THE VERTEBRATE
VISUAL SYSTEM

STEPHEN POLYAK · 1953

THE VERTEBRATE VISUAL SYSTEM

*Its origin, structure, and function and its manifestations in disease
with an analysis of its role in the life of animals
and in the origin of man*

*Preceded by a historical review of investigations of the eye,
and of the visual pathways and centers of the brain*

By

STEPHEN POLYAK, M.D.

Edited by

HEINRICH KLÜVER

THE UNIVERSITY OF CHICAGO PRESS *1957*

OPTOMETRY LIBRARY

The publication of this book has been aided by grants from the Dr. Wallace C. and Clara A. Abbott Memorial Fund of The University of Chicago; the John Simon Guggenheim Memorial Foundation; the United States Public Health Service; and the National Science Foundation

Library of Congress Catalog Number: 55–5153

THE UNIVERSITY OF CHICAGO PRESS, CHICAGO 37
Cambridge University Press, London, N.W. 1, England
The University of Toronto Press, Toronto 5, Canada

Foreword

"To achieve this, the lives of many gifted men, and infinite labor and patience were expended." Thus Dr. Polyak, on page 202 of the present book, recapitulates past efforts concerned with discovering "the principal features of the visual system, from the eye to the visual centers in the cerebral cortex. . . ." Almost thirty years of his own life were expended on work devoted to *The Vertebrate Visual System*—years of "almost continuous labor," to use his expression. But fortunately, unlike Kinnier Wilson's *Neurology*, Stephen Polyak's magnum opus was finally completed, although in a race with death. The present book, as the author modestly claims, ". . . treats the subject of vision chiefly as an anatomical problem." A glance at the Table of Contents, however, shows that this treatment rests on a very broad basis indeed and that the author's "desire to understand better the anatomical structures underlying vision, the way in which they work, and how they originated" has led him far beyond the confines of anatomical and histological problems into the pathology and biology of the vertebrate visual system and into long-continued researches dealing with the history of investigations in these fields. "For generations to come," Ragnar Granit recently wrote (Science, v. 122, p. 64, 1955) in an appraisal of Stephen Polyak's previous book, *The Retina*, "his work will be the leading source of reference for those interested in the way in which the retina collects and elaborates information for delivery to the higher centers." The present book, aside from embodying the results previously published in *The Retina* (1941) and in *The Main Afferent Fiber Systems of the Cerebral Cortex in Primates* (1932), represents an account—in fact, a rather condensed account—of the work to which Stephen Polyak devoted almost his entire scientific life and of the relevant findings on the visual system as reported by others in the world literature. There is little doubt that *The Vertebrate Visual System*, as a compendium of currently available knowledge in this field, will, for gen-

erations to come, be consulted by all investigators seeking information on the relations of vision to the retina, the visual pathways, and the subcortical and cortical visual centers, as well as by all students interested in the structure and function of the central nervous system in general.

It is evident from a study of this volume that the author, in analyzing problems of vision, starts from and always returns to anatomical structures and their interrelations. He took the occasion, again, to emphasize this chief concern with anatomical structures when he penned the Preface to this book in January, 1955. A few months later, on March 9, death terminated his activities, even the last day of his life having been spent in working on this book. It is of some interest in this connection that a century before his death, in 1855, Ludwig Edinger and Cornelis Winkler were born and that the decade between 1850 and 1860 saw the birth of men such as Marchi, Pick, Dogiel, Cajal, Pierre Marie, F. W. Mott, von Monakow, M. A. Starr, Bechterew, H. Oppenheim, Bernard Sachs, Mingazzini, and Nissl. Most of these men (their contributions figure prominently in the Bibliography of the present volume) were still alive or even publishing papers of far-reaching significance at the time Stephen Polyak was a student at the Medical School in Graz (Austria) from 1909 to 1914. They were men either famous for their pioneering in the anatomy and histology of the nervous system or imbued with the great importance of anatomical structures for nervous function. It does not seem surprising, therefore, that Stephen Polyak became deeply concerned with "structure" in his whole approach, thinking, and work. And yet it must be recalled in this context that it was only a few months before his passing away that Albrecht Bethe died—a man whose scientific activities spanned six decades and who, in 1897, still voiced the hope of explaining physiological phenomena on "an anatomical basis" but who, on meeting Apáthy in Naples before the turn of the century, soon insisted on substituting "functional" for "anatomical" explanations, to become one of the most vehement opponents of the neuron theory, that is, taking a stand radically different from the one taken in the pages of this book. While it is true that we now live in an age abounding in "functional" and "dynamic" approaches, such approaches again and again appear to demand a return to "form" and "structure." Even in a field as modern as enzyme research, the final goal, as Hugo Theorell (Science, v. 124, p. 467, 1956) has recently pointed out, can be nothing but "the filling of the yawning gulf between biochemistry and morphology."

The fact that "structure" was of central importance to Stephen Polyak does not mean that "function" was foreign to his thinking. It merely means that he could not conceive of a "physiology without anatomy" or of, what Flourens in 1824 called, *une anatomie sans physiologie*. If it had not been for a period of ill health during the last ten years of his life, he would have enlarged this book to include chapters dealing specifically with the physiology of vision and with "higher" visual functions and their disturbances. However, "their elimination seems now rather an advantage than a loss," he wrote in August, 1951, when commenting on various topics less directly concerned with the "principal theme: the anatomy of the vertebrate visual system." Under the circumstances, it was work on the blood supply of the vertebrate visual system and on the phylogenesis and biology of the organs of sight that received his special attention during the last years. His interest in function, as particularly the last two chapters of the book indicate, even extended to a wide range of behavioral phenomena. In describing manifestations of behavior he had the courage and, I believe, the wisdom to use the kind of language that was used by the great naturalists and biologists of the nineteenth century and which is capable of conveying so much more than the terminologies that came into existence with the "isms" and "schools" of psychology, including the varieties of an "objective" psychology.

Throughout the book, especially in the chapters dealing with the "principal theme," the author has made extensive use of data based on experimental work with monkeys and apes. Unfortunately, it was only a few months before

his death that the scientific world also lost Wood Jones and Arthur Keith, two of the investigators widely known for their studies of the comparative anatomy of the Primates. As regards the central nervous system, Stephen Polyak's statement of 1932—"the brain of the lower primates is . . . in its essential features and in its finer structure a simplified replica of the human brain"—will still go unchallenged among neuroanatomists and neurophysiologists, and his strong emphasis on material from non-human Primates will probably be even more readily appreciated now than it was several decades ago. It is not surprising, however, that the author, who himself, both in this country and in Europe, was a clinician for many years, felt that, no matter how convincing the deductions from experiments on animals, "the true sense of the reality is obtained only by a study of patients suffering from disturbed vision." There is no doubt that the part of the book dealing with the pathology of the retina and of the visual pathways and centers will be as much welcomed by clinicians as by those who are interested in a better understanding of the fundamental mechanisms operative in the visual sector of the central nervous system.

It is not surprising, furthermore, that Stephen Polyak should have become so greatly interested in the history of the investigations in his chosen field of research. In fact, it appears that he was destined to develop strong interests in the historical aspects of his scientific endeavors. Born in Yugoslavia, that is, in a part of the world which for centuries was the frontier between the Mohammedan East and the Christian West of Europe, he became at an early age sensitized to phenomena in the historical realm; he acquired a wide knowledge of ancient and modern European languages, including the Slavic tongues; his scientific training and his work in the research centers of various countries never suppressed his joy of discovery in tracing the origins of our present-day knowledge and seeing how certain problems were finally solved and how others, still unsolved, provided suggestions and stimulus for the investigations of tomorrow. But more than anything else, it was his deeply felt desire to give full acknowledgment to the work of others and do justice to the men on whose shoulders we stand that motivated his occupation with historical matters. As the result of his efforts, the historical part of this book has therefore turned into more than merely a history of investigations of the structure and function of the vertebrate visual system from the days of classical antiquity to the present day; it has turned into a general account of the growth of our knowledge of the brain and, in fact, into a masterly introduction to the history of neuroanatomy, neurology, ophthalmology, and allied fields that will not easily find its equal. It almost supersedes the necessity of perusing the preceding authors, except perhaps for those interested in more specialized lines of investigation. Besides, the book contains more than one hundred portraits: a memorial to those who, in the author's opinion, have contributed significantly to developing our knowledge of the visual system.

The Bibliography, covering three hundred pages, is probably unique in these days of joint authorship of papers with scanty references and in an age in which ignorance of past efforts often passes for originality. It is probably unique, not in the sense that it covers, or is meant to cover, the world's visual literature, but in the sense of being a monument to the heroic efforts of a modern investigator determined to collect, digest, and cope with that part of the literature that is relevant for his own area of research. As a rich source of information, the student of vision will again and again consult the references of this Bibliography culled from the literature of all ages and of all civilized nations and dealing with anatomical as well as numerous other aspects of the subject.

Even a preliminary study of the fifteen chapters of *The Vertebrate Visual System* is certain to convince the reader that it was the intention of the author to write not only for the scholar and advanced investigator but also—and perhaps first of all—for the student and beginner in neuroanatomy, neurophysiology, clinical neurology, ophthalmology, and related fields. It is told that a report to the Admiralty on methods of shipbuilding furnished in 1811 by Thomas Young, the "founder of modern physiological optics," called forth the comment: "Though science is much respected by their Lordships and your paper is much esteemed, it is too learned." In striving for lucidity and brevity; in adopting an "architecture" of presentation that makes for clarity and enables the reader to cope easily with an enormous amount of material conveniently organized into chapters with sections and subsections; in avoiding unnecessary technical terms and introducing, whenever possible, English terms, Stephen Polyak has produced a book that, aside from being a mine of information for the expert, is admirably suitable for purposes of teaching. No serious student will ever, like the Admiralty official of Thomas Young's days, find that the text is too heavy-going or "too learned."

Although not an anatomist *von Fach*, I had promised the author before his death to see his magnum opus through the press. I could perhaps lay claim to being, to some extent, at home in the general area of research considered in his book; I had known the author for almost three decades and was familiar with his outlook in scientific matters; I knew his intentions, aspirations, and high standards in regard to his own scientific work and the methods of presenting it; in fact, for many years we had shared monkeys, ideas, and books in the very building in which I am now writing and which housed our respective laboratories as well as a hundred and thirty thousand volumes of the Biological Library of the University of Chicago. Little did I realize at the time, it must now be admitted, that my promise would in the long run entail such an exacting and time-consuming job. The very fact that the book was in the process of being published at the time of the author's death led me to underestimate the magnitude of the undertaking. I did not realize, for instance, that the legends for the illustrations alone would represent a typescript of more than three hundred pages; that the proofs of the hundreds of illustrations would not be numbered; that the author had been unable to re-examine large parts of the manuscript after turning it over to the publisher or scrutinize carefully those galley proofs that he actually did read; that, in brief, I should find it necessary to check on thousands of points, including details of a scientific nature, quotations, references, and even microscopic sections. At the end of my efforts I am ready to conclude, however, that the book as it appears now is, to all extents, the book as it left Stephen Polyak's pen and represents in all its details the kind of book he wanted it to be. The 551 illustrations are those which he himself had carefully selected: none has been added and none has been eliminated. No doubt, if sufficient time had been his to finish the job himself, this would have been a more perfect book. And, if perfect health had been his, he would have continued with studies and experimentation in the laboratory (his files are full of "plans for further experiments"), and this book would not have been published for years to come—if ever.

It is often the fate even of eminent scientists that records of their lives rapidly vanish or become unobtainable. The author of this book, for instance, often failed to obtain the portrait of a man whom he wished to memorialize and at times even failed in the case of scientists who had made their great contributions as late as this century. It is fortunate that Stephen Polyak himself will not share the fate of such men, since Mr. Christian Abrahamsen, one of the prominent portrait painters in America now residing in Chicago, painted him in 1953, a reproduction of this portrait appearing as the Frontispiece in this volume. The friends and colleagues of the author, as well as all students of vision and future historians of science, owe a special debt of gratitude to Mr. Abrahamsen not only for granting permission to include this portrait but also for contributing the cost of making the engravings.

My work was immeasurably helped by Mrs. Donna Polyak, who put all material related to the book and its writing at my disposal, including the various versions of the manuscript preceding the final copy and including the original (and carefully numbered) illustrations. While I cannot hope that I have succeeded in eliminating all errors from the book and its

extensive Bibliography, my efforts would have been even less effective if it had not been for the help and expert advice of Mr. Ben C. Driver, librarian of the Biomedical Libraries of the University of Chicago. It is with particular pleasure that I acknowledge his kindness in assisting me in various ways and in helping me check thousands of references. I am grateful to Mrs. A. S. Overton for lightening the burden of proofreading and to Dr. P. P. H. de Bruyn for making arrangements to obtain some help in my editorial work. I am especially indebted to Mrs. Paddy Rudd Howes, who, by assuming the responsibility for preparing the Index, greatly eased my load and effectively removed one of the obstacles to a completion of the book.

The job of finishing this book has been a long one, since the work involved took two years or, more accurately, two years of my scientific life. At times I felt that the book, at least for me, would remain a *presque vu* phenomenon. If it had not been for my sincere belief that both the man Stephen Polyak and his work merited such a sustained effort on my part, I should, of course, not even have started on such an undertaking. I am thankful—and in this connection my thanks go also to the University of Chicago —that I was enabled to complete the task. One of the famous chemists, Berzelius, once expressed the opinion that, as regards the success of a scientist's life, "he himself has no sound judgment in this matter. Often enough such judgment is lacking even among his contemporaries." During his lifetime Stephen Polyak received few, if any, honors, and the world so far has not done much more than supply an inscription (paraphrasing the one chosen by David Hume for himself):

STEPHEN POLYAK

Born 1889   Died 1955

Leaving it to posterity to add the rest

In my way I have merely attempted—like Thomas H. Huxley did in the case of Hume— "to help posterity in the difficult business of knowing what to add" to such an epitaph. I myself, after his passing away, have "added" the following words (see Bibliography):

Being devoid of personal ambition, he lived a life in which ultimately nothing mattered except his scientific work, and the problems, demands, and

exigencies arising in connection with this work. Those words of Francis Bacon that have subsequently been used to introduce one of the most famous books ever produced in the history of Western thought appear to be the very words written across all of Stephen Polyak's scientific endeavors: *De nobis ipsis silemus. . . .*

HEINRICH KLÜVER

CULVER HALL
UNIVERSITY OF CHICAGO

During the last few years of Stephen Polyak's life he was in ill-health; sudden death or total blindness was his future. His constant worry was that one or the other might strike before he completed the manuscript for *The Vertebrate Visual System*. His long-time friend, colleague, and confidant, Heinrich Klüver, relieved him somewhat by promising to complete the work, should he leave it unfinished. Although Professor Polyak worked beyond normal endurance and part of the manuscript was in the hands of the publisher, much remained to be done at the time of his death.

Professor Klüver, true to his promise, laid aside his own scientific work and took on the full responsibility for bringing the book to publication. Some of the work was in unchecked page proof, some in galley proof, some in manuscript form; cuts had been made for the 551 illustrations and the legends written, but they had never been put together; the Index had to be made.

Day after day for two years Professor Klüver checked and re-checked, matched illustrations with legends, read proof, and prepared the Index. Because of his unflagging devotion, the work has come to publication in a form which, as he says in his Preface, "is, to all extents, the book as it left Stephen Polyak's pen and represents in all its details the kind of book he wanted it to be."

THE PUBLISHER

Fig. 518-A—Samples of fruit native of the Middle West of North America, or introduced from abroad. Center: Hawthorn apples of Red-Fruited Thorn (*Crataegus mollis*), of somewhat angular spherical shape, the largest measuring one-half inch diameter, crimson red in color, the smallest immature fruit orange colored. Right and left: clusters of Pimbina or Highbush Cranberry (*Viburnum opulus amer.*), fruit broadly ovoidal, one-third inch long, translucent bright scarlet or cardinal red. Upper center: Lance-leaved Buckthorn (*Rhamnus lanceolata*), fruit globular in shape, one-fourth inch in diameter, and purple-black in color. Below: a twig of Matrimony Vine (*Lycium halimifolium* or *L. barbarum*), native of Central Asia, with several ripe berries, ovoidal in shape, one-third inch long, red in color, with a few unripe smaller berries green in color, and a blossom with violet petals and yellow stamens. The ripe, brilliantly colored fruit vividly contrasts with the green foliage, while the unripe green fruit blends with it, hence it is difficult to see by the shape alone. The same is also true of the ripe dark-colored Buckthorn berries which can easily be seen against the clear sky between the leaves. The biological rôle of the red, orange, yellow, purple, blue, violet, black and white fruit is two-fold: one, to attract animals, principally Birds, capable of responding visually to it, and to use it as food; the other, to disperse fruit seeds through the agency of animals. In this way the evolution of the colored fruits and of the color sense became biologically beneficial in two ways: by furnishing food to animals, and by dispersing plants into new regions of the world.

Preface

This book, *The Vertebrate Visual System*, like its forerunner, *The Retina*, originated in the desire to understand better the anatomical structures underlying vision, the way in which they work, and how they originated.

The book is in four parts: historical, anatomical, pathological, and biological.

The first part is an attempt to present the development of our knowledge of the bodily mechanisms underlying vision from the earliest efforts through the following ages to our own time. Historical investigation not only satisfied my curiosity concerning the origin of the concepts and ideas and their interaction but revealed both the temporal sequence of the discoveries and, more important, the ideological motivation for subsequent investigations. This was also the source from which the stimulus for my own research originated. This section is also intended to be a memorial to the many workers who gave us our present knowledge.

The second part, the anatomical, describes the gross and fine structures which constitute the vertebrate visual system, principally in Man, Apes, and Monkeys.

The third part deals with the pathoanatomical basis of disturbed vision, especially of the various visual field defects. This part may be helpful not only in understanding the pathology of vision, but it may also materially add to our understanding of the organization of the visual apparatus and its normal function.

In the fourth part I discuss the intriguing problem of the origin and development of the vertebrate eye, how the eye may have initiated the formation of the brain, and how vision in turn has given an evolutionary impetus to the rise of the Primates, eventually culminating in the advent of Man.

The problem of vertebrate vision transcends the time limits and powers of any individual life, and I am aware of the many shortcomings of this book. Especially I regret not having been able to analyze the minute structure of the visual centers of the brain far more thoroughly,

as this is necessary for the understanding of vision. I hope, therefore, that this book will prove to be an incentive to further investigation of the visual organs and of the synaptical relationships of neurons in the nervous organs in general. It is here that we know least and here that the answer to the riddle of the material basis of vision, and of the brain in general, seems to lie.

The numerous illustrations were prepared or collected by myself or made from my own sketches by Esther Bohlman Patterson, Elaine Kern (Mrs. John R. Weigel), Hariette Elisabeth Story, and Agnes Nixon.

I borrowed, in addition, a considerable number of figures, mostly in order to illustrate the historical parts of the book. In all cases I have indicated the source from which the figure was taken.

The voluminous references I have mostly collected from the original sources.

The Vertebrate Visual System represents the almost continuous labor of nearly three decades. It was a great, and for the most part a pleasant, privilege to write it. Its success will be measured by its service as a source of instruction to all those in any way interested in vision and by the encouragement it may give to further research.

It is with pleasure that I mention here the friends and institutions that have helped me in my work: Dr. Heinrich Klüver, Professor of Experimental Psychology at the University of Chicago, for his help on numerous occasions, not the least of which were the many discussions and valuable advice about problems concerning the visual function; Dr. Donald George Marquis, Professor of Psychology at the University of Michigan, Ann Arbor, Michigan, for his active interest in the publication of this book; Professor Peter Clemens Kronfeld, of Chicago, and Dr. Frank S. Ryerson, of Detroit, for having helped me in my experiments; Dr. C. Wilbur Rucker, Professor of Ophthalmology at the Mayo Clinic, Rochester, Minnesota, for valuable human specimens; Dr. Hilarion Ortynski, of Tucupita, Venezuela, for many specimens of South American animals; the Rockefeller Foundation and the Dr. Wallace C. and Clara A. Abbott Memorial Fund of the University of Chicago for the grants-in-aid, received during many years, which made my work possible; the John Simon Guggenheim Memorial Foundation of New York for a grant of a fellowship for the completion of this work; the Public Health Service of the National Institutes of Health, in Washington, especially Dr. Pearce Bailey and Dr. Charles P. Huttrer, for the generous subsidies which enabled me to complete this book and to publish the numerous illustrations, including the colored plates; the National Science Foundation in Washington for a substantial contribution toward the publication of this book; Dorothy Prchal (Mrs. W. J. Gaspar) for the faithful and intelligent service given me during many years in my laboratory work; Olive Falls for the many ways in which she conscientiously assisted me; Edward Poser, M.D., ophthalmologist in Chicago, for his most generous attention to my difficult problems; and Donna Irene Polyak and Stephen Francis Polyak, my wife and son, for all the help given me, without which my task would have been even more burdensome.

The editing of the manuscript was expertly carried out by Ann Scott Overton, the typing by Mrs. Marvel D. Jensen, both of Chicago.

S. POLYAK

UNIVERSITY OF CHICAGO
January 19, 1955

Note on the Use of References

The terminal bibliography contains approximately 10,000 references and is reasonably complete. It consists principally of books and papers of immediate interest to the problem of vision and the visual organs and includes most publications related to the anatomy of this subject. However, only a selected number of items concerning the physiology, pathology, and biology of vision are included, which may serve as a source for further information.

The references appended to most sections, or in the text, give only the authors' names and years of publication. These will be of assistance in finding the complete references in the terminal bibliography.

In the case of two or more references quoted with the same author and date in the terminal bibliography, it will depend on the reader's discretion to identify the particular reference from the subject discussed in the text.

References to publications written by two or more authors are identified by the sign "&" instead of the word "and," the latter always indicating separate publications.

A very few references, difficult of access, remain incomplete and may be completed by those to whom they are of special interest.

In some chapters most or all references are found at the end of the chapter.

The cross-references within the text and the legends describing the illustrations give the chapter, section, and subsection in the following form: (*Cf.* chap. IV, 7 [1]). The first Arabic figure refers to the center heading so numbered, and the figure in brackets refers to the numbered subsection or side heading within that section.

Technical Note

Since the publication of *The Retina* in 1941 I have made further attempts to improve the staining of the retina with silver bichromate, the Golgi method. In these attempts other factors, such as the technique of injecting the eyeball with osmium and bichromate solution, the fixation, imbedding, cutting, and mounting of sections, and covering the slides with coverslips by a "dry procedure" were practiced as described in chapter IV of *The Retina*. In order to increase the probability of a successful stain, I found it advantageous to extend the time of fixation. A useful combination that, even with difficult material such as monkeys' and lizards' eyes, frequently gave good results, was as follows:

Fixation of the eyes in 1 part of 1% perosmic acid and 4 parts of 2 or 3% potassium dichromate 5 days at ordinary temperature, followed by 8–10 days in fresh fixative in incubator at 37° centigrade; leaving in same fixative for another 1–2 days at ordinary temperature; transfer to 0.5–0.7% silver nitrate (with or without 5 drops of pure formic acid to 250 cc.) for 30 minutes; transfer to same Golgi fixative for another 30 minutes; transfer to same 0.5–0.7% silver nitrate, and gentle shaking for a few minutes until visible precipitation is no longer formed; transfer into a fresh change of same silver nitrate for 2–3 days at ordinary temperature; dehydration in $\frac{1}{3}$ pure acetone and $\frac{2}{3}$ absolute alcohol in a bottle over a layer of dehydrated copper sulphate, in incubator at 55° centigrade, during 1–1½ hours; washing out in repeated changes of absolute alcohol to remove acetone; imbedding in thick celloidin (Randolph Products Co.) in refrigerator, in a "quick way" (during 2–3 hours); hardening in liquid chloroform; transfer for ½–1 hour to 75–80% alcohol (one or two changes); sectioning at 30–60 or more microns; clearing in 1:3 carbolic acid and toluene; mounting on slides in clarite or purified neutral Canada balsam; drying over a hot plate; covering in a "dry way"; pressing with weights.

Prepared in this way, slides remain preserved for many years and may be examined with high-power oil-immersion objectives which possess long working distance, such as the *Ultropak* systems of Leitz.

Table of Contents

INTRODUCTION 1

PART I. HISTORY OF INVESTIGATIONS OF THE STRUCTURE AND FUNCTION OF THE EYE AND OF THE VISUAL PATHWAYS AND CENTERS OF THE BRAIN

I. HISTORY OF THE INVESTIGATION OF THE STRUCTURE AND FUNCTION OF THE EYE AND THE DEVELOPMENT OF THE OPTICAL SCIENCES 9

  1. Earliest Investigations of the Eye and the Beginning of Optics 9
  2. Beginning of Optics among the Early Civilized Nations 13
  3. Arab Knowledge of the Structure and Function of the Eye and of Optics . . . 14
  4. Introduction of the Arab Arts and Sciences into Europe, and the European Renaissance . 21
  5. Early Modern Optics and Discovery of the Retinal Image 27
  6. Investigations of the Retina from the Earliest Times to the Rise of Modern Microscopy . 40
  7. Early Modern Investigation of the Structure and Function of the Retina 46
  8. The Problem of the Intrinsic Organization of the Retina and Modern Efforts To Solve It 58
  9. The Neuron Theory and the Modern Concept of Structure and Function of the Vertebrate Retina 67

II. INVESTIGATION OF THE VISUAL PATHWAYS AND CENTERS DURING CLASSICAL ANTIQUITY, THE MIDDLE AGES, AND THE EARLY PERIOD OF THE MODERN SCIENTIFIC ERA 73

  1. Investigation of the Visual System during the Early Period of Classical Antiquity . . 73
  2. Galen's Anatomy and Physiology of the Visual System 77
  3. Galen's Physiology of the Visual System 78
  4. Galen's Functional Interpretation of the Chiasma and of Other Features Peculiar to the Visual System 80
  5. Evaluation and Critique of Galen's Concept of the Visual Mechanisms 82
  6. Anatomy and Physiology of the Visual Pathways and Centers during the Middle Ages among the Nations Influenced by Arab Civilization 83
  7. Western European Knowledge of the Visual System preceding and during the Renaissance 86
  8. Vesalius and the Anatomy and Physiology of the Visual Pathways 92
  9. Post-Vesalian Period in Brain Anatomy and Physiology 96
  10. Earliest Mechanistic Explanation of the Visual System 100
  11. Anatomy and Physiology of the Visual Pathways and Centers from Des Cartes to Albrecht von Haller 105
  12. Investigations of the Visual System toward the End of the Eighteenth and during the Beginning of the Nineteenth Centuries 112

III. INVESTIGATION OF THE VISUAL PATHWAYS AND CENTERS DURING THE EARLY PERIOD OF MODERN BRAIN RESEARCH 117

  1. Anatomy and Physiology of the Cerebral Cortex during the Seventeenth and Eighteenth Centuries 117
  2. The Dawn of Modern Brain Physiology 119
  3. The Plurality Doctrine of the Functional Organization of the Brain 122
  4. Doctrine of Functional Omnivalence of the Cerebral Cortex 126
  5. Early Investigations of the Cerebral Cortex and of the Subcortical Fiber Systems . . 130
  6. Revival of the "Doctrine of Localization" or Functional Inequality of the Cerebral Cortex 138
  7. Early Attempts To Localize the Sense of Vision in the Cerebral Cortex . . . 147
  8. Localization of Vision in the Occipital Lobe; Cortical and Mental Blindness . . . 149
  9. Early Modern Investigation of the Infranuclear Division of the Visual System . . . 152

IV. Modern Anatomical, Experimental, Clinical, and Pathological Investigation of the
Visual Pathways and Centers 163

   1. Early Modern Attempts To Localize Visual Function in the Human Cerebral Cortex . 163
   2. Doctrine of the "Projection Centers" as Distinct from "Association Areas" of the Cerebral
      Cortex 170
   3. Myelogenetic Investigation of Visual Radiation 177
   4. Theory of Topographical Representation of the Retina in the Cerebral Cortex . . 179
   5. Hypothesis of "Diffuse" or "Plastic" Organization of the Visual Centers . . . 184
   6. Recent Investigations of the Infranuclear Division of the Visual System . . . 188
   7. Recent Investigations of the Supranuclear Division of the Visual System . . . 195
   8. Recapitulation of Past Efforts To Explain the Phenomenon of Vision in Terms of Physical
      Factors and Anatomical Structures 202

PART II. ANATOMY AND HISTOLOGY OF THE RETINA AND OF THE VISUAL PATHWAYS AND CENTERS OF THE BRAIN

V. Structure of the Vertebrate Retina 207

   1. Structure and Function of the Eye 207
   2. General Features of the Minute Structure of the Retina 213
   3. Visual Cells or Photoreceptors 220
   4. Bipolar Cells of the Retina 228
   5. Ganglion Cells of the Retina 237
   6. Association Cells of the Retina 246
   7. Efferent or Exogenous Fibers of the Retina 250
   8. The Functional Grouping of Retinal Neurons 252
   9. Supporting Structures of the Retina 255
  10. Optic Papilla or Disk, Central Area and Fovea, Yellow Spot or Macula, and Serrated Margin or Ora Serrata of the Retina 259
  11. Regional and Comparative Characteristics of the Vertebrate Retina . . . 278

VI. Optic Nerves, Chiasma, Tracts, and Subcortical Visual Centers 288

   1. Component Parts of the Visual System 288
   2. Origin and Course of the Optic Nerve 292
   3. Histology of the Optic Nerves, Chiasma, and Tracts 297
   4. Course and Termination of the Fibers of the Infranuclear Division of the Visual System in
      General 301
   5. Structural Peculiarities of the Infranuclear and Nuclear Divisions of the Visual System in
      the Lower Vertebrates and Infraprimate Mammals 309
   6. The Chiasma of the Optic Nerves and the Representation of the Homonymous Halves of
      the Retinae in the Lateral Geniculate Nuclei 323
   7. Topographical or Dimensional Representation of the Retinae in the Infranuclear Division
      of the Primate Visual System and in the Subcortical Visual Centers . . . 334
   8. Minute Structure of the Principal or Laminated Lateral Geniculate Nucleus . . 354
   9. Minute Structure of the Principal or Laminated Lateral Geniculate Nucleus as Revealed
      by Histoanalytical Methods 364
  10. The Pregeniculate Gray Nucleus and the Pupillary Reflex Pathway 376
  11. Summary of the Intrinsic Organization of the Infranuclear and Nuclear Divisions of the
      Vertebrate Visual System 385

VII. Visual Radiation 390

   1. Introduction; General Remarks concerning the Supranuclear Division of the Visual System 390
   2. Meninges and the Internal Makeup of the Cerebral Hemispheres—Their Relation to the
      Visual Pathway in General and to the Visual Radiation in Particular . . . 391
   3. Origin, Course, and Termination of the Visual Radiation in General . . . 398
   4. Functional Organization of the Visual Radiation and of the Striate Area . . . 409
   5. Elemental Composition of the Visual Radiation and the Transmission of Retinal Images
      to the Cerebral Cortex 420

6. Summary of the Intrinsic Organization of the Supranuclear Division of the Vertebrate Visual System 426
7. Connections of the Striate Area or Visual Cortex with Other Parts of the Brain . . . 434
8. Topographical Relationships of the Visual System 442

VIII. CORTICAL VISUAL CENTERS 446

1. External Configuration and Functional Organization of the Cerebral Hemispheres . . 446
2. Gross Anatomy of the Cortical Visual Centers 460
3. Phylogeny of the Human Calcarine Fissure and the Striate Area 467
4. Location, Extent, and General Characteristics of the Striate Area 487
5. Cell Layers of the Striate Area 496
6. Fiber Systems of the Striate Area 507
7. Minute Structure of the Striate Area as Revealed by Histoanalytic Staining . . . 510

IX. GENERAL THEORY OF THE ORGANIZATION OF NERVOUS SYSTEMS AND THE VISUAL FUNCTION . 540

1. Introduction 540
2. The Hypothesis of *Neuroreticulum* or the "Nerve Net" 541
3. The Neuron Theory 545
4. The Minute Organization of the Nervous Centers 560
5. The Structure of the Neuron Synapses and Their Probable Function 563
6. The Neuron Relationships in General 572
7. The Elemental Neuronal Associations and Their Probable Function 575
8. The Functional Grouping of Neurons in the Retina 581

X. THE BLOOD SUPPLY OF THE VERTEBRATE VISUAL SYSTEM 593

1. General Remarks on the Blood Supply of the Eye and of the Visual Pathways and Centers 593
2. The Blood Vessels of the Eye and of the Optic Nerve 597
3. The Arterial Circle of Willis and the Origin of the Cerebral Arteries 602
4. The Middle Cerebral Artery and Its Subsidiaries 607
5. The Posterior Cerebral Artery and Its Subsidiaries 609
6. The Calcarine Artery 611
7. Note on the Blood Supply in the Human Fetus and in the Monkeys and Apes . . . 615
8. Physiological and Pathophysiologic Implications of the Blood Supply of the Visual System 617
9. Summary of the Blood Supply of the Visual System 623

PART III. PATHOLOGY OF THE RETINA AND OF THE VISUAL PATHWAYS AND CENTERS OF THE BRAIN

XI. DISTURBANCES OF VISION AND THE ANATOMICAL ORGANIZATION OF THE VISUAL SYSTEM . 629

1. Introduction 629
2. Disturbances of Vision Caused by Pathology of the Retina, Optic Nerves, and Chiasma . 636
3. Disturbances of Vision Caused by Suprachiasmal Pathology of the Visual System . . 642
4. Types of Homonymous Hemianopia and Their Anatomical Basis 647
5. Partial Homonymous Hemianopias and Their Anatomical Basis 654
6. Hemiachromatopia and Hemiamblyopia 665
7. Scotomas, Field Rests, Crescentic and Other Field Defects and Their Interpretation . 668
8. Central Sparing in Homonymous Hemianopia: The Hypotheses and Speculations . . 680
9. Central Sparing in Hemianopia: The Underlying Functional and Anatomical Factors . 687

XII. CLINICAL AND PATHOANATOMICAL OBSERVATIONS OF CASES WITH DISTURBANCES OF THE VISUAL FIELDS 695

1. Materials and Methods 695
2. Case of the Chiasma Displaced by a Pituitary Tumor without Interruption of Chiasma . 696
3. Case of Complete Homonymous Hemianopia 698
4. Case of an Incomplete Homonymous Hemianopia 702
5. Case of a Quadrantic Homonymous Hemianopia Transformed into a Bilateral Incomplete Hemianopia 707

6. Case of a Pure Incomplete Quadrantic Homonymous Hemianopia 710
7. Case of a Superior Quadrantic Homonymous Hemianopia Associated with Quadrantic Hemiachromatopia 717
8. Case of Horizontal or Altitudinal Hemianopia and Mental Blindness 724
9. Case of Central Homonymous Hemianopic Scotoma 733
10. Case of Central Homonymous Hemianopic Scotoma with Post Mortem Examination . 735
11. Case of Incomplete Homonymous Hemianopia with Central Sparings 747
12. Case of a Lesion in the Lower Calcarine Lip and Occipital Pole 750
13. Case with an Encephalomalacic Focus along the Calcarine and Parieto-Occipital Sulci . 755

PART IV. ORIGIN, DEVELOPMENT, COMPARATIVE ANATOMY, PHYSIOLOGY, AND BIOLOGY OF THE VERTEBRATE ORGANS OF SIGHT

XIII. Origin and Development of the Vertebrate Eye and Visual System 763
1. Ontogenesis of the Vertebrate Eye 763
2. The Phylogenesis of the Vertebrate Eye 768
3. The Phylogenetical Origin and Functional Significance of Decussation of the Vertebrate Visual System 779

XIV. Biology of the Organs of Sight and of the Visual System of Vertebrates . . 794
1. The Role of Vision in the Maintenance of Animal Forms of Life 794
2. Northern Brook Silverside 803
3. Sunfish 810
4. Pike 814
5. Trout 825
6. Bullhead 831
7. Anole or "American Chameleon" 838
8. Swallow 847
9. Common Shrew 860
10. Tree Shrew 874
11. Squirrel 895
12. Tarsier 903
13. Miscellaneous Notes on the Visual Behavior of the Animals in Nature . . . 941

XV. Vision and Its Role in the Origin of Man 957
1. The Role of Vision in the Evolution of Vertebrates 957
2. The Role of Vision in the Origin of Primates 963
3. The Origin of Man 974
4. Infrahuman Primates as an Illustration of Man's Ancestors before They Assumed an Erect Posture and Bipedal Gait 985
5. Observation of the Monkeys and Apes in Captivity 1003
6. Darwin's View on the Origin of Man, and on the Causes of Man's Pre-eminent Place in Nature 1023
7. Analysis of Factors Responsible for the Origin of Man from an Infrahuman Primate . 1026
8. Man's Earliest Ancestors preceding and during the Assumption of Erect Posture and Bipedal Gait 1033
9. Reflections on *Australopithecus* and on the Origin of Mankind 1038

Epilogue 1046

BIBLIOGRAPHY

Bibliography 1059

INDEX

Index 1359

Introduction

1. THE PROBLEM OF VISION.—What vision is, has been and still remains one of the mysteries that have challenged human thought since the beginning of civilization. What agents and forces intervene between the observing eye and the observed object? How is the eye built, and how does it work in order to convey to the discerning mind the wealth of forms and colors that make up the visible environment? What are the cerebral mechanisms connected with the eye, how are they organized, and how do they work in order to elicit subjective visual responses to the visible objects that represent the surrounding world? These are the basic questions to which, for more than two thousand years, human intelligence has sought, and only partly found, the answers.

2. HUMAN INTEREST IN VISION.—As far back in the human past as there is a record, the supreme importance of vision and of its instrument, the eye, has been recognized. In the prescientific era the interpretation was purely allegorical. Very early, however, a practical interest was manifested in empirical attempts to preserve or restore the precious faculty of sight by the healing art of ancient civilized nations: Hindus, Babylonians, Chinese, Egyptians, and others.

During Classical Antiquity this persistent interest in vision, as in other bodily functions and in nature in general, gave rise to the doctrines and theories of Greek philosophers, naturalists, and medical men. The ancient Greek knowledge of the eye, of its function, its pathology and treatment, preserved during the Middle Ages by the learned men of the Arab world, finally developed in modern times into a great body of knowledge encompassing a number of allied fields, such as the anatomy, physiology, psychology, and pathology of the visual organs and centers. Intimately connected with these disciplines were efforts to discover the physical aspect of sight, in particular the nature and properties of "light" and its behavior under various conditions.

The result of these numerous and various efforts was the formulation of the laws of optics, the discovery of the structure of the eye and its connections with the brain, and the body of knowledge incorporated in modern physiology and pathology of vision and of the visual organs.

3. PRACTICAL AND TRANSCENDENTAL MOTIVATION OF INTEREST IN VISION.—The persistent interest in the organs of vision manifested by all advanced societies during enlightened epochs of the human past can easily be understood because of the overwhelming importance that vision has in human life. Anything likely to increase knowledge of the visual organs and centers and thus help to preserve their normal function or to restore defective eyesight may be expected to be held in high esteem and eagerly sought. But the nonutilitarian motives arising from intellectual and often unconscious emotional sources have played a great and probably decisive role in keeping the problem of vision alive. The fascination that the eye, its workings, and its intimate relation to psychic life have always held for the curious is revealed in numerous writings of the last twenty centuries. The obtrusive reality and indispensability of the subjective phenomenon of vision, the manifest connection of sight with its anatomical instrument, the eye, and the close relation of the eye to the brain, have always had a vivid appeal for all who have a profound interest in human nature.

The motives for the sustained interest of the thinking part of humanity in the organs of vision have been admirably expressed by Sir David Brewster, a great student of vision, in his *Letters on Natural Magic* (1862, p. 19) addressed to Sir Walter Scott, in the following words:

Of all the organs by which we acquire a knowledge of external nature the eye is the most remarkable and the most important. By our other senses the information we obtain is comparatively limited. The touch and the taste extend no further than the surface of our own bodies. The sense of smell is exercised within a very narrow sphere, and that of recognizing sounds is limited to the distance at which we hear the bursting of a meteor and the crash of a thunderbolt. But the eye enjoys a boundless range of observation. It takes cognizance, not only of other worlds belonging to the solar system, but of other systems of worlds infinitely removed into the immensity of space; and when aided by the telescope, the invention of human wisdom, it is able to discover the forms, the phenomena, and the movements of bodies whose distance is as inexpressible in language as it is inconceivable in thought.

The same conviction of the overwhelming importance of sight in the intellectual life of man and in his existence as the supreme intellectual being on earth is reflected in a single sentence of a lifelong student of the brain and the visual centers, Sir Grafton Elliot Smith, in an article published in *Nature* (v. 125, p. 822, 1930): "Vision is the foundation of intelligence and the chief source of our knowledge."

4. Scope and subject of this book: bodily mechanisms of vision.—The persistent interest of inquisitive minds in vision, in its bodily instruments and its physical factors, has resulted in an accumulation of information too great for any single person to master. It would be presumptuous for any but the specialist merely to review such fields as the photophysics and photochemistry, the physiology, psychology, and pathology, of vision and the visual organs. The accomplishments in these fields and the problems still to be solved constitute a task for those well acquainted with these subjects. The range of the present book is more limited. It treats the subject of vision chiefly as an anatomical problem. Whatever the factors are that make us see, vision as we know it and subjectively experience it is entirely dependent upon specific structures of the body maintained in proper working order. When these are interfered with or destroyed, the faculty of vision is impaired or destroyed. Vision, though absolutely dependent upon the physical world, is a performance of our visual apparatus.

One more step in this logical postulation brings us to the realization that "vision" is no more than an abstraction, the concrete reality of which is our bodily visual mechanism. We see as our visual system sees, that is, within the limits and capacities of its intrinsic, inherent organization. "Vision," in fact, is nothing more than our visual apparatus working under adequate physiological conditions.

5. The intrinsic organization of the visual system and vision.—Heretofore vision has mostly been treated as a psychophysiological problem, with structures playing a subsidiary role. Since, however, the various visual phenomena are manifestations of the activity of the visual system and vary with the intrinsic organization of its different parts and in different animal species and are variously disturbed by discrete pathological processes, it is quite proper to look upon the structural organization of this system as the core of the problem of vision.

In the physiology of the peripheral organ— the eyeball—and of the oculomotor apparatus, this is self-evident. This viewpoint is also accepted for the gross anatomical features of the visual pathways and centers of the brain. The minute structures that make up the peripheral photoreceptor—the retinal membrane of the eye—may likewise largely be interpreted in terms of the known manifestations of the visual phenomenon. However, beyond the retina, in the brain, few structures have been discovered so far which could be usefully interpreted either grossly or in their minute relationships. Yet, like the structures of the eyeball and retina, the remaining larger and more complicated part of the visual system must be viewed as the principal carrier of the processes which, in their totality, we summarize under the term "vision."

The first step in understanding the phenomenon of vision, therefore, is to disclose the intrinsic organization of the visual system as completely as present scientific technique permits. While it is possible to study separately the structure of the eye or of the visual pathways or of the visual centers of the brain, to understand the anatomical basis of vision it is necessary to consider the entire visual apparatus.

6. Gross anatomical relations of the visual system.—The vertebrate visual system, beginning with the retinal membrane, is principally an assemblage of nervous tissue; hence the same general approach has to be applied to its study as to that of any other part of the nervous system. Embryologically, the entire visual system proper, including the retina, is a derivative of the brain and, in its fully differentiated state, bears the character of, and in fact is a part of, the central organ. In the study of the visual system, the gross arrangement must first be determined, that is, the thickness, length, course, topographical relationships, and other particulars of the optic nerves, chiasma, and tracts; the subcortical terminal stations of the midbrain and betweenbrain; the visual radiations, their beginnings, course, topographical relations, and cortical termination; the striate areas of the occipital lobes where the radiations terminate, and their extent, shape, position, topographical relations, and connections with other areas of the cortex and subcortical regions.

Next, more important in the visual than in any other system is the topographical projection of the stimuli-receiving retinal surface on the intermediate subcortical stations and on the cortical terminal visual areas. On the proper elucidation of this depends the understanding of how the two discrete images formed in both eyes are projected upon the two visual cortical centers—the striate areas—by mediation of which they evoke a single visual impression in our consciousness.

Closely related to the subject of the topographical organization of the visual system is the problem of the oculomotor apparatus, including the muscles moving the two eyeballs; the nerves and subcortical and cortical centers by which the gaze of both eyes is co-ordinated and directed toward the common point of fixation; and the dioptrical systems of the eyes accommodated to the distance of the viewed object—all factors essential for the normal visual act.

One of the most important anatomical items is the blood supply of the eyes and of the visual pathways and centers. For, as elsewhere in the living body, no part of the visual system, whether a large or microscopic structure, can perform its proper function if not adequately supplied with blood. Knowledge of the blood supply is

of paramount importance in the pathology of vision; this, in turn, may elucidate certain subtle aspects of the organization of the central visual apparatus, such as the cortical representation of the all-important central foveae and areae, the "maculae" of the retina, and their preservation in disturbances of vision of cerebral origin.

This leads to the study of representative human pathological cases where impaired vision was observed during life. These, together with experiments executed on suitable animals, especially on manlike apes and monkeys, may reveal organizational points that could never be understood on the basis of an investigation of normal anatomical material alone. Human clinical observations are invaluable, especially when correlated with macro- and microscopic examination of pathological material, since this is the only way to make us understand the subtle and multifarious processes of the human pathology of vision and its related functions.

The last and perhaps the most important item in the problem of vision is general biology: How and from what incipient sources did the faculty of vision originate in the animal kingdom? What, especially, were the origins of visual organs in early animals that eventually culminated in the development of the eyes and visual organs of Vertebrates, including Man? In which of many ways, essentially similar and yet infinitely varying from species to species, have the different Vertebrates solved the problem of visual relationship to the environment in which they live? And how have they adjusted themselves, by means of varied visual mechanisms, to their particular conditions and satisfied their basic requirements, acquiring food, procreating, and saving themselves from extinction? By the answers to these questions the background necessary for an understanding of the individual roles of all living beings, large and small, may be acquired.

7. ROUTINE METHODS OF INVESTIGATION, THEIR USEFULNESS AND LIMITATIONS.—Whereas the gross anatomical and general histological methods spoken of previously have played a capital role in the collection of the information we now possess about the visual system, they did not penetrate to the core of its intrinsic or-

ganization. Since the inception of modern microscopy, particularly during the first half of the twentieth century, the minute structure of the eyeball, of the retinal membrane, and of the visual pathways and centers have been thoroughly investigated. The layer of retinal photoreceptors—the rods and cones—has been repeatedly studied in modern times, ever since the pioneer researches of Bowman, H. Müller, Koelliker, and M. Schultze. The various gray nuclei and cortical areas related to vision have also been the subject of much fine work. We know now in detail the composition of the photoreceptor layer in numerous animal species, the various structures of the brain stem, and the specific areas of the gray cover of the brain, or cortex, that are directly related to the normal act of vision; and we are rather well acquainted with numerous disturbances resulting from lesions of these various parts of the visual apparatus.

Furthermore, since modern anatomohistological and experimental physiological methods of investigation have been devised, numerous papers have been published describing in detail the character and arrangement of the nerve cells, fibers, and other constituent elements of each of the parts of the visual apparatus; and a good start has been made with modern electrophysiological methods, to reveal dynamic factors involved in vision. But, in spite of all this, the final answer to the question "What are the minute mechanisms of the brain that are the material basis of sight?" still eludes us.

8. Nervous constituents of the visual system: the nerve cells, carriers of visual function.—The particular function of every part of our bodily machine is understood to be an expression of its specific organization and relationships: the kind of structural elements constituting it, the way these elements are put together, the way they are related to one another and to other structures, and the influences by which they are regulated or through which they influence other parts. If the same principle is applied to the visual system, there is little doubt that the specific constituent "functional parenchyma" of this system is the nerve cells, or "neurons." By analogy with other parts of our organism, the neurons that make up our visual system are the true substratum or carriers of the specific faculty of vision. "Vision," potential and actual, is the total of specific responsiveness or activity of the living neurons of the visual system. All other parts of its tissue, such as the supporting connective and neuroglial cells and fibers and the blood vessels, necessary though they are, are merely a matrix or bedding within which the visual neurons are lodged, held in proper arrangement, and nourished. The gross physical and chemical constitution of the tissue, being much like that of other parts of the brain, likewise may be largely nonspecific.

The specific function of the visual mechanisms may be considered to be an expression principally of two factors: first, of the specific organization of the peripheral visual photoreceptor, the eye, and, above all, of the retina; and, second, of the particular kind of its constituent "neurons," their varieties, their mutual synaptical relationships, and their inherent dynamical capacities.

Since the structure of the eye and, in particular, the layer of photoreceptors are by now sufficiently well known, the principal remaining task is to find out what varieties of neurons there are in each link of the complex visual mechanism, how they are distributed and arranged with respect to one another, and, most important, in what synaptical relationship each particular neuron variety stands with other related neuron varieties. Such investigation may make it possible to identify the innumerable minute channels along which the nerve excitations, after being generated in the retinal rods and cones by light, are propagated; and a likely estimate therefrom may be made as to the probable changes in intensity, quality, spread, and other modifications which these excitations undergo as they pass from neuron to neuron.

When these questions are answered satisfactorily, an attempt may finally be made to correlate the various known visual phenomena with particular sets of neurons or their arrangement. This task, one of the most difficult in contemporary science, appears to be the only promising road to the interpretation of vision by means of concrete natural factors, above all, by means of the structures of the brain that are unquestionably the instruments by means of which we see.

What additional problems may arise, the future progress of man's knowledge alone will show.

9. Historical retrospect of past efforts to understand vision.—What vision—a faculty almost as overwhelmingly striking as life itself—is, has been, as initially stated, a problem in the focus of Man's attention ever since he began to reflect on himself and nature. Throughout Man's development he has tried to understand vision according to his means, from savages barely conscious of the precious gift they possessed to modern scientists measuring with the most refined instruments the wave lengths of light or trying to disentangle, by means of the microscope, the complex relationships of the visual nerve cells of the brain.

To learn about these efforts and to present them briefly has constituted one of the chief by-products of writing this book. To trace when, where, and why the first attempts were made and subsequent progress achieved in the optical sciences, in the anatomy and physiology of the eye and of the brain, and in the pathology and biology of vision was both absorbing and indispensable. In many instances it illuminated the problems of vision and pointed the way to their solution.

Such delving into ancient times reveals Man's character and his intellectual interests and strivings as essentially the same throughout the ages. From the darkness of barbarous ignorance, by a process of long, slow, laborious toil, helped by fortune and hampered by adversity, Man gradually learned to observe, to improve his tools of research, to profit from logic as well as from the errors of his predecessors, until he accumulated a knowledge of himself and of nature of which the gods of the past may well have been envious.

Torn between the flashy sophistry of the clever, verbose dialectic of a Plato and the methodical examinations and clear logic of an Aristotle, Man still plods on toward the goal which he has not attained, even though he may have advanced toward it: to know his place in nature, and thus to know himself. It is a formidable task, as indicated almost twenty-five centuries ago by Aristotle in his treatise *On the Soul* (*De Anima*, Περὶ ψυχῆς), book 1, par. 10: "To attain any assured knowledge about the soul is one of the most difficult things in the world."

The task becomes yet more formidable when the limitations of human existence are taken into consideration. With a sense of apology for the shortcomings of this book, I may quote a sentence attributed to Hippocrates, "father of medicine," from his *Aphorisms*, book 1, chapter 1 (Littré, IV, 458): "Life is short, art is long, opportunity is elusive, experience is deceptive, judgment difficult."

PART I

History of Investigations of the Structure and Function of the Eye and of the Visual Pathways and Centers of the Brain

Chapter I

History of the Investigation of the Structure and Function of the Eye and the Development of the Optical Sciences

SEC. 1. EARLIEST INVESTIGATIONS OF THE EYE AND THE BEGINNING OF OPTICS

1. ANCIENT ANATOMY OF THE EYE.—Knowledge of the structure of the eye, of its normal function, and of its ailments and their treatment closely reflects the intellectual and material conditions of the age and place which produced it. How much, or how little, the earliest civilized nations—the Sumerians, Assyrians, Babylonians, Egyptians, and Persians—knew about the eye is unknown, except for a few hints indicating an empirical-practical treatment of diseases of the eye. (*See* Wölfflin 1922; Krause 1933; Ranke 1933; Meyerhof 1940; Gordon 1942; Steindorff; Leix; Campbell Thompson; Elgood 1951; Laignel-Lavastine.)

The ancient Hindus, on the other hand, seem to have made some beginnings both in general medicine and surgery and in ophthalmology, according to Bidhyādar (1939). Since, however, the date of Suśruta's book *Samhitā Uttara Tantra*, a manual of medical methodology, is still in dispute, some claiming it was written about 1000 B.C., while others put its origin at the beginning of the present era (Esser 1934), the appraisal of early Hindu medicine remains a problem. In any case, Suśruta's description of the eye was extremely brief and inaccurate: the eye, according to him, is made up of six layers, two of which are the lids and four of which make up the eyeball proper. These may be identified tentatively as the cornea, containing the aqueous and possibly the lens, the ciliary region, the vitreous, and the retina. Despite the theoretical shortcomings of the Hindus, Dutt (1938) believes they were the first successfully to perform the operation for cataract. "India," according to Dutt, "is a land of cataracts.—No wonder that the first opera-

tion for cataract was devised and performed in India." (*Cf.* sec. 3 [2], this chapter, for conditions in Arab lands; sec. 3 [3] for cataract operation by Arabs.)

The early Greek writers were not much more advanced. Demócritos of Abdera (Δημόκριτος, 460–370 B.C.), according to H. Magnus (1900), described two tunics of the eye—a thick, firm outer one, called the "fibrous tunic" in modern terminology, comprising the cornea and sclera, in which he distinguished a "delicate tunic" (cornea), and a spongy inner tunic with a pupil (κόρη, kóre or "maiden"), that may be identified with the uvea, including the chorioid, ciliary body, and iris.

Aristotle ('Αριστοτέλης, Aristotéles, 384–322 B.C., *see also* Fig. 1; chap. II, 2), called "The Father of Natural Sciences," also discussed the eye very briefly, mentioning only the parts easily seen in a living person and saying that it contained water. His idea of the nature and property of light and of the visual act (*see* subsec. 2, below) was closer to modern views than that of most other Greek naturalists and philosophers. (*See* chap. II, 1 [4], for Aristotle's anatomy of nerve supply of the eyeball.)

A somewhat more detailed description of ocular structures is found in the writings of Hippocrates ('Ιπποκράτης, 460?–377 B.C.), "The Father of Medicine," according to Magnus. He distinguished three tunics: first, an outer white one (sclera), with an anterior transparent part (cornea); second, a delicate middle tunic, with an anterior colored portion (iris), a "crown" (ciliary body and root of the iris), and a central opening, or pupil (κόρη, kóre, "maiden"; ὄψις, opsis, "view" or "sight"), together forming what is now called the uveal tunic; the third was the inner tunic, the retina, of which nothing was known except that it was extremely delicate. Within the eyeball there was a single space filled with "water." The crystalline lens was not known. The water was believed to originate in the brain and was considered to be a true photoreceptor or photosensitive substance by the Hippocratic School.

The first truly scientific description of the structures of the eye dates from the Alexandrine or Hellenistic Period (323–212 B.C.). This late Greek anatomy of the eye is attributed to Heróphilos ('Ηρόφιλος, 344–280 B.C.), the first great pioneer in anatomy and physiology. His description is preserved in a treatise *On Medicine* by Aulus Cornelius Celsus (1st century, Christian Era), a Roman author, and in the

FIG. 1.—Aristotle of Stágeira (Aristotéles, 384–322 B.C.), "Father of Natural Science." The most encyclopedic naturalist of Classical Antiquity and one of the foremost philosophers of Ancient Greece. Teacher of Alexander the Great. Author of the earliest description of the vertebrate eye. Proponent of the most correct interpretation of the function of the eye and of vision in general ever made by the Greeks. A marble copy made in Roman times from a contemporary realistic portrait by an unknown sculptor of the late fourth century, according to M. Rostovtzeff (1926). Original in the Kunsthistorisches Museum (Museum of the History of Art), Vienna, Austria. Courtesy of Kunsthistorisches Museum, Vienna. (For other portraits of Aristotle *see* Bernoulli, *Griechische Iconographie*, v. 2, p. 96; Studniczka, *Das Bildnis des Aristoteles*, Leipzig, 1908; Hekler, *Die Bildniskunst der Griechen und Römer*; Hekler, *Bildnisse berühmter Griechen*; Charles Singer 1921, v. 2, Pl. II; G. Sarton, *Lychnos*, 1944–45.)

writings of Rûfos of Ephesos ('Ροῦφος, Rhû-phos; he flourished at the end of the first, and during the beginning of the second, century of the present era), and especially in the thick volumes of Galen of Pérgamos (Γαληνός, Galenós, A.D. 129–201?), the greatest authority of Antiquity on medical science except Hippocrates. Its merit was that it was based upon knowledge gained directly from dissection of animal eyes. This Alexandrine or Galenian anatomy of the eye became almost the only source of information during the subsequent Arab period, when, because of Mohammedan religious scruples, no dissection was practiced. Toward the end of the Middle Ages and at the beginning of the Renaissance, when the interest in anatomy and natural sciences revived, it was passed from the Arabs to the early European anatomists.

The Greek anatomists, exemplified by Rûfos and Galen, distinguished the following coats of the eyeball: the cornea (*keratoëidés hitón*, "horn-like tunic"); sclera (*leukós* or *sklerós hitón*, "white" or "horny tunic"); uvea or iris (*rhago-ëidés hitón*, "grapelike tunic"); chorioid (*chorio-ëidés hitón*, "chorion-like tunic"); the anterior lens capsule with the ciliary zonule or suspensory ligament of Zinn (*phakoëidés hitón*, "lenticular tunic," or *krystalloëidés hitón*, "crystalline tunic"); and the retina (older term *arach-noëidés hitón*, "spiderweb tunic," also *hyaloëidés hitón*, "glassy tunic," later term *amphiblestro-ëidés hitón*, "netlike tunic"). Their order or sequence was, roughly, correct. Of the transparent media which fill the eyeball, they knew the aqueous (*hydatoëidés hygrón*, "water-like humor"), vitreous (*hyaloëidés hygrón*, "glasslike humor"), and the crystalline lens (*krystalloëidés hygrón*, "icelike humor"). From this it is apparent that the ancient Greek anatomists correctly identified and appraised all the parts of the eye which could be observed without benefit of magnifying glasses or could be seen at low magnification (*see* sec. 2, this chapter). (For a more detailed history of early anatomical studies of the eye *see* Polyak, *The Retina*, 1941, 1948.)

2. GREEK PHYSIOLOGY OF VISION.—Whereas the Greeks missed or erred in but few of the anatomical details, their functional interpretation of the structures of the eye was, for the most part, faulty. They were mistaken when they be-lieved the lens to be in the center of the eye. Furthermore, since the laws of light refraction, and hence the formation of the retinal image, were unknown to them (*see* sec. 2, this chapter), they assumed that the lens was the actual photoreceptor or principal organ of sight. The retina, because of its numerous blood vessels, they came to consider as both an organ of nutrition for the lens and a conveyor of the "visual spirit"—the mysterious element or force by which vision was thought to be effected—to and from the lens. The chorioid, rich in blood vessels, they believed to be the nutritive organ of the retina, which they thought nourished the vitreous, which in turn nourished the lens, thus freeing the latter of obstructing vascular structures.

Nevertheless, it was the Greeks, and particularly Galen, who noticed the resemblance of the retina in color and consistency to the substance of the brain and correctly guessed it to be a displaced part of the cerebrum (*see* sec. 6 [1], this chapter, and chap. II, 5 [1]). They erred, however, in their belief that the optic nerves were hollow channels, wherein a peculiar, subtle substance, the "luminous air" or "visual spirit" (*pneuma*) originating in the cerebral ventricles, was supposed to circulate to the eye and reach the lens, whence, after meeting the "visual rays" returning from outside, the *pneuma* would again flow back to the brain charged with images of observed objects. (*See* chap. II, 2 and 3.)

The chief reason for this erroneous functional interpretation of ocular structures was the fact that nothing positive was known about physical "light," and but little about its dissemination (*see* sec. 2, this chapter). In order to explain the phenomenon of vision, the majority of Greek philosophers and students of nature, apparently beginning with Empeoclés ('Εμπε-δοκλῆς, 5th century B.C.), assumed the presence of certain "visual rays" (ὄψις, *ópsis*, originally meaning "look," "appearance," "vision," "eye-sight," or "view"; see Aristotle, *De Sensu*, book 2, chaps. 6–9; *Meteora*, chaps. 1, 2, 5, 6, 9, 18; and Plato, *Timáios*, pars. 45C, 46B). Galen compared these very thin rays to delicate threads of cobweb. Emerging from the eye—which in this respect the Greek scholars and philosophers compared to the sun (e.g., Helio-

dóros of Larissa, 4th century, Christian Era)—
these visual rays, they thought, spread with immeasurable speed in straight lines in the form of
a rectangular cone whose summit was in the
pupil and whose base was at the observed object. When these rays touched the object, the
visual act was consummated in a manner similar to a blind person finding his way about with
the help of a walking stick. This was the simplest version of the "emanation hypothesis of
vision" proposed by Pythagóras (Πυθαγόρας,
532 B.C.) and accepted by his followers Euclid
(Εὐκλείδης, *ca.* 290 B.C.), Hípparchos of Nicea
(Ἱππαρχος, 2d century B.C.), the most renowned astronomer of Antiquity, and by Théon
of Alexandria (Θέων, 4th century, Christian
Era). Under the influence of Euclid's authority,
this hypothesis found wide acceptance among
such students of geometrical optics as Héron of
Alexandria (Ἡρων, *ca.* 1st century B.C.), Ptolemy (Πτολεμαῖος, Ptolemáios, *ca.* A.D. 100–161
or 178), Cleomédes (Κλεομέδης, early 3d century, Christian Era), and Heliodóros of Larissa
(Ἡλιοδώρος Λαρισσαῖος, early 4th century,
Christian Era). During the centuries following
Pythagóras, the emanation doctrine of vision
underwent numerous changes and adaptations
to suit particular views.

Of the rival theories, the one proposed by
Demócritos stated that all objects continuously
send forth images of themselves to the surrounding air, which are somewhat like the imprint that a seal makes in wax. Another hypothesis, by Epícuros (Ἐπίκουρος, 341–270
B.C.), assumed a discharge of countless shell-
like casts or "eidols" (ἔιδος, *éidos*, "image,"
"form," or "shape") made up of very thin matter. These eidols, or "impressions," by moving
in straight lines, reached the visual organs and
caused objects to be perceived.

While, in the hypothesis of visual rays, the
subjective, and, in those of the eidols or impressions, the objective, factor dominated, each to
the exclusion of the other, the hypothesis of
"synaugy" (συναύγεια, *synáugeia*) or union of
inner and outer visual rays, advocated by Plato
(Πλάτων, 427–347 B.C.), represented an attempt to combine both. According to his view,
the rays of "inner light" issuing from the pupils,
in order to accomplish the visual act, were supposed to unite with the rays of "outer light"

originating from the source of light, such as the
sun, and reflected by the observed objects.

Common to all early hypotheses of the visual
act, in particular the one adhered to by the
Stoics, was the implication that the sensations
elicited in the crystalline lens are conveyed to
the brain along with the "luminous pneuma" or
"inner light," where they educe subjective visual appreciation. (*Cf.* chap. II, 3 [3].)

A very different interpretation of the visual
act was proposed by Aristotle in his treatises
De Anima (book 2, chap. 7; *Parva Naturalia,
De Sensu,* chap. 2). The essence of his speculation was the assumption of an immaterial mediator—the "something" or "transparency"
which, according to modern thought, corresponds to the "ether" (ἀιθήρ), by means of
which viewed objects affect the visual organs.
Aristotle's idea, which alone among those of the
Classical Period was capable of further development, was unfortunately opposed by the majority of Greek thinkers, even though it found vigorous support in some (for example, Alexander
of Aphrodisías, who flourished *ca.* A.D. 200).

Since the indispensable prerequisite—theoretical knowledge of light refraction—was lacking during the Classical Period, there could
have been no understanding then of the formation of the visual image on the retina or of the
true role of the dioptrical media of the eye.

It is of interest to note, however, that Galen's explanation of the flattened lentil-like
shape of the crystalline lens as more advantageous than a spherical shape for the reception
of visual stimuli indicates perhaps some vague
presentiment of the part the refractive surfaces
of the transparent ocular media play in the formation of the retinal image (*see* Galen, *De Usu
Partium,* or *On the Use of Parts,* book 10,
chap. 15).

References: Alexander of Aphrodisias; Allbut;
R. M. Allen; Aristotle; Barkhuus 1945; Ber-
noulli 1901; Bhāvaprakāśa (*see* Esser 1930);
Bidyādhar; Bouman 1934; Breasted; Brunet &
Mieli; Budge 1913; Campbell Thompson; Cas-
tiglioni 1947; Castillo y Quartiellers; Celsus;
Chapot; Chievitz 1904; Cohen & Drabkin 1948;
Contenau; Cumston 1927; Damianós (*see also*
Heliodóros); Daremberg; Demócritos; Dill;
Dutt 1938; G. Ebers; Elgood; R. H. Elliot;
Empedoclés; Epícuros; Esser 1930, 1934; Eu-

clid; Gage; Galen; Garrison; H. Gerlach; Gibbon; Gordon 1942; Gossen; Greenidge; Gruner; Haas; Haeser; A. Haller 1774–76; E. Hamilton; Hekler 1912; Heliodóros (*see also* Damianós); Hemneter; Henderson 1917; Herget; Hípparchos; Hippocrátes; Hirsch; Hirschberg 1887, 1890, 1898, 1899; Ilberg; Jones; O. Katz 1890; A. C. Krause 1933, 1934; Laignel-Lavastine 1936–49; Leake; Leix; Locy 1910, 1925; Mach 1925; H. Magnus; Marquart 1886; T. H. Martin; Neuburger 1906–11, 1910; Meyerhof 1940; Meyerhof & Prüfer; W. Ogle 1882; Pagel 1915; Pauly & Wissowa 1894–1937; Plato; Pliny; W. B. Pollock 1945; Polyak 1941, 1948; Porterfield; Ptolemy; Puschmann, Neuburger & Pagel 1902–5; Pythagóras; Ranke 1933; Renouard; Ross 1923; Rostovtzeff; Rûfos or Rûphos; Sarton; Seelig; Seneca; Shastid; Sichel; Sigerist 1951; Simon 1906; Singer 1921, 1922, 1925, 1928, 1941; Soury; Southall 1922; Steindorff; Stillwell; Studniczka 1908; Suśruta (*see* Esser 1934); F. A. Taylor; H. L. Taylor; H. O. Taylor 1922; Théon; Thorndike; Ullrich; Waghji 1937; Wheeler 1946; Whitney & Lanman 1905; Wiedemann 1890; Zacher 1874; E. Zeller 1920–23; Zielinski 1931; Zimmer 1948.

SEC. 2. BEGINNING OF OPTICS AMONG THE EARLY CIVILIZED NATIONS

1. DISCOVERY OF THE RECTILINEAR PROPAGATION OF LIGHT AND GREEK CATOPTRICS.— What the ancient nations of the Near East, such as the Babylonians, Phoenicians, and Egyptians, knew about light and how it behaves when it is reflected from polished and variously curved surfaces or when it passes through transparent bodies is unknown. It seems probable that they knew little more than could be deduced from simple observation of everyday phenomena.

With the Greeks it was otherwise. Such notable students of the physical phenomena of nature as Euclid, Archimédes ('Αρχιμέδης, 287–212 B.C.), Héron of Alexandria, and their successors, Ptolemy, Heliodóros of Larissa, and others, observed a fundamental property of light: that it travels in straight lines. In the course of time, the Greek physicists succeeded in collecting a considerable number of observations based upon this fact and in organizing them into a system. Their knowledge, however, was almost entirely limited to "catoptrics," or the study of light reflected from polished plane or curved surfaces, such as variously shaped mirrors: plane, concave, convex, spherical, and cylindrical.

2. GREEK DIOPTRICS.—The experience of the Greeks and their pupils, the Romans, in "dioptrics," or understanding the principles and rules according to which light is refracted when it passes through variously shaped and polished transparent bodies of different optical properties, in contrast with their knowledge of "catoptrics," was rather slight (Euclid, Héron of Alexandria).

Nevertheless, the ancient nations seem to have possessed enough empirical knowledge of dioptrics to make considerable practical use of it. A number of lenses manufactured of glass or of transparent stone, mostly of Greek and Roman origin, found at Nineveh (Assyria), Nola and Pompeii (Italy), Mainz (Germany), London, and various places in France are evidence of this. They all are of a biconvex or planoconvex type and of short focus.

The lens found in 1854 during the excavations in *Via Stabia* in Pompeii (destroyed A.D. 79), now preserved at Naples, is of a planoconvex shape, 4 cm. or $1\frac{9}{16}$ in. in diameter, and, according to Cuming, "with the edge ground as if it had been set in a frame." Another lens, a fragment of which was found in London, is biconvex, with a diameter of almost $5\frac{1}{2}$ cm. or $2\frac{1}{8}$ in., and had a thickness of 1 cm. or $\frac{3}{8}$ in. The dimensions of yet another lens found at Mainz, according to Sacken, are: diameter 5.5 cm., axial thickness 5.9 mm., marginal thickness 1.8 mm., probable focal length between 18 and 19 cm. (the lens could have been used as both a "reading" and a "burning glass").

It is probable that such lenses, as well as the *specula* (sing. *speculum*), or magnifying concave mirrors, were used by ancient artists as magnifying utensils in making miniature engravings of precious and semiprecious stones, such as the *cameos* and *intaglios*, and probably also in making dies for coins. At any rate, the minute details of design and their exquisite execution make such an assumption probable. (*See* M. Rostovtzeff, *A History of the Ancient World*, 1926, v. 1, pls. 59, 84; v. 2, pls. 12, 27, 83, for examples of superbly executed Greek and Roman coins; *see also* "Gems, in Art," *Encyclopaedia Britannica*.

There is also evidence that the magnifying property and the heat-collecting power of biconvex lenses and of spherical bottles filled with water were well known, even though not understood. In the case of the bottles the magnifying power was interpreted as the property of water itself (by Seneca; the only exception seems to have been Heliodóros of Larissa, who alone explained these phenomena by the refraction of light). In England such spherical bottles, precursors of the "crystals of augury" used by modern fortunetellers, were known as "Seneca's microscopes." In German lands they were called *Schusterkugeln*, or "cobblers' lamps," because they were used by the shoemakers in nightwork. Occasionally, similar illuminators are used at present in microscopy. That such bottles and lenses were in general use as "burning glasses" by surgeons in both Greece and Rome can be deduced from the writings of Aristophanes (*Clouds*, vs. 767), and of Pliny the Elder (*Plinius*, A.D. 23–79, *Hist. Nat.*, book 37, chap. 10). It is less certain whether the Greeks and Romans had any knowledge of concave lenses or polished stones and their optical properties. A passage in Pliny telling of the Emperor Nero's use of a concave emerald to correct his myopia when attending gladiatorial combats was interpreted in this sense by Rohr (1920) and by Landolt (1926). (*See* sec. 5 [2], this chapter, for a discussion of the origin of eyeglasses.)

Simple dioptrical phenomena, such as the apparent break in a rod or paddle when it is partly submerged in water (Lucretius); the "rising" of a ring or coin from the bottom of an empty vessel, which becomes visible when the vessel is filled with water (Cleomédes, Seneca, Ptolemy); magnification of letters when viewed through a bottle filled with water, and a more beautiful appearance of fruit when submerged in water, etc. (Seneca); perception of the sun and stars before they have actually risen or after they have set below the horizon (Cleomédes, Ptolemy), were recognized by many Greek and Roman writers as caused by refraction—although not of light but of "visual rays" coming from the eyes—at the point of entry into a denser or less dense medium. (*See also* Archimédes, Damianós, Heliodóros, Nemésios, Philipónos.)

Similar advanced views of optical phenomena were expressed, above all, by Ptolemy, celebrated Alexandrine astronomer, physicist, and geographer. His measurement of the relationships of the angle of incidence to the angle of refraction for different degrees of incidence and various combinations of transparent media—air and water, air and glass, and water and glass—may be considered the beginning of the science of dioptrics in the modern sense.

There is little doubt that the Greeks and Romans established a good foundation in optics. Unfortunately, the events which brought to an end the entire structure of Classical Civilization, its ethical, political, social, and economic disintegration, terminating in the invasion of the barbarians, stopped all advancement of science, in spite of a few late efforts by Théon of Alexandria and a few others.

References: Archimédes; Aristophánes; Badermann; Bock; Brunet & Mieli; Cantor; Cleomédes; Cohen & Drabkin 1948; Damianós (*see also* Heliodóros); Delambre 1817; Euclid; P. Harting 1866; T. L. Heath; Heliodóros (*see also* Damianós); Héron of Alexandria; Hoppe 1926; Landolt 1926; Lucretius; Mach 1925; T. H. Martin; Neugebauer; Pansier 1901; Pauschmann; Pliny; Priestley; Ptolemy; Rohr; Rostovtzeff; Sacken; Seneca; Théon of Alexandria; Wilde 1838–43.

SEC. 3. ARAB KNOWLEDGE OF THE STRUCTURE AND FUNCTION OF THE EYE AND OF OPTICS

1. THE RISE OF ARAB CIVILIZATION AND LEARNING.—After the moral and material disintegration of the Roman Empire and the Classical Civilization it preserved, there was a long period of political confusion and economic decay and a general intellectual reversion to pre-Classical primitiveness and barbarism throughout most of Europe. This epoch, the so-called Dark Ages, lasted from approximately the fifth to the tenth century. Only in the Near East, parts of Asia Minor, and Syria did a few scattered groups of scholars, principally the Nestorian and Jacobite Christians, manage to salvage vestiges of ancient Greek learning. Such were the religious communities in Urfa or Edessa (Al-Ruhāʾ), Antioch (Antakya), and Damascus (Dimashq al-Shām, Damas). Banished from the Byzantine Empire during the fifth and sixth centuries, these Christians finally found refuge in Persia or Iran, where the city of Gondē-Shāpūr became their center (probably the present village of Shahabad, near Kermanshah, in Khuzistan).

In Alexandria and in Egypt the ancient "Academy" was still continuing its precarious existence, pushed as it was into obscurity by cataclysmic events, the rise of an obscurantist intolerance, and a general decline of civilization.

From these scattered remnants of Greek learning, in the course of the seventh and eighth centuries after the rise of Islam to world importance, a new enlightenment developed known as "Arab Civilization." Its zenith was reached under the wise rule of the caliphs, or emperors, Al-Manṣūr (A.D. 754–75), Hārūn al-Rashīd (A.D. 786–809), Al-Maʾmūn (A.D. 813–33), and Al-Muʿtaṣim (A.D. 833–42). This Arab Civilization subsequently spread over all the Mohammedan countries, westward across Egypt and North Africa to Spain, and eastward across Persia to Central Asia, India, and, to some extent, as far as China. Within this spacious territory numerous centers of learning developed, the earliest and most splendid in Baghdad, capital of Iraq and residence of the caliph. The influence of this civilization upon the character of the nations within its sphere was profound and lasting.

It was through Arab Civilization that ancient Greek learning was preserved and transmitted to Europe. It was the fountainhead of the Renaissance and the foundation on which modern Western Civilization has been built. (*See* chap. II, 6.)

2. ARAB INTEREST IN OPHTHALMOLOGY AND SCIENCES RELATED TO THE EYE AND VISION.— Among the branches of learning to which the Arabs and other nations under their sway paid particular attention were the mathematical sciences, optics, astronomy, and medicine. Of the medical sciences, ophthalmology was one of the most favored. The obvious reason for this was the prevalence in the Near East of infectious eye diseases, especially trachoma, also called "Egyptian ophthalmia." (For the history of the term "trachoma" *see* Paparcone; for a vivid description of conditions in Syria and Palestine a century ago *see* Mark Twain's *Innocents Abroad*, chap. 45; for similar conditions prevalent in modern India *see* R. H. Elliot and C. G. Henderson; for conditions in ancient and modern Egypt *see* J. Hirschberg 1890 and Castiglioni 1947.)

The result of this persistent Arab interest in the eye is a considerable number of treatises on ophthalmology. The most ancient of them was written by Ḥunain ibn Isḥāḳ (Latin Johannitius, 809–73), a famous translator of Greek writings into Arabic. Other Arabic books on ophthalmology in their chronological order were those written by ʿAlī ibn ʿĪsā (ʿAlī ben ʿIssā, died 1010), ʿAmmār (*ca.* 1010), Zarrīn-Dast (1087), Ibn Abī Usaibiʿah (1203/4–70), Khalīfa (*ca.* 1260), and Ṣalāḥ al-Dīn (*ca.* 1297). Of these, the best known is *Kitāb Ḥunain ibn Isḥāḳ fī tartībi al-ʿaini wa-ʿilalihā wa-ʿilajihā ʿalā rāʾi Abukrāṭ wa Jālīnūs wa hiyā ʿashr makālāt*, or *The Book of Ḥunain ibn Isḥāḳ on the Structures of the Eye, Its Diseases, and Their Treatment, According to the Teaching of Hippocrates and Galen, in Ten Treatises*, written during the ninth century and translated into English by Meyerhof (1928). Another well-known book is *Tadhkirat al-kaḥḥalin*, or *The Oculist's Memorandum Book* by ʿAlī ibn ʿĪsā, a native of Persia, written during the eleventh century and translated by A. C. Wood (1936).

The most prominent of the Arabic treatises on optics is *Kitāb al-manāẓir*, or *Book of Optics*, known in Latin under the title *Opticae Thesaurus*, by Ibn al-Haitham (Lat. Alhazen or Alhacen, b. 965 A.D. at Basra, in Iraq; d. 1039 A.D. in Cairo, Egypt). This treatise, apparently based chiefly on Euclid and Ptolemy, was written in Cairo during the early part of the eleventh century. Arabic manuscripts, considered lost until a few years ago, have recently been discovered in Istanbul, Turkey; a few

Latin manuscripts have been preserved in Britain and elsewhere, while a printed Latin edition was published in Basel (1572). Another similar treatise, *Kitāb tanqīḥ al-manāẓir li-dawī al-abṣār wa al-baṣāʾir*, or *Making Optics Understandable for Those Who Possess Perspicacity and Insight*, by Kamāl al-Dīn Abūʾl Ḥassan al-Fārisī, a learned Persian, looked upon as a commentary to Ibn al-Haitham's *Book of Optics*,

important than the text, which are the earliest pictorial representations in existence of the structures of the eye, the optic nerves, and the brain. Such figures are found in the manuscripts of Ibn al-Haitham (MS dated 1083; Fig. 56), of Ḥunain ibn Isḥāk (MS dated 1197; Figs. 2, 3; *see also* Meyerhof 1928; Meyerhof & Prüfer); of Khalīfa (MS dated 1266; *see* Hirschberg 1908); of Salāḥ al-Dīn (MS dated 1296; *see*

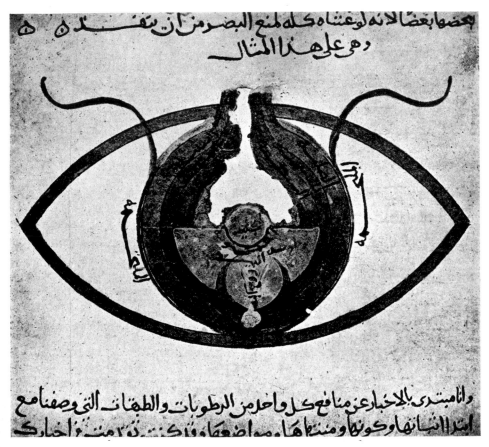

Fɪɢ. 2.—Photographic reproduction of a diagram of the eye from a manuscript written by Ḥunain ibn Isḥāk entitled *Ten Treatises on the Structure of the Eye, Its Diseases, and Their Treatment*. Date of the manuscript in which the figure was found, A.D. 1197; date of the manuscript from which it was copied, A.D. 1003; approximate date of the original manuscript, A.D. 860. From M. Meyerhof & C. Prüfer, Arch. f. d. Gesch. d. Med. (Sudhoff), v. 4, p. 163, 1911.

was written about 1316 and exists in both Arabic and Latin manuscripts, as well as in a modern Arabic edition (1928–30).

3. Aʀᴀʙ ᴀɴᴀᴛᴏᴍʏ ᴏꜰ ᴛʜᴇ ᴇʏᴇ.—A common feature of all Arabic treatises and textbooks on ophthalmology and optics is a detailed description of the structure and function of the visual organs. They also contain diagrams, even more

Hirschberg; Pansier 1903, p. 89); and of Kamāl al-Dīn Abūʾl-Ḥassan al-Fārisī (MS dated 1316; *see* Fig. 4). These and possibly other Arab diagrams mentioned by Pansier in the writings of Morched de Errafequy (Escorial Library No. 835, *encient* 830), Salāḥ Eddin (Bibliothèque Nationale, No. 1042 du Fond Arabe, Paris), and of Al-Quazwînî (Wiedemann 1912), as well as the texts, clearly show the extent and kind of knowledge that Arab ophthalmologists and writers on optics had of the structures of the eye and their mechanics. Since Mohammedan tenets prohibited dissection of the human and animal body even more strictly than did Christian beliefs, no active anatomical investigation was possible during the Arab period. This made Arab writers wholly dependent upon Greek sources. It is probable that the Arab diagrams also are copies of, or adaptations from, ancient Greek illustrations now lost, which makes them even more valuable as historical documents. (*Cf.* K. Sudhoff 1912.)

"water"—hence "waterfall" (καταρράκτης, or "cataract"). (*See* sec. 1 [1], this chapter, for information on Hindu operations for cataract.)

4. Arab physiology of vision.—The learned men of the Arab period, seriously handicapped as they were in their researches by their religious customs, also depended upon the Greeks for the functional interpretation of eye structures. It is to their credit that the most prominent among those ancient scholars raised their voices in protest against the "emanation hypothesis of vision." However, there was a

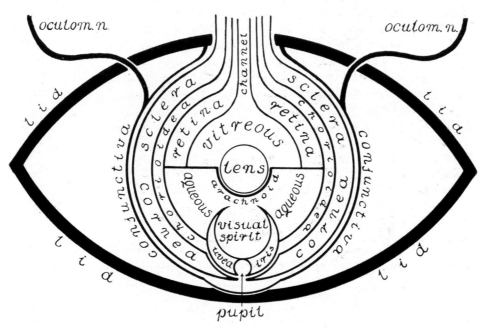

Fig. 3.—Drawing of the Arabic diagram shown in Fig. 2, with the various parts of the eye labeled in English

Knowing the derivative character of the Arab ophthalmological sciences, it is not surprising to see Arab students of the eye repeating all the familiar mistakes found in the Greek originals: central location of the crystalline lens; the belief that the optic nerves are hollow; belief in a "visual spirit"; the photoreceptor role of the crystalline lens; and the "emanation hypothesis" of vision. It is remarkable that, in spite of these theoretical errors, Arab ophthalmic surgeons devised the method of aspiration with a hollow needle for removal of a macerated lens in cases of cataract, which they, accepting the mistaken interpretation of their Greek teachers, considered to be an accumulation of

significant difference between the Arab and Greek criticism of this theory. Among the Greeks its opponents were students of nature, such as Demócritos, Alexander of Aphrodisías, Themístios, and Aristotle, against the speculators and clever dialecticians of the Platonic School; in the Arab Period the opposition to the absurd emanation doctrine arose chiefly from physicists and philosophers, against the practical ophthalmologists.

The following phrases of the most prominent Arab student of optics, Ibn al-Haitham, or Alhazen, leave no doubt as to his viewpoint in this matter: "The act of vision is not accomplished by means of rays emitted from the visual organ"; and "The belief of those who think that something comes out of the visual organ is false" (Alhazen, *Opticae Thesaurus*, 1572, book 1, chap. 5, theor. 23); and "Vision is accomplished by rays coming from external objects and entering into the visual organ" (*ibid.*, theor. 14). These were the ideas which almost literally repeat the words Aristotle used more than one thousand years earlier to oppose the emanation hypothesis of his contemporaries (*De Sensu*, chap. 2, *Parva Nat.*); insignificant though these ideas may seem to have been, they had a number of prominent adherents throughout the Arab world: Al-Fārābī (870–950), Al-Rāzī (Fahr al-Dīn al-R., Lat. Rhazes, *ca.* 850–932), Ibn Sīnā (Lat. Avicenna, 980–1037), Ibn Rushd (Lat. Averroës, 1126–98), and Ṣalāḥ al-Dīn. The full importance of Ibn al-Haitham's convictions became apparent much later, when the correct interpretation of the structures of the

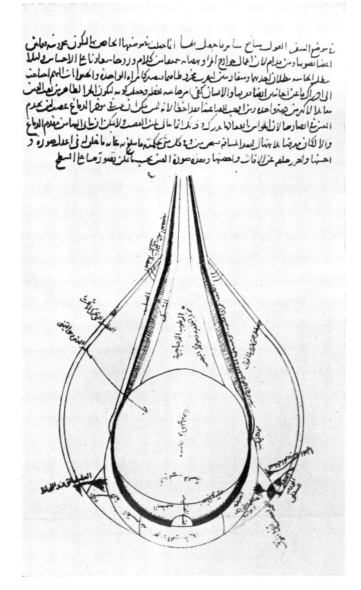

FIG. 4.—Eye diagram from an Arabic manuscript entitled *Tanquīḥ al-manāẓir* or *Explanation of Optics*, written A.D. 1316 by Kamāl al-Dīn Abu'l-Ḥasan al-Fārisī, a Persian writer on optics. Ahmet Salis Library, Topkapu Saray, Istanbul, Turkey.

eye was made possible by the advancement of optical sciences and optical technique (*see* sec. 5, this chapter).

5. ARAB OPTICS.—The knowledge of optics which Arab scholars adopted from their Greek masters was preponderantly catoptrics, or the science concerned with light reflected from polished plane and curved surfaces, e.g., variously shaped mirrors. Dioptrics, or the science of the refraction of light, was in its infancy during the Greek Period and experienced but little

advancement during the Arab Period. The lack of dioptrics, in turn, was an insurmountable obstacle to correct functional interpretation of the eye. The idea of the formation of a visual image which Ibn al-Haitham had was inadequate, even though it represented a step in the right direction. Its fundamental defect was that he considered perpendicular rays only, thus missing the main factor, which is the diverging radiation of light rays in all directions from every point of an illuminated surface. Another error of the Arab concept was placing the "visu-

FIG. 5.—Title-page of the oldest manuscript of *Kitāb al-manāẓir* or *Book of Optics*, written 1083 by Ibn al-Haitham, an Arabic scholar, known to the Latin West as Alhazen. Ayasofya Library, Istanbul, Turkey.

al pyramid" at the posterior surface of the "glacial sphere" instead of upon the retina (*see* Ibn al-Haitham, *Opticae Thesaurus*, book 1, chap. 5, theor. 24). If the glacial sphere in his figure be identified with the lens, the visual image would be far in front of the retina (Fig. 4). It is true that in a few places in Ibn al-Haitham's book the text lends itself to a different interpretation (book 2, chap. 1, theor. 8). According to this, the glacial sphere would comprise both the lens and the vitreous humor, which would put the image almost upon the retina. There is, however, reason to think that

inversion, and possibly also of the diminished size of the image. Since no refraction is involved in a simple pinhole camera, however, it is apparent that not much was gained thereby for the immediate development of ocular dioptrics. (*See* Polyak, *The Retina*, p. 133.)

Incidentally, Ibn al-Haitham's writings prove that the dark chamber (*camera obscura*, or "pinhole camera"), the precursor of the modern photographic camera, was well known to Arab scholars. They also support the view that the dark chamber was used by them (e.g., by Ibn al-Haitham and Kamāl al-Fārisī) in their

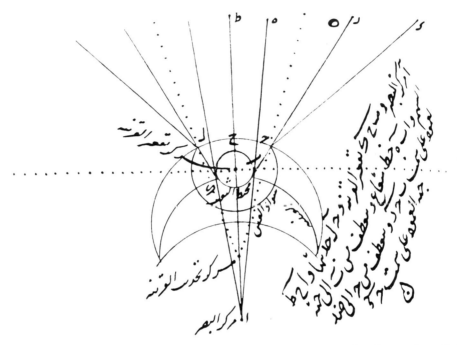

FIG. 6.—Diagram explaining the function of the eye, from *Kitāb al-baṣaʾir fī ʿilm al-manāẓir*, or *Book of Reflexions on the Science of Optics* by Kamāl al-Dīn Abuʾl-Ḥasan al-Fārisī, dated 1433. Ayasofya Library, Istanbul, Turkey.

the latter version was purely accidental and was caused by an insufficient acquaintance with the structure of the eye.

Be this as it may, Ibn al-Haitham advanced considerably beyond the Greeks, abandoning the emanation doctrine altogether. His frank comparison of the eye with a "dark chamber" went a long way toward the correct understanding of ocular structures (*op. cit.*, p. 17). From his detailed description of the "dark chamber" there is no doubt that he, as far as he went, had quite a correct idea of the formation of the image in it. This was true particularly of the

observations of solar and lunar eclipses centuries before it became known to Europeans (e.g., Leonardo da Vinci, Giambattista della Porta, and many others to whom its discovery has mistakenly been attributed).

(*See* Curtze; Pauschmann; Polyak; Wiedemann 1910, 1912, 1914, 1923; *Encyc. Brit.*, 14th ed., "Camera Obscura," unsigned article, prob. by J. Waterhouse.)

References: Abdallatif 1810; Al-Fārābī; Alhazen (Ibn al-Haitham); Al-Rāzī (Rhazes); Averroës (Ibn Rushd); ʿAlī ibn ʿIsā; ʿAmmār; Avicenna (Ibn Sīnā); Bergsträsser; Brockel-

mann; Browne; Brunet & Mieli; Budge; Butler
1902; Calvert & Gallichan; D. Campbell; Carra
de Vaux; Casanova 1923; Castiglioni 1947;
Chievitz 1904; Choulant; Curtze; Delambre
1817; De Lint; Diercks; Dozy; Dozy & Stokes;
Duhem; R. Duval 1899; Elgood 1951; R. H.
Elliot 1918; *Encyclopaedia Britannica*, 14th ed.,
v. 4, p. 658 (prob. J. Waterhouse); Fukala;
Furlani 1925; Furnari 1845; Gabrieli; Edw.
Gibbon; L. W. Gilbert 1812; Hell; Henderson
1917; Hirschberg 1890, 1908, 1918; Hirschberg
& Lippert; Hitti 1937, 1951; Holmyard; Howorth; Ḥunain ibn Isḥāk (Johannitius); Husson
1937; Ibn Abi Ussaibiʿah; Ibn al-Haitham (Al-
hazen); Ibn Rushd (Averroës); Issa Bey 1928;
Jones; Kamāl al-Dīn; Khairallah 1946; Khalīfa;
Koning; P. Kraus; M. Krause; Kremer; Le Bon;
Leclerc; McCallan; Mach 1925; Meyerhof;
Meyerhof & Prüfer; Mieli; Montucla; Muratori; Narducci; Nazif Bey; Pansier; Paparcone;
Pauschmann; Pollock 1945, 1946; Polyak 1941
or 1948; Rashīd al-Dīn; Rhazes (Al-Rāzī); Ritter & Walzer 1934; M. Rohr 1920, 1940; Ṣalāḥ
al-Dīn; Sarton; Schrutz; Sédillot; Sichel; Singer
1921; Sudhoff 1907, 1912, 1915; Thomas; J.
Waterhouse (prob.) 1932; Wiedemann 1910,
1912, 1914, 1923; Wilde; Wood 1936; Wüstenfeld 1840; Zarrīn-Dast.

SEC. 4. INTRODUCTION OF THE ARAB ARTS AND SCIENCES INTO EUROPE, AND THE EUROPEAN RENAISSANCE

1. THE ROLE OF ARAB LEARNING IN THE EU-
ROPEAN REVIVAL OF ARTS AND SCIENCES.—
Toward the end of the eleventh century, and
more especially during the twelfth, fragments
of Classical Greek medicine and other learning,
preserved, changed, and added to by Arab
scholars, began to filter into Western Europe.
To a small extent this knowledge came directly
from Byzantion by way of southern Italy (Con-
stantine the African of Monte Cassino; Magister Zacharias; Salernitan School; Sicily), but
arrived chiefly through Spain ("Translator
School" of Toledo, the "shiny center," founded
by Gerhardus Cremonensis, or Gerard of Cremona, 1114–87). After a millennium of intellectual darkness, the nations of Southern and
Western Europe began gradually to awaken by
a stimulus coming from the Arab world.

By a curious fate, this occurred at the time
when Arab Civilization itself showed signs of
decline: in 1058, Seljuk Turks under Togrul
conquered the city of Baghdad and with it almost the entire Near East; next, the Christian
Crusades stirred up an intolerant orthodox reaction among the Arabs; thereafter came destructive invasions by the Mongols, first under Temūchin or Genghis Khan, and later under Ti-
mūr i Leng or Tamerlane. A final blow was delivered by the Mongols under Hulagu in 1258,
by the destruction of Baghdad and by the
invasion of Ottoman Turks. In the West, Cór-
doba, in 1236, and Seville, in 1248, were re-
conquered by Christian Spaniards.

The time of early Arab influence upon Southwestern Europe may be considered the beginning of the Modern Period of Western Civilization. Here, too, as in the oriental model after
which it was patterned, medicine and the science of optics were among the most esteemed of
several branches of learning. The science of optics, since its introduction into Western Europe
at the beginning of the second millennium,
exerted a powerful influence upon generations
of learned men interested in the relationship of
the human mind to the body, in life, and in the
physical world in general.

Their interest eventually brought about the
discovery of the laws of optics, the correct understanding of ocular structures and their functions, and the invention of ingenious optical
instruments, such as the telescope and microscope.

Early Western anatomy and physiology of
the eye and early European optics were borrowed from the Arabs. The Arab treatises
translated into Latin (Ibn Sīnā or Avicenna,
Al-qānūn fī al-ṭibb, or *Canon of Medicine;* Ibn
al-Haitham, or Alhazen, *Kitāb al-manāẓir* or
Book of Optics; Kamāl al-Fārisī, *Kitāb tanqīḥ
al-manāẓir*, or *Making Optics Understandable*),
as well as many others, became standard texts
and remained supreme authorities for several
centuries to come.

2. EARLY WESTERN EUROPEAN TREATISES
ON OPTICS.—The nations of Europe, still deeply

enveloped in barbarism, were as yet ill prepared to accept and to digest the wealth of new information, and even less to add significant contributions.

The earliest Western treatises on optics, quite naturally, were hardly more than compilations from Ibn al-Haitham's *Thesaurus*, rendered into Latin sometime during the twelfth century by an unknown translator, possibly Gerard of Cremona or one of his Toledan "School of Translators." This was true of the first treatise written in Europe about 1270, the voluminous *Perspectiva* or *Ten Books of Optics*,

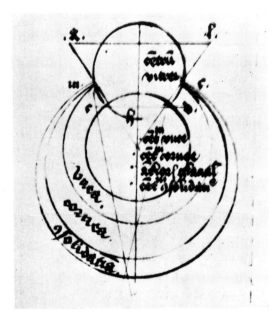

Fig. 7.—Geometrical eye diagram from *Opus Maius* by Roger Bacon, *doctor mirabilis*, the learned English Franciscan friar, of Oxford. From a fifteenth-century manuscript, at Bodleian Library, Oxford, England.

by Vitello (Witelo, incorrectly also Vitellio, 1220 or 1230–70 or 1278), a native of Silesia, then a part of Poland (he was therefore called *Thuringopolonus*, that is, a German-Pole).

Two other treatises, very similar to Vitello's book, written at about the same time in England, which became standard textbooks during the remainder of the Middle Ages, are the *Perspectiva* of the learned friar Roger Bacon of Oxford (1214–92) and the *Perspectiva Communis* of John Peckham, archbishop of Canterbury (approx. 1228 or 1240–91 or 1292). In these compilations the Greek sources then available (e.g., Euclid; Ptolemy; Apollónios, 3d or 2d

century B.C.; Theodósios, 2d century B.C.; Menélaos, end of 1st century, Christian Era; Páppos, end of 3d and early part of 4th century, Christian Era; Théon, 4th century, Christian Era; Próclos, 410–85) were likewise used, particularly by Vitello and Bacon; but the chief source remained Ibn al-Haitham's *Thesaurus* and, in the following centuries, apparently also Kamāl al-Fārisī's *Tanqîḥ*. The scope and standard of all these early Western books on optics was naturally Greek and Arab, with all the virtues and faults of the originals.

3. Early European anatomy and physiology of the eye.—The mistakes of the Greeks and Arabs concerning the structure of the eye and its functional interpretation are all encountered in the early Western treatises. For example, in the writings of Roger Bacon we find references to the central location of the crystalline lens, the lens as an actual photoreceptor, the cavity in the optic nerves, the "emanation hypothesis of vision," and the existence of a *pneuma* or "visual spirit." The problem of light refraction and of the formation of a visual image and hence the true functional significance of the retina remained as yet unconsidered. Nor did European anatomy and ophthalmic surgery of the Late Middle Ages, primitive and crude as they were, do much to advance knowledge or correct erroneous concepts. (Alcoatin 1159; Benevenutus Grassus of Jerusalem; Henry de Mondeville 1304; Mondino de'Luzzi or Mundinus 1315; Guy de Chauliac or Cauliacus 1363; Manfredi 1490; Fernel 1542; Du Laurens 1599.)

In fact, from that period until far into Modern Times, there was hardly any independent Western anatomy and physiology of the eye worthy of the name.

(On early European ophthalmology and surgery, *see* Pansier 1908, v. 2, p. 99, and Hirschberg 1908.)

4. Early Western eye diagrams.—Western dependence upon Arab sources is nowhere better manifested than in the various eye diagrams found in the manuscripts and early printed books and treatises on optics of this period, which are all adaptations from the Arabic originals. Even the best of these diagrams—for example, those found in the various Latin manuscripts of Roger Bacon (Figs. 7, 8), of John Peckham (Fig. 9), of Ibn al-Haitham's *Opticae Thesaurus* (Fig. 10), of Vitello's *Ten Books of Optics* (Fig. 11), and in other similar writings of the Late Middle Ages—are a jumble of circles and lines, with hardly a semblance of anatomical reality. Even so, all the early Western eye diagrams betray their Arabic, and hence Greek, origin, of which they are mostly inept, degraded copies. (Alhazen 1572; Avicenna; Bacon; Bar-

er of Anatomy" (1513 or 1514–64, portrait Fig. 15; *see also* Figs. 16, 17); in the figure of Felix Platter (1583, 1603; *see* Fig. 19); and in that of Aguilonius (1613, Fig. 20).

Not before the work of Girolamo Fabrizi d'Aquapendente (Lat. Hieronymus Fabricius ab Aquapendente, 1600, portrait Fig. 21), and of Christopher Scheiner (1619; *see* Fig. 22 and portrait, Fig. 30), both based upon personal experience, was there, in fact, a break with the

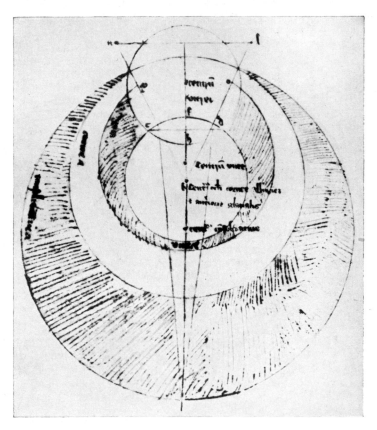

Fig. 8.—Another eye diagram by Roger Bacon, found in a fifteenth-century manuscript of his *Perspectiva*. Bodleian Library, Oxford, England.

tisch; *Codex Lipsiensis* No. 1183; Maurolycus; Peckham; Reisch; Ryff; Vitello; Vogtherr; *see also* Choulant; Crew; Polyak 1941 or 1948; Rohr 1924; Sudhoff 1907, 1915; *cf.* Figs. 12, 13, 14, 16, 18, 19, 20.)

Even later, Arab influence is still clearly noticeable. It can be traced in various sketches of the eye by Leonardo da Vinci (1452–1519), the encyclopedic genius of the Italian Renaissance; in the somewhat improved diagram and plate of Andreas Vesalius (1543), the "Reform-

erroneous views on the internal structure of the eye inherited from the Greek period of almost two thousand years before (*see also* R. Columbus). The cruder, external parts of the eye, in contrast, had already become better known from Vesalius' description (Fig. 17). (For further information on history, eye diagrams, legends, and quotations *see* Polyak 1941 or 1948.)

References: Alcoatin; Alhazen (Ibn al-Haitham); *Anonymus; Anonymus*-Winthrop; H. F.

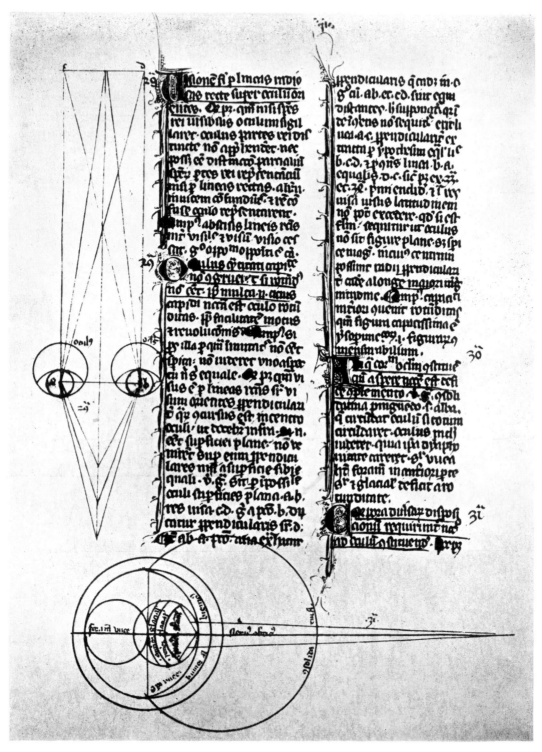

Fig. 9.—Two eye diagrams found in a fourteenth-century Latin manuscript of *Perspectiva* by John Peckham, the learned archbishop of Canterbury, written during the thirteenth century. The upper diagram purports to explain binocular vision; the lower diagram, the structure of the eye. Bodleian Library, Oxford, England.

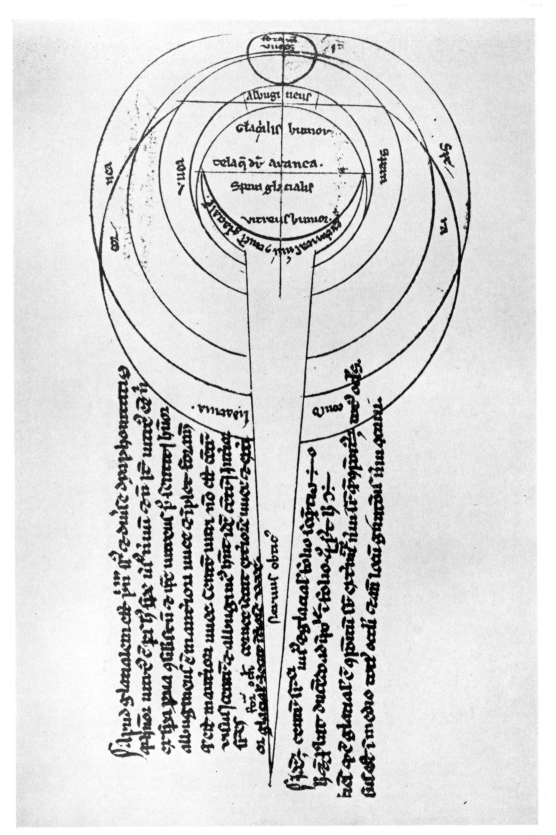

Fig. 10.—Geometrical eye diagram from a thirteenth-century Latin manuscript of Ibn al-Haitham's or Alhazen's *Opticae Thesaurus*, a translation from the Arabic original entitled *Kitāb al-manāẓir* or *Book of Optics*. Crawford Library, Royal Observatory, Edinburgh, Scotland. This and other similar diagrams illustrate the debased Western medieval knowledge and presentation of the visual organs as compared with the Arabic presentation. (*Cf.* Figs. 2, 4, 56.)

Aquapendens; Avicenna (Ibn Sīnā); R. Bacon; Baeumker; Ball; Barbensi 1947; Bartisch; Bauer; Bednarski 1935; Bock; Bouyges; Boncompagni 1871; Brunet & Mieli; A. H. Buck: Burckhardt; Burggraeve; Capparoni; Castiglioni 1947; Cauliacus (Guy de Chauliac); Chievitz 1904; Choulant; Chauliac (Cauliacus); R. Columbus 1559; Constantin Africanus (*see* Corner 1927, Pansier, v. 2, p. 157, and Sudhoff 1932); Corner 1927, 1931; Crew; Cullen; Curtze; Dampier; Da Vinci (Leonardo da V.); De Renzi; Diercks; Dozy; Dozy & Stokes; Du Laurens (Laurentius); W. Durant 1953; Edinger 1892; Girolamo Fabrizi or Hieronymus

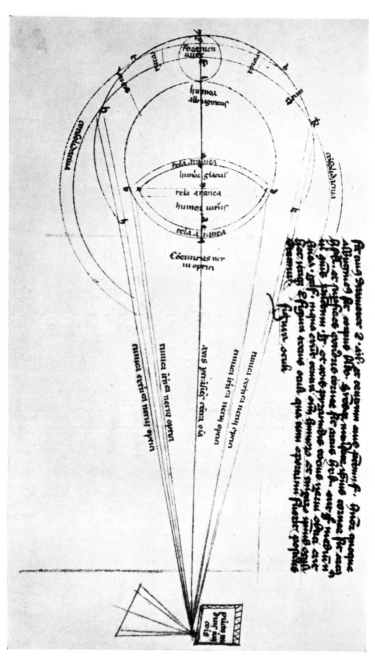

FIG. 11.—Another geometrical eye diagram found in a Latin manuscript of *Perspectiva* by Vitello, a native of Silesia, the first book on optics written in Europe after the downfall of Classical Civilization. Fourteenth-century manuscript, Bodleian Library, Oxford, England.

Fabricius ab Aquapendente; Fernelius; Fröbes; Gerard of Cremona (*see* Boncompagni 1851; Sudhoff 1914, 1930; Nallino); Benevenutus Grassus; Güdemann; Guy de Chauliac (Cauliacus); Haskins; Hirschberg; Hopstock; Hurd-Mead; Ibn Sīnā (Avicenna); Jourdain; Kamāl al-Fārisī; Krembs; Lenard; Lévi-Provençal; Leonardo da Vinci; Little 1914; Locy; Mach 1925; L. C. MacKinney; McMurrick; Manfredi; Maurolycus; Meyerhof 1920; Henry de Mondeville; Mondino de'Luzzi (Mundinus); Muratori; Nallino; Narducci; Pansier; Passera; J. Peckham; F. Platter; Polyak 1941, 1948; Priestley; Rashīd al-Dīn; Reisch; Riesman; Roger Bacon; Rohr 1924, 1940; Roth; Ryff; Sarton; Chr. Scheiner; Schnaase; Sédillot; Singer; Sorsby 1948; Southall 1922; Spielmann; Steele; Steinschneider; Sudhoff 1907, 1915; Suter; Symonds; Symonds & Smith; Thorndike; Vinci (Leonardo da V.); Vitello (Witelo); Vogl; Vogtherr; Wiedemann; Wilde; Würschmidt; Wüstenfeld; Zacharias; Zebrawski.

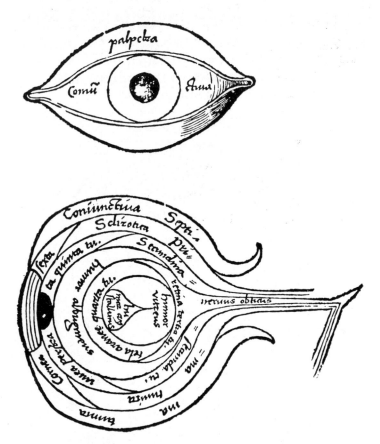

Fig. 12.—A somewhat more correct presentation of the external parts and of the internal structure of the eye and optic nerves published in *Margarita Philosophica* by Gregor Reisch, printed in Strassburg, 1504, betraying an Arabic, and hence a Classical Greek, influence. From K. Sudhoff, Stud. z. Gesch. d. Med., Fasc. 1. J. A. Barth, Leipzig, 1907.

SEC. 5. EARLY MODERN OPTICS AND DISCOVERY OF THE RETINAL IMAGE

1. KNOWLEDGE OF THE STRUCTURE OF THE EYE AND THE ADVANCEMENT OF EARLY WESTERN OPTICS.—Since the vertebrate eye is a dioptrical apparatus constructed according to the principles of physical optics, in particular those of light refraction, its correct interpretation was not possible until the basic laws of refraction had been formulated. In turn, the discovery of laws of refraction, or the behavior of light when it passes through the variously propertied and differently shaped transparent bodies, depended to a great extent upon the correct under-

standing of ocular structures. The solution of these mutually interdependent problems was a long process, which ultimately led to the highly advanced modern physiology of vision and modern optics.

2. INVENTION OF EYEGLASSES.—The earliest attempts at a practical application of dioptrics were made during Classical Antiquity (*see* sec. 2, this chapter). There is no sure evidence that the Greeks or Romans or any other nation of the Ancient World had either sufficient theoretical knowledge or practical experience in making objects of glass to make lenses that would be of much use as aids to defective vision (*see* sec. 2 [2], this chapter). It is certain that spectacles were not known during Classical Antiquity or during the greater part of the Middle Ages.

Neither is the thesis of a non-European ori-

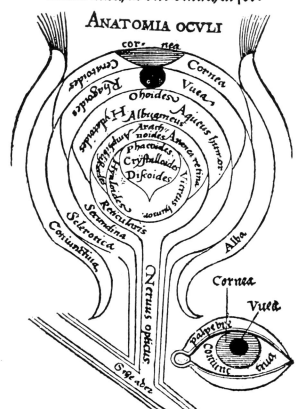

FIG. 13.—Structure and external view of the eye from *A New Most Highly Useful Little Book, and Anothomy of an Open Eye, Together with Its Explanation, Well-tried Purgation, Application, Poultice, Fine Salves, Powders and Waters, and How To Make Them and To Use Them*, by Heinrich Vogtherr, printed in Strassburg, 1539. Note all labeling in Latin except the optic nerve, which is also called, in German, *Sehader*, or "visual vessel," referring to the ancient concept of the optic nerves as hollow channels. From K. Sudhoff, Stud. z, Gesch. d. Med., Fasc. 1, p. 24. J. A. Barth, Leipzig, 1907.

gin of spectacles well documented. In China the use of spectacles cannot be traced with certainty earlier than the time of Marco Polo's travels (1271–95). It is probable that the knowledge of how to make spectacles had spread from Europe to China, rather than from China to Europe. This knowledge could most reasonably have been passed along the trade routes opened by the temporary political and economic unification of most of Eurasia in the wake of Mongol conquests initiated by Genghis Khan (Temūchin), the "Perfect Warrior," during the early part of the thirteenth century. A contrary statement by Cuming (1855) concerning the antiquity of Chinese spectacles and of the *ocularia* supposedly in use at Constantinople as early as A.D. 1150, requires careful modern verification. This applies also to a statement on the great age of Chinese lenses made in a pamphlet on *Ophthalmic Lenses, etc.*, published by Bausch & Lomb (1935).

The preliminary step toward the advancement of optics and toward a correct interpretation of structures of the eye was made with the discovery, doubtless purely empirical, of eyeglasses, about A.D. 1285. There is little reason to think that this discovery was made by Roger Bacon (1214–94), of Oxford, even though he may have gained some rudimentary knowledge of the action of convex and concave lenses (*Opus Maius*, 1268). Overwhelming evidence points rather toward Northern Italy.

The identity of the discoverer is uncertain. That this was S. d'Armato degli Armati, a Florentine nobleman, as was claimed, is not probable. There are some indications that the discoverer may have been A. Spina, a Dominican friar in Pisa (d. 1313). After sifting the scanty information on the subject, it appears probable that eyeglasses gradually developed from a "reading glass," a rather large planoconvex lens to be put upon a page in order to facilitate reading by making the letters bigger. At any rate, such reading glasses were mentioned by the poets and writers of the second half of the thirteenth century as one of the wonders of the age. (*See also* G. Ten Doesschate 1946.)

The earliest written mention of reading glasses was made by Heinrich Frauenlob (1250–1318), a German poet; the second by Bernhard Gordon of Montpellier in *Lilium Medicinae* (1303); the next by Guy de Chauliac (1363) and by the Italian poet Francesco Petrarca (Petrarch, 1304–74). Roger Bacon gave a good description of the use of the reading glass (*see* Clay & Court, pp. 4, 5). The subsequent step in the evolution of eyeglasses was to provide the reading glass with a handle in order to hold it close to the eye.

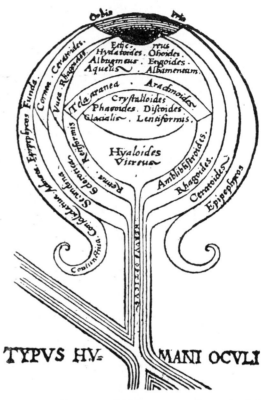

FIG. 14.—Structure of the human eye from a book by Walter Hermann Ryff printed in Strassburg, 1541. Note that the optic nerves are presented, as in the preceding figure, as hollow channels meeting in the chiasma. From K. Sudhoff, Stud. z. Gesch. d. Med., Fasc. 1. J. A. Barth, Leipzig, 1907.

The most likely locality of the first attempt to fit two smaller reading glasses together in a frame of horn, leather, bone, or metal and attach them close to the eyes was Venice, one of the great focal points of trade, wealth, and culture of the time. Or, rather, it was Murano, a Venetian suburb on the mainland, an ancient seat of the glass-blowing industry. In any case, the manufacture of *perspicilla, ocularia* or "beryls," *occhiali, besicles, antojos* or *anteojos, Brillen, Augenspiegel, ougspiegel,* and *spectacles,*

FIG. 15.—Andreas Vesalius (Witing, Vésale, 1514–64), the "Reformer of Anatomy," at the age of twenty-eight. Woodcut portrait engraved by an unknown artist from a drawing by Jan Stephan van Calcar, Vesalius' friend and illustrator of his famous textbook of anatomy, drawn in 1542. Frontispiece from the first edition of Vesalius' *De Corporis Humani Fabrica*, printed at Basel, 1543. From M. H. Spielmann, *The Iconography of Andreas Vesalius.* J. Bale, Sons & Danielsson (Staples Press, Ltd.), London, 1925. (*Cf. also* Fig. 64, and a portrait by Tintoretto in R. N. Wegner 1939, Fig. 6.)

as these early eyeglasses usually made of semi-precious beryllium or emerald were called in the various idioms, was well established in that region during the first half of the fourteenth century. (The original Greek word for emerald was ἡ βήρυλλοσ, ὁ βηρύλλιοσ, or ὁ βηρυλλιο-λίθος, diminutive το βηρύλλιον.)

With the development of other centers of manufacture at Nuremberg (Nürnberg), Rouen, and in Flanders, the use of eyeglasses became fairly common toward the middle of that century. For a long time, only convex glasses for the correction of presbyopia were made. It is significant that concave glasses for the correction of myopia did not appear until the middle or end of the fifteenth century, shortly after the invention of printing. Concave eyeglasses were first mentioned by Nicolaus Cusanus (1401–64) in his book *De Beryllo*, the earliest monograph on spectacles.

The oldest pictorial presentation of eyeglasses appears to be in a painting by Tommaso di Modena, dated 1352, at Treviso, in Northern Italy. This was a single reading glass or a magnifier held before the eye. Tommaso painted another picture in which a double glass was shown. Another example, which may be as old as the preceding, is in a picture by a painter of the Giotto School which is now in the Figdor Gallery in Vienna. The next oldest picture of eyeglasses seems to be in a miniature painting in a manuscript Bible of the year 1380, in the possession of the Bibliothèque Nationale in Paris. The third in chronological order is the painting by Conrad van Soest (C. de Susato), dated 1404, in the church in Niederwildungen, Germany. Another is the painting by Jan van Eyck, dated 1436.

Other early representations of spectacles mentioned by Sacken (1879) are those by Domenico dal Ghirlandajo in the church of S. Trinità, in Florence, and one by Quintin Matsys at Windsor. The first printed picture of eyeglasses appeared in Hartman Schedel's *Chronicle*, Nuremberg (Nürnberg), Bavaria, 1493. Hogarth, regarded as a "supreme pictorial satirist," immortalized nose-spectacles in his painting "The Politician." (*See* Sacken; *cf.* Figs. 23–26.)

The invention of eyeglasses and their gradual perfection, a slow process extending over several centuries, coincided with the beginning of a new era of civilization. It was a necessary technical prerequisite for the rise and advancement of the science of optics and, above all, of modern dioptrics. It was the first step which made possible the invention of the telescope and microscope, two instruments which have immeasurably increased our knowledge of life and the universe and have profoundly influenced the practical side of human affairs. (*See* Clay &

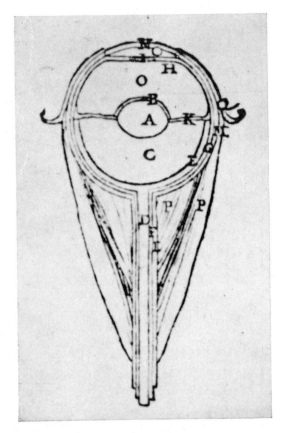

FIG. 16.—Eye diagram from the first edition of *De Corporis Humani Fabrica* by Vesalius, printed in 1543. Compare its essential features with the Arab diagrams in Figs. 2, 3, 4. Courtesy Professor J. F. Fulton, Yale University, New Haven, Conn.

Court 1932; Disney, Hill & Baker 1928, Gunther 1923–45.)

3. ITALIAN RENAISSANCE AND EARLY MODERN ATTEMPTS TO EXPLAIN THE DIOPTRICAL APPARAT S OF THE EYE.—The development of the glass industry and the invention of eyeglasses, lenses, and other optical instruments were part of a historical change which was taking place in Southern and Western Europe and, above all,

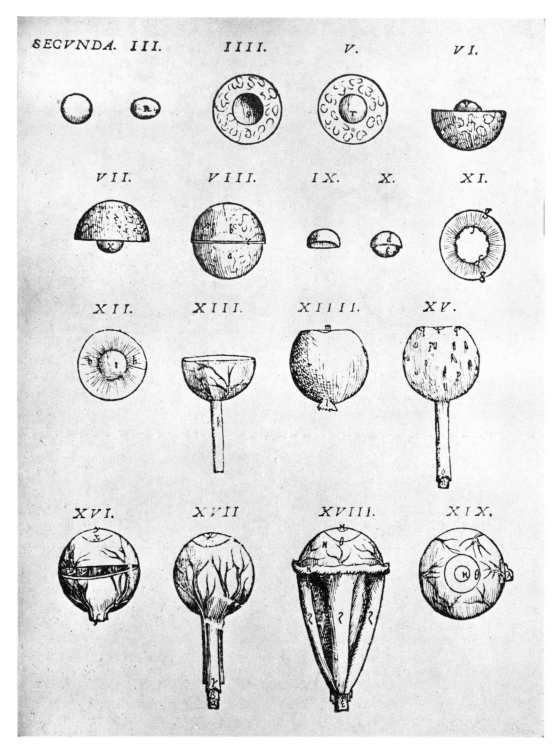

FIG. 17.—Woodcut plate showing parts making up the human eye. From the first edition of *De Corporis Humani Fabrica* of Vesalius (1543). Courtesy Professor J. F. Fulton, Yale University, New Haven, Conn.

in Italy. This period, thought of as a revival or rebirth of Classical Civilization, was, in fact, the beginning of a new epoch of human history which brought the Dark Ages to an end. This great material and intellectual change was manifested in the stability of political, economic, and social orders, which resulted in improved

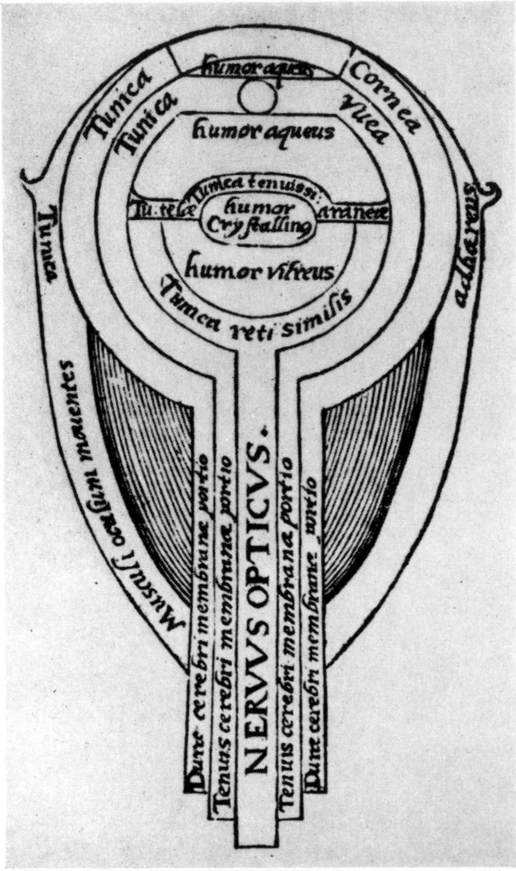

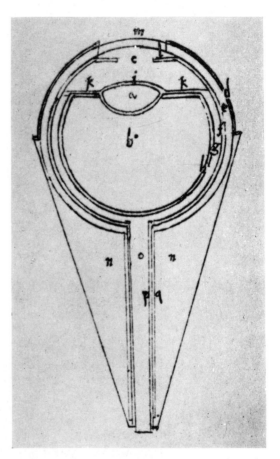

FIG. 18.—Eye diagram from the joint volume of Alhazen's *Opticae Thesaurus* and Vitello's *Opticae Libri X*, published at Basel, 1572. This diagram is obviously an adaptation of the figure found in Vesalius' *Fabrica* (Fig. 16) rather than of the diagrams found either in the Latin or in the Arabic manuscripts of Ibn al-Haitham's *Book of Optics*, known during the Late Middle Ages (Figs. 2, 3, 4, 9, 10, 11).

living conditions, gentler manners, and an awakening of interest in the arts and sciences, including knowledge of the human body and of nature in general.

Leonardo da Vinci (1452–1519, portrait Fig. 61), probably influenced by Ibn al-Haitham, Ibn Rushd, or Vitello, arrived at a full realization of the dioptrical role of the transparent

media of the eye. He became convinced that a visual image or images is or are formed in the eye, but he was not able to explain how. With the basic preliminary work in dioptrics still to be done, this was not yet possible. Another factor which helped obscure the problem was Leonardo's obsession with the idea of an erect image, which he, on logical and psychological grounds, postulated (for otherwise, he thought, one would see the object upside down!). Nor was his knowledge of ocular structures based

FIG. 19.—Eye diagram from Platter's *De Corporis Humani Structura et Usu*, published at Basel in 1603. It is an almost accurate copy of Vesalius' figure, with, however, one important innovation: the crystalline lens is now placed closer to the iris, even though it still does not touch it, while in Vesalius' presentation the lens has a central location, as in the Arabic diagrams.

upon personal experimentation. His attempts to solve the problem with pen and paper naturally failed. His fantastic sketches, showing a double refraction in the eye but no collecting action by the cornea and lens, were pure specu-

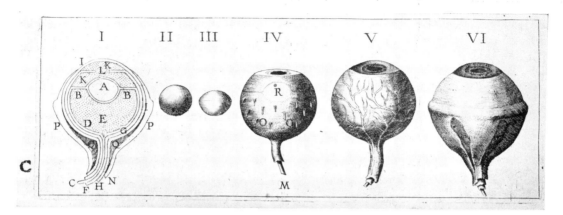

Fig. 20.—Component parts of the human eye, left-hand sketch representing a section showing the lens, the iris, and the several coats of the eye. From F. Aguilonius, *Opticorum Libri Sex*, Antwerpiae, 1613.

Fig. 21.—Girólamo or Gerónimo Fabrízio, Fabríci or Fabrízi d'Aquapendénte, or Hieronymus Fabricius ab Aquapendente (1537–1619), professor of anatomy and surgery at Padua, Italy. Pupil of Gabriele Falloppio and teacher of William Harvey. Investigator of the eye, ear, and the organ of voice. First demonstrated the correct position of the crystalline lens in the anterior portion of the eye, just behind the iris, instead of in the center of the eye, where it was believed to be by the Greeks, Arabs, and the early western Europeans: Vitello, Leonardo da Vinci, and Vesalius. From P. Capparoni, *Profili bio-bibliografici*, 1928–32. Original at Istituto Anatomico della Università, Padova, Italy.

lation, void both of anatomy and of all the essentials of physiological optics (*see* Polyak, *The Retina*, Fig. 24).

And yet, wrong as Leonardo was in all details, his thinking moved in the right direction. This was also true of many other men of that time who were eager for more knowledge. Maurolycus of Messina, Sicily, apparently was more successful (1494–1575; his book was written in 1554 but published in 1617). He was the first to understand that rays of light radiating from a luminous or illuminated point are again collected by a lens at one point. Unfortunately, Maurolycus, influenced by ideas from the past, primarily the belief in the photoreceptor function of the crystalline lens, failed to recognize that the sum of such focal points symmetrically distributed over the retina would form an image on it, instead of on the surface of the lens, where he placed it.

Even stranger is the case of Giambattista della Porta (1589, portrait Fig. 27). Following Daniello Barbaro (1568), he first added a convex lens to the pinhole camera, or *camera obscura*, in this way making the similarity of this contrivance to the eye more apparent. Yet, in spite of this, Porta never understood either the principles of dioptrics or their application to the eye, and he continued in his belief that the visual image was formed on the surface of the lens.

4. Discovery of the photoreceptor role of the retinal membrane by Platter.—The first clear pronouncement of the photoreceptor function of the retinal membrane and the subsidiary, purely physical, role of the crystalline lens of the eye was made by Platter, an anatomist at Basel (Platerus, 1536–1614, portrait Fig. 28; book published first in 1583 and again in 1603). For him the lens was not the true photoreceptor that it was to the Greek and Arab scholars and their European followers of the Middle Ages, but only a collector of the rays falling into the eye, a *perspicillum nervi visorii*, or "spectacle of the optic nerve" (that is, of the retina). The true photoreceptor, in his opinion, was the retina, while the lens merely collected light and distributed it over the expanse of the former.

It is true that the same idea was occasionally

expressed by others, for example, by Ibn Rushd, the famous Spanish-Arab scholar who lived four centuries earlier and from whose writings the students of the Renaissance, such as Leonardo da Vinci, Pozzi (*see* Edinger 1892), and indirectly possibly Vesalius, and even Platter himself may have received a suggestion. Yet the undeniable fact remains that in Platter's time the mistaken Greek idea of the photoreceptor role of the crystalline lens still found universal acceptance, as is attested by numerous celebrities in the fields of optics, anatomy, and physi-

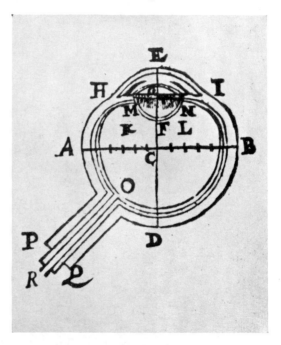

Fig. 22.—Earliest diagram of the human eye in which relative proportions and arrangement of structures approach the normal. From Christopher Scheiner's *Oculus*, etc., published at Innsbruck, Austria, 1619. Courtesy U.S. Army Medical Library, Washington, D.C.

ology, such as Maurolycus, Porta, Du Laurens, Bauhin, and even Hieronymus Fabricius ab Aquapendente himself.

In order to disprove it against formidable opposition Platter performed an experiment. In it he cut the so-called "araneal tunic"—now called suspensory ligament of the lens or zonule of Zinn—along which, according to the hypothesis of the photoreceptor function of the lens, the visual impulses were supposed to pass from the latter to the retina and thence to the optic nerve and brain. Since, in spite of the severance of the zonular attachment of the lens, vision was still possible, Platter's experiment demonstrated the functional role of the lens to be purely physical (*see* Plehn 1922, p. 204).

5. Kepler's evidence of the retinal image.—Platter's opinion, logical and based upon experimental evidence, did not seem to carry much weight with his contemporaries, principally because it lacked a clear dioptrical interpretation and was otherwise defective in certain

light that enter the eye through the pupil (as is the case in the simple pinhole camera with which Ibn al-Haitham compared the eye, a factor Leonardo da Vinci alone considered) but was a product both of the collecting and the refracting power of the cornea and of the lens. In fact, as Kepler insisted, the retinal image was an aggregation of as many focal points ("image points") of as many "pairs of cones" of light rays as there were points on the object seen ("object points"), the bases of the cones coin-

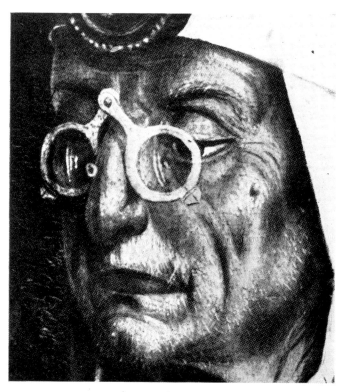

Fig. 23.—One of the earliest representations of spectacles and their use. From a painting in the parish church at Rothenburg ob der Tauber, in Bavaria, Germany, executed by F. Herlin in the year 1466. From A. von Pflugk, Ztschr. f. ophth. Optik, v. 14, p. 140, 1927.

details. It is probable that it would not have prevailed against the dominant view of the time, had it not come to the attention of Johannes Kepler (1571–1630, portrait Fig. 29), the foremost mathematician, student of optics, and astronomer of his time (for Kepler's biography see *Naturwissenschaften*, v. 30, 1930).

According to Kepler's explanation (1604), the visual image was not caught by the lens, as Porta insisted, but was "painted" on the retina. Furthermore, the retinal image was not the result merely of an intercrossing of the rays of

ciding with the portion of the lens not covered by the iris. In this way a "real" and inverted image, clear in detail, although diminished in size, was produced on the retinal backscreen.

This and other discoveries of Kepler (for example, a correct interpretation of presbyopic and myopic spectacles) not only gave a satisfactory explanation of ocular structures but also furnished a reliable basis for the modern science of optics (Mach 1925; Rohr 1925).

Kepler's efforts in optics and allied fields had opened a new era of investigation. Mach says:

"In his *Dioptrice* (1611) which has but eighty pages, Kepler established the fundamental scientific principles of dioptrics." Subsequently, Kepler's pioneer work was followed by a series of important discoveries by some of the most brilliant students of the physics and of the physiology of the eye, by which physical and

6. Scheiner's experimental demonstration of the retinal image.—The conviction of the reality of a retinal image became even firmer through the efforts of a series of notable students of optics during subsequent decades: Christopher Scheiner (1575–1650), Willebrord Snell (1591–1626), René Des Cartes (Cartesius,

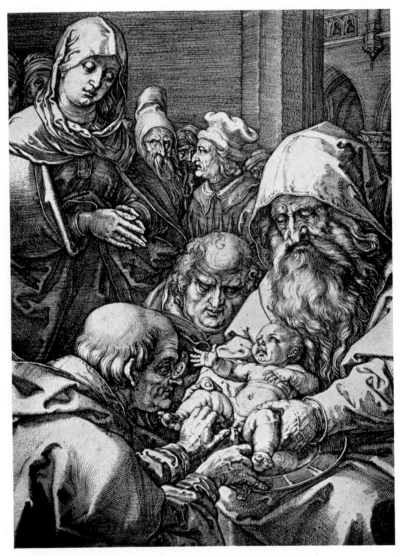

Fig. 24.—Picture of the circumcision of Jesus, in which the rabbi performing the operation uses *pince-nez*, or "nose-clip" eyeglasses, which permit the use of both hands. Part of an engraving made by C. Schoneus, 1594. Courtesy Professor W. Bloom, University of Chicago.

physiological optics was brought to its present state (Grimaldi, W. Snell, Huygens, Thos. Young, Porterfield, Euler, Fresnel, Malus, Arago, Brewster, Fraunhoffer, Fizeau, Gauss, Listing, Maxwell, Hertz, Donders, Helmholtz, Abbé, Mach, Michelson, Gullstrand, Rohr, *et al.*).

1596–1650), Christiaan Huygens (1629–95), Isaac Newton (1642–1727), Molyneaux (1692), Hamberger (1696), and others. Their merit was to have placed the study of ocular dioptrics and of optics in general on a solid scientific, experimental foundation.

Kepler's views were largely theoretical deductions based upon computations which, even though probable, required testing by experiment. The first practical proof of the presence of a retinal image, following Kepler's suggestion, was furnished by Pater Scheiner (portrait Figure 30). He made the image formed on the retina directly visible, first in animal eyes and then in the human eye, by removing part of the opaque coats in the back of the eyeball (1625; *see* Rohr 1919, p. 129). A similar experiment

ing the retinal image chemically. (Kühne 1877, 1878; *see also* Gerling; Grether 1940; Hidano; Lashley 1932; Uexküll & Brock; similar studies were recently made by D. D. Michaels.)

As a result of the preceding efforts, the view that "the eye is nothing but a natural pinhole camera, and that the pinhole camera in turn is an artificial eye" (Kohlhans, Sturm) became universally accepted, in spite of occasional opposition, such as that voiced by J. Campbell, De la Hire, Horn, Le Cat, Lehot, Mariotte,

Ochiali e lor uso.

Fig. 25.—Fitting eyeglasses in the shop of a seventeenth-century optometrist. From Cornelius Meyer, *Nuovi ritrovamenti*, Rome, 1689–96. According to R. Greeff, Ztschr. f. ophth. Optik, v. 7, 1919.

was performed even earlier by Aranzi (1595, p. 70), but, having been made before Kepler's lucid interpretation and with no knowledge of dioptrics, it remained without effect.

During the century following Scheiner, the experiment with the retinal image was repeated by numerous investigators, the more prominent among them being F. Sylvius de la Boë (1614–72), Kircher (1646; portrait Fig. 32; experiment, Fig. 33, *left*), T. Bartholin (1651), A. Haller (1769), Buzzi (1782), and Magendie (1816). In modern times, finally, it was possible to produce the permanent "optogram" by fix-

Mayer, Mery, Mühlbach, Plagge, Reade, Saint-Yves, Santorio, and John Taylor.

References: Adams; Adams & Tannery; Aguilonius; Albertotti; P. Allen; R. M. Allen; Arago; Aranzi (Arantius); Averroës (Ibn Rushd); T. Bartholin; Bauer; Bauhin 1621; Bausch & Lomb 1935; Baxandall; A. E. Bell 1947; E. Bock; Briggs; J. Burckhardt; Buzzi; Caesemaker; Camper; Cherubin d'Orleans; Clay & Court; Cousin; Crew; Cuming 1855; Curtze; Cusanus; C. G. Darwin; Day; Daza de Valdés; F. De la Boë (Sylvius); Dechâles (Deschâles); Doesschate 1946; Des Cartes (Cartesius); Disney, Hill & Baker; Donders; Dunscombe; W. Durant; Dyson; Eddington 1930; Edinger 1892; Emsley; Erggelet 1916; Euclid; Fahie 1921; A. J. Fresnel; Fröbes; Fukala; Gage; Galileo Galilei; Gassendus; Gehler; Gehrling; Gill & Eddington; Greeff 1913–14, 1917, 1918, 1919, 1921, 1923, 1924, 1925; Grether 1940; Haldane; Hallauer; A. Haller; Hamberger; J. Harris 1775; Hartsoëker; Helmholtz 1924–25; Hidano; J. Pergens; Peters; Pflugk; Pflugk & Rohr; F. Platter; Plehn; Polyak 1941, 1948; G. della Porta; Preston; Priestley; Rössler; Rohault; Rohr; Sacken 1879; Shyrley de Rheita; Chr. Scheiner 1619, 1626–30; Schnaase; G. Schott; Singer; Sirturus 1618; T. E. Smith; W. Snell; Solmis; Sorsby 1948; Southall 1922; Straet 1600; Straub 1908; Sturm; Swinne 1924; Sylvius (F. Du Bois or De la Boë); Symonds;

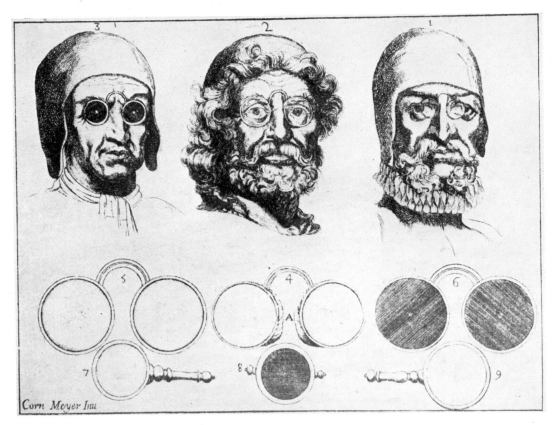

Fig. 26.—Varieties of eyeglasses used during the seventeenth century, including so-called "stenopaic spectacles," or *Lochbrillen* in German, an old-fashioned device for reducing the size of the blur circles and so improving a definition of the retinal image (*see* Southall 1937, p. 83). Note in *1* the improperly adjusted glasses, with their centers out of the line of vision, in contrast with diagram *2*, where the optical centers coincide with the lines of vision of the eyes. From Cornelius Meyer, *Nuovi ritrovamenti*, Rome, 1689–96. According to R. Greeff, Ztschr. f. ophth. Optik, v. 7, 1919.

Hirschberg; Hooke; Chr. Huygens; Ibn Rushd (Averroës); Joly & Waterhouse; J. Kepler 1604, 1611; A. Kircher; A. König 1937; Kohl; Kohlhans (Kolhansius); Kopff 1930; Krembs; Kühne; Lashley 1932; Leikind; Leonardo da Vinci; Lenard; Libri-Carucci 1838–41; Mach 1925; Magendie; Malgaigne; Manzini; M. Márquez; L. C. Martin; T. H. Martin; Maurolycus; Mees; Molinetti; Molyneaux; Napoli; Narducci; I. Newton; Pansier; Pauschmann; Symonds & Smith; G. Ten Doesschate 1946; Traber 1675; Uexküll & Brock; Vinci, Leonardo da; J. Waterhouse 1932; Werner; Wiedemann 1910, 1912, 1915; Wilde; G. Wilson 1855; A. Wolff; Woodruff; Würschmidt; Zahn; Zehender 1864. *See also* journal *Janus*, v. 19, 1914; and *Encyclopaedia Britannica*, 14th ed., articles "Camera obscura," "Ether," "Lens," "Light," "Photography," "Telescope," and "Vision."

SEC. 6. INVESTIGATIONS OF THE RETINA FROM THE EARLIEST TIMES TO THE RISE OF MODERN MICROSCOPY

1. INVESTIGATION OF THE RETINA DURING CLASSICAL ANTIQUITY.—The investigation of an organ apparently so insignificant as the retina could have been initiated only after its importance in vision had been established.

From what has been said about the development of physiological optics and the interpretation of the ocular structures, it is apparent that the true function of the retinal membrane as a photoreceptor or a sensitive backscreen of the living "dark chamber," the eye, had been recognized relatively late. It may, therefore, seem remarkable that the Greek anatomists of the Hellenistic or Alexandrine Period (*ca.* 300 B.C.) paid any attention to this membrane at all. This was probably because of the belief of the Ancients in the role of the retina as a conveyer of the "visual spirit" from the optic nerve, hence from the brain, to the crystalline lens, which, in their opinion, was the actual photoreceptor. Another probable reason was their belief that the retina served, in its second capacity, as a transmitter from which the visual impressions or sensations elicited in the lens passed to the optic nerve and along the optic nerve to the brain. In the opinion of the Greek anatomists and physiologists, the retina was well suited for both these functions, since it was attached to the lens by means of the araneal tunic, or zonular ligament, and was continuous with the optic nerve.

There was yet a third reason: the belief, be-

G. B. PORTA
(1536-1615)

FIG. 27.—Giambattista della Porta (1536–1615), an encyclopedic student and writer on physics, chemistry, optics, and various natural phenomena during the Italian Renaissance. An experimenter with the *camera obscura* or "dark chamber," a forerunner of the photographic camera. Author of *Natural Magick in XX Bookes*, a widely read compendium of that time. From E. Mach, *The Principles of Physical Optics*, Methuen & Co., London, 1925.

cause of its abundant blood supply, in the nutritive role of the retina, which the Greeks thought brought nourishment to the vitreous, that, in turn, nourished the crystalline lens, both therefore being able to preserve their transparency. (*Cf.* sec. 1 [2], this chapter.)

It is remarkable that even at that early date, when the science of optics and optical technology were practically nonexistent, an acute observer like Galen noticed the similarity between the appearance of the retinal substance and that of the brain, an observation whose true cause was discovered only in modern times. (*See* Galen, *De Hippocr. et Plat. Decr.*, book 7, chap. 5; *De Usu Part.*, book 10, chap. 1.) One is inclined to suspect that in Galen's case the reason for his emphasis on this structural similarity was his desire to discover a conveyer of the "visual

FIG. 28.—Felix Platter (Platerus, 1536–1614), professor of anatomy at Basel. First investigator definitely to consider the retinal membrane of the eye a true photoreceptor, and the crystalline lens as its "spectacle" or a dioptrical medium. In order to prove his view, he severed the suspensory ligament or Zinn's zonule, by which the lens is attached to the inner coats of the eye, without impairing the vision. In this way he demonstrated the falsity of the ancient Greek and Arab view, in which the lens was the true photoreceptor and the ciliary ligament and retina were conductors of the visual impressions to the optic nerve and brain. From a painting by Hans Bock, Sr., 1584, in the Oeffentliche Kunstsammlung, Kunstmuseum Basel, Switzerland.

spirit" from the brain to the crystalline lens via the optic nerve and retina, rather than actual observation (*see* chap. II, 3 [3]).

2. KNOWLEDGE OF THE RETINAL MEMBRANE DURING THE MIDDLE AGES.—During the Middle Ages, especially the darkest period from the sixth to the eleventh century, with an almost complete cessation of interest in the human

body and in nature in general, nothing was added to the knowledge of the retina or of the eye. Even the most zealous among the Arab scholars—Ḥunain ibn Isḥāḳ, ʿAlī ibn ʿĪsā, ʿAlī ibn al-ʿAbbās, and Ibn Sīnā—could do no other service than to preserve part of the anatomical knowledge bequeathed by the Greeks, since the Mohammedan religion forbade dissection.

In this connection it is of interest to mention

FIG. 29.—Johannes Kepler (1571–1630), court astrologer to the German emperor and one of the foremost mathematicians and astronomers of all times. Discoverer of the laws of planetary motion known as "Kepler's laws." Pioneer student of physical and physiological optics. First correctly interpreted the action of the dioptrical media of the eye and of the formation of the ocular image on the retina. From E. Mach, *The Principles of Physical Optics*, 1925, Methuen & Co., London. For biography *see* Naturwiss., v. 18, 1930.

the origin of the modern word "retina," which is a Latin translation of the Arabic word *al-shabakīyya*, or "the netlike tunic," which, in turn, was a translation of the Greek name ἀμφιβληστροειδὴς χιτών, or *amphiblestroëidés hitón*. This name was given to the retina by Herophilos, its discoverer, because of its resemblance, when collapsed, to a folded fishing net, as this membrane usually appears in a carelessly dissected eye. The Arabic term was preserved by Ibn Sīnā, or Avicenna, in his *Canon of Medicine*, a medical encyclopedia of the Middle Ages. After the translation of the *Canon* into Latin by Gerard of Cremona during the twelfth century, the term became generally known in Europe.

Productive investigation of the retina may be said to have begun with early microscopy. What was known about it by the compiling anatomists of the late Middle Ages and of early Modern Times went little further than a recognition of structures easily observable with the unaided eye: the blood vessels and bundles of myelinated nerve fibers, both of which could easily be seen in various domestic and other easily procured animals, e.g., a Hare and a Rabbit. The presence of retinal "veins" and nerve fibers was mentioned by several writers during the Middle Ages, for example, by ʿAlī ibn ʿĪsā (10th century), Alcoatin (1159), and Vitello, while the absence of color in the retina was noticed by Benevenutus Grassus (*ca.* 12th century), for which reason he called it *discolorata*. This may perhaps indicate the beginning, even at that early date, of an active interest in things anatomical.

Except for these few instances, even the foremost anatomists of the remainder of the Middle Ages and of early Modern Times up to Platter (1583), Kepler (1604, 1611), and Scheiner (1619) paid but little attention to the retina or ignored it altogether (Fernelius, Vesalius, Falloppio, Aranzi). Even later, after its function was known, it did not become the subject of more detailed investigation until optical technology had advanced enough to permit employment of magnifying glasses.

3. EARLY MICROSCOPIC INVESTIGATION OF THE RETINAL STRUCTURE.—The first investigator to examine the retinal structure microscopically was Antonie van Leeuwenhoek, a

learned draper, sexton, and town chamberlain of Delft, Holland (1632–1723, portrait Fig. 34). This remarkable autodidact ground his own biconvex lenses and made his own simple but effective "microscopes." (*See* Fig. 35; *see also* Allen 1940; H. Baker 1743; Carpenter 1901; Cittert 1933; Conn, 1948; Dobell; Leikind 1941; Locy 1901, 1910; A. W. Meyer; Priestley; Roseboom; Singer 1914; A. Wolff 1935; and Turtox Microscopy Booklet 1946.)

FIG. 30.—Christopher Scheiner (1579–1650), a Jesuit friar, born at Wald in Schwaben, Bavaria, Germany; died at Neisse, in Silesia. A noted astronomer still adhering to Ptolemy's geocentric hypothesis of solar system and a diligent student of the eye and of optics. First, in the wake of Platter's and Kepler's postulations, to furnish experimental evidence of the formation of a retinal image in the eye. From Albert König, *Fernrohre und Entfernungsmesser*, 1937. Courtesy J. Springer, Berlin.

An interesting piece of information on the equipment of Leeuwenhoek's microscopes may be found in a book entitled *The Microscope Made Easy* by Henry Baker, himself a pioneer microscopist, published in London in 1743. In a footnote to page 7, Baker writes:

Several writers represent the glasses Mr. Leeuwenhoek made use of in his microscopes to be little globules or spheres of glass, which mistake most probably arises from their undertaking to describe what they had never seen; for at the time I am writing this, the cabinet of microscopes left by that famous Man, at his death, to the *Royal Society*, as a legacy, is standing upon my table; and I can assure the world, that every one of the twenty-six microscopes contained therein is a double convex lens, and not a sphere or globule.

The structures which Leeuwenhoek observed on two occasions (1674 and 1684) in a cow and a frog specimen of the retina were blood vessels containing blood corpuscles and some small globules of rather oblong shape adhering to the vessels, which may have been either the rods and cones or the nerve cells.

Ruysch (1700), another deft Hollander, showed the retina to be composed of both blood vessels and nerve fibers. Thereafter many other anatomists and physiologists, physicists, and philosophers described and discussed various retinal structures, some real and others whose presence they postulated purely speculatively. Most of the investigators of this period believed the retina to be a simple expansion of the optic nerve, which may explain the German term

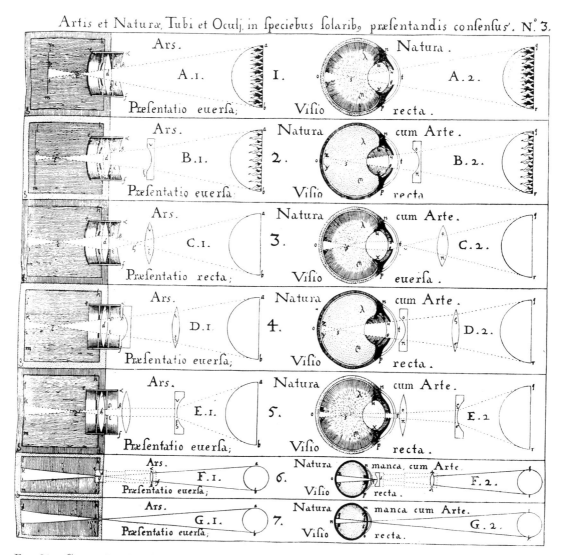

FIG. 31.—Composite plate from Scheiner's *Rosa Ursina*, published 1619–25, to illustrate the workings of the dioptrical mechanism of the eye.

Faserhaut, or "fibrous membrane," occasionally met with in older writings (*see* Burdach 1822, p. 177). Only a few, those more critically inclined, as, for example, Winslow, thought this membrane to be composed of cellular elements as well as of nerve fibers and blood vessels.

These observations and assumptions, still largely vague, began to acquire substance with the work of Briggs (1676), Morgagni (1719), Maître-Jan (1707), Zinn (1755), Valsalva (1740), Fontana (1782), and others. Fontana clearly showed for the first time that the retina contained not only blood vessels and nerve fibers but also a pulpy or medullary substance, made up of small, spheroidal bodies held together by very thin, transparent membranes and fine filaments. He found that these globules, which looked as if they were made of a transparent jelly, greatly resembled similar globules in the brain. What he saw both in the retina and in the brain undoubtedly were spherical nerve cells. The framework of delicate membranes which held the globules together, described by him, was very likely the neuroglial stroma.

Interesting as all these observations were, they were still a long way from answering the questions raised by those interested in the correlation of the retinal structures with the principal visual phenomena. One of these problems was the direct continuity between the retinal nerve fibers and the fibers of the optic nerve. Another concerned the size of the fibers and their distribution over the surface of the retinal membrane. While some investigators assumed a uniform distribution, others believed the fibers to be distributed unevenly. An observation made by Maître-Jan, that the retina was thicker in the fundus of the eye than near the *ora serrata*, seemed to support the latter view.

The "yellow spot," or *macula lutea*, and central fovea, both first observed by Buzzi in Milan (1782, 1784) and independently rediscovered by S. Th. Soemmerring (1795, portrait Fig. 37), could also have been held to contribute to this interpretation. These discoveries, important though they were, were but preliminaries to the wealth of information which followed the development of modern microscopy.

References: Albinus; Alcoatin; ʿAlī ibn ʿĪsā; ʿAlī ibn al-ʿAbbās; R. M. Allen 1947; Aranzi; Avicenna (Ibn Sīnā); H. Baker 1743; E. Brücke 1847; Carpenter; Clay & Court 1932; Diemerbroek; Doellinger; Eustachio; Falloppio; Fernelius; F. Fontana; Fragonard; Gabrieli; Gage; Galen; B. Grassus; Hirschberg 1908; Home; Hovius; Ḥunain ibn Isḥāḳ (*see also* Meyerhof); Ibn Sīnā (Avicenna); A. Jacob; J. Janin 1772; J. Kepler; Knox; Leeuwenhoek; Leikind 1941;

FIG. 32.—Athanasius Kircher (1601–80), Jesuit friar and scholar of optics, at the age of fifty-three. Author of a compendium *Ars Magna Lucis et Umbrae,* published at Rome, 1646. An engraving made in 1655. Courtesy Francesco Margi, S.J., professor of physical sciences at the Pontifical Gregorian University of Rome.

F. T. Lewis 1942; Locy 1901; Maître-Jan; Malpighi; A. W. Meyer; P. Michaelis; Moeller; Monro; Morgagni 1719; Polyak 1941 or 1948;

Porterfield 1759; Priestley 1772; Roseboom; Ruysch; Santorini 1724; Chr. Scheiner; Singer; D. W. Soemmerring 1818; S. Th. Soem- merring 1801; Sudhoff 1921; F. Sylvius; J. Taylor; Valsalva 1740; Vesalius; Vitello (Witelo); Wedel; A. Wolff; Woodruff; Zinn 1755.

SEC. 7. EARLY MODERN INVESTIGATION OF THE STRUCTURE AND FUNCTION OF THE RETINA

1. INVENTION OF THE COMPOUND MICRO- SCOPE AND THE RISE OF MODERN MICROSCOPY.— A systematic microscopic investigation of the aided eye or simple magnifying glasses, which required microscopes of high power. This was possible because of the development of optical

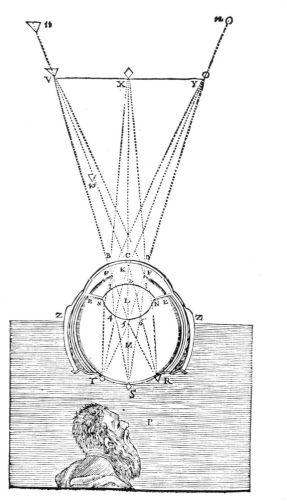
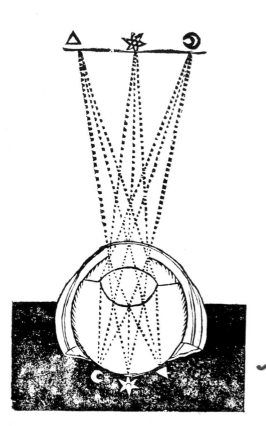

FIG. 33.—Diagrams showing the formation of the retinal image, *left* from Kircher in *Ars Magna Lucis et Umbrae* (1646); *right* from Des Cartes's *Tractatus de Homine* (1677). (*See also* Figs. 32, 68, 69, 70.)

retina began with the work of Treviranus (1835–38). In human anatomy, by this time, the organs and structures which could be investigated without the aid of strong magnifying glasses had become rather well known. Interest was now directed toward the study of structures small enough to be beyond the reach of the un- instruments, culminating in the discovery and perfection of the compound microscope. (*See* Abbé 1904–6; Adams 1746; R. M. Allen 1947; H. Baker 1743; W. B. Carpenter 1901; Clay 1938; Clay & Court 1932; Disney, Hill & Baker 1928; Gage 1941; Heschl 1880; F. Merkel 1893; *see* Figs. 38–41.)

2. DISCOVERY OF RODS, CONES, AND RETINAL GANGLION CELLS.—In the investigation of the retina two questions were of primary interest. The first concerned the identity of the structures to be considered true photoreceptors, capable of responding to stimulation by physical light. The second question concerned the way these photoreceptors were related to the optic nerve fibers. Treviranus (1776–1837), a German naturalist, believed he had answered both. He found a number of cylindrical, globular, and nipple-like structures which he called *papillae* and which he thought were the termi-

nal ends of optic nerve fibers. From his description and even more clearly from his diagrams interpreted in the light of present knowledge, it is certain that some of his *papillae* actually were rods and cones, while others were ganglion cells (Figs. 42, 43, 44).

Treviranus, unfortunately, never understood the real significance of all these structures. He was the first to describe retinal layers, but he presented them upside down, with the optic nerve fibers on the outside, facing the chorioid. The fibers, radiating from the disk of the optic nerve, he believed, turned in toward the vitre-

FIG. 34.—Antoni van Leeuwenhoek (1632–1723), the scholarly draper, sexton, and town chamberlain of Delft, in the Netherlands, at the age of fifty-four. Together with M. Malpighi (*see* Fig. 36), the principal pioneer of microscopy (the others being R. Hooke, 1635–1703, J. Swammerdam, 1637–80, and N. Grew, 1641–1712). Self-taught, made his own simple but effective microscopes, with which he investigated the minute structure of numerous parts of the human and animal bodies and plants, including the eye and the brain. First investigated the crystalline lens and the retina of the eye. Photo of the original painting by Jan Verkolje made in 1686. Courtesy Rijksmuseum, Amsterdam, Netherlands. (*Cf. also* following figure.)

ous, at points varying with each fiber. After penetrating the thickness of the retinal membrane, each fiber supposedly terminated either as an individual *papilla* or as several fibers merged into a single *papilla* of a larger size. Treviranus believed the *papillae*, which in his opinion were the true photoreceptors, to be on the vitreal side of the retina (as the ganglion cells actually are). In this way he satisfied the logical expectations of his time, according to which the photoreceptors were the first of the

errors were eliminated and the correct interpretation found.

First, Bidder (1839) found the correct topographical position of the rods and cones on the outer or scleral face of the retina, where they make up the second or bacillary layer (Fig. 128, *2*). In the functional interpretation of the rod structures, however, Bidder, under the influence of contemporary prejudice or misconception, was at fault. Since, according to the idea generally accepted at that time, the photoreceptors

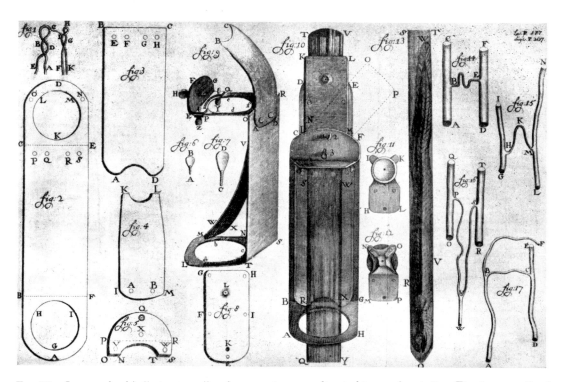

Fig. 35.—Leeuwenhoek's "microscope" and accessories, according to his own description. Fig. *1*, connection between arteries and veins; Figs. *2–7*, parts of a copper frame for the "microscope" shown in Fig. *9; L* in Fig. *8*, the "microscope" or a small biconvex lens mounted between two thin copper or silver plates fastened together by five small bolts; *K*, hole for a screw which held the lens plate to the frame; Fig. *9*, frame without the lens plate; Fig. *10*, complete "microscope," with all parts put together: *IKLM*, lens plate; *QRSTVWXY*, a glass tube for observation of living animals, in Fig. *13* shown separately containing a young eel; Figs. *14–17*, blood vessels. From A. Leeuwenhoek's *Arcana Naturae Detecta*, published in 1722.

retinal structures to be reached by rays of light entering the eye.

3. "Catoptric hypothesis" of rod func- tion.—The work of Treviranus, though erroneous in almost every point, was beneficial because it stimulated an immediate series of investigations (Huschke; Gottsche; G. A. Michaelis; Johannes Müller 1837; Valentin; Henle; Remak 1839; Hannover 1840). Step by step his

were to line the inner face of the retina, as they actually do in Cephalopods, Snails, the parietal eye of Tuatára (*Sphenodon*), and some other Lizards, Bidder decided that outwardly placed rods could not be the photoreceptors. For the same reason he denied even their nervous character. The rods, according to him, were merely some sort of mirror structures, a catoptrical mechanism, from which rays of light, after having passed through the thickness of the retina, are once more reflected in the opposite direction, toward the pupil. In this way light, passing for the second time through the optic nerve fibers spread over the vitreal face of the retina, which, to Bidder as to Treviranus, were the true photoreceptors, reinforced the stimulus elicited by the first passage. This "catoptric hypothesis" of the bacillary structures, an unwitting

4. DISCOVERY OF THE TRUE ORDER OF RETINAL LAYERS.—The prospects for unraveling the complex structure of the retinal membrane improved with Hannover's (1840) introduction of chromic acid into histological laboratory technique.

Until then the usual procedure had been to study the retina spread out in "whole-mounts,"

FIG. 36.—Marcello Malpighi (Malpighius, 1628–94), anatomist, physiologist, and botanist of Messina, Bologna, and Rome. Together with Leeuwenhoek (*see* Fig. 34), the principal pioneer microscopist of animal and vegetable tissues. Photo made from the original portrait by J. Tabor and presented by Malpighi to the Royal Society of London, of which Malpighi was a member. Courtesy Royal Society of London. For biography *see* A. W. Meyer in *Science*, v. 72, p. 234, 1930.

precursor of the functional explanation of the *tapetum* found in the chorioid membrane of many crepuscular and nocturnal Vertebrates, was widely accepted for a time. (*See also* Brücke, Goodsir, Hannover, Wilson 1855.)

while fresh and still transparent. Much of the confusion prevalent until that time, especially as to the number and sequence of layers, it seems, was caused by the difficulty of getting properly oriented in such preparations. In contrast to this, the fixation and hardening of the specimens in chromic acid permitted the making of sections vertical to the retinal surface.

Even better results were obtained with chromic salts, the "Müller solution," introduced by H. Müller (1859). With the use of this improved technique, Pacini (1845), Bowman (1849, portrait Fig. 45), Koelliker (1852–54, portrait Fig. 47), Vintschgau (1853), and, most important, Heinrich Müller (1856–57, portrait Fig. 46) described correctly the sequence of the retinal layers and their exact position relative to the outer and inner face of the membrane, with the bacillary layer on the outside, the optic nerve fibers and ganglion cells on the inside, and the granular layers in between.

When, in addition, Helmholtz (1843), Corti (1850, 1854), and Koelliker (1854) demonstrated the continuity of the nerve fibers and of the ganglion cells, a firm foundation was laid for the understanding of the retina and the nervous structure in general.

SÖMMERRING.

Fig. 37.—Samuel Thomas von Soemmerring (1755–1830), anatomist, physiologist, and physician at Mainz, Frankfurt, and Munich, Germany. Student of the structure of the eye, discoverer (with Buzzi of Milan) of the "yellow spot," or *macula flava*, and of the central fovea of the human eye. Investigator of the brain. Friend of Immanuel Kant, the famous German philosopher of Königsberg (Fig. 353). Postulated a homogeneous organization of the brain as a material substratum of the transcendental soul, contrasting with the concept of a composite organization championed by Gall (*see* Figs. 83, 84). Frontispiece in H. F. Kilian, *Die Universitäten Deutschlands*.

5. RODS AND CONES RECOGNIZED AS TRUE PHOTORECEPTORS.—Of the important problems that remained unsolved at that time, that of the true photoreceptors was one. Various structures had been suggested as the possible photoreceptors, but without wide acceptance.

It was fairly certain that the optic nerve fibers themselves were not photosensitive, an idea propagated by the sponsors of the "catoptric hypothesis" of the bacillary layer—Bidder, Hannover, and Brücke—because the optic disk, although it contains many fibers, is blind (corresponding to Mariotte's "blind spot" in the field of view). The other alternative, that the ganglion cells were photoreceptors, advocated by Bowman and by Helmholtz (1851), also was in clear disagreement with the absence of ganglion cells in the territory of the optic disk.

The vexing problem of the identity of the photoreceptors seemed to be approaching its solution, when H. Müller (1851) discovered the "radial fibers," which were named by Koelliker "Müller's fibers" (for biography *see* H. Müller 1872, Koelliker 1866–67, and Fig. 46). Arranged vertically, these fibers pass through nearly the entire thickness of the retinal mem-

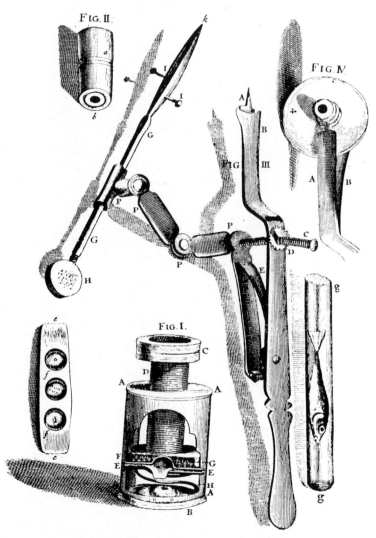

FIG. 38.—So-called "pocket microscope," *I*, of James Wilson (1702–3), with accessories: low-power magnifier used independently, *II;* one branch of the handle, *III*, to which, at *A*, one of seven magnifying lenses of different power could be attached (per sketch *IV*), while the examined object was held either by a mounting forceps *k* or on a small ivory carrier *H*, one side of which was white, the other black; *g*, a glass tube for viewing living objects (as in Leeuwenhoek's equipment). From Phil. Tr. Roy. Soc. London, v. 23, 1704.

brane (Figs. 48, 50). They seemed to be the structures connecting the bacillary layer with the layers of ganglion cells and optic nerve fibers. Contrary to Bidder's "catoptric hypothesis" of rod function and to Treviranus' *papillae* as photosensitive structures on the vitreal face of the retina, Müller's discovery showed that the elements of the bacillary layer may well be the terminal structures of the optic nerve fibers, hence the true photoreceptors, even though they are located on the outer, scleral face of this membrane.

These important discoveries helped to substantiate the thesis of the photoreceptor function of the rods and cones. Even when it was shown later that Müller's "radial fibers" belonged to the supporting neuroglial tissue and were, therefore, unfit to conduct nerve impulses, Müller's basic concept remained unshaken, since other, thinner threads and fibers, undoubtedly nervous and also arranged radially, were found that could well serve as the links connecting the outwardly placed rods and cones with the inner layers (Fig. 50). Additional evi-

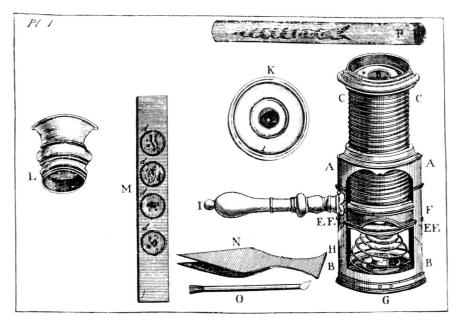

FIG. 39.—Wilson's "single pocket microscope" with accessories: *A*, *B*, body; *C*, movable tube; *EE*, brass plates to hold slide; *G*, near end of tube; *H*, steel spring; *I*, handle; *K*, one of six magnifying lenses of different power to be screwed onto *G*; *L*, low-power magnifier to be used independently; *M*, slide with four specimens mounted between plates of glass or mica; *N*, nippers; *O*, hair brush; *P*, glass tube for living objects "such as frogs, fishes, etc., in order to discover the blood, as it streams along the veins and arteries"; *, one of several brass rings of varying aperture used as diaphragms. The linear magnification claimed for this microscope was from 16 to 400×. The instrument was, accordingly, more versatile than Leeuwenhoek's but gave only a little more magnification. From Henry Baker, *The Microscope Made Easy*, London, 1743.

Müller (1853, 1854, 1856–57), furthermore, was able to furnish experimental physiological evidence of a photoreceptor function of the bacillary layer. This he did with the help of a parallactic displacement of shadows of the retinal blood vessels, which cause "Purkinje's figure" to be perceived entoptically. The distance computed by Müller proved to be identical with that between the larger blood vessels on the inner, vitreal, face and the bacillary layer on the outer, scleral, face of the retina, as measured in preparations.

dence gathered during the next several decades, mainly the discovery by Boll (1877) of rhodopsin, or erythropsin, also called "visual purple," a photosensitive substance contained in the outer rod segments, put Müller's claim beyond reasonable doubt.

References: Adams 1746; Arnold; Ammon; Babuchin; Baker 1743; Bergmann; Bidder; Bird & Schäfer; Boll; Borysiekiewicz; Bowman 1849; Brücke; Carpenter; Clay 1938; Clay & Court 1932; Conn 1948; Corti 1850, 1854; Dalrymple; Disney, Hill & Baker 1928; Ehrenberg;

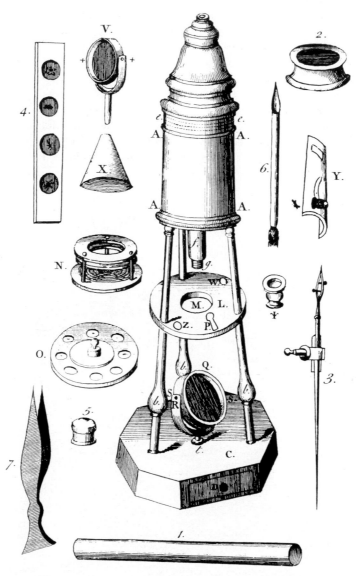

Fɪɢ. 40.—"Double reflecting microscope," a large compound magnifier of Marshall, improved by Culpeper and Scarlet. *A*, body; *b*, pillars; *C*, pedestal; *D*, drawer; *f*, smaller tube; *g*, lower end of small tube onto which one of five objectives or nosepieces could be screwed (focusing was accomplished by raising or lowering the tube); *L*, stage; *M*, hole in same; *N*, adapter for holding a slide to be put into hole *M; O*, circular brass slide with specimens, also exchangeable disks of ivory or ebony for observation in incident light for black or white opaque objects; *P*, slit in stage for the fitting of a button in the center of the circular slide; *Q*, concave mirror for transillumination; *V*, plano-convex lens, attachable to a hole *W* for observation of opaque objects in incident light; *X*, cone of black ivory, attachable beneath central opening of stage for dark-field illumination; *Y*, brass pan for mounting small fish for study of circulation; *Z*, hole in the stage for mounting a needle (*3*); *1*, glass tube for living objects; *2*, cell for fleas, lice, and mites fitting into *M; 3*, mounting needle and forceps; *4*, slide holding four specimens mounted between plates of mica or isinglass; *5*, box for isinglass; *6*, hair brush; *7*, nippers. From H. Baker, *The Microscope Made Easy*, London, 1743.

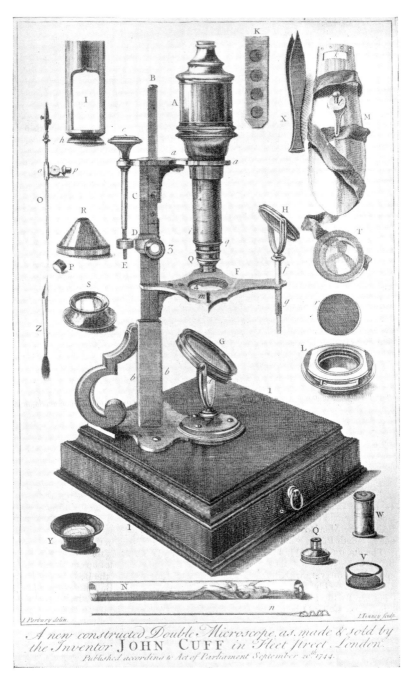

FIG. 41.—A compound microscope with accessories constructed by John Cuff, in London, 1744. From Henry Baker, *Employment for the Microscope*, London, 1753. Equipment similar to that in the preceding figure.

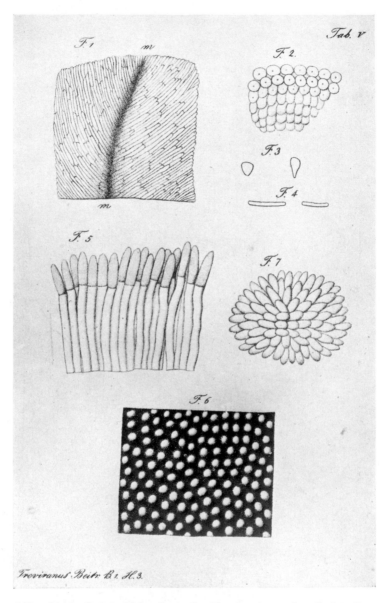

Fig. 42.—Some of the objects that could be observed with microscopes described in the preceding figures: *1*, flat view of a frog retina, showing "cylinders," obviously photoreceptors, parting at both sides of a line *m*; *2*, socalled *papillae*, evidently rods of frog retina, upper tiers in flat view, lower tiers in half-profile; *3*, two isolated papillae in profile; *4*, "stalks" of the papillae, with their pointed ends torn off; *5*, papillae of a frog tadpole in profile (doubtless photoreceptors); *6*, "inner face," but obviously the scleral or outer face, of a snake's retina in flat view, showing papillae surrounded by pigment; *7*, a bunch of retinal papillae. From G. R. Treviranus, *Beiträge zur Aufklärung der Erscheinungen und Gesetze des organischen Lebens*, Bremen, 1837. (*See also* following two figures.)

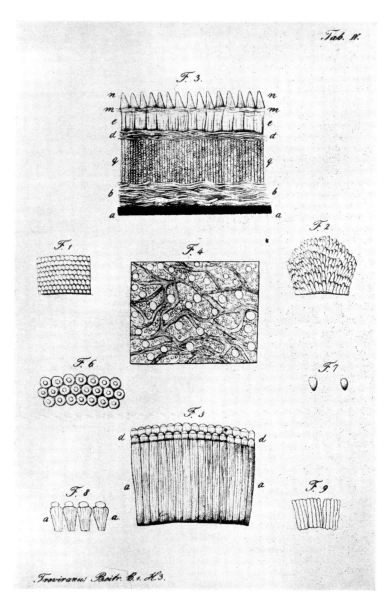

FIG. 43.—More retinal structures described by Treviranus (*see* preceding and following figures): *1*, papillae in a Starling's retina; *2*, papillae of a Swan's retina; *3*, vertical section through retina of a Crow fixed in alcohol: *a*, pigment layer; *b*, outer "fibrous and vascular layer"; *q*, vertical continuation of fibers of *b* disintegrated into "globules" (apparently outer nuclear layer); *d*, second "cellular layer," made up of central artery and nerve fibers (present inner plexiform layer); *e*, layer of thicker fibers from *q* that become even coarser in layer *m*; *n*, layer made up of papillae that were supposed to be the true photoreceptors coating the inner face of the retinal membrane; *4*, flat view of the vascular layer of a Fox retina; *5*, segment of a Turtle's retina showing papillae in *d*, *d*; *6*, vitreal, or, rather, scleral, aspect of three tiers of the papillae of *5*; *7*, two of the same papillae shown individually; *8*, papillae in profile; *9*, cylindrical structures, obviously photoreceptors. Note that sketch *3* is the earliest pictorial representation of the retinal layers in cross-section, although its interpretation was incorrect. From G. R. Treviranus, *Beiträge zur Aufklärung*, Bremen, 1837.

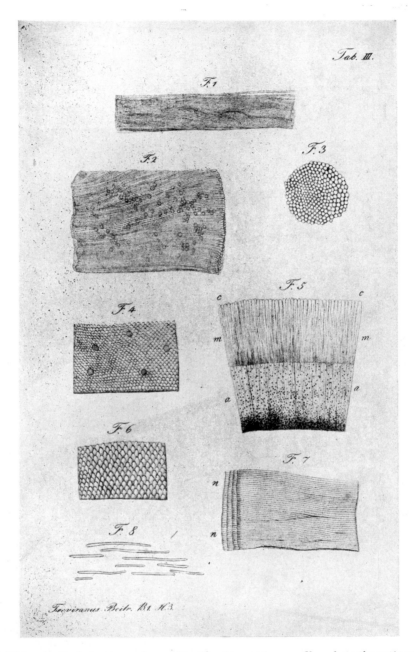

FIG. 44.—Additional retinal structures observed by Treviranus: *1*, nerve fibers from the optic nerve of a Sheep; *2*, vitreal view of Sheep retina, with nerve fibers terminating at right margin as papillae, with few seen through membrane as round globules; *3*, papillae of Sheep retina seen from the vitreal side (probably ganglion cells); *4*, papillae of a Rabbit's retina (probably ganglion cells); *5*, scleral view of the segment of a Mole's retina, showing, along its upper margin, nerve fibers terminating as papillae (probably at ora terminalis); *6*, vitreal view of a Mole's retina, showing papillae (probably ganglion cells); *7*, segment of an Owl's retina, supposedly showing at *nn* terminations of optic nerve fibers as papillae; *8*, cylindrical structures, possibly from the layer of nerve fibers. From G. R. Treviranus, *Beiträge zur Aufklärung*, Bremen, 1837. (*See also* preceding two figures.)

Ewart & Thin; Gage; Gerlach 1858; Gottsche; Goodsir; Hannover 1840; Hasse; Heinemann; Helmholtz 1843, 1851; Henle; Hensen; Heschl 1880; Hirschberg 1911 (on Bowman); Hoffmann; Hulke; Huschke; Th. Wh. Jones 1833; C. Krause; Koelliker 1852–54, 1866–67; Kuhnt; Langenbeck; Leydig; Merkel; G. A. Michaelis; H. Müller 1851–72; J. Müller 1837; W. Müller; Norris & Shakespeare; Nunnely; Pacini 1845; Ranvier; Reich 1874; Reichert 1841; Remak 1839; Retzius 1881, 1905; Ritter; Robertson & Edwards (on Bowman); Salzer; Schaffer; Schiess; M. Schultze; Schwalbe; Stieda; Tafani; Treviranus; Valentin; Vintschgau; Wagner; Welcker; Wilson 1855.

Fig. 45.—William Bowman (1816–92) at the age of forty-five. An anatomist, physiologist, and renowned ophthalmologist of London. Together with Helmholtz, Graefe, and Donders, a founder of modern ophthalmology. Discoverer of "Bowman's membrane" or the cornea and of "Bowman's capsule" in the Malpighian glomeruli of the kidneys. First who nearly correctly described and depicted the layers of the retinal membrane. From J. Hirschberg, in Graefe & Saemisch, *Handb. d. ges. Augenh.*, 2d ed., v. 14 (4), p. 203, 1914.

SEC. 8. THE PROBLEM OF THE INTRINSIC ORGANIZATION OF THE RETINA AND MODERN EFFORTS TO SOLVE IT

1. EARLY ATTEMPTS TO UNRAVEL THE MINUTE STRUCTURE OF NERVOUS TISSUE.—The information about the minute organization of the nervous system which the histologists of the eighteenth and the greater part of the nineteenth centuries possessed was acquired from studying fresh specimens or those fixed, though unstained, which were either "whole-mounts" or "teased preparations," that is, pieces of tissue dissected with needles.

Even after the introduction of the technique of fixation, hardening, and cutting of sections, and staining with various dyes, the appearance of structures composing a nervous organ—the nerve cells, the fibers and their various envelopes, the supporting tissue, and the blood vessels—was rather uniform. In such prepara-

tions, in spite of varying intensity and tint, the chance of determining subtle and intricate relationships of some particular histological constituents was small.

In what soon came to be regarded as the core of the problem of the histophysiological constitution of nervous tissue—the relationship of the nerve cells to one another—the primitive technique of early modern histology mostly failed. With much effort and disproportionate investment of time, histologists of the mid-

FIG. 46.—Heinrich Müller (1820–64), professor of anatomy, at Würzburg, Bavaria, Germany. A pioneer in modern anatomy and physiology of the eye and, in particular, of the retina. Founder of ophthalmic pathology. Described the principal layers of the retina and their correct arrangement, with rods and cones outermost. By a physiological experiment—the displacement of entoptically perceived shadows of the retinal blood vessels, or "Purkinje's vascular tree"—he furnished the evidence in support of the photoreceptor function of rods and cones. Described supporting structures of the retinal tissue, since called "Müller's radial fibers." Discovered the central area surrounding the foveal depression; the multiple foveae in the eye of Birds; the circular muscle fibers in the ciliary body; the smooth muscle of the eye socket, innervated by sympathetic nerves ("Müller muscle"), etc. Portrait enlarged by Mrs. J. R. Weigel (Miss Eileen Kern) from an original by J. Hirschberg, in Graefe & Saemisch, *Handb. d. ges. Augenh.*, 2d ed., v. 15 (2), p. 243, 1918.

nineteenth century—Remak (1839, 1853, 1854), Helmholtz (1843, portrait Figs. 102, 356), Corti (1850, 1854), Koelliker (1854, portrait Fig. 47), J. von Gerlach (1858), B. Stilling (1859), Deiters (1865), M. Schultze (1866, 1869, 1872, 1873, portrait Fig. 49), and others—succeeded in discovering the most important facts: that nerve fibers were not independent structures but were expansions of the nerve cells and that there were two kinds of such expansions, long ones, which were named "axis cylinders" or "axons," and short ones, named "dendrites." But the details of how the nerve cells and their expansions were related to one another remained outside the reach of available techniques. (*Cf.* Obersteiner 1892; Stieda 1899; S. Ramón y Cajal 1909–11; Edinger 1911; *see also* Conn 1948.)

FIG. 47.—Rudolf Albert von Kölliker (1817–1905), professor of anatomy, microscopy, and embryology at Würzburg, Bavaria, Germany. One of the most productive morphobiologists of his age. A pioneer of modern microscopy and a most accomplished connoisseur of bodily tissues in his time, according to C. S. Minot. Together with Heinrich Müller (Fig. 46), his friend and collaborator, he first determined the correct order of the retinal layers and analyzed the minute structure of the retinal tissue (Fig. 48). Engraving by H. Hanfstaengl, made in 1855 from a painting by Clementine Stockar-Escher. Courtesy Dr. Jeannette Obenchain and Professor R. R. Bensley, of the University of Chicago. For Kölliker's autobiography see *Erinnerungen aus meinem Leben*, 1899; W. Waldeyer 1906, and Haymaker & Baer, *The Founders of Neurology*, 1953.

2. Limits of preanalytic histological techniques as applied to the retina.—In the investigation of the retina the farthest point reached by the end of the third quarter of the nineteenth century is represented in the admirable work of Max Schultze (especially 1866, 1872–73, portrait Fig. 49; for biography *see* G. Schwalbe 1874). In it the principal features, such as the distribution of cellular and fibrous elements into ten layers, the appearance and distribution of the photoreceptors, the structural characteristics of the foveal cones, and many other details, were correctly presented (Fig. 50).

Also, Schultze was the first to suggest that the two varieties of photoreceptors were concerned with different functions, the rods being instrumental in nocturnal or scotopic vision, and the cones in daylight or photopic vision, an idea which has since developed into the modern "duplexity theory of vision" or "duplex retina" of Parinaud, Kries, *et al.*

Yet, fundamental as these discoveries were and in spite of the painstaking labors of Schultze, Schwalbe, and many other retinologists of that period, who relied chiefly upon the "maceration" and "teasing" technique, the problem of precisely how the various histological components of the retinal membrane are integrated into a complex tissue and what the particular functions of each of them are defied solution. A special obstacle proved to be the two plexiform layers, through which the fibers could not be followed with certainty.

Finally, Schultze felt it necessary to admit that a direct histophysiological connection of the photosensitive rods and cones on the scleral side with the optic nerve fibers on the vitreal side of the retinal membrane, believed in by most investigators since H. Müller's discovery of "radial fibers," was more a conviction than positive knowledge based upon observation.

3. Introduction of histoanalytical methods in the study of nervous tissue.—The possibility of a complete histological analysis of complex nervous tissue arrived when new neurohistological methods were devised.

The first, accidentally discovered by an Italian investigator, Camillo Golgi (1873, 1878, portrait Fig. 344), consisted in staining, in a weak silver nitrate solution, specimens previously fixed and hardened in a solution of potassium dichromate, in "Müller's solution," or in a mixture of potassium dichromate and osmium tetroxide: the "Golgi method." The sections made from such blocks showed a peculiarity not found in the preparations treated with any of the earlier methods, as, for example, Gerlach's carmine stain introduced in 1858. In-

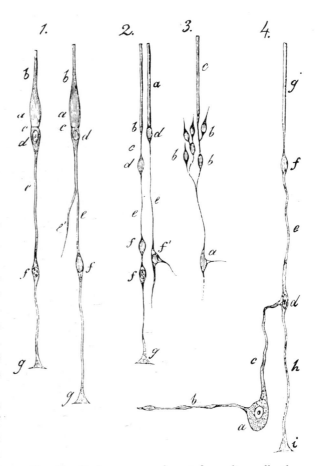

Fig. 48.—Rods, cones, nuclear and ganglion cells of the retina and their relationships, as conceived by Heinrich Müller (1852, 1854) and by Kölliker (1854). Sketch *1* illustrates the hypothetical connection of the cones (*b*), and sketches *2, 3,* and *4* that of the rods (*a, c, g*), with various cells of the retina, for example, with the outer nuclear cells (*d* in sketches *1* and *2; b* in sketch *3; f* in sketch *4*), with the inner nuclear cells (*f* in sketches *1, 2; a* in sketch *3; d* in sketch *4*), and with the ganglion cells (*a* in sketch *4*) by means of Müller's "radial fibers" (*c, e, g, h*). No distinction was as yet made between the nervous fibers proper and the supporting neuroglial fibers. In sketch *4* a nerve fiber *b* with typical spindle-shaped varicosities continues to the brain. From A. Kölliker, *Mikroskopische Anatomie oder Gewebelehre des Menschen* and *Manual of Human Microscopical Anatomy,* 1854, Figs. 392, 411.

stead of all cells and fibers being more or less diffusely stained, only some were found to be blackened, while the others remained unstained. In such preparations, if the nerve cells were stained completely, as often happened, the expansions could be followed to the very finest of their terminal branches, and their relationship to other nerve cells or to nonnervous structures could thus be determined.

lich (1886), consisted in injecting a weak solution of methylene blue, an aniline dye, into a living animal, whose nervous tissue made the blue dye colorless within a short time. When the tissue was exposed to the action of air, the nervous structures appeared selectively stained in blue. (For a description of methods of Golgi and Ehrlich *see* Polyak, *The Retina,* chap. 4, 1941, 1948.)

Fig. 49.—Max Johann Sigismund Schultze (1825–74), professor of anatomy at Halle and Bonn in Prussia, Germany. Pioneer of modern microscopy. Cofounder, with Theodor Schwann and M. J. Schleiden, of modern cell theory of animal tissues. A diligent student of the minute structure of the retinal membrane. Originator of the concept of the double function of the retina, or so-called "duplexity theory," later amplified by Parinaud and by Kries, according to which the cones are active in daylight and are instrumental in color vision, whereas the rods are instrumental in twilight vision. Frontispiece in Schultze's Arch. f. mikr. Anat., v. 10, 1874. (*See here* obituary by G. Schwalbe.)

With one stroke the Golgi method not only revealed an undreamed-of complexity of nerve centers but also furnished the means for a successful histological analysis of the entire nervous system.

Another histoanalytical method, the "vital methylene blue stain," discovered by Paul Ehr-

4. Influence of histoanalytical techniques upon concepts of the organization of the nervous system.—The effect of the methods of Golgi and Ehrlich upon the subsequent course of neurological disciplines was profound. It unleashed a flood of investigations which threw light on many parts of the nervous

system which had been obscure until then. Even more important was the effect of the new technique upon the general theory of the nervous system.

Until that time the concept of the minute organization and working of the nervous organs had been vague and confused. For example, J. Gerlach (1872), one of the leading anatomists of his time, believed that the nerve fibers of the nerve fibers to the central *reticulum* and to the nerve cells, however, remained undisclosed.

The idea of a "diffuse nerve net," "punctate substance," "neuropil," and what-not has persisted ever since, even though later investigations abundantly demonstrated the fallacy of Gerlach's concept. Golgi himself subscribed to it in describing a *rete nervosa diffusa*, or "diffuse nerve net."

Fig. 49*A*.—Jakob Henle (1809–85), professor of anatomy in Zürich, Heidelberg, and Göttingen. First described the pupillary membrane in the eye of an embryo, and the outer fiber layer of the retina named in his honor "Henle's outer fiber layer." Discovered "epithelium" as a lining of the surface of various organs. Described simultaneously with Meynert the alternating cell and fiber laminae in the human lateral geniculate nucleus. Author of the *General Anatomy of Bodily Tissues* and of the classical *Handbuch der systematischen Anatomie des Menschen* in three volumes. Reformer of physiological pathology, and a cofounder (with Pfeufer) of the Zeitschrift für rationelle Medicin. Frontispiece from F. Merkel, *Gedächtnisrede* (commemoration speech), 1909. For biography *see* F. Merkel, *Jacob Henle, ein deutsches Gelehrtenleben*, F. Vieweg & Sohn, Braunschweig, 1891.

posterior roots, after entering the spinal cord, divide into numerous branches, which together produce a diffuse nerve net, or *reticulum*, in the gray substance. The threads of this *reticulum*, by merging again, he thought, formed the anterior spinal roots. The precise relation of the

The most radical form this idea assumed in modern times was the concept of a "universal neuroreticulum" or *neurencytium*, which supposedly permeated the tissues of the whole organism and would be the guarantor of its functional unity (Held 1927, 1929). What the countless varieties of nerve cells and their connections were for and what the precise histophysiological basis of locally diversified functions of nervous organs was, the advocates of the "neuroreticulum hypothesis" have never explained intelligently. (*See* chap. IX.)

Very different ideas arose in the minds of another group of investigators, chiefly under the stimulus and influence of the newly discovered histoanalytical technique. The embryological studies of W. His (1886, 1889, 1904, portrait Fig. 343; *also* Mall 1905) led him to a conviction

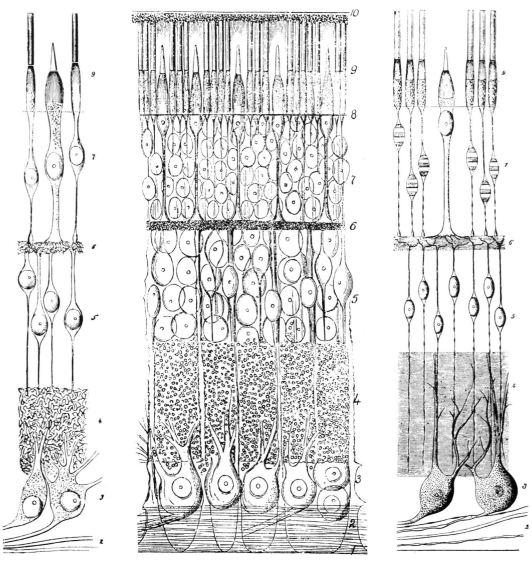

FIG. 50.—Arrangement and relationships of constituent nerve cells and fibers of human retina as conceived at the close of the pre-Golgi period of modern microscopy. Left-hand and middle diagrams from M. Schultze (1872, Figs. 344, 357); right-hand diagram from Schwalbe (1874, Fig. 51). Layer *1*, inner limiting membrane; *2*, layer of optic nerve fibers; *3*, ganglion cell layer; *4*, inner "granular," now inner plexiform layer; *5*, inner nuclear layer; *6*, outer "granular," now outer plexiform layer; *7*, outer nuclear layer; *8*, outer limiting membrane; *9*, bacillary layer of rods and cones; *10*, pigment epithelium. (For modern terms *see* Fig. 128.) In contrast with Kölliker's figure (Fig. 48), two varieties of "radial fibers" were now distinguished: nervous, identified with the outer and inner expansions of nerve cells, or rods and cones, and the nonnervous Müller's "radial fibers" which belonged to the supporting neuroglial framework. The nervous radial fibers were presented as intimately connected with plexiform layers *4* and *6*. The primitive histological technique exemplified in this figure left the principal problem, that concerning the true significance of the plexiform layers, unsolved. (*Cf.* Figs. 53, 54, 55.)

that in the early stages of fetal development the histological elements from which the nervous system is built are individual, independent young cells, the "neuroblasts," of rather uniform appearance. In pursuing the same line of thought, other neuroanatomists recognized that the relative independence or individuality of the nerve cells remains preserved in the more

experiments, finally crystallized in the "neuron theory." (*See* chap. IX.)

5. Neuron theory of the nervous system.—Following are the essential tenets of the neuron theory. Each individual nerve cell, with all its expansions or processes, is to be considered as a histological and functional entity, a

Fig. 51.—Ernst Abbé (1840–1905), mathematician and student of physical optics, at the age of forty-four. Considered the "world's greatest genius in scientific optics." Cofounder and research director of K. Zeiss Optical Company at Jena, Germany. Inventor of oil-immersion lenses and of the stage condenser for the microscope, which made the advancement of modern microscopy possible. From Abbé's *Gesammelte Abhandlungen*, G. Fischer, Jena, 1904–6.

advanced stages as well, including the fully differentiated tissue of the adult organs. The observations and interpretations of Forel, Waldeyer, Lenhossék, Gehuchten, Retzius, *et al.*, and, above all, the brilliant and indefatigable S. Ramón y Cajal (1888–1935, portrait Figs. 52, 131, 317), well substantiated by Harrison's

"neuron," which is to a certain degree independent of other neurons of the same organism. The individual neurons are related to one another not by "anastomosis," or merging of their processes, but by means of more or less intimate contact, and the boundaries at the points of contact are real. A *neuroreticulum* or *neuren-*

cytium is only apparent, owing to inadequate technique and to faulty interpretation. Each nerve cell, each neuron, is a morphodynamical microcosm whose various parts are differentiated into distinct functional organelles. The cell body and the shorter and usually more numerous "protoplasmic expansions" of Deiters, called "dendrites," are the receptor organelles of a neuron capable of receiving stimuli or impulses from other neurons or from other structures or agents. The other and usually single, long or short "axis cylinder" of Deiters, or "axon," the "nerve fiber" in common parlance, terminating at its far end in an arborization, or "teledendron," is a discharging organelle of the neuron, along which the "impulses" are transmitted to other neurons, glands, or muscles. The points at which a more or less intimate contact is established between the related neurons, called "synapses," barring a few exceptions requiring further study and interpretation, are organized unidirectionally or in a way which permits a flow of the influences in one direction only, specifically from the teledendron of one neuron to the cell body or dendrites of another related neuron, while at the same time inhibiting the influence from spreading in the opposite direction. This is called the "dynamic or functional polarity of a neuron."

The neuron theory, briefly, maintains that the entire nervous system is made up of countless dynamically or functionally polarized neurons of the most varied shapes and types, concatenated in an orderly manner into many different patterns, which, in addition, vary from place to place.

There is, furthermore, substantial evidence that the inherent functional capacities of morphologically differing neuron varieties are not of the same kind but vary from species to species of the nerve cell. In other words, each neuron variety should be regarded as dynamically responsive in one way only, and therefore functionally reacting in one way only, peculiar to or specific for it, different from the modes of reaction of all other neuron varieties of the same animal species. This is called "dynamic or functional specificity of neurons." The specific mode or modes of dynamic and, therefore, physiological reaction of a neuron is or are determined not only by such factors as the position of a neuron in the tissue or its synaptical relationship to

other neurons or tissues, and by various exogenous factors, such as the kind and intensity of the stimulus, but also especially by its own innate or inherent biochemical and biodynamical properties and capacities.

The organization of the nervous system, central and peripheral, according to these principles, fully accounts for both the diversity and the complex character of nervous functions and also seems a sufficient material substratum by means of which an individual organism is created and preserved as a biological and psychic entity.

The neuron theory as the basis of a concept of the intimate organization of the nervous system, tested by decades of hard experience and severe criticism, has, on the whole, been satisfactory in explaining the principal phenomena of normal nervous functioning and the reaction of nervous organs under pathological conditions. Also the theory has proved flexible enough to permit amplification, modification, and further adaptation in detail to the new and heretofore unknown facts or requirements arising from additional observations and wider experience.

References disapproving of, or questioning, the "neuron theory": Apáthy; Bethe; Bielschowsky; Boeke; Held 1927, 1929; Heringa; Marui; Nissl; Péterfi; Stöhr, Jr.; Tiegs; M. Wolff.

References favoring "neuron theory": Barr; Bartelmez; Bartelmez & Hoerr; Bodian; Bozler; Detwiler 1936; Fedorow; Fedorow & Matwejewa; Forel; Gehuchten; Hanström; Harrison; Heidenhain; Herzog & Günther; W. His; Lenhossék; Neal; Nonidez; Parker; Polyak 1941, 1948, 1949, 1953; S. Ramón y Cajal; Retzius 1905, 1908; Schaper 1899; Schiefferdecker 1906; Tello; Waldeyer; Windle & Clark; Woollard & Harpman.

References on "synapse": Adrian; Ariëns Kappers; Barr; Bartelmez & Hoerr; Bodian; Bronk; Eccles; Erlanger; Forbes; Fulton; Gasser; Gerard; Lillie; Lorente de Nó; Lucas & Adrian; E. Meyer; Monnier; Polyak 1941, 1948, 1949, 1953, 1955; J. Z. Young. *See also* Cold Spring Harbor Symposia, v. 4, and Trans Faraday Soc., v. 33, p. 911.

References, general: Barr; Bodian; Eccles 1936; Edinger 1911; Obersteiner 1892; Rasmussen 1947; Stieda 1899.

SEC. 9. THE NEURON THEORY AND THE MODERN CONCEPT OF
STRUCTURE AND FUNCTION OF THE VERTEBRATE RETINA

1. VARIETIES OF RETINAL NEURONS AND THEIR SYNAPTICAL RELATIONSHIPS.—The influence which the neuron theory exerted upon the concept of the minute organization of the retina and upon its interpretation in terms of functions was far reaching. The continuous connections of the photosensitive rods and cones and of the optic nerve fibers, which the older investigators—Treviranus, Koelliker, H. Müller, M. Schultze, Dogiel, Tartuferi, and many others—tried to establish, S. Ramón y Cajal proved did not exist (1888, 1892–93, 1909–11, 1934, 1935; Figs. 52, 131, 317). Instead, he found the retina to be composed of three superimposed series of neurons or individual nerve cells related to one another by means of synapses (Figs. 53, 54, 55). The first series, represented by the rods and cones, was the most

FIG. 52.—Santiago Ramón y Cajal (1852–1934), the foremost modern neurohistologist, at the age of fifty-five. Professor at the universities of Valencia, Barcelona, and Madrid. Most accomplished investigator of the minute structure of the nervous system, its development, and its pathology. Author of *Les nouvelles idées sur la fine anatomie des centres nerveux*, Paris, 1894; *Textura del sistema nervioso del hombre y de los vertebrados*, Madrid, 1897–1904, translated into French, *Histologie du système nerveux, etc.*, Paris 1909–11, etc.; Nobel laureate, with Golgi, for the year 1906. Portrait from München. med. Wchnschr., v. 54, 1907 (for other portraits *see* Figs. 131, 317). For autobiography *see* his *Recuerdos de mi vida* (also in English); for biography *see* Ariëns Kappers 1934; Lenhossék 1935; Sprong 1935; Tello 1935; Villaverde 1935; P. Lain Entralgo 1947; Haymaker 1948; Cannon 1949; Trueta 1952; Haymaker & Baer 1953; and Polyak 1953. *See also* Figs. 53, 54, 55.

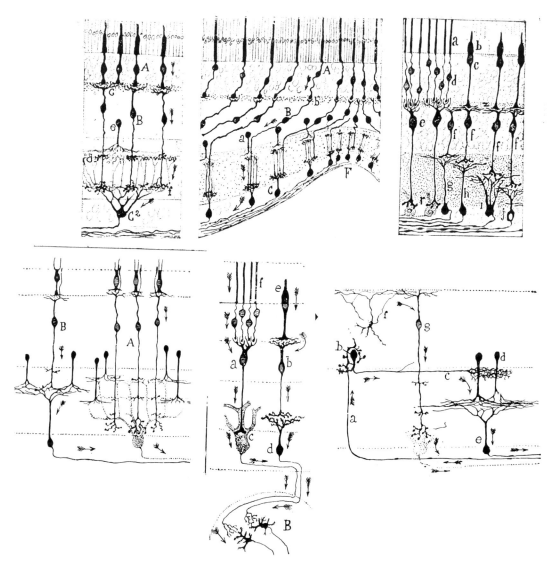

Fig. 53.—S. Ramón y Cajal's diagrams illustrating types of neurons of the vertebrate retina and visual system, their synaptical relationships, and their probable functional significance. *Upper row, left and middle sketch:* mechanism for color and visual space perception in retinal periphery and in the fovea (*F*), made up of cones (*A*), bipolars (*B*), and ganglion cells (*C*); right-hand sketch showing his concept of two sets or systems of receptors and conductors: the rod system instrumental in colorless twilight vision (*a, d, e, r*), and the cone system for color perception in daylight vision (*b, c, f, g, h, i, j*), embodying "duplexity theory" of Schultze, Parinaud, and Kries. *Lower row, left sketch:* synaptical relations of one cone to one bipolar cell (*B*), and through it to one ganglion cell and to two amacrine cells, and again three cones singly related to three bipolars (*A*), and through these to several amacrines and to one ganglion cell (all in Bird's retina); *central sketch:* illustrates achromatic (*f, a, c*) and chromatic (*e, b, d*) constituents of the visual system from the retina to the brain (*B*); *right-hand sketch:* illustrates complex relationships in Bird's retina: a centripetal pathway made up of a bipolar (*g*) and a ganglion cell (*shaded*), also a centrifugal pathway composed of a fiber (*a*) originating in the brain and terminating around an amacrine cell (*b*), which, in turn, by way of its axon fiber (*c*) and amacrine cells (*d*), influences a ganglion cell (*e*), and in this way influences the centripetal system of neurons. From Ramón y Cajal, *Recuerdos de mi vida,* 1923.

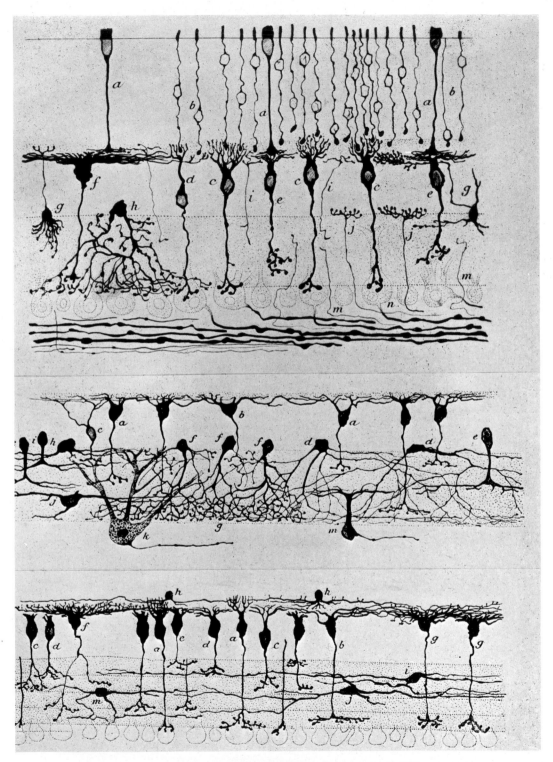

Fig. 54.—S. Ramón y Cajal's illustrations showing neuron varieties composing the retinal membrane and their synaptical relationships. Upper sketch represents Dog's retina: cones (*a*), rods (*b*), "rod bipolars" (*c*), "cone bipolars" (*e*), "giant bipolar" (*f*), cell with an ascending axon (*g*), amacrine cell (*h*), fibers and terminations probably of extraretinal origin (*i, j, m*), and ganglion cells in outline (*n*). Middle and lower sketches, from the retina of an Ox, showing bipolars, amacrines, ganglions, and horizontal cells. From Ramón y Cajal, Cellule, v. 9, 1892–93; and Trav. du lab. de recherches biol. Madrid, v. 28, 1933.

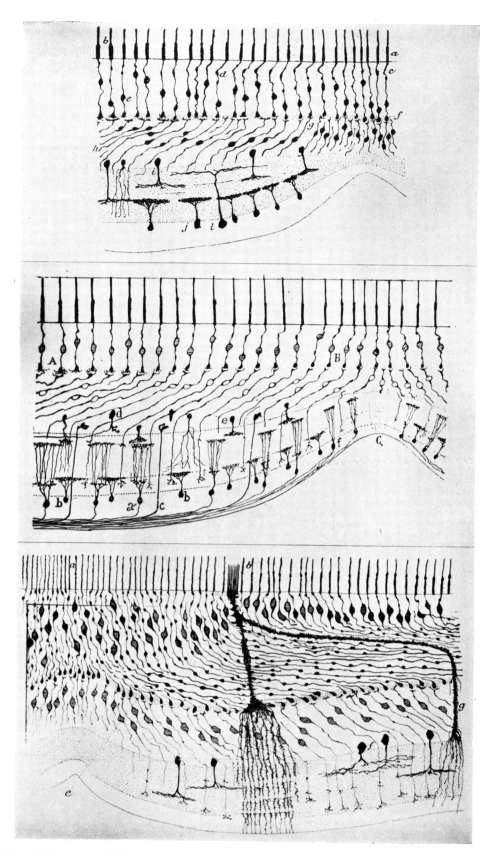

Fig. 55.—S. Ramón y Cajal's presentation of the minute structure of the fovea in various Vertebrates: upper sketch of a Greenfinch (*Fringilla* or *Ligurinus chloris*), middle sketch of a House Sparrow (*Passer domesticus*), lower sketch of a Chameleon (*Chamaeleon vulgaris*). Note that the cones of the bacillary layer are thinner and more numerous in the center of the fovea than outside; synaptical relationships of the foveal cones and bipolars are individualized; lateral displacement and slanting course either of bipolars or of both the cones and bipolars (as in Chameleon), all caused by the formation of a foveal excavation. From Ramón y Cajal, Cellule, v. 9, 1892–93, and Trav. du lab. de recherches biol. Madrid, v. 28, 1933.

peripheral (both topographically and in the functional sense). Here the electromagnetic vibrations of hypothetical "ether," which make up physical "light," elicit nervous "impulses" which are forwarded to the second series of neurons represented by the bipolar cells. From these, the "impulses" are further transmitted to the third series of neurons, the ganglion cells, along whose axis cylinders, or optic nerve fibers, they travel until they finally reach the brain.

2. Retinal structures, perception of light and colors ("duplexity theory"), and visual space perception.—The hypothesis of two functionally different varieties of photoreceptors proposed by Max Schultze suggested to S. Ramón y Cajal a similar cleavage or differentiation among the remainder of the structures of the retina and the visual pathways. Just as there are two kinds of photoreceptors, the rods and the cones, so there should be in the second series of the retinal neurons two varieties of bipolars—the "rod bipolars" related to the rods and the "cone bipolars" related to the cones.

Among the neurons of the third series, Ramón y Cajal distinguished several varieties, although he was less explicit in assigning them definite synaptical relationships. Even so, he assumed a separation of the two sets of neurons as far as the brain, one set conducting the impulses generated in the rods and the other conducting the cone impulses. This he regarded as an anatomical substantiation of the "duplexity theory" of Max Schultze, Parinaud, and Kries, according to which the cones are active only during the day and are instrumental in color perception (photopic vision), while the low-threshold rods mediate the perception of the various shades of colorless "gray" elicited by the weak stimuli under nocturnal conditions (scotopic vision).

Another important observation by Ramón y Cajal concerned the individual synapses between the cones and the bipolars and again between the bipolars and the ganglion cells. He found such a one-to-one synaptical relationship in the central fovea of Birds and Lizards and considered this to be the structural basis of the greater acuity of "central" or direct vision in the fovea, in contrast to the more diffuse synaptical relationships of the extrafoveal territory of the retina, corresponding with the less distinct "peripheral" or indirect vision.

Besides these basic structures, Ramón y Cajal found other types of neurons in the retina, such as the "horizontal cells" and "amacrine cells," and also efferent or exogenous fibers, which presumably serve more complex functions of "association."

3. Critique of S. Ramón y Cajal's interpretation of retinal structures.—Great as was the advance in the fundamental understanding of the retinal mechanism as a result of Ramón y Cajal's discoveries, much in his scheme and interpretation was doubtful and incomplete. The first objection is to the material used, for all of his work was done with the infraprimate Vertebrates, whose vision conceivably differs in many respects from Man, Monkeys, and Apes. Nor had there been a later systematic investigation of the primate retina by means of the histoanalytical procedures of Golgi and of Ehrlich. The few serious efforts of this kind, for example, by Dogiel (1891, 1892, 1893) and Balbuena (1922, 1923, 1925, 1929, 1936), unfortunately fell short of their goal.

The functional interpretation of the retinal structures given by Ramón y Cajal also appears to be weak. Experimental physiology and psychology of vision suggest that certain complex dynamic processes which had formerly been assigned to the brain take place in the photoreceptor organ. If Ramón y Cajal's schemes were truly representative of the relationships of the retinal neurons, this membrane would be comparable to an aggregation of simple receptors such as are found in the skin. Such structures would account only for the simple reactions to light stimuli and for the transmission of impulses to the brain, but not for the more complex processes—the reciprocal influencing, selection, intensification, and inhibition of the impulses, and the like—functions which, according to some physiologists, are carried out by the retinal neurons (Kohlrausch 1931; Granit; Bartley 1941).

Such a relegation of the role of the retina to a simple photoreceptor is disproved by even a casual examination of sections of successfully stained preparations, which show a remarkable wealth of nerve cells arranged in a way suggestive of a structure of higher nerve centers, especially of the cerebral and cerebellar cortex. It then becomes apparent that, in order to appreciate fully the functions which the retina performs in the visual act and to bring its morphology abreast of modern physiological concepts of the visual act, a complete analysis of this organ was necessary, particularly in various primate species and in Man.

(For a description of neuron varieties of the retina, their synaptical relationships, and their probable functional role, in Man and in other Primates, *see* chaps. V, IX; *see also* Polyak, *The Retina*, 1941, 1948; *Retinal Structure and Colour Vision*, in Doc. Ophth., v. 3, 1949, and the article "Eye," in *Encyclopaedia Britannica* 1955.)

References: Bach; Balbuena; Baquis; Bouin; Cattaneo 1922; Dogiel; Druault; Ebner; Eccles; Embden; Greeff 1898, 1900; Hosch; Kallius; Kolmer 1930, 1936; W. Krause 1895; Marenghi; Neumayer; Polyak 1935, 1936, 1941, 1948, 1949, 1953; S. Ramón y Cajal 1889, 1892–93, 1904, 1909–11, 1916, 1923, 1934, 1935; Rasmussen 1947; Renaut; Resnikov; Rozemeyer & Stolte; Schaper 1889; Tartuferi 1887; Uyama; Uyama & Miyake; Velhagen; Vermes; Verrier 1928; H. Vogt.

Chapter II

Investigation of the Visual Pathways and Centers during Classical Antiquity, the Middle Ages, and the Early Period of the Modern Scientific Era

SEC. 1. INVESTIGATION OF THE VISUAL SYSTEM DURING THE EARLY PERIOD OF CLASSICAL ANTIQUITY

1. IMPORTANCE OF THE VISUAL SYSTEM FOR THE UNDERSTANDING OF THE BRAIN.—Of the many parts of the nervous system, few attracted the attention of the philosophers, naturalists, and physicians of bygone ages as did those related to the eye. During ancient Greek and Roman Times, the Arab Period, and the Middle Ages in Europe, the ideas derived from the study of the eye and the optic nerves were a major influence in the formation of the concept of the structure and function of the entire nervous system. In modern times, too, no other part of the brain has been investigated with greater zeal than the visual pathway.

Indeed, it was precisely the visual system that in our time was used as a weapon with which some of the major battles were fought concerning the intimate organization of the brain, its function, and its reaction in pathological conditions. The review of past efforts directed toward the elucidation of visual mechanisms is, therefore, in great measure the history of neurology. The close relationship of the nervous system to the rest of the organism again connects the problem of the visual apparatus with the investigation of other bodily systems, their anatomical organization, and their function, all, in turn, having a share in forming our concepts of the brain and the sense organs.

2. BEGINNINGS OF ANATOMY.—What knowledge, if any, the ancient Egyptians, Sumerians, Assyrians, Babylonians, Hindus, and other preclassical civilized peoples had of the optic nerves and their connection with the brain is difficult to evaluate because of the scarcity of evidence and the lack of systematic investigations in this field. Whether sacrificial practices and customs, such as the embalming of human bodies in ancient Egypt, or the practical experience gained by surgeons in treating wounds of the head were in any way helpful in expanding knowledge of the visual organs and centers beyond the merest rudiments is doubtful. The crudity of their procedures may be judged from the writings of the "Father of History," Heródotos of Halicarnassós ('Ηρόδοτος 'Αλικαρνασσεύς, 484–425 B.C.; see Heródotos, *History*, book 2), and of Diodóros of Sicily (first century B.C.; *see* Le Clerc 1729, p. 712).

The same unfavorable impression is gathered from the Edwin Smith Papyrus and other sources. (*See* Breasted 1930; A. C. Krause 1933; Ranke 1933; Mendelsohn 1944.) Equally bad for any naturalistic approach to the study of the human and animal body were the conditions in India and in China, the other two ancient spheres of civilization, since the rise of the ruling religions of Brahmanism and Buddhism, both of which were inimical to scientific inquiry. (*See* E. Clark, Simhaji, Zimmer, Wong & Lien-Teh, *et al.*)

Until further indisputable evidence to the contrary is furnished, it must be concluded that knowledge of the structure of the human body and its workings and almost as much the understanding of disease and its treatment, in those vast territories up to and largely also during our own times, had been entirely dominated by magic and mysticism, qualified but little by

73

practical experience. (*See also* Le Clerc 1729; Daremberg 1869, 1870; Thorndike; Singer 1925, 1928, 1931; *cf.* chap. I, 1 [1].)

Only a small part of the foundation of modern knowledge of the human and animal body and of Western medicine in general is, accordingly, to be found in any of the Pre-Classical Civilizations. Rather, its origin is in the practical, everyday experience of the peoples and tribes that populated the region around the Mediterranean Sea before the dawn of recorded history. These peoples of the Balkan Peninsula and Italy and of other near-by parts of Europe and western Asia gained their livelihood from primitive agriculture and stock raising, subsisted upon herds of sheep, goats, and cattle and to some extent upon the wild animals which they hunted. They were not bound by the inhibitions of a too intricate and rigid system of taboos such as was already rising in India, Egypt, and elsewhere. Their food was derived to a considerable extent from their domestic animals. In their free consumption of animal food these ancient goatherds and shepherds merely continued a habit inherited from their Late Stone Age forefathers, for whom, as hunters, meat was a very important source of subsistence (*cf.* Breuil & Obermaier, N. Casteret, H. L. Movius). It was natural for them to assume that the animal food that was good for them was as palatable to the gods with which their fancy populated the fields, forests, skies, rivers, and caves of their native lands.

In offering animal sacrifices to their deities, they gradually developed a ritual performed according to certain rules. Such sacrificial practices, in turn, furnished ample opportunity to learn much about the principal organs, their appearance, size, location, and arrangement in the body. Upon this rich, varied, constantly exercised, and direct experience was gradually built the original anatomical terminology of the common Aryan language and its later derivatives: Greek, Latin, Celtic, Germanic, and Slavonic.

It was but a short step for the bright minds of late Mediterranean prehistory to make a comparison between animal and human organization and to draw conclusions concerning its similarities and differences, as Greek folklore and mythology amply illustrate. Their anatomical knowledge was further amplified and corrected by the observation of wounds inflicted in frequent combats between the numerous tribes and communities that constituted this primitive, atomized society. When, about the middle of the first pre-Christian millennium in post-Homeric Greece, more settled conditions emerged from this chaos, the Greek language already possessed a rich anatomical vocabulary, found most useful by the newly rising class of healers or precursors of medical professionals needed in an emerging urban civilization. When at last Ancient Greece blossomed out into a phenomenon unique in the Ancient World, conditions developed which permitted and fostered free inquiry into all the phases and phenomena of life: native gifts of the race, economic progress and urbanization, commercial freedom, and, probably most important, a lack of enforced religious, political, economic, and social uniformity. (*See* Daremberg 1865, 1869; Soury 1899; J. Jolly 1901; Hopf 1904; Rostovtzeff 1926).

3. Greek anatomy of the brain and of the visual system.—In contrast to the remainder of the Ancient World, the Greeks had already acquired, particularly during the time of Heródotos, considerable knowledge of the anatomy and physiology of the brain, as they had of practical medicine in general (the school of Hippocrátes of Cos, 'Ιπποκράτης, "Father of Scientific Medicine," 460–380 B.C.). The few scattered hints found in classical Greek writings indicate this. Alkmáion, or Alcmáeon of Croton ('Αλκμαίον, *ca.* 520 B.C.), a physician by profession, is reputed to have been the first to dissect human bodies. He knew the role of the brain in sensation, movement, and thinking and considered it to be the seat of *hegemonikón* or the "ruling soul." (*See* Soury 1899; W. Sudhoff 1914.) Anaxagóras of Klazomenai ('Αναξαγόρας *ca.* 500 B.C.) was the first to dissect the brain systematically. Another sage of Hellenized southern Italy, Philólaos of Croton or Tarent (Φιλόλαος, approx. 400 B.C.), considered the brain to be the seat of intelligence and the heart the seat of ἡγεμονικον (*hegemonikón*), or the principal of several souls animating the living body, and of sensation. (*See* Brunet & Mieli 1936.) The fact that the Hippocratic School considered the seat of epilepsy to be in the brain and interpreted it as being caused by a cerebral edema also shows that the early Greek physicians had arrived at the idea of the brain as a substratum of nervous action. (*See* Hippokrátes, Περὶ ἱερῆς νόσου or νούσου, *De Morbo Sacro*, or *On the Sacred Disease; see* Temkin.)

An advancement in the knowledge of the brain is even more probable during the time immediately preceding the Hellenistic or Alexandrine period (to 323 B.C.). During this period the natural sciences began to flourish, as evidenced by the writings of Aristotle (*cf.* chap. I, 1 [1]). Thereafter, for a hundred years or so, from 323 to 212 B.C., in Alexandria, Egypt, which was founded in 332 B.C. by Aristotle's pupil Alexander III of Macedon, after the establishment of Greek dominion in Egypt under King Ptolemy Sotér, Alexander's general, Greek science reached a level never equaled or even approached either before or after, until the advent of Modern Times.

During the Roman Empire and the subsequent ages of decadence following its disintegration, Hellenistic or Alexandrine anatomy and physiology, especially of the brain, served as a foundation and an inexhaustible source of instruction. Later, during the Renaissance in western Europe, this ancient Greek knowledge furnished the tools with which our own modern sciences and medicine were built. (*See* Breasted; Brunet & Mieli; Cantor; Le Clerc; Soury.)

4. ARISTOTLE'S KNOWLEDGE OF OPTIC NERVES AND THEIR CONNECTIONS.—The first written record of the anatomy of the brain and the cranial nerves dates from Aristotle, the encyclopedic Greek naturalist and philosopher (*see* chap. I, 1 [1]). His description of the connections of the eyes with the brain, however, is extremely sketchy:

From the eye there go three ducts to the brain: the largest and the medium-sized to the cerebellum, the least to the brain itself; and the least is the one situated nearest to the nostrils. The two largest ones, then, run side by side and do not meet; the medium-sized ones meet—and this is particularly visible in Fishes—for they lie nearer than the large ones to the brain; the smallest pair are the most widely separated from one another, and do not meet [Aristotle, Περὶ τα ζῷα ἱστορία, or *Historia Animalium*, chap. 16].

Tentatively, the largest of the three nerves related to the orbit may be identified with the fifth or trigeminal nerve, the medium-sized with the optic nerve proper, and the third and thinnest one probably with the olfactory nerve. The reference to the "meeting" of the medium-sized nerves of both sides clearly indicates the chiasma of the two optic nerves.

Aristotle's meager account is, perhaps, all that could be expected from a great naturalist and thinker, busy with the innumerable problems of life and the world and living in a time of cataclysmic events: the downfall of Greece as a political power, the conquest of Persia and Egypt by Alexander, the creation of Alexander's empire, with its rapid disintegration and the struggle of the Diadochs, or Alexander's "heirs," for the division of the spoils after Alexander's death.

Another detrimental factor which probably prevented him from paying more attention to the particular question of the optic nerves was his concept of the functional role of the brain in general. For in his opinion this organ was merely an accessory to the heart, which, by implication, was the true seat of the "soul." The brain, accordingly, was not supposed to feel and could not be connected with the sense organs. In any case, it is a strange conclusion by such an acute observer, who undoubtedly had dissected many and various animals. (*See* Aristotle Περὶ ζῴων μορίων, *De Partibus Animalium*, or *On the Parts of Animals*, book 2, chap. 7.)

The concept of the heart as the seat of the soul, at any rate of its highest principle, *hegemonikón*, was later accepted and further elaborated by the ideologists of early Christianity, for example, by Tertullian (*De Anima, Of the Soul*, ca. A.D. 210).

5. ANATOMY AND PHYSIOLOGY OF THE VISUAL SYSTEM DURING THE ALEXANDRINE AND EARLY ROMAN PERIODS.—The sketchy description of the nerves more or less related to the eye by Aristotle was soon followed by the first systematic anatomical investigation during the most advanced, the Alexandrine or Hellenistic, period of Greek science. This, according to the scanty information available, was based chiefly on the dissection of human bodies. In order, in the words of Celsus, to learn better "the correct position, color, form, size, relative situation, hardness, softness, smoothness, the connection, and the way the various internal organs, concealed by nature, are fitted into one another," Heróphilos and Erasístratos ('Ερασίστρατος, d. 258 B.C.), the pioneers of Alexandrine anatomy and medicine, it is said, dissected alive hundreds of criminals delivered to them by the order of the king. Their knowledge, accordingly, was obtained through direct observation.

It is probable that this was more than an allegation, in spite of the denial of some modern historians, judging by the vehement accusation against Heróphilos by Tertullian, "Founder of Latin Christianity" and an inveterate adversary of science, who calls him "that doctor or butcher, who hated man in order to learn about him." (*See* Tertullian, *op. cit.*, chap. 10, par. 4.)

An even more weighty indication that there was a concrete basis for Tertullian's complaint is found in a detailed discussion of the attitudes of the various medical "sects" or schools toward human vivisection, related by the famous Roman medical writer, Aulus Cornelius Celsus (*ca.* A.D. 20), in the first book of *De Re Medica*, or *On Medicine*, the oldest medical writing after Hippocrates. According to Celsus, some schools favored this practice, while others, e.g., the "Empirics," disputed its usefulness and also rejected it on ethical grounds. Celsus states his own opinion as follows: "How is it, in fact, possible to understand the seat of an illness, if one does not know the place of each internal organ? How to treat a sick organ without knowing what it is? And it is not cruelty, as many pretend, to sacrifice a few criminals in the interest of the innocent of the centuries to come!" (*Cf.* Vesalius, sec. 8 [1], this chapter.)

Whatever the truth in the matter of human vivisection, the unquestionable fact remains that the early part of the Alexandrine period (third century B.C.) was most fertile in advancing knowledge of the human body. Later, toward the beginning and during the first few centuries of the Christian Era, coinciding with the Late Roman Republic and the Empire after Caesar, when the humanitarian principles and religious prejudices of an overcivilized Roman public made the dissection of dead human bodies rare, animals, sometimes monkeys, were dissected almost exclusively, as expressly stated by Rûfos and by Galen (*see* Rûfos, *On Naming the Parts of the Human Body*; Galen, Περὶ τῶν ἀνατομικόν ἐνχειρήσεων, *De Anatomicis Administrationibus*, or *On the Practice of Anatomy*).

During the general decay of intellectual life that followed the collapse of the Western Roman Empire, during the Dark Ages, finally even the use of animal bodies was discontinued, and the few ignorant "medics" and barber-surgeons had to rely upon the scant information left from Classical times.

The earliest systematic description of the nervous system including the optic nerves is contained in a little book by Rûfos of Ephésos, entitled: Περὶ ὀνομασίας τῶν τοῦ ἀνθρώπου μορίων, or *On Naming the Parts of the Human Body*, apparently a compilation from older Greek sources, probably from Heróphilos, Erasístratos, and Éudemos (Εὔδημος, 3d century B.C.; *see* chap. I, 1 [1]). This description of the brain and the optic nerves is rather scanty. Rûfos mentioned the two meninges, the "varicose surface" or convolutions of the brain, the brain's base, cerebellum, ventricles, chorioid tunic—now called chorioid plexus and chorioid tela—and the spinal cord. Among the nerves, he distinguished sensory and motor, and, following the interpretation by Alkmaíon of Croton and by Demókritos of Abdera, he considered them to be hollow conductors or channels (*póroi, hodói,* or *ochetói*). The optic nerves (*póroi optikói* or "optic channels") he believed emerged from the base of the brain and divided into two branches, which, by coursing obliquely, entered the eyes. (*See also* Rûfos, *Anepígraphon*, par. 3, in Daremberg & Ruelle's trans.)

References: Aristotle; Barkhuus 1945; Bernoulli 1901; Bhiṣagratna; Breasted; Brunet & Mieli; Cantor; Caton; Castiglioni; Celsus; Chievitz 1904; E. Clark; Cohen & Drabkin 1948; Cole; Contenau; Cumston; Daremberg; Faller 1948; Galen; Garrison; Gordon; Gossen; A. Haller 1774–76; Hekler 1912; Hemneter; Hilgenberg & Kirfel 1941; Hippocrates (Hippokrátes); Hirschberg; L. Hopf 1904; Hyrtl 1835; J. Jolly 1901; Kaviratna & Kavibhushana; H. D. F. Kitto 1951; A. C. Krause 1933; Laignel-Lavastine 1936–49; F. A. Lange 1908; Leake; Le Clerc 1729; Leix; Locy; H. Magnus 1900; Mendelsohn 1944; Neuburger; Ogle 1882;

Pagel; Puschmann, Neuburger & Pagel 1902–5; Ranke 1933; Ross 1923; Rostovtzeff; Rûfos; Schwegler; Sarton 1954; Sigerist 1951; Simhajī; Chas. Singer; Skinner 1949; Soury; Steindorff; W. Sudhoff 1914; Studniczka 1908; Surśuta (*see* *also* Bhiśagratna); H. O. Taylor 1922; Temkin 1933; Tertullian; R. C. Thompson; M. Wellmann; Whitney & Lanman 1905; E. Zeller 1920–23; Ziehen 1902; Zielinski 1938; Zimmer 1948.

SEC. 2. GALEN'S ANATOMY AND PHYSIOLOGY OF THE VISUAL SYSTEM

1. GALEN'S MEDICAL WRITINGS AND THEIR INFLUENCE UPON ARAB AND EARLY WESTERN SCIENCE.—The most prolific writer of Classical Antiquity on anatomy, physiology, and other medical subjects was Galen, called the "Prince of the Physicians" (Γαληνός, Galenós). Born A.D. 129 in Pérgamos or Pérgamon, an ancient seat of learning in western Asia Minor, of Greek or Hellenized parentage, he enjoyed a careful medical and general education, first in his native city and later in other cities, including the most important, Alexandria, the medical center of the Roman Empire. Thereafter he practiced medicine, first in Pérgamos and later in Rome. Here he met with singular success, becoming a friend of the Emperor-Philosopher Marcus Aurelius Antoninus (A.D. 121–80). After a life filled with many varied activities, Galen died about A.D. 201 either in the capital or in his native city.

The influence of Galen's anatomy and physiology, of his views concerning the organization and workings of the brain and of every other part of the body, under both normal and pathological conditions, was profound and of long duration. The importance of his voluminous writings, which represent the best and most complete exposition of Greek knowledge of medical subjects, especially anatomy and physiology, was enormous because they became the chief source of information during the Arab period and, through the Arab writings, of western Europe during the period of Revival in the Late Middle Ages and early Modern Times.

A description of the nervous parts concerned in vision is found in several treatises: Περὶ χρείας μορίων or Περὶ χρείας τῶν ἐν ἀνθρώπου σώματος μορίων, *De Usu Partium Corporis Humani libri XVII*, or *On the Use of Parts of the Human Body*; Περὶ τῶν καθ'Ἱπποκράτην καὶ Πλάτονα δογμάτων, *De Hippocratis et Platonis Placitis libri IX*, or *On the Teachings of Hippocrates and Plato*; Περὶ τῶν ἀνατομικῶν ἐγχει-ρήσεων, *De Anatomicis Administrationibus libri XV*, or *The Practice or Procedure of Anatomy*; Περὶ νεύρων ἀνατομῆς βιβλίον τοῖς εἰσαγωμένοις, *De Nervorum Dissectione ad Tyrones Liber*, or *The Book on the Dissection of Nerves for Beginners*. (For translations *see* Daremberg, Töply, Wiberg; for biography, etc., *see* Allbutt 1921; Daremberg 1854–56, 1865, 1870; Ilberg 1905; Chas. Singer 1922, 1928; Ullrich 1919; J. Walsh; also private information from Mr. W. J. Wilson, Army Medical Library, Cleveland.)

2. GALEN'S DESCRIPTION OF THE NERVES RELATED TO THE EYE.—In general, Galen distinguished two varieties of nerves: "hard nerves," which he considered to be motor in function, and "soft," or sensory, nerves. The eye is supplied by both. The hard nerves are attached to the extrinsic eye muscles (actual oculomotor, trochlear, and abducent nerves). The optic nerves proper, on the contrary, are soft; and, following his Greek forerunners, Alkmáion, Demókritos, Heróphilos, and others, he believed them to be hollow or tubelike and thicker than any other nerves of the body. In spite of their softness, the optic nerves, like the other nerves, are much tougher, though not much harder, than the brain. In one respect, however, the optic nerves differ from other nerves: they are not true nerves but are expansions of the brain itself. (This idea, apparently was taken over from Aristotle, *see De Sensu*, chap. 2, in *Parva Naturalia*.) Even so, Galen counted the optic nerves as the first pair of cranial nerves. Incidentally, the application of the term "optic nerve" to the entire stretch from the eye to the subcortical visual centers, which also includes the optic tracts in modern terminology, as practiced by Galen, remained customary until Vicq-d'Azyr (1786–90) (*see* sec. 12 [7], this chapter).

Galen designated two localities of the brain as the origin of the optic nerves, precisely the sides of the two anterior cerebral cavities which he called *thalami* (sing. *thalamus*), now termed lateral ventricles, a discovery which, in his own words, had until then remained unknown to the anatomists. To make the optic nerves originate from the cavities seemed to him quite logical, in view of his idea about the origin of the "visual spirit" in the brain, and its role in vision (*see* sec. 3, this chapter, and chap. I, 1 [2]). It was therefore unavoidable for him to miss the large, solid masses of gray substance, to which the term *thalamus* is applied in modern anatomy, and their true relations to the optic nerves.

Galen's use of the Greek word θαλάμη, *thalámē* (meaning a "hole," "cave," or "cavity," akin to θάλαμος, *thálamos*, meaning an "inner room" or "chamber" of a house, or the "inner space" of a ship), thus becomes understandable. The term probably derived from the Egyptian word *thalam*, which meant the "inner space" or "sanctum" of a temple, and Galen's application of it to the cerebral ventricles bears its original sense.

In this connection it is perhaps of some interest to mention that the word *thalám* is now used in modern Malayalám, a composite Tamil-Sanskrit language spoken by the preponderantly Dravidian population along the Malabar coast of South India, the ancient "Land of Spices," according to Dr. L. Chacko. The meaning of the word in Malayalam is precisely the same as in Ancient Greek and Ancient Egyptian. This may, perhaps, not be pure coincidence, in view of the close commercial relationship between Ancient Egypt and India.

Galen also thought the substance of the brain softer in its anterior portion, where the sensory nerves were supposed to originate (forebrain), and harder posteriorly, where the motor nerves seemed to him to arise (cerebellum and the adjoining parts of the brain stem, in modern terminology). The "hard" oculomotor nerve was the only exception to this rule, since it originated from the anterior portion of the brain. In the chiasma the two optic nerves only ap-

parently intercross. In reality, they merely join here in order to bring their channels together.

The optic nerves terminate in the eyes by means of a thinned-out expansion, the retinal tunic, at the crystalline lens, in particular at its capsule, the lens in Galen's opinion being "the principal and essential organ of vision," or, in modern terminology, the actual photoreceptor. This concept of the photoreceptor function of the crystalline lens was later taken over by Arab scholars and bequeathed by them to their European pupils, among whom it was held in high esteem until the beginning of the seventeenth century (*see* chap. I, 1 [2]; 3 [3, 4]; 5).

Galen accepted and further elaborated upon the idea that the optic nerves were tubelike and functioned as conducting channels of the "visual spirit," proposed by Alkmáion, and taught by Demókritos, Heróphilos, and Éudemos, since, of all nerves, the optic nerves alone seem to show a visible *lumen* or opening. During the subsequent fifteen centuries this imaginary channel played a prominent role in shaping the concept of the functions of the visual system and of the brain. The Arab scholars and, among the European anatomists, Eustachio (in *Tabulae Anatomicae*, written *ca.* 1560, but published 1714) were firmly convinced of the reality of this channel and represented it regularly in their illustrations (Figs. 56–60; *see also* Figs. 7–12 in Polyak, *The Retina*, 1941, 1948).

References: Th. Beck; Brunet & Mieli; Castiglioni; Chievitz 1904; Cole; Daremberg 1854, 1865, 1870; Daremberg & Saglio 1877–1912; Deneffe 1896; Faller 1948; Galen; Garrison; Gordon; A. Haller 1774–76; Heinrichs; Hirschberg 1899; Homo 1930; Ilberg; Kassel 1911; O. Katz 1890; Meyer-Steineg 1913; J. S. Milne 1907; Neuburger; Pagel; Puschmann, Neuburger & Pagel; Révész 1917; Rostovtzeff 1926; Sarton 1954; J. Soury 1899; M. Simon; Chas. Singer; W. Sudhoff 1914; O. H. Taylor 1922; Ullrich; J. Walsh; J. Wilberg; E. Zeller 1920–23.

SEC. 3. GALEN'S PHYSIOLOGY OF THE VISUAL SYSTEM

1. THE GREEK HYPOTHESIS OF "PNEUMA" OR "SPIRIT" AS LIFE'S PRINCIPLE.—Even more interesting and far more important are Galen's

ideas about the factors involved in the visual act and about the role the brain plays in it. The eyes, in Man, he considered dominant sense organs. They are placed in the most elevated part of the body because of the obvious advantage deriving from this position. The brain is situated in the head because of the eyes, while all other sense organs, in turn, are placed in the head because of the brain's location there. (*Cf.* chap. XIII.)

From the heart, "a center of the arterial system," the brain receives through the arteries a "vital spirit" or "vital air" ($\pi\nu\epsilon\hat{\upsilon}\mu\alpha$ $\zeta\omega\tau\iota\kappa\acute{o}\nu$, *pneuma zoötikón*). The "vital spirit," in turn, is an elaboration of an elemental "natural spirit" ($\pi\nu\epsilon\hat{\upsilon}\mu\alpha$ $\phi\upsilon\sigma\iota\kappa\acute{o}\nu$, *pneuma physikón*), originating from the liver, "the center of the venous system," a mysterious substance indispensable for life. This relatively crude "vital spirit," arriving in the brain with the arterial blood, is further transformed therein into a more refined "animal spirit" ($\pi\nu\epsilon\hat{\upsilon}\mu\alpha$ $\psi\upsilon\chi\iota\kappa\acute{o}\nu$, *pneuma psychikón*). A necessary ingredient for this is the air inspired into the cerebral ventricles through the nostrils, the cribriform plate of the ethmoidal bone of the skull, the olfactory nerves, bulbs, and tracts.

The transformation of the "vital spirit" into an "animal spirit" takes place in the *rete mirabile*, a dense arterial network at the base of the brain. Here it may be mentioned that such a network is present in some mammals, such as sheep, but not in Man, where it may be homologized roughly with the branches of the inner carotid and the vertebral arteries, including their anastomoses, which together form the arterial circle of Willis and its subsidiaries (*see* Fig. 368). This and other similar features of Galen's description show that his knowledge was mainly or entirely based on the dissection of animal bodies, prevented, as he was, from using human bodies for his studies by current prejudice.

2. The brain—a repository of the "animal spirit" and of the "reasoning soul."—Most of the "animal spirit," according to Galen is deposited in the brain, an organ with which we think and which is the seat of the "reasoning soul" ($\psi\upsilon\chi\grave{\eta}$ $\lambda\omega\gamma\iota\sigma\tau\iota\kappa\acute{\eta}$, *psyché logistiké;* Aristotle's $\nu\acute{o}os$ or $\nu\omega\hat{\upsilon}s$, *nóös* or *nōōs*, "mind" or "reason"; this soul corresponds to the noblest of Plato's three souls, the $\dot{\eta}\gamma\epsilon\mu\omega\nu\iota\kappa\acute{o}\nu$, *hegemonikón*, or a ruling or supreme principle residing in the human body, immortal according to Plato, but hardly so according to Galen). A certain quantity of "animal spirit" was present in the entire brain, both the substance and the ventricles. The cerebral ventricles served as a special repository of the "animal spirit," an idea that originated with Heróphilos, as one learns from Galen's treatise *On the History of Philosophy* (*De Historia Philosophiae, liber spurius,* chap. 38; *see* W. Sudhoff, 1914, p. 154; *see also* Aaítios or Aëtios, *ca.* A.D. 500). This soul, filling the ventricles, Heróphilos named $\tau\grave{o}$ $\tau\hat{\eta}s$ $\psi\upsilon\chi\hat{\eta}s$ $\dot{\eta}\gamma\epsilon\mu\omega\nu\iota\kappa\acute{o}\nu$, or "the dominant spirit."

From the brain the "animal spirit" spreads to all nerves, including the optic, whose channels, in Galen's view, communicate directly with the cerebral ventricles. Since these ventricles expand and contract the way the heart does, the "animal spirit" is continuously being propelled from the brain into the nervous channels and in this way is distributed all over the body.

3. The eyes—repositories of the "visual spirit."—That part of the "animal spirit" which passes through the optic channels to the eyes is the "visual spirit" ($\pi\nu\epsilon\hat{\upsilon}\mu\alpha$ $\dot{o}\rho\alpha\tau\iota\kappa\acute{o}\nu$, *pneuma horatikón*). In the eyes the "visual spirit" spreads along the thinned-out portion of the brain—the retina—as far as the pupil. Finally, it passes to the crystalline lens, the supposed "principal organ of sight," or, in modern parlance, the "photoreceptor," to which Galen believed the retina was directly attached. This "visual spirit" or "luminous air," a sort of ethereal fluid, also fills the anterior chamber of the eye, where it mixes with the aqueous or albugineous humor. The anterior chamber and the pupil, therefore, are the localities where "outer light," coming from outside, and "inner light," coming from the brain, meet (*cf.* this with Plato's "synaugy," chap. I, 1 [2]). To Galen it seemed clear that the brain extends as far as the eyes in the form of the optic nerves, that these nerves become soft and membranous in the eyes (that is, are transformed into retinal membranes), and that the optic nerves alone are excavated (a tacit implication being that all these factors facilitate the intimacy of the contact with the supposed photoreceptor, the crystalline lens).

The flow of the "visual spirit" from the brain

to the eyes, however, is only a part of a complete process, the other part being a flow in the opposite direction, from the eyes to the brain. Both these movements, or processes, Galen obviously considered indispensable, the act of vision being consummated only when the "visual spirit" returns to the brain with the impressions received in the crystalline lens.

Galen's idea of the brain's importance, in contrast to the ideas of Aristotle and many other Greek naturalists and thinkers, was quite modern. For he was firmly convinced that the brain was "an organ where all sensations arrive, and where all mental images, and all intelligent ideas arise," a "place of imagination, memory, and comprehension." (*Cf.* chap. I, 1 [2], and 6 [1].)

References: Aáitios (Aëtios); Aristotle; Burdach 1819–22–26; Daremberg 1854, 1854–56, 1865, 1870; Galen; Haas 1907; A. Haller 1774–76; Ilberg; Isaac Newton; O. Katz 1890; Plato; Révész 1917; Sarton 1954; Simon 1906; Chas. Singer; Soury; W. Sudhoff 1914; Ullrich; Vesalius; Th. Willis; E. Zeller 1920–23.

SEC. 4. GALEN'S FUNCTIONAL INTERPRETATION OF THE CHIASMA AND OF OTHER FEATURES PECULIAR TO THE VISUAL SYSTEM

1. EXPLANATION OF THE DOUBLE CEREBRAL ORIGIN OF OPTIC NERVES.—Galen's analysis and interpretation of the anatomical features peculiar to the visual system is interesting and even ingenious, though in places naïve, obscure, and confused.

First, the reason Galen gives to explain why each optic nerve originates from the brain independently instead of together (even though a common origin would be more advantageous for the unity of the visual impressions) is fantastic: the necessity to place the cerebral infundibulum (through which the brain was supposed to discharge its impurities into the nasal cavity) at the very point of a potential central origin of the optic nerves, the central position of the infundibulum in turn being determined by the central position of the nose! As if Almighty Zeus or Mother Nature, had they so willed, had not been able to create two infundibulums and two noses, one on each side, in order to make the optic nerves originate from a single central point!

The arrangement of the parts which compose the visual system, Galen insisted, follows the principles of geometry and is determined during intrauterine development. From the point of their junction in the chiasma to the eyes, the optic nerves may be compared with two straight lines meeting in one point and placed in a single plane. The other principal constituents of the visual system: the visual axes and pupils of both eyes and the optic nerves from the *papillae* (where, according to Galen, the summits of the "visual cones," or visual axes, rest) to the chiasmal juncture all follow straight lines and are arranged in the same plane. In this way, Galen imagined, diplopia or double vision is avoided, and the single image is achieved in the binocular visual act or in seeing with both eyes.

2. FUNCTIONAL ROLE OF THE CHIASMA.—In discussing the functional significance of the junction of the optic nerves in the chiasma, Galen mentions several previous hypotheses made by those interested in this subject.

The first explanation was mechanical. According to this, the purpose of the chiasma was to avoid damage to the optic nerves, which might easily occur if they were straight and tightly drawn (presumably in the case of tension on the nerves when the eyes rotate).

Another opinion held that the function of the chiasma was to enable the optic nerves to exchange sensations or affections and thus to reduce the "pain" suffered by the stimulated optic nerve. This opinion was based upon an ancient doctrine, according to which all sensations were essentially painful. (*Cf.* the terms "pathos," "sympathy," "compassion," "passive," etc.)

According to a third view, the optic nerves, since they supply two different peripheral organs, must ultimately come together in one point, presumably in order to bring about unity of visual impressions received through both eyes.

Not being satisfied with any of these theories, Galen suggested as the most plausible function of the chiasma the proper distribution of the "visual spirit" coming from the brain to both eyes. In the case of shutting or losing one eye, all *pneuma*, he thought, would pass over to the other eye and, by doubling its power, would compensate for the loss. In order to prove his thesis, Galen describes the following test: if one holds a hand or a board vertical to the tip of the nose, one sees only imperfectly with each eye. But if one eye is shut, sight improves as if the visual power that was divided until then passed entirely to the other eye.

Still another purpose of the chiasmal junction, Galen thought, was to bring about simple binocular vision by eliminating diplopia or double vision, or, in modern parlance, the creation of a "functional cyclopean eye" (*cf.* chap. XIII, 3 [6]). These ideas of Galen's, which may have originated partly or entirely with the Alexandrine School, inadequate as they are, appear to be the earliest recorded attempt to interpret binocular single vision in terms of anatomical structures. (*See* sec. 11 [4, 5], this chapter.)

3. DIVINE FORCE—GALEN'S DEFENSE AGAINST THE PREJUDICE OF THE ROMAN PUBLIC.— Galen's effort to solve one of the riddles of the human constitution—binocular single vision—is of interest from yet another angle. The hypothesis of the chiasmal function, as well as the idea of a geometrical organization of the visual system, as he modestly admits, were, in reality, not his own but were suggested to him in a dream by a god not further identified. This god may have been Apollo, patron of the arts and of healing, or his son, Asklepiós or Aesculápius, God of Medicine, although Galen, like his imperial friend, Marcus Aurelius, and many other educated persons of his age, certainly was acquainted with the precepts of the Hebrews and the Christians, not to speak of the philosophical concepts professed by Socrates and Plato, which amounted virtually to monotheism.

Whether Galen, imbued as he was with religious feeling and superstition, sincerely believed this story or whether his introduction of the divine powers into the physiology of vision was merely a trick to guard himself against the fanaticism and religious prejudice of the reactionary Roman populace, and perhaps also designed to avoid adverse action of the jealous Roman doctors, his professional competitors, there is no way of telling.

From the remarks scattered in his writings, however, one is to believe that his friendship with the Emperor, his popularity with patients, and, most of all, his financial success must have aroused great envy among the greedy, narrow-minded, poorly educated, and numerous Roman "medics." Which reminds one of an old Latin proverb: *Homo homini lupus, medicus medico lupissimus!* or "Man is a wolf to another man, but most wolfish is a doctor to another doctor!"

Nor did the encyclopedic Galen, who loved to theorize, to speculate, and to criticize, alleviate this situation by his show of contempt for his professional Roman colleagues, who, as he complains, had no interest in such useless intellectual pursuits as "mathematics, astronomy, and music."

In these circumstances Galen, the successful but hated outsider, a *Graeculus* or "petty Greek," may have felt it advisable to hide behind a divine shield in order to avert a fate similar to the one which befell Socrates, and almost befell Plato and Aristotle: to be indicted and executed for "corrupting the youth" and "for introducing novel practices in religion."

Similarly, Galen's failure to mention human vivisection, a subject even more obnoxious to the spirit of his time, which Celsus had discussed at length less than two centuries earlier, may have been motivated by opportunism rather than by ignorance (*cf.* sec. 1 [5], this chapter).

References: Th. Beck 1909; Brunet & Mieli; Daremberg; Galen; Garrison; Gossen; A. Haller 1774–76; Helmholtz 1924–25; Hering; I. Ilberg; O. Katz 1890; Marquart 1886; Révész 1917; Sarton 1954; Simon 1906; Chas. Singer; J. Soury; W. Sudhoff 1914; Ullrich; J. Walsh; E. Zeller 1920–23.

SEC. 5. EVALUATION AND CRITIQUE OF GALEN'S CONCEPT
OF THE VISUAL MECHANISMS

1. SIMILARITIES AND DIFFERENCES BETWEEN GALEN'S THEORIES AND THE MODERN VIEW OF THE FUNCTION OF THE VISUAL SYSTEM.—Galen's views about the function of the visual system, which in a sense embody the best knowledge of Classical Greek and Roman times, in spite of many inaccuracies, are fundamentally, when properly translated into modern terms, amazingly close to our own.

The retina, for example, Galen, like Aristotle before him, correctly recognized as a displaced portion of the brain. This view, obviously, could not have been based upon histological and embryological data but was prompted by speculation. The closer and more intimate the relationship between the brain and the crystalline lens—the alleged photoreceptor—the easier the flow of the "visual spirit" from the brain to the lens and from the lens back to the brain (after having been charged with the impressions or sensations in the lens). Considering the general state of knowledge, especially the absence of dioptrics and magnifying apparatus, Galen's reasoning was the best that could be expected at that time. (*Cf.* chap. I, 1 [2] and 2.)

Of the visual pathway, Galen knew the infranuclear division, from the eye to the brain. The subcortical visual centers, visual radiations, and the visual centers in the cerebral cortex were all unknown to him and remained unknown until modern times (*see* chap. III, 7, 8, 9). Under the circumstances, it is to his credit to have made an effort to investigate those parts which he knew, especially the chiasma, and the "origin" of the optic nerves in the brain.

Galen's opinion that each optic nerve and tract remains on its own side of the brain, that is, that there is neither a partial nor a total crossing in the chiasma, remains, of course, inconsistent with the facts (*see* chap. VI, 4, 5, 6). If, however, one considers that until the beginning of the twentieth century some of the foremost microscopists (e.g., Koelliker) still struggled with the essential arrangement of fibers in the human chiasma and denied the partial decussation in it, our judgment of Galen's mistakes will be less harsh (*see* chap. III, 9 [3]). But the basic idea of the merging of the two "optic channels" in order to permit the "exchange" of the "visual spirit," archaic as it appears, is not far from the anatomical and physiological reality of a partial crossing of the optic nerve fibers and the functional collaboration of both eyes in single vision. To Galen, the function of the chiasma was to make it possible to compensate for the loss of one eye by doubling the power of the other. The modern interpretation is that its function is to bring about a stereoscopic effect in the normal binocular visual act and to enable both cerebral hemispheres to see the larger portion of the common cyclopean field of vision in case one eye is lost.

Galen's assumption of the presence of a hollow channel within the optic nerves was an outright error (except as it concerns the early period of embryonic development, of which he could have had no knowledge; *see* chap. XIII, 1, and Fig. 435). In his defense one should recall the channel-like cavity in the olfactory tracts and bulbs in many Vertebrates, with which he was probably familiar. Also, the excavation of the optic papilla may easily have suggested a "peripheral orifice" of a channel. A "central end" of a channel in the lateral ventricles, too, could easily have been found in the slitlike spaces between the "roots" of the optic tracts and the surrounding structures, especially around the hippocampal fissure. The difficulty of convincing one's self of the presence of a channel in the course of the optic nerve could also have been overcome if the analogy of empty, contracted blood vessels were invoked. For here, too, an arterial *lumen* or opening is often easier to assume than to see. Finally, an actual channel in the optic tract, probably resulting from developmental irregularities, has been described by J. Stilling (1882, p. 12, footnote) and may be seen on rare occasions (as I know from my own observation).

2. GALEN'S MISTAKES—THE RESULT OF HIS DESIRE TO EXPLAIN THE ORGANIZATION OF THE VISUAL SYSTEM WITH INADEQUATE MEANS.— The idea of a channel in the optic nerves through which an active principle—the visual spirit or visual *pneuma*—circulates is worthy of attention because of the general physiological interest which it represents.

Like the other Greek anatomists and physiologists, Galen was naturally ignorant of the bioelectric forces in the living nervous substance responsible for the "transmission" of "nerve impulses"—a basic concept of modern neurophysiology. He was, therefore, unable to conceive of the propagation of nervous influences through solids, such as the nerves, in fact, are.

In this connection one may recall similar difficulties encountered by the early modern microscopists and physiologists, e.g., Malpighi, Vieussens, Diemerbroeck, Ridley, A. Haller, S. Th. Soemmerring, and all investigators of the period preceding the discoveries of Galvani (1780) and Volta (1800). They, too, and for the same reason as Galen, were prompted to regard the myelinated nerve fibers as "tubes" with a hollow central lumen or passageway—which, in reality, was the axis cylinder enveloped in a myelin sheath—along which an extremely thin substance, a hypothetical *fluidum nerveum, succus nervosus*, or "nervous fluid" or "nervous juice," was supposed to circulate.

Galen's desire for a plausible explanation of nervous transmission logically demanded a palpable substratum. Such was the material "spirit" or *pneuma* moving within the visible space of the "nerve channels" from the brain to the eyes and back again to the brain, in analogy with the circulation of the blood in the arterial channels and particularly in the veins (inadequate as the Greek concept of the function of the vascular system otherwise was).

But, in spite of this seemingly mechanical analogy, a fluid vehicle or carrier of visual sensations, the "luminous air," imagined by Galen, was not so crudely material as the blood and other humors found in the organism. The "visual spirit," as conceived by Galen, was a principle, refined, subtilized, and sublimated to a degree where it almost ceased to be material. Obviously, only such an ethereal *pneuma* was fit to serve a function as subtle and delicate as Galen considered vision to be. Seen in this light, his concept of visual mechanisms approaches modern views much more closely, in spite of the naïve terms and phrases, long since outdated, in which his ideas are clothed.

References: Castiglioni; Cole; Daremberg; Galen; Garrison; A. Haller 1774–76; I. Ilberg; O. Katz 1890; Révész 1917; Chas. Singer; Soury; J. Stilling 1882; W. Sudhoff 1914; Ullrich; Willis; E. Zeller 1920–23.

SEC. 6. ANATOMY AND PHYSIOLOGY OF THE VISUAL PATHWAYS AND CENTERS DURING THE MIDDLE AGES AMONG THE NATIONS INFLUENCED BY ARAB CIVILIZATION

1. CESSATION OF SCIENTIFIC INTEREST IN EUROPE DURING THE DARK AGES; THE ARABS AS THE HEIRS OF GREEK SCIENCE AND MEDICINE. —During the thousand years or so following Galen's death (*ca.* 200, Christian Era), especially after the collapse of the Western Roman Empire and Classical civilization, interest in anatomy and physiology, as in the natural sciences in general, almost vanished. The arts and sciences created and accumulated during Classical times gradually disappeared from Europe in the chaos of the Dark Ages, which lasted well into the second millennium of the present era. In this process of gradual reversion to a barbarous state, a condition was reached where all incentive ceased, both for active research and for the preservation of previously acquired knowledge. Under such conditions of total cultural disinte-gration, most of the writings of the Greek scholars, including those of Galen, were lost in the European West.

A different situation, fortunately, obtained in the newly arisen Arab dominions of the Near East and among other nations influenced by Arab civilization. Here most of Galen's treatises were preserved and became the principal source from which Arab scholars derived their information about anatomy, physiology, and allied subjects (*see* chap. I, 3). Unfortunately, however, the Mohammedan creed, just as the Brahman, Buddhist, Jewish, and Christian creeds did until late into the Middle Ages, opposed the dissection of human and animal bodies, which circumstance proved to be an insurmountable barrier to progress in anatomical and medical research. Arab anatomy and physiology to a far greater degree than practical medicine, astronomy, mathematics, physics, including optics, chemistry, and other sciences, remained a passive digestion of ideas preserved in the Greek writings.

The presentation of the visual pathway, by Ḥunain ibn Isḥāḳ, for example, was in substance merely an abstraction from Galen, although arranged more logically than in the rambling Greek original (*cf.* Figs. 56–60). In it all the principal ideas—the hollowness of the optic nerves, their merging in the chiasma "so that their two cavities become one," the "origin" of the optic nerves from the cerebral ventricles, and the existence of a "psychic spirit" which constantly circulates from the ventricles to the eye in great quantity—are expressed in approximately the same way as in Galen's writings, the source being duly acknowledged by the author.

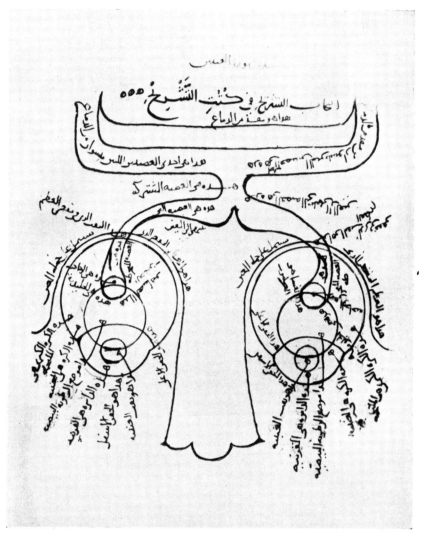

Fɪɢ. 56.—Diagram of the visual system from the oldest existing copy of *Kitāb al-manāẓir* or *Book of Optics* by Ibn al-Haitham or Alhazen. Manuscript written A.D. 1083, in possession of Fatih Library at Istanbul or Constantinople, Turkey. For English terms *see* Fig. 8, in S. Polyak, *The Retina*.

The same may be said about other Arab descriptions of the visual system found in the books of ᶜAlī ibn ᶜĪsā, Ibn al-Haitham (Alhazen), and others. The only exceptions were Al Rāzī (Rhazes or Rasis), and Ibn Sīnā (Avicenna), who described the optic nerves in the chiasma as completely crossed (*see* Avicenna's *Canon of Medicine*, book 3, fen 3, chap. 32).

2. IBN AL-HAITHAM (ALHAZEN), A PRECURSOR OF MODERN VIEWS ON THE FUNCTIONAL ORGANIZATION OF THE VISUAL SYSTEM.—Of considerable interest is Ibn al-Haitham's presentation of the physical side of the working of the visual mechanisms, which to him, primarily a physicist, was of principal interest. The title of the pertinent theorem 18, in the first book of his *Thesaurus of Optics* (early part of 11th century, *cf.* chap. I, 3 [2]), reads: "Distinct

sentiens ultimum, or "final arbiter" of all subjective photic experiences and responses.

These ideas of Ibn al-Haitham plainly express the rudiments of the concept of a "projection" or topographical representation of the retinal surface in the cerebrum, which in modern times has played a spectacular role in the investigation of the visual and other systems, although Ibn al-Haitham's concept of the physical process in vision, as the reference to "perpendicular lines" shows, was inadequate (*cf.* chap. I, 3 [3, 5]; chap. IV, 4; and sec. 10, this chapter).

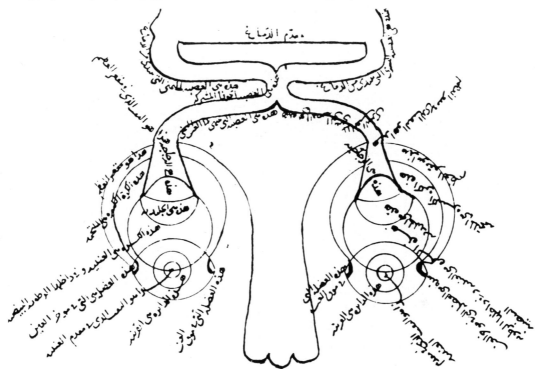

FIG. 57.—Diagram of the visual system from the earliest preserved manuscript of Kamāl al-Dīn Abuʾl-Ḥasan al-Fārisī, a Persian scholar, dated Anno Hegirae 716, or A.D. 1316. Courtesy of the Ahmet Salis Library, Topkapu Saray, Istanbul, Turkey. (*Cf.* Fig. 11 in S. Polyak, *The Retina.*)

vision is accomplished by means of perpendicular lines drawn from the objects seen to the surface of the organ of sight. In this way each point of the object is related to a point of the surface of the visual organ having the same position as in the object seen."

Ibn al-Haitham even contemplated an unaltered transmission of "figures" from the posterior surface of the "glacial sphere" or lens, where they were supposedly formed, along the retina and the hollow optic nerve, to the brain, which, in his opinion, was the *ultimum sensus,*

As the seat of the "final arbiter" of the visual functions Ibn al-Haitham, following Galen, designated the forebrain, where the optic nerves supposedly originated (Fig. 56; *see also The Retina,* Fig. 8). The functional role of the chiasma, according to him, was evidently decisive, since only after the superposition and fusion of the two monocular images in it, he thought, can the "final arbiter" unify them into a single visual experience. (*Cf.* chap. I, 3, 4 [1], and chap. XIII, 3.)

References: Alhazen (Ibn al-Haitham); ʿAlī

ibn ᶜĪsā; Avicenna (Ibn Sīnā); D. Campbell 1926; Castiglioni; E. Clark 1913; Elgood 1951; A. Haller 1774–76; Holmyard 1940; Hitti 1951; Ḥunain ibn Isḥāk; Ibn al-Haitham (Alhazen); Ibn Sīnā (Avicenna); Khairallah 1946; Khalīfa (*see* Hirschberg 1908); Koning 1903; Meyerhof 1926, 1945; Meyerhof & Prüfer; Mieli 1939; Soury 1899; W. Sudhoff 1914; Wiberg; Wüstenfeld. *See also* references at the end of secs. 3 and 4, chap. I.

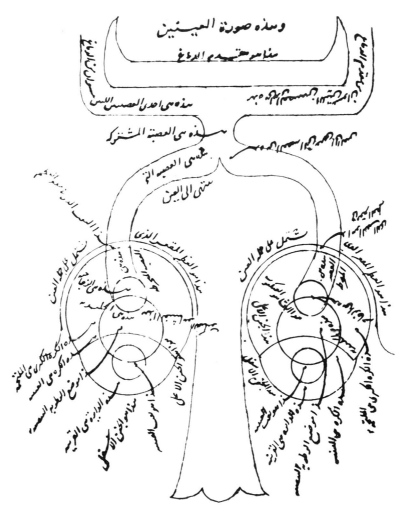

Fig. 58.—Diagram of the visual system from an Arabic manuscript of *Kitāb al-manāẓir* or *Book of Optics* by Ibn al-Haitham or Alhazen, dated A.H. 899 or A.D. 1493. Courtesy of the Ayasofya Library, Istanbul, Turkey.

SEC. 7. WESTERN EUROPEAN KNOWLEDGE OF THE VISUAL SYSTEM PRECEDING AND DURING THE RENAISSANCE

1. EARLY EUROPEAN ANATOMISTS AND THEIR KNOWLEDGE OF THE VISUAL SYSTEM.—During the later part of the Middle Ages, from the twelfth to the fifteenth centuries, western Europeans became acquainted with the Arab writings and, through them, with those of the Greek naturalists, anatomists, and writers on medicine. During this period the knowledge of the visual pathway and of the functions, ailments, and treatment of other parts of the human body, possessed by them, was limited to that found in the afore-mentioned writings. Even this was little understood by men who, for the most part, had never used a dissecting knife and therefore had no personal experience. Such were the earliest writers, mostly monastic schol-

ars: Alcoatin (1159), Vitello (*ca.* 1270), Roger Bacon (13th century), and John Peckham (13th century), some of them rated the foremost thinkers of their time. Theirs was pure book learning, and whatever they knew about the optic nerves, their "origin" in the brain, the

the newly organized universities: William of Saliceto (*ca.* 1215–*ca.* 1280), Mondino de'Luzzi (Mundinus, 1315), and Guy de Chauliac (Cauliacus, 1363). These were followed later by Manfredi (1490), Zerbi (1502), Achillini (1516), Berengario da Carpi, recte Barigazzi, or Car-

Fig. 59.—Visual system and its working, from an Arabic treatise on the practice of ophthalmology by Shams al-Dīn Mohammed Ibn al-Ḥasan al-Kaḥḥāl, a Persian eye doctor known as Bāward, dating from A.D. 1690. The sketch purports to show the itinerary of the "visual spirit" from the liver, lung, and heart (*lower part*) to the ventricle of the brain, whence it was, according to Galen's teaching, supposed to spread along the optic nerves to the crystalline lenses of the eyes. From M. Meyerhof & C. Prüfer, Arch. f. Gesch. d. Med. (Sudhoff), v. 6, 1913.

chiasma, and other details was taken from the Greeks, either directly or by way of the Arabs.

The first active anatomical investigation in the south and west of Europe came with the appearance of a class of practical surgeon-anatomists in Italy and in France, connected with

pensis (1521), Massa (1536), and Landi (1542).

Small as their anatomical knowledge was, these early investigators had already acquired considerable personal experience (*see* Singer 1917). They knew, for example, of the so-called "optic thalami," which they called *anchae*, *coxae, nates,* and *glutea,* meaning "hips" and "buttocks" of the brain, although they seem not to have recognized their relationship to the optic nerves. These terms were apparently applied to the entire mass of the basal nuclei, including the thalamus proper and the corpus striatum (*see also* Burdach 1822, p. 339; Stein 1834). On the question of the optic chiasma they disagreed, some assuming a complete crossing (e.g., Vitello), others merely a merging.

In all other respects, however, these early "Western" anatomists and physiologists echoed the mistaken Greek beliefs, especially as regards the hollowness of the optic nerves, in whose channels a visual spirit was supposed to circulate.

Along with this belief, and in strange contradiction to it, was a view already current at that early date, according to which the optic nerve and its termination, the retina, was made up of

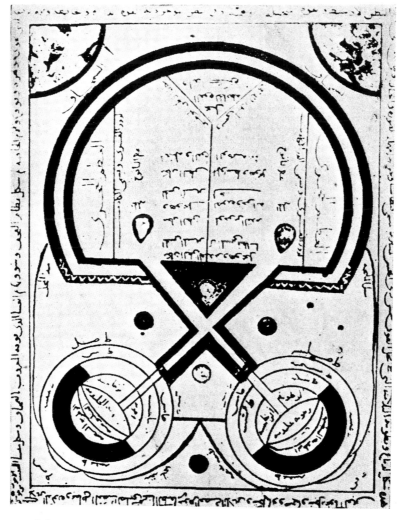

Fig. 60.—Diagram of the visual system and its relation to the brain. The upper part represents the two lateral ventricles, with the third and fourth ventricles of the brain in the mid-line. The ventricles are enveloped by hard and soft meninges on the outside, in turn inclosed by the *periosteum* and the bony shell of the skull. From the ventricles arise optic nerves which contain channels. The nerves decussate in the chiasma and form the two eyeballs (in the lower portion of the diagram). These consist of the fibrous tunic, the chorioid, and the retina. The other parts of the eyes are the vitreous, crystalline lens, arachnoid, aqueous, uvea (iris) with the pupil, the cornea, and conjunctiva. The interpretation follows, in general, that of other Arabic figures and the texts. The original diagram found in an Arabic manuscript of Khalīfa written about A.D. 1266 and published in A. Castiglioni, *A History of Medicine*, P. B. Hoeber, New York. The interpretation according to a schematized presentation by J. Hirschberg in Graefe & Saemisch, *Handb. d. ges. Augenh.,* 2d ed., v. 13, p. 151, 1908.

extremely delicate fibers (Vitello). Where this idea originated remains obscure, although it seems probable that it was taken over from Arab writers such as ᶜAlī ibn ᶜĪsā and Alcoatin (*see* chap. I, 6 [2]).

The visual center was considered to be in the anterior portion of the brain, a view also taken over from Galen via the Arabs.

The knowledge of the visual pathways possessed by the learned men of Europe during the later part of the Middle Ages was, on the whole, quite meager and sterile and amounted to even less than the little they knew about the structure of the eye (*see* chap. I, 4 [3]). Essentially, this knowledge consisted of a recognition of the fact that the peripheral organ of vision, the eye, was anatomically connected with the brain, which in some way was concerned with the function of vision. (*See* A. Haller 1769, v. 4, p. 51; and Singer.)

2. LEONARDO DA VINCI'S KNOWLEDGE OF THE VISUAL PATHWAYS AND CENTERS.—The almost complete ignorance of any part of the brain involved in vision had in no way been relieved during the general Revival of the Arts and Learning in Europe.

This situation is well attested by the figures of Leonardo da Vinci (1452–1519, portrait Fig. 61), the many-sided genius of the Italian Renaissance (Figs. 62, 63). These sketches, in spite of their artistic aspect, merely show how complete his ignorance was of the anatomy of the brain and especially of the parts related to the eye. Those details of his figures which show the superficial and therefore more accessible structures of the head he represented accurately. Contrasting with these are the deeper, hidden parts which are either distorted or are simply the naïve products of a rich imagination.

Contrary to Leonardo's principle, adhered to in his sketches of other parts of the body, where he truthfully depicted the anatomical structures which he actually saw, in the case of the brain and the visual system, evidently under the influence of Galen and the speculative scholastic writers, he permitted himself to draw imaginary organs which he could not have seen.

In one of his fantastic drawings, for example, the eye is shown connected by means of the optic nerve to a sausage-like cavity extending into the brain (Fig. 62). The cavity is subdivided into three compartments purporting to represent the three cerebral ventricles. These three spaces evidently correspond to the three hypothetical cerebral "cells," which the speculating anatomists and philosophers of the Middle Ages regarded as repositories of the three hypothetical principal mental faculties: a *cellula phantastica* for perception, a *cellula logistica* for thinking and reasoning, and a *cellula memorialis* for memory. (According to Flechsig 1896, p. 36, it was Nemesius, Church Father and philosopher of the fourth century, who originated the idea of three cerebral cells, a concept later accepted by Albertus Magnus, celebrated philosopher and "universal doctor" of the thirteenth century.)

This is the more astonishing, since, from Leonardo's own account and sketches, it is certain that he had dissected the brain and should have acquired a somewhat truer knowledge of the number, shape, and arrangement of the cerebral ventricles, of which he was the first to make wax casts (Fig. 63).

In Leonardo's figures, at last, Galen's idea of the cerebral cavities as the most important part of the central nervous system, considered by the latter as repositories of the all-important "animal spirit," until then clothed in the elastic phrases and ambiguous words of a clever, verbose *Graeculus*, had, in all its glaring impossibility, become exposed to the scrutiny of a merciless posterity (*see* sec. 3, this chapter). Leonardo's figures, if anything, show that no amount of ingenuity and imagination can compensate for the absence of positive knowledge based upon direct examination and logical judgment.

Leonardo's figures, jealously kept from publicity by their ignorant possessors, did not influence the development of anatomy. To the historian they are of interest because they show the farthest point reached by the dissecting knife and imagination of one of the keenest minds of his age.

Other anatomists of that time, true to the medieval spirit, blindly relied upon the Greek authorities, limiting themselves to inept abstracting of Galen's writings, instead of dissecting the structures they were describing. This state of affairs, exemplified by a perfectly sterile account of the visual system in the writings of Fernel (Joannes Fernelius Ambianates, 1542), lasted until the great reform brought about one year later by Andreas Vesalius (1543).

References: Achillini 1516; Albertus Magnus 1280; Alcoatin 1159; ʿAlī ibn ʿĪsā (10th century); Anonymus-Winthrop; Arnaldus de Villanova (d. *ca.* 1312); Roger Bacon; Barbensi; Berengario da Carpi (Berengarius) 1521; Bernard de Gordon (*ca.* 1302–5); Burdach 1822; J. Burckhardt; Carpensis, Carpus (*see* Berengario); Castiglioni 1947; W. Durant 1953; Guy de Chauliac (Cauliacus) 1363; Chevalier 1940, 1944; Corner 1927, 1930, 1931; De Renzi; Dryander (Eichmann) 1537; W. Durant 1953; Fernel (Joannes Fernelius Ambianates) 1542;

Fɪɢ. 61.—Leonardo da Vinci of Florence (1452–1519), the many-sided genius of the Italian Renaissance. An artist, architect, engineer-inventor, and a great student and illustrator of the human and animal body. A self-portrait in possession of the Royal Palace of Turin, in Italy. From J. P. McMurrick, *Leonardo da Vinci, the Anatomist*, 1930. Courtesy Carnegie Institution of Washington, D.C. (*Cf.* following two figures.)

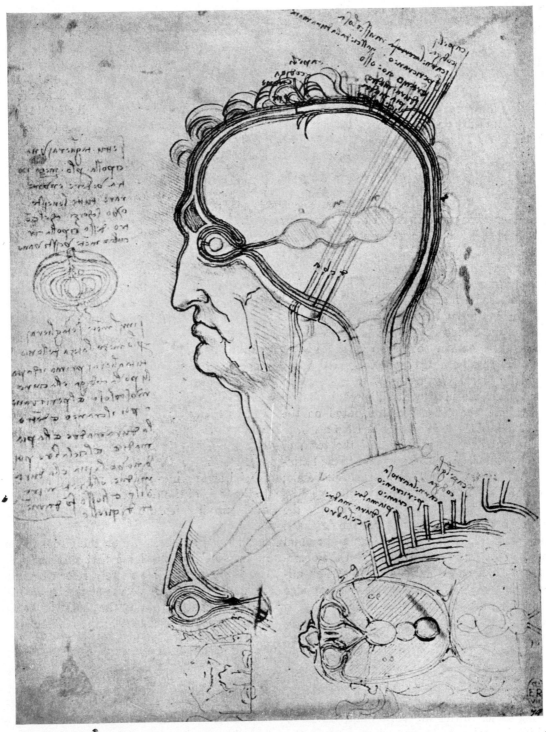

Fig. 62.—Sketches illustrating Leonardo da Vinci's concept of the contents of the human head, in particular, of the relationship of the eyes to the brain. In his own words: "If you cut an onion through the middle" (*see* left-hand sketch), "you will be able to see and count all the covers or rinds which surround its center on all sides. Just so if you cut a man's head in the middle, you will cut first hair, then the coating and the muscular flesh and pericranium, then the cranium and, within, the dura mater and pia mater and the cerebrum, then again the pia and dura mater, and the *rete mirabile* and the fundamentum of this, the bone." Noteworthy is the direct connection of the eyes, through the optic nerves, with the cerebral ventricles (*O, M, N*) which are presented as three round cavities arranged in a line and communicating with one another. From Leonardo da Vinci's *Quaderni d'anatomia*, v. 5, fol. 6, *verso*.

Flechsig 1896; Garrison; Giacosa; Bernard de Gordon; Haller 1776; Haskins 1927; Heinrichs; M. Holl 1905, 1910 (*see also* K. Sudhoff 1907); Hopstock 1921; R. H. Hunter 1931; Hurd-Mead; Landi 1542; Leonardo da Vinci; Mac-Kinney; Manfredi 1490; Massa 1536; McMurrick 1930; Henry de Mondeville (14th century); Mondino de' Luzzi (Mundinus) 1315; Neuburger; Neuburger, Sudhoff & Pagel; O'Malley & Saunders 1952; Passera; Peckham (13th century); Puschmann; Puschmann, Neuburger & Pagel; Putti; Riesman; M. Roth 1905, 1907; Salerno (Aforismi); Chas. Singer; Singer & Rabin 1946; Sinno; Soury; W. Sudhoff 1914; Stein 1834; Töply; Vesalius 1543; Vitello (Witelo, *ca.* 1270); Zerbi or Gerbi 1502.

SEC. 8. VESALIUS AND THE ANATOMY AND PHYSIOLOGY OF THE VISUAL PATHWAYS

1. The reform in anatomy introduced by Vesalius.—With the appearance of Andreas Vesalius' *De Humani Corporis Fabrica,* or *On the Structure of the Human Body* (1543), the first period of Postclassical European anatomy, characterized by a helpless dependence upon the written word of the Greek and Arab authorities, often erroneous or based upon animal rather than human sources, was at an end. (Vesalius was born 1513 or 1514; died 1564; originally called Wyting or Witting, assumed name Wesel, meaning "weasel," probably taken either from the town Wesel situated on the right bank of the lower Rhine or from a village of the same name southwest of the town of Nymwegen, where his family came from; Latinized form Vesalius or Wesalius, French Vésale; portrait Figs. 15, 64.)

Beginning with the work of Vesalius, the guiding principle in anatomy was the emphasis upon personal dissection of human and animal bodies and to some degree also upon the observation of human pathological cases and experimentation on living animals. The knowledge taken over from the past was, of course, by no means discarded. The reborn science of anatomy was neither strong enough for this nor so blind as not to see much that was good in the old books. But a more critical attitude was assumed toward the ancient authorities, especially Galen, and every tenet was tested at the dissecting table. In this way an unlimited field of inquiry into the structure and working of the normal and ailing human body was opened, and an age of fruitful study of nature in general was initiated. (For the similarity of the Vesalian viewpoint and that of the Ancient Greek and Roman writers *see* Celsus, in sec. 1 [5], this chapter.)

2. Improvement in neuroanatomy instituted by Vesalius.—The achievements of Vesalius and his immediate successors in the field of neuroanatomy and of the anatomy of the brain, in particular, in spite of the new spirit, were in no way overwhelming. His chief merit was a systematic, compact, and lucid presentation of the principal parts easily seen by the unaided eye during a careful dissection, in contrast to Galen's rambling description.

The lucidity of Vesalius' style was in no small degree assisted by the numerous artistic woodcuts executed by his friend, Jan Stevenszoon van Calcar or Kalcker, all materially helped by the printing process (*see* Figs. 16, 17, 65). But more than the concrete discoveries, careful arrangement of the material according to the logic of the dissecting procedure was the distinguishing feature of his chapter on the brain.

There is, in fact, little on the visual system in Vesalius' thick volume that was not mentioned by Galen. He merely referred to the "origin" of the optic nerves at the base of the brain, without indicating the thalamus or any other particular structure in the modern sense as related to the visual system.

3. Vesalius' skepticism about the cavity of the optic nerves.—The attitude of Vesalius toward the channel or cavity in the optic nerves, one of the dogmatic cornerstones of Galenian teaching, was skeptical. No matter how often he tried to find it in various anatomical specimens, for which purpose he dissected living animals, he was not able to convince himself of the existence of a channel. Undoubtedly, he used living animals because of Galen's assertion that the cavity was visible only in freshly

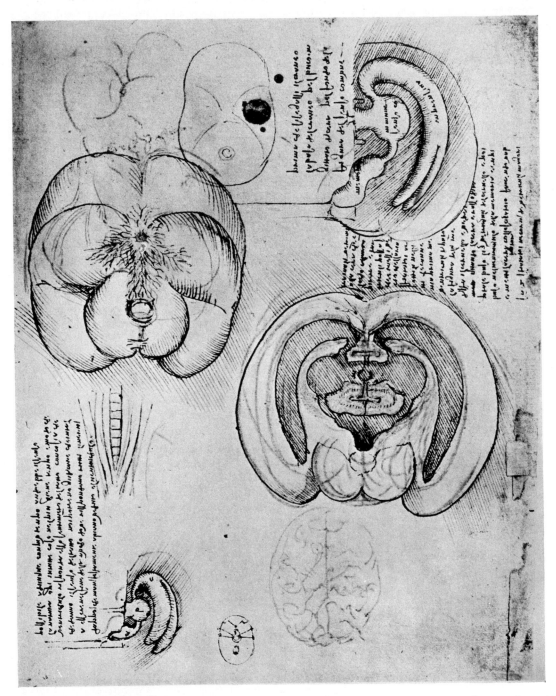

Fig. 63.—Leonardo da Vinci's presentation of the base of brain and of the cerebral ventricles, together with instructions for making casts of the ventricles by means of molten wax. From Leonardo da Vinci's *Quaderni d'anatomia*, v. 5, fol. 7, *recto*.

killed animals (*see* Galen, *De Hippocr. et Plat. Decr.*, book 7, chap. 4).

Nor was Vesalius more successful in finding a cavity in the human optic nerves he examined at executions, not more than a quarter of an hour after death and while the head was still warm and after having taken the precaution of immediately putting it into warm water (apparently in order to prevent or retard the loss of *pneuma*). The only probable exception was the chiasma, where he thought the cavity was noticeable.

Fig. 64.—Andreas Vesalius (1514–64), the "Reformer of Anatomy," at the age of twenty-eight. A steel engraving by Charles Onghena made around 1840 from the original woodcut portrait in Vesalius' *Fabrica* (*cf.* Fig. 15 in this book). Frontispiece in A. Burggraeve, *Études sur André Vésale*, Gand, 1841.

This bona fide skepticism of Vesalius is the more praiseworthy, since it went against the opinion of his times, expressed by another Renaissance anatomist and rival of Vesalius, Bartolommeo Eustachio (Fig. 66), who not only believed he had seen this cavity but took pains to depict it in one of his plates published posthumously. (*See also* Zinn, 1755.)

4. VESALIUS' VIEW ON THE STRUCTURE OF THE CHIASMA.—Concerning the relationship of

tion of his book, *Fabrica*, leaves no doubt about this.

Vesalius' view, notwithstanding its being a mistake, as his own figure shows (Fig. 65, *H*), was based on two observations: one of a youth whose eye, apparently as a punishment for some crime, had been torn out (!) a year before he died on the gallows, and another of a woman who suffered the same cruel fate and one of whose eyes had been atrophic since childhood (her crime may have been to look like a

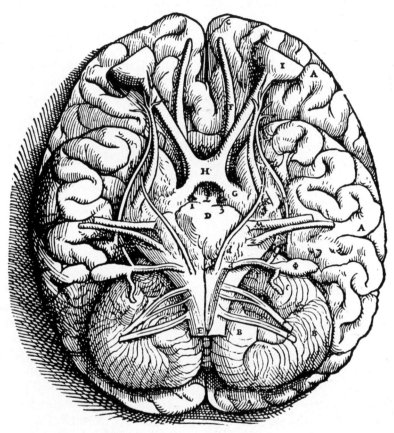

FIG. 65.—Woodcut figure from Vesalius' *Fabrica*, 1555, showing the basal aspect of the brain, with the origin of cranial nerves, and the brain stem. *A*, brain; *B*, cerebellum; *D*, origin of "spinal cord" (modern pons and medulla oblongata); *E*, cut-off stump of same; *F*, olfactory bulbs and tracts; *G*, optic nerves ("first cranial pair," according to Vesalius); *H*, optic chiasma; *I*, retina formed by the expansion of optic nerve; Φ, auditory and vestibular nerves. (*Cf.* Leonardo da Vinci's sketch of brain's base in Fig. 63.)

the two optic nerves in the chiasma, Vesalius' interpretation did not appreciably differ from Galen's. According to him, too, the connection was only an apparent one, each nerve, in fact, remaining on its own side along its entire course, from its apparent origin in the brain to its seeming termination in the eye at the same side. A small diagram given on page 329 of the first edi-

witch with an "evil eye"!). In both cases Vesalius' dissection showed the "nerve," or rather tract, on the side of the removed eye to be thinner, somewhat indurated, and of a reddish color.

Other cases of an absence of optic chiasma, apparent or real, were subsequently reported by Valverda, Fabricius ab Aquapendente, and Pasinus, as one learns from a remark in Henle's book (1879, p. 393; *cf.* Meckel 1812–18, v. 1, p. 398; Henle in his *Nervenlehre*, 1871, p. 348, or 1879, p. 393; Gudden 1879; Little 1886; Hovelaque, p. 49).

5. GALEN'S INFLUENCE ON VIEWS OF THE BRAIN'S FUNCTION PROFESSED BY VESALIUS.— In the functional interpretation of cerebral structures Vesalius was still under the spell of Galen's ideas (*cf.* sec. 3 [2], this chapter). For him, too, the brain was a place where the "animal spirit" was produced partly from the "vital spirit," which arrived with the blood from the heart, and partly from the air which entered through the nose. The "animal spirit," after having been further elaborated in the brain, was, in turn, propelled along the nerves to all sensory and motor organs of the body. The brain, accordingly, was a sort of nervous heart, and the nerves were its vessels, by analogy with the vascular system proper (forty years later, characteristically, Platter classified the nerves as *vasa*, or "vessels").

Concerning a more detailed interpretation of the function of the cerebral ventricles, the focal point of the brain in Greek, Arab, and early European anatomy and physiology, Vesalius, as on some other controversial questions, wisely abstained from committing himself. In this respect he favorably contrasts with most other anatomists of his time, whose thick volumes are filled with pages packed with learned nonsense.

References: J. M. Ball; J. Boeke 1914; Burggraeve; Castiglioni 1947; R. Columbus 1559; G. W. Corner; Cullen; Cumston 1926; Cushing 1943; De Feyer; De Lint; Faller; Falloppio 1561; Garrison; Garrison & Morton; A. Haller 1774–76; Heinrichs 1913; M. Holl 1910, 1915; H. R. Hunter; Knappert; Little 1886; Locy; Morley 1915; Paz Soldán 1944; Pettigrew; Révész 1917; Riesman 1935; Roth 1892, 1907; Saunders 1943; Saunders & O'Malley 1950; Chas. Singer 1925, 1942; Singer & Rabin; Soury 1899; Spielmann 1925; K. Sudhoff 1921; C. L. Taylor (*see* Cushing 1943); Töply 1898; Van der Kleij 1914; Van Leersum 1914; Vesalius.

SEC. 9. POST-VESALIAN PERIOD IN BRAIN ANATOMY AND PHYSIOLOGY

1. PERSISTENCE OF GALEN'S IDEAS ON THE BRAIN'S FUNCTION AFTER THE VESALIAN REFORMS.—The level which brain anatomy and physiology reached with Vesalius remained substantially the same for about two hundred years. Certain of his views, in fact, lasted until the beginning of the modern microscopic era, during the first half of the nineteenth century. During this long period many concepts incorporated in Galen's teaching still held sway, their replacement by more modern and, in general, more accurate views being quite slow.

Especially persistent and slow to be relinquished was the Galenian functional interpretation of the brain and the visual system. Here the quasi-material and, at the same time, almost transcendent *pneuma* or "visual spirit," that product of Greek speculation, still reigned supreme. It is remarkable—and significant for the appraisal of the maturity of scientific thinking of that period—that even the most emancipated among the "Vesalian Epigoni" (such as Platter, Du Laurens, Kepler, Scheiner, Willis, Des Cartes, and Vieussens) were still under the complete domination of the idea of a mysterious

"animal spirit" supposed to fill the brain ventricles.

According to Vieussens' definition (1684, portrait Fig. 75), this "animal spirit" was now conceived as an imperceptible, very thin, volatile substance of an ethereal nature, which, owing to its extremely subtle properties, could not be seen; whereas the *succus nervosus* or "nervous fluid," apparently identical with the cerebrospinal fluid, was a watery substance supposed to be secreted by the gray matter (*cf.* Burdach, v. 2, p. 264). A particular variety of *pneuma*, the "visual spirit," was believed to circulate in the visual pathways.

The only difference, in comparison with the past, was that the retina, finally recognized as the actual photoreceptor, was now considered the farthest point reached by the "visual spirit," and not the lens, to which was now assigned a passive, purely dioptrical, role in the visual act.

Even at that time, however, some lucid intellects, such as Wepfer (1658), Schneider (1660), and Stensen (1668, in Winslow's book 1733), either disclaimed the presence of the "spirit" in the brain or were quite critical of it.

Some residue of this intellectual inheritance from the dawn of Western Civilization, disguised in modern dress, has managed to survive until now and has played an important role in the shaping of certain contemporary concepts

to the understanding of the visual pathway. Falloppio (Fallopius or Falopius, 1523–62; book pub. 1561) paid no attention to the subject at all. Nor did Aranzi (Arantius, 1537–1619; book written before 1586, pub. 1595) produce anything of importance in this connection.

FIG. 66.—Bartolommeo Eustachio (Eustachius, *ca.* 1524–74), at the age of forty-nine. One of the founders of modern anatomy and among the first to recognize the connection of the optic nerves with the thalamus. From C. A. Manzini, *L'occhiale all'occhio*, Bologna, 1660.

of the working of the nervous system. (*See* chap. III.)

2. EARLY MODERN CONTRIBUTIONS TO THE ANATOMY OF THE VISUAL SYSTEM.—The immediate successors of Vesalius contributed little

Eustachio (Eustacchi, Eustachius, 1520–74, portrait Fig. 66) was first among the Westerners to depict in his *Tabulae Anatomicae* the visual pathway, more correctly recognizing the supposed "origin" of the "optic nerves" in the posterior portion of the thalamus instead of in the lateral ventricles, as Galen insisted. Unfortunately, since his plates, apparently completed around 1552, remained in obscurity until 1714, when they were published by Lancisi, his observation escaped notice of the subsequent anatomists (*see* Eustachio 1714, Pl. 17, Fig. 6).

For this reason Varoli (Varolius, 1543–78, book pub. 1573) seems to have been the first to publish a text with a figure adequately illustrating the infranuclear division of the visual pathways, including the eyes, optic nerves, tracts,

3. Du Laurens' view of the brain as the seat of a "general sense."—More information about the visual pathway and its function is to be found in the voluminous book of the noted French anatomist and physician Du Laurens (Laurentius, 1599, portrait Fig. 68).

He opposed the view both of a simple contact and of a complete crossing in the chiasma. His functional interpretation, however, was still quite Galenian, even though he never observed a cavity in the optic nerves. Concerning the

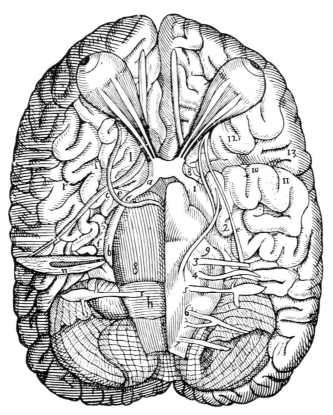

Fig. 67.—Basal aspect of human brain, from C. Varolio, *De Nervis Opticis*, Padua, 1573. Facsimile from J. G. de Lint, *Atlas of the History of Medicine*, P. B. Hoeber, New York, 1926. According to the common belief of the anatomists of that time, there were seven pairs of cranial nerves (*right half of figure*): *1*, origin of optic nerves; *2*, origin of oculomotor nerves; *3–7*, "all other nerves whose origin from the spinal cord was investigated by Vesalius"; *8*, locality where olfactory apparatus originates; *9*, beginnings of spinal cord; *10, 11*, "middle prominence of brain" (temporal lobe); *12, 13*, boundary of the frontal and parietal lobes toward temporal lobe. In the left half of the figure, *a* and *b* show a portion of the optic nerve, now termed "optic tract," unknown to Vesalius' contemporaries, which at *b* turns into posterior portion of "spinal cord" (present midbrain and thalamus); *h*, pons of cerebellum; *i*, origin of acoustic nerve.

their thalamic origin, and the chiasma (Fig. 67). This may explain why Platter, in his notable book (1603, p. 122), refers to Varoli as the discoverer of the origin of the optic nerves. (On other early anatomists who published illustrations of the brain's base, *see* S. Th. Soemmerring 1778.)

anatomical connections of the optic nerves with the brain, Du Laurens limited himself to Galen's view that the role of the brain was to unite all special sensations without being subservient to any one in particular. The brain, as the seat of a *sensus communis*, a "general sense," "neither sees, nor hears, nor feels."

In these words of Du Laurens the idea of a "functional equivalence" or "omnivalence" of all parts of the brain, as opposed to the concept of the "localization of cerebral functions," found its first expression. (*Cf.* Gall & Spurzheim, Flourens, Hitzig, Munk, Goltz, Flechsig, Monakow, Brodmann, Henschen, Lashley, *et al.*, in chaps. III and IV.)

4. The working of the "visual spirit" in the eye and brain, according to Du Lau-

in the lens and transmits the impressions of the seen objects to the brain, which acts in the role of a judge.

In the foregoing concept, expressed contemporaneously with Platter's quite different ideas and but a few years prior to the revealing work of Kepler (*see* chap. I, 5 [4–6]), there was hardly a hint of comprehension of the true functional significance of the dioptrical apparatus of the eye and of the formation of the retinal image. In his own words: "The eye, accordingly,

Fig. 68.—André du Laurens (Andreas Laurentius, 1558–1609) at the age of thirty-nine. Professor of anatomy at the University of Montpellier, in France, and a physician to the French King Henri IV and to Queen Marie de Médicis. Writer on visual organs, their anatomy, physiology, and pathology. Considered the brain as the seat of the *sensus communis* or a "general sense" uniting several special senses, without serving any one in particular. A copper engraving probably made by Jacques de Weert, in the 2d ed. of Du Laurens' *Historia Anatomica Corporis Humani*, Paris, 1600. Courtesy of Universitäts- und Landesbibliothek Halle a.S., Sachsen-Anhalt, Germany.

RENS.—In still another respect Du Laurens' idea about the working of the visual system is of interest. The *visilis spiritus*, or "visual spirit," coming from the brain, according to his view, spreads by means of the retina throughout the crystalline lens and over the entire eye. The same membrane in turn perceives the changes

seems to act like a mirror. It receives the images of the external objects without emitting anything. From the mirror the eye differs only in that in the former there is no animate principle by means of which the received image would be transferred to a higher resort which would act as an arbiter" (Laurentius 1599, p. 419).

5. LOCUS OF THE PERCEPTION OF VISUAL IMAGES, ACCORDING TO DU LAURENS.—Considering the various views as to whether the brain (since Galen's doctrine teaches that all sensation derives from it) or the pupil (according to Aristotle) or the "arachnoid membrane" of the eye (the lens capsule) or the chiasma of the optic nerves (according to Avicenna) is the locus of visual perception, Du Laurens expressed the following conciliatory opinion:

We believe the reception of the images to be in the crystalline lens, since this is the principal and foremost organ of sight, situated in the center of the eye, and different from other parts in its substance, its shape, and other properties. If you nevertheless desire to reconcile all the above-mentioned views, say that reception takes place in the lens, refraction in the tunics, perfection in the chiasma, perception in the brain [Laurentius 1599, p. 420].

This clever definition of the working of the visual mechanism, worthy of a true scientific opportunist, filled with meaningless words, was as empty as the words of a proverbial "windbag" politician, trying to satisfy everybody. It certainly was the least propitious way to try to find a successful solution of one of the most difficult problems of human organization.

6. GRADUAL EMERGENCE OF MODERN IDEAS CONCERNING THE RELATIONSHIP OF THE EYE AND BRAIN.—Better than a lengthy description, the preceding quotation shows how, at the end of the sixteenth century, even the leading authorities were uncertain and confused about both the anatomical mechanisms and the physiological processes involved in vision.

This ignorant hesitancy may seem the more remarkable, since a correct interpretation by Platter (1583, 1603), Kepler (1604, 1611), and Scheiner (1619, 1626–30) was already in sight

(*see* chap. I, 5 [4, 5, 6]). With the publication of their discoveries, computations, and experiments, the ancient Greek "emanation hypothesis" of the "visual rays" emitted from the eye, after having bedeviled scientific thinking for two thousand years, finally had to go.

The other source of confusion, Galen's "visual spirit," even though quite critically treated by Stensen (Steno 1668, Fig. 72), continued to circulate for a while in an unaccountable way from the brain to the eyes and back again.

In spite of this and other mental inhibitions inherited from the times of magic and ignorance, the idea of functional changes caused within the eye by external physical stimuli and a transmission of impulses, thus elicited, to the brain was by now becoming fairly well established. The problems which, from the early seventeenth century on, became gradually more apparent in the consciousness of the learned inquirers concerned with the problem of vision were more concrete and of a less magical character: the exact route by which the visual impulses reach the brain; the physiological nature of these impulses; and where in the brain, and precisely how, the central reactions to the photogenic impulses take place.

References: Aquapendens 1600; Aranzi 1595; Argentier 1565; Burdach 1819–22–26; Chievitz 1904; Coiter 1573; R. Colombo (Columbus); De Lint; Des Cartes; Du Laurens (Laurentius) 1599; Eustachio (Eustachius) 1552; Estienne (Stephanus) 1546; Falloppio or Fallopio (Fallopius) 1561; A. Haller 1774–76; Platter (Platerus) 1583, 1603; Riolan 1618; S. Santorio 1660; Chas. Singer; Soury 1899; Stensen (Steno) 1668; W. Sudhoff 1914; Valverda 1589; Varoli (Varolius) 1573; Vieussens 1685; Th. Willis 1664, 1682.

SEC. 10. EARLIEST MECHANISTIC EXPLANATION OF THE VISUAL SYSTEM

1. CARTESIAN SPECULATIONS ABOUT THE ANATOMICAL BASIS OF VISION.—During the early Modern period, in spite of the Vesalian reforms, most of Galen's ideas concerning the anatomy and physiology of the human body, particularly of the sense organs and the brain, were still firmly intrenched in the convictions of those concerned with these problems. There were notable exceptions, however. Some of the

keenest minds of that period, unable to find complete satisfaction in Galen's simple formulas, began to search for a more plausible explanation of the anatomical substratum of the human mind.

One of these pioneers was the French philosopher René Des Cartes (Descartes, Cartesius, 1596–1650, portrait Fig. 69). Among his numerous speculations, he produced a remarkable hypothesis of the intrinsic organization of the visual system which was far ahead of his time (1638, 1662). A confirmed dualist and a devout believer, he nevertheless tried his best to use the few positive anatomical facts known to him in order to explain the phenomenon of vision mechanistically. Even though he formally denied any direct dependence of the "psychic" functions upon the crudely material parts of the brain, the factors which he used in his hypoth-

esis were all essentially material and anatomical.

There were three such factors: the "spirits," which he conceived to be vapor-like or gaseous, originating from the heart (still essentially a Greek-Galenian idea of *pneuma*); the "pores" of the cerebrum, through which these "spirits" passed (this, too, was but a refined modification of the Greek idea of "visual channels"); and, lastly, the mode of distribution of the "spirits"

FIG. 69.—René Des Cartes de la Haye (Descartes, Cartesius, 1596–1650), scientist, mathematician, and philosopher. Author of the earliest mechanistic explanation of the intrinsic organization of the visual system, according to which each sensitive point of the retina of each eye has its own, discrete representation in the brain. Engraving by W. Holl from an original painting by Frans Hals in the Louvre, Paris. Courtesy Crerar Library, Dr. Sonnenschein Collection, Chicago. (For biography *see* E. S. Haldane 1905.)

in the "pores," or, in modern language, the arrangement of the nerve fibers in the visual system.

This new idea of "projection," in the light of modern knowledge the most important of the three factors, even though hinted at several centuries before by Ibn al-Haitham, was apparently Des Cartes's own.

2. Cartesian hypothesis of a topographical representation of the retina in the

Vesalius, thought of as completely separated from one another in the chiasma, the fibers and bundles pursue a course parallel with each other as far as the retina, where they "terminate" discretely (Fig. 71, *1*, *3*, *5*). To each point of the ventricular surface, accordingly, there corresponds a point in the sensitive retinal surface. By means of this mechanism, the images painted upon the retinal membrane are reproduced accurately and with fidelity in the cerebral ventricles. (*Cf.* sec. 11 [6], this chapter.)

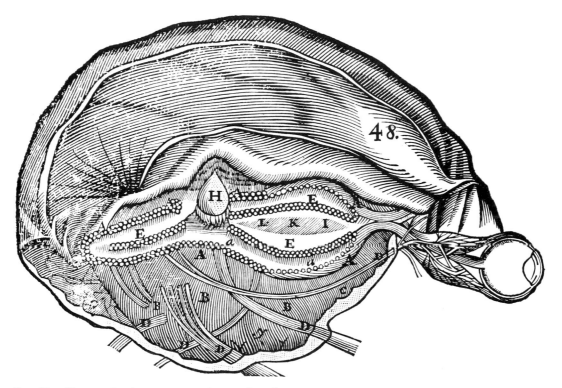

Fig. 70.—Human visual system, according to Des Cartes in his *Tractatus de Homine* or *A Treatise on Man*, written 1660, published 1686. The optic nerve consists of parallel fibers originating from evenly distributed points on the surface of the cerebral ventricles. In the chiasma the two optic nerves are supposed to be merely in contact, without exchanging their fibers. The peripheral end of the optic nerve merges with the retina of the eyeball. The extrinsic eye muscles are supplied by the branches of oculomotor nerve originating from the posterior extremity of the ventricle. Other peripheral nerves leave the brain in various directions. In the center of the brain is the pineal gland, *H*, which Des Cartes looked upon as the "seat of the soul," where ideas are formed. The figure illustrates a queer combination of the anatomical facts discovered since the time of Vesalius, and the products of speculation influenced by Galen's writings. (*Cf.* Fig. 71.)

BRAIN.—The nerve fibers which make up the visual system, according to Des Cartes, are not arranged haphazardly but follow a definite order. At their place of "origin" in the lateral ventricles of the brain, each fiber or a small bundle of fibers arises from a definite locality in the ventricular surface (Fig. 71, *2*, *4*, *6*). In the optic nerves and tracts, which he, like Galen and

Des Cartes likewise tried to explain the single subjective experience in the binocular visual act. According to him, the single monocular impressions impinging upon the "corresponding points" of both retinae were further transmitted to the pineal gland (*H*). This organ, because of its central location in the brain, its special connections with the optic nerves, and its rich blood supply, was, in Des Cartes's opinion, eminently suited to serve as a unifying focus.

In the pineal gland the distribution of nerves was also orderly, each monocular impression arriving from a "corresponding point" of one retina and meeting its "corresponding mate" from the other retina (*a, b, c*). In this way the two single monocular retinal impressions merged in the pineal gland, the "seat of the soul" or conscious appreciation, according to Des Cartes, into a single psychic experience. The meeting of the conjugated or syndynamical impressions in the central organ would be accomplished by a hypothetical partial crossing of the central conductors in the brain itself, instead of in the chiasma, where, following Galen and Vesalius,

tional values and arranged topographically in space to reproduce an accurate cerebral copy of the observed visual object.

Naïve and vacuous though Des Cartes's speculation may now appear, it is worth while to consider that it contained, for the first time, a clearly conceived and expressed idea of a topographical projection or representation of the retina in the brain (*cf.* chap. IV, 4; chap. VI, 7; chap. VII, 4, 5, 6). However subtle and elusive the forces, such as the "spirits" elicited by the stimulation of the retina, they had to follow preformed anatomical pathways on their way to the brain.

The essentially mechanistic character of Des Cartes's speculation is not weakened by his fan-

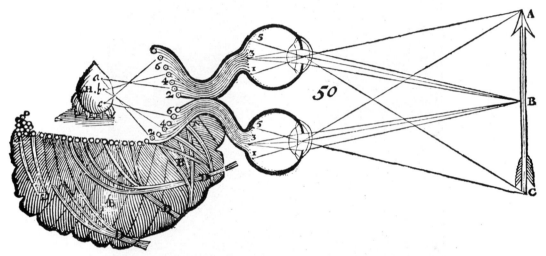

Fig. 71.—Binocular stereoscopic visual system and its working, as imagined by Des Cartes. The two retinal images of a single object are accurately, point-for-point, projected upon the surface of the cerebral ventricles, whence they are further transmitted to the centrally located pineal gland, *H*, the supposed "seat of imagination and common sense." Here the homonymous "corresponding" or "syndynamical" impressions merge into a single visual "idea"—for example, of the object point *A*, via two retinal points *1* and *1*, along the two ventricular points *2* and *2*, ultimately meeting in a common point *a* of the pineal gland (*H*). In this way a single binocular visual experience would be achieved, in spite of complete separation in the chiasma, a mistaken belief which Des Cartes took over from Galen and Vesalius. After the union of the two monocular images in the pineal gland, the impressions would be further transmitted to the brain substance, *B* and *B*, and deposited in it as a memory image. The problem of how the "corresponding impressions" are made to unite remained thus unexplained. From *Tractatus de Homine* or *Traité de l'homme*, written 1660 and published 1686. (*Cf.* also Figs. 33, 69, 70.)

Des Cartes assumed a complete separation of the optic nerves.

Altogether, Des Cartes tried to explain mechanically, by anatomical structures, not only a "point-to-point" transmission of each monocular retinal image upon its own area of the brain but also an orderly formation of a single cerebral mental image made up of "corresponding retinal points," united according to their func-

tastic elaboration upon it, according to which the "animal spirits" were supposed to enter from the ventricles into "pores" or minute spaces between the fibers of the optic nerves and tracts; the ventricular images were supposed to be further transmitted, first to the pineal gland, the "seat of the soul," where they formed the "ideas" of external objects, after which they were finally deposited in the brain substance itself, where they served as a substratum of the "memory" (Fig. 71, *B, B*).

3. Mistakes and merits of Des Cartes's speculations.—Whatever the obvious faults of Des Cartes's speculations in the light of present knowledge, the fact remains that he was the first to make an honest effort to explain the visual act in terms of anatomical structures known to him or conceived by him, instead of

duced Malpighi, one of the founders of modern microscopy, to correct its glaring inaccuracies, such as the supposed origin of the optic nerves in the cerebral ventricles and their hypothetical connection with the pineal gland (Malpighi 1687, v. 2, p. 123). But, with the erasure of Des Cartes's anatomical errors, his most valuable idea—that of a topographical relationship of a peripheral receptor surface, such as the retina, to the brain, first announced by Ibn al-Haitham

Fig. 72.—Niels Stensen (Nicolas or Nicolaus Steno, or Stenonius, 1638–87), noted Danish anatomist, active in Paris, Florence, and Copenhagen. From C. G. Cumston, *Introduction to the History of Medicine*, 1926. According to a painting made in 1669 by an unknown painter, now in Pitti Gallery, Florence, Italy. Courtesy of Pitti Gallery.

comfortably putting the entire burden upon the equipotentialist properties of a transcendental "spirit" or "soul." In this sense his hypothesis was a precursor of the modern idea of functional cerebral localization.

The influence of Des Cartes's hypothesis upon further efforts to understand the nervous system, unfortunately, was very small. It in-

half a millennium earlier (*see* sec. 6 [2], this chapter)—was also lost from the consciousness of the scientific world. In consequence, more than two centuries later this idea had to be rediscovered, until it now forms the very foundation of our concept of the visual system. (For an able critique of Cartesian ideas, *see* Steno's dissertation in Winslow's *Anatomy*, 1733, sec. 10,

par. 10, p. 56; for Briggs's and Taylor's speculations, *see* sec. 11 [2, 5, 6], this chapter; for Steno's portrait *see* Fig. 72.)

References: Ch. Bonnet 1775; Corner 1919;
Des Cartes (Cartesius) 1677; Diemerbroeck
1683; Galen; A. Haller 1774–76; Ibn al-Haitham; Malpighi 1664, 1687; Pirenne 1948;
Révész 1917; Soury 1899; Stensen (Steno)
1668; F. S. Taylor 1939; Winslow 1773; Ziehen 1902.

SEC. 11. ANATOMY AND PHYSIOLOGY OF THE VISUAL PATHWAYS AND CENTERS FROM DES CARTES TO ALBRECHT VON HALLER

1. BEGINNINGS OF MODERN NEUROANATOMY
AND THE VISUAL SYSTEM.—The earliest systematic presentation of the anatomy of the brain,
including the visual pathway, in Man and in
other Vertebrates, after the Revival of Learning
came from Thomas Willis (1621–75, portrait
Fig. 73). Through his book, *Cerebri Anatome*
(1664), the gap of the fifteen centuries—which
separated the last productive period of Greek
anatomy and physiology of the brain, represented by Galen, from modern times—was definitely bridged. His monograph not only embodied a
comprehensive survey of all that was known at
that time about the structure and function of
the brain but also included numerous personal
observations, especially comparative.

Following are the main points of Willis'
work, as far as it concerns the visual pathway.
The "optic nerves' (presently tracts) "originate" from parts of the brain called the "optic
thalami," or *thalami nervorum opticorum* (term
from Riolan 1618), *juga nervi optici, juga crurum medullarium,* or *secunda sectio crurum medullarium.* These are the backward extensions
behind the striate bodies, distinguished by their
somewhat darker color.

According to Willis' subdivision, the thalami
were a part of the *medulla oblongata,* to which he
assigned not only the midbrain, pons, and bulb
or *medulla oblongata* of modern terminology,
that is, the entire "brain stem," but also the
"striate bodies," including the lentiform nucleus. From the "optic nerves" (i.e., tracts) the
medullary processes extend toward the root of
the pineal gland. Apparently it was these structures that induced Des Cartes to include this
gland in the visual system (*see* sec. 10, this
chapter). Differing from Des Cartes, however,
Willis considered these processes to be a sort of
commissure between the two optic nerves (later
a similar view was suggested by Charcot, in order to explain the "contralateral amaurosis" of
one eye caused by unilateral brain lesion (*see*
chap. III, 9 [6]). Of the other parts of the brain
more or less related to the visual system, Willis
described the larger superior, and the smaller
inferior, colliculi, or *protuberantiae orbiculares
natiformes* or *nates,* and the *protuberantiae mi-
nores* or *testes,* in Galenian terminology, and
their connections

In contrast to his accurate presentation of
the anatomical facts, Willis' functional interpretation of the various parts of the visual system, of the production and distribution of "animal spirits," of the role of the optic chiasma,
and the like was completely Galenian.

Of interest, finally, is the fact that even so
assiduous an anatomist as Willis looked upon
the apparent origin of the optic nerves in the
thalami as the end of the visual system. His attention, like that of other contemporary anatomists, was still completely absorbed by the
lower parts of the central organ. Even though
he knew something of the *corona radiata,* he
entirely missed the supranuclear division, chiefly represented by visual radiation, and thus he
overlooked the importance of the cerebral cortex. This, in view of the technical difficulties of
his time, is understandable. (*See* Niels Stensen,
or Steno, 1668.)

Although Willis' anatomy of the visual system did not differ a great deal from Galen's, it
nevertheless showed some progress. In the first
place, it was accurate, the pleasing illustrations
drawn by Sir Christopher Wren, the "English
Leonardo da Vinci," celebrated architect and
builder of St. Paul's Church in London, adding
much to this. In both points Willis' work contrasts favorably with the verbose, vague, and
inadequately illustrated descriptions of most of
the preceding writers.

Nor was there any mention made by him of
the "channels" of optic nerves, which, until
then, had played a prominent role. The optic

nerves were not hollow tubes but were made up of bundles of nerve fibers, a fact confirmed and depicted but a few decades later by Briggs (1676–85, Fig. 74) and verified by a number of investigators of renown, such as Diemerbroeck (1683, p. 375), Vieussens (1684, p. 165, portrait Fig. 75), Bidloo (1685), and Malpighi (1687, v. 2, p. 121; portrait Fig. 36).

This and other fundamental discoveries in cerebral anatomy and physiology made at that time induced the more critical minds of the following period to doubt the whole Galenian concept of "animal spirits," their generation in the cerebral ventricles, and their propagation in the peripheral nerves, thus preparing the way for modern research. (*See* Steno 1668; Malpighi, *Op. Omn.*, 1687, v. 2, p. 121.)

2. SUCCESSORS OF WILLIS AND THEIR CONTRIBUTIONS TO THE KNOWLEDGE OF THE VISUAL

FIG. 73.—Thomas Willis (1621–75) at the age of forty-five. Professor of natural philosophy at Oxford, England. Physician and noted brain anatomist. Described the "arterial circle of Willis" at the base of the brain. Author of the *Cerebri Anatome*, 1664, the earliest modern comprehensive treatise on the brain. Writer on physiology and pathology of the nervous system (*De Anima Brutorum* or *On the Soul of Animals*). Founder of the Royal Society of London. Courtesy of Dr. Francis F. R. Walshe, London, England *See also* frontispiece in Willis' *Pharmaceutica Rationalis*, Oxford, 1673.

SYSTEM.—During the century and a half following Willis, there was but little advancement made in the anatomy of the visual pathways. In fact, until the first quarter of the nineteenth century, this subject stagnated at approximately the level to which it had been brought by the impetus of the pioneers of the Renaissance and their immediate followers.

An exception was Briggs, who in his *Nova Visionis Theoria* continued to speculate along

gained further ground, even though it was, as yet, based upon pure speculation.

Here mention may be made of a curious opinion of the French anatomist Vieussens, according to which the optic nerves continued as far as the cerebral cortex. This appears to be the earliest intimation of visual radiations and of the cortical visual centers (*cf.* Gratiolet, chap. III, 5 [5]). This suggestion, which might have redirected investigation of the brain into more

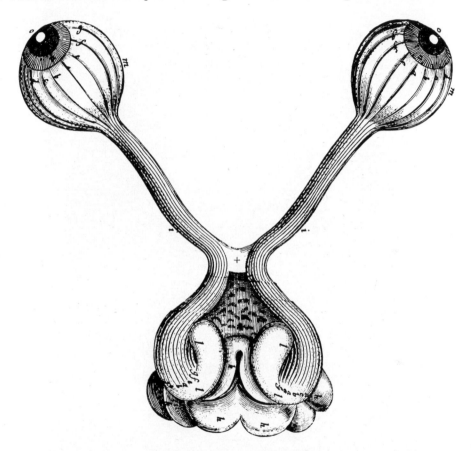

FIG. 74.—Visual system as represented by W. Briggs in his *Ophthalmo-graphia* (1685). The optic nerves (*i, i*) are composed of nerve fibers. Each fiber, or a small fiber bundle, was supposed to originate in a well-defined small area (*g, f, e, a, b, c, d*) of optic thalamus (*l, l*) and to terminate in a circumscribed area of the retina of the eye (*m*) marked by the same letter. The principle of a topographical projection of the retina upon the brain is similar to that of Des Cartes (*see* Fig. 71), except for the union of the homonymous "corresponding" fibers in the pineal gland. As in Des Cartes's figures, in Briggs's diagram also there is no interchange of fibers between the two optic nerves in the chiasma, each nerve remaining independent (Galen's doctrine). No optic fibers extend to the superior colliculi of the midbrain (*h, h*), and there is no mention made of a visual radiation to the cerebral cortex.

the lines of Des Cartes concerning the parallel course of the optic nerve fibers, placing their presumptive "origin," however, in the optic thalamus instead of in the cerebral ventricles (Fig. 74). Thus the idea of a topographical projection of the retinal surface upon the cerebrum

profitable channels, produced no results for a long time. The reason was that most anatomists, physiologists, and clinical neurologists of the period were still submerged in the struggle with elementary anatomical problems ("origin" of optic nerves, structure of the chiasma), the usual opinions expressed being taken literally from Vesalius and Galen.

The existence of a supranuclear division of the visual system remained, therefore, outside the sphere of immediate interest. The blame for this falls upon inadequate methods of investigation, among other factors, as pointed out by scientific interpretation of cerebral structures and functions. (*See* Wepfer 1658; Schneider 1660; Diemerbroeck 1683; Vieussens 1684; Morgagni 1719; Santorini 1724, 1775; Maître-Jan 1725; A. Haller 1769, v. 4, p. 206; Zinn 1755; Winslow 1773, 1776; *see also* H. Heinrichs 1913; W. Sudhoff 1914.)

FIG. 75.—Raymond Vieussens (1641–1716), professor of anatomy in Montpellier, France. Author of *Neurographia Universalis* (1684), a voluminous treatise on the anatomy of the brain, spinal cord, and nerves. From W. Stirling, *Some Apostles of Physiology*, Waterlow & Sons, London, 1902.

Steno. Also, not until approximately the middle of the eighteenth century were the anatomy and physiology of the brain completely emancipated from Galen's idea of "animal" and "visual" spirits that had so far hampered a truly

3. Confusion concerning the structure and functional significance of the optic chiasma.—One of the perennial problems of this period was the structure and function of the chiasma or junction of the optic nerves. In regard to this, opinions differed and continued to do so until the end of the nineteenth century. Vesalius, Aquapendens, Valverda, Des Cartes, Briggs, Riolan, Diemerbroeck, Plemp, Vesling, and many others, joining Galen, maintained that there was no exchange of fibers in the chiasma, an opinion conveniently followed by the majority.

Bauhin, Lud. Mercatus, Sennertus, and their partisans, however, considered the chiasma not a simple contact but a complete mixing of substance of the two optic nerves. Its function, they believed, was not so much to improve the sight of one eye when the other was lost, as Galen thought, but "to enable the spirits to pass easily from one eye to the other." This view was, of course, only a variation of Galen's inconsequential thesis, defended previously by Porta.

Still a third group, adopting the opinion of Rhazes and Avicenna, advocated a complete decussation (Zinn).

Nor did the few pathological cases accidentally coming into the hands of the anatomist-surgeons help to clarify the issue. In one such case observed by Caesalpinus (1590) and reported by Diemerbroeck (1683, p. 375) the atrophy of the optic tract, coinciding with the site of the blind eye and of the atrophic optic nerve, was a duplication of a pertinent observation by Vesalius (sec. 8 [4], this chapter). (*See also* Porterfield 1759, v. 1, p. 190, and v. 2, p. 282; A. Haller 1769, v. 5, p. 346; Soemmerring 1778; Burdach 1819–26; S. A. W. Stein 1834.)

4. Earliest announcement of a partial decussation in the chiasma by Isaac Newton.—Closer to the truth in explaining the anatomy and functional significance of the optic chiasma was Isaac Newton (1642–1727), the celebrated English natural philosopher and mathematician (*see* Newton, *Opticks*, 1704, book 3, query 15; portrait Fig. 76).

Searching for an explanation of simple binocular vision, Newton assumed its cause to be the union in the chiasma of the nerve fibers which originate from the homonymous sides of both eyes. This information he, himself not an anatomist, may have obtained from one of the contemporary anatomists, as a hint in his note indicates (*cf.* pars. 1 and 2, this section; *see also*

Fig. 71, where the fusion of homonymous "corresponding impressions" in the brain was clearly indicated by Des Cartes, although only in the pineal gland; for Ibn al-Haitham *see* sec. 6 [2], this chapter). Owing to this arrangement, the impressions from the homonymous halves of both retinae are transmitted either to the right or to the left half of the brain, the two cerebral impressions together producing one single mental experience. In modern times this idea assumed a concrete form in the concept of a "cyclopean eye" (Hering and Helmholtz). (*See* chap. XIII, 3.)

5. Earliest formulation of the "theory of identical or conjugate points."—The idea of a partial decussation in the optic chiasma serving as an anatomical arrangement that brings about a single impression in the binocular visual act, foreshadowed by Ibn al-Haitham, or Alhazen, during the eleventh century and later by Des Cartes and first clearly announced by Isaac Newton, was further taken up and elaborated upon by John Taylor (1727, 1750, portrait Fig. 77), a roving ophthalmic surgeon and adventurer.

According to Taylor's hypothesis, those fibers which are "akin," that is, similarly or syndynamically attuned, as are those which originate from the homonymous halves of both eyes, join in the central organ. In this way each point of the photoreceptive surface of one eye becomes anatomically and functionally correlated to a similar point of the contralateral eye. In Taylor's diagram (Fig. 78), fibers from the homonymous halves of both eyes are shown to join above the chiasma as two separate fascicles and to proceed together to their respective halves of the brain.

Taylor's hypothesis would be practically identical with the modern "theory of identical points" and "joining of homonymous fiber bundles" proposed by Johannes Müller and by Wilbrand (*Faszikelfeldermischung, see* chap. IV, 4 [5]), if it were not for the fact that the fibers from the ipsilateral and contralateral eye are depicted in his diagram as running parallel instead of being superimposed. On the other hand, far advanced though it was, Taylor's functional interpretation was inadequate, since it failed to recognize the true effect, which is stereoscopic vision, as a functional consequence of the peculiar anatomical organization of the visual system. (For continuation of this subject, *see* sec. 12 [7], this chapter; chap. IV, 4 [5]; and chap. XIII, 3.)

6. FURTHER ELABORATION OF THE IDEA OF TOPOGRAPHICAL REPRESENTATION OF THE RETI-

NAE IN THE VISUAL SYSTEM.—Of considerable interest also is Taylor's idea of the preservation of the relative positions of the optic nerve fibers along their course from the eye to the central organ or the topographical "projection" of the retina upon the brain. This idea, already suggested by Ibn al-Haitham (sec. 6 [2], this chapter), but first clearly expounded by Des Cartes

FIG. 76.—Isaac Newton (1642–1727), celebrated mathematician, physicist, and philosopher of Cambridge, England. Originator of the concept of "force of gravitation" as a basic factor in the universe. Student of the fundamental properties and nature of light ("corpuscular, emission, or emanation theory"). Showed white light to be a composite of homogeneous colored lights, together representing a visible "spectrum." Author of *Principia Mathematica*, 1687, and of "Opticks," 1704. First writer who clearly indicated the partial decussation of optic nerves in the chiasma to be a basis of the single subjective impressions in the binocular visual act, later expressed in the concept of a "cyclopean eye" by Hering and by Helmholtz. From E. Mach, *The Principles of Physical Optics*, Methuen & Co., London, 1925. (*Cf. also* Fig. 350.)

(sec. 10 [2, 3], this chapter), and again advocated by Briggs (par. 2, this section), as presented by Taylor, even though less explicit, appears closer to the modern viewpoint, since it is anatomically more correct. Its weakness was the lack of anatomical evidence. The earliest attempt to furnish such evidence was made by Zinn (1755, p. 193), who found that the number of fiber bundles in the optic nerve is constant and that they preserve the same relative order along the entire course of the nerve. (*Cf.* chap. IV, 4.)

IOHANN TAYLOR,
RITTER, DOCTOR DER ARTZENEY KUNST, VERSCHIEDENER
Hohen Königl. und Hoch Fürstl. Höfe Hoch bestalter Augen Artzt, wie auch
Mitglied vieler berühmten Academien in Deütschland, Franckreich, Schweitz u. Portugal

QUI VISUM VITAM DAT.

Effigiem Taylor, tibi qui demissus ab alto est,   Miranda praxi sublata ophtalmia, quævis
Turba alias expers luminis, ecce vides,   Artifici dextra gutta Serena cadit.
Nic maculas tollit, Cataractas deprimit omnes,   Ecce Virum, Cujus Cingantur tempora lauro
Irnissum Splendens excitat ille rubar.   Dignum, cui laudes Sæcula longa Canant.
Chevalier Riche Roma Pinx.   A. Reinhardt fe. Francofurti 1750.

FIG. 77.—John Taylor (1703–72), English ophthalmiatric "knight-errant" and, according to some historians, "the greatest charlatan among the oculists that ever lived." In spite of the adverse opinion of posterity about Taylor's character and professional accomplishments, it is only fair to admit that his view on the anatomical causes of single vision was remarkably modern: e.g., that the bundles composing the optic nerve, originating from the localities of both retinae used simultaneously in a binocular visual act, meet in one point in the brain and thus bring about a single subjective visual experience. Whether original or borrowed, this view was subsequently developed by Johannes Müller, H. Wilbrand, and others into the modern "theory of corresponding or syndynamical points" (*see* chap. II, 11, [5]). Frontispiece of Taylor's *Mechanismus*, 1750. (*Cf.* Fig. 78.)

7. SMALL INFLUENCE OF EARLY CLINICAL OB-SERVATIONS UPON THE UNDERSTANDING OF THE VISUAL SYSTEM.—The divergence of opinions concerning the visual system during the seventeenth and eighteenth centuries is astonishing, in view of a considerable number of clinical and pathoanatomical observations. It seems, in fact, that as the number of observed cases increased, so did the disagreement, until, as A. Haller, a leading physiologist of his time, remarked, nothing but well-performed physiological experiments could clarify the issues (A. Haller 1769, v. 4, p. 206, portrait Fig. 80).

The only subject on which there seems to have been general agreement concerned the channel in the optic nerves. At last this fantasmagoria was eliminated. Originating in the days of Heróphilos and Erasístratos and cleverly propagated by Galen, it easily survived the credulous Middle Ages and managed even to linger on into the modern era of magnifying glasses and microscopes, all the while interfering with sober research and clear thinking. It

was an illusion apparently caused by the central retinal blood vessels buried in the center of the optic nerve, which to an unaided eye may have simulated a collapsed channel (Zinn 1755). (*Cf.* Fig. 185.)

References: Aguillon (Aguillonius) 1613; Aquapendens 1600; Bauhin 1621; Bidloo 1685; Briggs 1676–85; Cherubin d'Orleans 1678; Diemerbroeck 1683; J. W. French 1923; A. Haller 1769, 1774–76; Helmholtz 1924–25; Hering 1931; J. Hirschberg 1911; Huygens 1654; Maître-Jan 1725; Malpighi 1687; Joh. Müller 1826, 1835–40; Morgagni 1719; Isaac Newton 1704; Pirenne 1948; Plempius 1632; Porterfield 1759; Rauber & Kopsch 1914; Riolan 1618, 1620; Santorini 1724; C. V. Schneider 1660; Soemmerring 1778; Southall 1937; Steno or Stensen 1668 (*see* Winslow); J. Taylor 1727; Tschermak-Seyssenegg 1942; Vater & Heinicke 1723; Vesling 1696; Vieussens 1684; W. C. Wells 1792; Wepfer 1658; Wilbrand; Th. Willis 1664; Winslow 1773, 1776; Zinn 1775.

SEC. 12. INVESTIGATIONS OF THE VISUAL SYSTEM TOWARD THE END OF THE EIGHTEENTH AND DURING THE BEGINNING OF THE NINETEENTH CENTURIES

1. TRANSITION FROM GROSS ANATOMY TO MICROANATOMY.—During the first half of the eighteenth century little progress was made in the anatomy and physiology of the visual system. The reason was not so much the lack of interest as the fact that the crude dissection of fresh specimens, heretofore used almost exclusively, was obviously approaching its inherent limits. By this time, most of the gross features easily studied without magnifying glasses, such as the size, consistency, and fibrous composition of the optic nerves and related parts of the brain, had been described. The next task was to study finer details. This, however, had to wait until the beginning of the microscopic era. But just before this, during the second half of the eighteenth century, as if in preparation for the age of microscopy, gross anatomical investigation not only increased in volume but became more subtle in technique and in its concept.

During the early part of the nineteenth century the investigation of the visual pathway was the logical continuation of the preceding period, both in understanding the problems and

in technical approach. The interest was still almost entirely confined to the surface features of the brain. So far as the deeper parts, especially the gray masses or nuclei and the various fiber tracts and sheets or laminae of the brain, were studied, the examination was done without the aid of optical apparatus. True, the microscope was now used more frequently than before, but only for the study of nervous tissue in general.

Even so, in the training of the anatomists, accumulated experience and maturity of scientific thinking advanced further in comparison with the past. In the investigation of the brain in general and of the visual system in particular, this led to a further refinement in analyzing the accessible structures. (On the influence of the perfection of microscope upon research *see* F. Merkel 1893; R. M. Allen; Clay & Court; *cf.* also chap. I, 7, and corresponding figures and references.)

2. CONFUSION CONCERNING THE "ORIGIN" OF OPTIC NERVES.—Among the numerous questions raised by gross anatomical investigation, some lacked adequate definition, since the general principles of organization of nervous tissues had not yet been formulated (*see* "neuron theory" chap. I, 8, and chap. IX). Only microscopy could have furnished these.

For the same reason, the various contradictory assertions relative to the "origin" of the "optic nerves" could have been neither confirmed nor refuted. In this respect almost every part of the brain not too distant from the optic nerves was claimed by someone as their presumptive origin. Among the parts so designated were the superior colliculi of the midbrain; the posterior colliculi and cerebellum; Vieussens' "oval center"; cerebral peduncles; tuber cinereum; the anterior portion of the corpus callosum and anterior commissure; the fornix; the corpus striatum; stria terminalis; thalamus and geniculate nuclei; lateral geniculate nucleus alone; the upper surface of the thalamus; the superior colliculi and lateral geniculate nucleus. Only those of the foregoing suggestions that could have been easily tested without the help of a microscope—for example, the hippocampal gyrus—could have been discarded as fallacious.

In summary, in the words of Soemmerring (1810), of all parts of the brain claimed to be related to visual function, this was certain only about the thalamus. But Burdach (1819–26), commenting on this, remarked that even this was doubtful. Hence, at the end of the first quarter of the nineteenth century, there was practically nothing known about the function of the great hemispheres of the brain, particularly about the gray superficial layer, the cortex. (*See* Soemmerring 1778; Gall & Spurzheim 1810–19; Burdach 1822; S. A. W. Stein 1834.)

3. The problem of the chiasma.—The other of the two chief problems of the visual system during this period—the structure and functional significance of the optic chiasma—remained unsolved.

The majority still followed Galen's and Vesalius' opinion of a unilateral arrangement, some being in this respect even more radical, denying any relationship between the two nerves. A few advocated a complete decussation, an opinion expressed, according to Burdach, by some

Greek anatomists before Galen; others a partial decussation; while still another group assumed an interlacement of fiber bundles without an actual crossing. In any case the evidence in favor of or against any of the foregoing views was inconclusive. This again served as a stimulus for many additional hypotheses, usually even less plausible (*see* Soemmerring 1778, p. 104).

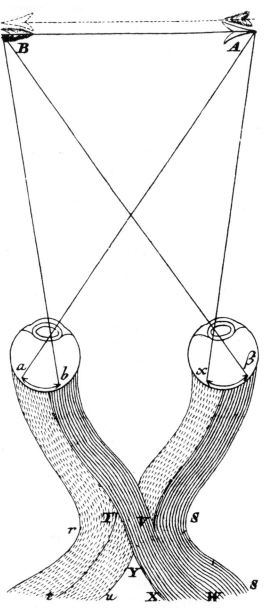

Fig. 78.—John Taylor's diagram showing partial decussation or crossing of optic nerve fibers in the chiasma as a basis of binocular single vision. From J. Taylor, *Mechanismus . . . des menschlichen Auges,* Fig. 5, Tab. V, published in Frankfurt a.M., 1750.

Only after the more careful anatomical studies by Michaelis (1790) and by the Wenzel brothers (1812) and after the observation of additional pathological cases, did the concept of a partial decussation become better substantiated. Such was a case reported by Rudolphi (1815), in which one eye was missing and where a strand was found to cross to the opposite tract

4. Earliest correct interpretation of homonymous hemianopia.—The first case of impaired vision in both eyes caused by a unilateral affection of the brain—apparently the earliest recorded clinical observation of homonymous hemianopia or half-blindness of either the right or the left half of the fields of view— was described by Morgagni (1719, *Epist. Anat.*

ANATOMICORUM PRINCEPS

Fig. 79.—Giovanni Battista Morgagni (1682–1771), professor of anatomy in Bologna and Padua, in Italy. The "Prince of the Anatomists," and "Founder of Pathological Anatomy." In 1719 described a case, apparently the first on record, of impaired vision in both eyes caused by a unilateral lesion of the brain, or homonymous hemianopia (half-blindness). From C. G. Cumston, *Introduction to the History of Medicine*, K. Paul, Trench, Trubner & Co., London, 1926; A. A. Knopf, New York, 1926; and R. N. Wegner, *Das Anatomenbildnis*, 1939. According to a sketch by Angelica Kauffman, made from a drawing by Nathaniel Dance. (*See also* P. Capparoni, *Profili bio-bibliografici*, Ist. Naz. med. farm. "Serono," Roma, 1926.)

from the normal optic nerve. (*See* Burdach 1822, p. 392; Gall & Spurzheim 1810, p. 112; A. Haller 1769; Henle 1871, v. 3, part 2, p. 348; Meckel 1812–18, 1815–20; Soemmerring 1778; for doubts raised later, *see* chap. III, 9 [3–6].)

16, art. 13, portrait Fig. 79; *see also* Soemmerring 1778, p. 104). The first correct interpretation of this disturbance in connection with a partial decussation of fibers in the chiasma was given by Vater & Heinicke (1723). A few years later a similar view was expressed by J. Taylor

(1727, 1750, Figs. 77, 78). Weber (1805, p. 306), in analyzing a case observed by Ackermann, coined the term "partial decussation" instead of a less adequate "semidecussation."

A clearly formulated hypothesis of partial decussation in the chiasma as an anatomical condition of binocular vision and of homonymous hemianopia was given by W. H. Wollaston (1824), famous English chemist and physicist and himself a student of optics and optical phenomena. It was based on an analysis of hemianopic scotomas, from which he himself suffered, and also deduced from the observation of homonymous hemianopia, with which several of his acquaintances were afflicted. (*See also* G. B. Airy; Arago 1824; Testelin; and chap. III, 9 [3].)

5. DISCOVERY OF THE PULVINAR OF THE THALAMUS.—Vicq-d'Azyr (1786–90), Gordon (1815), and Meckel (1817), followed by Burdach (1822), first called attention to the overhanging posterior portion of the thalamus. Vicq-d'Azyr named this prominence *tuberculum posticum*, and Meckel, *tuberculum ganglii postici posterius* or *tuberculum ganglii postici posterius superius*. Burdach gave it the present name *pulvinar thalami optici*, or "cushion" or "cushioned seat" of the thalamus (Burdach 1822, p. 117).

6. DISCOVERY OF THE GENICULATE BODIES OR NUCLEI.—The internal or medial geniculate nucleus seems to have been first described by Willis (1664). Santorini (1724) and Reil (1809) named it *corpus geniculatum* or "geniculate body." By Santorini (1724, 1775), Girardi (*see* Santorini 1775), and Malacarne (1780) it was considered one of the sources of the optic nerve. Soemmerring (1778) called it *tuberculum thalami inferius*.

The external or lateral geniculate nucleus had already been seen by Santorini (1724) and later by Soemmerring (1778), Vicq-d'Azyr (1786–90), Reil (1809, 1812), Cuvier (1809–10), Gall & Spurzheim (1809), Carus (1814), Gordon (1815), Meckel (1817), Treviranus (1816–20), and Burdach (1822). The present name *corpus geniculatum externum*, or "external geniculate body," was given to it, apparently by Burdach, in contradistinction to the *corpus geniculatum*

internum, or "internal geniculate body" (*see* Gall & Spurzheim 1809, p. 264; Burdach 1822, pp. 115, 118, 342). By Santorini, Reil, and Burdach it was considered to be a part of the thalamus.

Burdach found its core to be made up of a reddish-gray nucleus, covered on the outside by a layer of white substance belonging to the zonal stratum of the thalamus. "Sometimes both substances [that is, the gray and the white] interlace, like the tongues of a flame, almost as in the olives [that is, in the inferior olives]." The foregoing phrase definitely indicates that Burdach, for the first time, was describing the alternating layers which are characteristic of the structure of this nucleus, even though he did not recognize them clearly.

According to Burdach, the lateral geniculate connected with the superior colliculus by means of a brachium, inwardly adjoining the medial geniculate nucleus, its zonal stratum receiving one of the "roots" of the optic tract.

Gall & Spurzheim (1809, p. 264) observed both the lateral geniculate nucleus, their *corps articulé externe*, and the superior colliculus of the midbrain undergoing atrophy in a case where the optic nerve was damaged, and they correctly considered them, and not the thalamus proper, the true visual nuclei.

7. SEGREGATION OF THE OPTIC TRACTS FROM THE OPTIC NERVES.—The separation above the chiasma of the central portion of the optic nerve from the peripheral portion below had been made by Vieussens (1684). This was done more precisely by Vicq-d'Azyr (1786–89), who named the central portion *tractus opticus*, which was translated by Meckel and Burdach into the German *Sehstreifen*, or "optic stripe, band, or tract." They considered the optic tract a part of the brain itself, as distinct from the peripheral optic nerve.

8. MORE FACTS ABOUT THE "ORIGIN" OF THE OPTIC NERVES AND THE CHIASMA.—By the end of the first quarter of the nineteenth century, knowledge of the optic nerves and their relationship to the thalamus and adjoining parts of the brain stem reached the limit attainable by refined gross anatomical technique.

According to Burdach (1822, portrait Fig. 90), the fibers of the optic tract may, first, enter the tuber cinereum from the chiasma. Posteriorly the tract divides incompletely into two parts. The thinner medial portion passes underneath the medial geniculate nucleus to the midbrain tegmentum. The thicker outer or lateral portion enters into the lateral geniculate nucleus and into the pulvinar of the thalamus, where, in the superficial white medullary layer, the zonal stratum, it could be followed anteriorly. Other optic nerve fibers probably pass over to other parts of the brain stem—for example, the *substantia nigra* of the cerebral peduncles—and to the region adjacent to the quadrigeminal bodies.

While the precise origin—in the modern sense actually the termination—of the optic nerves was still uncertain, Burdach's analysis of the structure of the chiasma was remarkably clear. In it he found that the lateral or temporal fibers remained on the same side and that the medial or nasal fibers crossed to the opposite side. He further considered the possibility of the presence of commissural fibers, which, he thought, might connect the two optic nerves, or tracts, in the manner of loops (which he called *Hackenfasern*).

The idea of a commissural system was further developed by Johannes Müller (1826, portrait Fig. 355) in substantiation of his doctrine of "identical or conjugate points" of the two retinae in those species which possess binocular vision. At first, he assumed that each fiber divided, in the chiasma, into two branches, each branch passing to the identical or syndynamical point of one of the two retinae. Later on, however, Treviranus (1835, v. 2, p. 61), Volkmann (1836, v. 2, p. 10), Arnold (1839), and Johannes Müller himself (1837, p. xv) recognized a partial decussation in the chiasma, thereby moving the locus of the fusion of the two single retinal images farther into the brain. (*See* chap. III, 9 [3]; chap. VI, 4, 5, 6; and chap. XIII, 3.)

The final question as to whether or not the optic pathway continues beyond the brain stem to the cerebral cortex had not yet been raised. According to Burdach, the *corona radiata*, a fan-shaped system of nerve fibers connecting the various subcortical regions with the cerebral cortex, previously studied by Willis and by Vieussens and named by Reil (1809), had its center in the thalamus, whence it spread in all directions. Only Gall & Spurzheim (1810) hinted at the presence of a separate bundle or fiber tract from the lateral geniculate nucleus to the occipital lobe. The sagittal strata of the occipital lobe, the longitudinal and arcuate bundles, the forceps of the corpus callosum, and other fiber systems, through Burdach's studies, however, became recognized as definite anatomical entities. This marked the beginning of investigations of the fiber systems that make up the white subcortical mass of the cerebral hemispheres (*see* chap. III, 5 [2, 3]).

References: G. B. Airy 1865; Aquapendens 1600; Arago 1824; Aranzi (Arantius) 1595; Arnold 1839 (1838–42); Bauhin 1621; Besse 1701–2; Blasius 1673; Burdach 1819–22–26; Caldani (Caldanius) 1791; Carus 1814; Cheselden 1792; Collins 1685; R. Colombo (Columbus) 1559; Cuvier 1809–10; Diemerbroeck 1683; Gall 1825; Gall & Spurzheim 1809, 1810–19; F. Gennari 1782; Girardi (*see* Santorini 1775); J. Gordon 1815; A. Haller 1769, 1774–76; Hering 1868, 1931; J. Hirschberg 1911; Lieutaud 1742; Lancisi 1739; Lebensohn 1941; Malacarne 1780; J. Ch. A. Mayer 1779; Meckel 1815–20; Monro 1783, 1797; Morgagni 1719; Joh. Müller 1826, 1837; Reil 1809, 1812; Riolan 1618; Rudolphi 1802; Sabatier 1798; Santorini 1724, 1775; S. Th. Soemmerring 1778; S. A. W. Stein 1834; Stieda 1899; J. Taylor 1724, 1750; Testelin 1866; Treviranus 1816–20, 1835; Valverda 1589; Varoli (Varolius) 1573, 1591; Vater & Heinicke 1723; Vesling 1696; Vicq-d'Azyr 1786–90, 1805; Vieussens 1684, 1685; A. F. Volkmann 1836, 1846, 1856; D. Weber 1805; J. Wenzel & K. Wenzel 1812; Willis 1664, 1682; J. B. Winslow 1733; W. H. Wollaston 1824; J. G. Zinn 1755.

Chapter III

Investigation of the Visual Pathways and Centers during the Early Period of Modern Brain Research

SEC. 1. ANATOMY AND PHYSIOLOGY OF THE CEREBRAL CORTEX DURING THE SEVENTEENTH AND EIGHTEENTH CENTURIES

1. LATE START IN THE INVESTIGATION OF THE CEREBRAL CORTEX AND ITS CAUSES.—It is a remarkable fact that during the first three hundred years of independent research in modern anatomy, from its revival by Vesalius (1543) until approximately the middle of the nineteenth century, only sporadic attempts were made to investigate the minute structure of the great cerebral hemispheres and to determine their probable function. This was especially true of the cerebral cortex and its connections with the rest of the nervous system. It almost seems as if there had been a tacit agreement among the scientists not to intrude into the sacred precinct of human anatomy—the repository of the soul, the seat of the reasoning mind. The few who considered the cortex a possible substratum of the psychic faculties and mental functions—the Swedish mystic E. Swedenborg (1738), the anatomists Francis Joseph Gall (1809–25) and Charles Bell (1811)—were long disregarded.

It may be argued that there were notable exceptions, for example, the microscopic investigations of Malpighi (1664), Leeuwenhoek (1674, 1677, 1685), Vieussens (1684), Ruysch (1691) and a few others (*see* sec. 5, this chapter). While this is true, it is also true that the efforts of early microscopists were, of necessity, aimed at the solution of general histological problems of the nervous system—for example, whether the primitive elements which make up the white and the gray substance of the brain are "fibers," "globules," or blood vessels or whether they are a pithy, structureless substance called "pulp." The investigation of specific architectural problems—for example, the kind and distribution of the nerve cells and fibers, their patterns of arrangement, relationships, and connections, and the local variations of cortical structure in general—had to wait for greater understanding of the basic problems of bodily organization, as well as for better technique.

2. BELIEFS OF THE OLD ANATOMISTS CONCERNING THE FUNCTIONAL SIGNIFICANCE OF THE CEREBRAL CORTEX.—The almost total disregard by the pioneer microscopists of the minute structure of the cerebral cortex, which in Man represents the bulk of the gray matter of the central nervous system, which Swedenborg intuitively regarded as "the noblest substance of the brain," is not astonishing in view of the strange ideas current among them about its functional significance. Some of them (Malpighi, Vieussens, Bidloo, Le Cat, and Lamarck) considered it to be an excretory glandular tissue, reverting in this respect to the concept advocated by Aristotle two thousand years earlier. A similarly irrational view was expressed by no less an authority than the French Academy of Sciences, headed by the famous naturalist Cuvier (1808), in its dispute with Gall (1808). Ruysch also saw in the cortex nothing but a mesh of blood vessels. What probably was the lowest point in misconception of the cortex was reached when Bichat, "Pioneer of Scientific Histology" (1801–3), declared the nerve fibers in the brain to be hypothetical and artifacts. Burdach (1819) and Ehrenberg (1833, 1836), in turn, thought that the nerve fibers were made up of globules arranged in rows, even though Burdach noticed that the filaments appeared almost cylindrical when quite fresh and that the globular appearance increased with the lapse of time.

Such notions, entertained by the foremost authorities of the time, were not of the kind to stimulate profound interest in the cerebral hemispheres, particularly in the cortex. Nor was the understanding of the cellular composition of the body advanced enough to provide a basis for further research. The cellular theory of Schwann (1838), Schleiden (1839), and Max Schultze (1861) had as yet not been formulated.

3. THE IDEA OF A HOMOGENEOUS, INDIVISIBLE "SOUL" A DETERRENT TO THE INVESTIGATION OF THE CORTEX.—The most important factor which prevented early investigation of the cerebral cortex seems to have been ideological and speculative. It was the idea of the unity and homogeneity of the *anima*, or transcendental "soul," and its identity with the two complementary principles, the *vis vitalis*, or "vital force," and the *mens*, or abstract "mind."

This concept, absolutely dominant at that time, accepted equally by philosophers and scientists, gave no incentive to anatomists and physiologists to look for some particular mechanism responsible for the well-defined nervous and psychic functions. Just as, in the macrocosm, the idea of creation of the World and Life by a supernatural power was unsuitable for stimulating any investigation into the origin and development of animate and inanimate Nature, so in the problem of Man's microcosm rational understanding was precluded by the concepts inherited from the irrational, mystical past. Since the "soul," albeit manifesting itself in various ways, was conceived as a single, homogeneous, and indivisible principle—the *anima* or *mens integra*—the only legitimate question to be dealt with by the investigators and philosophers was: In what part of the cerebrum does the integral, transcendental "soul" reside or stand in contact with, or by what means does it act upon, the bodily machine; or is it, perhaps, diffused over the entire brain or body—as various religious and philosophical systems postulated.

4. SPECULATIONS CONCERNING THE RELATION OF THE "SOUL" TO THE BRAIN.—In contrast to the scarcity of concrete information about the structure of the brain was the profusion of speculation on the relationship between the brain and the transcendental "soul" or "mind" (*see* Neuburger 1897; Révész 1917; Corner 1919). That there was some relationship was taken for granted upon purely speculative, "logical" grounds. In emulation of the Greek philosophers and naturalists, one or another of the numerous anatomical subdivisions of the cerebrum was claimed as the special "seat of the soul." Des Cartes considered the pineal gland lodged between the colliculi of the midbrain to be a link tying the soul to the body (*see* chap. II, 10 [2]; *cf.* Figs. 70, 71). Other investigators gave preference to other parts of the cerebral anatomy: to the corpus striatum and cerebellum (Willis), the corpus callosum (Bontekoe, Lancisi, La Peyronie, Chopart, Bonnet), the oval center (Vieussens), the pons (Molinetti, Haller, Wrisberg), the spinal cord (Crusius, Mieg), or the cerebellum (Drelincourt). Still others, on the contrary, averse to such crass materialism, believed the entire cerebrum (Haller, Zinn) or the entire bodily organism (R. Whytt) to be the habitat of the soul. (For the views of the Hindus, Greeks, Romans, and Hebrews on the material substratum of the "soul," *see* Neuburger 1897; Brunet & Mieli 1936, p. 1149; and Révész 1917.)

5. SPECULATIVE PSYCHOLOGY AND EARLY ATTEMPTS AT A FUNCTIONAL CEREBRAL LOCALIZATION.—The analysis or subdivision of the mental process into elemental components, when undertaken at all in these early attempts at a psychophysical correlation, was carried out along the lines of the "speculative rational psychology" of the time. The partial functions assigned to certain territories of the brain were more or less highly complex psychological abstractions, such as "memory," "imagination," "judgment," "reasoning," "religion," "knowledge," and the like. J. Ch. A. Mayer (1779), one of the pioneer writers on functional cerebral localization, trying to place various faculties in particular regions of the brain, conjectured that "memory" was stored in the cortex and "imagination" and "judgment" in the subcortical white matter, although both these substances, he thought, also collaborated in the perceptive and cogitative processes (*see* sec. 3 [1], this chapter). "Apperception" and "will power," in his opinion, had their abode in the basal region of the cerebrum and close to the central termination of the nerves, while the role of the *corpus callosum* and of the *vermis* of the *cerebellum* was to integrate the impressions with the various particular functions.

6. LAST MANIFESTATION OF THE ANCIENT GREEK IDEA OF "PNEUMA" AS A PSYCHIC SUBSTRATUM.—As an example of the profundity of ignorance, the confusion of the principal issues, and the sophistry of the pseudo-scientific argumentation of that period in matters of cerebral physiology, S. Th. Soemmerring, one of the foremost authorities of his time, may be mentioned (portrait Fig. 37). As late as 1796 he proclaimed the cerebrospinal fluid that fills the ventricles of the brain to be a substratum of the "soul." His evidence in support of this fantasmagoria—the last manifestation of the Greek concept of *pneuma* or "spirit"— was the unity of the system of ventricular cavities and the apparent origin of the cranial nerves from these cavities. The underlying idea was that only a homogeneous substance, bringing into a common connection the origins of all cranial nerves, could possibly be a material substratum of the indivisible, homogeneous, transcendental "soul." (For a modified version of Soemmerring's hypothesis by Immanuel Kant, *see* Soemmerring's *Ueber das Organ der Seele*, p. 81; for Rolando's "galvanic or nervous fluid," *see* sec. 4 [1], this chapter; for similar ideas of Galen, expressed sixteen centuries earlier, *see* chap. II, 3, 5; *see also* Gall & Spurzheim 1810–19, v. 2, p. 214; Burdach, v. 2, p. 225; on Du Laurens, *see* chap. II, 9; on Des Cartes, *see* chap. II, 10.)

References: C. Bartholin 1645; Bichat 1801–3; Bidloo 1685; Bonnet 1775; Brunet & Mieli 1935; Burdach 1819–22–26; C. G. Carus 1814; Corner 1919; De la Peyronie 1709, 1741; Des Cartes (Cartesius) 1662, 1677; Ehrenberg 1833, 1834, 1836; A. Haller 1769, 1774–76; J. Ch. A. Mayer 1779; Immanuel Kant (*see* Soemmerring 1796); Lancisi 1739; F. A. Lange 1908; Le Cat 1740 (1744), 1767; Leeuwenhoek; Malpighi (*see also* A. W. Meyer 1930); Molinetti; Mott 1922; Neuburger 1897; Révész 1917; Ruysch; S. Th. Soemmerring 1796; Soury 1899; F. Tiedemann 1823; Vesalius 1543; Vieussens 1685; R. Whytt 1751; Willis 1664; Th. Ziehen 1902; Zinn 1755.

SEC. 2. THE DAWN OF MODERN BRAIN PHYSIOLOGY

1. PROBLEMS OF CEREBRAL PHYSIOLOGY AS FORMULATED BY A. HALLER.—Until the eighteenth century, interest in the visual pathway was almost wholly confined to the infranuclear division, from the eye to the "origin of the optic nerves," as pointed out in the preceding pages (chap. II, 11, 12). With the general advancement of the anatomy and physiology of the brain, this interest began to spread to the cerebral cortex. The chief reason seems to have been an increasing emphasis upon experimental physiology, as well as pathology. The rigid, preponderantly descriptive, anatomical treatment of the somatic sciences and the speculative "physiology" built upon them began to recede from their heretofore dominant position to a more proper place (*see* Neuburger). This advancement was due in no small measure to the great stimulus that the study of physiology received at that time, largely through the encyclopedic efforts of Albrecht von Haller (1769, portrait Fig. 80).

The questions about cerebral organization raised by Haller concerned the very foundations of the nervous system. The controversies which developed in the wake of his work stirred the minds of succeeding generations, and even now they are far from being allayed. These questions may be put into a single phrase: Is the brain an aggregation of many foci, each with a function of its own, or is this organ a common repository, wherein the impulses arriving from different peripheral sensory organs are transformed into a new composite, but homogeneous, process? (*See* A. Haller, *Elem. Physiol. Corp. Hum.*, 1769, v. 4, p. 396, par. XXVI, "An Diversae Diversarum Animae Functionum Provinciae"; for biography *see* Hübotter 1929–35.)

2. EVIDENCE FOR AND AGAINST FUNCTIONAL CEREBRAL LOCALIZATION.—Haller, to begin with, could not deny the obvious anatomical fact that the optic, olfactory, acoustic, and other cranial nerves have their apparent "origin" in distinct parts of the brain. An a priori assumption could, therefore, be made that each of the various tubercles and eminences described in the brain by the anatomists was a storage place for particular "images," "shapes," "impressions," "sensations," or their vestiges, brought to them by a particular nerve—for example, the "optic thalami" for the visual "im-

cerebral cortex and the subjacent white substance), as suggested by numerous clinical and pathological-anatomical observations, certain regions may be concerned with one or another of several sensory functions, while still others may be related to motility. (Pourfour du Petit's experiments with dogs indicated the presence of such a motor center.) Also, by that time, a number of clinical observations of blindness be-

Fig. 80.—Albrecht Haller (Albrecht von Haller, 1708–77), a native of Switzerland and a noted poet and philosopher, professor of anatomy and botany in Göttingen, in Prussian Brunswick, Germany. Founder of modern physiology and leading authority of his time in this field. Protagonist of a unitarian concept of the nervous system, according to which the entire brain, including the cerebellum and spinal cord, were homogeneously organized and functioned in the same way in all parts. Author of *Elementa Physiologiae Corporis Humani* (1757–66), the first comprehensive modern treatise on physiology. Courtesy of Professor R. N. Wegner, University of Greifswald, Germany. According to a painting by Sigmund Freudenberger (1773, with addition of the order painted 1776), now in possession of Mr. Albert de Haller, of Lausanne, Switzerland. For other portraits *see* Arthur Weese, *Die Bildnisse Albrecht von Hallers*, Bern, 1909. *Cf.* J. Hirschberg, in Graefe & Saemisch, *Handb. d. ges. Augenh.*, 2d ed., v. 14, 1911.

ages." The region of the pons or "bridge" of Varolius and the *medulla oblongata*, where several nerves originate, would, accordingly, be the seat of a complex mechanism incorporating many motor and sensory functions. In the brain itself (evidently Haller here had in mind the

came known, in which the pituitary gland or hypophysis, the pineal gland or epiphysis, or the optic nerve had been affected by a pathological process or in which the skull or the brain, meaning mainly the cerebral hemispheres, had suffered injury or the "optic thalamus" had been compressed. Of particular interest was a case of temporary blindness occurring after injury to one side of the head; and another case of blindness of long duration, which later cleared up, caused by an injury to the top of the head in the region of *bregma;* and, finally, a case of permanent blindness occurring after injury to the occiput.

Against this evidence, which pointed in the direction of functional localization, there were observations of other cases in which a single lesion had caused an impairment of several faculties. In one such case a tumor of the pineal gland was accompanied by headache, blindness, and deafness. These observations seemed to show that any major cerebral lesion may be followed by an impairment of several faculties.

3. HALLER'S VERDICT AGAINST FUNCTIONAL CEREBRAL LOCALIZATION.—After considering various clinical cases and other evidence known to him, Haller decided against the localization of special faculties in particular localities of the brain (for example, of vision in the region of the "origin" of the optic nerve or of hearing in the locality whence the acoustic nerve arises, and so forth). No nerve, he contended, has its own exclusive and limited territory in the brain stem or in the spinal cord, whence it emerges. Nor would it be proper, he thought, to express an opinion as to the purpose and the use of certain tubercles, for example, of the superior or inferior colliculi, of the midbrain, pons, striate bodies, cerebral hemispheres, or cerebellum, or to assign to any one of them a function which would differ from that of the brain as a whole. Haller declared the eminences and sulci of the brain to be the products of mechanical factors, such as pressure from the near-by pulsating arteries, or possibly to be caused by the weight of neighboring parts, and not an expression of specific functions.

According to Haller's definition of brain function, the concept of "equivalence" or "omnivalence" of all parts of the nervous centers reached an extreme. The entire brain, including the brain stem, cerebellum, and spinal cord, was to be regarded as a single great repository, into which various peripheral impulses pour and, as he seems to have implied, produce in it an entirely new psychophysical status identical with, or at any rate related to, and indispen-

sable for, the action of the transcendental, indivisible "soul."

4. REASONS FOR HALLER'S FAVORING FUNCTIONAL CEREBRAL OMNIVALENCE.—The failure of such a mind as Haller's to adopt a more adequate view of cerebral organization is remarkable! He did not deny the too obvious anatomical diversity of the nervous organ but, instead, satisfied himself with a naïve mechanistic explanation. He recognized the peripheral nerves as independent conductors. Following Galen, Willis, and Whytt, he also admitted that the nerve fibers and fiber bundles which compose various nerve trunks retain their individuality all the way from their apparent central origin to their termination in the peripheral organs—all of which shows that he was well aware of the functional importance of such an arrangement. Haller admitted the validity of the principle of "localization" or the "somatotopic" principle in the peripheral nerves, the function of the individual fibers being, in modern parlance, to transmit specific impulses without interference and independently from those transmitted by all other filaments. But he failed to make the next logical step and admit the validity of the same rule in the central nervous organ. To him, apparently, this was too crude, too mechanistic, to be acceptable as an architectural pattern for the substratum of the "soul" or "mind."

After toying with the idea of "localization of cerebral functions," Haller performed a logical somersault by rejecting it, and seized upon the broad and comfortable theory of integral cerebral "equipotentialism"! The responsibility for this seems to lie not only with the insufficient scientific evidence at his disposal but even more with various nonscientific factors and considerations. Plainly, supernaturalism and transcendentalism, even among the scientists of that period, were still too strong to permit an unbiased study of the brain with the same scientific approach as that used for the investigation of less sacred parts of human anatomy.

References: Burdach 1819–22–26; A. Haller 1769, 1774–76; F. A. Lange 1908; Neuburger 1897; Puschmann *et al.* 1902–5; Révész 1917; Soury 1899; J. A. Unzer 1746, 1768, 1771; Willis 1664, 1682.

SEC. 3. THE PLURALITY DOCTRINE OF THE FUNCTIONAL ORGANIZATION OF THE BRAIN

1. EARLY SPECULATIONS ON FUNCTIONAL LO-CALIZATION IN THE BRAIN.—The idea of localization of distinct functions in particular regions of the brain is quite ancient. According to Burdach (1826, p. 270), Galen suggested three basic forces or properties as making up the "soul," for which his successors assumed three chambers in the brain, which they called *cellulae, specus, sinus* or *cavernae.* The anterior chamber served as a repository of "perception" (φαντασία, *phantasia, anima imaginativa, sensus communis*), the middle chamber for the faculty of thinking (λόγος, διάνοια, νόος, νοῦς, φρόνησις, *anima cogitativa*), and the posterior for memory (μνήμη, *anima memorativa*).

This concept, which was probably taken over by Galen from the older Greek philosophers, was accepted by the early Christian writers, Nemesius (4th century), St. Augustin (354–430), and others (*see* W. Sudhoff 1914). Subsequently it was entertained by Albertus Magnus (1206–80), Roger Bacon (1214–94), Hieronymo Manfredi (1430–93), and many other writers of the late Middle Ages and is well demonstrated in Figure 81. During the early period of modern anatomy and even for many years thereafter, numerous writers accepted it. Chanet (1649) considered the frontal portion of the brain to be the seat of imagination, made up of many small organs. Willis (1664), Molinetti (1669, 1675), and Bonnet (1759) also regarded the brain as a composite organ whose parts have different functions. Vieussens (1684) believed that the "animal spirit" from certain cerebral regions entered particular nerves.

The efforts of French brain surgeons and experimenters of the eighteenth century were of special importance in the development of the idea of diverse functions of different parts of the brain (*see* Neuburger 1897; Soury 1899). Among these, Lorry (1760), with the discovery of a respiratory center in the medulla oblongata, demonstrated for the first time the dependence of an important somatic function upon a definite locality of the brain. Saucerotte (1768) deduced from his experiments with dogs that the forelimbs and hind limbs had separate motor centers in the brain. Finally, Sabouraut (quoted

by Soury 1899) postulated connections from every part of the body to a particular locality in the brain.

Dissatisfied with the dominant doctrine, which insisted that "the whole brain was a common sensorium" and that only "the extremities of the nerves were fitted to receive a peculiar impression; or that they were distinguished from each other only by delicacy of their structure, and by a corresponding delicacy of sensation"—and not at all by their diverse central connections and functional peculiarities—Charles Bell (1811), in England, and Magendie (1822–23), in France, initiated researches which led them to the discovery of the motor function of the anterior roots, and the sensory function of the posterior roots, of the spinal cord.

The following quotations from Charles Bell's writings show his opposition to the prevalent omnipotentialism: ". . . while the organ of sense is provided with a capacity of receiving certain changes to be played upon it, as it were, yet each utterly is incapable of receiving the impressions destined for another organ of sensation"; and ". . . properties of the nerves are derived from their connections with the parts of the brain . . . "; ". . . portions of the brain are distinct organs of different functions"; and "Through the nerves of sense, the sensorium receives impressions, but the will is expressed through the medium of the nerves of motion."

Such convictions, supported by experimental evidence, for a while helped save from oblivion the idea of functional cerebral localization, in spite of the great weight of adverse opinion resting upon such authority as Haller (1769) and J. G. von Herder (1784–91), a noted German philosopher and writer. Another exception in favor of cerebral functional localization was a pamphlet of J. Ch. A. Mayer (1779), an obscure Prussian writer.

2. GALL'S EVIDENCE IN FAVOR OF THE FUNCTIONAL DIVERSITY OF THE CEREBRUM.—The first systematic effort to give the idea of functional cerebral localization a scientific foundation and to bring it to the attention of the scientific world, was made by Francis Joseph Gall (partly in company with Spurzheim, 1809, p. 288; 1810–19; 1825; portrait Figs. 83, 84).

Gall proclaimed an anatomical and functional diversity of the central organ, which was contrary to the idea of structural uniformity or homogeneity of the brain and oneness of cerebral processes generally accepted at the time. The brain, in his opinion, was composed of a number of particular systems differing from one another both in structure and in function. The cranial nerves—the olfactory, optic, oculomotor, and so forth—not only were related to different peripheral sensory and motor organs but also originated from different nuclei, and in other respects differed among themselves. Functional difference was the result not only of different peripheral connections but also of discrete central relationships. The brain was a composite

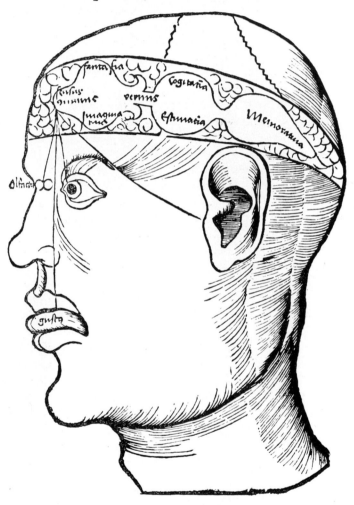

FIG. 81.—Medieval concept of the brain mechanisms serving higher or mental functions, according to a diagram from G. Reisch, *Margarita Philosophica*, printed in 1513. The brain was supposed, according to this, to contain three interconnected cavities or cells, each serving as a repository of a particular mental faculty. The frontal cell, a repository of common sense, fantasy, and imagination, alone would receive direct messages from the peripheral organs of sight, hearing, smell, and taste. The middle cell was the place of the thinking process and judgment, while the most posterior cell served the memory. The figure is one of the earliest Western pictorial presentations of the idea of localization of distinct faculties in definite localities of the brain, in which, according to the words of Hieronymo Manfredi (1490), "the soul performs its diverse operations, for which reason it is necessary that these parts be of different structure." From K. Sudhoff, Augenanatomiebilder, in Stud. z. Gesch. d. Med., Fasc. 1, 1907. (*Cf.* Fig. 62.)

organ made up of many systems, each with its own distinct function. The dispositions and properties of Man and animals were innate and were predetermined by organization.

3. Gall's system of intellectual and moral faculties and their localization.— The various "intellectual and moral faculties" bility, courage, cleverness, property sense, pride, ruling instinct, ambition, vanity, circumspection, memory, educability, perfectibility, orientation in space or local sense, visual memory, auditory speech memory, philological talent, color sense, auditory tone sense, mathematical talent, temporal sense, mechanical and artistic talent, intellect, metaphysical sense,

PETRUS CAMPER.

Fig. 82.—Pieter Camper (1722–89), Dutch anatomist whose ideas influenced F. J. Gall, originator of "cerebral organology" (*see* Figs. 83, 84). A frontispiece in Camper's *Discours, . . . sur le moyen de représenter d'une manière sûre les diverses passions qui se manifestent sur le visage*, Utrecht, 1792.

and traits of personal character, according to Gall, were stored in definite regions of the cerebrum and were not different manifestations of a single, uniformly organized substratum. Such faculties, according to Gall's classification, were: the instinct of procreation, love, socia- humor, causality, poetic talent, morality, compassion, honesty, conscience, goodness, avarice, irritability, religiosity, reason, and will power.

The more pronounced a trait was, the better developed was the corresponding cerebral territory. Outwardly this was manifested by the prominences on the cranium (several decades later Panizza believed he had demonstrated this in experiments with animals). Turning his argument the other way, Gall claimed it was possible to determine what faculty, trait, or feature of the character was particularly developed in a given person from the prominences of the cranium. He also believed that a mental or

the "vital" somatosensory and motor functions were thought of as being regulated by the brain stem and cerebellum (*see* Neuburger 1897).

Gall's "doctrine of the plurality of cerebral organs" in contrast to the unitarian concept, with its practical corollary, "craniognomy," a branch of "physiognomy," subsequently (especially under Spurzheim's influence) degener-

FIG. 83.—Franz Joseph Gall (1758–1828), brain anatomist and founder of the doctrine of functional cerebral localization. From G. Elliot Smith, *Essays on the Evolution of Man*, Oxford University Press, London, 1927. Courtesy Mrs. Grafton Elliot Smith. (*See* following figure.)

moral faculty, since it is localized, could be impaired or lost by damage to a particular locality of the brain.

It is remarkable that, in the system devised by Gall, only a few of the faculties he listed correspond to the simple sensory or motor functions as conceived at the present time. This, without doubt, was because at that time the forebrain was universally accepted as the exclusive seat of the "psychic functions," whereas

ated into "phrenology," which lacked any factual foundation and is still a pseudo-science with some following among the unenlightened (*see* Macalister & X). On the other hand, Gall's basic idea, favorably looked upon by such a reserved anatomist and thinker as Burdach, was intriguing enough to stimulate numerous investigators to test it by scientific methods. From then on, the idea of the localization of distinct functions in special regions of the cerebral cortex or the concept of the brain as a composite organ made up of a number of territories with locally varying structure and function did not fail to influence neurological research, in spite of the determined opposition it met and the disrepute in which it was held by many. (*See* sec. 6, this chapter.)

References: Ch. Bell 1811; Boring 1950; Burdach 1819–22–26; Camper 1792; Castiglioni 1947; Corner 1919; Froriep 1911; Gall 1810–19, 1825; Gall & Spurzheim 1809; H. Head 1920; B. Hollander 1899, 1928; F. A. Lange 1908; Liepmann 1909; Macalister & X; Magendie 1822–23; J. Ch. A. Mayer 1779; Möbius 1905; Neuburger 1897; La Peyronie 1741–44; Puschmann *et al.*; Révész 1917; G. Elliot Smith 1923, 1927; J. Soury 1899; Spurzheim 1833; W. Sudhoff 1914; J. A. Schwegler 1855; Th. Ziehen 1902.

SEC. 4. DOCTRINE OF FUNCTIONAL OMNIVALENCE OF THE CEREBRAL CORTEX

1. EARLY PHYSIOLOGICAL EXPERIMENTS AND THE PROBLEM OF THE FUNCTIONAL ORGANIZATION OF THE BRAIN.—The physiological experiments carried out during the eighteenth century by Pourfour du Petit, Haller, Zinn, Lorry, Fontana, and others, to determine the function of the brain, were continued with even greater zeal during the early part of the nineteenth century (*see* Neuburger 1897; Soury 1899). But the results of this early period of modern experimental physiology, in respect to the visual and other sensory and motor functions, were inconclusive. Pourfour du Petit (1710), experimenting upon dogs, observed contralateral paralysis when the corpus striatum was damaged, but only paresis or weakness if the lesion was limited to the cortex; vision, he thought, was impaired in the eye contralateral to the lesion. Lorry (1760), the discoverer of the respiratory center in the medulla oblongata, found that manipulations upon the brain did not elicit any reaction such as motion or sensation (for example, pain). Rolando (1809, 1828), in his numerous experiments upon the brains of various Mammals and other Vertebrates, either did not observe or ignored disturbance of vision, even when the thalamus and midbrain colliculi had been destroyed. His interest was wholly absorbed by the effects of his experiments on motor function. For him, as for many others among his contemporaries, the thalami were still the only visual centers. Rolando, opposing Gall's "doctrine of cranioscopy," as he called it, denied that the cortex of the cerebrum and cerebellum were composite structures or aggregations of organs with specific functions, as Gall contended, and considered these parts to be uniform, homogeneous masses. He was con-

firmed in this opinion by his observation of general convulsions which resulted from an application of galvanic current to the surface of the brain. The cortex, in Rolando's opinion, was the origin of an "electric or galvanic fluid," a kind of "nervous fluid," which was but a modern restatement of Galen's "vital or animal spirit" or *pneuma*. (*Cf.* chap. II, 3.)

2. FLOURENS' EXPERIMENTS ON THE BRAIN.—Of far greater significance to cerebral physiology were the experiments of P. J. M. Flourens (1824; portrait Fig. 85; for biography *see* Vulpian 1887). In these, because of their scope and completeness and because of Flourens' clear grasp of the essentials, the fundamental problem of cerebral organization seemed finally to have been solved. This problem—whether or not the various parts of the cerebrum that differed structurally had separate functions—raised by Haller and others, especially after Gall's advocacy of the "plurality doctrine," again became acute (*cf.* secs. 2 and 3, this chapter). The negative answer that the cortex itself is not the seat of diverse functions which Flourens gave, expected and desired by most of the contemporary investigators, received almost universal acclaim.

A reward, the coveted membership in the French Académie des Sciences, was also bestowed upon Flourens, a mere youngster, in 1822, at a session presided over by Cuvier. This august body but fourteen years earlier, under Cuvier's influence, refused admission to a great man, Francis Joseph Gall, on the grounds that the cortex of the brain has nothing to do with the processes of thinking!

As a consequence, Flourens' concept of the

organization of the brain exerted a powerful influence upon the scientific and philosophical thinking of his time. It was the period following the French Revolution and its aftermath, Napoleon's ascent to power and his downfall. The heirs both to the French Revolution and to Napoleon, after an exhausting struggle and bent on reinstating the principles of conservatism, were ill disposed toward any tampering with the approved foundations of established order, least of all to a dismemberment of the supernatural, homogeneous soul.

3. Concrete results of Flourens' physiological experiments.—Flourens introduced

a more adequate experimental technique than used by his predecessors. Instead of the crude, haphazard destruction practiced before, in which chance was the chief factor and where an effect upon the entire content of the cranial cavity was hard to avoid, he used a method of successive, careful ablations of circumscribed parts of the brain, with no damage to the others. Such a procedure could not fail to yield remarkable results. These, in summary, were: The two chief functions of the nervous system, sensation and motion, were distinctly localized. Only the peripheral nerves, spinal cord, medulla oblongata, and midbrain, when stimulated, produced immediate muscular contractions.

Fig. 84.—Franz Joseph Gall (1758–1828), originator of the "cerebral organology," in advanced age. Foremost student of the cerebral anatomy and physiology of his time. Proclaimed the cortex of the brain to be the seat of the psychic processes. Championed the idea of unequal structural organization and locally varying function of different parts of the brain, in opposition to the concept of functional equivalence of the entire brain defended by A. Haller (Fig. 80). Originator of the concept of localization of mental and moral faculties and traits in discrete parts of the brain, which, on the one hand, subsequently developed into modern teaching of cerebral functional localization and, on the other hand, degenerated into popular "phrenology." First indicated the seat of the faculty of speech to be in the frontal lobes, a suggestion further substantiated by Bouillaud (Fig. 94) and especially by Broca (Fig. 95). From a portrait by Félix Jean Marius Belliard, lithographed by F.-S. Delpech of Paris. For biography *see* Deutsch. med. Wchnschr., v. 35, p. 960, 1909; H. Head 1920; G. Elliot Smith 1923; P. J. A. Möbius 1905; B. Hollander 1928; and A. Froriep 1911. (*See* preceding figure.)

The cerebellum was an organ of co-ordination of movements initiated by the other parts. The cerebral hemispheres were the seat of the will. There were, accordingly, three principal nervous functions: (1) the will or perception, which is sensitivity; (2) the excitability which produces muscular contractions; and (3) the co-ordination of movements. The intellectual faculties, the "will," and the sensory performances or "perception" were localized in the cerebral hemispheres (i.e., cortex). In this way the functional subdivision of the central nervous system along anatomical lines into a forebrain, brain stem, cerebellum, and spinal cord was substantiated by experiment.

By distinguishing several functions and by localizing them in different parts of the central nervous organ, Flourens became one of the founders of the modern concept of functional cerebral localization. This appears substantially

Fɪɢ. 85.—Marie Jean Pierre Flourens (1794–1867), professor of comparative anatomy in Paris. Initiator of modern experimental brain physiology. Champion of the doctrine of functional equivalence or homogeneity of the entire cerebral cortex, as distinct from Haller's homogeneous organization of the entire cerebrospinal system and from Gall's concept of cerebral diversity. From an engraving by Aug. Lemoine. Courtesy Crerar Library, Dr. Sonnenschein Collection, Chicago.

correct, even though he himself insisted upon the view that, owing to the multiple interconnections and the functional interdependence of its constituent parts, the brain represents but one single complex, or *un système unique*.

4. RESTRICTION OF THE "OMNIVALENCE DOCTRINE" TO THE CEREBRAL CORTEX BY FLOURENS.—In consequence of Flourens' experiments, Haller's concept of the functional omnivalence or equivalence of the entire central nervous system had to be recognized as an error. "The nervous system," in Flourens' words (1842, p. 56), "is not a homogeneous system. The function of the cerebral lobes is not the same as that of the cerebellum, nor of the cerebellum as that of the spinal cord, nor the latter's in any way like that of the nerves." The cerebral cortex, however, was a notable exception. Here, Flourens insisted, the principle of functional equivalence was valid: "The cerebral lobes are the exclusive seat of all sensations and intellectual faculties" (p. 97). Through his experiments he became convinced that the cerebral and cerebellar cortex—since seemingly unexcitable to direct stimulation—served exclusively higher sensory functions of sight, hearing, instinct, and probably intellectual faculties also. These functions, however, did not, in his opinion, depend upon distinct localities of the cortex. They were, in fact, all manifestations of one single basic function distributed over the whole cortex.

In support of his thesis Flourens brought up his observation that a limited portion of the cortex may be removed without appreciable impairment of any or all of the several sensory functions. Nor did it matter which portion of the cortex was destroyed. The only factor of importance was the quantity or amount of substance eliminated. Beyond a certain minimum of destruction, all faculties became impaired, and, after complete destruction, all were equally lost. From this experience Flourens concluded that the various sensory functions were not separately stored in particular regions but were uniformly represented in the entire cerebral cortex. The lost faculties might be recovered through a vicarious function of parts remaining normal, provided that the damage was not too extensive. The entire cortex, according

to Flourens, functioned as a single, uniformly organized mass in which each part could substitute for any other part.

The only exception was sight, which in the case of unilateral destruction of the cortex was permanently lost in the contralateral eye. Flourens never recognized the hemianopic character of centrally caused visual disturbances, working as he did upon lower Vertebrates (Pigeons and Chickens), in which the optic nerves are completely or nearly decussated. (*Cf.* chap. VI, 5 [3].)

5. DOCTRINE OF CORTICAL OMNIVALENCE AND THE DOGMA OF THE UNITY OF "SOUL" OR "MIND."—In the "doctrine of cortical equivalence or omnivalence" proclaimed by Flourens, the concept of the unity of "soul" or "mind," adhered to by the majority of anatomists, physiologists, and philosophers of the preceding periods, not only was fully preserved but seemed to have been experimentally substantiated. Its strong point, besides apparent solid experimental evidence, was its reasonableness when compared with the preceding attempts to confine the "soul" or "mind" to a particular, minute organ, such as the pineal gland, as, for example, Des Cartes did (*see* chap. II, 10 [2]).

According to Flourens' version, the Ancient Greek *hegemonikón*, or "dominant soul," was neither distributed over the whole organism nor restricted to a minute fraction of the bodily machine but was stored in the large mass of gray substance covering the cerebral hemispheres, the cortex. Within that relatively large container, however, the "intelligence" was nowhere tied to a particular, small locality to the exclusion of the remainder. (*Cf.* sec. 1 [4], this chapter.)

In practice, the difference between Flourens' and Haller's teachings was small. On the one hand, the cortex was anatomically and functionally connected to other subdivisions of the brain and spinal cord. On the other, the spirit of the time was attuned almost exclusively to the idea of unity of the entire central nervous system, to the disadvantage of any moderating qualification.

6. FLOURENS' DISCOVERY OF THE DEPENDENCE OF VISION ON THE CEREBRAL CORTEX.—

The most important discovery of Flourens concerning the visual function was its dependence, chiefly or entirely, upon the cortex of the cerebral hemispheres and not exclusively upon the subcortical regions such as the thalamus or midbrain, as previously believed (Rolando). This was an important discovery, sufficient to correct the then dominant view of the forebrain as an exclusively "psychic organ" with no direct relation to the senses and motility (according to Du Laurens, the brain "neither sees, nor hears, nor feels"; *see* chap. II, 9 [3]). For reasons of doctrinaire prejudice, however, Flourens' declaration of a functional, and presumably also structural, uniformity, homogeneity, or omnivalence of the entire cortex made a more profound impression. It was a thesis agreeable to the majority. It was fascinating and yet controversial enough to furnish a subject for argument for the next fifty years.

The almost universal acclaim with which Flourens' experiments were received may also explain the absence of objections that could justly have been made to both his procedure and his interpretation. His experiments had, for the most part, been carried out on birds and, in general, on brains of small size. With these, even his advanced technique and skill were inadequate to prevent extensive interference. Also, the ignorance of finer comparative anatomy, in particular of the fiber tracts of the brain, would in any event have made anatomical control illusory (*cf.* sec. 5). The fact that in all his numerous experiments the locality of the "sizable portion" of the "cerebral lobes" removed was only vaguely indicated and that the destruction most often included the thalami and striate bodies remained unnoticed.

Whatever the other consequences of Flourens' notable work, it changed the outlook in the formulation of the problems of the visual system. The interest of the investigators, until then confined to the infranuclear division of the visual pathway, began now to extend to the cerebral cortex. From then on, as far as the visual functions were concerned, the cortex of the brain became the focal point, all evidence indicating it as the "final arbiter."

Flourens demonstrated that the two higher senses, sight and hearing, as well as functions and faculties of the higher category, such as volition, instinct, judgment, and the "intellect," in the advanced Vertebrates were preponderantly, or even exclusively, located in the cerebral cortex. If the cortex was destroyed, they were invariably and permanently lost. The fallacy of the view of the thalamic and mesencephalic regions as the only centers of visual function became obvious. Whether the highest or integrative functions of the brain were a homogeneous process or whether they were a synthesis wherein no partial functions could be recognized was a matter for further inquiry.

In conclusion, even though Flourens believed that the various functions abolished with the destruction of the cerebral cortex were but several outward manifestations of the same, essentially homogeneous, process uniformly distributed over the entire cortex of the brain, his work definitely pointed toward the cortex, instead of the whole brain, as the substratum of the perceptive and integrative processes.

References: Ch. Bell 1811; Boring 1950; C. G. Carus 1814; De la Peyronie 1709, 1741; Des Cartes 1662, 1667, 1677; Du Laurens 1599; Flourens 1824, 1842; Fontana; A. Haller 1769, 1774–76; F. A. Lange 1908; Lorry 1760; Neuburger 1897; Pourfour du Petit 1710; Révész 1917; Rolando 1809, 1828; Soury 1899; Vulpian 1887; Willis 1664; Th. Ziehen 1902; Zinn 1749.

SEC. 5. EARLY INVESTIGATIONS OF THE CEREBRAL CORTEX AND OF THE SUBCORTICAL FIBER SYSTEMS

1. SHIFTING OF INVESTIGATIVE INTEREST TO THE CEREBRAL CORTEX; DISCOVERY OF LOCAL VARIATION OF CORTICAL STRUCTURE.—Toward the end of the eighteenth and during the first few decades of the nineteenth centuries, the way was cleared for a systematic anatomical investigation of the cerebral hemispheres. Flourens' experiments furnished enough evidence to show the paramount importance of the cerebral cortex in the "higher" or "psychic" functions. They finally disposed of the ancient Hippocratic idea that the cortex is a gland and

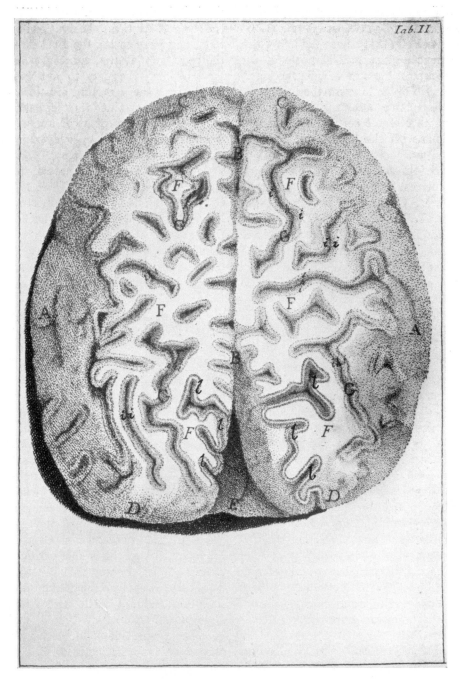

Fig. 86.—Gennari's figure, where, for the first time, structural variation in the cerebral cortex was demonstrated. Horizontal section through human brain *in situ*, with upper portions of both hemispheres cut off to show the newly disclosed intracortical stripe *l, l*, named in honor of its discoverer "Gennari's stripe or line" (later also named "Gennari & Vicq-d'Azyr stripe"). *Labeling: A, A*, right and left hemispheres; *B, B*, longitudinal fissure; *C, C*, frontal lobes; *D, D*, occipital lobes; *E*, tentorium of cerebellum; *F, F*, white subcortical medullary substance; *G, G*, gray cortical substance; *h, h*, fissures or sulci; *i, i*, newly discovered white intracortical layer of frontal lobes, which in some localities appears double; *l, l*, pronounced white intracortical stripe of the occipital lobes, or Gennari and Vicq-d'Azyr's line (*lower part of figure*), which more than a century later was recognized as indicating the visual center, or "striate area" of G. Elliot Smith. From Francesco Gennari, *De peculiari structura cerebri*, published in 1782, Parma, Italy. (*Cf.* Figs. 226–29.)

inadvertently vindicated the substance of Gall's teaching and the opinion of Swedenborg (1738) and of Charles Bell (1811), according to which "the cineritious and superficial parts of the brain are the seat of the intellectual functions." From now on, in order to know the brain's organization, it became necessary to study not only the structure of the cortex itself but also its connections with the brain stem and the peripheral nerves.

The pioneer investigators of this period, whose chief interest was in the finer structure of the cortex, were Gennari (1782), Cazauvieilh (quoted by Baillarger 1840), Vicq-d'Azyr (1786–90), and Meckel (1815), followed later by Baillarger (1840), Hannover (1844), and Koelliker (1854). They furnished evidence of the nervous nature of the cortical substance and made a significant discovery of local variation in cortical architecture. Gennari first noticed the white medullary stripe of the occipital lobe in the cortex, which has been named for him (Fig. 86, *l*). This observation was subsequently confirmed by Vicq-d'Azyr, Rolando (1828), Soemmerring, and others. Only much later was it realized that this area was the visual center. (*See* chap. IV, 7 [3]; and chap. VIII, 3, 4.)

Most successful of the investigators of this period was Baillarger (1806–91), a pupil of Esquirol, "Creator of the Science of Psychiatry" (*see* Magnan 1902; *see* portrait Fig. 86*A*). By mounting thin sections upon glass and examining them against light, he found the cortex to be composed of no less than six parallel layers, alternating white and gray and differing in structure (Fig. 87, 88). The arrangement and number of layers varied from region to region; in some places there were only two. He found the fibers entering into the cortex from the subjacent white subcortical substance most numerous in the summit of the gyri, fewer along the walls of the sulci, and least numerous around the sulcal floor, where they were arranged obliquely. There was also a difference in termination: in some localities the fibers terminated in the lowermost layers, in others in the layers closer to the cortical surface. Baillarger also realized that the white cortical strata were made up partly of fibers penetrating from the white subcortical substance and partly of the autochthonous fibers arranged parallel to the surface. All these observations induced him to consider the cortex the most important and the most complicated substance of the brain. He was also the first to anticipate modern views: that the advanced stratification of the human cortex signified its "perfection" in comparison with those of other animals and that isolated damage to distinct layers is possible in various pathological processes.

Another group of anatomists, Rolando (1809), Gall & Spurzheim (1809, 1810–19, portrait Figs. 83, 84), Reil (1809, portrait Fig. 89), Burdach (1819–26, portrait Fig. 90), and Arnold (1839, portrait Fig. 91), were engaged in an effort to disentangle the various fiber systems which form the white medullary core of the cerebral hemispheres. Even so, all these initial attempts, especially in fiber anatomy, were no more than guides to future research. (*Cf.* chap. IV, 7 [1, 2].)

2. Discovery of the corona radiata of the cerebral hemispheres.—The relatively slow progress in cerebral anatomy was chiefly the result of the primitive techniques employed during that period. Fixation and hardening of specimens were occasionally practiced by most early modern anatomists, and regularly by Malpighi (boiling); Vieussens (boiling in water and oil, a suggestion given to Vieussens by his friend Baylé, professor in Toulouse); Ruysch (injecting and boiling; also embalming by a secret process, perhaps first using alcohol followed by diluted nitric acid); Monro (same as Ruysch); Vicq-d'Azyr (alcohol and hydrochloric acid); Niemeyer (corrosive sublimate followed by diluted nitric acid); and Gennari (freezing). But only after Reil, who used alcohol or turpentine followed by alcohol, was the preliminary fixation recognized as an essential requisite for the study of cerebral fiber systems. Until then, the customary procedure was to work with fresh, unfixed, and often decaying material, where many original structures and relationships were lost (*see* Burdach 1822, v. 2, p. 243). For this reason the fibrous constitution of the cerebral hemispheres was little known.

Among the systems first recognized was the *corona radiata*, a huge fiber fan radiating from the base of the cerebral hemisphere toward all regions of the cerebral cortex. This system had already been observed by Thomas Willis (1664) and was subsequently described and depicted by Vieussens (1684, portrait Fig. 75). It was so named by Reil (1809, portrait Fig. 89), who considered it to be a continuation of the funiculi of the brain stem, spreading fanlike in the subcortical space. Reil described the apparent origin of the posterior portion of the *corona* in the yet undisclosed (*see* Reil 1809, p. 165; *see also* chap. II, 12 [8]).

3. DISCOVERY OF THE PRINCIPAL CEREBRAL FIBER SYSTEMS.—A related problem much discussed at that time was the course and arrangement of fiber bundles, particularly whether all fibers terminate in the cortex, or whether some also originate in it, or whether they simply turn

FIG. 86*A*.—Jules-Gabriel-François (J.-P.) Baillarger (1806–91), psychiatrist and pioneer investigator of the cerebral cortex. Author of the pamphlet *Recherches sur la structure de la couche corticale des circonvolutions du cerveau* (1840), which for the first time demonstrated the structural variation of different parts of the cortex. (*See* for biography Y. Magnan in France méd., v. 49, p. 473, and v. 50, p. 17; J. F. Fulton 1951; and Haymaker & Baer, *The Founders of Neurology*, 1953.)

thalamus and its termination in the occipital extremity of the hemisphere. This included the geniculo-calcarine fiber system, or visual radiation, the identity of which, except for a hint given by Gall & Spurzheim (1810), remained as around and pass back again to the brain stem. The many opinions expressed concerning this problem, mostly speculative, increased the existing confusion instead of clarifying matters (Burdach 1822, v. 2, p. 382). In spite of these

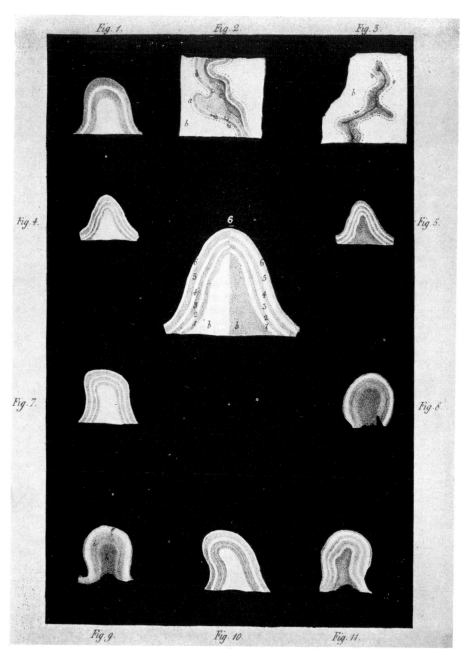

FIG. 87.—Baillarger's figure, which, together with the following figure, is the earliest presentation, after Gennari's, of a local structural variation of the cerebral cortex. *Labeling: 1*, white intracortical stripe of Gennari & Vicq-d'Azyr, indicating the visual center or striate area of G. Elliot Smith; *2*, Gennari's figure, exceptionally showing two white intracortical lines; *3*, another of Gennari's figures with usual single line; *4* and *5*, sheep cortex with six alternating gray and white layers, one in incident, the other in transmitted, light; *6*, same specimen slightly magnified, left half in incident, right half in transmitted, illumination (in the left half the myelinated layers *2, 4,* and *6* appearing white, in the right half the same appearing gray, whereas layers *1, 3,* and *5*, made up of nerve cells and only a few myelinated fibers, behave optically in an opposite way); *7*, human cortex in incident light with six alternating gray and white layers; *8*, local variation of human cortex in transillumination, with gray stripe, formed by closely packed lines *2, 3,* and *4*, still showing a vestige of transparent line *3; 9*, another variation showing subcortical white substance (*b*), inner zone of cortex composed of first four layers, of which *1* and *3* are poorly developed, and outer zone (*e*) chiefly made up of transparent gray matter containing little myelin; *10*, occipital cortex with a broad white intracortical stripe corresponding to fourth layer (in modern terminology "line of Gennari & Vicq-d'Azyr" or "Baillarger's outer layer"), and another much thinner white stripe corresponding to Baillarger's second layer (in modern terminology "Baillarger's inner layer"; *cf. 1* and *6* in this plate); *11*, cortex of a horse showing six layers in transmitted light. From J. G. F. Baillarger, *Recherches sur la structure de la couche corticale,* 1840. (*See* **Fig. 88.**)

difficulties, several distinct systems or "bundles" of fibers were identified in the core of the great hemispheres, some real, others artifacts. Such, according to Burdach, were the *tapetum, cingulum, fasciculus unciformis, f. longitudinalis inferior, f. arcuatus* or *f. longitudinalis superior*, and *f. baseos internus*. Later, when modern methods of making stained sections were developed, some of these systems, especially the *fasciculus longitudinalis inferior*, or the inferior longitudinal bundle, became of prime importance in the investigation of the visual pathway (*see* chap. IV, 2 [4], 3, 7 [4–10]). The callosal fiber system was also recognized as an independent anatomical entity. However, even the best authorities still remained silent about the connections of the cranial nerves with the cerebral cortex. (Burdach 1822, v. 2; Rolando 1828; F. Arnold 1838–42; *see also* chap. II, 12 [8].)

4. GRATIOLET'S INVESTIGATION OF THE FIBER SYSTEMS OF THE BRAIN.—During the beginning of the second half of the nineteenth century, the investigation of the brain was directed increasingly toward the cortex. Following the initial investigations of the fiber anatomy of the brain by Willis, Vieussens, Vicq-d'Azyr, Reil, Gall, Burdach, Arnold, and Foville, Gratiolet in a systematic study, chiefly of simian material, succeeded in bringing some degree of order into a subject which until then had been obscure (Gratiolet 1854, 1855; Leuret & Gratiolet 1857, v. 2, pp. 166, 179; portrait Fig. 92; for biography *see* Broca 1865). His technique consisted of "teasing" or careful dissecting of fixed and hardened specimens. By first removing the cortex and then gradually working deeper, he demonstrated the several layers or fiber systems which make up the subcortical white substance. These he found to be of several kinds: (1) the *fibres propres*, or short U-shaped association fibers connecting the adjoining gyri of the same hemisphere; (2) the anterior commissure; (3) the fibers originating from Reil's *corona radiata;* (4) callosal fibers; (5) radiations originating from the nerves related to special sensory functions; and (6) radiations from the "accessory ganglia," such as the quadrigeminal bodies, internal geniculate nucleus, and cerebellum.

5. DISCOVERY OF VISUAL RADIATION BY GRATIOLET.—Among these fiber systems passing to and from the cortex, that related to the optic nerve was of particular interest. It was believed in Gratiolet's time that this nerve had two chief "sources" or "roots": one in the quadrigeminal bodies, the other in the white medullary or zonal stratum that lines the dorsal face of the thalamus (*see* S. A. W. Stein 1834). In Mammals the second source was considered more important, and it was thought to be a direct continuation of the optic nerve. Beyond this, information did not go, and almost nothing was known about the pathway by which the visual impulses reach the cortex. Gratiolet's investigations seemed to indicate that the flat inner branch of the optic nerve or tract, after slipping beneath the medial geniculate nucleus, proceeded to the occipital pole of the cerebral hemisphere (Fig. 93). The thicker outer branch seemed to pass into the zonal stratum of the thalamus, where, after turning around the pulvinar, it continued in the oral direction. This root also surrounded the gray mass of the lateral geniculate nucleus. From it a small bundle passed directly to the superior colliculus. The bulk of its fibers, arranged in closely packed radii and rising from the outer edge of the lateral geniculate nucleus, was distributed along the entire superior margin of the hemisphere. The fibers of the optic tract, according to Gratiolet's interpretation, continued directly into the hemisphere, especially into the parietal and occipital lobes, where they spread in the form of a fan. The bundles of that fan, as they passed upward, gradually changed their position. Those from the outer division turned frontally, those from the inner division of the optic tract passed to the occipital lobe.

6. EFFECT OF GRATIOLET'S DISCOVERY ON VIEWS OF THE SIGNIFICANCE OF THE CEREBRAL CORTEX.—The visual pathway, as described by Gratiolet, offered several points worthy of attention. In the first place, the presence of a special sensory tract above the level of the brain stem was, for the first time, confirmed. This agreed with Flourens' experiments, which had demonstrated the importance of the cerebral cortex in the sensory functions, especially vision (*see* sec. 4 [4, 6], this chapter). Of equal

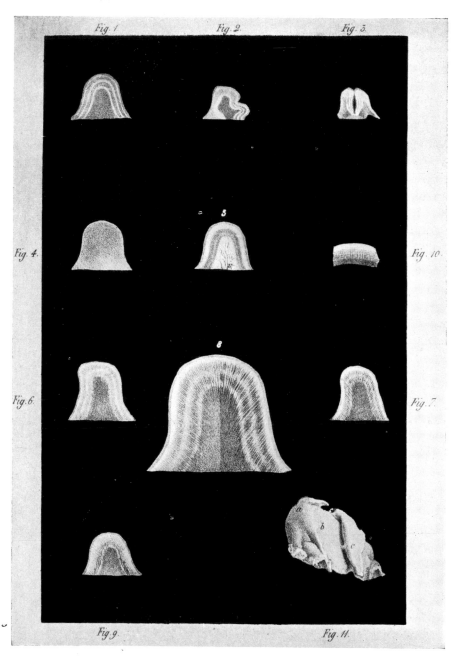

FIG. 88.—Another of Baillarger's plates showing local variation of structure in the cerebral cortex (*see* Fig. 87). *Labeling: 1*, six alternating white and gray layers in Dog; *2*, same in Cat, partly visible; *3*, same in Rabbit, next to corpus callosum; *4*, homogeneous appearance of cortex of a newly born baby in incident light; *5*, same in transmitted light, with several opaque gray stripes and blood vessels at *v; 6*, human cortex with two tiers of fibers in transmitted light; *7*, similar specimen of Pig with thicker and fewer fibers than in the preceding; *8*, composite and magnified figure, left half corresponding to *6*, right half to *7; 9*, Dog cortex showing faint transverse or horizontal fibers, besides the radial; *10*, Rabbit cortex showing vertical fibers crossed at right angles by numerous transverse or horizontal fibers; *11*, convolution of human brain, with an outer layer *c* flapped over to the right side from the region *b*, leaving the region *a* intact.

significance was the fact that the visual pathway terminated in a distinct area of the cortex. Even though this area, as indicated by Gratiolet, was large, there remained a considerable portion of the cortex outside direct reach of these fibers. This was a significant advance over the theory, current until then, that the entire cerebral hemisphere was a uniformly organized substratum of homogeneous function (*see* Flourens versus Gall, in sec. 4, this chapter).

Gratiolet's discovery clarified the mystery that until then had enveloped the cerebral hemispheres, particularly the cortex. The fact that at least one of the principal sensory pathways, the visual, continued to the cortex lent substance to the idea of the paramount importance of the gray coat, of which many investigators in the past had been dimly aware (Willis 1664; Pourfour du Petit 1710; J. Ch. A. Mayer 1779; Gall 1809, 1810–19; Charles Bell 1811; Foville & Delaye 1820; Baillarger 1840).

The notion of the anatomists of preceding centuries that "the brain," by which they really meant the cerebral cortex, "neither sees, nor hears, nor feels" but in a way presides over these functions proved to be fallacious (*see* Du Laurens, chap. II, 9 [3]). Also, Gall's and Burdach's concept, generally adhered to during the first half of the nineteenth century, which grew out of Du Laurens' concept that the cerebral hemispheres were not directly related to the sense organs and hence were exclusively a substratum of the so-called "psychic functions" above the level of a mere sensory experience (Johannes Müller, Longet, Vulpian), had to yield to the force of contradictory anatomical evidence. In this way Flourens' experiments, which indicated the localization of vision in the cerebral cortex, were vindicated anatomically.

In the light of Gratiolet's observations, the cerebral cortex had to be recognized not as a kind of anatomical abstraction outside the somatic sphere but as the highest level of the nervous system, whose roots reach to the very confines of bodily organization.

References: F. Arnold 1838–42; Baillarger 1840 (*see also* Magnan 1902, and Fulton 1951); Burdach 1819–22–26, 1848; Foville 1844; Gall & Spurzheim 1809, 1810–19; F. Gennari 1782; Gratiolet 1854, 1855 (*see also* Leuret & Gratio-

let 1857); Fulton 1937, 1943; Hannover 1844; Koelliker 1854; Leuret & Gratiolet 1839–57; Longet 1842; J. Ch. A. Mayer 1779; Meckel 1815, 1815–20; Joh. Müller 1840; Pourfour du Petit 1710; Reil 1809; Révész 1917; Rolando 1809, 1828; Soemmerring 1839–45; Soury 1899; S. A. W. Stein 1834; Vicq-d'Azyr 1786–89, 1805; Vieussens 1685; Vulpian 1866; Willis 1664, 1682.

Fig. 89.—Johann Christian Reil (1759–1813), professor in Halle and in Berlin, Germany. Pioneer investigator of fiber systems of the brain. First recognized the treatment of brain specimens in a fixing fluid, e.g., alcohol, as an essential prerequisite for anatomical investigation. Described fanlike spreading of nerve fibers of the white core of the brain, since known as Reil's *corona radiata* or "cerebral radiation," and described concealed part of the cerebral cortex, named in his honor *insula Reilii* or "Reil's Island." From München. med. Wchnschr., v. 60, 1913. *See also* R. N. Wegner, *Das Anatomenbildnis*, 1939. Courtesy Armed Forces Medical Library, Cleveland, Ohio.

SEC. 6. REVIVAL OF THE "DOCTRINE OF LOCALIZATION" OR FUNCTIONAL INEQUALITY OF THE CEREBRAL CORTEX

1. DISCOVERY BY BOUILLAUD OF THE CORTICAL LOCALITY CONCERNED WITH MOTOR SPEECH. —The idea of the functional omnivalence or equivalence of the entire cerebral cortex supported by the authority of Haller and Flourens reigned almost unchallenged throughout the greater part of the nineteenth century. Gall's premature and overly ambitious attempt to

the gray cortex, was structurally and functionally homogeneous is well illustrated by Gratiolet himself, who interpreted his anatomical discoveries in favor of Flourens, even though they pointed in the opposite direction (Leuret & Gratiolet 1857, p. 378).

The doctrine of cortical omnivalence, in spite of the high authority by which it was sustained,

FIG. 90.—Karl Friedrich Burdach (1776–1847), professor of anatomy at Dorpat, Tártu or Yúryev, in Russian Estonia, and at Königsberg (now Kaliningrad), and Breslau (now Wroclaw), both then in Prussia. Most encyclopedic writer of his time on the brain anatomy, physiology, and pathology and author of *Vom Baue und Leben des Gehirns*, in 3 vols., 1819–26. Pioneer investigator of the cerebral fiber systems: described the tapetum, cingulum, uncinate bundle, inferior longitudinal bundle, later recognized as the visual radiation, and the arcuate bundle, etc., of the brain, and the fasciculus cuneatus in the spinal cord and oblong medulla. Portrait and lithograph by Josef Kriehuber, 1832. From R. N. Wegner, *Das Anatomenbildnis*, 1939.

carry his "plurality doctrine" of cerebral functions to its logical consequence with insufficient means was not only no deterrent but lent positive support to the very idea he had tried to supplant. How firm and universal was the belief that the bulk of the brain, and especially

was, however, not accepted by all. In particular, certain observations accumulated by the clinicians disagreed with it. Flourens' teaching was first seriously questioned when Bouillaud (1825, 1839, portrait Fig. 94), leaving aside Gall's notion of the localization of "intellectual and moral faculties," applied his basic idea of functional plurality to the motor and sensory functions. Such a claim, in the first place, disputed the general aspect of Flourens' "equivalence doctrine." But, beyond this, Bouillaud's concept of the direct cortical influencing of the peripheral muscles was in outright opposition to Flourens, who, at most, admitted an indirect influence of the "will power."

A particular contention of Bouillaud was the dependence of the motor component of speech was brought about. This function of specific motor integration and its underlying mechanism differed both from the apperceptive or gnostic speech function (auditory word memory) and from the somatosensory and somatomotor mechanisms used in speech. In other words, Bouillaud assumed the presence of a cortical center for the co-ordination of the phonetic mechanism for the production of spoken words, a center of articulated language (a theory previously expressed by Gall). This "motor speech

Fig. 91.—Friedrich Arnold (1803–90), professor of anatomy in Zürich, Switzerland, and in Freiburg i.Br., Tübingen, and Heidelberg, Germany. Pioneer student of the human eye and nervous system, especially of fiber tracts of the brain. Described short or U-shaped association fibers, connecting adjoining gyri of the brain, and the "frontopontine tract of Arnold." According to a contemporary lithograph by M. Wieser, from R. N. Wegner, *Das Anatomenbildnis*, 1939. Courtesy Armed Forces Medical Library, Cleveland, Ohio.

upon a definite locality of the cerebral cortex. He distinguished three components in spoken language. One was a specific function of co-ordination of auditory word images with the executive organs of speech, implying the presence of a cortical substratum of "motor word images," through which the act of speaking center" he, like Gall, localized in the frontal lobes (orbital surface). In support of his claim and against formidable opposition (Andral, Longet, Claude Bernard, Vulpian, *et al.*), Bouillaud was able to cite several cases from his own observation in which post mortem examination revealed a more or less extensive injury to the frontal lobes, while the rest of the brain remained intact, and where other functions, with the exception of motor speech, had been unimpaired.

2. BOUILLAUD'S CONCEPT OF MOTOR AND SENSORY CENTERS OF THE CEREBRAL CORTEX.—Bouillaud's idea of the brain in general also appears surprisingly modern. In analogy with the motor speech center and based upon his experiments with various animals (1827), he postulated the presence of other motor and "intellectual"—now called sensory—centers in the brain. There was, for example, a distinct center for vision, the destruction of which caused either impairment of sight or blindness, and a similar

PARIS. — TYP. E. MARTINET.

PIERRE GRATIOLET

Mort à Paris le 16 février 1865.

FIG. 92.—Louis-Pierre Gratiolet (1815–65), anatomist and physiologist of Paris. Prominent student of comparative anatomy of the brain. Systematically investigated fibrous core of the brain and described its principal constituent fiber systems. First disclosed the fibers of visual or "Gratiolet's radiation," along which the impulses pass from the eyes to the cortex of the brain. Frontispiece in Mém. Soc. Anthropol., Paris, v. 2. For biography *see* Broca in same vol., p. cxii. (*Cf.* Fig. 93.) For other biographies *see* J. de conn. méd., Paris, 1865, v. 32, p. 95; Bull. Soc. méd. de l'Yvonne, Auxère, 1866, pp. 33–54, and 1868, pp. 17–37; Gaz. hebd. de méd., Paris, 1865, 2d ser., v. 2, pp. 161, 177; Union méd., Paris, 1865, 2d ser., v. 25, pp. 353–62; Wien. med. Wchnschr., 1865, v. 15, p. 345; and Gaz. d. Hôp., Paris, prob. 1865.

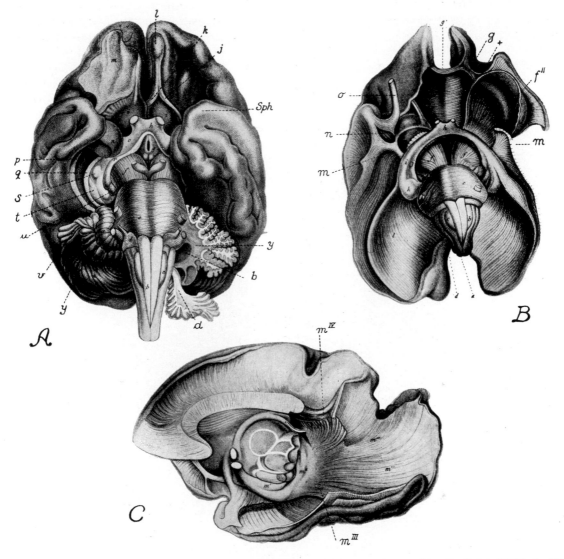

Fig. 93.—Visual pathway of Baboon *Papio* and of Capuchin Monkey, dissected by Gratiolet (1857). In this work, for the first time, a connection was shown between subcortical visual centers and cerebral cortex, the so-called "visual or optic radiation of Gratiolet"; and the importance of the cortex as the uppermost level in the cerebral hierarchy was anatomically demonstrated.

Labeling: A, view of the brain from below, with a part of the right temporal lobe removed to show the entry of optic tract *o* into subcortical visual centers: lateral geniculate nucleus (*s*) and pulvinar of thalamus (*t*); *B*, basal view of the dissected visual system of both hemispheres showing junction of optic nerves in the chiasma (*h*), external and internal "roots" of optic nerve (*i, j*), external or lateral geniculate nucleus (*k*), and the apparent continuation of optic nerve as a "visual radiation" (*l*) to the occipital lobe; *C*, medial view of right hemisphere showing visual pathway after removal of obstructing parts: the optic tract (*m*), inner and outer root of the same (*m^I, m^II*), the latter enveloping the external geniculate nucleus, with fiber fan of visual radiation (*m^III*) streaming toward the occipital lobe at right; *m^IV*, anterior fibers of radiation mingling with callosal fibers. From a specimen "teased" or dissected with needles, after a preliminary maceration. From Leuret & Gratiolet, *Anatomie comparée du système nerveux (atlas)*, 1857, Pls. 26 and 27.

auditory center. The makeup of the somesthetic system, he believed, was more complicated. Here each nerve, related to a particular region in the periphery of the body, terminated in a discrete portion of the brain, a lesion in the area of termination causing impairment of sen-

visual, and auditory. Furthermore, Bouillaud assumed the principle of "projection," or somatotopic representation of the peripheral receptor surfaces in the cerebrum, so far postulated only for the visual system (Ibn al-Haitham, Des Cartes, Briggs, Taylor; *see* chap. II, 6 [2],

FIG. 94.—Jean Bouillaud (1796–1881), professor of medicine in Paris. Follower of Gall and a precursor of Broca in the cerebral functional localization. From an engraving by Bornemann. Courtesy Crerar Library, Dr. Sonnenschein Collection, Chicago. For biography *see* C. Lian, in Dumesnil & Bonnet-Roy, v. 3, 1947.

sation in the corresponding territory. The concept of functional cerebral localization, as formulated by Bouillaud, was first extended to each of the several "primary" or "elemental" functions, such as the motor, somesthetic,

10 [2], 11 [2, 6], and Figs. 71, 74), to be valid also for the somesthetic system, long before Meynert gave it a more concrete definition and Munk proved it experimentally. In this way the problem of cerebral functional localization,

initiated by Gall's fantastic system, assumed for the first time a concrete form suitable for further research along modern scientific lines.

3. FURTHER ATTEMPTS TO LOCALIZE MOTILI- TY, VISION, AND SPEECH IN THE BRAIN.—Bouil- laud was not alone in claiming the functional diversity of the cerebral cortex. A few other pioneers of that period, in France and else- where, accepted the idea of cerebral functional localization, which to them seemed to promise more fruitful results than could be expected from an essentially negative concept of "corti- cal functional omnivalence." Foville & Pinel- Grandchamp (1825), for example, noticed dis- tinct impairment of motor, or somesthetic, functions in cases of cerebral lesions. Paralysis of a single limb meant to them that each had a separate center in the brain. The arm center, they believed, was in the thalamus, the leg cen- ter in the corpus striatum. Subsequent investi- gations showed this to be an error, but the idea of functional diversity of the cerebrum was kept alive through their efforts during a period which otherwise was mostly ill disposed to- ward it.

About the middle of the nineteenth century, Panizza (1855–56), in Italy, clearly under the influence of Gall's ideas, made a series of experi- ments with the visual system and studied cases of impaired sight in cerebral lesions. His work convinced him that the faculty of vision de- pended upon the posterior portion of the hemi- sphere and that the bilateral destruction of this locality produced complete blindness without affecting other cerebral functions. Unfortu- nately, Panizza's work failed to impress con- temporary scientific thought, which was still almost entirely dominated by Flourens' doc- trine of cortical functional omnivalence (*see* sec. 4, par. 2, this chapter, and chap. IV, 1).

Bouillaud's idea of cerebral organization re- ceived powerful support in Broca's discovery of a "motor speech center" (1861 and later, por- trait Fig. 95; for biography *see* Broca 1880). In- stead of localizing it in the orbital surface, as Gall and Bouillaud did, however, Broca placed this particular "center" in the posterior third of the left inferior frontal gyrus (Fig. 274). When this locality suffered damage, it resulted in "aphemia," now known as motor aphasia

(Trousseau) or apractic aphasia (Nielsen), a kinetic apraxia of speech in Liepmann's sense, that is, an inability to pronounce words, with understanding of spoken or written language more or less preserved and with other functions of the mouth, tongue, and throat, such as mas- tication and deglutition, remaining normal; (in left-handed persons the motor speech center is commonly assumed to be in the right frontal lobe; for references *see* Moutier 1908; Monakow 1914; Nielsen 1946). The idea of functional cor- tical localization gained further support in the obvious structural diversity of the brain in gen- eral, and in particular in the structural varia- tion of the cerebral cortex noticed by Gennari (1782), Baillarger (1840), Meynert (1866, 1868, 1869), Charcot (1876–80), and others, until it was considered a firmly established fact (*see* chap. IV, 7). In retrospect, powerful sup- port of the same concept was derived from the numerous clinical and pathoanatomical obser- vations of J. Hughlings Jackson (1861–88, por- trait Fig. 106), the noted English neurologist.

4. DISCOVERY OF SOMATOMOTOR AREA BY HITZIG.—The efforts of Bouillaud, Panizza, Broca, Meynert, and Hughlings Jackson, form- ing a continuous chain of evidence, did little at the time to dislodge the firmly intrenched "doc- trine of cortical functional omnivalence." Most contemporary investigators, especially physi- ologists, unable to elicit movements of the limbs or any other visible manifestation by stimula- tion of the cortex in living animals or at most observing generalized, unco-ordinated convul- sions and seeing no definite impairment or loss of well-defined function in cases of a partial de- struction of the cortex, persisted as before in favoring Flourens' doctrine of the unexcitability and functional equivalence of the entire cortex. (Longet, Claude Bernard, Vulpian, Schiff *et al.*)

This situation changed radically when Hitzig (1870, portrait Fig. 96), in collaboration with Fritsch, in experiments on dogs showed that motor response of the contralateral limbs may be elicited by electrical stimulation of a certain cortical area of the frontal portion of the brain. In the Monkey, as he later found (1873), this area corresponded to the precentral gyrus (Fig. 280). Hitzig's observation that when a liminal stimulus was applied, the response was restricted to one or to a few muscles was significant in contrast to the generalized convulsions regularly obtained by Rolando (*see* sec. 4 [1], this chapter). The discovery of the presence of small excitable motor foci was further amplified by Hitzig's observation that the limb whose ex-

firmed and variously augmented by numerous experimenters and observers of human pathological cases. In this way not only the presence of the cortical motor and somesthetic areas was demonstrated but also their composition of minute foci. In the motor area such foci repre-

FIG. 95.—Paul Broca (1824–80), professor of pathology at the University of Paris, at the age of forty-three. Famous as a brain anatomist and exponent of the idea of functional cerebral localization. First indicated the area in the lower portion of the left frontal lobe of brain on which the faculty to pronounce words, or "motor speech," in the normal right-handed persons, depended: "Broca's area" or "Broca's speech center." A pioneer anthropologist and craniologist. From an engraving by I. Lafosse, 1867. Courtesy Crerar Library, Dr. Sonnenschein Collection, Chicago. Biography by G. Cordier, in Dumesnil & Bonnet-Roy, v. 3, 1947; and Haymaker & Baer, *The Founders of Neurology*, 1953.

citable cortical focus was destroyed became paralyzed (duplication of Pourfour du Petit's observation made in 1710).

Hitzig's discovery was subsequently con-

sent individual muscles and muscular groups or, more correctly, particular detailed motions; in the somesthetic area the foci represent restricted portions or segments and parts of segments of the surface and of the deeper parts of the body. In this way, albeit belatedly, the essential ideas which Bouillaud had championed several decades earlier were ultimately vindicated. (For modern investigations of cortical representation of somaesthetic and motor functions *see* Ph. Bard; Bartholow; Bechterew; Leyton & Sherrington; Luciani; Luciani & Seppilli; Luciani & Tamburini; Mankowski; Marshall & Bard; Marshall, Woolsey & Bard; Mott, Schuster & Sherrington; Munk; Penfield; Penfield & Boldrey; Penfield & Erickson; Scarff; Schäfer; Sciamanna; C. & O. Vogt; Woolsey; Woolsey & Bard; Woolsey & Walzl.)

Fig. 96.—Julius Eduard Hitzig (1838–1907), professor of psychiatry at Halle a.S., Germany. His discovery, made 1870 conjointly with G. Fritsch, of electrically excitable foci in the cerebral cortex whose stimulation produces movements of various groups of muscles, limbs, etc., opened up the era of modern brain research. From Arch. f. Psychiat. u. Nervenk., v. 31 (3), 1899. For biography *see* Haymaker & Baer, *The Founders of Neurology*, 1953.

Beevor & Horsley; Berger; Boldrey & Penfield; G. Brown; Brown & Schäfer; Brown & Sherrington; Cushing; Ferrier; O. Foerster; Fulton; Fulton & Dusser de Barenne; A. Gordon; Grünbaum & Sherrington; M. Hines; Hines & Boynton; Horsley; Horsley & Schäfer; Lamacq 1897;

5. Overthrow of the "omnivalence doctrine" and its replacement by the "theory of functional cerebral localization."— The discovery of the "motor area" in the cerebral cortex by Fritsch & Hitzig disposed of the hitherto dominant thesis of the unexcitability of the cerebral cortex (Wepfer, Lorry, A. Haller, Rolando, Magendie, Flourens, Longet, Claude Bernard, Vulpian, Schiff, Brown-Séquard, *et al.*). Most important, however, Hitzig's work demonstrated an unequal physiological or functional significance of different localities of the cerebral surface, in opposition to the doctrine of functional equivalence.

In consequence of Hitzig's discovery and against formidable opposition (Schiff, Brown-Séquard, Goltz, *et al.*) numerous investigations were undertaken during the following decades, in Man and other Vertebrates, through which the principal "centers" in the cerebral cortex—somesthetic, visual, auditory, and others—were discovered. Also, certain localities concerned with definite "psychic" functions, such as memory for spoken or written language, music, and visual objects and the ability to execute skilled movements, such as writing or instrument playing, and many others, were more or less accurately plotted (*cf.* chap. VIII, 1 [4], and Figs. 274, 275).

These discoveries brought about a great change in the entire concept of the minute organization and function of the brain and of the nervous system in general. It became understood that "mind" or "intellect" was not a single, total, indivisible function of the entire cerebrum but a composite of numerous partial functions, many and perhaps all of which were bound to distinct localities of the cerebral cortex and subcortical regions and variously interlinked among themselves.

The discovery of excitable foci by Hitzig was, in a sense, the first experimental vindication of the principle of functional localization in the cerebral cortex, propounded by Gall and adhered to by a few advanced thinkers. But not all tenets of the "doctrine of cerebral functional plurality" were substantiated. The idea of the cortex as an exclusive repository of functions and faculties usually termed "higher" or "psychic" had to go.

In the light of Hitzig's disclosures, it became apparent that the huge mass of the gray substance which is the cortex of the cerebral hemispheres was as much an anatomical substratum of the "simple," "primitive," or "elemental" nervous functions, such as sensation and motility, and therefore an integral part of the bodily machine, as it was an instrument of those elusive phenomena and subjective experiences called "psychic" or "mental," to which ordinary terms and measures used in anatomy and physiology are not applicable.

References: Ades; Ades & Felder 1942; Andral 1840; Arndt 1867–69; Arnold 1851; Ph. Bard 1938; Bard & Brooks 1934; Bartholow 1874; Bechterew 1898, 1901, 1906, 1908–11; Beevor & Horsley 1886, 1888, 1891, 1894; H. Berger 1926; R. Berlin 1858; Bethe *et al.* 1927–31, vols. 9, 10; E. G. Boring 1950; Bouillaud 1825, 1827, 1830, 1839, etc.; Broca 1861, 1863, 1864, 1865, 1866, 1867, 1868, 1888; S. Brown 1888; Brown & Schäfer 1888; Brown & Sherrington 1911; T. Graham Brown 1927; Charcot 1876–80; H. Cushing 1909; Dejerine 1906, 1926; Dumesnil & Bonnet-Roy 1947; M. Duval 1887; Exner 1881; Ferrier 1874, 1875, 1878, 1881, 1886, 1889; Ferrier & Yeo 1884; Flourens 1824, 1842; O. Foerster 1923, 1931, 1934, 1936; Foerster & Penfield 1930; Foville & Pinel-Grandchamp 1825; Fritsch & Hitzig 1870 (*see also* Hitzig); Fulton 1934, 1937, 1943; Fulton & Dusser de Barenne 1933; Gall 1825; Gall & Spurzheim 1809, 1810–19; Gerdy 1839; Goltz 1881; A. Gordon 1907; A. S. F. Grünbaum & C. S. Sherrington 1901; A. Haller 1769; M. Hines 1929; Hitzig 1872, 1873, 1874, 1901, 1903, 1904, 1905 (*see also* Fritsch & Hitzig 1870); Horsley 1909; Horsley & Schäfer 1887; J. Hughlings Jackson 1925, 1931–32; Klüver & Bucy 1937, 1938, 1939; F. A. Lange 1908; Leyton & Sherrington 1917; Longet 1842; Luciani 1881, 1885, 1911–21; Luciani & Seppilli 1886; Luciani & Tamburini 1876, 1879; Mankowski 1929; Marshall, Woolsey & Bard 1941; Meynert 1866, 1868, 1869; Monakow 1914; Moutier 1908; Munk 1877, 1878–79, 1879, 1880, 1881, 1883, 1889, 1890, 1891, 1892–96, 1899–1901, 1910; Nielsen 1946; Nothnagel 1879, 1887; B. Panizza 1855–56; Penfield & Boldrey 1937; Penfield & Erickson 1941; A. Pick 1920; E. A. Schäfer 1887, 1888, 1889, 1900; M. Schiff 1858–59, 1894–98; E. Sciamanna 1882, 1905; Sherrington 1934; G. Elliot Smith 1923, 1927; Soury 1899; C. & O. Vogt 1919, 1926; Vulpian 1866; J. J. Wepfer 1658; C. Wernicke 1879; Woolsey, Marshall & Bard 1942; Woolsey & Walzl 1942.

SEC. 7. EARLY ATTEMPTS TO LOCALIZE THE SENSE OF VISION IN THE CEREBRAL CORTEX

1. VAGUENESS CONCERNING PROBABLE LOCA-TION AND BOUNDARIES OF THE CORTICAL AREA RELATED TO VISION.—The initial efforts to identify the locality and to delimit the area of the cerebral cortex related to sight produced, at best, only vague results. For this the blame lay with the anatomists of the preceding period. The terminal area of visual radiation indicated by Gratiolet (1854; *see also* Leuret & Gratiolet 1857), including, as it did, the entire occipital and part of the parietal lobes, was too large to be of great value to an experimenter (*see* sec. 5 [5, 6], this chapter, and Fig. 93). On the other hand, Meynert (1869), while emphasizing the termination of the radiation in the occipital lobe and disclaiming such in the parietal, un-fortunately maintained that almost the entire temporal lobe was also related to the visual pathway. This may in part explain the varied and often quite opposite views expressed during the subsequent period concerning the precise locality and extent of the cortical visual center.

First among the modern localists, Bouillaud (1827), while obtaining evidence of functional cerebral localization in general, failed to indi-cate the seat of the visual or any other sensory center (*see* sec. 6 [2], this chapter). Andral (1840), although not opposed to the principle of localization, had not found any evidence of a visual center in the pathological cases he had collected.

B. Panizza (1855–56) seems to have been the first to notice an impairment of sight in local-ized experimental brain lesions. Both in his ex-periments with dogs and in human pathological cases where the "parietal" lobe was destroyed, he noticed blindness in the contralateral eye, as he interpreted it, which, in fact, must have been homonymous hemianopia (*see* sec. 9 [4, 6], this chapter). Significantly, this was precisely the locality where, according to him, the fibers of the optic nerve "originate" (whether this ana-tomical knowledge was the fruit of Panizza's own effort or was obtained from Gratiolet is not clear). When both the "parietal" (really the oc-cipital) lobes were damaged, the result was com-plete blindness (*see also* sec. 6 [3], this chapter, and chap. IV, 1 [1]).

Next to consider the problem of visual lo-calization was F. H. Chaillou (1863). In one case of homonymous hemianopia observed by him the lesion involved the occipital lobe (for details, *see* chap. IV, 1 [1]). These observations of Panizza and Chaillou, few as they were and made by relatively obscure investigators, car-ried no weight against the general trend of the time, which, supported by the authority of Flourens, opposed localization. (*See also* chap. IV, 1 [1].)

2. LOCALIZATION OF VISION IN THE ANGULAR GYRUS BY FERRIER.—Of greater consequence, closely following, as they did, the striking dis-covery of Fritsch & Hitzig (*see* preceding sec-tion), were the experiments of David Ferrier (1873 and later, portrait Fig. 97). Having ob-served that when the angular gyrus of the Mon-key is stimulated by electricity, conjugate movements of the eyes to the contralateral side result, he declared it to be the visual center. Later, finding that a bilateral destruction of the angular gyrus alone was not sufficient to cause complete and permanent blindness, for which it was necessary to destroy the occipital lobes also, Ferrier thought that the area concerned with the visual function included both. He thought the angular gyrus to be more impor-tant, since in his opinion this locality was re-lated to the centers of the visual fields, or "ma-culae." The occipital lobes, Ferrier contended, may be injured, or "cut off bodily, almost to the parieto-occipital sulcus, on one or on both sides simultaneously, without the slightest ap-preciable impairment of vision."

3. PROBABLE CAUSES OF FERRIER'S MISTAKE. —Examined in the light of present knowledge, Ferrier's experiments appear crude and their post mortem anatomical control inadequate. The most likely factor to have caused the im-pairment of visual function following injury to the angular gyrus was an interference with the branches of the middle cerebral artery which supply the underlying visual radiation, as had been pointed out previously by Starr (1884) and by Schäfer (1888; *see* chap. VII, 3, 8, and chap. X, 4). Another misleading factor was the absence of a noticeable impairment of vision in the Monkey after a bilateral destruction of the occipital lobes. This may be explained by the relatively small size of the central scotomas caused by the removal of the "macular" cortex over the occipital opercula (a similar observation was made in Klüver's experiments, private communication; *see also* chap. IV, 7 [3]).

connection (*see* Ferrier's scheme, 1886, and compare with Figs. 400 and 401 in this book). According to his hypothesis, not all fibers related to the temporal halves of the retinae, which we now know remain uncrossed in the chiasma, pass in the midbrain to the opposite hemisphere, as was assumed by Landolt (1875) and Charcot (1876–80), but only those related to the "areae of clear vision," that is, to the foveae

Fig. 97.—David Ferrier (1843–1928), pioneer of modern experimental brain research. Photo by Maull & Fox, 187 Piccadilly, London, W., received from Professor J. F. Fulton, of Yale University, New Haven, Conn. For biography *see* Haymaker & Baer, *The Founders of Neurology*, 1953.

4. Ferrier's explanation of "central sparing" in hemianopia.—Ferrier missed, at first, the hemianopic character of the visual disturbance after a unilateral lesion of the brain. Subsequently (1881), under the pressure of contrary evidence furnished by Luciani & Tamburini (1879) and others, he acknowledged that in such cases both eyes were affected. His interpretation of "central or macular sparing" in homonymous hemianopia is interesting in this

or "maculae" of the two retinae (*cf.* sec. 9 [6], this chapter).

This view, illogical and contrary to the facts, has never been substantiated by any unequivocal anatomical and clinical evidence. In spite of this, however, the idea of a partial crossing or recrossing of the visual fibers at the level above the midbrain in the corpus callosum, for example, was later taken over by Wilbrand, Heine, Niessl von Mayendorf, R. A. Pfeifer,

O. Foerster, and others in their search for an explanation of "central sparing" in hemianopia. For this purpose they devised a hypothesis of bilateral total representation of each central fovea in both cerebral hemispheres, to be discussed elsewhere in this book (*see* chap. IV, 1; chap. VI, 4, 5, 11; and chap. XI, 8, 9).

5. THE SIGNIFICANCE OF FERRIER'S INVESTIGATIONS FOR FUNCTIONAL CEREBRAL LOCALIZATION.—For one point—his firm conviction of the existence of a well-defined cortical region concerned with the visual function—and in spite of his mistakes, Ferrier is entitled to unreserved praise. Also noteworthy was the general conclusion to which he was led through his researches: "that a functional equivalence or indifferentism of the various regions of the cortex and the theory of one region compensating for the loss of another are assumptions which involve anatomical impossibilities." In this way Ferrier boldly attacked the "doctrine of functional equivalence" of the entire cerebrum.

6. REVIVAL OF THE CORTICAL "EQUIVALENCE DOCTRINE" BY GOLTZ AND THE HYPOTHESIS OF "VICARIOUS FUNCTION."—Ferrier's claim to have discovered the principal centers in the cerebral cortex (motor, somesthetic, acoustic, visual, olfactory, gustatory, and others) precipitated a series of investigations whose purpose was to test and possibly to correct, or to refute, his observations.

Goltz (1875 and later), repeating Ferrier's experiments, arrived at different conclusions. For, irrespective of the part of the brain operated upon, the consequent disturbance, he claimed, was the same, always concerning more or less all functions, sensory as well as motor. The only difference was in degree, which in turn depended upon the quantity or amount of the substance destroyed. The reality of the cortical "centers," both sensory and motor, Goltz denied altogether, insisting that each cortical lo-

cality was related to all motor and sensory nerves of the body. Small lesions or even large ones, such as the removal of one-fourth of the brain, in Goltz's opinion, produced little impairment of either the motor or the sensory functions. This he interpreted as resulting from a "substitution" or "vicarious function" of the remaining portions of the brain (*cf.* Flourens, in sec. 4 [4], this chapter). Hitzig's and Ferrier's discoveries, through which functional localization in the cerebral cortex seemed to have been placed upon a solid basis, were again questioned in the light of Goltz's experiments, and the old doctrine of "functional equivalence" of Haller and Flourens was revived.

It is noteworthy that Goltz's exposition found a responsive audience. The prejudice against the novel idea of functional cerebral localization was obviously still deeply ingrained and was strong enough to influence many to disregard the glaring inadequacies of Goltz's technique, as well as his argumentation. And his technique was extremely crude: washing out parts of the brain with the help of a stream of tap water forcibly introduced into the cranial cavity, with no regard for the structures intended to be removed or those to be left intact or with any consideration of such factors of general pathology as infection. Even after Goltz had improved his technique, it would have been nothing short of a miracle, had his badly conceived and ineptly performed experiments resulted in anything but interference with the working of the entire brain.

References: Andral 1840; Bechterew 1908–11; Boring 1950; Bouillaud; Chaillou; Charcot 1876–80; J. C. Dalton 1881; Exner 1881; D. Ferrier; Ferrier & Turner; Fritsch & Hitzig (*see also* Hitzig); Goltz 1881, 1892, 1899; Gratiolet (*see also* Leuret & Gratiolet); Hitzig (*see also* Fritsch & Hitzig); Landolt 1875; Lannegrace 1889; Leuret & Gratiolet; J. Loeb 1884, 1885, 1886; Luciani & Tamburini; Meynert 1869; Panizza; Schäfer 1888; Schiff; Soury 1899; Starr 1884.

SEC. 8. LOCALIZATION OF VISION IN THE OCCIPITAL LOBE
CORTICAL AND MENTAL BLINDNESS

1. MUNK'S CRITIQUE OF GOLTZ'S EXPERIMENTS.—The challenge to the emergent modern concept of functional cerebral localization,

which, in spite of a slight concession to it, the views of Goltz and other advocates of the "omnivalence doctrine" represented, was ably taken up by Munk (1876, 1877 and later; portrait Fig. 98). The objections to Goltz's work were directed both against the substance of his doctrine and against his technique. To Munk it seemed inconceivable that "whereas in the lower centers the best harmony rules, on the upper levels there should be a complete confusion." Also, it was obvious that, with his opponent's experimental technique, no localized lesions were possible, since, because of increased intra-

Munk found that the anterior half of the cerebral hemisphere serves the motor functions and the posterior half the sensory functions. In particular, when in the posterior sensory sphere the occipital lobe was superficially damaged close to its pole, a locality which he labeled A_1, or the "visual area" (Figs. 99, 100), the result was a remarkable psychic disturbance of a transient character, which within four, five, or six weeks disappeared completely: *Seelenblindheit*

Fig. 98.—Hermann Munk (1839–1912), professor of physiology at the Veterinary Hochschule in Berlin. Pioneer in experimental investigation of the cerebral functional localization. First furnished the evidence in favor of localization of visual function in the occipital lobe of the brain and of auditory function in the temporal lobe. Defined mental or psychic blindness as distinct from cortical blindness. First proved experimentally the retinotopical or "point-to-point" organization of visual centers in the cerebral cortex. From Deutsch. med. Wchnschr., v. 35, p. 258, 1909. For obituary *see* Neurol. Centralbl., v. 31, p. 1343, 1912. (*Cf. also* Figs. 99, 100.)

cranial pressure and infection, all parts of the brain were necessarily interfered with. Goltz's experiments were, according to Munk, of no value as evidence against the concept of functional localization in the cerebral cortex.

2. Discovery of mental or psychic blindness by Munk.—From his own experiments

or "mental or psychic blindness," subsequently renamed "visual agnosia."

This defect manifested itself in an inability to understand the meaning or significance of visual objects which were familiar before the operation, although the same objects were recognized by means of other senses, e.g., hearing or smell. The behavior of the animal was the more remarkable, since signs of true blindness were absent: the animal apparently saw objects and was able to avoid running into obstacles, their symbolic meaning alone having been lost. In the course of time, however, the animal gradually relearned the significance of objects and persons seen, passing through a process of learning similar to that of young animals, although requiring less time. This visual disturbance Munk interpreted as caused by the loss of traces of past visual impressions or experiences, or mnemonic engrams (*Erinnerungsbilder*). (For human pathology *see* chaps. XI, XII.)

3. DEFINITION OF CORTICAL BLINDNESS.— The same area A_1 on the lateral face of the occipital lobe in the Dog, Munk assumed, represented also the locus of distinct or direct vision

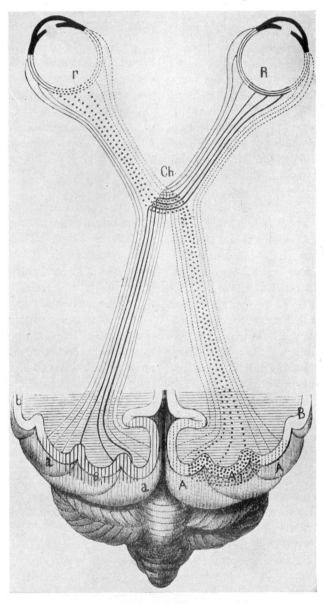

FIG. 99.—The representation of the retinae in the visual pathways and centers of the cerebral cortex in Dog, according to Munk (1879). *Labeling: AA*, right visual area; *aa*, left visual area; A_1 and a_1, centers of visual areae whose destruction supposedly produces "mental or psychic blindness"; *B* and *b*, auditory areae; *Ch*, chiasma of optic nerves; *R*, *r*, right and left retinae. Note that according to this scheme the ipsilateral and contralateral homonymous or "identical" portions of both retinae do not coincide, as now accepted, but are distinctly represented in the same area. (*Cf.* Fig. 100.)

in the field of view, homologous with foveal or "macular" vision in Man. When the occipital lobe was more extensively damaged or removed bodily, the result was not only loss of visual memory but true blindness. Munk thought at first that in the Dog the blindness concerned only the contralateral eye, thus repeating the erroneous interpretation of Pourfour du Petit, Flourens, Panizza, and Ferrier. In the further course of his work (1878, 1879), in both the Dog and the Monkey, because of a partial crossing in the chiasma found by Gudden, Munk recognized the defect to be homonymous hemianopia (this symptom was first, but less clearly, produced experimentally by Luciani & Tamburini 1877). When both occipital lobes were destroyed, the result was complete and permanent blindness. The blindness caused by destruction of the visual area of the cerebral cortex Munk named *Rindenblindheit*, or "cortical blindness," in contrast to the "mental or psychic blindness" described above.

4. Retinotopical organization of the cortical visual area.—Concerning the detailed relationship of the visual receptor organ —the retina—to the visual cortical area, Munk concluded that "the central elements of the visual area, where the optic pathway terminates and where perception takes place, are arranged in an orderly manner and continuously, as are the receptors in the retina where the fibers arise, viz., that the adjoining retinal units remain close to the same units in the cortex." With this, the problem of the cerebral representation of the retina was formulated, and a basis was given for subsequent investigations of the visual pathway (*see* chap. II, 10, 11 [2 & 6], and chap. IV, 4).

5. Occipital location of the visual area. —In opposition to Ferrier (*see* sec. 7 [2], this chapter), Munk found the visual center in the Monkey to be limited to the occipital lobe. Destruction of the occipital lobe produces a visual disturbance—contralateral homonymous hemianopia if the lesion is unilateral; complete and permanent blindness if it is bilateral. Munk found the angular gyrus, where, according to Ferrier, the most distinct vision corresponding to the fovea or "macula" was represented, to be a sensory-motor center for contralateral conjugate eye movements and for the winking reflex (*see* Munk & Obregia 1890).

6. Effect of Munk's work on subsequent brain research.—Munk's discoveries and his interpretation had a profound effect upon contemporary students of cerebral anatomy, physiology, and pathology, as well as psychology. In summary, they demonstrated, first, the localization of the distinct motor, somesthetic, visual, and auditory functions in particular regions of the cerebral cortex and, second, that both the "higher" or "psychic" and the "elemental" receptor and motor functions were located in the cortex.

Enthusiastically accepted by most, Munk's observations encountered an equally skeptical attitude in others. The errors in detail, e.g., Munk's assumption of separate representation of the ipsilateral and contralateral homonymous halves of the two retinae in the cortex, both in the Dog and in the Monkey, and the localization of the visual center on the lateral face of the occipital lobe in the Dog, however, in no way diminished the effect of his researches as a powerful stimulus to the further investigation of the brain in general and of the visual system in particular (*see* chap. IV, 4, 5).

References: Bechterew 1883, 1908–11; Boring 1950; Brown & Schäfer 1888; Exner 1881; Fritsch 1912; Goltz; Hitzig; Klüver & Bucy 1937, 1938, 1939; Lissauer 1890; Luciani & Seppilli; Luciani & Tamburini; Monakow 1905, 1914; Munk; Munk & Obregia; Roncoroni 1920; H. Sachs 1895; E. A. Schäfer 1887, 1888, 1889; Siemerling 1890; Soury 1899; Vitzou 1888, 1893; Weigandt 1900, 1901; Wilbrand 1887.

SEC. 9. EARLY MODERN INVESTIGATION OF THE INFRANUCLEAR
DIVISION OF THE VISUAL SYSTEM

1. Beginnings of modern ophthalmoneurology.—The modern period of investigation of the visual system, like that of modern ophthalmology in general, began with the discovery of the ophthalmoscope by Helmholtz (1851, Figs. 101, 102), the introduction of the plotting of fields of vision by Albrecht von Graefe (1856, portrait Fig. 103), and the invention of the perimeter by R. Förster (1867, portrait Fig. 104). The ophthalmoscope furnished the means of examination of the intraocular structures in the living—an advantage which inaugurated a new epoch in ophthalmology: in Graefe's own words, "Helmholtz has revealed to us a new world!" Perimetry made possible an accurate quantitative measurement of the visual functions and in pathological conditions, conjointly with anatomical considerations, the diagnosing of the seat of the lesion along the intra- and extracranial portions of the visual pathway.

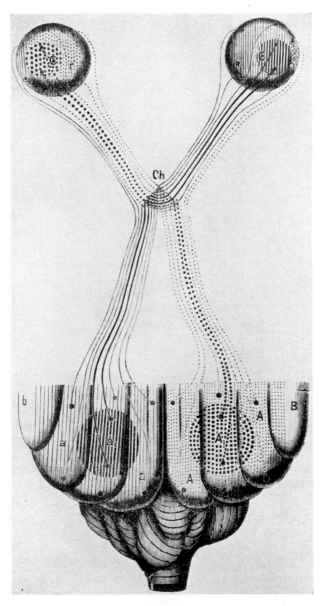

FIG. 100.—Representation of the two retinae in the visual pathways and cortical areae of Dog, according to Munk (1879). *Labeling: AA*, right visual area; *aa*, left visual area; A_1 and a_1, centers of visual areae whose destruction supposedly produces "mental or psychic blindness"; *B* and *b*, auditory areae; *C* and *c*, centers of the retinae, or central foveae ("maculae"); *Ch*, chiasma of optic nerves; *R* and *r*, right and left retinae. Note separate representation in each visual cortical center of the right and left homonymous or "identical" retinal halves, instead of in a coextensive territory, as now accepted. Each fovea or "macula," according to this diagram, is represented in the contralateral hemisphere only. (*Cf.* Fig. 99.)

These modern clinical methods of examination of the visual organs and their functions, combined with anatomy, physiology, and pathology, offered the means for a detailed analysis of the intrinsic organization of the visual system. (For biographies *see* F. Hübotter 1929–35; L. Königsberger; E. Michaelis 1877; J. Hirsch-

2. THE SEARCH FOR THE SUBCORTICAL VISUAL CENTERS.—Until long after the middle of the nineteenth century, no great progress was made toward solving the perennial problem of the "origin" of the optic nerves, beyond what Gall, Burdach, Stein, Gratiolet, and those who preceded them had known. According to the pres-

FIG. 101.—Hermann Ludwig Ferdinand Helmholtz (1821–94) in his younger years. Professor of physiology at Königsberg (now Kaliningrad), Bonn, and Heidelberg, and professor of physics at Berlin, Germany. Inventor of the ophthalmoscope (*see* Fig. 102). Authority on physiological optics, acoustics, electrophysics, etc. One of the most brilliant personalities in modern science. Portrait from his biography by L. Koenigsberger, 1902–3. (*See also* Fig. 356 and legend.)

berg; W. Schwagmeyer; for additional information on perimetry *see* J. Bjerrum 1884, Cushing *et al.*; H. Rønne 1911, 1917, 1921, 1924, 1927; C. W. Rucker 1946; Rucker & Keys 1950; Traquair 1946; C. B. Walker 1913, 1917, 1921, 1929; W. P. C. Zeeman 1925.)

entation of Panizza (1855–56), Meynert (1869, 1872), Gudden (1869, 1870, 1874, 1875, 1879, portrait Fig. 105), Forel (1872), Huguenin (1875, 1878), Tartuferi (1878, 1880, 1882), Henle (1879), J. Stilling (1880, 1882), Wilbrand (1881), Ganser (1882), Monakow (1889 and later), Bernheimer (1889, 1891), and others, there are three principal subcortical stations related to the optic nerves: the lateral geniculate nucleus, the pulvinar of the thalamus, and the superior colliculus of the midbrain. There was, however, some uncertainty as to whether the medial geniculate nucleus, the thalamus proper, Luys's body, the inferior collicus, the pons, and the tuber cinereum of the hypothalamus should not also be included. Flechsig

(1896), employing a more efficient technique, expressed doubts that any optic nerve fibers reached the thalamus proper (*see* chap. IV, 2 [3]). Dimmer (1899), applying the Marchi method to a human specimen, also found that most optic fibers terminated in the lateral geniculate nucleus; only a few in the superior colliculus; and hardly any in the pulvinar of the thalamus.

At this time little was known of the finer

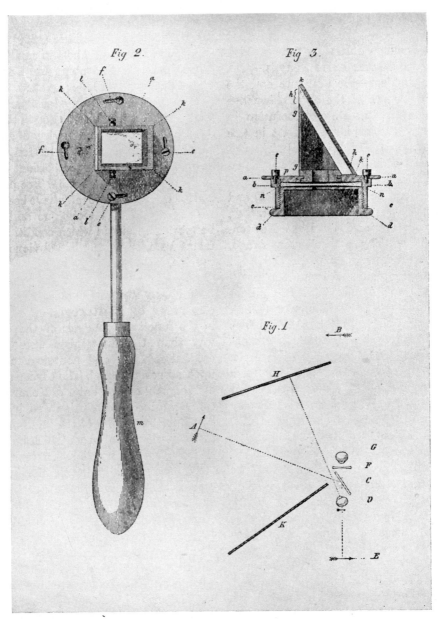

FIG. 102.—Original ophthalmoscope or "eye mirror" invented by Helmholtz (1851), an instrument that laid the foundation for modern ophthalmology. *1*, explanation of its principle; *2*, instrument assembled for use; *3*, horizontal section of the ophthalmoscope. (*See* W. Schwagmeyer 1952, and preceding figure.)

structure of the subcortical visual centers. The peculiar alternating cell and fiber layers or laminae of the lateral geniculate nucleus were first hinted at by Burdach (1822; *see* chap. II, 12 [6]). Burdach's casual remark, however, was forgotten until the laminar structure of this nucleus was more accurately described by Meynert and by Henle. Meynert's interpretation was that, of each two medullary laminae, one belonged to the tract and the other to the visual radiation, with one cellular lamina between them (*cf.* chap. VI, 6 [6]).

3. Partial versus complete decussation in the chiasma of the optic nerves.—The other vexing problem—the structure and the functional significance of the optic chiasma—remained, as before, in a state of confusion, in spite of the greatly increased interest in this problem (*cf.* chap. II, 11 [3]; 12 [3, 4]). The majority of early modern anatomists, physiologists, and clinicians—beginning with Treviranus (1835) and ending with Cramer (1898) and others—accepted "semidecussation," or, rather, partial crossing, proposed by Isaac Newton, Vater & Heinicke, Taylor, Wollaston, Arago, and Johannes Müller (*see* chap. II, 12 [3, 4]). This view was accepted by Alison (1836), Cruveilhier (1838, 1852), Arnold (1839, 1851), Longet (1842), Foville (1844), Hannover (1852), Sahmen (1854), A. Graefe (1856), J. Hughlings Jackson (1863, 1875), Testelin (1866), Alexander (1867), Hjort (1867), Zagórski (1867), Keen & Thomson (1871), Gudden (1874–79), Reich (1875), Hirschberg (1875, 1876), Schweigger (1876), Plenk (1876), R. Förster (1877), Pooley (1877), Munk (1877 and later), Hosch (1878), Nicati (1878), Gowers (1878), Baumgarten (1878, 1881), Henle (1879), Nieden (1879), Adamük (1880), Purtscher (1880), Mauthner (1881), Tartuferi (1881), Féré (1882), Stilling (1882), Ganser (1882), Bechterew (1883), Gnauck (1883), Noyes (1884), Starr (1884), Jatzow (1885), Singer & Münzer (1888), Siemerling (1888), Bernheimer (1889, 1900), Hebold (1891), Hüfler (1895), L. Jacobsohn (1896), and Hellendall (1897).

The opposition, however, represented by Biesiadecki (1861), Pawlowski (1869), Brown-Séquard (1872), Mandelstamm (1873, 1875), Michel (1873 and later), Cohn (1874), Scheel (1874), Schwalbe (1874), *et al.*, all of whom advocated the idea of a complete crossing of the optic nerve fibers in all Vertebrates, including Man, was hardly less formidable, especially in view of the fact that, in spite of Gudden's perfectly clear evidence to the contrary, it was backed by the authority of Koelliker (1896, 1899, 1900) and other histologists of note. As to Johannes Müller, his earlier assumption of division of each optic nerve fiber, with branches passing to the opposite halves of the brain, was later vindicated to some extent by S. Ramón y Cajal (1899) and Koelliker (1899). The former saw such bifurcating fibers in small numbers in the chiasma of the Rabbit and Rat, the latter in the Cat, Ox, and Dog (*see* chap. II, 12 [8]).

The refusal to acknowledge a partial decussation in the human chiasma and in that of higher Mammals was strange, in view of an increasing number of clinical cases of homonymous hemianopia caused by unilateral lesions of the visual pathway above the chiasma. The principal reason for this reluctance may have been the crudeness of anatomical technique and the use of vertebrate species in which conditions were different from, or at least less obvious than, those in Man

4. Early modern investigations of various types of hemianopia.—More successful in the functional analysis of the visual pathway than the anatomists were the clinical ophthalmologists and neurologists who relied upon human material. The earlier observations of Morgagni and of Vater & Heinicke but especially the lucid description and interpretation by Wollaston (1824) of the "half-blindness" or rather "half-vision" from which he and several of his friends suffered again revived interest among the clinical ophthalmologists in the nature of this affliction (*see* chap. II, 12 [4]; *see also* Testelin 1866). A. Graefe (1856), "founder of modern ophthalmology," found the right answer when he interpreted homonymous hemianopia—in his opinion a rather frequent disturbance—as caused by a unilateral cerebral lesion of the visual pathway above the place of partial decussation in the chiasma. Incidentally, the term with which this disturbance was first designated was "hemiopia," meaning "half-vision" or "half-sight"; the present terms "hemianopia'' and "hemianopsia," meaning "half-blindness," were subsequently introduced by Hirschberg (1875).

Graefe's work, well presented by Engelhardt (1865), was rapidly followed by numerous clinical and pathological studies of cases showing various types of defects in the fields of view. D. E. Müller (1861), Saemisch (1865), and Williams (1875) explained bitemporal hemianopia as caused by compression of decussating fibers in the chiasma, which leaves the nondecussating fibers intact, while Knapp (1875) interpreted binasal hemianopia as a consequence of interference with uncrossed fibers in the same locality, in his particular case through pressure exerted by atheromatous blood vessels.

FIG. 103.—Albrecht von Graefe (1828–70), professor of ophthalmology in Berlin, Germany. Man most deserving the title "Founder of Ophthalmology." Pupil of Johannes Müller (Fig. 355) and of Arlt, and a friend and collaborator of Heinrich Müller (Fig. 46), Du Bois-Reymond, Donders (Fig. 358), and Helmholtz (Fig. 101). First to use in clinical practice the ophthalmoscope invented by Helmholtz (Fig. 102); in Graefe's words, "Helmholtz gave us a new world!" First began systematic plotting of the fields of view in cases of defective vision. Brought about recognition of ophthalmology as an independent branch of medical science. Introduced numerous important practices into clinical ophthalmology. Founder of the Arch. f. Ophth., in 1854. Frontispiece in E. Michaelis, *A. v. Graefe, sein Leben und sein Wirken*, 1877. *See also* E. Michaelis 1877; and J. Hirschberg in Graefe & Saemisch, *Handb. d. ges. Augenh.*, 2d ed., v. 1 (1), 1910.

5. Solution of the problem of the chiasma.—The evidence from numerous clinical observations, verified by careful post mortem examinations accumulating toward the end of the nineteenth century and from physiological experiments, overwhelmingly favored the concept of "semidecussation" in the chiasma, a term introduced by Wollaston, which Alison later replaced by the more correct term "partial decussation" (*see* Hughlings Jackson 1875;

portion of the chiasma is made up of fibers, originating in the nasal halves of both retinae, which cross the mid-line from the respective optic nerves to enter the contralateral optic tract. The fibers from the temporal halves of the retinae do not decussate but, forming the lateral bundles of the chiasma, proceed to the optic tracts of the same side. The suprachiasmal portion of the visual pathway of each side (the optic tracts, lateral geniculate nuclei, visual

Fig. 104.—Richard Förster (1825–1902), professor of ophthalmology in Breslau (now Wroclaw), then Prussian Silesia. Inventor of the arc perimeter, an instrument with which to plot the normal fields of view and to study the various defects, such as hemianopias and scotomas. First suggested multiple blood supply of the occipital pole as the cause of the so-called central or "macular" sparing frequently found in homonymous hemianopia. From J. Hirschberg, in Graefe & Saemisch, *Handb. d. ges. Augenh.*, 2d ed., v. 15 (1), p. 160, 1918.

Wilbrand 1881; Bernheimer 1889, 1896; Delbrück 1890; Darkschewitsch 1891; Hebold 1891; Bechterew 1898; Cramer 1898; Dimmer 1899; S. Ramón y Cajal 1899; Siegrist 1899; Wilbrand & Saenger; A. Pichler 1900).

According to this view, now generally accepted, in Man and other Primates the central

radiations, and visual cortical centers) contains, accordingly, two sets of fibers, the crossed, which are somewhat more numerous, and the uncrossed, corresponding to the right or left homonymous halves of both retinae.

In lower Vertebrates (Fishes, Amphibians, Reptiles, Birds, and possibly also in the most primitive Mammals [*Echidna, Platypus*]), whose monocular fields are largely or entirely separated and whose vision is therefore preponderantly or entirely panoramic, decussation seems to be complete (Gudden 1874–79; Stilling 1882; Michel 1887; Singer & Münzer 1889; Sölder 1898; S. Ramón y Cajal 1899, 1909–11; Harris 1904; Lubsen 1921; C. J. Herrick 1944, *et al.*). In the infraprimate Mammals, beginning with Marsupials and Rodents, the relative number of homolateral nondecussating fibers increases with the increase of overlap of the two monocular fields of vision or with the perfection of binocular stereoscopic vision, which is the same

FIG. 105.—Bernhard von Gudden (1824–86), professor of psychiatry in Munich, Bavaria, Germany. Pioneer investigator in experimental neuroanatomy, in particular of the vertebrate visual system. Frontispiece from Gudden's *Gesammelte und hinterlassene Abhandlungen*, 1889. For biography *see* T. Meynert, in Wien. med. Bl., 1886; in Arch. f. Psychiat. u. Nervenk., v. 18; and in Haymaker & Baer, *The Founders of Neurology*, 1953.

thing. In the Mouse, Rat, and Rabbit the non-decussating fibers are believed to be few; in the Opossum and the Horse they amount approximately to one-fifth; in the Cat almost to one-third; in the Monkey and in Man almost to one-half (*see* Dexler 1897; S. Ramón y Cajal 1899; Minkowski; Brouwer; Brouwer & Zeeman; Barris, Ingram & Ranson; Bodian; for further details on the comparative structure of the chiasma *see* chap. VI, 4, 5, 6).

The fact of partial decussation in Mammals has been further confirmed by physiological experiment (Nicati 1878; Bechterew 1883; my own observation in Cat and Monkey). Anatomical experimental evidence of semidecussation of the foveal or "macular" fibers was furnished in the 1930's by Le Gros Clark & Penman (*see* chap. IV, 6 [5]; for the evidence presented in this book *see* chaps. VI, XI, XII).

6. Landolt's and Charcot's hypothesis of the decussation of optic nerve fibers in the midbrain.—A hypothesis proposed by Landolt (1875) and supported by Charcot (1876–80) may be mentioned in connection with the question of the chiasma and homonymous hemianopia. An increasing number of the observed cases of half-blindness caused by verified unilateral suprachiasmal cerebral lesions had induced Charcot to accept partial crossing in the chiasma and, consequently, homonymous hemianopia in unilateral lesions of the optic tract. Such, for example, was a case reported by Gowers (1878) of softening of the posterior portion of the thalamus and another by Hirschberg (1875), where one optic tract was compressed by a gliosarcoma. However, in order to explain the "amaurosis of the contralateral eye," which many at that time, following Flourens and Panizza, still believed to be caused by unilateral suprachiasmal brain lesions (*see* secs. 4 [4], 7 [1], this chapter, and chap. IV, 1 [1]), Charcot assumed an additional crossing in the region of the quadrigeminal bodies of the midbrain of those fibers which remain uncrossed in the chiasma (some of the older anatomists, e.g., Willis 1664, and Rolando 1809, believed the two optic nerves were united in the posterior commissure at the place of their apparent origin). The total effect of this arrangement in Man would be an amaurosis of the opposite eye in the case of a unilateral lesion of the visual pathway at the levels above the midbrain, the same as in the Lower Vertebrates, where decussation in the chiasma is considered to be complete (*cf.* chap. VI, 5). Such an arrangement would also agree with the early experiments of Pourfour du Petit, Ferrier, and Munk, who at first believed the unilateral destruction of the cortical visual center caused blindness only of the contralateral eye (*see* secs. 7 [4], 8 [3], this chapter). Even though this speculation was subsequently proved to be fallacious (*see* Starr 1884), the idea of a partial crossing or of a recrossing of the visual pathway above the midbrain level persists in the hypothesis of bilateral cortical representation of the fovea or "macula" (*see* chap. VII, 3 [4], 6; and chap. XI, 8).

7. Early modern attempts to discover the retinotopical organization of the infranuclear division of the visual system.—From the intensive study of clinical cases showing various forms of disturbance of the fields of view there gradually evolved the conviction that the intrinsic disposition or arrangement of its constituent fiber bundles was the core of the problem of the visual system and that through its study the dimensional relationship of the retinal surface to the brain and its functional and pathophysiological significance might be disclosed.

Most of the interest centered around the identity and course of the foveal fibers, usually termed "macular bundle," or the continuation of the "papillomacular fascicle" of the retina. The investigations of D. E. Müller (1861), Purtscher (1880), Samelsohn (1880, 1882), Uhthoff (1880, 1884, 1887), Vossius (1882), Bunge (1884), Jatzow (1885), Thomsen (1888), Schmidt-Rimpler (1889), Widmark (1897), and Dalén (1906) showed that this bundle is located in the center or axis of the optic nerves, chiasma, and optic tracts. The exception is the portion of the optic nerve close to the eyeball, where, to approximately the point of entry of the central blood vessels, the "macular bundle" holds a peripheral position at the lateral or temporal margin of the nerve. On cross-section, this area has the shape of a wedge lodged between the peripheral or "extramacular" fiber segments. Some uncertainty remained as to its position in the chiasma, the evidence pointing toward a dorsoposterior location immediately underneath the optic recess. The question of the ipsilateral uncrossed fibers was also much discussed; most authors favored a dorsolateral position in the chiasma and in the optic tracts.

The problem of quadrantic representation, among other topics, was discussed by Marchand (1882), who, anticipating Brouwer & Zeeman's modern work (chap. IV, 6 [4]), found the lateral segment of the optic tract related to the inferior portion of the retina. Whether the crossed and the uncrossed fibers in the chiasma and in the tracts are present as compact, separate bundles (Gudden) or whether they intermingle (Kellermann, Delbrück, Dimmer 1899) remained an open question, which was answered only in recent times (chap. VI, 6).

8. Henschen's scheme of retinotopical organization of infranuclear division of the visual system.—The effort of the preceding investigators, especially of Samelsohn and Jatzow, to find the arrangement of the retinal segments on a cross-section through the various levels of the infranuclear portion of the visual pathway was taken up and systematically carried on by S. E. Henschen (1890–92 and later; *see also* chap. IV, 4 [4–7]).

According to his scheme, "macular" or foveal fibers in the optic nerves, chiasma, and tracts form a separate bundle. Immediately behind the eyeball this bundle has the shape of a wedge located in the lateral or temporal half of the nerve. Farther up, above the portion containing the central blood vessels, the foveal bundle assumes a central position, being surrounded on all sides by fibers related to the extrafoveal portions of the retina. The four foveal quadrants are also arranged in a definite order. Close to the eyeball the two nasal quadrants are in the center and are flanked above and below by the upper and lower temporal quadrantic foveal fibers. The two bundles corresponding with the upper and lower extrafoveal temporal quadrants are in the same temporal half of the optic nerve but are kept apart by the foveal bundle. The two nasal extrafoveal quadrantic bundles are in the nasal half of the nerve and are contiguous. As the foveal bundle above the point of entry of the central vessels becomes axial,

the upper and lower temporal extrafoveal quadrantic fibers gradually merge along the temporal periphery of the nerve. In the chiasma, only the center is made up of crossed fibers, the lateral portions containing both crossed and uncrossed fibers intertwining in complicated loops and layers. In this locality the foveal bundle is located either centrally or in the dorsal portion of the chiasma. In the optic tracts the foveal-macular bundle preserves a central location in the same way as in the optic nerves, being flanked above by the temporal and below by the nasal extrafoveal quadrantic fibers. Henschen believed a similar arrangement to be present also in the lateral geniculate nuclei.

9. Critique of Henschen's views.—Henschen's scheme, as shown by investigations of Wilbrand & Saenger (1904), Rønne (1914), Minkowski (1920), and later Brouwer & Zeeman (1925, 1926), Brody (1934), Le Gros Clark & Penman (1934), and those presented in this book, was at fault in several respects (*see* chap. VI, 4–7). His first mistake was to assume that the ipsilateral and contralateral fibers took a separate course above the chiasma: he supposed the ipsilateral remained chiefly in the lateral, and the contralateral chiefly in the medial, portion of the tracts. He also assumed that each set terminated separately, by quadrants, in the lateral geniculate nuclei. Henschen's presentation of the foveal or "macular" fibers in the optic tracts as surrounded on all sides by the extrafoveal or "peripheral" fibers, was likewise an error. Nor was the arrangement of the upper and lower quadrants, either in the tracts or in the lateral geniculate nuclei, as given in Henschen's scheme, correct. Finally, Henschen failed to notice discrete terminations of ipsilateral and contralateral fibers in the alternating cell laminae of the lateral geniculate nuclei, discovered by Minkowski, and thus misunderstood the essential functional role of these internodes of the visual pathway (*see* chap. VI, 6). In spite of these errors, Henschen's work was of great merit, since it showed the road that subsequent investigators had to follow. (*Cf.* chap. VI, 4, 5, 6, 7.)

References: Adamük 1880; G. B. Airy 1865; H. Airy 1870; Alexander 1867; Alison 1836;

Ariëns Kappers, Huber & Crosby 1936; F. Arnold 1838–42, 1845–51; A. Bader 1933; Baumgarten 1878, 1881; Bechterew 1883, 1898; Bernheimer 1889, 1896, 1900; Biesiadecki 1861; Brewster 1865, 1866; P. Bunge 1884; F. Burdach 1883; K. F. Burdach 1822; Charcot 1876–80; H. Cohn 1874; A. Cramer 1898; J. Cruveilhier 1838, 1852; Darkschevitsch 1891; Delbrück 1890; Deutschmann 1883; Dexler 1897; Dimmer 1899; Engelhardt 1865; C. Féré 1882; Flechsig 1896; R. Förster 1867, 1869, 1877; A. Forel 1872; Foville 1844; S. Ganser 1882; Gnauck 1883; W. R. Gowers 1878; A. von Graefe 1856; B. Gudden 1874–79; A. Hannover 1852; W. Harris 1904; Hebold 1891, 1892; Hellendall 1897; H. Helmholtz 1851; J. Henle 1871 (1879); Henschen 1890–92 and later; J. Hirschberg 1875, 1876; Hjort 1867; Hosch 1878; E. Hüfler 1895; Huguenin 1873, 1875; J. Hughlings Jackson 1863, 1875; C. Jacobsohn 1896; Jatzow 1885; Keen & Thomson 1871; Kellermann 1879; J. H. Knapp 1875; Koelliker 1896, 1899, 1900; E. Landolt 1875, 1894; Lebensohn 1941; W. S. Little 1886; Longet 1842; Marchand 1882; Meynert 1869, 1872; J. Michel 1873, 1877, 1887; A. Mohr 1879; Monakow 1883–92, 1900; D. E. Müller 1861; Munk 1877 and later; Nicati 1878; Nieden 1879, 1883; Noyes 1884; Pawlowski 1869; Pick 1918; Plenk 1876; Pooley 1877; Purtscher 1880; S. Ramón y Cajal 1899, 1909–11; A. Richter 1885, 1889; Saemisch 1865; Samelsohn 1880, 1882; Scheel 1874; Schwalbe 1874; Schwagmeyer 1952; Schweigger 1876; Siegrist 1899; Siemerling 1888; Singer & Münzer 1889; Sölder 1898; Soury 1899; M. A. Starr 1884; J. Stilling 1880, 1882; Tartuferi 1880, 1882; Testelin 1866; Thomsen 1888; Tornatola 1889; Uhthoff 1880, 1887; Vater & Heinicke 1723; Vossius 1882; Wiethe 1884; Wieting 1898; Wilbrand 1878, 1881; Wilbrand & Saenger 1904; E. Williams 1875; Wollaston 1824; Zagórski 1867.

Chapter IV

Modern Anatomical, Experimental, Clinical, and Pathological Investigation of the Visual Pathways and Centers

SEC. 1. EARLY MODERN ATTEMPTS TO LOCALIZE VISUAL FUNCTION IN THE HUMAN CEREBRAL CORTEX

1. EARLIEST CLINICAL CASES OF VISUAL DISTURBANCES VERIFIED BY POST MORTEM EXAMINATION.—The observations of impaired sight, hearing, sensation, and motor function caused by the cerebral lesions that were occasionally recorded during the seventeenth, eighteenth, and first half of the nineteenth centuries produced no convincing evidence in favor of localization of the specific functions in particular territories of the cerebral cortex. Indeed, as Flourens' experiments indicated, such an intimate relationship was not to be expected (*see* chap. III, 4).

Concerning vision, the first breach in this, on the whole, negative situation was made by the experiments and the clinical and pathoanatomical investigations of Panizza (1855, 1856). In a case seen by him, a right-sided hemiparesis and hemianesthesia caused by a hemorrhage in the left thalamus was associated with "blindness of the right eye" (this was, of course, an erroneous interpretation of homonymous hemianopia accepted at that time, originating with Pourfour du Petit's and Flourens' experiments; *see* chap. III, 9 [6]). In another similar case there was a lesion in the thalamus and one in the posterior region of one cerebral hemisphere. Panizza also described a fiber tract originating in the posterior portion of the thalamus and terminating in the posterior superior gyri of the hemisphere —obviously the visual radiation of Gratiolet or a part of it (*see* chap. III, 5 [5]). Its interruption regularly produced, in Panizza's experience, "blindness of the opposite eye." In the case of a bilateral lesion the blindness was complete, with no impairment of other functions.

Another pioneer of that period, Chaillou (1863), reported a case apparently of right-sided homonymous hemianopia, with other symptoms, in an elderly person. It was caused by foci of softening, partly on the inner face of the left occipital lobe and partly in the posterior portion of the left thalamus.

Since in both Panizza's and Chaillou's cases cortical lesions were complicated by lesions in the thalamus, they in no way changed the trend of opinion, which, under Flourens' influence, was, in general, antilocalist (*see also* chap. III, 6).

2. INTRODUCTION OF PERIMETRY AND ITS EFFECT UPON NEURO-OPHTHALMOLOGY.—An important factor which made possible modern investigation of the visual pathway was the introduction of systematic testing of the fields of vision in disturbances caused by cerebral pathology by A. von Graefe (1856, portrait Fig. 103). The plotting of the fields, made popular by J. Hughlings Jackson (1863, portrait Fig. 106), became a routine procedure after the introduction of the perimeter into clinical practice by R. Förster (1867, portrait Fig. 104). Interest was at first quite naturally restricted to the infranuclear division of the visual system. Before long, however, the supranuclear division came to the fore. During this period the principal characteristics of visual field disturbances were discovered, and their various types classified. In apoplexy, for example, Graefe (1865) noticed a frequent occurrence of hemianopic symptoms, often with "sparing" of the central portions of the fields around the fixation points. In other cases the division line between the normal and the blind halves of the fields was straight, passing through the fixation points. The relative frequency of the hemianopic defects of vision in cerebral disease was emphasized by J. Hughlings Jackson (1875), Schweigger (1876), R. Förster (1877), and other clinicians. (For biographies *see* J. Hirschberg 1911; F. Hübotter 1929–35; E. Michaelis 1877.)

cus of the occipital lobes. The optic nerve, according to him, terminates both in the lateral and medial geniculate nuclei and also in the pulvinar of the thalamus. From these three localities, he thought, fibers arise that terminate partly in the ensiform and lingual gyri and partly in the hippocampal sulcus (the posterior

Fig. 106.—John Hughlings Jackson (1835–1911), physician at the National Hospital for Paralysed and Epileptic, Queen Square, London, England. Pioneer clinical neurologist and neuropathologist. Among the first to emphasize the importance of the ophthalmoscope and of the plotting of fields of view in clinical neurology. An early student of the cerebral functional localization in relation to clinical neurology. A unique observer and interpreter of the clinical manifestations of nervous disease. Courtesy Dr. F. M. R. Walshe, of London. For biography and writings *see* J. Taylor *et al.*, in Jackson's *Neurological Fragments*, 1925; *cf. also* his *Selected Writings*, 1931, and Haymaker & Baer, *The Founders of Neurology*, 1953.

3. EARLY ANATOMICAL SUGGESTION OF AN OCCIPITAL LOCALIZATION OF VISUAL FUNCTION.— Meynert (1869) was apparently the first to express an opinion concerning the location of the cortical visual center around the calcarine sul-

portion of that sulcus is identical with what is now called the "calcarine sulcus or fissure"; *cf.* Figs. 271, 273). Subsequently, this view was accepted by Huguenin (1878) and by Wilbrand (1881). It is also possible that Meynert's opinion was the source of Munk's idea of locating the visual center in the posterior region of the cerebral hemisphere (*see* chap. III, 8 [5]; on Meynert *see* J. Fritsch 1892; Jolly 1892; Anton 1930; De Crinis 1939; O. Vogt 1943).

4. First verified clinical cases suggesting the occipital seat of visual center.—The clinical cases of visual field defects observed with increasing frequency during this period were of far greater importance to the localization of visual function in the cerebral cortex than were the anatomical investigations. Most of these cases definitely indicated the presence of a center of sight in the occipital lobes. The observations reported by Levick (1866), Keen & Thomson (1871), Pooley (1877), Baumgarten (1878), Hosch (1878), Huguenin (1878), Curschmann (1879, 1881), Nothnagel (1879), and Westphal (1879, 1880, 1881) supported this theory. Unfortunately, evidence from human pathology was inconclusive. In almost all cases the pathological changes found in the brain were not confined to the occipital lobe, much less to a small portion of its cortex or subcortical fibers. Usually the destruction extended to the adjoining territories, mostly to the parietal or temporal lobes, occasionally as far as the insula, central region, frontal lobe, thalamus, and other parts. This insufficient evidence may, then, explain why some prominent investigators of that period (e.g., Goltz and Hitzig) remained faithful to the ancient thesis of a preponderance of the subcortical nuclei in the visual function. (*Cf.* chap. III, 4 [6]), 5 [6].)

Notwithstanding the afore-mentioned difficulties, Wilbrand (1881, portrait Fig. 107), after reviewing all known clinical observations, decided in favor of occipital localization of vision. This, of course, agreed with Munk's physiological experiments (*see* chap. III, 8 [5]), and with the occipital termination of visual radiation described in the Monkey by Gratiolet (1854–57), Huguenin (1878), and Wernicke (1881). The field defects found in homonymous hemianopia may, according to Wilbrand, be caused not only by lesions of the optic tract, thalamus, and adjoining structures but also by cortical and subcortical lesions affecting only a portion of the occipital lobe. An incomplete hemianopia, for example, may be caused by a focus close to or in the cortex, where the incoming visual fibers spread over a wide area, in analogy with the somatomotor monoplegias caused by a similar location of small lesions in the motor cortex or in the outgoing motor fibers. (On Wilbrand *see also* sec. 4, this chapter.)

5. Earliest suggestion of the striate area as a visual center.—Wilbrand's deductions were soon corroborated by Giovanardi (1881), who described the brain specimen of an *anophthalmos* or a baby with congenital absence of eyes and other parts of the visual system, where he found marked atrophy of the occipital lobes (Fig. 108). Even more to the point were two cases of homonymous hemianopia (Fig. 109) reported by Haab & Huguenin (1882). In one, a solitary tubercle and, in the other, a single embolic encephalomalacic focus in the contralateral calcarine region were found. It was logical, then, for Huguenin to suggest that the cortical area in the occipital lobe, distinguished by the presence of Gennari's and Vicq-d'Azyr's stripe, may be concerned with the visual function.

6. Starr's pathophysiological analysis of visual pathways.—Another clinical observer of that period, M. A. Starr (1884, portrait Fig. 110), after discussing more than two dozen cases of visual disturbances known at that time, became convinced that the visual center was located in the occipital lobes. The symptoms of homonymous hemianopia, according to him, may be produced not only by unilateral lesions of the optic tract but also by those of the pulvinar of the thalamus, of the posterior portion of the internal capsule, of fiber radiation to the occipital lobe, of the medullary portion of that lobe, and of its cortex. Each occipital lobe was anatomically and functionally related to the homonymous halves of both retinae. A unilateral lesion of the suprachiasmal portion of the visual pathway, therefore, did not make, according to Starr, the contralateral eye blind, as Flourens, Panizza, Charcot, and many others believed at that time, but instead it destroyed the function of the contralateral halves of both fields of vision. (*Cf.* chap. III, 4 [4], 9 [6], and par. 1, this section.)

Starr's analysis of the visual mechanism of

the brain was a far cry from the uncertainty which had existed only a few years earlier. Nevertheless, more well-observed clinical cases, documented by careful post mortem examination, were needed to duplicate Munk's animal experiments in Man by a detailed correlation of parts of the fields of vision with definite localities of the occipital cortex. (*See* chap. III, 8 [4].)

7. CLINICAL OBSERVATIONS POINTING TO THE CALCARINE FISSURE AS A LOCALITY CONCERNED IN VISUAL FUNCTION; EVIDENCE OF A QUADRANTIC REPRESENTATION OF HEMIRETINAE.—During this period, additional clinical observations made the localization of the visual center in the occipital lobe practically certain (Schweigger 1876, 1891; Wilbrand 1881, 1885, 1887, 1890, 1892; Haab & Huguenin 1882; Jany 1882; Marchand 1882; Noyes 1884; Féré 1885; Monakow 1885; Richter 1885, 1889; Gruening 1886; Reinhard 1886–87; Séguin 1886; Nothnagel 1887). Among these, a classical case observed

FIG. 107.—Hermann Wilbrand (1851–1935), professor of ophthalmology at Hamburg, Germany, at the age of seventy. Encyclopedic neuro-ophthalmologist and co-author, with A. Saenger and C. Behr, of *Die Neurologie des Auges* published in ten volumes, 1899–1927. Suggested bilateral representation of each complete fovea in the cerebral cortex as an explanation of central or so-called "macular" sparing in cases of homonymous hemianopia. Author of the hypothesis of syndynamical homonymous conductor units in the suprachiasmal portion of the visual pathway as the anatomical basis of the functional congruity of both monocular fields of view in the normal binocular visual act. From Klin. Monatsbl. f. Augenh., v. 66, p. 769, 1921.

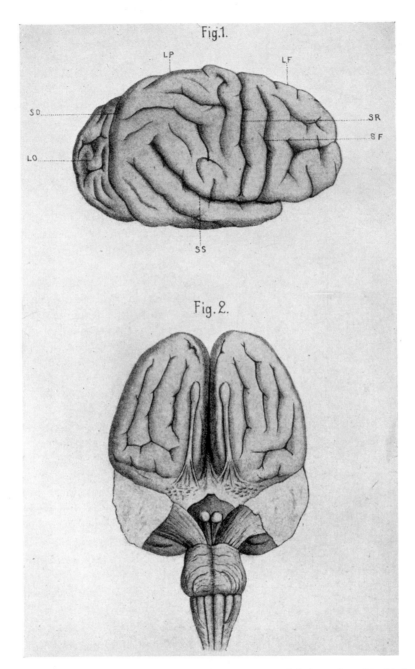

Fig. 1.

Fig. 2.

FIG. 108.—Brain of a fourteen-month-old child with a congenital anophthalmia, first of its kind, reported by Giovanardi as evidence of localization of vision in the occipital lobes of the brain. All parts making up the visual system were absent: the eyes, optic nerves, chiasma, tracts, and lateral geniculate nuclei, while the occipital lobes were underdeveloped. Upper figure shows the lateral view of the right cerebral hemisphere with the atrophic occipital lobe (*LO*), separated from the rest by a deep and long external parieto-occipital sulcus (*SO*) resembling simian sulcus (*cf. l* in Figs. 280, 282, 284). Lower figure shows the basal view of the brain. From E. Giovanardi in Riv. sper. di freniat., v. 7, p. 244, 1881.

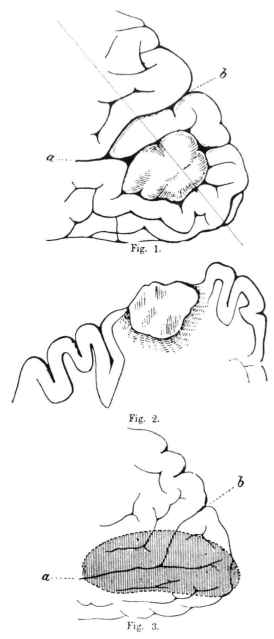

Fig. 1.

Fig. 2.

Fig. 3.

FIG. 109.—First verified cases of visual disturbance caused by localized lesions of the calcarine region of the occipital lobes, reported by Haab (& Huguenin). Upper sketch shows the inner face of the right occipital lobe with a solitary tubercle located in the calcarine fissure (*a*). Middle sketch shows same specimen cut along the indicated line. During life a left homonymous hemianopia was found. Lower sketch also shows the inner face of the right occipital lobe with the calcarine fissure (*a*) and parieto-occipital sulcus (*b*), the shaded area indicating the approximate extent of encephalomalacic region caused by embolism. Here, too, a left-sided homonymous hemianopia was present during life. From O. Haab (& Huguenin), in Klin. Monatsbl. f. Augenh., v. 20, p. 141, 1882.

by Henry Hun (1887), Professor of Diseases of the Nervous System at the Albany Medical College, was noteworthy (portrait Fig. 111; for biography *see* La Salle d'Archambault 1924). The plotting of the fields of view revealed a blindness confined to the left inferior homonymous quadrants of both sides (Fig. 112). A post mortem examination showed a single encephalomalacic lesion in the right occipital lobe, limited to the inferior margin of the cuneus, that is, to the upper lip of the calcarine fissure (*A* in same figure). This rather uncomplicated case was the next after Haab & Huguenin's to furnish evidence of localization of the visual center on the inner face of the occipital lobe (Huguenin, 1878, claimed that most fibers of the visual radiation terminate around the calcarine fissure).

But beyond this, Hun's case was also the first to demonstrate a quadrantic representation of the homonymous hemiretinae in the cerebral cortex: the upper quadrants above, the lower quadrants below, the calcarine fissure (in the fields, owing to the dark-chamber effect of the eyes, the arrangement of the quadrants is inverted). It also lent substance to the view, later expounded in detail by Flechsig, that only a relatively small portion of the occipital cortex, precisely where the visual radiation terminated, was the "gateway" for incoming visual impulses and therefore a substratum of "simple visual sensation." The remaining and larger territory of the occipital lobe, especially its lateral face, was the substratum of "higher," gnostic, mnemonic, and other "psychic" visual functions. (*See* chap. III, 8, and sec. 2, this chapter.)

With these observations, the presence of a "visual area" or "visual center" in each occipital lobe, located along the "calcarine sulcus," was established for those few who were qualified and willing to evaluate the available data objectively; (the term "calcarine sulcus" originated with Th. Huxley 1861; *see* chap. VIII, 1 [4]). A representation of the homonymous halves of the retinae by quadrants was also demonstrated. In this way the two principal points insisted upon by Munk, but as yet based only upon animal experiments, became substantiated for the human visual system also: the presence of a definite center of vision in the occipital cortex and a topographical representation of the retina in this center.

The next task was to determine more exactly the limits of the visual cortical area in the human brain, especially its identity with a definite cytoarchitectural territory; the precise representation of the various parts of the hemiretinae in it, primarily of the central fovea or "macu-

1877; Giovanardi 1881; A. Graefe 1856 (*see also* Engelhardt 1865); Gruening 1886; Haab & Huguenin 1882; Henschen 1923, 1925; Hosch 1878; Huguenin 1878; Hun 1887; Th. Huxley 1861; J. Hughlings Jackson 1863, 1878; Jany 1882; Ph. Jolly 1892; Keen & Thomson 1871; Lenz 1924; Levick 1866; Marchand 1882; Meynert 1869; Monakow 1885; Mooren 1888; Niessl

Fig. 110.—M. Allen Starr (1854–1932), professor of neurology at Columbia University, New York. An illustrious pioneer of American neurology. One of the early writers who successfully analyzed visual disturbances of central origin and correctly interpreted their pathoanatomical basis. For portrait and obituary *see* F. Tilney, in J. Nerv. & Ment. Dis., v. 77, p. 226, 1933; *see also* Haymaker & Baer, *The Founders of Neurology*, 1953.

la"; the microscopic study of its minute structure; its various fiber connections; and the clinical and psychophysiological analysis of its many functional manifestations.

References: Anton 1930; Baumgarten 1871, 1881; Chaillou 1863; Curschmann 1879, 1881; Exner 1881; Féré 1885; R. Förster 1867, 1869,

von Mayendorf 1904, 1905, 1926; Nothnagel 1879, 1887; Noyes 1884; Panizza 1855–56; Pooley 1877; Reinhard 1886–87; A. Richter 1885, 1889; Schweigger 1876, 1891; Séguin 1886; Starr 1884; O. Vogt 1943; Wernicke 1881; Westphal 1879, 1880, 1881; Wilbrand 1881, 1885, 1887, 1890, 1892.

SEC. 2. DOCTRINE OF THE "PROJECTION CENTERS" AS DISTINCT FROM "ASSOCIATION AREAS" OF THE CEREBRAL CORTEX

1. IMPROVEMENT OF LABORATORY TECHNIQUE AND THE ADVANCEMENT OF BRAIN RESEARCH.— The investigations of the cortical visual centers and their connections received a powerful stimulus toward the close of the nineteenth century from the anatomical investigations of normal brain structures, especially of the fiber systems and tracts. This, in turn, became possible because of a general improvement in histological making of thin sections, to which stains could be applied. It now became possible to study, in serial sections, the normal and degenerated fiber tracts of which the brain is largely made. The normal relationships of the various structural elements were much better preserved in such preparations than in the torn-off bits of tissue obtained by the maceration and "teasing" procedures in use until then.

FIG. 111.—Henry Hun (1854–1924), professor of diseases of the nervous system at the Albany Medical College, Albany, New York. Described one of the earliest clinical cases of quadrantic homonymous hemianopia, where post mortem examination revealed a single lesion limited to the upper lip of the calcarine fissure of the contralateral occipital lobe. This observation showed, first, the location of the visual center along the calcarine fissure and, second, the representation of homonymous hemiretinae, by quadrants, in the cerebral cortex. From Arch. Neurol. & Psychiat., v. 11, p. 711, 1924. For biography *see* La Salle d'Archambault in same volume. (*Cf.* following figure.)

laboratory technique introduced by Reil, Hannover, B. Stilling, Türck, H. Müller, J. Gerlach, Beneke, Waldeyer, Böttcher, Meynert, Blum, and others. The improvements consisted in the hardening of brain specimens in various chemical solutions, such as alcohol, chromic acid, and chromic salts, which permitted the With this technique, by following serial sections, the origin, course, relationships, and termination of discrete fiber bundles could be determined. Also, through the application of such dyes as carmine or cochineal and of hematoxylin or logwood dye, the thin, transparent sections were made more useful for the microscopic study of fine details, such as the nerve cells in the cerebral cortex, in the various nuclei of the brain, and in the spinal cord. When, as a further development of this trend, a number of special staining procedures were devised by Golgi (1873, 1878), Weigert (1882), Ehrlich (1885, 1886), Marchi (1886–87), Nissl (1894, 1895), S. Ramón y Cajal (1903, 1904), Bielschowsky (1904), and others, efficient tech-

Rasmussen 1943; Conn 1948; *cf.* also chap. III, 5 [2].)

2. INITIATION OF MODERN BRAIN RESEARCH; MEYNERT.—Among the first to apply the improved techniques to the brain in a systematic way was Theodor Meynert (1867–68, 1869, 1872), Professor of Psychiatry in Vienna (portrait Figs. 113, 311; *see also* sec. 7 [2], this chap-

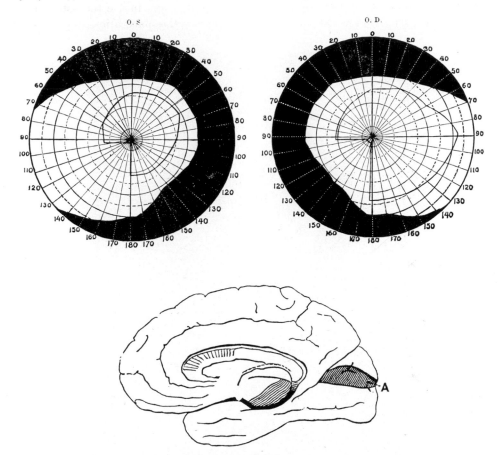

FIG. 112.—First recorded case of a quadrantic homonymous hemianopia caused by a limited cortical lesion along the calcarine fissure, verified by a post mortem examination, reported by Hun (Fig. 111). The fields of view of both eyes showed a complete loss of function in the left lower quadrants between the horizontal and vertical meridians, extending as far as the fixation points, the loss also extending into upper quadrants, including here an area larger than the monocular temporal crescent. A single lesion (*A*) was found on the inner face of the right occipital lobe, which destroyed the lower portion of the cuneus or the upper lip of the calcarine fissure. From H. Hun, Am. J. M. Sc., N.S., v. 93, p. 140, 1887.

niques had been found which made possible detailed structural analysis of the nervous organs. (For historical reviews *see* Burdach 1822, p. 243; Flechsig 1876, 1927; J. Stilling 1882; Gierke 1884–86; Stieda 1899; Neuburger 1910; Edinger 1911; Wallenberg 1926; R. Krause 1926–27; Polyak 1941–48; F. T. Lewis 1942;

ter). His fundamental investigations threw new light upon the complex organization of the brain and opened new vistas to subsequent investigators. One idea of the many which were to influence the coming generation was his concept of "projection," or topical representation in the cerebral cortex of the receptor surfaces of the sense organs, such as the retina, cochlea, skin, etc. (it is possible that Meynert, in turn, was influenced by similar ideas expressed previously by E. H. Weber, 1852, originator of the compass test for two-point discrimination of the tactile sense; for biography *see* Anton 1930 and De Crinis 1939).

3. DISCOVERY OF MYELOGENESIS; FLECHSIG. —The new ideas and the application of a new technique proved exceptionally successful in the hands of Paul Flechsig, Professor of Psychiatry in Leipzig (dates of publications 1872–1927, especially from 1894 on; portrait Fig. 114; for biography *see* Quensel 1917; Flechsig 1927; R. A. Pfeifer 1930). Early in his career Flechsig noticed that in the fresh unstained brain and spinal cord of newborn babies and fetuses only a few parts were myelinized, while the rest was without myelin. Even more distinct was the contrast between the myelinized and unmyelinized fiber tracts in the sections stained with

Fig. 113.—Theodor Hermann Meynert (1833–92), professor of psychiatry at the University of Vienna, Austria. Pioneer of modern investigation of the minute structure of the brain. He first systematically studied the cerebral cortex and showed its structure to vary in different localities. As early as 1867–68 he described the peculiar structure of the visual cortex, later called "striate area" by G. Elliot Smith, with its eight layers and "solitary cells," since then known as "Meynert cells." He created the concept of the "projection" of body surface and of the sense organs upon the cerebral cortex and named the principal fiber tracts, connecting body periphery and sense organs with the cerebral cortex, "projection systems," in contrast with short "association fibers," by means of which various parts of the cerebral cortex are interconnected. Portrait received from Frau Dora von Stockert-Meynert, Meynert's daughter, in 1946. (*See also* Fig. 311.) For biography *see* P. Jolly, in Arch. f. Psychiat., v. 24, p. iii, 1892; J. Fritsch, in Jahrb. f. Psychiat., v. 11, p. 1, 1892; G. Anton, in J. f. Psychol. u. Neurol., v. 40, p. 256, 1930; M. de Crinis, in Ztschr. f. d. ges. Neurol. u. Psychiat., v. 165, p. 17, 1939; O. Vogt, in Anat. Anz., v. 94, p. 49, 1943. and Haymaker & Baer, *The Founders of Neurology*, 1953.

carmine or, better yet, with Weigert's recently developed special hematoxylin method for staining myelin. Obviously, different tracts and systems of fibers in the central nervous organ develop their myelin sheaths at different periods of pre- and postnatal life. Those fibers, Flechsig found, which belong to the same system mature at approximately the same time, while those of

the olfactory system, the last the acoustic. This is Flechsig's "fundamental law of myelogenesis," an extension of the "biogenetical law" formulated by E. Haeckel (portrait Fig. 521).

4. FLECHSIG'S MYELOGENETICAL INVESTIGATION OF PROJECTION AND ASSOCIATION FIBER TRACTS OF THE BRAIN.—Flechsig, realizing the

AUS DEM "CORPUS IMAGINUM" DER PHOT. GES. BERLIN

FIG. 114.—Paul Emil Flechsig (1847–1929), professor of psychiatry at Leipzig, Saxony, Germany. One of the foremost students of the brain as an organ of the mind. Creator of the concept of the "projection centers" of the cortex, where the principal nerve tracts either terminate (olfactory, gustatory, somesthetic, visual, auditory) or originate (motor), as distinct from the much more extensive regions, the "association centers," where the impulses from "projection centers" meet and where they are integrated into composite processes. From Arch. f. Psychiat. u. Nervenkr., v. 91, 1930. (*Cf.* following figure; for biography *see* Quensel 1917; Flechsig 1927; R. A. Pfeifer 1930; and Haymaker & Baer, *The Founders of Neurology*, 1953.)

anatomically and functionally different tracts do so at different periods. The order or sequence of myelinization of particular fiber systems during individual development apparently repeats the phylogenetic appearance, the earliest being

importance of his discovery to cerebral anatomy, began systematically to investigate all the fiber tracts of the human brain and spinal cord. His labor, carried on for more than fifty years, had far-reaching consequences in understanding the basic organization of the human central nervous system and its workings.

The most positive results were achieved by Flechsig in his study of the afferent and efferent fiber tracts of the cerebral cortex, until then only superficially known from the work of Vieussens, Reil, Arnold, Burdach, Gratiolet, Meynert, Huguenin, J. Stilling, and Wernicke. Flechsig found (1894) that these great fiber tracts, which together make up Reil's *corona radiata* and which Meynert (1869; 1872, p. 697) termed "projection systems," related to the sense organs of sight, hearing, smell, and taste; to the peripheral somesthetic receptors of the skin, muscles, joints, and other tissues; and to the motor systems, are the first to mature in the baby's brain. Toward the end of intra-uterine development and during the first few weeks of extrauterine life, these fiber systems alone possess myelin sheaths and may there-fore be followed in serial sections from their respective origins in the subcortical nuclei to their respective terminal areas in the cerebral cortex (Flechsig's "autoanatomy"). In contrast, the systems of association fibers, by means of which the regions of the cortex are intercon-nected, develop their myelin sheaths at a later period.

5. Myelogenetical sensory spheres of the human cerebral cortex.—There are five "primordial regions" or "sensory centers or spheres" in each cerebral hemisphere of the hu-man brain that are myelinated at the time of birth, corresponding to the terminal areas of the principal afferent fiber tracts (Fig. 115). Each sensory sphere is associated with one of the primary fissures first to appear in the fetal brain—the somesthetic and somatomotor (*I*) in the posterior portion of the frontal gyri and in the pre- and postcentral gyri along the cen-tral sulcus of Rolando, which also includes the origin of the motor "pyramidal tract" and other efferent fiber systems to the pons, red nucleus, and elsewhere; the auditory sphere (*II*) in the transverse temporal convolutions of Heschl or auditory gyri of Flechsig, especially the first transverse gyrus, tucked into the posterior pocket of the lateral fissure or Sylvian fossa, emerging but little on the external surface; the visual sphere (*III*) around the calcarine fissure;

the olfactory sphere (*IV*) in the uncinate gyrus of the temporal lobe and in the inferior posterior portion of the frontal lobe; and the hippocampal gyrus, where a special fiber tract terminates which may possibly be related to the gustatory sense (*V*). The sensory spheres, Flechsig found, were not contiguous, nor did they spread over the whole hemisphere, as was assumed by Munk, but were relatively small patches sepa-rated by considerable distances, together com-prising less than one-third of the entire cortex. The various corticofugal, efferent, or descend-ing tracts, according to Flechsig, also originate either in the sensory spheres or in their imme-diate vicinity. In this way each sensory sphere is provided with a double connection, an affer-ent and an efferent one: Flechsig's "conjugate tracts."

6. Flechsig's association areas of the cerebral cortex.—The much more extensive cortical areas located between the sensory or projection spheres, comprising approximately two-thirds of the cortex, Flechsig (1894, 1895, 1896, 1927) found, become myelinized at a somewhat later date. First in order, discernible one month after birth, are the belts adjoining the sensory spheres, which, therefore, he named "marginal zones." The parts maturing last, more than one month after birth, Flechsig called "terminal regions." There are, according to him, four such intercalated regions (Fig. 115). The anterior comprises most of the frontal lobe (*VI*). Another is the *insula* or Reil's "island" buried in the Sylvian pit (*VII*). The greater part of the temporal lobe (*VIII*) repre-sents the third region, which is continuous with the fourth, comprising the larger portion of the parietal and occipital lobes (*IX*). In all these intermediate regions, Flechsig believed, both afferent and efferent fibers are absent; or, if present, their number is much smaller than in the sensory spheres, and they become invested with myelin at a much later period of develop-ment. The connection of these regions with the peripheral receptor organs was, therefore, not direct but via the sensory spheres, to which they are relayed by means of the short "associa-tion fibers" of Meynert and also by the callosal fibers (although Flechsig later admitted the possibility of their receiving collateral fibers branching off from the principal afferent tracts). Because he believed these intervening regions to be provided with association fibers only and also because of the intermediate location of some of them between the sensory spheres, Flechsig named these parts of the cortex "association centers" or "association areas" (*Assozia-tionszentren*) and considered them to be a substratum of the "psychic functions" (*geistige Zentren, Cogitationszentren*, meaning psychic or thinking centers). The association regions, because of their relatively large size in the human brain when compared with the infrahuman species, Flechsig looked on as a "specific human

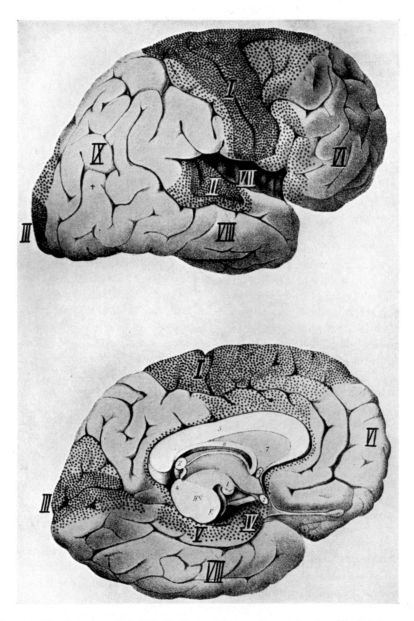

Fig. 115.—Lateral (*above*) and medial (*below*) views of human brain, showing Flechsig's sensory or receptor areas (*densely stippled*) surrounded by marginal zones (*less dense stippling*), with association areae in between (*without stippling*). *I*, somesthetic and somatomotor area; *II*, auditory sphere; *III*, visual sphere; *IV*, olfactory sphere; *V*, gustatory sphere; *VI*, frontal association area; *VII*, insula; *VIII*, temporal association area; *IX*, parieto-occipital association area; *1*, mammillary body; *2*, optic chiasma; *3*, anterior commissure; *4*, superior colliculus of midbrain; *5*, corpus callosum; *6*, fornix; *7*, pellucid septum; *Z*, pineal gland; *HS*, midbrain tegmentum; *F, pes* or foot of the cerebral peduncle. From P. Flechsig, *Gehirn und Seele*, Pl. IV, 1896.

acquisition" (*cf.* Figs. 274, 275). Phylogenetically, they are the latest to appear and are the material foundation of "Man's mastery over other creatures."

7. FUNCTION OF THE ASSOCIATION REGIONS OF THE BRAIN.—Flechsig believed that the function of the extensive cortical association areas filling the space between the sensory spheres was, in general, to serve as repositories of past impressions arriving through the afferent channels via the sensory spheres or, in his definition, to serve essentially as a substratum of "memory" and its integration or building of complex processes. The posterior association area, comprising a large portion of the parietal, occipital, and temporal lobes, would be concerned with the integration of the visual, somesthetic, and auditory impulses. Its task would be retaining visual, auditory, and somesthetic experiences and integrating them and also performing certain complex acts of the order of Liepmann's "praxias"—for example, reading and visual understanding of written language, understanding spoken words or auditory language, and the like. The function of the insular association area, hidden in the Sylvian fossa or pit, as yet little understood, may also in some way be related to language. The function of the largest association area comprising most of the frontal lobe would be uppermost in the hierarchy of cerebromental functions and faculties: consciousness of one's own personality, or *Ego*, conscious and purposeful planning and acting, will power, "character," logical thinking, and judgment. In a word, the frontal lobes would be the anatomical substratum of a "unified person, conscious of itself, and capable of free and independent action."

8. PROJECTION AND ASSOCIATION AREAS AND FUNCTIONAL SIGNIFICANCE OF THE CEREBRAL CORTEX.—The subdivision of the cerebral cortex into two fundamentally different categories of "centers"—one, the sensory and motor spheres or "projection centers," whose essential function was reception of incoming, and emission or discharge of outgoing, impulses; the other, the association areas or intellectual centers proper—at once threw light upon the most

vexing and obscure problem of modern neurology: the functional significance of the cerebral cortex. Flechsig showed this cortex, which in early times was looked upon as an inert mass, possibly a gland (Hippocrates, Aristotle, Malpighi, Vieussens, Cuvier, Lamarck), or at best as an organ where, in some unaccountable way, the "soul," "psyche," or "mind" was linked to the "body," to be an ingeniously constructed mechanism whose constituent parts have a reason and purpose: to conduct to, and to receive the various impulses arriving from, the peripheral sense organs; to integrate these impulses into compound processes and to store up their traces or "engrams"; and to make use of such relatively stable engrams by initiating and carrying out the various motor and secretory acts. In the light of Flechsig's interpretation, the many mental and sensory faculties, including those which are specifically human, e.g., language, not only were linked to the various structures of the same territory, such as particular groups of cells and fibers, as Munk supposed, but were a functional expression of an elaborate topographical differentiation and organization of the same cortex. The first prerequisite to an understanding of the intimate processes of which "mind" or "intellect" was a supreme manifestation was, then, to investigate the complex structure of the brain, especially of the cortex, and its connections.

9. MODIFIED CONCEPT OF FLECHSIG'S PROJECTION AND ASSOCIATION AREAS OF THE BRAIN.—Flechsig's concept of the subdivision of the human cortex into sensory and association areas, in spite of much opposition (e.g., from Sachs, Monakow, Niessl von Mayendorf, Hitzig, Siemerling, Weygandt, O. & C. Vogt, *et al.*), in the main remains valid. The idea of a fundamental difference between the functions of sensory spheres and association areas has since been corroborated by numerous clinical, pathoanatomical, and experimental observations. The primitive, elemental character of functional disturbances which accompany lesions of the sensory and motor spheres is, by now, fairly well established, especially when compared with more complex subjective and objective phenomena observed in the pathology of, or in experiments upon, the "association areas" (including those with conscious human subjects). (*See* O. Foerster 1923, 1926, 1929, 1931, 1934, 1936; Foerster & Penfield 1930; Löwenstein & Borchardt 1918; Mankowski 1929; Penfield 1937–38, 1938; Penfield & Boldrey 1937; Penfield & Erickson 1941; Penfield & Evans 1935; Penfield & Gage 1934; Penfield & Rasmussen 1950; Klüver & Bucy 1937, 1938, 1939; Scarff 1940.)

Flechsig's subdivision appears valid though his idea of cerebral organization must be qualified. Most of the association areas, except, perhaps, parts of the temporal lobe, are not without connections with the subcortical regions, as Flechsig thought, but are related, e.g., to the thalamus, through afferent fibers of their own (Monakow; Siemerling 1898; Probst 1900; d'Hollander 1922; Minkowski 1923–24; Polyak 1932; Le Gros Clark 1936; A. E. Walker 1938, 1940; Walker & Fulton 1938; Freeman & Watts). Also, fiber tracts such as the fronto-pontine system of Arnold, temporopontine system of Türck, frontonigral, occipitotectal, and other systems originate in some of them (Polyak 1932; P. M. Levin 1936; Levin & Bradford 1938; A. E. Walker 1938; Papez 1939; Peele 1942; *et al.*). The afferent connections of the association regions, however, seem to be of a different order, less direct, originating in thalamic nuclei which are not the terminals of the great afferent sensory tracts of the brain stem and which, therefore, apparently transmit impulses

of a complex nature, devoid of the character of concrete conscious objectivity.

References: Artom 1925; Bianchi 1900; M. Bielschowsky 1904; F. C. Burdach 1822; Le Gros Clark 1936, 1948; Döllken 1898; L. Edinger 1911; P. Ehrlich 1885, 1886; Flores; O. Foerster; O. Foerster & Penfield; P. Flechsig; Freeman & Watts; J. Gerlach 1858; Golgi 1873, 1878; E. Haeckel 1891; Hannover 1840; Hirako 1923; Hösel 1905; F. Hollander 1922; Klüver & Bucy 1937, 1938, 1939; Langworthy 1929; P. M. Levin 1936; Levin & Bradford 1938; F. T. Lewis 1942; Marchi 1886–87; Marchi & Algeri 1885, 1886; Meynert 1867–68, 1869, 1872; Minkowski 1923–24; Monakow 1905, 1914; Munk; Neuburger 1910; Niessl von Mayendorf 1903, 1907, 1920, 1921, 1922, 1926, 1930; Nissl 1894, 1895; Papez 1939, 1944; Peele 1942; Penfield 1937–38; Penfield & Boldrey 1937; Penfield & Erickson 1941; Penfield & Evans 1934, 1935; Penfield & Rasmussen 1950; Polyak 1932, 1941–48; S. Ramón y Cajal 1903, 1904, 1909–11 (v. 2, p. 862); A. T. Rasmussen 1943; Reil 1809; W. Riese 1940; Righetti 1897; Romanes 1947; Sabin 1905, 1910–11; H. Sachs 1892, 1896, 1897; Scarff 1940; Schultz 1897; E. Sciamanna 1882, 1905; Siemerling 1898; Soury 1899; Stieda 1899; B. Stilling 1882; J. Stoffels; Türck 1851, 1853, 1910; C. & O. Vogt; A. E. Walker 1938, 1940; Walker & Fulton 1938; Wallenberg 1926; E. H. Weber 1852; Weigert 1882, 1927; Weygandt 1900.

SEC. 3. MYELOGENETIC INVESTIGATION OF VISUAL RADIATION

1. ORIGIN OF VISUAL RADIATION IN THE LATERAL GENICULATE NUCLEUS.—Flechsig's investigation of the visual system (1874, 1876, 1881, 1883, 1889, 1894, 1895, and later) proved to be no less fruitful than that of the other systems. Visual radiation, discovered by Gratiolet (*see* chap. III, 5 [5]), had been, until then, little known. Meynert (1869; 1872, p. 721) described and illustrated it in the Monkey, though in a rather sketchy way (*see* sec. 1 [3], this chapter). In addition, he erred when he assumed that a portion of it terminated in the temporal lobe. Nor did Munk, in his notable experiments, indicate the exact location of the visual center (*see* chap. III, 8 [5]).

According to Flechsig, the afferent fiber

tract, by which impulses from the eyes reach the cortex, is the first of the several fiber systems of the occipital lobe to develop myelin sheaths. Because of this, he termed it *primäre Sehstrahlung*, "primary visual radiation." He at first assumed that its origin was in the lateral geniculate nucleus, in the pulvinar of the thalamus, and in the superior colliculus of the midbrain. Later, however, in contrast with his forerunners, he found that it originated in the lateral geniculate nucleus only (*see* chap. III, 9 [2]). The thalamus, in Flechsig's opinion, was not an internode of the visual pathway. The initial portion of the visual radiation, close to its origin, was the first to become myelinized, followed somewhat later by the section close to the cor-

178 *The Vertebrate Visual System*

tex. This process of maturing was interpreted by Flechsig as an expression of the ascending or corticopetal character of this fiber system. Another system, a descending or corticofugal tract, arising in the occipitotemporal cortex and terminating in the midbrain, remained distinct from the first, even though it was close to it. Since that fiber tract, the occipitotemporal efferent corticotectal system, becomes myelinized at a later period, Flechsig named it *secundäre Sehstrahlung*, or "secondary visual radiation."

2. The course of the visual radiation, according to Flechsig.—Flechsig (1896), describing the visual radiation in the human brain, first called attention to the peculiar course of the ventral fibers. These fibers, from their origin in the lateral geniculate nucleus, first go forward and downward in the temporal lobe. In the anterior portion of that lobe they turn under and around the inferior horn of the lateral ventricle and continue toward the occipital lobe, where they terminate. This sharp turn made by the visual radiation is known as Flechsig's "temporal knee " "temporal detour," or "temporal loop" (*see* Figs. 235, 236).

The "temporal loop" was subsequently studied by Niessl von Mayendorf, Hösel, Stauffenberg, Archambault, Löwenstein, A. Meyer, Zingerle, Monakow, Traquair, R. A. Pfeifer, Elze, L. L. Mayer, and Rasmussen (*see also* chap. VII, 3 [6]). Its discovery was erroneously attributed by some writers to A. Meyer and to H. Cushing (for Meyer's admission of Flechsig's priority, *see* Fox & German 1936, discussion).

In the occipital lobe the fibers of the visual radiation are arranged in a thick lamina, one of several deep fiber layers of the white medullary core concentrically enveloping the posterior horn of the lateral ventricle; Sachs (1892, 1893) described them as an "external" and "internal sagittal stratum" and a "tapetum" or "medial sagittal stratum" lining the ventricle.

The visual radiation, identical with the "inferior longitudinal fascicle" of Burdach (*see* chap. III, 5 [3]), was, according to Flechsig (1896), not a system of association fibers connecting the visual center in the occipital lobe with the auditory speech center in the temporal lobe, as it was considered to be by Wernicke,

Sachs, Edinger, Monakow, Dejerine, and many others, but a constituent of Reil's *corona radiata*. (*Cf.* sec. 7 [4], this chapter.)

3. Termination of the visual radiation in the striate area, according to Flechsig.—Visual radiation, Flechsig found, terminates in the brains of babies up to one month old in the part of the cortex of the occipital lobe around the calcarine fissure or sulcus, characterized by the intracortical stripe of Gennari & Vicq-d'Azyr, to which the term "striate area" was later given by G. Elliot Smith (1904; *see also* chap. VIII, 3 [5]). Here, according to Flechsig (1895), the main axis cylinders terminate. Soon, however, beginning with the end of the first postnatal month, the radiation fibers, probably collaterals, Flechsig thought, spread over a larger territory, which included the entire cuneus, lingual gyrus, and lateral face of the occipital lobe as far as, but not including, the angular gyrus that belonged to the parietal association region (1895, 1896). This whole extensive region belonged to the visual sphere in the wider sense. The larger part, that is, all but the striate area, was, however, a "marginal zone of the visual sphere," which Flechsig considered to be a substratum of the higher visual functions.

4. Effect of Flechsig's investigations upon the modern concept of cerebral organization.—Flechsig's anatomical investigations and his interpretation of cerebral organization made a deep impression upon those of his contemporaries interested in the problem of brain and mind, both adherents and opponents. Through his efforts, the pioneer work of Gratiolet and Meynert was splendidly developed and brought to a preliminary conclusion. From that time on, knowledge of the visual pathway, of the cortical visual center, and of the remainder of the brain rested on a solid anatomical foundation.

Especially valuable was Flechsig's indication of the calcarine region as the visual center. Even so, much remained uncertain. Both the precise origin of the radiation and its terminal area in the cortex, in Flechsig's description, were left somewhat vague. Nor was it quite certain from his presentation which of the constituents of the radiation were afferent and which efferent. Also, he made no attempt to analyze the functional makeup of the visual pathway from which any useful indication could be gleaned for the topographical representation, or "projection," of the retina in the cerebral cortex. But the reality of a specific pathway involved in vision, stretching from the lateral geniculate nucleus of the betweenbrain to the inner face of the occipital lobe along the calcarine fissure and to its pole, was now beyond reasonable doubt.

References: Artom 1925; H. Cushing 1921; L. E. Davis 1921; Dejerine 1895–1901; P. Flechsig 1874, 1876, 1881, 1883, 1889, 1894, 1895, 1896, 1898, 1899, 1900, 1901, 1903, 1904, 1905, 1907, 1908, 1920, 1927; Hösel 1905; La Salle d'Archambault 1905, 1906, 1909; A. Meyer 1907, 1912; Th. Meynert 1869, 1870, 1872; Monakow 1905, 1914; Niessl von Mayendorf 1903, 1907; Probst 1901; A. Th. Rasmussen 1943; Righetti 1897; Sabin 1910–11; H. Sachs 1892, 1893; J. Stilling 1882; Trolard 1906. (For additional references *see* end of sec. 7, this chapter.)

SEC. 4. THEORY OF TOPOGRAPHICAL REPRESENTATION OF THE RETINA IN THE CEREBRAL CORTEX

1. DEFINITION OF THE PROBLEM.—The problem of the relation of the eye, or, more correctly, of the retina, to the brain in general and to the cerebral cortex in particular may be divided into two parts. The first concerns the identity of the visual pathway or the fiber system along which the impulses from the eyes pass to the various subcortical centers and finally to the cortex. This also includes the precise locality, boundaries, and extent of the terminal areas of the visual pathway. How the solution of this question was foreshadowed by Des Cartes, Briggs, and J. Taylor, and how it was advanced by others, especially by Gratiolet and by Flechsig, have been dealt with in the preceding pages (*see* chap. II, 10 [2], 11 [2, 5, 6]; chap. III, 5 [5]; chap. IV, 3).

The other particular problem may be formulated as follows. The photosensitive retinal membrane represents roughly a surface of somewhat more than half of a hollow spheroid, each point of which has a definite functional value in two-dimensional space in relation to the central fovea or "fixation point" as a common point of reference. The problem, then, was to determine whether, and to what extent, the original spatial or dimensional relationships of the retina are preserved in the visual pathways and centers; and, if they are, how and where the various distinct localities of the retina, such as the fovea ("macula"), the extrafoveal periphery, the upper and lower quadrants, the monocular crescent, the vertical and horizontal meridians, and so forth, were represented on the various levels of the visual pathway and in the cerebral cortex.

The particular question of topographical representation of the retina in the brain is part of a wider problem concerning the relationship of the peripheral receptor surfaces to the cerebrum, clearly formulated and correctly interpreted by E. H. Weber (1852), "Originator of the Science of Psychophysics," and later more clearly defined by Meynert (1869, 1872).

2. EARLY EXPERIMENTS TO DETERMINE THE TOPOGRAPHICAL RELATIONSHIP OF THE RETINA TO THE CEREBRAL CORTEX.—The necessity for a stable dimensional relationship of the photosensitive receptor surface of the eye to the brain had been clearly foreseen by Ibn al-Haitham centuries earlier (*see* chap. II, 6 [2]). Des Cartes, Briggs, J. Taylor, Zinn, Hun, and others had accepted this idea as self-evident (*see* chap. II, 10 [2], 11 [2, 5, 6]). With most of them, however, this was no more than speculation based upon logical postulation, unsupported by factual evidence. Only modern experiment could have furnished this evidence.

Munk (1879, 1881) was the first to make an experimental attempt to solve the problem of the topographical representation of the retinal surface in the cerebral cortex, in pursuance of Weber's, Graefe's, and Meynert's ideas of "projection." From his experiments on dogs and monkeys he mistakenly concluded that the temporal portion of the retina was represented in the lateral portion of the ipsilateral visual area, and the much larger nasal portion of the retina in the larger medial portion of the contralateral visual area. He also found that in the Dog the upper half of the retina was related to the anterior portion, the lower half to the posterior portion, of the visual area (more than a quarter of a century later, this observation was confirmed by Minkowski; *see* sec. 7 [3], this chapter). On much firmer ground was E. A. Schäfer (Sharpey-Schäfer 1888, 1889, portrait Fig. 116), who was in fact the first to demonstrate a regular topographical distribution of oculomotor centers in the cortex of the occipital lobes, whence he postulated a similar organization of the adjacent visual area.

3. Opposition to stable representation of the retina in the cortex.—Munk's and Schäfer's concept, while favorably received by most clinicians, met with strenuous opposition from contemporary physiologists and experimenters—Goltz (1881), J. Loeb (1884), Luciani

Fig. 116.—Edward Albert Schäfer (Sharpey-Schäfer, 1850–1935), professor of physiology at the University College of London, and at the University of Edinburgh, Scotland. One of the leading British physiologists. First experimentally disclosed the topographic arrangement of stimulable points in the occipital lobe of the Monkey from which distinct conjugate eye movements could be elicited, in agreement with Munk's hypothesis of cortical projection of the retina. Also, he first produced experimentally, in the Monkey, "psychic blindness" and "change of character" after a bilateral removal of temporal lobes, which has recently become of interest in the light of experiments by Klüver & Bucy. Portrait courtesy of Dr. F. M. R. Walshe, of London. Obituary and portrait in Quart. J. Exper. Physiol., v. 25, p. 99, 1935.

(1885), Ferrier (1886), Brown-Séquard (1889, 1890, 1892), Monakow (1892, 1902–4, 1905, 1914), H. Sachs (1895), and, remarkably, also Hitzig (1901–3, 1905). While, by and large, they accepted the hemianopic character of visual disturbances following a unilateral lesion of the posterior portion of the cerebral hemisphere, the opponents questioned any detailed and stable relationship between the restricted portions of the retina and the well-defined segments of the cerebral cortex. The profit from their profuse criticism was, on the whole, rather modest: the discovery that, in the Dog, the visual area was located in the posteriormost portion of the hemisphere, instead of on the lateral surface of the occipitoparietal region, where Munk localized it, and that the ipsilateral and contralateral homonymous halves of the retinae had a common representation in the same cortical area, instead of being represented in separate areas placed side by side, as Munk originally assumed.

4. WILBRAND'S AND HENSCHEN'S ATTEMPT TO REVEAL THE FUNCTIONAL ORGANIZATION OF THE VISUAL PATHWAY.—The dispute between Munk and his adversaries about a detailed and stable projection of the retina in the brain was taken up by numerous investigators of the following generation.

First to substantiate the topographical organization of the visual cortical area by experiments with monkeys was A. E. Schäfer (Sharpey-Schäfer 1888, 1889, portrait Fig. 116), a London physiologist. A regular, topographical arrangement of the points at and close to the occipital lobe, from which synergic ocular movements could be elicited, was to him suggestive of a similar topographical organization of the cortical visual center.

Among the clinicians siding with Munk, the most notable were H. Wilbrand (pub. 1881–1929, portrait Fig. 107), of Hamburg, Germany, and S. E. Henschen (pub. 1892–1931, portrait Fig. 117), of Uppsala and Stockholm, Sweden. During their activity, spreading over almost half a century, these two indefatigable researchers systematically investigated all parts of the visual pathway, beginning with the optic nerves, subcortical visual stations, and visual radiation, and including the visual cortical centers. The way in which Wilbrand and Henschen attempted to solve the problem was partly through normal anatomy, but more especially through the study of visual disturbances in clinical cases, followed by a careful pathoanatomical analysis of brain specimens. The result of their efforts may be summarized, first, in their conviction of cortical preponderance in vision, in this respect breaking from the older school of Goltz, Hitzig, and others, who, still adhering to the former views, ascribed the principal role to the subcortical centers; the other important result of their work was the substantiation of a stable topographical representation of the retina in the brain, which they elaborated and documented in detail.

5. WILBRAND'S HYPOTHESIS OF SYNDYNAMICAL CONDUCTORS IN THE SUPRACHIASMAL DIVISION OF THE VISUAL SYSTEM.—Early in his career, Wilbrand (1890) was induced by his clinical campimetric work to accept Munk's "retinotopical principle," with, however, one notable qualification. From observations of congruous scotomas of central origin, he concluded that the two homonymous retinal halves were represented in a common cortical area, instead of independently, side by side, as Munk insisted. Out of this Wilbrand developed a hypothesis, according to which the two sets of optic nerve fibers arising from the "identical or conjugate points" of the homonymous halves of both retinae come to lie very close together in the visual pathway above the chiasma. The visual radiation, for example, he imagined to be made up of pairs of bundles, one corresponding to the ipsilateral, and the other to the contralateral, "identical point," each bundle terminating in a minute territory of the visual cortex. He also thought of the functional cortical units as each made up of two minute areas, an ipsilateral and a contralateral. The visual cortical center, as conceived by Wilbrand, was a mosaic of such double units, each representing a point in the ipsilateral and a point in the contralateral homonymous halves of the two retinae, the points which, in the normal binocular visual act, function syndynamically: the "hypothesis of associated or syndynamical homonymous conductor units" in the visual pathway (*Hypothese der Faszikelfeldermischung*).

...
x

Such complete, uniform, and accurate commingling of the syndynamical receptor, conductor, and perceptive units of both sides—which otherwise preserve their relative topographical position in the entire visual pathway from the retina to the visual cortex—was, in Wilbrand's opinion, the anatomical basis of the congruity of visual field defects of homonymous character, that is, of similarity in shape, size, Wilbrand 1907, 1925, 1925–26, 1926, 1930; Wilbrand & Saenger 1917, 1918; for the forerunners of Wilbrand's hypothesis, Des Cartes, Isaac Newton, John Taylor, and Johannes Müller, *see* chap. II, 10 [2], 11 [4, 5]; for Monakow, *see* sec. 5 [5], this chapter; *cf. also* chap. XIII, 3.)

6. Henschen's view of the visual system's intrinsic organization.—Henschen,

Fig. 117.—Salomon Eberhard Henschen (1847–1930), professor of medicine in Upsala and Stockholm, Sweden. One of the foremost modern students of the pathology of the brain and its clinical manifestations. An indefatigable champion of the idea of functional cerebral localization. A great figure in the field of neurology of his time and an opponent of the "diffuse" or "pliable" concept of cerebral organization championed by C. Monakow (*see* following figure). From Henschen's autobiography in L. R. Grote, *Die Medizin der Gegenwart in Selbstdarstellung*, v. 5, F. Meiner Verlag, Hamburg, 1925. *See also* Krabbe in Acta Psychiat. & Neurol., v. 6, 1931; Pötzl 1926; Minkowski 1932; Haymaker's *Guide*, 1948; and Haymaker & Baer, *The Founders of Neurology*, 1953.

and location of the blind areas in both monocular fields of view regularly found in the unilateral lesions of the brain which involve the suprachiasmal portion of the visual pathway. (*See* through his study of brain specimens of numerous cases in which various types of visual field defects had been found during life, also became convinced that there was a stable projection of the retina onto the subsequent links of the visual pathway, including the cerebral cortex; his dictum that the visual cortical center was a "replica of the retina" or, in fact, a "cortical retina" became famous and much disputed. (*Cf.* Monakow's *Abklatsch*-hypothesis in subsec. 4, following section.)

The following, in brief, is the internal organization of the visual system as outlined by Henschen. Within the optic nerve the fiber segments originating from particular quadrants of the retina have a definite position. The foveal or "macular bundle" is located approximately in the center of the nerve. In the lateral geniculate nucleus, the upper retinal quadrants were located in the upper, the lower quadrants in the lower, and the "macula" in the intermediate, segments (for the actual relationships *cf.* sec. 6 [4], this chapter, and chap. VI, 7). Of the three sagittal fiber layers of the occipital lobe described by Sachs, it is the external stratum that is the visual radiation, and not the internal, which is an efferent system. The dorsal bundles of the radiation terminate in the upper lip of the calcarine fissure; these represent the upper retinal quadrants or lower quadrants in the fields of view. The ventral bundles of the radiation, representing the lower retinal quadrants, or upper field quadrants, enter the lower lip of the fissure. The floor of the fissure receives fibers from both the upper and the lower bundles of the radiation. Functionally, it corresponds to the horizontal meridians of the retina (thus in Henschen's case *Eggert*, 1911; *see* Fig. 396, this book). However, Henschen was not able to indicate where the "macular" or foveal bundle was located in the radiation. On one occasion he suggested the possibility of "macular fibers" being spread in a thin layer on the inner, ventricular face of the radiation, with the "extramacular fibers" on the outside.

7. Location and functional organization of the cortical visual center.—The cortical visual center, Henschen was certain, was confined to the calcarine fissure. For a long time, however, he (1903, p. 93) was not sure whether it was identical with the striate area or whether the tip of the occipital lobe belonged to it. He was equally uncertain in locating the cortical fovea, or "macula." For a number of

years he believed it to be in the anterior portion of the calcarine region, at the point of junction of the calcarine fissure and parieto-occipital sulcus, and the extramacular retinal periphery to be in the occipital pole. He obstinately clung to this view, in spite of good evidence to the contrary (1890–96, 1900, 1907, 1911, 1917). Such was a notable case clinically investigated by R. Förster (1890) and anatomically studied by Sachs (1895), the first wherein Munk's "cortical blindness" was carefully tested. In this case both fields of view were blind, with the exception of central portions around the points of fixation; the pathological cause was symmetrical encephalomalacic foci in the territories of both posterior cerebral arteries, which spared both occipital poles (on the vascular mechanism by which such polar sparing may be explained *see* chap. X, 6 [3], 8 [4], and chap. XI, 8, 9).

Even more convincing was another similar case reported by Laqueur & Schmidt (1899; *see also* Laqueur 1899, 1904): a bilateral homonymous hemianopia with a minute central field "rest" of less than two degrees caused by a thrombotic encephalomalacia spreading over the medial face of both occipital lobes and sparing only the poles. In spite of this demonstration showing the "macula" or central fovea to be represented in the occipital pole and the retinal periphery in the anterior portion of the striate area, as advocated by Dejerine (1895–1901), Christiansen (1902), Beevor & Collier (1904), Laqueur (1904), Niessl von Mayendorf (1905), and especially Lenz (1909, 1910, 1914, 1924, 1926, 1927), Henschen refused to accept such an arrangement and did so only much later upon overwhelming evidence, especially of war injuries made known through Inouye (1909), Cantonnet (1915), Uhthoff (1915, 1916, 1922), Holmes & Lister (1916), Marie & Chatelin (1916), Monbrun (1917, 1919, 1924), Souques (1917), Souques & Odier (1917), Holmes (1918, 1919), Moreau (1918), Morax (1919), Morax, Moreau & Castelain (1919), Monbrun & Gautrand (1920), and other investigators (*see* sec. 7 [7], this chapter; *cf. also* chaps. XI, XII).

Summarizing the work of Wilbrand and of Henschen, it is fair to say that, even though they were not able to avoid all pitfalls—Wilbrand & Saenger, as late as 1918, localized the so-called "monocular crescent" in the occipital pole—progress in the knowledge of the visual system achieved during the following years was in no small degree the result of their labors and of the interest they kept alive.

References: Beevor & Collier 1904; Best 1917, 1919, 1920; Bolton 1900; Bolton, Bramwell & Robinson 1915; Briggs 1676–85; Christiansen 1902; Dejerine 1895–1901; Des Cartes 1662–77; D. Ferrier 1886; R. Förster 1890; Goltz 1881; S. E. Henschen 1892–1931; Hitzig 1901–3; G. Holmes 1918, 1919; Holmes & Lister 1916; Hun 1887; Ibn al-Haitham; Inouye 1909; Krabbe 1931; Küstermann 1897; Laqueur 1904; Laqueur & Schmidt 1899; Lenz 1909, 1910, 1914, 1916, 1921, 1924, 1926, 1927; Marie & Chatelin 1916; Minkowski 1932; Monakow 1905, 1914; Munk; Niessl von Mayendorf 1903, 1905, 1907, 1926; Pick 1918; Sachs 1895; Schäfer 1888, 1889; John Taylor 1727 and later; Vialet 1893, 1894; H. Wilbrand 1881–1930; Wilbrand & Behr 1927; Wilbrand & Saenger 1899–1927; Zinn 1754, 1755.

SEC. 5. HYPOTHESIS OF "DIFFUSE" OR "PLASTIC" ORGANIZATION OF THE VISUAL CENTERS

1. OBJECTIONS OF DECENTRALISTS TO STABLE FUNCTIONAL LOCALIZATION OF VISION.—The modern doctrine of detailed and fixed representation of the retinal surface in the brain, especially in the cerebral cortex, promulgated by Munk and further developed by Wilbrand and Henschen (*see* preceding section), was not unopposed. In fact, for several decades most of the nonclinical investigators disclaimed it. Hitzig, pioneer of functional cerebral localization, rejected it. Subsequently it was vigorously disputed by many, including some of the foremost authorities of the time (Brown-Séquard, Goltz, Loeb, Luciani, Gudden, Vialet, Bernheimer, Wehrli, Stauffenberg, S. I. Franz, Kalberlah, P. Marie, H. Sachs, *et al.*).

For a number of years, the recognized leader of this "decentralist school" in neurology was Constantin Monakow, Professor of Neurology in Zürich (portrait Fig. 118, pub. 1881–1928; for biography *see* Minkowski 1931, 1936, 1953; Winkler 1923; and R. A. Pfeifer 1925). To him, the basic concept of cerebral organization and of the visual system in particular, championed by Munk, Wilbrand, and Henschen, seemed too crudely mechanistic to be acceptable or even probable. It is true that Monakow never went to the extreme of denying altogether the idea that particular functions may be more closely related to certain localities of the cerebral cortex. In fact, the title of his last great contribution, *The Localization in the Forebrain*, would disclaim such an allegation. In this respect he contrasted favorably with the extremist leaders of the antilocalist trend of former days, A. Haller, Flourens, Goltz, Brown-Séquard, and others (*see* chap. III, 2, 4). What Monakow and his followers were opposed to was the insistence of the localists on a "rigid," "exclusive," and "insoluble" dependency of a certain function upon a definite cortical locality. The paramount importance of vision and the "enormous complexity" of the visual function, in Monakow's opinion, excluded the possibility of its dependence upon a single limited area of the brain, such as the "calcarine region," as claimed by the localists.

2. THE CONCEPT OF DIFFUSE OR MULTIPLE CORTICAL REPRESENTATION OF THE RETINA AS PROPOSED BY MONAKOW.—The starting point of Monakow's argumentation—and the source of his errors—was his assumption of three subcortical visual centers: the lateral geniculate nucleus, where, according to him, 80 per cent of the optic nerve fibers terminate; the pulvinar of the thalamus; and the superior colliculus of the midbrain (*cf.* chap. III, 9 [2]). His experiments and pathological studies suggested to him that each of the three stations might be related through its own fiber system to a particular locality of the cortex.

The representation of the lateral geniculate nucleus, which, according to him, was obviously the most important of the three stations, was almost identical with, or possibly somewhat larger than, the striate area, the latter being the most important part of the entire visual cortical sphere, its "nuclear zone." The pulvinar and the superior colliculus project upon parts of the cortex, apparently outside the striate area (here Monakow undoubtedly misinterpreted the corticofugal or motor character of the occipitotectal fiber system). There are, accordingly, three, and in any case no less than two, distinct "visual spheres" in the cerebral cortex. In each of these, possibly widely separated, visual centers the pattern or plan of retinal representation was possibly different. Again, apart from its principal terminal area, the fiber tract from each of the three subcortical stations of sight might spread over the adjoining cortex, the "accessory or subsidiary zone." There might even be a third extensive representation, a "conjoint visual sphere," common to all three subcortical stations.

The anatomical visual sphere of the cortex, according to Monakow, was neither so restricted nor so sharply outlined as advocated by the radicals of cerebral localization (e.g., Wilbrand, Henschen). In fact, it included not only the cuneus and the lingual and descending gyri but also the lateral face of the occipital lobe and, in addition, probably parts of the parietal lobe (*cf.* Figs. 271, 272, 273). The precise boundaries of this "wider visual sphere" whose bilateral destruction produces permanent cortical blindness were, according to Monakow, not yet known.

This view of the organization of the visual centers was maintained by Monakow even after Bechterew (1906), Kurzveil (1909), and, remarkably, also his own pupil Minkowski (1911) furnished adequate experimental evidence in favor of the striate area as the "physiological center of vision" (*see* sec. 7 [3], this chapter). (*See* Monakow 1914, pp. 373, 374, 379, 386, 394, footnote.)

3. MONAKOW'S OPPOSITION TO THE CONCEPT OF "THE CORTICAL RETINA."—Monakow was especially averse to the concept of a stable, detailed retinotopical arrangement, either in the visual pathway or in the visual cortex, such as was claimed by Wilbrand and by Henschen (*see* sec. 4 [4–7], this chapter). He refused to accept the "point-to-point" or "one-to-one" representation as an organizational principle in the visual system and in the nervous system in general. But, unlike Hitzig, who fanatically persisted in denying all retinotopical relationships

whatsoever, Monakow, at any rate, admitted a rough quadrantic representation. He believed that in the visual radiation the upper retinal quadrants are represented in the upper, the

FIG. 118.—Constantin v. Monakow (orig. Monáchov, in Russian, 1853–1930), professor of neurology in Zürich, Switzerland. An encyclopedic investigator of normal brain structure and its changes in pathological conditions and in experiment. First demonstrated experimentally the occipital location of visual functions. One of the leading figures of his time in neurology, and a champion of the "diffuse" or "pliable" concept of cerebral functional localization (as against a rigid concept, insisted upon by S. E. Henschen, *see* preceding figure). Author of *Die Gehirnpathologie*, 1905, and of *Die Lokalisation im Grosshirn*, 1914. From Schweiz. Arch. f. Neurol. u. Psychiat., v. 13, 1923. For biography *see* M. Minkowski in the same journal, v. 27, 1931, and Arch. internat. de neurol. v. 55, p. 531, 1936; *also* C. Winkler in Schweiz. Arch. f. Neurol. u. Psychiat., v. 13, p. 11, 1923; Haymaker's *Guide*, 1948; Haymaker & Baer, *The Founders of Neurology*, 1953; and Katzenstein, Neue Zürch. Zeitung, December 9, 1953.

lower quadrants in the lower, segments, agreeing in this point with Henschen. In the cortex he advocated representation of the upper retinal quadrants in the anterior, and of the lower

quadrants in the posterior, parts of the occipital cortex, constantly confusing this view with Henschen's scheme, according to which the upper retinal quadrants are projected upon the upper lip, and the lower quadrants upon the lower lip, of the calcarine fissure.

FIG. 119.—Vladímir Miháilovich Béhterev (Békhteryev, 1857–1927), together with I. P. Pávlov, the most assiduous Russian investigator of the structure and function of the nervous system, studied conducting pathways of the spinal cord and brain. Of importance were Béhterev's physiological experiments on localization of particular functions in distinct parts of the cerebral cortex, such as taste (in operculum), cutaneous and muscular sensibility (in parietal region), vision (in occipital lobe), and complex motor acts (in motor area). Especially revealing was his disclosure of the dependence upon the cerebral cortex of the function of the heart, of the numerous visceral organs and organs of generation, of respiration, of regulation of blood pressure and of temperature. Author of several books on anatomy and physiology of the nervous system and on clinical neurology, including *The Functions of the Nerve Centers* (*Die Funktionen der Nervencentra*, in German), 1908–11, in three volumes. Portrait from his anniversary book (Sbornik) published by Government Psychoneurological Academy and by Reflexological Government Institute for Brain Research, Leningrad, 1926. For biography *see* W. Haymaker's *Guide*, 1948; and Haymaker & Baer, *The Founders of Neurology*, 1953.

4. MONAKOW'S REJECTION OF DISCRETE CORTICAL REPRESENTATION OF THE FOVEA OR "MACULA."—Monakow was even less prepared to accept a representation of the fovea or "macula" in a restricted "island-like" portion of the cortex, such as was insisted upon by his principal opponents, Wilbrand and Henschen, and subsequently by Lenz. Instead, for several reasons, he advocated the concept of "diffuse representation" of the "macula" in a wide area.

To begin with, the "macular fibers" of the optic nerve and tract, he maintained, spread diffusely in the entire lateral geniculate nucleus. In this way, he believed all original retinal spatial, dimensional, or topographical relationships became obliterated. Furthermore, he assumed that the terminals of the "macular" fibers were not directly related to the nerve cells whose axons form the visual radiation, but to a special category of small nerve cells, which he called *Schaltzellen,* meaning "intercalated cells," the neurons belonging to Golgi's second type with a short axis cylinder. These intercalated cells, in turn, Monakow claimed, were related to the larger elements, his *Hauptzellen* or "principal cells," whence the fibers of the visual radiation originate.

Since all these contacts were "diffuse," that is, widespread and irregular, even if a part of the visual pathway were blocked off by a lesion, the "macular" influences could still spread to all parts of the lateral geniculate nucleus and could thus gain access to an extensive area of the cortex. A diffuse arrangement of this kind, furthermore, would facilitate a process which he termed *Umschaltung,* a "rearrangement," or "regrouping," of the original retinal relationships. A continuous isolated conduction in the visual pathway would, accordingly, not exist.

Nor was there a distinct and compact "macular bundle" in the visual radiation, according to Monakow. The representation of the "macula" in the cortex would be only "indirect," perhaps multiple, and spread over a wide area. It probably extended beyond the "anatomical visual sphere" proper (which in Monakow's jargon was apparently synonymous with the striate area) to the lateral face of the occipital lobe, possibly as far as the posterior portion of the angular gyrus, a reminder of a similar claim made decades earlier by Ferrier (*see* chap. III, 7 [2]).

Such an arrangement would, of course, preclude any fixed, "geometrical" retinotopical representation of the retina and "macula" in the visual system. An *Abklatsch,* meaning an accurate replica or a copy of the retina in the cerebral cortex, a "cortical retina," claimed by Wilbrand, Henschen, and other localists, was not present, and a transmission of unaltered retinal "figures" to the cerebral cortex did not take place. Logically, Monakow also doubted whether any strictly "macular" hemianopic scotomas of purely cortical origin were possible and whether they ever occur (for contrary observations, *see* chaps. XI, XII).

Monakow, on the other hand, rejected the hypothesis of bilateral representation of each total "macula," proposed by Wilbrand, correctly pointing out its inconsistency with the basic views of his opponents, who, according to him, "invented it" (*see* chap. VII, 6, 8; chap. XI, 8, 9).

5. INADEQUACY OF THE "DECENTRALIST" CONCEPT OF THE VISUAL SYSTEM.—The essential idea of cerebral organization held by Monakow was "plastic," nonmechanical. It was incompatible with the concept of a visual pathway composed of numerous, nearly equivalent, and largely independently functioning conductor units made up of cells and fibers arranged in such a way as to preserve topographical relationships between the retina and the cortex. The congruity and the precise linear outlines of homonymous hemianopic field defects, neatly explained by Wilbrand's hypothesis of "commingling of syndynamical ipsi- and contralateral conductor units," in terms of Monakow's doctrine, would remain a puzzle (*see* sec. 4 [5], this chapter). Such fundamentally "dimensional" functions as visual acuity and visual space perception were equally inexplicable.

The only symptom to which his doctrine could be applied with some profit was "macular sparing" in homonymous hemianopia (*see* chap. XI, 8 [esp. 5], 9). If there were partial damage

to the lateral geniculate nucleus, for example, the impulses from the "macula" could still pass over to portions remaining normal and thus attain the cortical level, since, according to Monakow, the "macular fibers" spread diffusely over the entire nucleus. Similar interpretations would also be applicable to cases with partial destruction of the visual cortical area. For here, too, because of widely scattered and possibly multiple representation, "macular" impulses could still find a sufficient cortical substratum, even though the calcarine cortex were largely destroyed. Functionally, this again would manifest itself by "sparing" the "macula," that is, the central or foveal portion of the otherwise blind fields of view (*cf.* chap. XI, 8).

6. CRITIQUE OF THE "DECENTRALIST" CONCEPT OF THE CEREBRAL ORGANIZATION OF VISION.—The deductions of Monakow, Hitzig, Bernheimer, and other decentralists concerning the functional organization of the visual pathway and centers suffered from two fatal weaknesses.

The first was the inadequacy of their investigative technique when measured not only by modern standards but also by those of their own time. Goltz's technique, for example, was inexcusable, even at the time at which it was practiced (*see* chap. III, 7 [6]). The experimental technique of other decentralists, not excluding Hitzig and Monakow himself, was also rather "sloppy." It did not permit accurate gauging of restricted functional defects, such as small scotomas.

Their laboratory procedures were also rather primitive and sometimes quite faulty. But the greatest weakness was their method of study and interpretation, which may be characterized as slack, undisciplined, and often illogical: thus when Monakow consistently used the terms "origin" and "termination" of the fiber systems vicariously, leaving in confusion the question of their functional character, whether sensory-afferent or motor-efferent, or when, while admitting a functional-anatomical organization of the visual radiation, he nevertheless refused to accept the unavoidable pathophysiological consequences of it. Nor could such defects, with glaring prejudices and intransigence, be covered by a profusion of questionable evidence, by additional gratuitous hypotheses, and by an endless torrent of persuasive, but empty, verbiage found in too many of the voluminous treatises of this school (*see* especially Hitzig 1900–1903, Weygandt, Monakow 1914, and Goldstein).

Small wonder, therefore, that the "decentralist" views held but little appeal for those used to disciplined and strictly causal anatomical and physiological thinking. The decentralists found, on the contrary, and still occasionally find sympathetic response among those, usually little acquainted with anatomy and biology in general, who habitually seek satisfaction in such nebulous concepts as are expressed by the terms "cerebral plasticity," "vicarious function," "total action," "diaschisis," "reorganization of functions," "dynamic factors," "pseudo-fovea," and the like and among those who generally favor the "dynamic" and "functional" viewpoint, as against the "anatomical" and "mechanical."

References: Bechterew 1906, 1908–11; H. Berger 1899, 1900; Bernheimer 1900; Bethe 1931, 1933; Bethe & Fischer 1931; Collier 1930; S. I. Franz 1911, 1912, 1923; K. Goldstein 1910, 1923, 1925, 1927, 1931; Goltz; B. Gudden 1886, 1889; S. E. Henschen 1892–1931; Hines 1929; Hitzig 1900–1903, 1904; Kalberlah 1903; W. Köhler 1947; Koffka 1931; Kurzveil 1909; Ladame 1919; Lashley; Lenz 1909, 1910, 1914, 1916, 1924, 1926, 1927; J. Loeb 1884, 1885, 1886; Luciani 1881, 1885, 1911–21; Minkowski 1911, 1936, 1953; Monakow 1881–1925; Monakow & Mourgue 1928; Munk; Soury 1899; Stauffenberg 1914; Vialet 1893, 1894; Vitzou 1897; Wehrli 1906; Wilbrand 1881–1929; Wilbrand & Saenger 1899–1927; Winkler 1923.

SEC. 6. RECENT INVESTIGATIONS OF THE INFRANUCLEAR DIVISION OF THE VISUAL SYSTEM

1. IMPROVED STANDARDS IN NEUROANATOMY AND THEIR EFFECT UPON THE INVESTIGATION OF THE VISUAL SYSTEM.—With the advent of the twentieth century, the demands upon the anatomy, physiology, and pathology of brain research increased, in harmony with the higher standards in other branches of natural science and medicine. The guessing and speculation characteristic of much clinical medical thinking of the preceding decades, with its self-bestowed freedom to create plausible hypotheses of anatomical structures whenever needed in order to explain away a difficult diagnostic situation, gradually became recognized as unsatisfactory. Clearly, only evidence which could be observed, verified, tested, and measured was acceptable as a criterion fit for the solution of pending problems.

The substantial achievements of Munk, Flechsig, Wilbrand, Henschen, and a host of other investigators in furthering knowledge of the brain under normal and pathological conditions, great as they were in comparison with the preceding period, did not seem binding in the opinion of many. There was too much left to the liberty of individual interpretation and to personal preference, to have the value of permanence and finality.

In the visual pathway the important question of the subcortical nuclei, undoubtedly related to the optic tracts, still had to be answered. Another problem was the exact projection of the extrafoveal retinal quadrants and of the fovea or "macula" upon the subcortical visual stations. Even less certain was the exact origin, course, and arrangement of the bundles of the visual radiation and the way they reached their respective terminal areas in the cerebral cortex. The basic question—whether or not the terminal cortex of the visual radiation was identical with the striate area—still remained to be answered. This uncertainty may have been responsible for the prolonged influence that the ideas of Monakow and other "decentralists" had upon their time. It became obvious, then, that the only way to clarify the internal organization of the visual pathway was through well-planned, systematic experimentation, supplemented by the study of selected pathological cases.

2. IDENTITY, COURSE, AND TERMINATION OF THE FOVEAL OR "MACULAR" FIBERS IN THE HUMAN OPTIC NERVE AND LATERAL GENICULATE NUCLEUS.—The first decisive move in the analysis of the fascicular composition of the infranuclear division of the visual system, in continuation of the pioneer work of D. E. Müller, Samelsohn, Purtscher, Uhthoff, Vossius, Bunge, Jatzow, Thomsen, Schmidt-Rimpler, Widmark, Dalén, Wilbrand, and Henschen (*see* chap. III, 9 [7–9]), was made by H. Rønne (Roenne 1914, portrait Fig. 120). Contrary to the claim of Monakow, Bernheimer, and other "decentral-

3. Early experimental evidence in favor of retinotopical organization of the visual system.—The experimental approach to the problem of the fascicular composition of the optic nerves and tracts was first used by Pick (1894), Pick & Herrenheiser (1895), Usher & Dean (1896), and H. Parsons (1902). In their experiments, in which they made small lesions in the retina, they studied the infranuclear sec-

Fig. 120.—Hennig Kristian Trappand Rønne (Roenne, 1878), professor of ophthalmology at Copenhagen, Denmark. Eminent investigator of the visual organs and a "chief exponent of quantitative perimetry" in modern time (according to Traquair). First correctly indicated the location of "macular representation" in the intermediate segment of the lateral geniculate nucleus and of the "macular fiber bundle" in the intermediate portion of visual radiation of the occipital lobe of the brain. Courtesy Professor H. Rønne.

ists," in several cases of central neuritis of the optic nerve caused by diabetes, alcohol, and tobacco, he found the "papillomacular bundle" to be a definite anatomical entity, terminating in a sharply outlined locality, corresponding approximately with the intermediate segment of the lateral geniculate nucleus.

tion of the visual system. The method used was that of Marchi's secondary degeneration, by which the course of fibers was determined. Even though in some of these experiments monkeys were used, as well as rabbits and cats, the results were of limited value, since the lateral geniculate nuclei were not examined.

Lubsen (1921), following Ariëns Kappers' suggestion, carried out similar experiments upon a fish, *Leuciscus rutilus*, and found detailed retinotopical representation in the midbrain tectum. Similar evidence of detailed retinal representation was obtained by Brouwer (1923, 1926), Brouwer & Zeeman (1925, 1926), Zeeman (1925), and Overbosch (1927), in the optic nerves, chiasma, and lateral geniculate nuclei of the Rabbit and Cat and in the contralateral superior colliculus of the midbrain in the Rabbit. A like situation was also found by Lashley (1934) in the Rat and by Bodian in the Opossum (1937).

4. Brouwer & Zeeman's experiments concerning the retinotopical organization of the infranuclear division of the simian visual system.—Far more fundamental and certainly more spectacular, because of the obvious human implications, were the experiments performed by Brouwer & Zeeman upon monkeys (1925, 1926, portrait Fig. 121). They found that in the optic nerve the "macular" fibers are gathered into a thick bundle. Close to the eyeball this bundle hugs the temporal margin of the nerve. Near the chiasma the macular bundle gradually shifts toward the center. In the chiasma its position is central, leaving the upper and lower margins to the fibers from the upper and lower extramacular nasal quadrants. In the optic tracts the crossed and the uncrossed fibers were not separated but were intermingled. They were, however, arranged retinotopically, with the upper quadrants in the dorsomedial, the lower quadrants in the lateroventral, and the "macula" in the intermediate segment of the tract. (*Cf.* chap. VI, 7.)

Brouwer & Zeeman recognized the lateral geniculate nucleus, the gray pregeniculate nucleus, and the superior colliculus of the midbrain as the subcortical terminal stations of the optic nerve. In none of the species (Rabbit, Cat, Monkey) was the pulvinar of the thalamus connected directly with the eye. In the Monkey there is no *fasciculus accessorius optici anterior* and no *tractus peduncularis transversus* of Gudden, found in the Rabbit and the Guinea Pig (*see also* Overbosch).

The most important result of Brouwer & Zeeman's fundamental work concerned the

lateral geniculate nucleus. In the Monkey, the bulk of the optic nerve fibers terminates here. Relatively few fibers pass over to the superior colliculus by way of the brachium, fewer in the Monkey than in the Cat and the Rabbit. On the contralateral side, these optotectal fibers are more numerous, apparently all originating in the extramacular parts of the retina. There is a slight suggestion of retinotopical projection in the colliculus also, the fibers from the upper retinal quadrants entering the posterior, those from the lower quadrants entering the anterior, segments.

In the lateral geniculate nuclei the upper extramacular quadrants are projected upon the inner or medial, the lower quadrants upon the outer or lateral, segments (the nasal quadrants in the contralateral, the temporal quadrants in the ipsilateral, nucleus). The much-disputed "macula," more correctly called the central fovea, sends fibers to the intermediate segment of the nucleus lodged between the two extramacular segments. The size of the "macular" representation is larger than that of the extramacular segments. Altogether, Brouwer & Zeeman were able experimentally to substantiate Rønne's observation of retinal representation in the human lateral geniculate nucleus, and in this point corrected Henschen's error (*see* chap. III, 9 [8, 9], and sec. 4 [6], this chapter).

Concerning the controversy between Henschen, who advocated a restricted and sharply localized projection of the "macula," and Monakow, who favored a diffuse spreading of the "macular" influences over most of the lateral geniculate nucleus, Brouwer & Zeeman were less explicit. Since, according to their observations, "macular" fibers appeared scattered over a larger portion of the nucleus and since there seemed to be partial overlapping of the "macular" and "extramacular" segments, "macular" impulses could, in their opinion, reach the entire nucleus and thus spread over an extensive portion of the visual cortical area, an obvious concession to Monakow's viewpoint. On the other hand, since only the "macular" fibers terminate in the intermediate segment, there was no doubt about a certain amount of localization of the "macula" also (a guarded compromise with Henschen's viewpoint). (*Cf.* secs. 4 [6] and 5 [4], this chapter; for detailed comparison with results presented in this book *see* chap. VI, 7.)

5. LE GROS CLARK & PENMAN'S AND BRODY'S EXPERIMENTS ON RETINOTOPICAL PROJECTION IN THE LATERAL GENICULATE NUCLEUS. —Brouwer & Zeeman's observations have been further amplified, and in several important points corrected, by the experiments, also made upon monkeys, of Le Gros Clark & Penman (1934, portrait Fig. 310), and by Brody (1934). In these, small lesions were made in different parts of the retina. The method by which the location and size of degenerated zones in the lateral geniculate nuclei were determined was "transsynaptic" or "transneuronal" atrophy-degeneration, which permits greater precision than the Marchi method. In various parts of

FIG. 121.—Bernardus Brouwer (1881–1949), professor of neurology at Amsterdam, Netherlands. An illustrious investigator of the visual pathways and centers. In association with W. P. C. Zeeman, first furnished experimental evidence in the Monkey of a quadrantic representation of the retina in the lateral geniculate nucleus. Courtesy Professor B. Brouwer, 1946. For obituary and portrait *see* Nederl. tijdschr. v. geneesk., v. 93 (4), p. 3866, 1949.

the nuclei a sharp projection was found, with no overlapping of the "macular" segment by the "extramacular."

The extent of the "macular" projection was also less, being restricted to approximately the posterior two-thirds of the lateral geniculate nucleus. Anteriorly it begins as a narrow segment, gradually expanding, until, close to the posterior extremity, almost the entire nucleus belongs to the "macula." The central fovea is apparently confined to the posterior third of the nucleus. Of the six cell layers, all belong in part to the macula-fovea, with separate layers representing the ipsi- and contralateral homonymous halves of the two maculae-foveae. "Macular" representation follows the same pattern as that found in the "extramacular" parts of the nucleus. Finally, the "fibers from the nasal half of the 'macula' undergo complete decussation in the chiasma, while those from the temporal half remain uncrossed."

6. The discovery of separate termination of crossed and uncrossed optic nerve fibers by Minkowski.—Cramer (1898) and S. Ramón y Cajal (1899) already anticipated that the two sets of optic nerve fibers—the nondecussating ipsilateral and the contralateral which decussate in the chiasma—terminate discretely. The question, however, was positively answered when Minkowski (1913, 1920, portrait Fig. 122) made the notable discovery that the two categories of fibers do not terminate in the same layer, but in different layers of the laminated lateral geniculate nucleus. In the Monkey, for example, if the left eye is removed, the cell laminae *1*, *4*, and *6* of the contralateral right geniculate nucleus—counting from the lowermost superficial layer at the hilum—degenerate, indicating a termination of the decussating fibers; in the nucleus of the left side, where the nondecussating ipsilateral fibers terminate, laminae *2*, *3*, and *5* are affected (for designation and terms *see* chap. VI, 8 [3]; *see also* Le Gros Clark 1941; Le Gros Clark & Penman 1934). In other words, the cell layers or laminae in the lateral geniculate nucleus represent two sets, one related to the ipsilateral, the other to the contralateral, homonymous retinal half.

In Man the arrangement is essentially the same, as was first found by Minkowski and subsequently confirmed by Schroeder (1929), Balado & Franke (1930), Lenz (1930), Le Gros Clark (1932), Sántha (1932), Hechst (1933), Juba (1933), Orlando (1933), and Barris (1935). (*See also* chap. VI, 6 [5], 8 [3].)

The effect of this peculiar mechanism, according to Minkowski, is a simultaneous transmission of impulses from the "corresponding or conjugate points" of the two homonymous retinal halves which work together in a normal binocular visual act, along two sets of fibers, to two sets of minute segments of two adjoining cell layers of the lateral geniculate nucleus. In this nucleus and also in the visual radiation, the two monocular channels still remain separate, although they are close together. The locality where the final union or fusion of the monocular impressions—if it is to be achieved—may take place seems, accordingly, to be the striate cortex of the occipital lobes of the brain.

Minkowski's discovery raised two problems. The first of them concerns the functional significance of the two or three layers which, in the Primate lateral geniculates, are assigned to each set of fibers (ipsilateral and contralateral). The other is the probable functional effect, or "purpose," of the double or triple supply of each point of the striate cortex by the fibers arising from the adjoining points of the two or three layers of both sets. (*See* chap. VI, 6 [6].)

7. The discovery of accessory subcortical visual centers.—In addition to the principal large stratified or laminated portion which, in Primates, makes up the bulk of the lateral geniculate nucleus, Minkowski found a smaller, caplike portion, the *griseum praegeniculatum* or *substantia grisea praegeniculata*, that is, the pregeniculate gray nucleus, attached to the former along the dorsomedial aspect in approximately the anterior half. This particular gray nucleus is also a terminal station for the optic nerve fibers, mostly decussated, as Minkowski believed. This small nucleus, first described by Nissl and Koelliker (*corpus geniculatum laterale ventrale*, *see* Koelliker 1896, pp. 542, 543), seen by Dejerine (1895–1901), and described by C. Vogt (1909) and by Friedemann (1911), must therefore also be considered one of the several subcortical visual centers. It partly degenerates if one eye is destroyed, but it remains normal when the visual radiation or the occipital lobe is damaged. (*See* chap. VI, 1 [4], 4 [4], 5 [4, 5, 6, 7], 7 [5], 10.)

Later Barris, Ingram, and Ranson (1935) added, in the Cat, to the three stations of the optic nerves already known: the dorsal portion of the lateral geniculate nucleus, the superior colliculus of the midbrain (dorsal part of the

lus. The number of crossed and direct fibers is about equal.

The ventral nucleus, the nucleus of the optic tract (*n. lentiformis mesencephali*), the pulvinar, the *pars posterior* of the pulvinar, and the nucleus of the posterior commissure receive no optic nerve fibers. No optic fibers cross the midline in the posterior commissure or between the superior colliculi. The anterior and posterior ac-

Fig. 122.—Mieczyslaw Minkowski (1884), director of the Institute for Brain Research in Zürich, Switzerland. An eminent modern experimental neuroanatomist. First produced experimental evidence of the identity of the striate area of G. Elliot Smith and of the visual cortical center. First disclosed a topographical or point-to-point representation of the striate area in the lateral geniculate nucleus. Also first demonstrated the termination of ipsilateral and contralateral homonymous retinal optic nerve fibers in distinct layers of the lateral geniculate nucleus in the Monkey. Courtesy Professor M. Minkowski, 1946.

stratum opticum), and the pregeniculate nucleus, also the rostral part of the pretectal area (the center for the constrictor of the pupil). The avenues to the superior midbrain colliculus and the pretectum are the zonal strata of the thalamus and the brachium of the superior colliculus

cessory optic tracts or fascicles are apparently absent in the Cat and in all Mammals above the Rodents. The same experimenters found that "fibers, the cell bodies of which lie within the dorsal nucleus of the lateral geniculate body, pass exclusively to the cerebral cortex."

They did not find evidence in favor of a geniculopulvinarian or geniculothalamic connection.

8. Functional organization of the infranuclear division of the visual system in primitive Mammals.—Because of the low taxonomic status of the investigated animal, the experiments on the visual system of the Opossum by Bodian (1937) are of no small interest. Here, too, the subcortical stations are the dorsal portion of the lateral geniculate nucleus, the superior colliculus, and the optic tegmental nucleus (where the posterior accessory optic tract, which is completely crossed, terminates). It is less certain whether a few fibers also terminate in the ventral portion of the lateral geniculate nucleus, in the pretectal nucleus, and in the accessory nucleus of the optic tract (the *noyau accessoire de la voie optique bigéminale* of S. Ramón y Cajal). No fibers of retinal origin, however, cross in any of the supraoptic commissures. The retinotectal fibers are preponderantly crossed. A remarkably detailed retinotopic projection is present both in the dorsal portion of the lateral geniculate nuclei and in the superior colliculi. In the latter, the binocular portion of the ipsilateral retina is represented in a way similar to that found in the lateral geniculates. (On cortical projection in the Opossum, *see* sec. 7 [10], this chapter.)

9. Investigation of the minute structure of the subcortical visual centers.—With the problem of the terminal nuclei of the optic nerves and their fiber connections with other regions of the brain, the problem of their minute structure, development, and comparative anatomy and the functional interpretation of their structures have absorbed a great deal of attention in modern times. The question of the homology of the dorsal and ventral portions of the lateral geniculate nucleus—first identified in this way by Koelliker (1896)—in various classes of Vertebrates and their gradual change during the process of evolution was ably presented by Le Gros Clark (1932). The structural analysis of the lateral geniculate nucleus, superior colliculus, and adjoining parts of the be-

tween- and midbrain, with the help of the Golgi method, was attempted by S. Ramón y Cajal (1899, 1909–11, 1923) and by his co-workers Tello (1904) and Taboada (1927–28), and further by Balado & Franke (1931, 1937), O'Leary (1938, 1940), and other investigators (*see* chap. VI, 9). A similar series of investigations was carried out in inframammalian Vertebrates by P. Ramón y Cajal (1890, 1891, 1894, 1896, 1897, 1898, 1899, 1917, 1922, 1943) and by Ch. J. Herrick (1917, 1925, 1933, 1934, 1935, 1936, 1938, 1939, 1941, 1942, 1943, 1944, 1948).

References: Ariëns Kappers, Huber & Crosby 1936; Balado & Franke 1929, 1930, 1931, 1937; Barris 1935; Barris, Ingram & Ranson 1935; Beccari 1943; Berl 1902; Bernheimer 1899, 1904, 1910; Bochenek 1908; Bodian 1937; Bouman 1905; Brody 1934; Brouwer 1923, 1924, 1926; Brouwer & Zeeman 1923, 1925, 1926; Casta'di 1923; Chasan 1927; Le Gros Clark 1931, 1932, 1941, 1942; Le Gros Clark & Penman 1934; Cramer 1898; Dalén 1906; De Vries 1913; Friedemann 1911–12; Glees 1941, 1942; Glees & Clark 1941; Hanke 1903; B. Hechst 1933; S. E. Henschen 1890–1931; Ch. J. Herrick 1917, 1925, 1933, 1934, 1935, 1936, 1938, 1939, 1941, 1942, 1943, 1944, 1948; Herrmann & Pötzl 1928; J. M. Jefferson 1941; Juba 1933, 1934, 1939; Koelliker 1889–1902 (v. 2, 1896); Környey 1928; Kosaka & Hiraiwa 1915; Lashley 1934; Lenz 1930; Leonowa 1896; Loepp 1912; Lubsen 1921; Magoun, Atlas, Hare & Ranson 1936; Magoun & Ranson 1935; Marburg 1903, 1942, 1947; Minkowski 1912, 1913, 1914, 1920, 1922, 1930, 1932, 1934, 1939; Monakow 1914; O'Leary 1940; Orlando 1933; Overbosch 1927; Papez 1929; Parsons 1902; W. Pavlow 1900; Pick 1894, 1918; Pick & Herrenheiser 1895; Probst 1901; Putnam & Putnam 1926; P. Ramón y Cajal 1890, 1891, 1894, 1896, 1897, 1898, 1899, 1917, 1922, 1943; S. Ramón y Cajal 1891, 1898, 1899, 1909–11, 1923; Rønne 1914; Sántha 1932; Sjaaf 1923; Sjaaf & Zeeman 1924; R. W. Sperry 1943–51; Ströer 1939, 1940; Taboada 1927–28; Tello 1904; Tsai 1925; Usher & Dean 1896; Vidal & Malbrán 1942, 1943; C. Vogt 1909; Wilbrand & Saenger 1899–1928; Widmark 1897; Winkler 1913; Woollard 1926; Zeeman 1925.

SEC. 7. RECENT INVESTIGATIONS OF THE SUPRANUCLEAR DIVISION
OF THE VISUAL SYSTEM

1. PROBABLE CAUSES OF THE LONG DELAY IN THE HISTOANALYSIS OF THE CEREBRAL CORTEX. —The reasons why it took so long to answer such an apparently elemental question as the presence and location of the visual center in the cerebral cortex were many. Among the most potent negative psychological factors were the beliefs, concepts, and prejudices inherited from earlier times. Another factor was the irrepressible inclination of the human mind to accept only those bits of information which fit into certain preconceived schemes (*cf.* sec. 5, this chapter). These and occasionally other even less excusable features of human character were apparently responsible for the fact that the perfectly valid evidence presented by Hun, Laqueur, and Flechsig in favor of a single visual center in the occipital lobe was declared insufficient or simply brushed aside.

Other reasons, undoubtedly of an objective nature, also contributed their share to the general retardation. The most important was the lack of proper orientation in the cerebral cortex. The sulci and gyri were structures too crude, which varied too much from species to species and from individual to individual, to serve as reliable landmarks. The attempts of early modern experimenters to determine the functions of the various cortical localities were quite vague. If an important discovery was made, such as that of Fritsch & Hitzig (*see* chap. III, 6 [4]), it was more an accident than a logical consequence of planned investigation.

There is nothing surprising, therefore, in the fact that in the early phases of modern brain research some of the brighter minds keenly felt the necessity of learning more about the minute structure of the cortex. And very little progress had been made in this field since Gennari (1782) and Vicq-d'Azyr (1786–90) first noticed the white stripe in the occipital cortex named after them, except the little information added by Baillarger (1840) and by a few other pioneer neurohistologists (*see* chap. III, 5 [1]). Theirs was, however, only preliminary work, carried out with primitive technique and concerned only with broad aspects of the problem.

2. MODERN INVESTIGATION OF THE MINUTE STRUCTURE OF THE CEREBRAL CORTEX. —The modern period of microscopic investigation of the minute structure of the cerebral cortex was initiated by Berlin (1858) and taken up by Arndt (1867–68) and in a more systematic way by Meynert (1865, 1867–68, 1869, 1872, and later; portrait Figs. 113, 311; for biography *see* Anton 1930; DeCrinis 1939; *see also* sec. 2 [2], this chapter). Among other parts of the cortex, Meynert studied the striate cortex of the occipital lobes (*cf.* chap. VIII, 4 [1]). Soon thereafter, Betz (1874, 1881) discovered giant ganglion cells in the precentral motor cortex.

In the course of the following decades the minute structure of the cerebral cortex became an object of increasing interest. As a result of the persistent efforts of numerous investigators, more or less complete charts have been plotted of the cerebral hemispheres of Man and of numerous other vertebrate species, especially of Primates and other Mammals, and, in addition, some work has been done on the structural analysis of the cortex with the Golgi method.

Of these contributions, the important ones are given below, the first contribution of each author being used as a chronological key: B. Lewis (1878); Lewis & Clarke (1878); Henschen (1892); Hammarberg (1893); Kaes (1893, 1907); S. Ramón y Cajal (1893, 1899–1904, 1900–1906, 1909–11, 1921, 1922, 1923, 1924, 1926); Nissl (1897); Schlapp (1898, 1902–3); Bolton (1900, 1901, 1903, 1911, 1933); G. Mann (1900); O. Vogt (1900, 1902, 1903–4, 1906, 1943); Hermanides & Köppen (1903); Brodmann (1903–18); A. W. Campbell (1904, 1905); C. & O. Vogt (1904, 1919, 1926); Köppen & Löwenstein (1905); Mott (1905, 1907); O. & C. Vogt (1906); G. Elliot Smith (1907, 1919, 1927, 1930); Marburg (1907); Watson (1907); Mauss (1908, 1911); Mott & Halliburton (1908, 1910); Mott & Kelley (1908); Ariëns Kappers (1909, 1911, 1928); Mott, Schuster & Halliburton (1910); Marinesco (1911); Mott, Schuster & Sherrington (1911); Flores (1911); Roncoroni (1911, 1927); Rose (1912, 1929, 1930, 1935); Lorente de Nó (1922, 1933, 1934, 1935, 1943);

Gray (1924); Economo & Koskinas (1925); Woollard (1925); Economo (1927, 1928, 1928–29, 1929, 1930, 1931); Filimonoff (1929, 1931–33); Le Gros Clark (1931, 1932, 1942); Hines (1934); Filimonoff & Sarkisoff (1935); Ariëns Kappers, Huber & Crosby (1936); Bonin (1938, 1939, 1942, 1945, 1947, 1950); Sarkisoff & Filimonoff (1938); Bailey & Bonin (1946); Krieg (1946, 1949); Lashley & Clark (1946); Bailey, Bonin & McCulloch (1950). (As standard reference works, Campbell, Brodmann, Economo & Koskinas, and Ariëns Kappers *et al.* 1936, may be most useful; for localization *see* chap. III, 6 [4].)

Before the first reliable cyto- and myeloarchitectural charts of the brain were available as guides, there were few places to look for indications of special functions. The most diligent experimental students of the visual system in the later part of the nineteenth century—Ferrier, Munk, and Monakow—did not have sufficient cytoarchitectural data to rely upon in their work. This may explain why the two former localized the visual center in the wrong place, while Monakow—except for having demonstrated, generally, that there was some sort of topographical relationship—became lost in a maze of learned "decentralistic" potentialities, assumptions, and hypotheses (*see* chap. III, 8; and sec. 5, this chapter).

3. Minkowski's demonstration of the identity of the striate area and the cortical visual center and of the stable representation of the retina in it.—The early experimental attempts to locate the cortical visual area resulted in an approximation, at best. Ferrier's "macular center" in the angular gyrus and Munk's "visual sphere" A_1 on the lateral face of the parieto-occipital region, none of them precisely outlined, were, as evidenced by subsequent research, obviously illusions caused by experimental interference with the visual radiation coursing underneath that locality on its way to the striate cortex. Monakow (1882 and later) and Bernheimer (1900) were able, from their own experiments, to indicate only generally the location of the visual center in the posterior portion of the hemispheres. The results obtained by Bechterew (1901,

1906), Agadschanianz (1906), and Kurzveil (1909) were only a little more positive.

The turning point in the long-lasting dispute between the "localists" and the "decentralists" in this quest finally arrived when Minkowski (1910, 1911, portrait Fig. 122) experimentally produced complete and permanent blindness in the Dog by removing the striate area of both occipital lobes. Through his crucial experiments the question, first asked by Huguenin (1882), of whether or not the striate area was identical with the "physiological visual center," as it was believed to be by Flechsig (1895), H. Sachs (1895), and others, was positively answered (*see* secs. 2 [5], 3 [3], this chapter). Furthermore, in other experiments with partial removal of the striate area, Minkowski (1912, 1913, 1914) found the upper halves of the retinae to be related to the anterior half and the lower halves to be related to the posterior half of the striate area—in this point confirming Munk's earlier observations. And, beyond this, by making small lesions in the Cat, variously placed in the striate area, each lesion causing a corresponding small segment in the lateral geniculate nucleus to degenerate, Minkowski was able to reveal the topographical organization of the supranuclear division of the visual system.

In this way, Minkowski proved experimentally that the striate area was the cortical visual center and that the retina was represented in it in a detailed and stable manner. His work was the more noteworthy, since it was carried out in Monakow's own institute. And although Minkowski, in drawing his conclusions, exercised due deference toward his chief, the deleterious effect of his experiments upon Monakow's decentralist doctrine was unavoidable.

4. Identity of the visual radiation and the inferior longitudinal bundle of Burdach.—Another step in the right direction were the anatomical investigations of Niessl von Mayendorf (1903, 1905, 1907), Hösel (1905), La Salle d'Archambault (1905, 1906, 1909), Redlich (1905), Probst (1906), K. Löwenstein (1911), Zingerle (1911), Stauffenberg (1914), Venderovich (Wenderówič 1915, 1916), Traquair (1922, 1931), R. A. Pfeifer (1925, 1930), Putnam (1926), Papez (1942), and Rasmussen (1943). In agreement with Flechsig's earlier observations (*see* sec. 3 [2], this chapter), they showed the "inferior longitudinal bundle" of Burdach—the "external sagittal stratum" of Sachs—to be identical with Gratiolet's "visual radiation," originating in the lateral geniculate nucleus and terminating in the calcarine cortex, rather than a long association system which it had been, until then, considered to be (*see* chap. III, 5 [3]). The "internal sagittal stratum" of Sachs, which Monakow and others mistook for the visual radiation, on the contrary, was revealed to be principally made up of efferent, corticofugal nerve fibers, arising in the posterior regions of the cortex and terminating in the superior colliculus of the midbrain and elsewhere.

5. REMAINING UNCERTAINTIES ABOUT THE VISUAL RADIATION.—In spite of these disclosures, there was still no general agreement on a number of important issues. One such was the precise origin of the visual radiation—whether it was in the lateral geniculate nucleus alone, as the localists following Flechsig believed, or also in the pulvinar of the thalamus and possibly in the superior colliculus of the midbrain, as Monakow and his followers claimed. Nor were the exact course, arrangement, and termination of fiber bundles as yet well known, in spite of numerous studies in this direction. (*See* Vialet 1893, 1894; Niessl von Mayendorf 1903, 1905, 1907, 1920, 1921, 1930; La Salle d'Archambault 1905, 1906, 1909; Weber 1905; Quensel 1906; A. Meyer 1907, 1912; Tsuchida 1907; Henschen 1910; Zingerle 1911; Winkler 1913; E. De Vries 1913; Monakow 1914; Stauffenberg 1914; Brouwer 1917; Holmes 1919; Rønne 1919; Minkowski 1923–24; Pfeifer 1925; Putnam 1926; and others.)

6. THE PROBLEM OF THE FUNCTIONAL ORGANIZATION OF THE VISUAL RADIATION AND THE IDENTITY OF THE FOVEAL OR "MACULAR" BUNDLE.—The arrangement of the various segments of the visual radiation related to particular quadrants of the fields of view, assuming that there was a regular arrangement, puzzled investigators for a long time. Even after World War I, one of the best-informed authorities could only express a guess, without offering specific indications. Thus G. Holmes (1918, portrait Fig. 123) wrote:

We are consequently forced to the conclusion that the fibres of the radiations are arranged regularly in laminae or series according to the origin of the impulses they carry. The defects in the fields are so frequently quadrantic, despite the gross nature of the injuries, that it is tempting to assume that even in the main mass of the radiations, those indirectly connected with the upper and the lower halves of the retinae are contained in distinct bundles, separated from each other by an anatomical interval; but this hypothesis seems *a priori* so improbable that it cannot be accepted without further evidence, and unless an anatomical basis for it can be discovered.

A similar view was also expressed by Monbrun (1919).

Least certain was the identity and arrangement of the "macular bundle," functionally related to the central foveae. Monakow, in conformity with his antimechanistic concept, assumed an intimate mingling of "macular" fibers with the extrafoveal or peripheral fibers in the entire visual radiation (*cf.* sec. 5, this chapter). Niessl von Mayendorf considered it possible that the macular fibers were contained either in the dorsal or in the ventral segment of the visual radiation, or in both. According to Henschen's opinion, macular fibers were spread out in a thin layer either on the inner or on the outer face of the visual radiation (*cf.* sec. 4 [6], this chapter).

A fourth possibility, that of the macular fibers filling in the "anatomical interval" of Gordon Holmes and of Monbrun and thus keeping apart the upper and the lower extramacular segments of the radiation related to the lower and upper extrafoveal field quadrants, suggested by H. Rønne (Roenne 1919, portrait Fig. 120), seemed too artificial to have wide appeal.

It was equally uncertain whether the striate area alone or a portion of it or perhaps, in addition, portions of the adjacent occipital and parietal cortex receive fibers of the visual radiation. Nor did R. A. Pfeifer's effort (1925, 1930) materially help to clarify the issue. As late as 1927, Lenz was justified in calling the internal organization of the visual radiation "exceedingly complicated and not yet in every respect clarified." (*Cf.* chap. VII.)

7. WAR INJURIES AND THE INTERNAL MAKE-UP OF THE VISUAL SYSTEM.—The influence which experience with war injuries had upon the localization of vision in the brain, and especially upon the understanding of the structure of the visual pathway and the organization of the visual centers was, contrary to what could be expected, relatively slight. During the enormous and confusing conflicts of modern war, there was apparently little disposition or opportunity for systematic study of a problem

and microscopic experience, cases of injuries to the occiput of the head, accompanied by disturbed visual function, were only rarely mentioned. The first report of twenty-three cases of hemianopias and central scotomas was made by Inouye (1909) from the Russo-Japanese War (1904).

In contrast with this scarcity was a fairly

FIG. 123.—Gordon Morgan Holmes (1876), of National Hospital for Paralysed and Epileptic, Queen Square, London, England. One of the most productive investigators of visual brain mechanisms, in particular of the cortical representation of the retina and of the pathology of vision. Courtesy G. Holmes, 1948. (*Cf.* following figure.)

whose utilitarian value seemed remote. In such adverse circumstances, few important cases of cranial injuries were carefully examined by competent neurologists, and fewer specimens of such cases ever came to be properly studied with modern histological techniques.

During the Franco-Prussian War (1870–71), because of insufficient theoretical knowledge

large number of cranial injuries observed during World War I (1914–18) and thereafter, which showed defects in the fields of vision. Prominent among these were the contributions by Axenfeld (1915), Bolton, Bramwell & Robinson (1915), Dimmer (1915), Marie & Chatelin (1914–15, 1915, 1916), Terrien & Vinsonneau (1915, 1916), Uhthoff (1915, 1916, 1922), Beauvieux (1916–17), Cérise (1916–17), B. Fleischer (1916), Holmes & Lister (1916), Morax (1916, 1917), Best (1917, 1919, 1920), Fuchs & Pötzl (1917), Souques (1917), Souques & Odier (1917), G. Holmes (1918, 1919, 1931, 1934), F. Moreau (1918), Szily (1918), Wilbrand & Saenger (1918), G. Jefferson (1919), Fleischer & Ensinger (1920), Lenz (1922, 1924, 1926, 1927), Balado, Adrogue & Franke (1928), R. A. Pfeifer (1930), Brouwer (1930, 1932), Balado & Malbrán (1932), *et al.* (*see* subsec. 10, this section). This abundant evidence, in the light of subsequent experience, unanimously supported the localist

the evidence mentioned above, G. Holmes and Wilbrand & Saenger, as early as 1918, were able to devise sketches of the arrangement of the retinal quadrants and of the fovea in the cortex of the calcarine region (Fig. 124). According to them, the upper extramacular quadrants are represented in the upper lip, the lower quadrants in the lower lip, of the calcarine fissure; the "macula" in the posterior extremity at the occipital pole; and the monocular crescent in the most anterior zone of the striate area, with the intermediate belts arranged in an orderly sequence between these localities. The vertical

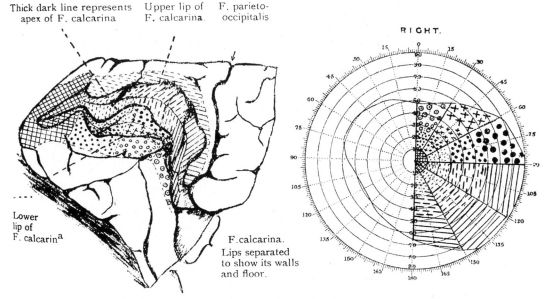

Fig. 124.—"A diagram of the probable representation of the different portions of the visual fields in the calcarine cortex. On the left is a drawing of the mesial surface of the left occipital lobe with the lips of the calcarine fissure separated so that its walls and floor are visible. The markings on the various portions of the visual cortex which is thus exposed correspond with those shown on the chart of the right half of the field of vision. This diagram does not claim to be in any respect accurate; it is merely a scheme." From G. Holmes, in Brit. J. Ophth., v. 2, p. 353, 1918.

concept. Unfortunately, only a small number of these cases were autopsied, and even fewer were competently examined with the help of modern histopathological techniques. The situation being what it was, it was possible for Klüver (1927), in his critical review, to venture a statement to the effect that it would not be difficult to compile as imposing a list of modern contributions in favor of a decentralist viewpoint and against Henschen's localist concept.

8. Sketch of a "cortical retina" in the human brain.—In spite of the shortcomings of

meridians or division lines between the heteronymous halves of the retinae would, according to these maps, run along the upper and lower boundaries of the striate area, with the horizontal meridians extending along the floor of the calcarine fissure from the anterior to the posterior extremity of the striate area.

9. Experimental-anatomical evidence of the retinotopical organization of the cortical visual centers.—Experimental evidence showing the retinotopical organization of the visual radiation and the striate area of the cortex in Primates was first produced by Minkowski (1920). According to him, the upper segment of the visual radiation and the striate area was related to the medial half, the lower segment to the lateral half, of the lateral geniculate nucleus. Van Heuven (1929) and also Brouwer, Van Heuven & Biemond (1929), continuing earlier experiments by Brouwer and his co-workers upon the infranuclear division of the visual pathway (*see* sec. 6 [4], this chapter), were able to confirm and amplify the essential points obtained from the study of human pathological cases.

This was further substantiated and elaborated by a series of experiments performed by the author (1932, 1933) in Monkeys, although with a different technique. Some discrepancy in detail was found, which, however, could be easily explained by a somewhat different configuration and development of human and simian brains. Whereas in Man, because of a tremendous expansion of the parieto-occipitotemporal association region, almost the entire striate area is pushed onto the medial face of the occipital lobe (Fig. 290), in lower Monkeys about half of it is still found on the lateral face, covering practically the entire occipital lobe or the "occipital operculum" (Fig. 280). The posterior limit of the striate area where the central fovea or "macula" is represented, which in Man usually just covers the tip of the occipital lobe, in the Monkey is a homologue of the portion of striate area close to its anterior boundary on the lateral face of the hemisphere, stretching along the simian sulcus. The representation of the monocular nasal portion of the retina that appears to be phylogenetically a more stable portion of the visual center, is located, both in Man and in the Monkey, at the anterior limit of the striate area on the medial face of the hemisphere (*see* chap. VIII, 2). The visual radiation, these experiments disclosed, is made of functional segments, with an axial segment belonging to the "fovea-macula" in the middle, filling the "anatomical interval" of Gordon Holmes and of Monbrun, and with the two "extramacular" segments flanking it above and below, representing the "extramacular" periphery. A fascicle of the visual radiation supposed to decussate in the corpus callosum, which, according to Heine, Niessl von Mayendorf, Lenz, O. Foer-

ster, R. A. Pfeifer, and others, was responsible for the "central sparing" frequently observed in homonymous hemianopia, was not found in these experiments (*cf.* chap. VII, 3 [4], and chap. XI, 8, 9).

10. FURTHER EVIDENCE OF THE DETAILED FUNCTIONAL ORGANIZATION OF THE STRIATE AREA.—While these experiments did away with the last possible doubt which could reasonably be entertained against a rough quadrantic representation of the retina in the cerebral cortex, the problem of a more detailed, or one-to-one, representation required further investigation. For, in their experiments, Brouwer & Zeeman, and their co-workers observed quadrantic changes, no matter what the size of the retinal lesion was and no matter where in the quadrant it was located. There was still some doubt, therefore, whether Monakow's decentralist concept and Pierre Marie's idea of "global quadrantic representation"—as against Wilbrand's and Henschen's concept of a "cortical retina"—may not have been correct after all.

In order to clarify this particular problem, the author made small, variously placed lesions in the striate area of Monkeys, some measuring 1 mm. or less in size (1932, 1933). By studying minute zones of degeneration caused by these cortical lesions in the lateral geniculate nucleus, clear evidence was obtained in favor of detailed retinotopical organization of the supranuclear division of the visual pathway. In still other experiments where lesions in the striate area were arranged to represent various "figures," the zones of degeneration in the lateral geniculate nucleus agreed rather accurately in shape and location with the lesions (for details, *see* chap. VII, 5 [3], and Figs. 248, 252, 256). A well-differentiated retinotopical organization of the striate area, though much below that found in Monkeys, had also been revealed in preponderantly nocturnal Rats by Lashley (1934) and in the Opossum by Bodian (1935, 1937).

Subsequent experiments and carefully studied pathological cases reported by Brouwer (1930, 1932), Pfeifer (1930), G. Holmes (1931, 1934), Juba (1933), Mackenzie, Meighan & Pollock (1933), Polyak & Hayashi (1936), Walker & Fulton (1938), and Polyak (1942), the noteworthy experiments of Foerster (1929) with electrical stimulation of the occipital lobe in conscious human subjects in which subjective photomas and hallucinations in various parts of the visual field were evoked, and the "plotting" of changes in the action potential over the striate areas in Monkeys whose retinas were stimulated with minute beams of light (*see* O'Leary & Bishop 1938; Talbot 1941; Talbot & Marshall 1941; Marshall & Talbot 1942) leave no doubt as to the essential retinotopical organization of the entire visual system. The cortical representation of the retina—with certain qualifications—may indeed be considered what Meynert, Munk, Flechsig, Wilbrand, Henschen, and most clinical neurologists and ophthalmologists have for many decades believed it to be: a "cortical retina."

It was a strange fate that the most solid support that Henschen's thesis was to receive should have come from experimental anatomy and physiology, precisely where he expected it least. (For complete experimental evidence, *see* chaps. VI, VII.)

In summary, we may now venture to say that the visual system of Man and his Primate relatives, the Monkeys and Apes, may safely be considered explored, in spite of a few belated doubts such as those expressed by Foerster (1929), according to which not only the "macula" but the entire retina were represented globally in both hemispheres, and by Hyndman (1939) and Balado & Malbrán (1932), according to which the macula had a second representation outside the occipital lobe.

References: Akelaitis 1940–44; Anton 1930; Arndt 1867–69; Ariëns Kappers, Huber & Crosby 1936; Ask Upmark 1932; Axenfeld 1915; Bailey & Bonin 1946; Bailey, Bonin & McCulloch 1950; Balado, Adrogue & Franke 1928; Balado & Malbrán 1932; Beauvieux 1916–17; Bechterew 1906, 1908–11; H. Berger 1900; R. Berlin 1858; Bernheimer 1900; Best 1917, 1919, 1920; Betz 1874, 1881; Bodian 1935, 1937; Bolton 1900; Bolton, Bramwell & Robinson 1915; Brodmann 1903–18; Brouwer 1917, 1930, 1932; Brouwer, Van Heuven & Biemond 1929; T. G. Brown 1927; A. W. Campbell 1904, 1905; Cérise 1916–17; Coppez & Fritz 1930; E. De Vries 1913; Dimmer 1899, 1915; Economo 1927, 1928, 1929; Economo & Koskinas 1925; Fleischer & Ensinger 1920; O. Foerster 1929; Fuchs & Pötzl 1917; German & Brody 1940; German & Fox 1934; Gurewitsch & Bychowsky 1928; K. Hammarberg 1893; S. E. Henschen 1890–1930, 1893, 1894, 1895, 1900, 1903, 1909, 1910, 1911, 1912, 1917, 1919, 1923, 1924, 1925, 1926; M. Hines 1929, 1934, 1942; G. Holmes 1918, 1919, 1931, 1934, 1945; Holmes & Lister 1916; Inouye 1909; G. Jefferson 1919; Juba 1933; Katzenstein 1932; Klüver 1927; Kronfeld 1929, 1931, 1932; Kurzveil 1909; La Salle d'Archambault 1905, 1906, 1909; Lashley 1934; Lenz 1910, 1916, 1924, 1926, 1927; B. Lewis 1878; Lorente de Nó 1922, 1933, 1934, 1935, 1943; Marie & Chatelin 1914–15, 1915, 1916; Marshall & Talbot 1942; A. Mayer 1907, 1912; Meynert 1867–68, 1869, 1872; Minkowski 1910, 1911, 1912, 1913, 1914, 1920, 1922, 1923–24, 1930, 1932, 1934, 1939; Monakow 1914; Monbrun 1917, 1919, 1920; Morax 1916, 1917, 1919; Morax *et al.* 1919; Moreau 1918; Mott, Schuster & Sherrington 1911; Mackenzie 1934; Mackenzie, Meighan & Pollock 1933; Niessl von Mayendorf 1903, 1907, 1911, 1921, 1926, 1930; O'Leary & Bishop 1938; Penfield & Rasmussen 1950; R. A. Pfeifer 1925, 1930; Pirenne 1948; Pötzl 1918, 1919, 1928; Pötzl & Urban 1935; Polyak 1930, 1932, 1933, 1941, 1942; Polyak & Hayashi 1936; Probst 1906; Putnam 1926; Putnam & Liebman 1942; Quensel 1927, 1931; Rønne (Roenne) 1914, 1916, 1917, 1919, 1944; H. Sachs 1895; G. Elliot Smith 1907, 1923; Souques 1917; Souques & Odier 1917; Stauffenberg 1914; Szily 1918; Talbot 1942; Talbot & Marshall 1941; Terrien & Vinsonneau 1915, 1916; Tsuchida 1907; Van Heuven 1929; Venderóvich (Wenderówič) 1916; Vialet 1893, 1894; C. & O. Vogt 1919, 1926; O. Vogt 1943; Walker & Fulton 1938; Weber 1905; Wilbrand 1925, 1925–26, 1926, 1930; Wilbrand & Behr 1927; Wilbrand & Saenger 1899–1927, 1918; Zingerle 1911.

SEC. 8 RECAPITULATION OF PAST EFFORTS TO EXPLAIN THE PHENOMENON OF VISION IN TERMS OF PHYSICAL FACTORS AND ANATOMICAL STRUCTURES

The effort to explain vision in terms of natural factors had its origin in Ancient Greece. This was not accidental. The inquisitive spirit of that gifted people, the relative peace and prosperity of the country, the religion which chiefly represented personified forces of nature relatively free from magic, the democratic organization of the political units, the resulting relative freedom of thought and speech, and the many contacts of a seafaring people with foreign countries—all contributed to conditions favorable to the rise of science. Nor is it an accident that the logically thinking Greek naturalists, taking the first step before proceeding further, began the investigation of the visual system with the eye (Aristotle, Heróphilos, Rûfos). However, impatient as they were to satisfy their thirst for knowledge, they invented the mysterious "visual spirit" and a channel in the optic nerve through which this spirit could reach the brain (Alkmáion, Heróphilos, Galen).

The Arabs and other Arabic scholars of the Middle Ages, hampered by the restrictive laws of Allah's prophet, added little to what they learned from their Greek teachers. Their merit was in having preserved the most important part of Greek intellectual heritage, which otherwise would probably have perished (Ḥunain ibn Isḥāḳ, ᶜAlī ibn ᶜĪsā, Ibn al-Haitham, Ibn Sīnā).

Another fortunate circumstance was a gradual improvement of living conditions in southwestern Europe during the second half of the Middle Ages, so that time and thought could again be given to the germs of learning coming from Arab lands, chiefly through the activity of Gerard of Cremona and the translator academy of Toledo in Spain. From then on, in many a secluded chamber of a monastery, away from the intrigues of the capitals and castles and from the battlefields, lights began to burn over the new Latin translations of the ancient Arabic manuscripts, and, as always, enlightenment followed study (Vitello, Roger Bacon, John Peckham, Albertus Magnus).

When, through this preparatory work, the Renaissance began, eagerness to learn more about Man and Nature became universal among the educated. Astronomy, physics, and medicine, for the first time since the collapse of the Classical World, began to make real progress. From obscure beginnings the glass industry emerged, producing eyeglasses for the comfort of the aged (A. Spina, Murano, near Venice). This put optical lenses into the hands of clever men, to experiment with and to lay the foundation of the modern science of optics (Maurolycus, Daniello Barbaro, Giambattista della Porta). Augmented by the *camera obscura*, or "dark chamber," such lenses finally helped to explain the true function of the eye's structures, especially light refraction in the dioptrical media and the formation of the retinal image (Plater, Kepler, Scheiner). With the discovery of the telescope (Kepler, G. Galilei), modern astronomy, which the genius of Copernicus had already foreshadowed, was born; and with the invention of the microscope, the all-important science of microscopy began its course (Malpighi, Leeuwenhoek).

The next step, after finding a correct functional interpretation of the eye's structures, was to discover just how the light stimuli, impinging upon the eye, elicit reactions in the brain which enable us to see. Whether it was with the help of some transcendental, immaterial medium or a palpable "visual spirit," it was obvious that special arrangements and connections in the nervous mechanism were at work. Early, crude anatomy could do little to reveal these, except to indicate in a rough way the optic nerves and their apparent origin (Leonardo da Vinci, Vesalius, Willis). Later on, even though anatomical knowledge had advanced but little, the first attempts were made to interpret the visual sense of space and binocular vision by means of a specific intrinsic organization of the visual pathway (Des Cartes, Newton).

But only in modern times, with the general development of natural science and medicine, were the principal features of the visual system, from the eye to the visual centers in the cerebral cortex, discovered.

To achieve this, the lives of many gifted men, and infinite labor and patience were expended. Nor was the road which led to our present considerable knowledge always smooth. It was difficult, rough, and often devious. There were many blind alleys, and much time and effort were wasted in retracing steps (Haller, Gall, Flourens). It was not all the fault of some and all the virtue of others. Most investigators erred in something and were right in other ways (Munk, Monakow, Wilbrand, Henschen).

Final success, then, is the result of the combined efforts of many, each contributing something, much or little, positive or negative, according to his character, ability, and material facilities (Bouillaud, Broca, Gratiolet, Hitzig, Munk, Flechsig, Monakow, Wilbrand, Henschen, Rønne, Minkowski, Brouwer & Zeeman, Holmes, Marie, S. Ramón y Cajal).

The remaining problems, inasmuch as they can now be formulated, are of two categories: first, a complete morphological, biochemical, and biophysical analysis of the minute structures which make up the visual system; and, second, a detailed correlation of these structures with the known visual functions. To know which particular sets of neurons and other associated structures serve, why and how, as the instruments of achromatic sensations and of color vision, of acuity, of visual form and space perception, of the intensities of subjective photic experiences, of contrasts and like phenomena, of binocular stereoscopic vision, of the various reflex actions, and, lastly, of the many higher or psychic functions of vision—this appears as the final purpose of the investigation of the visual system.

If, in addition, through greater knowledge of the mechanics of vision and its operation under normal conditions, and of the many factors underlying pathological disturbances, better methods are found to prevent or retard ailments of sight or to restore failing vision, the labor invested will be well repaid.

PART II

Anatomy and Histology of the Retina and of the Visual Pathways and Centers of the Brain

Chapter V

Structure of the Vertebrate Retina

SEC. 1. STRUCTURE AND FUNCTION OF THE EYE

1. STRUCTURAL PLAN OF THE VERTEBRATE EYE AND ITS WORKINGS.—The eye of all Vertebrates, including the human eye, is a peripheral sense organ by means of which the individual reacts to the physical radiant energy called "visible light." The first task of the eye is physical: to refract those rays of light falling into it in such a manner as to produce real images of the external objects from which the light rays emanate or are reflected—images that are symmetrically accurate, although reduced in size and inverted.

The other, and no less important, task of the eye is the sorting of nervous impulses, generated in the eye by the action of light, and the transmitting of them to the brain. In the brain the corresponding subjective reactions of "seeing" and of "visual appreciation" of seen objects take place, as a result of which the individual makes the necessary adjustments to his changing environment.

The first task—the formation of a physical image on the retina—is accomplished because of the eye's organization as a dioptrical apparatus. In this sense the vertebrate chamber eye may be looked upon as a living photographic motion-picture camera. How the dioptrical principles of the *camera obscura*, or "dark chamber," upon which the eye is built were discovered in the past is related in chapter I, 5 (*see also* Figs. 31, 33). The subject of the physical optics and dioptrics of the eye is exhaustively dealt with in a number of treatises, such as those of Gullstrand (1902), Helmholtz (1924–25), Preston (1928), A. König (1929), R. W. Wood (1934), Rohr (1937), Southall (1937), Emsley (1939), Tschermak-Seysenegg (1942), Le Grand (1946), Linksz (1950), Pascal (1952), Rüchard (1952), and others; whereas a discussion of the structure of the eye is to be found in

the books of Salzmann (1912), Ovio (1927), Duke-Elder (1932), Kolmer & Lauber (1936), Walls (1942), Detwiler (1943), Kronfeld *et al.* (1943), Rochon-Duvigneaud (1943), and E. Wolff (1948). For details concerning the retinal structures *see* the subsequent sections of this chapter and the monograph *The Retina* (1941, 1948) by this author.

The other, and much more complicated, function of the eye and of the central visual pathway connected with it is to generate and conduct nervous impulses to the brain—impulses varying in a great many ways: in quality, in intensity, in spatial and temporal distribution, etc. This role of the eye and of the remainder of the visual apparatus still remains largely obscure. The structures instrumental in this complex function and the role that each performs in the total process of vision are the principal themes of Part II of this book. (*Cf.* Helmholtz 1924–25; Piéron 1936, 1945; Bartley 1941; P. J. Bouma 1947; Granit 1947; Wright & Martin 1947; Pirenne 1948; Davson 1949.)

The eye, like other useful organs of the body, is adapted, in all the details of its intrinsic organization, to its physiological task (Fig. 125). Its shape is more or less spheroidal, the shape best suited for preventing distortion—a factor essential in a dioptrical apparatus. Its outer membrane is a tough fibrous tunic, which, together with the fluids filling its cavities and the intraocular pressure maintained by the heart's action, helps preserve the shape of the eye. Most of that outer tunic, the sclera (*scl*), is opaque, the opaqueness being made complete by the pigmented chorioid membrane (*chor*) and by the pigment epithelium of the retina (layer *1* in Figs. 127, 128, 129). The anterior segment, the cornea (*cor*), which faces the out-

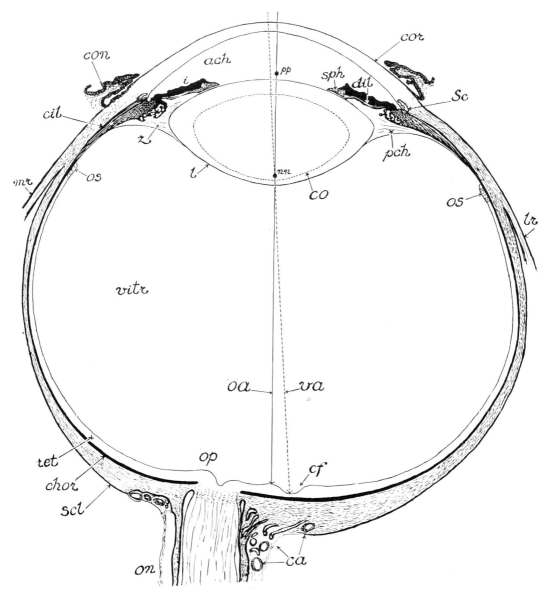

Fig. 125.—Horizontal section through the fully developed human eye drawn with the help of camera lucida, magnified approximately 6×. Right side temporal, left side nasal. *Labeling: ach,* anterior chamber; *ca,* ciliary arteries; *cf,* central pit or fovea; *chor,* chorioid membrane; *cil,* ciliary body; *con,* conjunctiva; *cor,* cornea; *dil,* dilator muscle of pupil; *i,* iris membrane; *l,* crystalline lens; *lr,* lateral rectus or straight muscle (tendon); *mr,* medial rectus or straight muscle (tendon); *nn,* double nodal point of eye; *oa,* optical axis; *on,* optic nerve; *op,* optic papilla, disk, or head of optic nerve; *os,* ora serrata, serrated margin of retina; *pch,* posterior chamber; *pp,* double principal point; *ret,* retina; *Sc,* venous scleral sinus or canal of Schlemm or Lauth; *scl,* sclera; *sph,* sphincter or constrictor muscle or pupil; *z,* ciliary zonule of Zinn or suspensory ligament of lens; *va,* visual axis; *vitr,* vitreal chamber and vitreal body. Actual length of visual axis, from anterior surface of cornea to posterior surface of retina, 21 mm.; length of transverse diameter, from retina to retina, 21.5 mm. Note varying thickness of all three coats, their thickest parts being in posterior portion; the thinnest locality of sclera is along nasal equator; of chorioid, along equator all around; of retina, at ora serrata; cornea is thinnest along its vertex; scleral radius of curvature varies considerably from point to point, being also different on nasal side from that on temporal, making the shape of eyeball asymmetrical. (*Cf.* Fig. 365.)

side world, is transparent, as are also the fluid and semisolid media within the eyeball itself, permitting free passage of light into the eye's interior—into the aqueous humor in the anterior and posterior chambers (*ach, pch*), the vitreous humor (*vitr*) in the large vitreal chamber, and the elastic lens (*l*) placed in between.

The light that enters the eye, however, cannot spread within it in a haphazard way but is forced to follow the laws of refraction. First, not all the light rays that enter through the transparent front window—the cornea—gain free entrance into the interior but only those that pass through the opening in the iris (*i*), the pupil. Here they are further compelled, by the refractive power of the lens, to change their direction until they are concentrated into the smallest possible dimension, or focused, on the photosensitive screen that coats the inside of the eye—the retina (*ret*). Changed in this way, the rays of light that are distributed over the expanse of the retina, like the rays from a motion-picture projector on a screen, reproduce in succession a variety of pictures of external objects, much reduced in size from the objects seen and in an inverted position.

The next step—the last in the eye, although first in the long chain of the neurodynamical changes and reactions of the visual apparatus—involves the minute structures of the retinal membrane and concerns their working. These structures, because of their chemical composition, number, histological peculiarities, special distribution, and connections with one another or isolation from one another, are capable of reacting specifically to the stimulation of physical light and of transmitting, combining, selecting, or otherwise modifying their reactions, which are then sent to the brain. Suffice it to say that, in general, the more the retinal structures are capable of reacting in detail to the locally and dynamically varying light stimuli, which, in the aggregate, form the physical ocular image, the more complete and accurate are the messages sent to the central arbiter, the brain, about the things and events in the world of light in which we live.

Briefly, the eyeball, complicated though its structure is, is no more than an elaborate container for the true peripheral photoreceptor—the retina—which alone, by virtue of its photo-sensitivity and specific organization, is capable of bringing the organism into photodioptrical relationship with the surrounding world.

2. Dimensions and dioptrical landmarks of the eyeball.—The normal human eye of an adult measures 24 or 25 mm., or approximately 1 inch, in diameter (Fig. 125). The approximate diameter of the eye of a Gorilla is the same; of a Chimpanzee, 21 mm.; of a Rhesus Macaque, 19 mm. (Fig. 126).

Several convenient landmarks and dioptrical lines and planes are customarily distinguished in the eyeball. The straight line (solid in the figure) connecting the anterior pole, or vertex, of the cornea with the farthest point at the posterior end of the eyeball is the *anatomical axis*. This line almost coincides with the *geometrical axis*, which, in turn, is practically identical with the *optical axis* (*oa*), or the sagittal line passing through the centers of rotation of the refractive optical media of the eye, the cornea, and the lens.

The *visual axis* (*va*), or the line of vision or gaze (indicated by an interrupted line in our figure), in the fundus deviates from the optical axis by 4°–7° laterally or temporally and is about 3°.5 below the horizontal meridian, as it passes through the center of the central fovea (*cf*).

A plane vertical to the visual axis, where this axis passes through the largest circumference of the eyeball, is called the *equator*. Other planes that pass through the visual axis of the eyeball are known as the *meridians*. Of the latter, the most important are the vertical meridian, oriented anteroposteriorly or sagittally, and the horizontal meridian. The first divides the eyeball into a nasal and a temporal half; the second into an upper and a lower half. Both divide the eyeball and its membranes into four *quadrants:* an upper and a lower nasal and an upper and a lower temporal.

3. Outer tunic of the eye: sclera and cornea.—The outermost of the three eye membranes is a tough, fibrous tunic. Its larger posterior portion, the sclera (*scl*), is opaque. The smaller, and more sharply curved, anterior portion—the cornea (*cor*)—is transparent under normal conditions of life. The cornea is made up of several regularly arranged layers. Normally it is devoid of blood vessels, but it contains numerous nonmedullated nerves and their terminals.

4. Uveal tunic and ciliary muscle.—The middle, vascular tunic, the *uvea* (black in Fig. 125; white in Fig. 126), is a nutritive organ, especially of the retina. The larger posterior portion of the uvea, called the *chorioid membrane* (*chor*), consists chiefly of blood vessels.

by approximately sixty to seventy minute, radially arranged folds, varying in length and in thickness and consisting largely of smooth muscle fibers and blood vessels.

The action of the ciliary organ—by relaxing the fibers of the *suspensory ligament*, or *Zinn's zonule* (*z*), one end of which is attached to the chorioid and the other end to the lens—increases the bulge or curvature of the lens and thus, by increasing the refractive power of the crystalline lens (*l*), serves to accommodate vi-

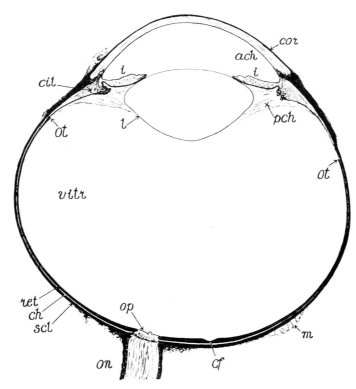

Fig. 126.—Horizontal section of a right eyeball of a Rhesus Macaque (*Macaca rhesa, M. mulatta*), magnified $4\frac{1}{2}\times$. Right side temporal, left side nasal. Actual length both of the optical axis (from anterior surface of cornea to posterior surface of retina) and of the transverse axis approximately 19 mm. *Labeling: ach*, anterior chamber; *ch*, chorioid membrane; *cf*, central fovea; *cil*, ciliary body; *cor*, cornea; *i*, iris; *l*, lens; *m*, portion of an extrinsic muscle; *on*, optic nerve; *op*, optic papilla; *ot*, ora terminalis or retinal margin; *ret*, retina; *scl*, scleral coat.

The uvea also is composed of numerous chromatophore cells containing dark pigment, which make it an opaque screen, lining the interior of the ocular cavities, which are filled with transparent media—the posterior chamber (*pch*) and the vitreal cavity (*vitr*).

The anterior portion of the uveal tunic, where it is firmly attached to the outer fibrous coat at the line where the opaque sclera passes into a diaphanous cornea, is transformed into a special organ, the *ciliary body* (*cil*), represented

sion for close range. Conversely, the relaxation of the ciliary muscle fibers increases the tension of the suspensory ligament, which in turn, by flattening the lens, decreases its refractive power, thereby adjusting the eye for distant vision. (*See* par. 8, this section.)

5. Iris and pupil.—The anterior portion of the uveal tunic, the *iris* (*i*), is a thin, circular membrane placed curtain-fashion in front of the lens. In the living, it is visible through the transparent cornea. Its individually varying color is caused by the different quantity of pigment stored in the cells of its tissue.

The nearly circular opening, the pupil, placed almost centrally in the iris, permits light from outside to pass through the lens into the inner, vitreal chamber of the eye (*vitr*). The black color of the pupil is caused by the very small quantity of light reflected from the interior of the eye, in comparison with the intense outside light.

The size of the pupil is determined by the action of two minute, antagonistically functioning, muscles contained in the iris tissue. One muscle, consisting of circular fibers near the pupillary margin, is called the *sphincter*, or *constrictor*, of the pupil (*sph*). This muscle, as well as the *ciliary accommodation muscle* (*cil*), responds to the stimuli of parasympathetic oculomotor nerves and nuclei of the midbrain (by way of the ciliary ganglion). The activation of the iris sphincter decreases the size of the pupil and thus cuts down the amount of light falling into the eye. This reflex action results from the stimulation of the retina by light.

The other muscle of the iris, composed of delicate fibers arranged radially, is the *dilator* of the pupil (*dil*). It is under the influence of the sympathetic ciliospinal center of Budge (which is located in the lowermost cervical and uppermost thoracic segments of the spinal cord) by way of the cervical sympathetic trunk, its superior ganglion, and its postganglionic fibers.

The iris membrane, which is lined on its inner side and up to its pupillary margin with a heavily pigmented, nonnervous extension of the retina, functions as an opaque curtain, preventing light from entering the vitreal cavity except through the pupil.

6. Retina.—The innermost membrane or tunic of the eye is the *retina* (*ret*). In contrast with the cornea, sclera, and uvea, the retina is an organ made up entirely of nervous tissue and blood vessels. It is the actual photoreceptor organ, or the structure which, stimulated by physical light entering the eye, elicits nervous reactions, which, transmitted to the brain, are manifested in the subjective experience of vision.

The retinal membrane develops as an outpocketing of the frontal end of the brain, one protuberance on each side, during the early period of embryonic life (*cf.* chap. XIII, 2, and Figs. 434, 435). The primary optic vesicle first formed contains a space which communicates freely with the ventricular cavities of the brain by means of a hollow optic stalk—the future optic nerve. During further development the anterior wall of the primary optic vesicle gradually caves in until it touches the back wall, whereupon the original ventricular space disappears. In this way the two sheets of the embryonic retina—the inner and the outer—join, forming the secondary optic vesicle, or optic cup. In this vesicle the outer sheet becomes the pigment layer, and the inner sheet the nervous retina proper. In the anterior nonnervous ciliary and iridial portion of the retina lining the ciliary body and the back face of the iris, both sheets retain the character of a simple epithelium loaded with pigment.

The larger, posterior nervous portion—the retina in the proper sense—is a highly transparent membrane, with the exception of the pigment layer. In the living, in those vertebrate species where this membrane contains blood vessels—as, for example, in Man, Monkeys, and Apes—the color of the retina is determined by the blood contained in its vessels. After death, with the emptying of most blood from the vessels, the retina appears as a glassy, colorless membrane. Within a short time after death, however, the tissue of the retina assumes a dull whitish coloring and loses its transparency, owing to the process of coagulation. (For details on the retinal structures, *see* subsequent sections in this chapter, and Polyak, *The Retina.*)

7. Chambers and humors of the eye.— The inner space of the eye is filled with transparent fluid and transparent bodies and is subdivided, by partitions, into three cavities or chambers.

The *anterior chamber* (*ach*), inclosed by the cornea, the iris, and as much of the anterior surface of the lens as is left exposed by the varying size of the pupil, is filled by a thin, watery fluid, the *aqueous humor*.

The *posterior chamber* (*pch*), which is limited by the posterior surface of the iris, by that part of the anterior surface of the lens which is not included in the pupil and is not covered by the iris, by the equatorial margin and the adjoining portion of the posterior surface of the lens, and also by a portion of the vitreal membrane, is a minute, meniscoidal space encircling the lens equator in a ringlike fashion. It is also filled with aqueous humor, which is here being secreted from the epithelium of the ciliary ridges containing blood vessels and capillaries.

The largest and most posterior chamber, the *vitreal cavity (vitr)*, which is inclosed by the retina, zonular ligament (*z*), the posterior surface of the lens (*l*), and the hyaloid membrane, is filled with a viscous and somewhat gelatinous fluid, the *vitreous humor*.

8. CRYSTALLINE LENS.—In Man and his primate relatives the crystalline lens (*l*) is an elastic body, resembling a lentil. It is characterized by a regular shape, smooth surfaces, high transparency, and a considerable index of refraction.

Anteroposteriorly the lens is somewhat flattened, with the curvature of its anterior surface less than that of its posterior surface. The lens is inclosed in a delicate, structureless envelope, whose two leaves—the anterior and posterior lens capsules—form a pillow-like casing, to whose equatorial edge the fibers of the suspensory ligament, or zonule, are attached. The tissue of the lens consists of numerous cells elongated into thin, long, elastic, fiber-like structures, the *lens fibers*, arranged in an intricate, but very regular, pattern.

Owing to its structure, the lens is endowed with an elastic property, permitting the lengthening of its sagittal axis and the shortening of the radii of curvature of its anterior and posterior surfaces. In a relaxed condition, relieved from the tension of the suspensory ligament (which, in turn, is sustained by intraocular pressure)—an effect normally brought about by the action of the ciliary muscle during the process of accommodation—the lens increases its refractive power and thus adjusts the dioptrical apparatus of the eye for close vision. Conversely, the pull of the suspensory ligament in the unaccommodated eye causes the two sheets to compress the lens, thereby counteracting the elastic tendency of the lens, and, by increasing the radii of curvature of its surfaces, causes the refractive power of the lens to decrease and

in this way adjusts it for distant vision. The pull of the suspensory ligament is made possible by the relaxation of the ciliary muscle. (*Cf.* par. 4.)

9. THE EYE AS A DIOPTRICAL APPARATUS.—As stated earlier, the eye may be compared to a dark chamber, *camera obscura*, provided with a dioptrical apparatus and a photosensitive back screen. The parts of the dioptrical apparatus of the eye are the cornea, which is stable, and the lens, which is changeable. The back screen in the eye is represented by the photosensitive retina. On it the light rays, when properly focused by the accommodation apparatus, are united in such a way as to form a sharp, inverted, and much diminished image of visible external objects toward which the visual axis is directed. In Man and other terrestrial Vertebrates most refraction takes place in the cornea; in the aquatic Vertebrates mostly, or only, in the lens.

The nervous reactions elicited in the retinal tissue, varying in many ways from point to point on the retinal surface, especially in intensity and quality, are further propagated to the brain, where they are subjectively interpreted as variously illuminated and colored objects of many shapes, sizes, and numbers, still or in motion, near or distant, and so forth. In the further course of the visual process, the seen objects are compared with those seen before and are either recognized as known, and identified with these, or as unknown; they are additionally evaluated as to their meaning and other properties—trains of subjective experiences designated as "higher," "psychic," or "mental" visual functions.

10. ACCESSORY ORGANS OF THE EYE.—The eyes are also equipped with extrinsic muscles, nerves, glands, and blood vessels. With these, the eyes are lodged in the bony orbits of the skull, which are filled with a fatty tissue. In addition, the eyes are protected by the lids, lashes, and brows. Together with the oculomotor centers of the brain and spinal cord, all these structures form an ingeniously devised apparatus serving binocular stereoscopic vision.

References: Abelsdorf & Wessely 1909; F. H.

Adler 1953; G. F. Alexander; Ames *et al.* 1932; Arey 1932; Ascher 1942, 1946; Th. G. Atkinson 1944; E. H. Bárány 1947; Bartelmez 1922; Bartley & Fry 1934; Bach & Seefelder 1914; Baillart *et al.* 1939; Ballantyne 1941; Barkan 1936; Basile 1938; Baurmann 1933, 1934; Bausch & Lomb (*see* Kronfeld *et al.*); Benoit 1926; Berens & Sells 1950; Berliner 1943–49; Bethe, Bergmann, Embden & Ellinger v. 12 (*Photoreceptoren*); Bradley 1934; Bonnet 1932; Brücke 1847; Bruno 1936; Bucciante 1933; Carlevaro 1943; Clerici 1943; Coblentz 1920; Cooper & Daniel 1949; Cooper, Daniel & Whitteridge 1949, 1950; Cowan 1932, 1946; D. J. Cunningham 1943; Damel 1936; Daniel 1946; Déjean 1926; Detwiler 1943; H. E. De Vries 1943, 1949; De Vries *et al.* 1950; Donders 1864; Duke-Elder 1932-38; Duke-Elder *et al.* 1940, 1943, 1948, 1949; Dvořak-Theobald 1934; Eisler 1930; F. P. Fischer 1938, 1940, 1947; Fralick 1941–42; Fralick & Crosby 1943–44; V. Franz 1913, 1934; Friede 1933; J. S. Friedenwald 1936, 1944; Friedenwald & Stichler 1935, 1938; Fujimori 1935; Fujita 1934; Gallenga 1932; O. Gasser 1935; K. F. Gauss 1841; Goedbloed 1934; Goldsmith 1939; Graefe & Saemisch 1874–1932; Greear 1942; Greeff 1899 (1900); Grether 1941; Groethuysen 1929; Gullstrand 1902; Hardy & Perrin 1932; Hartinger; Hegner 1937; Heine 1906; Helmholtz 1924–25; T. Henderson 1941; Hering 1905, 1905–20, 1931; R. Hesse 1929; Hesse & Doflein 1935; Hidano 1926; Hildreth 1940; Hotta 1906; Hovelaque 1927; E. Jackson 1941; Jokl 1918–19, 1923; Kinsey 1948; Kinsey & Grant 1944; Kirbey 1932, 1941; Kiss 1947; Knapp 1861; Koby 1930; Koelliker 1861; Koeppe 1918, 1920, 1921, 1937; Kolmer 1930; Kolmer & Lauber 1936; A. C. Krause 1934, 1942; W. Krause 1855; Kronfeld, McHugh & Polyak 1943; A. Kühl 1920; Lauber 1931, 1936; Leber 1903; Le Grand 1937, 1946; Leplat 1932; Leuckart 1876; Lindner 1934; Linksz 1950; J. B. Listing 1845, 1853, 1905; Llorca 1932; Lutz 1931; Maggiore 1924; Magitot 1921, 1946; I. C. Mann 1928, 1931, 1950; W. A. Mann 1944, 1945; Marchesini 1933; Mawas 1937; May 1949; Merkel 1885–90; Merkel & Kallius 1901; Merkel & Orr 1892; Metz 1868; Mollier 1938; McCotter & Fralick 1942; McReynolds 1929; Nippert 1931; Novotny 1934; J. Ohm 1943; Oppenheim 1940; Ovio 1927; Palumbi 1932; Parsons & Duke-Elder 1948; Pascal 1945, 1952; Pischinger 1938; Plate 1924 (*Sinnesorgane*); Polyak 1941, 1948, 1955; Polyak *et al.* 1946; Pütter 1908–12; Ramsay *et al.* 1941; Reese 1935; Rochon-Duvigneaud 1943; M. Rohr 1937; Ross 1949; Rüchardt 1952; Sala 1933; Salzmann 1912; B. Samuels 1935; Sanna 1930; Sattler 1876, 1887; Scammon & Wilmer 1950; Schieck & Brückner 1930–32; A. H. Schultz 1940; Schwalbe 1887; Scott 1945; Sendermann 1930, 1933; Senná 1932; Smaltino 1937; D. W. Soemmerring 1818; Sommers 1949; Southall 1937; Spalteholtz 1916; Spaeth 1941; R. Stein 1932; Streuli 1925; Studnička 1918, 1933, 1934; Sugar 1942; Tarkhan 1934; Ten Doesschate & Fischer 1948; Thorington 1939; Toldt; Traquair 1948; W. Trendelenburg 1943; Troncoso 1942; Tschermak-Seysenegg 1929, 1931, 1942; Van der Horst 1933; Velter 1934; Vidal & Damel 1944; Vila-Coro 1936; A. Vogt 1930–42, 1935, 1941, 1947; Waardenburg 1932; H. Wagner 1931; Wald & Griffin 1947; Walls 1942; Watanabe 1930; Whitnall 1932; Wiener & Alvis 1939; Wilbrand & Saenger 1904; Wilczek 1947; Wilmer & Scammon 1950; G. Winckler 1937; E. Wolff 1948; Zinn 1755; Zoth 1923. (On the blood supply of the eye *see* chap. X, 2; on ontogeny and phylogeny of the eye *see* chap. XIII, 1, 2.)

SEC. 2. GENERAL FEATURES OF THE MINUTE STRUCTURE OF THE RETINA

1. INTRODUCTORY REMARKS.—The histological elements which make up the tissue of the nervous or functioning portion of the retinal membrane, from the optic papilla to the *ora serrata*, resemble those found in the brain, whence this membrane derives, both phylogenetically and ontogenetically. The nervous parenchyma is represented here by nerve cells in the proper sense and by their expansions, both carriers of the specific retinal function. Another important constituent is the neuroglia, which forms the framework in which the nervous parenchyma is lodged. The third constituent is the pigment epithelium, a derivative of the outer sheet of the secondary optic vesicle of the early embryo (*see* chap. XIII, 1, 2). These three constituents, with the possible exception of microglia, are of ectodermal origin (*see* sec. 9 [3], this chapter). Numerous blood vessels, branches of the central artery and vein, penetrate the retinal membrane and form a dense capillary network in its vitreal half. These are of mesodermal origin. (*See* chap. X, 2 [3].)

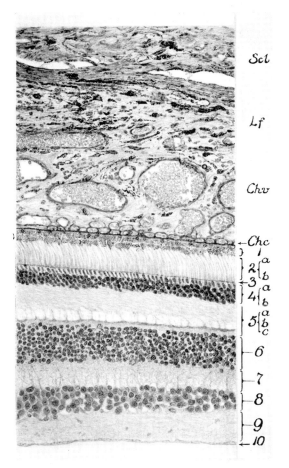

Fig. 127.—Vertical section through the tunics of human eyeball in the region of central area stained with haematoxylin and eosin. Upper half of figure shows portion of fibrous sclera containing pigment-bearing chromatophore cells and some blood vessels, more numerous in the chorioid membrane, which is principally vascular, containing also some chromatophores, and terminating next to the retina in a choriocapillary layer composed of minute vessels. Lower half of figure shows retinal membrane made up of cellular and fibrous elements arranged in regular, parallel layers. *Labeling: Chc*, choriocapillary layer; *Chv*, vascular layer of chroioid membrane; *Lf*, lamina fusca; *Scl*, less pigmented portion of scleral membrane; *1*, pigmented epithelium of retina; *2*, bacillary layer; *3*, outer limiting membrane; *4*, outer nuclear layer; *5*, outer plexiform layer; *6*, inner nuclear layer; *7*, inner plexiform layer; *8*, ganglion cell layer; *9*, layer of optic nerve fibers; *10*, inner limiting membrane of retina. Magnified approximately 150×.

The nerve cells and fibers and the elements of the supporting tissue are arranged in several distinct layers and zones parallel to the surface of the retina and to one another. These layers are noteworthy because of their regularity. In the human and simian retina, ten layers and sublayers, or zones, may be distinguished, beginning with the layer closest to the chorioid membrane (Figs. 127, 128), and are described below.

2. PIGMENT EPITHELIUM (1).—This is the outermost layer of the retina, immediately adjoining the chorioid. It was first well described by Th. Wharton Jones (1833). It is represented by a single layer of cuboidal cells, which, from the surface, appear pentagonal or hexagonal in shape. From the vitreal end of the cell body containing a nucleus, ragged, fringe-like protoplasmic expansions spread between the photoreceptors. These expansions and the near-by vitreal part of the body are filled with the granules and needles of a dark-brown pigment—the fuscin.

In numerous Vertebrates, such as Fishes, Amphibians, and Birds, the pigment changes its position according to the intensity of illumination. In strong daylight in the bright-adapted eye, the pigment migrates into protoplasmic expansions, closer to the external limiting membrane, reducing or preventing a lateral diffusion of light. In dim light in the dark-adapted eye, on the contrary, the pigment migration is the reverse, from the fringes into the cell bodies, thus exposing the photoreceptors to the full action of light of low intensity. There are indications that similar, although apparently less extensive, movements of the pigment may occur also in the Mammals, including the Primates. (*See* Genderen Stort 1886, 1887; Chiarini 1904–6; Garten 1907; Arey 1915, 1916, 1919, 1928, 1932; Detwiler 1916, 1923, 1943, 1944, 1945; Laurens & Williams 1917; Laurens & Detwiler 1921; Detwiler & Lewis 1926; Zikulenko 1926; Walls 1928, 1942; E. Scharrer 1929; Luppino 1930; Wigger 1937–38, 1939; Arey & Mundt 1941; Sverdlick 1942; Arey & Jennings 1944.)

3. BACILLARY LAYER (2).—Immediately vitrealad to, and partly enveloped by, the pigment epithelium is the second layer, composed of more or less rodlike or flasklike scleral ends of the visual cells or photoreceptors—the rods (*a*) and the cones (*b*).

In sections vertical to the surface of the retinal membrane, the bacillary layer, when well preserved, appears vertically striated, with the extensions of the lines directed toward the pupil of the eye.

In the human and simian retina there are two varieties of elements in the bacillary layer: the thinner, but somewhat longer and more numerous, rods and the thicker, shorter, and less numerous cones. Since each rod and each cone is, in turn, made up of an outer and an inner segment, with a short intermediary zone between, the bacillary layer may be further subdivided into two zones: *2-a*, represented by the outer segments, and *2-b*, represented by the inner segments. Because the boundary line between the outer and the inner segments is slightly closer to the sclera in the rods than in the cones, the division line between *2-a* and *2-b*, even though distinct, is not sharp but appears somewhat fuzzy (*cf.* Fig. 130).

The function of the bacillary layer is "photoreception," a specific reaction to physical "light." In this process probably all three constituents of the rods and cones—the outer and the inner segments, as well as the intermediary zone—participate, even though it seems probable that the initial reaction takes place in the outer segments. (*Cf.* sec. 3 [5], this chapter.)

Formerly, the bacillary layer was termed "Jacob's membrane," or "Jacob's tunic"; and, together with the retinal pigment epithelium, the capillary layer of the chorioid membrane, and Bruch's glassy membrane, it was known as the "membrane of Ruysch or Doellinger."

4. Outer limiting membrane (3).—This term is applied to a structure that appears as a sharp line separating the bacillary layer from the layers below. The line, visible in both stained and unstained preparations, represents a membrane-like structure produced by the joining of the top ends of the supporting neuroglial "radial fibers" of Müller. In the flat view the outer limiting membrane appears perforated by countless openings, somewhat pentagonal and hexagonal in shape, for which reason it was

also called the "reticular membrane." The smaller and more numerous of these openings serve for the passage of rods; the fewer larger ones, for the passage of cones.

The function of the outer limiting membrane seems to be that of providing stable support for the lower ends of the rods and cones proper, by which they are firmly kept in place. This membrane was first described and named by M. Schultze (1866), even though it had been seen by others earlier.

5. Outer nuclear layer (4).—The relatively thick fourth layer is formed by closely packed bodies of photoreceptor cells containing the nuclei of the rods and cones. The larger nuclei, which in stained preparations are paler and fewer in number, are the cone nuclei. These are oriented with their longer axes more or less vertical. Their position, spacing, and number closely agree with those of the cones proper of the bacillary layer in each particular locality of the retina.

With the exception of the foveal center, the cone nuclei are found in a single row immediately below the outer limiting membrane, where they form zone *4-a*. In the center of the central fovea they are at some distance from this membrane and are present in several tiers (Figs. 129, *I*, and 161). The smaller, darker, and, in Primates, far more numerous rod nuclei, filling the fourth layer as far as its vitreal boundary, form zone *4-b*. Their number also closely corresponds with that of the rods in the bacillary layer, in a given locality of the retina. In the foveal center both the rods and the rod nuclei are absent (*see* above-mentioned figures).

6. Outer plexiform layer (5).—The fifth layer is located between the outer and the inner nuclear layers. In most regions of the retina it is relatively thin (Fig. 129, *IV*, *V*, *VI*). In the region of the axis, corresponding to the central area, however, the outer plexiform layer attains considerable thickness (Figs. 127, 128, 129, *II*, *III*). Here, also, it is further differentiated into three sublayers.

The outer zone, *5-a*, composed of the inner rod and cone fibers, shows a parallel striation. Outside the central area this striation is more or less vertical (Fig. 129, *V*). In the periphery

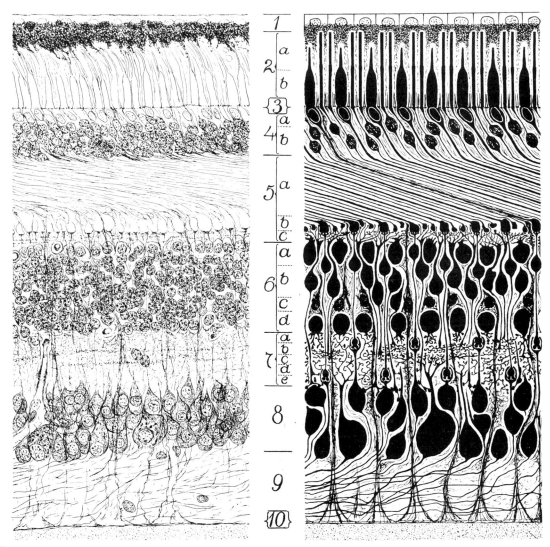

Fig. 128.—Structure of human retina as it appears in sections vertical to its surface, from central area midway between areal periphery and central fovea. Left half of figure shows the appearance of a preparation stained with haematoxylin and eosin, right half showing constituent cellular and fibrous elements of retinal tissue disclosed with the help of "analytical" methods of staining such as Golgi (silver dichromate) and Ehrlich (vital methylene blue stain). Layers: *1*, pigment epithelium; *2*, bacillary layer; *3*, outer limiting membrane; *4*, outer nuclear layer; *5*, outer plexiform layer; *6*, inner nuclear layer; *7*, inner plexiform layer; *8*, ganglion cell layer; *9*, layer of optic nerve fibers; *10*, inner limiting membrane. Note that zone *2-a* of bacillary layer is made up of outer segments, zone *2-b* of inner segments of thinner rods and thicker cones; *3*, outer limiting membrane resulting from joining of top-ends of supporting radial fibers; zone *4-a* formed of larger and paler cone nuclei, zone *4-b* of smaller, darker, and more numerous rod nuclei; *5-a*, outer fiber layer of Henle representing inner fibrous expansions of rod and cone cells, *5-b*, terminal swellings of same (smaller rod spherules and larger cone pedicles), *5-c*, outer expansions of bipolars and all expansions of horizontal cells, the last two zones representing the first synaptical field in the retina and in the visual system; *6*, inner nuclear layer, comprising bodies and nuclei of horizontal cells, bipolars, amacrines, a few displaced ganglion cells, and most radial fibers; *7*, inner plexiform layer formed by expansions of sixth and eighth layers, such as bipolars, amacrines, and ganglion cells; layer *10* or inner limiting membrane formed by joining of lower expanded ends of supporting radial fibers, a boundary toward vitreous fluid. *Cf.* Figs. 127, 129.

of the central area the striation is oblique (Figs. 127, 128). Close to and within the central fovea the obliquity of the striation increases so as to become almost horizontal, owing to a peculiar slant of the much elongated inner rod and cone fibers of the central pit, the "outer fiber layer" of Henle (Fig. 129, *I, II, III*).

The intermediate zone, *5-b*, is also present throughout the whole of the retina, being most distinct in the central area (Figs. 127, 128, 129,

II, III). It is composed of swollen vitreal ends of the inner fibers of photoreceptors, smaller and more round in the rods—the rod spherules; larger and somewhat conical in the cones—the cone pedicles.

In the slope of the central fovea, in a belt where the inner fibers of the centralmost rodless foveal territory terminate, zone *5-b* is made up of a single row of regularly arranged, cuboidal cone pedicles (visible in Fig. 129, at the right

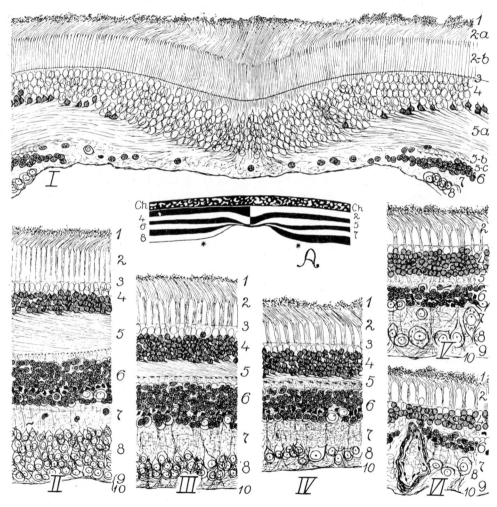

Fig. 129.—Regional variation of retinal structure in Rhesus Macaque. *I*, center of central fovea showing greatly lengthened, much thinner, and more numerous central cones (slightly disarrayed), which, together with their nuclei in the fourth layer, are alone present in the central "rodless area"; at some distance from center, smaller and darker rod nuclei in *4* begin to appear singly and in groups (*cf.* Figs. 127, 128, 161); lower layers below *4*, in the center, are much reduced, fibrous zone *5-a* greatly so, while zones *5-b* and *5-c* are entirely absent, as are also layers *6–9*; *A*, sketch at lower magnification of central fovea and its immediate vicinity of central area, ** marking the limits of the foveal pit; note a well-developed chorioid membrane, *Ch; II*, perifoveal region with five tiers of ganglion cells; *III*, perifoveal region in the periphery of central area, with ganglion cell layer reduced to three tiers; *IV*, near periphery, with ganglion layer represented by a single continuous cell row; *V*, middle periphery with a partly discontinuous layer of much larger ganglion cells; *VI*, far periphery of retina along ora serrata or ora terminalis; *VII* (not represented), where ganglion cell layer is disrupted by more or less considerable intercellular intervals.

and left ends of sketch *I*). Outside this foveal belt, in most of the central area and in the entire extra-areal periphery, zone *5-b* contains both the cone pedicles and the rod spherules (Fig. 128).

In number and spacing, these two structures —the pedicles and spherules—closely correspond to the number and spacing of the two varieties of photoreceptors in the *2-b* zone of the bacillary layer. In the foveal center the *5-b* zone is absent (Figs. 129, *I*, and 161).

The inner zone, *5-c*, is made up of external or scleral expansions of the nerve cells of the inner nuclear layer (Fig. 128). Together with *5-b*, this zone corresponds to the classical "outer plexiform" or "outer reticular layer" of earlier writers.

Zones *5-b* and *5-c* are the place of a synaptical contact of photoreceptors or neurons of the first order and of the bipolars and horizontal cells or neurons of the second order in the visual system. The fifth layer, particularly zones *5-b* and *5-c*, represents, accordingly, the first "synaptical field" in the retina and in the visual system.

7. INNER NUCLEAR LAYER (6).—The sixth layer, apparently most voluminous in the primate retina except in the foveal center, is formed by closely packed cell bodies and nuclei that belong to the various categories of the nerve cells. Some of the nuclei are somewhat larger than those in the fourth layer, while others are about equal in size; but all are smaller than the nuclei of the eighth layer. Also they vary considerably in size among themselves.

This layer may be further subdivided into four ill-defined zones (Fig. 128). The uppermost zone, *6-a*, predominantly represents the "horizontal" cells (*c*). Zone *6-b* is made up of the nuclei of bipolar cells (*d, e, f, g, h*). Zone *6-c* contains, in Man, in addition to the bipolar nuclei, most of the nuclei of the supporting "radial fibers" of Müller (*u*). The lowermost zone, *6-d*, contains chiefly the bodies and nuclei of the "amacrine cells" (*i, k, l*) and of a few displaced ganglion cells ("Dogiel's cells") and an occasional bipolar nucleus. The position of the nuclei of Müller's "radial fibers" varies in different species (closer to, or farther away from, layer *7*).

The inner nuclear layer has been named by Henle the "outer ganglion layer," and by W. Müller the "ganglion of the retina." This layer and the layers below contain blood vessels belonging to the system of the central retinal artery and vein, whereas the layers above contain no blood vessels (*see* chap. X, 2). In the center of the foveal pit the sixth layer and the layers below it are practically absent (*see* Figs. 129, *I*, and 161; *cf.* sec. 10 [6], this chapter, and Fig. 512).

8. INNER PLEXIFORM LAYER (7).—The thick seventh layer, which has a fine granulated appearance, is almost entirely fibrous. In it are found, here and there, only a few nuclei belonging to the nerve and neuroglial cells and also to the endothelial cells of capillaries, besides those of an occasional larger blood vessel.

A closer study reveals an indistinct vertical, as well as horizontal, striation. The coarser vertical striping, more pronounced close to the ganglion layer, is chiefly caused by the thick trunklike main pillars of Müller's radial fibers, which may be continuously followed in the extra-areal periphery as far as the tenth layer. The finer vertical striation, where discernible, is due to the ascending and descending protoplasmic and axonal expansions of the nerve cells of the adjoining layers, *6* and *8*. The horizontal stripes, Ramón y Cajal's "granular lines," are caused by the evenly arranged terminal and preterminal dendritic and teledendric expansions of the nerve cells (compare left and right sides in Fig. 128).

Since these expansions vary from level to level in number, thickness, and other details, the texture of the meshwork of the inner plexiform layer also varies somewhat, being finer or coarser or otherwise differing from level to level. Using these criteria, five zones—*7-a, 7-b, 7-c, 7-d,* and *7-e*—may sometimes be distinguished in this layer, at least in the central area and close to it.

Analytical studies show the inner plexiform layer to be the place of synaptical contacts between the bipolars and amacrines, or neurons of the second order, and the ganglion cells, or neurons of the third order (right half in Fig. 128). This layer, accordingly, is the second "synaptical field" in the retina and in the visual system.

9. GANGLION CELL LAYER (8).—The ganglion layer consists of larger elements more closely resembling the typical nerve cells of the brain or spinal cord than those found in the two nuclear layers (for this reason, some have called it "layer of brain cells"). In well-stained preparations, not only the nuclei of these cells, but their bodies as well, may easily be seen (Fig. 127 and left half in Fig. 128).

There are not less than five, and possibly more, varieties of ganglion cells in the primate retina (*m, n, o, p, r, s*). The size of the cell bodies and nuclei varies more than in the other two cellular layers, *4* and *6*. The total number of the ganglion cells, however, is less than the number of cells in either the outer or the inner nuclear layers.

In most of the retinal expanse there is only one, often a discontinuous, row of cells in the ganglion layer (Fig. 129, *IV, V, VI*). In the human and simian retina, in the central area alone, except in the foveal pit, the ganglions are found in more than one tier; close to the central fovea, there are as many as six to eight tiers (Figs. 127, 128, 129, *II, III*).

By far the greater majority of the nuclei of the ganglion layer are those of nerve cells proper, with only a few belonging to the neuroglial cells. The latter are typical small astrocytes and microglia and a few displaced nuclei of the radial fibers of Müller. There are also some nuclei of blood vessels.

The ganglion layer has been named by Henle the "inner ganglion layer," and by W. Müller the "ganglion of the optic nerve."

10. LAYER OF OPTIC NERVE FIBERS (9).—The ninth or optic fiber layer is composed of axis cylinders, probably mostly of ganglion cells, both of those whose bodies are in the eighth layer and of those of the few displaced ganglions in the inner zones, *6-c* and *6-d*, of the sixth layer. Possibly some fibers belong to the "exogenous axons" of extraretinal origin.

Because of their varying course, the nerve fibers in customary vertical sections, depending upon the locality and orientation of the plane of cutting, are seen arranged either horizontally or assembled into bundles, cut across. The more or less vertically arranged striation of this layer is caused by the inner, conically swollen ends of the thick pillars of Müller's radial fibers which form the supporting frame of the retina.

The ninth layer has been termed by Henle "inner fiber layer." Its nerve fibers, as soon as they leave the eyeball, form a thick nervelike trunk known as the "optic nerve." They continue as the optic tracts and terminate in the subcortical or primary visual centers of the midbrain and betweenbrain (chap. VI, 4 [3, 4, 5]).

Normally, in the human and simian retina, the optic nerve fibers do not possess myelin sheaths; and, because of their transparency and lack of color, they therefore remain invisible in routine ophthalmoscopic examination. Occasionally, as an anomaly, streaks and patches of myelinated fibers are found. Myelin investments are provided in the extraocular portions of fibers beyond the cribriform or sievelike lamina, in the optic nerves and tracts. In some animals, e.g., the Rabbit, the intraocular sections of fibers are also myelinated in certain places. (On the arrangement and course of bundles of optic nerve fibers in the human and simian retina, *see* chap. VI, 2.)

11. INNER LIMITING MEMBRANE (10).—The tenth and innermost layer of the retina appears as a sharp, thin line bounding the retinal tissue toward the vitreous (Figs. 127, 128). It is composed of flattened vitreal ends of Müller's radial fibers, which are joined to one another. It is not, therefore, a detachable membrane but a part of the retinal supporting or neuroglial tissue. This membrane-like structure is not identical with the hyaloid membrane which adjoins it from underneath and which belongs to the vitreous. The inner limiting membrane was first described by Pacini (1845).

Throughout the retinal tissue, beginning with zone *2-b* and continuing as far as the inner limiting membrane, there are supporting elements—important and indispensable structural and functional constituents (*see* sec. 9, this chapter). In the primate retina, blood vessels are present only in the inner layers, from *5-c* to *9*, inclusive. The outer layers, from *1* to *5-b*, inclusive, rely for their nutrition upon the chorioid membrane. (*See* chap. X, 2 [3].)

The stratification of the retina in sections vertical to its surface shows important variations in certain regions, depending upon the function of a particular locality. Most markedly, this stratification deviates from the type just described in the central area and fovea, in the papilla or disk of the optic nerve and in the region of the *ora serrata* (*see* secs. 10, 11, this chapter).

References: Arey 1915, 1916, 1919, 1928, 1932; Arey & Jennings 1944; Arey & Mundt 1941; Babuchin 1863–64; A. J. Ballantyne 1946; Bowman 1849; Cattaneo 1922; Chiarini 1904–6; Detwiler 1916, 1923, 1938, 1940, 1942, 1943, 1944, 1945; Detwiler & Lewis 1926; Doellinger 1818; Duke-Elder 1932; Eisler 1930; Estable 1947; Garten 1907; Genderen Stort 1886, 1887; Greeff 1899 (1900); Hecht 1927; J. Henle 1841, 1855–71, 1861, 1864, 1871 (1879); H. Herzog 1905; A. Jacob 1819; T. L. Jahn 1946; Th. Wh.

Jones 1833; Koelliker 1854; Kolmer & Lauber 1936; Krause & Sibley 1946; Kuhnt 1877; Kuffler 1953; Laurens & Detwiler 1921; Laurens & Williams 1917; Lindeman 1947; Luppino 1930; I. Mann 1950; Menner 1929, 1930, 1931; Merkel 1869; Morano 1872; H. Müller 1851–72; W. Müller 1856–57, 1872; Ovio 1927; Pacini 1845; Parker 1932; Polyak 1941–48; Pütter 1908–12; Raehlmann 1907; Rochon-Duvigneaud 1943; Ruysch 1737; E. Scharrer 1929; M. Schultze 1859–73; Schwalbe 1874, 1887; Sverdlick 1940, 1942; Valentin 1837; Verne 1925; Verrier 1934, 1938, 1945; Vintschgau 1853; Vonwiller 1945–46; Walls 1928, 1942; Welch & Osborn; Wigger 1937–38, 1939; E. Wolff 1940. (For historical data *see* chap. I, 7, 9.)

SEC. 3. VISUAL CELLS OR PHOTORECEPTORS

1. General features of rods (*a*) and cones (*b*).—The photoreceptors are nerve cells or neurons of the retina, specially adapted in structure and in physiological, chemical, and probably also physical properties to react to the physical form of energy called "light" (Fig. 130).

They are considered "neuroepithelial cells" by some authorities. Such a distinction, as far as it denies the nervous status or nature of the photoreceptors, appears to have little justification and is otherwise meaningless; for both histogenetically and in adult form the photoreceptors possess certain features characteristic of typical nerve cells. In the cones these are a large vesicular nucleus containing a nucleolus, a typical teledendron at the end of the inner cone fiber, and synaptical junctions with undoubted nerve cells of the retina.

Other characteristics of nerve cells, however, are absent. There are no chromophile granules of Nissl and probably no neurofibrils. Instead, the photoreceptors have special features of their own, the rod- and conelike scleral ends of the bacillary layer, which are present in this form nowhere else in the organism.

Each photoreceptor cell has a "body," with a "nucleus" in the outer nuclear layer; in the cone cells, this body has a typical spherical "nucleolus." The nucleus is sometimes, but rarely, displaced into the rod or cone proper, in zone *2-b*, above the outer limiting membrane.

When this occurs, it is called an ectopic nucleus.

From the scleral end of the body an expansion usually arises, the "outer fiber," much thinner in the rods than in the cones. This outer fiber, as it slips through one of the openings in the outer limiting membrane, *3*, becomes either a rod or a cone proper of the bacillary layer, *2*. When the nucleus is close to, or immediately underneath, the outer limiting membrane, as is the case in almost all cones except those in the center of the central fovea (Figs. 129, 161), the outer fiber is short and thick or is absent altogether, and the body continues directly into a rod or cone proper.

Ordinarily, just before passing through the outer limiting membrane, the outer rod or cone fiber increases to the thickness of its rod or cone proper. At the point of passage through that membrane, there is usually a slight dent, indicating a groove where the ring of the opening of the limiting membrane is fitted. Above the dent there is often a slight flaring of the base of the rod or cone proper.

2. Outer bacillary expansions, or rods and cones proper.—The part of the photoreceptor cell which is in the bacillary layer is a peculiar structure composed of an "inner segment" and a slightly shorter "outer segment" kept together by a narrow zone, the "intermediate link."

In the rods, both segments have straight

sides, and the difference between the outer and the slightly thicker inner segment is small. This gives the rods their characteristic slender form (*a*, in Fig. 130).

In the cones, the inner segment is also only a little thicker in the central fovea (Fig. 161); outside the fovea the swollen inner segment, however, is considerably thicker than the outer segment and has somewhat curved, bulging sides (*b*, in Fig. 130).

The outer cone segment is much more delicate than the inner and is much longer in the

(Fig. 161). Here the inner segment is but little thicker than the outer segment, which is also much longer than the inner.

The rodlike appearance of the cones in the foveal center, however, in no way changes their true cone character, as shown by the typical cone nuclei, thick inner fibers, and relatively large spheroidal or cuboidal pedicles, or swollen lower ends, which are very different in shape and size from the much smaller rod spherules. The slenderness of the central foveal cones, therefore, is not evidence that would permit

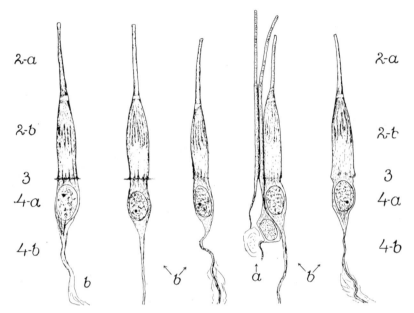

Fig. 130.—Elements of bacillary and outer nuclear layers from a "teased," unstained preparation of the retina of an adult Rhesus Macaque freshly fixed in osmium vapors (preparation of Professor G. W. Bartelmez). Region of central area. Thinner structures represent rods (*a*); thicker structures, cones (*b*). In rods note uniformly cylindrical shape, inner segments in *2-b* only slightly thicker than outer segments in *2-a* and separated from latter by a very narrow intermediate zone. In cones outer segments slightly cylindrical and much thinner than the flask-shaped inner segments, both segments separated by a clear intermediate zone consisting of a highly refringent substance. In two cones the neuroglial outer limiting membrane (*3*) with its "fiber baskets" is still attached. Larger cone nuclei include typical spherical nucleoli. Both rod and cone bodies continue inward as "inner fibers," a few still surrounded by their neuroglial sheath. Camera lucida drawing, approximate magnification 550×.

fovea. Outside the fovea the outer segment is almost the same length as the inner. It has a slender conical shape, a narrow tip, and a somewhat widened base, where it is continuous with the intermediate link. This gives the central foveal cones a rodlike appearance and the extrafoveal cones a flasklike appearance and thus accounts for the name "bulbs" formerly given the latter.

In the central fovea the cones are thinner and longer, and the longest and most attenuated are found in the very center of the central fovea

confusing—much less identifying—them with genuine rod photoreceptors (discussed in par. 4, this section). The staining properties of the central cones also differ from those of the adjoining rods. (*Cf.* also Figs. 157, 158, 159; *cf.*, however, Fig. 512.)

The regular, even appearance of the rod- and conelike parts of the photoreceptors is found only in preparations expertly made from perfectly fresh specimens. In routine material the regular form is usually lost and is replaced by various artifacts, such as bulbous swellings and other deformities. These artifacts are most often found in the outer segments, which is indicative of their extreme fragility.

The rods and cones proper, that is, their inner and outer segments, where the initial process of photoreception takes place, form a solid, continuous "mosaic" or "pavement" throughout the entire retinal membrane (*see also* sec. 10 [5], this chapter). With the exception of a minute rodless area in the center of the central fovea or pit (Figs. 150–56), corresponding to direct vision in the axis of the visual field, and a transitional circular belt around the central fovea, where the rods are few (Figs. 157–60), the rods and cones are mixed in almost even numbers in each particular territory, forming the double photoreceptor apparatus of the retina. The exact gradient in various meridians, however, is yet to be determined.

The anatomical fact of the presence of both kinds of photoreceptors suggested to Max Schultze (1866) the idea of functional difference in the rods and cones. This idea was subsequently elaborated by Parinaud, Kries, and others into the "theory of the duplex retina." This theory considered the retina to be made up of a double photoreceptor-conductor mechanism, one a cone apparatus active during daylight or photopic conditions of illumination and characterized by high acuity, responsiveness to colors, and other peculiarities; and the other a rod mechanism functioning in dim light and much more responsive to low intensities but not reacting specifically to different wave lengths of light.

The photoreceptor mosaic, while fairly homogeneous in each particular small retinal territory, exhibits considerable variation in the relative numerical composition of the constituent rods and cones. This is demonstrated by sections cut through the retina parallel to the surface or by well-made whole-mounts of the retina. Such preparations show the gradual appearance of the rods, singly and in groups (Figs. 157–59), from the rodless center of the fovea, where only cones of minute size are present (Figs. 150–56), through the extrafoveal belt of the central area, where each cone is surrounded by a row of rods (Fig. 160), to the extra-areal territory, where there are three or more rods between each two adjacent cones, with a corresponding wider spacing of the cones. (*See* sec. 10, this chapter, for a discussion of the photoreceptors of the central fovea and area.)

3. Photosensitive substances of the rods and cones.—The outer segments of the rods and, to a lesser extent, those of the cones stretch into the pigment epithelium (layer *1*) and are imbedded between its pigment-filled protoplasmic fringes (Figs. 127, 128, 129). In the living eye, especially in one which is dark-adapted, the outer rod segments contain a peculiar photosensitive chemical substance of an extremely unstable nature, which acts as a mediator in the process of photoreception. This photomediator has been variously named "rhodopsin," "erythropsin," or "visual purple," and it may be partly responsible for the pink color which the retinal membrane has in life. (In the Fish retina a similar substance with slightly different spectral properties is known as "porphyropsin" or "visual violet"; and there are other substances, such as "visual yellow," "visual red," and "visual blue," as well as others not yet identified, according to Dartnall 1950.)

Visual purple has lately been identified as a complex "color protein" or "chromoprotein," that is, a conjugate protein containing vitamin A or carotene and probably other compounds as well, which are its indispensable constituents (Wald 1936, 1938, 1939, 1942, 1943, 1944, 1945, 1945–46, 1948, 1950; Broda, Goodeve & Lythgoe 1940; Godding 1945). Vitamin B_2 has also been shown to be concerned in the synthesis of photochemical substances (R. A. Morton 1944).

Visual purple and the pink color of the retina may be preserved for some time in a freshly dissected retina or in an extract solution, if the specimen is kept in darkness at a low temperature (between pH 5.2 and 10). Visual purple is believed to be produced by the outer rod segments without the aid of pigment epithelium (Tansley 1933).

Soon after it is subjected to the action of light, visual purple disintegrates into "transient orange," "indicator yellow" (formerly called "visual yellow" and "retinene"), and finally into a colorless substance, "leucopsin" or "visual white," the end-product being vitamin A_1, or visual violet vitamin A_2 (Wald).

Through the process of bleaching, probably

by initiating a change in the electrical potential, visual purple acts as a nerve stimulus and hence brings about the sensation of "light" (Dartnall 1948; Tansley 1950).

The presence of visual purple in the retina can be demonstrated by partly exposing a freshly enucleated eye to light. When this is done, the rhodopsin partly disintegrates, leaving on the retina figures of various shapes that may be rendered permanent by the action of an appropriate fixative (Kühne's "optograms").

Under normal conditions visual purple is in a constant state of regeneration, a process that is still not completely understood (Tansley 1950). It is always present in quantities sufficient for the activation of the retina, especially so in the scotopic or dark-adapted eye.

Since the discovery of visual purple by Boll (1877, 1881), its chemical and physiological properties have been much studied by W. Kühne (1877, 1878, 1882), Ewald & Kühne (1877), and others, and again in modern times by Hecht (1921, 1924, 1931, 1937, 1938, 1940, 1944), Tansley (1931, 1933, 1950), A. C. Krause (1934, 1942), Lythgoe (1937), Wald (1938, 1942, 1944), Wald & Clark (1938), and others (*see also* Granit 1950).

Visual purple is considered to be a substance indispensable for the light reaction of the rods. It is extremely light-sensitive. Its absorption curve, approximately determined by Trendelenburg (1904), was first accurately plotted by Lythgoe (1937). Its maximum absorption has been found to be about the wave length of 0.5 micron, or the greenish-blue part of the visible spectrum, corresponding to a quantum yield of 1 (by which one quantum of light destroys one molecule of visual purple; Dartnall, Goodeve & Lythgoe 1938).

The photosensitivity or absorption curve of visual purple agrees with the human dark-adapted, or scotopic, luminosity curve, illustrating the distribution of brightness for a dark-adapted eye to a spectrum of low intensity (Schneider, Goodeve & Lythgoe 1939; *et al.*). All evidence, accordingly, indicates that "visual purple mediates scotopic vision by virtue of the photochemical changes it undergoes on exposure to light" (Dartnall 1948).

It has been claimed that a similar, but colorless, chemical photomediator, the "cone substance" or "iodopsin," is contained in the cones (Studnitz 1936–37, 1937–38, 1940, 1941; Wald 1937, 1938, and later publications). Its absorption curve is supposed to correspond to the distribution of sensitivity or luminosity of radiation in a photopically adapted human eye or to the daylight luminosity curve for cone vision. The maximum of this photopic luminosity curve in a daylight-adapted eye, with the cones dominating or even suppressing the scotopic rod–visual purple mechanism, is at the wave length of light of 0.56 micron, that is, in the greenish-yellow segment of the visible spectrum. It is, accordingly, considerably shifted toward the long end of the spectrum in comparison with the scotopic maximum, which is at the wave length 0.5 micron, corresponding to the greenish-blue part of the spectrum ("Purkinje shift" or "Purkinje phenomenon"; *see* Helmholtz' *Treatise on Physiol. Opt.*, v. 2, Pl. II).

The chemical composition of "iodopsin" is not known, but indirect evidence indicates that it is a carotenoid protein, closely related to the rod photopigments, rhodopsin and porphyropsin (Wald 1945–46). Another hypothesis, however, claims that the photomediator both in scotopic rod vision and in photopic cone vision is visual purple (Dartnall 1948). This hypothesis has been questioned by Granit (1950).

The basic question whether the photopic photomediator of the cones is a single, homogeneous substance responsive to all color hues of the visible spectrum that can be distinguished or whether there are several chemical photomediators in the cones more or less structurally closely interrelated has not been answered. It is the belief of the author that this problem is infinitely complex, beyond the capacity of an exclusively anatomical, physiological, biochemical, or electrophysiological analysis.

The photoreceptor role of the outer rod segments is supported by the following evidence: the presence of visual purple in the outer rod segments, the insulation of these segments by the pigment in the bright-adapted eye, and their exposure to full action of light in the dark-adapted eye, which is also assisted by the movement of the outer rod segments closer to, or farther from, the outer limiting membrane through the action of the myoid component of the inner rod segments observed especially in Lower Vertebrates, the reverse of the movement of the photopic cones (the so-called photokinetics of the retina).

The intermediate links, largely refractory to dyes in stained preparations and therefore improperly called "vacuoles," are found in freshly prepared specimens of retinae of Birds and some Lizards to be red, orange, or green in color. These "colored globules" have, therefore, been interpreted as "filters," by means of which the spectral composition of physical light passing through them to the photoreceptor outer segments is variously modified (Walls & Judd 1933; Walls 1942). This interpretation has been disputed by Studnitz (1940).

4. Differential characteristics of primate rods and cones.—Ever since the formulation of the duplexity theory of the retina, the problem of the structural and functional similarity or dissimilarity of rods and cones has been periodically discussed. Especially alluring was the concept of the identity of the rods and cones in the foveal center. The rodlike appearance of the slender cones in the very center of the fovea, when examined superficially, encouraged such an interpretation.

Nothing could be more erroneous and misleading than to insist upon the identical nature, and hence identical function, of the central cones and rods proper. Whatever their common phylogenetical and ontogenetical origin, the two varieties of photoreceptors are as different in the fully differentiated state found in the mature human and simian retina as any closely allied histological elements could be. Additional evidence of this difference is found in their different synaptical relations with other neurons of the retina, discussed elsewhere. (*Cf.* secs. 8, 10, 11, this chapter, and chap. IX.)

Following are the principal characteristics by which the rods and the cones may be differentiated in the primate retina.

The rod nuclei residing in the outer nuclear layer are considerably smaller in size, angular in shape, and have a crude inner framework with larger meshes and several crude nodules or granules in it. In hematoxylin and eosin or phloxin preparations they stain more sharply than the cone nuclei and in a darker, decidedly blue-black hue. The cytoplasm enveloping the nucleus and forming the body of the rods is scanty. From it, a thin, filamentous inner fiber descends to the outer plexiform layer, where it terminates in the shape of a minute, more or less oval, "spherule."

The cone nuclei are larger, smoother in outline, and less frequently angular in shape. In the retinal periphery they are oval or elliptical; in the fovea they are spherical. The inner framework is composed of much finer and more numerous meshes and trabecules and is much more delicate and regular in appearance. The cone nuclei stain in a characteristic, decidedly pink or purplish hue, in contrast to the sharp, dark, "steel-engraving" hue of the rod nuclei. They are enveloped by a relatively thick layer of cytoplasm, which forms the body, from which a stout fiber descends to the outer plexiform layer, where it terminates in the form of a sizable "pedicle," more or less conical or bulbous in shape.

In the primate retina these features are present in all regions, including the central fovea. By means of them, two categories of photoreceptors may be easily distinguished. There is little doubt that these morphological and tinctorial characteristics indicate a profound difference in the chemical, and therefore physiological, properties of the two varieties of photoreceptors. (*Cf.* E. Wolff 1941.)

Another important and easily ascertained fact is the identity of appearance, and hence identity of function, of all cones in any given small territory of the retina. In the very center of the fovea, for example, all cones are of much the same diameter, shape, and hue and hence must possess identical functional properties. Slight differences in the shape and size and in the saturation of staining, observable in many cones, do not follow any pattern of distribution that could reasonably be expected from a homogeneously organized photoreceptor mosaic. (*Cf.* cones in Figs. 157–59.)

The histological and cytological characteristics just discussed are easily discerned in any good microscopic preparation of a human or simian retina. They all indicate that the properties of the cones are essentially identical in the entire retina and are different from the properties possessed by the rods. This definition in no way precludes functional differences among the cones of different retinal regions, as, for example, different spectral responsiveness between the central cones compared with the cones in the periphery of the retina.

5. REFLECTIONS ON THE INTERPLAY OF PHYSICAL AND STRUCTURAL FACTORS IN THE INITIAL PROCESS OF PHOTORECEPTION.—Since H. Müller (1853) presented the evidence which demonstrated the photoreceptor role of the bacillary layer and Boll (1877) announced the discovery of visual purple, the question of the mechanics and location of the initial process of photoreception has been considered. By what interplay of various essential factors is it made possible, and in precisely which structures does it occur? Although much knowledge has been accumulated since then, we are still far from able to give a fully satisfactory answer. For this a deeper knowledge of basic photophysics and biochemistry will be necessary.

The first step in photoreception seems to take place in the outer segments. The location of these segments as the ultimate parts of the rod and cone cells still freely entered by light, before light is impeded by the optical barriers of retinal and chorioidal pigment, and the continuity of the outer segments with the inner segments, the cell bodies, and inner fibers indicate this. The intermediary links between the outer and the inner segments must also be essential. The disproportionately small size of the outer cone segments, representing but a fraction of the volume of the inner segments in the entire retina except the outer fovea, is not necessarily contrary to this interpretation. In a sense, the outer segments may act as triggers whose action discharges the more bulky inner segments (Fig. 130).

In the very center of the outer fovea, where the outer cone segments exceed the inner segments in length, the disproportion may be much smaller and may, in fact, be reversed in favor of the outer segments, in spite of their extreme thinness (Fig. 161).

The difference in bulk of the outer and inner segments of the rods is much smaller in all regions of the retina. This and the presence of visual purple seem to confirm the role of the outer segments as primary photoreceptors.

The slender conical shape of the outer segment in the majority of cones may be indicative of their function as collectors of rays of light, by which the intensity of the stimulus, transferred to the inner segment, is increased. The great lengthening of the outer segments in the very center of the outer fovea, with a slight shortening and a striking thinning of the inner segments, is additional evidence in favor of the outer segments being the principal photoreceptors in this particular locality.

Next to be considered is the distribution of the photosensitive substances. This is a problem to be solved by microphysics and microchemistry conjointly with histological methods, and no reliable solution is to be expected by hypothesizing. There are many questions concerning this matter. Is the photosensitive substance uniformly spread through the entire photoreceptor? Or is it preponderantly, or entirely, accumulated in part of it? Is this part its core, its surface, the inside, or the outside of its surface, or both, forming a sort of two-faced membrane? Or is the photosensitive substance accumulated in some special way, perhaps in seriated layers, fibrils, a network, or micelles? The separation of the outer rod segments into a great number of thin plates resembling a roll of coins has been interpreted as indicating preformed structures. No comparable separation has been observed in the outer cone segments, which seem to have, when fresh, a uniformly plastic constitution, which would indicate a rather uniform, homogeneous distribution of the photosensitive substance.

There is still another question. Since the light entering the layer of photoreceptors must first pass through the inner segments and intermediate links, it is logical to suppose that the process of photoreception may begin here but can be consummated only in the outer segments. Is this initial phase a purely physical, optical one, in which the inner segment "guides" and "collects," hence intensifies, the rays of light before they enter the outer segment? Or is it a chemical process, or a combination of both? In any case, the inner segment does not seem to be a mere vehicle for the light rays passing through it to the outer segment, nor merely a conductor of impulses passing back from the outer segment, but probably is also a contributing generator to these impulses.

The thesis which postulates active participation of the inner segments in the process of photoreception is further supported by the essential role which their diameter plays in the perception of space, or visual acuity. This is evidenced by the following considerations.

The structural arrangement postulates that light must pass through the inner segment and intermediate link, no matter what it does in these two parts, before it enters the outer segment. Since the inner segments are several times as thick as the outer segments, in the entire retina except in the very center of the outer fovea, the sensitive points in the visual space must be separated by blind intervals, corresponding to the intervening spaces. It should, then, be possible to determine experimentally whether or not the smallest stimulable points correspond to the diameter of the outer, or to the diameter of the inner, cone segments.

Since the inner cone segments outside the very center of the outer fovea have a respectable diameter, ranging from roughly 2 to 3 microns in the foveal periphery to 6 or 8 microns in the far periphery of the retina, each cone could accommodate more than one ray, including the rays of the long waves, for example, orange and red (from 650 to 700 millimicrons in diameter). This would indicate that more parallel rays can enter the thicker cones of the retinal periphery than can enter the cones close to and in the central fovea.

This raises a further question as to whether or not the thicker cones are capable of responding discretely to more than one ray. This aspect of the cone function touches the fundamental problem of the nervous system dealt with in detail in chapter IX. In the light of what is said there, it appears that each individual "neuron" or nerve cell is capable of responding to one or more simultaneous stimuli always in a rather global way, as a unit (even though varieties of synaptical contacts found in most neurons indicate a modulation of such global response).

Each cone, accordingly, may always react as a single, indivisible unit, no matter how thick it is or how many elemental rays of light may stimulate it. Each cone may, at any given short period of time, respond in one way only.

The way to increase the number of stimulable points on the receptor surface of the retina is to increase the number of individual cones per surface unit, which occurs in the central fovea, maximally so in the center of the outer fovea. Here the cone thickness, in Man and Monkey, is reduced roughly to 1 micron and may be even a little less in individual cones. The diameter of central cones, then, is just large enough comfortably to accommodate precisely one ray of light of any wave length of the visible spectrum (Figs. 154, 155). The reduction of cone diameter in the very center, in turn, is compensated for by greater length, obviously to increase the bulk or volume of the outer segments which contain the photosensitive substance.

In the eyes of certain species believed to possess extremely high visual acuity, for example, the Golden Eagle (Fig. 171), the thinnest cones are much thinner than the thinnest foveal cones in Man or Monkey, approximating $\frac{1}{3}$ micron. This gives pertinence to the question of whether the usual concept, adhered to by physicists, of the "ray" of light as the ultimate physical entity is correct, or whether there are perhaps other properties of light that would allow a use of angular values much smaller than those corresponding to the diameter of the thinnest cones in the human and simian retina (1–1.5 microns, or 12–18 seconds of arc), as indicated by the "aligning power of the eye" or the Nonius or Vernier methods of measuring. In order to remain within accepted concepts, we may consider the possibility that in the case of keen-sighted species, such as the Eagle, light of short wave lengths can still be comfortably accommodated within cones measuring not much more in thickness than $\frac{1}{3}$ micron (corresponding to a visual angle of 4 seconds of arc) and is preponderantly or exclusively utilized.

6. Inner expansions or fibers of rods and cones.—The vitreal ends of the bodies of photoreceptor cells are thinned out into inner fibers, filamentous in the rods and of considerable thickness in the cones. These "inner fibers" enter in the outer plexiform layer, forming zone 5-a (Figs. 140, 145, 146, 147, and colored schemes in 177, 178, 179).

In the peripheral extra-areal regions of the retina the inner rod and cone fibers are short and arranged vertically to the surface of the retina; in the rods and cones, whose bodies adjoin the fifth layer, these fibers are practically nonexistent.

In the central area the inner photoreceptor fibers are of considerable length, the longest being in the cones and in the few rods of the central fovea (*see* sec. 10, this chapter). Here they are arranged obliquely and stretch for hundreds of microns in Henle's outer fiber layer to reach their related bipolars in the sixth layer, which is displaced laterally by the formation of the foveal depression (*see* Fig. 161; also 512).

7. Inner terminations of photoreceptors; rod spherules and cone pedicles.— The inner photoreceptor fibers terminate with enlarged, swollen ends. The "cone pedicles" are larger and somewhat conical or bulbous, the "rod spherules" are smaller and spherical, oval, or pyriform in shape. Both these terminal swellings form, in the aggregate, the intermediate zone, *5-b*, of the outer plexiform layer (Figs. 128 and 140; and also 146, 147, and colored schemes in 177, 178, 179).

The lower ends or bases of the cone pedicles are all strung along a line which corresponds exactly with the boundary line between zones *5-b* and *5-c*. In the extrafoveal regions, half-a-dozen or so short, barbel-like "basal filaments" spread from each pedicle in zone *5-c*, some of them carrying minute swellings at their ends (*b* in Fig. 141). In the central fovea the basal filaments are mostly absent.

The rod spherules, filling the gaps between the cone pedicles in several closely packed rows, are not all in direct contact with zone *5-c*, the majority remaining at some distance from it. This difference in arrangement has some bearing upon the kind of synapses which the two varieties of photoreceptors undergo with the bipolars and horizontal cells (*see* secs. 4, 6, and 8, this chapter).

References: Arey 1928, 1932; Bach 1895; Balbuena 1929, 1930, 1936; Ball *et al.* 1948; Baquis 1890; E. Baumgardt 1952; Baumgardt & Bujas 1952; Bayliss, Lythgoe & Tansley 1936; Bidder 1839; Bliss 1943, 1946, 1948; Boll 1877, 1881; Bouma 1947; Braun 1861; E. Brücke 1844; A. M. Chase 1938, 1948; B. Clark *et al.* 1946; Dartnall 1937, 1948, 1950; Dartnall, Goodeve & Lythgoe 1936, 1938; Davson 1949; Detwiler 1916–44; Detwiler & Laurens 1921; Detwiler & Lewis 1926; H. E. De Vries 1946, 1949; Dogiel 1884, 1891–92; Donner 1950; Donner & Willmer 1950; Ebner 1902; Ehrenberg 1836; Ewald & Kühne 1877; Fortin 1925, 1926; V. Franz 1934; Gobrecht & Oertel 1953; Godding 1945; Gottsche 1836; Granit 1947, 1950; Grundfest 1931, 1932; C. Haig 1948; Hannover 1840; E. Hanström 1940; Hartridge 1947; Hasse 1867; S. Hecht 1921, 1924, 1927, 1928, 1929, 1930, 1931, 1934, 1935, 1937, 1938, 1940, 1942, 1944, 1948; Hecht *et al.* 1936, 1937, 1945; Heine 1902; Held 1905; Henle 1839, 1841, 1861, 1864; R. Hesse 1903, 1904; Hibben 1950; Hosch 1895; Hosoya, Okita & Akune 1938; Huschke 1835; Kallius 1894; Koelliker 1851, 1854; Kolmer 1925, 1930; Kolmer & Lauber 1936; A. C. Krause 1934, 1942; W. Krause 1861, 1867, 1867–68, 1868, 1873, 1876, 1881; Kühne 1877, 1878, 1882; Larsen 1922; Leeuwenhoek 1684; Leydig 1853; Loken 1942; Lythgoe 1937, 1938; Lythgoe & Goodeve 1937; Lythgoe & Phillips 1938; Lythgoe & Quilliam 1938; Maggiore 1929, 1930; Mandelbaum & Mintz 1941; Mandelbaum & Sloan 1947; Mawas 1910; Menner 1930; Merkel 1869, 1870, 1876, 1877; G. A. Michaelis 1838; Moroff 1922; R. A. Morton 1944; Morton & Godwin 1944; H. Müller 1851, 1852, 1856–57, 1872; Mureddu 1930; Murr 1930; Østerberg 1935; Pacini 1845; Pirenne & Denton 1953; Polyak 1941, 1948; Pratt 1947; S. Ramón y Cajal 1892–93, 1894, 1896, 1899–1904, 1909–11, 1917; Rand 1946; Rüchardt 1952; Salzer 1880; Saxén 1954; Schaffer 1890; Schaper 1893; W. J. Schmidt 1951; Schneider, Goodeve & Lythgoe 1939; Schwalbe 1874; M. Schultze 1866, 1867, 1869, 1872, 1873; Sloan 1950; R. Stern 1905; Stiles 1939, 1946; Stiles, Thomson & Pirenne 1945; Studnitz 1937–38, 1940, 1941, 1950; Studnitz *et al.* 1942, 1943, 1943–44; Sverdlick 1940; Tansley 1931, 1933, 1950; Tartuferi 1887; Thompson 1949; Tonner 1943–44; Tonner & Weber 1943–44; Trendelenburg 1904; Treviranus 1835, 1837, 1838; Valentin 1840; Verrier 1934, 1935, 1936, 1938, 1945; Verrier & Escher-Desrivières 1936; Verrier & Pannier 1936; Wald 1936, 1938, 1939, 1942, 1943, 1944, 1945, 1945–46, 1948, 1950; Wald &

Clark 1938; Wald & Zussman 1938; Walls 1928, 1934, 1935, 1942, 1943; Walls & Judd; Walters & Wright 1943; Weale 1953; Willmer 1944, 1946, 1949, 1950; Willmer & Wright 1945; Wislocki & Sidman 1954; E. Wolff 1941; W. D. Wright 1939, 1940, 1942, 1943, 1944, 1947; Wright & Granit 1938; Zewi 1939, 1941. (For Leeuwenhoek and other historical data *see* chap. I, 6 [3], 7 [2]; for central fovea and yellow spot *see* secs. 10, 11, this chapter.)

SEC. 4. BIPOLAR CELLS OF THE RETINA

1. General features of retinal bipolar cells.—These neurons have received their name because of their bipolar appearance. The "bodies" of the bipolar cells (*d, e, f, h*), with their "nuclei" wrapped in scanty protoplasm, are closely packed in the inner nuclear layer, *6* (Figs. 132, 133, 134, 143, 144, 146, 147 and colored schemes in 177, 178, 179). Only exceptionally is one or the other bipolar nucleus found displaced in the outer plexiform layer. The bodies are usually irregularly spherical, oval, or somewhat like a short spindle.

Usually, from each body two processes arise which are oriented vertically. The shorter "scleral process" extends into the outer plexiform layer (*5*), and the "vitreal process" stretches into the inner plexiform layer (*7*). The former may be considered a dendritic expansion, the latter an axis cylinder of the differentiated, functionally polarized neurons (*cf.* chap. I, 8 [5], and chap. IX). In the two plexiform layers, both processes divide into secondary, tertiary, etc., branches, different in morphological appearance and synaptical relationships.

Several distinct varieties of bipolar cells may be distinguished in the primate retina according to their appearance, anatomical contacts, and probable functional role. These represent two groups: "common," "polysynaptic rod and cone bipolars" (*d, e, f*, possibly also *g*), which are in synaptical contact with both kinds of photoreceptors, and "monosynaptic bipolar" (*h*), which is related only to the cones.

2. Mop bipolar (*d*).—This bipolar variety is morphologically clearly characterized. Usually, from the upper end of the "body" a single, relatively thick, main "dendritic or scleral process" extends in the scleral direction. In the inner zone of the outer plexiform layer (*5-c*) this process divides repeatedly until a small mop of delicate, filamentous terminal branches is formed (thus in Fig. 134, lower center). Occa-sionally, a single, somewhat stouter, filament extends as far as the outer nuclear layer, re-sembling the "club of Landolt" found in the Lower Vertebrates (left end of middle sketch, in Fig. 133).

The fine filaments of the mop spread out in zone *5-b*, where they cling to the sides of the cone pedicles and rod spherules. Both the rod spherules close to zone *5-c* and those that re-main at some distance from it are in contact (Fig. 140). In this way, each mop bipolar be-comes synaptically related to a compact group of photoreceptors, rods as well as cones. This is the multiple and common axodendritic type of synapse.

Another noteworthy feature is the reciprocal partial overlapping of the dendritic mops of the adjoining mop bipolars (thus at left end in middle sketch, in Fig. 133, and in lower center in Fig. 134). Because of this, a group of photo-receptors related to a single mop bipolar is also partly related to the adjoining mop bipolars; that is, the separation of a functional group of photoreceptors related to a single mop bipolar from the similar functional groups of the adjoin-ing mop bipolars is not abrupt, but gradual.

The third feature is the overlapping or mingling of the dendritic expansions of the mop bipolars with those of the other bipolar varieties and of the horizontal cells.

In other words, a group of the rods (*a*) and cones (*b*) synaptically related to a single mop bipolar (*d*) is simultaneously related not only to the adjoining mop bipolars (*d*) but also to a few cells of the other bipolar varieties (*e, f, h*) and to the horizontal cells (*c*).

3. Synapses of the mop bipolar with pho-toreceptors.—The synaptical relationships described above indicate a potential influencing of the mop bipolars (*d*) both by the rods (*a*) and by the cones (*b*), which may take place either simultaneously or successively. This influencing is, of necessity, diffuse, that is, less precisely limited in space than in the *h*-bipolar, involving, as it always does, a group of mop bipolars.

The influencing of a single mop bipolar either by a single cone or by a minute group of rods and cones seems to be ruled out on morpho-

logical grounds, because of dendritic overlapping and multiple contact with the photoreceptors.

Nor does it seem probable that an influence arising either in the rods or in the cones, or in both, could be restricted to the mop variety of

1 Mayo de 1922.

S. Ramón Cajal

FIG. 131.—Santiago Ramón y Cajal (1852–1934) at the age of seventy. One of the most brilliant investigators of the structure of nervous system and sensory organs, in particular of the retina, and an ingenious interpreter of their functions. From *Libro en honor de D. S. Ramón y Cajal*, Madrid, 1922, v. 1, Frontispiece. Courtesy Instituto Cajal, Madrid. (*See also* Figs. 52, 317.)

bipolars, except, perhaps, by a raised threshold of responsiveness in the remaining bipolar varieties (*e–f, h*).

Finally, a restriction of the mop bipolar to the influences of either the rods or the cones, on grounds of synaptical relationship, appears possible only in situations where either the one or the other category of photoreceptors ceases to be responsive to the stimulus of physical light.

Fig. 131*A.*—Stephen Polyak (1889–1955), author of the present book, at the time of completion of the manuscript of *The Retina.* A snapshot taken during the summer of 1939 by Professor Friedrich Wassermann, of the University of Chicago.

This could possibly take place in a system maximally adjusted either for scotopic or photopic vision.

4. Synapses of the mop bipolar with ganglion cells.—The "vitreal process," "axis cylinder," or "axon" of the mop bipolar, usually much thinner and provided with spindle-shaped varicosities characteristic of nerve fibers elsewhere, descends to the lowermost part of the inner plexiform layer (*7–e*). Here it divides into two or three short, thick, swollen branches terminating with crude, irregularly spherical varicosities. The nodular varicosities of this simple teledendron adhere directly to the surface of the bodies of the ganglion cells of the eighth layer adjoining the seventh layer. This is the axosomatic type of synapse.

There are usually also one or two short twigs branching off from the axon higher up, in the third or fourth zone of the seventh layer, whose terminal swellings touch one or another of the thick main ascending dendrites of the ganglion cells. This is the axodendritic synapse.

Since the teledendric axonal arborizations of the mop bipolars do not penetrate into the deeper parts of the ganglion layer, it is probable that the synapses of the ganglion cells whose bodies are buried deeper in the thick ganglion layer found in the central area are accomplished through the above-mentioned short collateral twigs of the mop bipolars somewhere in the vitreal half of the inner plexiform layer.

The number of ganglion cells related to a single mop bipolar is two, three, or at most four. There is apparently no selection of ganglion cell varieties to which the mop bipolars are related, while, on the other hand, the ganglion cells related to the mop bipolars are simultaneously also related to other bipolar varieties. A ganglion cell may be related to two or more of the adjoining mop bipolars, as well as to other bipolar varieties. The functional interpretation of these anatomical arrangements indicates a diffusion of influences, passing through the mop bipolars upon all ganglion cell varieties, and a relatively small localizing value.

5. Distribution and history of mop bipolar.—The mop variety of bipolars, in Primates, is present in great numbers in all regions of the retina. It is present in the central area and fovea to the limit of the rodless area, that is, to the edge of the foveal floor. Only in the rodless area of the central fovea, corresponding to the minute centralmost territory, where the photoreceptor layer is represented exclusively by the cones, has the presence of the mop bipolar not been ascertained.

The mop bipolar may have been seen by Tartuferi (1887) and by other investigators and was named "rod bipolar" by S. Ramón y Cajal (1892–93, 1909–11).

6. Brush and flat-top bipolars (e, f, g).—The bipolar cells of these two or three varieties usually also have a single main "dendritic expansion," which may be either slender or fairly stout, ascending to the fifth layer, and a thin "axonal process," descending to the seventh layer.

When the body adjoins the fifth layer, several thin dendritic branches arise directly from it. The dendritic ramifications of one type resemble a brush with the tips of its thin, bristle-like filaments cut off straight (e, right lower corner in Fig. 134). The other type has undulating branches which sweep laterally (f, upper center, in same figure). In both they differ from the branches of mop bipolars, in that they are strictly confined to the inner zone of the outer plexiform layer, *5-c*. Except for an occasional larger or smaller varicosity, frequently found in flat-top bipolars, all dendritic branches in both varieties just reach the division line separating zone *5-b* from zone *5-c*. The strict adherence to this boundary is remarkable because of the minute dimensions of the structures involved.

Careful study reveals that the filamentous dendrites, in both brush and flat-top bipolars, just touch the vitreal faces of the cone pedicles (that largely determine the boundary line between *5-b* and *5-c*) and the lowermost of the rod spherules (Fig. 140). The lateral faces of the cone pedicles and those rod spherules situated farther up in the intermediate zone, *5-b*, which are in contact with the dendritic filaments of mop bipolars, remain out of reach of brush and flat-top bipolars.

7. Synapses of brush and flat-top bipolars with photoreceptors.—The peculiar synaptical relationships of brush and flat-top bipolars with the photoreceptors, different from those found in mop bipolars, are undoubtedly an indication of their specific function.

The feature common to all three "diffuse" bipolar varieties so far considered (d, e, f, and the freakish form g) is their relationship to both the cones and the rods, even though many, per-haps the majority, of the rods are in no contact with brush and flat-top varieties.

Another resemblance is the overlapping of their adjoining dendritic tops both by those of the same variety (thus d by d, e by e, f by f), and by those of other varieties (d by e and f, e by d and f, f by d and e). A minute group of photoreceptors, both rods (a) and cones (b), related to a single brush bipolar, accordingly, also influences the adjoining brush bipolars, even though to a lesser degree. The same group of rods and cones simultaneously influences the adjoining flat-top bipolars (f), as it also does the mop bipolars (d), and the midget bipolars (h); the cones also influence the horizontal cells (c). From the synaptical contacts it appears that the emphasis in brush and flat-top bipolars is less upon influences arising in the rods than is the case in mop bipolars.

Finally, the fact that a part of the synaptical surface of the cone pedicle, its lateral sides, is used by the mop variety (d), while the other part, the vitreal face of the same pedicle, is in contact with the brush, flat-top, and midget varieties (e, f, h), as illustrated in detail in Figure 140, indicates a separation or sorting of influences originating from the common source —the cones—and their direction into several channels, each serving as a passage for a specific influence.

In other words, the peculiar and specific synaptical arrangements of each diffuse bipolar variety with the rods and cones are indicative of their specific responsiveness to influences arising from a common source, the photoreceptors.

8. Synapses of brush and flat-top bipolars with ganglion cells.—The terminal axonal ramifications and synapses of brush and flat-top bipolars in the inner plexiform layer (*7*) differ even more from those of mop bipolars than do their dendritic synapses in the outer plexiform layer (*5*). They are, in general, more delicate, consisting of a small clump of thin, short twigs, swollen in places into varicosities and with minute buttons at the ends, occasionally all twisted into a fine meshwork.

They are, furthermore, conspicuous because of the locality in which they are found. Whereas the teledendrons of mop bipolars (d) are always located in the lowermost zones of the seventh layer (zones 7-*d* and 7-*e*), those of brush (*e*) and flat-top bipolars (*f*) spread exclusively in approximately the scleral half of the same layer (zones 7-*a*, 7-*b*, and 7-*c*).

The synapses they undergo with the ganglion cells likewise differ. In brush and flat-top bipolars the contact is either with the twigs or with the main trunk of the dendritic processes,

and never with the bodies of the ganglion cells (axodendritic synapses), whereas the principal contact of mop bipolars is with the ganglion cell bodies.

In one respect, all diffuse bipolar varieties are alike: there is apparently no selection of the ganglion varieties to which they are synaptically related, all ganglions (*m, n, o, p, r, s*) being

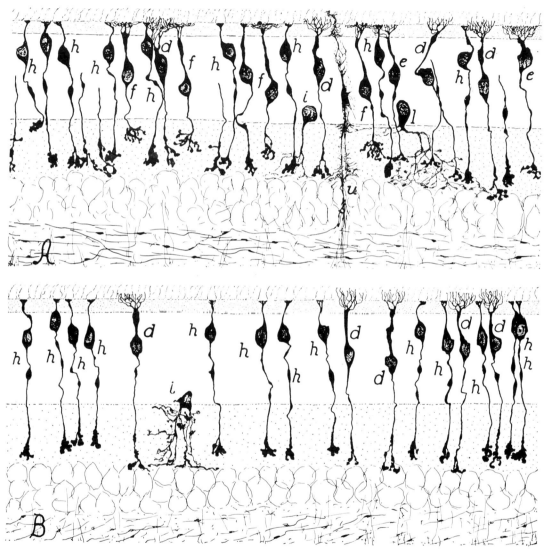

Fig. 132.—Bipolar cells of different varieties of the retina of a Rhesus Macaque stained with the Golgi method. Selection from the periphery of a single section, from central area not far from the papilla of the optic nerve. Individual bipolars or groups of bipolars drawn as found in the preparation, either singly or in groups, to show synaptic relationships with lower ends of photoreceptors (given in outlines in the upper tier of each sketch) and with ganglion cells (their bodies outlined in the lower tier). *Labeling: d,* mop bipolars; *e,* brush bipolars; *f,* flat-top bipolars, which all represent diffuse or common rod and cone bipolars; *h,* midget bipolars, which are the individualized cone bipolars; *i, l,* so-called amacrine cells; *u,* radial fiber of Müller belonging to supporting structures of the retina. Note the individual contact of *h* bipolars with cone pedicles and the absence of overlapping with other *h* bipolars; presence of overlapping in diffuse *d, e,* and *f* bipolars among themselves and with *h* bipolars. Only a small number of the cells were stained in this preparation, making it possible to study various details. (*Cf.* Figs. 143, 144.)

related to both brush and flat-top bipolars, as they are to mop bipolars. These relationships are multiple, less restricted in space, several bipolars of diffuse varieties being related to each ganglion cell, especially of the larger varieties (*m, n, p*), few in the central area, and many in the extra-areal periphery.

In still another way a multiple synaptical relation is assured, since several ganglions, especially of the midget variety (*s*) in the central area, are related to each brush or flat-top bipolar. Moreover, each brush and flat-top bipolar may be related to several ganglion cells of different varieties.

Finally, neither the territories of brush and flat-top bipolars nor those of their related ganglion cells are completely separated from one another but overlap, and more so in the extra-areal periphery than in the central area of the retina.

9. DISTRIBUTION AND HISTORY OF BRUSH AND FLAT-TOP BIPOLARS.—Both brush and flat-top bipolars are present in great numbers in the entire retina, including the central fovea. They have been found alone in the centralmost area of the fovea, where the rods are missing. Whether or not this is an accident of the Golgi stain used in this work, future investigation alone can determine.

Whether brush and flat-top bipolars are one or two distinct varieties also remains uncertain. The similarity of their synaptical contacts, in spite of their somewhat different appearance, suggests that both may be but slight variations of the same type. This seems to be even more true of the *g*-variety, which is probably a freak. A more detailed investigation in various vertebrate species may solve this problem.

Brush and flat-top bipolars were first seen by Tartuferi (1887), who called them *cellula a pennachio*, and were described by S. Ramón y Cajal (1892–93, 1909–11) as "cone bipolars."

10. MIDGET BIPOLAR (*h*).—This variety, because of its appearance and its synaptical connections, is the most conspicuous bipolar neuron of the human and simian retina (Figs. 132, 133, 134, 140, 146, 147, and colored schemes in 177, 178, 179). Its small body is usually in one or

both of the scleral zones of the inner nuclear layer (*6-a* and *6-b*).

The "dendritic expansion" in most cases is a short, thin fiber passing straight into the outer plexiform layer. The division into a ramification ordinarily takes place quite close to the boundary line separating zone *5-b* from *5-c*. This terminal dendritic ramification is quite peculiar and is found almost nowhere else in the nervous system. It consists of a dozen or so thin and very short branchlets, all of about the same length and all remaining close together (*see* lower sketches in Fig. 133, and right-hand sketches in Fig. 134, and especially Fig. 140). Each minute twig carries at its end a tiny spherical or globular swelling, all the globules about the same size and arranged in approximately the same plane.

The terminal dendritic "bouquet" or "rosette" resembles a minute basket, cup, or tray, whose shallow floor is formed of closely packed terminal globules. Seen in profile and at low magnification, the entire structure appears as a single, solid, cup-shaped, or funnel-like expansion (thus some in Fig. 132) and has been described as a minute "plaque" in the fovea of Birds (S. Ramón y Cajal 1892–93, 1909–11) and as a "meniscus" in the simian retina (Fortin 1925). However, the employment of appropriate oil-immersion lenses of high magnification (Leitz's Ultropak and other objectives that have a long working distance) reveals its composite structure.

11. SYNAPSES OF MIDGET BIPOLAR WITH PHOTORECEPTORS.—An attentive study of the relationships of the dendritic bouquets of midget bipolars shows them all strung along a line just beneath the intermediate zone of the outer plexiform layer, *5-b* (Figs. 128, 129, 161).

The bouquets are separated from one another by intervals. These intervals vary in length, depending on the region. In the central area, especially in the fovea, the midget bipolar bouquets are short and very closely spaced, the separating intervals between them measuring not more than about one-third the length of a single bouquet. Farther away, the spread or size of the bouquets, as well as the separating intervals, rapidly increases until in the extra-areal periphery the intervals are several times the length of a single bouquet.

The most centrally located midget bipolars have the smallest bouquets. They are in the fovea, where they are found as far as the margin of the foveal floor or foveola; that is, as far as cone pedicles are present in zone *5-b* (*cf.* middle sketch in Fig. 161). In routinely stained preparations the dendritic bouquets of midget bipolars appear at low magnification as a broken line of short and somewhat more intensively stained segments (Fig. 127). On closer scrutiny, each of these segments is revealed to be made up of a number of minute granules (they have, therefore, been named "granular clods" by Dogiel 1884). Their spacing corresponds exactly to that of the cone pedicles in zone *5-b*. In hematoxylin and eosin- or phloxin-stained preparations the pedicles appear pale and, because of this, have been erroneously interpreted by Balbuena as "vacuoles." It is not difficult to notice, in fact, that to each cone pedicle there

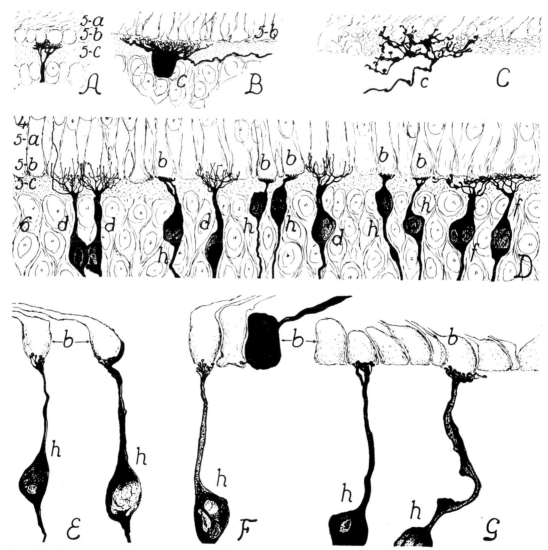

Fig. 133.—Details of bipolar and horizontal cells of the retina of a Rhesus Macaque at various magnifications. Golgi method. *Labeling: c*, horizontal cell (body in sketch *B*, terminal ramification or teledendron in sketch *C*); *d*, mop bipolars, first from the left in middle sketch with Landolt's fiber extending as far as the outer nuclear layer *4*; *f*, flat-top bipolars; *h*, midget or individualized cone bipolars. Note overlapping of dendrites in *d* and *f* bipolars, the first spreading into zone *5-b*, the latter remaining in zone *5-c* of the outer plexiform layer; strict individual synapses of each midget bipolar with a single cone pedicle (*b*), except in sketch *A* (polysynaptic midget bipolar). (*Cf.* Figs. 146, 147, and color Figs. 177–79.)

is attached one "granular clod" from the vitreal side, that is, a dendritic bouquet of one midget bipolar.

In preparations stained with the histoanalytical method of Golgi it has been found that in the central area and particularly in the fovea of Man, Monkey, and Ape, one bouquet of a midget bipolar clings to the underside of each cone pedicle (*b*). The diameter of the bouquet is usually somewhat smaller than the diameter of the pedicle to which it clings (Fig. 133, *E*, *F*, *G*; Fig. 134, *C*, *F*, *G*; Fig. 140, upper two rows). In the retina of the Chimpanzee and less frequently in that of Man and the Rhesus Macaque, midget bipolars are found outside the central area which are the same as those in

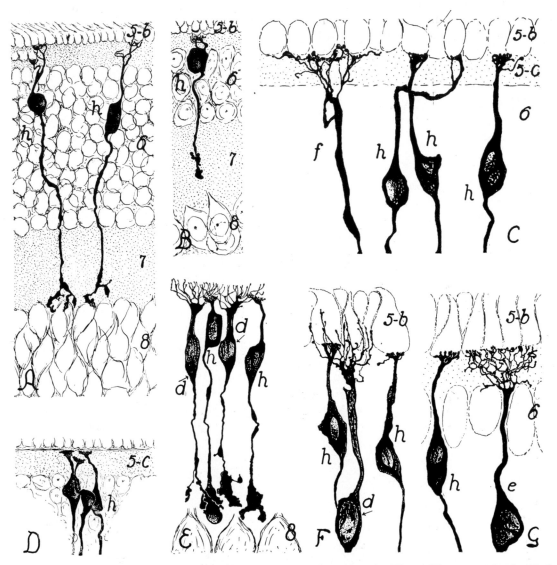

FIG. 134.—Synapses of different varieties of bipolar cells of the retina of a Rhesus Macaque stained with the method of Golgi. *d*, mop bipolars; *e*, brush bipolar; *f*, flat-top bipolar; *h*, midget or individualized cone bipolars. Left-hand sketches drawn at moderate magnification, right-hand sketches at high magnification. In sketches *C*, *F*, and *G* note multiple synapses of *d*, *e*, and *f* bipolars, each related in its own way to the lower ends of photoreceptors, the rods and cones (in zone *5-b*), and strictly individualized synapses of *h* bipolars with the cones alone. Note also structural composition, location, spread, and attachment of upper parts of bipolars, especially of midget "bouquets," to a particular locality of the lower ends of photoreceptors, the mop of *d* bipolar clinging to the sides of both the rods (smaller outlines) and cones (larger contours), *e* and *f* bipolars touching the lower faces of rods and cones, while *h* bouquets touch only the lower faces of individual cone pedicles. Sketch *A* shows two polysynaptic midget bipolars. (*Cf.* Figs. 146, 147, 177, 178, 179.)

the central area in all details, except that each
has two or three bouquets related to as many
adjoining cones (*h-h*). In Figure 139 all these
polysynaptic midget bipolars are labeled with
a single *h*. (*See also* such a bipolar in the lower
right-hand corner, in Fig. 144, and a much more
magnified detail labeled *VI* in Fig. 140.)

The Golgi-stained preparations also show
that midget bipolar bouquets have no contact
with rod spherules or structures belonging to
any other neuron variety. (*Cf.* Fig. 133; *see also*
detail at the right-hand end of first row in Fig.
140, and colored schemes in 177, 178, 179.)

12. Functional significance of synapses
of midget bipolar with photoreceptors.—
The peculiar anatomical relationship of the
dendritic bouquets of midget bipolars to the
cone pedicles, especially in the central area and
fovea, described in the foregoing subsection, indicates the presence of an individual or "private" synapse (*b* & *h*). In other words, midget
bipolars are monosynaptic, individual, or "private bipolars." Furthermore, since they are related only to the cones, they must be considered
as the true "cone bipolars."

Because of the arrangement described above,
each cone in the central area and fovea is
capable of influencing a single midget bipolar,
without influencing directly either the immediately adjoining or the more distant midget
bipolars.

Those midget bipolars of the extra-areal
periphery that have several dendritic bouquets
each and are related to as many cones are an
exception. They, too, are exclusively cone bipolars, although, being related to several cones,
they may be termed "polysynaptic cone bipolars" (*h-h*).

The cone influences in the central area and
fovea, in so far as they are concerned with the
midget bipolars, are all individualized. Since,
however, each cone is synaptically related also
to mop (*d*), brush (*e*), and flat-top bipolars (*f*),
it is capable of influencing these too, simultaneously or successively, although in a less restricted way spatially or dimensionally. There
is still a third channel by means of which a
given cone may be able to exert an influence:
the horizontal association cells (*c*). (*Cf.* sec. 6,

and Figs. 146, 147, this chapter, and colored
schemes 177, 178, 179.)

13. Individual synapses of midget bipolar with ganglion cells.—The synaptical relationships of midget bipolars with ganglion
cells are no less remarkable (*see* above-mentioned figures). A thin "vitreal fiber" or "axis
cylinder," often provided with a fairly large
varicosity, one to each bipolar, descends to the
inner plexiform layer, where it terminates with
a few lumpy swellings of compact appearance
(Fig. 132). These teledendrons are arranged in
two tiers, one in the upper, the other in the
lower, half of the inner plexiform layer, approximately corresponding with zones γ-*b* and
γ-*d*. They remain, however, at a distance both
from the inner nuclear layer and from the layer
of ganglion cells. They do not come into contact
with the bodies either of the amacrines or of the
ganglion cells, their synapses being exclusively
with the dendritic processes in the plain substance of the inner plexiform layer.

The mode of their synapsing depends upon
the cell variety. With the small or midget ganglions (*s*) their synapses are strictly individual.
Each minute, lumpy midget bipolar teledendron is enveloped by the delicate twigs of a dendritic basket of a single midget ganglion cell. In
this way a peculiar "axosomatic synapse" of
the type called "cog or joggle synapse" by
S. Ramón y Cajal, or "hand-clasp synapse" by
Herrick is formed. In exceptional cases a midget
ganglion is found that has two dendritic baskets
related to two midget bipolars (*s-s* in Fig.
143), a counterpart to the bi- or polysynaptic
midget bipolars of the extra-areal periphery.

In the great majority of cases, however, the
h and *s* synapses are strictly individual or
"private," especially in the central area and
fovea. In this way a chain of three conducting
neurons is formed in the retina: cone (*b*) and
midget bipolar (*h*) and midget ganglion cell (*s*).
Through this chain, in and around the visual
axis of the eye, an individual stimulus may be
conveyed from each cone along its own private
optic nerve fiber to the brain (*cf.* middle sketch
in color Fig. 177).

14. Multiple synapses of midget bipolar
with ganglions and other retinal nerve

CELLS.—In addition to individual synapses with midget ganglion cells (*s*), midget bipolars (*h*) are also related to other ganglion cell varieties designated as "diffuse ganglions" (Figs. 146, 147). These synaptical relationships, however, are different. Each of the ganglion varieties, such as parasol (*m*), shrub (*n*), small diffuse ganglion (*o*), and garland ganglion (*p*), all of which possess more or less widespread dendritic ramifications in the inner plexiform layer, also undergoes a synaptical association with the midget bipolars (*h*). These relationships are not individual or "private" but multiple or polysynaptic, since each of these ganglion cells is related to a larger or smaller number of midget bipolars (as well as to a number of mop, brush, and flat-top bipolars).

By means of this arrangement, in addition to those impulses that arrive via the "diffuse varieties of bipolars" (*d*, *e-f*), less individualized, diffuse, or global, and apparently summated cone impulses are transmitted from larger areas of the photoreceptor layer through the midget bipolars and conveyed to the brain.

Finally, the centrifugal bipolars (*i*) and the so-called amacrine cells (*k*, *l*) are also synaptically related to the midget bipolars and may in this way be influenced by the cones.

15. HISTORICAL NOTE ON THE DISCOVERY OF MIDGET BIPOLARS.—The midget variety of bipolar had been seen a number of times, although usually only in part, and had, therefore, been neither accurately described nor correctly interpreted. Certain structures observed by Merkel (1869, 1876, 1877), Gunn (1877), Tafani (1883), Dogiel (1884), Borysiekiewicz (1887, 1894), Kuhnt (1890), S. Ramón y Cajal (1892–93, 1909–11), Schaper (1893), Held (1905), Fortin (1925), Balbuena (1929, 1930), and Kolmer (1930, 1936) evidently were dendritic bouquets or rosettes of midget bipolars. Their true nature and relationships, and hence their functional significance, had heretofore remained unknown. (*See also* Polyak 1934, 1935, 1936, 1941, 1948.)

References: Arey 1932; Bach 1895; Balbuena 1929, 1930 (*see also* Rochon-Duvigneaud 1943, Figs. 25, 26); Baquis 1890; Dogiel 1884, 1885, 1888, 1891–92, 1893, 1895; Ebner 1902; Eisler 1930; Fortin 1925; Greeff 1899 (1900); Gunn 1877; Held 1905; Hosch 1891, 1895; Kallius 1894; Koelliker 1854; Kolmer 1930; Kolmer & Lauber 1936; Kuhnt 1890; Merkel 1869, 1876, 1877; H. Müller 1856–57, 1872; Polyak 1934, 1935, 1936, 1941, 1942, 1948, 1949; S. Ramón y Cajal 1889, 1892–93, 1894, 1896, 1899–1904, 1904, 1909–11, 1919; Renaut 1893–99; Retzius 1881, 1905; Rochon-Duvigneaud 1943; Schaper 1899; M. Schultze 1872; Schwalbe 1874; Tafani 1883; Tartuferi 1887; Uyama 1926. (For additional references *see* chap. I, 8, 9.)

SEC. 5. GANGLION CELLS OF THE RETINA

1. GENERAL REMARKS ON THE CLASSIFICATION OF RETINAL GANGLION CELLS.—The ganglion cells of the retina represent the third link in the chain of retinal neurons which carries impulses to the brain (Figs. 135–39, 146, 147, and colored Figs. 177, 178, 179).

In the simian and human retina there are at least five distinct varieties of ganglion cells, differing greatly from one another in body size and even more in the locality and manner in which their expansions are spread and in their synaptical connections. These varieties may be subdivided into two groups, depending on whether their expansions overlap and are in contact with numerous bipolars of all varieties, or whether overlapping is absent and they are related to a few bipolars only or even to a single midget bipolar. The first group is represented by diffuse, polysynaptical ganglion cells (*m*, *n*, *o*, *p*, and possibly *r*); the other group contains the single individual, oligosynaptic or monosynaptic ganglion variety (*s*).

There are certain features common to all ganglion varieties. Most have a body in the ganglion cell layer (*8*, in Figs. 127–29). In a few the body is displaced into the inner zone of the inner nuclear layer (*6-d*), these are the so-called "Dogiel's cells" (one such cell is found in each of Figs. 136 and 139). In any case, the dendritic expansions of the ganglion cells spread in the inner plexiform layer. Those with a body in the eighth layer, the majority, spread in the direction of the sclera; the few with bodies in the inner nuclear layer spread their dendrites in that layer in an inverted fashion, in the direction of the vitreous, hence superficially they resemble the "amacrine cells" (*k, l* in Figs. 142, 143).

There is one axis cylinder or axon in each ganglion cell. It is thick in the large cells, and delicate in the small. All axons, or optic nerve

fibers, pass into the layer of optic nerve fibers (*9*), whence they reach the optic papilla (Fig. 138).

After they leave the eyeball, these axons are assembled into a trunk, the optic nerve, and continue to the brain as the optic tract (chap. VI, 3). Apparently, there are no side branches

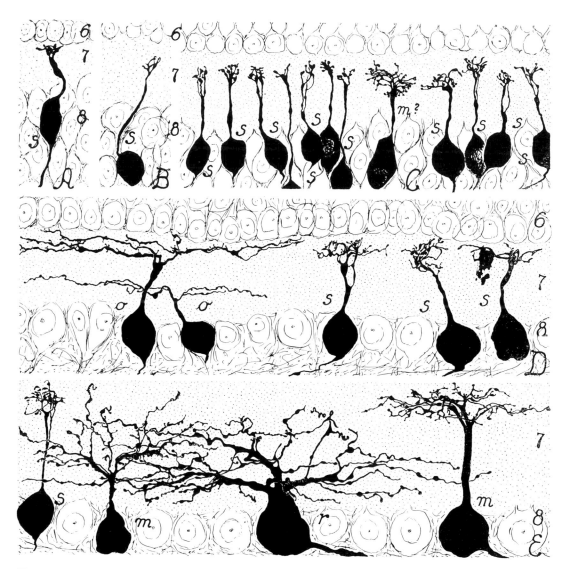

Fig. 135.—Types of ganglion cells of the retina of a Rhesus Macaque stained with the Golgi method: *m*, parasol variety; *o*, small variety with horizontally placed dendrites; *r*, giant ganglion; *s*, midget ganglions. Sketches *A, B*, and *C* from central fovea or just outside it; *D* and *E* from region outside the central area. Dimensions of ganglions in and close to visual axis are much smaller than away from it, a reverse from the number which is the greatest around the axis. However, all varieties of ganglions appear to be present everywhere. Note the restricted size of dendritic treetops in midget ganglions of the fovea (*upper sketches*) compared with more robust appearance of the same in the extra-areal regions (*middle and lower sketches*). Owing to its small size and few synaptical contacts, each ganglion cell in the fovea and close to it makes connections with only a few bipolars as compared with the extrafoveal periphery; also, its photoreceptor area is much smaller here, the visual resolution therefore much greater in the axis of the field of view. This is further enhanced by the individual synapses that each foveal and areal midget ganglion undergoes with a midget bipolar, which, in turn, is related to only one cone cell. (*Cf.* Figs. 146, 147, 177, 178, 179.)

or collaterals in the axis cylinders during their course in the retina. Nor do the optic nerve fibers in Man, Ape, Monkey, and other higher Mammals normally possess myelin sheaths within the eyeball; but as soon as they penetrate the cribriform lamina of the sclera and form the optic nerve, they become sheathed. (*See* chap. VI, 2, on the origin and course of optic nerve fibers in the human and simian retina.)

2. Umbrella or parasol ganglion (*m*).— These medium- to large-sized cells (Figs. 135–39) have an approximately spherical body from which one or several stout, trunklike main dendrites stretch into the inner plexiform layer. Here, by dividing repeatedly, an arborization resembling an umbrella or parasol is formed. This arborization is conspicuous because of its density and flatness, being limited to one or two zones, usually *7-b* or *7-d*. The horizontal extent or spread of the dendritic treetop is small in the central area (Fig. 138) and gradually increases to giant proportions in the extra-areal periphery (Figs. 136 and 139).

The synapses of the terminal dendritic twigs occur with the numerous brush (*e*), flat-top (*f*), and midget bipolars (*h*); those of the body with a few mop bipolars (*d*). The synaptical relationships indicate a summating function little restricted in space.

3. Shrub ganglion (*n*).— This ganglion (Figs. 137, 138) has a body of relatively small size and a loose dendritic ramification, made up of a few thin, twisted branches terminating with contorted, hook-shaped twigs carrying tiny swellings at the ends. In a given segment, the dendritic ramification spreads over the entire thickness of the inner plexiform layer. The terminal dendritic branchlets form a number of ill-defined baskets, into which clumpy axonal teledendrons of a group of midget bipolars (*h*) are fitted. The teledendrons of the brush (*e*) and flat-top bipolars (*f*) are also enmeshed in the dendritic twigs of the shrub ganglion, while those of the mop bipolars (*d*) are in contact with its body. The synaptical relationships indicate a summating role of a special kind and are somewhat more restricted in space than in the parasol variety.

4. Small diffuse ganglion (*o*).— This variety (Figs. 135, 136, 138) is conspicuous because of the diminutive size of the cell body, probably the smallest of all retinal ganglion varieties. The few long, but delicate, filamentous dendritic branches spread horizontally or somewhat obliquely in the sixth layer. The synapses are with a small number of bipolars of all varieties.

5. Garland ganglion (*p*).— This ganglion variety (Figs. 136, 137, 139) has a body of medium size, from which a few main dendrites arise. These divide into a small number of rather thin, but very long, secondary and further branches, the longest of all ganglion varieties, spreading in wavy lines for great distances in the seventh layer. The terminal dendritic twigs, which hang from the longer branches like moss and have minute swellings at the ends, make the entire arborization resemble festoons and garlands.

The bipolar cells whose axonal teledendrons lie enmeshed between the dendritic twigs of the garland ganglion belong to the brush (*e*), flat-top (*f*), and midget varieties (*h*), while the mop bipolars (*d*) are in contact with the body of the garland ganglion.

Considering the great number of bipolar cells related to each single garland ganglion cell, especially in the extra-areal periphery, it is plausible to assume that the function of this variety is a summation of the rod and cone excitations from relatively large areas of the photoreceptor layer.

6. Giant ganglion (*r*).— These unusually large ganglion cells (Fig. 135) are found in a more distant part of the extra-areal periphery (*cf.* Fig. 129, sketches *V*, *VI*). They resemble either parasol or garland cells, except that they are larger. They may be merely large varieties of one or another of the afore-mentioned varieties.

7. Midget ganglion (*s*).— The midget ganglion cells of the human and simian retina are conspicuous because of their small, uniform size, extremely reduced dendritic ramifications, mode of synapsing, and numerousness (Figs. 135–39). In fact, the majority of cells in the central area and fovea are midget ganglions.

Their spherical, oval, or pyriform bodies may be found anywhere in the thick eighth layer. A single, thin main "dendritic shaft," either short or long, depending on the position of the body, usually arises from it. If long, the shaft has one or more spindle-shaped swellings that make it resemble a short axis cylinder (thus in Fig. 138).

All dendritic shafts are oriented vertically, more or less, and stretch into the inner plexiform layer. Here each divides into a few secondary and tertiary branchlets, altogether forming a minute dendritic basket whose diameter is usually less than the diameter of its own cell body. These baskets are turned in the direction of the sclera, except in the few midget ganglions with bodies displaced into the inner nuclear

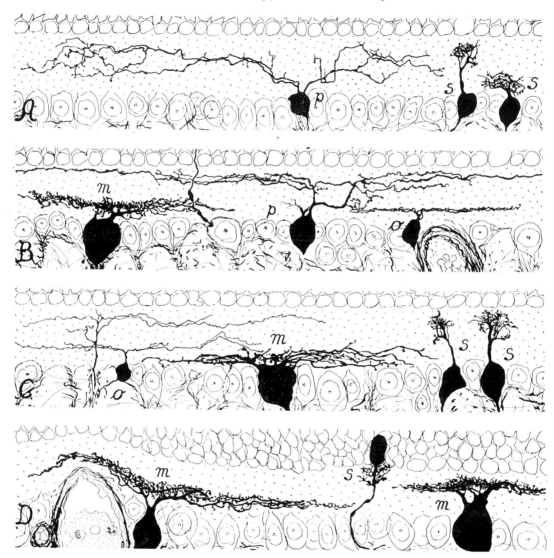

Fig. 136.—Types of ganglion cells of the retina of a Chimpanzee stained with the Golgi method. Extrafoveal and extra-areal periphery. *Labeling:* m, parasol variety; o, small ganglions with horizontal dendrites; p, garland ganglions; s, midget ganglions. Note long meandering dendrites of p variety, compared with diminutive dendritic treetops of s variety, whereas the size of their bodies remains the same; large bodies and compact dendritic treetops, restricted to a narrow zone of the inner plexiform layer, characterize the m variety. In lowermost sketch the body of a midget ganglion is displaced in the inner nuclear layer, its dendrites spreading in the usual manner in the inner plexiform layer, where they undergo synaptical contacts with the bipolars. Since larger varieties have a wide dendritic spread, permitting synaptical contacts with numerous bipolars, in turn gathering impulses from an extensive area of photoreceptor layer, such varieties may be considered as "collectors" or "summators" of impulses. By the same token, midget ganglions are "specialized conductors" of territorially restricted impulses. (*Cf.* Figs. 146, 147, 177, 178, 179.)

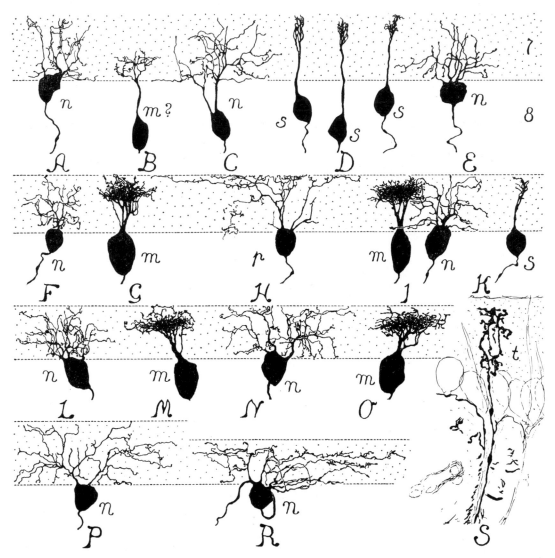

FIG. 137.—Types of retinal ganglion cells of Chimpanzee mostly from central area, stained with the Golgi method. *Labeling: m,* parasol variety; *n,* shrub ganglion; *p,* garland ganglion; *s,* midget ganglions; *t,* termination of a nerve fiber in inner plexiform layer, probably of extraretinal origin. Note the wide spread and loose appearance of the dendritic branching in the *n* variety extending over the whole thickness of the seventh layer, contrasting with the minute treetops in the *s* variety, which, in addition, are restricted to a narrow zone of the same layer, even though the size of the body differs but little in both varieties. In the *m* variety, again, the dendritic treetops are also relatively restricted but are much richer and more compact, whereas the bodies are much larger than in either *n, p,* or *s* ganglions. These morphological differences, interpreted functionally, may indicate the collecting of fewer bipolar impulses from a wider photoreceptor territory by the *n* variety than by the *m* variety, which collects a denser stream of impulses from a smaller territory. In the *s* ganglions, again, both the density and the territorial extent of impulses are further reduced. Other qualities of impulses to which each ganglion variety responds undoubtedly also vary, contributing to the complex structural mechanism of the retina. (*Cf.* Figs. 146, 147, 177, 178, 179.)

layer whose dendrite is inverted, and oriented upside down (one such *s* ganglion is to be found in the lowermost sketch in Fig. 136).

Midget ganglion cells are also conspicuous because of the placement of the dendritic baskets in two tiers, approximately corresponding with zones *7-b* and *7-d* of the inner plexiform layer. These tiers are identical with those where the tiny, lumpy teledendrons of the midget bipolar cells (*h*) are placed.

8. INDIVIDUAL SYNAPSES OF MIDGET GANGLION WITH BIPOLARS.—Direct evidence shows that the tiny axonal teledendrons of the midget bipolars (*h*) are individually enmeshed in the dendritic baskets of the midget ganglion cells (Figs. 146, 147, and colored schemes in 177, 178, 179). In this way two series of exquisitely individual or "private" axosomatic synapses are formed (*h* & *s*), one in the upper, the other in the lower, story of the inner plexiform layer (*7-b* and *7-d*).

On rare occasions one meets with a small ganglion cell which resembles a typical midget ganglion in all details, except that its main dendrite divides into two branches, each forming a basket, one of which is sometimes incomplete (*s s* in Fig. 143). Such a bisynaptic midget ganglion cell is related to two midget bipolars (Fig. 177, right-hand sketch). Most of the midget ganglions in the central area and fovea, however, are strictly monosynaptic; that is, they are related to single midget bipolars (Figs. 146, 147, and colored Figs. 177, 178, 179).

In the extra-areal periphery small ganglion cells are present which resemble typical midget ganglions of the central area but are cruder and larger in every detail. They are also relatively and absolutely fewer in number, in comparison with ganglions of larger varieties found outside the central area.

9. MULTIPLE SYNAPTICAL RELATIONSHIPS OF MIDGET GANGLION CELL WITH BIPOLARS.—In addition to their relationship to midget bipolars (*h*), each midget ganglion is simultaneously related to bipolars of other varieties (*see* same figures). The synapses with mop bipolars (*d*) are axosomatic, those with brush (*e*) and flat-top bipolars (*f*) are axodendritic. Frequently, an unusually long teledendric twig of a brush or flat-top bipolar is found touching the main dendritic shaft of a midget ganglion, with its terminal varicosity just below the point where the ganglion divides into a terminal basket. However, the relationships with diffuse bipolar varieties are not monosynaptic, that is, they are not single or "private," since several midget ganglions are related to a single mop, brush, or flat-top bipolar; conversely, several diffuse bipolar cells may be related to a single midget ganglion cell.

10. FUNCTIONAL SIGNIFICANCE OF THE SYNAPTICAL RELATIONSHIPS OF MIDGET GANGLION CELL.—The complex synaptical relationships of the midget ganglion cells may, in general, indicate a variety of functions.

First, the individual synapse with midget bipolars is obviously an arrangement by means of which individualized cone impulses are transmitted to midget ganglions, along whose axons they reach the brain: monosynaptic receptor-conductor channel (*b* & *h* & *s*).

Second, the synapses with diffuse bipolars appear to be a mechanism by which that part of the cone impulse passing along the bipolars and all impulses originating in the rods in some way influence the midget ganglion cells: polysynaptic receptor-conductor channel (*a* & *def* & *s*).

How these synaptical relationships are fitted into the total and more complex mechanism of the retina is discussed in section 8 of this chapter and in chapter IX.

11. HISTORY OF INVESTIGATIONS OF THE GANGLION CELLS.—The retinal ganglion cells, that is, their bodies, were probably seen by Leeuwenhoek (1674, 1684) and by the subsequent early microscopists Fontana (1782), Arnold (1832), R. Wagner (1833), Ehrenberg (1833, 1836), Langenbeck (1836), and especially by Treviranus (1835–38), who called them *papillae* (*see* chap. I, 7 [2]). The fact that they are true nerve cells, however, was recognized only by Valentin (1837), Hannover (1840, 1843), Pacini (1845), Bowman (1846, 1849), and a few others. They have since been studied in detail by many investigators; e.g., Corti (1850, 1854), H. Müller (1851, 1856–57, 1862), Remak (1853), Bergmann (1854), Koelliker (1854), M. Schultze (1872), and Schwalbe (1874).

The retinal ganglion cells were first studied with the analytical methods of Golgi and Ehrlich by Tartuferi (1887) and by Dogiel (1891, 1892, 1893, 1895). The most complete information and classification derives from S. Ramón y Cajal (1889, 1892–93, 1894, 1896, 1899–1904, 1904, 1909–11).

In spite of these efforts, knowledge of the ganglion cell varieties, their synaptical relationships, and probable function, is still extremely limited.

The failure of students of the retina to identify the midget ganglion variety (*s*), to which most of the ganglion cells in the central area and fovea of Man and of the Simians belong and which is obviously of paramount impor-

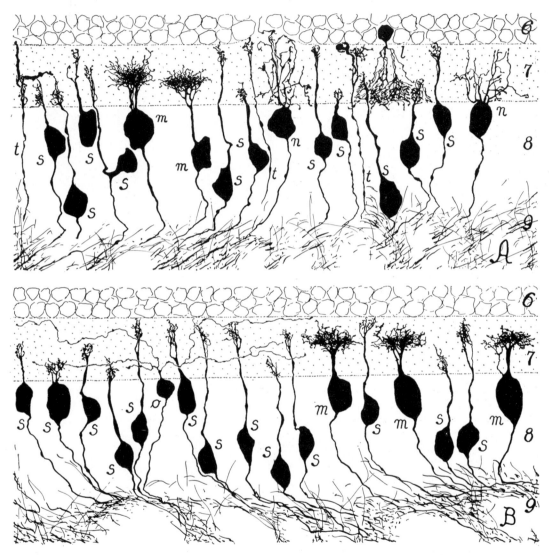

Fig. 138.—Types of nerve cells, mostly ganglions, from central area of the retina of a Chimpanzee, stained with the Golgi method. *Labeling:* *l*, so-called amacrine cell that in this instance does not possess an axon fiber; *m*, parasol ganglions; *n*, shrub ganglions; *o*, small ganglion with long, loose dendritic branches; *s*, midget ganglions; *t*, terminations of nerve fibers in inner plexiform layer, probably of extraretinal origin (so-called exogenous or centrifugal fibers). Note generally reduced dimensions of all varieties in comparison with the same varieties found in extra-areal periphery of retina shown in Fig. 136; characteristic compact appearance of the treetops in *m*, and the loose appearance of same in *n* and *o* varieties; the minute dimensions and delicate structure of the treetops in the *s* variety located either close to the inner nuclear layer (*6*) or close to the ganglion layer (*8*); descent of all axis cylinders, the actual "optic nerve fibers," down to the fiber layer of retina (*9*), where they pass over to optic disk, eventually to form the optic nerve. Functional interpretation same as in preceding figure. (*Cf.* Figs. 146, 147, 177, 178, 179.)

tance both for visual acuity and for color vision, was conspicuous.

References: F. Arnold 1832; Bach 1895; Bergmann 1854; Birch-Hirschfeld 1900; Bowman 1846, 1849; Cattaneo 1922; Corti 1850, 1854; Dogiel 1891–92, 1893, 1895; Ehrenberg 1833, 1836; Fontana 1782; Greeff 1899 (1900); Han-

nover 1840, 1843; Hosch 1895; Kallius 1894; Koelliker 1854; Kolmer & Lauber 1936; Langenbeck 1836; Leeuwenhoek 1674, 1684; Leinfelder 1938, 1940; Marenghi 1900; Merkel 1869, 1876, 1877; H. Müller 1851, 1856–57, 1862, 1872; Mureddu 1930; Oshinomi 1830; Pacini 1845; Polyak 1934, 1935, 1936, 1941–48; S. Ra-

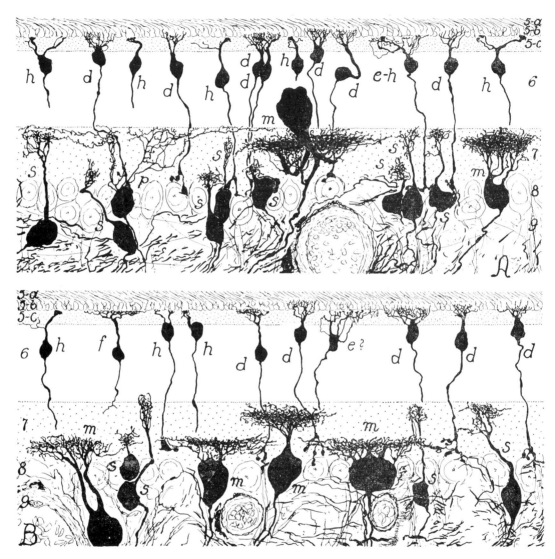

FIG. 139.—Types of ganglion cells and bipolars from extra-areal regions of the retina of a Chimpanzee, stained with the Golgi method. *Labeling:* d, mop bipolars; e?, an irregular brush bipolar; e–h, another irregular type that has a "bouquet" of a midget bipolar h, and other twigs resembling those found in the brush bipolar e; h, midget bipolars, some of a strictly monosynaptic type, with a single bouquet, the others of an irregular type, with two bouquets, one of which may be smaller or incomplete or just indicated by an accessory twig; m, bulky parasol ganglions, one in the upper sketch with its body displaced in the inner nuclear layer, so-called "Dogiel's cell," its treetop built by recurved branches formed in the usual way; large spread and loose appearance of treetops in garland ganglion p and restricted size and compact structure of treetops in midget ganglion cells s; flat, densely constructed treetops in bulky parasol ganglions m, spreading horizontally in one zone of the inner plexiform layer. The impression gained is that of imperfectly differentiated structures indicative of the less specialized function of extra-areal regions of the retina, in comparison with the central area and fovea. (*Cf.* Fig. 138.)

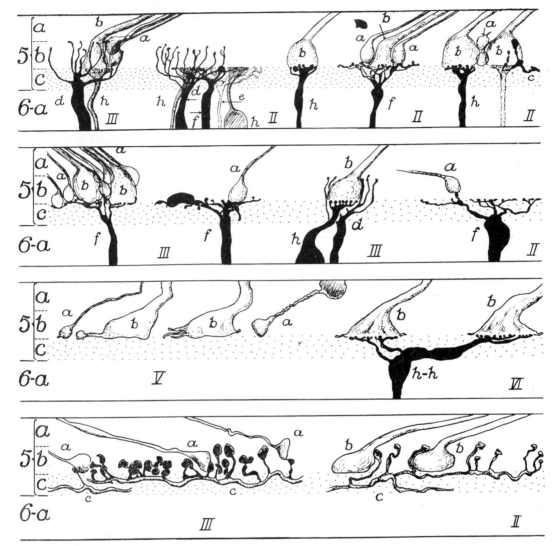

Fig. 140.—Samples of the synapses and synaptic relationships found in the outer plexiform layer of the retina of a Rhesus Macaque, stained with the Golgi method. Sketched with the help of a camera lucida and oil-immersion objectives at high magnification. Beginning with the left upper corner, the following details are presented (Roman numerals indicating retinal belts; Arabic numbers and letters along the left margin indicating retinal layers). *Uppermost sketch:* d, brush, and h, midget bipolar, delicate dendrites of first clinging to a cone pedicle b, some touching rod spherules a, while midget bouquet is in contact with lower face of same cone pedicle; natural group of five bipolars, h, d, f, e, and h, showing the presence of overlapping in diffuse varieties and the absence of such between midget bipolars; an individual synapse of a cone pedicle b and a midget bipolar h; synapse of a single flat-top bipolar f with a cone pedicle b and two rod spherules a, other structures not stained; two cone pedicles b, each related singly to a midget bipolar bouquet h, the interval between pedicles filled with rod spherules a, which remain unrelated to midget bipolars; in addition, a terminal twig of an axon fiber of a horizontal cell c clinging to the side of a cone pedicle. *Second sketch:* a compact group of cone pedicles b and rod spherules a synapsing with a single flat-top bipolar f; single flat-top bipolar f synapsing with a single rod spherule a, other details unstained; combined synapse of a single cone pedicle b with d and h bipolars, branches of first clinging to the sides of the pedicle, the bouquet of the latter to the lower face; a single flat-top bipolar f touching with one of its synaptic buttons a single rod spherule, other details unstained. *Third sketch:* two rod spherules a and two cone pedicles b, showing their topography in the outer plexiform layer; a polysynaptic midget bipolar h–h with two dendritic bouquets, each related to one cone pedicle b. *Fourth sketch:* part of a terminal ramification or teledendron of an axon fiber of a horizontal cell c with numerous twigs, each carrying a terminal swelling, some attached to the three rod spherules a, other details unstained; same, but with terminal buttons of horizontal cells attached to the sides of two cone pedicles b, with other details unstained. (*Cf.* Figs. 145, 146, 147, and colored Figs. 177, 178, 179.)

món y Cajal 1892–93, 1894, 1896, 1899, 1899–1904, 1904, 1909–11, 1919, 1923, 1933; Remak 1853; Renaut 1899; Rushton 1949, 1950; M. Schultze 1872; Schwalbe 1874; Tartuferi 1887; Tepljaschin 1894; Treviranus 1835–38; Valentin 1837; Wagner 1833.

SEC. 6. ASSOCIATION CELLS OF THE RETINA

1. General remarks.—The function of the retinal neurons so far discussed—the photoreceptors, bipolars, and ganglion cells described in the preceding pages—is obviously to react to physical "light" and to convey those reactions to the visual centers of the brain. There are other varieties of nerve cells in the retina whose function, speaking broadly, is to distribute photogenic impulses in the retinal tissue itself and thus in some way, either by facilitation or by inhibition or some similar influence, to modify the streams of impulses transmitted to the cerebrum. As far as is known, there are three categories of such neurons: the horizontal cells (*c*), the centrifugal bipolars (*i*), and the amacrine cells (*k*, *l*).

2. Horizontal cells (*c*).—These neurons were so named by S. Ramón y Cajal because of the horizontal spreading of their axon fibers (Figs. 141, 143, 146, 147, and colored Fig. 179). Their oval or irregularly spherical bodies, generally somewhat larger than the bipolars, are found in the one or two uppermost rows of the inner nuclear layer (*6-a* in Fig. 128). The scleral end of the cell is somewhat elongated into a short neck, from which a few short, thick, primary dendrites arise. Spreading in the inner zone of the outer plexiform layer (*5-c*), each of these dendrites divides into half-a-dozen or more minute preterminal and terminal branches which carry at the ends minute spherical varicosities (*c* in Fig. 141). These branchlets and varicosities are assembled into diminutive cups or baskets, not unlike the dendritic bouquets or rosettes of midget bipolars. In shape and size these baskets fit the vitreal faces of the cone pedicles (*b* in Fig. 141; *see also* Figs. 146, 147, and colored Fig. 179). Seen in flat view, a horizontal cell has the appearance of an octopus, with its basket-carrying dendrites spreading in all directions (*c* in Fig. 141).

The size of the cell body, the number of baskets to each cell, and the length of its dendrites vary considerably, depending upon the region.

The smallest cells, which have only a few short dendrites and not more than half-a-dozen baskets, are found in the central fovea. The cells increase gradually in size, in the length of dendrites, and in the number of baskets, until in the extra-areal periphery they attain giant size and have several dozens of baskets (thus in the left upper corner, in Fig. 141).

A single axis cylinder originates from the neck of the cell body or from one of its main dendrites. It spreads in a somewhat horizontal direction through the inner zone of the outer plexiform layer (*5-c*), occasionally dipping for a short distance into the inner nuclear layer. At a distance of several hundreds of microns the axon fiber splits repeatedly into a great number of secondary, tertiary, and further branches. The terminal twigs carry minute, approximately spherical swellings at their ends (lowermost sketch in Fig. 140). These together form a fan-shaped terminal arborization or teledendron, which spreads over a territory considerably larger in size than the dendritic spread of the same cell (several such complete arborizations are presented in Fig. 141). There is apparently neither definite nor prevalent direction or orientation; the axis cylinders crisscross in all directions. Both the dendrites and teledendrons in the adjoining cells partially overlap.

The synaptical relationships of the horizontal cells are relatively simple. The dendrites of each cell are in contact with the pedicles of a group of cones. No dendrites are related to the rods. The teledendrons of the axis cylinders, on the contrary, are synaptically related both to the cones and to the rods. Interpreted functionally, this relationship indicates that only the cones are able to activate the horizontal cells, which, in turn, stimulate, at some distance, a group of both rods and cones.

3. Centrifugal bipolar (*i*).—The body of this neuron variety is in the inner nuclear layer (Fig. 142). Its scleral, or outer, and its vitreal, or inner, expansions are oriented vertically; in this respect it closely resembles the expansions of the centripetal bipolars described in section 4 of this chapter. The expansions, however, differ in appearance. While in the centripetal varieties the morphological features indicate a functional polarity that signifies a flow of excitations from the photoreceptors to the ganglion cells, in the centrifugal bipolar the reverse seems to be the case.

The body and nucleus of the centrifugal bipolar is placed in the lower zones of the inner nuclear layer (*6-c* and *6-d*). The nucleus is

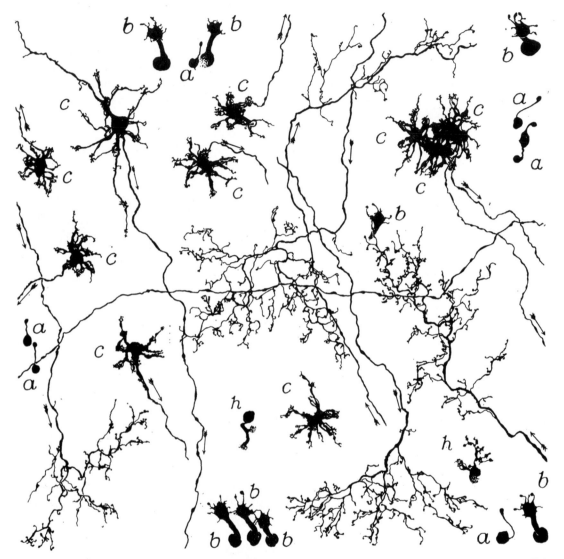

Fig. 141.—Details of structures making up the outer plexiform layer as seen in flat preparations cut parallel to retinal surface. Adult Rhesus Macaque, Golgi method. *Labeling: a*, rods, larger ends representing bodies or inner segments, smaller oval swellings terminal spherules; *b*, cones, their pedicles extending into barbel-like basal filaments, each of which carries a minute terminal varicosity; *c*, horizontal cells, each with several dendritic branches terminating in a cluster of minute twigs forming a basket to fit the lower end of a cone pedicle, and each cell giving rise to a single axon fiber; *h*, midget bipolars of the polysynaptic type with two bouquets, found in extra-areal periphery. Each axon fiber of horizontal cells, provided with spindle-shaped varicosities, terminates with an elaborate ramification or teledendron made up of numerous branches and terminal twigs, each carrying at its end a minute varicose swelling (*see* preceding figure). The arrows along the axons indicate the direction of the spread of the nervous impulses, from the cell body to the teledendron. In the left lower corner and close to lower margin of diagram, two complete teledendrons. In upper left corner a large horizontal cell from extra-areal periphery, other smaller cells from central area. In right upper corner a cluster of several horizontals, showing an overlapping of their ramifications.

usually somewhat larger than that of the centripetal bipolars.

The scleral process, which is a single, relatively thin fiber, with or without spindle-shaped varicosities, meanders between the nuclei of the sixth layer until it reaches the fifth layer. In the inner zone of this layer (5-c) it divides into a few short secondary branches. By further division into tiny twigs, each terminating with a small, occasionally a sizable, varicosity at the end, the fiber produces a terminal arborization. The fiber and its arborization appear as an axon with a teledendron. The terminal varicosities of this arborization touch the vitreal faces of the photoreceptors.

The vitreal expansion may be single, or there may be several main branches arising directly from the vitreal end of the cell body. The subdivision into numerous secondary and further branches produces a cluster resembling a dendritic ramification, the terminal twigs of which carry rather large varicosities, and all spread in the inner plexiform layer. The lowermost twigs of the vitreal arborization are in direct contact

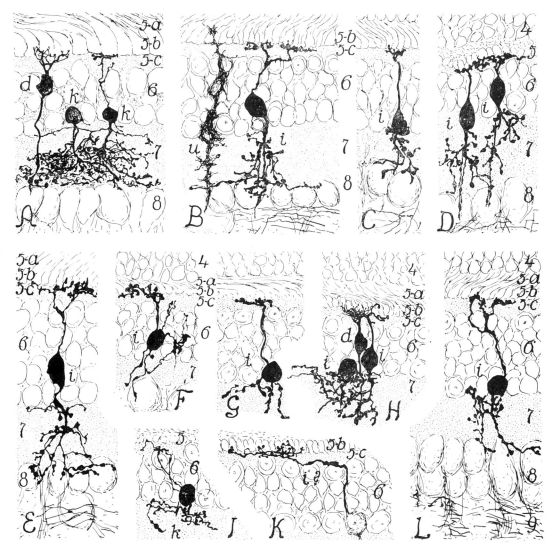

Fig. 142.—Various types of so-called "centrifugal bipolars," formerly identified with "amacrine cells," or elements without an axonal expansion. In centrifugal bipolars the axon-like process ends with a terminal ramification touching the lower extremities of rods and cones in zone 5-b of the outer plexiform layer. The descending expansions have the appearance of dendritic arborizations spreading in the inner plexiform layer (7), where they are in contact with bodies of ganglion cells (8). These cells have been interpreted by the author as dynamically polarized or oriented in the direction opposite to that of the "centripetal bipolars" d, e, f, and h, hence transmitting impulses from the ganglion cells back to the photoreceptors.

with the bodies of the upper most row of the ganglion cells of the eighth layer. The others, spreading in the plain substance of the inner plexiform layer, apparently undergo synapses with the dendritic expansions of the ganglion cells and of the centripetal bipolars.

The dynamic orientation of this neuron variety remains uncertain. The appearance of its expansions indicates a function opposite to that of the centripetal bipolars: transmission of influences from the ganglion cells, and possibly from the centripetal bipolars, back to the photoreceptors. Such influences may possibly be inhibitory. (*Cf. i* in Figs. 146, 147, and in colored Fig. 179.)

4. AMACRINE CELLS (*k, l*).—These neurons were so named by S. Ramón y Cajal because of

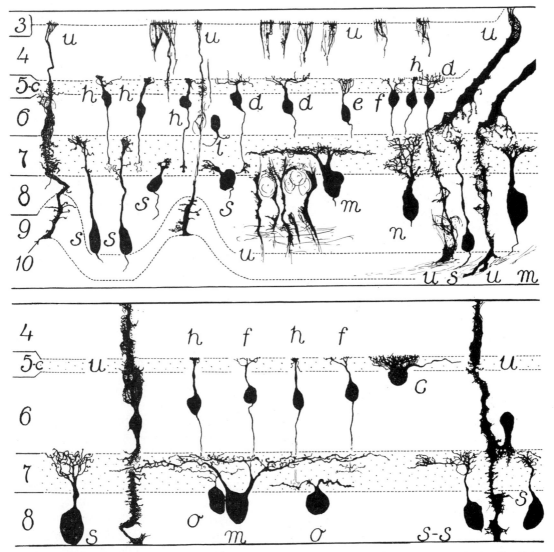

FIG. 143.—Elements of human retina stained with the Golgi method. Upper sketch from a six-month-old fetus; lower sketch from one eight months old. *Labeling: c*, horizontal cell; *d*, mop bipolars; *e*, brush bipolar; *f*, flat-top bipolar; *h*, midget bipolars; *l*, amacrine cell; *m*, parasol ganglion; *n*, shrub ganglion; *o*, small ganglion with horizontally running dendrites; *s*, midget ganglions; *s–s*, bisynaptic midget ganglion; *u*, radial fibers of Müller or their top ends, with so-called "fibrillar baskets." At the right, in upper sketch, radial fibers have already assumed a slanting course, as found in the fully developed fovea and close to it. Note characteristic features by which each neuron variety may be recognized, even though the neurons have still far to go to assume their final form. The notable feature at the earlier age is the "diffuse character" of neurons. Here many collateral branches, thus in *h* and *s*, are still present, which later become discarded. In the advanced age the neurons almost attain their final, streamlined form. These gradual changes are to be interpreted as a functional specialization of various types of neurons in the process of maturing, which appears to be the essence of growth. (*Cf.* following figure.)

the alleged absence of an axis cylinder (Fig. 142, left-hand cell labeled with *k*; Fig. 138, *l*). The cells are conspicuous because of their appearance, great numbers, and enigmatic connections and function.

The amacrine cell body (somewhat larger than that of other cells of the inner nuclear layer but considerably smaller than that of displaced ganglion cells) is in the lowermost zone of the inner nuclear layer (*6-d*). From it one or several main processes descend, which by repeated subdivision produce an "arborization" spreading in the inner plexiform layer.

The arborization is loose, composed of a few long, thin, smooth branches dividing but little, with only a few spindle-shaped varicosities and with terminal spherical and globular swellings. In the other amacrine cells, on the contrary, the arborization is dense, compact, made up of many branches and twigs carrying numerous swellings, buttons, spines, and varicosities of various shapes. The arborization, especially if large, spreads over the entire thickness of the inner plexiform layer, its lowermost twigs touching the bodies of the ganglion cells. In smaller amacrines the arborization, usually at the end of a single descending process, is small and spreads in only one or two of the several zones of the inner plexiform layer.

According to the appearance, size, and area in which the arborizations spread, several varieties of amacrine cells may be distinguished. Future investigation will show whether there is a morphological and functional basis for such subdivisions. In typical amacrines there is no scleral process. In many, however, the vitreal expansion resembles that of one type of centrifugal bipolars (*i*); and perhaps these amacrines are simply incompletely stained centrifugal bipolars.

We must also consider the possibility that some amacrines, especially the larger ones, may possess a horizontal axis cylinder spreading in the inner plexiform layer; fibers often found there which have the character of an axon suggest this (Figs. 146, 179, cell labeled *l*). If this supposition is substantiated, such neurons could be called the "internal horizontal or association cells"—the counterpart of the "external horizontal cells" (*c*) of the outer plexiform layer described in paragraph 2, of this section.

The amacrine cells are present in great numbers in all regions of the retina. They differ only in size—the smaller are found in the slope of the fovea and central area, and the larger ones in the extra-areal periphery.

References: Dogiel 1891–92, 1893, 1895; Kallius 1894; Marenghi 1900; Polyak 1941, 1948; S. Ramón y Cajal 1892–93 (1933), 1899–1904, 1909–11; Renaut 1899.

SEC. 7. EFFERENT OR EXOGENOUS FIBERS OF THE RETINA

The structures of the retina described in the preceding sections of this chapter are all instrumental in some way in the transmission of impulses from the photoreceptors to the brain. The visual pathway, accordingly, would be a one-way avenue. Under these circumstances, while the brain could be influenced by impulses arriving from the retina, there would be no means by which the action of the retina could in any way be modified by the central organ, the brain (except antidromically).

Certain fibers resembling terminal arborization of axons, apparently originating outside the retina, possibly in the midbrain, may be the structures through which the retina is influenced by the brain. The so-called exogenous or centrifugal fibers described by several investigators, notably by S. Ramón y Cajal (1909–11)

and by Bouin (1895), are of this type. They seem to terminate on or around the bodies of the amacrine cells placed in the lowermost zone of the inner nuclear layer (*6-d*).

This is most probable in the case of avian retinae. It is less certain in other Vertebrates, particularly Mammals. However, similar teledendron-like terminal arborizations have been found by this author in the retina of the Chimpanzee (*t*, in Figs. 137, 138, and colored Fig. 179). The retina may be directly influenced along such efferent fibers by the subcortical visual centers, e.g., the lateral geniculate nucleus (R. A. Pfeifer), the superficial gray layer of the superior colliculus (Edinger, Brouwer), the *ganglion isthmi* (Wallenberg 1898), or the hypothalamus (Weber 1945). A detailed study of this category of neurons in various Vertebrates, especially in Birds, where it is most promising, is sorely needed.

When, in Man, an eye has been missing for a long period of time, the optic nerve of that side shows complete degeneration and absence of all myelinated fibers when stained for myelin (*see* chap. VI, 2 [1], 4 [2]). Since it is probable that in the human optic nerve all fibers are myelinated (*see* chap. VI, 3 [2]), this could be interpreted to mean that there is no centrifugal fiber system. The evidence, however, is not conclusive, since there is possibly a retrograde degeneration of the centrifugal fibers whose terminals have been cut off.

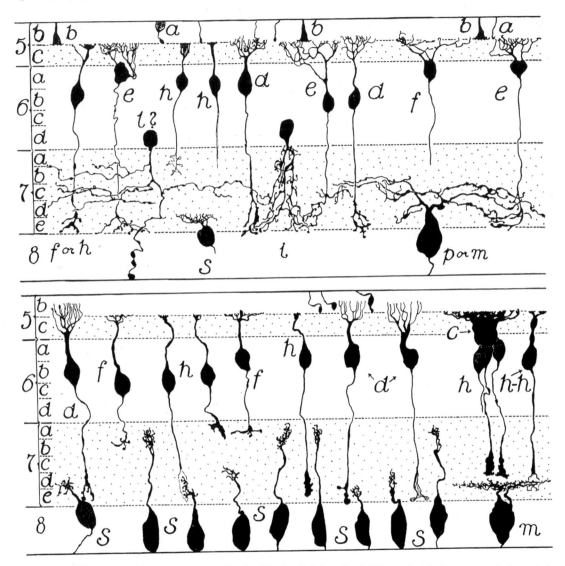

FIG. 144.—Elements of human retina stained with the Golgi method. Upper sketch from a newly born infant; lower sketch from an adult. *Labeling: a*, lower ends of rods; *b*, lower ends of cones with cone pedicles; *c*, horizontal cell accidentally stained with a group of bipolars, simulating Cajal's "giant bipolar"; *d*, mop bipolars; *cne* with an oversized Landolt fiber; *e*, brush bipolars; *f*, flat-top bipolars; *h*, individual midget bipolars; *h–h*, bisynaptic midget bipolar with two complete "bouquets"; *i*, typical so-called amacrine cell without an axon fiber; *l?*, a somewhat similar cell which apparently is a displaced ganglion or "Dogiel's cell," its axon fiber descending to the layer of optic nerve fibers; *m*, parasol ganglion; *p* or *m*, garland or parasol ganglion; *s*, midget ganglion cells. Note immature appearance of neurons in upper sketch, even though they have advanced further toward the adult form they attain in the lower sketch. When comparing mature human and simian retinae, their similarity becomes striking, the cell varieties, in fact, being identical, indicating a practically identical function of the retina in all advanced Primates. (*Cf.* preceding figure.)

References: Arey 1916; Bouin 1895; Brouwer 1936; Cattaneo 1922; Dogiel 1895; Monakow 1914; Elsberg & Spotnitz; R. A. Pfeifer 1930; Polyak 1941, 1948; S. Ramón y Cajal 1889, 1892–93 (1933), 1894, 1895, 1899–1904, 1903, 1909–11; Rozemeyer & Stolte 1931; Wallenberg 1898; A. Weber 1945.

SEC. 8. THE FUNCTIONAL GROUPING OF RETINAL NEURONS

1. GENERAL REMARKS CONCERNING FACTORS WHICH DETERMINE THE FUNCTIONAL RESPONSE OF THE RETINA.—The photoreceptors and other nerve cells of the retina, representing more than a dozen distinct neuron varieties, are woven into an intricate and stable tissue pattern (Figs. 146, 147, and colored Figs. 177, 178, 179). This pattern, it must be assumed, in its gross features and in all its numerous details, is a structural expression of functions, of which the constituent neurons of the retina are carriers. It should then be possible, by piecing together the facts which have already been discussed, to single out from the total pattern the systems of neurons that are likely to form various channels along which dynamical changes are propagated. This may show which of the neuron relationships are of primary importance and which are purely accidental, in no way instrumental in generating, propagating, and transmitting specific nervous impulses. (*See* chap. IX on the organization of nervous tissue.)

The criterion by which we may determine functional relationships is synaptical contacts, through which alone these relationships are established. Since, however, all retinal neurons are directly or indirectly connected with one another through their synapses, it is further necessary to assume that their varying modes of reaction are also regulated by the specific responsiveness intrinsic to each neuron variety, in addition to the variation in quality and intensity of the external stimulus, physical light.

With this in view, several neuron systems may be singled out from the permanent retinal structural pattern, depending on whether one or the other, or both, of the two distinct photo-receptor varieties—the rods and the cones—are put into action by light stimulus.

2. ROD SYSTEM (*a* & *def* & *mnoprs*).—The rod system of the retinal neurons (Fig. 145, sketch *A*) is represented by the rods (*a*), by all mop bipolars (*d*), by some brush and flat-top bipolars (*e, f*), and apparently by all ganglion cells (*m, n, o, p, r, s,* in our diagram symbolized by *m* and *s*). Excluded from it are the cones (*b*), midget bipolars (*h*), horizontal cells (*c*), and centrifugal bipolars (*i*); (*cf.* Figs. 146, 147, and colored Figs. 177, 178, 179). Its functional units are composed of a group of rods, a group of diffuse bipolars synaptically related to them, and a group of ganglion cells related to the diffuse bipolars. The localizing value of impulses mediated by this system, even though its conductors are arranged parallel to one another, is somewhat restricted because of partial overlapping. The rod system may be thought of as embodied under conditions when the high-threshold cones cease to be responsive because of decreased intensity of stimulus.

3. CONE SYSTEM (*b* & *defh* & *mnoprs*).—The cone system of the retinal neurons (Fig. 145, sketch *D*) is represented by the cones (*b*), by various bipolars, including the midget variety (*d, e, f, h*), and by all ganglion cell varieties (*m, n, o, p, r, s,* symbolized by *m* and *s*). Only in the rodless central portion of the fovea do the mop bipolars (*d*) appear to be missing (colored Fig. 177, middle sketch). The constituent functional units of the cone system are made up of the same neurons as in the rod system, with the addition of midget bipolars, except that the photoreceptors are the cones instead of the rods. The localizing value of the impulses mediated by the cone system is limited as in the rod system, and for the same reason: the multiple and partly overlapping synaptical relationships of its polysynaptical constituent neuron varieties (all except *h* and *s*).

In the rodless central territory of the fovea the modified cone system (without *d*) seems to be present as a permanent structural arrangement. Outside the rodless foveal center the cone system is present as a functional potentiality, realized only in case the rod function is eliminated or suppressed (color Fig. 177, lateral sketches).

4. Combined rod and cone system (*ab & defh & mnoprs*, latter symbolized by *m* and *s*) and "pure" or "private" cone system (*b & h & s*).—The first of these two systems of retinal neurons is realized under conditions when both rods and cones are simultaneously activated

(Fig. 145, sketch *H*). In this case all neuron varieties related to the two types of photoreceptors participate functionally, forming a "combined rod and cone system." On the other hand, the individual synapses between the cones and midget bipolars and between the latter and the midget ganglion cells suggest that under certain dynamical conditions the cone impulses may be restricted to these neu-

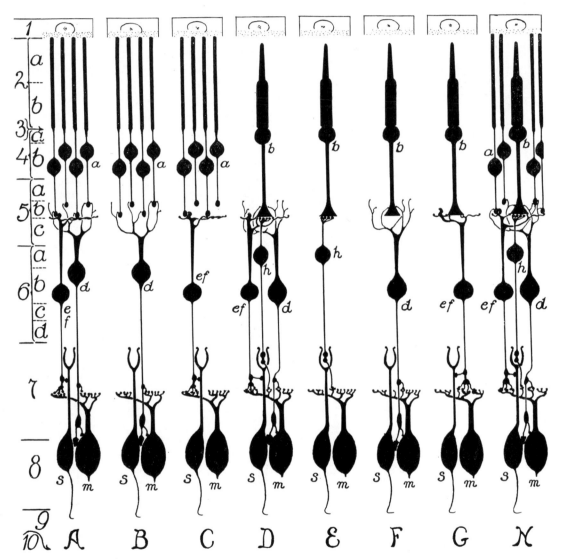

Fig. 145.—Grouping of neurons of the primate retina into functional systems. *Labeling: A*, rod system; *B*, reduced rod system with only the mop bipolar as an intermediary link; *C*, same with only the brush or flat-top bipolar linking rods to the ganglion cells; *D*, cone system, complete, with rods omitted and with all bipolar varieties linking cones with the ganglion cells; *E*, reduced or pure cone system, with rod and cone bipolars omitted, the cones linked to the ganglion cells by the midget bipolars alone; *F* and *G*, constituent elements of the cone system, with either the mop, brush, or flat-top bipolars as intermediary links; *H*, mixed or complete rod and cone system as actually found in the normal duplex primate retina. In this diagram the parasol ganglion (*m*) symbolizes all so-called "diffuse" ganglion varieties (*m, n, o, p, r*), while *s* is the midget ganglion closely related to the cones. (For details *see* sec. 8, this chapter.)

rons, or that a portion of the cone excitation may be transmitted as a distinct dynamic entity through these monosynaptical links (*b & h & s* chain of neurons), while the remaining cone excitation, if any, may pass over to the polysynaptic bipolars and ganglion cells (*b & def &*

mnops) and, in addition, to the horizontal cells (*c*), centrifugal bipolars, and amacrines (*i, k, l*).

The set of monosynaptic neurons (*b & h & s*) may, therefore, be considered a "private," or "pure cone," system of the retinal conductor neurons (Fig. 145, *E*, minus diffuse ganglions

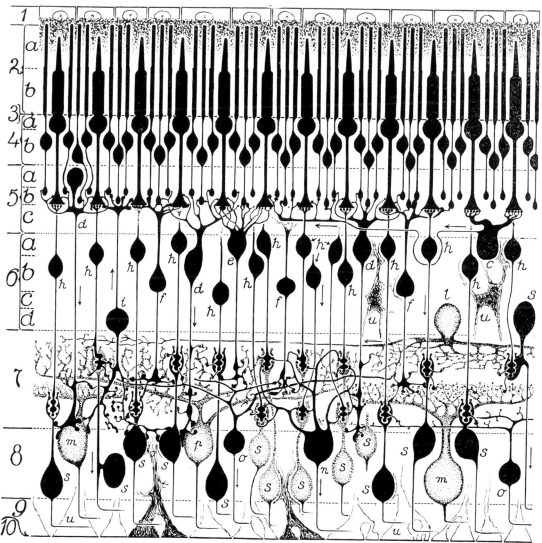

Fɪɢ. 146.—Schematic presentation of neuron varieties of primate retina and their synaptic relationships, with the essential features preserved, based on the Golgi method of staining. Layers and zones, indicated along the left margin, same as in Fig. 128. In the upper part of the diagram are photoreceptors, both rods (*a*) and cones (*b*), the bacillary parts sticking into the pigment layer, the inner fibers of the rods terminating with round spherules, and those of the cones, with conical pedicles, which form zone *5-b* of the outer plexiform layer. Here the synaptical contacts are made with upper or dendritic expansions of horizontal cells (*c*), along which the impulses spread in adjoining parts of the retina, and with the bipolars of centripetal varieties (*d, e, f, h*), along which they pass to the inner plexiform layer, where synaptical contacts are established with the ganglion cells (*m, n, o, p, s*). From the ganglions arise nerve fibers which, as the optic nerve, enter the brain. Other types of neurons, called "centrifugal bipolars" (*i*), may condition photoreceptors under the influence of the ganglion cells, hence in a direction opposite to that of the centripetal bipolars (*d, e, f, h*). There may be still other neuron varieties whose connections are lateral, spreading in the inner plexiform layer (*l*). This indicates that the primate retina is a complex organ whose function is not only to react to physical light as an external stimulus but also to sort the generated impulses in many ways before they are further transmitted to the brain. (*Cf.* Fig. 147, and colored Figs. 177, 178, 179.)

symbolized by *m*). It is a system organized strictly on a spatial principle, most perfectly expressed in the central fovea, and progressively less so in the para- and perifoveal parts of the central area, with further roughening in the extra-areal periphery. In the axial region of the retina and in its portion of the visual pathway, the private cone system of the conductor neurons makes possible the transmission to the brain of an impulse originating in a single cone as a single dynamic entity, evoking a very restricted subjective photic experience.

5. Intraretinal association or integration system.—This system of neurons, as far as it could be identified, is represented by the horizontal cells (*c*) and by the various amacrine cells, including the centrifugal bipolars (*i, k, l*). The synaptical relationships of the horizontal cells indicate a lateral diffusion of cone influences upon more or less distant groups of photoreceptors, both rods and cones (Figs. 146, 147). A similar diffusion of rod influences appears to be not feasible anatomically. A lateral spreading of influences through the association "amacrine cells" (*k, l*), provided that their axons spread laterally in the inner plexiform layer, also seems to be possible. The function of the centrifugal bipolar (*i*) would be the diffusion of influences from the ganglion cells (*m, n, o, p, s*) and centripetal bipolars (*d, e, f, h*) upon the photoreceptors (*a, b*). Finally, if the presence of exogenous fibers of extraretinal origin (*t*) were substantiated, the means by which brain influences could reach the retina would be identified.

6. Dependence of retinal response upon an interplay of anatomical, physiological, and physical factors.—On purely anatomical grounds it is apparent that bipolars of diffuse varieties (*d, e, f*) serve as links in both the rod and the cone systems (Figs. 146, 147). For the same reason, the five or more ganglion cell varieties (*m, n, o, p, r, s*) must be considered the constituents of either system. Whether these bipolars and ganglions function in the capacity of mediators of rod or of cone influences or as a "common pathway" or in a selection or combination of influences may depend, in the first place, on whether one or the other photoreceptor variety, or both, are activated by an external physical stimulus.

In the case of a simultaneous stimulation of both kinds of photoreceptors, a complex situation ensues wherein the neurons in question serve as a common pathway. In this case relative rod and cone emphasis in the total response of the conductor neurons may be determined by less conspicuous secondary factors, such as the relative intensity of the initial rod and cone process, the "quality" of a given physical stimulus, such as the wave length, the varying physiological state of the nervous substance following stimulation, or the degree of "fatigue," and many other external and internal factors yet to be determined.

The problem of interpreting the sets of retinal neurons so far known in terms of the basic functional components of the phenomenon of vision—the perception of light, color, and space—is the theme treated in chapter IX of this book.

References: Brooks & Eccles 1947; Chabrun 1926; Eccles 1936; Granit 1947, 1950; Kolmer & Lauber 1936; D. D. Michaels 1952; Motokawa 1942, 1945, 1949; R. W. Pickford 1947, 1951; H. Piéron 1945; Pirenne & Denton 1953; Polyak 1941, 1948, 1949; S. Ramón y Cajal 1892–93 (1933), 1909–11, 1923; J. Roux 1898; Seidel 1919.

SEC. 9. SUPPORTING STRUCTURES OF THE RETINA

1. General remarks.—The tissue of the retina, like that of the brain from which it phylogenetically and ontogenetically derives, consists essentially of two components. One is represented by the parenchyma proper—the nerve cells and their expansions; these are the carriers of its specific function. The other constituent is nonspecific in the strict sense, forming, as it does, an appropriate stroma or framework within which the nerve cells and their expansions are lodged. This supporting retinal tissue, as in the brain and in the spinal cord, is the neuroglia, which is also mainly of ectodermal origin. The retinal neuroglia is chiefly represented by the sustentacular cells called "radial fibers," also known as "Müller's fibers," after

H. Müller who discovered them (1851), and to a lesser extent by the accessory neuroglia. (For details and additional figures *see* Polyak, *The Retina*.)

2. Radial fibers (*u*).—These structures, peculiar to the retina, are considered to be modified astrocytes of neuroglia found elsewhere in the central nervous system. They form the bulk of the retinal supporting framework (Figs. 142, 143, 146, 147).

Each radial or Müller's fiber is a cell with a body, inclosing a nucleus, and its expansions. The nuclei of most radial fibers, conspicuous

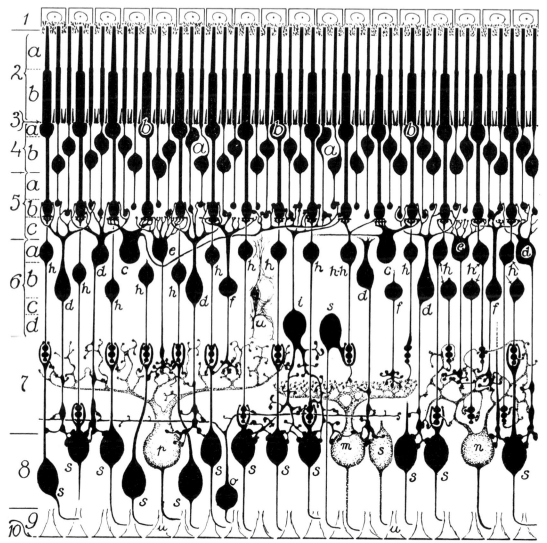

Fig. 147.—Another schematic presentation of constituent neurons of primate retina and their synaptical relationships. Note the multiple relationships of each neuron variety, making it possible for additional so-called functional and dynamic factors to modulate in many ways the reaction elicited in the retinal structures. As an example, an impulse generated in the first cone in the left upper corner, if stimulated by a restricted ray of light, would be transmitted directly to the first midget bipolar from the left (*h*), and through it to the first midget ganglion (*s*). Another impulse generated in the same cone would pass over to the first mop bipolar from the left (*d*), and further to the first two midget ganglions (*s*). The impulse passing through the first midget ganglion (*s*) would necessarily be a cone impulse and would possess a localizing value much better defined than that passing through the first mop bipolar (*d*), since the latter is also a "common path" for the second cone from the left, as well as for a group of rods, being, in addition, related to a diffuse group of ganglion cells (first and second *s* and *p*), hence having a much more diluted "local signature"; and so forth. In summary, the retina is an ingeniously contrived mechanism capable of reacting in many locally and qualitatively different ways to the variety of photic stimuli playing upon its photoreceptor surface. (*Cf.* Fig. 146 and colored Figs. 177, 178, 179.)

even in routinely stained preparations because of their darker hue and angular shape, are located in Man in the third zone of the inner nuclear layer (*6-c; see* Figs. 128, 129). The zone varies, however, with the vertebrate or primate species. A few nuclei are found displaced in the seventh, eighth, or ninth layers.

Enveloped in scanty cytoplasm, the cell body extends from the nucleus in the shape of a narrow pillar, traversing the thickness of the retina bounded by the two limiting membranes (*3* and *10*). The substance of the body incloses one or more thick fibers, whose broadened scleral and vitreal ends, in the aggregate, form the limiting membranes. The cytoplasm, enveloping the main pillar-like fibers and the finer fibers imbedded in it, expands into a multitude of sheets, lamellae, and excrescences, which, by joining with the similar lamellar expansions of the adjoining radial cells, form a complicated meshwork and system of cavities. The details of this latticework vary from layer to layer and even from zone to zone, depending upon the character of the nervous parenchyma they have to support.

The outer limiting membrane (*3*), as mentioned previously (*see* sec. 2 [4], this chapter), is perforated by countless openings, smaller for the rods and larger for the cones. Scleralad to this membrane, minute needle- or spinelike processes stretch along the base of each inner rod and cone segment (visible along line *3*, in Fig. 143). These reinforcements lie imbedded in delicate sheaths, individually enveloping each photoreceptor—the "fibrillar baskets."

In the outer nuclear layer (*4*) the delicate neuroglial lamellae form a dainty honeycomb of as many sockets as there are cell bodies to envelop. The spaces of the larger shells and sockets hold the cone bodies, the smaller ones those of the rods. In this way each body of a photoreceptor is incased in its own individual compartment, separating and insulating it from the adjoining rod and cone bodies.

The inner and outer fibers of the rods and cones are also enveloped in neuroglial sheaths which insure perfect insulation. This is especially apparent in the central area, where the outer zone of the fifth layer, Henle's "outer fiber layer" (*5-a*), is quite thick. Here the neuroglial sheaths and fibers, in fact, produce as

many tubes as there are nerve fibers (one such tubelike sheath is schematically presented in Fig. 128). The position of these tubes, conforming to the position of the inner rod and cone fibers which they insulate, is oblique in the central area and vertical or nearly so outside it.

In the middle zone of the outer plexiform layer (*5-b*) the supporting and insulating husks or sockets are very small, as are the rod spherules and cone pedicles that make up this zone. The terminal swellings of the photoreceptors, however, are not completely incased, since their vitreal and parts of their lateral sides, where the expansions of bipolars and horizontal cells are in contact with them, are left free.

In the inner zone of the fifth layer (*5-c*) the feltwork of fine neuroglial fibrils resembles a delicate plexus, except for the thick main radial pillars passing through it. Similar plexus-like felting is present in the seventh and ninth layers.

In the sixth and eighth layers (*6* and *8*) the arrangement is similar to that in the fourth layer, except that the sockets are larger. In the layer of optic nerve fibers (*9*) the conically expanded inner ends produce numerous horizontally placed sheets and tubes incasing the fibrous elements. The inner limiting membrane (*10*), finally, appears as a solid, continuous sheet, even though, in reality, it is composed of juxtaposed broadened inner ends of Müller's radial fibers.

The radial fibers and the supporting and insulating framework they produce are present in essentially the same form everywhere in the retinal membrane. In the central fovea and area they are more delicate, made up of finer sheets, narrower tubes, and smaller sockets, altogether forming a finer framework, within which the smaller but more numerous nerve cells and fibers are incased.

3. ACCESSORY NEUROGLIA (*v, x, y*).—The accessory neuroglia of the retina is represented by several elements.

The *neuroglial amacrine cells* or *interstitial spongioblasts* (*v*) of W. Müller (1874) resemble the *k*-variety of the amacrines in the location of their bodies in the innermost zone of the inner nuclear layer (*6-d*) and in the form and size of their expansions, which spread in the inner plexiform layer (in Fig. 143, one such cell may be seen in the right lower corner, still connected to its radial fiber).

The *astrocytes* (*x*) are mostly found in the inner layers near and in the optic papilla. They resemble the astrocytes elsewhere in all respects, except that they are smaller. Also, two varieties among them may be distinguished: *fibrous astrocytes*, with relatively long and smooth processes, and *protoplasmic astrocytes*, whose expansions are covered with numerous minute, raglike, cytoplasmic sheets and appendages. Their true nature is revealed by the presence of "sucker feet," with which they are attached either to the typical radial fibers or to the capillaries or to larger blood vessels.

The third element, the *microglia* (*y*) of Río-Hortega, with all the features characterizing it elsewhere—a minute body containing an oblong nucleus and a few contorted and twisted expansions covered with a small number of short needle-like spines—is present in the seventh layer. The oligodendroglial cells, in Primates, seem to be absent as a normal structure.

4. FUNCTIONAL SIGNIFICANCE OF SUPPORT-ING RETINAL STRUCTURES.—The supporting neuroglial framework formed by Müller's radial fibers and by the accessory neuroglia produces in the retina, in the aggregate, an extremely complicated "honeycomb," with countless minute spaces, slits, interstices, tubes, shells, and husks, into each of which a cell body, an axis cylinder, a dendrite, a branch, or a twig of a nerve cell is wrapped.

The only localities where the insulating neuroglial sheaths are absent are parts of the outer plexiform layer (*5-b*) and parts of the inner plexiform layers (*7*), the two "synaptical fields" of the retina, where a direct contact between the neurons is established. This arrangement apparently insures complete insulation of each neuron and guarantees it against interference by other neurons. The impulses, in this way, are forced to spread along the channels formed by the substance of the neurons and the synaptical contacts.

The neuroglial framework of the retina serves, accordingly, as a mechanical support and a dynamic insulator, holding in place and keeping separated the nervous structures. In this way the neuroglia preserves the countless anatomical and functional relationships as they have developed during the period of embryonic growth and postembryonic maturing process. Without such a supporting and insulating system, the propagation and proper distribution of infinitesimally delicate dynamic changes, varied in quality and intensity, which are called "impulses," through the complex retinal structures during a process of photoreception would be impossible.

But, beyond these two functions—mechanical support and dynamic insulation—it is possible and even probable that the neuroglial structures perform other essential functions concerned with normal metabolism, as they also do in various pathological processes.

A problem closely related to the foregoing concerns the relationship of the neuroglial cells to one another. The indications, in this respect, do not favor the concept of a continuous syncytium advocated by Hardesty (1904), Held (1904, 1927, 1929), Holzer (1923), Metz & Spatz (1924), Franz (1927), Akkeringa (1934), and partly also by Alzheimer (1910). Observations tend rather to support the idea that the neuroglial cells, like the nerve cells proper, also preserve a measure of independence as structural elements, a view propounded by S. Ramón y Cajal (1897, 1909–11, 1913, 1932), Achúcarro (1915), Río-Hortega (1916, 1928, 1932), Joseph (1928), *et al.* Even so, in a fully mature retinal tissue, under normal conditions, the honeycomb produced by the supporting structures appears to be mechanically sealed. The insulation of the nervous parenchyma within the retinal honeycomb, however, is only relative, since a means of free exchange of fluids and of the many constituent chemicals dissolved in these fluids must be fully preserved.

5. HISTORY OF INVESTIGATIONS OF RETINAL SUPPORTING STRUCTURES.—The elements of the supporting tissue of the retina were previously observed by Fontana (1782), but were definitely described by H. Müller (1851, 1853, 1856–57), Koelliker (1852, 1854), and Remak (1854).

M. Schultze (1866, 1867, 1869, 1872, 1873) was first to give a comprehensive analysis of the

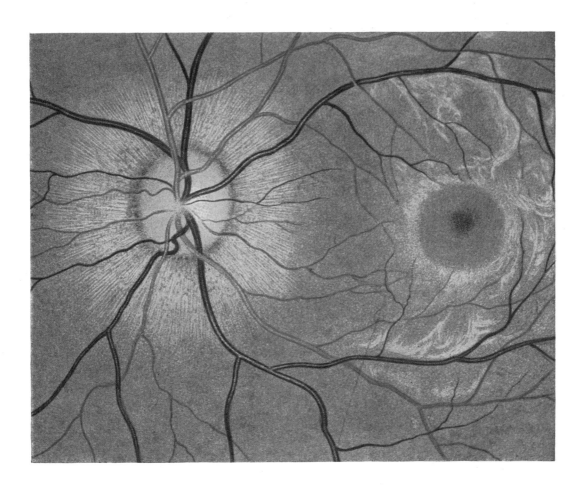

Fig. 148—Fundus or interior of the left eye of a dark-haired English girl 20 years old. Mottled chorioid stroma indistinctly seen in the background. Translucent optic nerve fibers may be traced for a short distance beyond the disk. A circular foveal excavation, encircled by a reflex ring, encloses a cherry-red center, the foveola. A reflex along the arteries (bright red) and veins (dark red) visible. (From G. L. Johnson, *Philos Trans. Roy. Soc. London*, ser. *B*, vol. 194, pl. 1, year 1901.)

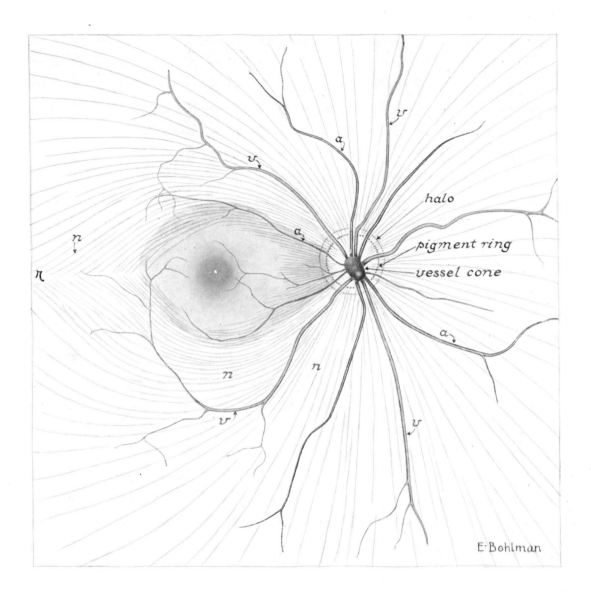

Fig. 149—Fundus or interior of the right eye of a Philippine Tarsier (*Tarsius carbonarius* or *T. philippinensis*) seen ophthalmoscopically in red-free light. Optic papilla encircled by a halo and a pigmented ring, with arteries (*a*, red) and veins (*v*, blue) radiating in all directions. Translucent vessel cone protruding from the papillar center. Bundles of optic fibers (*n*) show a radial arrangement on nasal side (right), and arching above and below the central fovea on the temporal side (left), with a meeting line or *raphé* (*r*) along the horizontal meridian. Macula or yellow spot is represented by a large pear-shaped area with its handle at the papilla, and its expanded portion embracing the foveal excavation, with finer pigmentation and deeper orange tint in the fovea. The fovea is relatively small, its diameter about one-half of that of the papilla. A faint dot-like light reflex indicates the very center of the foveal depression. Note the size of the yellow pigmented area many times larger than the fovea. The central area and fovea are well supplied with blood vessels that approach the fovea, which remains free from visible vessels. (Water-color painting from a sketch made during life by Dr. Frank Stuart Ryerson of Detroit.)

retinal supporting framework; but only the analytical investigations of S. Ramón y Cajal (1889, 1891, 1892–93, 1909–11) clarified its essential features. The neuroglia of the human retina, especially of the central area, found a competent student in Dogiel (1893).

The retinal neuroglia was examined by modern methods by López Enríquez (1926, 1948), Marchesani (1926, 1927), Kolmer (1930, 1936), Díaz (*see* Balbuena 1930), Bulač (1931), and Akkeringa (1934).

Some of their views, e.g., those concerning the structure and the relationships of the outer limiting membrane (Fortin 1926, 1930), on the nonsupporting character of Müller's radial fibers and their peculiar role in photoreception (Police 1928, 1932) and the presence of Held's "universal network" or continuous glial-neuro-fibrillar *syncytium* (Akkeringa 1934) are at variance with the available evidence.

References: Achúcarro 1915; Akkeringa 1934; Alzheimer 1910; W. Andrew 1943; Andrew & Ashworth 1945; Arey 1932; Bach 1895; Bulač 1931; Dejean 1926; Díaz (*see* Balbuena 1930); Dogiel 1893; Dougherty 1944; Felix Fontana 1782 (1795); Fortin 1926, 1930; Greeff 1894, 1899 (1900); Griño 1948; Hardesty 1904; Held 1904, 1927, 1929; Holzer 1923; Hosch 1895; Joseph 1928; Kallius 1894; Koelliker 1854; Kolmer 1930; Kolmer & Lauber 1936; Leboucq 1908–9; López Enríquez 1926, 1927, 1930, 1948; Marchesani 1926, 1927, 1930; Marenghi 1900; Menner 1930; Merkel 1870; Metz & Spatz 1924; H. Müller 1851, 1853, 1856–57, 1872; W. Müller 1874; Penfield 1928, 1932; L. Pines 1899; Police 1928, 1932; Polyak 1941, 1948; S. Ramón y Cajal 1889, 1891, 1892–93 (1933), 1897, 1899–1904, 1909–11, 1913, 1920, 1925, 1928, 1929, 1932; Remak 1854; Río-Hortega 1916, 1932, 1941; M. Schultze 1866, 1867, 1869, 1872; Schwalbe 1874; Serra 1922; Silver 1942; Stricht 1922; Tartuferi 1887.

SEC. 10. OPTIC PAPILLA OR DISK, CENTRAL AREA AND FOVEA, YELLOW SPOT OR MACULA, AND SERRATED MARGIN OR ORA SERRATA OF THE RETINA

1. GENERAL REMARKS ON THE LOCAL VARIATION OF THE RETINAL STRUCTURE.—The structure of the retina proper is not exactly the same in all its expanse but shows considerable regional variation, depending upon the special functional requirements of a particular locality (Fig. 125). Generally, the refinement of structures is greatest in the region where the visual axis touches the membrane (Fig. 129, *I, II*). Conversely, the internal makeup is less refined in the extensive territory outside the axial region, with the crudest structures present along its anterior boundary, the *ora serrata* (*V, VI*). The gradual structural perfection toward the axis or functional center of the retina is expressed, on the one hand, in a numerical increase in the nerve cells of all varieties, including the photoreceptors, and, on the other hand, in decreased dimensions of the individual cellular and fibrous elements. In this way, spatially much more restricted and more delicately diversified reactions of the structures to minute photic stimuli are possible in the center than in the extra-axial periphery, where the reactions necessarily are of a cruder nature.

Five especially differentiated localities are customarily distinguished in the retina of Man and other Primates: optic papilla or disk (*op*); central area and *macula lutea* or yellow spot; central fovea or central depression, dimple, or pit (*cf*); extra-areal periphery, representing most of the retinal expanse; and the narrow *ora serrata, margo undulato-dentatus*, the serrated, undulating, or dentate margin (*os*) in Subhuman Primates, called the *ora terminalis* (*ot* in Fig. 126).

2. OPTIC PAPILLA, DISK, HEAD, COLLICULUS, OR "HILLOCK" OF OPTIC NERVE.—The spot where the optic nerve is implanted in the eyeball, seen from the retinal side, appears as a more or less circular area nasal to the axial center of the retina (Figs. 148, 149, 165–70). It is composed of optic nerve fibers streaming in from the entire territory of the retina and gathered at the point where they leave the eyeball (*see* chap. VI, 2 [2–5] on the course of optic nerve fibers). After passing through the cribriform or sievelike membrane, a portion of the sclera provided with numerous perforations, the bundles of nerve fibers are assembled into a trunk, the optic nerve (Fig. 125, *on*).

Only the nerve fibers, blood vessels, and neuroglia of the retinal structures are present in the papilla; the nerve cells, photoreceptors, and pigment epithelium are absent. Since the chorioid membrane with its pigment-carrying melanophores and blood vessels is also absent, the color of the living papilla is a light shade of pink caused by the blood contained in its moderately developed vascular network.

Several large blood vessels, branches of the central retinal artery and vein, emerge from the tissue of the papilla, usually from a slight dimple, the physiological excavation, and spread in various directions (*see* chap. X, 2 [3], and Figs. 148, 149, 165–70). Since the photosensitive rods and cones are absent in the papilla and since the nerve fibers are insensitive to light, the optic papilla is blind. It corresponds in the field of view to the "blind spot" of Mariotte, situated on the temporal side of the visual axis and not far from it.

3. CENTRAL AREA AND MACULA OR YELLOW SPOT.—The central area of the retina is a specially differentiated locality around the visual axis, where the ganglion cells of the eighth layer (*8*) are accumulated in several tiers (Fig. 129, *II, III;* also Figs. 127, 128). In the human retina the nasal boundary of the central area is at the temporal margin of the papilla. On the temporal side, along the horizontal meridian, the central area extends almost an equal distance beyond the foveal center, its total diameter measuring approximately 6 mm. Ophthalmoscopically, the central area roughly corresponds to a central circular territory encircled by the larger blood vessels.

The central area is further characterized by the presence of a peculiar yellow pigment permeating all layers below the outer nuclear layer (*6, 7, 8, 9*), the "yellow spot" or *macula lutea* or *macula flava*, or simply *macula* (Fig. 149). It is probable that the outer plexiform layer or parts thereof, like the thick outer fiber layer of Henle or zone *5-a*, also contain this pigment in the living, as Segal (1951) indicated, but this should be verified in quite fresh material. A careful ophthalmoscopic study in red-free illumination may also help solve this problem.

The pigment of the yellow spot is not granular or crystalline, but diffuse, of the character of a "lake" (*lac, lakh*). In the living, ophthalmoscopically, it is not noticeable except in red-free light (A. Vogt, Koeppe). (*See* sec. 11 [1], this chapter, for discovery of the yellow spot.)

In a freshly opened human or simian eye the pigmented area is visible as a yellow patch temporal to the optic papilla. It may best be seen after a freshly dissected retina has lost its natural transparency and has assumed a whitish coloring because of the coagulation of the protoplasm of its cells and fibers. The color is a clear canary or lemon yellow with a slight tinge of green (the orange-yellow color of the fovea seen ophthalmoscopically during life is caused by the chorioid pigment seen through the thinned-out fovea; *see* following section). A small ring-shaped area corresponding to the ridge surrounding the central fovea is most intensively pigmented. The center of the foveal depression, called the *foveola*, itself is almost colorless. Toward the periphery of the central area the coloring fades rapidly. After death and under the action of histological fixatives, especially alcohol, the pigmentation soon disappears.

Chemically, the pigment of the yellow spot has been identified as a hydroxy-carotenoid protein or xanthophyll, probably lutein or leaf xanthophyll (Wald 1945, 1945–46, 1949). In the opinion of Segal (1951) the macular pigment consists of carotenoids identical with the photolytic products of visual purple, apparently mostly of the type of transient orange of Lythgoe and of the transient or indicator yellow. (*Cf.* also E. Hanström 1940.)

The probable function of the macular pigment is to filter out much of the blue segment of the visible spectrum, thus protecting the low-threshold rods of the central area, especially of the fovea, from the dazzling effect of strong daylight. The yellow pigment, together with the ventral layers, is practically absent in the very center, the foveola, coextensive with the external fovea, where only high-threshold cones are present and no such protection is required. The advantage of this arrangement is to preserve the scotopic rod system around the visual axis during the photopic condition for ready use in a rapid transition to scotopic vision. (*See also* Berger & Segal 1949; Segal 1951.)

In this connection it would be of interest to examine ophthalmoscopically and histologically, for the presence of a pigmented spot, those species which have only an incipient fovea or none at all but have a distinct central area definitely used for fixation and binocular sterescopic vision. An easily procurable animal with such a retina is the Domestic Cat, and probably the Dog, and possibly many other species with primarily nocturnal habits.

A well-formed, though small, fovea, together with a large pigmented yellow spot, was found ophthalmoscopically, in red-free light, in the which the foveal center, containing only cones, alone remains free from yellow pigmentation. (*See* chap. XIV, 12.)

The human retina attains its maximum thickness of about 400–500 microns close to the center of the central area, just outside the foveal depression. This is chiefly caused by great accumulation of nerve cells and to a smaller extent because of the lengthening of photoreceptors and fibrous elements, especially in zone *5-a*, of this locality (Henle's layer). According to an

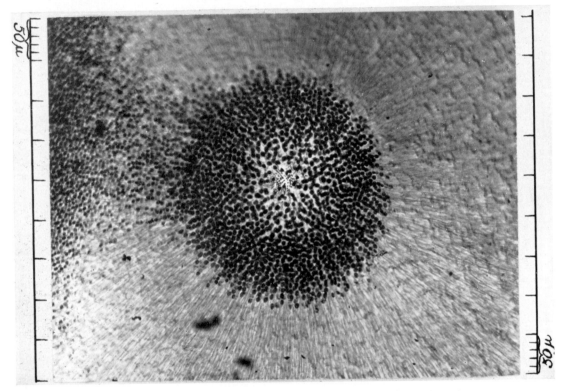

Fig. 150.—Microphotograph of a flat section through the central fovea of the retina of a Rhesus Macaque. In the center a circular accumulation of nuclei of the outer nuclear layer, with a few centralmost cones in the very center, indicating the deepest portion of the outer fovea (*cf.* Fig. 161, *middle sketch*). Bundles of the outer fiber layer of Henle, or zone *5-a*, of the central area radiating in all directions, to hook up with respective parts of the inner nuclear layer displaced laterally, owing to the formation of a foveal depression at the expense of the inner retinal layers. In the upper left corner the central nuclei are continuous with the more distant nuclei of the outer nuclear layer caused by an uneven spread of the specimen. Hematoxylin and phloxin stain, actual magnification in microns indicated along lateral margins.

Philippine Tarsier. The pigmented area apparently also includes the foveal center (*see* colored Fig. 149). The screening-off of the very center of the fovea by yellow pigment, in order to reduce the dazzling effect of strong daylight in the Tarsier, a strictly nocturnal species with no identifiable cones, is to be expected, in contrast with the diurnal Rhesus Macaque and Man, in approximate estimate, half of all ganglion cells of the retina reside in this restricted territory. The proportion may also be much the same in the case of the cones. For this reason, in spite of the much reduced size of the cells, the thickness of all layers is considerably increased in this locality. This is especially noticeable in the eighth layer, where the number of cell rows, in the vicinity of the foveal pit, increases to as many as six, seven, or eight (Figs. 129, 161).

4. CENTRAL DEPRESSION, PIT, OR FOVEA; FOVEOLA AND DARK SPOT.—Approximately in the center of the central area or of the pigmented territory known as the "yellow spot," is per sketch in Fig. 161). Its gently rounded fundus or floor is called "foveola" or "little fovea." In most monkey species the outlines of the foveal depression or dimple resemble an inverted pan with a flat floor (Fig. 129, *A*). There is considerable variation in detail in various simian species (Figs. 166–69). The smallest,

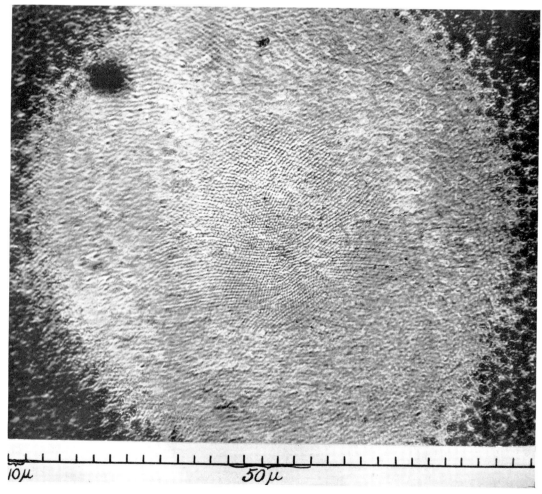

FIG. 151.—Flat section through central fovea of a Rhesus Macaque, stained with hematoxylin and phloxin, photographed with Bausch & Lomb fluorite 4.3-mm. 1.00 oil-immersion objective at 443× magnification, with actual dimensions indicated in microns on the accompanying scale. In the very center a circular territory entirely populated by the cones, the smallest being in its geographic center. The cones are arranged in a continuous, compact formation, without any gaps. The rows of cones intersect in various directions, preponderantly radiating from the geographic center, altogether forming an even-grained mosaic, hence precluding lines of predilection. The area where the cones are visible corresponds to the outer fovea and is surrounded, first, by a belt of less regular structures corresponding to the inner cone segments mixed with rods, and, on the outside, with the dark outer nuclei. (*Cf.* following figures.)

found a small circular excavation or depression, the "central" or "inner fovea." In sections vertical to its surface the outlines of the foveal depression resemble, in Man and Anthropomorphous Apes, a bowl with sloping sides (up-though well-defined, fovea is present in the South American Night Monkey, *Nyctipithecus* or *Aotes trivirgatus*, and in the Asiatic Tarsier (*Tarsius carbonarius* or *T. philippinensis*) (Figs. 149, 512). The concavity of the fovea faces the transparent center of the eye filled with the vitreous and is directed toward the pupil (*cf.* in Figs. 125, 126). (*See* sec. 10, this chapter, for history and comparative anatomy.)

In the living, the foveal pit is difficult to examine ophthalmoscopically because of the transparency of the retinal tissue. Its location, shape, and dimensions may, nevertheless, be

excavation (370 microns or more) and, because of the absence of blood vessels, there is no sheet of blood to screen off the dark retinal and chorioidal pigment (Figs. 148, 149). This dark patch is, in clinical parlance, falsely called "central fovea," and also "macula," but in fact corresponds only to the very center, the foveola.

In fixed anatomical specimens where the

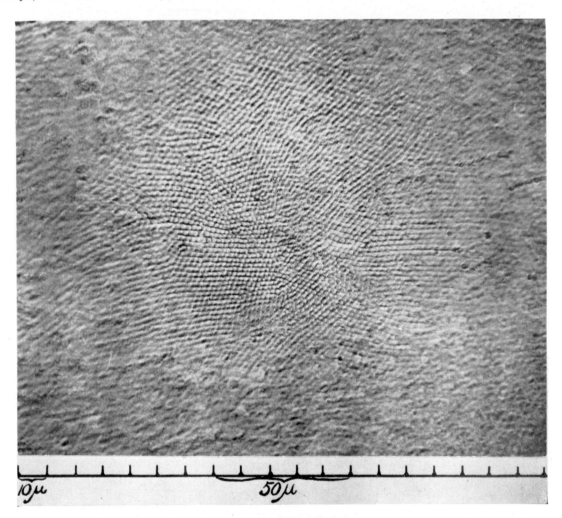

Fig. 152.—Flat section through central fovea of a Rhesus Macaque, presented in the preceding figure, here photographed magnified almost twice (732×), with actual size indicated in microns on the accompanying scale. The even-grained arrangement of the central cone mosaic, resembling a cobblestone pavement, is clearly seen, with intersecting rows radiating in a somewhat irregular way from the geographic center. The smallest cones are present in the very center, gradually and rather rapidly increasing toward the periphery. (*Cf. also* following figures.)

determined with the help of certain landmarks. Its center—the foveola—has a deeper, more saturated appearance than the remainder of the retina, because the thickness of the retina is here reduced to 130 microns or almost one-third of what it is immediately outside the foveal

retinal membrane has a whitish color and the red sheet of blood is absent, this dark center is particularly conspicuous and is called "dark macula," or "black spot," *macula nigra, punctum niger*, of S. Th. Soemmerring. Ophthalmoscopically, this deepest central portion, the foveola, is usually marked by a minute reflex of light, the "reflex of the foveola."

Another somewhat circular light reflex surrounding the first at some distance indicates the thick margin or ridge that marks the boundary of the foveal pit, the "foveal (falsely called macular) reflex" (Fig. 363). The retinal blood vessels converge toward it from all sides (*see also* Figs. 148, 149).

The diameter of the entire foveal depression from margin to margin measures, in Man, no less than 1.5 mm., corresponding to 5° in the field of view; the diameter of the foveola alone being approximately 0.4 mm., or 1°20′ of arc in the field of view. In the Rhesus Macaque the corresponding measures of the fovea and foveola are 1 mm., and from 0.25 to 0.35 mm., respectively. The distance of the fovea from the temporal margin of the optic papilla measures approximately 3 mm. in Man and 2 mm. in the Macaque.

The excavation of the central fovea sur-

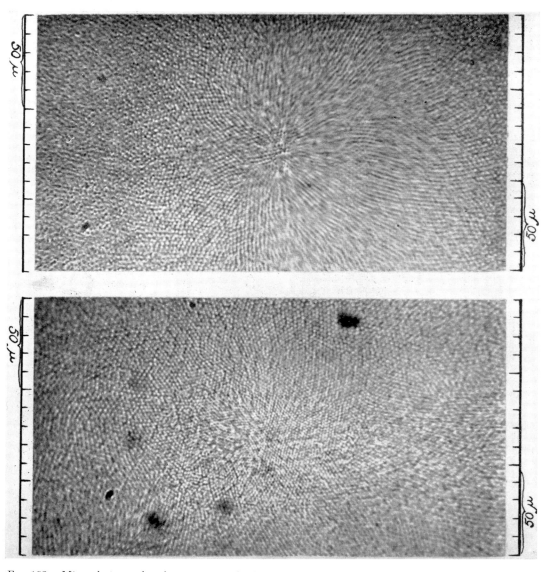

Fɪɢ. 153.—Microphotographs of two unstained whole-mount preparations of the retinae of adult Rhesus Macaques showing individual variation of the pattern of the cone mosaic in the very center of the fovea. In the upper photo many, in the lower photo only a few, of the cones have been laid flat in the center, the majority being arranged in a cobblestone pattern. Taken with a Leitz *Ultropak* oil-immersion objective 60×, and ocular 6XB, with transmitted light, at a linear magnification of 635×. Actual magnification indicated in microns on the accompanying scales.

rounded by its wall usually appears ophthalmo-scopically somewhat elliptical in shape, although in reality it is circular, as is seen in well-preserved specimens. In some specimens it has a hue slightly brighter, in others a more saturated color, than the orange-red or vermilion of the region surrounding it.

Another conspicuous feature is the arrangement of the larger blood vessels, which circle above and below and at some distance from the fovea (*cf.* same figures, especially Figs. 148, 162). Only smaller branches are seen streaming from all sides toward the foveal margin; their terminals, the precapillary arteries and veins,

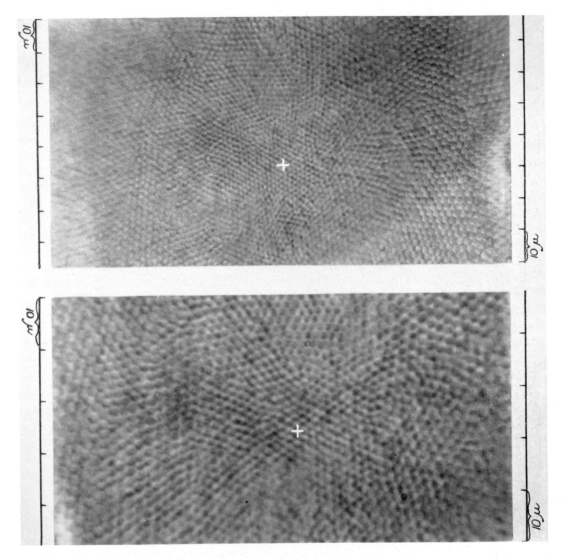

Fig. 154.—Cone mosaic from the very center of the fovea of an adult Rhesus Macaque as seen in an unstained whole-mount preparation of the retina. Microphotographs taken with Leitz *Ultropak* oil-immersion objective 100×, the upper photo with ocular 6XB, the lower photo with ocular 10XB, at the respective magnifications of 1,130× and 1,866×. The actual linear magnifications are indicated in microns on the accompanying scales. Note the characteristic honeycomb appearance of the cone mosaic, resembling a cobblestone pavement; hexagonal shape of individual cones, where clearly visible in sharp focus; the arrangement of cones in irregularly intersecting rows; the smallest cones in the geographic center, indicated by a white cross, from which the cones gradually increase in size toward the periphery; the absence of any gaps whatsoever in the solid cone formation, except for the thin neuroglial partitions visible as grayish lines; the absence of any rods in the central territory, indicating the "rodless area"; the even "grain" of the cone mosaic in a minute territory in the very center, measuring barely 20 microns in diameter, or about one dozen of cone diameters, where the cones are most reduced in size, corresponding with the "focusing" or "fixation point," or rather area, of the field of vision. (*Cf.* preceding and following figures.)

just slip over the margin into the foveal pit. In a small area, corresponding to the deeper portion of the foveal pit, even the precapillary vessels are absent (Fig. 364). This area, in the horizontal meridian, in Man usually measures not less than 550 microns across, or approximately 0.5 mm., which corresponds to 1°50′ of arc in the field of view. The foveola, where, because of the absence of all inner layers, all blood vessels, including the capillaries, are also absent, measures only 400 microns across. In the field of view this avascular or vessel-free area corresponds to 1°20′ of arc, more or less. The extent of this area varies individually. (*Cf.* chap. X, 2 [3].)

It is here that a few words may be added to clarify the confusion still existing concerning the use of the terms "fovea" and "macula." The first, a Latin term meaning a "pit," should be used to connote the excavation, whereas *macula lutea* or "yellow spot" should be reserved for the much larger area containing the yellow pigment visible only in red-free light (Fig. 149). The center of the fovea, appearing ophthalmoscopically as a minute, dark-red patch, is the *foveola* or "little dimple" or "little pit," marked by a foveolar reflex, and is much smaller than the actual excavation of the entire fovea, which is bounded by a circular foveal reflex ring (*cf.* Fig. 363). In this center alone all blood vessels are absent, and the yellow pigmentation, if present at all, is reduced to a minimum.

5. Foveal or central photoreceptors.— The photoreceptor layer (*2*) is considerably thicker in the fovea than outside, because of the lengthening of the bacillary portions of the cones (Figs. 129, 161). This layer is thickest in the very center. Here the length of the photoreceptors is almost twice what it is in the foveal periphery. In order to accommodate the greatly lengthened central photoreceptors, the outer limiting membrane is pushed inward, toward the vitreous, forming a shallow dip named the "outer fovea" by Kuhnt and Dimmer (the very center, the deepest point, of this dip is filled with a few centralmost cones; *see* Fig. 150).

The diameter of this locality, where the photoreceptors attain their greatest length in Man, measures approximately 400 microns across,

corresponding to 1°20′ of arc in the field of view. This area, accordingly, is practically coextensive with the deepest portion of the inner fovea, or foveola. Likewise, it is the same area that is free from all blood vessels, including capillaries (*see* chap. X, 2 [3]).

In this minute central territory or in a slightly larger area, measuring roughly from 500 to 600 microns across, the photoreceptor layer consists exclusively of cones (Fig. 161, upper sketch, rodless area in layer *2* between broken lines; *see also* Fig. 129). This fact is even more clearly demonstrated in microphotographs in Figures 151–56. In the field of view this rodless center approximately corresponds to from 1°40′ to 2° of arc.

The rodless and avascular center is encircled on the outside by a belt corresponding to the foveal slope, where the rods begin to appear, first singly, or in small groups or short chains, gradually becoming more numerous toward the periphery of the foveal excavation (Figs. 157–60).

In the Rhesus Macaque the central rodless territory is smaller, measuring approximately 200 microns across. Both in Man and in the Monkey the rodless central area, accordingly, is considerably smaller than the foveal excavation, amounting to about half the total foveal diameter, but less than half its area.

The greater length of the foveal cones is caused principally by the lengthening of their outer segments, whereas the inner segments appear, in fact, to be shorter. In a minute area, in the very center, measuring in Man from 50 to 75 microns across, the long, slender cones are all of almost uniform length. They attain their greatest length in the entire retina here; and here alone, or more than elsewhere, their scleral tips are imbedded in the pigmented epithelium (Fig. 161). The thickness of the cones, on the contrary, decreases toward the foveal center, the most centrally located foveal cones being the most delicate in the entire retina.

The length and thickness of the cones in the foveal center vary, depending upon the species. In Man, in the very center, they are approximately 70 microns long and from 1 to 1.5 microns thick in their inner, and 1 micron thick in their outer, segments, corresponding to 14″–21″ of arc in the field of view.

The separating dead intervals between the adjoining cones in the very center, filled by the enveloping neuroglial sheaths, measure hardly more than 0.3 micron, which corresponds to 4″ of arc in the field of view.

Toward the periphery of the outer fovea the thickness of the cones increases rather rapidly, and the length decreases, while the separating intervals also become greater. Just outside the foveal depression the inner segments of the cones are from 3.5 to 4 microns thick, and the outer segments 1.3 microns thick.

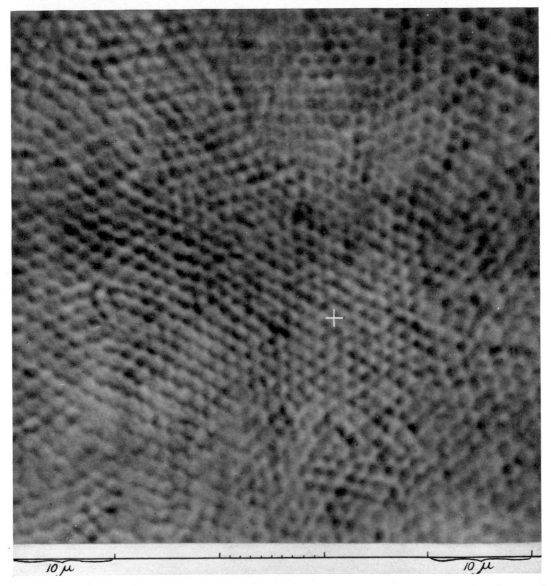

FIG. 155.—Cone mosaic from the center of central fovea from the same preparation presented in the preceding microphotographs (Fig. 154), much more magnified. Actual linear magnification 3,718×, indicated in microns on the accompanying scale. Leitz *Ultropak* oil-immersion 100× objective used with transmitted light. This photo, even better than the preceding one, shows the arrangement of the central cone mosaic, with the following noteworthy details: blunt hexagonal shape of individual cones in optical cross-section; smallest cones in the geographic center, approximately indicated by a white cross, their size gradually increasing away from the center; characteristic and somewhat irregular pattern of cone rows intercrossing in three ways at approximate angles of 60°; marked individual difference in cone diameter in each particular small territory; solid, continuous cone formation, without any gaps and without any rods. This is the part of the photoreceptor screen structurally most fit functionally to resolve the physical retinal image, caught by it, into the most minute details and transmit the stream of nerve impulses to the brain for further mental processing.

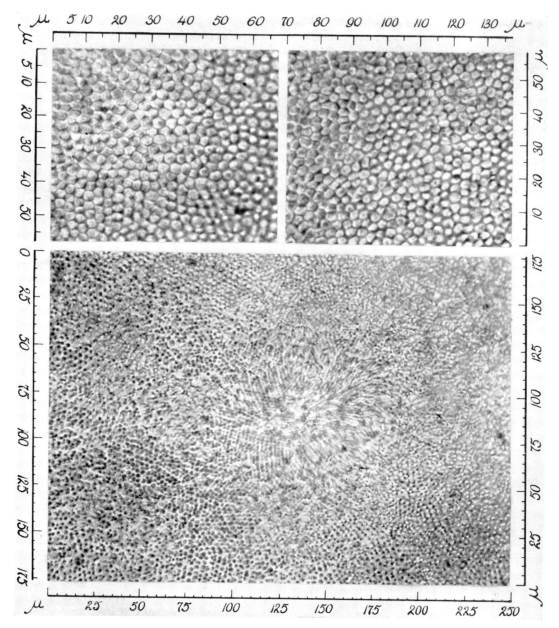

FIG. 156.—Microphotographs of the adult human foveal cone mosaic from a central rodless area. Specimen fixed in 10 per cent formalin, whole-mount unstained preparation, dehydrated in graded alcohols, cleared in terpineol and toluene, mounted in clarite, and covered with a coverslip on a paper frame. Larger photo, taken at $665\times$, shows a portion of the rodless central area of the fovea, with the foveal center, partly out of focus, approximately in the center of the photo and with cones slightly disarrayed. Smaller photos, magnified $1,227\times$, also from the same rodless area, but at some distance from the very geographic center, left photo slightly more distant from the center than the right one. Actual magnifications indicated on the accompanying scales. Leitz *Ultropak* oil-immersion objectives $60\times$ and $100\times$, used with transillumination. Note in the larger photo an arrangement in intercrossing rows similar to that of the Monkey shown in preceding figures, with smallest cones located in the geographic center. The smaller photos show distinctly the character of the central photoreceptor cone mosaic, with irregularly hexagonal individual cones, much varying in shape, size, and arrangement but, on the whole, forming a fairly uniform, evenly grained mosaic. No gaps in normal, well-made preparations are found in the cone mosaic. (*Cf.* preceding figures.)

The number of cones in the territory of the central fovea is absolutely and relatively greater per unit area than anywhere in the extrafoveal regions (Figs. 151–56). In the outer fovea, which is practically coextensive with the foveola, in a circular area measuring about 400 microns across in Man, 20,000 cones may be counted in a whole-mount human specimen. In the field of view this corresponds to 1°20′ of arc.

In the very center of the outer fovea, a minute, irregularly circular island, measuring not more than 100 microns across, is filled with 2,000 of the thinnest cones of practically uniform diameter, the "bouquet of central cones" of Rochon-Duvigneaud. This minute central territory may correspond to 20′ of arc in the field of view.

In the central rodless territory, where the bacillary layer consists of cones alone, measuring about 500 microns asross, which corresponds to 1°50′ of arc in the field of view, the approximate number of cones is 35,000.

In the territory of the entire depression of the central fovea, computed to be 1.75 sq. mm., the number of cones is from 100,000 to 115,000.

In the simian retina the corresponding figures are smaller. The "central bouquet" of a Rhesus Macaque may contain not more than 400–500 cones. In the entire outer fovea, in the same species, measuring approximately 300 microns across, corresponding to the flat foveal floor, the number of cones is approximately 17,000.

In good preparations cut vertically to the retinal surface, the bacillary portions of the central cones appear perfectly straight, with their axes parallel and perpendicular, instead of oblique, as alleged by Koeppe.

In flat preparations of the retina, the "whole-mounts," both fresh unstained and fixed and stained, the cones in the region of the central fovea are closely packed into a solid formation, without any gaps; the entire formation here resembles an evenly distributed mosaic, like the cobblestones in an old-fashioned pavement (Figs. 154, 155, 156). An irregular distribution described by Fritsch and by Kolmer is to be considered an artifact, owing to improper technique.

The smallest cones of the mosaic are around the very center, indicated in our photographs by a white cross. From that center the cones gradually, though somewhat unevenly, increase in size toward the periphery along all radii. There are no gaps in this mosaic, except for the extremely narrow spaces between the adjoining cones. These spaces are filled with delicate sheaths of neuroglia, the "fiber baskets" of Müller's radial fibers, and the vitreal expansions of the retinal pigment epithelium, both already mentioned (sec. 2 [2], and 8 [2], this chapter).

The elements of the foveal photoreceptor mosaic, the individual cones, as they appear in a whole-mount preparation, are mostly hexagonal, less frequently pentagonal in shape, much like the "cells" of a honeycomb (Fig. 156). As in a honeycomb, they are arranged in fairly distinct rows, somewhat arching and cutting across one another in three definite ways at approximately 60°. The pattern is not mathematically regular, as depicted by M. Schultze, but shows numerous irregularities and deviations from a theoretically postulated arrangement.

The arrangement of the "grain" of the central foveal cones as described indicates small preference, if any, for certain directions, lines, or shapes. Each minute hexagonal or pentagonal field of the mosaic of the central photoreceptors corresponds to an individual cone in an optical cross-section.

The smallest cones in the very center in Man measure from 1 to 1.5 microns, in the Macaque from 1–1.3 to 1.5 microns, which corresponds to from 12″ to 18″ of arc in the field of view. The separating glial partitions and blind intervals amount to from one-fifth to one-third of these figures.

The distance from center to center of the adjoining cones in the very center of the fovea, both in Man and in the Rhesus Macaque, is from 1.6 to 2 microns. Considering the minimum (one-tenth) and the maximum (one-fourth) of possible shrinkage caused by the action of the chemicals to which the specimen was subjected during fixation and imbedding, the diameter of the centralmost cones may be estimated, both in Man and in the Rhesus Macaque, at from 1.1 to 2 microns, their inter-center distance at from 2 to 2.6 microns. (My latest measurements show the linear shrinkage not to exceed one-tenth of the original size.)

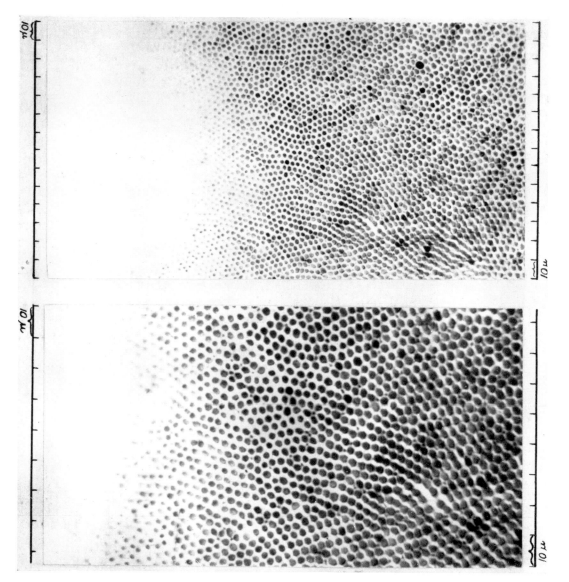

Fɪɢ. 157.—Microphotographs of a flat section of the retina of an adult Rhesus Macaque stained with hematoxylin and phloxin, showing photoreceptor mosaic of the central fovea next to the central rodless area, with most centrally located rods (*dotlike structures*) appearing between the cones (*larger structures*). Unstained left ends of photos represent a portion of central rodless area, with the very center farther to the left, outside the photos. Taken with Leitz *Ultropak* oil-immersion objective 60×, and transillumination, upper photo with ocular 6XB, lower photo with ocular 10XB, at the respective magnifications of 635× and 1,053×, with actual magnifications indicated on the accompanying scales. Note complicated and irregular, although even, cone pattern of triply intercrossing rows, with a gradual increase of cone diameter from the center (*left ends*) to the foveal periphery (*right ends* of photos), the gradual increase to right being caused partly by a lower level of the plane of cutting, closer to the base of the cones; few larger and darker cones are those with ectopic nuclei displaced into bacillary layer *2-b*. The much smaller rods appear at first singly between the large cones, gradually appearing in pairs and further increasing in number toward the periphery of central fovea at the right end of the photos (continued in subsequent three figures).

These dimensions of the smallest physiological units harmonize well with the *minimum visibile* of 16″.5 to 21″ in the Monkey, as found experimentally (Klüver 1933, pp. 230, 231).

The diameter of the inner segments of the central cones, on which the "grain" of the cones and hence the visual resolution depend, was variously estimated by preceding investigators, the given values exceeding more or less considerably the figures given above. These figures, in microns, are: M. Schultze 2–2.5 (Man), 2.8 (*Macaca cynomolga*); H. Müller 3 or less (Man); Koelliker 3 (Man); Merkel 3 (Man); Krause 3 (Man); Kuhnt 2–2.5 (Man); Wadsworth 2.5 (Man); Koster 4.4–4.6 (Man); Schaper 2 (Man); Welcker 3.1–3.6 (Man); Greeff 2.5 (Man); Dimmer 2.3–2.5 (Man); Bird & Schäfer 2.1 (Man); Fritsch 1.5–1.8–4.5–6 (Man); Heine 4 (Man); Rochon-Duvigneaud 1.5–2–2.5 (Man); Henle 2 (Man); Wolfrum 1.2 (Rhesus Macaque); Kolmer 1.5 (*Macaca nemestrina*); Neumann 1.7 (Rhesus Macaque), 1.5 (*Cercoce-*

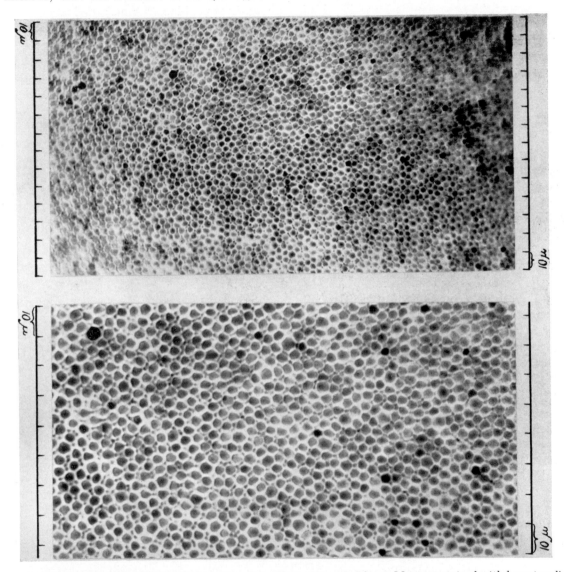

FIG. 158.—Microphotographs of a flat section of an adult retina of a Rhesus Macaque stained with hematoxylin and phloxin, showing a belt of photoreceptors from the foveal periphery outward to that shown in the preceding figure. Same technique and magnification used. The number of dotlike rods has increased considerably, now appearing frequently in pairs, or in short chains or groups of threes or more, although the total distribution pattern is remarkably uniform in spite of the irregularity of the detail. Most cones (*larger structures*) still adjoin their neighbors directly, with a few darker ectopic nuclei found here and there. (*Cf.* preceding and following figures.)

bus torquatus atys); Polyak 2.3–3 (Rhesus Macaque), 1.2–1.5–1.8 (Man), 0.3–0.4 (Golden Eagle, central fovea), 1 (Golden Eagle, temporal fovea); Hartridge 2 (Man, cone diameter), 3–4.1 (Man, intercenter distance).

6. Inner layers of central fovea.—The structure of the retinal tissue in and around the central fovea is dominated by the formation of the foveal excavation, a process which takes place during the phylogenetic and ontogenetic development. The mechanism by which this is accomplished is a lateral displacement, from the center toward the periphery, of the various histological elements, such as the bipolars, horizontal cells, amacrines, and ganglion cells. The result of this is a reduction in thickness of the inner layers below the photoreceptor layer, small in the periphery of the fovea and maximal in its center (Fig. 129, *I, A;* and Fig. 161).

In the human fovea the lateral displacement begins in the outer nuclear layer (*4*), here made up entirely of cone nuclei, and progresses in the successive inner layers (Fig. 161, lower sketch). In the very center only two or three somewhat scattered tiers of cone nuclei remain, whereas away from the center the cone nuclei increase to a dozen or so rows, the greatest accumulation in the entire retina being found here.

In the center of the simian fovea (Fig. 129, upper sketch) this thinning of the outer nuclear layer is only slightly indicated, or, speaking phylogenetically, the center of the simian fovea shows merely an incipient process of rarefication of the outer nuclear layer. In the Tarsier the greatest accumulation of the outer nuclei is precisely in the very center of the fovea (Fig. 512).

The outer fiber layer of Henle (*5-a*) composed of inner cone fibers, both in Man and in Monkey, is likewise quite thin in the very center. Its fibers are swept aside as if pulled by centrifugal force. The middle zone (*5-b*) and the inner zone (*5-c*) of the outer plexiform layer, representing synapses of the foveal neurons, are entirely pulled away from the center, more completely in Man than in the Monkey, thus forming the floor of the fovea, or foveola. Here only a few scattered nuclei belonging to the inner nuclear layer (*6*) and an occasional ganglion cell remain as a residue of the inner layers. As a result, almost all structures between the inner limit of the outer nuclear layer (*4*) and the transparent vitreous which fills most of the eyeball are removed, almost completely in the very center and decreasingly so toward the periphery of the foveal excavation.

The importance of this arrangement is discussed under paragraph 7, following. Here it suffices to point out that, in forming the foveal excavation, the synaptical relations between the three categories of conducting neurons (the photoreceptors, bipolars, and ganglions) are as fully preserved as if the arrangement had remained vertical, as it originally was and remains in most of the extrafoveal regions of the retina. The preservation of the original synaptical relations is made possible by the slanting course taken by fibrous elements, in the primate fovea chiefly those of the rods and cones (in *4* and *5-a*), and to a lesser extent also the bipolars and ganglions, in the fovea of Birds and Lizards of all three elements.

The outer nuclear layer is remarkable precisely in the foveal center. Whereas in the extrafoveal regions, including the extrafoveal portion of the central area, the cone nuclei form a single discontinuous row immediately beneath the outer limiting membrane, *3* (thus in *II–VI*, in Fig. 129; *see also* zone *4-a* in Figs. 127, 128), this zone is greatly augmented in the center of the foveal excavation, in conformity with the greatly increased number of cones precisely in this territory. In the flat foveal floor of a Rhesus Macaque there are from seven to eight tiers of cone nuclei. In the periphery of the human outer fovea, from eight to ten tiers may be counted. In the very center, exactly beneath the "bouquet of central cones," their number in Man is again reduced to about two or three rather loose rows.

In the territory roughly corresponding to the central locality, all outer nuclei belong to the cones. Here the photoreceptor layer (*2*) is greatly thickened and made up exclusively of cones, the "outer fovea." This central territory coincides with the rodless area. In the human fovea the rodless portion of the outer nuclear layer measures at least 500 microns across, being somewhat more extensive than the floor of the foveal excavation (Fig. 161). In the Rhesus Macaque the most centrally located rod nuclei also invade the periphery of the augmented central portion of the outer nuclear layer, considerably restricting the extent of the central rodless area (Fig. 129). In the Philippine Tarsier, a nocturnal Primate, all nuclei in the central fovea belong to the rods (*see* chap. XIV, 12, and Fig. 512).

The factors causing the displacement of cells and fibers from the center, which results in the formation of the foveal excavation, remain unknown. It is more than a guess that they are not purely mechanical but are rather combined biochemical, biophysical, and "dynamic" processes which it is not possible further to define at present. The formation of the foveal depression is apparently a result of the natural forces that make living things grow and, for the present, is as much of a mystery as the factors that make a

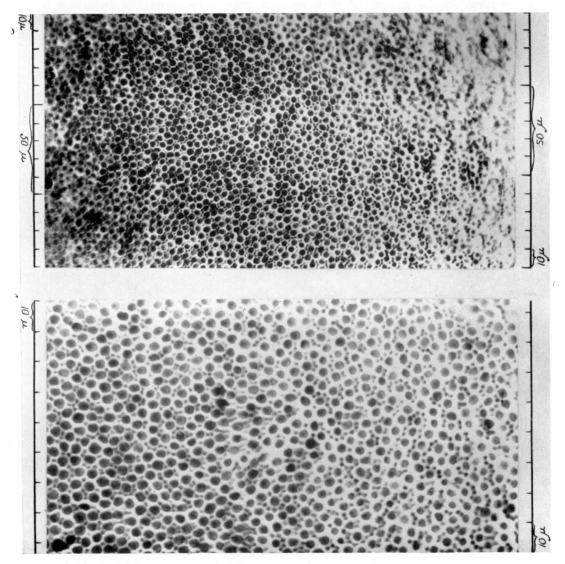

FIG. 159.—Microphotographs of a flat section of the retina of a Rhesus Macaque prepared with the same technique as the preceding photos, showing the photoreceptor mosaic from a circular belt encircling the one presented in the preceding figure, corresponding to the periphery of the central fovea. The cones have further increased in diameter, and the more numerous rods have taken up much of the intervening space, in places encircling individual cones almost completely, with numerous cones, however, still adjoining their neighbors directly. The plane of the cutting at the right end of the lower photo is somewhat higher in the bacillary layer, passing through the cones where they begin to taper, leaving more intervening space between the individual cones. The few cones stained dark are those containing ectopic nuclei. Magnification same as in preceding figure, actual magnification in microns indicated on the accompanying scales. (*Cf.* preceding and following figures.)

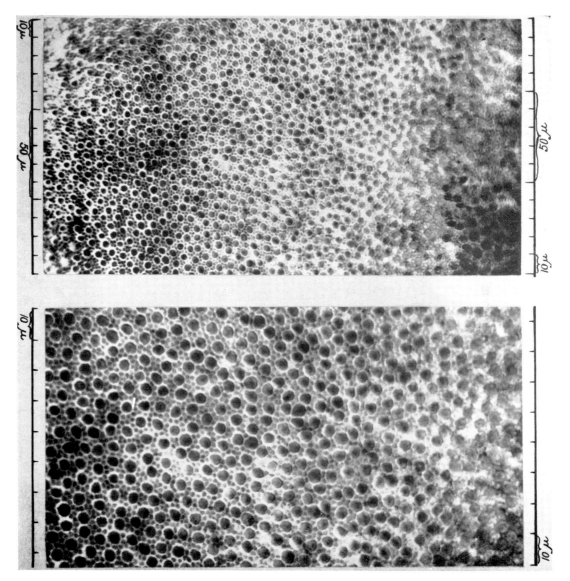

Fig. 160.—Microphotographs of the same series as the preceding photos of flat sections of the retina of a Rhesus Macaque from a locality 750 microns distant from the foveal center, hence just outside the foveal depression (*cf.* Fig. 129). Same technique and same magnification as in the preceding photos. The plane of the cutting at the right ends of photos passes through the outer limiting membrane, in the center of photos through the inner segments, and at the left end of the photos through the outer segments of the photoreceptors. Actual magnifications indicated on the accompanying scales. In this locality of the central area the cones are much stouter, possess smooth, round, or oval contours because here they are not pressing against one another as they do in the central rodless area and are not arranged in very distinct rows. Most of the cones are now encircled by a row of rods, which in places increases to two rows. In other instances the cones still adjoin their neighbors directly along one or the other side, which makes their intercenter distance shorter. Occasionally three or more cones touch one another directly with one of their sides, producing short chains. The rods also increase their diameter in comparison to the thin, most centrally located rods next to the central rodless area in the fovea. But in spite of these slight local variations in size and distribution, the double photoreceptor screen appears remarkably uniformly organized, with no predilection for certain shapes or directions. (*Cf.* preceding figures.)

fertilized ovum or a seed develop into a complex living animal or a plant made up of a multitude of variously differentiated tissues, forming a harmonious whole.

7. FUNCTIONAL SIGNIFICANCE OF FOVEAL DEPRESSION.—From the preceding it is fairly evident that whatever the unknown factors of phylogenetic and ontogenetic mechanics and dynamics involved in the formation of the foveal depression are, the removal of most of the nervous and supporting structures and of most blood vessels from in front of the photoreceptive bacillary layer serves the dioptrical purpose of the eye admirably (Figs. 125, 126, 129, *I*, *A*, 161).

Even though all these structures of the inner layers are normally highly transparent during life, they represent an appreciable dioptrical impediment. The countless irregularly curved surfaces formed by the walls of cell bodies and of their innumerable processes, all of different sizes and undoubtedly of different coefficients of refraction, each acting as a minute lens of different power, taken together form an optical labyrinth in which passing rays of light are multifariously deflected, diffracted, and deviated from their theoretical rectilinear course. That such interference, even though it be relatively slight, would perceptibly reduce the sharpness of definition of the visual image in the layer of photoreceptors of the central fovea, where the need for precision is greatest, is evident. Teleologically, it was in order to avoid this, and not for the purpose suggested by Walls (1937, 1940, 1942), that the foveal excavation was formed by the lateral displacement of optically undesirable inner layers which would otherwise screen off the photoreceptors.

The vertical arrangement of cones in the central area and fovea, as well as in the remainder of the retina, substantiates the foregoing interpretation. If the refractive function of the slanting slopes of the foveal excavation was to increase the size of the foveal image, as suggested by Walls, it would, first, be entirely annulled by the vertical position of the photoreceptors in the bacillary layer, and, second, the increased image area would counteract the resolving power of the foveal photoreceptors, the very purpose for which the diameter of these photoreceptors was reduced to the minimum. Besides, the large size of the flat foveal floor directly contradicts Walls's hypothesis.

The effect of the displacement of the inner layers in the foveal excavation is obvious: a greatly thickened, but spatially delicately organized, bacillary layer of the axial photosensitive cones, as it were, becomes exposed to the undiminished action of light. Above all, this arrangement permits the maximum advantage to be taken of the biologically superior property of "light," viz., its propagation in straight lines. (*See* chap. VI, 2 [2, 3, 4] on the arciform course of fibers in the primate central area, teleologically serving the same purpose by removing the thick fiber bundles from the axial portion of the retina.)

8. STRUCTURAL FEATURES OF EXTRAFOVEAL REGIONS.—The extrafoveal, especially the extra-areal, regions of the primate retina, in contrast with the central fovea and area, are structurally uniform. From the fovea on, the basic architecture of the membrane becomes imperceptibly cruder until in the region of the *ora serrata* it is confused and partly lost (Fig. 129, *VI*).

The most prominent feature of that extensive territory is the presence of both kinds of photoreceptors, rods and cones. Their relative number, however, changes but little. In the vicinity of the fovea, both in Man and in Monkey, there is usually only one rod interposed between two adjoining cones (*II*, in same figure).

In the periphery of the central area two rods separate the cones (*III*). Outside the central area the number of intercalated rods increases to three, or not more than four; this ratio remains constant as far as the *ora serrata* (*IV*, *V*, *VI*).

The thickness of the inner cone segments gradually increases from 4 to 5 microns in the vicinity of the fovea to 5 or 6 microns just outside the central area, and to 7, 8, and, finally, 9 microns close to the *ora serrata*.

The distance between the two adjoining cones also widens from 1–3 microns near the fovea to from 3 to 5 microns in the areal periphery, slowly increasing from 6 microns just outside the area to 8 microns close to the *ora serrata*.

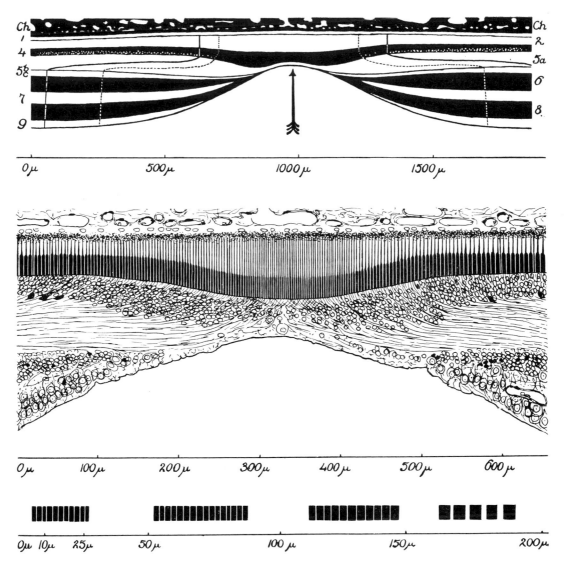

Fig. 161.—Central fovea of human retina. Upper sketch shows semidiagrammatically, in a vertical section, the shape of the central fovea, the arrangement and relative thickness of layers, and the anatomical and synaptical relationships of photoreceptor layer *2* and the outer nuclear layer *4* to the subjacent layers *5–9*. Broken lines in layer *2* indicate the most centrally located rods, their nuclei in layer *4* marked with white dots, the region thus bounded indicating the central territory free from rods—the rodless area. Solid lines in *2* mark the territory of lengthened photoreceptors, called "outer fovea," mostly filled with greatly lengthened and thinned-out central cones. Note synaptical relationship of this outer fovea to the much larger inner fovea, a pit caused by a lateral displacement of all layers below *5-a*. The middle sketch shows the actual structural composition of the deepest portion of the foveal pit. Note the length and thinness of the central cones, their points reaching into the pigment layer. Layer *4* is made up entirely of cone nuclei (*circles*), the few rod nuclei (*shaded*) appearing only outside the outer fovea. In the very center, all layers below *4* are either absent or greatly reduced in thickness, this layer itself being much thinned out, thus facilitating the unimpeded passage of light rays to the photosensitive cones (the course of light from the pupil indicated by an arrow in the upper sketch). Lower sketch shows the relative size and number of cones, from the center of the fovea (*left*), the slope and edge of the outer fovea, and the periphery of the central area (*right*). The accompanying scales indicate actual dimensions in microns. *Ch*, chorioid membrane. (*Cf*. Fig. 512 showing central fovea of a Tarsier containing exclusively rodlike photoreceptors.)

276

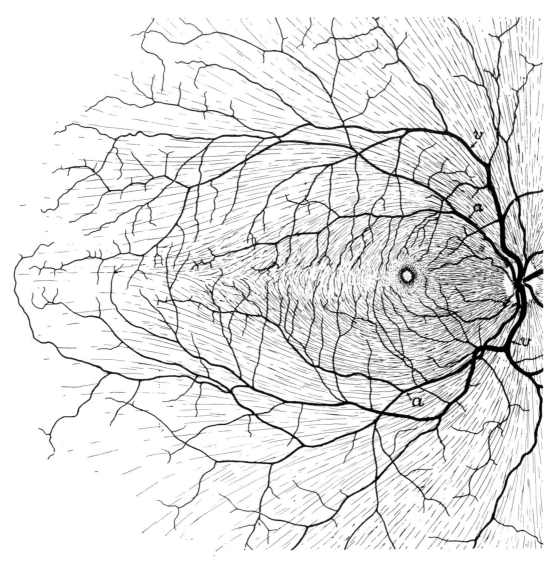

FIG. 162.—Fundus or inside appearance of the right eye of a Rhesus Macaque drawn from a whole-mount preparation of the retina stained during life, or intravitally, with methylene blue. Close to the right margin is the oval optic disk or papilla. From it emerge central retinal blood vessels, the thinner arteries (*a*), and the thicker veins (*v*). These spread in all directions over the retina, repeatedly dividing into smaller branches which ultimately form a continuous capillary network (not seen here, *cf*. colored Fig. 364). This network supplies the layers of the retina inward to the inner plexiform layer, whereas the outer layers are supplied by osmosis via the chorioidal system (colored Fig. 365). The arrangement of blood vessels varies in different parts. In the nasal half of the fundus, not included in this figure (at the right end), vessels radiate from the disk, like the spokes of a wheel. In the larger temporal half of the fundus shown here, the vessels arch above and below the central area of the retina in order to leave it relatively free. Especially is this the case with the central fovea, whose floor, inclosed by a stippled circle, is entirely free from blood vessels, including capillaries. In this way most structures which would impede the free access of light rays to the central foveal photoreceptors are removed (*cf*. Figs. 129, 161). The optic nerve fibers, arising from retinal ganglion cells, indicated by thin, smooth lines in the figure, gather from all points of the fundus toward the optic disk, where they leave the eyeball and form the optic nerve. Their arrangement is similar to that of the blood vessels. They, too, and for the same reason stated above, part above and below the central fovea and area. The line along the horizontal meridian, from the fovea to the temporal margin (*left* in the figure), called *raphé* or "seam," indicates the partition. This line is important for the understanding of the genesis of quadrantic scotomas and hemianopias and for the so-called macular sparing in visual field pathology. (*Cf*. chap. XI, 8, 9.)

The thickness of the rods likewise increases from approximately 1–1.5 microns in and close to the central fovea to 2 microns just outside the central area, and to 2.5 microns and, finally, to 3 microns in the extreme periphery.

The numerical maximum of rods in Man is attained in a belt just outside the central area, approximately 4 mm. distant from the fovea. In the Rhesus Macaque the maximum has already been attained in the periphery of the central area, and it so remains for a short distance outside it.

Other layers also show a proportionate roughening toward the *ora serrata* or *ora terminalis*, where, both in Man and in the Simians, large vacuolar spaces are found. All this, in physiological terms, means a roughening of the function, especially of visual space perception or acuity, outside the central fovea, which, together with the added factor of polysynaptical relationships, further decreases the number of physiological units toward the periphery of the field of view.

References: F. H. Adler 1953; Atkinson 1937; Bach & Seefelder 1914; Bedell 1929, 1950; Bergmann 1854; Bird & Schäfer 1895; Chevallereau & Polack 1907; Chievitz 1887, 1888, 1889, 1890, 1891; Cohen & Weisberg 1950; Dartnall & Thomson 1949–50; Davson 1949; Detwiler 1938, 1939, 1940, 1943; Di Marzio 1937; Dimmer 1894. 1902, 1907; Dogiel 1892; Cl. DuBois-Reymond 1881, 1886; Ebner 1902; Eisler 1930; Erggelet 1929; Fleischl 1883; Fortin 1925; V. Franz 1913, 1934; Fritsch 1907, 1908; H. Goldman 1949; Goldschmidt 1950; Greeff 1899 (1900); Grether 1941; Guillery 1894–1931; Gullstrand 1902, 1906, 1907, 1918; Haden 1947; Hamilton & Goldstein 1933; Hartridge 1947; Hecht 1922, 1940; Heine 1900, 1901, 1902, 1926, 1935; Hensen 1865, 1867; Hirschberg 1882; J. Hoeve 1912; Holm 1922; Hurvich & Jameson 1953; Jameson & Hurvich 1953, 1954; G. L. Johnson 1892, 1894, 1896–97, 1901; Jones & Higgins 1947; Kahmann 1935, 1936; Köllner 1920; Koeppe 1918, 1920, 1921, 1937; Kolmer 1930; Kolmer & Lauber 1936; Kühl 1920; Kugelberg 1932, 1934, 1937; Kuhnt 1881; Landolt 1871; Leber 1880; Leuckart 1876; Libby 1925; Lineback 1927; Lo Cascio 1924; Loddoni 1930; Low 1951; Ludvigh 1941, 1949; Maggiore 1924; Mandelbaum & Sloan 1947; I. Mann 1950; Martin & Pearse 1947; E. Marx 1909; Merkel 1869; Miles 1949; H. Müller 1856–57, 1859, 1861, 1863, 1872, 1881; Mureddu 1930; Neumann 1921; Nordenson & Nordmark 1928; Østerberg 1935; Pavía 1937; Polyak 1941, 1948; Pütter 1908–12; S. Ramón y Cajal 1892–93 (1933), 1899–1904, 1909–11; Ramsay *et al.* 1941; Riedinger 1932; Rand 1946; Ritter 1864; Rochon-Duvigneaud 1907, 1920, 1934, 1943; Rønne (Roenne) 1944; Rollet & Jacqueau 1898; Rucker & Keys 1950; M. Sachs 1891; Salomonson 1921; Schaper 1893; Schirmer 1864; Schmidt-Rimpler 1874, 1875, 1904; M. Schultze 1861, 1866, 1867, 1872; Schwalbe 1887; Scullica 1928; Segal 1950, 1951; Sloan 1950; Slonaker 1897; Sobotta 1929; S. Th. Soemmerring 1795, 1795–98; Stiles 1939, 1946; Stiles *et al.* 1945; L. C. Thomson 1947, 1949, 1951; Thomson & Wright 1947; F. Tonner 1943–44; Tonner & Weber 1943–44; Van der Velden 1944; Verrier 1938, 1939, 1945; A. Vogt 1918, 1921, 1930–42, 1937; Wadsworth 1881; Wald 1945, 1945–46, 1949; W. C. Wallace 1836; Walls 1937, 1940, 1942, 1943; Walls & Mathews 1952; Walters & Wright 1943; R. A. Weale 1951, 1953; K. S. Weaver 1937; E. H. Weber 1852; Weinstein & Grether 1940; Welcker 1863; Wertheim 1887; Wilcox 1932; Wilcox & Purdy 1933; E. N. Willmer 1944, 1946, 1949, 1950; Willmer & Wright 1950; W. H. Wilmer 1934; Casey H. Wood 1917; Woollard 1926, 1927; W. D. Wright 1939, 1940, 1942, 1943, 1944; Wright & Granit 1938; Zigler *et al.* 1930; O. Zoth 1923; Zwanenburg 1915. (*See* following section for references on comparative anatomy of central area, macula, fovea, etc.; *see* chap. X, 2, for blood supply.)

SEC. 11. REGIONAL AND COMPARATIVE CHARACTERISTICS OF THE VERTEBRATE RETINA

1. Discovery of yellow spot and central fovea.—The fact that the retinal membrane was not of identical construction in all its parts and that various species of Vertebrates possess peculiarities of their own was recognized relatively late. True, the local peculiarities, either

actually observed or merely assumed, were discussed quite early. Kepler (1604 and later), on theoretical grounds, postulated a more perfect structural organization of the retina in the fundus of the eye than in the parts closer to the *ora serrata*. Valsalva, Morgagni, Briggs, Zinn, and Fontana all described the characteristic fanlike arrangement of optic nerve fibers in the Rabbit

macula lutea or *macula flava*, and of the "central depression" or "central pit," the *fovea centralis*, by Buzzi (1782, 1784) and by S. Th. Soemmerring (1795, portrait Fig. 37). At first, however, both the structure and the function of this most important area of the retina were misunderstood. Soemmerring, for example, thought that the fovea, which, because of its frail struc-

Fig. 163.—André Rochon-Duvigneaud (1863), eminent ophthalmologist of Paris, France, and a lifelong student of the vertebrate eye. Author of numerous papers and monographs on the structure of the eye, and of the book *Les Yeux et la vision des vertébrés*, Paris, 1943. Courtesy of Professor A. Rochon-Duvigneaud.

and the Hare, while Maître-Jan noticed that the retina was thicker close to the optic papilla than it was farther away. Other regional peculiarities had been observed by Moehring, Lobé, Hevermann, and others.

The systematic investigation of the regional characteristics of the retinal membrane began with the discovery of the "yellow spot," the

ture, can be easily ruptured during dissection precisely in the center, where it is thinnest, was a hole, perforation, or orifice and named it *foramen* or *foraminulum centrale*. He thought that it was responsible for Mariotte's "blind spot" in the field of vision.

For more than four decades this "central orifice," together with the *plica transversa* or *centralis retinae,* a "transverse or central fold," were looked upon as normal retinal structures and were thus described and depicted by F. Arnold (1839), until both were finally recognized as artifacts and post mortem changes. But not until G. A. Michaelis (1838) and especially Bergmann (1854) and H. Müller (1856–57) correctly described and interpreted the pe-

2. Discovery of the arching course of nerve fibers in the human retina.—The peculiar arrangement of the optic nerve fibers in the human retina, circling from above and from below around the fovea, discussed in detail in chapter VI, 2 (2, 3, 4), was first described by W. C. Wallace (1836) and was later confirmed by a number of investigators (Dogiel 1892;

Fig. 164.—Gordon Lynn Walls (1905), professor of physiological optics and optometry, University of California at Berkeley, California. One of the most proficient and assiduous modern investigators of the vertebrate eye. Courtesy of Professor G. L. Walls, 1947.

culiar structural features of the central fovea, was the true functional significance of this area as mediator of "central" or direct vision understood and recognized; and not until then were the various erroneous interpretations by Johannes Müller, Home, Blumenbach, Berres, Desmoulins, and others done away with. (*Cf.* sec. 9 [3, 4, 5, 6, 7], this chapter.)

Greeff 1900; Koelliker 1854; Koelliker & Müller 1853; Koeppe 1920, 1937; Kolmer & Lauber 1936; C. Krause 1842; W. Krause 1895; G. A. Michaelis 1838–42; Michel 1874; S. Pappenheim 1842; Schwalbe 1874, 1887; A. Vogt 1921, 1937; and others).

The ophthalmoscopic appearance of the human fundus was much studied by clinical oph-

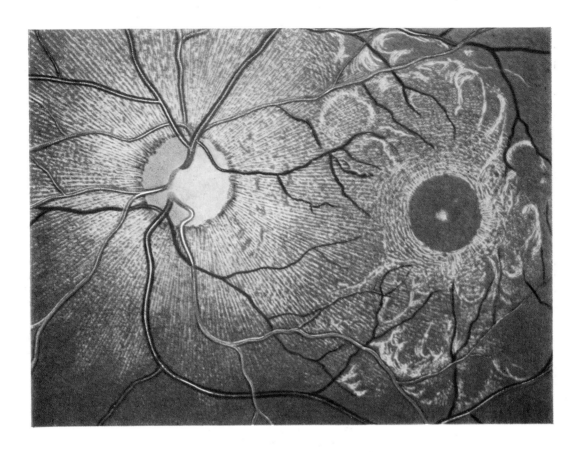

FIG. 165—Fundus or interior of the left eye of a Nubian youth aged 17. Color chocolate-brown, reflexes pronounced, extending over whole central area. Translucent bundles of optic nerve fibers can be traced for a great distance beyond the disk, with the arching above and below fovea well presented (*compare* Figs. 148, 166, 167, 168, 169, 363). Central fovea surrounded by a brilliant circular reflex ring contains a minute reflex in its center. Chorioid vessels not visible. (From G. L. Johnson, *Philos. Trans. Roy. Soc. London*, ser. *B*, vol. 194, pl. 1, year 1901.)

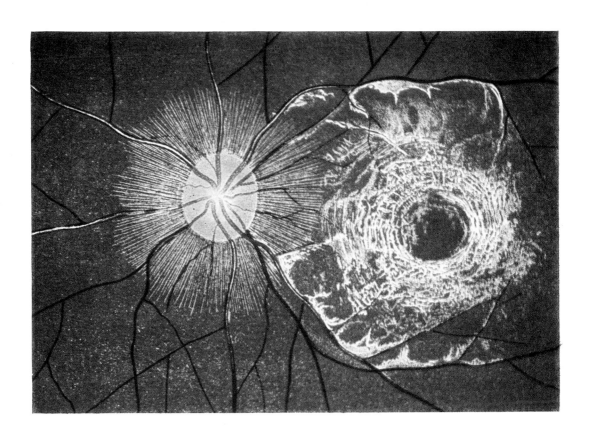

Fig. 166—Fundus or interior of the left eye of a Chimpanzee (*Troglodytes niger*), strikingly resembling that of the Nubian youth in the preceding figure. (From G. L. Johnson, *Philos. Trans. Roy. Soc. London*, ser. *B*, vol. 194, pl. 2, year 1901.)

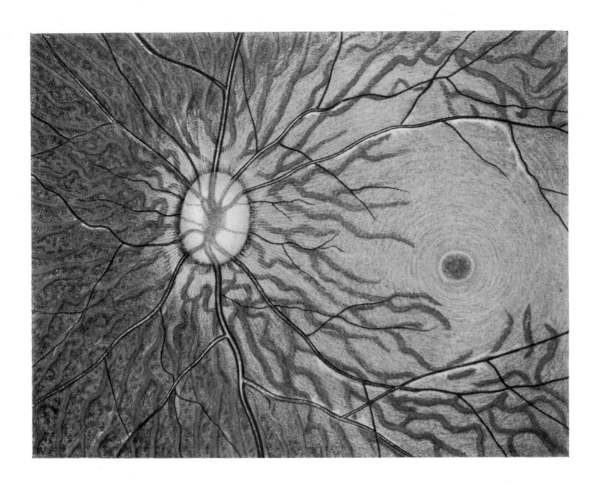

Fig. 167—Fundus or interior of the left eye of a White-Handed Gibbon (*Hylobates albimanus*). Bundles of optic nerve fibers and reflexes prominent. Foveal excavation small. Brown chorioidal stroma covered with black dots can be seen outside the central area where it is obscured by reflexes. On all sides bifurcating chorioidal vessels radiate from the disk ; these can be traced to the periphery. (From G. L. Johnson, *Philos. Trans. Roy. Soc. London*, ser. B, vol. 194, pl. 2, year 1901.)

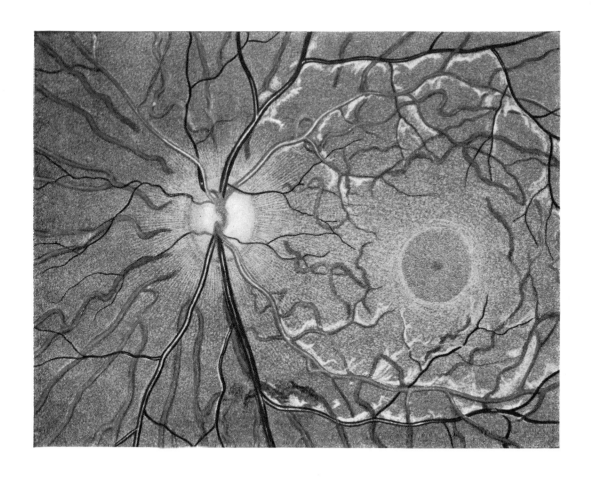

FIG. 168—Fundus or interior of the left eye of a Java Macaque (*Macacus cynomolgus*). The background is without dots, and the chorioidal vessels are arranged as in the Gibbon, being much fewer in number, however. The central fovea resembles human fovea. (From G. L. Johnson, *Philos. Trans. Roy. Soc. London*, ser. *B*, vol. 194, pl. 3, year 1901.)

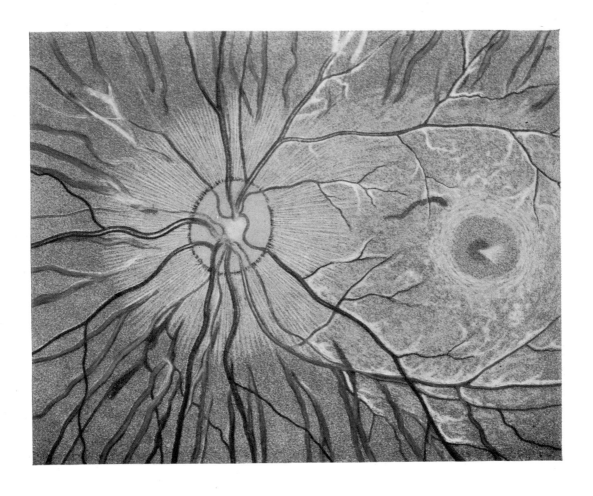

F<small>IG</small>. 169—Fundus or interior of the left eye of a Black-Headed Spider Monkey (*Ateles geoffroyi*), closely resembling that of the Java Macaque. (From G. L. Johnson, *Philos. Trans. Roy. Soc. London*, ser. *B*, vol. 194, pl. 4, year 1901.)

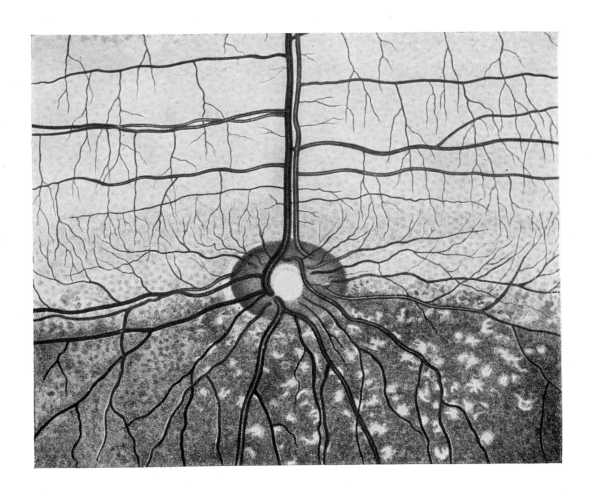

Fig. 170—Fundus or interior of the eye of an Indian Ox (*Bos indicus*), representative of nearly all Ruminants. Papilla is large and horizontally oval, with a central circular depression. From the papilla arise numerous arteries (bright red) and veins (dark red). Principal artery and vein run straight up, giving off strong secondary branches running horizontally. From these numerous smaller twigs descend to a broad, rose-colored, horizontally placed central area, instrumental in acute vision. This area they supply conjointly with other numerous vessels coming from below partly directly from the papilla, and partly arising from larger vessels spreading over lower region of the retina. Lighter colored upper segment of the fundus sharply terminating just below the band-like central area contains so-called *tapetum lucidum* (*t. fibrosum*), a specially constructed tissue layer of the chorioid membrane which reflects light and makes "shining eyes" in nocturnal animals. (From G. L. Johnson, *Philos. Trans. Roy. Soc. London*, ser. *B*, vol. 194, pl. 12, year 1901.)

thalmologists and was later well presented by A. Vogt (1918, 1921), Wilmer (1934), Atkinson (1937), Di Marzio (1937), and Clerici (1943) (for history *see* Rucker & Keys 1950). The eye fundus of the Primates and of numerous other Mammals and Submammalian Vertebrates was well described and beautifully illustrated by G. L. Johnson (1894, 1896–97, 1901, 1927), and in Birds by C. A. Wood (1917). (*Cf.* Figs. 148, 165–69, 172–76.)

3. COMPARATIVE STUDIES OF CENTRAL FOVEA AND YELLOW SPOT IN MAN, APES, AND MONKEYS.—After the great functional importance of the central fovea and its vicinity was recognized, much attention was paid to it by investigators. Its exact location, size, shape, and other details were studied, and the various light reflexes seen with the ophthalmoscope were noticed; also the extent and other peculiarities of the pigmented yellow spot were described (Dimmer 1907; Holm; Johnson 1892, 1894, 1896–97, 1901; Kreiker 1930; Kühne 1878; Landolt; Leber 1880; Merkel 1869; P. Michaelis; H. Müller 1856–57; Reil 1797; Rollet & Jacqueau; Schirmer 1864; Schmidt-Rimpler; M. Schultze 1866; Wadsworth; Welcker).

The presence of pigmentation in the yellow spot during life was a much debated topic. While accepted by most (Chevallereau & Polack; Ewald; Hoeve 1912; Holm; E. Home 1798; Kolmer & Lauber 1936; Kühne 1878; Riccò; Walls & Judd), it was considered by others to be a post mortem phenomenon (Gullstrand; Nordenson & Nordmark), until it was demonstrated ophthalmoscopically in the living, with the help of red-free light (Koeppe 1918, 1921, 1937; A. Vogt 1918, esp. Pl. 1; also 1921, 1937). A large yellow spot was found in the Tarsier (Fig. 149).

In modern times the central area and fovea were intensively studied. Both, without exception, are present in all Monkeys and Apes, diurnal as well as nocturnal (Figs. 149, 166–69). The size and shape of the fovea, however, vary considerably in different species. The same is true of the structures, especially the cones. The most delicate cones so far have been found in the foveal center in the African Mangabeys (Kolmer 1930). The few nocturnal Primates, such as the South American Three-banded

Night Monkey or Douroucouli (*Nyctipithecus* or *Aotes trivirgatus*) and the Asiatic Tarsier (*Tarsius spectrum*), have been considered by most investigators, including modern ones, as having no fovea (M. Schultze, Woollard, Detwiler). However, L. Johnson (1901), a reliable observer, found ophthalmoscopically a well-formed macula in the Night Monkey. A rudimentary fovea was described by Kolmer (1930) in the Three-banded Douroucouli (*Nyctipithecus* or *Aotes trivirgatus*) which was missed by M. Schultze (1872) in the kindred Feline Douroucouli (*Nyctipithecus* or *Aotes felinus*).

In the Philippine Tarsier (*Tarsius carbonarius* or *philippinensis*) Dr. F. S. Ryerson, then assisting the author, found in ophthalmoscopic examination in red-free light a large, yellow-pigmented "macula," with a small fovea and the typical arching arrangement of optic nerve fibers and blood vessels characteristic of all Primates, except the Tree Shrews (*see* Fig. 149; *cf.* also chap. XIV, 12 [9]).

A microscopic examination of sections of the retina of the Tarsier revealed in the corresponding locality a small, shallow, but typical and otherwise well-developed, central fovea in the central area. It was surprising to find in the Tarsier's fovea, including the very center, typical rods, present here as in the rest of the retina, to the complete exclusion of the cone type of photoreceptors: a pure rod retina (Fig. 512).

A well-formed fovea and central area, with an arching arrangement of blood vessels, was also found in a specimen of a Three-banded Night Monkey. (*Cf.* Detwiler 1940, 1941, 1943; Home 1798; Johnson 1901; Kolmer & Lauber 1930, 1936; Menner 1931; Neumann; Max Schultze 1872; Woollard 1927; *see also* chaps. X, 2 [3]; XIV, 12.)

4. CENTRAL AREA AND ITS RELATION TO FOVEA.—In numerous Vertebrates below the Primates H. Müller (1861) found in the axial region of the retina, instead of a foveal depression, merely an accumulation and a general refinement of photoreceptors and nerve cells, which he called "central area." This especially differentiated area is apparently a forerunner in the process of structural and functional perfection of the axial region which eventually culminates in Primates, many Birds, Lizards, and

Fishes in the formation of a true foveal depression.

In species where a foveal excavation is present, it is practically always found in the central area, as is regularly the case in the Primates.

A fovea without an areal development, according to Kolmer, seems to be present rarely, if ever (Swallows, Kingfishers). A contrary arrangement, a central area without a fovea, has been found in the representatives of all five classes of Vertebrates: Fishes, Amphibians, Reptiles, Birds, and Mammals.

Not all species of a class or an order, but only those with well-developed sight, also have a foveal excavation. Still others which depend little upon sight have neither an area nor a fovea.

In Mammals, which, except for the Primates, have been investigated little, the structural perfection of the axial region of the retina is usually only slight, being expressed merely in a more or less pronounced refinement of the photoreceptors, a moderate accumulation of nerve cells, and the arching course of the blood vessels.

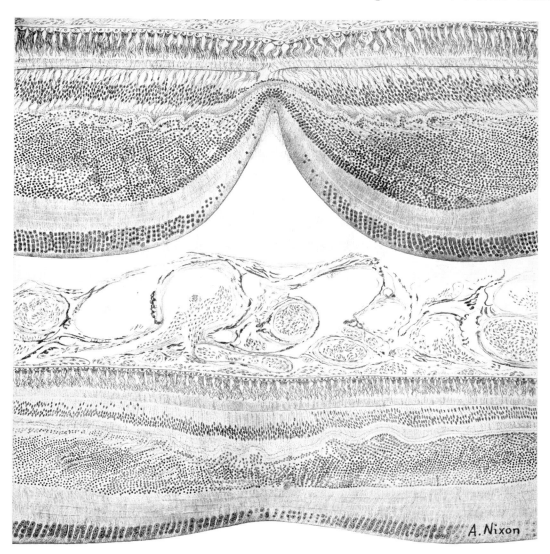

Fig. 171.—Upper figure shows a vertical section through the deep, funnel-shaped central fovea of an American Golden Eagle (*Aquila chrisaëtos*), the lower figure showing a shallow but wider lateral or posterior fovea of the same species. The first is believed to be used independently while in flight by this eminently keensighted bird of prey when scanning the country for prey, the second being used together with the lateral fovea of the opposite eye in binocular estimating of the distances, or essentially in stereoscopic vision. Approximate magnification 150×. (*Cf.* two foveae in each eye of the Barn Swallow, in Fig. 469; *see also* Fig. 172.)

This arrangement is present in the Philippine Tree Shrew (*Urogale everetti*), considered now to be the lowest in the order of Primates (*see* chap. XIV, 10). In a few species investigated, such as Cat and Dog, there is also a shallow, rudimentary, or perhaps orimental fovea, associated with a typical arching course of optic nerve fibers.

In many diurnal Rodents, such as Squirrel,

5. REGIONAL STRUCTURES OF BIRDS' RETINA. —The Vertebrates whose retina shows the greatest variety in locally differentiated structures are the Birds (Figs. 171–76). Frequently two foveae are found in each eye: a central, nasal or anterior, and a lateral, temporal or posterior, area and fovea.

In the Golden Eagle (*Aquila chrisaëtos*) the central fovea is a deep, narrow, funnel-shaped

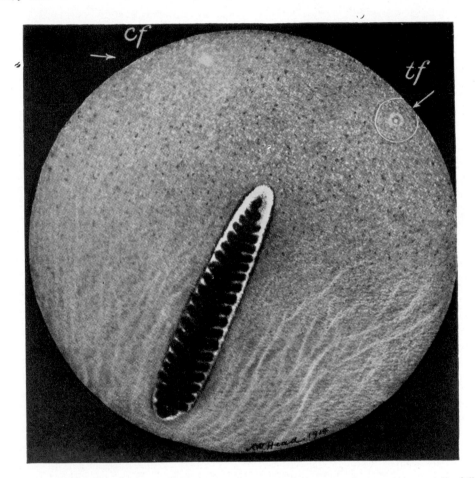

FIG. 172.—Fundus of the left eye of a Bald Eagle (*Haliaëtus leucocephalus*) showing two specially differentiated localities of the retina, one a central fovea and area (*cf*) of a somewhat blurred appearance, situated left above the pecten or "comb" (black corrugated structure), and a temporal or posterior fovea and area (*tf*) to right, behind the pecten. Seen ophthalmoscopically during life, the latter structure appears as a brilliant, round, white dot surrounded by a small light-green reflex ring inclosed in a brilliant, narrow, green circle indicating the temporal area. Photo of a colored plate taken from C. A. Wood, *The Fundus Oculi of Birds*, Chicago, 1917. (*Cf.* preceding figure.)

Chipmunk, Prairie Dog, and Woodchuck, the cone mosaic is very fine grained in an extensive territory, which may function as a fovea (Walls 1934; *see also* chap. XIV). In Ruminants there usually is a stripelike central area stretching across the retina (Fig. 170).

pit, the lateral fovea a shallow, wide depression (Fig. 171). In the former the photoreceptors are thinner and more numerous; in the latter, a wider area is used for sharp vision. Two foveae are typical of the diurnal birds of prey, such as the Eagles, Hawks, and their diminutive insectivorous counterparts, the Swallows (*see* chap. XIV, 8). Here the two lateral foveae of both eyes apparently serve as an instrument in binocular stereoscopic vision, while the central foveae function independently.

The avian visual apparatus represents a three-pronged mechanism with three visual axes—a common binocular axis directed for-

described in detail by a number of investigators (Chard & Gundlach; Chievitz 1891; Detwiler 1940, 1943; V. Franz; Fritsch; Hirschberg 1882; Kahmann; Kajikawa; Kolmer & Lauber 1930, 1936; W. Krause 1894; H. Müller 1863; Polyak 1941–48; Pütter; Rochon-Duvigneaud; Slonaker; Walls 1937, 1940, 1942; C. A. Wood 1917).

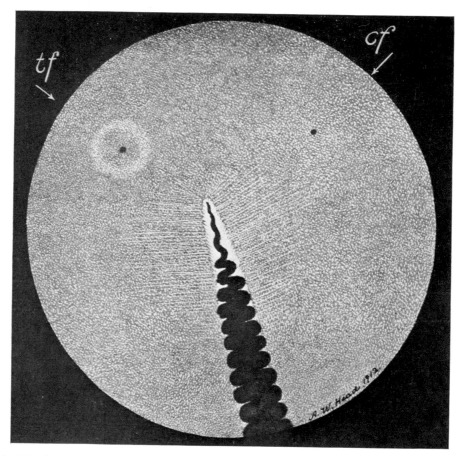

Fig. 173.—Fundus of the right eye of a European Chimney Swallow (*Hirundo* or *Helidon rustica*), identical with American Barn Swallow (*Helidon erythrogaster*), with two specially differentiated localities of the retina, both at about the same level above the upper extremity of the pecten. As in the Eagles, one is the central or anterior (*cf*) fovea, the other the temporal or posterior fovea (*tf*). In the living both foveae appear as small brown dots. The temporal fovea is surrounded by a circular light reflex made up of minute gray dots. Thin bundles of grayish, opaque optic nerve fibers radiate from the disk, to which is attached the pecten or "comb." Photo of a color plate from C. A. Wood, *The Fundus Oculi of Birds*, Chicago, 1917. (*Cf.* Figs. 172, 469.)

ward and two monocular axes on the sides, the "visual trident" of Rochon-Duvigneaud (*see also* Alaerts; Best 1930; Delage; Franz 1934; Portier; C. A. Wood 1917). In other species of Birds the number, shape, size, location, coloring, and other peculiarities of the locally differentiated retinal structures vary a great deal, depending on the modes of life, and have been

6. Central fovea of Reptiles, Fishes, and Cephalopods.—In the Reptiles (Lizards, Snakes, etc.), in conformity with their diurnal habits, a well-developed central area and fovea are often present—for example, in the Collard Lizard, Fence Swift, Skink, Agama, Iguana, Varanus, Tuatara (*Hatteria punctata* or *Sphenodon punctatum*) and *Dryophis*.

A relatively large, pitlike foveal depression, with a smooth, gently sloping surface, is present in the American Chameleon (*Anolis virginiensis; see* chap. XIV, 7), and a slightly smaller one in the Horned Lizard (*Phrynosoma cornutum*). The sharp-sighted Chameleon probably has the most differentiated fovea of all Vertebrates, a veritable "living microscope" (Del Duca 1930; Detwiler 1938, 1940; Detwiler & Laurens; V. Franz; G. L. Johnson 1927; Kahmann; Kal-

gneaud; Rochon-Duvigneaud & Roule; Schiefferdecker; Verrier; Wunder). Even a Cephalopod, *Bathyteutis*, has been found in possession of a foveal formation (Chun).

7. INVESTIGATION OF MINUTE FOVEAL STRUCTURES.—The minute structure of the central area and fovea was much studied, in particular in Monkeys, Apes, and Man. Since this work was mostly done with routine, nonanalyti-

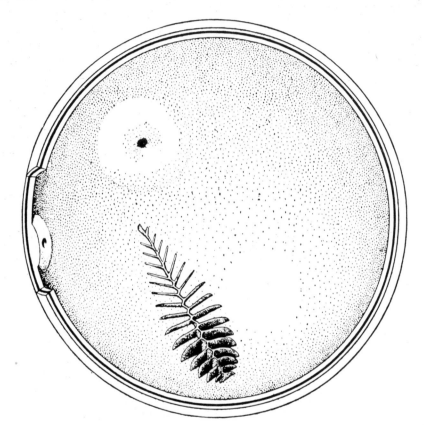

FIG. 174.—Fundus of the right eye of a British Kingfisher (*Alcedo ispida*). Example of a type of avian eye with two foveae-areae, a larger central one above the pecten and a smaller lateral or posterior fovea back of the pecten (*at left, in a cutaway*). From C. A. Wood, *The Fundus Oculi of Birds*, Chicago, 1917.

lius 1892; Knox 1823; Kolmer 1936; W. Krause; Laurens & Detwiler; H. Müller 1862; Osawa; S. Ramón y Cajal 1892–93, 1911; Rochon-Duvigneaud 1917, 1933, 1943; Rochon-Duvigneaud & Roule; Verrier 1930, 1933, 1935; Walls 1934, 1942).

Of the Fishes, practically all maritime Teleosteans have a more or less developed fovea, most pronounced in the species capable of extensive eye movements (Brauer; V. Franz; Gulliver; Kahmann; Kolmer; McEwan; Rochon-Duvi-

cal technique, important results have been obtained only with regard to the photoreceptor layer.

A systematic investigation of the synaptical relationships of neurons in the fovea and its vicinity with the Golgi method has so far been carried out only by S. Ramón y Cajal (1892–93, 1911) in the Chameleon and in some Birds, and with Golgi and Ehrlich methods in the Primates by the author of this book (Polyak 1941–48).

References: Alaerts 1935; F. Arnold 1851;

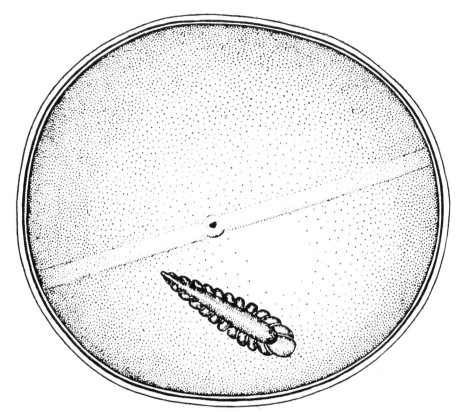

Fig. 175.—Fundus of the right eye of a Black-bellied Plover (*Squatarola squatarola*), with central fovea located within a long, narrow, stripe-shaped area or "retinal band" extending across the entire fundus. From C. A. Wood, *The Fundus Oculi of Birds*, Chicago, 1917.

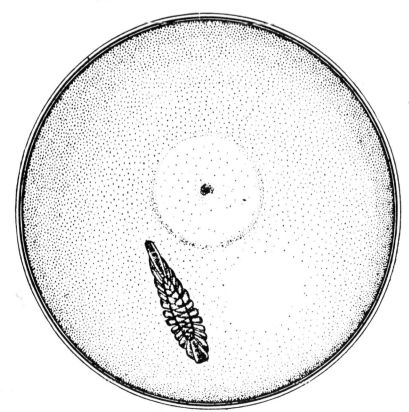

Fig. 176.—Fundus of the right eye of a Yellow-billed Cuckoo (*Coccyzus americanus*). This fundus has but a single circular and unusually large central area in front and above the upper extremity of the pecten, with a fairly spacious, funnel-shaped excavation in its center. From C. A. Wood, *The Fundus Oculi of Birds*, Chicago, 1917.

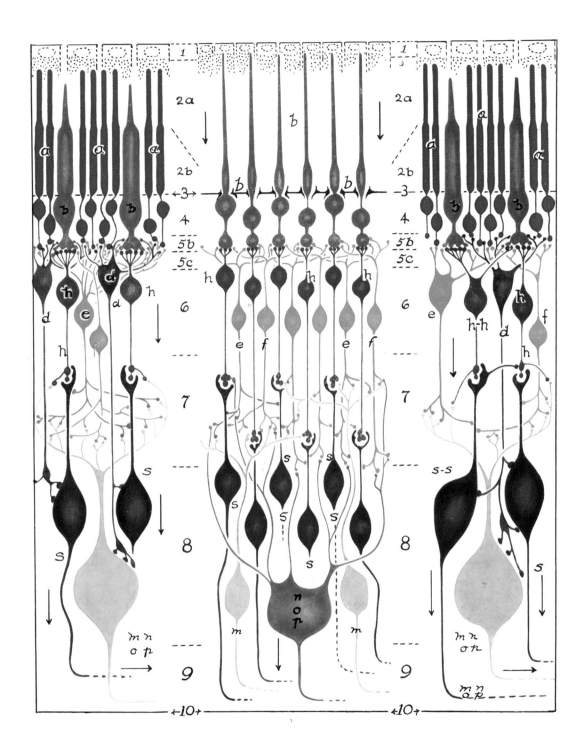

FIG. 177—General scheme of the synaptical connections of the primate retina : right and left sketches from the rod-bearing extra-foveal periphery, middle sketch from the rodless center of central fovea. Layers and zones are indicated in vertical columns separating the three sketches, with pigment epithelium (1), next to the chorioid membrane, the uppermost, and with the inner limiting membrane (10), next to the vitreous, the lowermost. *Abbreviations: a* rods ; *b* cones ; *d* mop bipolar ; *e* flat-top bipolar ; *f* brush-top bipolar ; *h, h-h* midget or cone bipolars ; *m, n, o, p* diffuse ganglion cells ; *s, s-s* midget ganglion cells. (*Compare* Figs. 146, 147, 178, 179.)

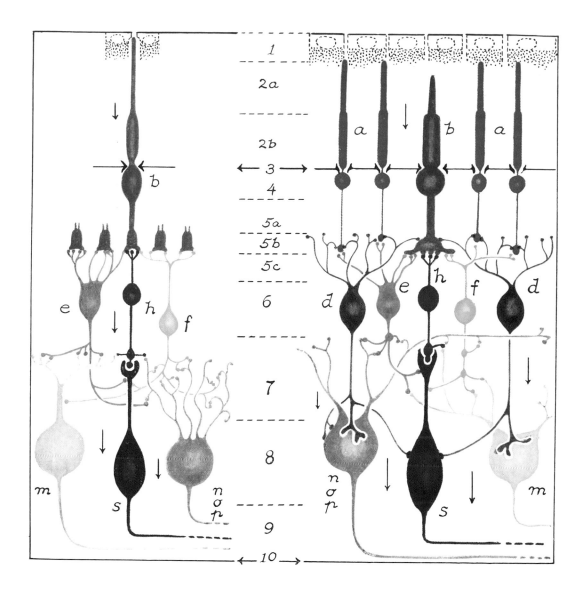

Fig. 178—Diagrams illustrating neuron constituents of the centripetal retinal pathways along which impulses are passed on to the brain, the left-hand sketch from the rodless foveal center, the right-hand sketch from the rod-bearing extra-foveal periphery. In the left-hand sketch all impulses are generated in the cones (*b*), whence they are transmitted to the bipolars and ganglion cells. Of the bipolars there are three varieties (*e, f, h*), the fourth variety (*d*) not being found here (so far). In the right-hand sketch both rods (*a*) and cones (*b*) are a source of impulses which are transmitted to all four bipolar varieties (*d, e, f, h*), and further to the ganglion cells (*m, nop, s*). Some rod and cone impulses, accordingly, use, on the bipolar level, the same structures (*d, e, f*), while the midget bipolars (*h*) are used for cone impulses alone. On the ganglion level all cell varieties serve both for the rod and cone impulses. The factors which determine the locality, quality, and intensity of the impulse ultimately entering the brain are many, and are as yet little understood : structural, pertaining to the kind and organization of synaptical organelles, and the very character of the constituent substance ; and the physical and dynamical factors which multifariously vary from case to case, as well as according to situation. (*Compare* Figs. 146, 147, 177, 179.)

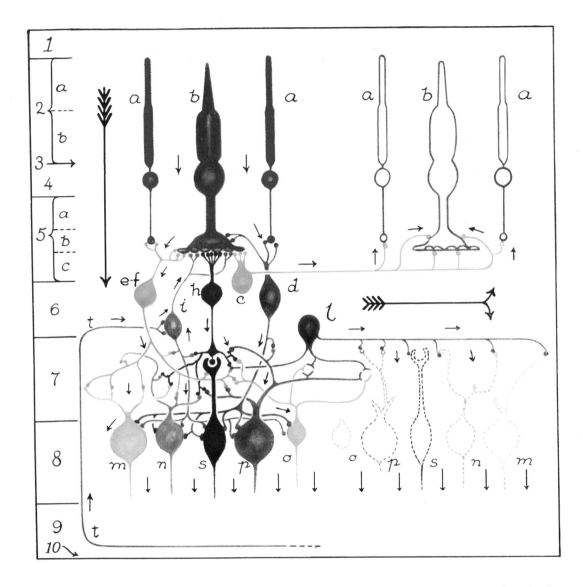

FIG. 179—Diagram of the essential constituent neurons and their synaptical relationships in the primate retina. The left solidly drawn half of the diagram symbolizes the structures used as a direct pathway of impulses from a given stimulated group of photoreceptors to the brain. The right half of the diagram given in outlines indicates structures surrounding the first group which are not directly stimulated by physical light, and are influenced only indirectly by way of associational neurons : the horizontal cells (*c*) and associational " amacrine " cells (*l*). In case the cones (*b*) are stimulated alone, all bipolars are activated, which in turn stimulate all varieties of ganglion cells ; the rods (*a*) in this setup remain inactive. When the rods (*a*) alone are stimulated, all bipolars except the midgets (*h*) are activated, again stimulating all ganglion varieties even though in a different way. When the cones are stimulated, in addition to the activation of bipolars, the horizontal cells (*c*) are also activated which would remain inactive if the rods alone were stimulated. The stimuli from the horizontal cells in turn are transferred upon a group of both varieties of photoreceptors at some distance from the point stimulated by the physical light. This influence may be interpreted as an active inhibition. A similar role may be ascribed to the centrifugal bipolars (*i*) by which the same group of stimulated cones is again influenced from the ganglion cell level, or from the brain via the centrifugal exogenous fibers (*t*). What role other associational neurons (*l*) play is as yet beyond calculation except that in some way they " condition " the structures surrounding the stimulated locality. (*Compare* Figs. 146, 147, 177, 178.)

Atkinson 1937; Bach & Seefelder; Bartels 1920, 1925, 1931; Bergmann 1854; Berres; Best 1930; Bichat 1800 (examined eyes of freshly guillotined victims of French Revolution, according to Koelliker 1851); Blumenbach; Bird & Schäfer 1895; Brauer 1902, 1908; Buzzi 1782; Chard & Gundlach 1938; Chevallereau & Polack 1907; Chievitz 1889, 1891; Chun 1903; A. Clerici 1943; Cohen & Weisberg 1950; Coiter 1573; Delage 1920; Del Duca 1930; Desmoulins; Detwiler 1924, 1938, 1939, 1940, 1941, 1942, 1943; Detwiler & Laurens 1921; Di Marzio 1937; Dimmer 1907; Dogiel 1892; Ewald; Fortin 1925; Fragonard (quoted by D. W. Soemmerring 1818, p. 25); V. Franz 1934; Fritsch 1911; H. Goldman 1949; Greeff 1899 (1900); Gulliver 1868; Gullstrand; Hartinger 1927, 1938; Hasse 1867; Heine 1926; Henle 1852; Hensen 1865, 1867; Hirschberg 1882; Hoeve 1912; Holm 1922; E. Home 1798; Hulke 1868; G. L. Johnson 1892, 1894, 1896–97, 1901, 1927; Kahmann 1933, 1934, 1936; Kajikawa 1923; Kallius 1898; J. Kepler 1604; Knox 1823; Koelliker 1851, 1854; Koelliker & Müller 1853; Koeppe 1918, 1920, 1921, 1937; Kolmer 1911, 1912, 1924, 1927, 1930, 1931; Kolmer & Lauber 1936; C. Krause 1842; W. Krause 1894, 1895; Kreiker 1930; Kühne 1878; Landolt 1871, 1901; Laurens & Detwiler 1921; Leber 1880; Leonardi 1930; Leuckart 1876; Lineback 1927; McEwan 1938; I. C. Mann 1950; Menner 1930, 1931, 1938; Merkel 1889; G. A. Michaelis 1838–42; P. Michaelis 1796; Michel 1874; H. Müller 1856–57, 1858–62, 1861, 1862, 1863, 1872; J. Müller 1826, 1840; Neumann 1921; Nordenson & Nordmark 1928; O'Day 1940; Osawa 1898, 1899; Pappenheim 1842; Polyak 1941, 1948; Portier 1923; Pütter 1902, 1908–12; S. Ramón y Cajal 1892–93 (1933), 1909–11, 1923; Reil 1797; Riccò 1876; Rochon-Duvigneaud 1917, 1933, 1943; Rochon-Duvigneaud & Rode 1943; Rochon-Duvigneaud & Roule 1927; Rollet & Jacqueau 1898; Rucker & Keys 1950; Schaper 1893; Schiefferdecker 1886, 1887; Schirmer 1864; Schleich 1922; Schmidt-Rimpler 1874, 1875, 1904; M. Schultze 1861, 1866, 1871, 1872; Schwalbe 1874, 1887; Slonaker 1897, 1902, 1918, 1921; D. W. Soemmerring 1818; S. Th. Soemmerring 1795, 1798; Sorsby; Stricht; Studnitz; Tansley 1950; Uyama; Vermes; Verrier 1927, 1928, 1929, 1930, 1932, 1933, 1935, 1936, 1937, 1938, 1940, 1945; Vintschgau 1853; Virchow 1901; A. Vogt 1918, 1921, 1937; H. Vogt 1902; Wadsworth 1880; W. C. Wallace 1836; Walls 1934, 1937, 1940, 1942; Walls & Judd; Welcker 1863; Wigger 1939; Wilmer 1934; Wolfrum 1908–23; C. A. Wood 1917; Woollard 1926, 1927; Wunder 1925, 1926, 1927, 1930; Zürn 1902. (*See* preceding section for additional references.)

Chapter VI

Optic Nerves, Chiasma, Tracts, and Subcortical Visual Centers

SEC. 1. COMPONENT PARTS OF THE VISUAL SYSTEM

1. GENERAL PLAN OF THE VERTEBRATE VISUAL SYSTEM.—The chain of physiological processes subjectively experienced as "sight" or "vision" is initiated in the retinal photoreceptors, the rods and cones, through the action of the luminous form of radiant energy called "light." From the photoreceptors of the eyes, the impulses pass along the optic nerves to the central nervous organ, the brain. In this organ reactions take place by means of which the individual adjusts himself in a suitable way to the environment whence the photic stimuli emanate or are reflected.

The visual adjustment may be either simple, immediate, and automatic or of varying degrees of complexity and remoteness in time. To use a few simple biological examples, when a cloud which has obscured an area moves away, the intensive light stimulus causes the pupils of the eyes to contract, and the stimulus is cut down. A very different situation arises when a shadow of specific shape, size, and motion—cast, for example, by a flying Eagle or Hawk—moves across the photoreceptor surface of the retina of a potential object of prey, such as a Rabbit. Even though this elicits but an infinitesimal dynamic change in the nervous structures of the retina, the "symbolical value" or the "specific biological significance" which such a stimulus represents for a Rabbit releases a complex chain of reactions whose purpose is the avoidance of danger of extinction. Its obverse takes place in the visual system of an Eagle or a Hawk, cruising for hours over the prairies and forests, deliberately scanning and mentally evaluating countless objects before its visual apparatus fulfils the biological role assigned to it: the acquisition of food or the meeting of a mate, both fundamental tasks in the maintenance and preservation of the individual and the species.

Some physiological demands upon the visual system, accordingly, are simple. To satisfy these smoothly and speedily, a relatively simply organized central mechanism suffices, which for the most part works automatically. Other situations, on the contrary, require complex machinery whose prompt response is largely determined by traces of past individual and phylogenetic experience stored in the cerebral substance.

2. AFFERENT VISUAL PATHWAY OR SYSTEM.—Whatever the visual stimuli, the impulses elicited in the retinal structures must be conveyed to the central nervous system and distributed therein, in order to serve any useful purpose. For in Vertebrates, as far as is known, there are no other avenues by means of which motor or other responses could be elicited by light. (Humoral agents, too, must act via the brain or spinal cord; local skin reflexes which do not lead directly to a change in animal behavior are excluded from present considerations.) The anatomical set of structures serving that purpose may be called the *afferent visual pathway or system*. It is made up of agglomerations of nerve cells and of bundles and tracts of nerve fibers organized into a complex mechanism, all held together by supporting and other structures which assure its physical existence and keep it in proper functioning order.

The visual system of Man and his primate relatives, the Monkeys and Apes, may be roughly subdivided into three parts according to anatomical features, location, and connections

(Fig. 180): (1) infranuclear or peripheral division (*r, on, ch, otr*); (2) subcortical visual nuclei, which represent the intermediate division (*cols, lgn, pgn, pulv*); and (3) supranuclear or central division (*vis rad, stra*). Each component structure of this system has its own peculiar features, in addition to those common to several or all. Each is connected with the others in some way, and all these components together form an intricately built and interdependently functioning mechanism.

3. INFRANUCLEAR DIVISION OF THE VISUAL SYSTEM.—This division of the visual system is composed of the retinae of the eyes (*r*), the two optic nerves or bundles (*on, nervi* or *fasciculi optici*), the bridgelike union or apparent intercrossing of the optic nerves, called the chiasma (*ch, χίασμα,* or *chiasma nervorum opticorum*), and of the two optic tracts (*otr, tracti optici*), by which the optic nerves apparently continue beyond the chiasma to the brain.

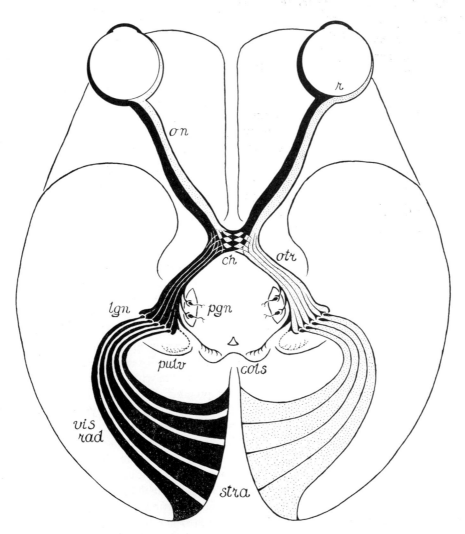

FIG. 180.—Diagram of the human visual system drawn into an outline of the brain. The infranuclear division is made up of the eyes, including the retinae (*r*), optic nerves (*on*), chiasma (*ch*), and optic tracts (*otr*), the latter terminating in subcortical visual centers, the principal one of which is the lateral geniculate nucleus (*lgn*), with subsidiary pregeniculate nucleus (*pgn*), superior colliculus (*cols*), and possibly also the pulvinar of the thalamus (*pulv*). The supranuclear division consists of the visual radiations (*vis rad*) originating in the lateral geniculate nuclei and terminating in the striate areae (*stra*) of the occipital lobes. Fibers originating in the inner or nasal halves of the retinae intercross in the chiasma. In consequence, while each optic nerve represents the retina of its own eye, the portions of the visual system above the chiasma represent ipsilateral homonymous halves of both retinae or contralateral halves of the fields of view.

4. Intermediate division of the visual system or subcortical visual centers.— The subcortical visual nuclei, centers, or stations are those parts of the brain in which the optic nerve fibers, originating in the retinae, terminate, or where the efferent fibers that terminate in the retinae originate. In each half of the brain there are, in Man and other Primates, at least three and possibly more such centers.

The principal and most elaborately organized center is the laminated lateral geniculate nucleus or body, or *l.g.n.* in the restricted sense (*lgn, nucleus geniculatus lateralis dorsalis* or *corpus geniculatum laterale dorsale*). It is a homologue of the dorsal portion (*pars dorsalis*) of the geniculate nucleus of Infraprimate Mammals.

The other subcortical visual center is a smaller, cap-shaped nucleus of gray substance adjoining the first on the dorsal, dorsomedial, and medial sides, the pregeniculate gray substance or nucleus (*pgn, substantia grisea praegeniculata, nucleus praegeniculatus, corpus geniculatum laterale ventrale*). This nucleus, in turn, is a homologue of the ventral portion (*pars ventralis*) of the geniculate nucleus of the Lower Mammals.

Both these nuclei, first described in this way by Nissl (*see* Koelliker 1896, pp. 540–43), and the medial geniculate nucleus (a constituent of the auditory system), represent the "metathalamus." With the hind part of the thalamus, called *pulvinar* or "cushion" (*pulv*), which also may be in a slight degree directly related to the visual system, they form a part of the inter- or betweenbrain, or *diencephalon*, one of the principal subdivisions of the brain.

The fourth subcortical visual center is the superior or anterior hillock (*cols, colliculus superior,* or *c. anterior*). It is a part of the midbrain or *mesencephalon* (another major subdivision of the brain), in particular, that called *tectum* or "roof." Each of the three or four nuclei is differently organized structurally, has its own particular connections with other parts of the brain and its own specific function.

5. Supranuclear division of the visual system.— The supranuclear or central division of the afferent visual pathway is represented by two bulky systems of nerve fibers originating from the nerve cells of the two laminated lateral geniculate nuclei, the visual or optic radiations, one in each cerebral hemisphere (*vis rad, radiatio optica*). In addition, those portions of the cerebral cortex directly related to the visual system, the striate areae, one area in each occipital lobe (*stra, area striata*), where the fibers of the visual radiations terminate, are also considered constituents of the supranuclear division.

The afore-mentioned nervous structures, peripheral, nuclear or subcortical, and cortical, are all in one way or another concerned in the transmission or reception of impulses generated in the photoreceptors of the retinae—the rods and cones. In some of these centers the retinal impulses initiate more or less subconscious reflex acts, automatic in character, which regularly accompany the visual act, for example, the constriction of the pupils of the eyes. Again, in other centers, especially in the laminated lateral geniculate nuclei and in the striate areae, the messages arriving from the retinae are further elaborated into physiological processes that underlie a conscious subjective experience of vision.

6. The visual system in a wider sense.— The structures discussed in the preceding paragraphs represent the afferent visual pathway and centers of the visual system in the restricted sense. There are numerous other structures, nervous and nonnervous, anatomically and functionally closely related to the afferent visual system which make its harmonious working possible. These are, on the one hand, the extrinsic and intrinsic eye muscles and the coordinating centers of the brain stem and cortex. Their task and that of other related structures, such as the various tracts, nuclei, and nerves, both sensory and motor, is to furnish a machine which can direct the gaze toward the object of visual attention and form sharp retinal images. On the other hand, to a visual system in the wider sense also belong portions of the occipital, parietal, and temporal regions of the cerebral cortex outside the striate areae, which are considered a substratum of the psychic visual functions.

References: Ariëns Kappers, Huber & Crosby 1936; Bender & Kanzer; Brouwer 1936; Coppez

& Fritz; D. J. Cunningham 1937; M. J. Dejerine 1895–1901; Foix & Nicolesco 1925; H. Gray
1942; M. Hines 1942; Ingvar 1925; Juba 1939;
Koelliker 1896; Kolmer & Lauber 1936; Kuhlenbeck 1937; O. Marburg 1942; Merkel 1874,
1885–90; Merkel & Kallius 1901; M. Minkowski 1930, 1939; H. Morris 1942; H. Obersteiner

1912; R. A. Pfeifer 1925, 1930; G. A. Piersol
1930; Poirier & Charpy 1901, 1904; Polyak
1941–48; T. J. Putnam 1942; Quain 1909–12;
S. Ramón y Cajal 1909–11; Rasmussen 1941;
Rønne 1944; Spalteholtz 1926; Tandler 1926–
29; Wilbrand & Saenger 1904; E. Wolff 1948;
Th. Ziehen 1899–1934.

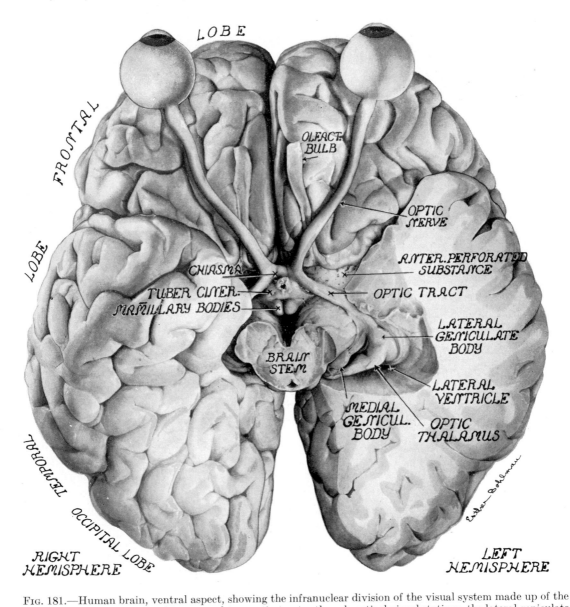

Fig. 181.—Human brain, ventral aspect, showing the infranuclear division of the visual system made up of the two eyeballs, optic nerves, the chiasma, and two optic tracts; the subcortical visual stations, the lateral geniculate body or nucleus and the pulvinar of the thalamus, are made visible on the left side (*right* in the figure) by removing portions of the temporal and occipital lobes of the brain. The right hemisphere of the brain intact, the brain stem with superior colliculi and the hypophysis removed.

SEC. 2. ORIGIN AND COURSE OF THE OPTIC NERVE

1. ORIGIN AND FUNCTIONAL SIGNIFICANCE OF OPTIC NERVE FIBERS.—The optic nerve fibers of the infranuclear division of the afferent visual pathway preponderantly, if not entirely, originate as axis cylinders or axons of the retinal ganglion cells (layer *8* in Fig. 128; *cf. also* chap. V, 2 [9, 10], 5). It is probable that the axons of all or almost all nerve cells in the eighth layer of the retina and those in the sixth layer designated as "displaced ganglion cells" or "Dogiel's cells" help make up the optic nerves.

When, in a monkey, an optic nerve, a tract, or a lateral geniculate nucleus is cut or destroyed, if care is taken to avoid any damage to the blood supply of the eyeball, the ganglion cells of the eighth layer suffer a retrograde degeneration within a few days and disappear almost completely in a few weeks. (This occurs in the entire expanse of the retina if the optic nerve of that eye is cut and in the corresponding homonymous halves only, when one optic tract is interrupted or one lateral geniculate nucleus destroyed.) The few remaining ganglion cells also show more or less pronounced pathological conditions: reduction in size, uneven outlines, displaced nuclei, and poor staining. The loss is especially pronounced in the central area close to the edge of the foveal depression. Here the ganglion layer, normally containing from six to eight tiers of well-formed, deeply stained, and closely packed cells, is reduced to a single or double discontinuous row of pathologically changed cells intermingled with a few nuclei which belong to the blood vessels and to the supporting tissue. A few nerve cells, however, remain in fairly good condition for as long as one year after the experiment.

Why some ganglion cells of the retina survive, even after a prolonged lapse of time, is a question to which no positive answer can be given at present. By way of conjecture, it is possible to assume that the surviving ganglion cells are a part of the intraretinal association system, whose axis cylinders do not leave the membrane but terminate in it not far from their origin, in analogy with the horizontal cells, *c* (*see* chap. V, 6 [2]). Another possibility is that these are aberrant or freak cells, incompletely differentiated and in some ways not conforming

to type; such cells are found in small numbers among other categories of the retinal elements, notably among the bipolars.

Whether all axis cylinders of the optic nerve, in Man and other Primates, belong to the category of afferent neurons—that is, those conveying impulses generated in the retina to the brain—or whether there are also efferent axons, or those originating in the brain and terminating in the retina, by means of which central influences may reach the photoreceptors, is a problem still to be solved. From the investigations of S. Ramón y Cajal (1888, 1889, 1892–93, 1895, 1911), Bouin (1895), Dogiel (1895), Weber (1945), and others, the presence of such fibers is fairly certain in Birds and in Axolotl, but they have not yet been definitely shown to exist in Mammals. (*Cf.* chap. V, 7.)

2. COURSE OF OPTIC NERVE FIBERS WITHIN THE RETINA.—In the ninth layer of the retina, the optic nerve fibers are assembled into numerous bundles, fewer and containing coarse fibers in the retinal periphery and more numerous and made up of a great number of delicate fibers in the axial or central region.

Examined in suitably made whole-mount preparations, for example, stained intravitally with methylene blue (Fig. 162) or observed ophthalmoscopically with proper technique (Fig. 148), all fiber bundles on the nasal side are seen to converge in straight lines, like the spokes of a wheel, toward the hub represented by the optic papilla or disk. On the temporal side, however, only a few of the many short, delicate fiber bundles, those originating from the nasal edge of the fovea and passing directly to the temporal margin of the papilla, take a straight horizontal course. All other bundles above the horizontal meridian originating in the upper, lower, and temporal segments of the foveal pit circle in more or less distinct arches or sweeping curves above and below the fovea to the papilla. This is as true of the bundles arising from the upper, lower, and temporal segments of the central area surrounding the fovea, which, in the aggregate, form the "papillomacular bundle," as it is of those bundles arising from the corresponding portions of the extra-areal temporal

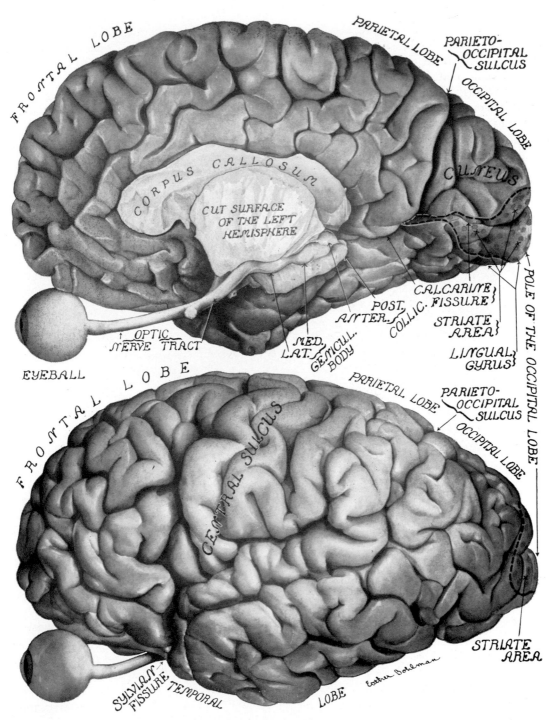

FIG. 182.—Human brain, upper figure showing the inner aspect of the right hemisphere, lower figure showing the outer aspect of the left hemisphere. Visible parts of the visual system are the eyeballs, optic nerves, chiasma, optic tracts, lateral geniculate nucleus or body, anterior or superior colliculus, and striate areae of the occipital lobes (*coarsely stippled*).

periphery and the adjacent zone of the nasal retinal half.

The arciform bundles of the optic nerve fibers follow rather closely the larger arteries (*a*) and veins (*v*), which, from above and below, encircle the central area, into which they send numerous smaller blood vessels. An obvious result of this arrangement is the elimination of the obstructing optic nerve fibers from the central area and fovea. An arching course of the periaxial fibers, similar to that found in Man, Monkeys, Apes, and the nocturnal *Nyctipithecus* and Tarsier (Fig. 149), is also found in some other Mammals, such as the Cat, which possess a distinct central area, even though they do not have a pronounced foveal depression. (*Cf.* chap. V, 10 [7], 11 [2].)

vision line, called the *raphé* or "seam," stretching on the temporal side from the fovea along the horizontal meridian to the *ora serrata* (Figs. 149, 162). It is a line which separates bundles of nerve fibers originating in the upper temporal quadrant from those originating in the lower temporal quadrant. This anatomical cleavage, found in the human and simian retina and in that of the Tarsier, is an important architectural arrangement whose effect continues in the visual pathway as far as the visual centers of

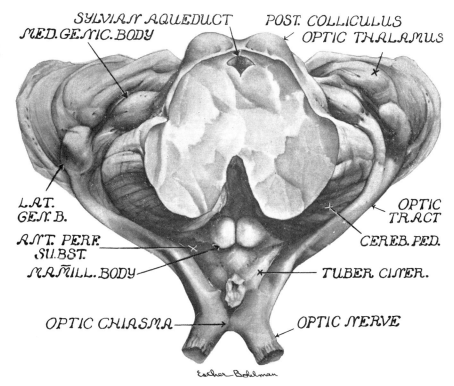

Fig. 183.—Posterior aspect of the human midbrain and betweenbrain, showing optic nerves joined in the chiasma and continuing, as optic tracts which terminate in subcortical visual centers, in the lateral geniculate nuclei or bodies, and seemingly also in the thalami.

3. Temporal raphé or seam of the retinal nerve fibers.—Another noteworthy feature of the primate retina, directly related developmentally and functionally to the formation of the foveal depression, is a horizontal di-

the cerebral cortex. It is the anatomical basis of the homonymous quadrantic hemianopias of central origin. (*Cf.* secs. 6, 11, this chapter; chap. VII, 3 [3], 4, 6; chap. X, 8, 9; and chap. XII, 6, 7, 8.)

The separation of the optic nerve fibers along the horizontal meridian temporal to the central fovea is somewhat less distinctly duplicated by a "vascular raphé." In this zone only small blood vessels and capillaries cross the horizontal line; the larger arterial and venous stems are absent here.

In living persons of the white race, the arciform course of the retinal optic nerve fibers, ordinarily not visible ophthalmoscopically, may be seen only when red-free light is used (A. Vogt 1918, 1921, 1937; *see also* colored plates in Heine 1918; Wilmer 1934; Kolmer 1936; Atkinson 1937; Di Marzio 1937; for early references *see* chap. V, 11 [2]). In colored races the peculiarly arranged fibers around the optic disk and central area are noticeable as translucent streaks (Johnson 1901).

4. Functional and pathophysiological significance of the arching perifoveal optic nerve fibers.—The obvious functional effect of the peculiar arrangement of optic nerve fibers in the vicinity of the central fovea is precisely the same as that of the foveal depression. Since, because of developmental and teleological-creative factors (*see* chap. XIII, 1, 2), light must first pass through the entire thickness of the retinal substance, in order to reach the photoreceptor layer situated outside (*2*, in Fig. 161), an inordinate thickening of the inner layers (from *10* to *4*) and, in particular, of the optic nerve fibers (*9*) would be an unwelcome impediment precisely in the axial region where their numerical increase, necessitated by the refinement of spatial discrimination, is greatest. It is therefore logical to find the inner layers of the retina in this locality displaced laterally, a process most completely carried out in the foveal center, the foveola (*see* chap. V, 10 [7]). Conversely, this displacement unavoidably results in the ridgelike accumulation of nerve cells around the foveal pit and, at a somewhat greater distance from it, of the more mobile optic nerve fibers. What evolutionary and developmental factors brought about such highly purposeful and useful arrangements remains at present entirely unknown.

The anatomical, physiological, and pathological consequences of the lateral or centrifugal displacement of nerve cells and fiber bundles in the central area are easier to understand. Anatomically, the result is a separation of the upper from the lower extrafoveal fibers by those that originate in the foveal depression and its immediate vicinity. That this should be so along the stretch between the fovea and the optic papilla—since the fibers of the retina are arranged in a flat plane—is self-evident. The effect of the interposition of the "papillomacular bundle" and foveal pit between the upper and the lower extrafoveal fibers, however, is felt far beyond the central area. For only by circuitous routes can the fiber bundles arising from the more distant extra-areal zones of the two temporal retinal quadrants reach the papilla, while avoiding an overlapping of the foveal pit and its fibers. This, in turn, necessitates separation of the upper quadrantic fibers from the lower all along the temporal stretch of the horizontal meridian as far as the ora serrata. Literally, the extra-areal optic nerve fibers of the upper and lower temporal quadrants become separated by the interposition of the foveal-areal or "macular" fibers. The significance of this fact for the understanding of the intrinsic organization of the entire visual system, especially of the mechanism responsible for quadrantic hemianopia, has been studied by Rønne (1909, 1917, 1919, 1944) and is dealt with in detail in chapters VII, 4, 6; IX, 8; and XII, 6, 7, 8, in this book.

The peculiar arciform arrangement of the circumfoveal fiber bundles is apparently responsible for a curious entoptical phenomenon seen under certain conditions and known as "blue arcs of the retina" (Purkinje 1825; H. Müller 1859; Ladd-Franklin 1926, 1928; Judd 1929; B. Friedman 1931; Newhall 1937). At any rate, the arrangement of these fibers is practically identical with the "blue arcs" found by Dolecek & Launay (1945). The interesting question concerning the mechanism and factors involved in the production of "blue arcs" still remains to be answered. The impedance of the rays of light normally passing through the thick fiber bundles or their change in quality and intensity in comparison with the surrounding regions, where the rays have a freer course, is the probable cause of different responsiveness in the archlike zones of the photoreceptors, which are normally relatively screened off by corresponding bundles, which, during the entoptical stimulation, may produce this peculiar subjective phenomenon.

5. Fascicular composition of the optic papilla.—The individual bundles of optic nerve fibers which originate in limited segments of the retinal surface, in spite of the arciform course in and around the central area, preserve, on the whole, their relative position as they stream toward the papilla (*optpap* in Fig. 225; *see also* Figs. 148, 149). In the nasal region of the retina, where the arrangement of bundles is almost perfectly radial, this is obvious. Here all fibers from a given narrow wedge-shaped segment at the papillar margin also appear to be of a more or less semicircular shape. Here the extra-areal fibers streaming from the peripheral regions, because of their dislocation in order to avoid the central area and fovea, are assembled principally at two points on the papillar margin: in the left eye, as seen with the ophthalmo-

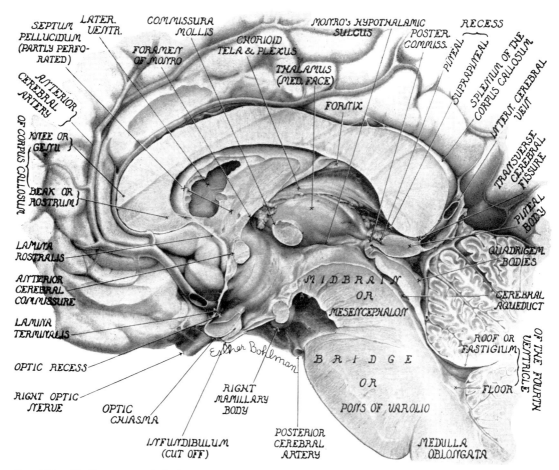

Fig. 184.—Median aspect of the human betweenbrain and brain stem cut along sagittal plane (*right half*). The parts of the visual system visible are a stump of the right optic nerve, the cut surface through the optic chiasma, and the quadrigeminal bodies or colliculi of the midbrain. Note structures and spaces immediately adjacent to optic chiasma, which are: the lamina terminalis; the optic recess of the third cerebral ventricle; the infundibulum or "funnel" of the diencephalon (with hypophysis torn off); the anterior cerebral artery in front of the chiasma; and the posterior cerebral artery behind the infundibulum and mammillary body in the interpeduncular fossa. Note also the position of the quadrigeminal bodies relative to the pineal gland and to the cerebral aqueduct, through which the third ventricle, and through it the two lateral ventricles, communicate with the fourth cerebral ventricle, all structures important in normal exchange of cerebrospinal fluid and in the cerebral pathology of this region. (For further topography *see* accompanying figures, and X-ray figure of the head in chap. VIII, and also colored plates in chap. X.)

segment converge toward the same point in the papilla.

In the temporal region, because of the arciform course of bundles around the central area and fovea, the areas that belong to a given fiber

scope in an upright picture, those from the upper quadrants between approximately 1 and 2 o'clock, and those from the lower temporal quadrants between 4 and 5 o'clock, at the papilla; and in the right eye between 10 and 11 and between 7 and 8 o'clock at the papilla, respectively. Between these two sections there is a rather wide intermediate temporal sector, in the left eye corresponding to between 2 and 4 o'clock, and in the right eye to between 8 and 10 o'clock, where the numerous thin bundles from the central area and fovea reach the papilla: the "papillomacular bundle."

In the papilla, accordingly, fibers from the axial region of the retina occupy an approximately wedge-shaped temporal segment, surrounded from above and below by bundles originating in the extensive extra-areal portions of the upper and lower temporal quadrants.

Since in the optic nerve there is a further shifting of the bundles by which the axial or areal-foveal fibers are gradually brought into a central position, it is possible that such displacement is being prepared during the intra-retinal course. For example, the extreme peripheral fibers, originally superficial, may grad-

ually sink deeper and be the first to slip into the papilla, in this way leaving the fibers from regions closer to the central fovea and area on the papillar surface and thus bring them closer to the center of the papilla.

References: Arey & Gore; Atkinson 1937; Best 1919, 1920; Cone & Macmillan 1932; Deyl 1896; Di Marzio 1937; Dogiel 1892; Dolecek & Launay 1945; J. N. Evans 1939; Friedman 1931, 1942; Greeff 1899 (1900); Heine 1918; Hines 1942; J. Hoeve 1919; Igersheimer 1918–20; G. L. Johnson 1894, 1901; Judd 1927; Koelliker 1854; Kolmer & Lauber 1936; C. Krause 1842; W. Krause 1895; Ladd-Franklin 1926, 1928; Lauber 1927; Loddoni; Michaelis 1836, 1842; Michel 1874; H. Müller 1859; Newhall 1937; Pappenheim 1842; Polyak 1941, 1942, 1948; Purkinje 1825; Putnam 1942; Rønne 1909, 1917, 1919, 1944; Schwalbe 1874, 1887; Sjaaff 1923; Sjaaff & Zeeman 1924; Traquair 1939; A. Vogt 1918, 1921, 1937; Wallace 1836; A. Weber 1945; Wilmer 1934.

SEC. 3. HISTOLOGY OF THE OPTIC NERVES, CHIASMA, AND TRACTS

1. GENERAL REMARKS ON THE OPTIC NERVE. —The optic nerves—also termed *optic fascicles,* since, for embryological reasons, they may be compared with the fiber tracts of the brain—are thick, tough, and more or less cylindrical structures, one to each eye, by means of which the eyeballs are connected with the brain. At present, however, only the portions between the eyeballs and the chiasma are customarily called "optic nerves" (*on* in Fig. 180; *see also* Figs. 181, 182, 183, 184). The portions between the chiasma and the subcortical visual nuclei of the brain are called "optic tracts" (*otr* in Fig. 180, also above-mentioned figures; *see* chap. II, 12 [7]).

Each optic nerve is made up of a considerable number of bundles of myelinated optic nerve fibers—preponderantly, if not entirely, axis cylinders of the retinal ganglion cells—firmly held together by supporting tissue (Fig. 185). The appearance of the optic nerve on a cross-section varies. In the longer intraorbital portion it is fairly round or cylindrical in shape; in the posterior segment inclosed in the bony optic foramen or channel, just before it joins the nerve from the opposite eye in the bridgelike

chiasma, it becomes somewhat flattened in the dorsoventral sense. The diameter, without the arachnoid and dural sheaths, varies, accordingly, from 3 to 5 mm., more or less. The length of the optic nerves, in adult human individuals, attains approximately 5.5 cm., or slightly more than 2 inches. In a fully grown male Gorilla, the famous "Bushman" of Lincoln Park Zoo in Chicago, a dorsoventral diameter of the optic nerve was 3 mm., a transverse diameter 5–6 mm., and the total length of the nerve the same as in Man.

It remains an open question whether, in addition to the fibers that are the axis cylinders of the retinal ganglion cells, there are other fibers in the optic nerve whose origin is in the brain and which may terminate in the retina. The fact that a severed optic nerve degenerates completely does not necessarily militate against the presence of such efferent fibers, as pointed out previously (chap. V, 7).

2. STRUCTURE OF THE OPTIC NERVE.—In its anterior portion close to the eyeball, the optic nerve, in Man and other Primates, appears, on cross-section, to be an assemblage of approximately five hundred bundles of varying sizes and shapes (Fig. 185). Each bundle is made up of a number of myelinated optic nerve fibers differing considerably in thickness (fibers devoid of myelin sheaths, found in many Lower Vertebrates, according to Bruesch & Arey, are absent in Man and Monkey). The bundles are separated from one another by rather coarse septa (sing. *septum*, in Latin) or partition-like sheets of interstitial connective tissue repre-

themselves. This tissue appears to be exclusively neuroglial, chiefly represented by the astrocytes and their fibrous expansions. Blood vessels of any kind, including capillaries, seem to be absent in the fiber bundles.

The pattern of the bundles and partitions is not the same along the whole length of the optic nerve but changes considerably in different localities and possibly also in different individuals. In the distal portion of the nerve close to

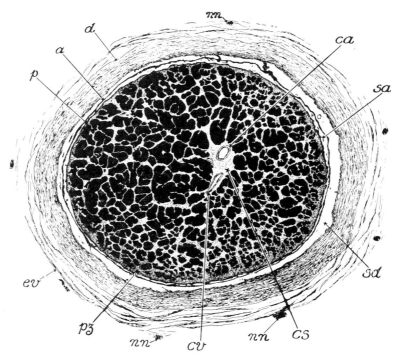

Fig. 185.—Cross-section of the human optic nerve close to the eyeball. The nerve proper is made up of numerous larger and smaller bundles of myelinated nerve fibers (*solid black*) separated from one another by *septa* (sing. *septum*), or partitions of connective tissue containing blood vessels. The connective tissue is most abundant in the center, where it forms a "central supporting tissue strand" (*cs*) containing the central artery (*ca*) and central vein (*cv*). Just underneath the pial membrane (*p*) a peripheral zone of connective tissue (*pz*) may be distinguished. On the outside the optic nerve is surrounded by three sheaths or vaginae: the pia mater (*p*) and arachnoid (*a*), which are thin and interconnected by strands and inclose the subarachnoid space (*sa*), and the thick and tough dural sheath (*d*), whose epivaginal connective tissue (*ev*) is the outermost. The space inclosed by the dura and arachnoid is the subdural space (*sd*). Attached to the dura from outside are several thin dural nerves (*nn*). Weigert method of staining, magnified 20×.

sented by the connective cells and fibers (collagenous and elastic).

In a cross-section through the nerve, the interstitial septa appear as a network in whose meshes bundles of nerve fibers lie imbedded. Small blood vessels, both arteries and veins, the majority of which are apparently of pial origin, are present in fair numbers in the interfascicular partitions. Contrasting with this is a delicate network of interstitial tissue within the bundles

the eyeball the largest accumulation of connective tissue is in its center. Here it forms the central connective tissue strand (*cs*), in which the central blood vessels, an artery (*ca*), a vein (*cv*), and a few smaller branches are imbedded. In the longer proximal portion of the orbital division of the optic nerve closer to the optic foramen, this structure and the central vessels are absent. (*See* chap. X, 2, on central vessels.)

The immediate investment of the entire

trunk of the optic nerve proper and, in fact, a part of its substance is a thin layer, the most superficial, of the connective tissue framework: the pia mater or pial sheath (*p*). It contains numerous small blood vessels, both arteries and veins, whose branches penetrate with the connective septa into the thickness of the nerve which they supply with blood. Outside the pial sheath and not far from it is the second envelope of the optic nerve, which, owing to its thinness, is called the arachnoid membrane or spider-web sheath (*a*). This delicate membrane is devoid of blood vessels. It is attached to the underlying pial sheath by numerous thin threads, filaments, and strands. The narrow space inclosed by it and the pial sheath is the subarachnoid space (*sa*). The pial and arachnoid sheaths, because of their thinness, are called leptomeninges or "thin envelopes" (sing. *leptomeninx*).

The third and outermost investment of the optic nerve is a thick, tough fibrous sheath, the dura mater or dural sheath (*d*). Because of its thickness and toughness, it is called *pachymeninx*. It is composed principally of a thick, dense, inner circular layer and a more loosely arranged outer layer of connective tissue cells and fibers. The latter, principally made up of longitudinal fibers, is the epivaginal connective tissue or zone (*ev*). The dural sheath contains but few small blood vessels, mostly in the epivaginal zone, and a fair number of thin nerves (*nn*) in the same zone, each nerve made up of a few thick, well-myelinated nerve fibers. The space between the dura and the arachnoid is the subdural space (*sd*). It is crossed by a small number of somewhat thicker trabecules or threads.

At the proximal or central end of the optic nerve the three investments—the two thin inner leptomeninges, and the single outer thick pachymeninx—are continuous with the corresponding envelopes of the brain—the pia, arachnoid, and dura mater. At the optic channel the dural sheath merges with the periosteal lining of that locality and of the fundus of the orbital cavity, the periorbita. At the distal, peripheral, or bulbar end the dural sheath of the optic nerve alone is continuous with the scleral tunic of the eyeball, whereas the two leptomeninges terminate blindly here.

The arrangement and other peculiarities of the constituent nerve fibers seen in cross-section show noteworthy variations in different sections of the optic nerve. In most of the bundles the fibers vary more or less in thickness or caliber. That is, in addition to the thin fibers, there are always some thick ones. The average thickness of fibers, however, varies considerably from place to place. In the portion of the nerve at some distance from the eyeball, the coarsest fibers are found in a peripheral zone along the circumference, the width of that zone not exceeding one-tenth to one-eighth of the nerve diameter. Conversely, the thinnest fibers are assembled in the centrally located bundles surrounding the central connective tissue strand containing central blood vessels. Here the bundles are thickly packed with a great number of very thin fibers, the thinnest in the nerve and the most nearly uniform in caliber and distribution. In the immediate vicinity of the eyeball, bundles composed largely of thin fibers are found along the temporal margin.

3. STRUCTURE OF THE OPTIC CHIASMA AND TRACTS.—The **X**-shaped junction of the optic nerves, named the *chiasma* by the ancient anatomists because of its similarity to the Greek letter chi (χ), is a short, stout bridge, through which, in Mammals, a partial exchange of fibers between the two nerves is made. Those fibers which, in Man and other Primates, originate in the somewhat larger nasal half of the retina, pass from one nerve, through the chiasma, and join the opposite optic tract, whereas the fibers arising from the temporal side of the retina proceed in the lateral portions of the chiasma, without decussation, from the optic nerve to the corresponding optic tract.

In anatomical appearance, histological structure, physiological significance, and phylogenetic origin and perfection, the optic chiasma is unique among all cranial nerves and probably among all nerves of the peripheral nervous system, approaching in its peculiar arrangement that of the "commissures" of the brain and spinal cord.

The gross anatomical appearance of the chiasma is subject to considerable individual variation, in the length, width, and thickness of the bridgelike portion and in the four angles formed by the four nervous bars which it joins.

There are short and stout forms of the chiasma with acute anterior and posterior angles and obtuse lateral ones. The other extremes are those where the bridge is broadened and flattened, with resulting wide anteroposterior angles. Various anomalies are transitions to pathology, with a separation of one or another part as a distinct bundle, or atrophy, an abnormality which, in the extreme, culminates in the absence of the chiasma. (*Cf.* chap. II, 8 [4].)

In histological makeup the chiasma and the optic tracts vary somewhat from the optic nerves, in that the former largely lack connective tissue partitions. In a cross-section through the optic tract the nerve fibers appear, therefore, more evenly distributed. In the chiasma, however, owing to the partial crossing, numerous minute fiber bundles intertwine in various ways, producing a peculiar pattern which resembles in places the "herringbone" weave in cloth.

Both the chiasma and the optic tracts are invested by the meningeal sheaths: a rather thick pia mater containing numerous blood vessels and bounded on the outside by a thin, avascular arachnoid membrane. The exception is the side where the chiasma and the tracts are attached to the brain. Here the leptomeningeal investments are absent, and the chiasma and tracts merge directly with the cerebral substance. A special dural or pachymeningeal sheath, on the other hand, is absent both in the chiasma and in the optic tracts and is represented by a common dural envelope incasing the entire cerebrum. (*See* sec. 5, this chapter, on the comparative anatomy; *see* sec. 6, on the fascicular composition of the chiasma.)

4. FIBER NUMBER IN THE OPTIC NERVES OF VARIOUS VERTEBRATE SPECIES.—The number, kind, and arrangement of fibers in the optic nerve vary a great deal, depending upon the biological importance and use of the visual system in a particular vertebrate species. In general, in those animals in which vision is the most important sense, the optic nerve is relatively thick and rich in fibers. In contrast is the thin optic nerve of species relying chiefly upon other senses, such as smell, taste, and hearing.

The optic nerves of Primates and Birds, in which sight has become the dominant sense, contain by far the greatest number of fibers. In the human optic nerve, for example, the number of the fibers which may be counted on a cross-section reaches and even exceeds the formidable figure of 1,000,000 (W. Krause; Polyak 1941, 1948; Bruesch & Arey 1942). This is in remarkable contrast with the fibers in the human auditory nerve, which, on the average, number only 30,000, although hearing is second in importance to sight (Rasmussen 1940).

In the Macaque, the number of optic nerve fibers, according to Bruesch & Arey (1942), is as high as 1,200,000. Other figures, according to the same authors, are: Hagfish 1,579; Brook Lamprey 5,217; Dogfish Shark pup 113,000; Guitar Fish 74,600; Sting Ray 39,700; Shovelnosed Sturgeon 13,500; Bowfin 114,000; Goldfish 53,000; Bullhead 26,000; *Necturus maculosus* 362; *Ambystoma tigrinum* 2,004 (6,000–10,000, according to Herrick 1941); Toad 15,500; Frog 29,000; Turtle 105,000; baby Alligator 105,000; Horned Toad 129,000; Duck 408,000; Chicken 414,000; Pigeon 988,000; Canary Bird 428,000; Duck-Bill or *Platypus* 32,000; Opossum 82,100; Small Brown Bat 6,940; Cat 119,000; Dog 154,000; Rabbit 265,000; Pig 681,000; Sheep 649,000.

The small number of fibers in Fish and in Amphibians living in a poorly lighted habitat (Bullhead, Goldfish, *Necturus*, *Ambystoma*) or in those that are largely parasitic (Hagfish, Lamprey) is remarkable. The macrosmatic or nocturnal Fishes, such as the Shark and Sturgeon, are little, if any, better supplied.

The largely nocturnal Mammals, such as the Opossum, Dog, and Cat, rank considerably below the lowly Rabbit in the number of optic nerve fibers; but most poorly provided of all are the macroacoustic Bats.

The Birds, with their exquisitely developed sight, equal in this respect, on the whole, the Primates, whose visual system is the best developed among Mammals. The great number of optic nerve fibers in the Pigeon, Pig, and Sheep is noteworthy.

Another interesting fact obtained by Bruesch & Arey is the absence of fibers devoid of myelin in most Mammals, including the Monkey and Man, and in all Birds which they investigated. This appears to indicate an improvement of performance or quality of function, in comparison with the lower ranks of Vertebrates, in which a considerable number of fibers are without myelin.

The observation of these authors that in man "some 38% of all fibers entering or leaving the central nervous system do so by way of the optic nerves" appears of particular significance. This fact, compared with the relatively small number of fibers in the auditory nerve found by Rasmussen, does as much as a lengthy analysis to prove the overwhelming importance of human vision. A true appraisal of the importance of vision in living beings, however, may be expected only after a systematic investigation of all principal factors concerned: anatomical, physiological, and biological. (*Cf.* chap. XIV.)

References: Adrian & Matthews 1927; Arey & Bickel; Arey, Bruesch & Castanares; Arey & Gore; Arey & Schaible; C. Behr 1935; Brouwer 1936; Bruesch & Arey 1940, 1942; Chacko 1948; Charlton 1933; Cone & McMillan; Davenport & Barnes; Deyl 1895; Greeff 1899; B. Gudden 1874–79; Gundlach 1933; Fleischl 1883; Haden 1947; Haller von Hallerstein; Henckel 1898; C. J. Herrick 1941; Hesse & Doflein; Hovelaque 1927; Kolmer & Lauber 1936; W. Krause 1880; Kuhnt 1879; Lauber 1902; Leuckart 1876; López Enríquez 1926–48; Merkel 1874, 1885; Merkel & Kallius 1901; Mureddu 1930; Palmer 1912; Penfield 1932; R. A. Pfeifer 1930; Polyak 1941, 1948; Pütter 1908–12; F. Salzer 1880; Salzmann 1912; Sanna 1930; Schwalbe 1887; Walls 1942; E. Wolff 1948; Zwanenburg 1915.

SEC. 4. COURSE AND TERMINATION OF THE FIBERS OF THE INFRANUCLEAR DIVISION OF THE VISUAL SYSTEM IN GENERAL

1. ANATOMICAL PROCEDURES FOR THE STUDY OF THE COURSE AND TERMINATION OF THE OPTIC NERVES.—There are many methods by means of which it is possible to determine where a certain nerve or bundle of nerve fibers originates and terminates in the brain. The first step, ordinarily, is to examine gross specimens and sections without the aid of elaborate magnifying apparatus, such as a microscope, or with the help of slight magnification only. This may be followed by a careful dissection of well-fixed specimens. In this way, by duplicating the procedure of the anatomists of the past, much may be learned about the optic nerves and tracts and about the various related nuclei and centers of the brain (Figs. 181–84). As pointed out previously, however (*see* chaps. II, III, IV), this method permits us to determine with some certainty only relatively crude connections, while the minute relationships cannot be definitely determined in this way. More information may be gained through the study of a series of sections of specimens stained by one of the modern methods (e.g., Nissl's, Weigert's; *see* Polyak, *The Retina*, chaps. II–VI).

Far more reliable results may be obtained by combining one of the histological methods with the experiment. The procedure of Marchi is such an experimental histopathological method, much utilized in the investigation of the fiber

systems of the brain and spinal cord. It is based upon the property of selective staining in black against the lighter background of those myelinated nerve fibers or bundles of fibers that have been damaged and in consequence have degenerated. These may then be easily followed in serial sections as far as the stations of the brain where they terminate. The results of experiments upon the infranuclear division of the visual system of several representative species where this technique was applied are described in the following paragraphs.

2. COURSE OF THE FIBERS IN THE OPTIC NERVES, CHIASMA, AND TRACTS AND SUBCORTICAL VISUAL NUCLEI, AS DETERMINED BY EXPERIMENT.—When an eye is removed in an experimental animal, for example, Monkey, Pigeon, Rat, Guinea Pig, or Cat, the optic nerve fibers originating in that eye degenerate and may conveniently be studied along their course as far as their termination in the various subcortical visual stations or nuclei of the brain (*see* Figs. 186, 190, 191, 192). Such a series of sections shows that the optic nerve on the side of the removed eye degenerates completely in all animals. Whereas, however, in Birds the opposite or contralateral tract alone shows degeneration, in nearly all investigated Mammals both optic tracts degenerate, even though only partly, the degree of involvement of the ipsilateral tract depending upon the species. The optic nerve of the opposite side, corresponding with the intact eye, remains normal or practically so in all cases.

The fact that the optic nerve of the remaining eye does not contain degenerated fibers indicates that there are probably no commissural fibers directly linking the two eyes, as was assumed by a number of investigators of former times (F. Arnold 1839; Pagano 1897; Myers 1901; Parsons 1902; Dubreuil & Dupuis-Dutemps 1904).

In the chiasma of the optic nerves, both in

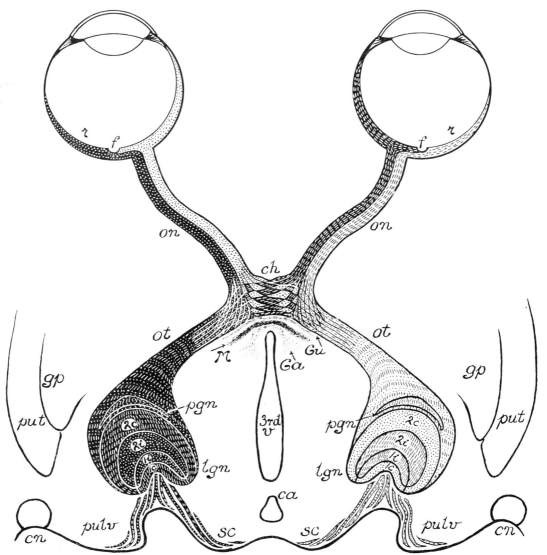

Fig. 186.—Infranuclear and intermediate or nuclear divisions of the visual system of a Monkey (Rhesus Macaque). Optic nerve fibers originating from the retinae (r) of both eyes are assembled in the two optic nerves (on). After a partial crossing of nasal fibers in the chiasma (ch), they continue as optic tracts (ot) and terminate in the subcortical visual nuclei: laminated lateral geniculate nuclei (lgn), pregeniculate gray nuclei (pgn), superior colliculi of the midbrain (sc), and possibly also in the pulvinars of the thalami ($pulv$). No other nuclei of the brain, such as the globus pallidus (gp), the putamen (put), and the caudate nucleus (cn) of the striate bodies, or the commissures of Gudden (Gu), Meynert (M), and Ganser (Ga) are directly related to the visual system. Other abbreviations: ca, cerebral aqueduct; f, central fovea; $3rd\ v$, third cerebral ventricle. Note the termination of nondecussating ipsilateral and decussating contralateral fibers in separate layers of the laminated nucleus (to be identified by corresponding stippling) and a conjoint termination of both fiber categories in the pregeniculate nucleus and the superior colliculus. Based on an experiment where one eye was removed and the specimen was stained with the Marchi method for secondary degeneration of nerve fibers. (*Cf*. Figs. 190, 191, 192.)

the Cat (Fig. 192) and in the Monkey (Fig. 186), it is found that almost half the fibers cross from the severed optic nerve to the contralateral tract, while a little more than half pass over to the tract of the same side. Not all decussating bundles, however, take the shortest course. Some deviate from it, describing more or less complicated circuitous routes. The detouring is more pronounced on the inferior than on the superior levels of the chiasma. In general, the bundles closer to the anterior limit of the chiasma make a loop-shaped detour in the terminal portion of the opposite optic nerve, and the bundles in the posterior edge of the chiasma make a detour in the initial portion of the ipsilateral tract, before they cross over to the contralateral optic tract.

In Man and in the Monkey the phenomenon of the detouring chiasmal fibers is even more pronounced (*see* sec. 6, this chapter, and Figs. 193, 196, 198). While crossing, the decussating bundles spread over the entire anteroposterior expanse of the chiasma. As soon as they enter the contralateral optic tract, the decussating fibers, streaming in numerous bundles, spread over the entire thickness of that tract. The nondecussating fibers arising from approximately the temporal halves of the two retinae are confined to the lateral zones of the chiasma, leaving the larger intermediate section entirely to the two decussating systems. The nondecussating fibers also spread over the entire thickness of their own tract as soon as they enter it.

The supraoptic commissures and other similar decussating fiber systems of the adjacent region of the hypothalamus, of varying development and appearance in different species, apparently have no direct connection with the visual system except topographically (*cf.* Probst 1905; Herzog 1906; Ariëns Kappers *et al.* 1936). At least three such systems may be distinguished in Man and in the Monkey. On the lower levels and immediately adjoining the chiasma along its posterior margin is the inferior posterior, or ventral, supraoptic commissure of Gudden, made up of a great number of delicate myelinated fibers (*Gu*, in Fig. 197). Next to it at a somewhat higher level and separated by it from the chiasma proper is the superior posterior commissure of Meynert (*M*), consisting of a few bundles of slightly thicker

and much more deeply stained fibers, which can be traced back along the tracts for some distance. The third, closest to the anterior limit of the third cerebral ventricle, is the dorsal supraoptic, or anterior hypothalamic, decussation or commissure of Ganser and Forel (*Ga*). In Man it is composed of two or more loose strands of extremely delicate myelinated fibers skirting the third ventricle, along whose sides they can be followed back into the hypothalamus, leaving the columns of the fornix laterally (*F*, in Fig. 197). Still other similar fiber systems have been announced by Hannover & Obersteiner ("ansate commissure"), Marie & Lerie, and Moeli ("residual bundle"); (*see* Obersteiner 1912, p. 501).

In the optic tracts the fibers, both crossed and uncrossed, spread over the entire thickness, as soon as the region of the chiasma is passed. The fibers are uniformly distributed, indicating an intimate and uniform mingling of the two systems, the decussating and the nondecussating. The exception is the inner-lower, or ventromedial, corners of the tracts, where the crossed fibers from the extreme anterior segments of the nasal halves of the retinae alone are present, the "monocular fibers." The relative number of fibers, however, increases from the wedge-shaped, ventromedial end to the bulkier, club-shaped, dorsolateral extremity; conversely, the thickest fibers are found in the first, the thinnest near the surface in the latter, part of the tracts.

The fibers remain confined to these structures along the entire length of the tracts in Man, Monkey, and Cat. The only exception is, perhaps, a few fibers which, in the Cat, enter a locality in the hypothalamus along the inner contour of the tract for a short distance. In Monkey and in Man, however, no myelinated optic nerve fibers pass into the various nuclei of the hypothalamus and subthalamus, such as the supraoptic nucleus or basal optic ganglion, ectomammillary ganglion, isthmic ganglion, etc. Nor could any side tracts described in the Lower Mammals and Inframammalian Vertebrates, such as the transverse peduncular tract of Gudden (*tractus peduncularis transversus*) or the anterior and posterior accessory optic tracts or bundles of Bochenek (*fasciculus* or *tractus opticus accessorius anterior* and *posterior* or "basal optic root"), be identified in Man, Monkey, and Cat. If there are such connections within the brain stem in the visual system of these species, they must be represented by non-myelinated fibers (on these *see* S. Ramón y Cajal 1911, Fig. 255; *see also* Bruesch & Arey 1942). Hence it is probable that, especially in Primates, unlike some Lower Mammals and Inframammalian Vertebrates, there are no optic connections below the level of the lateral geniculate nucleus or that, if present, they are, at most, only slight. (*Cf.* sec. 5, this chapter.)

All optic nerve fibers from the retinae, as far as evidence from experiments with the Monkey, Pigeon, Rat, Guinea Pig, and Cat indicate, terminate in the subcortical visual nuclei of the brain stem (Figs. 186, 190, 191, 192; *see also* sec. 5, this chapter). There is no certain indication that any of these fibers continue farther up or that any reach the cerebral cortex (as formerly believed, e.g., by Gudden). In the Cat and in the Monkey and presumably also in Man, the greater majority of all optic fibers and practically all thick ones terminate in the laminated or dorsal portion of the lateral geniculate nucleus (*lgn*). Those that continue beyond are thin fibers, with only a few thicker ones interspersed (Fig. 187). These delicate fibers enter the pregeniculate and pretectal nuclei and the superior colliculus of the midbrain. The number of these direct optopregeniculate and optotectal fibers is approximately equal on both sides, both in the Cat and in the Monkey, indicating that each eye contributes about an equal share of decussating and nondecussating fibers to both the right and the left sets of these subcortical visual nuclei. The way these fibers are distributed in each nucleus is further dealt with in detail in the following paragraphs and sections of this chapter.

3. The termination of optic nerve fibers in the laminated lateral geniculate nucleus.—When degenerated optic nerve fibers are followed from the chiasma to their terminal stations in a continuous series of sections, treated by Marchi's technique, through the optic tracts and adjoining parts of the brain of a monkey, where one eye had been removed 2 or 3 weeks before the animal was sacrificed, it is found that both tracts are about equally affected and that both lateral geniculate nuclei receive about an equal number of degenerated fibers.

By far the greatest majority of degenerated optic nerve fibers enter the laminated lateral geniculate nucleus. They invade it in dense streams through its frontal extremity and also from the inferior aspect around the hilum. Other aspects of the nucleus, especially the lateral and the upper, are used less or not at all.

The thickest optic nerve fibers enter the lateral nucleus at its ventral or inferior aspect. They come from the inner-lower pointed "wedge" of the optic tract. Their termination is in two segments, a ventromedial and a ventrolateral, flanking the "notch" or hilum of the nucleus. These fibers, exclusively decussated, arise from the anteriormost segment of the contralateral nasal retina and correspond to the opposite monocular temporal crescent in the field of view, as discussed in section 11, in this chapter. The medium-thick and the fine fibers from the remaining larger portion of the tract, including its bulky upper end, are the mixed decussating and nondecussating fibers from the binocular portions of the homonymous halves of both retinae, coincident with the side of the examined geniculate nucleus (nasal half of the left retina and temporal half of the right retina in the case of the right-side geniculate nucleus; and vice versa). Spreading in numerous bundles, which approximately continue the slanting anteroposterior course of the tract fibers, they are distributed according to their topographical relationships to various segments (on coronal cross-sections) and levels of the nucleus (in the longitudinal sense) in which they terminate (*see* sec. 7, this chapter). Their principal mode of distribution is through the arciform and somewhat longitudinally arranged bundles, apparently largely coinciding with the intercellular fibrous laminae.

Except in the inferior and medial aspects of the lateral geniculate nucleus, only relatively few afferent optic nerve fibers are included in the thick perinuclear fibrous capsule enveloping the entire laminated nucleus. Most fibers of the perinuclear capsule, especially at the dorsolateral and posterior aspects of the nucleus, as well as the "triangular field" of Wernicke, are accordingly made up of geniculocortical and possibly corticogeniculate fiber systems (*see* chap. VII, 3 [2]).

Each preterminal arciform bundle consists of thinner fibers intermingled with a few thicker ones. The average thickness of the fibers decreases from the region of the hilum, where the coarsest fibers are found, toward the upper rounded extremity of the nucleus, where the fibers are most delicate. The pattern of distribution in the laminated lateral geniculate nucleus in that respect closely resembles the distribution of the thick and thin fibers in a cross-section through the optic tract (*see* preceding subsection, in this section).

Since numerous fibers terminate at a greater or lesser distance from the point of entry at the anterior extremity of the nucleus where it is joined to the tract, they have to pass through a longer or shorter stretch of the nucleus. This is especially true of the delicate fibers arising in the homonymous halves of the two foveae and central areae. In order to reach their destination at the posterior extremity of the nucleus, these are obliged to traverse almost its entire anteroposterior extent (*cf.* sec. 7 [3–5], this chapter).

4. THE TERMINATION OF THE OPTIC NERVE FIBERS IN PREGENICULATE AND PARAGENICULATE GRAY NUCLEI.—The relatively large laminated geniculate nucleus of the Primates is the principal subcortical visual station where most optic nerve fibers and almost all the thicker ones terminate. The other terminal station is a small, crescent-shaped area resembling a skullcap, pressed at a slant to the dorsal convex extremity of the laminated nucleus: the pregeniculate gray nucleus, *substantia grisea praegeniculata*, or *griseum praegeniculatum* (*pgn* in Figs. 186, 187). This nucleus is found along approximately the anterior third or half of the longitudinal extent of the bulkier laminated portion, or the lateral geniculate nucleus in the restricted sense (*see* nucleus marked with * in Figs. 200, 214, 215). (*See* sec. 10, this chapter, and *pgn* in Figs. 210, 212, 222, for structural details of the nucleus.)

In Man and in the Monkey the pregeniculate nucleus is made up of one or more somewhat disconnected rows of minute fiber bundles (*pgn* in Fig. 187, *A*) and a considerable number of mostly small fusiform nerve cells, with a few of

rather fair size (Figs. 211, 212, 213, 222). The bundles consist of delicate myelinated nerve fibers. In transverse coronal sections these bundles appear cut at a somewhat oblique angle. In the experiment where one eye is removed, these fibers degenerate in great numbers, approximately equal on both sides, manifesting their origin from the optic tracts and hence from the retinae, both crossed and uncrossed. Their passage from the tract to the pregeniculate nucleus is gradual, the fibers becoming detached on successive posterior levels.

The fibers which enter the pregeniculate nucleus are of the same fine caliber as are the delicate fibers which fill the central-areal and foveal segments of the subjacent laminated nucleus along its upper convex margin, whence some of them emerge. The experimental evidence shows that they all arise from the central area in and around the fovea of both retinae (*cf.* sec. 7, this chapter, and Figs. 202, 203, 204). Whether these fibers represent axis cylinders of a special variety of retinal ganglion cells or whether they are merely collateral branches of the same optic nerve fibers whose principal teledendrons or terminal arborizations are in the laminated nucleus can be determined definitely only with the help of good Golgi preparations. Considering their great number, a guess may be ventured that they are side branches of fine axis cylinders, whose ganglion cells of origin reside in the central area and fovea of both retinae and whose principal termination is in the intermedioposterior areal-foveal segment of the laminated nucleus.

In approximately the middle third of the longitudinal extent of the laminated nucleus, after the cap-shaped portion of the pregeniculate nucleus disappears, a narrow strand of small and medium-sized fusiform nerve cells is found closely attached to the medial or inner margin of the laminated nucleus: the parageniculate nucleus or *griseum parageniculatum*. This strand may be followed farther in the subthalamus, with whose cells it merges (thus *pgn* in Fig. 209; *see also* Figs. 211, 212, 215). It contains nerve cells of the same appearance as those found in the more dorsally situated pregeniculate nucleus, with which it is continuous. The cell strand marks the avenue along which the pre- and parageniculate nuclei have mi-

grated during their ontogenetical and phylogenetical development from the subthalamus.
Some of the fine bundles of afferent fibers described earlier enter that region also, as at *x*,
in Figure 187, *B*. (*See* secs. 7, 8, and 9, this
chapter, for additional anatomical details; *see*
sec. 10, this chapter, for probable function.)

5. THE TERMINATION OF OPTIC NERVE FIBERS
IN THE PULVINAR OF THE THALAMUS AND IN THE
SUPERIOR COLLICULUS OF THE MIDBRAIN.—The
thick perigeniculate fibrous capsule which envelops the laminated lateral geniculate nucleus
does not cease at the caudal end of that nucleus
but continues for some distance posteriorly
(Fig. 187, *C, D, E*). Especially those fibers that
form the ventral segment of this capsule gradually shift medially and join those that form the
medial segment of the same capsule. In this way
a narrow, compact "intergeniculate fiber lamina" (*il*) is formed, separating the lateral geniculate nucleus (*lgn*) and pulvinar of the thalamus (*pulv*) on the lateral side from the medial
geniculate nucleus on the medial side (*mgn*).
Farther back, this "intergeniculate lamina"
splits into two thin superficial fiber layers. One
of these becomes the zonal stratum of the pulvinar, specifically of its inferior or posterior nucleus, whose inferior surface it lines (*z*). The
other layer (*y*) covers, in a similar way, the exposed inferolateral surface of the medial geniculate nucleus.

Most of the fibers of both these superficial
strata gradually turn medially and proceed to
the superior colliculus (*sc*) of the same side by
way of the brachium (*bsc*), where this brachium
forms a superficial medullary layer (*y*). A few of
these medullated fibers enter the thin zonal
layer of the colliculus and the gray superficial
cell layer. A similar course is pursued by the
decussating optic nerve fibers in the opposite
half of the brain in order to reach the "cap" of
the contralateral colliculus (Fig. 187, *F*). In this
way both superior colliculi receive direct optic
nerve fibers from each eye; that is, each colliculus is supplied by both the decussating and
the nondecussating fibers originating in the
homonymous halves of the two retinae. In the
Monkey, the number of fibers of both categories
is approximately equal.

In the zonal stratum of the medial geniculate

nucleus, the majority of fibers which eventually
pass over to the superior colliculus are quite
fine, with a few thicker ones interspersed. In the
zonal stratum of the pulvinar, the optic fibers
are all thin. Whether or not these fibers also
terminate in this structure, there is, unfortunately, no way of telling. Undoubtedly, part of
them, probably the majority, use this locality
merely as a passage, along which they rejoin the
rest (*y*), eventually passing over to the brachium (*bsc*) and thus reaching the colliculus
(*sc*). All along their course in the two zonal
strata (*z, y*) and in the brachium (*bsc*) these
fibers remain close to the surface, immediately
underneath the pial cover.

The terminal distribution in the colliculus of
these direct optic nerve fibers is peculiar (*sc*).
Here they enter a narrow zone at the base of the
"cap," which, if viewed from above, would appear circular. The center or summit of the colliculus receives no myelinated optic nerve fibers
(Fig. 187, *E, F*). A considerable number of direct fibers may reach the pretectal nucleus as
well as the colliculus proper, an observation less
certain in the Monkey than in the Cat.

The direct optotectal nerve fibers do not
decussate in the midbrain, either in the posterior commissure or in the fiber systems which
connect the superior colliculi of the right and
left sides. Each superior colliculus, accordingly,
is a terminal station of fibers coming from the
optic tract and lateral geniculate nucleus of its
own side: the right-hand colliculus receiving
nondecussating fibers arising from the temporal
half of the retina of the right eye and fibers
arising from the nasal half of the retina of the
left eye decussating in the chiasma; and vice
versa. The relation of the two retinae to the
optic tectum in the Monkey, accordingly, duplicates that of the lateral geniculate nuclei, according to the principle of homonymity.

Since no direct optic fibers cross in the midbrain, there is no way for the fibers decussating
in the chiasma to recross to the side of the midbrain ipsilateral with the side of their retinal
origin—an arrangement which would annul the
effect of the chiasmal decussation. Nor do the
fibers not decussating in the chiasma pass over
to the contralateral side in the midbrain, as was
assumed by Landolt, Charcot, and Ferrier in
their attempts to explain "macular sparing"
(*see* chap. III, 7 [4], 9 [6], and chap. XII, 8).

The system of direct optic nerve fibers terminates principally in the superficial medullary stratum, to a lesser extent in the zonal stratum, of the superior colliculi and probably in the pretectal nuclei and perhaps also in restricted territories of the tegmental region of the midbrain of both sides just above the medial geniculate nuclei, adjacent to the brachia of the superior colliculi. It is noteworthy that no other parts of the midbrain, e.g., deep layers of the superior colliculi, the whole of the inferior colliculi, the tegmentum, the periaqueductal gray substance, and the oculomotor nuclei, receive such fibers. It is also very probable that the direct optic nerve fibers passing through the zonal layer of the medial geniculate nucleus do so without entering into synaptical and functional relationships with that nucleus, being in but loose contact with it.

In summary, the optic nerve fibers of retinal

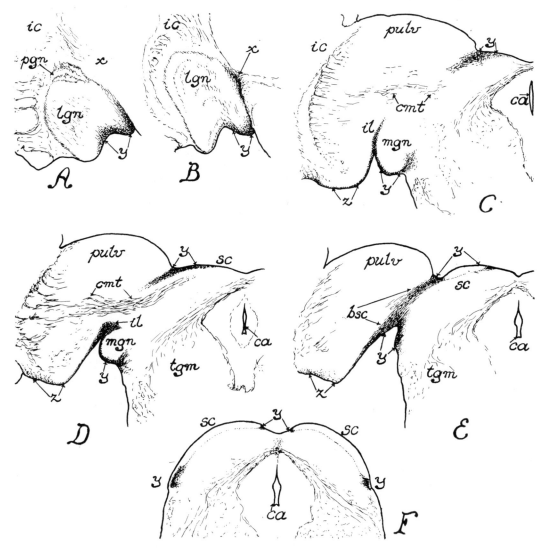

Fig. 187.—Termination of optic nerve fibers other than those in the laminated lateral geniculate and in the pregeniculate nuclei, as found in a Rhesus Macaque where one eye was removed experimentally and where the degenerated fibers were stained according to the Marchi procedure (degenerated fibers indicated by stippling). The following systems of fibers of retinal origin were found: *x*, direct fibers to parageniculate nucleus and subthalamus; *y*, similar direct system to superior colliculi of midbrain; *z*, system of direct optic nerve fibers to the pulvinar of the thalamus (poorly developed and doubtful). *Labeling: ca*, cerebral aqueduct; *cmt*, cortico-mesencephalic tract from occipital lobe (remaining normal in this experiment); *bsc*, brachium of superior colliculus (in part degenerated); *ic*, internal capsule; *il*, intergeniculate lamina (in part degenerated); *lgn*, laminated lateral geniculate nucleus; *mgn*, medial geniculate nucleus; *pgn*, pregeniculate nucleus; *pulv*, pulvinar of thalamus; *sc*, superior colliculi of midbrain; *tgm*, midbrain tegmentum. (*Cf.* preceding figure and Fig. 221.)

origin terminate, in both the simian and the feline brain, principally in the laminated lateral geniculate nuclei, whence the visual radiations to the striate areae of the occipital lobes originate (*see* chap. VII, 3). Few, if any, of them may enter the adjacent zone of the subthalamus; in the Cat some perhaps may enter the hypothalamus. A considerable number of mostly delicate optic nerve fibers, probably collaterals of the thicker ones terminating in the laminated geniculate nucleus, enter the pregeniculate gray nucleus (whence a special fiber tract, the indirect optomesencephalic system, described in section 10 in this chapter, proceeds to the subthalamus and the tegmentum of the midbrain). Still other numerous thin, and a few thicker, direct optic nerve fibers, probably also collaterals, pass by way of the intergeniculate lamina, the zonal stratum of the pulvinar of the thalamus, and the medial geniculate nucleus, over to the "cap" of the superior colliculus of the same side by way of its brachium. No optic nerve fibers of retinal origin reach directly any part of the thalamus proper, with the possible exception of the inferior-posterior nucleus of the pulvinar; nor do any extend as far as the periaqueductal gray substance of the midbrain and the oculomotor nuclei.

Not all fibers in the superficial medullary layer of the superior colliculus are of retinal origin, some apparently being branches of the somesthetic, vestibular, auditory, and descending occipital corticotectal oculomotor pathways (*see* S. Ramón y Cajal 1909–11, and others). The great number of direct fibers of the visual pathway reaching the superior colliculi, however, testifies to the importance of that system, whatever its function may be. It is noteworthy that this system, obviously a phylogenetic residue of a much bulkier one in Inframammalian Vertebrates, should be as well developed, if not better, in the Monkey as in the Cat, even though the "encephalization" or migration of the visual function from the brain stem toward the forebrain is assumed to be further advanced in the Monkey than in the Cat. Indications are that in Man, too, a direct optomesencephalic system not only is present but is an important and essential component part of the central visual mechanism (Juba 1939).

What the proper function of the system of direct optic nerve fibers terminating in the superior colliculi may be remains to be determined by future investigation. In the Lower Vertebrates, particularly in Fishes, where there is no forebrain cortex, all optic nerve fibers necessarily terminate in the brain stem, principally in the optic lobes—which may be considered homologues of the superior colliculi of the more advanced Vertebrates. At this phylogenetic level the optic tectum is the uppermost station of the visual system, also performing the higher or psychic functions of a commemorative or mnestic, integrative, and reproductive nature.

On successively higher phylogenetic levels, most of these functions are gradually transferred to the cerebral cortex, until in the Primates, especially in Man, practically all of them are dependent upon the cortex. As Klüver demonstrated in his experiments with monkeys, however, a notable residue of the original functions still remains, even after a complete removal of both striate areae of the occipital lobes of the brain. Such are certain primitive or elemental photognostic reactions which may be defined as "the ability to respond differentially to various quantities of light or differences in luminous flux densities at the eyes"; even though an animal thus mutilated and gnostically blind is not able to recognize either the size, color, or distance of visual objects, it still can choose those whose total amount of emanated or reflected photic energy is greater, regardless of whether the cause is the greater intensity, the greater size, or the lesser distance, than that of other objects simultaneously offered. Whether the superior colliculi alone, with, perhaps, parts of the midbrain, or together with the thalamus (posterior or inferior nucleus of the pulvinar, pregeniculate nucleus) are responsible for this elemental visual function remains an open problem.

This much by now appears certain: the visual pathway necessary to elicit a constriction of the pupils on stimulation of the retinae by light does not pass through the superior colliculi but is subtectal. The experiments involving the removal of the superior colliculi where no substantial impairment of the pupillary light reflex was observed do not leave much doubt about this (Knoll; Bechterew 1883; Ferrier & Turner

1898; Levinsohn 1904, 1909; Bernheimer 1909; Keller & Stewart; Magoun 1935). In agreement with this are other experiments where neither a constriction nor a dilatation of the pupils was seen on stimulation of the superior colliculi (Ranson & Magoun 1933). The evidence seems to point toward a subtectal location of the pupillary reflex pathway: an indirect or pre-geniculo-tectal pathway, originating in the pre-geniculate gray nucleus and terminating in the periaqueductal gray substance around the oculomotor nuclei. (*See* sec. 10 [3], this chapter, and Fig. 223 for more complete information on the pupillary reflex pathway.)

References: Abelsdorff 1919; Ariëns Kappers 1929; Ariëns Kappers, Huber & Crosby 1936; F. Arnold 1839; Aronson & Papez 1934; Balado & Franke 1929, 1937; Barris 1935, 1936; Barris & Ingram 1934; Barris, Ingram & Ranson 1935; Beccari 1943; Bechterew 1883; Bellonci 1888; Berl 1902; Bernheimer 1889, 1891, 1907; G. H. Bishop 1933, 1935; Bishop & O'Leary 1940, 1942; Bochenek 1908; Bodenheimer & Korbsch 1929; Bouman 1905; Brouwer 1923, 1926, 1927, 1934, 1936; Brouwer & Zeeman 1925, 1926; Chacko 1948; Chang & Ruch 1946; Le Gros Clark 1931, 1932, 1942, 1943; Cooper 1945; A. Cramer 1898; Crosby & Henderson 1948; Crosby & Woodburne 1940; Dejerine 1895–1901; Dimmer 1899; Dubreil & Dupuis-Dutemps 1904; Dupuy-Dutemps 1911; J. N. Evans 1939; A. Ferraro 1926; Ferrier & Turner 1898; Finkelstein 1935; Foerster, Gagel & Mahoney 1936; Foix & Nicolesco 1925; Forel 1907; E. Frey 1933, 1935, 1937, 1938; Friedemann 1911–12; Fuse 1936; Gagel 1928; Ganser 1878, 1882; Geiringer 1938; Geist 1930; Ghiselli 1937; Gilbert 1934, 1935; Gillilan 1941; Gillilan & Fellow 1939; Glees & Clark 1941; Greving 1925; B. Gudden 1870, 1874–79, 1881, 1885, 1889; Harman & Solnitzky 1944; F. Herzog 1906; Hüfler 1895; Huber & Crosby 1929, 1933, 1934, 1943; Juba 1939; Keller & Steward 1932; Klossowski 1930; Kodama 1928–29; Koelliker 1896; Kosaka & Hiraiwa 1915; Lenz 1927, 1928–29; Loddoni 1930; Loepp 1912; Magoun 1935; Magoun & Ranson 1942; Magoun *et al.* 1936; Malone 1910, 1914; Marburg 1903, 1942; L. L. Mayer 1940; Meader 1939; Meynert 1867, 1872; J. Michel 1873, 1877, 1887; Minkowski 1920, 1922, 1930, 1934, 1939; Monakow 1883–92, 1914; Montalti 1928; Mussen 1923; Myers 1901, 1902; Nicati 1878; Obersteiner 1912; Overbosch 1927; Ovio 1927; Pagano 1897; Parsons 1902; M. Pavlow 1900; Pines 1927; R. A. Pfeifer 1930; Pötzl 1938; Probst 1905; S. Ramón y Cajal 1909–11; Ranson & Magoun 1933, 1939; Riese 1926; Rioch 1929–31; Schaltenbrand & Cobb 1930; Schlagenhaufer 1897; Singer & Münzer 1889; Solnitzky & Harman 1943; Ströer 1939, 1940; Tartuferi 1878, 1879, 1880, 1885; Thuma 1928; Traquair 1931, 1939; Tsai 1925; Tsang 1937; Vidal & Malbran 1943; Vogt 1909; Weaver 1936; Wilbrand & Saenger 1899–1927; Zeeman 1925; Zeeman & Tumbelaka 1916; Ziehen 1903; Zondek 1933.

SEC. 5. STRUCTURAL PECULIARITIES OF THE INFRANUCLEAR AND NUCLEAR DIVISIONS OF THE VISUAL SYSTEM IN THE LOWER VERTEBRATES AND INFRAPRIMATE MAMMALS

1. VARIATIONS OF THE VISUAL SYSTEM IN VERTEBRATES.—The general plan according to which the vertebrate visual system is organized is basically identical, in the entire Chordate Phylum, beginning with the class of the Cyclostomes at the bottom of the phylum, through the various Fishes, Amphibians, Reptiles, Birds, to and including the Mammals at its top. Everywhere the photoreceptors are represented by two symmetrically placed retinae incased in the eyeballs, each connected crosswise by an optic nerve or its equivalent to the contralateral visual centers of the brain. The deviation introduced into this uniform organization by the emergence of an additional peripheral photoreceptor, the parietal or "pineal eye," in Lampreys and some Reptiles, and of the parapineal eye of the Lampreys, is only an apparent one, since its frequent presence as an orimental organ or as a rudimentary vestige shows it to be an original structure of the vertebrate organization. The phylogenetical and ontogenetical factors responsible for the uniform organization of the vertebrate visual system are discussed in chapter XIII, 2, 3.

The basically uniform organization of the

vertebrate visual system, however, is merely a background for an infinity of detailed execution. This concerns not only such elemental facts as the thickness of the optic nerves, the number of optic nerve fibers, the way the optic nerves reach the primary visual centers, and the mode of their termination therein, but also the distribution of fibers to the various subcortical stations, the shifting of emphasis from the mesencephalic centers to those of the diencephalon, with the resulting transference of most of the visual functions to the forebrain cortex. Finally, the introduction of a partial decussation in Mammals culminates, in the Carnivora and in the Primates, in the creation of a frankly binocular, stereoscopic, visual apparatus, bringing about the rearrangement or reorganization by which the basic character of this system is modified.

In the following paragraphs the visual system of a few representative Vertebrates is briefly described, and the pertinent functional factors discussed. (*See also* chap. XIV.)

2. STRUCTURE OF THE OPTIC CHIASMA IN INFRAMAMMALIAN VERTEBRATES.—The structure of the chiasma varies a great deal in different classes, orders, and even smaller subdivisions and individual species of Vertebrates (Figs. 188, 189). It is commonly believed that in all Vertebrates below the Mammals there is complete decussation, e.g., in Fishes, Amphibians, Reptiles, and Birds. This belief is to some extent based on theory, as well as on factual observations. Only in Mammals, it is believed, does a portion of the optic nerve fibers, small in the lower orders (e.g., Cetacea, Insectivora, Rodentia) and increasing toward the Order of Primates, remain on the same side and terminate in the ipsilateral hemisphere of the brain. Even, however, in orders where decussation is complete, or seems to be so, there is much variation in detail. While in some species there may be a simple crossing, whereby the two optic nerves decussate in bulk, without undergoing any more relationship than that of a contact, in others the two optic nerves may be separated into a smaller or larger number of bundles or sheets, intertwined and interlaced in many different ways. Even in the same species the pattern may vary from level to level. In the Golden Eagle

(Fig. 189), for example, the crossing appears in some planes to be massive, in bulk, while in other planes it is a complicated plaiting of several small interlaced bundles, forming an intricate pattern.

Where the crossing is in bulk, one optic nerve simply passes above or below the other. There seems to be no rule determining which nerve is above and which below. In the Northern Pike (*Esox estor* or *E. lucius*), for example, in one individual the right, in another individual the left, nerve is above. Only a systematic study of the various species, on a statistical basis, could determine whether or not there is some preference in this respect. (*See* chap. III, 9 [5]; and chap. XIV for additional information.)

The distribution of the afferent optic nerve fibers that enter the optic tectum varies according to the phylogenetic standing of the vertebrate species. In the Rabbit, according to Pavlow, Berl. Minkowski, Brouwer & Zeeman, and Overbosch, only the contralateral superior colliculus receives such fibers in great numbers, indicating a complete or nearly complete decussation of the phylogenetically older portion of the infranuclear visual system. In the more advanced Mammals, such as the Cat and the Monkey, according to Overbosch and Minkowski, both superior colliculi are the terminals, with the contralateral receiving the majority, the optic nerve fibers terminating in the superficial gray layer. The lateral geniculate nuclei, according to Ariëns Kappers (1929), receive fibers from both eyes, whereas each superior colliculus, as a phylogenetic reminiscence, receives fibers only from the contralateral eye. (*Cf.* following subsections, this section.)

The side tracks of the visual pathway also seem variously developed in different species. The "transverse peduncular tract" (*tractus peduncularis transversus*) of Gudden, and the "accessory optic tract" (*fasciculus accessorius optici*) of Bochenek, according to Overbosch, both degenerate when one eye is removed, but only in the Rabbit and Guinea Pig and not in the Cat and the Monkey.

The functional interpretation of complete decussation given by Johannes Müller (1826) was the absence of stereopsis in the Inframammalian Vertebrates. Subsequent investigations, however, incontestably demonstrate the erroneousness of this generalization. Beginning with the Fishes and increasing in various degrees in the higher classes of Vertebrates, stereoscopic binocular vision is present. This caused a number of investigators in modern times to question or completely reject Müller's opinion, according to which partial decussation of the optic nerves is regarded as the basis of stereoscopic vision in the Higher Mammals, including Man (Ovio 1927; Walls 1942). Further considerations, however, indicate that this is another extreme even less justified than the first. More in accord with observed anatomical and physiological facts is the assumption that the problem of providing Vertebrates with binocular stereopsis has been variously solved by the various vertebrate classes. What may be the particular mechanism of stereopsis in Birds, which gives them the ability to judge depth and distance visually with exquisite precision, in spite of

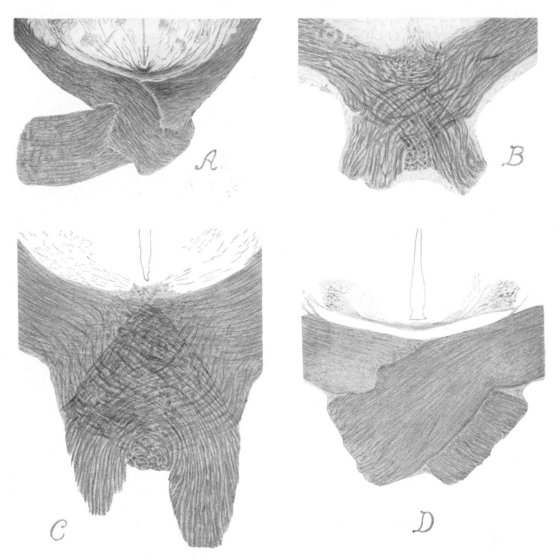

Fig. 188.—Structure of the chiasma of optic nerves in various Vertebrates. *A*, Collared Lizard (*Crotaphitus collaris*), showing a massive decussation; *B*, Guinea Pig (*Cavia porcellus*) with chiasma made up of intertwining fiber bundles; *C*, Rabbit (*Lepus cuniculus*), where chiasma is also made up of numerous intertwining bundles; *D*, Golden Eagle (*Aquila chrisaëtos*), showing at this level a massive decussation of thick optic nerves which on other levels show a complicated pattern of interdigitation (*see* following figure). Note also the entrance of fine fiber bundles into ventralmost portion of hypothalamus just below the slitlike third ventricle, in *B* and *C*. (*Cf.* following figures.)

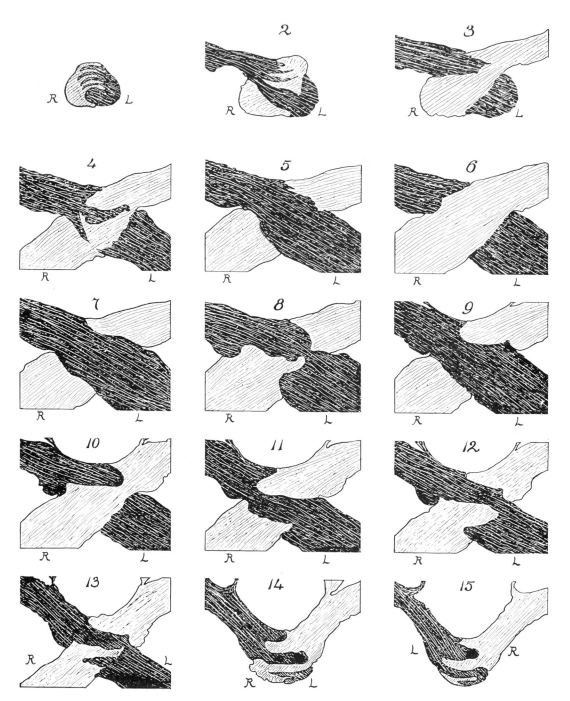

FIG. 189.—Chiasma of the optic nerves of a Golden Eagle (*Aquila chrisaëtos*) presented serially at approximately equal intervals from the rostral (*1*) to the caudal (*15*) levels. *L*, optic nerve of the left eye; *R*, optic nerve of the right eye. Note a massive decussation on the intermediate levels (shown also in *D*, in the preceding figure) and a splitting-up into fibrous laminae on the anterior (*1, 2*) and on the posterior levels (*14, 15*) through the chiasma.

complete or almost complete decussation, is a subject to be discussed separately. (*Cf. also* chap. XIII, 2, 3; and chap. XIV.)

3. THE VISUAL SYSTEM OF THE PIGEON.—The visual apparatus of Birds is an object of great scientific interest. This is motivated both by the structural perfection of the Bird's eye and retina and by the role that sight plays in this class. Additional interest stems from the problem of the nature of the neuromechanical organization which achieves such a high degree of tridimensional stereoscopic vision in Birds (a fact easily observed in such common species as the Sparrow or Pigeon) and is possessed in a remarkable degree by such good fliers as Hawks, Eagles, Kites, Swifts, and Swallows.

When one eye is enucleated in a Pigeon, the optic nerve of that eye is found to be apparently completely degenerated, while the other nerve remains normal (Fig. 190). When sections of a specimen stained by the Marchi technique are examined serially, the fibers are seen to continue directly from the affected optic nerve (*on*, black) to the contralateral optic tract (*otr*), which is found to be solidly degenerated. The decussation in the chiasma is complete, and no fibers pass over to the ipsilateral tract, in contrast with the partial decussation found in Mammals (Figs. 186, 191, 192). The structure of the chiasma is typically "plaited," with normal bundles from the intact nerve alternating with degenerated ones from the affected nerve, with no exchange of fibers between the two systems (*cf.* Fig. 189). Above the chiasma the optic fibers, after a shorter or longer course, are distributed over the various parts of the midbrain, where they terminate.

By far the greater majority of optic fibers terminate in the contralateral half of the diencephalon. First, a dense formation of coarse fibers accumulates in a narrow but compact formation next to the initial portion of the optic tract. From here these fibers pass into the reticular-like formation of the large oval core of the midbrain. They completely avoid both the thick periventricular area and the compact bundle of medullated fibers in the ventral region of the rotund core. These coarse fibers scatter between the cells of the latter formation in approximately its inferior fifth, where they ter-

minate. Caudal to the chiasma, this portion, representing perhaps as much as one-fifth of the optic fiber system, becomes superficial, lying on the exposed ventral face of the brain just lateral to the tuber cinereum of the hypothalamus, being flanked on the lateral side by the ventralmost extremity of the optic tectum. Another accumulation of nerve cells, the lateral geniculate nucleus (*lgn*), immediately adjoining the optic tract, is entered by a fair number of optic nerve fibers; other similar but more numerous fibers pass more laterally for some distance into a crescent-shaped formation just lateral to the rotund core.

The majority of optic nerve fibers, mostly thin, spread over the surface of the contralateral optic lobe, or optic tectum (*optec*), whose thick superficial medullary fiber layer, the optic stratum (*strop*), they largely form. From this coating they gradually enter into layers of the cortex-like gray substance of the lobe immediately subjacent to the optic stratum and terminate therein.

Not all optic nerve fibers, however, terminate in the contralateral half of the cerebrum, as one would be led to expect from the completeness of decussation in the chiasma. The exception is two small fiber sheets in the supraoptic area. The first one detaches itself, immediately after decussation of the optic nerves in the chiasma, from the contralateral optic tract, and as a slender stream of thin fibers hugging the ipsilateral optic tract it enters the so-called lateral geniculate nucleus of the ipsilateral side. The other similar fiber system arises from the contralateral tract at a little distance from the first, and, in the closest proximity of the periventricular gray substance, it proceeds into the ventral area of the rotund core of the ipsilateral side.

In summary, the subcortical visual apparatus of the Pigeon is overwhelmingly decussated, with optic nerve fibers originating in the retina of one eye terminating in the centers of the contralateral half of the meso-diencephalon. There are no indications that any fibers of one optic nerve join the ipsilateral tract during decussation in the chiasma, or above it after decussation, in order to reach the ipsilateral optic tectum. Nor do any fibers of retinal origin which have crossed to the contralateral optic

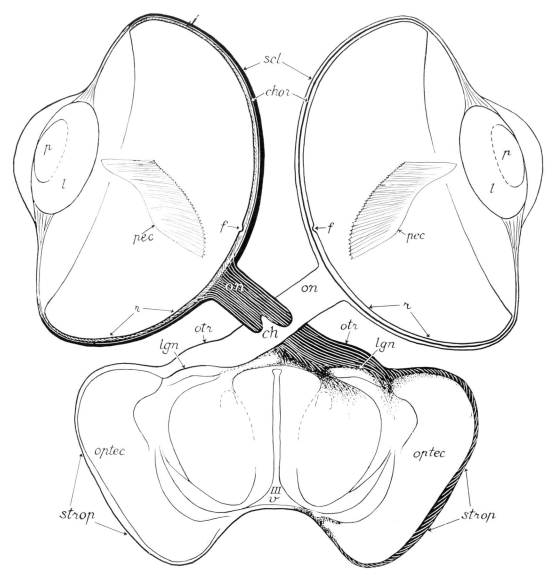

Fig. 190.—Diagram of the visual system of a Pigeon (*Columba livia domestica*). The left eye was experimentally removed (*black in figure*), and degenerated optic nerve fibers (*black*) were followed to their terminal stations in the brain. Marchi stain. The left optic nerve (*on*) degenerated completely, the right nerve remained normal, demonstrating a complete decussation in chiasma (*ch*). Beyond the chiasma the majority of fibers pass over to the optic stratum of contralateral optic lobe (*strop, optec*) of the midbrain, with numerous coarse fibers also entering the core of the brain, some entering the so-called lateral geniculate nucleus (*lgn*). However, two smaller fiber systems deviate from the principal decussating stream and recross to the ipsilateral side, where they enter the lateral geniculate nucleus and the core of the midbrain. These recrossing fibers may account in part for the ipsilateral pupillary reflex and in part for the presence of an overlapping of both monocular fields of view found by J. Levine (1945) and may indicate a phylogenetical beginning of a partial decussation found in almost all Mammals (*cf.* following figures). No retinal fibers recross in the roof of the midbrain (at *III v*), in the Pigeon. *Labeling: ch*, chiasma; *chor*, chorioid; *f*, fovea; *l*, lens; *lgn*, lateral geniculate nucleus; *on*, optic nerve; *optec*, optic tectum; *otr*, optic tract; *p*, pupil; *pec*, pecten; *r*, retina; *scl*, sclera; *strop*, optic stratum of midbrain (optic lobes); *III v*, third cerebral ventricle.

lobe recross to the optic lobe of the same side, for example, by way of the intertectal or posterior commissures. The only exception is two minute fiber systems, which, after decussation in the chiasma, recross in the suprachiasmal region to terminate in the ipsilateral core of the mesencephalon and the lateral geniculate nucleus on the side where they originate. None of these recrossing fibers reaches the ipsilateral optic tectum, however. What further connections, if any, there may be between the diencephalic nuclei, mentioned above, and the ipsilateral optic tectum and possibly the forebrain unfortunately remains unknown.

A remarkable feature of the avian visual system is its complexity, comprising a variety of subcortical visual centers directly related to the retinal fibers. This, in addition to the relatively enormous size of the optic lobes and the elaborate structure of the optic tectum, which far exceed their mammalian homologues, the superior colliculi of the midbrain, and equal the structure of the mammalian striate cortex, indicates a functional emphasis upon the midbrain in the organization of the avian visual apparatus.

Whether or not the preceding presentation of the avian visual system is valid for all representatives of this class can be determined only by additional investigation. It is possible that an almost complete decussation is found only in species in which vision is completely or largely panoramic. This assumption is borne out by the visual behavior of the Pigeon, with very restricted simultaneous use of both eyes (*cf.* Levine 1945). Other avian species in which the simultaneous use of both eyes in a binocular visual act has definitely been ascertained, for example, the Golden Eagle and the Barn Swallow, may conceivably possess a visual system in which a fair portion of the optic nerve fibers recrosses in the suprachiasmal region to the ipsilateral side, effectively creating a condition similar to the partial crossing of advanced Mammals, such as the Primates, which have binocular stereoscopic vision. (*Cf.* chap. XIII, 2, 3, and chap. XIV.)

4. The visual system of the Rat.—When one eye is removed in a rat, the optic nerve of that side degenerates solidly, while the nerve of the preserved eye remains normal (Fig. 191). In the chiasma, most degenerated fibers are seen decussating to the contralateral optic tract, a very small number proceeding to the tract of the same side. The proportion of decussating to nondecussating fibers is approximately ten or twenty to one.

The decussation in the chiasma is fairly massive, in thick bundles, with much intertwining of the right and left bundles. The majority of decussating fibers are rather coarse; they represent the bulk of the chiasma and subsequently the larger lateral portion of the tract. The finer fibers are in the posterior segment of the chiasma; in the initial portion of the tract these form the inner division next to the hypothalamus.

In the region of the chiasma, most degenerated fibers appear to keep strictly within the boundaries of this structure. The exceptions are a few localities where the optic nerve fibers leave the chiasma and tracts and enter the substance of the hypothalamus.

The first such area is the thin floor of the third ventricle between the chiasma and the ventricle. The fibers entering this locality are fairly coarse and compactly arranged. This formation is the "hypothalamic optic root" of Frey or "the intermediate hypothalamic optic bundle" (Fig. 191, *iaot*). A few of these fibers indicate their termination by a slight scattering in the adjoining ventralmost area of the hypothalamus, representing the floor of the third ventricle.

Another locality where the fibers leave the chiasma and optic tract is a narrow zone next to the chiasma but slightly lateral to the first area between the chiasma and the floor of the third ventricle, where a few fibers are seen to spread out within the adjoining portion of the hypothalamus (*laot*, in same figure). These fibers are found on the contralateral side only. It is not possible to determine from the degenerated myelin alone whether or not these fibers terminate here.

In a third system of deviating optic nerve fibers found on levels throughout the posterior segment of the chiasma and caudal to it, this is more certain. Upon closer examination, posterior levels of the chiasma are found to be made up of thinner fibers, contrasting with the coarser fibers which make up the anterior,

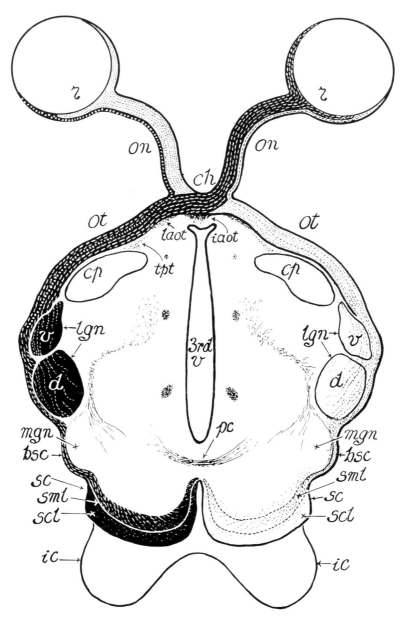

Fig. 191.—Infranuclear and nuclear divisions of the visual system of a Rat (*Mus norvegicus*). Note the overwhelming preponderance of nasal decussating and the minute size of temporal nondecussating portions of optic nerves; the relatively large size of the ventral portion (*v*) of the lateral geniculate nuclei (*lgn*), compared with the dorsal portion (*d*); the large size of the superior colliculi (*sc*); the distribution of optic nerve fibers to both portions of the lateral geniculate nuclei; the termination of almost half of all optic fibers in superior colliculi; no communication between superior colliculi by means of afferent optic nerve fibers; the presence of accessory or collateral optic tracts in hypothalamus (*iaot, laot*). *Labeling: bsc*, brachium of superior colliculus of midbrain; *ch*, chiasma of optic nerves; *cp*, cerebral peduncle; *d*, dorsal portion of lateral geniculate nucleus; *iaot*, intermediate accessory optic bundle; *ic*, inferior colliculus of midbrain; *laot*, lateral accessory optic bundle; *lgn*, lateral geniculate nucleus; *mgn*, medial geniculate nucleus; *on*, optic nerve; *ot*, optic tract; *pc*, posterior commissure; *r*, retina; *sc*, superior colliculus; *scl*, superficial cell layer of superior colliculus; *sml*, superficial medullary layer of superior colliculus; *tpt*, transverse peduncular tract; *v*, ventral portion of lateral geniculate nucleus; *3rd v*, third cerebral ventricle.

bulkier, principal portion. These posterior thin chiasmal fibers may be followed into the contralateral tract; they constitute the inner division of this tract, next to the hypothalamus. Whereas the compact, more laterally situated, coarse-fibered division proceeds up in the tract toward the lateral geniculate nucleus and midbrain, the medially situated inner, thinner fibers hug the inferior contour of the hypothalamus, where they make connection with two cell nests, one of them in the most lateral region next to the cerebral peduncle, the other situated about midway. The latter is the "lateral hypothalamic optic bundle" (Fig. 191, *tpt*). Part of this system of deviating optic nerve fibers, also entirely decussated, may be tentatively identified with Frey's "basal optic root of the hypothalamus," the "transverse peduncular tract" of Gudden, and the "posterior accessory optic bundle" of Bochenek and Tsai. The employment of the Golgi or some other analytical method alone may show whether or not these deviating fibers actually terminate where they seem to. The remaining larger territory of the hypothalamus and the subthalamus appear to receive no fibers belonging to the visual system.

The greater majority of optic nerve fibers and practically all coarse fibers remain within the optic tracts to their termination. The tract contralateral to the removed eye appears solidly degenerated. In the ipsilateral tract, only a few degenerated fibers are seen. On the contralateral side, numerous thick and thin bundles and single coarse and medium-thick fibers enter the lateral geniculate nucleus, where both its ventral and its dorsal divisions are invaded (*v*, *d*). In the dorsal nucleus (the phylogenetic oriment, or beginning, of the laminated lateral geniculate nucleus of advanced Mammals, especially Primates), the entering optic nerve fibers are arranged in regular bundles parallel to the outline of the nucleus. On the ipsilateral side the degenerated fibers in the tract and lateral geniculate nucleus, identically arranged, are numerically only a fraction, perhaps one-twentieth, of the decussated optic nerve fibers in the contralateral optic tract and subcortical visual centers.

Beyond the lateral geniculate nucleus the degenerated optic nerve fibers proceed, on the contralateral side, in great numbers to the pulvinar of the thalamus, where they form its thick zonal stratum. Some of these fibers pass into the substance of the pulvinar, where they scatter between its cells, indicating their termination therein. In all three terminal stations of the betweenbrain—the ventral and dorsal portions of the lateral geniculate nucleus and the pulvinar—the incoming optic fibers are most numerous close to the surface, next to the zonal stratum, gradually decreasing in numbers as deeper layers are entered. The entire extent of the zonal stratum of the pulvinar of the thalamus is abundantly degenerated, medially as far as the dent separating the thalamus from the habenular nucleus, which remains free. On the ipsilateral side the degenerated optic fibers behave in a similar way, except that numerically they represent but a fraction of the fibers found in the diencephalic nuclei of the contralateral side. Other parts of the betweenbrain, especially the medial geniculate nucleus, with the exception of its superficial zonal stratum, made up of fibers passing to the midbrain, receive no afferent visual fibers.

Posteriorly to the betweenbrain, the optic nerve fibers continue to, and into, the superior colliculus, which they enter by way of its brachium or arm. On the contralateral side the brachium is solidly degenerated; on the ipsilateral side not at all. Whereas, then, the contralateral geniculate nucleus in both the dorsal and the ventral parts, the pulvinar of the thalamus, and the contralateral superior colliculus of the midbrain are abundantly supplied with afferent optic nerve fibers, on the ipsilateral side the diencephalic stations receive a small number of fibers, while none enter the superior colliculus.

In the contralateral superior colliculus of the midbrain, the optic fibers enter the superficial medullary layer in great numbers. These fibers are fairly coarse, soon dividing into an abundance of fine and very fine granules of myelin, filling the entire layer. Numerous fine granules, droplets, and "dust," in streams, invade the superficial cell layer of the colliculus from below, indicating their termination herein. The zonal stratum and the layers ventral to the superficial medullary layer, with the possible exception of a few degenerated fibers immediately beneath the latter layer, remain entirely free. In the colliculus the decussated optic nerve fibers spread exactly to the mid-line, where they abruptly stop, none of them recrossing to the ipsilateral colliculus.

In summary, the visual system of a phylogenetically low-ranking Mammal such as the Rat is preponderantly crossed. This is entirely the case with the phylogenetically older portion of the system terminating in the superior colliculus. This portion of the Rat's visual system duplicates the conditions of a practically completely decussated visual system of the Inframammalian Vertebrates, such as the Birds (see Fig. 190), Reptiles, Amphibians, and Fishes (*cf.* also chap. XIV). The diencephalic connections in the Rat, however, are different. Here, even though at least nine-tenths of the optic fibers decussate, a small, yet not negligible, fraction remains ipsilateral, on the side of origin, and terminates in the lateral geniculate nucleus and the pulvinar of that side. The central visual mechanism, such as that found in a Rat, accordingly, represents an incipient stage in a phylogenetic process of reorganization which culminates in the frankly semidecussated system of visually advanced mammalian orders, such as the Carnivora and the Primates.

Still another fact about the Rat's visual system appears noteworthy. Whereas the number and thickness of optic nerve fibers that terminate in the midbrain are much above the number and caliber of the delicate fibers terminating in the superior colliculi of the Monkey, in the Rat possibly amounting to as much as one-third or more of the total number, the abundant terminations in the lateral geniculate nucleus and pulvinar of the contralateral side in the Rat indicate the increasing importance of the diencephalon even in the lowest mammalian ranks. The relative distribution of the afferent visual fibers in the Rat already shows a definite tendency to shift the emphasis from the midbrain, where it is dominant in the Inframammalian Vertebrates, to the forebrain, an evolutionary transformation completed in the advanced Mammals, the Monkeys, Apes, and Man. (*Cf.* sec. 7, this chapter, and chap. XIV.)

5. THE VISUAL SYSTEM OF THE GUINEA PIG. —The constituents of the infracortical division of the visual system of a Guinea Pig are essen-

tially the same as those found in the Rat. There are, however, some important differences.

The optic nerve of the removed eye degenerates completely, the nerve of the intact eye remains normal. The structure of the chiasma is plaited, thin sheets of fibers of the right and left nerve interdigitate as they cross to their respective tracts. The chiasmal decussation is almost complete, the number of fibers, mostly of coarse caliber, which pass to the ipsilateral tract, is quite negligible, amounting to barely 1 per cent of the total. The "intermediate hypothalamic optic bundle" consists of a fair number of thin myelinated fibers scattered in a small area in the ventralmost zone of the hypothalamus, beneath the third ventricle. The "lateral hypothalamic optic bundle" is thin, consisting of a few dozen delicate myelinated fibers. This system, as in the Rat, is present on the contralateral side only. It does not terminate in the hypothalamus and may be followed beneath the cerebral peduncle for quite a distance in the caudal direction. However, it was not possible to find its terminal locality with certainty (possibly it is the "tegmental optic nucleus" of Tsai). No other system of optic fibers deviating from the principal pathway and terminating in the between and midbrain was found, which contrasts with the multifarious connections described by some modern investigators (Frey; *see also* Ariëns Kappers *et al.* 1936).

The distribution of the afferent optic nerve fibers to the lateral geniculate nucleus, the pulvinar of the thalamus, the pretectal area, and the superior colliculus closely resembles that in the Rat. Roughly, about half the fibers may terminate in the lateral geniculate nucleus, including both divisions, the dorsal and the ventral, and in the pulvinar, the other half terminating in the pretectum and the superior colliculus. The diencephalic termination is almost entirely contralateral; the mesencephalic, exclusively so. In the two divisions of the lateral geniculate nucleus the incoming optic fibers spread over the whole thickness of the nuclei. In the cap of the contralateral superior colliculus, the fibers terminate in the entire superficial cell layer, gradually decreasing in number and fiber size toward the zonal stratum, which remains free.

In summary, the peripheral division of the visual system of the Guinea Pig is almost completely decussated, in this respect more closely resembling the conditions of the Inframammalian Vertebrates than does the visual system of the Rat. In both species the connections with the dorsal portion of the lateral geniculate nucleus and the thalamus, both frankly cortical dependencies, are, by comparison with the Carnivores and Primates, restricted; and the connections with purely subcortical stations, such as the ventral portion of the geniculate, the superior colliculus of the midbrain, and others, still prevail. This intimate connection with the noncortical dependencies of the brain stem is even more emphasized in the Guinea Pig by a greater abundance of optic fibers terminating in the midbrain.

In the light of this observation, the Guinea Pig appears even less removed than the Rat from the probable conditions of hypothetical early Mammals and their phylogenetic ancestors, in which the mesencephalic centers of vision predominated.

6. The visual system of the Cat.—The feline visual system is especially instructive because of the clear-cut results obtained in experiments involving the enucleation of one eye and the subsequent application of the Marchi method of staining (Fig. 192).

The optic nerve of the side where the eye is removed, as in other Vertebrates, degenerates completely. Many fibers are coarse and therefore easy to follow to their terminal stations. The "intermediate hypothalamic optic bundle" is absent, since no fibers pass from the chiasma into the hypothalamus beneath the floor of the third ventricle. If there is such a connection, it must be by way of the nonmyelinated fibers. The proportion between decussating and non-decussating fibers is almost equal. In the two tracts the fibers keep strictly within these structures, and there is no "basal optic root" or "lateral hypothalamic optic bundle" to be found.

The principal terminal stations of the optic tracts are the lateral geniculate nuclei, especially the laminated or dorsal portions. The geniculate nuclei of both sides receive about an equal number of fibers, or the contralateral receive, at most, slightly more than half. The distribution of incoming fibers is asymmetrical, that is, the

ipsilateral and contralateral fibers terminate in different layers of the nuclei (*cf.* sec. 6 [5], this chapter).

The ventral nucleus, which preserves its original position beneath the laminated dorsal nucleus fairly well in the Cat, is also entered by a great number of optic fibers. Being thin and scantily myelinated, however, these fibers can easily be overlooked when the attention is concentrated upon the principal stream of coarse fibers passing over to the laminated portion. An attentive examination shows minute bundles and single degenerated fibers scattering in the gray substance, indicating that in the Cat, too, as in the Rat, Guinea Pig, and Monkey, the ventral portion of the lateral geniculate, or pre-geniculate, nucleus is one of the subcortical visual centers. (*Cf.* O'Leary 1940.)

Beyond the lateral geniculate nucleus the optic nerve fibers continue in great numbers to the pretectal region and to the tectum of the midbrain. They are, however, all of fine caliber in comparison with the coarse fibers terminating in the betweenbrain. A few of these fibers may enter the pulvinar of the thalamus, but the greater majority pass to the superior colliculi, where they form the superficial medullary layer. There is no appreciable difference between the right and the left superior colliculus in the number of optic nerve fibers which terminate there.

The visual system of the Cat is noteworthy because of the features in which it resembles that of the Rodents and because of those in which it differs from it and approaches that of the Primates. The degree of reorganization attained by the Cat is most striking. The Guinea Pig, in this respect, represents the lowest level, the reorganization in this species being in an incipient stage, with only a few fibers passing over from the chiasma to the tract of the same side. In the Rat this process advances further, with probably not less and possibly more than 5 per cent of the fibers remaining on the same side. In the Opossum, according to Bodian (1937), about one-fifth of the fibers do not decussate. In the Cat, with almost as many fibers remaining on the same side as those that cross, the reorganization of the visual system has attained a level indistinguishable from that found in the Monkey.

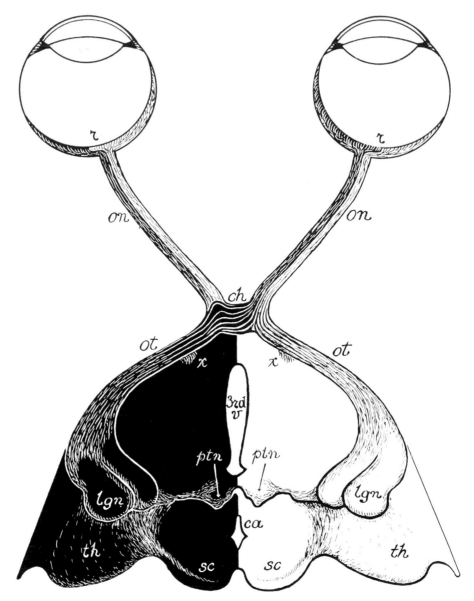

Fig. 192.—Infranuclear and intermediate or nuclear divisions of visual system of a Cat (*Felis domestica*), based upon an experiment where one eye was removed and where degenerated fibers, stained according to the Marchi technique, were followed as far as their terminal stations. The fibers originating in the right homonymous halves of both retinae, right temporal and left nasal, are presented in black lines on white ground; fibers originating from the left retinal halves are presented in white lines on black ground. In the optic chiasma, tracts, and subcortical visual centers, the fibers originating in the right eye alone are drawn, to show their course, arrangement, and termination. Note the clear-cut division of decussating and nondecussating fibers in the chiasma; the spreading of decussating fibers over the entire anteroposterior width of the chiasmal bridge, with the anterior bundles describing detours into the contralateral optic nerve before passing over into the contralateral tract, where they are distributed over its entire thickness; the similar spreading of nondecussating fibers in the ipsilateral tract after passing through the chiasma, of which they form the lateral portion; the different arrangement of crossed and uncrossed fibers in the right and left lateral geniculate nuclei, but the identical arrangement on both sides in all other nuclei; about an equal division into decussating and nondecussating fibers, thus producing a semidecussation or equal division of crossed and noncrossed fibers in the Cat's visual system. *Labeling: ca*, cerebral aqueduct; *ch*, chiasma; *lgn*, lateral geniculate nuclei; *on*, optic nerves; *ot*, optic tracts; *ptn*, pretectal nuclei; *r*, retinae; *sc*, superior colliculi; *th*, thalamus; *x*, uncertain termination of optic fibers in hypothalamus; *3rd v*, third cerebral ventricle. (*Cf.* Figs. 186, 190, 191.)

A profound change has also taken place, in a definite shifting of the emphasis toward diencephalic and hence toward cortico-telencephalic connections, as compared with the Rodents. Whereas in the Guinea Pig and almost as much in the Rat a goodly half of the retinal fibers continue to the superior colliculus, this tectal connection in both rodent species being exclusively contralateral (as in the Inframammalian Vertebrates), in the Cat the superior colliculi of both sides are included, even though proportionately much less than in the Rodents. In both features referred to, the organization of the visual system of the Cat is approached, though not attained, by the Opossum, a nocturnal marsupial Mammal with partly carnivorous habits (*see* Bodian 1937).

A third way in which the Cat differs from the Rodents is the emancipation of its visual system from the hypothalamic and other accessory connections (even though in Rodents these also need to be further investigated, particularly with histoanalytical methods).

The feature which remains common to all mammalian species is the termination of the optic nerve fibers in both the ventral and the dorsal divisions of the lateral geniculate nucleus. Such a connection, easy to demonstrate in Rodents, had until now been questioned in the Cat (Barris, Ingram & Ranson 1935). Its presence in this species, as well as in the Monkey (*see* par. 7, this section), makes it a uniform occurrence in all Mammals so far investigated; aside from its relative obscurity, the ventral geniculate nucleus suffers because of the luxuriant development of the dorsal laminated geniculate nucleus as a station included in the afferent cortical pathway. (*Cf.* sec. 10, this chapter.)

7. SIMILARITIES AND DIFFERENCES BETWEEN THE PRIMATE AND INFRAPRIMATE VISUAL SYSTEMS.—The peculiarities of a primate visual system, for example, that of the Monkey, and those of the Infraprimate Mammals may advantageously be studied after the removal of one eye and the treatment of specimens of the brain according to the Marchi method of staining. In such serial sections all myelinated fibers which degenerate may be followed along their course to the various stations at which they

terminate. The detailed arrangement of fibers in the Monkey is presented in section 4 of this chapter, while in this subsection only those features are dealt with which appear characteristic of the Primates in contrast with the visual mechanisms of the Infraprimate Mammals. (*Cf.* Fig. 186.)

In the Monkey, as in the other Vertebrates, the optic nerve on the side of the removed eye apparently degenerates completely. If there are any normal fibers left, they are lost to view in the mass of degenerated ones. In the contralateral normal nerve, however, a few scattered degenerated fibers may be found. The supra-optic commissures of Gudden, Meynert, and Ganser appear normal. An "intermediate hypothalamic optic bundle" in the center, between the chiasma and the deepest point of the third ventricle, cannot be identified with certainty. A small number of slender, tangentially cut bundles, made up of very fine myelinated fibers, spreading in the lowermost zone of the hypothalamus next to the chiasma, may possibly be interpreted in this way. The presence, however, of such a connection could be made certain only with the application of the Golgi method or of Ehrlich's vital methylene blue stain, which alone could demonstrate the actual teledendric terminations.

The similarity between the primate visual system and that of the Lower Mammals, such as the Rodents, manifests itself, in general, in the termination of the optic nerve fibers in both divisions of the lateral geniculate nucleus, the dorsal and the ventral. In the Monkey, the dorsal division is represented by the larger laminated nucleus (*lgn*); the ventral, by the smaller pregeniculate gray nucleus (*pgn*). Because of a rotation during the process of development, the relative positions of the two are reversed in comparison with the original phylogenetical condition, the larger laminated nucleus assuming, in the Monkey, a ventral, the pregeniculate nucleus a dorsal, position. The difference in size of the two nuclei, already noticeable in Rodents, becomes even more accentuated in Primates, with a great increase in bulk and an elaborate lamination of the dorsal division and a relative recession of the ventral.

Both divisions of the lateral geniculate nucleus, as the experimental evidence clearly shows. are richly supplied with afferent optic nerve fibers. The kind of fibers terminating therein differs, however; those in the laminated nucleus are relatively coarse, while those passing to the pregeniculate nucleus are uniformly thinner. The number of fibers terminating in the pregeniculate nucleus, while probably much smaller than that terminating in the laminated nucleus, is still quite large, even though they are less conspicuous because of their thinness. The pregeniculate fibers spread in numerous delicate bundles to all parts of the nucleus except its upper extremity, from which depart fibers which originate in it. They stop at the nuclear boundary and must therefore be interpreted as actual terminals and not as "fibers of passage."

The luxuriant development of the simian laminated nucleus indicates that it serves as a cortical dependency. In contrast with it is the relative reduction of the pregeniculate nucleus in the Monkey, which has no ascending connections with the forebrain cortex. All this is the consequence of a general tendency of the visual apparatus to become directly incorporated in the cortical mechanism. This tendency, noticeable in the Inframammalian Vertebrates, such as Lizards, and in the Lower Mammals, such as the Rat and Guinea Pig, is here only in its incipient stage, the corticalization of the visual apparatus attaining its maximum in the Order of Primates.

The mesencephalic connections of the primate visual system are in contrast with the diencephalic. Here an opposite trend is noticeable. Whereas in all Mammals so far investigated, from the lowest to the highest, part of the retinal fibers continue directly to the midbrain optic tectum, this direct optotectal connection undergoes a gradual decline in the Carnivora, which is even more marked in the Primates, where it is reduced to a very tenuous relation by delicate myelin fibers.

In the Monkey these direct optotectal fibers are included in the zonal stratum of the pulvinar of the thalamus and of the medial geniculate nucleus and in the intergeniculate lamina, whence, assembled in the brachium of the superior colliculus, they reach the roof of the midbrain. The number of these fibers is but a minute fraction of the number of thick and medium-thick fibers terminating in the laminated nucleus and is also much below the fine fibers which enter the pregeniculate nucleus. The numbers of ipsilateral and contralateral optotectal fibers in the Monkey are almost equal, with perhaps a slight preponderance of the contralateral, a faint phylogenetic reminiscence of a preponderantly or entirely decussated visuotectal system in Lower Vertebrates.

It is not possible to ascertain, on the basis of Marchi preparations alone, whether or not these direct optotectal fibers in the Monkey terminate in the pulvinar of the thalamus and in the medial geniculate nucleus. It is apparent from a complete absence of degenerated myelin in these nuclei that their superficial zonal layers are used merely as a convenient passage to the colliculus.

The termination of the vestigial optotectal fibers in the Monkey is in the superficial medullary and cell layers of the superior colliculus, precisely the same place in which the abundant and much thicker fibers of the Rodents terminate.

Another point worth mentioning is the strict observance of the barrier between the right and the left superior colliculus by the incoming optotectal fibers. Whether these fibers enter only the contralateral colliculus, as in the thick, numerous, and completely decussated optotectal fibers of the Guinea Pig and Rat, or pass over to both colliculi, as in the Cat and Monkey, they never recross in the intercollicular commissure. A "tectal decussation" of afferent optic fibers, assumed by some, does not exist. This and other features of the intrinsic organization of the vertebrate visual system indicate certain deep-seated tendencies, probably based upon definite functional requirements—tendencies which remain dominant whether or not a certain part of the central visual apparatus is well developed or remains vestigial and in spite of a profound change introduced by a partial crossing in the chiasma. (*Cf.* chap. XIII, 2.)

Finally, in no Mammal do the optic fibers continue so far as the inferior colliculus, the tegmental region of the midbrain, or the oculomotor and other nuclei related to the visual and other functions, aside from the few exceptions mentioned in the preceding paragraphs. (*See* sec. 10, this chapter, for other details.)

References: Abbie 1934; Ariëns Kappers 1939; Ariëns Kappers, Huber & Crosby 1936; Bard & Rioch 1937; Barris, Ingram & Ranson 1935; Bartels 1925; Beattie 1927; Beauregard 1875; Beccari 1943; Bellonci 1888; Bischoff 1900; Bochenek 1908; Bodian 1935, 1937, 1942; Bouman 1905; Brouwer *et al.* 1923; Bucher & Bürgi 1950; Burr 1928; Cairney 1926; Castaldi 1923–26; Charlton 1933; Chu 1932; Le Gros Clark 1924, 1928, 1929, 1930, 1931, 1932; Clausen & Mofshin 1939; Craigie 1928, 1931; Craigie & Brickner 1927; Crosby 1917; Crosby & Henderson 1948; Crosby & Woodburne 1940; Crouch 1934; De Lange 1913; Dendy 1910; Dexler 1897; Durward 1930; L. Edinger 1895, 1896, 1899, 1908–11; Edinger & Wallenberg 1899; Forel 1907; Frankl-Hochwart 1902; Frederikse 1931; Frey 1933, 1935, 1937, 1938, 1947–48; Ganser 1882; E. Gaupp 1899; Ghiselli 1937; Gilbert 1934, 1935; Gisi 1907; Goldby 1934, 1941, 1942; Groebbels 1922–24; Gross 1903; Grünthal 1930; Gudden 1870, 1889; Gurdjian 1927; Haller von Hallerstein 1934; Harris 1904; Hatschek 1903; D. O. Hebb 1938; C. J. Herrick 1910, 1917, 1922, 1925, 1933, 1935, 1938, 1939, 1941, 1942, 1943, 1944, 1948; Holmgren 1918, 1922; Huber & Crosby 1926, 1929, 1933, 1934, 1943; Huber, Crosby, Woodburne, Gillilan, Brown & Tamthai 1943; Ingram 1940; Ingram, Hannett & Ranson 1932; Ingvar 1923, 1925; Jansen 1929, 1930; J. M. Jefferson 1940, 1941; Juba 1939; Koelliker 1896, 1899, 1900; Kosaka & Hiraiwa 1915; K. Krause 1898; Kuhlenbeck 1937; Kupffer 1890, 1894; Larsell 1929; Lashley 1934; Lenhossék 1922; Leonowa 1886, 1896; Leydig 1891, 1896; Loepp 1912; Lubsen 1921; Marburg 1903, 1942; May & Detwiler 1925; Meader 1934; A. Meyer 1892; J. Michel 1887; Minkowski 1939; Mirto 1895; Morin 1948; Morrison & Bohn 1929; Münzer & Wiener 1898, 1902; Muskens 1929, 1930, 1936; Myers 1901, 1902; Nauta & Van Straaten 1947; Neumeyer 1895; Nichterlein & Goldby 1944; Nissl 1913; Ohata 1929; O'Leary 1940; Overbosch 1927; Ovio 1927; Packer 1941; Palmgren 1921; Papez 1932, 1934; Papez & Freeman 1930; G. H. Parker 1903; M. Pavlow 1900; Perlia 1889; Plate 1922; Rabl-Rückhard 1894; Rádl 1915; P. Ramón y Cajal 1891, 1896, 1897, 1898, 1917, 1922, 1943; S. Ramón y Cajal 1891, 1903, 1909–11; Ramsay 1901; Rendahl 1924; F. Ris 1899; Röthig 1923, 1924, 1926, 1927; Shanklin 1930, 1933; G. E. Smith 1921; Sperry 1943, 1944, 1949; R. Staderini 1917, 1928, 1934, 1937; Ströer 1939, 1940; Studnička 1905; Szily 1927; Tello 1904; Thuma 1928; Tretjakoff 1915; Tsai 1925; Tsang 1937; Unger 1906; Wallenberg 1898, 1903, 1904, 1913, 1934; Walls 1942; F. J. Warner 1931; Watkinson 1906; Willard 1915; Winkler & Potter 1911, 1914; Wlassak 1893; Woollard 1925, 1926; Woollard & Beattie 1927.

SEC. 6. THE CHIASMA OF THE OPTIC NERVES AND THE REPRESENTATION OF THE HOMONYMOUS HALVES OF THE RETINAE IN THE LATERAL GENICULATE NUCLEI

1. PATHOLOGICAL AND EXPERIMENTAL EVIDENCE OF THE PARTIAL DECUSSATION OF THE OPTIC NERVES.—When one eye is removed in a human subject or an experimental animal, the fibers in the respective optic nerve degenerate after a few days or weeks. The brain specimen of such a case, when treated with the staining method of Marchi and cut into serial sections, permits the course of selectively stained degenerated nerve fibers to be traced from the point of lesion to their termination in the subcortical visual centers (*see* sec. 4 [1], this chapter). Such series of sections show the severed optic nerve to be completed degenerated, while the nerve of the opposite intact eye remains normal.

In the chiasma the behavior of degenerated fibers varies according to the vertebrate class, as pointed out in the preceding sections. Whereas in the Inframammals, the Fishes, Amphibians, Reptiles, and Birds, the degenerated fibers simply pass over to form the contralateral optic tract (Figs. 188, 189, 190), in Mammals some fibers enter the tract of the same side (Figs. 186, 191, 192). In the Lower Mammals—for example, the Rat, Guinea Pig, and Rabbit—a few fibers only do not decussate; in the advanced Mammals, such as the Cat, Monkey, and Man, almost half the optic nerve fibers do not cross but pass to the tract of the same side.

In Mammals and especially in the Primates,

a partial crossing in the chiasma, accordingly, brings about a fundamental rearrangement, which changes the anatomical, physiological, and pathological character of that entire portion of the visual system which is above the chiasma; whereas below the chiasma each optic nerve is related to its own eye, in the suprachiasmal portion and as far as the cerebral cortex each half of the visual pathway is related to both eyes.

This evolutionary rearrangement of the completely decussating visual system characteristic of the Lower Vertebrates into the partially

lyze the peculiar structure of the human and simian optic chiasma, tracts, and lateral geniculate nuclei and their functional significance.

2. Fascicular composition of the chiasma.—The intermediate bridgelike portion of the chiasma in the Cat, Monkey, and Man is formed by the crossing fibers originating from the two slightly larger inner or nasal halves of both retinae. The decussating bundles turn toward one another and intermingle in complicated ways as they cross to the opposite tracts. The mingling, however, is by no means hap-

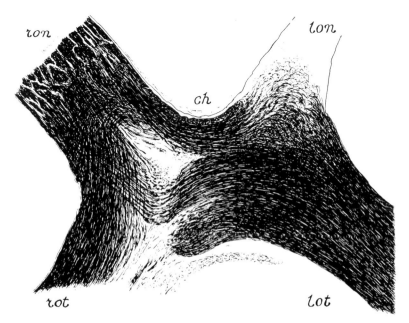

Fig. 193.—Fascicular composition of human optic chiasma in a case whose left eye was lost twenty-four years before death, as revealed in horizontal sections. The left optic nerve (*lon*), right in the figure, is completely degenerated, the right (*ron*) remained normal. The chiasma (*ch*), as well as both optic tracts (*rot, lot*), are partly degenerated. Note the detouring fibers in both nerves. Weigert method of staining; magnification 7×. (*Cf.* following figures.)

crossed mammalian visual system is the result of a long phylogenetic process of adaptation to the more perfect utilization of inherent potentialities of visual space perception. There is good reason to view this rearrangement as neither accidental nor irrelevant. For reasons discussed elsewhere in this book, partial decussation of the afferent visual pathway must be declared an essential anatomical factor upon which the three-dimensional binocular vision of Man and other Primates is based (*cf.* chaps. IX, XIV, XV).

In the following an attempt is made to ana-

hazard but rather orderly, according to a fixed, stable plan.

In Man the initiation of a partial exchange of fibers takes place in the proximal portions of the optic nerves, 3–4 mm. before the chiasma is reached (Figs. 193–97). This, as far as it is possible to judge from the arrangement of fiber bundles in human cases with one eye missing, consists of a longitudinal rotation of the optic nerve around its own axis, amounting to about 90° (clockwise in the left nerve and counterclockwise in the right one when viewed from behind). In this way, approximately the inner half of the fibers originating in the nasal half of the retina come to lie on the lower side of the optic nerve, making the monocular-crescentic fibers originating in the most anteronasal portion of the retina lowermost (Fig. 225).

The monocular fibers, the stoutest in the nerve, enter the ventralmost zone of the chiasma, where, pursuing a somewhat oblique course, they cross to the contralateral optic tract. Here they arrange themselves into a narrow crescent-shaped zone in and around the somewhat pointed ventromedial margin of the tract. On

they occupy approximately the upper two-thirds, from below the center to as far as the dorsal surface adjoining the hypothalamus (Figs. 202, 203; *cf.* following section). The remaining fibers, originating from the successive zones of the binocular portion of the extra-areal periphery of the retina, are arranged in an orderly way in the remainder of the available space in the chiasma (Fig. 225).

In crossing, few bundles take the shortest course. Most, in fact, describe larger or smaller loops, some shallow, others sharp, in all parts of

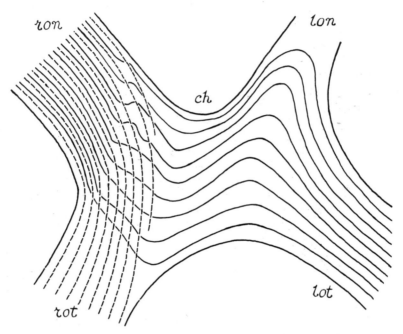

Fig. 194.—Schematic presentation of the preceding figure to show the fascicular composition of the human chiasma. The nondecussating fibers drawn in interrupted lines, the decussating fibers in solid lines. The mingling of the two fiber systems in the right optic nerve (*ron*) is only an apparent one caused by the twisted position of that nerve, the actual course of fibers being presented in the following figure. *Labeling: ch*, middle, connecting link or bridge of chiasma; *lon*, left optic nerve, degenerated owing to the loss of that eye; *lot*, left optic tract; *ron*, right optic nerve; *rot*, right optic tract.

ventral levels through the chiasma, these crescentic fibers, after crossing, seem to form the lateralmost portion, that is, the deepest part of the crotch formed by the junction of the ipsilateral nerve and the tract. Since these fibers, corresponding to the monocular crescent, are totally crossed, they degenerate in one tract only, namely, that opposite the removed eye or injured optic nerve.

The central-areal and foveal fibers, or "macular bundle," are located in the middle third of the longitudinal extent of the chiasma, where

the chiasma, from its anterior to its posterior extremity (Fig. 193).

The loops that push, for as much as 2 mm., into the adjoining portion of the optic nerves, named "anterior knee" by Wilbrand, are conspicuous. Attention was called to this peculiarity by Michel (1887), Koelliker (1896), Cramer (1898), Wilbrand (1904, 1926, 1930), and others. These anterior loops can be studied particularly easily in cases where one eye has been missing for some time. Such preparations show the loops more pronounced in the human than in the simian chiasma (*cf.* Figs. 186, 198, 199, with Figs. 193, 194, 195, 196). The detouring loops are flatter and invade the optic nerves to a lesser extent on levels through the upper portion of the chiasma, closer to the hypothalamus, than on levels closer to the inferior surface of the chiasma.

Only a part of these arches belong to the contralateral decussating fibers (after they have crossed in the chiasma), the others, mixed with the former, are the ipsilateral decussating fibers (just before they enter the chiasma). The

The nondecussating ipsilateral fibers, on the whole, deviate least from the shortest course. Only in the adjoining portion of the optic nerve are some of these fibers fitted into the anterior loops (Fig. 193). But even these soon join the rest and pass over to the optic tract of the same side in a solid formation, hugging, in the lateral portion of the chiasma, the lateral crotch formed by the nerve and the tract.

On the ventral levels through the chiasma (Fig. 197) the two systems of nondecussating fibers are far apart, being separated by the de-

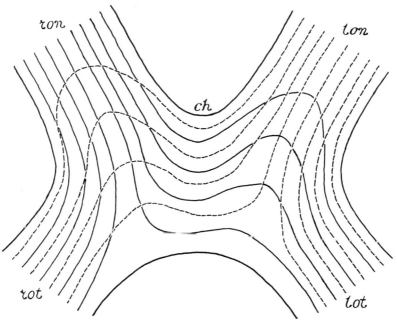

Fig. 195.—Fascicular composition of human chiasma showing decussating and nondecussating fibers of both optic nerves side by side; separation of the nasal fibers in the chiasma, their detouring course and spreading over the entire anteroposterior thickness of the chiasma and their entrance into contralateral tracts, where the crossed and noncrossed homonymous fibers, apposited to their respective syndynamic mates, spread out over the entire thickness of the corresponding tract. Fibers originating from the right optic nerve drawn in solid lines; those from the left nerve in interrupted lines. *Labeling: ch,* chiasma; *lon,* left optic nerve; *lot,* left optic tract; *ron,* right optic nerve; *rot,* right optic tract. (*Cf. also* a similar arrangement in the chiasma of the Monkey and of the Cat, in Figs. 186, 192, 198, 199.)

third element of these loops in the proximal portion of the optic nerve is the ipsilateral nondecussating fibers.

In the final analysis, the deviating fiber loops of the optic nerves just in front of the chiasma belong to the nasal fibers of both sides, the ipsilateral (before crossing) and the contralateral (after having crossed in the chiasma) and, in addition, to some nondecussating ipsilateral temporal fibers. No comparable detouring fiber bundles have been found in the initial portions of the optic tracts.

cussating fiber bundles, in particular the monocular-crescentic. On the dorsal levels the two systems approach each other somewhat, coming closer together, without, however, touching in the chiasmal bridge (Figs. 192, 402). It is noteworthy that even in their own territory the nondecussating fibers do not seem to be entirely separated from the decussating ones with which they intermingle.

The fiber pattern in every normal human chiasma is probably always basically the same except for nonessential details. Exceptions are aberrations, where, e.g., decussation is absent or where, on the contrary, there are no ipsilateral fibers (on both of these, unfortunately, information is scanty; *see* chap. II, 8). Individual variations in detail, sometimes pronounced, concern such particulars as a broader, longer, and flatter, or a shorter and stouter middle portion; an acute or obtuse angle of juncture of the

looping course resembles that of Man and Monkey; the detours, however, are less extensive (Fig. 192).

Another question to be considered concerns the character of the nerve fibers which make up the chiasma. It is to be assumed that, in order to preserve the individuality of the impressions of the two retinae as far as the visual centers,

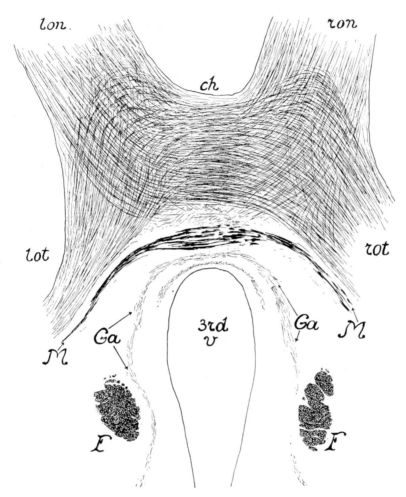

Fig. 196.—Horizontal section through the human optic chiasma and the adjacent region of the betweenbrain (hypothalamus), showing the course and arrangement of decussating and nondecussating optic nerve fibers and their topographical relations to the system of supraoptic commissures, to the third ventricle, and to other nearby structures. Weigert method. Level of the section dorsal relative to that of the following figure. Magnification 7×. *Labeling: ch*, chiasma of optic nerves; *F*, fornix; *Ga*, Ganser's commissure; *lon*, left optic nerve; *lot*, left optic tract; *M*, Meynert's commissure; *ron*, right optic nerve; *rot*, right optic tract; *3rd v*, third cerebral ventricle. Note detouring fibers in the initial portions of both optic nerves, resembling those in the Monkey and in the Cat (*see* Figs. 186, 192).

two optic nerves and tracts; and the like. In the simian chiasma the arrangement of fiber bundles closely resembles the human, except for the flatter course of detouring loops (Figs. 186, 198, 199). In the feline chiasma, too, the

the fibers should remain undivided. As S. Ramón y Cajal found in the Rabbit and Koelliker in the Cat, however, a small number of fibers bifurcate, that is, each fiber divides into two branches, with one of them entering each optic tract (rarely do both fibers continue in the same tract).

Whether or not similar bifurcating fibers are present in Higher Mammals, particularly in Primates, including Man, is not known. Perhaps such branching fibers, found only in the Lower Mammals but absent both in the higher ones and in the Inframammalian Vertebrates, indicate a phylogenetic initiation of a partial crossing, or a beginning of the separation of fibers destined to join the ipsilateral tract from those that pass over to the contralateral.

3. ARRANGEMENT OF DECUSSATING AND NONDECUSSATING FIBERS IN THE OPTIC TRACTS.—

The course of decussating and nondecussating fibers in the optic tracts is peculiar and of fundamental importance to the function of the visual system.

In the lateral portions of the chiasma and in the initial portions of the optic tracts, the crossed nasal fibers already mingle with those from the temporal half of the retina that do not cross (Figs. 195, 199). The decussating fibers join, in a strictly orderly way, their respective

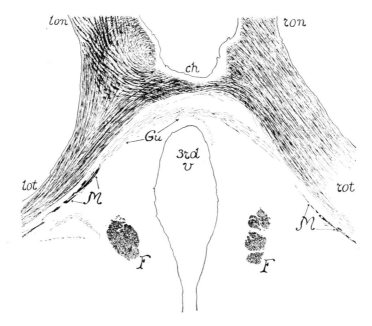

FIG. 197.—Horizontal section through the human optic chiasma and adjoining parts of the hypothalamus on a level ventral to that shown in the preceding figure, to show the topography of the visual system and of the supraoptic commissures. *Labeling: ch,* chiasma; *F,* fornix; *Gu,* Gudden's commissure; *lon,* left optic nerve; *lot,* left optic tract; *M,* Meynert's commissure; *ron,* right optic nerve; *rot,* right optic tract; *3rd v,* third cerebral ventricle. Weigert method of staining; magnification 5×. (*Cf.* preceding and following figures.)

It may be assumed that in the Lower Vertebrates—Fishes, Amphibians, Reptiles, and Birds—where complete decussation is present, there is neither need nor occasion for bifurcation. The Higher Mammals, e.g., the Primates, on the other hand, are already beyond the initial stage, with nondecussating fibers clearly differentiated from those which still pursue the original plan of complete decussation. (*See* chap. II, 8, 12 [3, 4, 8]; chap. III, 9 [3–6]; chap. IV, 6 [6], for the investigation of the chiasma in the past; *see* chap. XI, 2, for clinical interpretation.)

"corresponding" or homodynamic mates or bundles that do not decussate. The mingling of the two sets of fibers appears to be not entirely homogeneous but rather occurs in thin sheets, although the entire arrangement of the segments of the tract is according to retinal topography, as further described in section 7 in this chapter.

Each tract, accordingly, is made up of fibers originating from the homonymous halves of both retinae arranged topographically. The only part of the tract that contains but one set of fibers, the decussating, is the inner, ventromedial, wedge-shaped margin, where fibers from the anterior monocular portion of the nasal half of the contralateral retina alone are present.

In other words, the right tract contains direct, or nondecussating, ipsilateral fibers from the temporal half of the right retina and the decussating contralateral fibers from the nasal half of the left retina; in the left tract the situation is reversed. Functionally, because of the "dark-chamber" effect of the eye, the right tract represents the left halves, the left tract the

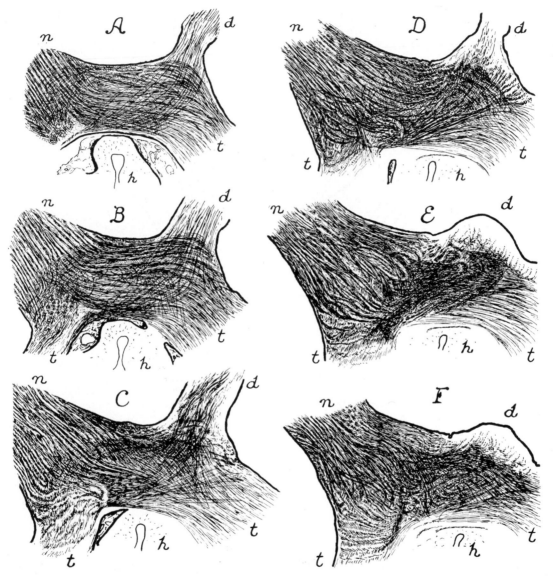

FIG. 198.—Fascicular composition of the optic chiasma of a Rhesus Macaque where the right optic nerve degenerated almost completely (*d*), owing to the scooping-out of the retina of right eye after birth two years earlier. A composite figure showing horizontal sections at approximately equal intervals through the ventral half of the chiasma, section *A* being close to the ventral surface, section *F* corresponding to a level passing through the middle of the chiasma. Note an extremely complex arrangement of countless intertwining bundles, their true arrangement given schematically in the following figure; spreading of decussating fibers over the entire anteroposterior thickness of the middle portion of the chiasma; decussating fibers making detouring loops in the contralateral nerve, much flatter than those found in the human chiasma; separation of nondecussating fibers in the lateral portion of the chiasma, and their entering the ipsilateral optic tract; few fiber bundles in the right optic nerve remaining normal owing to incomplete destruction of the right retina. Weigert stain. *Labeling: d*, degenerated optic nerve; *h*, hypothalamus next to third ventricle; *n*, normal optic nerve; *t*, optic tracts. (*Cf.* following and preceding figures.)

right homonymous halves, of the two monocular fields of vision (*see* chap. I, 5 [5, 6]).

What time and effort it took for these simple anatomical and physiological facts to become understood and generally accepted, since they were first correctly interpreted by Isaac Newton, was discussed on several occasions in the chapters dealing with history. The most weighty evidence in support of partial crossing in the chiasma is, of course, the hemianopia or half-blindness observed in a unilateral lesion of the suprachiasmal portion of the visual pathway (*see* chap. XI). The anatomical study of the chiasma and tracts in Man, Monkey, and Ape, in particular in pathological cases and in experi-

mentally; for example, in a monkey by a complete transection of one optic tract. In such an experiment the cutting of the optic nerve fibers causes retrograde degeneration of the retinal ganglion cells. In Nissl-stained horizontal sections through both eyes, the degeneration appears strictly limited to the ipsilateral retinal halves homonymous with the damaged tract, while the contralateral halves remain normal in every respect. In such an experiment the cleavage line separating the normal from the degenerated retinal halves, corresponding with the principal vertical meridians which are invisible in histological preparations of the normal retina, is clearly shown to pass exactly through the

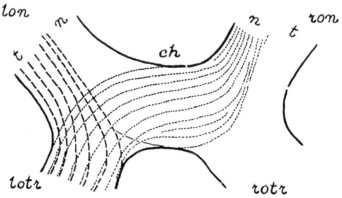

Fig. 199.—Position of the homonymous temporal nondecussating fibers (*broken lines*) in the temporal half of the left optic nerve (*lon*) and of the nasal decussating fibers (*dotted lines*) in the nasal half of the right optic nerve (*ron*) and the manner of their joining in the left optic tract (*lotr*), based on an experiment with a Rhesus Macaque illustrated in the preceding figure. Note while in the optic nerves the corresponding fibers occupy half, they spread over the entire thickness of the chiasma and tract as soon as they enter these structures, and, in the tract, each corresponding bundle joins its homonymous mate; hence each tract is made up of both categories of fibers, that is, representing ipsilateral homonymous halves of both retinae and contralateral halves of both monocular fields of view.

ments, heretofore played a lesser role (*see* chap. III, 9).

Ophthalmoscopically an absence of the optic nerve fibers may be determined in vivo in corresponding retinal halves in patients suffering from homonymous hemianopia caused by lesions of the optic tract or the lateral geniculate nucleus (Lauber 1927).

4. Experimental evidence of the separation of ipsilateral from contralateral fibers along the vertical retinal meridians.—Clear evidence of the separation of the nasal from the temporal optic nerve fibers in the retinae of both eyes along the principal or dividing vertical meridians may be obtained experi-

centers of both foveae and foveolae. The separation of the nasal from the temporal halves of the retinae along the principal vertical meridians, accordingly, is complete and is wholly extraretinal, being caused by the crossing of nasal fibers in the chiasma.

The experiments referred to show, in the first place, the anatomical basis of the homonymous organization of the supranuclear division of the primate visual system, owing to which unilateral lesions manifest themselves in homonymous hemianopia. In addition, they show that the foveal or "macular" optic nerve fibers, originating from the right or left foveal halves, do not cross the vertical dividing meridian either in the retina or in the optic nerve, contrary to a view held by some investigators to explain the "central" or "macular sparing" in many cases of homonymous hemianopia. (*Cf.* chap. XI, 8, 9.)

5. Separate termination of ipsilateral from contralateral optic nerve fibers in the laminated lateral geniculate nuclei. —The crossed and uncrossed optic nerve fibers, apparently evenly and fairly intimately intermingled in the optic tracts, become disentangled again in the principal, laminated, lateral geniculate nuclei, where they terminate in separate layers, as first observed by Minkowski (*see* chap. IV, 6 [6]; *see* secs. 1, 4, 8, this chapter; and Figs. 180, 210, 215, etc., for terminal stations and the structure of the lateral geniculate nucleus).

The evidence for this is easy to furnish. When, e.g., in a monkey, one eye is removed experimentally and Nissl-stained sections through both laminated nuclei are examined several months or years later, the nuclei are found partly degenerated (Fig. 200). This may also be observed in human cases where one eye was lost some time prior to death. Since the affected nerve cells are not damaged directly, the process is termed transsynaptic or transneuronal atrophy or degeneration. In each laminated nucleus certain cell laminae or layers are found to be degenerated, while others remain normal. In particular, those layers which degenerate in the nucleus of one side remain normal in the contralateral nucleus; and vice versa. In this respect the two laminated geniculate nuclei appear as a positive and a negative. Still another noteworthy fact becomes apparent: the normal and degenerated layers either alternate or adjoin.

A detailed analysis of a continuous series of sections reveals that in the anteriormost portion of the laminated lateral geniculate nucleus (Fig. 200, G) there are four layers; two magnocellular, made up mostly of large cells ($1i$, $1c$), and two parvocellular layers, composed mostly of small cells ($2i$, $2c$; compare also Figs. 210, 211, 213). In an experiment in which the retina of the left eye of a newly born Macaque was scooped out and the animal sacrificed two years later, on the side of the damaged eye the two inner layers which form the core of the nucleus

—one magnocellular ($1i$) and one parvocellular ($2i$)—were found to be degenerated (white layers in the figure); in this way these two layers reveal their connection with the ipsilateral nondecussating optic nerve fibers (L columns in Fig. 200, sketch G). The remaining two layers, also one magnocellular ($1c$) and one parvocellular ($2c$), preserved the normal structure because their relationship to the contralateral decussating fibers had not been disturbed (layers in solid black, in sketch G of the L columns). In the lateral geniculate nucleus contralateral to the removed eye, the arrangement of the normal and degenerated cell layers was precisely the reverse (sketch G in R columns). After a lapse of considerable time, the histopathological changes in the affected layers of either side consist in a complete disappearance of most of the nerve cells and a considerable increase in the neuroglia. A few less affected cells are found here and there, however. The process of degeneration in the two magnocellular layers is, on the whole, less severe.

In the much larger posterior portion of the laminated lateral geniculate nuclei, particularly in their intermediate foveal-areal segments (*cf.* secs. 7 and 11, this chapter; and Fig. 225), the arrangement of normal and degenerated layers is more complicated (Fig. 200, sketches F–A). Here the number of layers increases to six or even more by the splitting of each of the two original parvocellular layers ($2i$, $2c$) into two ($2i\alpha$, $2i\beta$; $2c\alpha$, $2c\beta$), a process of differentiation fully carried out only in the posterior or caudal tip of the nucleus (sketch A, same figure).

Of these six layers, on the side of the removed eye (L columns), in addition to the inner magnocellular layer ($1i$) and the parvocellular layer which adjoins it ($2i\alpha$), another layer containing small cells is degenerated ($2i\beta$), thus showing its relationship to the ipsilateral optic nerve fibers. The other three layers, a magnocellular ($1c$), and two parvocellular ($2c\alpha$ and $2c\beta$), which are the terminal stations of the contralateral fibers, remain normal. In the geniculate nucleus contralateral to the removed eye (R columns), the arrangement of the normal and degenerated cell layers is exactly the reverse.

In summary, in the less differentiated and apparently phylogenetically older anterior portion of the lateral geniculate nucleus (sketch G,

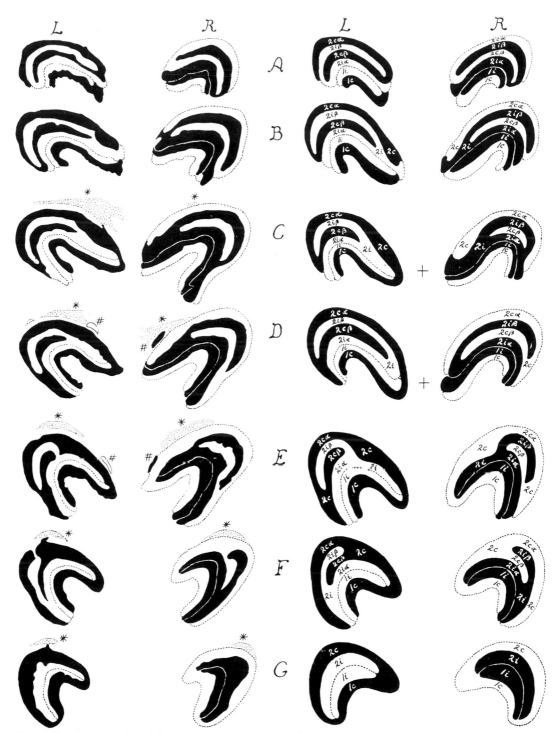

FIG. 200.—Anatomical and functional representation of homonymous retinal halves of both eyes in separate cell layers of the laminated lateral geniculate nucleus of the brain, as revealed experimentally in a Rhesus Macaque whose left retina was removed at birth. The two left columns represent camera lucida drawings of coronal sections through the left (*L*) and right (*R*) nuclei at approximately equal intervals, the two right columns being schematized presentations of the same. The sketches from *A* to *G* show levels from the most posterior to the most anterior extremities of the nuclei. The normal layers are given in solid black; the degenerated layers in white. The pregeniculate nuclei, in the left columns given in stippling, are marked with asterisks (*), the displaced portions of laminated nuclei, solid black or white, are marked by double crosses (#). The sketches in right-hand columns, marked with simple crosses, represent variations in detail of the arrangement of laminae. The numerals and small Latin and Greek letters indicate laminae and sublaminae.

partly also sketches *B–F*) each ipsilateral layer —one magnocellular and the other parvocellular—is juxtaposed with its particular magno- and parvocellular contralateral mate. Where six (or more) layers are present (partly in sketch *F* and increasingly so toward sketch *A*), a similar arrangement makes possible an intimate contact of the additionally differentiated layers, the ipsilateral to its contralateral mate (*2iα* to *2cβ* and *2iβ* to *2cα*).

6. Probable functional significance of the separate termination of the ipsilateral and contralateral fibers in the laminated lateral geniculate nuclei.—The effect of the complicated arrangement in the principal subcortical visual station, the laminated lateral geniculate nucleus, described in the foregoing paragraph is obviously to bring close together those ipsilateral and contralateral optic nerve fibers (nondecussating and decussating) whose origin is in the functionally synergical or homodynamical portions of the homonymous halves of both retinae—the "corresponding points"—bundle for bundle, point for point; even though, as yet, the two systems or sets of conductors do not merge into a single, common pathway.

Since each set of fibers, ipsilateral and contralateral, is related to two, and in the larger posterior portion, the foveal-areal segment, of the geniculate nucleus, to three, cell laminae, it is probable that there are two or three categories or varieties of optic nerve fibers in each set. Each fiber variety or combination of varieties arises from a particular variety, or combination of varieties, of the retinal ganglion cells. Each fiber variety or category is related to one particular cell lamina, and all varieties or categories of each set are juxtaposed in an orderly way with their functional homodynamical contralateral mates, according to the retinotopical principle, bundle alongside bundle.

This assumption also agrees with, and in turn explains, the observation that in minute injuries to the striate cortex the zones of degeneration pass through all cell laminae of the ipsilateral geniculate nucleus, indicating a common origin in narrow, serially arranged segments of the nucleus, and a common termination of fibers of all sets and of both sides, four or six fiber categories in all, in the same minute territories of the striate area (*see* chap. VII, 5).

In summary, in the intermediate or nuclear and in the supranuclear divisions of the visual system, including the laminated lateral geniculate nuclei and the visual radiations, the homodynamical "corresponding retinal points" are in the closest proximity, without, however, as yet merging into single binocular functional units. (*Cf. also* sec. 9 [10], this chapter; and Figs. 219, 220, 361, 439.)

The probable original condition from which the phylogenetic perfection of the primate laminated lateral geniculate nucleus developed was apparently represented by two cell layers: one related to the ipsilateral, the other to the contralateral, set of optic nerve fibers. The impetus for this early differentiation may have been given by the inception of stereopsis, conjointly with the beginning of partial decussation of the optic nerve connected with it. With further differentiation of the geniculate nerve cells into two neuron varieties—the second step in the progressive elaboration of vision—each of the original two layers divided into two, one magno- and one parvocellular layer, four layers in each nucleus. This, in order to make possible a close apposition of the ipsilateral and contralateral homodynamical bundles of retinal fibers (presumably also differentiating into two varieties), necessitated an arrangement by means of which the crossed and the noncrossed small-cell layers came to lie alongside each other. When, by a further differentiation of neurons, the small-cell layers again divided into two each—a third step—the same principle was observed by which each category of optic nerve fibers and geniculate cells of one side lay alongside its functional counterpart or mate of the other side, while at the same time preserving the original retinotopical relationships.

The segregation of the nerve cells of the laminated lateral geniculate nucleus into distinct layers appears to be a process which, both phylogenetically and ontogenetically, marks an organizational perfection of the visual system. In the Inframammalian Vertebrates geniculate stratification is not noticeable, or, at best, it is in its incipient stage. Here such an arrangement is apparently obviated by an elaborate organization of the optic lobes of the midbrain. Information is as yet scanty on conditions in species in which vision is a leading or dominant sense. It is noteworthy, however, that even at the base of the primate tree, in the Tree Shrew (*Tupaia, Urogale*), the cells of the dorsal portion of the lateral geniculate nucleus show a definite tendency toward laminated arrangement. In other primitive representatives of the Order of Primates, e.g., Mouse Lemur, Coquerell's Dwarf Lemur, *Lemur catta*, and quite definitely in the Lower Monkeys, lamination is already completed (Le Gros Clark 1932; *see* chap. VIII, 3, and chaps. XIV, XV, this book, on primate phylogeny).

In the human embryo up to the age of twenty weeks and more, the cell distribution shows no trace of stratification. In the early postnatal period the stratification of the human lateral geniculate nucleus, though completed, is still of a simple pattern, bearing a marked resemblance to that of an adult Chimpanzee (Fig. 214). Also there is sufficient evidence to support the view that in human adults there is considerable individual variation in the pattern and complexity of the arrangement of the cell and fiber layers of the nucleus. (*See* Figs. 209, 215, and secs. 8 and 9, this chapter.)

References on chiasma, lateral geniculate nucleus, etc.: Bakker 1921; Bartels 1925; Beckmann & Kubie 1929; C. Behr 1931; Bernheimer 1889, 1891, 1896, 1907; Best 1920, 1930; Bogaert 1929; Bollack 1920; Bouman 1905, 1909, 1910; Bridgman & Smith 1945; Brouwer 1931, 1936; Chacko 1949; Le Gros Clark 1940, 1947, 1948, 1949; Clark & Chacko 1947; *Concilium Ophthalmologicum* 1929; Cooper 1945; D. J. Cunningham 1943; Cushing 1929; Cushing & Eisenhardt 1929; De Kleyn 1912; Dejerine 1895–1901; Dexler 1897; Dimmer 1899; Dupuy-Dutemps 1911; Dupuy-Dutemps, Lagrange & Favory 1925; Evans 1939; Favory 1926; Fleischer 1914; Flechsig 1920, 1921, 1927; Geist 1930; Gudden 1874–79, 1881, 1885, 1889; Harman & Solnitzky 1944; W. Harris 1904; Hatschek 1903; Hellendall 1897; Henle 1871; Henschen 1912, 1925, 1926; Herrmann 1928; Hines 1942; G. Holmes 1929, 1946; Hovelaque 1927; Hyndman 1939; Jacobsohn-Lask 1924, 1928; Josefsohn 1915; Koelliker 1896, 1899, 1900; Krieg 1946; Kronfeld 1932; Lillie & Lillie 1928; Lutz 1928, 1930, 1937; Mackenzie *et al.* 1933; Malbran 1939, 1940; L. L. Mayer 1940; Michel 1887; Moeli 1891, 1898; Joh. Müller 1826; Myers 1901, 1902; Ogata 1912; Ovio 1927; Pagano 1897, 1899; R. A. Pfeifer 1930; Pichler 1900; Probst 1905; Putnam 1942; Rademaker 1937; S. Ramón y Cajal 1909–11; Reitmann 1904; Rioch 1929–31; Rioch *et al.* 1940; Rønne (Roenne) 1944; Schaeffer 1924; L. Scheel 1874; Schweinitz 1923; Schweinitz & Holloway 1912; Siemerling 1888; Singer & Münzer 1889; Solnitzky & Harman 1943; Steinach 1890; Taylor-Harrison 1928; Traquair 1930, 1931, 1939; Traquair, Dott & Russell 1935; Tschermak 1914; Uhthoff 1923; C. B. Walker 1915, 1916, 1930; Walker & Cushing 1918; F. B. Walsh 1947; Walls 1942; Wilbrand 1925, 1926, 1927, 1929, 1930; Wilbrand & Saenger 1904, 1915, 1918; Zeeman 1925; Ziehen 1899–1934. (For additional references on chiasma *see* chap. II, 8, 12; chap. III, 9; chap. VII, 8; chap. XI, 2.)

References on retinal representation in layers of the lateral geniculate nucleus: Balado & Franke 1933, 1937; Barris 1935; Le Gros Clark 1932, 1941; Clark & Penman 1934; Cramer 1898; Czermély 1939; Hechst 1933; Horánszky 1936; Horn & Helfand 1932; Juba 1933; Juba & Szatmári 1937; Lenz 1930; Mackenzie 1934; Minkowski 1913, 1920, 1922, 1930, 1932, 1934, 1939; Orlando 1933; S. Ramón y Cajal 1898, 1899; Rogalski 1946; Sántha 1932; Schroeder 1929.

SEC. 7. TOPOGRAPHICAL OR DIMENSIONAL REPRESENTATION OF THE RETINAE IN THE INFRANUCLEAR DIVISION OF THE PRIMATE VISUAL SYSTEM AND IN THE SUBCORTICAL VISUAL CENTERS

1. General remarks.—The belief that the optic fibers originating from various restricted areas or "points" of the retinal surface are not scattered haphazardly in the optic nerves, tracts, and visual centers but are arranged according to a certain stable order is quite old. Ibn al-Haitham of the Arab Period, Des Cartes, Briggs, John Taylor, Zinn, and Munk, to men-

tion only the most important philosophers and investigators of the past, entertained this idea, believing that such an anatomical arrangement might be a factor responsible for the exquisitely spatial character of the sense of sight (*cf.* chap. II, 10 [2]; 11 [2, 6]). How this concept gradually gained ground with the coming of modern clinical and experimental research, in spite of persistent opposition, is dealt with elsewhere. (*See* chap. III, 9 [7–9]; chap. IV, 4–7.)

In recent times it was especially the clinical and pathoanatomical work of Wilbrand, Henschen, and Rønne (Roenne), followed by the experiments of Brouwer (1923, 1926), Brouwer, Zeeman & Houwer (1923), Brouwer & Zeeman (1925, 1926), Zeeman (1925), Brody (1934), Penman (1934), and Le Gros Clark & Penman (1934), that not only substantiated this belief but also clarified the essential makeup of the infranuclear division of the visual system (*see* chap. IV, 6).

The results of these efforts may be briefly summarized as follows. The areal-foveal or "macular" bundle in the optic papilla and in the section of the optic nerve close to the eyeball is located in the temporal segment. At some distance behind the eyeball the areal-foveal bundle gradually assumes a central position. On the outside it is surrounded by the extra-areal fibers oriented according to the four retinal quadrants, the temporal and nasal quadrants preserving their respective places in the temporal and nasal halves of the optic nerve. In the proximal portion of the nerve, the areal-foveal bundle assumes a dorsal position (Zeeman). In the chiasma and the optic tracts, the same bundle preserves its dorsal position and terminates in the intermediate segment of the lateral geniculate nucleus along the dorsal outline (Widmark, Rønne). Henschen's view, according to which the "macular bundle" had a central position throughout its entire course as far as the lateral geniculate nucleus, was in this way corrected.

The exact arrangement of the retinal quadrants was revealed through the experiments of Brouwer & Zeeman and Le Gros Clark & Penman. These investigators found the upper homonymous quadrants to be represented dorsomedially, the lower quadrant ventrolaterally, and the fovea-macula in the intermediate seg-

ment between. In the tracts, geniculate nuclei, and superior colliculi of the midbrain, because of the decussation of the nasal fibers in the chiasma, only the homonymous halves of both retinae are represented. The anterior monocular portion of the nasal retinal half is represented singly in the contralateral tract and geniculate nucleus.

In order to make clear the internal organization of the infranuclear division of the afferent visual system, several selected experiments performed upon Rhesus Macaques are described. In each individual a minute lesion was made in one eye by means of an electrolytic needle, in each case in a different part of the retina. The lesions were made under ophthalmoscopic control and were examined ophthalmoscopically during life. In most experiments *intra vitam* sketches were made of the location, size, and shape of the lesion, and in all cases a careful study was made of both fresh and preserved specimens, and the sketches were corrected or remade.

Two weeks after the operation the animals were sacrificed, and the specimens were investigated histologically, according to the Marchi and Nissl techniques, the eyes for the exact location and extent of the lesions; the optic nerves, chiasma, and brain for the study of secondarily degenerated fibers.

An acknowledgment for technical assistance in these experiments is due here, in the first place, to Dr. P. C. Kronfeld, to Dr. B. L. Gifford, and to Dr. F. S. Ryerson, all at that time connected with the University of Chicago.

2. Experiments with the interruption of papillomacular fibers in the retina (Expts. 1 and 2).—In Experiment 1 a single, well-outlined lesion of oval shape was made between the ridge of the foveal pit and the papilla (Fig. 201, *les*). Most of the lesion was below the horizontal meridian. From comparison with the arrangement of optic nerve fibers in this area as found in the same simian species (*see* Fig. 162), it was reasonably certain that all fibers interrupted in this experiment belonged to the decussating variety originating from the nasal half of the foveal depression, the majority belonging to the lower nasal quadrant, and some to the adjoining portion of the upper nasal

quadrant, of the central fovea, in addition to those of the adjoining portion of the extrafoveal central area whose cells of origin were destroyed directly by the lesion.

In the optic nerve of the affected side a single well-outlined area of degeneration was found (Fig. 201). On levels next to the eyeball (*A*) the area corresponded to a radius stretching on the

ter. The affected bundles were rather solidly degenerated, being surrounded by a narrow zone of scattered degeneration. On a level corresponding to the entrance of the central vessels, the zone of degeneration became slightly displaced toward the center, with its inner tail now pointing downward along the central vessels and with some fibers extending to the lower

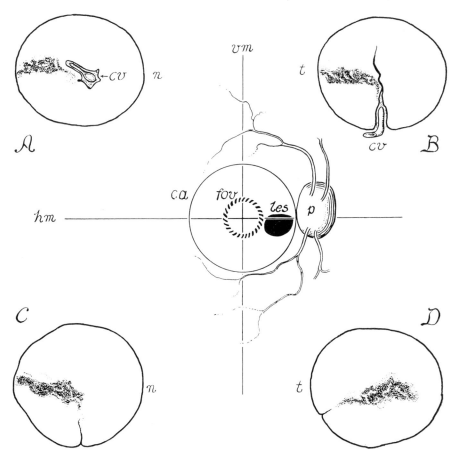

FIG. 201.—Foveal or so-called papillomacular bundle of the right optic nerve of a Rhesus Macaque degenerated in consequence of an experimental lesion made in the retina of the right eye between the central fovea and optic papilla (Expt. No. 1). Marchi method of staining. The center of the figure shows the fundus of the right eye with the oval optic disk (*p*), from which emerge central retinal blood vessels, on the temporal side enveloping a central area (*ca*) and fovea (*fov*) in its center, with vertical and horizontal meridians indicated (*vm, hm*). The single, sharply localized lesion (*les*), given in solid black, is mostly below the horizontal meridian. The four sketches show sections through the optic nerve at the following levels: *A*, just behind the eyeball; *B*, at the point of entrance of central blood vessels (*cv*); *C*, midway between the above-mentioned point and the optic chiasma; *D*, close to the chiasma. The nasal and temporal margins of the nerve are indicated by *n* and *t*. Note a temporal marginal position of the foveal bundle in most of the optic nerve and its gradual assumption of a central location only in the portion of the nerve close to the chiasma. (*Cf.* following figure.)

temporal side, in the horizontal meridian, from the central vessels (*cv*) to the periphery of the nerve. The bulk of the foveal fibers were assembled somewhat closer to the temporal periphery, with a tail stretching toward the cen-

surface of the nerve (*B*). Midway between the entrance of the central vessels and the chiasma, the zone had definitely reached the center of the nerve, even though it still preserved its original shape and compactness fairly well, maintaining its contact with the temporal periphery of the optic nerve (*C*). As the proximity of the chiasma was approached, the foveal bundle severed its contact with the temporal surface of the nerve (*t*) and, by a further shift in the nasal direction, assumed a central location (*D*).

A noteworthy feature of the areal-foveal bundle of fibers of the optic nerve was its compactness, permanence of shape and position, and preponderantly temporal location. Another peculiarity was the relatively large degenerated area and the great number of fibers composing it. Even if the generous assumption were made that most of the fibers originating from the nasal half of the foveal pit were interrupted, the estimated area on a cross-section of the optic nerve that would have to be attributed to the entire central area and fovea would hardly be less than one-third, and probably more, of the total area of the optic nerve.

In Experiment 2 a lesion of approximately the same size and only slightly differently located from that in the preceding experiment was made (Fig. 202). The lesion (*les*) resembled a cleft, given in solid black, surrounded by a less affected belt, indicated by stippling in the figure. Judging from the arrangement of optic nerve fibers in Figure 162, the axons of the ganglion cells residing in the upper nasal quadrant of the foveal pit alone were interrupted, in addition to those of the adjoining extrafoveal portion of the central area, whose residing cells of origin were affected directly.

In the optic nerve of the eye experimented upon, as in the preceding experiment, a single well-delimited area of degeneration was found. On levels immediately behind the eyeball the degenerated area appeared roughly of the same size and shape (*on1*). This agreed with the almost identical size of the lesion made in a similar locality of the retina. The location of the degenerated area, however, was slightly above the one in the preceding experiment, accounted for by the location of the lesion above the horizontal meridian. At the entrance of the central vessels the degenerated fibers began to gather closer to the central vessel cleft, while the peripheral end of the zone, still extending as far as the temporal margin of the nerve (*t*), touched it at a higher point (*on2*). Midway between the entrance of the central vessels and the chiasma,

the areal-foveal bundle had become central, preserving contact with the temporal margin of the nerve by means of a narrow trail of scattered fibers (*on3*). Closer to the chiasma, preparatory to decussation, the bundle changed considerably in shape (*on4*). It preserved its central location, producing a new pointed limb spreading toward the lower face of the nerve. In addition to the principal one, another minute degenerated bundle could be followed on all sections along the upper periphery of the optic nerve; this small bundle was probably made to degenerate by the needle piercing the coats of the eyeball, in its upper periphery, during the experiment.

In the chiasma (*ch*), on the anterior levels (upper sketch), the areal-foveal bundle, while still retaining for a space its former compact structure, gradually moved toward the center, its fibers spreading over more than the upper half of the bridge as far as its upper limit immediately adjoining the hypothalamus. On the middle levels these fibers gradually passed to the other side and, for the most part, arranged themselves close to the upper contralateral corner of the chiasma (lower sketch). Other parts of the chiasma were relatively free of these fibers, and the two lateral extremities and approximately the ventral third were entirely free.

The tracing of degenerated areal-foveal fibers in the suprachiasmal portion of the infranuclear and nuclear divisions of the visual system was quite easy. The first noteworthy fact was the complete crossing of all fibers that were caused to degenerate in this experiment. All fibers above the chiasma were found on the contralateral side (right, in figure), and none on the ipsilateral side (left, in figure). This agreed well with the size and location of the retinal lesion, by which only the fibers originating in the nasal half of the foveal pit and central area were interfered with, while those originating in the temporal half of the fovea and area, circling at some distance above and below the first, remained unimpaired (*cf*. Fig. 162).

In the contralateral optic tract the zone of degeneration resembled a narrow wedge, with its broad upper end at the upper rounded contour and its sharp lower extremity pointing to the narrow lower edge of the tract (*otr*, right side, in Fig. 202). The most delicate and most

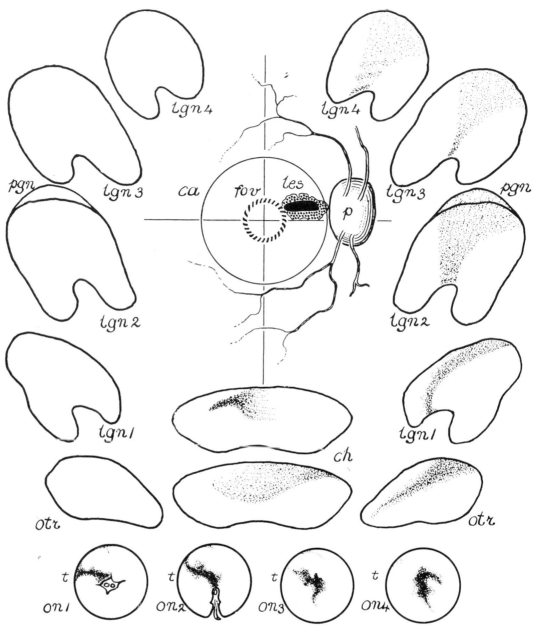

Fig. 202.—Central foveal or "papillomacular" bundle of a Rhesus Macaque demonstrated experimentally along its entire course from the origin in the retina and as far as the termination in the subcortical visual centers of the brain (Expt. No. 2). Degenerated fibers given in stippling of various density, as found in various sections, made visible with Marchi stain. Upper center represents right fundus, with the papilla of the optic nerve (*p*), with radiating central blood vessels encircling the central area (*ca*) and fovea (*fov*), divided by a vertical and horizontal meridian. The lesion, made with an electrolytic needle, is located between the fovea and the papilla, its intensively destroyed center given in solid black, its less affected periphery indicated by coarse stippling. The four lowermost sketches represent the following levels through the right optic nerve: *on1* just behind the eyeball; *on2* at the point of entry of central vessels; *on3* midway between the latter and the chiasma; *on4* close to the chiasma. The foveal bundle at first has a radial position between the temporal margin (*t*) and the central vessels, gradually disengaging itself from the margin and becoming central close to the chiasma. The foveal fibers keep within the dorsal half or so in the chiasma and are entirely decussated, since, in this experiment, the lesion was located in the nasal half of the central area. The fibers enter the left optic tract (right *otr*) and left lateral geniculate nucleus (right-hand sketches), where they may be followed from the anterior (*lgn1*) to the posterior level (*lgn4*). They take a position in the intermediate segment of the tract and nucleus and also enter into the pregeniculate nucleus (*pgn*). No degenerated fibers in this experiment enter the ipsilateral, right, tract and nucleus (left-hand sketches in figure), since the temporal half of the central area and fovea was spared. Note the laminated arrangement of fibers in *lgn 4*.

numerous fibers were assembled at the top, the coarser ones in the lower, pointed extremity of degeneration. The inferior limit of the zone corresponded fairly well to the axis of the tract, indicating the approximate position of the horizontal meridian.

In the lateral geniculate nucleus the zone of degeneration also resembled a wedge, with the broad end at the upper extremity and the narrow end at the hilum. On the anterior levels, the zone was narrow and placed in about the inner or medial half of the nucleus (*lgn1*). On the central levels the zone widened considerably (*lgn2*), again becoming somewhat reduced toward the posterior extremity of the nucleus (*lgn3* and *lgn4*). The most numerous, though most delicate, fibers were found on the posterior levels. The boundaries between the degenerated and the normal segments of the nucleus were found to be surprisingly sharp.

Another noteworthy feature was the termination of the areal-foveal fibers in the pregeniculate gray nucleus of the contralateral side (*pgn*).

3. Experiment with lesion in the central fovea (Expt. 3).

—A very small, practically microscopic, lesion (*les*) measuring in diameter barely one-fourth of a millimeter, and sharply outlined, was confined to the upper nasal quadrant of the foveal depression (Fig. 203). It is fair to assume from the minute size of the lesion and its location that all degenerated optic nerve fibers found in the visual pathway in this experiment belonged to the "foveal" or "macular" bundle. The overwhelming majority of fibers was found passing through the upper segment of the chiasma (*ch*) to the contralateral tract and geniculate nucleus (right, in the figure). The degenerated fibers were numerous and all of delicate caliber. The thinnest and most numerous fibers were found along the upper margin of the tract and geniculate nucleus.

In the tract the fibers were assembled into a fairly compact, wedge-shaped sector, whose sharp lower end pointed toward the narrow ventromedial margin and whose blunt end spread along the convex dorsolateral extremity of the tract (right *otr*, in figure). The narrow core of the area, also bladelike or wedge-shaped, was most intensively degenerated.

Since the minute lesion in the fovea was lo-cated close to the horizontal meridian, it is fair to regard the inferior lateral side of the narrow, intensively degenerated zone, approximating the axial line of the tract, as representing the horizontal meridian (*hm*).

On the rostral or anterior levels through the lateral geniculate nucleus (right *lgn1*), the degenerated area was still wedge-shaped, gradually becoming wider on the middle levels (right *lgn2* and *lgn3*) until, toward the caudal or posterior extremity of the nucleus (right *lgn4*), it expanded over somewhat more than its dorsomedial half. Also in the latter locality the area extended down to the ventral margin at the hilum of the nucleus. The fibers, obviously nearing their termination, spread over an area larger than that on the anterior levels of the nucleus, where they were assembled into a compact sector made up of "bundles of passage."

4. Features distinguishing representation of the central fovea in the optic nerves, chiasma, tracts, and lateral geniculate nuclei.

—The experiment just described (Fig. 203), in addition to the two preceding experiments (Figs. 201, 202), was illuminating in several points.

First, it showed that the "central fovea," or "macula" in clinical parlance, is projected onto the posterior portion of the lateral geniculate nucleus, somewhat wedged between the medial and lateral segments belonging to the extra-foveal parts of the homonymous retinal halves, including the monocular crescent.

Furthermore, the termination of the fibers from the upper foveal quadrant in the medial half or so of the lateral geniculate nucleus, in the posterior extremity (right *lgn4*), indicated an arrangement of the "foveal" or "macular" quadrants in the geniculate nucleus according to the rule found by Brouwer & Zeeman for the retina as a whole: the upper quadrants medial, and the lower quadrants lateral.

Next, the experiment demonstrated a relatively large area of the cerebral representation of the fovea when compared with its small size in the retina. Also, the thinness and great number of the foveal fibers agree with the small size and great number of the ganglion cells in, and close to, the foveal pit (*see* chap. V, 2 [9], 5 [1, 7], 9).

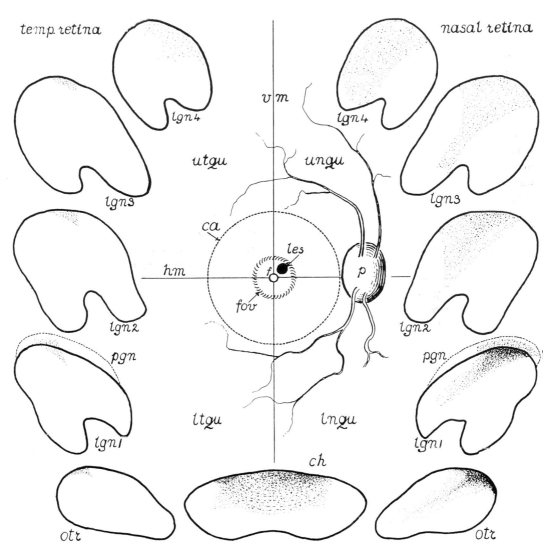

Fig. 203.—Central or "papillomacular" bundle, its origin and termination demonstrated in an experiment (Expt. No. 3). A single, minute, sharply outlined lesion (*les*) was made with an electrolytic needle in the upper nasal quadrant of the fovea (*fov*) of the right eye of a Rhesus Macaque. The lesion extended almost to the flat foveal floor (small circle *f* in the very center), and possibly slightly affected adjacent portions of the upper temporal and lower nasal quadrants beyond the vertical and horizontal meridians (*vm, hm*). Degenerated fibers, stained with the Marchi method, were found to decussate almost entirely in the chiasma (*ch*) to the left or contralateral side (right-hand sketches in the figure), with only a few fibers forming a minute bundle which passed over to the right or ipsilateral side (left-hand sketches). In the chiasma (*ch*) foveal fibers were confined to the upper two-thirds. In the tracts and nuclei these fibers spread over a wedgelike segment in the intermediate portion, with a broad end at the upper margin and a sharp point facing down, toward the hilum of the nucleus. The fibers were very numerous and delicate, the thinnest along the top, the thicker in the sharp point. Very fine fibers entered from the laminated nuclei into pregeniculate nuclei of both sides (*pgn*). Only a few fibers were found in the intergeniculate lamina, and none in the superior colliculi of the midbrain or in the pulvinar of the thalamus. Note remarkably sharp outlines of the degenerated segment; its stable shape and location on the cross-sections and the gradual widening of terminal area of the segment as the fibers approached their destination in the posterior extremity of the nuclei. This experiment makes it possible to determine the approximate position of the vertical and horizontal meridians and of the fixation points along the entire course of the infranuclear and nuclear divisions of the visual system. *Labeling: ca*, central area; *ch*, chiasma; *f*, foveola or foveal floor; *fov*, central fovea; *hm*, horizontal meridian; *les*, lesion; *lgn*, laminated lateral geniculate nuclei; *lnqu*, lower or inferior nasal quadrant; *ltqu*, lower temporal quadrant; *otr*, optic tracts; *unqu*, upper nasal quadrant; *utqu*, upper temporal quadrant; *vm*, vertical meridian. (*Cf.* preceding and following figures, especially Figs. 162, 204, 205.)

Finally, in this way was demonstrated the separate course of the "foveal" or "macular" bundle in the dorsal or upper portion of the chiasma (*ch*) and in the intermediate sector of the optic tract (right *otr*), here extending as far as the upper blunt margin of the tract but not reaching the pointed lower margin, as well as the course of the "macular" bundle through the entire longitudinal extent of the laminated lateral geniculate nucleus before reaching the posterior end of the nucleus.

In the same experiment, additional hints concerning the minute organization of the infranuclear division of the visual pathway may be gleaned from the small zone containing degenerated fibers on the side ipsilateral to the operated eye (left, Fig. 203). In position and shape this zone resembled the contralateral degenerated area just described, except that it was much smaller. It was located at the blunt upper margin of the tract (left *otr*) and the nucleus (left *lgn1* to *lgn4*). The zone of degeneration was sharply outlined against the normal parts (white in the figure) and was composed of minute bundles of delicate fibers solidly packed in a triangular field. The bundles remained close together throughout their course in the tract and in most of the laminated lateral geniculate nucleus. In the posterior fourth of the nucleus (left *lgn4*), however, they scattered over approximately the upper inner fourth. This minute degeneration was apparently caused by a slight encroachment of the lesion upon the adjoining upper temporal quadrant of the fovea, beyond the invisible vertical meridian or line by which the area of decussating fibers is separated from that of the nondecussating optic nerve fibers.

The preceding observations were noteworthy in several respects. First, the small size of the degenerated foveal bundle originating in a fraction of the foveal surface showed the representation of the fovea in the brain to be not merely "global," or roughly "quadrantic," as was alleged by some investigators (e.g., Pierre Marie, Brouwer & Zeeman, and others), but rather detailed and restricted to the posteriormost fourth of the nucleus (*cf.* chap. IV, 6 [4]).

Considering the relative crudity of the experimental technique used, the minute dimen-

sions of the degenerated bundle, its compactness and sharp outlines, and the fact that it did not mix with the adjoining bundles which remained normal—all these factors strengthened the belief that, minute though the actually demonstrated representation of the fovea was, it was still far more gross than the minuteness of the actual foveal representation in the lateral geniculate nucleus. Considering, further, that the observed minute zone of degeneration contained at least several hundred fibers, it seems that in the portion of the visual pathway related to the central fovea each elemental conductor unit is made up of more than a single neuron and a single axon or nerve fiber. This last-mentioned conclusion corresponds favorably with the minute structure of the central fovea previously described (*see* chap. V, 9, 10).

5. Fiber connections of the central fovea with the pregeniculate gray nucleus.—In Experiments 2 and 3, in addition to the coarser fibers terminating in the large laminated lateral geniculate nucleus, numerous and quite delicate fibers that pass over to the smaller cap-shaped pregeniculate nucleus were of interest (right-side *pgn* in Fig. 202, and *pgn* on both sides in Fig. 203). These fibers, obviously, are identical with the thin myelinated fibers of similar location described elsewhere (sec. 10, this chapter). Like the coarser optic fibers which terminate in the laminated nucleus, the thin fibers terminating in the pregeniculate nucleus are also of retinal origin, as the experiments with the enucleation of one or both eyes show (*cf.* secs. 4 [4], 5, this chapter). The fibers in question are homologous with the portion of optic nerve fibers terminating in the ventral geniculate nucleus of the Infraprimate Mammals described in section 5 (*see* Fig. 191).

These numerous thin afferent optic fibers are worthy of attention, and for several reasons. One is their origin in the central fovea and area of the retina, whence the pupillary light reflex can most readily be elicited (C. Hess 1907, 1908, 1916; Gasteiger 1934). The other reason is the linkage of the pregeniculate nucleus, and hence of the macular segment of the infranuclear division of the visual system, to the oculomotor nuclei of the midbrain by means of a fiber tract originating in the pregeniculate nucleus, the pregeniculo-mesencephalic tract (*cf.* sec. 10, this chapter).

All this evidence supports the opinion that the delicate optic fibers passing from the laminated geniculate nucleus to the pregeniculate nucleus are part of the pupillary reflex pathway. This opinion, in turn, agrees fairly well with the pathway of pupillary light reflex plotted experimentally by Ranson & Magoun (1933) and Magoun *et al.* (1936). It is also noteworthy that within this geniculo-pregeniculate connection a marked degree of localization is found, as evidenced by the experiments here presented.

6. EXPERIMENTS WITH LESIONS IN THE CENTRAL AREA (EXPTS. 4 AND 5).—In another experiment (Expt. 4) a somewhat larger lesion (*les*) was made (Fig. 204). It spread over almost the entire upper temporal quadrant of the fovea (*fov*) and over a portion of the adjoining quadrant of the central area (*ca*), besides probably also slightly impinging upon the upper nasal quadrant of both.

In the tracts and geniculates the degenerated fibers were found to be, as expected, overwhelmingly confined to the side ipsilateral with the operated eye (left, in the figure), with only a few fibers found on the contralateral side (right, in the same figure). In the chiasma the degenerated area, with the exception of a few decussating fibers, was entirely confined to the ipsilateral corner, which in the preceding experiments had remained unaffected. In the ipsilateral tract (left *otr*) and in the geniculate nucleus (left *lgn1* to *lgn4*), the degeneration appears as a cruder mirrored replica of the area of degeneration on the contralateral side in Experiment 3 (right, in Fig. 203). Since in Experiment 4, as in Experiments 2 and 3, the lesion extended practically to the horizontal meridian, the temporal demarcation line of the degenerated zones in all three cases indicated the position of the horizontal meridian in the tract and in the lateral geniculate nucleus. Again, since only the central area and fovea were damaged, the area of degeneration was confined to the intermediate areal-foveal sector. The innermost portion of the medial segment, both in the tract and in the lateral geniculate nucleus, remained normal, since fibers originating from the extensive un-

damaged extra-areal regions of the upper temporal quadrant of the retina were not affected. Finally, as in Experiments 2 and 3, delicate degenerated fibers were found passing from the principal degenerated area of approximately the anterior half of the laminated lateral geniculate nucleus (*lgn1* and *lgn2*) to the pregeniculate nucleus (*pgn*).

In Experiment 5 a small circular lesion (*les*) was made in the upper temporal quadrant of the central area not far from the edge of the foveal pit (Fig. 205). Considering the peculiar arching and somewhat radiating course of bundles of the optic nerve fibers emerging from the fovea (*cf.* Fig. 162), it is likely that only part of them were interrupted, the principal damage having been done to a compact nest of ganglion cells forming the wall of the foveal pit.

Owing to the location of the lesions at some distance from the horizontal meridian, it is fair to assume that neither the ganglion cells nor the outgoing fibers of the lower areal and foveal quadrants, separated as they are by the raphé, were affected. Since, as in Experiment 4, by far the greater number of degenerated fibers remained on the ipsilateral side (left, in the figure), the indication is that, in spite of the proximity of the lesion to the principal vertical meridian, very little damage was done to the upper nasal quadrant.

Unlike the preceding experiments, the degenerated area in the chiasma (*ch*) did not expand so far as the upper margin, and practically all degenerated fibers were of a nondecussating variety.

In the ipsilateral tract (left *otr*) the wedge-shaped area also did not extend to the upper margin. This was also true, to some extent, of the ipsilateral geniculate nucleus (left *lgn1* to *lgn4*), where the most extensive degeneration was found close to the hilum along the axial line. The considerable difference in distribution of degenerated fibers in the posterior fourth of the geniculate (left *lgn4*), where, unlike the preceding experiments, the area of degeneration approached, but did not quite reach, the dorso-medial margin, agrees with the extrafoveal location of the lesion.

On the other hand, the lateral boundary of the degenerated area, although the location of the lesion was at a considerable distance from the lower quadrant, was identical with that found in Experiments 2, 3, and 4, suggesting either an interruption of all fiber bundles down to the horizontal raphé or a vascular interference as far as the raphé which marks the horizontal meridian.

The confinement of degeneration to the inner or medial approximate half of the geniculate nucleus agrees with the preceding observations, the lesions, in all these experiments so far considered, being in portions of the retina above the horizontal meridian. Again, the portions of the medial segment in the anterior three-fourths of the lateral geniculate nucleus which remained

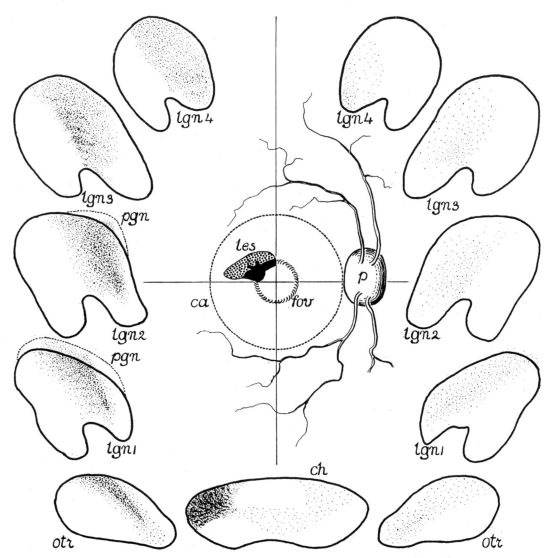

Fig. 204.—Representation of the central area of the retina of a Rhesus Macaque in the chiasma, optic tracts, and geniculate nuclei (Expt. No. 4). A single small lesion (*les*) was made electrolytically in the upper temporal quadrant, most intensively damaging the rim of the foveal depression (*solid black*), with less extensive damage spreading into the adjacent extrafoveal portion of the central area in the same quadrant as far as the vertical and horizontal meridians (*coarse dotting*). In the chiasma almost all degenerated fibers passed over to the tract and geniculate nucleus of the same side (*left* in figure), ipsilateral with the eye operated upon, with only a few fibers decussating to the contralateral side (*right* in figure). This experiment shows fairly accurately the location and extent of the upper foveal and areal quadrant, of the horizontal meridian, and of the fixation point in the optic tract and laminated lateral geniculate nucleus. The few decussating fibers may have been affected by the location of the lesion close to the vertical dividing meridian and could be followed into the opposite tract and nucleus (*right* in figure). Note an indication of a lamellar arrangement of fibers in the ipsilateral laminated nucleus and the entrance of fine fibers into the pregeniculate nucleus from the subjacent degenerated segment. Labeling same as in Fig. 203.

free from degeneration (left *lgn1* to *lgn3*), as in the preceding experiments, indicated the terminal areas of fibers originating from the extensive central-areal and extra-areal territories of the upper temporal quadrant, which in Experiment 5 also remained undamaged.

In contrast with the preceding two experiments, however, the number of delicate degenerated fibers passing over to the pregeniculate nucleus (*pgn*, in left *lgn1*) in the fifth experiment was negligible. Since the foveal excavation was not affected, this suggests that the fovea is the principal source of afferent geniculo-pregeniculate fibers serving as a pupillary reflex pathway.

7. Experiment with a lesion along the boundary of central area (Expt. 6).—In the

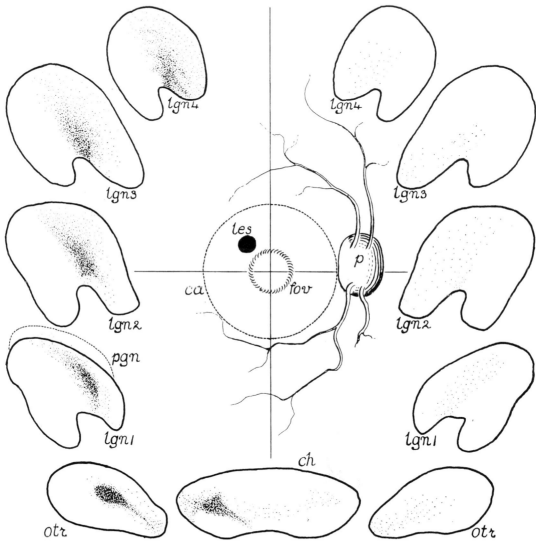

Fig. 205.—Representation of the central area of the retina of a Rhesus Macaque in the chiasma, in the optic tract, and in the lateral geniculate nucleus (Expt. No. 5). A single, small, circular, sharply outlined lesion (*les*) was located in the upper temporal quadrant of the central area (*ca*) outside the central fovea (*fov*), at an almost equal distance from the vertical and horizontal meridians. In the chiasma (*ch*), tract (*otr*), laminated geniculate nucleus (*lgn*), and pregeniculate nucleus (*pgn*), degenerated fibers were found almost entirely on the side ipsilateral with the operated eye (right side, *left* in figure), the few decussating fibers being caused to degenerate by the general conditions unavoidable in the experiment. This experiment shows principally the location and extent of the extra-foveal fibers of the central area in the optic tract and lateral geniculate nucleus and also indicates the position of the horizontal meridian. Very few fibers pass over from the laminated nucleus into the pregeniculate nucleus, indicating the foveal depression as the principal origin of this system (*see* preceding figures). Labeling same as in Fig. 203.

sixth experiment, a small, oblong lesion (*les*) was made along the upper boundary of the central area, astride the principal vertical meridian, apparently extending almost equally in the upper nasal and in the upper temporal quadrants (Fig. 206).

Because of the symmetrical location and to some extent also because of the peculiar course of the optic nerve fibers circling around the central fovea (*see* Fig. 162) and the similar distribution of blood vessels in the central area and fovea, the fiber bundles and cell areas affected by the lesion in both upper retinal quadrants must have been somewhat similar, extending chiefly along the upper circumference of the central area (*ca*). Because of this, a roughly semicircular zone in the upper periphery of the central area and in the region outside it, extending for some distance in the temporal direction along the horizontal raphé, must have been destroyed. In any case, the central fovea (*fov*) and the fibers originating in it, the "papillomacular bundle," were spared. These factors may explain the somewhat similar shape, extent, and location of degenerated areas in both tracts (*otr*) and lateral geniculate nuclei (*lgn*), the degeneration on the contralateral side (right, in the figure) being only slightly more intensive, though spreading a bit less, in the intermediate central-areal segment than on the ipsilateral side (left, in the figure).

The degeneration in approximately the medial half of both geniculate nuclei, as in the preceding experiments, agrees with the location of the lesion in the upper retinal quadrants above the horizontal meridian.

The course of degenerated fibers, both decussating and those remaining on the same side, particularly in the chiasma (*ch*), at first slants downward toward the mid-line, where they touch the inferior margin; in this way they assume the ventral position which they maintain in both tracts (*otr*).

In the lateral geniculate nuclei (*lgn1* to *lgn4*) it is also the ventromedial margins that are most heavily degenerated. The contrast between Experiment 6 and Experiments 2, 3, and 4 is especially apparent in the posterior fourth of the lateral geniculate nuclei. Whereas in the latter experiments (Figs. 202, 203, 204, *lgn1* to *lgn4*) the central foveal fibers terminate as far

as the upper convex margin of the nucleus (this is especially evident on the ipsilateral side of Expt. 3, left, in Fig. 203) and while in Experiment 5 the fibers, mostly extrafoveal from the central area, do not quite reach the upper margin of the nucleus (Fig. 205, *lgn4*), in Experiment 6 the situation is precisely reversed (Fig. 206, *lgn4*). Here the larger upper portion, close to the convex extremity of the nuclei, remains free, the degeneration being confined to a zone in the ventromedial tip and around the hilum of both the right and the left nucleus. The larger dorsal portion in the posterior half of the lateral geniculate nucleus, accordingly, is the terminal area of those optic nerve fibers that have their origin in and near the central fovea.

It is remarkable that the fibers from the fovea in Experiment 6 escaped injury—in spite of the proximity of the lesion and unavoidable damage to some branches of the upper temporal artery and vein! The collateral connections with the surrounding vessels that remained intact—that is, with the descending branches of the upper temporal artery and vein and also with the lower temporal vessels, but principally with the macular arterioles, venules, and capillaries—were apparently sufficient for the maintenance of blood supply in the entire foveal pit and in most of the central area (*see* Figs. 148, 162).

Another noteworthy feature in this experiment is the delicate fibers to the pregeniculate gray nucleus, which remained normal. This again, as in Experiment 5, indicated that most, if not all, of these fibers originate in the central fovea, as shown in Experiments 2, 3, and 4.

8. Experiments with lesions in extra-areal periphery (Expts. 7 and 8).—In the seventh experiment a small circular lesion (*les*) was made in the upper temporal quadrant above the large blood vessels (Fig. 207). Owing to the location of the lesion, both fibers from the locally damaged ganglion cells and others sweeping to the optic papilla in wide arches from the more distant periphery of the upper temporal quadrant were interrupted and were caused to degenerate (*cf.* Fig. 162). Since the lesion was not far from the principal vertical meridian, some damage also occurred in an adjoining group of ganglion cells and nerve fibers in the upper nasal quadrant. Hence the areas of degeneration in the two tracts and geniculates were almost identical, the reaction on the ipsilateral side (left, in the figure) being somewhat more intensive.

The first point of interest in this experiment concerned the restriction of degeneration to the ventromedial tip of the tracts (*otr*) and the geniculate nuclei (*lgn*). As in the preceding experiments, the medial location agreed with the damage to the upper retinal quadrants. The confinement of degeneration to the most ventral zone both in the tracts and in the geniculate nuclei was in contrast with Experiments 2, 3, 4, and 5, and resembled Experiment 6. In this respect, Experiment 7 was the reverse of those experiments in which the central area or fovea was damaged and degeneration in the upper portion

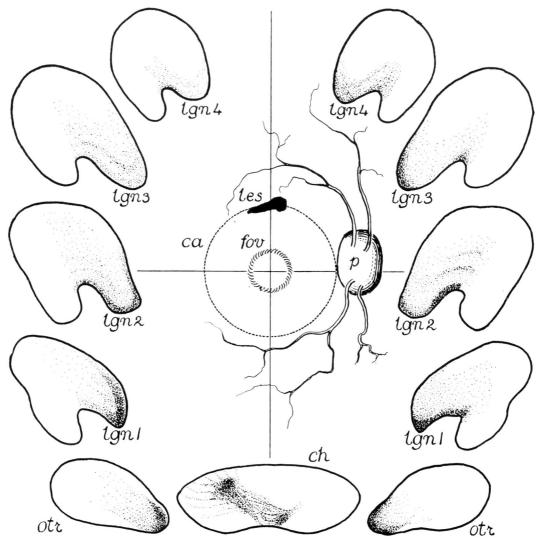

FIG. 206.—Representation of the periphery of the central area along the vertical dividing meridian in upper retinal quadrants in a Rhesus Macaque (Expt. No. 6). A single, small, oblong, and sharply localized electrolytic lesion (*les*) was made in the upper periphery of the central area (*ca*) astride the vertical meridian in the upper retinal half. The degenerated fibers, partly decussating in the chiasma, were found to be in numbers, location, and area of distribution almost the same on the ipsilateral side as on the contralateral. This experiment, owing to the fact that no damage was done to the central fovea, shows no degeneration in the tip of the posterior fourth of the lateral geniculate nuclei (*lgn4*), precisely the parts where foveal fibers were found to terminate (*cf*. Fig. 203). It further demonstrates the separation of nondecussating from decussating fibers by the vertical meridian and indicates the approximate location of the horizontal meridian in the tracts and geniculate nuclei. Labeling same as in Fig. 203.

of the nucleus was found. The portions of the retinae located at some distance from the central fovea and area and closer to the ora serrata, accordingly, are represented in the dorsomedial and ventrolateral edge of the optic tracts and in the ventral margins of the lateral geniculate nuclei which flank the hilum.

Noteworthy, further, was the small number or relative scarcity of degenerated fibers in this experiment. Here their number was only a frac-

tion of the degenerated fibers found in Experiments 2, 4, and 5 and was far below the number of fibers in Experiment 3, with a much smaller lesion. Obviously, the number of optic nerve fibers from the same surface area is many times larger in the central area, especially the fovea, than in the far periphery—a fact that agrees with the direct observation of the number of ganglion cells and fibers found in different regions of the stained whole-mounts and cut sec-

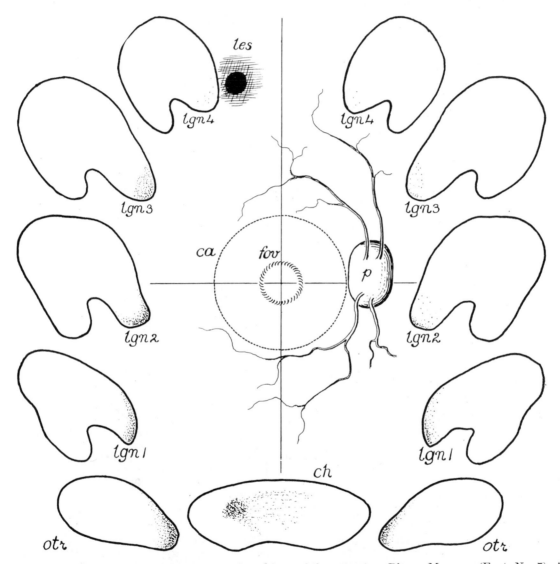

Fig. 207.—Representation of the extra-areal periphery of the retina in a Rhesus Macaque (Expt. No. 7). A small, circular, and somewhat diffusely outlined lesion (*les*) was made electrolytically in the upper temporal quadrant not far from the vertical meridian, but at a considerable distance from the central area (*ca*) and its arching fibers. The areae of degeneration were found to correspond fairly closely on both sides, the number of fibers being somewhat less on the contralateral, left side (*right* in the figure). In the lateral geniculate nuclei the zones of degeneration were confined to the extreme ventral tips of medial segments. This experiment shows the location of fibers originating from the distant retinal periphery in the lateral geniculate nuclei. No fibers were found to enter the pregeniculate nucleus. Labeling same as in Fig. 203.

tions (Fig. 129). Another interesting observation showed that in this experiment, where fovea and central area were spared, the delicate fibers to the pregeniculate nucleus did not degenerate.

In Experiment 8 a small circular lesion (*les*) was made in the upper nasal quadrant not far from the optic papilla (Fig. 208). Because of the peculiar arclike arrangement of the intraretinal optic nerve fibers described before (Fig. 162), a large sector of the retinal bundles was destroyed. This sector included a portion of the

extra-areal periphery of the upper temporal quadrant extending as far as the raphé, excepting its farthest periphery (*cf.* Fig. 207, where fibers from the distant periphery alone degenerated).

In addition, a portion of the adjoining upper nasal quadrant was damaged directly. On the other hand, the fiber bundles arising from the central fovea and area, in spite of the proximity of the lesion to the papillomacular bundle, escaped entirely.

Since the portion of the temporal quadrant

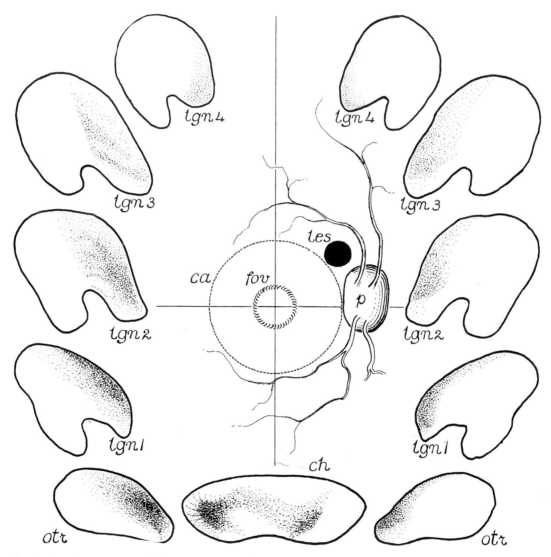

Fig. 208.—Representation of the extra-areal retinal periphery with, perhaps, a part of the adjacent central area, in a Rhesus Macaque (Expt. No. 8). A single, small, circular lesion (*les*) was made electrolytically at the upper extremity of the optic papilla (*p*), just touching the upper nasal quadrant of the central area (*ca*). Owing to the peculiar arching course and the convergence of optic nerve fibers close to the papilla, illustrated in Fig. 162, somewhat different segments in the two upper retinal quadrants were obliterated, indicated by the asymmetric areae of degeneration in both lateral geniculate nuclei (*lgn*). Note an absence of degeneration in the foveal segments of the nuclei (*lgn4*), and a laminar arrangement of degenerated fibers in *lgn2* and *lgn3*. Labeling same as in Fig. 203.

destroyed differed from that eliminated in the nasal quadrant, the degeneration in the two tracts and geniculates also varied considerably in size, shape, and location. In the optic tract of the ipsilateral side (left *otr*, in Fig. 208) and in approximately the anterior half of the ipsilateral geniculate nucleus (*lgn1* and *lgn2*), the degeneration in the medial segment spread as far as the axial line; the lateral segment contained no degeneration, since its fibers originate in the unaffected lower quadrants separated by the horizontal raphé.

Obviously, the fibers from the upper and lower extra-areal quadrants meet, in the anterior half of the lateral geniculate nucleus, along a portion of the mentioned axial line, precisely as they do along the horizontal raphé in the temporal half of the retina. In the posterior half of the nucleus, on the contrary, the two quadrantic sets of the extra-areal fibers, the upper and the lower ones, are separated, leaving between them a wedgelike central-areal and foveal representation, which widens toward the posterior extremity of the nucleus until it spreads over almost the entire nucleus (left *lgn3* and *lgn4*, in Fig. 208).

In the contralateral geniculate nucleus the area of degeneration is even smaller and more limited to the medial sector, leaving free a greater area around the axis of the nucleus. This negative evidence also shows the intermediate posterior segment to be a terminal region of the central-areal and foveal fibers, which agrees with the positive evidence shown in Experiments 2, 3, and 4 (*lgn4*, in Figs. 202, 203, 204).

The extra-areal segments in the lateral geniculate nucleus, accordingly, flank the intermediate central-areal and foveal segment on both sides, repeating the arrangement found in the retina, where the central area and fovea and the "papillomacular bundle" are encircled by fiber bundles originating from the extra-areal parts of the retina from above, below, and on the temporal side (*cf.* Fig. 162). In the contralateral tract and geniculate nucleus (right *otr* and *lgn1–lgn4*, in Fig. 208), the area of degeneration hugging the medial margin does not extend into the ventromedial tip of the nucleus, avoiding a part of the zone where fibers from the distant retinal periphery terminate (shown in Figs. 206, 207).

Also, the area is demarcated toward the center of the nucleus on the contralateral side by a curved, instead of a straight, line, as found in Experiments 3–6, as well as on the ipsilateral side of the same experiment except on the posterior levels, *lgn4* in Figure 208. Since no central-areal and foveal fibers of the nasal quadrant were damaged, the intermediate segment in the tract and the geniculate, particularly in the posterior extremity of the latter, remained intact (right *lgn3* and *lgn4*, in figure).

Finally, as in other experiments where the lesion was outside the foveal pit, no delicate fibers from the principal laminated nuclei to the pregeniculate gray nuclei degenerated in this experiment.

9. Summary of the topographical representation of the retinal surface in infranuclear and nuclear divisions of the primate visual system.—Taking into consideration the principle of symmetry on both sides of the horizontal meridian, the evidence from the experiments on monkeys described in the preceding paragraphs makes it possible to devise a scheme of detailed topographical representation or "projection" of the retinal surface in the infranuclear division of the visual system, and especially in its principal terminal station, the laminated lateral geniculate nucleus (Fig. 225; *see also* sec. 11, this chapter).

In the optic nerve (as in the papilla), along approximately three-fourths of the postbulbar stretch, the areal-foveal fibers are located in the temporal half of the nerve (Figs. 201, 202). Only gradually, in the proximal fourth of the nerve close to the chiasma, does this bundle definitely assume a central location. The bundle is organized quadrantically, the upper temporal and nasal quadrants being above, the lower temporal and nasal quadrants below, a line which corresponds to the horizontal meridian (*optpap* in Fig. 225). The extra-areal portions of the respective quadrants, close to the eyeball, are then next nasal in line in the nerve, with the temporal crescent fibers most inward, along the nasal margin of the nerve.

Closer to the chiasma, the areal-foveal bundle assumes a more central location and becomes surrounded on all sides by the extra-areal fibers, arranged according to the quadrants (*optn* in same figure). Along this proximal stretch of the nerve, however, the position of the quadrants changes, owing to a rotation of the optic nerve around its axis, with the upper quadrants becoming more nasal and the lower quadrants more temporal. The monocular crescentic fibers, in consequence, form the ventromedial margin of the nerve, a position they preserve after decussation in the contralateral optic tract.

In the chiasma the areal-foveal or "macular" bundle occupies a dorsal position (Fig. 225). The decussating halves of the fibers of this bundle, mainly on intermediate levels through the chiasma, occupy, closer to the center, about the upper two-thirds of the chiasma immediately underneath the hypothalamus; the two nondecussating halves forming the two dorsolateral corners of the chiasma, an approximate position maintained by them and their contralateral mates, after decussation, in the tracts as far as the geniculate nuclei. (This result from the experiments with monkeys agrees in substance with the position of macular fibers in the human chiasma as described by Rønne 1910.) The remainder of the chiasma, roughly represented by the inferior half, is formed by the extra-areal fibers, with the monocular crescentic bundles being situated ventral- and posteriormost.

In the suprachiasmal portion of the visual system each side represents only half of both retinae. According to the scheme (Fig. 225), each optic tract and lateral geniculate nucleus, on a cross-section vertical to its longitudinal axis, may be thought of as composed of a series of thin lamellae or sheets of fibers arranged roughly parallel to one another. The pattern of distribution of these lamellae fairly well resembles the arrangement of the quadrants and zones of the retinal surface. Owing to a partial decussation in the chiasma and the resulting doubling of the homonymous fibers, each tract and lateral geniculate nucleus represents homonymous halves of both retinae or of the crossed homonymous halves of both monocular fields of view.

The representation of the retinal surface in the geniculates and tracts, even though highly accurate, is not absolutely identical. The first qualification is introduced along their course by a slight shifting of fibers with respect to one another, owing to which the complete pattern becomes somewhat changed, even though the essential features of the retinal arrangement are preserved. In spite of the shifting, the individual conductor units at both ends remain close to their original neighbors, that is, they keep the same relative order in the terminal station, the lateral geniculate nucleus, that is present at the origin of the cable in the retina.

The second qualification is caused by the necessity to tie up in an orderly way, with the original topographical relations fully preserved, the retinal units arranged two-dimensionally, with their respective homodynamical cell groups in the lateral geniculate nucleus arranged according to a tridimensional pattern.

The third qualifying factor is the difference or change in the relative size of the receptor units of the retina and the corresponding terminal units in the lateral geniculate nucleus. This change takes place in the nucleus in an opposite sense from that found in the retina. In the foveal center the receptor units are identical with the single cones; outside it, with the increase in cone diameter and with the addition of the rods, wider spacing, and polysynaptical grouping, the photoreceptor units gradually increase in area toward the retinal periphery. In the lateral geniculate nucleus the opposite tendency is observed. Here the largest units are in the posterior intermediate segment, where the foveal center or foveola is represented, the smallest units being in those sectors where the extreme retinal periphery is represented.

There are, finally, indications that the representation of upper and lower quadrants is not exactly symmetrical with respect to the horizontal meridian as a divide, but is rather somewhat lopsided, a greater area or volume being related to the upper than to the lower quadrants on both sides of the line representing that meridian. This would indicate a somewhat greater importance of the inferior halves of the fields of view, especially so in Man, with his upright posture and terrestrial habit, in comparison with the arboreal species of the Primate Order, most of which use all four extremities for locomotion (*see* chap. XV).

Figure 225 summarizes in detail the retinal "projection" in the lateral geniculate nucleus of the Monkey. In it the right-eye retina (viewed from the front) is divided into two halves by the principal vertical meridian (*vm*), passing through the foveal center. The larger nasal half, in black, sends its fibers to the contralateral geniculate nucleus (right, in the figure), the smaller temporal half, in white, to the ipsilateral nucleus (left, in the figure). A horizontal meridian (*hm*), likewise passing through the foveal center, further divides each half of the retina into two quadrants, upper and lower, separating the retinal surface into four quadrants, upper and lower nasal (black) and upper and lower temporal quadrant (white).

A further subdivision is established by concentric smaller and larger circles, all centered in the foveal center (corresponding to the "points of fixation" in the fields of view). Each quadrant and zone is differently shaded, the upper quadrants with vertical, the lower quadrants with horizontal, lines, the density of the shading increasing from the periphery to the foveal center.

The smallest circle, closest to the fixation point, incloses the foveal center, corresponding to the deepest portion of the foveal excavation, or foveola, which practically coincides with the rodless central territory free of blood vessels. The next belt, encircling the rodless area, corresponds to the slopes of the fovea as far as the rim of the foveal excavation. The third circle from the fixation point represents the extrafoveal portion of the central area, on the nasal side extending as far as the optic papilla (*op*). The largest circular belt surrounding the central area corresponds to the spacious extra-areal periphery of the retina. On the temporal side (left, in the figure) this belt extends as far as the ora serrata or serrated margin of the retinal membrane. It incloses that larger portion of the retina which, in the normal binocular visual act, co-operates with, or is functionally overlapped by, the same portion of the retina of the opposite eye. On the nasal side (extreme right, in the figure), the retina extends for some distance beyond the binocular portion. This crescent-shaped portion of the retina corresponds to the monocular portion of the field of view, which does not have a counterpart in the field of view of the opposite eye.

While the arrangement of the quadrants and belts in Figure 225 is accurate, their relative

sizes, for purposes of more lucid presentation, are given at a different relative magnification. The area of the rodless and vessel-free center of the central fovea, e.g., actually amounting to approximately 2 per cent of the field of view in the horizontal meridian, is increased in the scheme almost tenfold (area inclosed by the first circle from the center). The central area (third circle from the center), on the other hand, was magnified less. (For the actual figures *see* chap. V, 10.)

The optic tracts and lateral geniculate nuclei, being above the chiasma and hence above the point of decussation of the nasal fibers, represent the homonymous halves of both retinae or the hemiretinae because of a suprachiasmal doubling. The ipsilateral tract and geniculate nucleus (left, in the figure) represent the temporal half; the contralateral tract and geniculate (right, in the figure) represent the nasal half of the right retina. The horizontal meridian, represented by fairly straight lines placed approximately in the center of the tracts and geniculates, divides each of these structures into two halves, each half corresponding to one retinal quadrant. The upper quadrants are located on the dorsomedial side of the horizontal meridian, the lower quadrants on the ventrolateral side. This meridian, in turn, terminates at its upper extremity with a small semicircle (*f*), indicating the position of the centralmost foveal fibers, corresponding to a minute nest of very small foveal cones named by Rochon-Duvigneaud the "bouquet of central cones." It is these cones that function as the centralmost point of the visual apparatus or, in the field of view, as the "point of fixation."

The various belts and quadrants, as is easily understandable from the figure, have a definite location, size, and shape in the tracts and geniculates. In Figure 225, these are represented according to their actual relative sizes. The salient feature is the location, shape, and size of the central fovea (densely shaded areas at the upper extremities of the sketches). In the tracts, where the foveal fibers are close together, they form a narrow wedge at the blunt upper end, with the axis following the horizontal meridian, the sharp end of the wedge pointing toward the medioventral, attenuated extremity of the tract. The foveal-areal wedge does not quite reach the middle of the horizontal axis and shows a flaring along the rounded upper contour of the tract.

In the lateral geniculate nucleus the foveal representation on the anterior levels close to the optic tract is still restricted, since the foveal fibers here are only "fibers of passage." On the middle level of the longitudinal extent of the geniculate nucleus, the foveal representation begins to increase in area, doing so rapidly in the posterior half, until in its posterior fourth the foveal fibers spread over most of the nucleus. Here, as in the tract and in the retina, the fovea preserves its central location. Whereas, however, in the tract and close to the anterior end of the geniculate it is flanked by fibers representing all belts of the retina, the farthest being the monocular crescentic fibers, the flanking belts gradually decrease in size toward the posterior end of the nucleus until the monocular representation ceases to exist. In this way it is possible to preserve a very accurate topographical relationship of the retinal surface in a compact tridimensional structure like a lateral geniculate nucleus.

The remainder of the hemiretinal surface is arranged in an orderly fashion around the hemifovea in approximately the same order as in the hemiretina: first, the extrafoveal portion of the central area outside the fovea; next, the extraareal binocular periphery outside the central area, and the monocular crescent outside the extra-areal binocular periphery. In the tract, the respective quadrants meet across the horizontal meridian, forming an approximately semicircular belt arranged concentrically with respect to the fixation point (*f*). In the lateral geniculate nucleus the upper and lower quadrants of the monocular crescent are separated by a notch or dent, the hilum, in this structure. The extra-areal binocular quadrants on anterior levels are held together only by a slender bridge squeezed between the notch below and the areal-foveal core above.

This process of separation is completed on the middle levels. Here the areal core breaks through the extra-areal binocular belt and establishes direct contact with the hilum. The separation, on caudal levels, proceeds further, with the extrafoveal quadrants of the central area also eventually separated from each other, permitting the foveal segments direct access to the hilum. It is likely that this separation culminates in a similar pushing aside of the upper and lower segments of the periphery of the fovea, leaving the representation of the rodless foveal center, or foveola, alone, to form the caudal tip of the lateral geniculate nucleus.

The general mechanical causes that have brought about these changes in the internal topography and external configuration of the lateral geniculate nucleus are: an inclusion of the space-requiring nerve cells, together with their dendritic expansions; the presence of teledendric ramifications of the incoming optic and probably other categories of nerve fibers; and the addition of a greatly increased vascular net, indispensable for the greater metabolism required by a nerve center.

The other factor is a disproportionate numerical increase in the nerve cells in the foveal and areal core of the nucleus, only partially compensated downward by the reduced size of the cells in the same foveal core. This appears to be the principal factor causing the upper contour of a cross-section of the lateral geniculate nucleus to assume a round, evaginated shape, instead of the straight line which the principal vertical meridian in the retina, represented by it, actually is. The same necessity that, in the retina, caused an accumulation of histological elements in a thickened central area, especially in the foveal ridge, produced a rounded bulge in the geniculate nucleus, in order to accommodate the greatly increased number of central-areal and foveal cells.

The configuration of the lateral geniculate nucleus, both external and on a cross-section, varies in different species of the Primate Order. In spite of this variation, the principal features are easily recognized, and accurate topographical homologies may be established. (*See* secs. 8, 9, this chapter, and accompanying figures for the minute structure of the lateral geniculate nucleus; *see* chap. VII, 5–7, for the functional organization of the supranuclear division of the visual system.)

10. Dimensional organization of the visual system in Infraprimate Verte-

BRATES.—The topographical representation, or, as it is also called, the "point-to-point" or "one-to-one projection," of the retinal surface in the infranuclear and nuclear divisions of the visual pathway has been studied most thoroughly in the Primates, because of its great importance for the understanding of the functional organization of the human visual system and its pathology. Also, since the laminated lateral nucleus is the principal terminal station of the optic tract, most attention was paid to its topographical relation to the retina.

The available information, scanty though it be, shows that a similar topographical relation is present in other subcortical visual stations. Such an arrangement was demonstrated experimentally in the superior colliculi of the midbrain in various infraprimate species, e.g., Opossum, Rat, Rabbit, and Cat (Brouwer 1923; Overbosch 1927; Lashley 1934; Bodian 1937).

Concerning the Inframammalian Vertebrates, unfortunately, there is little positive knowledge. Lubsen (1921) showed the presence of retinal projection in a Fish. This was further confirmed, and a similar arrangement found in *Triturus taeniatus*, a European Newt, by Ströer (1939, 1940).

These observations, because of the low phylogenetic standing of the Fishes and Amphibians, are of great interest, since they show the "point-to-point" representation of the retinal surface to be a basic plan of organization of the vertebrate visual system. In the American Newts *Ambystoma* and *Necturus* and in the Cat-fish *Ameiurus*, however, Herrick (1941, 1942, 1948) was able only partially to confirm Ströer's observations by finding, in addition to a generalized, diffuse, nonspecific system of thick optic nerve fibers, another system of thin and more numerous fibers that are possibly organized retinotopically.

The investigation of the intrinsic organization of the visual system of the Inframammalian Vertebrates and its interpretation in the light of the specific habits of a particular species still remain largely a task of the future. As far as is known, it justifies the assumption that a more or less elaborate "dimensional" organizational plan may be expected in all species except those whose vision has been eliminated. Such expectation is based upon indirect evidence: large eyeballs, an advanced differentiation of retinal structures, a formidable optic nerve made up of a great number of fibers, and well-developed visual centers of the midbrain possessing a structure resembling that of the mammalian cortex. Such features are characteristic of many Fishes, Lizards, and most Birds. In many cases, such as Birds of Prey, Insectivorous Birds, and certain Lizards (Chameleon, *Anolis*, *Agama*), a "point-to-point" organization of the central visual apparatus, in its structural refinement and functional performance, may equal, and occasionally surpass, that found in the best "visual Mammals," the Primates, including Man. Such a postulation is in accord with the notable experiments upon the visual apparatus of Salamanders and Frogs executed by Stone *et al.* and by Sperry. (*Cf. also* chap. XIV.)

References: Ariëns Kappers, Huber & Crosby 1936; Balado & Franke 1930; Barris 1935; Bodian 1935, 1937; Brouwer 1936; Brouwer & Zeeman 1925, 1926; Brouwer, Zeeman & Houwer 1923; Chacko 1948; Le Gros Clark 1932; Le Gros Clark & Penman 1934; Coppez & Fritz 1930; Dalén 1906; Delbrück 1890; Dimmer 1899; Harrington 1939; Hechst 1933; Henschen 1890–92 and later; Herrmann & Pötzl 1928; C. J. Herrick 1941, 1942; Jatzow 1885; Juba 1933, 1939; Kellermann 1879; Kuschel 1924; Lashley 1934; Lenz 1930; Lubsen 1921; Mackenzie, Meighan & Pollock 1933; Marburg 1942; Minkowski 1913, 1920, 1922, 1932, 1934, 1939; D. E. Müller 1861; Orlando 1933; Overbosch 1927; H. Parsons 1902; Penman 1934; Pick & Herrenheiser 1895; Polyak 1941, 1948; Purtscher 1880; S. Ramón y Cajal 1899, 1909–11; Rasmussen 1945; Rønne (Roenne) 1910, 1913, 1914, 1944; Samelsohn 1880, 1882; Sántha 1932; A. H. Schröder 1929; Sperry 1944, 1945, 1948, 1949; Ströer 1939; Stone 1944, 1946; Thomsen 1888; Uhthoff 1880; Usher & Dean 1896; Vossius 1882; Widmark 1897; Wilbrand 1881, 1925–26, 1927, 1929, 1930; Wilbrand & Saenger 1904, 1906, 1915, 1918; Zeeman 1925.

SEC. 8. MINUTE STRUCTURE OF THE PRINCIPAL OR
LAMINATED LATERAL GENICULATE NUCLEUS

1. General remarks.—The laminated lateral geniculate nucleus, or body, of the simian and human brain is the principal and structurally most elaborate subcortical visual center (Fig. 209, *LGN*; also Fig. 210 and sec. 1 [4], this chapter). It is probable that, together with the pregeniculate gray nucleus *(pgn)*, the laminated

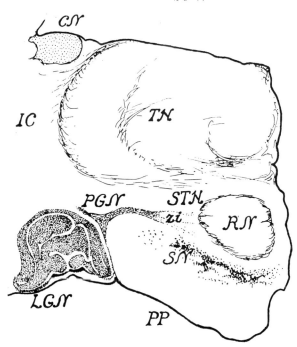

Fig. 209.—Cross-section through half of the human diencephalon, or betweenbrain, showing the topographic relationships of the principal constituent structures: laminated lateral geniculate nucleus *(LGN)*, pregeniculate nucleus *(PGN)*, subthalamus *(STH)*, zona incerta of subthalamus *(zi)*, red nucleus *(RN)*, substantia nigra or dark substance *(SN)*, pes pedunculi of "foot" of the cerebral peduncle *(PP)*, thalamus *(TH)*, internal capsule *(IC)*, and caudate nucleus *(CN)*. Note that the pregeniculate nucleus *(PGN)*, laterally attached to the laminated nucleus *(LGN)* and medially extending through the zona incerta to the red nucleus *(RN)*, indicates a path along which the lateral geniculate complex, represented by the laminated nucleus (dorsal portion of lateral geniculate nucleus) and the pregeniculate nucleus (ventral portion of lateral geniculate nucleus of Lower Mammals) migrated during phylogenesis and ontogenesis. *(Cf.* Figs. 210–15, and also Figs. 183, 186, 191.)

nucleus represents the "lateral geniculate nucleus" of the betweenbrain of the Infraprimate Mammals *(lgn* in Fig. 191).

Phylogenetically, the larger laminated or lat-

eral geniculate nucleus proper of the Primates appears, then, as a homologue of the "dorsal portion" or *pars dorsalis* (*d*, a derivative of the thalamus proper), the smaller pregeniculate gray nucleus as a homologue of the "ventral portion" or *pars ventralis* (*v*, a derivative of the subthalamus) of the primitive Mammals.

The reverse topographical arrangement found in the primate brain, with the principal laminated nucleus ventral and the smaller pregeniculate nucleus assuming a more or less dorsal or dorsomedial position, is caused by a great increase in size of the primate thalamus, which, in turn, results in a complex displacement during the phylogenesis and ontogenesis of the laminated nucleus in a lateral, posterior, and downward direction (*see* Környey 1928; R. A. Pfeifer 1930; Le Gros Clark 1932).

According to the ontogenetical and phylogenetical investigations of the lateral geniculate nucleus from the lowermost Mammals to the highest, including Man, by Le Gros Clark (1932), the dorsal laminated nucleus differentiates out of the lateral portion of the ventral nuclear mass of the thalamus proper.

The ventral nucleus is a more primitive visual center, showing a progressive reduction in the Higher Mammals (*cf.,* however, sec. 10 [1], this chapter). It appears to be a differentiated lateral segment of that part of the *pars ventralis diencephali* which is called the subthalamus (in Gilbert's terminology "ventral thalamus"). This is indicated by its topographical relations, the similarity of its nerve cells, its gradual grading into *zona incerta* (*zi* in Fig. 209), all features noticeable both in primitive Mammals, such as the Tree Shrew, and also in the Tarsier, and likewise seen both during human ontogenesis and in the mature human brain (Figs. 212, 214, 215).

The ventral nucleus, accordingly, is phylogenetically an old subthalamic visual center with tegmental connections (*see* sec. 10 [2], this chapter, on connections). In the Primates the ventral nucleus is preserved in the pregeniculate gray nucleus, *griseum praegeniculatum* or *substantia grisea praegeniculata,* of O. and C. Vogt (1909). In the adult human and simian brain this nucleus remains permanently continuous with the subthalamus. (*Cf. also* S. Ingvar 1923, 1925; M. S. Gilbert 1935; E. R. A. Cooper 1945.)

The lateral geniculate nucleus, with the medial geniculate nucleus, which is a subcortical station of the auditory pathway, forms the *metathalamus* or hind part of the thalamus proper, from which both nuclei became differentiated (*cf.*, however, Kuhlenbeck 1935–36).

The laminated geniculate nucleus is anatomically, functionally, and trophically closely related both to the infranuclear and to the supranuclear divisions of the visual system. Its nerve cells, irrespective of whether they belong to the neuron variety with a long axon (Golgi type *I*) or have a short axon (Golgi type *II*), are closely trophically dependent on the optic nerve fibers under whose exclusive influence they are ("monopoly of afferent relationship"). When separated from them, they atrophy or die completely, a phenomenon known as "transsynaptic or transneuronal degeneration." This is a reverse of a process of retrograde degeneration taking place, e.g., in the ganglion cells of the retina in consequence of their separation from the laminated nucleus.

A similar, though less intimate, relationship is possibly present between the pregeniculate nucleus and the optic nerve fibers and their cells of origin in the retina; this, however, requires further study.

In another sense the trophic interdependence of the infranuclear and nuclear neurons differs markedly. Whereas the cells of the laminated nucleus degenerate when they are cut off from their afferent influences, the retinal ganglion cells show but a slight reduction of staining properties in experiments where the supranuclear division of the visual system (the visual radiation or the striate area) is damaged, provided that no damage is done to the terminations of the optic nerve fibers in the laminated nucleus or to the latter's blood supply (*see* the author's observations in Klüver's paper 1937, p. 388; *cf. also* Lauber 1927 and Kolmer & Lauber 1936).

The axis cylinders or axons of the larger or principal nerve cells of the laminated lateral geniculate nucleus represent the visual radiation which terminates in the striate cortex of the

occipital lobe of the cerebral hemisphere (*see* chap. VII, 1 [2]). When these fibers are interrupted or their terminations in the striate cortex are cut off or in any way seriously interfered with, their cells of origin in the laminated nucleus show signs of irritation, which finally ends in their complete wasting or disappearance or retrograde degeneration.

To what extent the geniculate nerve cells in an adult state are capable of regeneration or what is the maximum of interference to their axons and teledendrons after which anatomical integrity and normal functioning still can be restored remains an open problem. Experimental evidence points with certainty toward a delicate adjustment, in which any mechanical interference with the terminations in the striate cortex is followed by degeneration and complete disappearance of the entire neuron.

In a severe insult, e.g., a complete interruption, not only the principal cells whose axons are severed but also the association cells of the laminated nucleus degenerate. The process of retrograde degeneration of the nervous parenchyma is accompanied by an increase of neuroglial elements. (*Cf.* chaps. VII and XII.)

The cells of the pregeniculate nucleus do not seem to suffer in consequence of an interference with the visual radiation. This, owing to an absence of cortical connection in this nucleus, is understandable. (*See* sec. 10 [2], this chapter.)

2. SHAPE AND TOPOGRAPHICAL RELATION OF THE LAMINATED LATERAL GENICULATE NUCLEUS.—The shape and the lamellated structure of the lateral geniculate nucleus proper in the various primate species are similar, even though they vary in detail (*cf.* Le Gros Clark, *Brit. J. Ophth.*, v. 16, 1932; also 1941, 1942; *see also* Solnitzky & Harman 1943; and Harman & Solnitzky 1944). In the Lower Monkeys, e.g., a Rhesus Macaque, the shape of the nucleus in the customary coronal sections resembles that of a horseshoe, with its apex or convex extremity pointing dorsolaterally, and its lower indented side facing down (Figs. 186, 210, 211). In the Anthropomorphous Apes (Fig. 214) and in Man (Figs. 209, 215) the nucleus is more or less club-shaped, with its bulky end turned medially and its short, attenuated handle extending in the lateral direction and down, although compact

forms of the human nucleus are also found occasionally.

The axial line by which the lateral geniculate nucleus may be divided into two fairly symmetrical halves is inclined laterally with its upper end, this line inclosing, with the horizontal line, an angle of approximately 45° (Fig. 211). The ventral notch or hilum (*h*) and the

terisk in Fig. 200, sketches *C–G*; Figs. 210, 211; Fig. 214, sketches *E, F*; Fig. 215, sketches *G–I*).

The two nuclei are separated from each other by a thick, curved fiber lamina, the "circumgeniculate capsule" (*cgc*), which incases the entire circumference of the laminated nucleus. On anterior levels this capsule is largely made up of the incoming retinal fibers from the optic tract.

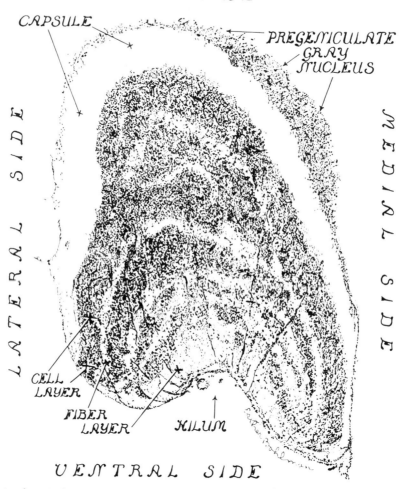

Fig. 210.—Lateral geniculate nucleus of a Rhesus Macaque, showing cell laminae in a Nissl-stained section through the middle third of the anteroposterior extent of the nucleus. Note the fiber layers, relatively free from cells, by which the cell laminae are separated, and the much thicker fiber capsule, entirely free from cells, by which the caplike pregeniculate nucleus is separated from the laminated nucleus. (*Cf.* preceding and following figures.)

two ventral extremities flanking it are part of the basal cerebral surface, the rest being imbedded in the substance of the brain. Dorsomedially, on anterior levels, much of the lateral geniculate nucleus is surrounded by the pregeniculate nucleus (*pgn* or marked by an as-

On posterior levels, especially above the apex of the nucleus, the circumgeniculate capsule consists mostly of the outgoing geniculate axons that form the initial portion of the visual radiation. Here this capsule increases in thickness, forming an area somewhat triangular in shape, called the "field of Wernicke" (*W* in Fig. 213); from it a long, narrow strand of obliquely cut fibers extends along the lateral face of the thalamus (Fig. 230).

Other important structures adjoining the lateral geniculate nucleus are the posterior thalamic nuclei on its dorsal and dorsomedial sides (*Th* or *th* in Figs. 209, 213), the subthalamus (*STH* or *sth* in Figs. 209, 215), the medial geniculate nucleus or body (Figs. 181, 183) or the cerebral peduncle on the medial side (*PP* in Figs. 209, 230), and the posterior extremity of the internal capsule of the brain on its lateral side. The lateral geniculate nucleus is separated from the hippocampal gyrus of the temporal lobe by a cleft, the chorioid fissure, which belongs to the space outside the brain (Fig. 230). Between the nucleus and the inferior horn of the lateral ventricle are the *fimbria* and *taenia* of the *hippocampus*, the blood vessels, and the chorioid plexus of this region (Fig. 230).

3. LAMINATION OF THE LATERAL GENICULATE NUCLEUS.—The nerve cells and fibers which constitute the laminated lateral geniculate nucleus in the Monkey, Ape, and Man are assembled into several parallel and alternating cell and fiber layers or laminae.

In the Macaque the laminae are "everted," that is, bent in a semicircular fashion around a ventral notch, the hilum (Fig. 200; also *h* in Figs. 210, 211). In the Anthropomorphous Apes and in Man the eversion or ventral curving, with the concavity facing down, is less pronounced and is noticeable, if at all, only in the anterior or rostral half of the nucleus (Fig. 214, *D–F;* Fig. 215, *E, H*).

In the posterior or caudal portion the "inversion" or curving, with the concavity facing up, is more pronounced (Fig. 214, *A–C;* Fig. 215, *A–D*). In the posterior tip of the nucleus, in fact, this inverted curving alone is present (Fig. 214, *A, B;* Fig. 215, *A–D*).

This particular feature of the principal or laminated lateral geniculate nucleus found in the phylogenetically highest Primates resembles the arrangement found in the Lower Primates, the Lemurs, and in the insectivorous relative of the primate ancestors, the Tree Shrew *Tupaia* (*cf.* Le Gros Clark in *Brit. J. Ophth.*, v. 16, Fig.

6, 1932, and lower photo in Fig. 213; *see also* sec. 6 [6], this chapter).

The number of the cell laminae of the laminated lateral geniculate nucleus and their arrangement vary somewhat in detail in different primate species. They also vary on different levels of the geniculate nucleus of the same species. In the anteriormost portion, at the anterior pole of the nucleus, where the fibers of the optic tract enter, there are four cell laminae in all simian species and in Man (Fig. 200, *G;* Fig. 214, *F;* Fig. 215, *H*).

Of these, the lower two magnocellular laminae are narrow and composed mostly of large nerve cells, the largest in the nucleus, though fewest numerically. The first or lowermost magnocellular lamina, *1c*, is related to the decussating optic nerve fibers from the nasal half of the contralateral retina, as discussed in detail in section 6 (5), this chapter. The next layer, *1i*, also magnocellular, is related to the nondecussating fibers from the temporal half of the ipsilateral retina.

The two upper parvocellular laminae, much thicker and made up of smaller but more numerous nerve cells, are also terminals of fibers from the same homonymous retinal halves: *2i* of the nondecussating ipsilateral and *2c* of the decussating contralateral.

In the much larger posterior portion of the nucleus the number of the laminae increases by a further subdivision of each of the parvocellular laminae into two, which makes four parvocellular and two magnocellular laminae. Of these, the *1i*, *2ia*, and *2iβ* are related to the ipsilateral fibers, and *1c*, *2ca*, and *2cβ* are related to the contralateral.

In the middle third or so of the longitudinal extent of the nucleus in the Monkey, however, the six laminae are found only in the intermediate foveal-areal segment (*see* Fig. 200, e.g., *E* or *F*). In the medial and lateral segments of the nucleus, where fibers from the upper and lower extramacular quadrants terminate (*see* Fig. 225 and sec. 7, this chapter), the number of the laminae in the Monkey remains limited to four or five.

In the Chimpanzee a sesquilaminal differentiation is present in the entire medial segment, in most of the posterior two-thirds of the nucleus (Fig. 214, *A–D*). In the medial extra-areal

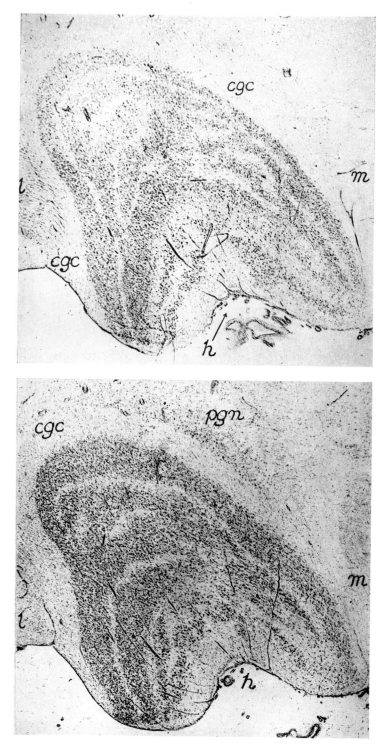

Fig. 211.—Microphotographs of Nissl-stained sections of the lateral geniculate nucleus of a Rhesus Macaque, showing the arrangement of cell laminae, separated from one another by fiber laminae relatively free from nerve cells. The upper photo is from a more posterior level through the nucleus than the lower photo; hence the pregeniculate nucleus is found only in the latter. For a complete presentation of the laminar pattern changing from level to level *see* Figs. 200, 214, 215. *Labeling: cgc*, fiber lamina surrounding the laminated nucleus and, in the lower photo, separating it from the pregeniculate nucleus; *h*, hilum of the nucleus; *l*, lateral face; *m*, medial face; *pgn*, pregeniculate nucleus. (*Cf.* Fig. 210.)

segment in the Monkey, in particular, the limitation to four basic laminae remains throughout the length of the geniculate nucleus. In the extreme posterior tip alone, in the Macaque, the differentiation of the four into six cell laminae is complete or almost so (Fig. 200, *A*).

In Man, in the entire posterior third of the nucleus (Fig. 215, *A–C*), in the Chimpanzee in the posterior tip only (Fig. 214, *A*, left), the number of the laminae is again reduced to the original four, the two thin lower laminae containing large cells and the two thicker upper ones composed of small cells.

In the Macaque, an ill-defined supplemental lamina of scattered medium-sized cells is also found in the closest proximity to the ventral

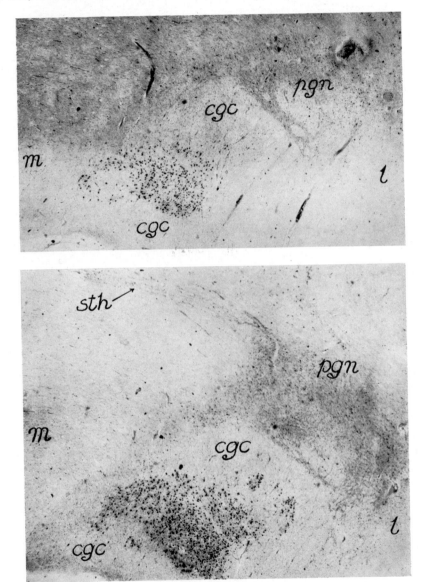

Fig. 212.—Microphotographs of the lateral geniculate nucleus of Man, showing, in Nissl-stained sections passing through anterior extremity, both portions of the nucleus: the larger laminated one made up of large, intensively stained nerve cells, enveloped by a thick fiber lamina (*cgc*) free from cells, and a paler, diffusely outlined pregeniculate gray nucleus (*pgn*) containing a great number of minute, fusiform cells which continue along a strand into subthalamus (*sth*), whence they have migrated during phylogenesis and ontogenesis, as shown in Fig. 209. The levels of these photos pass through the anterior extremity of the nucleus, where the pregeniculate nucleus is well developed, the same nucleus gradually disappearing on posterior levels shown in Fig. 213. Medial and lateral sides indicated by *m* and *l*. (*Cf.* also Fig. 215.)

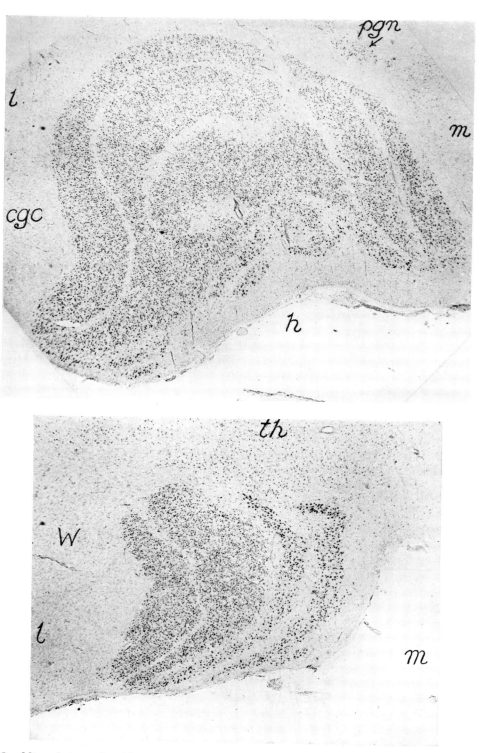

Fɪɢ. 213.—Microphotographs of human lateral geniculate nucleus, showing on posterior levels the laminated portion fully developed and the pregeniculate nucleus (*pgn*) much decreased before its final disappearance. In the lower photo, which shows a section through the posterior extremity of the nucleus, only four cellular laminae are present, two made up of small cells, the other two of large cells. This photo represents a level where the entire nucleus belongs to the fovea and may be considered a "geniculate fovea," its exquisite function being reflected in its regular arrangement and the great number of cells. (*Cf.* Fig. 215.)

surface at the hilum (Figs. 210, 211). A vestige of this formation, in Man and in the Ape, is the few stray nerve cells imbedded in the ventral portion of the circumgeniculate fibrous capsule at the hilum of the nucleus.

The intertwining of the secondary and tertiary extensions of the cell laminae in all species is most pronounced in the middle third of the longitudinal extent of the nucleus, in the intermediate areal-foveal segment, while the two magnocellular laminae are in many places broken up into discontinuous rows of larger and smaller groups and islands of cells.

A considerable difference in detail is found in individual specimens, even though the underlying basic quadri-, quinque-, and sesquilaminal pattern is always apparent. This is especially noticeable in human geniculates. In some individuals the cell laminae are smooth, evenly outlined, and regularly arranged, resembling the relatively uncomplicated pattern of the Macaque, while in others, e.g., Figure 215, the original simple pattern is much complicated by the secondary twisting and intertwining. (*See* sec. 6 [6], this chapter, and chap. VII, 3, for the functional significance of lamination of the lateral geniculate nucleus.)

4. Varieties and distribution of nerve cells of the lateral geniculate nucleus, in general.—The bodies of the neurons which make up the laminated lateral geniculate nucleus have, in general, a more or less spherical or globular shape. Some, however, resemble a short spindle or are irregular. The majority of the cells are multipolar. The large cells, measuring in Man up to 20×30 microns, constitute the two lower or ventral, magnocellular laminae (*1c, 1i*), while the upper or dorsal, parvocellular laminae (*2i, 2c*) and their derivatives (*2ia, 2iβ, 2ca, 2cβ*) are made up of cells half the diameter of the larger ones.

In the magnocellular laminae, in addition to the larger cells which are in the majority, there are also smaller cells similar in size and shape to those filling the parvocellular laminae. In the latter, close scrutiny reveals that the size of the cells also varies, with the medium-sized elements predominating. Occasionally an exceptionally large solitary cell is found here also. Small groups and clusters of larger cells resembling those in the magnocellular laminae are found in places along the medial and lateral fringes of the nucleus close to or among the smaller cells.

All cells of the laminated lateral geniculate nucleus, large and small, stain intensively with toluidine blue and thionin modifications of the Nissl method (Figs. 210, 211, 212, 213). In this respect they contrast with the somewhat paler cells of the adjoining portions of the thalamus, and considerably more with the even paler cells of the pregeniculate nucleus (Fig. 212).

At low magnification the entire cell body appears to be rather uniformly and diffusely stained. High magnification reveals the presence of numerous minute granules, threads, and specks of Nissl's chromophile substance filling the cytoplasm of the entire pericaryon or cell body. Most intensively stained are the rod-shaped granules in the immediate vicinity of the nuclear membrane. In all cells, large and small alike, in the adult human and anthropomorphous simian specimens, abundant yellowish-brown pigment is found.

The conspicuous difference in cell size between the dorsal parvocellular laminae (*2c, 2i;* or *2ca, 2cβ, 2ia, 2iβ*) and the ventral magnocellular laminae (*1c, 1i*) is apparently an expression of their different functional character. Again, the fact that in places there are four or more parvocellular laminae (*2ca, 2cβ, 2ia, 2iβ*) indicates further differentiation of cells of the two original parvocellular laminae (*2c, 2i*) into two or more distinct neuron varieties, one in *2ca* and *2iβ*, and another in *2ia* and *2cβ*.

According to this concept, each laminated lateral geniculate nucleus is made up of two sets of neurons, one ipsilateral (*1i, 2i;* or *1i, 2ia*, and *2iβ*), and the other contralateral (*1c, 2c;* or *1c, 2ca*, and *2cβ*). Each set of neurons, in turn, is represented by two, three, and possibly more distinct neuron varieties, depending upon the number of cell laminae in the particular locality of the nucleus. The arrangement is such that the same neuron varieties are found in each two adjacent laminae, one ipsilateral and one contralateral, e.g., *1i* and *1c; 2i* and *2c;* or *2ia* and *2cβ*; and *2ca* and *2iβ*.

All the neuron varieties in question represent Monakow's "principal cells" (*cf.* chap. IV, 5 [4]). The axis cylinders of these cells form the

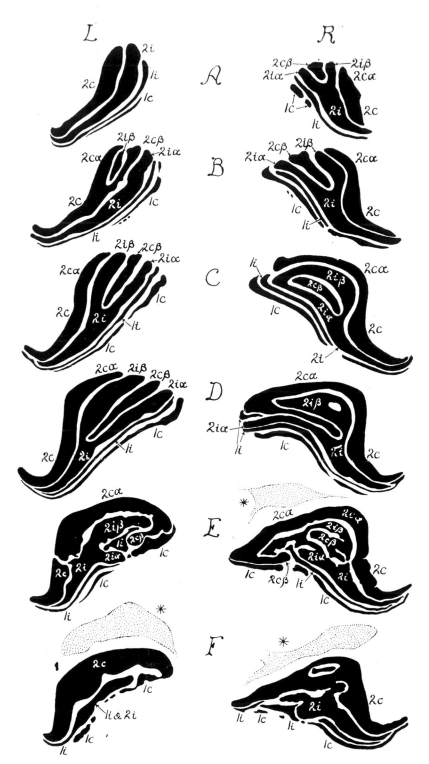

Fig. 214.—Lateral geniculate nuclei of an adult Chimpanzee showing the laminar pattern at approximately equal spacing from the most posterior extremities (*A*) to the anterior ends of the nuclei (*F*). *L* and *R* columns represent serially arranged levels through the left and right nucleus. The layers where the nondecussating ipsilateral retinal fibers terminate are *1i, 2i, 2ia, 2iβ*; the layers where the contralateral decussating fibers terminate are *1c, 2c, 2ca, 2cβ*. The pregeniculate nuclei, given in stippling, are marked by asterisks (*). (*Cf.* Figs. 200, 215.)

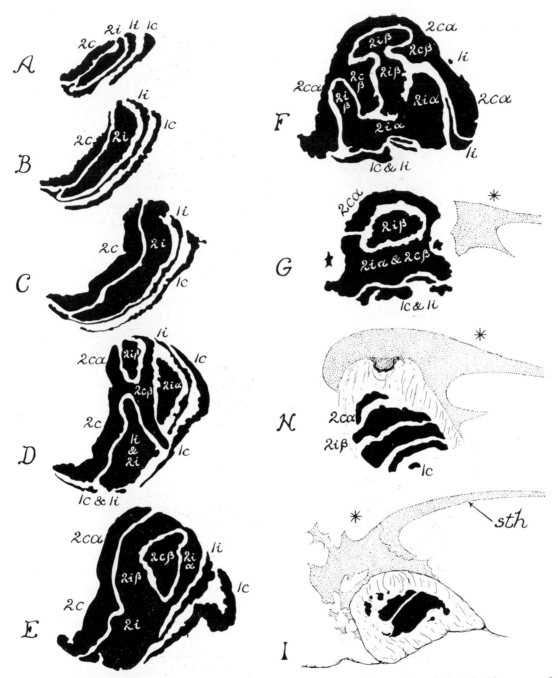

Fig. 215.—Coronal sections through the normal human lateral geniculate nucleus of the left side, arranged at approximately equal intervals from the posterior tip (*A*) to the anterior extremity of the nucleus (*I*). The layers where nondecussating ipsilateral retinal fibers terminate are *1i, 2i, 2ia, 2iβ*; the layers where contralateral decussating fibers terminate are *1c, 2c, 2ca, 2cβ*. The pregeniculate nucleus, given in stippling, is marked with asterisk (*). Compare the complex laminar pattern in this specimen, which was of an eminent microscopist of superior visual performance (Dr. F. B. Mallory), with simpler arrangement in the Chimpanzee (Fig. 214) and in the Rhesus Macaque (Figs. 210, 211), and see photos of the same specimen in Figs. 212, 213. Note the large size of the pregeniculate nucleus, its elaborate structure, and its connections with the subthalamus (*sth*). (On the brain of the same case *see* chap. XII, 10.)

363

visual radiation, which terminates in the striate cortex of the occipital lobe. They are, therefore, representative of Golgi type *I*, or neurons with a long axon. In addition to the neurons mentioned, however, there are smaller nerve cells in every one of the several laminae whose axis cylinders divide into teledendrons within the nucleus itself. These are representatives of Golgi type *II*, or neurons with a short axon (*see* following sec. 9).

In experiments and in pathological cases where one eye is removed, both types of neurons undergo transsynaptic or transneuronal degeneration. Also, they both degenerate when the visual radiation is interrupted or the striate cortex destroyed. The neurons with short axons or "association cells," as they may be called, are present in the simian lateral geniculate nucleus (*see* sec. 9 [3], this chapter), and have also been found in the Infraprimate Mammals, such as the Cat and Rabbit (O'Leary). This trophic interdependence is indicative of the intimate and exclusive anatomical and physiological relationship between these two neuron varieties. (*See* chap. IV, 5 [4] on Monakow's "intercalated cells"; *see* sec. 6 [6], this chapter, on functional interpretation of neuron varieties.)

5. Termination of optic and other nerve fibers in the lateral geniculate nucleus. —The optic nerve fibers enter the laminated lateral geniculate nucleus by continuing the sagittal course they pursue in the optic tracts. How they are distributed in the various segments of the nucleus according to their particular origins in the retina has been dealt with in section 7 of this chapter.

In general, in the core of the laminated nucleus the entering optic nerve fibers spread in the manner of a fan, dividing into several thin sheets or fiber laminae, each composed of numerous minute bundles and each separating two adjoining cell laminae. In coronal sections the fiber laminae appear curved in the same general sense as the cell laminae, in conformity with the general outline of the nucleus. In sagittal sections the fiber laminae are fairly straight, with the fibers running in the anteroposterior direction. The fiber laminae, alternating with the cell laminae, are mostly not solid but made up of numerous small bundles. Their numerical distribution on transverse coronal sections also varies, more fibers being assembled closer to the periphery of the nucleus than in its core, with the medial and ventral margins composed of a solid mass of fibers.

The shape, extent, arrangement, place, synaptical relationships, and other particulars of the terminal arborizations of the optic nerve fibers, in Man and in the Simians, are described in section 9 [4, 5], of this chapter.

References: Ariëns Kappers, Huber & Crosby 1936; Crouch 1934; Aronson & Papez 1934; Balado & Franke 1929, 1931, 1937; Barris 1935; Beattie 1927; Bellonci 1888; Bodian 1939–40; Brugi 1937, 1939; Brunner & Spiegel 1918; Chacko 1948, 1949; G. Clark 1948; Le Gros Clark 1928, 1929, 1930, 1931, 1932, 1940, 1941, 1942, 1949; Clark & Chacko 1947; E. R. A. Cooper 1945; H. Deutsch 1929; Friedemann 1911–12; M. S. Gilbert 1935; Geist 1930; Goldby 1941; Gurdjian 1927; Harman 1949; Harman & Solnitzky 1943, 1944; S. E. Henschen 1930; J. M. Jefferson 1940; Koelliker 1896; Környey 1928; Kuhlenbeck 1926, 1929, 1935–36; Minkowski 1920, 1922, 1932, 1934, 1939; Mussen 1923; Nichterlein & Goldby 1944; O'Leary 1940; Oshinomi 1929; Packer 1941; R. A. Pfeifer 1930; Pines 1927; Powell 1952; S. Ramón y Cajal 1899–1904, 1909–11; Rioch 1929–31; Rioch & Wislocki 1940; Solnitzky 1938, 1945; Solnitzky & Harman 1943; Tartuferi 1882, 1885; Toncray & Krieg 1946; Tsai 1925; C. Vogt 1909; A. E. Walker 1938; Walker & Fulton 1938; Walls 1953; Woollard 1926; Woollard & Beattie 1927. (For additional references *see* secs. 9 and 10 of this chapter.)

SEC. 9. MINUTE STRUCTURE OF THE PRINCIPAL OR LAMINATED LATERAL GENICULATE NUCLEUS AS REVEALED BY HISTOANALYTICAL METHODS

1. Introductory remarks.—The constituent structures of the laminated lateral geniculate nucleus as revealed by the Golgi method of staining go a long way toward amplifying those which can be demonstrated by the routine methods of hematoxylin and eosin, Van Gieson, and the like, and by some selective methods, such as those of Weigert and of Nissl. They show this nucleus to be more complex in its intrinsic makeup than is commonly assumed. In fact, in the light of the information furnished by histoanalytical methods, the lateral geniculate nucleus appears to be, not a simple "relay station" included in the visual pathway, but a true subcortical center, where a certain amount of reciprocal influencing of the constituent neurons takes place.

The histological elements of the simian and human laminated lateral geniculate nucleus are represented by several categories. First are the larger nerve cells whose bodies make up the bulk of the cellular layers: the principal nerve cells. Next are the smaller neurons interspersed among the larger ones: the association cells. The third element is represented by various terminations of optic nerve fibers or axis cylinders of the retinal ganglion cells. Still another category of terminations are those whose cells of origin are unknown (they possibly reside in the brain). Interspersed between the elements mentioned, which constitute the nervous parenchyma proper, is the stroma or supporting framework made up partly of neuroglia, which is ectodermal in origin, and partly of the interstitial connective tissue and blood vessels, which are mesodermal.

2. REVIEW OF PRECEDING HISTOANALYTICAL INVESTIGATIONS.—The investigations of the lateral geniculate nucleus of Mammals with the histoanalytical method of Golgi are few in number and incomplete. Ehrlich's vital methylene blue method was never used.

As far as the available record goes, Koelliker (1896) was first to apply the Golgi method to the lateral geniculate nucleus. Thereafter Tello (1904), S. Ramón y Cajal (1899–1904, 1909–11), Henschen (1925, 1926, 1931), Taboada (1927–28), Balado & Franke (1937), and O'Leary (1940) used this technique. Additional information was obtained with the reduced silver stain by Barris, Ingram & Ranson (1935), Glees & Clark (1941), and Glees (1942). Mention may also be made of the numerous publications by P. Ramón y Cajal (1890–1943) and by C. J. Herrick (1914–48) dealing with the brain stem, including the visual pathways and centers of

the Inframammalian Vertebrates. In the following, the essential results of these studies are briefly summarized.

Koelliker described the cells in the dorsal nucleus of the Rabbit and Cat as the "shrub variety" (*Buschzellen*), with a round body and with rather short dendrites. These cells resemble in appearance the "principal cells," which have a long axon, according to the present classification. The other smaller category found in the Mouse had a short axon. The "radiating cells" (*Strahlenzellen*), which Koelliker found in the ventral nucleus, are typical of that structure. Some of the large radiating cells located in the optic tract discharge an axon which, with or without collateral branches, joins the tract fibers. These neurons, he guessed, are homologous to those which, according to P. Ramón y Cajal, Van Gehuchten, and Koelliker, are the origin of the centrifugal fibers of the retina. (Judging from their appearance, these neurons may also be the principal cells of the ventral or superficial lamina whose axons enter the visual radiation.) In the human geniculate Koelliker mentions only the shrub variety. He also describes and depicts a dense plexus in the thalamus and lateral geniculate nucleus of afferent optic nerve fibers made up of terminal tufts and of several collaterals.

Tello (1904), besides correctly identifying the dorsal and the ventral geniculate nuclei of the Cat, gave additional information. He described three series or tiers of terminations in the dorsal nucleus of this species resembling cypress trees, corresponding to the three cellular laminae (Fig. 216). There is apparently an overlapping of the adjoining terminal tufts belonging to the individual optic nerve fibers. The nerve cells vary in size and shape, and all categories are distributed uniformly over the entire nucleus. Judging by the length of the axon, two varieties are present: neurons with a long axon and numerous dendrites, some with, others without, "spines" (Golgi type *I*), and neurons of Golgi's type *II*, of small size, with an axon which divides not far from the cell body into a scattered terminal ramification. Since both neuron varieties are enveloped by the terminal plexus of the incoming optic nerve fibers, the short-axon neurons cannot be interpreted as Monakow's "intercalated cells" mediating the transmission of impulses from the fibers to the principal neurons and farther to the cortex. Finally, Tello also described certain terminals which he regards as arising from the cells residing in the cerebral cortex.

The principal object of Taboada (1927–28) in his study of the simian lateral geniculate nucleus was to determine the exact relationship of the cell laminae to one another. His observation corroborated Minkowski's opinion of the existence of a laminar independence against the observations of Henschen (1925) and of Brouwer &

fibers. In the ventral magnocellular laminae, each glomerulus consists of from 12 to 15 cells; in the middle laminae, from 30 to 40; and in the upper laminae at the convexity of the nucleus, from 60 to 100. In the thinner ventral magnocellular laminae the glomeruli correspond to segments passing through their entire thickness; in the dorsal parvocellular laminae, especially in the intermediate "macular" portion, the glomeruli take up only a fragment of the thick lamina. The capillary network is denser in the cellular

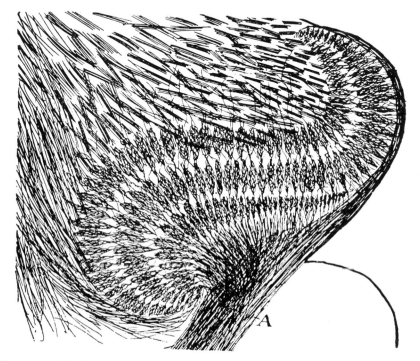

Fig. 216.—Structure of the lateral geniculate nucleus of the Cat stained with the Golgi method. *A*, optic tract entering the nucleus from underneath, its fibers forming terminal arborizations around the cells arranged in regular, parallel layers. From J. F. Tello, "Disposición macroscópica y estructura del cuerpo geniculado externo," Trab. del lab. de invest. biol. Madrid, v. 3, p. 39, 1904. (*Cf.* Figs. 192, 217, 218.)

jections of Henschen (1925) and of Brouwer & Zeeman (1926). In addition, Taboada found cells closely packed into glomeruli, or nests, with a denser intercellular substance in the center. The cells are of multipolar type, with three to four and even five to six dendrites, all belonging to the same variety. The dendrites are always confined to the same lamina where the body resides. Moreover, the processes of all cells that form a glomerulus remain within its territory. This, in his view, indicates that each glomerulus functions as a unit and receives terminal arborizations of a group of optic nerve

than in the fiber laminae. The association neurons, seen by Koelliker and Tello, and the terminations of fibers, Taboada did not discuss.

The most complete and most careful analysis of the structural makeup of the lateral geniculate complex was made in the Cat, by O'Leary (1940). In the dorsal nucleus, he found, as Koelliker and Tello had before, two categories of nerve cells present in all laminae. The larger principal cells give origin to axons, which, usually without emitting any or only a few initial collaterals, leave the nucleus and become the visual radiation or geniculostriate fiber tract.

The axons of the smaller cells are short and terminate within the same lamina of the nucleus in which their cell bodies reside.

There are apparently two short-axon varieties of neurons: one with a loose, scattered teledendron, the other terminating in baskets enveloping the bodies of the principal cells. There are several categories of the principal cells also: the axons of the large cells do not have the initial collaterals, whereas such are present in the medium and small cells. Some axons of the principal cells may pass over to the midbrain (this interpretation is clearly contradicted by the experimental observation showing all geniculate cells undergoing degeneration, thus indicating their dependence on the cortex; *see* chap. VII, 1, 3). The neurons of the ventral nucleus, of smaller size, send their axons, with collaterals, either in the anterior direction or to the optic tract.

The thick afferent optic nerve fibers terminate in the dorsal nucleus. The thin fibers give off collaterals to the ventral nucleus, in which they form a dense tangle, whereas their principal branches probably pass over to the superior colliculus (*cf.* S. Ramón y Cajal 1904 or 1911; *also* secs. 5, 7, 10, this chapter). Other categories of fibers may possibly also terminate in the ventral nucleus.

All thick fibers bifurcate into two branches, one thick, one thin. Each thick branch arborizes in the dorsal nucleus, with secondary terminals, whereas the thin branches may terminate elsewhere. Occasional brushlike collaterals are found just before the terminal arborization. In the thin laminae the terminal teledendrons extend across the entire thickness, in the thick laminae over only a part of the lamina.

It is an important observation that no single optic nerve fiber produces terminal tufts for more than one lamina (which is in agreement with Minkowski's separate termination of the ipsilateral and contralateral fibers in discrete laminae and with a similar observation made by Taboada).

It is probable that each principal geniculate cell is synaptically related to several afferent axons (*cf.* following subsection). There is probably abundant synaptical contact, both on the cell bodies and on the dendrites (unfortunately not illustrated). A dense tangle of overlapping terminal arborizations, both of the exogenous optic nerve fibers and of the endogenous short axons of association neurons, envelops the cells. Short axon arborizations deriving from the adjoining laminae suggest a reciprocal influencing (*see* par. 4, this section).

The connections of the ventral nucleus are apparently more complex than expected. Its

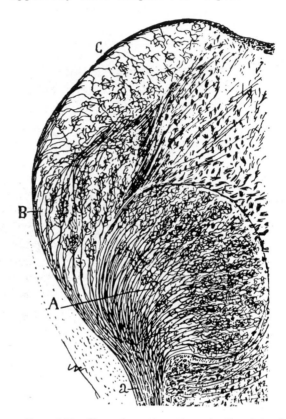

Fig. 217.—Coronal section through the lateral geniculate nucleus of a Cat a few days old, stained with the Golgi method, showing elaborate terminal arborizations of optic nerve fibers of retinal origin around the cells of the nucleus. *A*, inferior, *B* and *C*, superior segments of the nucleus; *a*, optic tract. From S. Ramón y Cajal, *Histologie du système nerveux*, v. 2, 1911. (*Cf.* Figs. 216, 218.)

cells are enveloped by a dense tangle of the afferent collaterals of a thin variety of optic fibers, to which tangle neither the collaterals of the thick fibers terminating in the dorsal nucleus nor the short-axon association cells residing in the latter nucleus contribute. These thin afferent fibers of the ventral nucleus apparently belong to a special variety of the retinal neurons instead of being the branchings of the thick fibers terminating in the dorsal nucleus. (This is of interest because it reverses an earlier belief expressed by Gudden [1889] and Westphal [1898], according to which the thin fibers represent a cortical pathway, the thick that of the pupillary reflex circuit; *see* Kolmer in Möllendorff's *Handb. d. mikr. Anat.*, v. 4, p. 494.)

In the dorsal nucleus there is no rich plexus of the afferent collaterals, but, significantly, one of the short-axon terminations. Since the affer-

nerve fibers. The short-axon cells may function as synchronizers of the groups of related principal cells (*see* O'Leary 1937; O'Leary & Bishop 1938).

Finally, O'Leary believes his work lends support to Lorente de Nó's concept of a "partially shifted overlapping" of the terminal arborizations of the tract fibers in the dorsal nucleus, denying the possibility that an individual axon

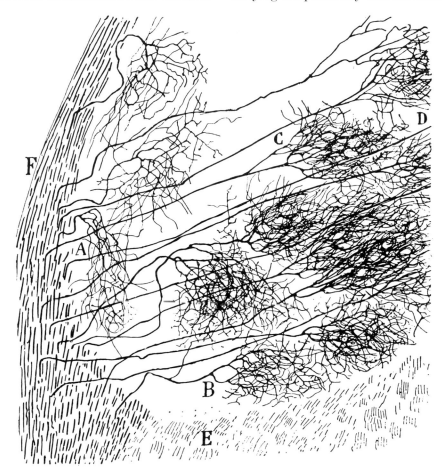

Fig. 218.—Portion of the "inferior segment" of the lateral geniculate nucleus of the Cat, showing at higher magnification terminal arborizations of optic nerve fibers of retinal origin stained with the Golgi method. *A*, superficial arborizations; *B, C, D*, similar arborizations located in deeper parts of the nucleus; *F*, superficial layer of nerve fibers arriving from the optic tract. From S. Ramón y Cajal, *Histologie du système nerveux*, v. 2, 1911. (*Cf.* preceding figures.)

ent optic nerve fibers are related directly both to the bodies and to the dendrites of the principal cells, the short-axon cells are not interneurons in the sense of Monakow (*see* chap. IV, 5 [4]). Judging from the synaptical connections, both the principal long-axon neurons and the short-axon association neurons receive retinal impulses simultaneously via the afferent optic

has ever provided an exclusive relationship to a single principal cell or to a small group of such cells. The fact that the Cat has no true fovea, its photoreceptors being exclusively rods, the number of fibers in its optic nerve being only one-tenth of those in Man and Monkey, makes one wonder whether the synaptical arrangements not found in the feline visual system may well be a regular equipment of the Primates, whose visual acuity is far superior to that of the Cat (*cf.* sec. 3 [4], this chapter, and pars. 5–9, this section).

Glees & Clark (1941) and Glees (1941, 1942) investigated the form and mode of termination of the optic nerve fibers in the lateral geniculate nucleus of the Monkey, Rabbit, and Cat by means of reduced silver nitrate stain. They showed, in addition to the termination of the ipsilateral and contralateral fibers in discrete cell laminae, that each individual fiber terminates in an arborization related to half-a-dozen cells. The terminal nodules are attached to the cell bodies (axosomatic synapse), each cell being in contact with a single nodule. There seems to be no overlapping of the terminal arborizations. In the Cat, the terminal buttons are attached both to the bodies and to the dendrites, with the axodendritic synapses preponderating numerically over the axosomatic synapses. Glees was inclined to think that in the Cat each geniculate cell may be synaptically related to more than one optic nerve fiber, each cell having, altogether, about 40 of both kinds of synaptical contacts. Whether these contacts belonged to one or to several fibers, it was not possible to ascertain, even though the latter was probable. The optic nerve fibers do not terminate as free endings but in the form of nodules. More than ten cells may be related to a single optic nerve fiber, and each cell, in turn, may be related to more than one fiber, which indicates the presence of an overlap in the geniculate terminations. An absence of an overlap in the Monkey and the presence of such in the Cat may be interpreted as "an arrangement providing for the utmost precision in the recording" of the retinal image in the first species and as "an anatomical basis for a high degree of sensitivity in low intensities of illumination" in the latter species. In the Rabbit, both axosomatic and axodendritic synapses are present. The number of the first is about ten to each cell. An overlap is probable.

3. PRINCIPAL NERVE CELLS.—The bulk of the cellular elements of the laminated lateral geniculate nucleus in Man and in the Monkey is represented by the larger nerve cells. When these cells are stained completely in Golgi prep-

arations, including all their dendrites, they have the appearance of typical multipolar neurons.

From a more or less spherical body, commensurate in size and shape with the bodies seen in Nissl preparations, half-a-dozen stout principal dendrites arise and soon divide into secondary, tertiary, and further branches. These branches are all of approximately the same length, radiating in all directions, thus giving the cells an asteriform or star-shaped appearance. Cells along the periphery of the cellular laminae are exceptions; their dendrites are all turned inward, in this way avoiding the extralaminar territory. Only occasionally does a dendrite penetrate into the circumgeniculate fibrous capsule or into one or another fiber layer separating the cell laminae. The rule is, however, that each cell spreads its dendrites in the cell lamina where its body resides.

The dendrites carry a moderate number of typical "spines," giving a dendritic branch the appearance of a more or less twisted twig of a thorny bramble. The "spines" are all of approximately the same length and usually carry minute spherical nodules at their ends.

The diameter of the dendritic spread of a large nerve cell is, on the average, from 300 to 500 microns or from $\frac{1}{3}$ to $\frac{1}{2}$ mm. across, the size of the spread being commensurate with the size of the cell body. A reciprocal overlapping of dendrites of the adjoining principal cells amounting to half the spread, more or less, is the rule throughout the nucleus. A preferential orientation of dendrites is not noticeable, except in small cells of the parvocellular layers at the apex of the nucleus, whose dendrites somewhat follow the lines vertical to the surface of the nucleus—an arrangement apparently caused by the emergent bundles of fibers of the visual radiation.

A single axis cylinder emerges directly from the cell body, usually with a typical "hillock," and is soon lost in the surrounding fiber layers. Its direction is toward the circumgeniculate fiber capsule.

4. ASSOCIATION CELLS.—The cell body of this category of neurons of the laminated nucleus of Man and Monkey is of a spherical or oval shape, approximately half the diameter of that of the larger principal cells of the immediate neighborhood, which are in the majority (Fig. 219). From one side of the body one or a few main dendrites arise and gradually divide into half-a-dozen secondary branches, altogether forming a loose, tree-shaped arborization, spreading over a territory which includes about fifty nerve cells. The dendrites carry a relatively small number of terminal twigs and spines, some twigs forming minute clusters or baskets. Most of the terminal twigs and spines are swollen into minute spherical "gemmules" or nodules at the very ends. These are the terminal varicosities.

A single, relatively thin, axis cylinder originates at the opposite pole of the body, dividing into half-a-dozen secondary branches, which, by further subdivision, produce a loose teledendron. The terminal twigs of this teledendron, all provided with nodules and a terminal varicosity, twist in various ways between the cells for which they form baskets, closely adhering to the surface of their bodies, in this way undergoing the axosomatic synapses. The number of principal cells synaptically related to an association cell approximates one dozen, all cells belonging to the same cellular lamina in which the body of the association cell resides.

5. General remarks on axonal terminations.—The terminal arborizations in the simian and human laminated nucleus, revealed by Golgi's silver bichromate method of staining, produce, by repeated division in the nucleus, an exceedingly rich and dense plexus surrounding the cells and their expansions.

This plexus is made up of coarser and finer terminal branches and twigs variously bent and twisted, many carrying varicosities of different shapes and sizes. Such varicosities or protoplasmic swellings may be found either along the course of the fibers or at the end of the terminal twigs, or the terminal "spines" may be without a swelling. Again, the terminal branches and twigs may stand alone, or they may be assembled into groups or clusters touching the surface of the body of a related geniculate cell, or they may be clasping a dendrite of a cell, or in some other way be attached to it.

In every case the terminals of the retinal fibers are in direct contact with the surface of the related geniculate neuron. Altogether, the terminal branchings or teledendrons of retinal origin produce an exceedingly dense plexus around the cells and their expansions, resembling, when stained completely, baskets that practically envelop the cells in shell-like casings.

A careful analysis of this terminal intercellular plexus reveals it to be made up of individual constituents belonging to teledendrons of different types, originating from distinct varieties of retinal and other ganglion cells, and of distinct functional significance.

Several varieties of terminal ramifications of the afferent optic nerve fibers may be distinguished, according to type, as far as it was possible to determine by number and distribution of terminal twigs, size and shape of the spread, and the orientation relative to the cell and fiber laminae of the geniculate nucleus.

From the well-established fact of the presence of several distinct varieties of retinal ganglion cells described in chapter V (5), several distinct categories of terminal ramifications may be expected in the laminated lateral geniculate nucleus. The difficulty in solving this problem arises, however, not only because of the "fickle" character of the Golgi technique, but even more because of the great distance intervening between the cells of origin of the fibers residing in the retina and their terminals in the brain. (This difficulty was largely absent in the study of retinal neurons, because of the shortness of their axons.) Unfortunately, there are no sure criteria by which a particular type of termination could be assigned to a definite variety of nerve cells as its probable origin. The only way, therefore, by which such identification may be attempted consists of circumstantial evidence.

Experience shows that in the nervous system in general, each particular neuron variety has a certain "character" with which all parts of that neuron variety, by and large, agree. As an example may be cited the parasol (m) and midget ganglions (s) of the retina. The first possess a rather large body with several robust dendrites dividing into a considerable number of short twigs, which, together, form a compact treetop of limited extent. The teledendrons of this ganglion variety may, accordingly, be expected also to be of rather robust appearance and of limited size. In the case of the midget ganglion

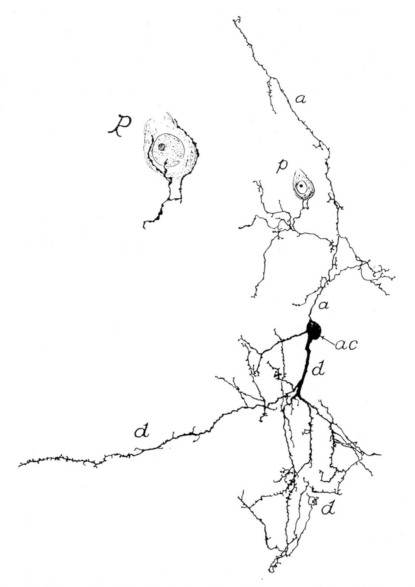

Fig. 219.—An "association cell" (*ac*) from the laminated lateral geniculate nucleus of a Rhesus Macaque, with the expansions completely stained. The axis cylinder or "nerve fiber" (*a*) arises from a spherical body and soon divides into a terminal arborization made up of a limited number of branches, each provided with a few short branches carrying terminal twigs and varicosities or swellings. Some varicosities are also found along the course of the branches themselves. All such terminal arborizations of axis cylinders form loose baskets, spreading in the cell lamina of the nucleus where the cell body resides. The terminal twigs and varicosities undergo synaptical contacts with the bodies of the "principal nerve cells" of the same lamina, as shown in the upper left corner at a higher magnification (*P*): a terminal branch embracing the body of a principal cell with several twigs, its smaller and larger varicosities adhering to the surface of the cell body. From the other end of the body of the association cell (*ac*) arise two dendrites (*d*), one shorter and thinner and the other much thicker, both dividing into an elaborate dendritic arborization. This dendritic arborization, formed by more numerous and more robust branches than those of the axonal arborization, is also provided with short terminal twigs which carry terminal varicosities or swellings. The dendritic arborization also spreads in the same cell lamina where the body of the association cell resides. The probable function of association cells is to condition in some way the groups of the principal cells around them, possibly under the influence of terminal teledendrons of retinal optic nerve fibers or also of fibers whose origin is somewhere in the brain, possibly in the striate area. Golgi method; larger sketch magnified 280×, detailed sketch 660×.

cells the teledendrons may also be expected to be of small dimensions and of delicate appearance. Again, the location and the relative number of a particular ganglion variety in a particular locality or region of the retina may be a clue to its identity. Since the midget ganglions represent the greater majority of ganglion cells in the central area, it is legitimate to expect their terminations to prevail numerically in the portion of the lateral geniculate nucleus, where, according to the experiments described in section 7 of this chapter, the central fovea and area are represented.

Lastly, the location and orientation of the terminal ramifications may be an important indicator concerning the identity of fiber terminations. As the experiments described in section 7 of this chapter show, no retinal fibers are to be found in the apical segment of the circumgeniculate lamina, with the exception of delicate fibers terminating in the pregeniculate nucleus (which nucleus is limited to about the anterior third of the laminated nucleus). Any robust fiber entering from the internal capsule of the brain, in the posterior third of the nucleus, and spreading in it, is likely to be of nonretinal origin.

Using the preceding and other less explicit morphological criteria which long experience with the method of Golgi suggests and always bearing in mind the tentative character of the interpretation, in the following subsections an attempt is made to classify the various types of terminal arborizations in the simian and human laminated geniculate nucleus, and their probable functional significance is discussed.

6. Terminations of axons of umbrella or parasol ganglions (*M*).—This type of terminal arborization conforms to the classical concept of a teledendron (Fig. 220, *a, t*). A relatively stout axon fiber usually emerges either from the ventral portion of the circumgeniculate fiber capsule at the hilum of the nucleus or from one of the several fiber laminae. Such fibers terminate in one of the adjoining cell laminae by dividing into a few dozen of rather short and twisted secondary, tertiary, and further branches and twigs, in many places swollen into spherical or irregular varicosities and nodules, and altogether forming a crude terminal

arborization. The ultimate twigs usually terminate with a minute spherical nodule. A single teledendron of this type spreads over the territory of a compact group of nerve cells of the particular lamina. Two dozen or more cells are to be found in such a group in the parvocellular laminae, next to the axis of the geniculate nucleus.

The size and appearance of the teledendron vary somewhat, depending upon the portion of the nucleus in which it is found. In the intermediate segment, corresponding with the representation of the central area and fovea, the size is more restricted and the twigs are more delicate than in the ventral magnocellular layers, where the extra-areal retinal periphery is represented. Some of the branches are oriented vertically with regard to the cell lamina, others meander in all directions.

The size and arrangement of the terminal twigs suggest basket-shaped synapses applied to the bodies of the laminar nerve cells, each pericellular basket being formed by the branches contributed by a number of individual teledendrons of the same variety.

The synapses formed by this variety of terminal arborization are of an axosomatic type; the terminal varicosities, or short terminal twigs carrying such varicosities, are closely applied to the surface of the body of the related cell.

Whether this arborization found in the entire laminated geniculate nucleus truly represents a single variety or whether similar, though functionally slightly different, types of the same variety of teledendron are present in the several laminae of the two sets, the crossed and the uncrossed, possibly indicating a different function in each lamina, it is not possible to determine on morphological grounds alone.

7. Terminations of axons of shrub ganglions (*N*).—A conspicuous, although very delicate, variety of termination is the axons arranged according to the radii of the laminated nucleus (Fig. 220, right-hand sketch). At moderate magnification they appear as long, fine, and rather straight threads passing up and down the layers, their lower ends pointing toward the hilum. Oil-immersion objectives reveal them to be very thin, but otherwise typical,

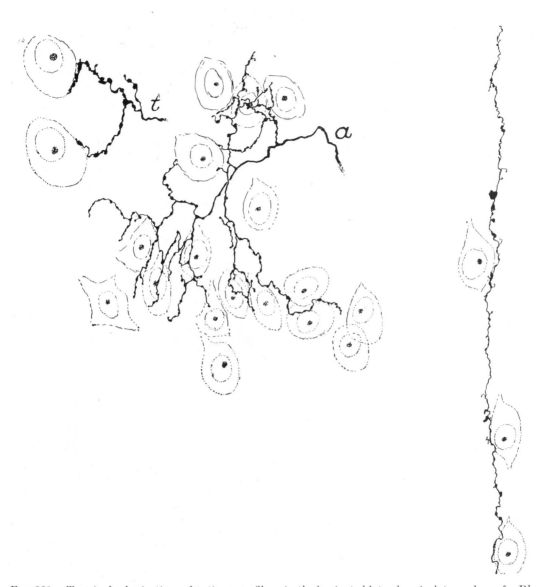

Fig. 220.—Terminal arborizations of optic nerve fibers in the laminated lateral geniculate nucleus of a Rhesus Macaque made visible with the Golgi method of staining: *a*, an elaborate arborization of a single nerve fiber, apparently of retinal origin, made up of branches, gradually dividing into terminal twigs, each in places swollen into varicosities and each terminating with a larger or smaller varicosity, each arborization terminating around a nest of "principal nerve cells" within a single lamina of the nucleus, whence the axon fibers of visual radiation originate; *t*, a single terminal twig of an arborization at a higher magnification with outlines of two principal cells showing in profile the attachment of varicosities to the surface of the bodies of cells, together forming an axosomatic type of synapse. The right-hand sketch represents the termination of a single afferent nerve fiber of unknown origin, possibly also retinal, of very thin diameter and long, straight course, arranged according to the radii of the laminated nucleus, with numerous minute terminal twigs and varicosities attached to the surface of principal nerve cells, the cells, interconnected in this way, forming narrow functional segments or columns passing through several cell laminae. There are indications of still other types of termination in the laminated nucleus, some probably of cerebral origin, altogether showing this nucleus to be an elaborate center wherein retinal impulses are processed in many ways before they are dispatched to the cerebral cortex. Camera lucida drawings, Leitz *Ultropak* oil-immersion objective 60×, transillumination, approximate magnification: center and right-hand sketch 270×, left upper sketch 450×.

terminal axons exhibiting numerous minute twists and curves, with an occasional minute varicose swelling in their course or with such a varicosity attached to the fiber. An occasional varicosity may be of much larger size than the average. A few minute twigs or "spines," usually curved in the form of a hook and with an infinitesimal budlike swelling at the usually undivided ends, are found along the fiber.

The remarkable fact about this variety of terminals is their length and the mode of their synapsing. Whereas the M and S terminals contact a compact cluster of cells roughly spherical in shape, occupying a minute area anywhere in one of the several cell laminae, the N terminals freely pass in a straight course from one cell lamina across the fiber lamina to the next cell lamina. In this way the cells of the adjoining laminae, independently related to the M and S terminals, are again joined with one another across the separating fiber laminae by means of the connecting N terminals.

The synapses of the N terminals are made by direct contact with the surface of the bodies of a string of nerve cells nearest to them.

8. TERMINATIONS OF AXONS OF MIDGET GANGLIONS (S).—This variety of terminal ramifications somewhat resembles the M variety, though much richer and composed of much more delicate branches and twigs. The space taken by it is likewise roughly spherical, representing but a tiny area of a cell lamina. The terminal twigs are variously contorted, forming dainty baskets for the bodies of the laminar cells with which they form axosomatic synapses.

9. TERMINATIONS OF FIBERS OF CEREBRAL ORIGIN (X).—A variety of terminal arborizations differing from the preceding in appearance, location, and orientation possibly belongs to axons of neurons residing in the brain itself. These rather thick fibers enter the laminated nucleus anywhere along its convex dorsal, dorsomedial, or dorsolateral aspect. Within the territory of the nucleus each fiber divides into a few fairly thick, long branches parting in opposite directions. The branches, thickened in places into small varicosities, carry a moderate number of terminal twigs and "spines," each terminating with a minute nodule. The

area over which this type of arborization spreads is large and may be populated by several hundreds of nerve cells of a given lamina. This variety of teledendron is present in all parts of the laminated nucleus, mingling indiscriminately with the terminations described earlier as possibly those of the retinal fibers. Because of the fact that the X terminations do not arise from fibers of the optic tract, it is a fair guess that they originate from neurons residing in the brain, probably somewhere in the occipital cortex.

10. SUMMARY OF THE INTRINSIC ORGANIZATION OF THE PRIMATE LAMINATED LATERAL GENICULATE NUCLEUS.—Because of the incompleteness of our knowledge of the actual structures, any plan of the intrinsic makeup or functional organization of the laminated lateral geniculate nucleus of Primates must be made with emphasis upon its tentative character.

Beginning with the nerve cells of the nucleus, it is certain that, in general, these resemble the neurons in the remainder of the central nervous system. Each cell has a body, several protoplasmic dendrites, and a single axis cylinder or axon. On the basis of whether the axon leaves the nucleus or terminates within its territory, two categories of neurons may be distinguished that conform to types I and II of Golgi. Strictly observable facts do not as yet permit us to go beyond this. At cursory examination, the principal neurons in all layers of the nucleus have about the same appearance. The only obvious difference is in dimension, which, in both Nissl- and Golgi-stained preparations, appreciably exceeds, in the ventral layers, the dimensions of the smaller cells making up the laminae closer to the rounded circumference of the nucleus.

True, mere size would not suffice as a criterion for further classification. Its consistent observance, making the neurons in the various layers oscillate around a certain mean size, however, indicates a specific functional differentiation. In other words, each cell lamina is made up of principal neurons which are functionally different from the principal neurons making up the other cell laminae of the same set. Since each nucleus contains two laminar sets, one set related to the ipsilateral, and the other to the contralateral optic nerve fibers arising from the two homonymous halves of both retinae, both sets must contain, in the homodynamic laminae, e.g., in *1c* and *1i* or in *2cα* and *2iβ*, neurons capable of reacting in the same way. There must be, in the binocular portion of the nucleus, at least two, and close to the fixation point not less than three, neuron varieties, crossed and uncrossed, arranged on a cross-section vertical to the longitudinal axis of the nucleus according to the retinotopical principle. In the extreme flanks of the nucleus representing the monocular portions of the contralateral retinae, there may be a single variety only of the principal neurons. (*Cf.* sec. 6 [6], this chapter.)

Before proceeding further in our attempt to understand the functional organization of the geniculate complex, it will be useful once more to emphasize the structural independence of the homolateral from the heterolateral set of the cellular laminae, first revealed by Minkowski (*see* chap. IV, 6 [6]). Henschen (1925, 1926, 1930, 1931), until his death, refused to accept such independence, even though his evidence was based upon defective preparations, as Taboada (1927–28) correctly pointed out. Minkowski's observation and interpretation have since been corroborated beyond reasonable doubt and are well illustrated by the experiment presented in Figure 200.

According to present knowledge, the four (in the extra-areal binocular flanks) or six (in the intermediate foveal-areal segment) cell laminae of the nucleus are arranged alongside one another in a way permitting the closest possible approach of the two sets of neurons related through the optic nerve fibers to the "corresponding" or "homodynamical" points of both homonymous retinal halves. This fact indicates the necessity of some sort of reciprocal influencing or co-operation of the two sets of neurons (counterbalancing the other factor, that of separation, because of which the cellular laminae became segregated from an original homogeneous matrix).

When two "corresponding points" of both retinae, for example, *a* and *a₁* or *b* and *b₁*, are stimulated by two identical or almost identical stimuli—because of an automatic direction of lines of view of both eyes toward the same object in the normal act of vision—the impulses converge upon the single "corresponding point" either of the left or of the right lateral geniculate nucleus. Here, depending upon the proximity to, or distance from, the "fixation point" and the "principal vertical meridian" (*F*), a minute segment of the nucleus is activated. This segment passes through all four or six cell laminae, narrow in the two ventral magnocellular laminae (*1c*, *1i*) and gradually widening toward the thicker laminae filled with smaller cells along the convexity of the nucleus (*2i*, *2c*, or *2iα*, *2cβ*, *2iβ*, *2cα*). From the particular segment of each lamina arises a bundle of axon fibers, which passes over into the visual radiation, eventually terminating in the striate area of the same cerebral hemisphere.

Each bundle of the visual radiation is, accordingly, made up of two sets of fibers, one set originating in the laminae related to the temporal half of the ipsilateral retina, the other originating in the laminae related to the nasal half of the contralateral retina. The constitution of the elementary conducting units, beginning with those related to the foveal center, is increasingly simplified toward the monocular periphery, where the units are probably made up of neurons and axons of a single variety, related only to the contralateral retina.

The problem of why the two sets of the geniculate laminae—the ipsilateral and the contralateral—are neatly juxtaposed, the "corresponding" or "syndynamical" points of one set exactly matching the "corresponding mates" of the other set, has been discussed by a few investigators. Minkowski (1920) believed that there must be some relationship of a "reciprocal inhibitory nature" (in Sherrington's sense) between the ipsilateral and contralateral laminae, perhaps mediated by the "intercalated cells." This, in his opinion, would agree with the (1) binocular contrast, (2) struggle of the fields of view, (3) above all, the binocular color mixing of Hering (1879, 1905). According to this, the hue and the brightness of the resulting subjective experience is always an intermediary between the two monocular impressions, between which it may oscillate, approaching now the one, now the other, without ever becoming a simple addition or superposition, as is the case with monocular mixing when the lights of different hues act upon the same retinal point.

Observations by R. W. Pickford (1947) are of importance in this connection. In binocular combinations, no color pairs completely fail to fuse or give perfect combinations when each eye is stimulated by a separate color; all colors show a strong combination tendency when presented independently to each eye in pairs; complementaries are very difficult to combine; bright colors are difficult to combine with dark; red and green can be combined to a certain extent, but only with considerable difficulty.

All this gives little support for the trichromatic theory of color perception of Young & Helmholtz but clearly sustains the four-color theory of Hering and Houston, according to which the opposite colors combine by a "neutralizing process" in one eye but not when presented separately to both eyes, whereas neighboring colors would combine readily in either way. "The fact that complementary colours are extremely difficult to combine when presented separately one to each eye, but very easy to combine in one eye alone, also throws doubt on the theory that all colour combinations take place in a single locus of the brain, and not in the retina. It is more likely that complementaries combine in the eye, though neighbouring colours may combine in the brain."

From the experiences of physiologists it appears that the principal portion of the visual mechanism instrumental in color mixing is the retina. Certain mixing also takes place in the brain. The cerebral mechanism responsible for this may, to some extent, be the laminated lateral geniculate nucleus; the final arbiter, however, is the striate cortex. The presence of geniculate connections relaying the ipsilateral and contralateral homonymous cell laminae of that nucleus makes such interpretation mandatory. This indicates that, contrary to prevalent belief, the laminated geniculate nucleus may play some role in color perception, just as it does in the other basic function—visual perception of space. In fact, the laminar organization of this internode appears, in primate vision, to be essential for both functions, as discussed elsewhere. (*Cf.* sec. 6 [6], this chapter.)

References: Balado & Franke 1937; Barris 1935; G. H. Bishop 1933, 1935, 1941; Bishop & O'Leary 1940, 1942; Brugi 1937, 1939; Chacko 1948, 1949; Le Gros Clark 1940, 1941, 1942, 1943, 1947, 1948, 1949; Clark & Chacko 1947; Edinger 1908–11; Glees 1941, 1942; Glees & Clark 1941; Hecht 1928; Henschen 1925, 1926, 1930, 1931; Koelliker 1896; Powell 1952; P. Ramón y Cajal 1890, 1891, 1896, 1897, 1898, 1917, 1922, 1913; S. Ramón y Cajal 1894, 1899, 1904, 1909–11; Spofford 1942; Taboada 1927–28; Tello; Van Gehuchten 1900; Walls 1953.

SEC. 10. THE PREGENICULATE GRAY NUCLEUS AND THE PUPILLARY REFLEX PATHWAY

1. The pregeniculate nucleus, its structure and relationships.—The primate pregeniculate gray nucleus (*pgn* or * in Figs. 200, 209–15) is an accumulation of mostly small nerve cells along the upper extremity and medial margin of the principal laminated lateral geniculate nucleus. It has also been named *corpus geniculatum laterale ventrale, corpus praegeniculatum,* and *substantia grisea praegeniculata* by various investigators (*see* Koelliker 1896; C. Vogt 1909; Friedemann 1911–12; Minkowski 1920; Ariëns Kappers, Huber & Crosby 1936). It is a homologue of the phylogenetically older ventral nucleus, the pars ventralis, of the primitive Mammals, as discussed in section 8 (1) in this chapter (*v* in Fig. 191).

The pregeniculate nucleus of Primates is smaller than the laminated nucleus, even though it is not insignificant or "vestigial," as one might judge from the literature. Topographically it is closely related to the principal laminated nucleus, which is a homologue of the dorsal and phylogenetically younger portion of the lateral geniculate complex of primitive Mammals (*d, pars dorsalis,* in Fig. 191; *cf.* secs. 1 [3] and 8 [1], this chapter).

The shape of the pregeniculate nucleus is roughly triangular, resembling a skullcap, and irregular on anterior levels. The nucleus extends from the anterior tip of the principal laminated nucleus to a varying distance in the posterior direction. In the Rhesus Macaque (Fig. 200) the posterior limit lies as far back as the boundary between the caudal two-fourths. In the

Chimpanzee (Fig. 214) and in Man (Fig. 215) this nucleus extends not quite to the mid-length of the laminated nucleus. Everywhere the pregeniculate nucleus closely applies to the laminated nucleus, or rather to the latter's thick fibrous circumgeniculate capsule. On coronal sections the position of the pregeniculate gray nucleus varies. On the anterior levels it covers the top or the apex, in Man the lateral side of the laminated nucleus also, and becomes more posteriorly displaced along its medial margin.

The pregeniculate gray nucleus, as its name implies, is made up chiefly of nerve cells and their unmyelinated fibrous processes. A number of minute bundles of thin myelinated fibers found in it are arranged singly, in groups or in short rows (*pgn* in Fig. 187, sketch *A;* also Fig. 221). A row of thin bundles marks the upper boundary toward the internal capsule and subthalamus. By far the greater majority of its nerve cells are small, more or less fusiform in shape, and with little cytoplasm (*pgn* in Figs. 210, 211, 212). Owing to a less-developed chromophile substance and apparently also to a lesser chemical affinity of that substance for aniline dyes, such as toluidine blue, the cells appear pale in preparations treated with routine modifications of the Nissl method, in contrast with intensively stained cells of the laminated nucleus. Hence, especially in improperly treated material, the pregeniculate nucleus may easily be overlooked or its considerable size underestimated. The irregular shape, poor staining qualities, and peculiar arrangement of cells in intertwining rows and strands, which sometimes undermine and disrupt the adjacent fibrous substance in the manner of the "reticular substance," all make the pregeniculate gray nucleus markedly resemble sympathetic or vegetative nuclei elsewhere, e.g., in the "lateral gray columns" of the spinal cord.

From the medial edge of the pregeniculate nucleus (Fig. 209, *PGN*) a thick strand composed of similar oblong, pale, and mostly fusiform cells directly continues into the subthalamus of the betweenbrain (*STH*), where it may be followed as a continuous band between the ventral margin of the thalamus proper (*TH*) and the cells of the *substantia nigra* (*SN*) almost as far as the lateral margin of the red nucleus

(*RN*). This strand, observed by Koelliker (1896, p. 544) and Minkowski (1920) and well presented also in Figure 212, *sth,* and Figure 215, *I,* marks the road traveled by the pregeniculate nucleus during phylogenesis and ontogenesis from its origin in the *zona incerta* to its final location on the lateral face of the subthalamus. (For this, *see* Le Gros Clark in *Brit. J. Ophth.,* v. 16, 1932; and M. S. Gilbert in *J. Comp. Neurol.,* v. 62, 1935.)

In addition to the smaller elements described, a few somewhat larger and more intensively stained nerve cells are found singly or in clusters in the pregeniculate nucleus. Some of these cells may reach proportions exceeding those of the cells that make up the parvocellular layers of the laminated nucleus. Owing to the well-developed Nissl granules, these large solitary cells stain intensively. Other medium-sized cells, usually of multipolar shape, are scattered in fair numbers between the smaller fusiform cells. Their chromophile granules are well developed; but they, too, apparently because of their small chemical affinity for dyes, appear paler than the intensively stained cells of the laminated nucleus.

The large size of the pregeniculate gray nucleus in human specimens is surprising (Fig. 215, stippled areas marked with *; *pgn* in Fig. 212). This is contrary to what one would expect from the literature on comparative anatomical investigations, where a gradual decrease in the relative size of this nucleus in the ascending phylogenetical scale of Mammals and its absence in Man have been claimed (Woollard 1926; Le Gros Clark 1932; Toncray & Krieg 1946; and others). The imposing size of this nucleus in Primates in general and in Man, in particular; the number of its nerve cells, which, owing to their small size, may not be much below that of the laminated portion; and their variety, as well as the connections with the midbrain tegmentum dealt with in the following paragraph, all indicate the important function that this nucleus performs in the central visual mechanism.

The several varieties of the nerve cells in the pregeniculate nucleus, furthermore, are indicative of its complex structure. In Man a small oval nest of minute, tightly packed cells lodged in a notch in the tip of the thick circumgenicu-

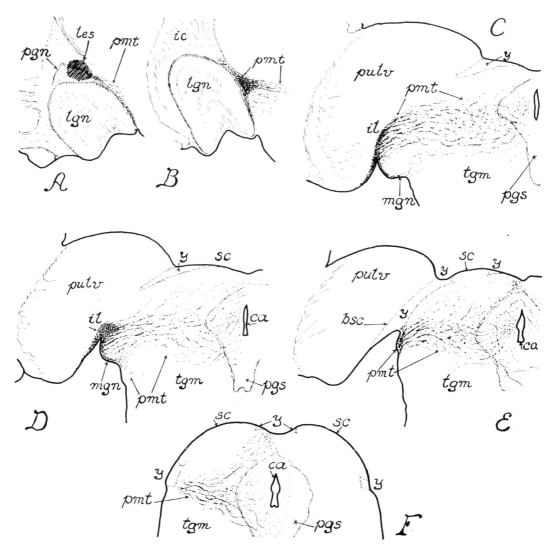

FIG. 221.—Origin, course, and termination of the pregeniculo-mesencephalic or indirect optomesencephalic tract (*pmt*), as revealed by experiment in a Rhesus Macaque. A minute lesion, *les* (*shaded area* in sketch *A*) was made with an electrocoagulating stereotaxic instrument of Horsley, Clark & Ranson in the cap-shaped pregeniculate nucleus (*pgn*). The degenerated nerve fibers, indicated by stippling and broken lines, stained with the Marchi method, enter partly into the hypothalamus (sketch *B*), with the majority forming the intergeniculate lamina (*il*, in sketches *C* and *D*) tucked between the pulvinar (*pulv*) and the medial and lateral geniculate nuclei (*mgn*, *lgn*), thence passing through the substance of the midbrain tegmentum (*tgm*), finally to reach the periaqueductal gray substance (*pgs*) around the nuclei of the oculomotor or third nerve of the brain (sketches *C, D, E, F*). Very few of these fibers enter into superficial layers of the superior colliculus (that was shown to be in part a terminal station of the direct opto-mesencephalic system, in Fig. 187), and only a few of them may decussate to the opposite half of the periaqueductal gray substance. It is probable that this system represents a central link in the pathway of the pupillary light reflex and that, when interrupted, it causes partially "frozen pupil" or Argyll-Robertson's symptom. *Labeling: ca*, cerebral aqueduct; *bsc*, brachium of superior colliculus; *ic*, internal capsule; *les*, lesion; *lgn*, laminated lateral geniculate nucleus; *mgn*, medial geniculate nucleus; *pgn*, pregeniculate nucleus; *pulv*, pulvinar of thalamus; *sc*, superior colliculi; *y*, system of direct optomesencephalic fibers, which in this experiment remained normal but degenerated in the experiment illustrated in Fig. 187. (*Cf.* Figs. 222, 223; and *see* W. H. Magoun & S. W. Ranson in Arch. Ophth., v. 13, p. 791, 1935.)

late fiber lamina which surrounds the principal laminated nucleus is a conspicuous feature (Fig. 215, sketch *H*). Such a pronounced structure in the approximate place where the horizontal meridian must be looked for is likely to be concerned with some particular function, e.g., constriction of the pupils during fixation.

The appearance of the neurons of the pregeniculate nucleus in Golgi preparations is shown in Figure 222. The relatively large size of some of its nerve cells is remarkable; the majority, however, are small. Another peculiarity

impulses reach the pregeniculate gray nucleus is represented by delicate myelinated fibers which enter it, partly directly from the optic tract and partly by way of the subjacent laminated lateral geniculate nucleus (*pgn* in Figs. 186, 202–5). These fibers emerge from the intermediate foveal-areal segment of the tract and geniculate nucleus, as described in section 4 (4). The origin of these afferent fibers is almost exclusively in the pit of the central fovea of both eyes, ipsilateral and contralateral, and in the region next to the fovea, as evidenced by experi-

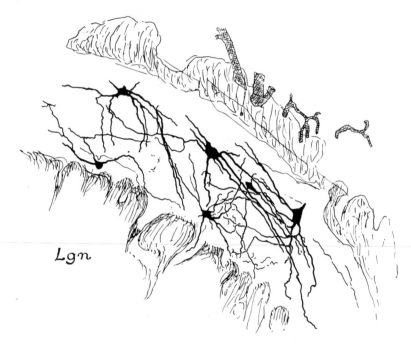

Lgn

FIG. 222.—Pregeniculate nucleus of a baby Rhesus Macaque showing nerve cells and their expansions, stained with the Golgi method. A few blood vessels along the upper margin are also impregnated. *Lgn*, dorsal extremity of the principal or laminated portion of lateral geniculate nucleus. (*Cf. pgn*, in Figs. 210, 211.)

is the confinement of dendritic expansions to the territory of the nucleus. The dendrites carry a considerable number of short "spines" with minute globules at the ends. Along these run long, fine threads, apparently teledendrons of collateral branches originating from the axons of retinal origin whose principal terminals are in the laminated nucleus. Each cell of the pregeniculate nucleus gives off a single axis cylinder, which turns in the median direction, toward the subthalamus and intergeniculate fiber lamina.

2. CONNECTIONS OF THE PREGENICULATE NUCLEUS.—The avenue by which the retinal

ments described in section 7 (5), in this chapter. In spite of their great numbers, in view of the observations of O'Leary (1940), these collateral branches apparently belong to the axons of special retinal neurons whose principal termination is in the laminated nucleus (*see also* S. Ramón y Cajal 1899–1904 [Figs. 576, 577]; and Tello 1904). Whether the pregeniculate nucleus receives additional afferent or efferent fibers from other parts of the nervous system, e.g., from the somatosensory, somatomotor, auditory, and so forth, including the cerebral cortex, is not known.

The efferent connections of the pregeniculate

gray nucleus are revealed by experiment (Fig. 221, sketch *A; cf.* Fig. 187). When, in a monkey, a minute lesion (*les*) is made in this nucleus, for example, by means of an electrocoagulating needle attached to a stereotaxic instrument of Horsley and Clarke (*see* Clarke & Henderson and Ranson & Ingram), the axis cylinders of the nerve cells of this nucleus degenerate, making it possible to follow them in Marchi preparations along their course as far as their termination.

The "pregeniculo-mesencephalic" or "indirect optomesencephalic tract" (*pmt*), revealed in this way, consists of fibers noticeably thicker than the very fine direct optomesencephalic fibers mentioned in the preceding paragraph and described in sections 4 (4) and 7 (5), in this chapter. Close to the origin, both systems of fibers, direct and indirect (*pmt* and *x* & *y*), partly commingle in the narrow "intergeniculate lamina" (*il*) squeezed between the lateral geniculate nucleus and the pulvinar, on the one hand, and the medial geniculate nucleus, on the other hand. Soon, however, the thicker fibers of the pregeniculo-mesencephalic tract leave the common roadbed and pursue their own course. The anteriormost turn at once medially into the subthalamus along the subthalamic strand of nerve cells described in one of the preceding subsections (*pmt* in Fig. 221, sketches *A, B; cf. PGN* in Fig. 209, and *sth* in Figs. 212, 215, sketch *I*). Their direction is oblique-medial and at the same time posterior. Eventually, these fibers reach the pretectal region, in front of and below the anterior exit of the cerebral aqueduct (*ca*). Whether anywhere along their course these fibers give off collaterals and undergo synapses with the cells of the subthalamus, and especially of the pretectal region, is a problem which must be solved with the help of histo-analytical methods like Golgi's.

The remaining pregeniculo-mesencephalic fibers, apparently the majority, for a while follow a more direct caudal course in the "intergeniculate fiber lamina" (*il* in sketch *C*, in Fig. 221). They enter the zonal-like fiber layer which coats the exposed lateral and ventral face of the medial geniculate nucleus (*mgn*). From this fibrous layer they successively turn in the medial direction, pushing in scattered bundles through the plain substance of the medial geniculate nucleus and farther on through the

substance of the midbrain tegmentum (*tgm*) underlying the superior colliculus (*sc*) and as far as the posterior end of that structure (back of sketch *F*). Whether these fibers undergo synaptical connections anywhere along their passage through the medial geniculate nucleus and tegmentum could not be determined by the method used.

Some of the pregeniculo-mesencephalic fibers reach from underneath the base of the superior colliculus (*sc*) of the same side, where they probably terminate (in sketches *D, E, F*). They do not enter the collicular brachium (*bsc*) or the circular zone in the superficial caplike portion of the colliculus (*y, y* in sketch *F*), where much finer direct optotectal fibers, referred to in section 4 (4), terminate (*y, y* in sketch *F*, in Fig. 187). The bulk of the indirect pregeniculo-mesencephalic fibers proceed to the central gray substance (*pgs*) surrounding the cerebral aqueduct (*ca*). In it they are found as far as the mid-line, with a few penetrating for a short distance beyond this line, within the periaqueductal gray substance, above and below the aqueduct. Also, only a few of these fibers may, by this route, reach the base of the contralateral superior colliculus. A small region on the ipsilateral side just lateral to the aqueduct appears best supplied with these pregeniculo-mesencephalic fibers. The nests of cells, both of the somatic and of the vegetative or Edinger & Westphal's divisions of the oculomotor nucleus, seem less well provided with these fibers, with none spreading as far as the inferior colliculus and nucleus of the trochlear nerve.

The number of fibers of the pregeniculo-mesencephalic tract coincides fairly well with the number of the nerve cells in the pregeniculate gray nucleus. The course and termination of this tract, since it remains subcortical throughout, explain the observation that the cells of the pregeniculate nucleus are unaffected in experiments or pathological cases where extensive portions of the parieto-occipital cortex have been destroyed (Minkowski, Polyak, A. E. Walker).

From the description of the course and termination of the optic nerve fibers which directly, without synaptical interruption, reach the midbrain, as given in section 4 [5], it is evident that the retinal fibers are not directly related to the nuclear complex of the oculomotor nerve. Such a connection, as described in this section, is established indirectly, through the pregeniculo-mesencephalic system, with the synapses in the pregeniculate nucleus. (*Cf*. Figs. 180, 223.)

3. Probable function of the pregeniculate nucleus and of the pregeniculo-mesencephalic fiber system.—Unlike the fiber systems originating in the laminated lateral and medial geniculate nuclei, in the pulvinar, and in most parts of the thalamus (A. E. Walker, Le Gros Clark), the fibers from the pregeniculate nucleus do not reach the cortex. The pregeniculo-mesencephalic system represents a subcortical side track to the great corticopetal afferent visual pathway. Terminating, as it does, in the closest proximity to the oculomotor nuclei, it is most appropriate to consider it a central link in the circuit of the pupillary light reflex, especially concerned with constriction.

Such an interpretation appears well substantiated by the close agreement between the origin, course, and termination of this tract and the faradic plotting of stimulable points from which the pupillary constriction may be elicited experimentally (Magoun, Atlas, Hare & Ranson 1936; *see also* Ranson & Magoun 1933; Hare, Magoun & Ranson 1935; Magoun & Ranson 1935; Magoun, Ranson & Mayer 1935; *cf. also* Karplus & Kreidl, who in their faradic experiments in 1913 unknowingly severed precisely this fiber tract on both sides of the oculomotor nuclei and described pupillary constriction in a medial cut and an absence of such constriction of the pupil in a lateral cut).

The observations presented in section 7 (5) of this chapter, showing that most, if not all, afferent fibers from the optic tract to the pregeniculate nucleus originate in the central fovea and area of the retina, precisely the region from which a constriction of the pupils may most promptly be elicited on direct stimulation with light (C. von Hess 1907, 1908, 1916; Gasteiger 1934), agree well with the interpretation of this tract as a central link in the pupillary reflex pathway. Also in agreement with this interpretation are those experiments which indicate that the superior colliculus of the midbrain is not indispensable for the maintenance of the pupil-

lary reflex, showing its pathway to have a location below the tectum, that is, in the subjacent tegmentum of the midbrain (Magoun 1935; *see also* Knoll 1869; Bechterew 1883; Ferrier & Turner 1901; Levinsohn 1904, 1909; Bernheimer 1909; Keller & Stewart 1932; Ranson & Magoun 1933).

4. Pregeniculo-mesencephalic tract and the pathology of the pupillary reflex.—Ever since the value of the pupillary reflex to light stimulation in the clinical diagnosis of syphilitic and metasyphilitic affections of the central nervous system became known by Argyll Robertson (portrait, Fig. 224), innumerable attempts have been made to discover the anatomical basis of this reflex.

As the anatomical mechanism responsible for the transmission of light stimuli from the retinal photoreceptors to the sphincter muscle of the iris of the eye became better known, the problem was gradually limited to the stretch of the reflex pathway intervening between the termination of the optic nerve fibers in the brain and the oculomotor nuclei of the midbrain.

During the past few decades this gap has been bridged by numerous investigations, mostly physiological-experimental, such as those of Karplus & Kreidl (1913), of Lenz (1927, 1929), and especially of Ranson & Magoun (1933) and of Magoun & Ranson and their associates (1935, 1936).

This section of the pupillary reflex circuit, as revealed by electrophysiological plotting, in the Cat and Monkey passes beneath the base of the superior colliculus, through the upper zone of the midbrain tegmentum, from the brachium of the superior colliculus laterally, to the pretectal nucleus medially. The superior colliculus is apparently not related to the constricting phase of the pupillary reflex, whereas the posterior commissure, though of some importance, seems not to be a major structure involved.

This gratifying agreement still left two specific questions to be answered. The first concerns the precise linking of the optic fibers to the plotted pupillary tract in the midbrain. The other deals with the exact relation of the pupillary tract to the sphincter nucleus of the oculomotor nerve. Finally, in order to produce convincing evidence, the pupillary tract of the midbrain had to be demonstrated anatomically. The pregeniculo-mesencephalic tract described in the preceding subsection seems to go a long way toward meeting all three requirements (Fig. 223). Even so, it is only fair to say that an adequate understanding of the central pupillomotor mechanism will not be attained until this entire apparatus has been thoroughly analyzed with the Golgi or a similar method.

With the interpretation of the pregeniculo-mesencephalic tract as a central afferent link of the pupillary reflex pathway, the pathology of the pupillary reflex may also be brought into harmony. In order to explain the selective impairment of the afferent pupillomotor fibers, a suggestion was made by Ingvar (1928) of their vulnerability. Since, according to C. Hess and others, however, the pupillary reflex may most readily be elicited from the central fovea, those localities where the foveal fibers are superficially located must be especially considered (* in Fig. 223).

From the presentation of this subject in section 7 (2, 3) of this chapter, it is plain that only in the distal portion of the optic nerve (on) and in the chiasma (ch) are the foveal and areal fibers located next to the surface. In the remainder of the infranuclear division of the visual system the foveal fibers are deeply sheltered within the nerves, tracts, and lateral geniculate nuclei and are therefore less exposed to extraneous agents.

Concerning the pregeniculo-mesencephalic tract, the situation is similar. In one locality, on the ventral surface of the lateral, and on the lateroventral surface of the medial, geniculate nuclei, this tract is superficial, located immediately beneath the pial cover (* at pmt). The noxious agents established in the meninges, as, for example, in chronic luetic meningitis, may therefore affect this tract directly and quasi-selectively. Another locality where the pregeniculo-mesencephalic fibers are close to the surface is their termination in the gray substance lining the cerebral aqueduct close to the posterior floor of the third ventricle (* at caq). Here again these fibers may be damaged by a pathological process, such as an inflammation of the periaqueductal gray matter, with or without vascular changes, accompanied by hemorrhages.

In the case of chronic meningitis or aqueductal ependymitis such as frequently accompany "neurosyphilis" and "metasyphilitic" affections of the central nervous system, e.g., general progressive paresis or paralytic dementia, tabes dorsalis, and a few other ailments, it is therefore possible for the pregeniculo-mesencephalic fibers to become affected either along their course or close to their termination, with a resulting interruption of the afferent link of the pupillary reflex pathway. The constriction of the pupils which regularly accompanies a volitional impulse for convergence and accommodation of the eyes to close range, as well as sight in general, may in the same cases remain preserved for the following reasons. Their particular pathways, one from the cortex to the pupillo-constrictor center of the midbrain, the other from the retinae via the laminated geniculate nuclei to the cortex, are both at some distance from the surface. Both pathways would therefore remain out of reach of the superficial pathological process, as would the oculomotor nucleus itself, and thus would not be affected, and the motility of the eyes and visual acuity would not be impaired. The retrograde affection of the pregeniculate nucleus, separated from the optic tract, by the synapses of its own cells, would also not affect the principal nerve fibers which terminate in the laminated nucleus.

The dissociation of the two functions, one abolished (constriction of pupils to the stimulation of retinae by light), the other preserved (constriction of pupils on accommodation and convergence), is the principal sign of the phenomenon of Argyll Robertson and is of great diagnostic value in clinical neurology.

Whether partially "frozen pupils," pathognomonic for neurosyphilis and metasyphilis of the brain, are always caused by a superficial pathological process of meningitis or ependymitis is a problem requiring further investigation. It is conceivable that in some cases the symptom of Argyll Robertson is not caused by inflammatory pathology but rather by a selective degeneration of the pregeniculo-mesencephalic fiber system, owing to the action of metasyphilitic virus or toxins circulating in the body fluids. This may also be true of the central sympathetic mechanism for the dilatation of the pupils, whose impairment appears to be respon-

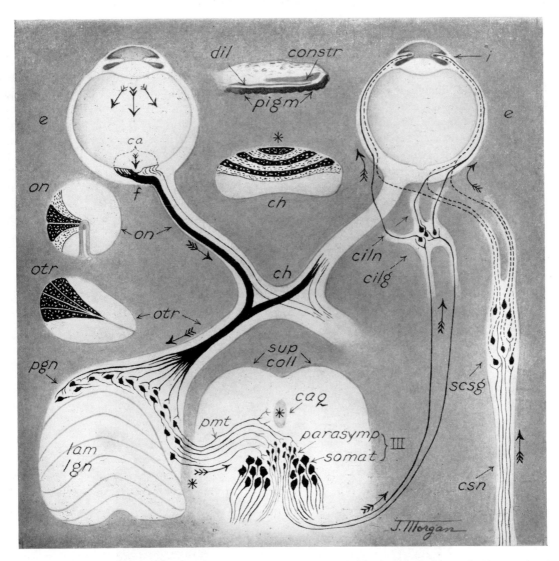

Fig. 223.—Diagram of the pathway of pupillary light reflex as revealed by pathological investigation, anatomical and physiological experiments, and clinical experience. The light that enters the eye (*e*, in *upper left*) stimulates the retina, principally the central fovea (*f*) and area (*ca*). These impulses are transmitted along decussating and nondecussating optic nerve fibers to the lateral geniculate nuclei of both sides, where they enter the pregeniculate nuclei (*pgn*). From here the impulses are further transmitted along the pregeniculo-mesencephalic tract (*pmt*) through the midbrain tegmentum to the central gray substance around the Sylvian aqueduct (*caq*), where they are synaptically related to the small-celled parasympathetic Edinger & Westphal portion of the oculomotor nucleus (*parasymp III*), and along its delicate axon fibers to the ciliary ganglion (*cilg*). After once more synapsing, the impulses finally reach, via short ciliary nerves (*ciln*), the smooth-muscle fibers of the pupillary constrictor in the margin of the iris (*constr*, in *upper center*), cutting down the amount of light entering the eyes. The superior colliculi of the midbrain (*sup coll*), situated above the pregeniculo-mesencephalic tract (*pmt*), and the large-celled somatic portions of oculomotor nucleus (*somat III*) apparently do not take part in a direct pupillary light reflex. The sympathetic fibers, originating in the lower segments of the cervical portion and the upper segments of the thoracic portion of the spinal cord, pass up the cervical sympathetic trunk (*csn*) to the superior cervical sympathetic ganglion, whence fibers arise which, by devious ways, reach the eyeball via long ciliary nerves and finally the smooth radially arranged muscles of the pupillary dilator (*dil*, in *upper center*). *Labeling:* ca, central area and fovea; *caq*, Sylvian aqueduct; *ch*, chiasma; *cilg*, ciliary ganglion; *ciln*, ciliary nerve; *constr*, constrictor or sphincter of pupil; *csn*, cervical sympathetic nerve or trunk; *dil*, dilator of pupil; *e*, eyeballs; *f*, central fovea; *i*, iris; *lam lgn*, laminated geniculate nucleus; *on*, optic nerve; *otr*, optic tract; *parasymp III*, parasympathetic or Edinger & Westphal nucleus; *pgn*, pregeniculate nucleus; *pigm*, pigment layer of iris; *pmt*, pregeniculo-mesencephalic tract; *somat III*, somatic portion of oculomotor nucleus; *sup coll*, superior colliculi; *scsg*, superior cervical sympathetic ganglion; *, points at which pupillary reflex pathway is most exposed to noxious agents. The arrows indicate the course of impulses from the retina via the oculomotor motor center to the sphincter or constrictor muscle of the pupil.

sible for pupillary miosis. (For other details *see* F. B. Walsh 1947.)

The ventral nucleus is a constant constituent of the lateral geniculate complex, beginning with the lowest and including the highest Mammals. In Man, although much smaller than the laminated nucleus, it is by no means "vestigial," that is, on the verge of being eliminated.

It may be pertinent to inquire whether the regulation of the amount of light to be admitted into the eye chamber exhausts the function of the pregeniculate nucleus and of the pregeniculo-mesencephalic pathway, or whether some other similar function associated with vision is also to be attributed to it. This question is particularly pertinent with regard to the Lower

FIG. 224.—Douglas Argyll Robertson (1837–1909), Scottish ophthalmologist. Disciple of A. Graefe and of W. P. Bowman. Discovered "Argyll-Robertson's sign or symptom," or partially "frozen pupil," one of the most important tests in clinical neurology. In his own words, this symptom consists in the following: "Although the retina is quite sensitive, and the pupil contracts during the act of accommodation for near objects, yet an alteration in the amount of light admitted to the eye does not influence the size of the pupil" (Edinburgh M. J., v. 14, p. 696; v. 15, p. 487, both 1869). Portrait from J. Hirschberg, in Graefe & Saemisch, *Handb. d. ges. Augenh.*, 2d ed., v. 14 (4), p. 414, 1914. *See* obituary by G. Mackay in Klin. Monatsbl. f. Augenh., v. 1, p. 308, 1909. Biography in Haymaker & Baer, *The Founders of Neurology*, 1953.

Its good development in all Primates is understandable in the light of the foregoing interpretation as a link in the pathway of the pupillary light reflex.

Mammals, in which the ventral nucleus is relatively larger than in the advanced Mammals. Its subthalamic origin, connections, and relatively large size indicate that this nucleus may be essentially vegetative in nature, serving a more complex function in the vision of primitive Mammals. (*See* Fig. 191.)

References: Abelsdorff 1919; Bach 1905, 1909; Balado & Franke 1931; C. Behr 1924, 1931; Bender 1945; Bernheimer 1901, 1904; Berteau & Jones 1950; Best 1908; Bouman 1905; Brouwer 1919–20; Bumke & Trendelenburg 1911; Le Gros Clark 1932; Collier 1927; Crouch 1934; Danis 1948; Foerster, Gagel & Mahoney 1936; Friedemann 1911–12; Gagel 1928; Gasteiger 1934; Hare, Magoun & Ranson 1935; A. J. Harris *et al.* 1944; W. Harris 1935; Herrmann 1928; C. Hess 1907, 1908, 1916; Hodes 1940; Hodes & Magoun 1942; Hyndman & Dulin 1939; Ingram 1940; Ingram *et al.* 1931, 1932; Jaffe 1950; Karplus 1937; Karplus & Kreidl 1913; Környey 1928; Keller & Stewart 1932; Kronfeld 1927; Kuhlenbeck & Miller 1942; Langworthy & Tauber 1937; Lenz 1927, 1929; Levinsohn 1904, 1909; Lowenstein & Loewenfeld 1950; Magoun 1935; Magoun & Ranson 1935; Magoun, Atlas, Hare & Ranson 1936; M. Marquez 1924; Merrit & Moore 1935; Mingazzini 1928; Minkowski 1939; L. R. Müller 1931; Münzer & Wiener 1902; Mussen 1923; Neimer 1946; Papez 1938; Papez & Rundles 1938; M. Pavlow 1900; Peterson & Henneman 1948; R. A. Pfeifer 1930; Pines 1896; Ranson & Magoun 1933; Rea 1941; M. Reichard 1918; Shafik 1937–38; D. Sheehan 1941; Spiegel & Sommer 1944; Spiegel & Nagasaka 1927; Toncray & Krieg 1946; Tsai 1925; U. Tsuchida 1906; Ury & Oldberg 1940; C. Vogt 1909; F. B. Walsh 1947; Watanabe 1930; Wick 1923; Wilbrand & Saenger 1904, 1922, 1927; Wilbrand & Behr 1927; Woollard 1926.

SEC. 11. SUMMARY OF THE INTRINSIC ORGANIZATION OF THE INFRANUCLEAR AND NUCLEAR DIVISIONS OF THE VERTEBRATE VISUAL SYSTEM

1. RETINAL ORIGIN OF OPTIC NERVE FIBERS. —The infranuclear or peripheral division of the visual system by which the photogenic impulses arising in the retinae of the eyes reach the brain is represented by the photoreceptors and other neurons residing in the retina itself and by the optic nerve fibers or axis cylinders of the retinal ganglion cells. In the retina, whose ninth layer they form, these optic nerve fibers, in general, pursue a radiating course as they converge upon the optic papilla or disk. In the region of the central area and temporal to it, the fibers from the upper and the lower quadrant are separated from one another by a horizontal division line, the raphé or "seam." In this locality the two sets of fibers are not arranged in straight radial lines but describe arches above and below the central area and fovea.

The optic nerve fibers in Man and other Higher Mammals normally do not possess myelin sheaths along the stretch in the eye; they obtain these sheaths after leaving the eyeball through the numerous small openings in the cribriform or sievelike lamina of the scleral tunic. In Rodents, e.g., the Hare and the Rabbit, a portion of the intraretinal section of the optic nerve fibers is normally provided with myelin sheaths.

2. COURSE AND ARRANGEMENT OF OPTIC NERVE FIBERS IN THE RETINA, PAPILLA, AND OPTIC NERVE.—The optic nerve fibers preserve a certain stable order while still in the retina. In general, each small bundle which originates from a limited territory keeps its relative position, to some extent, with respect to other bundles that originate from adjacent areae. A certain degree of interchange and displacement, however, occurs, especially because of the archlike course in and around the central area.

The "papillomacular bundle," a broad stream of delicate fiber bundles arising from the central area and fovea, passes over to the papilla in a rather straight horizontal course or in slight arches, being surrounded above and below by bundles of thicker fibers from the extra-areal portions of the two temporal quadrants and from the adjacent zone of the nasal quadrants.

At the temporal margin of the papilla the arrangement is similar, with the areal and foveal fibers located next to the horizontal meridian and flanked from above and from below by the upper and lower extra-areal temporal fibers (Fig. 225, *optpap*). Along the nasal margin of the papilla the arrangement is less complicated, each wedge-shaped retinal segment sending its bundles directly to the nearest point at the papilla.

In the optic nerve close to the eyeball, essentially the same arrangement is preserved. Here the foveal-areal quadrants are located along the horizontal meridian between the temporal margin and the central blood vessels, flanked above and below by the extra-areal temporal fibers and surrounded nasally by the fibers from the nasal extra-areal quadrants, including those from the extreme peripheral monocular crescent.

Farther away from the eyeball, in the optic nerve, the foveal-areal fibers become central and are surrounded on all sides by the extra-areal fibers of the four quadrants (Fig. 225, *optn*). Close to the chiasma the optic nerve seems to be rotated around its axis, resulting in a tilting of its temporal, and a lowering of its nasal, margins.

3. COURSE OF OPTIC NERVE FIBERS IN THE CHIASMA AND IN THE TRACTS.—The first great change takes place in the chiasma or junction of the optic nerves (Fig. 225, *chiasma*). This is accomplished by the crossing of fibers originating from the somewhat larger nasal halves of both retinae and joining the respective uncrossed fibers in the contralateral optic tracts originating from the somewhat smaller temporal retinal halves. In spite of the apparent confusion during their decussation, the fibers preserve a modicum of stable order: those from the central areae and foveae being in the upper portion of the chiasma, the monocular fibers in the lower portion, while the remainder from the binocular extra-areal portions of the two nasal retinal halves are arranged in between.

The cleavage line along which the fibers from the nasal half of the retina separate from those of the temporal half is, accordingly, entirely extraretinal, being caused by a partial decussation in the chiasma. Although not visible in a normal retina, this cleavage line is nevertheless real, as manifested by the visual field defects in various types of hemianopia and by experiment. Whereas each optic nerve contains all fibers from the corresponding eye, the middle portion of the bridge of the chiasma is made up of decussating nasal fibers of both eyes, and the optic tracts of decussating nasal fibers of the opposite eye and of the nondecussating tem-

poral fibers of the eye of the same side. The lateral portions of the chiasma contain nondecussating temporal fibers, the right portion from the right eye, the left portion from the left eye. Functionally, the middle part of the chiasma represents the nasal halves of the two retinae; in its two lateral portions it represents the right and the left temporal halves. The tracts, being composed both of the crossed nasal and of the uncrossed temporal fibers, functionally represent the homonymous halves of both retinae: the right tract the right halves, and the left tract the left halves.

In the fields of vision—the eye being a camera obscura or dark chamber, where only the crossed rays of light are utilized—the effect is reversed: in the chiasma the middle portion represents the two temporal halves, and the two lateral ends represent the right and the left nasal half of the two fields of view. For the same reason, each optic tract represents the two homonymous contralateral halves of the two monocular fields of view, an ipsilateral nasal and a contralateral temporal. Essentially the same anatomical arrangement and functional representation as in the tracts remain in the lateral geniculate nuclei and in the supranuclear division of the afferent visual pathway.

4. RETINOTOPICAL ORGANIZATION OF THE OPTIC TRACTS AND LATERAL GENICULATE NUCLEI.—As soon as the decussating fibers pass the lateral portion of the chiasma, they spread over the entire thickness of the initial portion of the tract (Figs. 195, 199). Here they meet the nondecussating bundles, which spread in the same fashion over the entire tract. In this way the two systems of fibers meet, each decussating bundle joining its nondecussating homonymous functional mate (Fig. 225, *r.opt.tr.*, *l.opt.tr.*). In the tracts, after mingling, the fibers are rather uniformly distributed over the cross-section.

Through this arrangement the right and the left homonymous synergical fiber bundles arising from the "corresponding points" of the homonymous halves of both retinae come to lie very close together. The fiber bundles are arranged in an orderly way, bundle by bundle, according to the homodynamical quadrants, or parts thereof, in the retinae and in the fields of view, with some qualification.

In the dorsomedial sector of each tract and

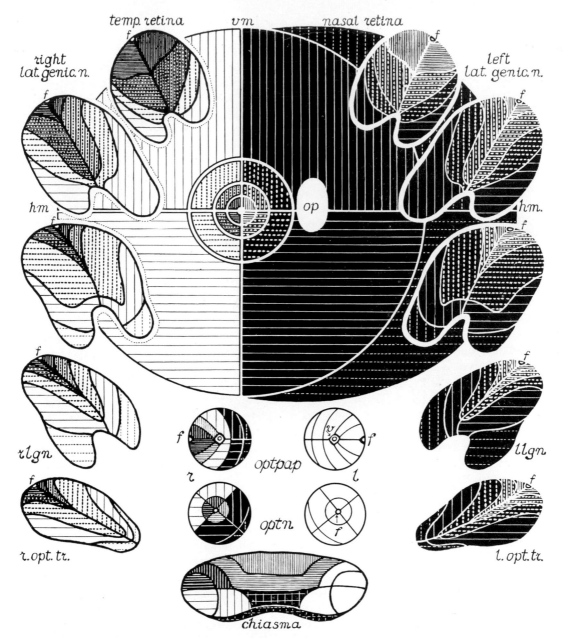

FIG. 225.—Topographical representation or "projection" of the retinal surface of the right eye in the infranuclear and nuclear divisions of the visual system of a Rhesus Macaque, determined in experiments described in section 7 of chapter VI, in this book. In the upper center the surface of the right retina is presented facing the observer, with the nasal half black and the temporal half white. Right-hand sketches represent, in black with white shading, cross-sections through the left optic tract and laminated lateral geniculate nucleus; the left-hand sketches represent, in white with black shading, the same of the right tract and the geniculate nucleus. The sketches in lower center show cross-sections through the optic papillae, optic nerves, and the chiasma, with the left papilla and nerve (*right* in the diagram) given only in outlines. The various patterns of the retinal belts or zones are carried throughout the visual pathways and centers and may be followed as far as the cortical visual centers (*see* Figs. 259, 260). In the center of the retina a small white circle indicates the fixation point. First circle surrounding it, divided into four quadrants, shows the foveola; the second circle, the periphery of the central fovea; the third circle, the remainder of the central area; and the fourth and largest complete circle, the extra-areal binocular portion of the retina, with the semilunar zone, which has no counterpart in the temporal half, representing the monocular nasal portion (corresponding to monocular temporal crescent in the field of view). By following variously shaded patterns from the right optic papilla (*optpap*) through the right optic nerve (*optn*) and the chiasma to both tracts and geniculate nuclei, it is possible to locate in this figure each belt or quadrant of the retina at any point in the visual pathway, including the supranuclear division. *Labeling: f,* fixation point; *hm,* horizontal meridian; *l,* left optic papilla or nerve (*optpap, optn*); *llgn,* left lateral geniculate nucleus; *l.opt.tr.,* left optic tract; *op,* optic papilla or disk; *r,* right optic papilla or nerve (*optpap, optn*); *rlgn,* right lateral geniculate nucleus; *r.opt.tr.,* right optic tract; *v,* central blood vessels; *vm,* vertical meridian.

lateral geniculate nucleus, the binocular portions of the upper ipsilateral homonymous retinal quadrants or of the lower contralateral homonymous field quadrants are represented. In the ventrolateral sectors of the tracts and geniculates, the binocular portions of the lower ipsilateral homonymous retinal quadrants or of the upper contralateral homonymous field quadrants are represented.

The fibers originating from the homonymous halves of the two central areae and foveae, both decussating and nondecussating, are assembled according to their homodynamic quadrants between the above-mentioned two extra-areal segments in an intermediate wedgelike segment of the tract and geniculate, whose sharp lower end points ventromedially and whose bulky end forms the dorsolateral convexity of the tract or geniculate. In the fields of view this intermediate segment represents the contralateral homonymous halves of the foveal or central field quadrants (*cf.* Figs. 202, 203).

At the inner or ventromedial extremity of the cross-section of the tracts, the monocular fibers from the extreme nasal portion of the contralateral retina are assembled in a narrow, superficial zone, the upper quadrantic fibers above, the lower ones below, representing the lower and upper portions of the contralateral monocular field of view. In the lateral geniculate nucleus the same fibers terminate in the two lowermost extremities on both sides of the hilum.

The long, slanting axis of the cross-section of the tract represents the horizontal meridians in the ipsilateral homonymous halves of both retinae or in the contralateral homonymous halves of both fields of view. The point at which the axis touches the upper contour of the tract is the fixation point (*f*). The fibers originating along the principal vertical meridians (*vm*), which divide the right from the left homonymous hemiretinae, are strung along the lateral margin of the tracts. In the lateral geniculate nucleus the principal vertical meridians and fixation points have a similar location.

The relative position of the superimposed homonymous quadrants in the tracts and geniculates is, accordingly, essentially the same as in the retinae, except for certain adjustments necessary to accommodate the fibers to the changed

shape of the tracts and geniculates when compared with the homonymous retinal halves. A slight displacement of the areal-foveal bundles seems also to take place along the horizontal meridian, inasmuch as the sharp wedge of the intermediate areal-foveal segment is pushed deep into the nucleus toward its ventromedial extremity, or hilum, in the posterior half of the nucleus completely separating the upper from the lower extra-areal segment. Or, in other words, the homonymous halves of the two central areae and foveae, the "hemimaculae," which in the retinae are located practically in the central corners of the upper and lower quadrants, in the optic tracts are somewhat, and in the lateral geniculate nuclei completely, displaced and are squeezed between the upper and the lower extra-areal quadrants, in this way in the tract nearly, and in the geniculates entirely, splitting up the raphé into a "gap" which they fill.

The peculiar topographical arrangement of the quadrants in the tracts, resembling a complete separation of the upper from the lower extra-areal fiber bundles by the "papillomacular bundle" close to and in the temporal margin of the optic papilla of the eye, remains essentially the same in the laminated lateral geniculate nucleus and also farther up in the visual radiation, where the separation of the two extra-areal quadrants by the intercalated areal-foveal quadrants becomes complete (*see* Figs. 259, 260, *LVR* and *RVR*). In the striate cortex, the extra-areal quadrants again join each other (*LSA* and *RSA*, in same figures).

5. Representation of the central fovea or "macula" in the infranuclear and nuclear divisions of the visual system.—The fovea or "macula" of each eye is represented in the infranuclear division of the visual pathway and in the laminated lateral geniculate nucleus according to the same general principle that holds for the extrafoveal parts of the retina (Fig. 225).

Each fovea is divided by a vertical meridian into a nasal and a temporal half, a hemifovea, owing to a partial decussation in the chiasma. The fibers from the ipsilateral temporal and the contralateral nasal hemifovea join in the tract and geniculate nucleus. Furthermore, as in the peripheral extrafoveal fibers, the foveal fibers are also subdivided into an upper and a lower homonymous hemifoveal quadrant. The two foveal quadrants are separated by a virtual axial line representing the horizontal meridians (*hm*), the line terminating at a point of the upper margin where the fixation points are represented (*f*).

The indications are that the representation in the foveal segments of the optic tracts, and even more so in the geniculates, is extremely minute or detailed and that it may, in fact, approach the theoretically postulated elemental conductor units, each represented by only a few neurons. In the greater portion of the optic tracts and geniculates such units are double, being composed of both the ipsilateral and the contralateral synergical or homodynamical fibers. In the monocular portion of the tracts and lateral geniculate nuclei the elementary conductor units are made up of decussating fibers only.

This view is supported by a similar shape and location of the areas of degeneration in the two tracts and geniculates in experiments where the retinal lesion similarly affects the two symmetrical localities on both sides of the principal vertical meridian, or where it straddles that meridian. It also agrees with and, in turn, explains in terms of anatomical factors the congruous boundaries of the functional defects in cases of homonymous hemianopias and hemi-anopic scotomas in complete and incomplete unilateral lesions of the optic tract (*see* chaps. XI, XII). Sharp boundaries observed in minute zones of degeneration in the lateral geniculate nucleus in experiments with monkeys, where small lesions were made in the visual cortex in one half of the brain, likewise support this view (chap. VII, 5).

The fact that the two sets of the homonymous fibers terminate in different cell laminae of the lateral geniculate nucleus indicates that, even though the two constituents of the elemental units, the "corresponding points," are close together, a certain measure of independence is preserved. By means of this arrangement, the fusion of the two similar homonymous retinal impressions in the infranuclear division and in the subcortical centers is merely prepared, its consummation, however, taking place in the striate cortex of the occipital lobes.

References: Ariëns Kappers, Huber & Crosby 1936; Balado & Franke 1937; Best 1920; Brouwer 1931, 1936; Brouwer & Zeeman 1925, 1926; Le Gros Clark 1942; Clark & Penman 1934; Coppez & Fritz 1930; Henschen 1890–1930, 1917, 1919, 1923, 1926; Hines 1942; Lashley 1942; Mackenzie, Meighan & Pollock 1933; Marburg 1942; L. L. Mayer 1942; Minkowski 1930, 1939; Penman 1934; Polyak 1941, 1948; Rønne (Roenne) 1944; Wilbrand 1926, 1929; Wilbrand & Saenger 1899–1927; Zeeman 1925.

Chapter VII

Visual Radiation

SEC. 1. INTRODUCTION; GENERAL REMARKS CONCERNING THE SUPRANUCLEAR DIVISION OF THE VISUAL SYSTEM

1. RELATION OF NUCLEAR TO SUPRANUCLEAR DIVISIONS OF THE VISUAL SYSTEM.—The optic nerve fibers, which originate in the ganglion cells of the retina, terminate in several nuclei or subcortical visual stations of the brain, as described in the preceding chapter. Structurally, the most elaborate of these is the laminated lateral geniculate nucleus, or body, where the bulk of the optic fibers terminate (Fig. 180, *lgn*). Next in importance is the smaller pregeniculate gray nucleus, which is the terminal station of the delicate optic nerve fibers or their collateral branches (*pgn*). The superior colliculi of the midbrain (*cols*) also receive numerous delicate optic fibers, while a few of these fibers may possibly enter the pulvinar of the thalamus (*pulv*). (*See* chap. VI, 4, 5, on other terminal structures of the visual system, in particular in the Infraprimates.) From the nerve cells of each of these four structures, one of each in each half of the brain, originate fiber systems along which the impulses generated in the two retinae of the eyes are further propagated and distributed to the various parts of the brain.

2. VISUAL RADIATION—ITS ORIGIN, COURSE, AND TERMINATION.—Only the tract or fiber system originating in the laminated lateral geniculate nucleus may be considered an avenue along which the visual impulses are transmitted to the highest brain center of vision—the striate area. This tract is the visual or optic radiation (*radiatio optica, vis rad* in Fig. 180), also called the geniculo-calcarine tract and Gratiolet's radiation (*see* chap. III, 5 [5]). The tracts which originate from the three other subcortical visual stations remain outside the scope of the present topic: the indirect pregeniculo-tectal system and the fibers that originate from the superior colliculi, because they are wholly subcortical (*see* chap. VI, 10), and fibers of the pulvinar of the thalamus to the cortex, because few optic nerve fibers, if any, enter that part of the brain and because there is, so far, no positive experimental, clinical, and pathological evidence to show that the pulvinar is a link in the afferent visual pathway.

The visual radiations of Gratiolet are systems of fibers of considerable magnitude which form part of the white fibrous core of the posterior portion of the cerebral hemispheres (Fig. 180, *vis rad*). They are made up of axis cylinders or nerve fibers of the principal cells of the laminated lateral geniculate nuclei of the betweenbrain. In the occipital lobe the fibers of the visual radiation are included in the thick fiber lamina known as the sagittal fiber layer (Figs. 226, 227).

Each visual radiation originates in the lateral geniculate nucleus and terminates in the striate area of its own cerebral half or hemisphere. The striate area of G. Elliot Smith (1904) *stra* in Fig. 180, one in each hemisphere) is that portion of the superficial gray cortical lining in and around the calcarine fissure and the pole of the occipital lobe, distinguished by a thin, whitish line, the stripe of Gennari and Vicq-d'Azyr, visible on a cut surface through the cortex (Figs. 226, 227). Other terms for it are "field *17*" (Brodmann), "visuo-sensory area" (Campbell), and "area *OC*" (Economo).

3. GENERAL CHARACTERISTICS OF VISUAL RADIATION.—The visual radiation in its general makeup, its subcortical origin, its course within the fibrous core of the cerebral hemisphere, its termination in the occipital cortex, its blood supply, its minute structure, and its elemental functional properties resembles other great afferent fiber systems of the brain, especially the somesthetic and auditory pathways. Its specific function in normal conditions and its reaction in disease are the expression of several factors: its minute structure and the innate properties of its living nervous substance, its blood supply, its topographic relationships, and its intrinsic functional organization. In the following sections of this chapter the basic facts of the anatomy and physiology of the visual radiation are discussed, the rest being treated in chapter VIII.

References: Balado & Franke 1933; Brouwer 1917, 1936; Coppez & Fritz 1930; Elze 1929; Flechsig 1920, 1927; M. Hines 1942; Kronfeld 1929, 1931; L. L. Mayer 1940; A. Meyer 1907; Minkowski 1920, 1922, 1923–24, 1930, 1934, 1939; Niessl von Mayendorf 1903, 1907, 1921, 1930; R. A. Pfeifer 1925, 1930; Polyak 1926, 1927, 1930, 1932, 1941, 1948; Probst 1906; Putnam & Liebman 1942; Putnam & Putnam 1926; Rasmussen 1943, 1945; Rønne (Roenne) 1919, 1944; Traquair 1922; Venderóvich (Wenderówič) 1916.

SEC. 2. MENINGES AND THE INTERNAL MAKEUP OF THE CEREBRAL HEMISPHERES—THEIR RELATION TO THE VISUAL PATHWAY IN GENERAL AND TO THE VISUAL RADIATION IN PARTICULAR

1. BRAIN ENVELOPES OR MENINGES.—The brain consists of various tissues arranged in a definite, characteristic way. These tissues and their arrangement are revealed by cutting the brain into slices and by careful examination of the exposed structures. An instructive way is to cut the entire brain by horizontal section at about the level of the posterior extremity of the lateral fissure or fossa of Sylvius—Flechsig's cut (Figs. 226, 227). Another way is to make coronal sections (Figs. 228–33). Such preparations permit general orientation concerning the various parts of both hemispheres, their appearance, size, shape, location, and relative arrangement.

The outermost of the various cerebral structures are the meninges or tunics, in which the brain is enveloped. There are three of these. The outermost is the *dura mater*, or *pachymeninx*, a thick, tough, fibrous membrane, which adheres to the cranium. The dural membrane also forms two firm partitions. The more conspicuous, placed between the two hemispheres, is the *falx*, or "sickle," of the cerebrum (Fig. 228). In the posterior portion of the cranial cavity the falx is continuous with another similar, tough, fibrous partition, the *tentorium*, or tent, placed transversely and separating the larger anterior forebrain above it from the smaller cerebellum, or little brain, below and behind. These two partitions, firmly attached at one end to the inside of the skull, form a secure support which holds the various parts of the brain in place. By splitting into two sheets along the lines where they are attached to the bony wall of the cranium, the dural partitions form the venous sinuses through which the blood leaves the brain and skull.

The other two meningeal tunics within the dura are thin and soft and are therefore called *leptomeninges* (sing. *leptomeninx*). The one closer to the dura is the arachnoid membrane. It does not carry any blood vessels, and it adheres to the innermost tunic by means of numerous delicate threads and trabeculae. The space between the dura and the arachnoid is the subdural space.

The third tunic, the *pia mater*, is the innermost, closely adhering to the surface of the gyri and sulci of the brain. It penetrates all dents and depressions of the cerebral surface, everywhere carrying both large and small blood vessels, from which numerous branches penetrate into the cerebral substance. The pia mater is the principal avenue by which the nutritive blood reaches the brain, especially the more superficial parts. The space between the pial and arachnoid membranes is the subarachnoid space.

Both the subdural and the subarachnoid spaces in the living are filled with a watery cerebrospinal fluid, as are the inner cavities, called the *cerebral ventricles*, where the fluid is produced by the chorioid plexus. The cerebrospinal fluid, by filling the ventricular cavities and by providing a cushion upon and in which the brain floats, is an important mechanical factor maintaining the normal conditions necessary for the existence and function of the brain.

2. GRAY AND WHITE SUBSTANCE OF THE BRAIN.—The first feature noticeable on a cut surface of a brain specimen is that it is composed of two kinds of substance: the darker, gray matter and the white matter (Figs. 226, 227, 228).

In a freshly prepared specimen the color of the gray substance is grayish-brown, with a slight tinge of reddish, or ocher. This color is caused by countless bodies and by innumerable protoplasmic expansions or dendrites of the nerve cells and by a dense network of minute blood vessels and capillaries, the principal constituents of the gray substance. The nerve fibers possessing myelin sheaths here are relatively few.

The white substance, on the contrary, consists principally of axis cylinders or nerve fibers, mostly enveloped in myelin sheaths of varying thickness, arranged in sheets, laminae, and sys-

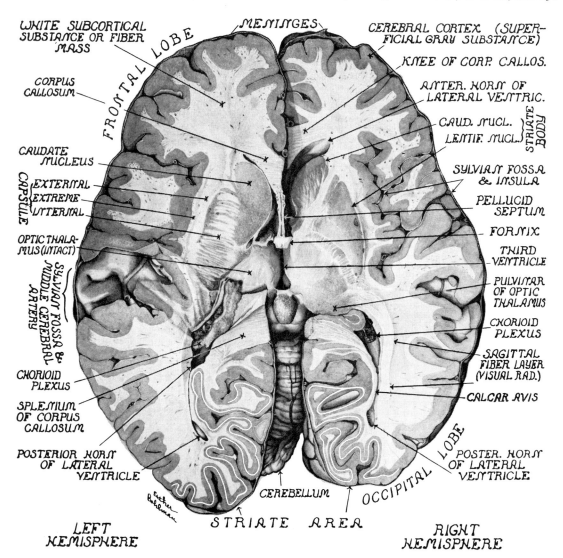

FIG. 226.—Human brain with upper parts of the hemispheres removed by a horizontal section to show the various structures which compose it. The cut through the right hemisphere is carried through a deeper level than on the left side. The superficial gray layer, the cerebral cortex or "rind," lines all gyri and sulci or furrows in between and varies in thickness. The deepest pocket is the Sylvian fossa or pit. Note the third ventricle in the center and close to it the two lateral ventricles extending from the frontal to the occipital lobes; pineal body and quadrigeminal colliculi in mid-line; white lines in the occipital cortices indicate the striate areae or visual cortical centers in both occipital lobes; the visual radiation, a thick whitish fiber lamina extending from the thalamus to the striate area, may be seen in the right occipital lobe.

tems. There are blood vessels in the white substance also, but their network is less dense. It is this fibrous composition, the myelin content, the absence or scarcity of the cell bodies, and the relative scarcity of blood vessels that impart a white coloring to the subcortical substance of the cerebral hemispheres. The same

—the supporting neuroglia, a special nervous interstitial tissue—is present in both the gray and the white matter.

The distribution of gray and white substance in various localities of the brain varies, the two usually being segregated from each other. Most of the gray matter forms a relatively thin super-

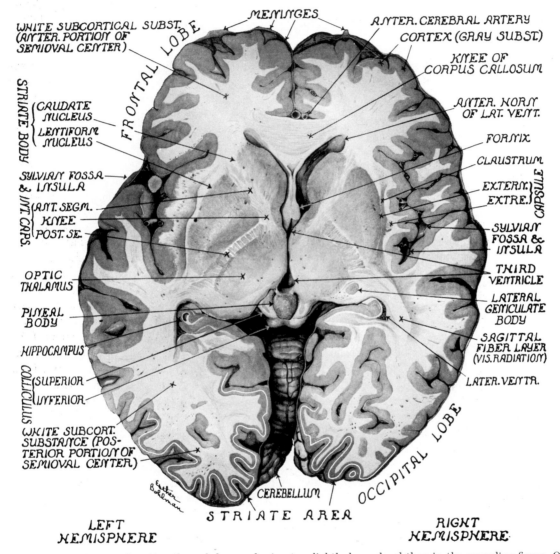

FIG. 227.—Horizontal section through human brain at a slightly lower level than in the preceding figure. On the right side the initial portion of the visual radiation and a part of the lateral geniculate nucleus are visible. The striate areae, marked by white intracortical lines, are clearly visible in both occipital lobes.

factors are also responsible for the varying appearance of different localities of the core of the brain, the brain stem, the cerebellum, the spinal cord, and the peripheral nerves and ganglions in the rest of the body.

The third constituent of the brain substance

ficial coating, which lines all convolutions or gyri and all furrows or sulci of the brain—the cortex, "rind," "bark," or "crust," of the brain. The thickness of the cortex varies considerably, depending upon the locality, partly because some of the gyri and sulci are cut more or less tangentially and partly because of the varying thickness of the cortex in different localities. On close examination one or more thin, and usually faint, whitish stripes may be observed in the cortex with the unaided eye. The most prominent of these is the stria of Gennari and Vicq-d'Azyr, found along the inner sides and at the poles of the occipital lobes, which, as mentioned, indicates the striate areae or the cortical visual centers.

The remainder of the gray matter is chiefly accumulated in the center of the brain in several solid masses, called *basal nuclei* (Figs. 226, 227)—the *thalami*, which flank the third ventricle, and the *striate bodies*, each of which, in turn, is made up of a *lentiform* and a *caudate nucleus*.

The white subcortical mass or substance of the brain (white in Figs. 226, 227, and dark in Fig. 230) forms the core of the two hemispheres —the semioval center of Vieussens. It also passes into every gyrus, of which it forms the central ridgelike portion. Sheets and segments of the white substance also separate the basal ganglia from one another and from the cortex: the internal, the external, and the extreme capsule.

The internal capsule is one of the best-known and pathophysiologically most important localities of the white subcortical core of the brain (Figs. 226, 227). It is a thick sheet resembling the letter **V**, with the point, the *genu*, or "knee," facing toward the third ventricle. The anterior limb or segment of the internal capsule separates the caudate nucleus, the posterior limb or segment separates the thalamus, from the lentiform nucleus.

The internal capsule contains important fiber tracts: the great corticobulbar and corticospinal or "pyramidal tracts" for skilled, detailed voluntary movements (which frequently are damaged in cases of cerebral hemorrhage, thrombosis, or "stroke," producing motor paralysis of the opposite half of the body); the great corticonigral and corticopontine tracts for the semiautomatic and postural movements of the limbs and body; the abundant fiber systems connecting various nuclei of the thalamus with most of the cortex and largely serving the transmission of somesthetic impulses from the body to the somesthetic areas of the cortex; and others.

3. Sagittal fiber layers of the occipital lobes.—In the posterior portion of the white subcortical core, corresponding with the parietal, occipital, and adjoining parts of the temporal lobes, a thick fiber lamina becomes apparent which may be traced from the posterolateral extremity of the thalamus along the posterior horn of the lateral ventricle in the direction of the tip or pole of the occipital lobe— the sagittal fiber layers of H. Sachs (Figs. 226, 227).

The exact number and arrangement of the fiber sheets which compose the sagittal layer may be examined more accurately in a brain whose posterior ends have been cut off (Fig. 228). In such a specimen the surface of the cuts through the two occipital lobes shows fiber bundles obviously arranged sagittally, or lengthwise, in the center of the white subcortical core. Because of their uniformly compact arrangement and the fact that they have been cut across, these bundles are somewhat grayish in color and have a texture somewhat different from the remainder of the white fibrous core.

The shape of these particular fibrous sagittal layers varies from plane to plane, usually somewhat resembling an irregular horseshoe (*see* Figs. 229, 231–33). The two ends of the horseshoe point inward, toward the medial face of the hemisphere, the horseshoe inclosing in its concavity the more or less collapsed posterior horn of the lateral ventricle (*v*), together with a deep furrow—the calcarine sulcus or fissure (in Fig. 229 marked with *).

Attentive examination of the sagittal fiber tracts reveals that they are composed of three parallel layers or strata (Fig. 228): an external, an internal, and a medial sagittal layer or *tapetum* (H. Sachs 1892). The tapetum is the innermost, closest to the posterior horn of the lateral ventricle, and is separated from it only by a microscopically thin ependymal lining. The thin, white fibrous coating on the medial side of the posterior horn is the subcortical layer of the calcarine fissure—the calcarine layer, or *stratum proprium*, coating the *calcar avis*.

In horizontally cut or dissected specimens this structure is noticeable as a curved, white bulge in the medial wall of the lateral ventricle, for which reason it was named *calcar avis*, or "bird's claw," the *hippocampus minor* of Vicq-d'Azyr (*cf.* Figs. 226 and 229). The lateral or collateral eminence of Meckel caused by the collateral sulcus is another bulge in the floor of the lateral ventricle, but lateral to the one just mentioned.

Of the several sagittal, longitudinally arranged fiber layers of the posterior portion of the hemisphere, the external stratum is chiefly afferent, containing practically all geniculo-calcarine fibers or the actual visual or optic radiation (for evidence, *see* secs. 3 and 4, this chapter, and accompanying figures).

From the early period of modern anatomy until recently, this conspicuous tract was thought by some investigators to be a system of long association fibers: the lower portion—the inferior longitudinal bundle, *fasciculus longitudinalis inferior* of Burdach—supposedly connecting the occipital with the parietal lobe; the upper portion—the superior longitudinal bundle, *fasciculus longitudinalis superior*—supposedly uniting the occipital with the parietal lobe (*see* chap. III, 5 [3]; chap. IV, 3 [2], 7 [4]).

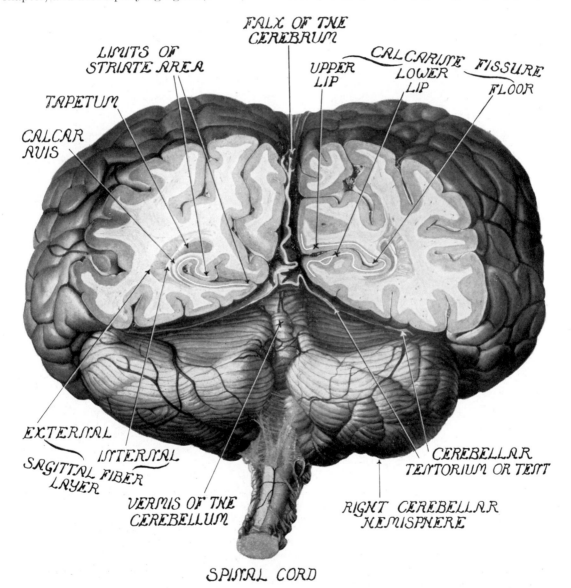

Fig. 228.—Back view of the human brain, with the caps of both occipital lobes cut off by a vertical section, in order to show on the cut surface the shape, size, and position of both calcarine fissures, the extent of the striate areae marked by white intracortical stripe of Gennari and Vicq-d'Azyr, the position of the sagittal fiber layers, which include the visual radiations, and other details. The *falx* or "sickle" of the dura mater of the brain's meningeal envelopes, and the tentorium of the cerebellum, both somewhat distorted, are left *in situ*. The translucent arachnoid and pial membranes covering the oblong medulla are also left in place. (*Cf.* preceding and following figures.)

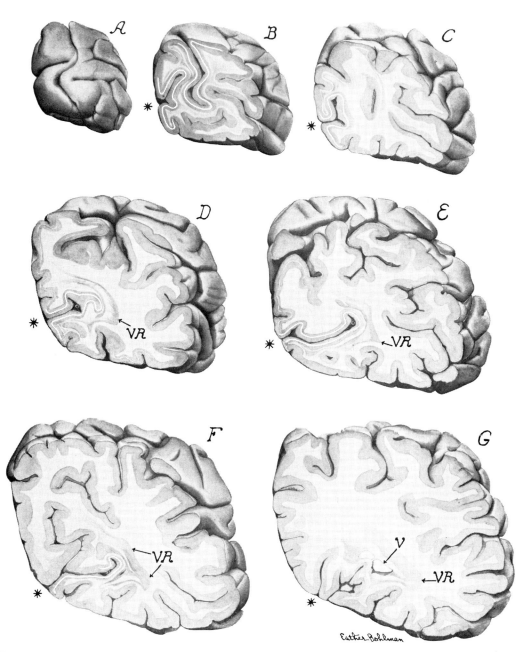

Fig. 229.—Sections through the right occipital lobe beginning with the pole (*A*) and terminating with the level passing through the posterior horn of the lateral ventricle (*G*). Note the calcarine fissure, marked with asterisks (*), representing in *G* a rather shallow sulcus medial to the lateral horn (*v*), not as yet lined by striate cortex; same fissure in *F* becoming quite deep and lined in its lower lip and floor with the striate cortex (identified by Gennari's white line), which extends from *E* on into the upper lip of the calcarine fissure and further expands over the lateral face of the occipital pole (in *B, A*), where it also lines the vertically placed lateral or posterior calcarine sulcus. *Labeling: v*, lateral ventricle; *vr*, saggital fiber layers which include the visual radiation. (*Cf.* Figs. 231, 232, 233, 271, 278, 288.)

The intermediate or internal sagittal stratum is composed largely of the efferent, or cortico-fugal, fibers arising in the para-peristriate area of G. Elliot Smith, or fields *18* and *19* of Brodmann, of the parieto-occipital lobes; it terminates in the subcortical centers, in part in the cap of the ipsilateral superior colliculus of the midbrain (*see* Fig. 268). The tapetum is made

The layer covering the calcar avis contains various fiber systems entering into, or leaving, the striate cortex, including the short subcortical association fibers of that and the adjoining cortical areae (Fig. 238).

The external sagittal stratum, in the anatomical sense, is not a pure afferent system, since efferent fibers of the internal stratum and also

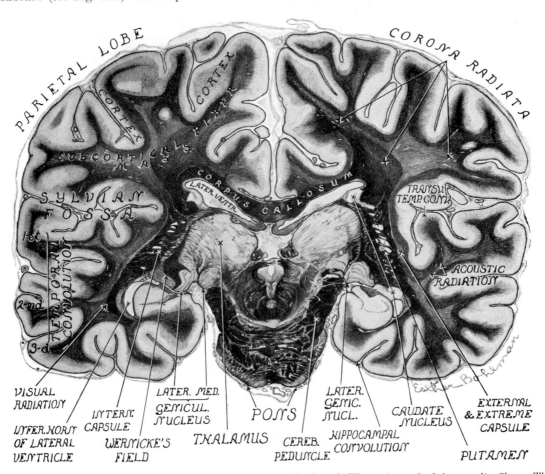

FIG. 230.—Coronal section through the human brain stained with Weigert's method for myelin fibers. The plane passes through both cerebral hemispheres, held in mid-line by the corpus callosum and by the brain stem. The parts of the visual system which are visible are the two lateral geniculate nuclei (next to the medial geniculate bodies, thalamus, cerebral peduncles, and internal capsule) and the visual radiations contained in the sagittal fiber layers of the temporal lobes (above and lateral to the inferior horns of the lateral ventricles). Note the meningeal covers; the gyri and sulci of the brain, lined with cerebral cortex, the core of the brain and of the gyri, made up of fiber systems, one of which is the visual radiation; the pronounced lamination of the lateral geniculate nuclei; and the topographical relations of the visible parts of the visual system. (*Cf.* following figures.)

up entirely of the ipsilateral and contralateral commissural fibers passing through the splenium of the corpus callosum from the occipital lobe of one hemisphere to that of the other (Fig. 267). A fourth layer, *stratum sagittale extremum*, just lateral to the external sagittal layer, has been distinguished by R. A. Pfeifer (1925).

the callosal fibers of the tapetum and numerous association fibers pass between its bundles to and from the respective points of the cortex which lines the upper, lateral, and lower faces of the parietotemporo-occipital region. The same is also true of the internal sagittal stratum, through which pass bundles of the callosal fiber system of the tapetum on their way to and from the cortex. (For further details on the visual radiation *see* the following sections in this chapter.)

The striate area, or the visual cortical center in the limited sense, recognizable without magnification by a sharp, whitish, intracortical stripe—the stria of Gennari and Vicq-d'Azyr or the outer stripe of Baillarger—is found in the calcarine fissures and around the poles of the occipital lobes. Its location and extent are given in Figures 226–29 and 231–33.

The position and extent of the striate areae over the occipital poles, in this case asymmetric, are shown in Figure 288. (*See* chap. VIII, 1 and 2, for further details on striate area.)

The two spacious cavities of the brain—the lateral ventricles, one in each hemisphere—are oriented longitudinally (Figs. 226, 227; *cf. also* Fig. 269). The rostral extremities of the lateral ventricles, called anterior horns, are close together and are separated from one another by a thin partition only—the pellucid septum—and by the anterior portion of the corpus callosum. The posterior extremities—the posterior horns —located in the occipital lobes, on the contrary, diverge from one another. The third expansion of the ventricular cavities—the inferior horns— are in the temporal lobes (Fig. 230). At the anterior ends, underneath the fornix, the lateral ventricles communicate by means of two passages—the foramens of Monro—with the third

ventricle, placed in the middle between the two thalami (Fig. 226). The third ventricle, in turn, communicates through the narrow, tubelike cerebral aqueduct of Sylvius with the fourth and hindmost of the cerebral cavities (*see* Fig. 269).

The cerebrospinal liquor or fluid, secreted by the chorioid plexuses, chiefly in the two large lateral ventricles, passes through the foramens of Monro to the third ventricle. From here the fluid enters through several small openings in the wall—the foramens of Luschka and of Magendie—in the subarachnoid space outside the brain, from which it is resorbed by Pacchioni's granulations into the venous blood system. In the living, the secretion of cerebrospinal fluid is continuous, and the ventricles are in a moderately expanded state. In an anatomical specimen, unless specially prepared, the ventricular cavities are often found collapsed, if they are not pathologically extended. (*See* Fig. 269 for the topography of cerebral ventricles in the living person.)

References: F. Arnold 1838–42; Brouwer 1917, 1936; Burdach 1819–26; Gratiolet 1854, 1855 (*see also* Leuret & Gratiolet 1839–57); Hochstetter 1942; Th. H. Huxley 1861; La Salle d'Archambault 1905, 1906, 1909; K. Löwenstein 1911; A. Meyer 1907; Monakow 1914; R. A. Pfeifer 1925, 1930; Polyak 1932; Putnam & Putnam 1926; Rasmussen 1943, 1945; H. Sachs 1892; A. Šercer 1951; Stauffenberg 1914; Trolard 1906; Vicq-d'Azyr 1805.

SEC. 3. ORIGIN, COURSE, AND TERMINATION OF THE VISUAL RADIATION IN GENERAL

1. Origin of the visual radiation in the laminated lateral geniculate nucleus.— The visual or optic radiations take their origin from the principal nerve cells of the laminated lateral geniculate nuclei of the betweenbrain (Fig. 180).

The details concerning the initial portion of the axis cylinders close to the geniculate cells, particularly whether or not they possess collateral branches and what course they take, where the termination of such collaterals may be, and also whether there is more than one variety of axis cylinder in the visual radiation— all unfortunately remain unsolved problems.

Only by circumstantial evidence—an absence of certain retrograde degeneration of nerve cells in the laminated nucleus in experiments and in human pathological cases where parts of the brain other than the visual radiation or the striate cortex were damaged—may the inference be drawn that there are no such collaterals or that, if present, they are short and probably terminate not far from the nerve cells in the nucleus itself.

The same experiments and pathological cases may also be adduced as evidence that the laminated lateral geniculate nucleus is the sole origin of the visual radiation and that the striate area is its exclusive terminal territory in the cerebral cortex. From the same evidence it is also apparent that the visual radiation, from its subcortical origin to its cortical termination, is strictly unilateral, no part of it crossing by way of the corpus callosum to the contralateral cerebral hemisphere. (For evidence *see* subsec. 4, this section, and secs. 4 and 5, this chapter; *see also* chap. XI, 8, 9.)

2. Course of visual radiation and its topographical relationships.—The initial portions of the axon fibers of the radiation at first pass through the layers of the lateral geniculate nucleus. Most of them emerge along its upper and lateral contours, a few along its medial contours, and apparently none along its lower contour (*cf.* chap. VI, 4 [3]).

After leaving the confines of the nucleus, the

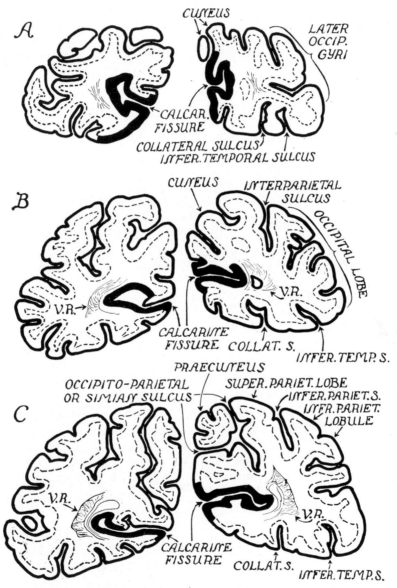

Fig. 231.—This and the following two figures show a succession of outlines of sections of the human brain, ⅓ inch apart, beginning with the occipital poles (in sketch *A*) and ending with the level of the lateral geniculate nuclei (in sketch *H* in Fig. 233). Note the position, size, and general topographic relations of the calcarine fissures of both sides and of the two striate areae (given in *solid black*), showing the extent and location of the same areae in the fissures; note also the topography of visual radiations (*V.R.*), from their beginnings in the lateral geniculate nuclei (in sketch *H*, in Fig. 233) to their terminations in the striate areae of the occipital lobes, and also the relation of the radiations to the lateral ventricles (*L.V.*) and to the gyri and sulci of the temporal lobes.

fibers fan out in various directions, mostly dorsally, laterally, anteriorly, and posteriorly, as they stream over to the posterior portion of the internal capsule. Here they form an almost complete circle around the lateral geniculate nucleus: perigeniculate fiber lamina. The broad dorsolateral segment of this fibrous ring is known as the triangular field of Wernicke (Fig. 230, left).

Posterior to its exit from the geniculate nucleus, in the *carrefour sensitif*, or "crossroad of the sensory pathways," of the French authors, the radiation is in immediate proximity to other important fiber systems (Fig. 237). One is the auditory radiation (*ar*), which, originating from the medial geniculate nucleus, slips just above and somewhat in front of the lateral geniculate nucleus on its way to Heschl's transverse temporal gyri (*Ttr*) of the Sylvian fossa (*FS*). The other is the somesthetic radiation (*sr*), which emerges from the lateral side of the thalamus and passes through the internal capsule to the cortex around the central sulcus of Rolando (*C*).

In this locality, where the three principal pathways are close together, they may all be easily damaged by a single lesion, e.g., a hemorrhage or encephalomalacia, resulting in an impairment of all three important functions: vision, audition, and bodily sensation; whereas closer to the cortex, where the three fiber systems are far apart, they may be damaged individually, if the lesion is small enough.

Outside the lateral geniculate nucleus the fibers of the visual radiation, assembled into bundles, are arranged in a thick, compact lamina in the posterior segment of the posterior limb of the internal capsule (Figs. 226–33). The position of this fiber lamina in the fibrous core of the temporal lobe is on the lateral side of, and somewhat slanting along, the inferior horn of the lateral ventricle (*V* and *L.V.*). The inferior margin or edge of this fiber lamina (*V.R.*) is bent in, with the concavity facing inward and parallel to the curve of this part of the ventricle. The bent-in lower edge of the lamina thins out into a narrow fiber sheet, which slips medially underneath the ventricle and becomes the core of the hippocampal gyrus (Fig. 230). It is very probable that the most inferior and medial bundles of this fiber lamina of the temporal lobe

are in no way concerned with the visual function.

In any case, the inferior margin of the sagittal fiber system of the temporal lobe comes to lie quite close to the floor of the inferior temporal and collateral sulci. The inferior segment of the visual radiation may, therefore, be easily damaged by any local pathological process spreading on the inferior face of the temporal lobe, involving an interference with its blood supply by a tumor, hemorrhage, encephalomalacia, abscess, mechanical injury, or other pathology (*cf.* sec. 8, this chapter, and chap. X).

In the occipital lobe the thick fiber sheet or lamina of the visual radiation, the most external of the three sagittal strata of Sachs, identical with Burdach's "inferior longitudinal fascicle," is found lateral to the posterior horn of the lateral ventricle (Figs. 228, 229). In coronal sections the external stratum includes in its concavity both inner sagittal strata, the tapetum, closest to the ventricle, and the internal—in fact, middle—sagittal stratum in between, which, together with the posterior horn of the lateral ventricle, are encircled by it from above, from below, and from the lateral side. To these must be added the deeper portion of the calcarine fissure and the fiber layer which covers that fissure on the ventricular side—the calcar avis.

The shape of the visual radiation changes considerably from level to level, resembling either an irregular horseshoe, a triangle, or a crescent with its concavity facing inward. It may be subdivided roughly into two or three segments: more posteriorly, close to the posterior limit of the ventricle, there is an upper and a lower segment; more anteriorly, through the occipital lobe, an upper, an intermediate, and a lower segment or branch are distinguishable.

The calcarine fissure, again, may be divided into an "upper or dorsal lip" and a "lower or ventral lip" (Fig. 228). The junction of the two lips is the "floor" of the fissure. It is this deepest portion, coated with a fiber layer, which protrudes into the ventricle and which, because of its peculiarly curved shape, noticeable in specimens cut horizontally or dissected, has been named calcar avis.

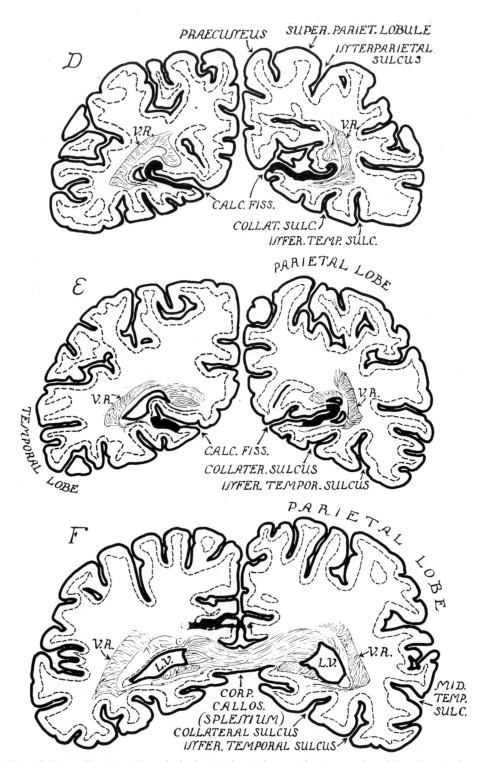

Fig. 232.—Outlines of sections through the human brain showing the topography of the calcarine fissures (*Calc. Fiss.*), striate areae (*solid black*), and visual radiations (*V.R.*) in the brain, and especially their relation to the posterior horn of the lateral ventricle (*L.V.*). (*Cf.* preceding and following figures.)

3. Functional segmentation of visual radiation.—An attentive examination of the coronal sections through the human or simian occipital lobe, stained for myelinated fibers, e.g., by Weigert's method or one of its modifications or according to Marchi's technique, reveals further details concerning the arrange-

ment and course of the visual radiation (Figs. 235, 236; and *see* par. 6, this section).

Those bundles which make up the upper segment of the external sagittal stratum gradually become medially displaced as the more posterior levels of the lobe are reached. After turning the upper corner of the lateral ventricle,

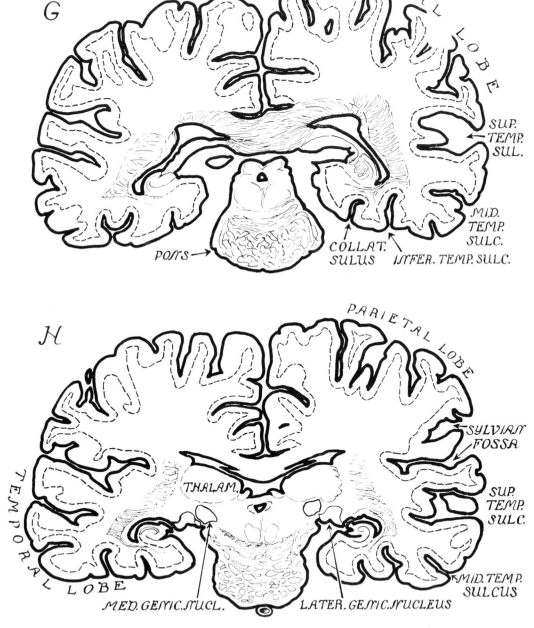

Fig. 233.—Outlines of sections through the human brain showing the topography of visual radiations, lateral geniculate nuclei, and lateral ventricles. (*Cf.* two preceding figures.)

these bundles finally slip into the upper lip of the calcarine fissure. A similar course is pursued by those bundles which form the lower segment of the radiation, except that they turn underneath the ventricle and thus pass beneath it into the lower lip of the calcarine fissure. The other fibers, those which are directly lateral to the ventricle and on most sections seemingly have no connection with the calcarine fissure, may be followed beyond the tip of the ventricle toward the pole of the occipital lobe.

The visual radiation, accordingly, is made up of several segments: the upper segment, which supplies the upper lip of the calcarine fissure; the lower segment, which supplies the lower lip; and the intermediate segment, which takes a more direct course along the lateral side of the ventricle to the occipital pole. As is apparent, the anterior portion of the striate area, closer to the splenium of the corpus callosum, is supplied by fibers which constitute the upper and lower segments of the radiation, while the intermediate segment of radiation supplies the striate cortex in the posterior portion of the calcarine fissure close to, and around the pole of, the occipital lobe.

Additional facts, especially those obtained experimentally, described in section 4, suggest a comparison of the visual radiation with a fan made up of many parallel ribs, each represented by a minute fiber bundle or segment of the radiation and each segment with a stable position relative to the other segments. The uppermost and the lowermost bundles of the fan are the first to turn medially around the lateral ventricle and enter the anteriormost portion of the striate area. The next upper and lower bundles, also turning above and below the ventricle, reach the next successive and somewhat more posterior segments of the striate cortex in the upper and lower calcarine lip, respectively; and so on. The intermediate bundles, which represent the axis of the fan, proceed directly to the farthest, posteriormost portion of the striate cortex at the occipital pole. Along the greater part of the calcarine fissure, bundles which turn above the ventricle and those which turn below meet in the fiber layer which coats the calcar avis along a line more or less corresponding to the floor of the calcarine fissure.

A simple principle of the "vertical articulation" just described, according to which the visual radiation is organized, in spite of the apparent irregularities and confusion, is strictly observed both in the Monkey and in Man. In the latter, however, this arrangement has to be somewhat qualified concerning the afferent fiber supply of the anteriormost portion of the striate area. Here the upper lip on a short stretch usually does not contain the striate cortex, this being confined to the lower lip alone (thus in Figs. 228, left side; 229, *F;* and 232, *D, E*).

Contrary to expectation, this portion of the striate cortex receives fibers not only from the lower segment of the visual radiation but also from the upper. The disagreement with the proposed scheme, however, is only apparent, as close study reveals: the fiber bundles deriving from the lower segment reach the inner half of the striate cortex closer to the inner edge of the lower calcarine lip, whereas the fibers from the upper segment of the radiation descend through the fiber layer coating the calcar avis and reach the outer half of the striate cortex closer to the floor of the calcarine fissure in the same lip. If the striate cortex be imagined as displaced in such a way that equal parts come to lie in both lips, the typical condition present in most of the calcarine fissure described in the preceding paragraphs would be restored.

The peculiar supply of the anterior portion of the striate area in Man, just described, makes possible an interruption of its afferent fibers by a single pathological focus, e.g., one situated underneath the lower calcarine lip or one destroying this lip directly, causing a defect in the extreme part of the contralateral field of view both above and below the horizontal meridian. (*See* sec. 8, this chapter, and chap. VIII, 3, for additional topographical details; *see also* chaps. XI, XII.)

4. UNILATERALITY OF VISUAL RADIATION.— The visual radiation is anatomically a unilateral fiber system, precisely as are the other great afferent fiber systems of the brain: the thalamocortical, auditory, and pyramidal-motor (*see* Polyak 1932). That is, no part of the radiation passes over to the contralateral hemisphere by way of the corpus callosum. The *fasciculus corporis callosi cruciatus* of Niessl von Mayendorf, R. A. Pfeifer, and others, does not exist. The

evidence in support of this view is experimental, pathological, and clinical.

When, in a monkey, one occipital lobe is removed, only the lateral geniculate nucleus of the same side degenerates in the retrograde sense, and it does so completely, with the contralateral geniculate nucleus retaining its normal appearance (Fig. 234). Also, whenever any portion of the radiation is interrupted experi-

eral homonymous halves of both retinae or contralateral homonymous halves of both fields of view. (*See* chaps. XI, 8, 9; XII; and XIII, 3, for the physiological and clinical implications, especially the cortical representation of the central fovea.)

5. Terminal area of the visual radiation in the cerebral cortex.—The terminal

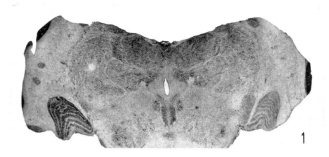

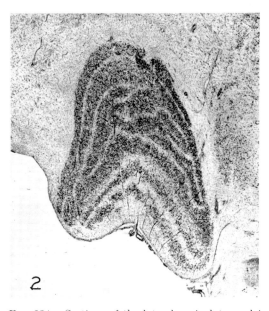

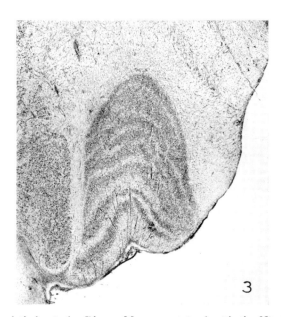

Fig. 234.—Sections of the lateral geniculate nuclei and thalami of a Rhesus Macaque stained with the Nissl method to show the origin of the visual radiation. The upper photo shows, at low magnification, the effect of the retrograde degeneration upon the nerve cells of the right-hand nucleus on the side where the occipital lobe, together with the striate area, was amputated and the visual radiation interrupted. On the opposite side, left, where no damage was done, the nucleus remained normal. The two lower photos show, at a somewhat higher magnification, on the left side the laminae of the lateral geniculate nucleus filled with normal cells, whereas on the operated right side the cells have been reduced in size and in their staining properties, the layers, in addition, being filled with greatly increased neuroglial cells. From S. Polyak, "A contribution to the cerebral representation of the retina," J. Comp. Neurol., v. 57, p. 541, 1933. (*Cf. also* Fig. 251.)

mentally, it can be followed to the occipital cortex of the same side only (Figs. 238–43). Functionally, however, because of a partial decussation of the optic nerve fibers in the chiasma, the visual radiation of each side represents ipsilat-

area of the visual radiation in the cerebral cortex is identical with the striate area of G. Elliot Smith, with Brodmann's field *17*, or with Economo's occipital area *OC*.

The evidence in support of this statement is

manifold (*see* Polyak, *The Main Afferent Fiber Systems of the Cerebral Cortex in Primates*, 1932). In experiments with monkeys, whenever a portion of the radiation was interrupted, degenerated fibers, without exception, entered the striate cortex, and that alone. The limits of the cortex supplied by the fibers of the visual radiation are sharp and are indicated by the stripe of Gennari and Vicq-d'Azyr (Figs. 238–43). In other experiments a retrograde degeneration in the laminated lateral geniculate nucleus of the same side was found exclusively when the striate area was damaged completely or in part (Figs. 252–58, and secs. 4, 5, this chapter; *also* Polyak 1933).

Observations of suitable human pathological cases agree with these experimental results (chap. XII). In these, the laminated lateral geniculate nucleus was found degenerated completely or in part only when the visual radiation or the striate area of the same side was affected by a pathological process. In cases where the para-peristriate areae were damaged without the involvement of the striate area, the lateral geniculate nucleus remained intact, the zones of degeneration having been found in the pulvinar of the thalamus.

6. Presentation of the visual radiation by dissection.—A useful method of demonstrating not only the origin, course, and termination of the visual radiation but also its basic internal or functional organization is a careful dissection or "teasing" of well-fixed and hardened brain specimens. Such "old-fashioned" preparations go a long way toward solving problems of long standing, which, by modern methods of serially stained sections, could be answered only by laborious plastic reconstruction.

The dissection method, used as a routine technique during the early period of modern brain research by Vicq-d'Azyr, Gall, Reil, Arnold, Foville, Gratiolet, Meynert, J. Henle, J. Stilling, and others, became largely outdated through the development of modern microscopy. A number of investigators, however, applied this method in modern times to the study of various fiber tracts of the brain, including the visual radiation: Trolard (1906), A. Meyer (1907, 1911), J. B. Johnston (1908), Curran (1909), H. J. H. Hoeve (1909), E. B. Jamieson (1909), Herrick & Crosby (1918), L. E. Davis (1921), S. W. Ranson (1921), H. Cushing (1922), Tandler (1926–29), Büttner (1927), C. Elze (1929), J. W. Hultkrantz (1929, 1935), and J. P. Martin (1937).

Lately the dissection method has been used by Rasmussen (1943) for a restudy of the question of the "temporal loop" of the visual radiation. According to the classical presentation by Flechsig (1896, 1920), repeated by A. Meyer (1907), Cushing (1922), R. A. Pfeifer (1925), and Elze (1929), those bundles which constitute the inferior segment or margin of the radiation, after emerging from the lateral geniculate nucleus, first turn anteriorly, toward the pole of the temporal lobe, before turning back to the occipital pole, describing, in Flechsig's designation, a "temporal knee" or, in A. Meyer's terminology, a "temporal loop" (*see* chap. IV, 3 [2]).

Confirming these and a similar observation of La Salle d'Archambault (1909), Rasmussen found the fibers of the visual radiation in the temporal lobe to extend anteriorly as far as the lateral surface of the amygdaloid nucleus and the vicinity of the anterior commissure and "almost as far anteriorly as the extreme tip of the inferior cornu of the lateral ventricle, in the roof and lateral wall of which they are located." The recurrent detour of the visual radiation proceeds anteriorly fully 2 cm. or almost 1 inch before again turning in the posterior direction.

The visual radiation and, in fact, the sagittal fiber layers of the posterior half of the human brain are a very definite anatomical entity, easily demonstrable by careful dissection of hardened specimens (Figs. 235, 236). In a lateral aspect, after scraping off most of the cortical substance from the lateral face of the hemisphere below the Sylvian fissure (*Sylv*) and the intraparietal sulcus (*is*), but leaving intact the cortex around the occipital pole, and after gradually peeling off the sheets of various systems of short association fibers which make up the core of that portion of the hemisphere, the visual radiation may be demonstrated in its entire extent.

The visual radiation—the classical "inferior longitudinal fascicle" of Burdach—appears as a broad, though relatively thin, lamina, composed

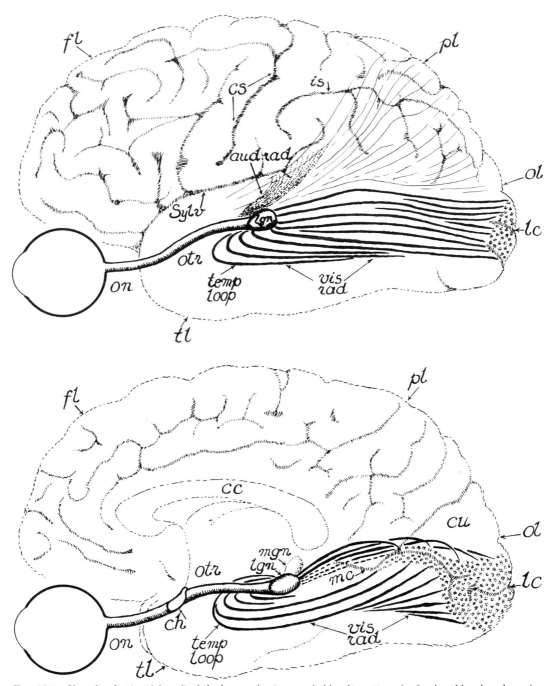

Fig. 235.—Visual radiation (*vis rad*) of the human brain revealed by dissection of a fixed and hardened specimen. Upper diagram represents a lateral aspect of the left hemisphere, lower diagram a medial aspect of the right hemisphere. Visual radiation given in thick lines, striate area in stippling. In the upper diagram bundles of fibers making up the radiation are arranged parallel to one another. They mostly follow a straight course from the lateral geniculate nucleus to the striate area at the occipital pole (*lc*). Lower bundles describe a detour of almost 1 inch, first being directed toward the pole of the temporal lobe (*tl*), then turning back again toward the occipital lobe: "temporal loop" of Flechsig and A. Meyer. The forming of a "temporal loop" and its entire course from its origin in the lateral geniculate nucleus to its termination in the lower lip of the calcarine fissure are shown in the lower diagram. Fibers that form the upper bundles of the visual radiation, not visible in the upper diagram, are seen in the lower diagram. They are shorter, have a straighter course, and terminate in the upper calcarine lip, in the cuneus (*cu*). Most of the striate area spreads over the medial face of the hemisphere along the calcarine fissure (*lower diagram*), only a small portion spreading over the occipital pole (*upper diagram*). Nonvisual radiations of the posterior half of the brain are indicated by thin lines, the auditory radiation by thin broken lines (*aud rad*). Note that the area of visual radiation, when projected on the lateral face of the hemisphere, remains well below the level of the Sylvian fissure (*Sylv*). (*Cf.* Figs. 182, 228–33, and especially Figs. 236, 269, and 271.) *Labeling: aud rad*, auditory radiation; *cc*, corpus callosum; *ch*, chiasma of optic nerves; *cs*, central sulcus; *cu*, cuneus; *fl*, frontal lobe; *lc*, lateral or posterior calcarine fissure; *lgn*, lateral geniculate nucleus; *mc*, medial or anterior calcarine fissure, separated in this specimen from the lateral calcarine fissure by a cuneo-lingual gyrus; *ol*, occipital lobe; *on*, optic nerve; *otr*, optic tract; *pl*, parietal lobe; *Sylv*, Sylvian fissure; *temp loop*, temporal loop of visual radiation; *tl*, temporal lobe; *vis rad*, visual radiation.

of a considerable number of rather thin, parallel fiber bundles (Fig. 235, upper diagram). The bundles extend in a fairly straight course from the region of the thalamus to the occipital pole, the length of the radiation amounting to considerably more than the posterior half of the length of the entire cerebrum. Anteriorly, the radiation approaches to within less than 1 inch from the anterior pole of the temporal lobe, whereas its lower margin is nowhere more than $\frac{1}{2}$ inch, and in the occipital lobe even less, from the inferior surface of the cerebral hemisphere. The uppermost bundles of the radiation, determined according to their point of origin in the lateral geniculate nucleus and their termination in the striate cortex, slightly bulging about midway of their longitudinal extent, remain well below the horizontal level of the Sylvian fissure.

The origin, course, and termination of each particular segment of the visual radiation or of the individual constituent bundles may be revealed more easily and more instructively by dissection than by serial sections. Such a preparation (Fig. 235, upper diagram) shows the lateral segment of the radiation, best seen from the lateral side, to be made up of bundles which pursue a fairly straight anterioposterior course. This segment, situated on the lateral side of the lateral ventricle, contains fibers related to the central fovea and area of the retina ("the macular bundle").

The lower bundles of the radiation, however, as they emerge from the lateral geniculate nucleus, are first seen directed anteriorly, toward the temporal pole. Slipping above the anterior horn of the ventricle, the bundles make a sharp turn laterally and backward—the "temporal loop"—and in this way come to lie on the lateral face of the ventricle. Gradually, these bundles slip underneath the ventricle and pass over to the lower lip of the calcarine fissure (Fig. 235, lower diagram).

Those bundles that form the upper segment of the radiation pursue a similar spiral course above the ventricle to reach the upper lip of the calcarine fissure. The only difference is that they do not form a "loop" but pursue a straight course back from their origin, bending only a little medially as they enter the upper calcarine lip (Fig. 235, lower diagram).

Altogether, the visual radiation can be seen to resemble a fiber fan made up of a great number of minute bundles exhibiting a remarkably orderly arrangement, with individual bundles arranged parallel to their neighbors and with hardly any mixing or intertwining of the bundles.

The fibers of the visual radiation are a part of the sagittal fiber system of the brain, with which they are continuous. The "inferior" and "superior longitudinal bundles" of the parieto-temporo-occipital lobes of the older anatomists as they appear in macroscopically dissected specimens are a single, solid fiber lamina, precisely as it appears in microscopic sections stained for fibers (Fig. 230). There are no visible features by which parts of this lamina belonging to the visual system may be distinguished from those serving other functions. The only criterion for such differentiation is the origin of a particular segment of this lamina in a subcortical nucleus with a known function, e.g., the lateral geniculate nucleus, and its termination in a cortical area whose functional significance is ascertained, e.g., the striate cortex. (*See* sec. 4, this chapter, for experiments on the functional organization of the visual radiation; *see* sec. 8, this chapter, for additional topographical data.)

References: Best 1919, 1920; Braus & Elze 1932–40; Bridgman & Smith 1945; Brouwer 1917, 1936; D. J. Cunningham (Le Gros Clark) 1943; Cushing 1922; L. E. Davis 1921; Dejerine 1895–1901; Edinger 1911; Elze 1929; Flechsig 1895, 1896, 1920, 1927; German & Brody 1940; German & Fox 1934; Gratiolet 1854, 1855 (*also* Leuret & Gratiolet, vol. 2, 1857); Hines 1942; Hösel 1905; G. Holmes 1919; Hultkrantz 1929, 1935; Hyndman 1939; Jamieson 1909; J. B. Johnston 1908; Juba 1935, 1944; La Salle d'Archambault 1905, 1906, 1909; Löwenstein 1911; Marburg 1910; I. P. Martin 1937; P. Martin 1925; L. L. Mayer 1940; A. Meyer 1907, 1911; Minkowski 1912, 1913, 1914, 1930, 1939; Monakow 1914; Niessl von Mayendorf 1903, 1905, 1907, 1914, 1920, 1921, 1926, 1930, 1932; Obersteiner 1912; Ostertag 1944; Papez 1942; R. A. Pfeifer 1925, 1930; Polyak 1932, 1933, 1941, 1948; Polyak & Hayashi 1936; Powell 1952; Probst 1906; Putnam & Putnam 1926; Ranson 1921; Rasmussen 1943, 1945;

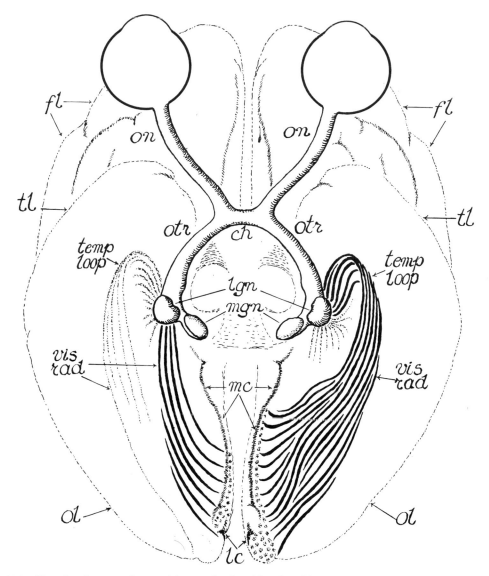

Fig. 236.—Visual radiations, dissected from a fixed and hardened human brain, in ventral aspect. In the right hemisphere (*left* in the figure) solid lines represent upper bundles of the right radiation originating from the medial segment of the lateral geniculate nucleus, pursuing a straight course and terminating in the upper calcarine lip. The lower bundles, which form the middle and lower segments of the radiation, are merely indicated by stippled lines. These bundles, which in part form Flechsig-Meyer's "loop" or "temporal detour," originating from the lateral and intermediate segments of the lateral geniculate nucleus, are drawn in solid lines in the left hemisphere (*right* in the figure), where they are seen to terminate in the lower calcarine lip and around the occipital pole. In each calcarine fissure only the lip or portion of the striate area supplied by the solidly drawn bundles of the radiation is indicated by stippling. Note straighter and shorter bundles supplying the upper lip (in the *left half*), and longer, detouring bundles supplying the lower calcarine lip (*right half* of the figure). (*Cf.* Figs. 182, 228–33, and especially Figs. 235, 269, and 271.) *Labeling: ch,* chiasma of optic nerves; *fl,* frontal lobe; *lc,* lateral or posterior calcarine fissure; *lgn,* lateral geniculate nucleus; *mc,* medial or anterior calcarine fissure; *mgn,* medial geniculate nucleus; *ol,* occipital lobe; *on,* optic nerve; *otr,* optic tract; *temp loop,* temporal loop of visual radiation; *tl,* temporal lobe; *vis rad,* visual radiation.

Redlich 1905; Rønne (Roenne) 1944; Rosett 1933, 1936; Rubinstein & Davis 1947; Sanford & Bair 1939; Settlage 1939; Stauffenberg 1914; J. Stilling 1882; Tandler 1926–29; Traquair 1922, 1931; Tsuchida 1907; Venderóvich (Wenderówič) 1916; Volkmann 1936; Zingerle 1911.

SEC. 4. FUNCTIONAL ORGANIZATION OF THE VISUAL RADIATION AND OF THE STRIATE AREA

1. TOPOGRAPHICAL PROJECTION, OR QUADRANTIC REPRESENTATION, OF THE RETINA IN THE SUPRANUCLEAR DIVISION OF THE VISUAL SYSTEM.—The surface of the retinal membranes is represented in the visual radiations and in the cerebral cortex according to a topographical

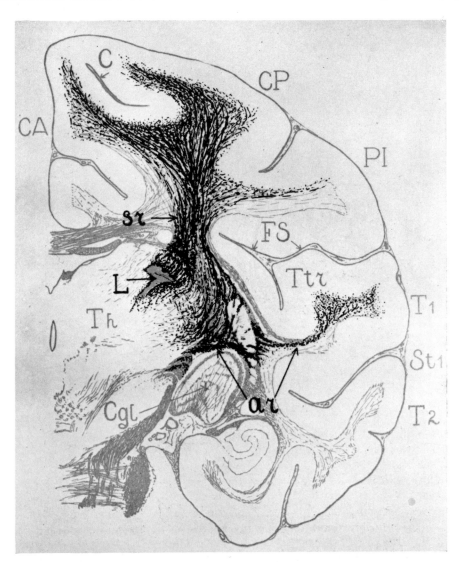

FIG. 237.—Section through the cerebral hemisphere of a Rhesus Macaque, where, in an experiment, a lesion *L* interrupted parts of the somesthetic (*sr*), auditory (*ar*), and visual radiations (*vr*, latter to be seen in subsequent sections), and the degenerated fibers were made visible by Marchi stain. *Labeling: ar*, auditory radiation; *C*, central sulcus of Rolando; *CA*, anterior central gyrus; *CP*, posterior central gyrus; *Cgl*, laminated lateral geniculate nucleus; *FS*, Sylvian fissure; *PI*, inferior parietal gyrus; *sr*, somesthetic radiation; *St1*, superior temporal sulcus; *Th*, thalamus; *T1, T2*, first and second temporal gyri; *Ttr*, transverse temporal gyrus of Heschl. This and the following Figs. 238–43 taken from S. Polyak, *The Main Afferent Fiber Systems of the Cerebral Cortex in Primates*, Berkeley, 1932.

principle or plan. According to this view, each minute area of the retina has its own discrete representation in the visual radiations and in the visual centers of the cerebral cortex, the striate areae of the occipital lobe.

The mode of the "projection" of the retinal surfaces in the infranuclear and nuclear divisions of the visual system was described in chapter VI, 7. Detailed evidence was also given in support of the concept of "retinotopical projection." In section 3 (preceding), anatomical evidence was adduced in support of the theory of the retinotopical organization of the visual radi-

How this idea originated and the opposition it met with, until it became generally recognized, was dealt with in the preceding pages (*see* chap. II, 6 [2], 10 [2], 11 [2, 6]; chap. III, 2 [4], 6 [2], 8 [4], 9 [7–9]; chap. IV, 1 [7], 4–7; chap. VI, 7).

The evidence from gross anatomical investigation which suggests a "vertical functional articulation" of the visual radiation was presented in section 3. Even more important is the evidence furnished by observation of human clinical cases in conjunction with the study of pathological material (*cf.* Part III, this book).

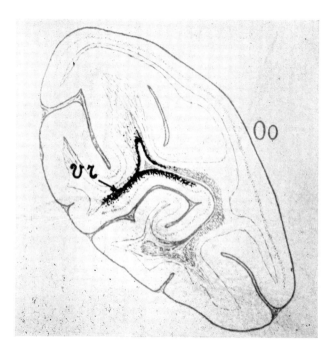

Fig. 238.—Cross-section of the occipital lobe of a Rhesus Macaque, showing the degenerated upper horizontal branch of the visual radiation (*black*), entering the upper lip of the calcarine fissure. Same experiment, Marchi stain. Note the extent of the striate cortex marked by a stippled line, supplied by the afferent visual fibers as far as its medial limit. *Labeling: Oo*, occipital operculum or occipital lobe; *vr*, visual radiation. (*Cf.* preceding figure.)

ation. Abundant clinical and pathoanatomical evidence in support of the same theory is presented in chapters XI and XII.

The accumulated evidence, anatomical and experimental, including cases of congruous homonymous hemianopic defects of the fields of view, particularly the quadrantic, and the "scotomas" or "blind patches" caused by unilateral injuries to the visual radiation or to the cortical center of vision, makes mandatory the acceptance of the concept of the detailed retinotopical organization of the visual system.

The anatomical and physiological experiments with monkeys and apes, of which a few are described in the following subsections, are of decisive importance because of the clarity of the procedure, which permits a detailed analysis of the visual pathway (for a complete presentation *see* Polyak 1932, and papers 1933 and 1936).

In these experiments both the visual radiation and the striate area were damaged in various ways. The resulting degeneration was then determined with the help of two technical procedures. In one, the degenerated fibers of the radiation, stained selectively by the Marchi method, were followed from the point of lesion, where they were interrupted, to the respective area in the cortex where they terminated; or a damaged portion of the radiation, after degenerated fibers had disappeared, was determined in serial sections treated by the Weigert method or one of its modifications for staining normal myelin fibers. The other procedure aimed at

In this way it was possible to determine for each major segment of the visual radiation, and thus indirectly for each retinal quadrant, its subcortical origin, its location and course within the fibrous core of the parietotemporo-occipital lobes, and its cortical termination in the striate area.

2. Origin, course, and termination of the upper segment of the visual radia-

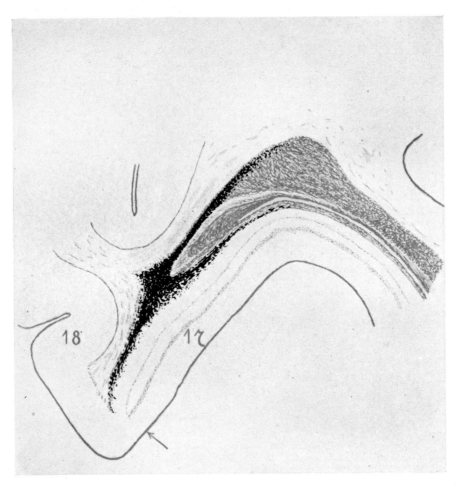

Fig. 239.—Upper lip of the calcarine fissure of a Rhesus Macaque showing the afferent fibers of visual radiation, made to degenerate experimentally, entering into that lip from the sagittal fiber layers of the occipital lobe. Marchi stain. Note the degenerated fibers passing over into the striate area as far medially (*to left*) as the stripe of Gennari (*stippled and marked with number 17*), beyond which point, marked with an arrow, no afferent degenerated fibers enter into the part of the cortex marked *18*, which is the parastriate area. Medium magnification. (*Cf.* preceding figures.)

producing restricted lesions in the striate cortex, with subsequent study of the resulting zones of retrograde degeneration in the laminated lateral geniculate nuclei, stained by the Nissl method.

tion.—When, in a monkey, a definite segment of the laminated lateral geniculate nucleus is destroyed, a well-defined portion or segment of the visual radiation degenerates. The degenerated fibers may be followed in serial sections as far as the terminal segment in the striate area of the occipital lobe of the same side. If the lesion is limited, for example, to the medial segment of the nucleus, the same area where fibers originating from the upper extrafoveal homonymous quadrants of both retinae terminate (as found in experiments described in chap. VI, 7), the upper segment or upper horizontal branch of

corner of the ventricle, then descend to the upper lip of the calcarine fissure, where they enter the striate cortex. The fiber bundles, which constitute the upper segment of the visual radiation, must accordingly describe a flat spiral turn above the posterior horn of the lateral ventricle, precisely as found in a dissected specimen of the human brain, in order to reach

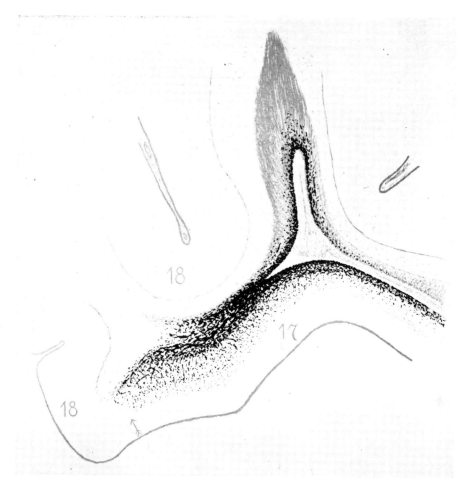

Fig. 240.—Similar experiment as in the preceding figure showing, in a Rhesus Macaque, degenerated fibers of the upper horizontal branch of the visual radiation entering the upper lip of the calcarine fissure. Note the abrupt cessation of fibers entering the striate area (*17*) at the point indicated by an arrow where the Gennari stripe ceases and the parastriate area (*18*) begins. Marchi method of staining, medium magnification. (*Cf.* preceding figures.)

the visual radiation degenerates (*vr*, in Figs. 238, 239, 240).

The degenerated fibers of this segment, stained black by the Marchi method and thus contrasting with the normal fibers, which remain unstained, gradually turn around the thick upper margin of the internal sagittal layer and of the tapetum, and around the upper

the upper lip of the calcarine fissure from their origin in the lateral geniculate nucleus (*see* Figs. 235, 236).

Since these bundles originate in the medial geniculate segment and since the destruction of the upper calcarine lip produces, in both Man and Monkey, a contralateral inferior quadrantic homonymous hemianopia, sparing the cen-

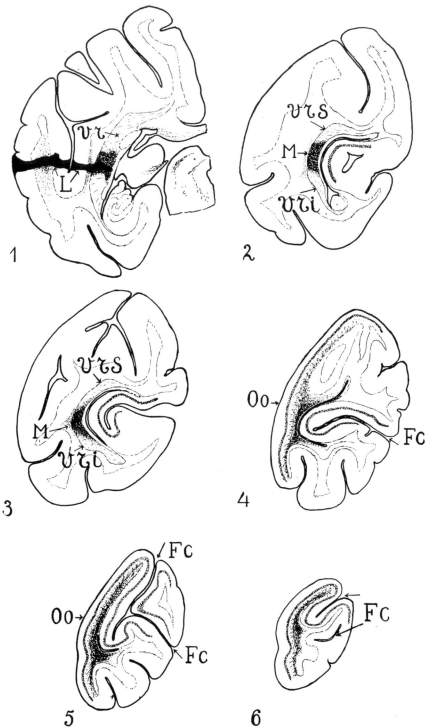

Fig. 241.—Sections through the occipital lobe of a Rhesus Macaque where a stabbing lesion (*L*) was made with Graefe's knife in one hemisphere at level *1*, which interrupted the intermediate foveal-macular segment (*M*) of the visual radiation. Note on subsequent posterior levels *2–6* the degenerated fibers passing over exclusively to the striate cortex on the lateral face of the occipital lobe (*Oo, left* in the figures), corresponding to the foveal-macular projection, leaving the upper and lower horizontal branches of the radiation (*vrs, vri*) and the two lips of the calcarine fissure (*Fc*) entirely free. The extent of the striate area or visual cortical center is indicated by the intra-cortical stripe of Gennari or Vicq-d'Azyr (*stippled line*). This experiment shows the intermediate branch of radiation and the opercular portion of striate area to belong, in the Monkey, to the central area and fovea, while the extrafoveal periphery is represented in the upper and lower branches of the radiation and in the anterior portion of the calcarine fissure, facing medially (*to the right*, in the figures). (*Cf.* preceding figures.)

ters of the fields of view around the fixation points, the conclusion is warranted that the upper segment of the visual radiation represents the upper extrafoveal quadrants of both homonymous retinal halves.

A duplicate of this experiment, with exactly the same result, may be attained when the lesion is located in the upper tier of the pos-

visual radiation; the adjoining parastriate area, or field *18*, beyond the limits of the stripe of Gennari and Vicq-d'Azyr, receives none (Figs. 239, 240).

When, in another experiment, the lesion, because it is in a slightly different location, interrupts a segment of the radiation somewhat closer to the axis of the fiber "fan," while leav-

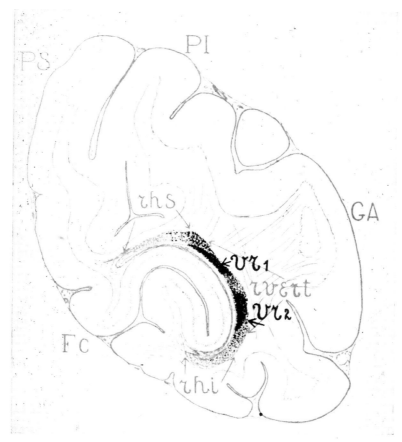

Fig. 242.—Another experiment in a Rhesus Macaque where two stabs were made with Graefe's knife in the intermediate or foveal-macular branch of the visual radiation (*rvert*), causing the degeneration of two fiber bundles (*vr1, vr2*), which could be separately followed to two distinct regions on the lateral face of the occipital lobe (*see* following figure). This experiment shows the composition of the visual radiation of nearly parallel fiber bundles which originate from distinct segments of the laminated lateral geniculate nucleus and terminate in distinct parts of the striate area. (*Cf.* Fig. 235). *Labeling: Fc*, calcarine fissure; *GA*, angular gyrus; *PI*, inferior parietal gyrus; *PS*, superior parietal gyrus; *rhi, rhs*, inferior and superior branches of the visual radiation; *rvert*, intermediate or vertical branch of the visual radiation. Marchi stain; low magnification. (*Cf.* preceding figures.)

terior limb of the internal capsule at some distance from the lateral geniculate nucleus. Here, too, the upper segment of the visual radiation alone degenerates and may be followed as far as the upper lip of the calcarine fissure.

These experiments, incidentally, also demonstrate that only the striate cortex, or Brodmann's field *17*, is supplied by the fibers of the

ing the marginal segment intact, the degenerated fibers are seen to stream to the posterior portion of the calcarine fissure around its ascending prong (Fig. 238). In the anterior portion of the fissure, only a narrow zone close to the floor receives degenerated fibers, whereas the marginal zone in the upper lip receives none. This experiment also shows that when a seg ment of the striate area on more posterior levels of the occipital lobe becomes marginal, the afferent fibers strictly observe the boundary of the striate cortex (*17*), marked by the stripe of Gennari and Vicq-d'Azyr (indicated in Fig. 239 by an arrow).

3. ORIGIN, COURSE, AND TERMINATION OF THE INTERMEDIATE OR AXIAL SEGMENT OF THE VISUAL RADIATION.—When a lesion (*L*, Fig.

lowing sections, the opercular portion of the striate area in the Monkey is homologous with the posterior or polar portion of the human brain, it is apparent that the intermediate or axial segment of the visual radiation is related to both ipsilateral homonymous hemifoveae and central hemiareae of the retinae.

By the same token, the upper and lower segments of the radiation that flank the intermediate or axial segment, which in this experiment

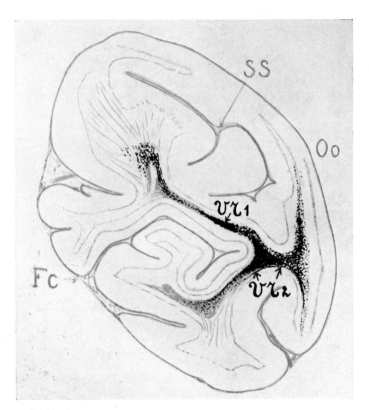

FIG. 243.—Section through the occipital lobe in the same experiment as in the preceding figure showing, on posterior levels, the Marchi-stained inferior degenerated fiber bundle (*vr2*) passing over to the lower segment of the striate area on the lateral face of the occipital lobe or operculum (*Oo*), while the upper bundle (*vr1*) reaches its destination in the upper segment of the same cortex, to appear on levels farther back. (*Cf.* preceding figures.)

241, sketch *1*) interrupts the intermediate or axial segment of the visual radiation (*M*), that segment alone degenerates, whereas the upper (*vrs*) and the lower (*vri*) segments remain normal. In such an experiment the degenerated fibers of the intermediate segment may be followed continuously to the occipital operculum (*Oo*).

Since, on the basis of comparative anatomy (*see* chap. VIII, 2, 3) and from the experiments described in the remainder of this and the fol-

remained unaffected, represent the extrafoveal and extra-areal parts of the homonymous halves of the two retinae. The similarity thus revealed between the position of the foveal-areal fibers in the radiation and the position of the "papillomacular bundle" of the retina, flanked from above and below by the arching extrafoveal bundles, found close to the optic papilla or disk, becomes apparent (*cf.* chap. VI, 2).

When, in another similar experiment, two small bundles not far from each other (*vr1* and *vr2*) are interrupted in the intermediate or axial segment of the radiation (*rvert*), they may be followed separately to two different localities of the occipital operculum (*Oo*), placed one above the other (Figs. 242, 243). As in the preceding experiment, here, too, no degenerated fibers pass to either lip of the calcarine fissure on the medial face of the hemisphere (*Fc*).

the lower lip of the calcarine fissure is underneath the lateral ventricle (Fig. 244).

When, in the Monkey, one temporal lobe is removed and the inferior segment of the visual radiation is interrupted, the ventrolateral segment of the laminated lateral geniculate nucleus is found to be degenerated (Fig. 244, *d*, in upper sketches; *cf. also* experiments in chap. VI, 7).

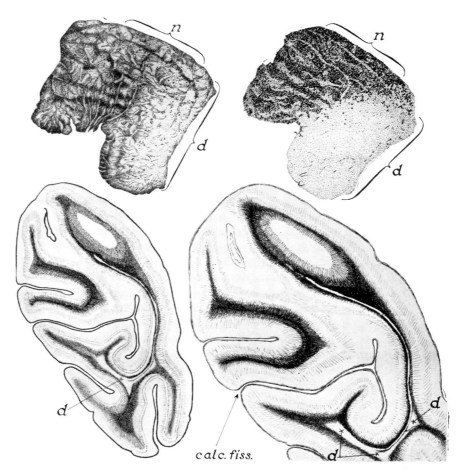

FIG. 244.—Sections through the lateral geniculate nucleus (*upper figures*) and through the occipital lobe (*lower figures*) of the brain of a Rhesus Macaque, where the temporal lobe of the same side was removed and the lower horizontal branch of the visual radiation was cut. As a consequence, the ventrolateral segment of the nucleus, *d* in upper sketches, degenerated in a retrograde sense, and in the occipital lobe the lower horizontal branch of the radiation, *d* in lower sketches, degenerated secondarily toward the striate cortex, specifically extending into the lower lip of the calcarine fissure (*calc.fiss.*). This experiment shows the origin of the lower horizontal branch of the visual radiation in the ventrolateral segment of the lateral geniculate nucleus and its termination in the striate cortex of the lower lip of the calcarine fissure.

4. Origin, course, and termination of the lower segment of the visual radiation.—Another experiment shows that the lower segment of the visual radiation originates in the ventrolateral segment of the laminated lateral geniculate nucleus and that its course to

The intermediate and dorsomedial segments of the geniculate nucleus, where the foveal-areal and upper extrafoveal fibers of the retinae terminate, are found to be normal (*n*). In the occipital lobe the lower segment of the external sagittal fiber layer is found to be devoid of fibers as far as the inferior calcarine lip (*d*, lower sketches, same figure).

5. Additional experiments on the retinotopical organization of the visual radiation.—Another and technically easier experimental method of analyzing the internal makeup of the supranuclear division of the visual pathway is to remove portions of the striate cortex of various sizes and from different locations and study the segments of the lateral geniculate nucleus showing retrograde degeneration. In these experiments it is preferable to use the Nissl method of staining.

When, with this purpose in mind, two lesions are made in a monkey on the medial side of the occipital lobe, the larger lesion undermining a substantial part of the striate cortex in the lower calcarine lip (marked with * in Figs. 245, 246) and the smaller lesion superficially damaging the striate cortex in the upper calcarine lip close to the ascending prong of the calcarine fissure (marked with # in same figures), two zones are found in the laminated lateral geniculate nucleus of the same side where cells have degenerated in the retrograde sense (Figs. 247, 251, photo *1*). The larger zone is located in the ventrolateral (*), the smaller zone in the ventromedial (#), segment of the nucleus.

This observation confirms, on the one hand, the projection of the lower extrafoveal quadrants upon the ventrolateral segment and of the upper extrafoveal quadrant of the two homonymous halves of the retinae upon the ventromedial segment of the lateral geniculate nucleus, as described in chapter VI, 7 (Fig. 225). On the other hand, the same experiment also confirms the origin and termination of the various segments of the visual radiation, as determined by a different technique in experiments presented in the preceding subsections of this section.

The large intermediate segment of the nucleus, flanked by the two partly degenerated segments, is found intact. It is in this segment where the foveal and central-areal fibers of the two retinae terminate, as found in chapter VI, 7. This observation corroborates the fact that the striate cortex over the occipital operculum was not interfered with. The evidence favoring the striate area over the simian occipital oper-

culum as the locality where the homonymous halves of the foveae and central areae are represented in turn corroborates its homology with the posterior portion of the human striate area close to, and at the pole of, the occipital lobe (*see* chap. VIII, 2, 3).

Positive evidence that the striate area, which lines the lateral convexity of the occipital lobe,

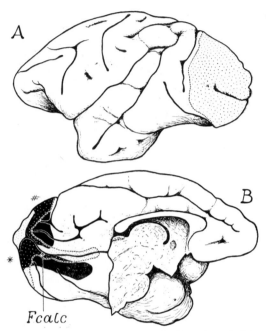

Fig. 245.—Lateral face (sketch *A*) and medial face (sketch *B*) of the brain of a Rhesus Macaque where both lips of the calcarine fissure (*Fcalc*) were undermined experimentally (*black*). The extent of the damage is presented in serial sections in the following figure, which shows the lesion in the lower calcarine lip, marked with an asterisk (*), larger than that in the upper lip (#). A larger and a smaller zone of retrograde degeneration in the ventrolateral and medial segments of the lateral geniculate nucleus of the same side were found, showing these segments to be related to the striate cortex of the two calcarine lips (*white stippling* in sketch *B*), while the occipital operculum (*black-stippled* area in *A*), where the foveal-macular fibers terminate, and the intermediate segment of the nucleus, where they originate, remained normal. (*Cf.* two following figures, and photo *1*, in Fig. 251.) (This and Figs. 246–58 taken from S. Polyak, "A contribution to the cerebral representation of the retina," J. Comp. Neurol., v. 57, p. 541, 1933.)

represents the homonymous foveal and central-areal halves of the two retinae is furnished by the following experiment.

A large portion of the cortex over one occipital operculum of a monkey was destroyed (Fig. 248, upper figure, lesion in solid black). There was also some damage done to the underlying vertical or intermediate segment of the visual radiation (Fig. 249). In the lateral geniculate nucleus of the same side, the intermediate segment was found solidly degenerated, while the lateral and medial segments remained normal (Fig. 248, lower figure; Fig. 250, degeneration given in black; *also* photos *2* and *4*, Fig. 251).

In this way the chain of experimental anatomical evidence is completed. It demonstrates

the same plan as in the Monkey. Here, too, the upper bundles arising from the medial portion of the laminated lateral geniculate nucleus terminate in the upper lip, and the lower bundles originating in the lateral portion of the geniculate nucleus terminate in the lower lip of the calcarine fissure. Those bundles which arise from the intermediate segment of the nucleus and represent the axis of the radiation terminate in the posterior portion of the striate area

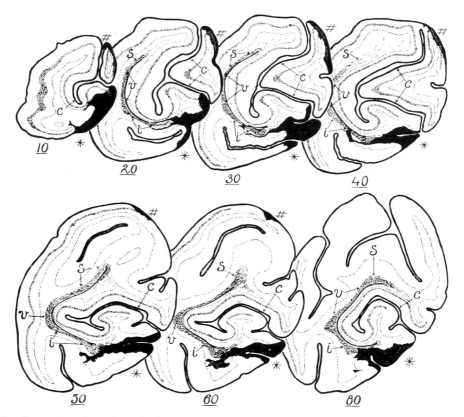

FIG. 246.—Coronal sections through the occipital lobe of a Rhesus Macaque, approximately equally spaced, showing the two lesions in the upper and lower lips of the calcarine fissure (*c*) made experimentally (* and #; *see* preceding figure). The lesion in the lower lip (*i*) is more extensive than that in the upper lip, the first also undermining the lower horizontal branch of the visual radiation, the other damaging only superficially the striate cortex, recognizable by the stippled intracortical stripe of Gennari. The upper (*s*) and the vertical branches (*v*) of the radiation remained undamaged. As a consequence, a larger (*) and a smaller zone (#) of retrograde cell degeneration were found in the lateral geniculate nucleus of the same side, showing the relationship of the two cortical and geniculate localities to each other. (*Cf.* following figure.)

a discrete representation, by quadrants, of the extrafoveal periphery of the homonymous retinal halves and of the central foveae, both in the visual radiation and in the visual cortical center, the striate area of the occipital lobes (Figs. 259, 260).

In Man the gross arrangement of the segments of the visual radiation follows essentially

at the occipital pole. A study of carefully dissected brain specimens (Figs. 235, 236), with the analysis of the pathological cases described in Part III of this book, does not leave any doubt on this point.

As an over-all result, the positive evidence indicates that the two peripheral receptor surfaces—the retinae—are represented in the two striate areae and in no other territory of the cerebral cortex. They are here represented not *in toto*, as O. Foerster (1929) imagined, but according to a strictly topographical principle; each single point of the monocular portion of one retina and each two "corresponding points" of the binocular portions of both retinae are represented in a single locality of either the one or the other striate area.

Outside the striate area the retinae are not represented either globally or in detail. This must be especially emphasized in connection with the central fovea-area, or "macula," for which a "second representation" outside the striate area, possibly outside the occipital lobe, has been claimed (Monakow, Balado *et al.*, Hyndman, Putnam, Fox & German, and others). The evidence reveals the fovea to be represented, like the remainder of the retina, in its own discrete segment of the striate area, namely, at the occipital pole. (*See* chap. XI, 8, 9, and chap. XII, 10, for additional discussion of the prob-

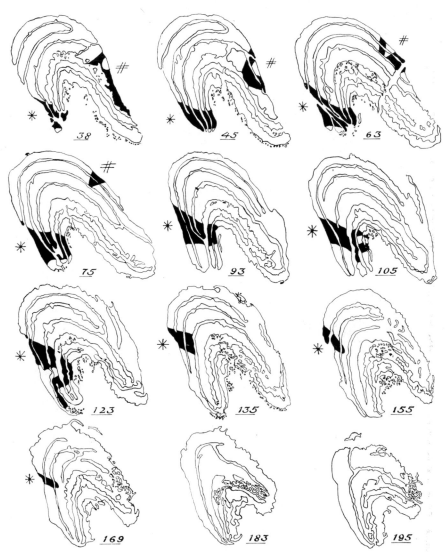

Fig. 247.—Serial sections through the lateral geniculate nucleus of the same cerebral hemisphere where two lesions were made, the larger in the lower lip and the smaller in the upper lip of the calcarine fissure (*see* preceding figures). In the lateral geniculate nucleus two zones were found where the cells degenerated in a retrograde sense: a more extensive one in the ventrolateral segment (*) and a smaller one in the medial segment (#). This experiment, where a different method was used, shows a topographical relationship of the upper and lower calcarine lips to the medial and lateral segments of the lateral geniculate nucleus, demonstrating a discrete cortical representation of the retinal surface in the striate area of the occipital lobes. (*Cf.* Figs. 237–44.)

lem of cortical representation of the fovea-macula.)

References: Ariëns Kappers, Huber & Crosby 1936; Balado, Adrogue & Franke 1928; Balado & Franke 1933, 1937; Balado & Malbrán 1932; Braus & Elze 1940; Brouwer 1917, 1936; Brouwer, Heuven & Biemond 1929; Elze 1929; Evans 1939; O. Foerster 1929; Fox & German 1936; Hartline 1942; Henschen 1890–1930, 1923, 1926; Hines 1942; Hoff & Pötzl 1935; G. Holmes 1918, 1919, 1931, 1934; Hyndman 1939; Juba 1934, 1935, 1944; Klüver 1927, 1942; Lashley 1942; Marshall & Talbot 1942; Minkowski 1911, 1913, 1914, 1920, 1930, 1939; Monbrun 1919; Morax 1919; Morax, Moreau & Castelain 1919; Papez 1942; Penard 1935; R. A. Pfeifer 1925, 1930; Pötzl 1918, 1928; Polyak 1932, 1933, 1941 (1948), 1942; Polyak & Hayashi; Putnam & Liebman 1942; Putnam & Putnam 1926; Rønne (Roenne) 1917, 1919, 1944; Rogalski 1946; Traquair 1922; Van Heuven 1929; J. Warschawski 1927; Weekers 1928. (*See* chap. IV, 4 and 7, and chaps. XI, XII for additional references, especially clinical.)

SEC. 5. ELEMENTAL COMPOSITION OF THE VISUAL RADIATION AND THE TRANSMISSION OF RETINAL IMAGES TO THE CEREBRAL CORTEX

1. GENERAL EVIDENCE IN SUPPORT OF DETAILED RETINOTOPICAL ORGANIZATION OF THE VISUAL RADIATION.—In the preceding sections

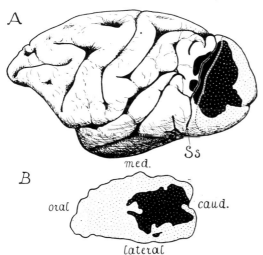

FIG. 248.—Lateral face of the brain of a Rhesus Macaque (sketch *A*), where a single lesion, shown in black, was made in the striate area (*stippled*) of the occipital operculum along the simian sulcus (*Ss*). In the lateral geniculate nucleus of the same side a zone of retrograde cell degeneration (*black*) was found in the intermediate or foveal-macular segment, shown serially in Fig. 250, whose dorsal view is given in sketch *B*. This experiment shows the projection of the intermediate segment of the nucleus, and hence of the fovea-macula, upon the portion of the striate area located on the lateral face of the occipital operculum, a homologue of the occipital pole in the human brain. (*Cf.* following figures.)

of this chapter experimental anatomical evidence has been adduced in substantiation of the claim that the upper and lower extrafoveal quadrants of the homonymous halves of both retinae and also the homonymous halves of

both central foveae and areae are separately represented in the visual radiation and in the striate area. It is now necessary to examine whether the representation of the surface of the two retinae in the laminated lateral geniculate nuclei, in the visual radiations, and in the striate areae is more than roughly quadrantic, and, if so, whether the minuteness or the "grain" of the cortical representation approaches the one theoretically postulated. (*See* chap. IV, 4, on the problem of retinal representation in the brain.)

A general indication that the retinal representation in the visual radiation and in the striate area is more than "global" or roughly quadrantic is evidenced by a sharp linear demarcation between the normal and degenerated fiber segments in the radiation or between the zones of the normal and degenerated cells in the laminated lateral geniculate nucleus. This is the rule, no matter what the size and location of the segments or zones, provided that the lesions in the radiation or in the striate area are well defined. Such localized and sharply outlined zones of degeneration as those depicted, e.g., in Figs. 251 (*2, 4*) and 255, are difficult to reconcile with the hypothesis of a diffuse, haphazard arrangement of the conductor units. They agree, however, with the concept of an orderly two-dimensional or "spatial" arrangement both of the nerve cells and of their axis cylinders or fibers on a cross-section through the supranuclear division of the visual pathway, in a way similar to that found in the infranuclear division (chap. VI, 7).

2. Experiments on detailed anatomical representation of the retinal surface in the visual radiation and in the striate area.—In order to determine experimentally how detailed the intrinsic organization of the visual radiation was, several minute lesions were made in the striate area of a monkey on the convex, lateral aspect of the occipital lobe, the "occipital operculum" (*a, b, c, d,* in Fig. 252, upper figure). The lesions were small enough to be confined to the cortex without involving the subcortical fiber substance and were separated from one another by strips of normal cortex (Fig. 253). They varied somewhat in shape and in size, which facilitated the identification of the resulting zones of degeneration.

between the latter and the lowermost lesion (*d*), which, in turn, was closest to the inferior boundary of the striate area.

In the laminated lateral geniculate nucleus of the same side, cut serially, four minute zones of degeneration were found, each passing through all six cell layers (Fig. 254; *also* Fig. 255). These zones closely correspond with the four lesions in size and location. Zone *a* was closest to the posterior extremity and in the ventrolateral half of the nucleus (sketches *2–5*). Beyond the gap of forty sections there were three other zones (*b, c, d*) running almost parallel with one another and at somewhat varying distances from one another: the distance between *b* and *c* was only half that between *c* and

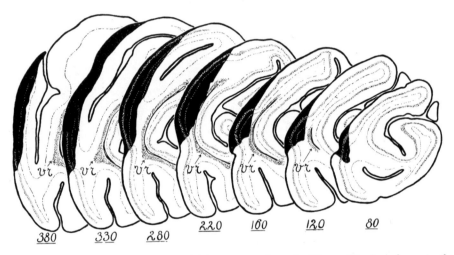

Fig. 249.—Serial sections through the occipital lobe or operculum of a Rhesus Monkey shown in the preceding figure, to demonstrate the extent of the lesion (*black*) and the damage done to the striate area (*stippled*) and to the visual radiation (*vr*). Since in this experiment the opercular portion of the striate area, or its fibers in the vertical branch of the radiation, alone suffered damage, the zone of retrograde degeneration also was confined to the intermediate or foveal-macular segment of the lateral geniculate nucleus. The striate area is identified by the stippled intracortical stripe of Gennari. (*Cf.* preceding and following figures.)

The principal feature of each lesion was its location in the striate area. Of the four lesions which in this particular experiment produced recognizable zones of retrograde degeneration in the laminated lateral geniculate nucleus, the smallest lesion (*a*) was closest to the anterior boundary of the striate area along the simian sulcus (*Ss*). The other three lesions (*b, c, d*) were all farther back and at about the same distance from that sulcus. The largest of these (*b*) was close to the superior margin of the hemisphere. The distance separating it from the middle lesion (*c*) was smaller than the distance

d. Also, all four zones were located in the somewhat smaller posterior half of the nucleus (secs. *264–390*), the anterior half of the nucleus showing no degeneration (secs. *391–600*).

Considering the topographical relationship between the retinal surface and the laminated lateral geniculate nucleus found in the preceding experiments (chap. VI, 7) and the relationships between that nucleus and the visual radiation and striate area described in sections 3 and 4 in this chapter, the interpretation of this experiment offers no difficulties. The confinement of all four zones of degeneration to the posterior half of the nucleus is obviously because all four lesions are located in the external, opercular portion of the striate area, which, in the Monkey, represents the homonymous halves of the central areae and foveae, as pointed out in section 4 (3) in this chapter, and in chapter VIII, 2, 3.

Zone *a*, closest to the posterior tip of the nucleus, shown in the right lower sketch in Figure

the simian sulcus *Ss*. The relative distances between these three zones and their relative sizes are also an accurate copy of the sizes and distances between the three lesions in the striate area. Taking all these facts together, it is obvious that the zones of degeneration in the lateral geniculate nucleus in this experiment are, in all particulars, an accurate copy of the lesions made in the striate area of the same side.

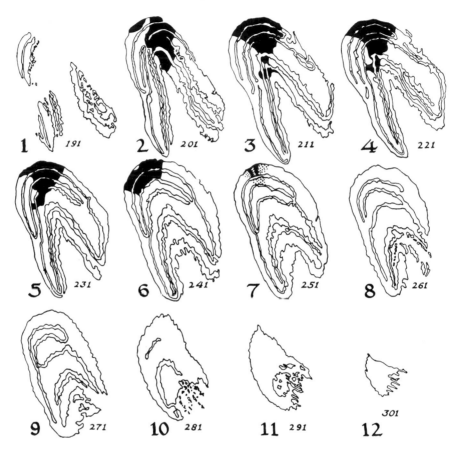

Fig. 250.—Serial sections through the lateral geniculate nucleus from its posterior (*1*) to its anterior extremity (*12*), from the experiment with a Rhesus Macaque where a single lesion was made in the occipital operculum of the brain (Fig. 248). A single zone of solidly degenerated nerve cells was found in the intermediate segment of the nucleus, showing this locality and the operculum to be related to the foveal-macular, or "central," vision. (*Cf.* preceding figures, and photos *2* and *4* in the following figure.)

252, standing alone, in its relationships resembles lesion *a* close to the "anterior," but, actually, the posterior, limit of the striate area which represents the vertical meridians. Zones *b*, *c*, and *d* are all found at approximately the same distance from the caudal tip of the nucleus, just as the corresponding three lesions are located at about the same distance from the "posterior" boundary of the striate area along

The foregoing experiment and other similar experiments clearly suggest a stable two-dimensional arrangement of the minute fiber bundles in the visual radiation, beginning with their geniculate origins and extending to their respective terminations in the striate area. The principle which seems to be strictly observed is that the fibers which originate from the adjoining cell groups in the geniculate nucleus also ter

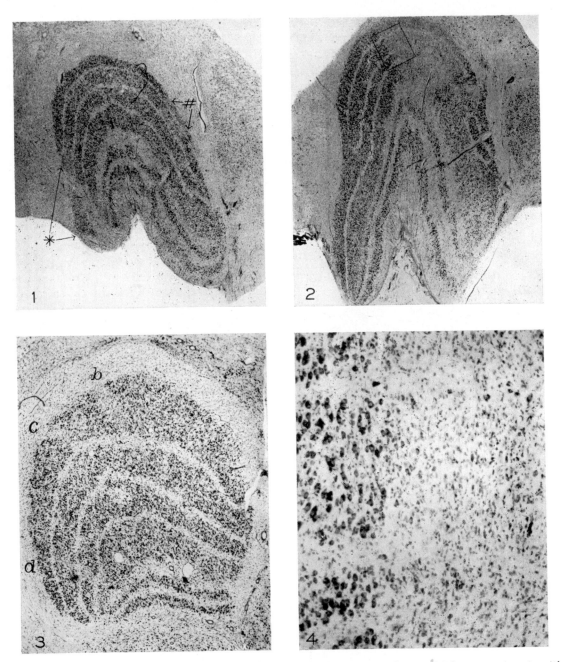

F_{IG}. 251.—Microphotographs of Nissl-stained sections of the lateral geniculate nuclei from experiments with variously located lesions in the visual system of the Rhesus Macaque to show the resulting zones of retrograde cell degeneration. Photo *1* from the experiment where two lesions were made in the calcarine fissure, resulting in two degenerated zones, a larger one in the ventrolateral segment (*) and a smaller one in the medial segment (#) of the nucleus (*cf.* Figs. 245, 246, 247). Photos *2* and *4* show a single zone in the intermediate segment at low and high magnification; note shrunken and poorly stained nerve cells and increased neuroglial nuclei (*cf.* Figs. 248, 249, 250). Photo *3* shows three of the four minute zones of retrograde degeneration in the lateral geniculate nucleus (*b, c, d*) of a Rhesus Macaque, where the opercular striate area was slightly damaged in four places (*cf.* Figs. 252–55). Note the remarkably straight, almost linear, demarcations of the zones of degeneration.

minate close together in the striate area. Since exactly the same arrangement, except for the crossing of the nasal fibers in the chiasma and

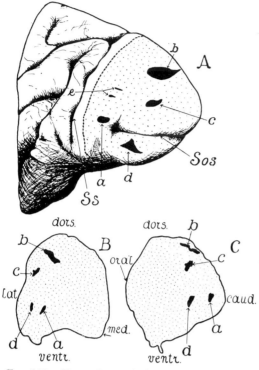

FIG. 252.—Upper figure *A* shows a lateral aspect of the left occipital lobe or operculum of a Rhesus Macaque with four small lesions (*a, b, c, d*) made in the foveal-macular portion of the striate area (*stippled*), its boundary parallel to the simian sulcus (*Ss*), the occipital lobe showing a slight horizontal dent: the incipient lateral calcarine sulcus (*Sos*) further discussed in chap. VIII. The four lesions caused cells to degenerate in four minute zones of the lateral geniculate nucleus of the same side which, in their size and topographic arrangement, were a replica of the four cortical lesions. The two additional lesions *e*, because of their almost microscopic size and superficial location, however, did not reveal themselves by a noticeable retrograde degeneration. Sketch *B* shows a posterior aspect, sketch *C* a lateral aspect, of a plastic model of the left lateral geniculate nucleus, with the surface arrangement of the four degenerated zones as follows: zone *a*, smallest of the four zones, was located close to the posterior tip of the nucleus, since lesion *a* was close to the anterior limit of the striate area; the larger three zones, *b, c,* and *d*, were located in front of it and arranged in a straight line, as were the three larger lesions in sketch *A*. (*Cf.* following four figures.) *Labeling: caud,* caudal or posterior extremity of lateral geniculate nucleus; *dors,* dorsal or upper extremity of same; *lat,* lateral side of same; *med,* medial side of lateral geniculate nucleus; *oral,* oral or anterior extremity of same nucleus; *Sos,* lateral calcarine sulcus; *Ss,* simian sulcus; *ventr,* ventral or inferior face of lateral geniculate nucleus. (For further details *see* S. Polyak, "A contribution to the cerebral representation of the retina," J. Comp. Neurol., v. 57, p. 541, 1933.)

their doubling-up in the tracts with the uncrossed fibers, is present in the infranuclear and nuclear divisions of the visual system, the conclusion cannot be avoided that the distribution of the functional units in the striate areae resembles their distribution in the retinal membranes.

The only points in which the fidelity of the cortical representation of the retinae, in addition to the doubling-up of the ipsilateral and contralateral homonymous fibers, needs to be qualified are the relative sizes of the units and their slight shifting or displacement in order to become adapted to a different surface configuration in the cortex.

In the retina, owing to the compelling physical factor—the nature of light—the foveal units are very small, especially in the central fovea, gradually increasing in size in the extrafoveal regions. In the striate area, where space is less severely restricted and function obviously demands a greater mass of the nervous substance in each unit, exactly the opposite is true, the units gradually increasing in size toward the fixation points. The mass of the functional units and the number of constituent cells are very much greater in the central nervous system than in the peripheral.

3. EXPERIMENTAL ANATOMICAL EVIDENCE FOR A TRANSMISSION OF "FIGURES" FROM THE LATERAL GENICULATE NUCLEUS TO THE CEREBRAL CORTEX.—In order to verify the correctness of the deduction made from the preceding experiments, various lesions, resembling simple figures, were made in the occipital operculum in a number of monkeys. Due consideration was given, first, to the blood supply, also that the lesions remained cortical, and, finally, that they were not complicated by damage to the intervening cortex.

In the following experiment the "cortical figure" resembled a reversed letter *C* (Fig. 256, upper figure *A*). When the occipital operculum of the simian brain is imagined turned back and the striate area spread in one plane, a condition is created resembling that normally found in the human brain. In this case, the **C**-shaped lesion was located in the posterior foveal-areal portion of the striate area, the concavity of the letter facing the corpus callosum (lower sketch *C*).

In the lateral geniculate nucleus of the same side, in the posterior half, a complex zone of retrograde degeneration was found (Fig. 258). In spite of its complexity, when taking into account the information obtained from the preceding experiments it was possible to make an accurate correlation between various parts of

The result of this experiment shows that the arrangement of the cell and fiber units which compose the supranuclear division of the visual system is very detailed, permitting an accurate transmission of two-dimensional retinal "figures," greatly varying in shape, size, and location, via the laminated lateral geniculate nucleus to the striate area of the same side. This

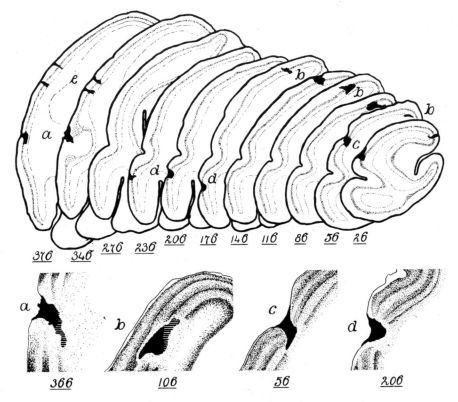

FIG. 253.—Upper diagram shows serial sections through the left occipital lobe of a Rhesus Macaque (Fig. 252), with the four small lesions of the striate area, *a*, *b*, *c*, and *d*, resulting in four minute zones of retrograde degeneration in the lateral geniculate nucleus (Fig. 254), and the two almost microscopic lesions *e* whose zones could not be detected. The four sketches in the lower row show, slightly magnified, the four lesions where they attain their maximum size. Note the smooth boundaries of the lesions and their almost strict limitation to the cortex. (*Cf.* preceding and following figures.)

the cortical lesion and the geniculate zone of degeneration.

Particularly striking was the similarity between the lesion in the striate area and the zone of degeneration in a model of the lateral geniculate nucleus. Presented in this way, the zone of degeneration, in its location and shape, appeared as only a slightly distorted replica of the cortical lesion (Fig. 256, middle sketch *B*).

agrees with clinical experience and recent physiological experiments.

References: Best 1919, 1920; Brouwer 1936; Henschen 1890–1930, 1923, 1926; Hines 1942; Lashley 1942; Marshall & Talbot 1942; Minkowski 1930, 1939; Penard 1935; R. A. Pfeifer 1925, 1930; Polyak 1932, 1933, 1941–48, 1942; Rønne (Roenne) 1944; Wilbrand 1925, 1925–26, 1930; Wilbrand & Saenger 1899–1927.

SEC. 6. SUMMARY OF THE INTRINSIC ORGANIZATION OF THE SUPRANUCLEAR DIVISION OF THE VERTEBRATE VISUAL SYSTEM

1. GENERAL REMARKS.—The visual system of Man and other Primates and of the Vertebrates in general is a well-defined and elaborately organized system of neurons (Fig. 180). It is composed of three subdivisions, an infra- and a supranuclear and an intermediate linking the two.

The infranuclear division is represented by the photoreceptors and other nerve cells that constitute the retinal membranes, including the

axis cylinders of the retinal ganglion cells, commonly called optic nerve fibers. These fibers form the two optic nerves, their junction, or the chiasma, and the two optic tracts. The chiasma, specifically its middle portion, is made up of decussating fibers which originate in the larger nasal halves; its lateral parts consist of the non-decussating fibers originating from the smaller temporal halves of the two retinae. The optic tracts, accordingly, are mixed, each tract con-

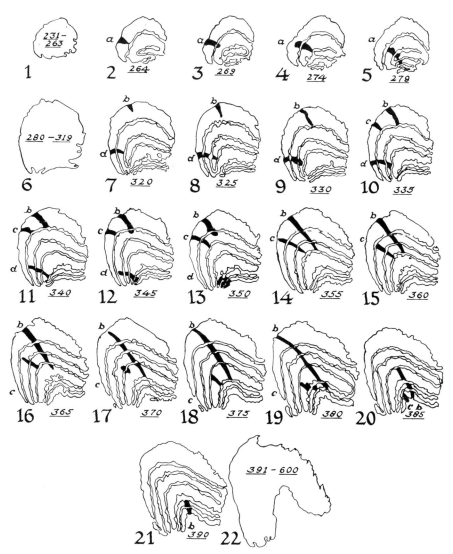

FIG. 254.—Serial sections through the lateral geniculate nucleus of a Rhesus Macaque from its posterior tip (*1*) to its anterior extremity (*22*), showing the four retrograde zones of degeneration caused by the four minute lesions made in the striate area of the occipital operculum (Figs. 252, 253). The size and the location of the zones are in fair agreement with those of the four lesions shown in the preceding figures.

taining both decussating and nondecussating fibers originating in the ipsilateral homonymous halves of both retinae.

The optic nerve fibers terminate in the subcortical visual centers of the brain stem, which represent the intermediate or nuclear division of the visual system. There are at least four such centers in each half of the brain: the laminated

cleus, the identical homonymous decussating and nondecussating fiber bundles terminate close to each other in segments of two sets of separate but adjacent cell laminae.

The supranuclear division of the visual system is represented by the axis cylinders originating from the nerve cells of the laminated lateral geniculate nuclei. Other extensive fiber sys-

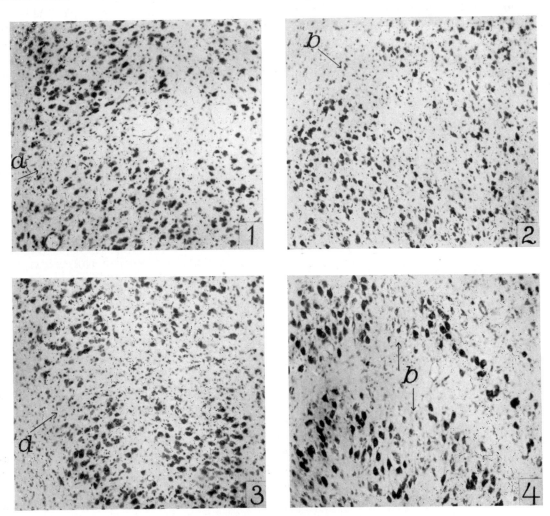

FIG. 255.—Microphotographs of three of the four minute zones found in the lateral geniculate nucleus of a Rhesus Macaque where the nerve cells degenerated in a retrograde sense, in an experiment where four small lesions were made in the striate area of the occipital operculum. Note advanced state of shrinkage of the nerve cells, straight boundaries of the zones, their passage through several cell laminae, and an increase in neuroglial nuclei in the zones. This experiment shows the detailed "projection," or representation, of very small territories of the retinal surface upon the striate area, or visual center, of the brain. (*Cf.* Fig. 251, photo *3*, and Figs. 252, 253, 254.)

lateral geniculate nucleus or body, which is the principal station; the gray pregeniculate (and parageniculate) nucleus; the superior colliculus of the midbrain; and the pulvinar of the thalamus. In the laminated lateral geniculate nu-

tems which originate in the pulvinars of the thalami, as far as is known, are not concerned with the direct transmission of unmodified visual impulses to the cerebral cortex and may therefore not be regarded as parts of the afferent

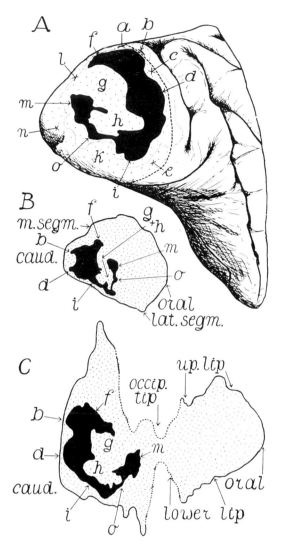

FIG. 256.—Upper sketch *A* shows a lateral view of the posterior portion of the right hemisphere of the brain of a Rhesus Macaque with the **C**-shaped lesion (*black*) made in the striate area (*stippled*) of the occipital operculum. Lower sketch *C* shows the entire right-sided striate area spread in a single plane, showing the position of the **C**-shaped lesion in the posterior opercular portion of the area. The middle sketch, *B*, shows the upper aspect of a plastic model of the right lateral geniculate nucleus, with the location of the retrograde degeneration, caused by the lesion in the striate area. The lettering, identical in all three sketches, shows the various details of the lesion or of the degeneration. Note great similarity between the lesion and the zone of degeneration (which, however, are inverted in sketches *B* and *C*). This experiment furnishes evidence in support of the "point-to-point representation" of the retinal surface in the visual cortical center, which makes possible an accurate transmission of images from the eyes to the brain. (*Cf.* following figures.) *Labeling: caud,* caudal or posterior extremity; *lat.segm.,* lateral seg-

visual pathway in the usual restricted sense. The pregeniculate nuclei and the superior colliculi give rise to fibers which do not pass over to the cerebral cortex.

The fibers which originate in the laminated lateral geniculate nuclei form the visual radiations contained in the external sagittal fiber layers of the parietotemporo-occipital lobes. Each visual radiation is strictly a unilateral system, no part of it crossing to the contralateral hemisphere by way of the corpus callosum. The "decussating callosal bundle" of Heine, Niessl von Mayendorf, Pfeifer, and others does not exist.

The fibers of the visual radiation terminate in the cortex, which lines the calcarine fissures as far as the poles of the two occipital lobes. The terminal areae coincide with the striate areae, distinguished by the white intracortical stripe of Gennari or Vicq-d'Azyr. No portion of cortex outside the striate areae receives afferent visual fibers.

2. RETINOTOPICAL ORGANIZATION OF THE SUPRANUCLEAR DIVISION OF THE VISUAL SYSTEM.—From its origin in the laminated lateral geniculate nuclei to its termination in the striate areae of the cerebral cortex, the supranuclear division of the visual system is elaborately organized topographically. In this way the detailed two-dimensional representation or "projection" of the retinal surfaces is continued as far as the striate areae (Figs. 259, 260; *cf.* Fig. 225).

The arrangement or representation of the retinal quadrants on various levels is as follows: the right upper extrafoveal-areal homonymous binocular quadrants of both retinae (black with white shading in *LR* and *RR*, Fig. 259) are in the dorsomedial segment; the right lower extrafoveal-areal quadrants of the retinae are in the ventrolateral segment; the corresponding homonymous quadrants of the central foveae and areae are in the intermediate segment; the extreme nasal monocular portion of the left retina

ment of lateral geniculate nucleus; *lower lip,* lower lip of calcarine fissure; *n.segm.,* medial segment of lateral geniculate nucleus; *occip.tip, o.t.,* pole of occipital lobe; *oral o.,* anterior extremity of lateral geniculate nucleus; *up.lip,* upper lip of calcarine fissure.

is in the lower inner edge, of the right optic tract (right *OT*).

In the right laminated lateral geniculate nucleus (right *LGN*) the arrangement is the same, except that the lateral and medial extrafoveal-areal segments decrease, while the intermediate foveal-areal segment increases in size toward the posterior extremity of the nucleus. Topographical representation is also present in the pregeniculate nucleus and in the superior colliculus.

In the right visual radiation (right *VR*) and in the calcarine striate area of the right occipital lobe (*RSA*) the upper and lower right homonymous retinal quadrants are represented in a

mous retinal quadrants. The zones or belts of the right homonymous halves of both hemiretinae are arranged in succession along the right half of the horizontal meridians, approximately corresponding to the floor of the calcarine fissure of the right occipital lobe (*f–HM* and *f–hm*).

The most peripheral nasal monocular portion of the left retina (in *LR*) is represented in the anteriormost segment (close to the right-hand *HM* or *hm*, in *RSA*), the foveal centers in the posteriormost, polar portion (next to *f*), with the remainder arranged in an orderly manner, zone after zone, in the rest of the right striate area.

The fixation points are at the occipital pole

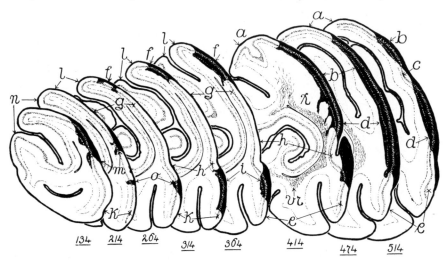

FIG. 257.—Serial sections through the occipital lobe of the preceding figure, to show location and extent of the lesion (*black*) in the striate cortex indicated by the presence of a stippled cortical stripe of Gennari or Vicq-d'Azyr. Note that in only a few localities the lesion extends as far as the sagittal fiber layers containing visual radiation, *vr* (thus at *x* in section *414*), remaining in other sections confined to the striate cortex and its immediate vicinity. (*Cf.* preceding and following figures.)

similar way: the upper extrafoveal-areal quadrants in the upper segment, the lower extrafoveal-areal quadrants in the lower segment, and the foveal-areal quadrants in the intermediate or axial segment of the radiation, flanked by the two extrafoveal-areal segments.

The foveal-areal fibers, accordingly, fill in the "anatomical interval of radiation" of G. Holmes (1918, 1931) in the same way as the "papillomacular bundle" does in the retina, as suggested by H. Rønne (1919).

In the striate area of the right calcarine fissure, the upper lip approximately represents the upper, the lower lip the lower, right homony-

(*f*), the right halves of both horizontal retinal and field meridians (*HM*, *hm*) approximately along the floor of the right calcarine fissure, whereas the principal vertical meridians are identical with the posterior boundary of the striate area at the right occipital pole (*VM*, *vm*).

The left homonymous halves of both retinae (lightly shaded in *LR* and *RR*) are symmetrically represented in the same way in the optic tract, lateral geniculate nucleus, visual radiation, and striate area of the left cerebral hemisphere (left sketches in Figs. 259, 260).

The representation of the surface of the retinal membranes in the visual pathways and centers, however, is not merely by quadrants but is much more detailed, approaching, in fact, a physiologically postulated point-to-point representation. The entire afferent visual system may be compared to a complex cable made up of individual conductors arranged throughout the whole system essentially according to the same plan.

small, numerous, and close together. Farther away they are larger and separated by larger intervals. The keys in each keyboard are grouped from the center to the periphery along the meridians, each having its own definite space value in the two-dimensional plane of the keyboard.

In the initial portion of the system, in the two optic nerves, the same approximate relative

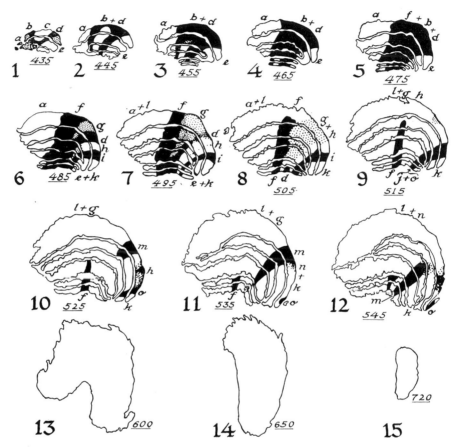

Fig. 258.—Serial sections through the lateral geniculate nucleus of the right side from its posterior (*1*) to its anterior extremity (*15*), to show the location and extent of the complex zone of retrograde degeneration caused by the **C**-shaped lesion in the occipital operculum. The lettering makes possible the identification and correlation of the various parts of the zone and of the lesion. Note the passing of the zone (*black*) through all cell layers of the nucleus down to the hilum, and its confinement to the posterior half of the nucleus (from section *435–545*). (*Cf.* preceding two figures.)

The two peripheral photoreceptors—the retinae—may be compared in this respect with two large keyboards made up of hardly less than one hundred thousand keys each. Every key is connected by its own independent conductor to the subcortical intermediate station and, through it, to the terminal station in the cortex. In the centers of the keyboards the keys are very

arrangement as in the retinal keyboards obtains. This is also true of the next section, the optic tracts, except for the decussation of the nasal fibers and their joining with the fibers which do not decussate.

In the subcortical relay stations—the lateral geniculate nuclei—the isodynamic or synergical bundles of fibers originating from the "corre-

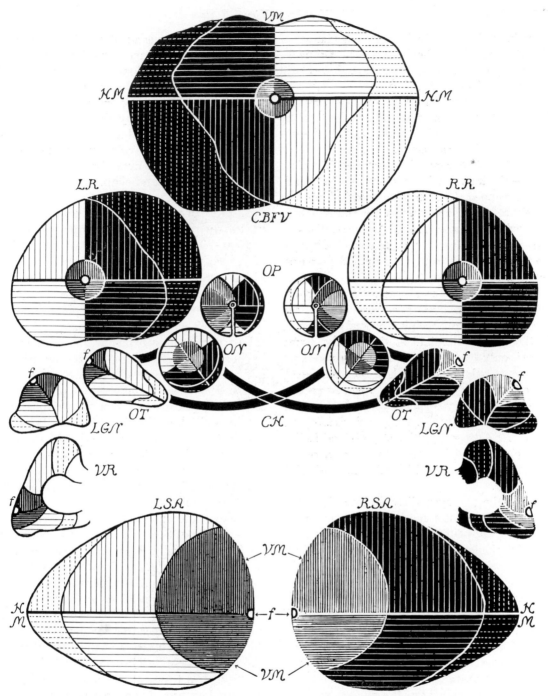

Fig. 259.—Topographic representation or "projection" of the common binocular field of view (*CBFV*, *above*), and of the left and right retinal surfaces (*LR*, *RR*) in the visual pathways and centers of the brain, in Man and in other Primates. The two monocular fields of view, superimposed over each other as in the normal binocular vision, are divided by a vertical meridian (*VM*) into a right and a left half, and again each half is subdivided by a horizontal meridian (*HM*) into an upper and a lower quadrant. A small white circle in the very center indicates the point of fixation. The next circle surrounding it, divided into four small quadrants, represents the central fovea (relatively much enlarged). The largest complete circle represents the extrafoveal parts of the binocular field of view. It is flanked on each side by the monocular temporal crescents. Each half and each quadrant are marked in the same way throughout the entire scheme: in the two retinae (*RR*, *LR*), optic papillae or disks (*OP*), optic nerves (*ON*), chiasma (*CH*), optic tracts (*OT*), lateral geniculate nuclei (*LGN*), visual radiations (*VR*), and the striate areae of the brain (*RSA*, *LSA*). The position of the fixation points (*f*), vertical and horizontal meridians, their approximate orientation in each locality, and the relative size of each quadrant are also indicated. (*Cf.* Figs. 125, 260, 381.)

sponding points" of the homonymous halves of the two peripheral keyboards—the retinae—come very close together, even though they still preserve their identity.

In the supranuclear division, the arrangement of the units on cross-section through the conductor cables—the visual radiations—remains essentially the same.

On the two central screens—the striate areae—the individual conductor units are similarly arranged. The terminal cortical pattern closely repeats the pattern of the retinal receptor keyboards, except for the nonessential displacement required by a somewhat different shape and surface configuration of the cerebral hemispheres.

There are, however, also some important differences. Whereas in the peripheral organs—the eyes—there are two recipient retinal keyboards, in the central terminal station in the cortex there is only a single screen; for each striate area represents only half, though of both retinae. If the common binocular field of view, as present in the normal physiological visual act, be considered (*CBFV*, in Fig. 259), each striate area (*LSA*, *RSA*) sees only the contralateral half of this field. Both striate areae together, therefore, represent a complete binocular field of view (Fig. 439).

Since the two eyes, directed by a delicately adjusted visuomotor mechanism, always work in unison, they function somewhat in the manner of a single median "cyclopean eye" of appropriate size. It is therefore logical to consider the two striate areae also as a single complete cortical center—in fact, as a single "cerebral eye." (*See* chap. XIII, 3, for further details.)

Another difference concerns the relative size of the functional units. In the peripheral receptor keyboards of the two retinae—because of the peculiar character of the physical stimulus, light, to be responded to—the smallest units are in the central foveae; in the terminal cortical screens, on the contrary, the largest functional units are found in those portions of the striate areae where the hemifoveae are represented. In the striate areae the foveal portions appear to be relatively larger and expanded, in comparison with the extra-areal periphery, which is relatively reduced in size. This again raises the question of the importance of the mass, or volume, of the nervous substance in the working of the visual system and of the brain in general. The apparent functional superiority of the foveal cortex as manifested in the "fixation points" last to become extinguished in general narcosis, and so probably also in death, may be based upon the much larger size of the foveal cortex and its relatively greater resistance, which results from a much better blood supply (*cf.* chap. X, 6, 8, and chap. XI, 8, 9).

3. Physiological implications of the retinotopical organization of the visual system.—The foremost functional consequence of the elaborate intrinsic organization of the visual system described in the preceding subsections and sections of this chapter and in chapter VI, 7, is that whenever a single point or, in the binocular visual act, two syndynamical "identical or corresponding points" of both retinal keyboards are stimulated, a message arrives, and a signal flashes in a single, definite locality of the central screen, always in precisely the same point (mostly in one of the striate areae).

The position of the signal is fixed, being determined by the relative position of the activated key or keys with respect to the center or centers, the fixation points, and the meridians of the two peripheral receptor keyboards as the points and lines of reference.

Briefly, the number, arrangement, size, shape, and position of messages flashed upon the "cerebral eye" will be fairly accurate copies or replicas of the "figures" painted on the two retinal keyboards. Whatever other structures there are to serve special visual functions, such as an eliciting of special reflexes and a reciprocal influencing of the receptor and conductor units, the intrinsic organization of the afferent visual pathway makes possible a maximum of fidelity of the figures transmitted from the retinae to the visual centers of the cerebral cortex.

The other and hardly less important functional consequence of the intrinsic organization of the afferent visual pathway is the automatic fusion of both images, separately caught on the two retinae, into a single image painted upon the cyclopean cerebral eye. (*See* chap. XIII, 3, for further elaboration of this theme.)

References: Austin, Lewey & Grant 1949; Best 1919, 1920, 1930; Braus & Elze 1940;

Brouwer 1926, 1930, 1936; Brouwer & Zeeman 1925, 1926; Le Gros Clark 1942; O. Foerster 1929; Foerster & Penfield 1930; Helmholtz 1924–25; Henschen 1890–1930, 1923, 1926; Hines 1942; Hoff & Pötzl 1934; G. Holmes 1918; Jacobsohn-Lask 1924, 1928; Klüver 1927, 1942; Lashley 1942; Lenz 1924, 1926, 1927; Marshall & Talbot 1942; Minkowski 1930, 1939; Monbrun 1919; Penfield & Rasmussen 1950; R. A. Pfeifer 1925, 1930; Pötzl 1918, 1928; Polyak 1932, 1933, 1941–48, 1942; Polyak & Hayashi 1936; S. Ramón y Cajal 1899, 1899–1904, 1909–11; Rønne (Roenne) 1919, 1944; Warschawski 1927; Wilbrand 1925, 1925–26, 1927, 1930; Wilbrand & Saenger 1899–1927, 1918.

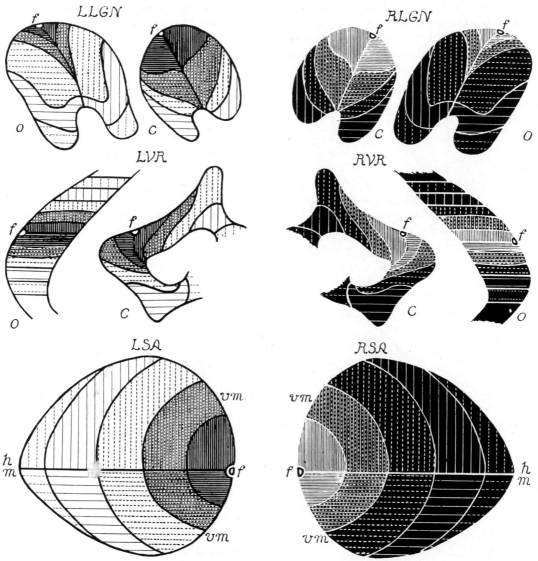

FIG. 260.—Topographic representation or "projection" of the right and left lateral geniculate nucleus (*RLGN*, *LLGN*) in the right and left visual radiation (*RVR*, *LVR*) and in the right and left striate area (*RSA*, *LSA*) in the brain of a Rhesus Macaque, determined experimentally. Shading of the quadrants similar to that in Figs. 225, 259. In the nuclei and in the radiations two levels are represented, an oral or anterior (*o*) and a caudal or posterior (*c*). In the striate areae the pointed extremities at *hm* are oral or anterior, the blunt ends facing each other correspond to the posterior extremities next to the simian sulci or, in Man, at the poles of the occipital lobes, where fixation points (*f*) and vertical meridians (*vm*) are represented. The central foveae around the fixation points (*densely shaded*) have a distinct representation next to the central areae (next zones, shaded with straight and broken lines). Note the relatively large size of the central foveae and areae on all levels, in comparison with the extra-areal peripheries, and a relative shrinkage of the inferior halves, in comparison with the upper halves of the fields.

SEC. 7. CONNECTIONS OF THE STRIATE AREA OR VISUAL CORTEX WITH OTHER PARTS OF THE BRAIN

1. GENERAL REMARKS.—The impulses generated in the peripheral photoreceptor organs of the visual system—the retinal membranes of the eyes—are transmitted along the optic nerves, chiasma, and tracts to the laminated geniculate nuclei of the betweenbrain, and from these nuclei, traveling along the visual radiations, they eventually reach the striate areae of the occipital lobes of the brain. The striate areae, accordingly, are the "gateways" through which the retinal impulses enter the cortex and

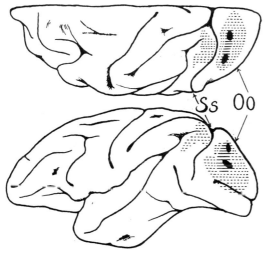

FIG. 261.—Upper and lateral views of the left hemisphere of the brain of a Rhesus Macaque, where two small and strictly cortical lesions in the striate area (*black oval patches*) were made experimental, in order to determine the territories which receive association fibers: the larger shaded area indicates the portion of the striate area, the smaller shaded area indicates the portion of the para-peristriate areae relayed to the two localities destroyed. *Labeling: Oo*, occipital lobe or operculum; *Ss*, simian sulcus. For the course and termination of fibers *see* Figs. 262–66. From S. Polyak, *The Main Afferent Fiber Systems*, etc., Berkeley, 1932.

from which they are further distributed to other cortical areae and regions.

Other visual subcortical stations—the hypothalamus, the pregeniculate gray nucleus, the pulvinar of the thalamus, the superior colliculi, and possibly the adjoining parts of the midbrain—do not participate in the transmission of retinal impulses to the cortex, partly because of their scanty connections with the visual system (pulvinar) and partly owing to the fact that

their connections remain subcortical (pregeniculate nucleus, superior colliculus). The various sidetracks supposedly connecting the laminated nucleus to the thalamus, described by some investigators (Ferraro 1926; Klossowski 1930), have also not been substantiated either by the normal anatomical methods of investigation or by experiment.

From the evidence adduced in this and the preceding chapter it is fairly certain that the only avenue by which retinal impulses reach the cerebral cortex is the visual radiation or that part of the visual system mediated by the laminated lateral geniculate nuclei and terminating in the striate areae along the calcarine fissures.

In order to pursue further the course of the retinal impulses, it is necessary to follow the connections of the striate cortex, or Brodmann's field *17*. From a general knowledge of the structural organization of the brain, the striate area may be expected to be connected with other parts as follows: (1) by short relays from neuron to neuron, this connection remaining wholly confined to the substance of the cortex, or intracortical; (2) by subcortical association fibers of various lengths arising from the nerve cells residing in the striate cortex and passing into the white subcortical fibrous substance, eventually terminating in the extrastriate cortical areae surrounding the striate area of their origin, and at different distances from it, all in the same cerebral hemisphere; (3) by commissural fibers arising in the striate cortex of one cerebral hemisphere and decussating by way of the corpus callosum to the opposite hemisphere, where they may terminate in the contralateral striate area, producing a "homotopical connection," or in any one or a group of the extrastriate areae, thus establishing a "heterotopic connection," or in both the striate and the extrastriate areae of the cortex; (4) by fibers arising in the striate cortex and descending to any one, or to several, of the many subcortical structures in the core of the brain and the brain stem, such as the caudate nucleus, the putamen and globus pallidus of the striate body, the thalamus and other parts of the betweenbrain, parts of the midbrain, especially the superior colliculi, and possibly elsewhere; (5) in the reverse, by association fibers arising in any one of the several extrastriate cortical areae of the same cerebral hemisphere and terminating in the striate area; (6) in the reverse, by the callosal commissural fibers originating either in the striate area or in the extrastriate areae or in both of the contralateral cerebral hemispheres; (7) in the reverse, by the fibers originating in one of the subcortical structures other than the laminated lateral geniculate nucleus and ascending to one or to both striate areae.

On the basis of probability, it may be expected that not all the possibilities mentioned are actually realized. The presence of some connections and the absence of others may give important indications as to which way the retinal impulses spread and what their functional significance may be.

In the following a single example based on experiments with monkeys is presented. A complete survey of the outgoing and incoming fiber connections of the striate area is a problem which, because of its magnitude, must remain outside the framework of the present book. Its importance should make it an attractive object of a special investigation.

2. ASSOCIATION FIBERS OF THE VISUAL CORTEX.—When a few minute lesions are made in a Rhesus Macaque, measuring from 1 to 2 mm. in diameter and strictly localized to the striate cortex of one occipital lobe (black, in Fig. 261), a great number of short, thin myelinated fibers degenerate secondarily and may be followed to the point of termination in preparations stained according to the Marchi technique (Figs. 262–66). The caliber of the overwhelming majority of these fibers is fine to very fine, with a few of medium thickness interspersed, indicating that, for the most part, they originate from cells of small size.

In the striate cortex immediately adjoining the lesion, except in the lowermost layer, there are no degenerated fibers of any length to be seen coursing away from the lesions (Figs. 262, 263). In particular, the stripe of Gennari or Vicq-d'Azyr, indicated by stippling, approximately corresponding to the intragranular layer *4-b*, remains free from any degenerated myelin. This layer, though medullated, accord-

ingly does not contain intracortical myelinated fibers of any appreciable length. All the long axon fibers originating from the nerve cells in the destroyed portions of the striate cortex (L_1, L_2) leave this cortex and enter the subjacent subcortical fiber substance, where they sort themselves into several categories.

The first variety, exceedingly numerous, are short association fibers. Immediately after entering the subcortex, these very fine fibers turn horizontally, keeping quite close to the striate

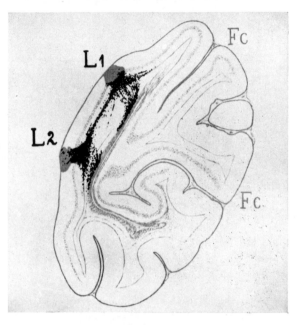

Fig. 262.—A section through the occipital lobe of a Macaque showing two small, cortical lesions (*L1*, *L2*) in the striate area (Fig. 261), whence fibers emanate to other regions of the brain. The stripe of Gennari or Vicq-d'Azyr, marked by stippling, indicates the striate area, partly buried in the calcarine fissure (*Fc*) and partly extending over the lateral face of the occipital lobe where the lesions were located. Note the great number of short association fibers (*black lines*) spreading below the cortex and within it, while others pass into the subcortical fiber substance. Marchi method of staining. (*Cf.* preceding and following figures.)

cortex, some re-entering its lowermost zone. A few of these fibers remain within the cortex, where they pursue a horizontal course in the lowermost zone next to the subcortex. The short association fibers are most numerous in the immediate vicinity of the lesion in an area measuring approximately 2 mm. across. From the vicinity of the lesion these short subcortical association fibers gradually and rapidly decrease in number until, at an approximate distance of 5 mm. on all sides of the lesion, the last of them have disappeared. Their lateral spread, accordingly, amounts to a circular area, shaded in our figure, measuring approximately 10 mm. in diameter, or almost half the extent of the striate area covering the lateral face of the occipital operculum at this level (*cf. Oo*, in Fig. 261).

Anteriorly, along the simian sulcus (*Ss*), these short association fibers attain the limit of the striate cortex (in Figs. 263 and 264 the striate cortex is clearly indicated by a stippled in-

sagittal fiber strata of the occipital lobe, into which they are fitted (Figs. 262, 263). They are confined to the sagittal strata, the thicker ones with preference for the internal stratum and the thin ones entering the extreme stratum. They remain in these strata until they reach the level of the well-developed annectent gyri, where some terminate (Fig. 264). The remaining and slightly longer association fibers, the majority, continue for a short distance in the sagittal strata in the rostral direction, gradually entering the surrounding fibrous core of the occipital

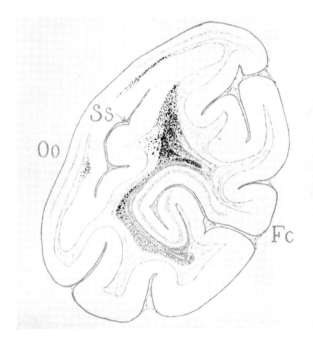

Fig. 263.—A section slightly anterior to the preceding one, located in front of the two small lesions, showing short association fibers passing in great numbers to the striate cortex immediately adjacent to the lesions, while other fibers pass over into the sagittal fiber layers underneath the cortex in the floor of the simian sulcus (*Ss*). *Labeling: Fc,* calcarine fissure; *Oo,* occipital operculum; *Ss,* simian sulcus. Marchi method. (*Cf.* preceding and following figures.)

tracortical line marking the extent of the stripe of Gennari). An attentive examination of the serial sections makes it appear probable that a zone of the adjoining parastriate cortex in the free lip of the simian sulcus also receives these short strio-parastriate association fibers as far as the floor of that sulcus (*Ss*).

In the second category the fibers originating in the striate cortex are longer. They are fewer in number, also mostly thin, although the caliber of some is slightly thicker. They descend in parallel, gently curved bundles directly to the

lobe. This is especially evident on levels where the angular gyrus (*GA*) becomes fully developed (Figs. 265, 266). It is the cortex of this gyrus, particularly that part lining its exposed ridge, within which these longer association fibers terminate. They are worthy of attention on account of their remarkably regular course, bundles arranged along bundles. In the fibrous core of the occipital lobe, these fibers correspond to the bundles radiating from the sagittal strata in the center toward the cortex lining the surface of the hemisphere. A few thicker fibers do not follow this course but curve away from the bulk, toward the cortex lining the anterior segment of the inferior occipital sulcus.

On levels in front of the angular gyrus, a few degenerated fibers are still found in the sagittal strata of the parietotemporal lobes (Fig. 266). Some of them, both thin and a few thicker ones, may be followed with some doubt through the pulvinar toward the superior colliculus of the same side. Similar, very fine, degenerated fibers possibly enter the tip of the lateral geniculate

Anterior to the level of the pulvinar of the thalamus (*Pulv*) no degenerated fibers could be found either in the fibrous core of the hemisphere or in the various gyri of the temporal and parietal lobes. Specifically, no long association fibers could be found in this experiment to the pre- and postcentral gyri (motor and somesthetic areas), to the orimental transverse temporal gyrus of the Sylvian fossa (auditory area), or to any other cerebral structure, cortical or subcortical. (*Cf.* Fig. 261.)

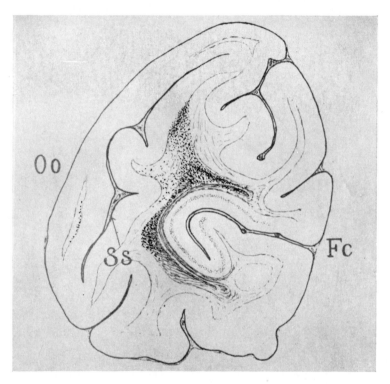

Fig. 264.—A section placed farther anteriorly through the occipital lobe and close to the lip of the simian sulcus (*Ss*), showing the reduced striate area and fewer short association fibers, whereas the somewhat longer fibers now begin to emerge from the sagittal layers to enter the cortex in the floor of the simian sulcus, including the annectent gyrus. *Labeling: Fc*, calcarine fissure; *Oo*, occipital lobe or operculum. (*Cf.* preceding and following figures.)

nucleus; either they are descending corticogeniculate fibers, or they are fibers of the visual radiation which, owing to some damage to their terminations in lesions L_1 and L_2, have undergone a retrograde degeneration. A few thin bundles of very delicate fibers could be followed in the poorly developed tapetum (*Tap*) all the way from the occipital lobe to the posteriormost segment of the splenium of the corpus callosum, and through it over to the contralateral hemisphere.

3. EVALUATION OF THE ANATOMICAL CONNECTIONS OF THE STRIATE AREA.—The remarkable fact which was demonstrated in this experiment is that most fibers undoubtedly originating in the striate area are short association fibers, terminating either within this area or in the areae of the cortex immediately adjoining it.

First are the short intracortical fibers originating from, and terminating around, the nerve cells residing in the striate cortex itself. Through these, each minute territory of the striate cortex is connected by relays with the remainder of that cortex and thus with the entire cerebral cortex.

The others are short subcortical association fibers. These are noteworthy, in the first place, because of their great numbers. They represent the majority of all fibers which leave the striate area. The other noteworthy feature is their direction or pattern of spreading. From each minute locality a great number of them enter into the subjacent subcortical substance, immedi-

short association fibers must be formidable. Through them, every point of the striate area is connected both ways with its immediate environment and, through this, by intracortical and subcortical relays, with the rest of the striate area and the remainder of the cerebral cortex.

The mechanism represented by the system of short association fibers makes the striate area an "integrated collective" or "aggregation of functional units." In this collective the most

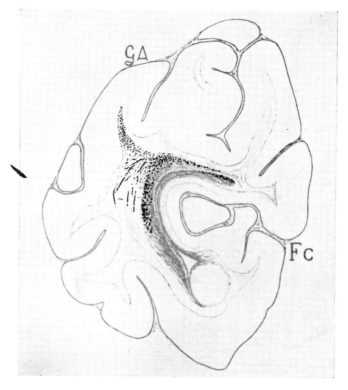

Fig. 265.—A section through the simian hemisphere in front of the occipital lobe, passing through the angular gyrus (*GA*), into which somewhat longer association fibers from the striate area enter, while others still remain in the sagittal fiber layers, with a few distributed to the near-by cortex of the parietal and possibly temporal lobes. *Labeling: Fc*, calcarine fissure. (*Cf.* preceding and following figures.)

ately spreading to right and left, fore and aft, in order eventually to re-enter the same striate cortex.

In this manner each particular point of the striate cortex is interconnected both ways with a fairly large segment of the same cortex. According to a rough estimate, the functional units of this kind may amount to at least one-sixth of the entire striate area covering the external face of the occipital lobe of a monkey's brain (Fig. 261, shaded). The total number of

intimate and direct connection of any particular point is with its immediate neighborhood. The intimacy gradually fades toward the periphery, the connection with the remaining and much larger portion of the striate area being indirect, mediated through the next adjoining units.

The somewhat longer subcortical association fibers connecting the striate area with the paraperistriate areae lining the annectent gyri and the angular gyrus are also noteworthy because of their abundance and orientation. The territory which they supply is closest to their point of origin in the striate area. Moreover, this territory is considerably larger in extent than the striate territory, whence they originate. As in the distribution of the short, subcortical, striate association fibers, the longer strioparaperistriate fibers also spread out at the place of their termination, indicating a collection of re-

transformed retinal impulses from the striate area reaches, as the next station, the paraperistriate areae, whence other influences may originate, which may further spread to more distant parts of the cortex and to the subcortex (Figs. 267, 268).

In any case, if the subcortical association fibers, because of greater thickness and better myelinization, indicate greater speed and vol-

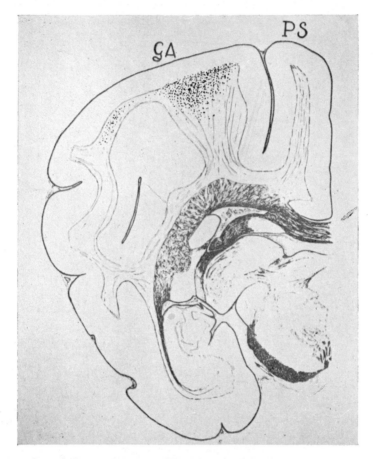

Fig. 266.—A section through the angular gyrus (*GA*), where it is fully developed, to show the distribution of the long association fibers originating in the striate area which enter that gyrus, as found in this experiment. It is doubtful whether similar fibers pass over to other parts of the brain. (*Cf.* preceding figures.)

ciprocally overlapping units. Briefly, each minute territory of the striate cortex is related by medium-long subcortical association fibers to a larger territory of the para-peristriate cortex, with a reciprocal overlapping of the adjoining units.

Since no other cortical areae of the same cerebral hemisphere receive association fibers originating from the striate cortex, it is permissible to conclude that the principal stream of

ume or intensity of propagated impulses in comparison with the thinner and poorly myelinized, short, intracortical relays, the transformed retinal impulses may at first spread only as far as the para-peristriate areae.

A fair amount of localization is preserved in this spreading, since each point of the striate cortex transmits impulses to one particular territory of the para-peristriate areae, the remainder having no such direct connections with that particular point. The fact, however, that each minute territory of the striate area transmits impulses to a much larger territory of the para-peristriate areae and that the areae of distribution overlap shows that, besides a possible point-to-point relationship, there is a much wider one of more diffuse character, owing to which a change in the dynamic state is brought about in a wide area.

Altogether, the evidence points toward a

poorly developed, if possibly they are not entirely absent. This agrees with the very reduced tapetal stratum found in the posterior portion of the occipital lobe as a distinct fiber formation in a few localities only, as, for example, next to the upper and lower corners of the posterior horn of the lateral ventricle. Equally uncertain are direct connections of the striate area with the subcortical parts of the brain, especially the superior colliculus of the midbrain.

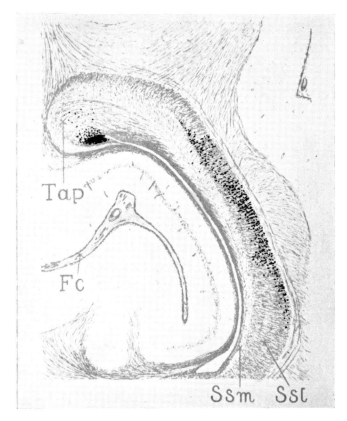

Fig. 267.—A section through the sagittal fiber layers of the occipital lobe of a Rhesus Macaque, where, in an experiment, a portion of the para-peristriate area was damaged, resulting in a secondary degeneration of two systems: a bundle in the tapetum (*Tap*), which eventually passes over to the contralateral hemisphere, and of other fibers descending to the superior colliculus of the midbrain (in *Ssl*). *Labeling: Fc*, calcarine fissure; *Ssl, Ssm*, lateral and medial sagittal layers; *Tap*, tapetum. (*Cf.* following figure.)

complex relationship between the striate and the para-peristriate areae in which many numerous structural and dynamic factors may work together. To identify these, a systematic investigation, both in the analysis of fine structural details of the striate cortex and by means of physiological experiments, is necessary.

The direct connections of the striate area with the contralateral hemisphere appear to be

One of the unexpected results of the experiment described is an absence of truly long association fibers from the striate area to other principal sensory and motor regions of the same and contralateral hemispheres of the brain. Even more remarkable is a development so poor that it amounts to an absence of commissural callosal fibers by which the two striate areae of both occipital lobes would be connected into a functional team. If there are such connections, they are not direct but are mediated through other nonstriate areae.

This contrasts with the manifest association of the two striate areae into a team by virtue of a partial decussation of the optic nerve fibers in the chiasma and a resulting welding of the two homonymous retinal sets into two twofold halves in the suprachiasmal portion of the visual system, as described in the preceding sections of this chapter and in chapter VI, 6. Hence the task of producing a single visuomental image in a common binocular visual act, resulting in single stereoptic vision, is a process commenced by the semidecussation in the chiasma, its consummation taking place in the striate areae of the two occipital lobes of the brain.

ing parts of the para-peristriate areae is also of interest in still another respect, that is, because the operculum is a locality where the central foveae and areae of both retinae are represented. An abundant connection is here to be expected, in view of the functional supremacy of the fovea in visual space perception, especially in acuity. The central fovea and its immediate vicinity is a principal retinal gateway for the most detailed or epicritic visual im-

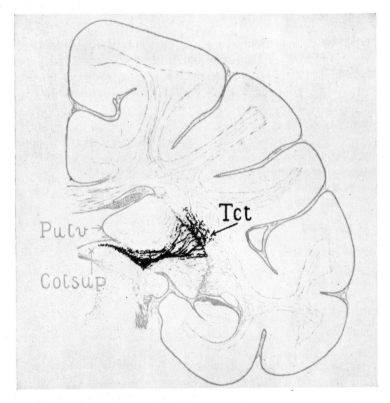

Fig. 268.—A section through the occipital lobe of a Rhesus Macaque, where a portion of the para-peristriate areae was damaged, resulting in a secondary degeneration of fibers descending through the pulvinar of the thalamus to the superior colliculus of the midbrain. *Labeling: Colsup,* superior colliculus of midbrain; *Pulv,* pulvinar of thalamus; *Tct,* occipital corticotectal tract.

The extraordinary wealth of association fibers arising in the striate area of the occipital operculum and their termination in the adjoin-

pulses. Hence its cortical representation in the posterior or polar portion of the striate area not only is relatively the largest but is also well supplied with association fibers. Through these a broad avenue is kept open for the epicritic foveal impulses to pass over to the para-peristriate and other areae of the cortex, there to combine into composite traces of a higher order. (*Cf.* chap. VIII, 3.)

References: Bailey, Bonin & McCulloch 1948; Bonin, Garol & McCulloch; Le Gros Clark

1941, 1942; Clark & Sunderland 1939; Flechsig 1894, 1920, 1927; Mettler 1935; Mingazzini 1922; Niessl von Mayendorf 1920; Polyak 1926, 1927, 1930, 1932; Probst 1901, 1902; Rosett 1933, 1936; Van Valkenburg 1908, 1913, 1926; C. & O. Vogt 1919, 1926; Vialet 1893, 1894; Villaverde 1924, 1931.

SEC. 8. TOPOGRAPHICAL RELATIONSHIPS OF THE VISUAL SYSTEM

1. GENERAL REMARKS.—The visual system, beginning with the peripheral organs—the eyes—and terminating with the striate areae of the occipital lobes, extends along the longer axis of the head, from the anterior to the posterior limit. Throughout this long stretch it is topographically related to numerous structures: the bony parts of the cranium, parts of the brain, the nerves, blood vessels, and other structures. This close relationship, partly anatomical-functional, partly purely physical, makes knowledge about it important in theoretical as well as practical respects.

In surgical operations, by keeping at some distance from the visual pathways and centers, serious injury to vision may be avoided. Dangerous procedures—for example, the posterior puncture of the lateral ventricles and other similar techniques which are likely directly to damage parts of the visual radiations and of the striate areae—may thus be avoided.

2. TOPOGRAPHICAL RELATIONSHIPS OF EYE-BALLS.—The visual system is, in general, located close to the base both of the skull and of the brain (Fig. 269).

The eyes, sheltered in the orbital cavities, with the anterior poles of the corneae fairly accurately coinciding with the anterior poles of the cerebral hemispheres, are close beneath the overhanging frontal lobes. The distance between the upper pole of the eyeball and the orbital surface of the frontal lobe is but a few millimeters. This space is taken up by the muscles, glands, fat, and other tissues filling the orbital cavities; by the thin bony partition made up of the orbital portion of the frontal bone and of the *ala parva* or "small wing" of the sphenoidal bone; and by the cerebral meninges and meningeal spaces.

3. TOPOGRAPHICAL RELATIONSHIPS OF THE OPTIC NERVES.—The course of the optic nerve in the orbital cavity is not straight but meanders somewhat in three dimensions, thus allowing necessary excursions to the eyeball during the converging movements and the lateral and vertical shifting of the gaze.

The point where the nerve is implanted in the eyeball is at a slight distance nasal to the posterior pole, where the optical axis touches the fundus of the eye. In the orbital cavity or eye socket, the optic nerve is imbedded in, and surrounded by, various tissues, such as the extrinsic eye muscles, oculomotor and sympathetic nerves, glands, the plastic fatty tissue which functions as a "cushion," and abundant blood vessels that fill the remaining space.

At the posterior, narrow, funnel-shaped end of the orbital cavity, the optic nerve slips through a short bony channel which varies in length from individual to individual. This channel is the optic foramen, formed by the small wing (ala parva) of the sphenoidal bone, in which the optic nerve is firmly lodged, and thus reaches the cranial cavity, in particular, the middle fossa or pit. Viewed *in situ*, from below or from above, the two optic nerves form an angle of approximately 60°.

4. TOPOGRAPHY OF THE OPTIC CHIASMA.—As soon as the optic nerves have entered the cranial cavity, they unite, producing a short, bridgelike junction—the chiasma—by means of which they are firmly linked together. The chiasma, in turn, is loosely lodged in the chiasmal sulcus, a shallow groove in the middle portion of the sphenoidal bone at the base of the skull (Fig. 269).

Two paired protrusions—the anterior and posterior clinoid processes—surrounding a nichelike depression, in which the hypophysis or pituitary gland is lodged, together form a smooth socket, the *sella turcica*, or "Turkish saddle," from which locality the two optic tracts continue to the brain. Important cranial nerves, such as the oculomotor, abducent, trochlear, and trigeminal, and the internal carotid artery with its branches, essential for the nutrition of the brain, are in the immediate vicinity of the sella, which also is filled with, and surrounded by, a rich, spongy, venous network—the cavernous sinus.

The region of the sella and of the optic chiasma is in the closest proximity to the base of the brain, in particular to the hypothalamus, which contains important centers for the regulation of various vegetative functions of the organism— growth, metabolism, temperature, reproduction, and emotional reactions.

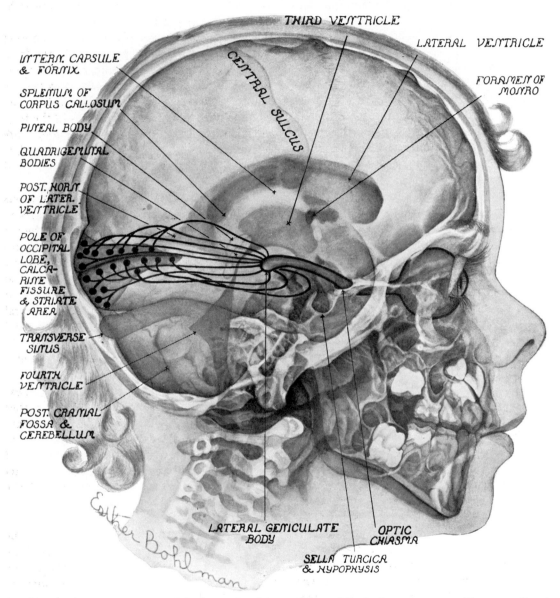

FIG. 269.—Normal structures of the human head, in particular of the brain, as seen on an X-ray negative, in a side view, of an eight-year-old child (University of Chicago Clinics No. 50749). Visual system drawn in its normal position: from the eye the optic nerve passes through the optic foramen of the orbit, extending through the chiasma and optic tract to the lateral geniculate body or nucleus, whence bundles of the visual radiation, indicated by thick lines, pass over to the striate area in the calcarine fissure of the occipital lobe, where they terminate (*black dots*). Note the topographic relations of the constituent parts of the visual system to the various parts of the skull and brain; the composition of the visual radiation of shorter upper bundles with a flatter curving course, terminating in the upper calcarine lip; of longer ventral bundles describing considerable detours, before turning back to the lower calcarine lip (so-called "temporal loop" of Flechsig and Meyer); and of intermediate bundles pursuing a straight course to the occipital pole.

On rare occasions the chiasmal junction is absent. In such cases each optic nerve continues as an optic tract on the side of the brain where it originates (for references, *see* chap. II, 8 [4]).

5. Topography of optic tracts.—The optic tracts are dorsoventrally somewhat flattened central continuations of the optic nerves attached to the base of the brain. In particular, they surround the exposed parts of the hypothalamus from the lateral sides: the *tuber cinereum*, which continues as a narrow, funnel-shaped *infundibulum* and connects it with the *hypophysis*, and the two rotund mammillary bodies. In their further course, the tracts remain closely attached to the ventral and lateral sides of the two cerebral peduncles, along which they finally reach the parts of the betweenbrain and midbrain, where they terminate.

6. X-ray topography of the visual system.—In a side view of a radiogram of the human head (Fig. 269) the optic foramen or channel appears as a small, oval opening at the end of the slanting roof of the orbit, not far behind the tip of the temporal lobe. Close behind the inner mouth of the optic foramen, in front of the anterior clinoid processes, the optic nerves unite and form the chiasma, determinable by the position of the sella turcica. From here on, the optic tracts take a slightly slanting, ascending course in the posterior direction.

There are several landmarks which may help determine the position of the structures at the base of the brain, useful in a region filled with thick fiber trunks and small interconnecting cavities. One, below the optic tract, is the round pocket of the sella. The other is the faintly outlined, funnel-shaped infundibulum and its slender stalk, to which is attached the hypophysis, or pituitary gland, lodged in the sellar fossa. The infundibulum, in turn, is continuous with the lower portion of the third ventricle, whose small supraoptic recess is well outlined at the coronal level of the anterior commissure (which, in turn, is found below and slightly in front of Monro's foramen).

Posteriorly, the shadow of the infundibulum continues into the gently sloping floor of the posterior portion of the third ventricle, which

leads directly to the anterior orifice of the cerebral aqueduct of Sylvius and thus to the midbrain. In this locality the lateral geniculate nuclei or bodies and the initial portions of the visual radiations are found. Most of the third ventricle is located above the optic tracts, being outlined along its upper boundary by the arching internal capsule and the fornix.

The spacious and sharply outlined cavities of the lateral ventricles extend partly in the frontal lobes, where they terminate with blunt, expanded anterior horns. Posteriorly, they may be followed as a curved, semicircular shadow, descending partly as the inferior horns in the temporal lobes and partly as a shorter and more slender shadow—the posterior horns of the lateral ventricles, pointing toward the occipital poles.

The position of the lateral geniculate nucleus in a lateral view is at the anteroventral *tegmentum* of the midbrain, corresponding with the red nucleus. This location is much more anterior and more ventral than indicated in a model by Cushing (1922), whose location of the lateral geniculate at the pineal body is inaccurate. For this reason, the detour described by the ventral bundles of the visual radiation, the "temporal loop," is somewhat shorter than indicated in Cushing's model and in other similar presentations (*cf.* Figs. 235, 236).

The fiber complex of the visual radiation, except the "temporal loop," represents a rather straight anteroposterior tract. Its lower margin runs close to and fairly parallel with the inferior outline of the occipitotemporal lobes and not far from the transverse venous sinus, its upper margin reaching the lower level of the callosal splenium.

7. Topography of the striate area.—The shape of the striate area projected upon the lateral aspect of a roentgenogram of the human head is that of an elongated triangle, with its sharp end turned anteriorly (dotted area at the left end of the figure). The anterior limit of the striate area extends approximately to the middistance between the lateral geniculate nucleus and the occipital pole. Its polar end extends downward as far as the internal occipital protuberance and the transverse sinus, the outward landmark being the external occipital protuberance or *torus*. Its surface extent, projected onto the occipital poles, does not quite reach the lambdoid suture of the parieto-occipital bones.

References: Arey 1932; F. Arnold 1939; Ch. E. Beevor 1909; Bertwistle 1946; R. Bing 1923, 1924, 1940; Braus & Elze 1932–40; Brodmann 1918; Brouwer 1936; Bruce & Walmsley 1939; Cone & Macmillan; Corning 1909; D. J. Cunningham (& Le Gros Clark) 1943; D. J. Cunningham (& V. Horsley) 1892; Curran 1909; Cushing 1921, 1922, 1930; Cushing & Eisenhardt 1929; Cushing & Heuer 1911; Cushing & Walker 1912, 1915, 1916, 1918; Dandy 1948; Davidoff 1951; Deaver 1904; Dejerine 1895–1901; De Schweinitz 1923; Elsberg 1932; Elze 1929; Fawcett 1896; Fay & Grant 1942; Fazakas 1932; G. Gerard 1904, 1911; Gradley 1923; H. Gray 1942; Greving 1926; Hack 1909; Hafferl 1953; J. Henle 1871, 1879; Hermann 1908; R. T. Hill 1946; Hochstetter 1943; Hoeve 1909; Hovelaque 1927; Hovelaque & Reinhold 1917; Hultkrantz 1929, 1935; Jaboulay 1886; Jamieson 1909; Kolmer & Lauber 1936; Kronfeld, McHugh & Polyak (Bausch & Lomb); Larsell 1942; Le Double 1902; D. Lewis *et al.* 1948; McCotter & Fralick 1942; P. S. McKibben 1937; Magitot 1907; Marie & Chatelin 1914–15; Merkel 1874, 1885–90; Merkel & Kallius 1901; H. Morris 1942; D. Munro 1938; Orley 1949; Ostertag 1944; Peet 1948; R. A. Pfeifer 1925, 1930; Pfister 1890; G. A. Piersol 1930; Poirier & Charpy 1901–4; Polyak 1932, 1941–48, 1942; Polyak, McHugh & Judd 1946; Quain 1909–12; Ranson 1921, 1943; Ranson & Clark 1947; Rasmussen 1943; Rea 1943; Reitmann 1904; Rønne (Roenne) 1944; Rubinstein & Davis 1947; Salzmann 1912; Schirmer 1909; Schwalbe 1881, 1887; Sená 1932; A. Šercer 1951; D. W. Soemmerring 1818; Spalteholtz 1926; Stanculéanu 1902; Tandler 1926–29; Tandler & Ranzi 1920; Thorek 1949; Toldt 1904 and later eds.; Truex & Kellner 1948; Vossius 1883; Wallis 1917; F. B. Walsh 1947; Watanabe 1930; Whitnall 1921, 1932; Wieczorek 1935; E. Wolff 1948; G. Young 1922; R. Zander 1896.

Chapter VIII

Cortical Visual Centers

SEC. 1. EXTERNAL CONFIGURATION AND FUNCTIONAL ORGANIZATION OF THE CEREBRAL HEMISPHERES

1. GENERAL REMARKS CONCERNING THE VERTEBRATE BRAIN.—The bulky nervous organ which fills the spacious cavity of the cranium is the brain or cerebrum. It is made up of countless nerve cells or neurons of varied shapes, sizes, types of expansions, and synaptical relationships, held together by supporting neuroglial tissue, blood vessels, and meningeal envelopes.

In all its complexity the brain is the product of a long process of phylogenesis. From modest beginnings in the fishlike ancestor of the Vertebrates, probably somewhat resembling the present-day Lancelet (*Branchiostoma* or *Amphioxus*), where the primitive *prosencephalon* or "brain" is merely a slight vesicular expansion of the anterior end of the neural tube or spinal cord, the brain has increased immensely in bulk and in its structural and functional complexity, until in Man and his nearest relatives it has become the dominant part of the organism (*see* figures in chap. XIV).

The development of the brain into the central nervous organ may be considered to be a result of the direct relation of the rostral end of the spinal cord to the principal sense organs, above all, to those of sight, followed in evolutionary chronology by those of gustation and olfaction. In further consequence of its special relation to the sources of stimuli, elaborate centers of locomotion and balance have developed in the brain. In a word, owing to its favored location at the head-end of the body, the brain has become the leading and dominant part of the central nervous system, the managing center of the entire organismic "individual." (*Cf.* chap. XIII, 2, 3.)

In the Lower Vertebrates such as Fishes and Urodele Amphibians (Salamanders), although unquestionably a leading or central organ, the brain is still small and of relatively simple external and internal makeup. In particular, the endbrain, from which the bulky cerebral hemispheres developed in the advanced Vertebrates, is still little more than a ganglion of olfaction. The cerebral cortex is still in its infancy at this evolutionary stage.

In the Anuran Amphibians (Frogs, Toads), Reptiles, Birds, and Lower Mammals the brain has increased considerably, with the cortex definitely beginning to evolve, though still exhibiting rather primitive features. The cerebral hemispheres, e.g., of the Bat, Mole, Mouse, Rat, Rabbit, or Shrew are lissencephalous, or smooth, without gyri and sulci. The phylogenetically older part—the *paleocortex*, related to the olfactory function, and the midbrain—is relatively larger than the *neocortex* of the *telencephalon* or front brain, which is concerned with the integration of somesthetic, auditory, and visual impulses (*see also* chap. XIV).

In the larger Rodents, Ungulates, and Edentates, and in practically all Carnivorous Mammals, the brain has attained considerable size, and the surface of the hemispheres has become complex, gyrencephalous, or folded into gyri.

The most complicated surface of the cerebral hemispheres is found in large Mammals such as the Whale and the Elephant and, in general, in the Primates, among Simians in the Anthropomorphous Apes, and most complicated of all in Man. Here the cortex has grown to a bulk much exceeding the total mass of the remainder of the gray substance of the entire brain and spinal cord. In complexity and local and individual variation of minute structure the cortex also exceeds all other parts of the nervous system put together. (*See* chap. XIV for comparative data on the brains of various Vertebrates.)

2. EARLY OR PRIMORDIAL NEOPALLIAL SULCI AND FISSURES OF THE HUMAN FETAL BRAIN.— The conspicuous feature of the external surface of the adult human brain is the numerous furrow-like depressions called sulci and fissures,

could otherwise not take place may be established between its neurons.

When one examines the human brain, the first impression is of great irregularity. A closer study, especially of a developing human fetal brain, and an acquaintance with the brains of monkeys and apes, however, help reveal the essential features of the complicated sulcal pattern and its relative stability.

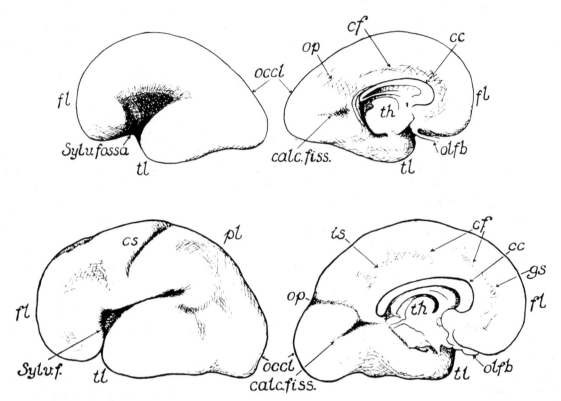

FIG. 270.—Lateral (*left-hand figures*) and medial aspects (*right-hand figures*) of the left cerebral hemispheres of human fetuses drawn while still fresh, in order to show the early development of sulci and gyri of the cortex. The upper figures of a fetus of an estimated age of four and three-quarters menstrual months, or nineteen to twenty weeks, the lower figures of a fetus of an estimated age of six and a half menstrual months, or twenty-six weeks. The lateral face of the younger brain is still perfectly smooth, lissencephalous, except for a wide-open Sylvian fossa, the brain at this stage markedly resembling that of a Tarsier (*cf.* Figs. 279, 516). The inner face, on the contrary, shows several quite shallow, barely perceptible principal or primordial sulci appearing first. In the older brain the primordial calcarine and Sylvian fissures are further deepened, owing to an expansion of the adjoining cortex, in addition to other sulci which appear now, some still vague depressions. At this developmental stage the brain somewhat resembles that of a Monkey (*cf.* Fig. 280). Slightly reduced. *Labeling: calc.fiss.*, calcarine fissure; *cc*, corpus callosum; *cf*, cingular or fornicate sulcus; *cs*, central sulcus (Rolando); *fl*, frontal lobe; *gs*, genual sulcus; *is*, intercalate sulcus; *occl*, occipital lobe; *olfb*, olfactory bulb; *op*, occipito-parietal or parieto-occipital sulcus; *pl*, parietal lobe; *Sylv.f.*, *Sylv.fossa*, Sylvian fossa or pit; *th*, thalamus; *tl*, temporal lobe.

separating the folds, called convolutions or gyri, from one another (Figs. 182, 271). In this way the area of organized gray matter of the cortex covering the hemisphere becomes much greater than if it were smooth, and the topographic and synaptical relationships which

During approximately the first half of the intrauterine development of the human fetus, no neopallial furrows in the proper sense of this word are seen, either on the lateral or on the medial face of a freshly examined specimen. In a ten-week-old human embryo, for example, the lateral surface of a cerebral hemisphere is as smooth as in a lissencephalous Mammal, such as a Shrew, Bat, or Mouse. The only uneven locality on the otherwise unbroken surface is a wide, shallow depression from which the Sylvian fossa or pit, the "lateral fissure," later develops. This condition remains substantially unchanged until approximately the second half of the fifth fetal month (Fig. 270, upper left-hand sketch).

The various "transient fissures" supposedly developing during the early weeks of fetal life and described by some investigators as a normal feature are post mortem artifacts caused by the action of the fixing fluid in which the specimen is preserved. When, for example, a fresh brain of that age is placed in 10 per cent formalin solution, the surface that was perfectly smooth becomes disfigured within a few weeks by the appearance of crisscrossing furrows, even though a proper quantity of sodium chloride may have been added to make the solution isotonic.

The first true neopallial sulci or fissures normally appear on the medial face of the brain at about the twentieth intrauterine week (Fig. 270, upper right-hand diagram). One such short, shallow depression is the calcarine fissure (*calc. fiss.*), another, the parieto-occipital or occipitoparietal sulcus (*op*), both as yet independent of each other. The brain of a human fetus at this stage somewhat resembles the brain of an adult Mouse Lemur, a diminutive primitive Primate, and even more that of a Tarsier (*cf.* Fig. 279, *D, E*). A third shallow, smooth, and barely perceptible depression is the cingular or fornicate sulcus (*cf*), the posterior portion of which may be homologized with the intercalate sulcus, the anterior portion with the genual sulcus, of the Infraprimate Mammals.

The calcarine fissure, significantly, appears among the earliest neopallial furrows in the human fetal brain, just as this fissure is the first to appear during phylogenesis (*cf. c* in the brains of *Tupaia*, Lemur, Tarsier, Marmoset, and *Loris* in Figs. 279, 306, 307). Equally noteworthy seems the circumstance that, from its inception during human ontogenesis, that portion of the calcarine fissure appears first and quite independently of the other sulci which subsequently becomes transformed into a medial

or anterior calcarine sulcus of the adult human brain (*mc*). The lateral or posterior calcarine sulcus (*lc*), which in the adult human brain forms the posterior extremity of the complete, fully developed calcarine fissural complex next to the occipital pole, appears much later during fetal development, duplicating ontogenetically its late appearance phylogenetically (for details *see* sec. 2, this chapter).

Other sulci and fissures begin to appear at a considerably later period, at a fetal age of six and one-half menstrual months (Fig. 270, lower diagrams). Some of these sulci form important boundaries by which the cerebral hemispheres are subdivided into major portions or lobes. On the lateral face the central sulcus of Rolando (*cs*) develops, separating the hemisphere of the brain into two almost equal halves, a frontal lobe anteriorly and a posterior portion (*cf. c* in Fig. 271). The posterior portion, in turn, is subdivided at this stage by the now much deeper, but narrower, lateral or Sylvian fissure (*Sylv. f.*) into an upper portion, the parietal lobe (*pl*), and a lower portion, the temporal lobe (*tl*). Posteriorly, both these lobes are directly continuous with the posteriormost portion of the hemisphere, the occipital lobe (*occl*). Several vague depressions identifiable as the incipient superior frontal, intraparietal, and other sulci at this stage become noticeable on the previously smooth surface.

On the medial face of the brain the most marked furrow is the calcarine sulcus or fissure (*calc. fiss.*). It is further deepened and lengthened and is now joined with the occipitoparietal sulcus (*op*). Toward the end of the prenatal period this simple fissural pattern of the human fetal brain is complicated by the appearance of secondary and tertiary sulci, which produce the final complex fissuration and gyration of the adult human brain (Figs. 182, 271).

3. Sulci and gyri of the adult human brain and the principal anatomical subdivisions of the cerebral hemispheres.— On the external or lateral face of the human cerebral hemisphere, five principal subdivisions, called lobes, are customarily distinguished (Fig. 271, upper diagram): frontal (*fl*), parietal (*pl*), temporal (*tl*), and occipital lobes (*ol*), and the

insula or "island" of Reil (concealed in the Sylvian fossa or pit, *Syl; see* Figs. 275, 301).

On the lateral face of the frontal lobe (*fl*) two principal furrows are usually found, the superior (*sfs*) and inferior frontal sulci (*ifs*), which separate three convolutions or gyri, the superior (*sfg*), middle (*mfg*), and inferior frontal gyri (*ifg*). The frontal sulci, however, extend only as far as the precentral sulcus (*precs*), which, usually broken up into several components, follows at some distance in front of and more or less parallel to the central sulcus (*c*), separating the anterior central, or precentral, gyrus from the rest of the frontal lobe. The orbital gyri (*og*) and the *gyrus rectus* or straight gyrus (*gr*, lower diagram), together with orbital sulci and the olfactory sulcus, in which the olfactory tract and bulb are lodged, form the inferior face of the frontal lobe (*see also* Fig. 272).

The parietal lobe (*pl*) is the region roughly outlined by the central sulcus (*c*) anteriorly, by the lateral or Sylvian fissure (*Syl*) inferiorly, and by an approximate vertical line beginning at the upper end of the parieto-occipital or occipital perpendicular sulcus (*po*) posteriorly. The convolution along the central sulcus—the postcentral gyrus—is more or less separated from the remainder of the parietal lobe by the postcentral sulcus (*pocs*), which, in turn, is usually broken up into a superior and an inferior component.

The rest of the parietal lobe, again, is subdivided by a horizontally placed or arching intraparietal sulcus (*ip*, in Figs. 271, 273; *ips*, in Fig. 272) into a superior and an inferior parietal lobule, the latter of which is composed of a supramarginal gyrus (*smg*, at the end of the lateral fissure) and an angular gyrus behind (*ag*). Sometimes a third, most posterior, division is distinguishable, the inferior posterior parietal gyrus of Retzius (*ippg*).

Below the parietal lobe and largely separated from it by a deep and spacious pocket of the lateral or Sylvian fossa or pit (*Syl*) is the temporal lobe (*tl*, in Fig. 271). This lobe is subdivided on the lateral face by a superior temporal, or parallel, sulcus (*sts*) and usually by a fragmented medial temporal sulcus (*mts*) into a superior (*stg*), middle (*mtg*), and inferior temporal gyrus (*itg*).

A large part of the cortex lies deeply hidden in the lateral fissure of Sylvius (*Syl*) beneath the overhanging surrounding parts, the frontal, parietal, and temporal opercula (Fig. 271). The deepest part or floor of the pit represents the insula or "island" of Reil, consisting of one long and several short gyri. The covered portion of the temporal lobe usually exhibits one long, broad convolution, placed obliquely, and one or two shorter ones in the posterior pocket of the pit. These are the transverse temporal gyri of Heschl (*H1* and *H2* in Fig. 274).

On the inner or medial face of the hemisphere (Fig. 271, lower diagram; also right diagrams in Figs. 272, 273), the gyrus next to the corpus callosum (*cc, gen, spl*) and encircling it from the front, from above, and from behind is the fornicate or cingular gyrus (*fcg*). The portion of the frontal lobe above it belongs to the superior frontal gyrus (*sfg*), here called marginal gyrus (*mg*). The paracentral lobule (*pcl*) is the medial extension of the anterior and posterior central, or precentral and postcentral, gyri. The quadrangular area just behind it is the precuneus (*precu*). The posterior boundary of the precuneus, and thus of the parietal lobe, separating the latter from the occipital lobe, is a deep furrow—in fact, a pit or fossa, the medial parieto-occipital fissure or sulcus (*po*), extending down to the calcarine fissure (*mc*).

The triangular area inclosed by the parieto-occipital and calcarine fissures is the *cuneus* or "wedge" (*cu*). The convolution just below the calcarine fissure which extends to the inferior face of the temporal lobe (*tl*) is the lingual gyrus (*lg*); its apparent continuation is the hippocampal gyrus (*hig*), terminating with the *uncus* or "hook" (*u*). Just outward to the latter gyri, also on the inferior face of the occipitotemporal region, is the fusiform or spindle-shaped gyrus (*fusg*), separated from the former by the collateral sulcus (*cols*). The furrow separating the fusiform gyrus from the inferior temporal gyrus (*itg*) is the inferior temporal sulcus (*its*).

Behind the parietal and temporal lobes, and only incompletely separated from them on the lateral face by the posterior descending extremity of the intraparietal sulcus, called the transverse occipital sulcus of Ecker (*tos*), and on the medial face of the hemisphere by the parieto-occipital sulcus (*po*), is the occipital lobe (*ol* in

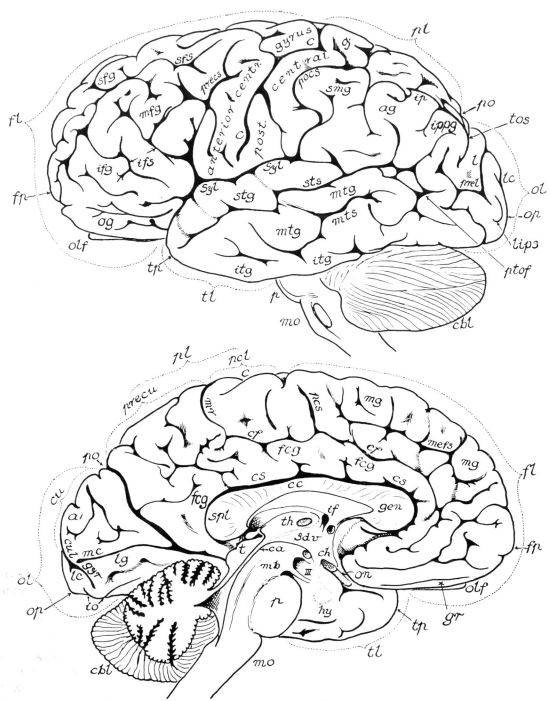

FIG. 271.—Adult human brain showing sulci and gyri in a lateral view (*upper diagram*) and in a medial view (*lower diagram*). *Labeling* for this and for the following Figs. 272, 273: *a1*, posterior cuneal gyrus; *c*, central sulcus of Rolando; *ca*, cerebral aqueduct of Sylvius; *cbl*, cerebellum; *cc*, corpus callosum; *cf*, cingular or fornicate sulcus; *ch*, chiasma of optic nerves; *cl*, cuneal or upper lip of calcarine fissure; *cs*, the sulcus of the corpus callosum; *cu, cun,* cuneus or "wedge"; *cul, cul gyr,* posterior cuneolingual gyrus of Cunningham, descending gyrus, or extreme lobule of Ecker; *fcg*, fornicate or cingular gyrus; *fl*, frontal lobe; *fp*, frontal pole; *fusg*, fusiform or occipitotemporal gyrus; *gen*, genu or "knee" of corpus callosum; *gr*, gyrus rectus or straight gyrus; *hif*, hippocampal fissure; *hig*, hippocampal gyrus; *hy*, hypophysis or pituitary gland; *if*, interventricular foramen of Monro; *ifg*, inferior frontal gyrus; *io*, inferior occipital sulcus; *ip, ips,* intraparietal sulcus; *ippg*, inferior posterior parietal gyrus or lobule of Retzius; *isth*, isthmus of fornicate or cingular and hippocampal gyri; *itg*, inferior temporal gyrus; *its*, inferior temporal sulcus; *l*, lunate or simian sulcus, *Affenspalte*; *lg*, lingual gyrus; *lc*, lateral or posterior calcarine sulcus; external calcarine sulcus of Cunningham; lateral calcarine sulcus of Ingalls and Kuh-

Fig. 271; *see also* Figs. 272, 273). The sulcal and gyral configuration of the occipital lobe frequently more or less resembles the conditions regularly present in the simian brain, its phylogenetic predecessor, with a lunate sulcus (*l*), a homologue of the simian sulcus or *Affenspalte*, and an occipital operculum (*op*) behind it (*cf.* Figs. 280, 282, 284, 286, 293, 294).

From the lunate sulcus a branch may extend for a varying distance into the parietal lobe. This is the prelunate sulcus (*prel*). If there is no lunate sulcus or if the lunate sulcus and the occipital operculum have been pushed back as far as the occipital pole, the lateral face of the occipital lobe is split by a number of short, twisted sulci into several irregular convolutions, the lateral occipital gyri (*og* in Fig. 296), the homologues of the annectent gyri of the simian brain, which have emerged onto the surface (*ag* in Figs. 282 and 284).

In many human brains, perhaps even in most of them, however, the original primate sulcal and gyral pattern can be revealed by careful examination. Such an examination will show the presence of a calcarine fissural complex, which, on comparative-anatomical and embryological grounds, may be subdivided into a medial or anterior calcarine sulcus (*mc*) and a lateral or posterior calcarine sulcus (*lc*), as will be discussed in detail in sections 2 and 3 of this chapter. Together, these three sulci form the classical posterior or horizontal occipital sulcus of Henle, better known as the calcarine sulcus or fissure of T. H. Huxley. A careful inspection of the external configuration of the occipital lobe in numerous specimens suffices to reveal the simian homologies of its components. In other complex and dubious instances the only safe criterion is the relation of the striate cortex or visual cortical area to the sulci and gyri in question.

4. FUNCTIONAL LOCALIZATION IN THE HUMAN CEREBRAL CORTEX.—Since the observations and speculations of Francis Joseph Gall (1809, 1810–19, 1825) and of Jean Bouillaud (1825, 1839), but more definitely since the discovery of the motor speech center by Paul Broca (1861) and the presence of stimulable points by Fritsch and Hitzig (1870), the ancient concept of functional omnivalence of the entire cerebral cortex, rooted in the belief in a single, homogeneous, and indivisible transcendental "soul" or "mind," has been gradually replaced by another concept, that of the composite nature of cerebral functions. Just as the whole human organism is made up of numerous diverse parts and organs, each performing its own particular work, in harmony with other parts and organs, so each given locality, nucleus, cortical area, or any other accumulation of nerve cells possesses its own functional properties different from the properties of all other nuclei, areae, or foci of the brain.

The brain is an extremely complex organ, composed of diverse parts that possess their own functional properties, all parts being intricately interconnected to form a composite whole. The many efforts through which the present concept of functional cerebral organization was achieved are presented in Part I of this book, especially in chapter III, 3, 6, and chapter IV, 7, whereas the question of the basic organi-

lenbeck; triradiate sulcus of Landau; lateral intrastriate sulcus of Elliot Smith; ypsiliform sulcus of Ariëns Kappers; *lips*, lateral inferior paracalcarine sulcus; *ll*, lingual or lower lip of calcarine fissure; *lsps*, posterior superior paracalcarine sulcus; *mb*, midbrain; *mc*, medial or anterior calcarine sulcus; stem and posterior calcarine fissure of Cunningham; proper, limiting, or prestriate calcarine sulcus together with retrocalcarine sulcus of Elliot Smith; medial striate or intermediate portion of calcarine fissure of Kuhlenbeck (in part); *mefs*, medial frontal sulcus; *mfg*, middle frontal gyrus; *mg*, marginal gyrus; *mips*, medial inferior paracalcarine sulcus; *mo*, medulla oblongata; *mr*, marginal ramus of cingular or fornicate sulcus *cf; msps*, medial superior paracalcarine sulcus; *mtg*, middle temporal gyrus; *mts*, middle temporal sulcus; *og*, orbital gyri; *ol*, occipital lobe; *olf*, olfactory bulb and tract; *olfs*, olfactory sulcus; *on*, optic nerve; *op*, occipital pole; *p*, pons or "bridge"; *pcl*, paracentral lobule; *pcs*, paracentral sulcus; *pl*, parietal lobe; *pms*, paramedian sulcus of Elliot Smith; *po*, parieto-occipital sulcus; *pocs*, postcentral sulcus; *precs*, precentral sulcus; *precu*, precuneus or quadrate lobule; *prel*, prelunate sulcus; *ptof*, parietotemporo-occipital fossa or pit; *rhif*, rhinal fissure; *sfg*, superior frontal gyrus; *sfs*, superior frontal sulcus; *smg*, supramarginal gyrus; *spl*, splenium of corpus callosum; *stg*, superior temporal gyrus; *sts*, superior temporal or parallel sulcus; *S, Syl*, lateral fissure or pit of Sylvius; *t*, tectum or quadrigeminal bodies or colliculi of midbrain; *th*, thalamus; *tl*, temporal lobe; *tos*, transverse parietal or occipital sulcus; *tp*, temporal pole; *u*, uncus or "hook" of hippocampal gyrus; *3dv*, third cerebral ventricle; *III*, third cranial or oculomotor nerve.

zation of nervous tissue is dealt with in chapter I, 9, and in chapter IX.

The functional organization of the human brain, an organ which has been called "the most intricate living substance on this planet," is a problem which must still be regarded as far from solved. Much remains uncertain, even if

principal senses and motility will be mentioned briefly, to serve as a background or framework for the function of vision, the principal theme of this book.

The *sense of vision*, or sight, is bound to the occipital lobes of both hemispheres of the brain (*Vision*, in Fig. 274; *cf*. Figs. 300, 301). The stri-

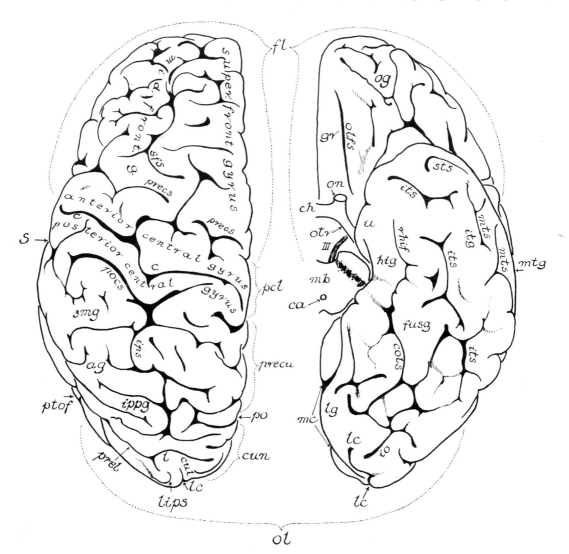

Fig. 272.—Left hemisphere of an adult human brain seen from above (*left diagram*) and from below (*right diagram*), showing major subdivisions besides sulci and gyri. Same specimen as the one represented in Figs. 271 and 273. (For *labeling see* legend of Fig. 271.)

we disregard the subtle question of the minute concatenation of the many types of nerve cells into complex associations and their interpretation in terms of function and limit ourselves to more or less gross functions. In the following, therefore, only those functions related to the

ate area or "striped cortex," so named by Elliot Smith because of a whitish line visible on a cross-section through it without magnification, or Brodmann's field *17*, lining the calcarine fissure on the medial sides and at the poles of the occipital lobes (given in close shading in the same figure), is, as far as now known, the "gateway" for all impulses entering the cortex which originate in the retinae of the eyes. From here the impulses are further distributed into adjoining para- and peristriate areae of Elliot Smith, or Brodmann's fields *18* and *19*, and beyond.

The striate area appears to be a carrier of the visual sensations of a more elemental character, such as the perception of light, colors, and localization of external objects in space whence the stimuli arrive (*see ELEMENTAL VISUAL*

participation of the adjoining parts of the parietal, temporal, and occipital lobes in vision is even less clear, the indications being in favor of the localization of certain highly complex visual functions, such as reading and writing, in these territories (*cf.* also "Comment on Figure 274," this section).

The conjugate movements of the two eyes are also partly directed by the cortex of the occipital lobes, other similar centers being in the frontal lobe just in front of the precentral gyrus and apparently also in other localities,

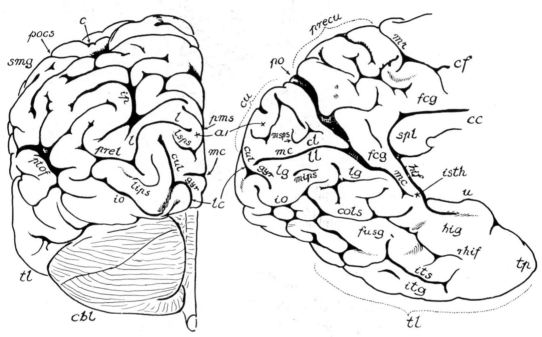

Fig. 273.—Left occipital lobe of the same human brain represented in preceding two figures, seen from behind (*left diagram*) and from a medial aspect (*right diagram*), showing the arrangement of sulci and gyri. (For *labeling* see legend of Fig. 271.)

SENSATIONS between sulci *l* and *lc*, in Fig. 275). The para-peristriate areae, in turn, seem to be a material repository of complex visual functions, such as visual memory of the shape, color, and movements of objects which have been observed and of the symbols or meanings of these objects or situations (*see 5*, in Fig. 274; and *COMPLEX VISUAL MEMORY* in Fig. 275).

To what extent these two categories of functions are tied to either the striate or the para-peristriate areae, or whether the first does or does not participate in the commemorative functions at all, remains an open question. The

such as the vicinity of the auditory center in the temporal lobe.

The *sense of hearing* is localized in the posterior pocket of the Sylvian fossa or pit and in the temporal lobe. Here again a projection area or "gateway" for the auditory impulses, identical with the termination of the auditory radiation, roughly coinciding with the transverse temporal gyri of Heschl (*H1, H2*), is distinguished from the surrounding spacious areae comprising most or all of the temporal lobe, with, perhaps, the adjoining portions of the Sylvian fossa and parts of the parietal and occipital lobes.

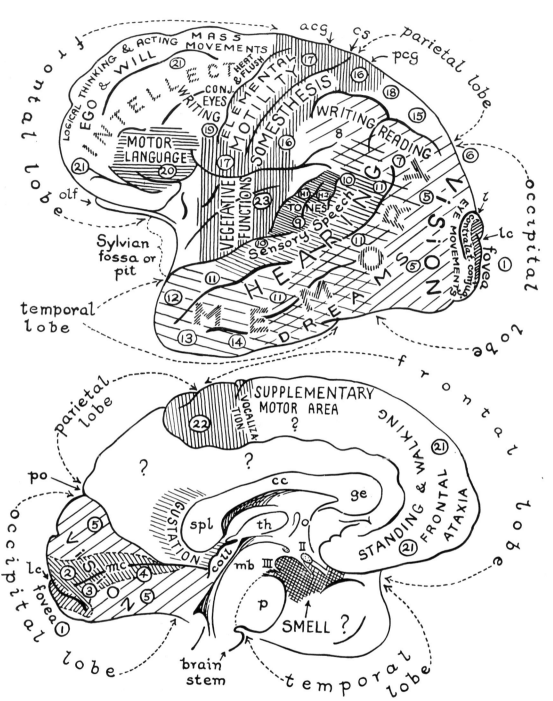

Fig. 274.—Principal functional centers of the human brain as determined by the physiological experiments, clinical observations, pathoanatomic investigations, and neurosurgical experience during the past hundred years (*cf.* chaps. III and IV). Upper figure represents the lateral face of the left cerebral hemisphere, with the opercular portions of the frontal and parietal lobes pulled away from the temporal lobe, in order to show the concealed parts of the Sylvian fossa. The lower figure represents the inner face of the left hemisphere. Sensory and motor centers are indicated by close shading. *Labeling: acg,* anterior central gyrus; *cc,* corpus callosum; *coll,* midbrain colliculi; *cs,* central sulcus; *ge,* genu or "knee" of corpus callosum; *H1, H2,* first and second transverse temporal gyrus of Heschl; *l,* lunate or simian sulcus; *lc,* lateral calcarine sulcus; *mc,* medial calcarine sulcus; *mb,* midbrain; *olf,* olfactory bulb; *p,* pons or "bridge"; *pcg,* posterior central gyrus; *spl,* splenium or "bandage" of corpus callosum; *th,* thalamus; *II,* chiasma of optic nerves; *III,* oculomotor nerve. (*Cf.* the following figure and Figs. 81, 115, 271, 272, 273, 300, 301; for further description and for the explanation of encircled figures and for the sources, *see* chap. VIII, 1 [4, 5].)

The cortex of Heschl's gyri apparently serves as a substratum of simple, elemental auditory perceptions, such as the intensity, pitch, and other tonal qualities of sound, the tones being arranged according to their proper position, from the highest to the lowest (Fig. 275). The temporal region appears to be a repository of the gnostic and commemorative qualities, such as auditory or vocal language or the recognition and understanding of spoken words and sentences and of their semantic meaning, including grammar and syntax, harmonies and melodies, and symbolic meanings of the various noises.

The *somesthetic sense*, the third principal faculty upon which human intellect is founded, is localized in and around the central sulcus (*cs*, in Figs. 274, 275). This sense may be subdivided into two categories, each with special localization. The one category comprises touch, especially "two-point discrimination," and also to some extent the sense of pain and thermal sense, or exteroceptive qualities with a subjective attribute of the externality; this category depends upon the posterior central gyrus (*pcg*), including the posterior wall of the central sulcus. The other category comprises sensations from the deeper parts of the body, particularly from the locomotor organs, such as the muscles, tendons, and joints of the limbs, which together contribute to the tridimensional sense of space or position of the limbs, or the so-called stereognostic sense; this faculty also depends, according to the latest neurosurgical experiences, upon the postcentral gyrus; but it may also be localized in the anterior central gyrus (*acg*), including the anterior wall of the central sulcus, and perhaps also to some extent in the adjoining parts of the frontal lobe. The numerous afferent fibers originating in the thalamus and terminating in the precentral gyrus and near-by parts of the frontal lobe indicate this (*cf.* Polyak 1932).

Closely allied with the somesthetic sense is the *somatomotor function*, represented by foci whence distinct movements on the contralateral side may be elicited by stimulation or paralysis may result from their damage. Such foci are chiefly in the precentral gyrus (*acg*). The postcentral gyrus directs only crude contralateral movements.

The exteroceptive sense of the bodily surface is represented in an orderly way, by segments and parts thereof, in the contralateral postcentral gyrus (*pcg*), with the mouth, tongue, and lips localized in the parietal *operculum* next to the Sylvian fossa, followed by segments representing the face, thumb, fingers, hand, arm, the trunk, leg, foot, toes, and *perineum* (Fig. 275). The parts which have more elaborate function, such as the tongue, lips, face, hand, and fingers, especially the thumb, have a proportionally larger areal representation than those where the sense is coarse, as on the trunk. In a similar way the numerous small muscles of the hand and arm, performing elaborate skilled movements, are represented in a more detailed way in a larger portion of the precentral gyrus (*cf.* motor and sensory *Homunculus*, in Figs. 9, 10, 22, 114, and 115, in Penfield & Rasmussen 1950).

The exteroceptive postcentral and the motor precentral representations are arranged fairly symmetrically on both sides of the central sulcus for each part or segment of the body. It is probable that this holds also for the proprioceptive qualities in the precentral gyrus.

Other motor centers, such as the frontal oculogyric center for the associated contralateral eye movements, are outside the somatomotor area proper in the frontal lobe, while the other similar optogyric foci for associated eye movements, distributed according to their spatial values, are located along the boundary of the striate area in the occipital lobe, with still other similar auditogyric eye foci attached to the auditory center in the Sylvian fossa and in the temporal lobe.

The other two faculties, the sense of *smell* and of *taste*, of capital importance on the lower levels of the vertebrate scale, in all Primates including Man are relegated in importance to a secondary role. The olfactory function, besides being localized in the olfactory bulb and tract (*olf*), is obviously served by those parts of the brain anatomically related to the first, particularly the prepyriform and periamygdaloid cortex. The gustatory sense is possibly related to the posterior portion of the fornicate or cingular gyrus and/or to the "island" of Reil in the Sylvian fossa.

Human *speech* or *language*, a function intimately related to Man's intellect, is a complex performance in which various parts of the cerebral cortex work together. Its two principal components are the auditory or sensory and the motor.

The sensory-auditory speech center of Wernicke is located in the superior temporal gyrus next to the terminal area of the auditory radia-

sentences, with pronunciation more or less preserved.

The other component of speech, the motor, is localized in the posterior portion of the inferior frontal gyrus, or Broca's area. The usually accepted view assumes the presence of Broca's

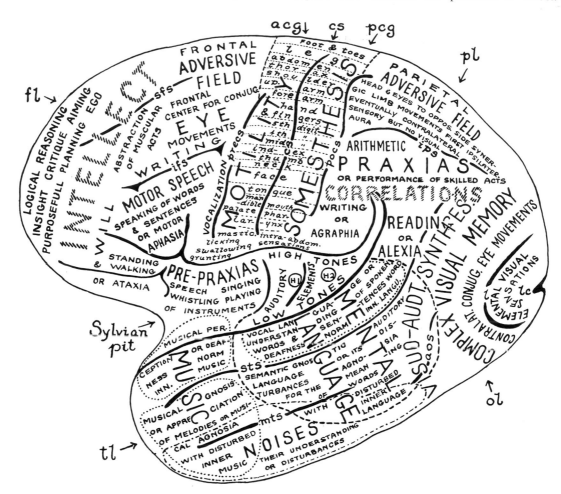

Fig. 275.—Functional map of the motor, sensory, and mental faculties in the human cerebral cortex based upon clinical observations, pathoanatomic investigations, and neurosurgical experiments. Lateral face of the left hemisphere of the human brain with Sylvian pit wide open. *Labeling: aos*, anterior occipital sulcus; *cs*, central sulcus of Rolando; *fl*, frontal lobe; *H1, H2*, first and second transverse temporal gyrus of Heschl; *ips*, intraparietal sulcus; *l*, lunate or simian sulcus; *lc*, lateral or posterior calcarine sulcus; *mts*, middle temporal sulcus; *ol*, occipital lobe; *pl*, parietal lobe; *pocs*, postcentral sulcus; *precs*, precentral sulcus; *sfs*, superior frontal sulcus; *sts*, superior temporal sulcus; *tl*, temporal lobe. (*Cf.* preceding figure and Figs. 115, 271, 272, 273, 300, 301; for further information *see* chap. VIII, 1 [4, 5].)

tion in the transverse temporal gyri of Heschl (*H1, H2*). It serves as a repository of complex auditory memory or auditory gnosis, or recognition and identification of verbal images and sentences. Its impairment results in an auditory word deafness or agnosia for heard words or

center in right-handed people in the left hemisphere of the brain, and in left-handed people in the right hemisphere. Whether this is valid for all or for the majority of individuals, whether perhaps there are exceptions, or whether the cerebral mechanism of language is essentially bilateral, in analogy with the cerebral mechanisms of sight, audition, somesthetic sense, olfaction, gustation, and motility, future investigations alone may show.

5. Comment on Figure 274 on functional localization in the cerebral cortex.—Additional information on the functional localization in the human brain gathered from various sources is indicated by encircled numbers in this figure.

1. Representation of the central fovea and the points of fixation, where in stimulation experiments with conscious subjects various photomas, such as stars, placed straight ahead and standing still, frequently white, or in red, green, blue, and yellow colors, in the shape of diamonds, wheels, disks, or balls, or flashes of bright light, or visual aura of flame, were obtained; when this locality is damaged, homonymous scotomas in and around the points of fixation result, extending to the very dividing meridians (according to this author) or leaving central or "macular" sparing (*see* chap. XI, 8, 9, for the opinions of other authorities).

2. Scintillating photoma or a star moving from the contralateral side below toward the center.

3. Scintillation moving from the contralateral side above toward the center.

4. Lively scintillations or stars coming from the opposite side toward the center.

5. Substratum of complex visual memory; when artificially stimulated, producing either simple subjective sensations, such as lively photomas, bright stars, or balls, either colorless or in colors, flames, a sea of fire; or complex visual images, such as fog or black clouds moving toward the observer, various objects moving from the ipsilateral to the contralateral side, as, e.g., gaudy figures or butterflies coming from the opposite side toward the center, and changing rapidly one after another, or dancing lights; in stimulation experiments always associated with a strong deviation of eyes and turning of the head toward the contralateral side; in epilepsy frequently initiated by a complex visual aura; in damage followed by a contralateral loss of visual memory for shapes, colors, and the arrangement of visual objects, and/or a visual disorientation in space (possibly when damage also includes parts of the cortex labeled with encircled numbers *6, 7, 8,* and *15*).

6. Hallucination of being "far away," or of micropia or micropsia.

7. Repository of the visual verbal images; of the meaning and understanding of written language; when this locality is damaged, the inability to read, called *alexia*, results.

8. Ability to write or to perform kinetic hand and arm movements; a repository of engrams of "kinetic melodies" for writing; its loss results in agraphia or inability to write; a locality whose stimulation produces the inability to speak, or a parietal aphasic arrest.

9. Transverse temporal gyrus or gyri of Heschl (*H1, H2*), a cortical termination of the auditory radiation; the cortical auditory receptor area and distributor center of auditory impulses; when this area is destroyed, the result is central deafness (especially if bilateral); when stimulated, the result is turning of the eyes and the head and correspondingly co-ordinated movements of the body and limbs toward the opposite side; in auditory hallucinations it produces an auditory aura.

10. Wernicke's area, or auditory word transformer; this is the repository of auditory verbal images necessary for the understanding of spoken words and sentences; when it is impaired, perceptive word deafness results, without impairment either of motor or of inner language.

11. Repository of the meaning of auditory language or word semantics; substratum of auditory gnosis or understanding of words, of grammar and syntax; when this is destroyed, sensory aphasia of Wernicke, or agrammatism of Pick (1909), associative word deafness of Henschen, or commemorative word deafness results, with motor speech still possible, but with understanding of spoken language impaired and inner speech lost; when this locality is experimentally stimulated in a conscious human subject, inability to speak results, or the temporal area aphasic speech arrest of Penfield & Rasmussen; a probable localization of bodily vestibular balance; a substratum of complex auditory aura or hallucinations; the origin of Türck's fiber bundle.

12 and *13*. Repository of musical gnosis, or understanding of tonal qualities or pitch of single tones, of melodies, harmonies, or chords, and of rhythm and musical phrases; when damaged, lack of musical understanding results, or sensory amusia, or musical deafness, with inner music either preserved (when *12* destroyed) or impaired (when *13* damaged), with preserved tonal values and melodies, in spite of inability to understand them (musical agnosia); stimulation experiments are accompanied by fear and sensations in the abdomen, associated with movements of the hands.

14. Repository of the recognition or the meaning, or semantic values, of various noises.

15. Localization of the sensation of the position of the body in space; when stimulated, the sensation of dizziness or hallucination of falling results.

16. Center of bodily sense or somesthesis of the contralateral side, that is, of the superficial touch, including two-point discrimination, probably also partly of pain, temperature, and position of the limbs in tridimensional space, or stereognosis, in the opposite half of the body, face, head, and limbs, with the largest areal representation of the most used or most distal parts, such as lips, tongue, hand, fingers, and thumb; when damaged, numbness or hemianesthesia of the opposite half of the body, face, and limbs occurs; or the hallucination of numbness, tingling, pressure, or constriction in the corresponding half or parts results; a locality whence, when stimulated, crude movements of the opposite limbs may be elicited; but no lasting paralysis is produced when damaged.

17. Detailed action of individual muscles or groups of muscles of the contralateral side of the body and limbs or a transient complete contralateral hemiparalysis, with a return of crude movements of limbs and a residual lasting loss of detailed movements of the fingers and of the thumb, associated with spasticity or hypertonia on that side; or, when parts of the precentral gyrus alone are destroyed, resulting in monoplegia of the same character, limited to a particular muscular group or movement.

18. Parietal adversive field or area from which complex synergic movements of the contralateral limbs and eventually also of the ipsilateral ones may be obtained on stimulation, associated with turning of the eyes and head contralaterally; area where poorly localized sensations or sensory aura may be obtained in the contralateral limbs, but no visual aura.

19. Vocalization of inarticulate, nonverbal sounds *ah! oh! ugh!*, on stimulation of either hemisphere, which apparently stimulates the entire sound-producing apparatus, including the mouth, larynx, thorax, diaphragm, and abdomen.

20. Motor speech center; repository of the engrams of complex muscular movements, Monakow's "kinetic melodies" of speech, necessary for the enunciation of words and sentences and for singing, which may be possible, even though the auditory area of Wernicke (*10*) and its surroundings (*11*) may be damaged, resulting in Broca's motor aphasia, or inability to speak, with understanding of heard and written language still more or less preserved (provided that areae *7–14* and their connections escape injury); area whence interference with motor speech may be obtained on stimulation, or the frontal area of aphasic arrest.

21. Hypothetical substratum of abstract thinking; frontal center for equilibrium, or balance in standing, walking, and maintaining direction; when damaged, ataxia results, associated with change of character, irritability, moodiness, illogical thinking and acting, decrease of memory, eventually terminating in dementia.

22. Presumable motor and somesthetic centers for the contralateral leg and toes (according to Scarff 1940), or centers for the contralateral toes, for genitalia, and for the rectum (according to Penfield & Rasmussen 1950).

23. Centers for poorly localized sensations and involuntary movements of the alimentary system of organs and of intra-abdominal sensations (according to Penfield & Rasmussen 1950); centers for the regulation of blood pressure, respiration, and gastric motility (according to B. L. Hoffman 1951).

The preceding account and the diagrammatic representation of the present knowledge of the functional cerebral localization given in Figures 274 and 275 is a far cry from the "phrenology" of Gall, devised almost a century and a half ago, discussed in the historical part of this book. In it the tremendous efforts of countless anatomists, physiological experimenters, and clinical and pathoanatomical observers are incorporated. Even so, as yet we have no more than a good foundation on which future investigators may build. In conclusion, it is fitting here to emphasize again the necessity for a thorough analysis of synaptical structures of the cerebral cortex, of which hardly a beginning has been made by S. Ramón y Cajal and a few other investigators, a work essential and indispensable to the proper understanding of the cortical mechanism (*cf.* sec. 7, this chapter).

Figures 274 and 275 represent a diagrammatic synthesis taken from several sources, chiefly from S. E. Henschen (*J. f. Psychol. u. Neurol.*, v. 22, 1918; *Ztschr. f. d. ges. Neurol. u. Psychiat.-Orig.*, vs. 47 and 52, 1919), Quensel & Pfeifer (*Zentralbl. f. d. ges. Neurol. u. Psychiat.*, v. 30, 1922; *Deutsche Ztschr. f. Nervenheilk.*, v. 77; *Ztschr. f. d. ges. Neurol. u. Psychiat.*, v. 81, 1922–23), O. Foerster (*J. f. Psychol. u. Neurol.*, v. 39; *Arch. Neurol. & Psychiat.*, v. 24, 1929), Foerster & Penfield (*Brain*, v. 53, 1930; *Ztschr. f. d. ges. Neurol. u. Psychiat.*, v. 125, 1930), J. M. Nielsen (*Agnosia*, etc., 1946), and Penfield & Rasmussen (*The Cerebral Cortex of Man*, 1950).

References: Ades & Felder 1942; Ades & Raab 1948; Alajouanine 1948; R. Anthony 1928; Ariëns Kappers 1913, 1929; Ariëns Kappers, Huber & Crosby 1936; Bárány & Vogt 1923; Ph. Bard 1938; D. H. Barron 1948; E. Beck 1928, 1929, 1930; Bender & Nathanson 1950; Bernhard, Gellhorn & Rasmussen 1953; T. L. Bischoff 1868; Boeke 1934; Boldrey & Penfield 1937; Bolton 1900, 1933; Bonin, Garol & Mc-Culloch 1941; Bouillaud 1825, 1839; Broca 1861, 1863, 1864, 1865, 1868, 1888; T. G. Brown 1927; Brummelkamp 1943–45; Bumke & Foerster 1935–37; Connolly 1936, 1940, 1941–43, 1950, 1953; Clark & Russell 1938; C. D. Cunningham 1890, 1891, 1892, 1943; Dandy 1930, 1933, 1946, 1948; Dejerine 1926; Ecker 1873; L. Edinger 1908–11; Feuchtwanger 1923; Filimonoff 1929, 1947; Foerster 1923, 1926, 1929, 1934, 1936; Foerster & Penfield 1930; Franz 1923, 1924, 1927; Friant 1940; Fritsch & Hitzig 1870; Fulton 1943; Fulton & Dusser de Barenne 1933; Gooddy 1949; Haller von Hallerstein 1934; Halstead 1948; Harman 1946; Henle 1871; S. E. Henschen 1890–1930, etc.; C. J. Herrick 1921, 1943; R. L. Heschl 1878; Hesse & Doflein 1935; M. Hines 1921, 1929, 1934, 1942; W. His 1904; Hochstetter 1919–29; M. Holl 1907, 1908, 1909; W. H. Hollinshead 1954; G. Holmes 1918, 1919, 1931; Jakob & Onelli 1911; Johnston 1909, 1910; H. H. Joy 1948, 1949; K. Kleist; Klüver & Bucy 1937–39; R. Klose 1920; Kornmüller 1932–37; Kuhlenbeck 1922, 1927; Larsell 1942; Liddell & Phillips 1951; Lieberman 1951; H. Liepmann; Liepmann *et al.*; McCulloch *et al.* 1942; McFie *et al.* 1950; Mall 1914; Mankowski 1929; Mettler 1942; Mills 1927, 1929; Minkowski 1928; K. Mollweide 1925; Monakow 1902, 1914; H. Morris 1942; Nielsen 1946, 1950; Niessl von Mayendorf 1908, 1911, 1922–23, 1925, 1927, 1930, 1933–37, 1936; Pansch 1868; Penfield 1937–38, 1938; Penfield & Boldrey 1937; Penfield & Erickson 1941; Penfield & Evans 1934, 1935; Penfield & Gage 1934; Penfield & Rasmussen 1940; R. A. Pfeifer 1920, 1921, 1925, 1930, 1932, 1936; A. Pick 1920; Pötzl; Pötzl *et al.*; Quensel; Quensel & Pfeifer; Ranson & Clark 1947; C. von Rad 1931; Reichert 1859–61; G. Retzius 1896, 1898, 1901, 1906; Révész 1917; L. Roberts 1951; Robinson & Pribram 1951; Rose 1912, 1929; M. Roth 1949; T. C. Ruch *et al.*; G. Rylander 1939; Scarff 1940; Schepers 1948; G. Elliot Smith 1903, 1904, 1907, 1909, 1919, 1923; J. Soury 1895, 1895–96, 1896, 1899, 1901; Spalteholtz 1926; Spiegel & Sommer 1944; Strassburger 1941; H. Strauss 1925; Streeter 1906; Strong & Elwyn; Tilney 1928; Toldt 1907; O. A. Turner 1948; C. & O. Vogt 1919, 1926; Waldeyer 1895; R. Wagner 1860–62; W. Wagner 1937; Walker & Weaver 1940; Walshe 1942; Wernicke 1875; Woodburne & Crosby 1938; Woolsey, Marshall & Bard 1942; Woolsey & Walzl 1942; Ziehen 1903–34, 1920, 1924; Zuckerkandl 1894, 1902–5, 1903, 1904, 1906, 1908, 1910; Zuckerman & Fisher 1937; Zuckerman & Fulton 1940–41.

SEC. 2. GROSS ANATOMY OF THE CORTICAL VISUAL CENTERS

1. MORPHOLOGY OF THE HUMAN CALCARINE FISSURE.—The calcarine sulcus or fissure, described and named by T. H. Huxley (1861; portrait, Fig. 276), also called the calcarine or striate fossa or pit by G. Elliot Smith (portrait, Fig. 277), is a locality of the cerebral cortex directly related to the visual function. The evidence in support of this view is given in chapter VII and is further discussed in chapters IV, XI, and XII.

below the splenium of the corpus callosum (*spl*) about as far as the tip or pole of the occipital lobe (*mc* and *lc* in Figs. 271, 273). The anterior portion is rather shallow, the posterior stretch is a deep and spacious pocket that includes a considerable area of the cortex (Fig.

FIG. 276.—Thomas Henry Huxley (1825–95), professor of physiology in London. A notable biologist and foremost advocate of Darwin's "theory of evolution." First described and named the "calcarine sulcus" of the occipital lobes of the primate brain. From Stirling, *Some Apostles of Physiology*, Waterlow & Sons, London, 1902.

rectly related to the visual function. The evidence in support of this view is given in chapter VII and is further discussed in chapters IV, XI, and XII.

The calcarine fissure is a long furrow extending on the medial face of the occipital lobe in a roughly horizontal direction from the isthmus (*isth*) of the fornicate or cingular gyrus (*fcg*)

278). The reverse situation is occasionally found in individual cases, with the anterior portion much more roomy than the posterior or polar portion.

The human calcarine fissure embodies morphological features common to all advanced Primates, Monkeys, Apes, and Man, in addition to those that must be considered specifically human. It is an evolutionary product, frequently sketchy and incomplete, of a merging or fusion of two distinct sulcal components arising within the territory of the striate area: (1) the medial or anterior calcarine sulcus (*mc*) between the fornicate-hippocampal isthmus and the posterior cuneolingual gyrus; and (2) the lateral or posterior calcarine sulcus behind

cipital pole. Usually it is curved, making one or more arches, with their convexities facing up or down. Also, either the fissure may be close to the lower margin of the medial face of the occipital lobe, making for a large cuneus, or the arches of the fissure may be considerably pushed upward, reducing the cuneus to half its usual size.

Photo by F. W. Schmidt, Manchester
By permission

Grafton Elliot Smith

Fig. 277.—Grafton Elliot Smith (1871–1937), professor of anatomy at the University College of London, a life-long student of the brain, especially of the cerebral cortex and of the visual center ("striate area," "lunate sulcus"), and an imaginative investigator of Man's origin (from J. Anat., v. 71, 1937). Courtesy J. Anat., and F. W. Schmidt, photographer, Manchester, England. *See*, for biography, Haymaker & Baer, *The Founders of Neurology*, 1953. For Smith's contributions to neurology *see* H. H. Woollard, in J. Anat., v. 72, p. 280, 1938.

the posterior cuneolingual gyrus (*lc*); (*cf*. par. 2, this section, and sec. 3, this chapter).

The configuration of the calcarine fissure varies much in individual brains and in each hemisphere of a particular brain. It is rarely a single, fairly straight, horizontally placed furrow running from the isthmal region to the oc-

The calcarine fissure usually meets the medial parieto-occipital fissure (*po*) at a point about one-third the distance between the callosal splenium and the occipital pole, or farther away from the splenium. The posterior end of the calcarine fissure, often forked, may be precisely at the occipital pole, or may be short of it, or may turn for a shorter or longer stretch around it onto the posterolateral face, or may be turned up or down.

Two lips—an upper cuneal or cuneofornicate (*cl*, dorsal *labium*) and a lower or lingual lip (*ll*, ventral *labium*)—are distinguished along most of the stretch of the calcarine fissure (Fig. 273, right diagram; Fig. 278). Frequently these lips are separated from the remainder of the cuneus and the lingual gyrus by secondary sulci running more or less parallel with the calcarine sulcus: the medial and lateral superior and inferior paracalcarine sulci (*msps*, *mips*, *lsps*, *lips*, in Figs. 273, 293).

When the lips of the calcarine fissure are drawn apart, the details of its floor, otherwise concealed, become visible (Fig. 278). In the anterior or precuneal portion, one or two small curved gyri are found hanging from the upper lip and oriented somewhat parallel to its margin: the cryptocalcarine gyri. Frequently, the anterior, attenuated, wedgelike portion of the cuneus continues in the anterior calcarine fissure, as an extension of the upper or cuneal lip, for quite a distance beneath the overhanging posteriormost gyrus of the precuneal cortex of the parietal lobe.

In the cuneal portion of the fissure one or more short, more or less vertical, or slanting gyri are found connecting the cuneus with the lingual gyrus: the anterior and posterior cuneolingual gyri of Cunningham. (According to Cunningham, one or the other gyrus is absent in from 8 to 10 per cent of brain specimens; according to others, these gyri are less frequent; according to our own experience, these gyri or their vestiges are present in most brains, the posterior one being a more stable feature.)

In some brains, or hemispheres, the cuneolingual gyri are not submerged and are visible on the medial surface, breaking up the calcarine fissure into two or more segments, the original constituents of the fissure (*cula*, *culpo*, in Fig. 295). Usually the posterior cuneolingual gyrus alone is on the surface, separating the anteromedial (*mc*) from the posterolateral (*lc*) calcarine sulcus (*see* right diagram, in Fig. 273). On occasion there are two anterior cuneolingual gyri, an upper one hanging from the upper lip and a lower one situated slightly more anteriorly, both gyri fitted to one another like the

teeth of two cogwheels (Fig. 295, lower diagram). In still other cases no cuneolingual gyri whatever are found, and the entire calcarine fissure is a continuous, deep, smooth furrow (Fig. 293, lower diagram).

Altogether, the configuration of the calcarine fissure shows almost an infinity of individual variation of essentially the same sulcal and gyral pattern, in close association with, and dependence upon, the development of the adjoining regions of the occipital, parietal, and temporal lobes. No two brains and no two hemispheres of the same brain are exactly alike in all details of the calcarine fissural complex, although specimens are occasionally encountered in which the configuration in both hemispheres attains a remarkable degree of similarity. (*See* Zuckerkandl 1906; G. E. Smith; and Antoni, for additional data on the calcarine fissure.)

Hidden in the calcarine fissure is the calcarine artery, a branch of the posterior cerebral artery (Fig. 278). It gives off several twigs of various sizes for the two lips and for the cuneus. These arteries, in part, emerge with their terminal branches upon the cuneus, lingual gyrus, and the surface around the occipital pole. The same calcarine artery usually also gives off a large branch for the parieto-occipital sulcus, the posterior parietal artery. Another branch passing to the collateral sulcus—the collateral artery, a branch of the posterior temporo-occipital artery—spreads over the ventral face of the occipital lobe. (*See* chap. X, 5, 6, 8, and corresponding figures, for additional information on blood supply.)

2. Morphology of the simian calcarine fissure.—In the simian brain the calcarine fissure has, in general, the same position on the inner or medial face of the occipito-parieto-temporal lobes as in the human brain. In the Indian Rhesus Macaque (Fig. 280), for example, and also in most other Monkeys its posterior extremity regularly forks into an ascending and a descending ramus or branch (*mc*, in *D* and *G*, in same figure; *see also* Connolly 1936, 1950).

The similarity of configuration of the simian and human calcarine fissure, however, is only apparent. In reality, the calcarine fissure of the Monkey is homologous only with approxi-

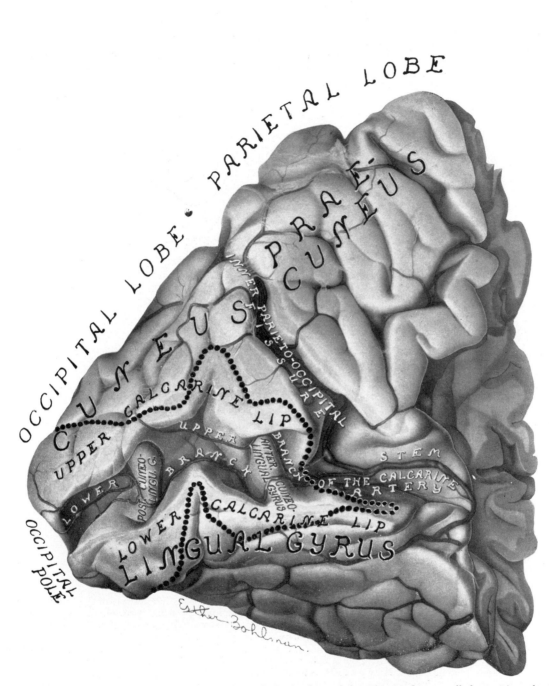

Fig. 278.—Left occipital lobe viewed from the medial side. Lips of the calcarine fissure pulled apart in order to show the inner configuration, in particular the two cuneo-lingual gyri, and the distribution of the calcarine artery. Dotted line indicates the boundary of the striate area. (*Cf.* Figs. 288, 290, 293, 294, 295, 296.)

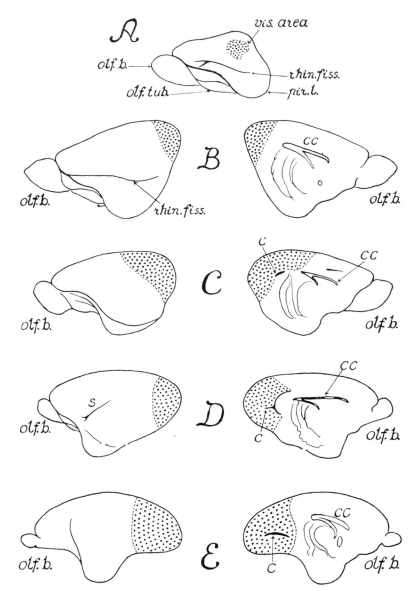

Fig. 279.—Composite drawing showing successive increase in size and change in shape and position of the cortical visual center, the striate area (*stippled*), in the forerunners and in the early representatives of the Primate Mammals, in dependence upon the mode of life: *A*, Jumping Shrew (*Macroscelides;* Africa; terrestrial, diurnal, moderately macrosmatic, large eyes, large anterior colliculi, but small and structurally poorly differentiated striate area; figure from Le Gros Clark 1928); *B*, Pen-tailed Shrew (*Ptilocercus lowii;* Borneo, Sumatra, Banka; arboreal, nocturnal, with small eyes and small, poorly differentiated striate area; figure from Le Gros Clark 1926); *C*, Tree Shrew (*Tupaia minor;* Malaya; mostly arboreal, diurnal, insectivorous, and fructivorous; rather large eyes; well-differentiated striate area spreading over a large part of hemisphere, on inside as far as calcarine sulcus, *c*, phylogenetically first to appear here; figure from Le Gros Clark, 1931); *D*, Mouse Lemur (*Microcebus murinus;* Madagascar; thoroughly arboreal, nocturnal, insectivorous, and fructivorous; eyes large; large striate area partly lining the calcarine fissure, *c*, which is here further extended in comparison with the Tree Shrew; figure from Le Gros Clark 1931, represents the "most primitive type of lemuroid brain"); *E*, Tarsier (*Tarsius spectrum;* Malaya; arboreal, nocturnal, subsists on insects, lizards, and other small animals; eyes very large, owl-like, relatively largest of all Mammals; striate area, comprising almost one-third of the cortex, surrounds and lines the calcarine fissure, *c*; figure from Woollard 1926). Note the gradual recession of olfactory parts (*olf.b., olf.tub., pir.l.*) as the striate area expands. *Other labeling: cc*, corpus callosum; *olf.b.*, olfactory bulb; *olf.tub.*, olfactory tubercle; *pir.l.*, piriform lobe; *rhin.fiss.*, rhinal fissure; *vis. area*, striate area. (For further information on Jumping Shrew, Tree Shrew, and Tarsier *see* chap. XIV, 10, 12.)

mately the anterior two-thirds or so of the human fissure, exactly from its anterior extremity at the fornicate-hippocampal *isthmus* or "neck" (*isth*, Fig. 273) to about midway or a little more of its cuneal stretch, or precisely as far back as the posterior cuneolingual gyrus (*cul gyr*). This portion corresponds to the "stem" and the "posterior calcarine fissure" of Cunningham; to the "proper," "limiting," or "prestriate calcarine sulcus," together with the "retrocalcarine" of G. E. Smith (*see* G. E. Smith, Tr. Linn. Soc. 1902, p. 386); or to the "medial striate" or "intermediate portion of the calcarine fissure" of Kuhlenbeck. In the terminology adopted in this book this portion of the calcarine fissure of the simian brain and its human homologue, for reasons dealt with in the subsequent pages, is called the *medial* or *anterior calcarine fissure* (*mc* in the accompanying illustrations).

In the Monkey, the portion of the cortex homologous with the posterior third or so of the human calcarine fissure (*lc*, in Fig. 273), the "external calcarine sulcus" of Cunningham, is still located on the lateral, convex face of the cerebral hemisphere. It is not yet included in the fissure, and it still remains wide open: the occipital operculum of the simian brain (*oo*), largely identical with the simian occipital lobe (*ol*, in Fig. 280, *A*, *B*, *C*, *E*, *F*).

In most Old World Monkeys—for example, in large specimens of the Macaque—there is found an incipient invagination of the opercular striate cortex, from which the human polar calcarine fossa or pit (*lc*) behind the posterior cuneolingual gyrus develops (Fig. 280). This invagination is usually indicated by a shallow, but well-marked, sulcus, less often merely by a slight depression, on the lateral face of the occipital lobe (*lc*, same figure). This is the "superior" or "horizontal occipital," "occipital diagonal," "lateral intrastriate," or "opercular sulcus," more correctly called the "external calcarine sulcus" by Cunningham and "lateral calcarine sulcus" by Ingalls.

Occasionally, there may be two short and shallow lateral sulci arranged in succession, one close to the simian sulcus, the other curving around the occipital pole and embracing the inferior prong of the medial calcarine sulcus from beneath, obviously an intermediate arrangement indicating a beginning of the merging into a complete lateral calcarine sulcus of the simian brain. In still other cases only a short dent beneath the inferior prong of *mc*, with or without a slight depression close to *l*, indicates the very beginnings of the formation of a lateral calcarine sulcus.

Because of the usual three-pronged, shamrock-like formation of the lateral calcarine sulcus in the Anthropomorphous Apes (*lc*, in Figs. 284, 286), it was named "triradiate sulcus" by Landau, "ypsiliform sulcus" by Ariëns Kappers, "sulcus *x*" by others, and, because it is located within the lateral portion of the striate area, "lateral intrastriate sulcus" by G. Elliot Smith. For reasons to be discussed subsequently, this sulcus is simply called "lateral or posterior calcarine sulcus or fissure" (*lc*) in this book.

Except for this "oriment," or phylogenetical beginning, of what, during further evolutionary stages, develops into a posterior, foveal-areal segment of the human calcarine fissure at the occipital pole, in contrast with the complicated configuration of the human hemisphere, the lateral face of the occipital lobe is rather smooth in most of the Lower Simians, especially the Catarrhines.

Also, in the catarrhine Simians the occipital lobe is sharply separated from the rest of the hemisphere by a deep furrow or cleft, the lateral or external parieto-occipital sulcus or fossa, called the "external or perpendicular fissure" by Gratiolet and by Huxley, and known since Rüdinger (1882) as the "simian sulcus or fissure," *sulcus* or *fissura simialis* or *f. simiarum*, and *Affenspalte* or "monkey cleft or slit" (*l*, in Figs. 280–86).

How the "calcarine sulcal complex" of the advanced Simians and of Man developed from these original component oriments of the simian brain is treated in section 3, in this chapter.

References: J. Anthony 1943; R. Anthony 1928; Antoni 1914; Ariëns Kappers, Huber & Crosby 1936; Bolton 1900, 1933; Brodmann 1909 (1925); Brouwer 1936; Le Gros Clark 1934, 1942; Connolly 1933, 1936, 1941–43, 1950; C. D. Cunningham 1890, 1891, 1892, 1943; Ecker 1873; Economo & Koskinas 1925; Filimonoff 1931–33; Friant 1940; Geist 1930;

Gray & Goss 1948; Hartman & Strauss; M. Hines 1934, 1942; M. Holl 1907, 1908, 1909; G. Holmes 1918, 1919, 1931; Hulshoff 1917; T. H. Huxley 1861; Ingalls 1914; Kohlbrugge 1903; Kükenthal & Ziehen 1895; Kuhlenbeck 1928; E. Kurz 1924; Landau 1915, 1916; Mauss, 1908, 1911; Mettler 1933; Mingazzini 1893, 1928; Monakow 1902; Morris 1942; Pansch 1868; Papez 1929; G. Retzius 1895, 1898, 1906; Roch 1941; Rüdinger 1882; G. Elliot Smith 1900–1903, 1903, 1904, 1907, 1908, 1909, 1910, 1929; Tilney 1928; Waldeyer 1895; Ziehen 1896, 1903, 1903–34; Zuckerkandl 1894, 1902–5, 1903, 1905, 1906, 1910.

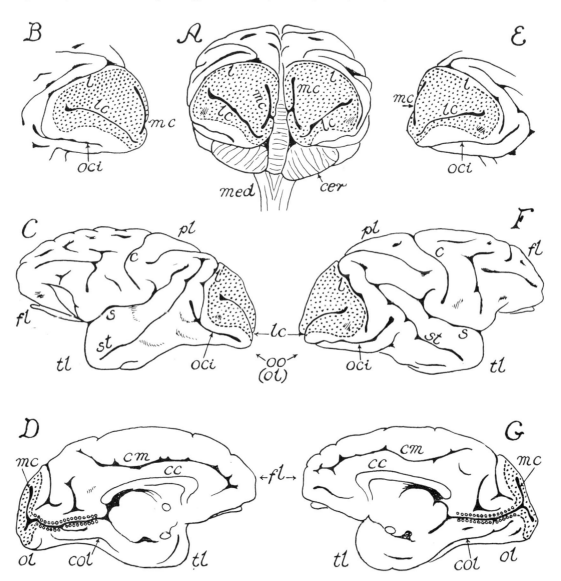

Fig. 280.—External configuration of the brain of a Rhesus Macaque showing the extent and location of the visual cortex, or striate area (exposed portion stippled; concealed portion marked by circles). *A*, posterior view of both hemispheres showing two occipital lobes in relation to each other and to the rest of the brain; *B*, posterolateral aspect of left occipital lobe (operculum); *C*, lateral, *D*, medial views of left hemisphere; *E*, posterolateral aspect of right occipital lobe (operculum); *F*, lateral, *G*, medial views of right hemisphere. *Labeling:* c, central sulcus of Rolando; cc, corpus callosum; cer, cerebellum; cm, callosomarginal sulcus; col, collateral sulcus; fl, frontal lobe; l, lunate or simian sulcus; lc, lateral calcarine sulcus; mc, medial calcarine sulcus; med, medulla oblongata; oci, inferior occipital sulcus; oo (ol), occipital operculum or occipital lobe; pl, parietal lobe; S, Sylvian fissure; st, superior temporal sulcus; tl, temporal lobe. Reproduced slightly reduced. Note the relatively large size of the striate area compared with the rest of the cortex; the occipital lobes are almost entirely taken over by the striate cortex.

SEC. 3. PHYLOGENY OF THE HUMAN CALCARINE FISSURE
AND THE STRIATE AREA

1. ORIGIN OF THE HUMAN CALCARINE FISSURE AND OF THE STRIATE AREA FROM THE VISUAL CENTERS OF INFRAHUMAN MAMMALS.—The peculiar anatomical features of the calcarine fissure of the fully developed, mature human brain and the topography and functional organization of the human striate area can be understood only if due consideration is paid to all those phases of the long process of phylogenesis which

isfactory phylogenetical explanation. This is the more necessary in view of the otherwise detailed retinotopical homology of the striate area of Man and his lesser relatives, the Monkeys and the Apes, abundantly demonstrated both by experimental investigations and by clinical and pathological-anatomical observations. (*See* in chap. VI, 7; chap. VII, 4, 5, 6; and Part III this book.)

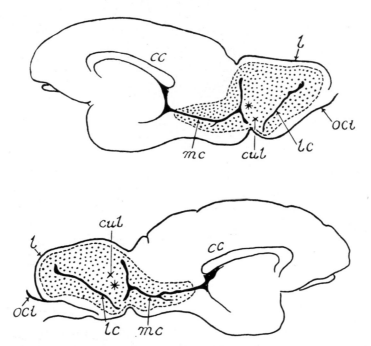

FIG. 281.—Right (*upper diagram*) and left cerebral hemisphere (*lower diagram*) of an adult Rhesus Macaque, with the occipital opercula represented turned back in order to align the lateral calcarine sulcus (*lc*) with the medial calcarine sulcus (*mc*), to conform to the condition usually found in the human brain. Both striate areae are represented in flat view. *Labeling: cc,* corpus callosum; *l,* lunate or simian sulcus; *oci,* inferior occipital sulcus. Asterisks (*) mark the position of the original occipital poles serving as hinges around which, during the process of phylogenesis, the simian occipital opercula rotate backward and medialward. Note the extraordinary relative length of the calcarine sulcal complex (*lc* and *mc*) and of the striate area (*stippled*), equaling two-thirds of the entire hemisphere. Compare with the conditions in Ateles (Figs. 282, 283), Chimpanzee (Figs. 284, 285), Gorilla (Fig. 286), and Man (Figs. 289–96). Reproduced at less than natural size.

have brought into existence the human cortical centers of sight.

Above all, the striking fact that in Man almost the entire striate area is found buried in a long and deep calcarine fissure wholly, or almost wholly, located on the medial face of the hemisphere, whereas in the lower Primates not less than half of the striate area is spread over the lateral face of the occipital lobe, requires a sat-

The complete retinotopical homology of that portion of the striate area which covers the simian occipital operculum, or the "primitive occipital lobe," with the posterior third or so of the human calcarine fissure is clearly supported by the experiments already referred to.

Other evidence also supports this thesis, for example, the obvious fact that almost the entire cortex of the occipital operculum of the lesser Primates belongs to the striate area (Fig. 280) and, above all, the mechanics of the phylogenetical process, because of which the striate area was gradually dislocated backward in the Primates, from the lowest to the highest.

The use in this connection of phylogenesis as evidence appears permissible, at least as an illustration of the probable stages of an evolutionary process through which the human cortical center of vision has passed, even though the now living and the known extinct representa-

tives of the various suborders of Primates may not represent a "true phylogenetical series," since they may not be in every respect identical with the direct lineal ancestral links which preceded Modern Man. (*See*, for the phylogeny of Primates, Charles Darwin 1859, 1871 and subsequent editions; E. Haeckel 1866, 1891, 1894–96; Chapman 1904; G. Elliot Smith 1919, 1927, 1930; Le Gros Clark 1925, 1934, 1935, 1947; Regan 1930; Gregory 1934, 1935, 1951; Zuckerman & Fulton 1934; Parker & Haswell 1940;

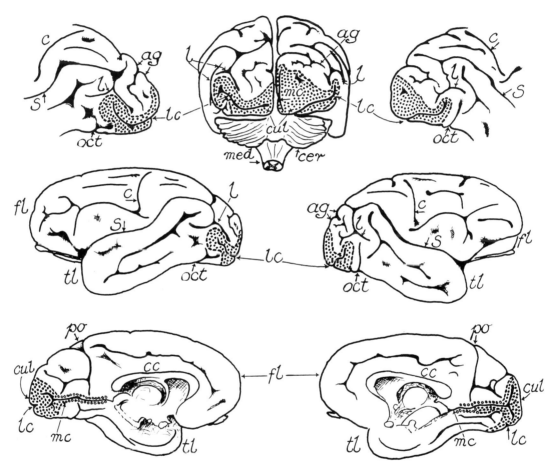

FIG. 282.—External configuration of the brain of a Red Spider Monkey (*Ateles paniscus?*; *cf*. preceding figure). This type represents the phylogenetical advancement in the evolution of the calcarine sulcal complex and striate area, compared with the Rhesus Monkey (Figs. 280, 281) and approaches somewhat the Anthropomorphous Apes (Figs. 284, 286). Arrangement and designation of diagrams same as in preceding figures. Lateral calcarine sulcus (*lc*), now fully developed, includes much of striate cortex that spreads less over exposed face of occipital lobes. In this way a condition is prepared which is realized in the brain of Anthropomorphous Apes. Another notable difference in comparison with the Macaque is an areal expansion of the cortex adjoining the striate area manifested by an emergence of annectent gyri (*ag*) and an anterior displacement of parieto-occipital sulcus (*po*) over the medial face. In addition, there is a general increase in area and in sulcal-gyral elaboration of the entire brain, bringing the Spider Monkey in this respect closer to the Anthropomorphous Apes, an advancement reflected in higher mental capacities resembling those of the Chimpanzee (Klüver). *Labeling: ag*, annectent gyri; *c*, central sulcus; *cc*, corpus callosum; *cer*, cerebellum; *cul*, cuneolingual gyrus; *fl*, frontal lobe; *l*, lunate sulcus; *lc*, lateral calcarine sulcus; *mc*, medial calcarine sulcus; *med*, medulla oblongata; *oct*, occipitotemporal sulcus; *po*, parieto-occipital sulcus; *S*, Sylvian fissure; *tl*, temporal lobe. Reproduced below natural size.

Romer 1943, 1945; G. G. Simpson 1949; and especially W. L. Straus, Jr. 1949; *see also* corresponding sections of chaps. XIV and XV.)

2. Cortical visual centers of the Tree Shrew, Lemur, Tarsier, and the Lower Monkeys.—The probable course of phylogeny, which, starting from the original "basal primate stock," the primitive Prosimians or Protoprimates

iae or Lemurs of warm parts of Asia and of Africa, especially Madagascar (Lemuroidea, Fig. 279, *D;* Fig. 307). In these families, because of the gradual change from a terrestrial to an arboreal mode of life, increased use of the visual organs caused an expansion of the striate area in comparison with that of their subprimate precursors, the nonarboreal Insectivorous Mammals, exemplified by the Soricide Shrews,

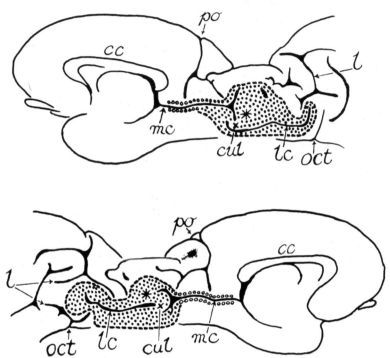

Fig. 283.—Calcarine fissural complex and its relation to the striate area and adjoining sulci and gyri in the brain of a Red Spider Monkey (*Ateles paniscus?*), presented in the same way as in Fig. 281. Right (*upper diagram*) and left cerebral hemisphere (*lower diagram*). Exposed parts of the striate areae stippled, parts buried in the calcarine fissures indicated by circles. Both striate areae presented in a flat view. Note a slight decrease of striate cortex in proportion to the remainder of the cerebral cortex, compared with the Rhesus Macaque. Most of the striate cortex is still along and in the lateral or posterior calcarine sulcus (*lc*), and at the occipital pole (*), and only a little along and in the medial or anterior calcarine sulcus (*mc*). However, both segments of the calcarine sulcus (*lc* and *mc*) are better aligned than in the Rhesus Macaque in preparation for the next stage found in Apes and Man. Cuneolingual gyri (*cul*) well developed. (*Cf.* preceding figure.) *Labeling: cc,* corpus callosum; *cul,* posterior cuneolingual gyrus; *l,* lunate sulcus; *lc,* lateral or posterior calcarine sulcus; *mc,* medial or anterior calcarine sulcus; *oct,* occipitotemporal sulcus; *po,* parieto-occipital sulcus.

mates, had gradually culminated in the visual centers of the human brain, may be imagined to have progressed somewhat as follows:

The first phylogenetical stage in the process of anthropogenesis, just above the level of the Terrestrial Shrews, may be exemplified by the partly arboreal Tree Shrews or Tupaiidae of Southeastern Asia (*Ptilocercus lowii, Tupaia tana, T. minor, Urogale everetti,* etc., *see* Fig. 279, *B, C;* and chap. XIV), and by the Prosim-

Hedgehog, Elephant Shrew, Jumping Shrew, *Solenodon, Centetes,* etc. (Fig. 279, *A*).

The early Tarsiers (Tarsioidea, Fig. 279, *E*) and the true Monkeys, which have developed from them (Lower Anthropoidea, Figs. 280, 281, 302, 306) may serve as an illustration of the next, the second, stage. This further trend was apparently also caused by a continued emphasis upon vision as the leading sense, necessitated by a more complete change from a terrestrial to an arboreal mode of life. In the Monkeys the visual projection center, the striate area of the cerebral cortex, concerned with an immediate utilization of visual impressions, attained its relative maximum of surface expansion.

Anatomically, this evolutionary phase culminated, in the words of G. Elliot Smith, in the development of "a mushroomlike outgrowth," a large occipital operculum (*oo*), with the opercularization of a part of the extrastriate cortex hitherto exposed, and in the formation of a simian sulcus (*l*), found in most of the modern Monkeys, both American Platyrrhines and Old World Catarrhines, especially in the Cercopithecidae (Mangabey, Macaque, Baboon, etc.); the most primitive species, e.g., the Marmosets, are an exception (*see* Figs. 306, 307).

3. CORTICAL VISUAL CENTERS OF THE ADVANCED MONKEYS AND APES.—The anatomical peculiarities of the cortical visual centers found in the large modern Anthropomorphous Apes were foreshadowed by conditions present in certain Catarrhines of the Old World, for example, the Langur or Langoor of India (*Semnopithecus* or *Presbytis*, Fig. 304), and decidedly so in the larger Platyrrhines of the New World.

In this, the third, phylogenetical stage the striate area exposed on the convex face of the occipital lobe is already noticeably reduced and somewhat displaced backward, to the occipital pole. In the *Ateles* or Spider Monkey, considered to be the most advanced of the Platyrrhines, this transformation is quite striking (*see* Figs. 282, 283). The examination of its brain and a comparison with that of the Macaque (Figs. 280, 281) suggest that this "decline and recession" of the occipital operculum was induced not by an originally lesser expansion of the striate area in comparison with the Lower Catarrhines, but—since, in fact, in the *Ateles*, the Chimpanzee, and the Gorilla that area either is as extensive as in the Macaque or even increases in surface—by a genuine increase and elaboration of the cortex surrounding the striate area. The relative size and the sulcal and gyral elaboration in the *Ateles* indicate that all adjoining regions—the parietal, temporal, and extrastriate occipital—had contributed to this development. The greatest contribution appears to have been from the cortex sunk in the

deep simian fossa or pit, found in the Lower Monkeys, such as the Macaque, largely comprising the cytoarchitectural para-peristriate area of G. Elliot Smith, the fields *18–19* of Brodmann, or the visuopsychic area of Campbell.

The incipient augmentation of this cortical locality is indicated, in the Rhesus Macaque, by several small gyri entirely concealed in the simian pit, named by Gratiolet (1854) *plis de passage*, also called *Brückenwindungen*, or "annectent gyri," meaning gyri connecting the parietal and occipital regions (*see also* Zuckerkandl 1906; Holl 1907, 1908; Hulshoff; Anthony 1928, 1943; Economo 1930; Mettler 1935; Connolly 1936, 1950; Kinosita 1942–44).

The cortex forming the annectent gyri and lining the remainder of the simian pit (*l*) evidently served as an "oriment" or "phylogenetical starting point," which, from modest beginnings, through gradual augmentation and expansion—the stages represented by the Mangabey, Spider Monkey, and Gibbon—developed into the next phylogenetical stage found in the large Anthropomorphous Apes (Chimpanzee, Orangutan, Gorilla; *see ag* in Fig. 284, *A*, *B*, *E*; Fig. 286). The prime factor responsible for this fourth phylogenetical stage seems to be a shift in the functional emphasis from what was originally largely a perceptive to an apperceptive or "psychic" utilization of visual and other impressions. Such an "intellectualization," in turn, necessitated a further expansion of the entire cortex between the visual, somesthetic, and auditory centers, resulting in the development of the spacious posterior parietotemporooccipital "association area" of Flechsig (*see* chap. IV, 2; and Fig. 115, *IX*).

Owing to this expansion of the cortex in a limited space, manifested in a gradual emergence of the annectent gyri upon the free surface of the brain, and an over-all increase of the cortex intervening between the terminal areae of the three principal afferent pathways—the visual, auditory, and somesthetic—the original simian occipital lobe or occipital operculum was rolled back, and the lateral portion of the striate area displaced backward and rolled in to form the lateral or posterior calcarine sulcus of the hominoid and hominid brain (*lc*).

The other consequence of this transformation was an alignment and a more or less complete fusion of the lateral calcarine with the medial calcarine sulcus (*mc*), the beginning of which is well illustrated in Figure 285 (upper diagram). In this way the phylogenetically younger lateral component became merged with the older medial component. This fusion may be considered a preparation for the final phylogenetical stage, a calcarine fissural complex of the mod-

ern human brain, where in some cases such fusion may be complete to a degree where all traces of the original constituents are obliterated. During this evolutionary process, owing to a turning-back and folding-in of the opercular portion of the striate area, the posterior cuneolingual gyrus is formed (*cul*, in Figs. 285, 286).

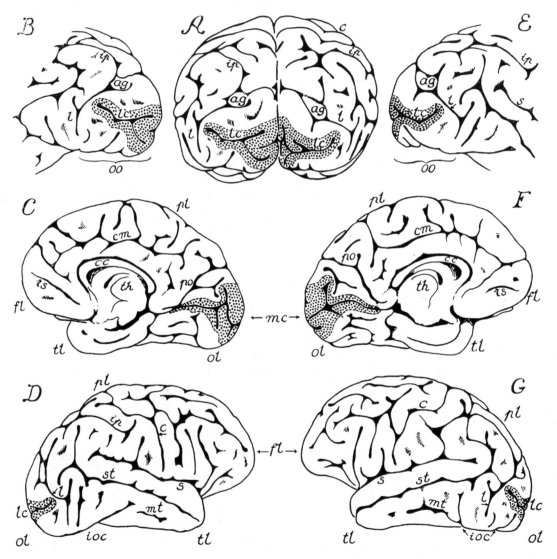

FIG. 284.—External configuration of the cerebral hemispheres of a four-day-old baby Chimpanzee and the extent and location of the visual cortical center, the striate area (*stippled*), in the intact brain. *A*, posterior view of both hemispheres, showing the two occipital lobes in relation to each other and to the rest of the brain; *B*, posterolateral view of left occipital lobe; *C*, medial, *D*, lateral views of right hemisphere; *E*, posterolateral view of right occipital lobe; *F*, medial, *G*, lateral views of left hemisphere. Reproduced at less than natural size. *Cf*. following figure. (For blood supply of Chimpanzee brain *see* Fig. 376.) *Labeling: ag*, annectent gyrus; *c*, central sulcus; *cc*, corpus callosum; *cm*, callosomarginal sulcus; *fl*, frontal lobe; *ip*, intraparietal sulcus; *l*, lunate sulcus; *lc*, lateral calcarine sulcus; *mc*, medial calcarine sulcus; *mt*, middle temporal sulcus; *ol*, occipital lobe; *oo*, occipital operculum; *pl*, parietal lobe; *po*, parieto-occipital sulcus; *rs*, rostral sulcus; *S*, Sylvian fissure; *st*, superior temporal sulcus; *th*, thalamus; *tl*, temporal lobe; *mt*, middle temporal sulcus; *st*, superior temporal sulcus.

4. Cortical centers of vision in prehistoric human races.—It must be assumed that the above-outlined trend in the phylogenetical development of the primate cortical visual centers continued in those Hominoids which gradually became transformed into various pithecanthropine and early prehistoric human races, in preparation for the anatomical conditions found in Modern Man.

human races and their immediate precursors: *Australopithecus africanus* (Dart), *Plesianthropus transvaalensis* (Broom), and *Paranthropus robustus* (Broom), and the various races of *Homo primigenius* that followed: *Homo soloensis* or Solo Man, *Pithecanthropus erectus* or Java Ape-Man, and *Sinanthropus pekinensis* or Peking Man (Fig. 287). In these, the details of the surface of the parieto-occipital lobes, especially

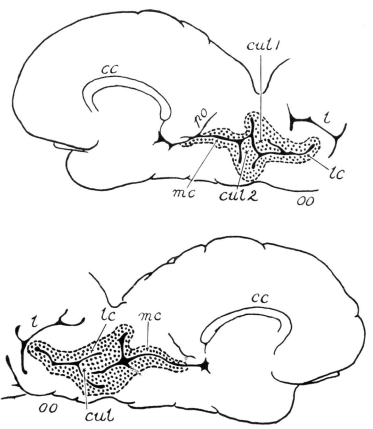

Fig. 285.—Right (*upper diagram*) and left cerebral hemisphere (*lower diagram*) of the same brain of a baby Chimpanzee as that shown in Fig. 284. Both striate areae fully exposed, and occipital opercula (*oo*) turned back to simulate a terminal evolutionary phase found in the human brain, with more or less the entire calcarine fissural complex displaced onto the medial face of the brain's hemisphere (*cf.* Fig. 290). Constituent parts of the calcarine fissural complex: the medial (*mc*) and lateral calcarine sulcus (*lc*) in the human brain usually form a single sulcus when examined superficially. In the Ape they may still be separated by a cuneolingual gyrus (*cul*) into their original constituents, as shown in lower diagram. Or the two sections may actually merge into a continuous furrow, as in the upper diagram, the two vestiges of the posterior cuneolingual gyrus (*cul1, cul2*) merely indicating a polar "hinge" around which the occipital flap begins to rotate. *See* similar conditions in the Macaque (Fig. 281), Spider Monkey (Fig. 283), and Man (Figs. 289, 292, 293, 294, 295). *Labeling: cc,* corpus callosum; *l,* lunate or simian sulcus; *oo,* occipital operculum; *po,* parieto-occipital sulcus. Note the considerable length of the calcarine sulcal complex (*mc* and *lc*) and of the striate area (*stippled*), equaling half the length of the hemisphere.

This fifth phylogenetical stage, more or less human, as much as can be judged from available data obtained from the study of endocranial casts, seems to have been attained by the earliest and most primitive known incipient

a lunate sulcus (*l*) and a pronounced occipital operculum with the posterior calcarine sulcus (*lc*), have been described and strongly resemble those of the present Anthropomorphous Apes (*cf. A* in Fig. 284, and upper sketch in Fig. 286, with the left lower sketch in Fig. 287; *see also* Shellshear 1926; Shellshear & Smith; G. E. Smith 1927; A. Keith; Ariëns Kappers 1935; Ariëns Kappers & Bouman; Weidenreich; Broom & Schepers 1946; *see*, however, Clark, Cooper & Zuckerman, 1936; and Packer 1949).

In the light of these observations it is fairly evident that, just as in the features characteriz-

ing their skeletal remains, the ancestors of modern humanity which populated distant parts of the Old World in remote times appear to have been an intermediary between the prehominid precursors, from which they developed, and *Homo sapiens* or Modern Man, into whom they slowly and painfully became transformed. (*Cf.* chap. XV.)

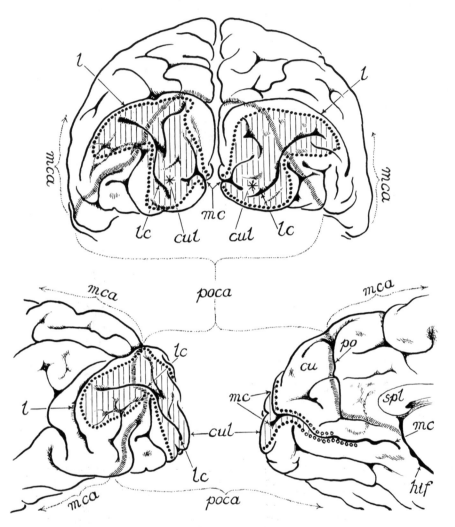

Fig. 286.—Occipital lobes of "Bushman," an adult Gorilla, showing striate areae and their relation to the sulcal and gyral configurations and to the middle and posterior cerebral arteries. *Upper sketch*, back view of both occipital lobes; *left lower sketch*, lateral view of left occipital lobe; *right lower sketch*, medial view of same lobe. Boundaries of striate areae marked by dotted lines, solid where on the surface, circles where concealed within fissures. Striate areae marked by vertical shading. Note slight asymmetry of occipital opercula; oblique position of lateral calcarine sulci (*lc*); considerable extent of opercular striate areae; polar position of cuneolingual gyri (*cul*) separating medial (*mc*) from lateral calcarine sulci (*lc*); shaded line separating arterial territories passing obliquely across occipital opercula, leaving extreme segments of striate areae closest to lunate sulci (*l*) in the territories of the middle cerebral arteries (*mca*), and the larger polar portions, together with portions along medial calcarine sulci in the territories of the posterior cerebral arteries (*poca*). *Labeling: cu*, cuneus; *cul*, cuneolingual gyrus; *hif*, hippocampal fissure; *l*, lunate sulcus; *lc*, lateral calcarine sulcus; *mc*, medial calcarine sulcus; *mca*, territory of middle cerebral artery; *po*, parieto-occipital sulcus; *poca*, territory of posterior cerebral artery; *spl*, splenium of corpus callosum. Poles of occipital lobes marked by asterisks (*). Reproduced below natural size.

5. Cortical visual centers of Modern Man.—The anatomical features of parts of the human brain related to sight, like other parts of the brain, and the remainder of Man's bodily organization necessarily and unavoidably resemble those of his prehuman ancestors. Some of these features are almost identical with the simian, whereas others are more or less changed, in many cases being transformed to a degree where only a thorough study of all pertinent

centage of the brains of some living human races considered to be primitive: Egyptian Fellahs, Sudanese, Malayans, Negroes, Javanese, Indonesians, Dayaks of Borneo, Bushmen, and particularly characteristic of the aborigines of Australia (G. Elliot Smith; Karplus; Brodmann 1906; Ingalls; Kooy 1921; Ariëns Kappers, Huber & Crosby; Murphy; Shellshear; Connolly 1943, 1950).

Other investigations, however, have dis-

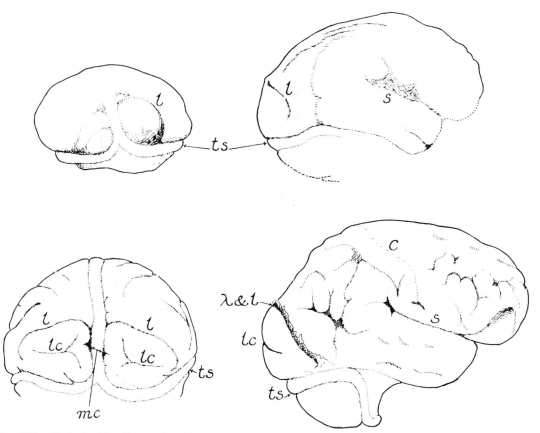

FIG. 287.—Posterior (*left diagrams*) and lateral aspect (*right diagrams*) of endocranial casts of two most primitive known prehistoric human or human-like races: *Pithecanthropus erectus*, or Java Ape-Man, with a cranial capacity of 855 cc. (*upper diagrams*, from G. Elliot Smith 1927), and *Sinanthropus pekinensis*, or Early China Man (*lower diagrams*, from Shellshear & Smith 1934). Note the large occipital opercula and typical pithecoid shape and arrangement of the lunate, lateral, and medial calcarine sulci in both races, approaching those in modern Anthropomorphous Apes (*cf.* Figs. 284, 286). *Labeling: c*, central sulcus; *l*, lunate sulcus; *lc*, lateral or posterior calcarine sulcus; *λ & l*, lambdoid suture and lunate sulcus; *mc*, medial or anterior calcarine sulcus; *S*, Sylvian fissure; *ts*, transverse sinus.

points may reveal the ancient traits and homologies, if they can be found at all.

One remaining feature of primitive "pithecoid" conditions much studied by anatomists is the well-developed, more or less typical, crescent-shaped lunate sulcus (*l*) and the large occipital operculum observed in an important per-

closed the presence of a clearly marked, though usually smaller and irregularly shaped, vestige or vestiges of a lunate sulcus in numerous instances in the brains of Chinese, Japanese, and the following Caucasians: Ashkenazic Jews, Germans, Swedes, Poles, English, Russians, and others (Weinberg; Antoni; Goldstern; Kuhlenbeck 1928; G. Elliot Smith 1929; Economo 1930; Levin 1936; Ngowiang 1936; Chi & Chun Chang 1941; Connolly 1943, 1950).

A lunate sulcus, much less a vestige of it, may therefore not be considered a "sign of race," and even less a "stigma of racial inferiority or degeneracy," since it was found in the brains of such eminent persons as Mendeleyev, the Russian chemist who discovered the "periodic law of elements" (Levin 1936); C. Monakow, a celebrated lifelong investigator of the brain (R. Anthony 1935); and a number of other outstanding individuals.

From the published figures of the brains of some of the most prominent thinkers and arttists—Helmholtz, Mommsen, Bunsen, and Menzel—the presence of a more or less well-formed lunate sulcus and of a lateral or posterior calcarine sulcus appears either fairly certain or at least probable (Hansemann 1899, 1907). A similar situation may have obtained also in the case of Mallory, a prominent American pathologist (*see* chap. XII, 10).

It is possible, however, that where an unusually well-developed lunate sulcus and an occipital operculum are frequently found and where the striate area extends to a considerable distance beyond the occipital pole and where other "simian features" of configuration of the occipital lobes are consistently met with, as, for example, in the Australian aborigines (Shellshear), these peculiarities cannot be discounted as of no anthropological significance. Unfortunately, because of the lack of systematic large-scale investigations, it is at present impossible to pass any valid judgment on this important and intriguing problem.

A large occipital operculum, marked off from the rest of the hemisphere by a deep, crescent-shaped lunate sulcus, and a striate area extending over the convexity of the occipital lobe much farther than is usually found in the so-called "advanced" races of mankind are, in any case, features strikingly resembling, and for reasons discussed elsewhere in this chapter homologous with, the anatomical conditions in the Infrahuman Primates, especially in the Anthropomorphous Apes.

An illustrative example of pithecoid conditions found in numerous human brains is a specimen depicted in back view in Figure 288.

It is of a human male, of Polish nationality, of Roman Catholic denomination, born in 1888 in "Congress Poland," which at that time had been for approximately one hundred years a part of the Russian Empire, of parents who were born and died in the same country—all circumstances showing it to be highly probable that the individual was "racially a pure Pole." A careful examination of the sulcal and gyral configuration and of the cortical structure in both occipital lobes revealed conditions remarkably resembling those typical for the Anthropomorphous Apes (*cf.* Figs. 284, 286).

On the left side a "triradiate" lateral or posterior calcarine sulcus (*lc*), surrounded above and below by posterior, superior, and inferior paracalcarine sulci and separated from the posterior forked end of the medial or anterior calcarine sulcus (*mc*) by a posterior cuneolingual gyrus (*cul*), was found (Fig. 289, lower diagram). A long, deep, semicircular lunate sulcus (*l*), together with a well-developed prelunate sulcus (*prel*), set off a typically simian occipital operculum from the rest of the hemisphere.

The striate area, indicated by stippling, partly lined the medial (*mc*) and the entire lateral calcarine (*lc*) sulci, including the inferior and part of the superior posterior paracalcarine sulci, as well as the terminal segment of the inferior occipital sulcus (*io*). The lunate sulcus (*l*), along its entire extent, remained approximately 3 mm. beyond the posterior boundary of the striate area.

In the right occipital lobe a similar situation was found, except that the lunate sulcus consisted of two components and the striate area did not extend over the pole as far as on the left side (Figs. 288, 289, upper diagram).

In another brain specimen whose race could not be determined but which, because of a high degree of pigmentation, may have been that of an American Negro, a very similar situation, with some differences, was found (Fig. 290). Here, too, the medial calcarine sulcus (*mc*) was found separated from the lateral calcarine sulcus (*lc*) on both sides symmetrically, by a posterior cuneolingual gyrus (*cul*), with a well-developed lunate sulcus (*l*) encircling the back ends of the calcarine sulcal complexes and marking off typical pithecoid occipital opercula. As in the brain of the Pole, here, too, the striate areae remained a few millimeters behind the lunate sulci. Whereas, however, in the brain of the Pole the left occipital operculum was considerably larger, in the presumably Negro brain both opercula and the exposed parts of the striate areae were approximately equal. (*Cf. also* Figs. 291–95.)

Whether these features of the visual center are in any way to be considered racially charac-

sulcal and gyral pattern, which alone may be misleading, but, above all, an exact determination of the limits of the striate area. This is a task not offering serious difficulty, since the stria of Gennari in fresh or well-preserved material can be easily seen without the aid of a magnifying glass or at slight magnification.

The sixth and final evolutionary stage of the phylogenesis of the calcarine fissure is possibly

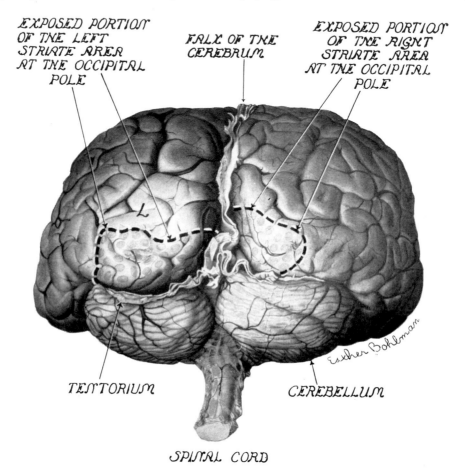

EXPOSED PORTION OF THE LEFT STRIATE AREA AT THE OCCIPITAL POLE

FALX OF THE CEREBRUM

EXPOSED PORTION OF THE RIGHT STRIATE AREA AT THE OCCIPITAL POLE

TENTORIUM

CEREBELLUM

SPINAL CORD

Fig. 288.—Back view of an adult human brain showing well-formed occipital opercula, with extensive exposed portions of striate areae (marked by *circles*), and other so-called simian features characteristic of Apes (*cf.* Figs. 284, 286). Note a lunate sulcus (*L*) on left side, marking off an occipital operculum larger than on the right side, an asymmetry considered normal in the human brain. The specimen from a person of pure Polish extraction (*see* text). *See* following figure and compare with Figs. 290–96. Falx cerebri, tentorium, cerebellum and spinal cord left *in situ*.

teristic or are merely individual peculiarities is an important problem that can be solved only by thorough, careful work. For this, in the first place, abundant material in a good state of preservation is necessary, permitting conclusions valid from the statistical viewpoint. The other indispensable condition, heretofore rarely met with, is not only the examination of the

represented by those brains of Modern Man— allegedly the majority in the Caucasian races— in which the occipital operculum and the lunate sulcus, the vestigial remnants of simian conditions, have largely or entirely disappeared (Fig. 296). Here, apparently owing to a great expansion of the extrastriate cortical areae, the entire striate area has been pushed onto the medial surface of the hemisphere and largely rolled in or invaginated into a deep posterior segment of the calcarine fissure. In such cases a pithecoid lunate sulcus and an occipital operculum are absent or, at any rate, are difficult to identify. (*Cf.* Fig. 290.)

But even here the original morphological ele-

ments of which the final evolutionary result is composed are usually still more or less recognizable. The short, but deep, sulci hidden within the posterior section of the calcarine fissure, running in front of and behind the posterior cuneolingual gyrus, usually noticeable by superficial dents in the lips of the closed fissure, are

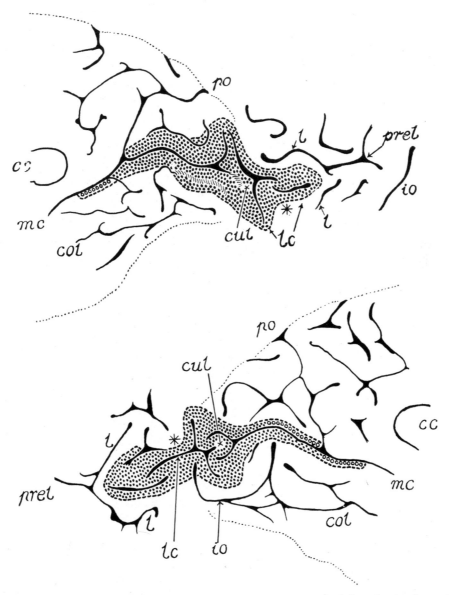

FIG. 289.—Right (*upper diagram*) and left sulcal complex (*lower diagram*) of the calcarine fissures of a person of Polish extraction depicted in the preceding figure. Both occipital opercula are turned backward, in order to align them with the plane of the medial face of the brain's hemisphere. Thus straightened out, the identity of various parts of the sulcal and gyral pattern with the simian becomes apparent (*cf.* Figs. 281, 285). The portions of the striate areae spreading on the exposed surface are indicated by solid dotting, those buried in the anterior calcarine sulci by circles. Occipital poles marked by asterisks (*). Brain outlines indicated by dotted lines. (*Cf.* Figs. 281, 283, 285.) *Labeling: cc,* corpus callosum; *col,* collateral sulcus; *cul,* posterior cuneolingual gyrus; *io,* inferior occipital sulcus; *l,* lunate sulcus; *lc,* lateral calcarine sulcus; *mc,* medial calcarine sulcus; *po,* parieto-occipital sulcus; *prel,* prelunate sulcus.

the vestiges of prongs of the lateral calcarine sulcus and of the ascending and descending rami with which the original medial calcarine fissure of the Monkeys and Apes terminates at its posterior extremity. (*Cf.* Figs. 280–86 with Figs. 289–92.)

6. PROBABLE PHYLOGENETIC FACTORS RESPONSIBLE FOR THE FORMATION OF THE CORTICAL VISUAL CENTERS OF MAN.—The ideas expressed in the preceding subsections concerning the probable course of the phylogenetic development of the cortical visual centers of the advanced human races from the initial conditions found in the infrasimian, prosimian, and lower simian representatives of the Primates are further supported by the following considerations.

In the catarrhine Monkeys, exemplified by the Rhesus Macaque (Figs. 280, 281), the occipital pole, marked with an asterisk (*), divides the striate area into two approximately equal halves, the medial, largely buried in the phylogenetically older medial or anterior calcarine sulcus (*mc*), and the lateral, that spreads over the lateral face of the occipital lobe (*ol*) or occipital operculum (*oo*), which, with the exception of a shallow lateral or posterior calcarine sulcus (*lc*), lies exposed on the lateral face of the brain. These two constituents of the future calcarine fissural complex of the Ape and Man, the older originating on the medial face (*mc*) and the younger on the lateral face (*lc*), still remain separated at the phylogenetic stage represented by the Macaque.

In the brain of the advanced Platyrrhines, such as the *Ateles* or Spider Monkey (Figs. 282, 283), the situation remains roughly similar, with, however, some significant changes. The two calcarine constituents (*mc* and *lc*) are still separated, but the occipital opercular portion of the striate area is partly folded into a deep posterior calcarine sulcus, thus reducing the extent of this area on the free face of the lobe. All these changes have obviously been induced by a considerable expansion of the surrounding extrastriate cortex, manifested in the emergence of the annectent gyri (*ag*), and a general increase in surface and in the sulcal and gyral elaboration of the entire cerebral cortex in the *Ateles* as compared with the Macaque.

In the Anthropomorphous Apes—for ex-

ample, in the Chimpanzee and the Gorilla (Figs. 284, 285, 286)—slightly more of the opercular striate cortex than in the Spider Monkey is buried within a deep, more or less three-pronged lateral calcarine sulcus (*lc*), the remainder still being exposed along this sulcus. In spite of this, however, the general situation remains the same as in the Macaque, although it more strikingly resembles that found in the Spider Monkey.

In the Chimpanzee additional significant changes are noticeable, indicating a further elaboration of the visual cortical centers. First, the inner extremities of the lateral calcarine sulci (*lc*) facing the occipital poles are forked. On the left side the two prongs encompass the lower prong of the medial calcarine sulcus (*mc*), an arrangement that appears to be a common simian heritage (*cf.* lower diagrams in Figs. 283 and 285). The two calcarine fissural elements (*mc* and *lc*) are still kept apart by a < or rather ≳-shaped intervening fold of the striate cortex (*cul*), precisely as is found in some human brains (Fig. 289, lower diagram; Figs. 291, 292, upper diagrams).

In human brains the same fold (*cul*) is known as the posterior cuneolingual gyrus, and so, by the same token, the fold in the Chimpanzee's brain must be considered a homologue of the same gyrus. In the Spider Monkey the homology with the Chimpanzee is also quite apparent (*cul*, in both diagrams in Fig. 283), even though the anterior extremities of *lc* are not forked and the intervening fold is therefore simpler, somewhat resembling the situation found in the Rhesus Macaque (Fig. 281). All this evidence shows the bridge of the cortex separating the medial (*mc*) from the lateral calcarine sulci (*lc*) in the Macaque to be, in fact, an oriment or primordium of the posterior cuneolingual gyrus of the more advanced Primates, including Man. A similar situation also obtains in the Gorilla (Fig. 286).

In all four otherwise widely separated representatives of the Primates—a catarrhine Macaque, a platyrrhine *Ateles*, the hominoid Chimpanzee and Gorilla, and Man—in the specimens described the essential arrangement of the primitive constituents of the "calcarine fissural complex" (*mc* and *lc*) accordingly remains the same (even though, undoubtedly, in the Ape, and

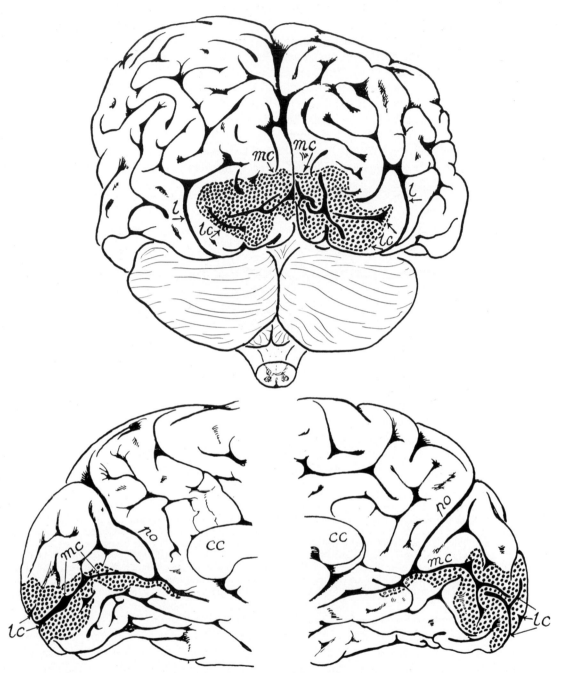

Fig. 290.—Back view (*upper diagram*) and medial aspect (*lower diagram*) of right and left occipital lobes, possibly of an American Negro, with pronounced lunate sulci (*l*) setting off large, symmetrically developed occipital opercula, with sizable parts of striate areae exposed over the occipital poles. These features markedly resemble those found in Anthropomorphous Apes (Figs. 284, 286) and in prehistoric human races (Fig. 287), in contrast to conditions in some brains of the Caucasian or White Race, where the striate areae are entirely moved to the medial face of the cerebral hemispheres and where the lunate sulci and occipital opercula are absent (Fig. 296). A symmetrical arrangement of opercula may also be an ancient feature, whereas in the White Race the left occipital operculum is larger (Fig. 288). Striate area indicated by stippling. Specimen somewhat out of shape, owing to careless handling. *Labeling: cc,* corpus callosum; *l,* lunate sulcus; *lc,* lateral calcarine sulcus; *mc,* medial calcarine sulcus; *po,* parieto-occipital sulcus.

even more so in Man, their relationship is obviously increasingly more intimate).

The right calcarine fissure of the same baby Chimpanzee affords an illustration of the next step in the process of calcarine fusion (Fig. 285, upper diagram). In this instance, the cuneolingual gyrus is broken through (*cul1* and *cul2*), and an actual fusion of the medial (*mc*) and the lateral calcarine sulcus (*lc*) into a continuous furrow has taken place (even though the original constituents are still clearly recognizable).

the actual pole of the occipital lobe (* in Fig. 281), in an advanced Monkey (*cul*, in Fig. 283) and in an Anthropomorphous Ape (*cul*, in Fig. 285) becomes a cuneolingual fold. This fold, even though it still represents the pole, definitely assumes the shape of a posterior cuneolingual gyrus, identical with the same gyrus in the human brain, where it may or may not be at the pole (Figs. 289, 295).

The posterior cuneolingual gyrus, the original "occipital pole" of the Lower Simians, clearly

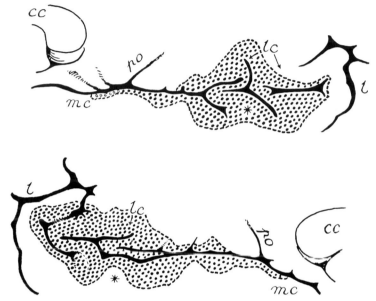

Fig. 291.—Right (*upper diagram*) and left calcarine sulcal complex (*lower diagram*) of the brain shown in Fig. 290, with sulci left *in situ*. Both occipital opercula are presented turned back, in order to bring the lateral calcarine sulci (*lc*) in line with the medial calcarine sulci (*mc*), as normally found in many specimens. In the upper diagram the composition of the calcarine fissure of a series of discontinuous sulci is apparent; in the lower diagram the calcarine appears in this view as a continuous fissure, its makeup of several constituents being revealed in Fig. 292. Exposed portions of striate areae indicated by stippling; portions buried in rostral segments of fissure indicated by circles. Occipital poles marked by asterisks (*). Note large segment of striate cortex along the lateral calcarine sulcus beyond the occipital pole, larger than found in Fig. 289. (*Cf.* following figure.) *Labeling: cc*, corpus callosum; *l*, lunate sulcus; *lc*, lateral calcarine sulcus; *mc*, medial calcarine sulcus; *po*, parieto-occipital sulcus.

In a similar human specimen the fusion of the medial and lateral calcarine components has also advanced to what appears as a single, continuous calcarine fissure when inspected superficially (Fig. 291, lower diagram). The examination of the sulci and gyri concealed in the fissure even in this case shows the original sulcal and gyral elements still present, including an anterior bifurcation of the lateral calcarine sulci and a posterior bifurcation of the medial (*lc* and *mc*, in Fig. 292, lower diagram).

The preceding examples and considerations show that a point which in a Lower Monkey is

functions as a "pivot" or "hinge" around which, during the process of anthropogenesis—owing to an overexpansion of the extrastriate regions of the cortex—the occipital operculum rotates and is turned back. In this way the lateral or posterior portion of the striate area is brought in line with the medial or anterior portion. This is the situation found in advanced human brains (Fig. 296). The lateral calcarine sulcus of the Infrahuman Primates becomes the posterior portion of the composite calcarine fissure of advanced humanity, variously called by different investigators three-pronged or shamrock-shaped *sulcus triradiatus*, external or lateral calcarine sulcus, *sulcus extremus* or *fissura extrema* of Seitz, and the like.

Since, however, the expansion concerns not only the parts of the extrastriate cortex in the simian fossa proper but also those along the upper and lower margins of the occipital operculum, the latter is not only turned back but also rolled or folded in, leaving but a small part of the striate cortex, or none at all, on the ex-

original boundary between the medial and the lateral sections of the original simian calcarine fissural complex.

The paramount single factor responsible for the notable mechanical changes in the phylogenesis of the primate cortical centers of vision, instead of merely a uniform surface and volume increase of the striate and extrastriate cortex, appears to be the topographical representation of the retinae in the striate area. A discrete rep-

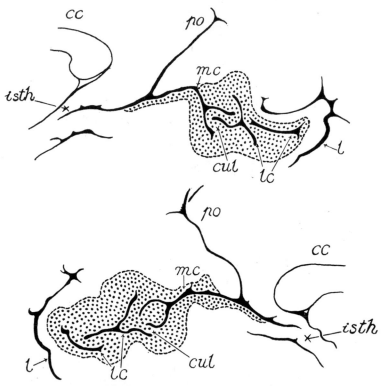

FIG. 292. Right (*upper diagram*) and left calcarine sulcal complex (*lower diagram*) of the same brain specimen shown in Figs. 290 and 291, with fissures opened, in order to demonstrate the original sulcal composition. Note posterior cuneolingual gyrus (*cul*) in both diagrams separating the medial (*mc*) from the lateral calcarine sulcus (*lc*), although this is not apparent in lower diagram of the preceding figure, where the calcarine fissure appears continuous; the composition of the lateral sulci of several distinct sulcal components, one of them a typical triradiate sulcus. *Labeling: cc*, splenium of corpus callosum; *cul*, posterior cuneolingual gyrus; *isth*, isthmus of fornico-hippocampal gyrus; *l*, lunate sulcus; *lc*, lateral calcarine sulci; *mc*, medial calcarine sulcus; *po*, parieto-occipital sulcus.

posed face of the occipital lobe around the pole (as, e.g., in Figs. 293, 296).

Thus it comes about that what in most human brains is the occipital pole is the region which in the Monkey still remains on the lateral face of the hemisphere, more or less close to the simian sulcus, and that the original simian occipital pole in many, perhaps most, human brains is displaced medially and anteriorly, marking as a posterior cuneolingual gyrus the

resentation of various parts of the retinal surface in distinct parts of the striate area implies a functionally unequal importance of the various segments of this area. The lateral or posterior portion of the striate area in all Primates, from Monkeys through Apes to Man, represents the two homonymous central-foveal and areal halves or hemifoveae and hemiareae, as described in chapter VII, 4 and 5 (*see* Figs. 259, 260).

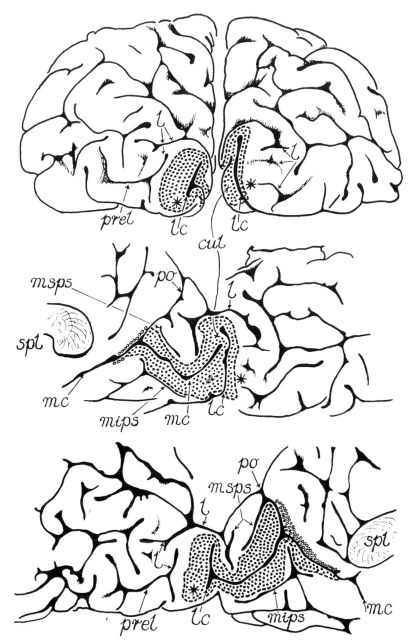

Fig. 293.—Occipital lobes of a human brain of unknown racial origin showing the configuration of the calcarine sulcal complex. *Upper diagram*, posterior view of both occipital lobes; *middle diagram*, right-side calcarine complex; *lower diagram*, left-side calcarine complex. Occipital poles indicated by asterisks (*). Medial calcarine sulcus (*mc*) in right occipital lobe separated from lateral calcarine sulcus (*lc*) by a posterior cuneolingual gyrus (*cul*), in left lobe both sulci merging into a continuous calcarine fissure. Lunate sulcus (*l*) on both sides broken up into several constituents. The striate area is indicated by stippling (where superficial) and by circles (where submerged). The left polar portion of the striate cortex slightly larger than the one at the right occipital pole, both, however, much smaller than those in specimens represented in Figs. 288 and 290. *Labeling: cul*, posterior cuneolingual gyrus; *l*, lunate sulcus; *lc*, lateral calcarine sulcus; *mc*, medial calcarine sulcus; *mips*, medial inferior paracalcarine sulcus; *msps*, medial superior paracalcarine sulcus; *po*, parieto-occipital sulcus; *prel*, prelunate sulcus; *spl*, splenium of corpus callosum.

Since the central foveae and areae, in virtue of their peculiar structural organization and location, are parts of the peripheral photoreceptive membranes—the retinae—most essential for direct, distinct, epicritic, or gnostic vision, it is legitimate to assume that most gnostic retinal impulses are transmitted to the cerebral cortex via the foveal-areal portions of the striate areae. In particular, with the gradual perfection of vision in the course of primate phylogeny, especially its "intellectualization," the foveal-areal portions of the central visual pathways and of the striate areae became the principal avenues and stations for the visual impulses that became the basis of primate intelligence.

In the long process of anthropogenesis or

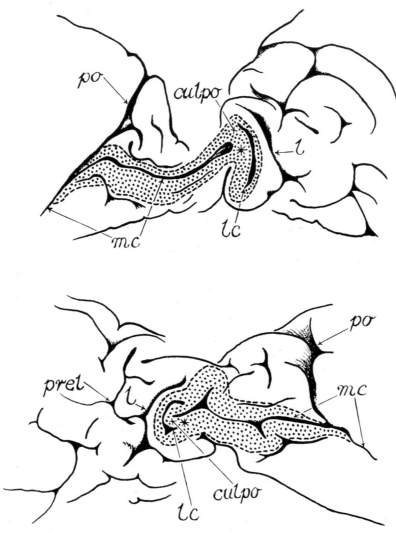

Fig. 294.—Right (*upper diagram*) and left occipital lobe (*lower diagram*) of a human brain of an undetermined race, with both inner and outer faces presented in one plane. Sulci and gyri drawn *in situ* (not opened). Both lobes show a symmetrical and remarkably pithecoid or Chimpanzee-like configuration, with a deep, sickle-shaped lunate sulcus (*l*) sharply setting off a typically simian "occipital operculum" from the rest of the hemisphere (*cf*. Fig. 284). Lateral calcarine sulci (*lc*) are semilunar furrows resembling lunate sulci. The fact that they are lined by the striate cortex shows their true nature, that is, to be parts of the calcarine fissural complex. The occipital poles, indicated by asterisks (*), are either on the posterior cuneolingual gyrus (*culpo*) or close to it. The medial calcarine fissures (*mc*) in their cuneal stretch are unusually deep and completely lined by the striate area, except in the precuneal stretch, where they are lined only along their floors. The lateral calcarine sulci (*lc*) are quite shallow. The anterior cuneolingual gyri **are** small and completely concealed in the medial calcarine sulcus. The striate areae are indicated by stippling. *Labeling: culpo*, posterior cuneolingual gyrus; *l*, lunate or simian sulcus; *lc*, lateral or posterior calcarine sulcus; *mc*, medial or anterior calcarine sulcus; *po*, parieto-occipital fissure; *prel*, prelunate sulcus.

"rise of Man," therefore, not only did the opercular portion of the simian striate area expand fastest and transform a shallow "lateral" or "diagonal" sulcus into an incipient posterior calcarine sulcus of the hominoid and hominid or human brain, but also that portion of the extrastriate or para-peristriate areae that surrounds it expanded most.

On anatomical and physiological grounds it is legitimate to think that the opercular extrastriate cortex, in virtue of its close association with the foveal portion of the striate area, became the principal repository of the "psychic" or gnostic visual "engrams" or traces of past impressions and experiences (*cf.* chap. VII, 7).

In consequence, this cortical territory, which in the Lower Monkeys lies chiefly buried in the simian sulcus, increased most in the advanced Monkeys, in the Apes, and even more in Man, necessitating, in turn, a displacement backward and inward precisely of the exposed areal-foveal portion of the striate area that ultimately formed the posterior, polar segment of the calcarine fissure of the human brain.

In this light the major factor contributing to the full development of the extensive occipito-temporo-parietal association region of Flechsig located between the three centers most important for the human intellect—the visual, auditory, and somesthetic—appears to be the stream of gnostic visual impulses from the central foveae via the posterior calcarine sulcus to the surrounding cortex (*see* chap. IV and Fig. 115, *IX*). It is not astonishing that the posterior calcarine sulcus shows such a diversity of topography and configuration, in view of the tremendous individual variation in the faculty of vision, particularly its "psychic" aspects; and similar reasons may be responsible for the racial peculiarities of this region, still to be studied in detail.

The least active, most inert, and hence, in an evolutionary sense, most conservative or stable part of the primate cortical visual center is the ontogenetically and phylogenetically oldest portion of the striate area in and along the medial calcarine sulcus (*mc*), close to the fornicate-hippocampal *isthmus*, where the extreme monocular nasal periphery of the contralateral retina is represented (*cf.* Figs. 259, 260). This portion and the adjoining part of the para-peristriate area necessarily experience the smallest surface expansion and suffer the least shifting of their position relative to the other parts of the brain in the course of an evolutionary process that has brought about the profound changes described in the preceding.

As an over-all result of the facts and considerations given in the preceding pages, there emerges a realization of the unity of the visual cortical centers in the entire Order of Primates, from the lowliest Monkeys through the various intermediate stages to Man. In that entire order the calcarine fissural complex, its relation to the striate area, and the topographical representation of the retina are laid down according to the same plan.

This forces one to make two important deductions. One concerns the functional factors that, in the final analysis, are responsible for the anatomical identity, or at least the homology, of all principal features of the calcarine-striate complex: these must be adjudged to have been the same from the phylogenetic emergence of the Primate Order until now. The other deduction related to the preceding concerns the systematic or taxonomic classification of all Primates into a single, closely knit group, irrespective of any further subdivisions based upon the other, sometimes less essential, features of the bodily organization of the same group. (*Cf.* chap. XV.)

References: Abel 1931; Addison & Donaldson 1933; Alouf 1929; J. Anthony 1943; R. Anthony 1913, 1928, 1935; Antoni 1914; Appleton; Ariëns Kappers 1913, 1914, 1921, 1929, 1933, 1935, 1936, 1937; Ariëns Kappers & Bouman; Ariëns Kappers, Huber & Crosby 1936; Bean 1905–6; Beddard; Beattie 1927; D. Black 1915, 1932, 1933; Bolk 1910; Bolton 1900, 1933; Bonin 1938, 1939, 1942, 1944, 1945; Bork-Feltkamp 1939; Boule & Vallois 1952; Brodmann 1904, 1908, 1909 (1925), 1913, 1918; Broek 1908; Brongersma 1942; Broom 1934, 1942, 1946; 1948; Broom & Schepers 1946; Brummelkamp 1940, 1943–45; Bushmakin 1928; Carlsson 1910, 1922; Chang & Chang 1941; Chapman 1904; Le Gros Clark 1924, 1927, 1928, 1929, 1931, 1933, 1934, 1935, 1945, 1946, 1947, 1950, 1954; Clark, Cooper & Zuckerman; Cohn & Papez; Connolly 1933, 1936, 1941–43, 1950; D. J. Cunningham

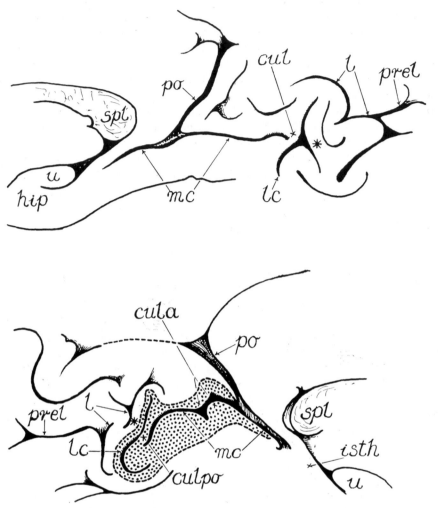

Fig. 295.—Occipital lobes of two different human brains of undetermined racial origin, presented with both inner and outer faces spread in one plane, with sulci drawn *in situ. Upper diagram,* right lobe; *lower diagram,* left lobe. In upper diagram the medial calcarine sulcus (*mc*) is a continuous furrow, terminating without forking next to the posterior cuneolingual gyrus (*cul*). The lateral calcarine sulcus (*lc*), of a typical three-pronged shape, a triradiate sulcus, is accompanied caudally by an accessory posterior calcarine sulcus. The entire calcarine sulcal complex is set off posteriorly by a double lunate sulcus (*l*). The cuneus (between *po* and *mc*) has the usual shape of a wedge. In the left hemisphere (*lower diagram*) the middle calcarine sulcus (*mc*) forms two arches, reducing the cuneus to half its usual size. The lateral calcarine sulcus (*lc*), in its semilunar shape and vertical position, simulates a lunate sulcus; the fact that it is lined by striate cortex reveals it to be a posterior component of the calcarine complex. The true lunate sulcus (*l*) is represented by two sulci, the lower one with a long prelunate extension (*prel*). The striate area is indicated by stippling. Anteriorly it extends in the lower calcarine lip almost as far as the fornico-hippocampal isthmus (*isth*). Along most of *mc* the striate cortex extends more over the lower lip, this possibly being related to the presence of anterior cuneolingual gyri, one in each lip (*cula*), making for a shallow fissure in this locality, becoming deep close to *culpo*. In the posterior lip of the posterior calcarine sulcus, the striate cortex in part does not emerge onto the exposed surface. Poles of occipital lobes marked by asterisks (*). *Labeling: cul, culpo,* posterior cuneolingual gyrus; *cula,* anterior cuneolingual gyrus; *hip,* hippocampal gyrus; *isth,* fornico-hippocampal gyrus; *l,* lunate sulcus; *lc,* lateral calcarine sulcus; *mc,* medial calcarine sulcus; *prel,* prelunate sulcus; *po,* parieto-occipital sulcus; *spl,* splenium of corpus callosum; *u,* uncus of hippocampal gyrus.

1890, 1891, 1892, 1943; J. T. Cunningham 1919–20; Dart 1948, 1949; Chas. Rob. Darwin 1871 and later editions; Dietel 1931; Donaldson 1892; Dräsecke 1906; Dubois 1894, 1898, 1899, 1924, 1933, 1940; Duckworth 1908, 1915; Economo 1930; L. Edinger 1905, 1908–11; T. Edinger; Filimonoff 1931–33; Flashman 1908; Flores 1911; Flower 1863; Gadow 1902; Gates 1948; Geist 1930; Goldstern 1915; Gratiolet 1854; W. K. Gregory 1916, 1927, 1927–29, 1930, 1934, 1935, 1951; Hansemann 1899, 1907; Hatschek 1908; Hayashi & Nakamura 1913–14; Heschl 1878; J. P. Hill 1919; M. Holl 1907, 1908, 1909; G. Holmes 1918, 1919, 1931; Hooton

Schuster & Halliburton 1910; Murphy 1910; Ngowyang 1935, 1936, 1937; Niessl von Mayendorf 1908; S. Oppenheim 1913; Oppenoorth 1937; Osborn 1916, 1928; Packer 1949; Pansch 1868; Papez 1927, 1929, 1930; Parker 1910, 1949; Parker & Haswell; Peden & Bonin 1947; Pittard 1943; Pocock 1919–20; Poynter & Keegan 1915; Regan 1930; G. Retzius 1896, 1898, 1900, 1906; Roch 1941; Romer 1943, 1945; Sander 1875; S. Sergi 1904, 1908, 1909; D. M. Sernow 1877, 1878; Shellshear 1926, 1933, 1936, 1937, 1939; Simpson 1931, 1949; G. Elliot Smith 1902, 1903, 1907, 1908, 1909, 1910, 1911, 1919, 1919–20, 1920, 1921, 1925, 1926, 1927,

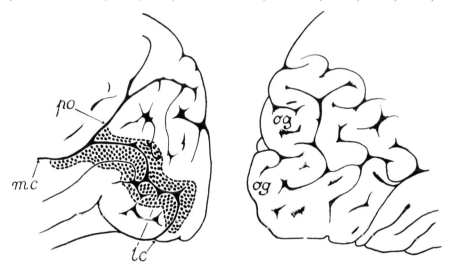

Fɪɢ. 296.—Right occipital lobe of a well-developed, healthy boy of Italian parentage, five years and six months old, who died of acute appendicitis. Left figure represents the medial or inner face of the lobe, the right figure the lateral or outer face. Both constituents of the calcarine fissure, the medial (*mc*) and the lateral (*lc*), form a single, continuous furrow with a somewhat arching course toward the cuneus. The posterior extremity of the fissure does not reach the occipital pole but turns downward instead. The striate area (*stippled*) is entirely confined to the medial face of the occipital lobe. No vestige of a lunate sulcus could be ascertained in this case. (*Cf.* lower right-hand diagram in Fig. 290.) *Labeling: lc*, lateral calcarine sulcus; *mc*, medial calcarine sulcus; *og*, occipital gyri; *po*, parieto-occipital sulcus.

1947; Hulshoff 1917; T. H. Huxley 1861; Ingalls 1914; Jakob & Onelli 1911; Jefferson 1915; Karplus 1902; Keegan 1916; Keith 1929, 1931, 1939, 1946, 1947; Kinosita 1942–44; Koenigswald 1940; Klaatsch 1900, 1911; Kohlbrugge 1903, 1906, 1908, 1909; Kükenthal & Ziehen 1895; Kuhlenbeck 1928; Kurz 1924; Kuzuoka; Landau 1914, 1915, 1916; Lapique 1907; Leche 1905; G. Levin 1936; Loo 1930–31; Lyon 1913; Malayev 1934; Mauss 1908, 1911; McBride 1919–20; Marquis 1935; Mettler 1933; Meynert 1877; Mingazzini 1893, 1928; Mitchell 1919–20; Monakow 1902, 1905; Mott 1907; Mott & Halliburton 1908; Mott & Kelley 1908; Mott,

1928, 1929, 1930; Sonntag 1924; Stangier 1937; L. Stieda 1907; Symington 1916; Thone 1946; Tilney 1927, 1928; Vallois 1946; Van Valkenburg 1909, 1913; Vint 1934; R. Wagner 1860–62; Waldeyer 1891, 1894, 1895; Walker & Fulton 1937; Weidenreich 1928, 1936, 1937, 1938, 1939, 1940, 1941, 1942, 1943, 1945, 1946; Weil 1929; Weinberg 1896, 1905, 1907; Wen 1933; Wilson 1933; Wood-Jones 1918, 1919, 1926, 1929; Woodward 1919–20; Woollard 1925, 1929; Zeuner 1946; Ziehen 1896, 1903, 1903–34; Zuckerkandl 1894, 1902–5, 1903, 1905, 1906, 1910; Zuckerman 1940; Zuckerman & Fisher 1937; Zuckerman & Fulton 1934.

SEC. 4. LOCATION, EXTENT, AND GENERAL CHARACTERISTICS OF THE STRIATE AREA

1. DEFINITION OF THE CORTICAL CENTERS OF VISION.—The cortical centers of vision are those portions of the superficial gray substance covering the cerebral hemispheres which are directly or indirectly concerned with the visual function. Specifically, in a restricted sense the striate areae of the occipital lobes where fibers of the visual radiations terminate are to be considered the cortical visual centers. In a wider sense all parts of the cerebral cortex which, according to experimental, clinical, and pathological evidence, serve any of the receptive, associative or integrative, and motor functions of vision may likewise be considered to belong to the visual sphere. (*Cf.* chap. VI, 1.)

2. LOCATION AND EXTENT OF THE STRIATE AREA IN THE HUMAN BRAIN.—The portion of the cerebral cortex where the afferent fibers of the visual radiation terminate, named by G. Elliot Smith the "striate area," identical with the "visuosensory area" of Bolton and Campbell, "field *17*" of Brodmann, or "area *OC*" of Economo, is located in the occipital lobe of each cerebral hemisphere (Figs. 298, 300, 301).

This area is distinguished by a pronounced, pale, and relatively wide stripe approximately in the middle of the thickness and parallel to the surface of the cortex. The line is visible to the unaided eye on a surface cut through a fresh or preserved specimen. It is called the outer stripe of Baillarger or, more commonly, the stria of Gennari or Vicq-d'Azyr (*see* Fig. 87, *1, 10,* in chap. III, 5; and Figs. 226–29).

In the human brain the striate area is located in and around the calcarine fissure, being mostly or entirely confined to the inner, medial face of the occipital lobe (Figs. 278, 288, 290, 293–96, 300, 301).

The location, shape, extent, and boundaries of the striate area vary greatly individually, as illustrated by the accompanying figures. The boundary of the striate area by which it is delimited from the adjoining "parastriate area" of G. Elliot Smith, or "field *18*" of Brodmann, is marked by an abrupt cessation of the stripe of Gennari (in unstained preparations or those stained for myelinated nerve fibers, e.g., by Weigert's method, Fig. 316, right half), or by a cessation of a double inner granular layer in Nissl preparations (Figs. 312, 313).

Its anterior boundary usually begins a short distance in front of the junction of the inner parieto-occipital sulcus (*po*) and the calcarine fissure (*mc*), not far from the splenium of the corpus callosum (*cc* or *spl*, in Figs. 289, 290, 291, 292, 293, 294, 295, 296). At this end, the striate cortex is ordinarily found only in the lower lip of the fissure, the upper lip belonging to the cortex surrounding the striate area, the "paraperistriate areae" of G. Elliot Smith, or "fields *18–19*" of Brodmann (Fig. 278). A striate area completely displaced into the lower lip is a rare occurrence (Ngowyang, Landau, Brodmann, Hoesel). A reverse arrangement, with the striate cortex in the upper lip and with none in the lower lip or with the striate cortex lining both lips more or less symmetrically, is only rarely found.

In the cuneal stretch of the calcarine fissure the striate cortex spreads over both lips, emerging also to a varying extent upon the free medial surface in a zone along both sides of the fissure, usually less along the upper or cuneal than along the lower or lingual lip.

At the tip or pole of the occipital lobe the striate area usually spreads a little over the posterior or posterolateral, convex face of the hemisphere (Fig. 293). In other cases where there is a persistent occipital operculum, the posterolateral exposed portion is considerable, both sides being fairly equal and symmetrical in shape or, on the contrary, of unequal size, with the left one usually the larger (Figs. 288, 290). In still other specimens the striate area falls short of the pole, as discussed in the preceding section (Fig. 296).

Ordinarily, the portion not concealed in the sulci amounts to less than half the total area, with more than half the striate cortex concealed within the sulci of the calcarine complex (Figs. 228, 229, 290, 291). The proportion of the striate cortex concealed in the sulci and that spreading over the inner and outer faces of the occipital operculum, as well as the longitudinal extent and, in particular, the shape, size, and location of the occipital operculum and opercular striate cortex, vary considerably individually and may also vary according to race, as discussed in the preceding section.

When one area, usually the left, is larger, a more or less pronounced asymmetry results (Fig. 288; *see* G. E. Smith 1907; Brodmann 1918). Such asymmetry is ordinarily, though causes of this peculiar arrangement, already found in the prehistoric human races and occasionally also in Monkeys and Apes, are little understood but are apparently complex, being both developmental-mechanical and architectural-functional. (*See* Figs. 282, 287; *see also* G. Elliot Smith 1907; Brodmann 1918; Le Gros Clark 1934.)

Fig. 297.—Alfred Walter Campbell (1868–1937), neurologist, neuropathologist, and alienist of Sydney, Australia. Pioneer investigator of the minute structure of the cerebral cortex. Author of the classical monograph *Histological Studies on the Localisation of Cerebral Function,* 1905 (from M. J. Australia, January 22, 1938). Courtesy of Professor Sydney Sunderland, of the University of Melbourne, Australia. *See also* Haymaker & Baer, *The Founders of Neurology,* 1953.

not regularly, associated with the "skew asymmetry" of the brain and of the cranium and with an unequal division of the venous sinuses at the "torcular of Herophilos," where the superior sagittal sinus proceeds mainly to the right, the straight sinus mainly to the left. The

The surface of the striate area in an adult human brain, according to Cunningham (1943) (G. Elliot Smith and Le Gros Clark), amounts to about 3,000 sq. mm., varying in different brains and hemispheres from 2,700 to 4,000 sq. mm. According to the investigations of Brod-

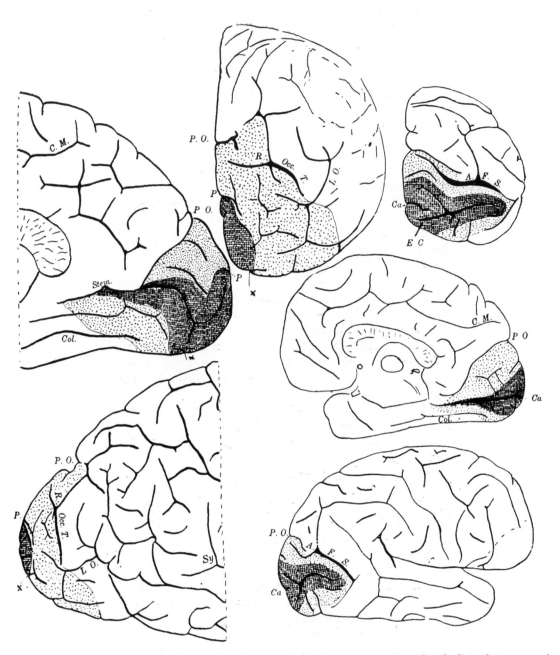

Fig. 298.—"Drawings to illustrate the distribution of the visuo-sensory (cross-hatched) and visuo-psychic (dotted) areas in the human being and orang. The three figures to the right are from the ape, and the wide lateral extension is to be specially noticed; observe, also, that the visuo-sensory area closely follows the fissure marked *E.C.*, the so-called 'external calcarine' fissure (the sulcus intrastriatus lateralis of Elliot Smith) [termed in this book 'lateral calcarine sulcus' (*lc*)] and that the visuo-psychic field is closely related to the 'Affenspalte' (*A. F. S.*). In the human brain the ramus occipitalis transversus (*R. Occ. T.*) seems to form a corresponding visuo-psychic limit. *Ca.* = calcarine fissure. *Stem* is placed above the division distinguished by that name. *Col.* = collateral fissure. *P.O.* = parieto-occipital fissure. *C.M.* = calloso-marginal fissure. *L.O.* = lateral occipital fissure of Eberstaller. *Sy.* = Sylvan fissure. *P.* = superior polar fissure of Bolton. × = inferior polar fissure of same writer." From A. W. Campbell, *Histological Studies on the Localisation of Cerebral Function*, p. 119, 1905. (*Cf.* Figs. 280, 284, 286.)

mann (1911), the size of the striate area varies between 2,950 and 4,400 sq. mm., being, on the average, 3,450 sq. mm. Filimonoff (1932) found the size of the same area to vary from 2,208 to 2,877 sq. mm., the mean extent being 2,613.

Since the area of the retina of a normal adult human eyeball is approximately 350 sq. mm., the ratio of its area to that of the striate area is roughly 1 to 7.

3. Location and extent of the striate area in Infrahuman Primates and in other Mammals.—In the brain of the Macaque and in other Old World Monkeys, almost the entire occipital lobe or operculum, sharply separated from the rest of the hemisphere by the simian or external occipitoparietal or lunate sulcus (*l*) and by the inferior occipital sulcus, is taken up by the striate area (Figs. 280, 302). Only a narrow zone along these sulci belongs to the adjoining extrastriate cortex. In the large Platyrrhines and in the Anthropomorphous Apes the portion of the striate area exposed on the posterolateral face of the occipital lobe is already noticeably reduced in comparison with most catarrhine Monkeys, even though it is still relatively larger than in Man (Figs. 282–84, 286, 303).

On the inner side of the hemisphere, in the Monkey, the striate area remains concealed in the calcarine fissure, except at the posterior pole along the ascending and descending prongs of the fissure.

In most Infraprimate Mammals the striate area is relatively smaller in extent than in the Simians (Figs. 308, 309). It is an area approximately semilunar in shape, close to or at the occipital pole, extending for some distance along the upper margin of the hemisphere anteriorly and posteriorly and in most species also spreading over the upper, inner, and lower surfaces of the hemisphere. In Mammals with poorly developed sight, such as the African Jumping Shrew (Fig. 279, *A*) and the European Hedgehog (Fig. 309, *B*), the striate area is quite small and is located at the occipital pole or close to it on the convex face of the hemisphere.

During life and in fresh specimens the striate area over the simian occipital lobe is of a peculiar pale yellowish-orange color and also has a characteristic arrangement of the blood vessels, features by which it may readily be distin-

guished from the surrounding cortex. (*Cf.* chap. X, 7.)

4. The striate area—a single, homogeneous, uniformly organized cortical territory.—The striate area, both in Man and in the Simians, has a remarkably uniform structure in all its parts. Morphologically, contrary to the statement of some investigators, it is not possible to notice any abrupt or sufficiently pronounced local differences which could be accepted as landmarks or boundaries by means of which the striate area could be further subdivided into smaller component territories or subareae.

This observation is at variance with the opinion of those students who insist that the striate area is made up of a number of subareae (Klempin 1921; Gurewitsch & Bychowski 1923, 1928; Volkmann 1926; Alouf 1929; G. Elliot Smith 1929–30; Beck 1930; Beck & Kleist 1931; Ngowyang 1934). Local variations, found in total thickness or thickness of particular layers of the striate cortex in so extensive an area, are merely expressions of physical factors caused by the surface configuration, if they are not plain artifacts.

The histological uniformity or homogeneity of the striate area, however, does not mean that its finer structural details are precisely the same in all parts. It means only that those changes that do occur do so gradually, almost imperceptibly, without alteration of the basic structural pattern, which remains essentially the same in the entire extent of the striate area. In its structural uniformity the striate area resembles the retina, of which it is a cortical representation. The variation concerns merely the less essential features. What differs is the number and size of the nerve cells and their expansions and, because of this, the total thickness and structural fineness of the cortex. But the kinds or varieties of neurons and their arrangement remain everywhere essentially the same.

The thinnest striate cortex in Man is in the posteriormost portion, contained in the pocket of the lateral or posterior calcarine fissure, close to or at the occipital pole, where the hemifoveae are represented. Conversely, the thickest cortex, approximately twice the thickness of the polar, is at the opposite, anterior, extremity of the striate area, where the monocular nasal portion of the contralateral retina is represented. In the Monkey the foveal-areal cortex is on the lateral face of the occipital lobe close to the simian sulcus, while the peripheral, extra-areal cortex remains buried in the anterior segment of the calcarine fissure on the medial face of the hemisphere.

The locality of the striate cortex related to the central foveae is also most delicately organized, while the locality representing the far and the extreme retinal periphery is relatively

FIG. 299.—Korbinian Brodmann (1868–1918), the neuroanatomist. Together with A. W. Campbell (*see* Fig. 297), founder of modern cytoarchitecture of the cerebral cortex of Man and of other Vertebrates (from J. f. Psychol. u. Neurol., v. 24, p. i, 1919). For biography *see* O. Vogt in the same volume, and Haymaker & Baer, *The Founders of Neurology*, 1953. (*See also* W. Spielmeyer in München. med. Wchnschr., v. 65, p. 1138, 1918; F. Nissl in Ztschr. f. d. ges. Neurol. u. Psychiat. [Orig.], v. 45, p. 329, 1919; L. Schwarz in Schweiz. Arch. f. Neurol. u. Psychiat., v. 4, p. 184, 1919–20.)

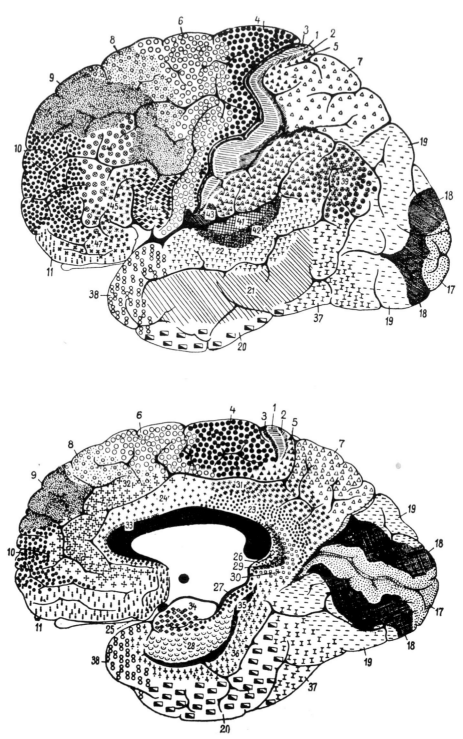

Fig. 300.—Brodmann's cytoarchitectural charts of the human cerebral cortex. *Upper figure*, lateral view of the left hemisphere; *lower figure*, medial view of the right hemisphere. Principal subdivisions: *1, 2, 3*, postcentral areae; *4*, gigantopyramidal precentral area (motor); *6*, frontal agranular area; the *4* and *6* together forming the precentral agranular region; areae *8, 9, 10, 11, 44, 45, 46,* and *47* compose the frontal granular region; areae *17, 18,* and *19* constitute the occipital region, of which the first is the striate area, *18*, the parastriate area, and *19*, the peristriate area of G. Elliot Smith; areae *20, 21, 22, 36, 37, 38, 41,* and *42* constitute the temporal region; areae *23, 24, 25, 31, 32,* and *33* comprise the cingular region; areae *26, 29,* and *30* make up the retrosplenial region; areae *27, 28, 34,* and *35* are the hippocampal region. The insular region (*13, 14, 15, 16*) is not indicated in these diagrams. From K. Brodmann, *Vergleichende Lokalisationslehre der Grosshirnrinde*, 1909. (*Cf.* Figs. 274, 275, 301.)

492

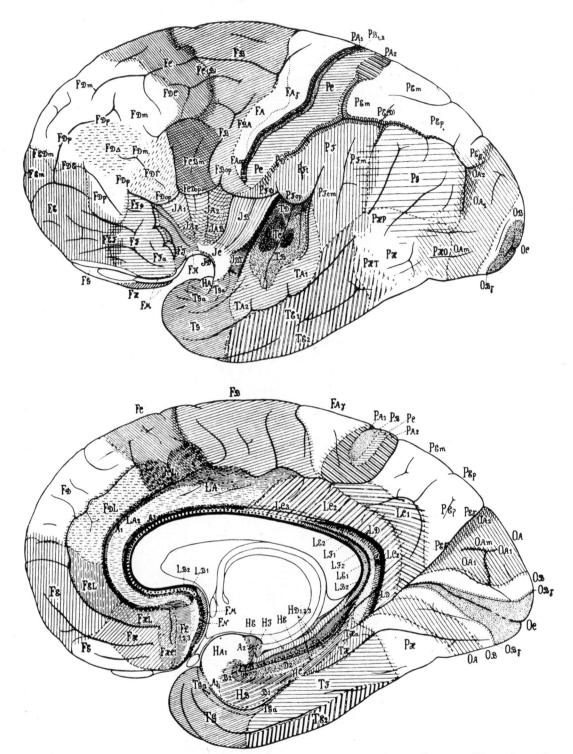

Fig. 301.—Cytoarchitectural charts of the human cerebral cortex, according to Economo. Upper figure shows lateral view of the left hemisphere; the lower figure a medial view of the right hemisphere. The principal receptor areae containing relatively the greatest number of granule cells or the most pronounced parts of the so-called *koniocortex* ("dusty cortex"), are: *Oc*, occipital granular area of Economo, identical with striate area of G. Elliot Smith, or with field *17* of Brodmann; *PA, PB, PC, PD*, make up the anterior parietal region of Economo, or postcentral region (areae *1, 2, 3*) of Brodmann; *TB, TC, TD*, represent the granular supratemporal area of Economo, approximately coinciding with the transverse temporal areae *41* and *42* of Brodmann. From Economo & Koskinas, *Die Cytoarchitektonik der Hirnrinde*, etc., 1925. (*Cf.* Figs. 274 and 275, showing functional localization, and Brodmann's charts in Fig. 300.)

493

crude. The intermediate zone filling the territory between these two extremes keeps the balance between both. But the differences, as pointed out above, are unessential and gradual. The rather vague boundaries, by means of which several beltlike zones may be distinguished in the retina, are smoothed over in the

striate area. Nor do such structural extremes as are found, for example, in the central fovea, on the one hand, and in the zone close to the ora serrata of the retina, on the other hand, have a clear counterpart in the striate area. The reason for this striking difference is rather obvious: in the central fovea, where the cones are most

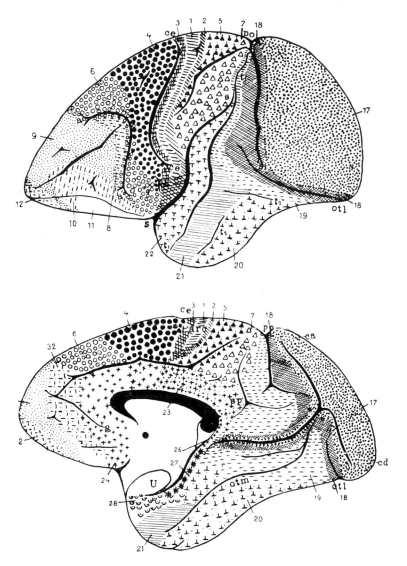

Fig. 302.—Cytoarchitectural charts of the brain of an African Cercopithecus Monkey. Upper figure represents a lateral view of the left hemisphere; the lower figure a medial view of the right hemisphere. The striate area, field *17*, or the cortical visual center (*medium stippling*), covers on the lateral face almost the entire occipital lobe or *o. operculum*, extending not quite to the simian sulcus (*si*) and to the inferior occipital sulcus (*otl*). On the medial face, field *17* spreads over a portion of the occipital lobe along the ascending and descending prongs of the medial calcarine sulcus (*ca, cd*), whereas along the main stem of this sulcus it is submerged, indicated by asterisks (*). The numbering of the areae same as in Fig. 300. From K. Brodmann, *Vergleichende Lokalisationslehre der Grosshirnrinde*, 1909. (*Cf.* Figs. 280, 281, and 306.) *Labeling: a*, arcuate sulcus; *ca, cd*, calcarine sulcus (medial, *mc* in Fig. 280); *ce*, central sulcus; *f*, frontal pole; *g*, genual sulcus; *otl*, lateral occipitotemporal sulcus; *otm*, medial occipitotemporal sulcus; *Parc*, paracentral lobule; *po*, parieto-occipital sulcus; *si*, simian sulcus; *S*, Sylvian or lateral fissure; *sp*, subparietal sulcus; *t₁, t₂*, superior and medial temporal sulci; *U*, uncus of hippocampal gyrus.

numerous and concentrated in a relatively small area, the vitreal layers, through which the rays of light would otherwise have to pass, are pushed aside in order to increase the central acuity, whereas in the cortical representation of the fovea, where much more space is available, the transition of the layers from point to point is smoothed over. (*Cf.* chap. V, 10 [5].)

References: Addison & Donaldson 1933; Aldama 1930; Alouf 1929; J. Anthony 1943; Antoni 1914; Ariëns Kappers 1909, 1911, 1913, 1914; Ariëns Kappers, Huber & Crosby 1936; Bailey & Bonin 1945, 1946; Bailey, Bonin &

1925; Filimonoff 1929, 1931–33; Flores 1911; Geist 1930; Gerhardt & Kreht 1933; Goldstern 1915; Gray 1924; Gurewitsch & Bychowsky 1923, 1928; B. Haller 1908, 1910; Harman 1947; Hermanides & Köppen 1903; Hines 1934, 1942; Horn & Helfand 1932; Klempin 1921; Köppen & Löwenstein 1905; Krieg 1946; Kurzveil 1909; Landau 1916; Lashley & Clark 1946; Marburg 1907; Marinesco 1911; Mauss 1908, 1911; Mott 1907; Mott & Halliburton 1908; Mott & Kelley 1908; Mott, Schuster & Halliburton 1910; Nayrac 1930; Ngowyang 1934, 1935, 1936, 1937; Nissl 1897; Packer 1941; Peden & Bonin

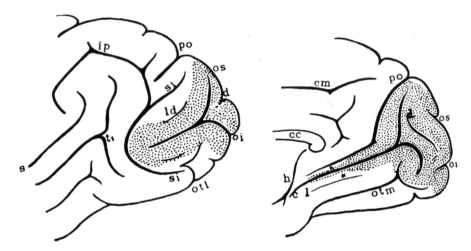

FIG. 303.—Striate area of an Orang-utan (*Simia satyrus, Pongo satyrus*). The left figure shows the lateral side of the left occipital lobe, the right figure the medial side of the right occipital lobe. The asterisks (*) indicate points at which the striate cortex, buried within the anterior segment of the medial calcarine fissure (*c*), emerges on the exposed surface. From K. Brodmann, *Vergleichende Lokalisationslehre der Grosshirnrinde*, 1909. (*Cf.* Figs. 284, 285, 286, 298.) *Labeling: cc*, corpus callosum; *cm*, callosomarginal sulcus; *d*, so-called descending sulcus of Ecker; *ip*, intraparietal sulcus; *l*, lingual sulcus; *ld*, dorsal limiting sulcus; *oi* and *os*, inferior and superior opercular sulci (our "lateral calcarine sulcus," *lc* in Figs. 284 and 285); *otm*, medial occipitotemporal sulcus; *otl*, lateral occipitotemporal or inferior occipital sulcus; *po*, parieto-occipital sulcus; *S*, Sylvian or lateral fissure; *si*, simian fissure; *t1*, superior temporal sulcus.

McCulloch 1950; Beck 1930, 1940; Beck & Kleist 1931; Bodian 1935; Bok 1929; Bolton 1900, 1903; Bonin 1934, 1938, 1942, 1945, 1950; Bonin & Bailey 1947; Brodmann 1903, 1904, 1905, 1906, 1908, 1909 (1925), 1911, 1913, 1918; Brouwer 1936; Brummelkamp 1943–45; Brunner & Spiegel 1919; A. W. Campbell 1904, 1905; Le Gros Clark 1925, 1931, 1934, 1942; Cobb 1925; Cohn & Papez 1930; Donaldson 1891–92; Drooglever Fortuyn 1914; Economo 1926, 1927, 1928, 1929, 1930, 1931; Economo & Koskinas

1947; Popoff 1927; Riese 1940, 1943, 1946; Riese & Smyth 1940; Roch 1941; Rogalski 1946; Roncoroni 1911; Rose 1912, 1930, 1935; Schlapp 1898, 1902–3; Senn 1942; Shellshear 1936; G. Elliot Smith 1907, 1909; Solnitzky & Harman 1946; Sonntag & Woollard 1925; Thorner 1910; M. Vogt 1929; O. Vogt 1906, 1943; Vogt & Vogt 1919, 1926; Volkmann 1926; G. A. Watson 1907; Wilson & Smith 1909; Woollard 1925.

SEC. 5. CELL LAYERS OF THE STRIATE AREA

1. GENERAL HISTOLOGICAL CHARACTERISTICS OF THE PRIMATE STRIATE AREA.—The striate area of Man, Ape, and Monkey, when examined in appropriately stained microscopic sections, e.g., by Nissl or Weigert methods, is characterized partly by features common to other localities of the cerebral cortex and partly by features found nowhere else. The arrangement of the bodies of nerve cells and of the thicker and thinner myelinated nerve fibers grossly follows the pattern found elsewhere. One general peculiarity is a more or less pronounced stratifica-

in the floor of the fissures, the thickest on the summit of the gyri. The thinnest striate cortex apparently is found at the occipital pole, where in Man the central foveae are represented, or in Monkeys close to the simian sulcus.

The striate area is, on the whole, much richer in nerve cells than the remainder of the cerebral cortex. The size of its cells, on the contrary, is much smaller, the intercellular spaces reduced, and the distribution of cells more uniform. The result of this is the dense, relatively homogeneous appearance of this cortical locality, for

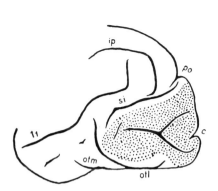 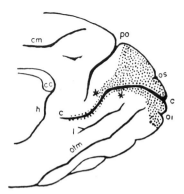

FIG. 304.—Striate area of a Langur or Hanuman Monkey (*Presbytis cephalopterus, Semnopithecus leucoprymnus*) of Ceylon, a catarrhine cercopithecid Old World Monkey. Left diagram represents the lateral view of the left occipital lobe; the right diagram the medial view of the right occipital lobe. The asterisks (*) indicate points in the upper and lower calcarine lip at which the striate cortex emerges from the calcarine fissure (*c*) upon the exposed surface of the lobe. From K. Brodmann, *Vergleichende Lokalisationslehre der Grosshirnrinde*, 1909. (*Cf.* Figs. 282, 283, 284, 285, 286.) *Labeling: c*, calcarine fissure (medial, *mc* in our Figs. 280, 282); *cc*, corpus callosum; *cm*, callosomarginal sulcus; *h*, hippocampal sulcus; *ip*, intraparietal sulcus; *l*, limiting calcarine sulcus; *oi*, inferior branch of lateral calcarine fissure; *otl*, inferior occipital sulcus; *otm*, medial occipitotemporal sulcus; *po*, parieto-occipital sulcus; *si*, simian sulcus; *t₁*, superior temporal sulcus.

tion parallel to the surface of the cortex. Another is the columnar arrangement of cells, vertical to the surface, less well defined here than in some other localities.

The striate cortex is thin when compared with the other cortical regions and fields—for example, with the precentral motor cortex. In Man its average thickness is from 1,300 to 1,600 microns, or 1.5 mm., more or less; in the Rhesus Macaque it is approximately 1,000 microns, or 1 mm. The thickness varies considerably even on the same level, depending on the plane of cutting and also on the physical factors that mold the sulcal and gyral relief, including the presence or absence of blood vessels and the like. Ordinarily, the thinnest striate cortex is found

which reason it has been named by Economo *koniocortex* or "dusty cortex," meaning "granular cortex."

When examined without the aid of a magnifying apparatus and even more so at slight magnification (50×), a vertical section through the striate cortex stained by the Nissl method reveals an unequal distribution of nerve cells. Close scrutiny shows at least eight parallel and alternating layers, five dark ones rich in cells (*2, 3, 4-a, 4-c, 6*) and three of lesser density (*1, 4-b, 5*, left numbers in Fig. 312, also Fig. 314).

In approximately the middle of the thickness there is a conspicuous belt where the cells are relatively few (*4-b*). The upper limit of this rarefied zone roughly coincides with the boundary between the upper and the lower half, the lighter zone itself being approximately one-sixth the thickness of the entire striate cortex. This lighter zone almost coincides with the bulk of the stria or stripe of Gennari or Vicq-d'Azyr visible by the unaided eye as a white line in fresh and fixed specimens and in Weigert-stained preparations as a dark belt (thick fiber belt *G*, in right half of Fig. 316). Another even sharper, but less wide, rarefied cellular zone is close to the lower boundary of the striate cortex (*5*, left half in Figs. 312, 313).

The stripe of Gennari divides the striate cortex roughly into two halves of almost equal thickness (right diagram in Fig. 316). The upper

Externally, the territory of the striate cortex rich in cells (layers *2–6*) is separated from the pial membrane (*p*) by a plexiform layer, where the nerve cells are almost absent (layer *1*). The thickness of this layer equals approximately one-eighth of the belt of the cortex containing cells. The inner boundary of the striate cortex toward the white subcortical matter (*Al*) is fairly sharp. A boundary line where the striate cortex adjoins the surrounding parastriate cortex is well marked along its entire circumference.

2. STRATIFICATION OF NERVE CELLS OR CYTO-ARCHITECTURE OF THE PRIMATE STRIATE AREA.

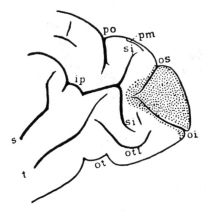 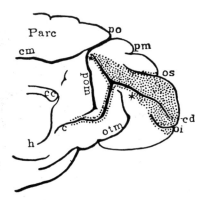

FIG. 305.—Striate area of the platyrrhine South American Woolly Monkey (*Lagothrix lagotricha* or *L. humboldtii*). Left diagram shows the lateral view of the left occipital lobe; right diagram the medial view of the right occipital lobe. Asterisks (*) indicate a portion of the striate area concealed within the anterior segment of the calcarine fissure (*c*). From K. Brodmann, *Vergleichende Lokalisationslehre der Grosshirnrinde*, 1909. (*Cf.* Figs. 282, 284, 286, 303, 304.) *Labeling: c, cd,* calcarine fissure (medial); *cc,* corpus callosum; *cm,* callosomarginal sulcus; *h,* hippocampal sulcus; *ip,* intraparietal sulcus; *oi* and *os,* inferior and superior branch of lateral calcarine sulcus; *ot,* occipito-temporal incisure; *otl,* inferior occipital or lateral occipitotemporal sulcus; *otm,* medial occipitotemporal sulcus; *Parc,* paracentral lobule; *pm,* paramesial sulcus; *po,* parieto-occipital sulcus; *pom,* medial parieto-occipital sulcus; *S,* Sylvian or lateral fissure; *si,* simian sulcus; *t,* temporal sulcus.

half, closer to the surface, situated above the stripe, is made up preponderantly of small, uniformly distributed cells not greatly different in size. The columnar arrangement, although not pronounced, is noticeable here. The lower or inner, deeper half of the striate cortex below the stripe of Gennari is less homogeneous. It comprises the inner rarefied zone (*5*) between the two denser ones (*4-c*, *6*). The cells here are less uniform in size, and the columnar arrangement somewhat less prominent. The few large cells, the largest in the striate cortex, found in groups and singly at irregular intervals in both rarefied zones (*4-b* and *5*), are conspicuous here.

—The nerve cells of the striate cortex in Man, Ape, and Monkey, according to a generally accepted view, are arranged in several more or less distinct horizontal layers parallel to the cortical surface. Following Brodmann's suggestion, eight layers may be distinguished—a greater number than in any other locality of the cerebral cortex (left numbers in Fig. 312). In the striate area, however, since it is a part of the *neocortex* or "new cortex" of the great cerebral hemispheres, the characteristic basic six layers are readily identified (right numbers in same figure), the increase being caused by a splitting of the fourth layer into three sublayers

(*4-a, 4-b, 4-c*). As in the remainder of the neocortex, the layers or sublayers of the striate cortex, even when clearly recognizable, with the exception of the first layer, are nowhere completely separated from one another by layers or zones devoid of cells, as is the case in the retina and in the laminated lateral geniculate nucleus (*see* chap. V, 2, and chap. VI, 8, 9).

The features by which the particular layers may be identified are the number, size, shape,

cortex into layers being in a sense an artifact. For, in reality, all superimposed layers of the striate cortex, as of the neocortex elsewhere, are structurally intimately tied up, the entire cortex forming, in fact, a single, solid nervous mass.

In spite of this intimate relationship of the several layers of the striate cortex, the undeniable structural differences from stratum to stratum are to be accepted not merely as accidental

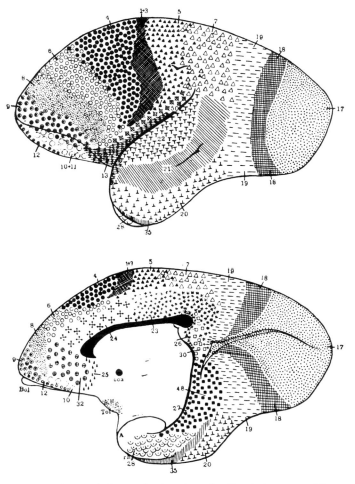

Fig. 306.—Cytoarchitectural charts of the cerebral cortex of a South American Marmoset Monkey (*Hapale jacchus*). Upper figure shows the lateral view of the left hemisphere; lower figure the medial view of the right hemisphere. Striate area, or field *17*, indicated by medium stippling. Numbering same as in Figs. 300 and 302. From K. Brodmann, *Vergleichende Lokalisationslehre der Grosshirnrinde*, 1909. (*See also* following figure.)

distribution, density, and other possible characteristics of the constituent nerve cells and fibers. While each of these features may vary from place to place of the areal extent, the transition from one layer to the next is everywhere continuous, the subdivision of the striate

features useful as landmarks but as a true morphological expression of a locally varying function. Each layer, although a part of the total structure, is to be looked upon as a differentiated cortical mechanism performing its own specific function, the function of the cortex being, accordingly, the sum total of the functions of its constituent specific structures.

The layers which in the primate striate cortex may, with fair justification, be distinguished in preparations stained by the Nissl method are as follows.

3. PLEXIFORM LAYER (*1*).—The first layer, identical with the "zonal lamina" of Brodmann,

equal in size to the medium-sized cells of the intermediate lamina of the inner granular layer (*4-b*). These larger cells may be present in any part of the plexiform layer, either close to the second layer, immediately underneath the pial membrane, or anywhere in between. They are mostly irregular, multipolar, and sometimes fusiform or spindle-like in shape. Of the smaller nerve cells, some are pyramidal, resembling

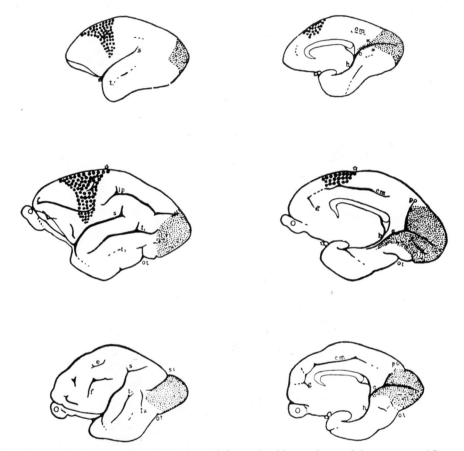

FIG. 307.—Lateral (*left*) and medial (*right*) views of the cerebral hemispheres of three species of Lower Primates, indicating the shape, position, and extent of the motor area (*coarsely stippled*) and of the striate area (*finely stippled*): *upper figures*, South American Marmoset (*Hapale jacchus*); *middle figures*, a Lemur of Madagascar (*Lemur macaco*); *lower figures*, an Indian Loris (*Nycticebus tardigradus*). From K. Brodmann, *Vergleichende Lokalisationslehre der Grosshirnrinde*, 1909.

or "molecular layer" of Economo, in Man comprises approximately one-eighth the total thickness of the striate cortex and less in the Monkey (*1*, in Fig. 314). It is closest to the pial membrane coating the surface of the cortex.

In the plexiform layer there are only a few true nerve cells, mostly of small size. Some cells, however, are considerably larger than the diminutive cells of the second layer (*2*) and are

those of the second layer, but the majority are irregularly spherical or triangular. Occasionally, a group of a dozen or so of these small cells is arranged in a row parallel to the general arrangement of the layers. The number of neuroglial elements is likewise small.

Owing to the scarcity of nerve cells, the plexiform layer appears empty, contrasting in this respect with all inner layers taken together

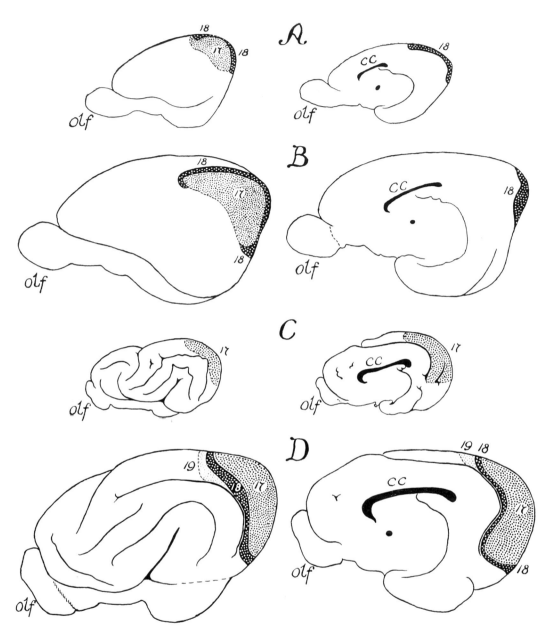

FIG. 308.—The shape, extent, and location of the striate (17), parastriate (18), and peristriate (19) areae of various representative Mammals. A, European Spermophile or Ground Squirrel (*Spermophilus citillus, Zieselmaus* in German, *Súslik* in Russian, $1\frac{3}{5}\times$ magnification); B, Rabbit (*Lepus cuniculus*, $1\frac{3}{5}\times$ magnification); C, Stone- or Beech-Marten (*Mustela foina*); D, Kinkajou (*Cercoleptes* or *Potos caudivolvulus*, $1\frac{1}{5}\times$ magnification). *Labeling: cc,* corpus callosum; *olf,* olfactory bulb. From K. Brodmann, *Vergleichende Lokalisationslehre der Grosshirnrinde,* 1909. (*See* following figure.)

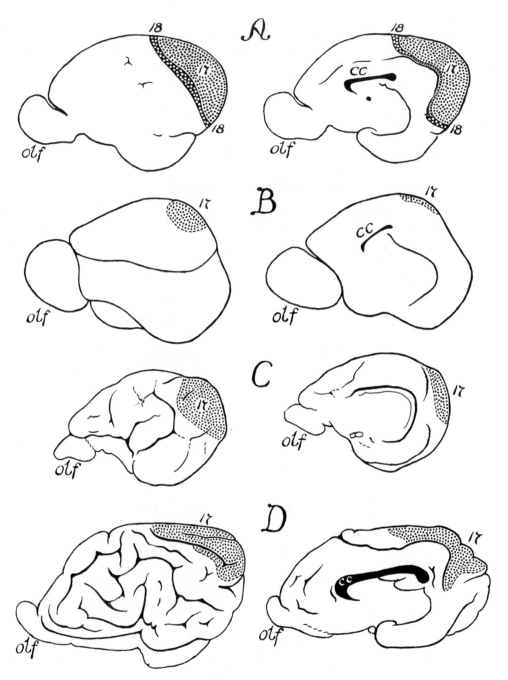

Fig. 309.—The shape, extent, and location of the striate (*17*) and parastriate (*18*) areae of some Mammals. *A*, Flying Fox or Fruit-eating Bat (*Pteropus edwardsii*, $1\frac{3}{4}$× magnification); *B*, European Hedgehog (*Erinaceus europaeus*, $2\frac{1}{4}$× magnification); *C*, Kangaroo (*Macropus penicillatus*); *D*, Domestic Goat (*Capra hircus*). From K. Brodmann, *Vergleichende Lokalisationslehre der Grosshirnrinde*, 1909. (*See* preceding figure.) *Labeling: cc*, corpus callosum; *olf*, olfactory bulb.

(2–6). In spite of this, the plexiform layer is part of the striate cortex. This fact is best shown by the spreading here of the numerous expansions of nerve cells residing in the subjacent layers, to be described subsequently.

4. Outer granular layer (2).—The second layer, identical with the "external granular

apical dendrite directed toward the surface and spreading within the first layer. The thin layer of cytoplasm of the cell body contains a scanty chromophile substance. Occasionally there is found a somewhat larger cell of an irregular spherical or oval shape, which more properly deserves the name "granule cell." The "granular" impression to which the layer owes its

Fig. 310.—Sir Wilfrid Le Gros Clark (1895), professor of anatomy in Oxford, England. An eminent student of the nervous system, in particular of the visual, and of Man's phylogenetical origin. Courtesy Professor Clark.

lamina" of Brodmann, or "outer granular layer" of Economo, is represented by the uppermost condensation of the cellular territory of the striate cortex next to the plexiform layer (2, in Fig. 314).

The cells of the outer granular layer are very small, among the smallest in the striate cortex. They are of a short pyramidal shape, with an

name is, however, caused by the small size of most of the cells, their great number, and density of arrangement.

5. Pyramidal cell layer (3).—The third layer, identical with the "pyramidal lamina" of Brodmann or "pyramidal layer" of Economo, is the inner continuation of the second layer and is approximately five times as thick. Its nerve cells, although similar in shape, are appreciably larger than those of the second layer. Although not so dense, the cells of this layer may, because of their great number, represent, in Man, almost one-fourth or perhaps more of the nerve cells of the entire striate cortex. They gradually increase in size from the vicinity of the second to the subjacent fourth layer. The larger of the tinct vertical columns. A cell of typical pyramidal shape and of a size equal to that of the largest elements, with pronounced Nissl granules, is rarely found in this layer. These may be considered displaced giant ganglion cells characteristic of the fifth layer (*4-b*).

6. OUTER LAMINA OF THE INNER GRANULAR LAYER (*4-a*).—The fourth layer, identical with

FIG. 311.—Theodor Hermann Meynert (1833–92), professor of psychiatry in Vienna, Austria. One of the foremost pioneers of modern brain research. (*Cf.* Fig. 113, and the appended references on biography.)

elements are mostly of pronounced pyramidal shape, with a fairly long apical dendrite pointing toward the surface of the cortex and a few shorter and thinner basal dendrites spreading in a more or less horizontal direction. Certain of these cells are more or less globular or spherical and multipolar.

The cells in this layer are agglomerated into small clusters, from two or three to six cells, the clusters in turn arranged in indis-

the "superficial internal granular lamina" or *4-a* of Brodmann and Economo, like the second layer, appears to be a condensation of the rather uniform, many-celled outer, or supra-Gennarian, half of the striate cortex. It immediately adjoins the subjacent and rather vacant fifth layer of Gennari and Vicq-d'Azyr (*4-b*).

It appears denser in comparison with the third layer (*3*) and even more in comparison with the fifth layer (*4-b*), because of the presence of small nerve cells of irregular globular shape, the typical "granules." There are also a few cells of somewhat larger pyramidal type, essentially identical with those in the third layer. On occasion, one of the larger cells characteristic of the fifth layer (*4-b*) may also be present, containing well-formed intracellular chromophile granules. The number of the granule-like cells in this lamina, however, is but a fraction of the number of similar cells in the deep inner lamina of the fourth layer (*4-c*).

7. MIDDLE LAMINA OF THE INNER GRANULAR LAYER (*4-b*).—The fifth layer, identical with the "intermediate internal granular lamina" or *4-b* of Brodmann and of Economo and largely with Gennari's or Vicq-d'Azyr's fiber layer, situated approximately midway in the cortex, is characterized by a relatively small number of cells. It separates the outer cortical half, made up of layers *1* to *4-a*, from the inner, represented by layers *4-c* to *6*, both of which are packed with nerve cells. These halves are of almost equal thickness.

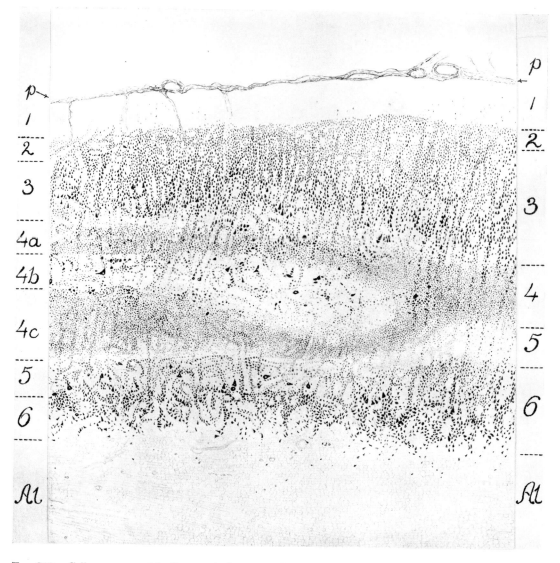

FIG. 312.—Cell arrangement in the marginal portion of human striate cortex stained with Nissl–toluidine blue method (Lenhossék's modification), showing the merging of the three sublayers of the inner granular layer of the striate area (*4-a, 4-b, 4-c*) into a single layer *4* in the parastriate area at the right end of the figure. (*Cf.* microphoto in Fig. 313; for stratification *see* Fig. 316.)

The elements found in the *4-b* layer are of several varieties. The bulk is represented by neurons of a size slightly larger than the typical granules of layers *4-a* and *4-c*, usually of spherical, pyriform, elliptical, or ovoidal shape. Other cells, somewhat larger than the cells of the *4-a* layer, always with their long axes horizontal, with an abundant chromophile substance, and expansions spreading in various directions, are conspicuous. The larger of these multipolar ganglions, among the largest nerve cells of the striate cortex, are characteristic of this layer. Their well-developed chromophile granules,

separated by intergranular lines or channels, and their robust expansions are indicative of their essentially "motor" nature. These large neurons, possibly identical with the "solitary cells" originally described by Meynert (1872), are found at irregular intervals, usually singly, sometimes in the company of one or more smaller similar cells. These elements, because of their location, may be termed "outer solitary or giant cells" of the striate cortex (*cf.* par. 9, this section). Less frequently, these giant cells are displaced into the adjoining layers *4-a* and *4-c*. Such large and medium cells are more numerous

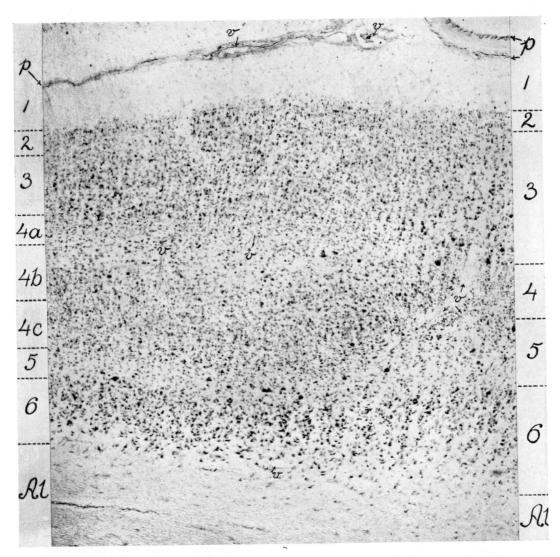

FIG. 313.—Microphotograph of a Nissl-stained section of the human striate area close to its boundary, showing the merging of the three sublayers (*4-a, 4-b, 4-c*) of the inner granular layer (left portion of the photo) into a single layer of the parastriate area (*4*, at the right of the photo). *Labeling: Al, alba,* or white subcortical fiber substance; *p,* pial membrane or vascular cover of brain; *v,* blood vessels. (For stratification *see* Fig. 316; *cf.* preceding figure.)

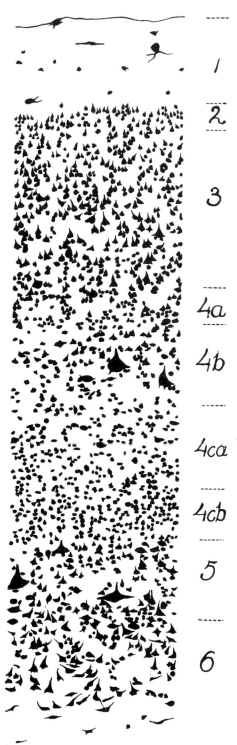

in the Monkey than in Man. Scattered among these varieties are nerve cells of a diminutive size which perhaps belong to the true "granules."

8. Inner or deep lamina of the inner granular layer (4-c).—The sixth layer, identical with the "deep internal granular lamina" of Brodmann and of Economo, is the richest cell layer in the infra-Gennarian half, comprising approximately from one-fifth to one-sixth the total thickness of the striate cortex.

The bulk of its cells are typical "granules" of small size and of spherical or irregular shape, with scanty cytoplasm and chromophile substance. Because of this, the sixth layer presents a rather homogeneous and somewhat paler appearance than the remainder of the striate cortex. In addition to the granules, there is a considerable number of cells of globular, ovoidal, or irregular shape, approaching in size the medium-sized elements of the fifth layer (4-b), containing distinct chromophile granules. Cells somewhat resembling small pyramids, with an apical dendrite pointing toward the surface, are few. A columnar arrangement of the cells is indicated. The greatest condensation of this layer is in a deep zone adjoining the ganglion layer, zone 4-cb. Here also the distribution of cells is most homogeneous, the larger and somewhat less dense cells being confined to the zone closer to the fifth layer, zone 4-ca (see Fig. 314).

9. Ganglion cell layer (5).—The seventh layer, identical with the "ganglion lamina" of Brodmann or "ganglion layer" of Economo, appears as a narrow break between the sixth (4-c) and the eighth (6) layers. Cells of large and medium size, found singly and in small clusters, are conspicuous in it. In size, shape, and other details they are practically a counterpart of the large "solitary cells" of Meynert in the fifth layer (4-b). Because of their location, they may be called "inner solitary or giant cells" of the striate cortex (see par. 7, this section).

Some of the small nerve cells scantily filling

Fig. 314.—Cell layers of the human striate cortex from the lower lip of the calcarine fissure, stained with the Nissl–toluidine blue method. Camera lucida drawing magnified 120×. *Stratification: 1*, plexiform layer; *2*, outer granular layer; *3*, pyramidal cell layer; *4a, 4b,* *4c*, outer, middle, and inner lamina of the inner nuclear layer; *4ca, 4cb,* outer and inner zone of *4c; 5,* ganglion cell layer; *6,* multiform cell layer. (*Cf.* Figs. 312, 313, 316.)

this layer are irregularly multipolar in shape, while not a few resemble small pyramids with an ascending apical dendrite. In the Monkey the majority of the large multipolar and pyramidal nerve cells are found not in this but in the eighth layer (layer *6*). Because of this, the ganglion layer here appears more empty of cells and with more precise boundaries than in Man.

10. MULTIFORM CELL LAYER (*6*).—The eighth, or innermost, layer of the striate cortex, adjoining the subcortical white matter, identical with the "multiform lamina" of Brodmann or the "layer of fusiform or spindle-shaped cells" of Economo, is a narrow zone filled with cells small in size and irregular in shape. Their visible dendrites are relatively long, some resembling the ascending apical dendrites, others spreading in various directions. Not a few cells are triangular, ovoidal, elliptical, or oblong fusiform, their narrow, horizontally or obliquely placed bodies extending at both ends into long, thin dendrites. In the Monkey this layer is distinguished by the presence of numerous large and medium-sized nerve cells resembling Meynert's "solitary cells." Some of the largest ganglions, which in Man are confined to the seventh layer (*5*), are found in the Monkey in the eighth (*6*).

References: Aldama 1930; Ariëns Kappers 1928; Ariëns Kappers, Huber & Crosby 1936; Bailey & Bonin 1945, 1946; Bailey, Bonin & McCulloch 1950; Beck 1925, 1930; Bielschowski 1921; Bonin 1938, 1939, 1942; Bonin & Bailey 1947; Brodmann 1904, 1906, 1908, 1909 (1925); A. W. Campbell 1905; B. Campbell 1951; Chasan 1927; Le Gros Clark 1942; De Crinis 1938; Economo 1927; Economo & Koskinas 1925; Geist 1930; M. Hines 1934, 1942; E. Landau 1915, 1938; Lashley & Clark 1946; Th. Meynert 1872; Mott *et al.* 1908, 1910; Ngowyang 1937; S. Ramón y Cajal 1899–1904, 1900–1906, 1909–11; Roch 1941; M. Rose 1930, 1935; D. Senn 1942; Solnitzky & Harman 1946; C. & O. Vogt 1919, 1926; M. Vogt 1929; O. Vogt 1943.

SEC. 6. FIBER SYSTEMS OF THE STRIATE AREA

1. GENERAL REMARKS ON THE MYELOARCHITECTURE OF THE PRIMATE STRIATE AREA.—The striate area contains numerous axis cylinders enveloped in myelin sheaths of various thicknesses, easily made visible by the appropriate staining technique, e.g., by Weigert's, Kultschitzky's, and other similar methods.

The arrangement or distribution of the myelinated nerve fibers, in this locality as elsewhere in the cerebral cortex, is not uniform, the fibers being assembled in more or less pronounced layers or strata and in bundles. The pattern into which the various fiber layers, bundles, and nettings in the striate cortex are arranged, even though essentially the same as in the remainder of the neocortex or "new cortex," is a peculiar one and characteristic of the striate cortex, not found anywhere else in exactly the same arrangement.

The fiber pattern, like the cell pattern, of the striate area is essentially the same in its entire extent, nowhere exhibiting sufficient differences to warrant further subdivision of this area into secondary fields. The fiber structure of the entire striate area, accordingly, is a uniformly organized field with slight local changes in detail which are accomplished only gradually. In contrast with its uniform fibrous structure, its boundary toward the surrounding parastriate area is quite sharp (Fig. 315). The striking peculiarities of its fibrous structure, in contrast with other areas of the occipital lobe and of the rest of the brain, define the striate area as a special territory of the cortex, with a function of its own.

2. FIBER SYSTEMS OF THE STRIATE CORTEX. —In a preparation cut vertical to the brain surface, the bulk of the myelinated fibers appears confined approximately to the inner or lower half of the striate cortex (Fig. 316, right figure). This territory comprises the conspicuous stripe of Gennari or Vicq-d'Azyr (*G*), whose upper limit is slightly above the level separating the outer from the inner half of the cortex.

In the inner or lower half of the striate cortex, corresponding with the cell layers *4-b* to *6*, most of the well-stained fibers are arranged in vertical bundles, grossly parallel to one another, extending from the subcortical fibrous substance (*Al*) to the stripe of Gennari, above which a few thin bundles may be seen for a short distance.

Other systems of fibers in the infra-Gennarian half are arranged obliquely, some assuming a horizontal course, cutting the vertical bundles at approximately right angles. When examined at high magnification, the vertical bundles appear to be made up mostly of fine and quite fine

In addition to these coarse fibers, there are many thin and very thin ones, crisscrossing in various directions and forming a fine fuzz or meshwork between the vertical bundles. The character of the fibrous plexus changes somewhat, however, from level to level of the infra-Gennarian region. Most dense and containing the most coarse fibers is the plexus closest to the subcortical fibrous substance, corresponding to

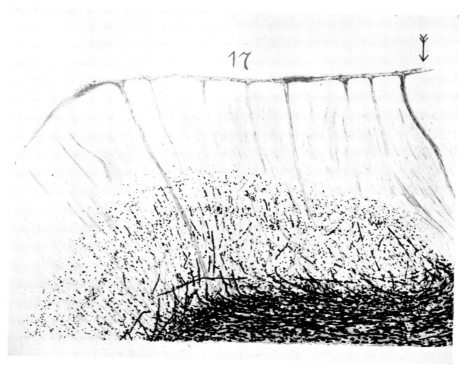

Fig. 315.—Upper lip of the calcarine fissure of Fig. 238 reproduced at higher magnification (about 45×) and turned upside down, to show the termination of the afferent visual fibers or of the visual radiation in the striate area of the Monkey brain. The striate area of G. Elliot Smith, identical with Brodmann's field *17*, contains a characteristic structure which stops abruptly at the point indicated by an arrow. The uppermost and widest of the several layers, placed approximately in the middle of the cortex, corresponds to the stripe of Gennari or Vicq-d'Azyr. The degenerated afferent visual fibers, in this case experimentally interrupted at a distant point in the radiation, are seen as black lines and specks streaming from the underlying subcortical fiber substance into the cortex as far as Gennari's layer. In the ventral layers these fibers observe a slanting course, as found by S. Ramón y Cajal in the human cortex (fibers marked *a* in Figs. 327 and 328). In their greater thickness and oblique course, the fibers of the visual radiation contrast with other fiber categories which remained normal in this experiment. Note also rapid decrease of the layers of the striate cortex before their cessation at the boundary line of that cortex. From S. Polyak, *The Main Afferent Fiber Systems*, etc., Berkeley, 1932.

fibers, a few only are of medium thickness, with the thicker fibers more frequently close to the subcortical fiber substance. Of the system of oblique and horizontal fibers, some are of medium thickness or even quite thin, while a considerable number of them are quite coarse, the coarsest fibers attaining a caliber ten or more times greater than that of the thin fibers.

layers *5* and *6*. Less dense and made up of less coarse fibers is the plexus in layer *4-c*. In the stripe of Gennari or Vicq-d'Azyr, principally corresponding to *4-b* and partly also to *4-c* of the cell layers, there are only a few somewhat coarser fibers, but the fuzz of thin and very thin myelinated fibers is particularly dense. Fine fibers pursue an irregular course here, winding and twisting in all directions. A horizontal direction prevails, however, although the individual fibers can be followed for but a short distance. The same is also true of the thick infra-Gennarian fibers which can be followed as far as Gennari's stripe.

In the supra-Gennarian half of the striate cortex, abutting on the surface of the cortex, the arrangement of the myelinated fibers is much simpler. Here the vertical bundles are mostly absent except in layer *4-a*, where their broken-off tips may be followed for a short distance into layer *3*. The meshwork of the fine, irregularly arranged fibers also becomes thinner here. In the second cell layer the fibers again increase in number (Kaes & Bechterew's plexus), until, close under the pia, a somewhat denser layer of mostly horizontal fibers of medium and thin

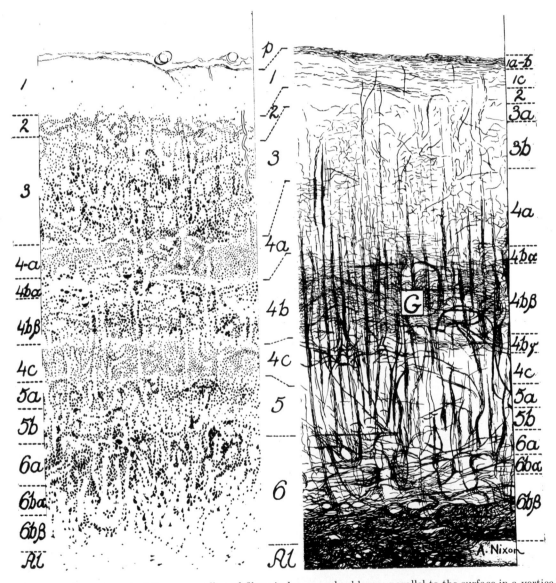

FIG. 316.—Arrangement of the nerve cells and fibers in layers and sublayers parallel to the surface in a vertical section through the human striate area or visual cortical center. The right-hand sketch from a preparation treated according to Kultschitzky's modification of Weigert's stain, showing only the nerve fibers; the left-hand sketch from a preparation stained with the Nissl–toluidine blue method, which shows only the bodies of the nerve cells. The numbers along the right and left margins indicate the layers according to C. and O. Vogt (1919); the middle column indicates the designation of layers adopted in this book. Approximate magnification 75×. For stratification *see* Fig. 314. *G*, fiber layer of Gennari or Vicq-d'Azyr.

caliber is formed. This is the plexus of Exner.

References: Bechterew 1891; Beck 1925, 1930; Le Gros Clark 1942; Th. Kaes 1907; Kawata 1927; Koikegami & Imogawa 1937; Lashley 1942; Lungwitz 1937; T. Mauss 1908, 1911; Niessl von Mayendorf 1907; S. Polyak (Poliak) 1932; S. Ramón y Cajal 1899–1904, 1900–1906, 1909–11; M. Rose 1935; A. H. Schroeder 1927–29; D. Senn 1942; Spiller 1901; C. & O. Vogt 1919, 1926.

SEC. 7. MINUTE STRUCTURE OF THE STRIATE AREA AS REVEALED BY HISTOANALYTIC STAINING

1. INTRODUCTORY REMARKS.—The methods of staining the microscopic sections of the striate area, as is also true of other parts of the nervous system, are many, from the most simple, employed routinely, to special procedures. The first are used in daily laboratory practice to show the entire structure; the others, to reveal special constituents of the tissue. Of the first, the most used are the several variations of the hematoxylin and eosin or phloxin method, which stains all tissue constituents fairly equally.

Of the special procedures, the most useful are the Nissl staining of the nerve cells and that of Weigert, which stains the myelinated nerve fibers. Both of these, in comparison with the hematoxylin and eosin stain, show more distinctly the particular tissue components, for example, the varieties, number, and arrangement of the nerve cells or fibers in a particular locality (Figs. 313, 316).

Useful as the methods of Nissl and Weigert are, they bring out only the cruder parts or the "skeleton" of the tissue, while the finer details, such as the relationships of cells and fibers to one another and, in particular, the synapses, remain mostly undisclosed. The methods capable of showing such relationships, especially the synaptical contacts of the terminal twigs of the nerve fibers with the bodies of the nerve cells, are the Golgi method and that of Ehrlich, or to some extent the various modifications of the silver staining by Bielschowsky, S. Cajal, Davenport, and Bodian.

Both the Golgi and the Ehrlich methods, however, have their limitations, in that they put a considerable demand upon the skill, experience, and patience of the investigator. Owing to this, few parts of the nervous system have been thoroughly investigated by these methods—the cortex of the brain, the carrier of the higher or intellectual functions, still remaining almost entirely unexplored.

The first impression one receives while examining a Golgi-stained preparation of the striate cortex of a human or simian specimen is of unbelievable complexity. The nerve cells, with their countless expansions crossing in all directions, intermingling and overlapping in the most varied ways, seem to produce real or apparent interrelationships beyond the power of human intellect and patience to analyze in a single lifetime. It may, indeed, be doubted whether even the well-planned diligence of a team of trained investigators could uncover more than a portion of the synaptical relationships present in the cortex of the human brain.

It is in this light that the following description of the constituent elements of the striate cortex, partly condensed from the work of the preceding investigators, is to be accepted and understood. A vast task remains still to be accomplished by those future investigators interested in penetrating more deeply into the organization of the brain.

In the following, first, the work of Santiago Ramón y Cajal on the minute structure of the human striate area is briefly summarized. In this, for the sake of uniform presentation, the naming of the layers and sublayers was rearranged according to the basic six-layer type introduced by Brodmann and adopted in this book. In addition, O'Leary's paper on the striate area of the Cat, studied by the Golgi method, was considered. To this, finally, we have added our own observations; these are based entirely upon primate material, human and from the Rhesus Monkey, of various ages, including full grown. In this way some general idea may be formed about the types of neurons, their arrangement, and something of their synaptic concatenations. The synaptical relationships and their functional interpretations, in this and in other parts of the cortex, remain a problem for the future.

2. Santiago Ramón y Cajal's investigation of the striate cortex.—In the following is given a brief summary of the studies of the striate cortex made six decades ago by S. Ramón y Cajal (Fig. 317), almost the only investigator paying attention to the types and synaptical relationships of neurons of this and other parts of the cerebral cortex. His work, isolated striate area than in other cortical regions, is made up largely of the expansions of the nerve cells residing in the subjacent layers: the small pyramidal cells of the second layer, the medium-sized pyramids of the third layer, and especially also the apical dendrites of the larger pyramids whose bodies are placed in the infra-Gennarian half of the cortex. There are, in addi-

Fig. 317.—Santiago Ramón y Cajal (1852–1934) at the age of seventy-three. Snapshot by the author made during a visit to the Instituto Cajal in Madrid in 1925. (*See also* Figs. 52, 131, and J. Comp. Neurol., v. 98, 1953.)

as it is, shows not only the brilliance of mind and character of this great investigator but also the formidable difficulties encountered in this work, and an astonishing lack of enterprising spirit and reluctance in the subsequent generations to follow his splendid example. (*See* Polyak, *J. Comp. Neurol.*, v. 98, 1953.)

Plexiform layer.—This layer, thinner in the tion, a few star-shaped cells that possess a short axon fiber here, and some whose axon fiber spreads horizontally, parallel to the cortical surface (*E, F, G,* in Fig. 318).

Outer granular layer.—This layer contains true pyramidal cells of small size and other numerous cells with short axon fibers, one variety with a double dendritic ramification, the other whose ascending axon fiber divides in a more or less horizontal fashion.

Pyramidal cell layer.—The pyramid-shaped cells which form the third layer in the striate area are smaller than those in the motor cortex. No mention is made by Cajal, however, of the "granules," corresponding to Brodmann's sublayer *4-a*, which apparently have been included by him in the pyramidal layer, even though this is not expressly stated. Possibly the inner granules are the unusually formed neurons found by

is the large star-shaped cells whose expansions are oriented sidewise, instead of toward the cortical surface, as in the pyramids. The other characteristic feature is a rich fiber plexus, corresponding to the stripe of Gennari and Vicq-d'Azyr, by which the cells are largely crowded out from this level. (*See* Figs. 327, 328.)

The large star-shaped cells, the outer solitary cells of Meynert, have an ovoidal or triangular body whence originate thick dendrites spreading up and down or horizontally (layer *A* in Fig.

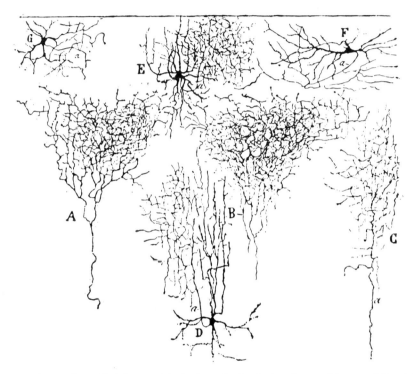

FIG. 318.—Types of axonal ramifications or teledendrons in the first and second layers of the striate cortex in a fifteen-day-old child. *A* and *B*, a dense plexus in the layer of small pyramidal cells; *C*, same, though less dense; *D*, small neuron with an ascending axon fiber, *a*, producing a similar terminal arborization; *E*, spider-shaped asteriform or star-shaped cell with a dense axonal arborization in the first or plexiform layer; *F*, *G*, other small neurons with short and little-ramified axonal expansions. From S. Ramón y Cajal, *Studien über die Hirnrinde des Menschen*, J. A. Barth, Leipzig, 1900–1906.

Cajal either in this layer or in sublayer *4-a:* their long dendrites are oriented vertically, and so are their delicate axonal arborizations, which pass in the form of long, narrow streamers or ribbons, interconnecting narrow vertical segments of several superimposed layers, possibly sublayers of the inner granular layer (*E*, *F*, in Fig. 320).

Inner granular layer.—This layer, as presented by S. Ramón y Cajal, is especially characteristic of the visual cortex. One of its features

319). They divide in the same layer and spread for long distances. The horizontal dendrites are most numerous and quite long. None of the dendrites spreads as far as the first or plexiform layer, thus easily distinguishing this neuron variety from the true pyramids.

The thick axon fiber originates from the inferior face of the cell body or from a dendrite, passing almost vertically through all subjacent layers down to the subcortical fiber substance. Close to its origin, the principal axon fiber gives off recurrent or horizontally running collateral branches spreading in the Gennarian fiber layer of the fourth layer.

Another constituent of the fourth layer is the pyramidal cells, that evidently became displaced from the third layer. Still another element is the star-shaped cells, which are provided with a short axonal fiber ascending into the suprajacent layers (*A, B, C, D*, in Figs. 320 and

off collaterals in the fourth layer and divides in the second layer into terminal arborization. Cajal also found similar neurons in the Cat (Fig. 323).

Of another type in the inner granular layer, according to Ramón y Cajal, are small star-shaped neurons, now called inner granules (Fig. 321). In his description, however, he mentions only those granules which, in the aggregate,

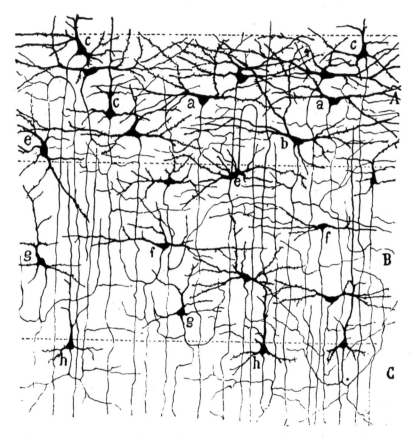

Fig. 319.—Asteriform or star-shaped cells from the calcarine fissure of a twenty-day-old child. *A*, layer of large star-shaped cells, corresponding to Brodmann's sublayer *4-b; B*, layer of small star-shaped cells or Brodmann's sublayer *4-c; C*, layer of small pyramidal cells with recurrent axons, probably Brodmann's layer *5* (in part); *a*, semilunar cells; *b*, horizontal spindle-shaped cells; *c*, neuron with a thin descending axon fiber; *e*, cells with recurrent axons; *f*, horizontally oriented spindle-shaped cells; *g*, triangular cells with thick recurrent collaterals; *h*, pyramidal cells with recurrent axons situated at the boundary of the sublayer *4-c*. From S. Ramón y Cajal 1900–1906.

322). These cells are irregularly scattered in the fourth layer. They possess an ovoidal or triangular body, whence arise short dendrites, covered with "spines," spreading not far from the body. The axon fiber divides close to the body into numerous branches directed horizontally or downward, coming into contact with the bodies of the large star-shaped cells. Another variety possesses an axon fiber that gives

form zone *4-c* of Brodmann, since he did not notice similar granules in zone *4-a* (*cf.* following subsection).

The first granular variety, fairly numerous, resembles the small cells scattered among the large outer solitary cells of Meynert in zone *4-b*. The others are small star-shaped cells, or true "grain," which give zone *4-c* its characteristic appearance. The body is spherical, fusiform, or star-shaped, usually not more than 10 or 12 microns in diameter. Each of these midget neurons possesses four, five, or more thin dendrites radiating in all directions, dividing repeatedly, and never spreading beyond the zone where they reside. Each granular neuron also gives rise to a very delicate axon fiber, which, by preference, spreads in an ascending direction. Close to its origin the axon fiber pursues a meandering course, and at some distance it splits up into a loose arborization, which, with other such arborizations, forms a dense plexus enveloping the bodies of the large and medium-sized solitary cells of Meynert in zone *4-b* (*d*, in same figure).

The function of the inner granular cells, in Ramón y Cajal's view, would be to intensify the impulses transmitted by way of afferent visual fibers from the laminated lateral geniculate nucleus, and hence from the retina, to the large

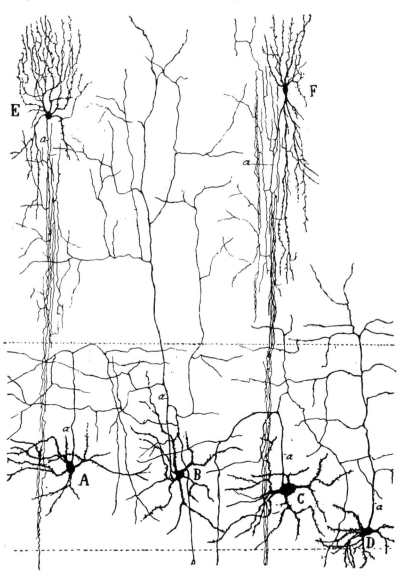

Fig. 320.—Types of neurons from the fourth layer of the visual cortex of a fifteen-day-old child. *A*, cell whose axon spreads in the upper zone of the fourth layer; *B*, cell with an axonal spread in the third and fourth layers; *C*, cell with an axonal spread in the third layer and in the zones *4-b* and *4-c* of the fourth layer; *D*, cell whose ascending axon spreads in the fourth layer and in the adjoining zone of the third; *E*, *F*, small neurons of the layer of the medium pyramids (or possibly of the adjoining sublayer *4-a?*), possessing a double dendritic tuft and a long, narrow axonal expansion, *a*, oriented vertically and interconnecting several superimposed layers (possibly sublayers *4-a*, *4-b*, and *4-c* of the fourth layer). From S. Ramón y Cajal 1900–1906.

outer solitary cells of Meynert, and in this way to the striate cortex. One way would be by a direct termination of the afferent fibers at the solitary cells; the other by an interposition of the granular cells and an interruption at the synapses of their short axons at the same solitary cells.

S. Ramón y Cajal further described other minute neurons in the fourth layer resembling neuroglia. These are provided with numerous

and third layers, instead of passing downward into the subcortical white substance; some of the axonal collaterals occasionally descend into the fifth and sixth layers (*h*, in Fig. 319). The second variety is the large star-shaped neurons, with numerous radiating dendrites and an axon fiber splitting up in the third and fourth layers (*f* in same figure; *a* in Fig. 324). The third is small and large pyramidal cells, few in number, with an apical dendrite ascending as far as the

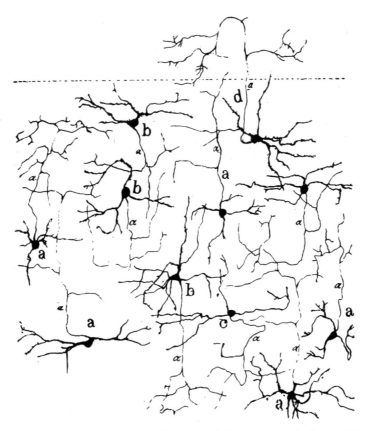

FIG. 321.—"Grains" or granular cells from the sublayer *4-c* of the inner granular layer of Brodmann, with short, variously oriented axonal expansions, as they appear in Golgi-stained preparations of a one-month-old child. *a*, type with a thin ascending axon; *b, c*, cells with a descending axon; *d*, a somewhat larger cell with an axonal spread apparently in the sublayer *4-b;* small italic letter *a* indicating axonal expansions. From S. Ramón y Cajal 1900–1906.

short, fine, varicose dendritic expansions and an axonal fiber that terminates with an arborization of very fine and dense branches around the small star-shaped neurons (*E* in Fig. 322).

Finally, there are in the inner granular layer, according to Ramón y Cajal, the following types of neurons present in small numbers (Fig. 325). The first variety (*c, e*) are pyramidal or ovoidal cells, with a fine axon fiber arching upward and probably terminating in the second

first or plexiform layer and with an axon fiber descending to the subcortical fiber mass (*b* in Fig. 325).

According to our own estimate, the bodies of the last two varieties reside in the upper tier of the fifth layer of the striate cortex as classified in this book, just above the level of the internal solitary or ganglionic cells.

Ganglion cell layer.—This layer is characterized by the presence of giant pyramidal cells which may be called "inner solitary cells" of Meynert (*see* sec. 5 [7, 9], this chapter). These cells are arranged in a single tier, at some distance from one another (*a*, in layer *B*, in Figs. 325, 326). In Golgi preparations one sees the base of their bodies expand into thick and extremely long dendrites, which spread strictly horizontally to the cortical surface, their length sometimes exceeding that of the apical den-

form layer; and large and medium cells of polygonal shape whose thick axon fiber spreads in a somewhat horizontal direction and whose long and obliquely or horizontally spreading branches seem to form nests around the giant pyramidal cells.

Other medium pyramids send an apical dendrite as far as the superficial plexiform layer and an axon fiber, which, after descending for a

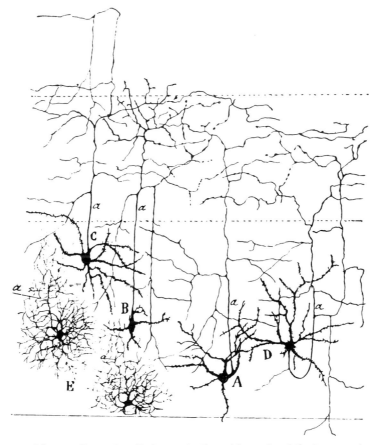

Fig. 322.—Neurons with ascending axis cylinders, *a*, in the sublayer *4-c* of the inner nuclear layer of the striate cortex of a fifteen-day-old child, stained with the method of Golgi. *A*, *B*, cells whose axon ramifies in the layer of large asteriform cells or *4-b; C*, same except that a few branches spread into the layer of medium pyramids (*4-a* or *3*); *D*, cell whose recurrent axon spreads in the sublayers *4-b* and *4-c* and in the fifth layer; *E*, a very small cell with a short ascending axon (*a*). From S. Ramón y Cajal 1900–1906.

drites. These horizontal dendrites divide, and, together with those of the adjoining similar cells, produce a horizontal dendritic plexus or tangle.

Other cells in this layer are small pyramidal cells with an arching axon fiber (*i, j, k*, in Fig. 325) resembling those in the fourth layer; small star-shaped cells whose ascending axon fiber possibly extends as far as the first or plexi-

short distance, turns upward, where it splits in the plexus of the fourth layer (Gennari's layer), with one collateral descending to the subcortical white substance (*g*, in Fig. 326).

Still other neurons accompany giant pyramids, such as the large star-shaped cells whose thick axon fiber ascends to the plexiform layer, after giving off a few collaterals for the fifth and sixth layers, besides the large and small star-

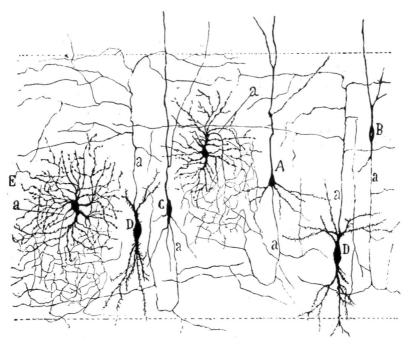

FIG. 323.—Various types of neurons from the layer of asteriform or star-shaped cells (*4*) of the visual cortex of a twenty-day-old Cat. *A, B, C*, small pyramids and spindle-shaped cells with a recurrent ascending axon fiber; *D*, large spindle-shaped cells with ascending axons; *E*, spider-shaped cells with a short axonal expansion; *a*, axonal expansions. From S. Ramón y Cajal 1900–1906.

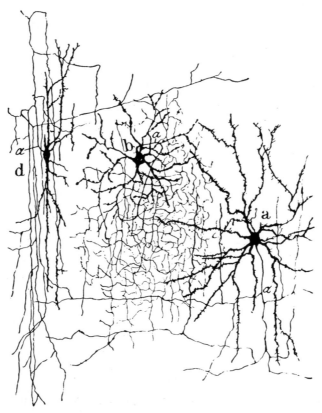

FIG. 324.—Types of neurons with short axonal expansions from the layer of star-shaped cells (*4*) of a twenty-day-old Cat stained with Golgi's method. *a*, large star-shaped cell provided with a descending axon fiber spreading in the fourth layer (in Man in the sublayers *4-b* and *4-c*); *b*, small, spider-shaped cell with a richly ramified, delicate, and dense axonal expansion; *d*, spindle-shaped cell provided with an axonal expansion spreading ribbon-like and oriented vertically. From S. Ramón y Cajal 1900–1906.

shaped cells with a short axon fiber ramifying in the same layer.

Multiform cell layer.—The cells of fusiform shape have two dendritic expansions, an ascending and a descending one, and an axon fiber passing down into the subjacent white substance. The others are medium-sized pyramids with a descending axon, and perhaps some other neuron varieties.

ate area and which terminate in that area. These fibers are distinguished by considerable thickness and a slanting course as they enter the striate cortex, where they branch among its cells.

In preparations stained for myelin (Weigert method) one sees in the sublayer *4-c* and in a part of sublayer *4-b* a dense fiber plexus of mostly horizontally arranged fibers. This is

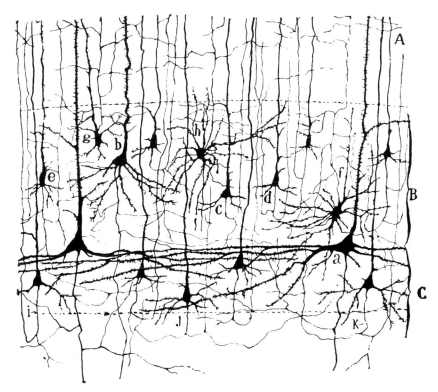

Fig. 325.—Neurons from the fifth and sixth layers of the visual cortex of a fifteen-day-old child. *A*, sublayer *4-c*; *B* and *C*, parts of the fifth and sixth layers; *a*, giant pyramidal cells, the inner solitary cells of Meynert as here classified; *b*, medium-sized pyramidal cell provided with a long descending axon fiber; *c*, small pyramidal cell with a recurrent ascending axon fiber; *d*, pyramidal cell with an axon fiber with two loops; *e*, pyramidal cell with an axonal expansion dividing into several ascending branches; *f, g, h*, star-shaped cells with axon fibers spreading in *4-c* and in the fifth layer; *i, j, k*, pyramidal cells with recurrent axon fibers ramifying in the fifth and sixth layers. From S. Ramón y Cajal 1900–1906.

Fiber systems of the striate area, according to S. Ramón y Cajal.—S. Ramón y Cajal recognized two principal constituent categories of fibers of the striate area. The first is made up of the fibers which, in a general way, may be termed "centrifugal"; these originate from the cells residing in that area, particularly from the large star-shaped and pyramidal neurons, and terminate outside the striate area. The other category, which may be termed "centripetal" fibers, is of those whose origin is outside the stri-

Gennari's or Vicq-d'Azyr's stripe, a whitish line visible without the aid of a magnifier on a surface cut through the striate cortex (Figs. 226–29). In Golgi-stained preparations one may see these fibers as far as their terminal arborizations (Figs. 327, 328).

These fibers, because of their unusual thickness, are quite conspicuous as they pass through the subcortical substance into the cortex. Their course as they pass through the ventral layers as far as the fifth layer (inner solitary or ganglionic cells) is usually oblique. Here they assume a horizontal course, divide into long, horizontally meandering branches, and remain confined to the same horizontal level. Some of these afferent fibers go as far as the upper limit of sublayer *4-b*, where they also split up and ferent optic fibers climbs higher than the upper limit of sublayer *4-b*: hence the small and medium pyramids of the second and third layers are not directly related to these fibers. This, however, is not quite certain, since fine collaterals occasionally ascend from these fibers

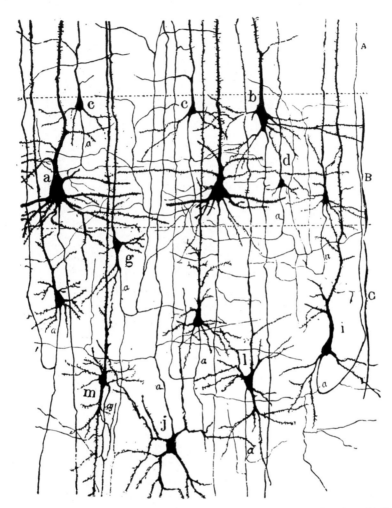

FIG. 326.—Types of neurons of the deep layers of the visual cortex of a twenty-five-day-old Cat stained with the Golgi method. *A*, lower zone of the layer of star-shaped cells (*4-c*); *B*, layer of giant pyramids (*5*); *C*, layer of medium pyramids with a recurrent axon fiber (also part of *5*); *a*, giant pyramids; *b*, medium-sized pyramids with a descending axon fiber; *c, d*, pyramids with descending and bifurcating axon fibers ramifying around giant pyramids; *g*, triangular cell with a recurrent axon fiber and descending collaterals; *i*, pyramid-shaped cell with a recurrent ascending axon fiber; *j, l*, a star-shaped and a triangular cell of the fusiform or spindle-shaped layer *6*, one provided with an ascending axon fiber, the other with a descending axon fiber; *m*, spindle-shaped cell provided with a descending axon fiber. From S. Ramón y Cajal 1900–1906.

become horizontal. During their passage they usually give off a few collateral branches for the neurons of the fifth and sixth layers.

These coarse afferent fibers give off the thickest branches only after they have entered sublayer *4-b*, where they divide. None of these af- and penetrate into the marginal zone of sublayer *4-a* (Fig. 327, *D*).

The afferent fibers produce a thick plexus in the striate cortex of the human fetus in sublayer *4-c* and a similar but much thinner tangle with fewer secondary branches in sublayer *4-b*.

A good representation of this plexus is given in Figure 328. Here layer *B*, corresponding to sublayer *4-c* of the inner granular layer in Figure 314, shows a dense tangle, with nests left vacant in which are lodged the granules and the star-shaped cells with an ascending axon fiber, while layer *A* with looser plexus, corresponding to sublayer *4-b*, envelops large star-shaped cells, the outer solitary cells of Meynert.

caliber corresponding rather well with the thick fibers originating from the laminated lateral geniculate nucleus. In this respect they resemble the thick afferent fibers of the sensory-motor and olfactory regions of the cortex, while such fibers are absent in Flechsig's association areas of the brain. Also, clinical and anatomical evi-

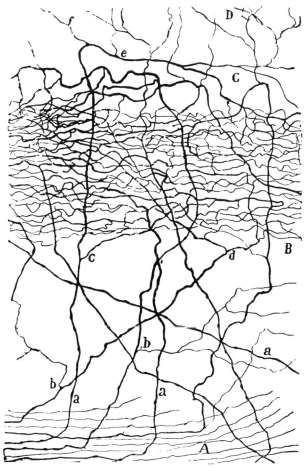

FIG. 327.—Entrance of fibers of the visual radiation into the visual cortex or striate area in a three-day-old child, Golgi stain. Thick axis cylinders arising from the subcortical fibrous substance (*A*) divide and in this way form a plexus-like formation, the stripe of Gennari or Vicq-d'Azyr. *B*, layer of small star-shaped cells or sublayer *4-c* of Brodmann; *C*, afferent fibers turning horizontally in the fourth layer, probably in *4-b*; *D*, layer of medium pyramids, probably identical with sublayer *4-a* or *3* in Nissl-stained preparations; *a*, principal afferent visual fibers; *b*, collateral branches destined for the deeper layers of the striate cortex; *c, d*, collateral branches ascending into Gennari's plexus. From S. Ramón y Cajal 1900–1906.

sublayer *4-b*, envelops large star-shaped cells, the outer solitary cells of Meynert.

S. Ramón y Cajal gives the following reasons to support his view of the formation of Gennari's stripe by the terminations of afferent optic nerve fibers arriving by way of the visual radiations. First, these fibers are much thicker than the association and callosal fibers, their

dence indicates the termination of Gratiolet's visual radiation in the calcarine cortex.

The contention of S. Ramón y Cajal was subsequently fully substantiated by my experiments on cats and monkeys. These experiments showed the presence of such thick fibers with a slanting course in the infra-Gennarian half of the striate cortex and terminating in Gennari's or Vicq-d'Azyr's stripe, hence proving that they are those of the visual radiation originating in the laminated lateral geniculate nucleus. (*Cf.* thick, slanting fibers *a* in Fig. 328, with similar fibers in Fig. 315; *see also* Polyak, Berkeley, 1932, and *J. Comp. Neurol.*, v. 44, p. 197, 1927; *see* following subsection and figures.)

There are, however, other categories of fibers, according to S. Ramón y Cajal, in addition to infra-Gennarian layers, especially from the pyramids that possess an arching axon fiber (*b*, in Fig. 328), also the collaterals of axon fibers of the large- and medium-sized star-shaped cells of sublayers *4-b* and *4-c* and the terminal arborizations of the granular and other small cells provided with short axons.

These minute cells, the "grain" of the inner granular layer, representing the bulk of the

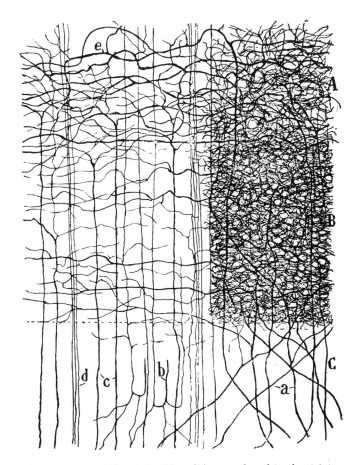

Fig. 328.—Fiber plexus in the stripe of Gennari or Vicq-d'Azyr as found in the striate area or visual cortex of a twenty-day-old child, Golgi stain. *A, B,* sublayers *4-b* and *4-c* of the inner granular layer; *C,* fifth layer; *a,* afferent visual fibers; *b,* recurrent axon fiber of a cell of the fifth layer; *c,* ascending axon fibers of pyramidal cells of the sixth layer; *d,* axon bundles of medium and small pyramidal cells (from second and third layers); *e,* loops of afferent visual fibers with collateral branches ascending into sublayer *4-a.* From S. Ramón y Cajal 1900–1906.

those originating in the lateral geniculate nucleus, which contribute to Gennari's stripe. These may possibly be the association fibers originating in the extrastriate parts of the cortex, even though Cajal was not able to identify their cells of origin. Certainly there are fibers originating from the cells residing in the striate cortex itself, for example, from those in the small neurons of sublayers *4-a* and *4-c,* appear to be partly responsible for the myelinated appearance of Gennari's stripe, to which, because of their great numbers and compact arrangement, they contribute a share, in spite of the shortness of their axonal expansions and poor myelinization. In any case, long and well-myelinized fibers are not found in Gennari's

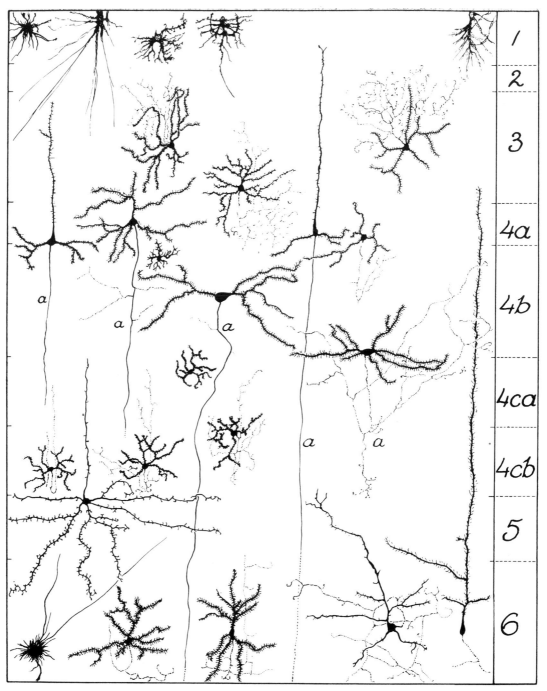

Fig. 329.—Types of nerve cells or neurons and of neuroglial cells from the foveal portion of the striate cortex of an adult Rhesus Macaque stained with silver bichromate or the Golgi method. Note the shape and size of the cell bodies and their location in the layer or sublayer given at the right margin and the character and location of the dendritic and axonal (*a*) expansions, according to which several neuron varieties may be distinguished. *Cf.* similar subsequent figures. For description *see* text. Approximate magnification 100×.

stripe, as the absence of such fibers in that stripe in an experiment of Le Gros Clark (1941) and in that described in chapter VII, 7, in this book shows.

The observation that the stripe of Gennari is not entirely missing in the human pathological cases where the visual radiation was destroyed or was absent also tends to corroborate the concept that the terminal arborizations of the afferent visual fibers in that stripe are only one of several contributing factors, albeit they seem the most important. (*See* chap. XII.)

3. Comment on Cajal's investigation of the striate area.—In our own attempt to verify and to amplify S. Ramón y Cajal's work, advantage was taken of Leitz's Ultropak oil-immersion objectives, in addition to the less powerful dry optical systems. This advantage is the superior optical resolution which the Ultropak apochromates afford in studying the thick preparations which the Golgi technique requires, compared with the poor resolution which the usual dry objectives give. Covering the slides with cover slips, according to a "dry procedure" described in *The Retina*, was an additional advantage, since this made possible easy use of the oil-immersion systems of the Ultropak design. Following are a few remarks which seem worthy to be added to those of S. Ramón y Cajal recorded under the preceding subsection.

The various types or parts of neurons found in the simian striate area are illustrated in Figures 329–41. Whether or not they represent all types, future study of abundant material of Golgi-stained sections alone may show. Such study may also decide how far the various types described by S. Ramón y Cajal are true neuron varieties constantly found in the primate striate area or to what extent they are merely adaptations of one or another standard type to secondary factors, such as the crowding into available space of a particular layer or sublayer, and so forth.

In examining our illustrations, beginning with the first layer and down to the sixth, no certain nerve cells are found in the first or plexiform layer. This is possibly caused by the scarcity of true neurons in this layer and by the haphazard character of the Golgi method. Contrasting with this are numerous expansions of the several types of neurons spreading in this layer whose body resides in any one of the subjacent layers down to the sixth. These expansions bear the character either of dendrites or of axonal teledendrons. The impression one gains is that this layer is principally or preponderantly made up of such expansions, together with the marginal neuroglia and its fibers, in addition to blood vessels.

The second layer is made up of small, closely packed cells of more or less pyramidal shape, corresponding with those found in the Nissl stain. Unlike the latter, however, the Golgi method shows these cells to vary in their expansions and hence in their functional character. Some of the cells may represent Golgi type *I*, their delicate axon fibers passing down to the subcortical substance, to terminate in other parts of the brain. Such axons, while still close to their body of origin, as a rule emit a few collateral branches which ramify around neighboring cells in the second and possibly the third layers. Some collaterals may traverse considerable distances in the striate cortex before terminating. Exactly where the principal axon fibers terminate remains a problem to be further determined by the various methods, including experiments, e.g., by the study of retrograde cell degeneration after destruction of distant parts of the brain.

Other small neurons of the second layer, also pyramidal in shape, certainly belong to Golgi type *II*. Their delicate axonal expansion spreads not far from the place where the cell body resides. Whether such cells belong to a single variety or represent several varieties, further careful study may determine. The impression one gains is that there may be several such neuron varieties, distinguished by their external features. In one type the body and the dendritic expansions, provided with numerous thorny "spines," resemble the type just described, while their axonal expansion splits into several branches and twigs, spreading in a small area in the first, second, and third layers. In another type found in the second and third layers, characterized by smooth dendrites, almost entirely devoid of any "spines" and oriented rather vertically, the very thin axonal expansions run up and down like streamers arranged in long but narrow

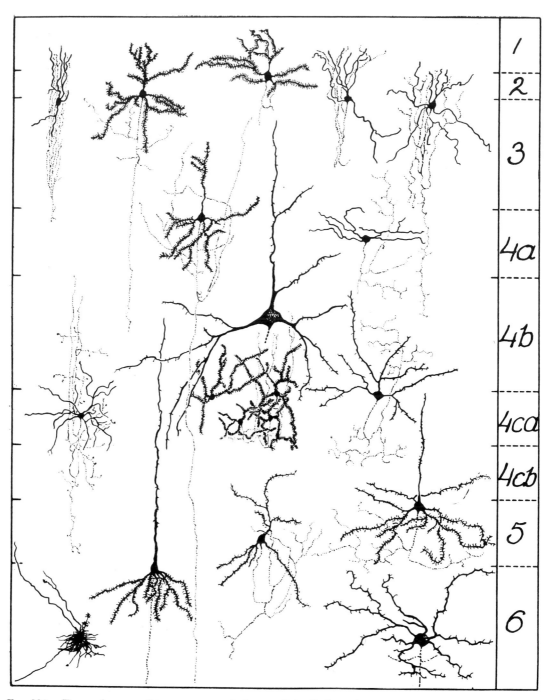

FIG. 330.—Types of nerve cells or neurons and of neuroglial cells from the foveal portion of the striate cortex of an adult Rhesus Macaque stained with silver bichromate or the Golgi method. Note the shape, size, and location of the cell bodies and the character and location of the dendritic and axonal processes in different neuron varieties. Layers indicated along the right-hand margin. *See* preceding and subsequent figures. For description *see* text. Approximate magnification 100×.

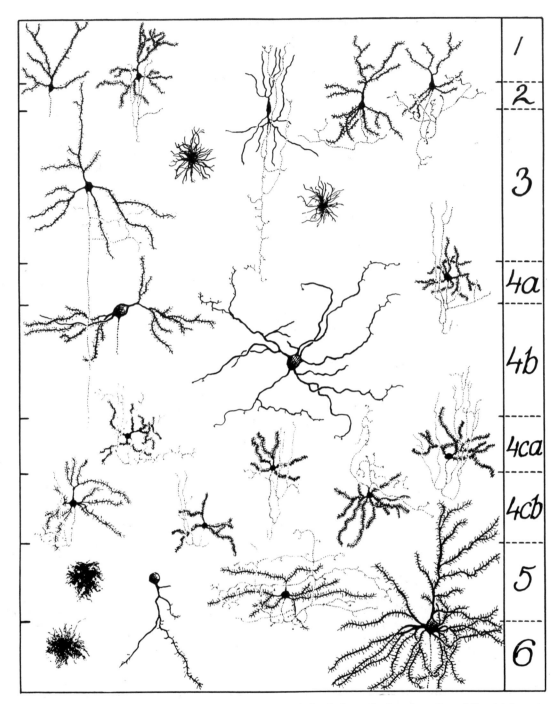

Fig. 331.—Types of nerve cells or neurons and of neuroglial cells from the foveal portion of the striate cortex of an adult Rhesus Macaque stained with silver bichromate or the Golgi method. Note the variation of detailed structures in different types and their essential identity in the same type, and compare the same details in the preceding and in the following figures. Layers indicated along the right-hand margin. For description *see* text. Approximate magnification 100×.

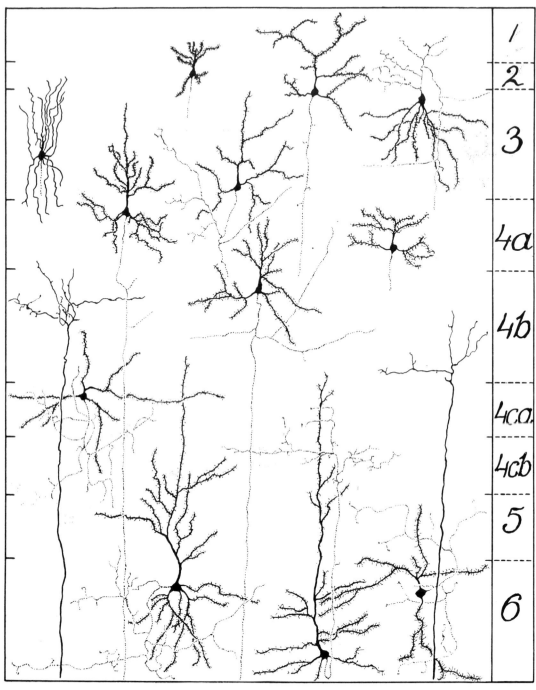

Fig. 332.—Types of nerve cells or neurons from the foveal portion of the striate cortex of an adult Rhesus Macaque stained with silver bichromate or the Golgi method. Compare other similar figures in this chapter. For description *see* text. Approximate magnification 100×.

bands, reaching up to the first layer and descending as far as sublayers *4-a* and *4-b*. Remarkable are, finally, the neurons which resemble the granular cells or "grain" which are typical of the fourth layer, especially *4-a* and *4-c*. Their delicate axis cylinder divides into a number of contorted twigs, which, together, form a dense and almost inextricable plexus or tangle, within which the cell body and its dendrites are quasi-suspended, as in a tiny cloud.

The neurons whose bodies reside in the third layer also belong to several types. They, in general, resemble the neurons of the second layer, being, however, larger in body and in their expansions. Some of them, of the shape of small and medium pyramids, possess dendritic expansions abundantly provided with thorny "spines." Their axonal fibers descend in a rather straight course through the subjacent layers down to the subcortical fiber substance. Several collateral branches of the axon are given off to neighboring cells. Other neurons, with their dendritic branches radiating in a more even way and all of about the same length, may be more justly compared with a star. Their axonal expansion, abundantly ramified, spreads in a part of the second, third, and fourth layers.

The neurons of the fourth layer appear more diversified than in the remainder of the striate cortex. They vary much in the shape, size, and distribution of their bodies and in the varieties of their dendritic and axonal expansions. The most conspicuous are the large solitary ganglion cells of Meynert. Their ovoid, horizontally placed body is usually confined to sublayer *4-b*. Their thick dendrites, covered with numerous robust "spines" terminating with spherical nodules, are mostly oriented horizontally or obliquely (Figs. 337, 338). Their axons, few of which we were able to pursue any distance from the body, descend toward the subcortical substance. Whether all these neurons send their axon fibers away from the striate cortex is more than questionable. As shown in Figure 329, the axis cylinder may split up into several branches, which further divide and spread over a considerable area of sublayers *4-b* and *4-c*, terminating around its cells. Still other similar cells, instead of confining their dendrites to a somewhat restricted horizontal zone of sublayer *4-b*, stretch these in an octopus-like fashion in all directions, including sublayers *4-a* and *4-c* (Fig. 331). A further variety of Meynert's solitary ganglion cells possesses a robust apical dendrite which ascends as far as the superficial layer of the cortex, resembling in this way a large motor pyramidal cell (Fig. 330). It may be of considerable physiological interest to compare the dimensions, especially the volume or mass, of the giant solitary cells with those of the diminutive granular cells, as depicted in Figure 337.

The other neuron variety of the fourth layer, conspicuous because of its great numbers, is among the smallest neurons of the entire nervous system. These are the "granular cells" or "grain." These diminutive neurons, confined to sublayers *4-a* and *4-c*, when completely stained with silver nitrate, have a characteristic appearance. Their short dendritic expansions, carrying a moderate number of small thorny "spines," are restricted to a narrow territory around the cell body, where they twist in all directions (Figs. 337, 339). Their delicate axonal expansions, one to each grain, usually descend and soon divide into a few branches, which, after making a turn, spread vertically toward the upper layers. Their axonal side branches, however, are numerous and together form an inextricable feltwork between the cell bodies. Together, these teledendric axonal expansions of the inner granular cells represent a vast mechanism connecting sublayers *4-b* and *4-c* and probably also *4-a*, but especially the granular cells of sublayer *4-c*, with one another. In their aggregation these countless minute grain neurons form a concatenated pad made up of countless short synaptical circuits.

Similar to the typical granular cells, but perhaps a bit larger and with longer dendrites spreading in all directions, provided with only a few spines or none at all, are cells of sublayer *4-ca*. Their delicate axonal expansions spread mostly in the manner of ribbons in a narrow vertical zone, fusing superposed segments of sublayers *4-a*, *4-b*, *4-c*, and *5* into functional units, whose elements are activated simultaneously. Other larger neurons with dendrites radiating in all directions, residing in the transitional zone between *4-b* and *4-c*, interconnect larger segments of these sublayers into functional units. Further investigation is required to identify these neurons with one or another ele-

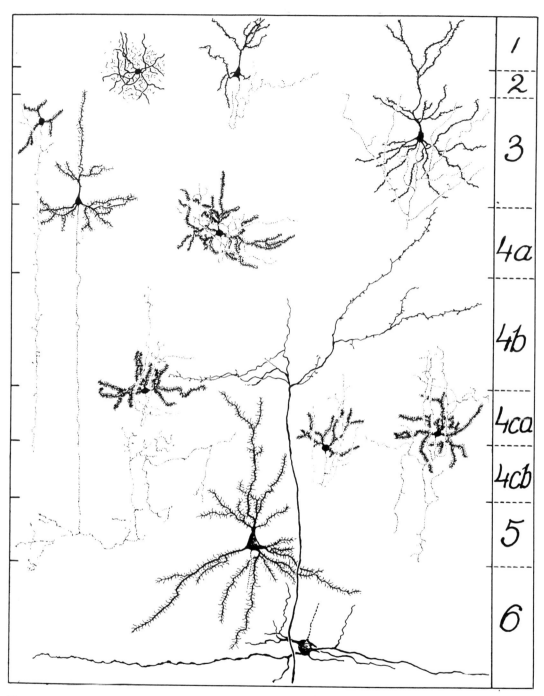

Fig. 333.—Types of nerve cells or neurons from the foveal portion of the striate cortex of an adult Rhesus Macaque stained with silver bichromate or the Golgi method. Layers and sublayers indicated along the right-hand margin. For description *see* text. Approximate magnification 100×.

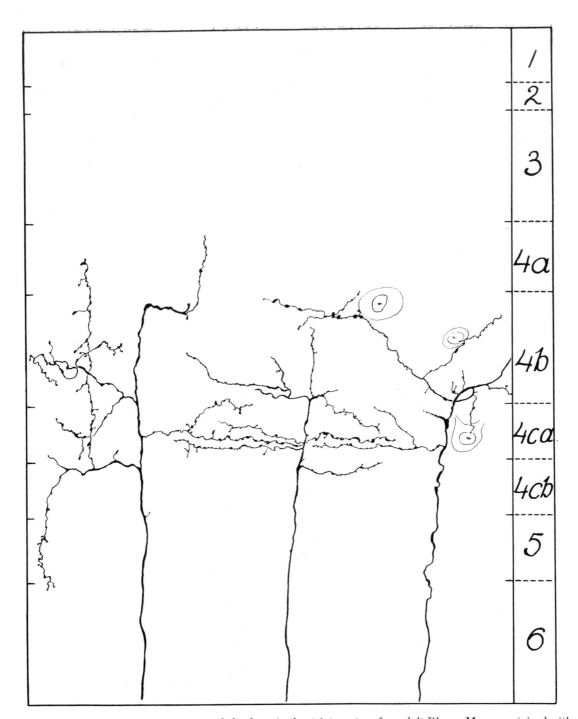

1

2

3

4a

4b

4cα

4cb

5

6

Fig. 334.—Terminal arborizations or teledendrons in the striate cortex of an adult Rhesus Macaque stained with silver bichromate or the Golgi method. Note the course of the visual fibers as they enter the fourth or inner granular layer, the character of the terminal arborizations, their location and spread, and the terminal nodules. Some branches have been omitted in order to make details clearer. Note a few terminal nodules in contact with the surface of the nerve cells given in outline. Freehand drawing at an approximate magnification of 100×.

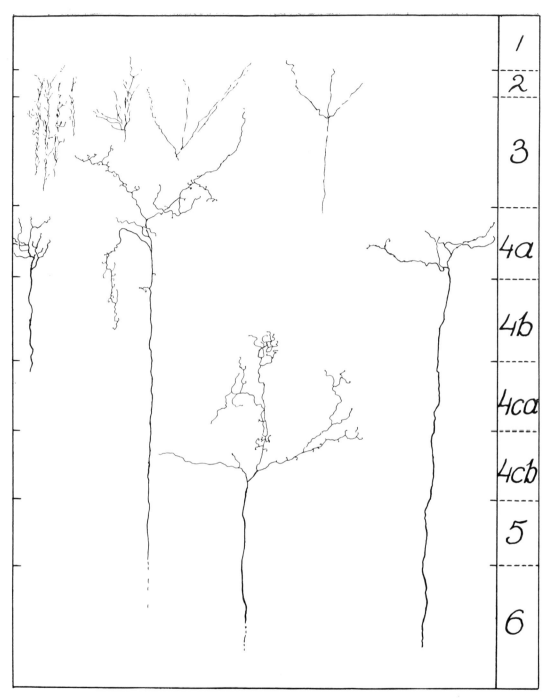

FIG. 335.—Diverse types of the terminal axonal arborizations or teledendrons in the striate cortex of an adult Rhesus Monkey found in preparations stained with silver bichromate or the Golgi method. It is very likely that many more different types will be found when the same cortex is further investigated. Freehand drawing at an approximate magnification of 100×.

ment visible in Nissl-stained preparations or, better yet, in those stained with the Klüver stain (personal communication; *cf. also* Klüver & Barrera 1953, 1954).

The numerous neuron varieties populating ventral layers *5* and *6* of the striate cortex are also conspicuous by their unequal size and distribution. Their particular morphological details and connections are as yet little known. The impression is that many more neurons residing here are oriented laterally, in a horizontal direction, than in the layers above. There are,

however, some conspicuous exceptions represented by the small pyramidal cells whose body is located in layer *6* and whose apical dendrite ascends as far as layer *3*. Altogether, the number of the second type of Golgi or association neurons in these two layers may be much larger than heretofore suspected.

Of the afferent fibers entering the striate cortex and terminating here, we may describe only those which, according to their location and spread, may be the axis cylinders of the cells of the laminated lateral geniculate nucleus. Such

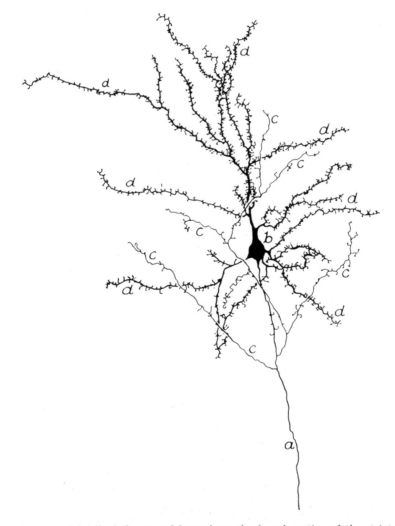

Fig. 336.—Small pyramidal cell of the second layer from the foveal portion of the striate area of an adult Rhesus Macaque stained completely, including all terminal twigs and nodules. Leitz *Ultropak* oil-immersion objective, transillumination, camera lucida drawing, 600× magnification. Rapid Golgi method. Note the pyramid-shaped body (*b*), from which several principal dendritic expansions (*d*) spread in all directions, carrying numerous "spines" or minute terminal thornlike twigs, each terminating with a small spherical nodule; from the lower end of the body a single axonal fiber (*a*) descends to the subcortical fiber mass or "white substance" of the brain; from the axon fiber two or three thin collateral branches (*c*), also carrying a few terminal twigs with spherules, differently shaped than the dendritic "spines," spread within the cortex in the same territory where the dendrites ramify.

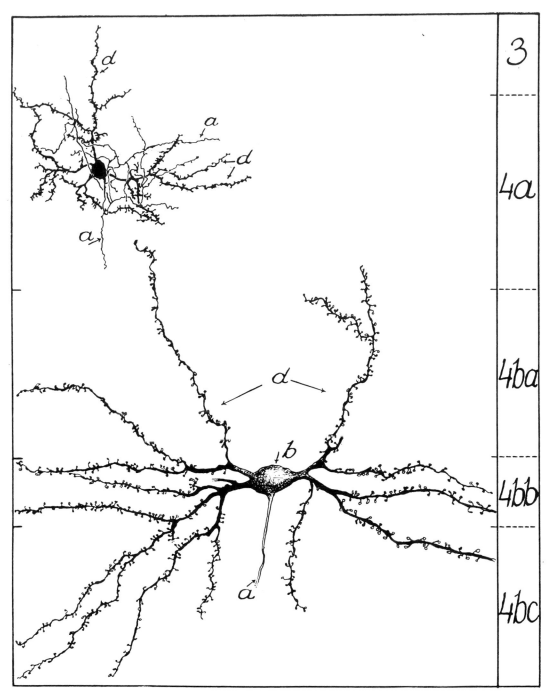

Fig. 337.—Large "solitary cell" of Meynert, with its ovoidal body in sublayer *4-bb* compared with a minute granular cell of the outer lamina of the inner granular layer (*4-a*). Foveal portion of the striate cortex of an adult Rhesus Macaque. Rapid Golgi method, Leitz *Ultropak* oil-immersion objective, transillumination, camera lucida drawing, 600× magnification (*cf.* following figure). Note body (*b*) of the "solitary cell," containing in its volume several times the volume of the body of the granular cell; the long and robust dendrites (*d*) of the solitary cell, covered with numerous minute twigs carrying spherical terminal nodules, spreading preponderantly in a horizontal direction; the smooth and straight axon fiber (*a*) of same cell, descending from the lower face of the body; different appearance of the same detailed structures in the granular neuron, the most conspicuous being the axon fiber (*a*), which divides into a few delicate and contorted threads spreading within the same territory in which the thicker bramble-like dendrites also spread.

are the teledendric ramifications in sublayer *4-b* of Gennari (*see* Figs. 332–35). These terminations are conspicuous because of their robust build, as pointed out by S. Ramón y Cajal (*cf.* Figs. 327, 328). In the foveal portion of the striate cortex of a baby Rhesus Macaque the horizontal spread of an individual fiber of this type may measure, on the average, from 100 to 150 microns and on occasion as much as 250–300 microns. This, computed for the occipital operculum, where the hemifovea and, in fact, the ipsilateral homonymous halves of both central foveae are represented, would give at least 10,000–15,000 independently stimulable functional units to each vertical foveal half. This, in turn, is in fair agreement with the number of cones populating the foveal territory (*see* chap. V, 9 [5]). The number of the stimulable units in the entire central foveal cortex, comprising parts of both striate areae, would, accordingly, be twice the indicated number. In the same foveal portions of the human striate areae, the number of units would be correspondingly larger, in order to satisfy the greater number of central foveal cones of human foveae.

These afferent fibers, as we said, terminate in the middle sublayer or *4-b* of the inner granular layer. However, they are not arranged in exactly the same way but are staggered, some being closer to sublayer *4-a*, the others closer to *4-c*. Whether this has any functional significance requires further study.

Another question pertains to the variety of the afferent fibers in the striate area. Even disregarding all other terminations, such as those of the numerous fibers originating in parts of the cortex outside the striate area of one and of the other hemisphere and omitting short association fibers arising in the same striate area, which, as Le Gros Clark's and our own experiments indicate, are extremely numerous, it is legitimate to expect more than one variety of termination in each minute territory of the striate area. This, at any rate, is probable, since, in the experiments with retrograde degeneration, all cell laminae of the lateral geniculate nucleus are affected whenever a lesion above a certain minimal size is made in the striate area, provided that the lesion involves the inner granular layer or layers ventral to it (*see* chap. VII, 5). The synaptical contacts of the terminal twigs

and nodules of the afferent geniculate fibers apparently apply to the multitudinous nerve cells and their expansions, which, in the aggregate, form the three sublayers *4-a, 4-b,* and *4-c* of the inner granular layer. It is very difficult to be certain of this, even in the abundant and successfully stained Golgi sections and with the best available optical systems, such as the Ultropak oil-immersion apochromates. This special problem requires further methodical investigation. The close approach of the branches of the terminal afferent arborizations to the dendritic expansions of the minute grain cells compactly filling sublayer *4-c* may indicate this. The same may also be true of the similar granular cells of sublayer *4-a*. It may also be true with respect to the pyramid-shaped neurons whose bodies lie above the stripe of Gennari and whose horizontal and ventral dendrites also spread in *4-b* or close to it.

The following functional interpretation of the course of retinal impulses in the striate cortex arriving by way of the coarse afferent visual fibers, in view of our incomplete knowledge, must remain tentative (Fig. 342). These impulses, after passing through the laminated lateral geniculate nuclei, are first transmitted to sublayers *4-a* and *4-c* of the striate areae of the occipital lobes of the brain. Here the stimulation is directly transmitted to the countless grain cells, their involvement depending on the place of the stimulated portion of the retina or retinae. In the granular sublayers the excitation is propagated from neuron to neuron. At the boundary of the excited territory the excitation quickly becomes exhausted in the labyrinth of countless minute synapses through which the granular cells are concatenated into a solid pad. Here the granular excitation dies down, since the granular cells act as a functional barrier. However, other and somewhat larger neurons, with somewhat longer and more widely spreading expansions, especially axonal, may continue to propagate a portion of the impulse in a less intensive way into wider parts of the striate area, while still other neurons may transmit another share of the impulse to other cortical areae of the same and of the opposite hemisphere of the brain. A residue of this excitation may remain as a permanent trace, the "memory." Still other and more robust neurons may respond by eliciting various motor acts that automatically accompany the visual act: the turning of the eyes toward the source of stimulus, the regulation of the size of the pupil and the amount of light entering the eyes, and so forth.

Just how such varied impulses, generated in the retinae and transmitted by way of the afferent visual fibers to the inner granular layer of the striate area, may be multifariously changed and modulated, depending, on the one hand, upon the initiating external physical stimulus and, on the other hand, upon their passage through the synaptical labyrinth of interconnected neurons, differing in many ways in their innate properties and responsiveness, and how fusion of the two ocular images into a single cerebral phenomenon is finally produced are exceedingly complex problems. Our present knowl-

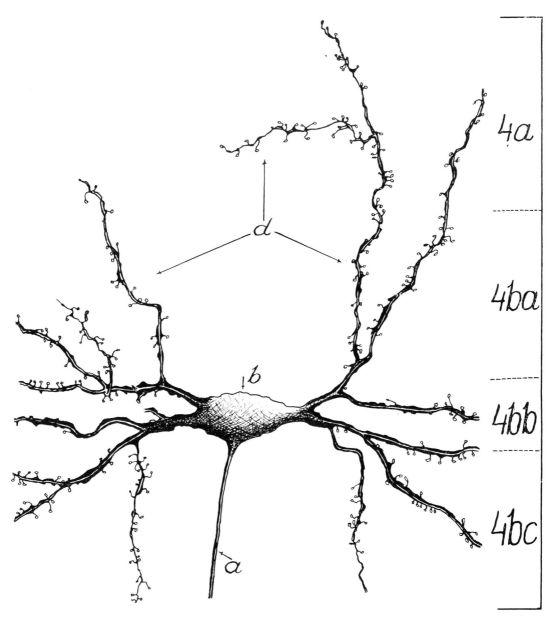

Fig. 338.—Same "solitary ganglion cell" of Meynert as in the preceding figure, approximately 1,200 × magnification. Note the absence of "spines," "nodules," and "varicosities" along the initial portions of dendrites (*d*) and in the axon fiber (*a*); varying shape, size, and distribution of the "spines," these structures being interpreted as organelles whose function is the reception of the nervous impulses. (*Cf.* Fig. 341.)

edge, unfortunately, is too meager to make further speculation along this line profitable. The morphological and functional analysis of the striate cortex is thus suggested here as one of the important problems for future research.

In conclusion, mention must be made here of the neuroglia and the blood vessels, both essential constituents of the striate cortex. The neu-

pansions which loop back so that they both originate and terminate in the limiting membrane of the brain, just beneath the pial membrane, which, in the aggregate, they form. Other neuroglial fibers pass between the nerve fibers proper, the axis cylinders, and dendrites, thus, together with the numerous minute, ragged neuroglial sheets and excrescences, form-

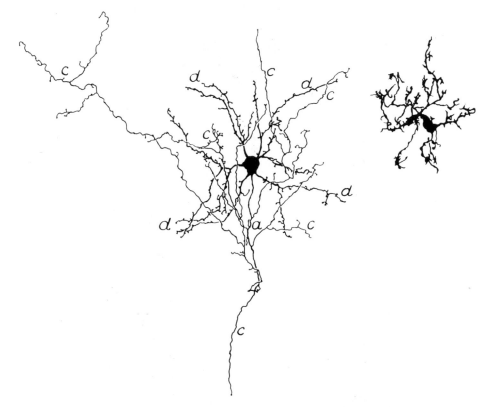

Fig. 339.—Granular cell or "grain" (*left sketch*) and a microglial cell (*right-hand sketch*) stained with silver bichromate or the rapid Golgi method. From the inner sublayer of the inner granular layer (*4-ca*) of the foveal region of the striate cortex of an adult Rhesus Macaque. Leitz *Ultropak* oil-immersion objective, transillumination, camera lucida drawing, 600× magnification. Note that from the spherical body of the granular cell several dendritic expansions (*d*) spread in all directions; they carry numerous "spines" or minute thornlike twigs, except in the initial segments close to the body; each "spine" terminates with a minute spherical nodule; from the lower face of the body a single smooth axon fiber (*a*) descends for a short distance, dividing into several delicate collateral branches (*c*), each carrying a few minute twigs terminating with nodules, different from the dendritic "spines." Note also that the entire teledendric ramification of the axonal fiber is located within the territory of the dendritic processes, or not far from it. The microglial cell also has many minute twigs, which, however, seldom carry terminal nodules but end in sharp points.

roglial cells and their expansions are abundantly present in all parts of the striate cortex. In the most superficial stratum the neuroglial bodies and nuclei are arranged in a row, forming the marginal neuroglia. From here expansions pass down into the first layer, where they radiate in various directions. There are some curious ex-

ing the sustaining and metabolic stroma for the specific nervous structures or parenchyma.

Some of these neuroglial fibers pass farther down into the subjacent second and third layers of the cortex. A number of the evidently originally marginal neuroglial cells are detached from the limiting membrane, to which, however, they are still held by one or more expansions. Still other similar neuroglial cells are entirely separated from the limiting membrane and are, with all their expansions, imbedded in the first layer. These elements, in their morphological appearance, resemble the neuroglial astrocytes elsewhere. Some of them possess rather smooth fibers radiating from the nucleus-containing body, whereas the others have fibers beset with minute ragged fringes, labeling them as the protoplasmic variety of astrocytes. However, the fickleness of the Golgi stain must also be taken into consideration, owing to which some cells may assume the appearance of protoplas-

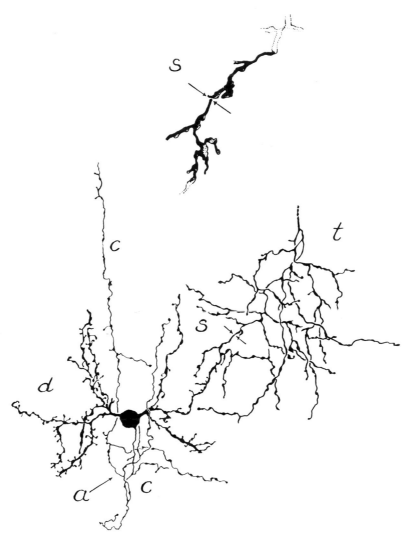

Fig. 340.—Inner granular neuron from the foveal portion of the striate cortex of an adult Rhesus Macaque stained completely, with all its expansions, in addition to a terminal arborization of an afferent fiber. Rapid Golgi stain, Leitz *Ultropak* oil-immersion objective, transillumination, camera lucida drawing, principal magnification 600×, upper sketch 1,400×. Left lower end of the figure shows an inner granular neuron, complete with all its dendrites (*d*) and with a single and thinner axis cylinder (*a*), from which several delicate collaterals branch off. The dendritic expansions are much thicker, carrying numerous short terminal twigs, practically all ending in spherical nodules or terminal thickenings. Along their course the dendrites also show spindle-shaped varicosities of different size. Similar but smaller varicosities and a few spines with terminal nodules are present also in the axon fiber and its collateral branches. The lower right-end part of the figure represents a terminal ramification or teledendron of an axon fiber belonging to another neuron, possibly residing in the laminated lateral geniculate nucleus: an afferent visual fiber of a special variety (*t*). At the point indicated by arrows (*s*), one terminal twig of the teledendron approaches a terminal twig of a dendrite of the granule cell almost close enough to touch it, apparently in a synaptical junction, this being shown at higher magnification in the upper sketch.

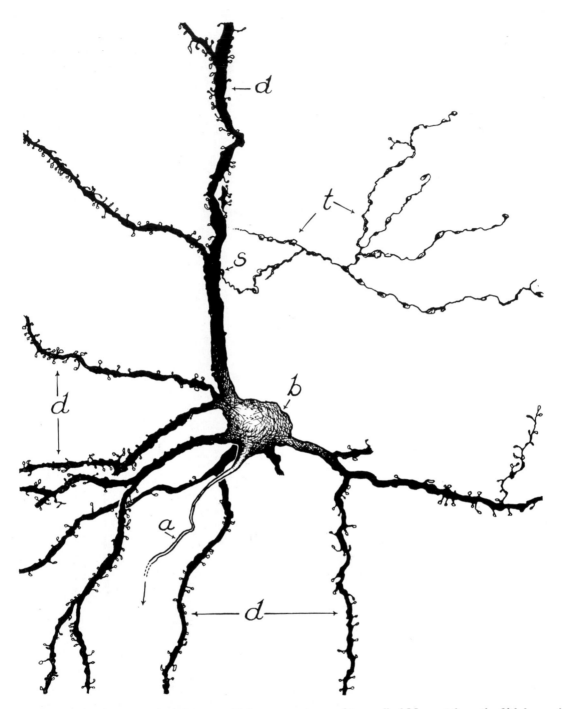

Fig. 341.—Principal parts of a large pyramidal neuron or inner solitary cell of Meynert from the fifth layer of the foveal portion of the striate area of an adult Rhesus Macaque stained with the rapid Golgi method. Leitz *Ultropak* oil-immersion objective, transillumination, camera lucida drawing, magnification *ca.* 850×. Note numerous synaptical buds or nodules attached to the dendrites (*d*), except in the parts proximal to the cell body (*b*), and none present in the single and smooth axon fiber (*a*). The right upper corner of the figure shows a terminal ramification or teledendron (*t*) belonging to a fiber of another neuron residing elsewhere. Its several branches show numerous spindle-shaped varicosities and a few twigs and terminal nodules of a different character. At the point indicated by *s*, by the accident of stain one of these terminal nodules is shown attached to the surface of the stout apical dendrite with which it undergoes a synaptical juncture. The number of the synapses in a large neuron of this variety may be considerable, since the number of the synaptical buds in this particular cell was roughly one thousand, which does not include the synapses with the smooth parts of the dendrites or of the cell body.

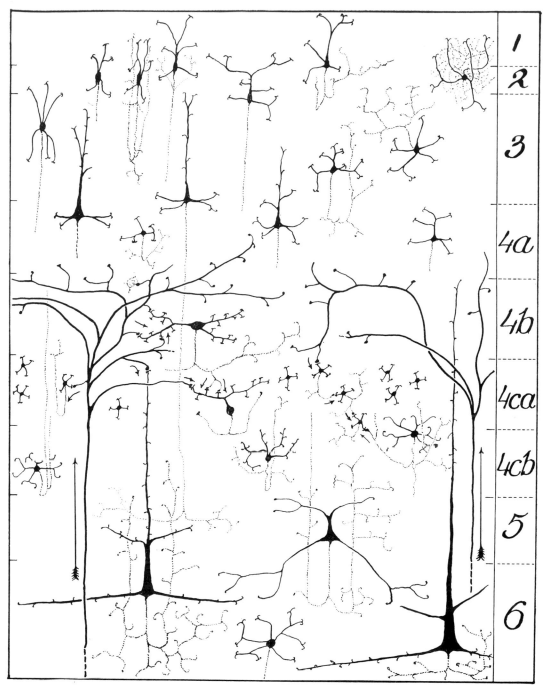

Fɪɢ. 342.—Preliminary scheme of the types and synaptical relationships of neurons in the primate striate cortex, based on the study of Golgi-stained preparations. The fibers of the visual radiation, marked with large arrows at the right and left, terminate in the inner granular layer (4), principally 4a, 4b, and 4c. Along these fiber terminals arrive impulses from the two retinae of the eyes via the laminated lateral geniculate nuclei. These retinal impulses are transmitted to a variety of neurons, to some directly, to others by means of various intermediary neurons. The most important and most numerous, although smallest, of the striate cortex appear to be the so-called granular cells of sublayer 4ca and 4cb, with a few also present in 4a. These "granular" cells are synaptically directly related to the afore-mentioned terminals. Other neurons of various sizes and shapes also undergo direct synaptical relationship, while still others are related indirectly to the same terminals. In addition, the granular cells are synaptically connected among themselves, as well as with other large and medium sized neurons, and are likewise related to other terminals of fibers originating in various areas and regions of the same and of the contralateral hemisphere of the brain, including fibers arising in the striate area itself. The composing structures and synaptical concatenations of the striate area appear exceedingly complex, requiring further investigation. Only a few of these are presented in this figure. The spreading of the impulses is indicated by the arrows.

mic astrocytes, the others that of fibrous astrocytes, even though they may be essentially the same.

The same type of neuroglial astrocytes are present in all layers of the striate cortex down to the sixth layer, and also in the subcortical white substance. In the latter they appear frankly as fibrous astrocytes. Of the other types the presence of the mesodermal microglia of Río-Hortega, typical in appearance and provided with characteristic thorny spines, was ascertained with the high-power Ultropak oil-immersion apochromates. The oligodendroglia, probably also present, however, requires further investigation.

References: Lorente de Nó 1922, 1933, 1934, 1935, 1943; O'Leary 1941; S. Ramón y Cajal (various publications, especially 1900–1906 and 1909–11; *also* S. Polyak 1953); Spiller 1901. For other references *see* terminal bibliography. *See* chapters I–IV for the history of investigations of the retina and of the nervous system in general; *see* chapter X and the appended references for the blood vessels.

Chapter IX

General Theory of the Organization of Nervous Systems and the Visual Function

SEC. 1. INTRODUCTION

1. NERVOUS SUBSTANCE, THE ANATOMICAL SUBSTRATUM OF VISION.—In the response of the vertebrate organism to stimulation by physical light, called "vision" or "sight," two different organs or sets of organs are involved. First are the peripheral organs—the eyes—constructed upon the principles of geometrical optics. Their task is the formation of retinal images. This part of the process of vision is entirely physical, if we disregard the fact that the dioptrical media and most other ocular structures are made up of living tissue (the formation of retinal images does not differ basically from that in the photographic camera). The interpretation of this part of the eye's structure is the object of physiological optics.

The obtrusiveness of the eyes as the organs of sight makes it easy to slight the other and equally important realization that the eyeball is nothing more than an elaborate dioptrical container of the delicate retinal membrane. It is this membrane that must be considered the true photoreceptor (*see* chap. I, 5 [4, 5, 6]).

In the retina and in the nervous structures that make up the remainder of the visual system, processes take place which are subjectively interpreted as vision. In order to understand these processes, it is necessary to know both the basic organization of the nervous system and the composition of the nervous constituents of the visual pathways and centers.

The gross and minute features of the optic nerves, chiasma, and tracts and of the subcortical and cortical visual centers are described in chapters V, VI, VII, and VIII. The nervous constituents making up these parts are the veritable material substratum or carrier of vision, including the higher or psychic functions of sight. An attempt to solve the age-old problem of "psychophysical parallelism" must, accordingly, begin with a general analysis of the nervous structures and their correlation with those functions that are the manifestations of their activity.

2. THE PROBLEM OF THE GENERAL ORGANIZATIONAL PRINCIPLE OF THE NERVOUS TISSUE.—An attempt at a correlation of the various aspects of the faculty of vision with the nervous constituents of the visual system and any other similar attempt concerning audition, the somesthetic sense, motility, and many other functions of the body, regulated or chiefly performed by the nervous system, must be preceded by a discussion of the general principles upon which the nervous system is organized. It is legitimate to assume that these principles are observed in all parts of the nervous system, even though their application may vary in detail.

Everywhere in the nervous system, especially in the brain and spinal cord, a basically similar arrangement is found: numerous nerve cells of different shapes and sizes, connected with, or separated from, one another by a multitude of nerve fibers of varying thickness, all imbedded in a supporting neuroglial stroma and interlaced by blood vessels and connective tissue. The first problem with such composite tissue is to determine the general character of the reciprocal relations of its constituent structures. In an agglomeration of countless structures not greatly varying in size or other observable properties, their reciprocal relationship may be expected to play a decisive role.

3. HISTORICAL REMARK.—The present advanced knowledge of the intrinsic makeup or basic organizational plan of the nervous system is the result of an effort extending over more than a century and a half. It began with Felix Fontana (1782) and Ehrenberg (1833–36), and it culminated toward the end of the nineteenth and during the beginning of the twentieth centuries in the classical work of Santiago Ramón y Cajal and his contemporaries—Golgi, Gehuchten, Retzius, Koelliker, and others. In this effort the investigation of the retina and of other parts of the visual system played a substantial role (Treviranus, Hannover, Bidder, Corti, Remak, Heinrich Müller, Koelliker, Max Schultze, S. Ramón y Cajal, and others). (*See* chap. I, 6–9, and chap. IV, 2, 3; for the figures to illustrate this chapter *see* chap. V, 3–8; chap. VI, 9; and chap. VIII, 7.)

References: Ariëns Kappers 1916–17, 1920, 1927; Ariëns Kappers *et al.* 1936; Barker 1901; Bielschowsky 1928; Heidenhain 1911; Henle 1879, v. 3(2), p. 27; Lenhossék 1910; Parker 1929; S. Ramón y Cajal 1908, 1909, 1909–11, 1923, 1934; G. Retzius 1905; Stieda 1899; Schiefferdecker 1906; J. P. Turner 1940; Verworn 1900; Waldeyer 1891, 1895.

SEC. 2. THE HYPOTHESIS OF *NEURORETICULUM* OR THE "NERVE NET"

1. The state of neurohistology during the early period of modern microscopy.— At the beginning of the modern microscopic era, around the middle of the nineteenth century, knowledge of the origin, development, morphological character, and interrelationships of nerve cells and, in general, even of their identity was slight. This is understandable, since histological technique was then still in its infancy, as only bits of fresh tissue, after being "teased" or dissected with needles, were examined with "dry" objectives.

The preliminary fixation of tissue, first in chromic acid, introduced by Hannover (1840), and then in chromic salts, used by H. Müller (1852), only gradually began to be accepted. But even when thin translucent sections were studied by H. Müller and serial sections cut and stained with carmine by Gerlach (1858), diffusely stained preparations showed but little contrast of finer structural details. The optical equipment of that period also was a handicap before the problems of stage illumination, of oil-immersion systems, and of the construction of apochromatic objectives and compensating eyepieces were solved by Abbé (1872, 1878, 1886).

It is remarkable that under these circumstances the pioneers of modern microscopy were able to make important discoveries, such as the connections of nerve fibers with cell bodies (Corti 1850) and the fact that each nerve cell possesses two kinds of expansions, several short ones and a single long one that becomes a nerve fiber (Deiters 1863).

Efforts to trace the tortuous processes within the "gray substance" and learn the nature of Leydig's "punctate substance" or "neuropil" that fills the space between the cells of the brain and the spinal cord, however, failed. This was much more regrettable, since precisely this substance was suspected of containing peculiar arrangements that could throw light upon the true relationships of the nerve cells and fibers.

It was, perhaps, unavoidable that the idea gradually gained ground that most or all nerve cells were in some way directly connected with one another. In the opinion of Gerlach (1872), for example, the posterior spinal root fibers, after entering the gray substance of the spinal cord, were supposed to divide into a net surrounding the nerve cells and would again assemble at the other end and leave the cord as anterior root fibers. The concept of the "nerve net" became popular for a while and was supported by most of the hard-working authorities of the day, who were diligently hunting for the "anastomoses" in their preparations and happily presenting them in illustrations in their papers.

It is significant that even at that time a few clearer minds dared to oppose the then fashionable theory held by the crowd of numerous lesser lights now forgotten. Meynert (1872), in the same volume of Stricker's *Handbook* in which Gerlach championed his theory of "nerve nets," considered the "separation" of the nerve fibers and their "isolation" as a basic feature of the nervous tissue, while Max Schultze (1871) in the same handbook expressed grave doubts about the general occurrence of anastomoses between the nerve cells.

Ever since then the "nerve-net concept" has

had its sympathizers, some of them championing their cause to the bitter end (thus Held's animosity toward S. Ramón y Cajal). After having seemingly been defeated by the advocates of the "neuron concept," the Proteus of the "nerve net" managed on several occasions to stage a come-back, sometimes almost winning a temporary victory, for example, when Bethe (1903) and Apáthy (1894, 1897, 1907, 1908) proclaimed the neurofibrils to be the "principal nervous substratum."

2. Tenets of the Neuroreticular Hypothesis.—The essentials of the nerve-net hypothesis, briefly, are as follows:

The constituent elements of the nervous system, the nerve cells and nerve fibers, are more or less interconnected by protoplasmic bridges, forming sets or systems along which the excitations are propagated.

From its phylogenetical beginning in the lowliest multicellular animals and from its earliest ontogenetical inception until its full maturity, the nervous system represents a cellular and fibrous *syncytium*, wherein the "cells" are little more than local condensations or foci distributed in an otherwise more or less continuous and uniform mass.

The nerve fibers, especially of the long peripheral nerves, and the various fiber systems of the brain and spinal cord either are preformed (Hensen) or arise by fusion of the numerous cells that thus form a syncytial chain (Schwann, Balfour, O. Schultze), or else the axis cylinders grow along the pre-existing plasmatic bridges called "plasmodesms" or "neurodesms" (Held 1909).

A similar principle would obtain during the process of regeneration of the nerve fibers (Bethe, Spielmeyer, and others). In no way could the nerve cells be regarded as even remotely genetically, structurally, and functionally independent units, as insisted upon by the sponsors of the "neuron theory."

3. Hypothesis of Neurencytium.—The nerve-net hypothesis attained its most extreme form in the concept of a "universal nervous network," or *neurencytium*, espoused by Golgi, Apáthy, and Bethe, but in particular by Held (1927, 1929). According to this concept, all nerve elements of an organism were fused into a "general network" permeating the entire body, merging even with neuroglia and other tissues. The "nerve cells" were merely locally differentiated foci or condensations in this continuum, with no clear boundaries between the cells. The neurofibrils were the only conducting structures, the neuroplasm of the cells and fibers being little more than a living vehicle of the fibrils (Apáthy, Bethe, Péterfi). The neurofibrils were supposed to be the products of special cells and passed indiscriminately from cell to cell, irrespective of the apparent barriers (Apáthy, Nissl, Held). The synaptical boundaries between the territories of the individual nerve cells were nonexistent.

In the final analysis, the universal bodily nerve net was the instrument by means of which the unity of the organism was brought about and was maintained (Held). Theoretically, in the nervous system thus organized—if the term "organized" is applicable to it at all—the excitations or nervous impulses, no matter where they arose, would spread in an unaccountable way in any direction without change in quality or quantity.

The questions concerning the purpose of the countless morphologically differing nerve cells and their various modes of reciprocal interlocking, how the various patterns of the arrangement of nerve cells should be interpreted in terms of concrete physiological manifestations, and how the hypothetical continuity of the nervous system could be made to harmonize with the numerous locally varying functions had never been answered by the champions of neuroreticularism, except in ambiguous generalities.

4. The Neurofibrils and Neuroreticulum.—The hypothesis of the nerve net had been variously modified to suit the particular idea of the individual investigator. After periods of relative oblivion, it had been repeatedly revived, and even today it is being championed with a stubbornness worthy of a better cause.

At present, the crude protoplasmic anastomoses, cocksurely championed by the older school of Gerlach, Tartuferi, Golgi, Dogiel, Carrière, B. Haller, and others, are rarely mentioned. In the modern "neuroreticularist" version the task of welding countless nerve cells into a "whole" is usually assigned to more subtle structures. These are the "neurofibrils" first noticed by Remak (1843, 1853), Leydig (1857, 1885), Deiters (1866), Koelliker (1867), Ehrlich (1886), Flemming (1893), and Lugaro (1896), but clearly seen only by Max Schultze (1866, 1870, 1871, 1872, 1873), H. Schultze (1879), Kupffer (1883), Apáthy (1892), Dogiel (1893, 1895), Flemming (1895), Bethe (1898), and Simarro (1900).

Precise knowledge of the neurofibrils, however, dates from the publications of Apáthy (1894, 1897, 1907, 1908), Bethe (1903), S. Ramón y Cajal (1903, 1904, 1906), and Bielschowsky (1904, 1927, 1928, 1935). From that time the role of the unifying neuroreticulum was assigned to these subtle, often elusive, threads. The neurofibrils, as the neuron-combating neuroreticularists insisted, continuously pass from one nerve cell to another, regardless of apparent cell boundaries, and are present even outside the nerve cells proper.

Since the protagonists of this concept had exalted the neurofibrils to the role of the only conducting nervous structure, they had, by the same token, relegated the cytoplasm of the nerve cells and axoplasm of the nerve fibers to a secondary role. In this way the genetical and structural individuality and relative functional independence of the nerve cell had been contested or denied outright, and the whole "neuron" concept either trimmed to a point where it could not be recognized (thus by Bielschowsky 1928, p. 119) or condescendingly deposited upon the historical scrap-heap of useless mistakes (by Abderhalden; Klarfeld 1925; P. Schröder 1926; Tiegs 1926, 1927, 1929, 1931; Held 1927, 1929; E. T. Brücke 1929, p. 771; Péterfi 1929; Boeke 1936, 1938, 1940, 1941–42, 1943–45, 1949; Beritoff-Beritashvili; and others).

The uncompromising opposition of reticularists to the "neuron" concept was to some extent motivated by subjective factors. Golgi was against it because, as a sympathizer of the "cerebral equipotentialism" of Flourens and of Goltz, he was against any form of functional cerebral localization (*see* chap. III, 4 and 8). Again, Held's idea of an organism required a material substratum as a carrier of its unifying activity which he believed he had found in his *allgemeines Grundnetz*, or "general elemental reticulum" (Held 1929, pp. 23, 41).

Similar motives of a rather philosophical order may have been responsible for the origin of Bethe's doctrine of "plasticity," for the highly speculative "resonance hypothesis" of P. Weiss, and the like, all difficult to harmonize with any clear structural and functional delimitation within the nervous system. To other opponents, again, the whole "neuron" concept was simply obnoxious. Stöhr, Jr., for example, declared it an outright "invention."

5. CRITIQUE OF THE HYPOTHESIS OF "NEURO-RETICULUM."—A charitable verdict, fully justified upon the evidence given in chapters V, VI, and VIII of this book, concerning the reticularist doctrine is that it served a useful role as a counterpoise to the exaggerations of the advocates of "neuronism." Its stubborn opposition and its sometimes violent critique aroused efforts among its adversaries which, without it, would very likely never have been made.

For the rest, the work and ideological presentation of the reticularists are largely wasted effort. Their critique was mostly negative. The obligation squarely resting upon them to give a lucid, reasoned explanation of how the undeniable fact of numerous locally varying functions in the nervous system could be made to harmonize with their doctrine has been consistently dodged or sidetracked into a realm of semi-mystical "dynamism."

Their pretense of being in revolt against the "old-fashioned" Schwann-Schleiden-Schultze concept of the "cell" as a structural element of the bodily organization impresses one as meaningless scientific faddism. Their claim to have proved the presence of a "continuous nerve net," a *continuum*, a *Grundnetz*, a *neurencytium*, a special "gray substance," or a "molecular substance of the brain," and what not, as a nervous substratum existing outside and besides the regular nerve cells and their expansions, wherein the latter would be dissolved as individual structures, must be considered meaningless after the evidence given in the preceding chapters.

In particular, the fantastic schemes of Apáthy, Bethe, and especially of Nissl (*see* Péterfi 1929, p. 128) have never been substantiated by positive evidence, while Held's and Boeke's presentation of the peripheral nervous system lends itself to a different interpretation (*see* Nonidez 1936–37). Held's belief, to which he clung to the last (Held 1929, p. 5), viz., that the "gemmules" or "spines" of the dendrites were terminal buttons of the afferent nerve fibers, an argument which he repeatedly used to prove a wholesale merging of the nerve cells and their expansions, was long since revealed by S. Ramón y Cajal (1896, 1909–11, 1934, p. 92) to be an error and is easily refuted by any cursory examination of a good preparation stained with silver bichromate and examined by high-power oil-immersion Ultropak apochromatic objectives (*cf.* Figs. 337, 338, 341).

The continuity of the neurofibrils, supposed by the neuroreticularists to pass directly from one cell to another, has been refuted by a number of modern investigators. Tello (1931) showed the intracellular neurofibrils of the cochlear and vestibular sensory epithelium to be in no direct connection with the neurofibrils of the terminal branches of the cochlear and vestibular nerves. S. Ramón y Cajal (1932, 1934) and, in an especially clear way, Bartelmez & Hoerr (1933) and Bodian (1937 and later) have demonstrated the distinctness of the neurofibrils in the afferent terminals from those in the cytoplasm of the body of the related neuron, being separated from each other by a "synaptical membrane."

That the "neuropil" or Leydig's "punctate substance," a finely granulated mass characteristic of many localities of the gray nervous centers, is not the continuous nonsynaptical network which it had been proclaimed to be by the neuroreticularists and by adherents of the concept of functional equivalence of the brain, but is a tangle of interlacing neuron processes and is therefore to be regarded as a "synaptical field," has been convincingly demonstrated by C. J. Herrick in his numerous studies of the central nervous system of Lower Vertebrates (Herrick 1934). A similar composition of the molecular layer of the cerebral cortex and of other parts of the brain was made certain by my own study of the best Golgi-stained preparations with the help of oil-immersion objectives of the Ultropak type (magnifications used up to 2,000×).

The continuity of the neurofibrils in the somatic motor nerve terminations with the myofibrillar substance by means of the "periterminal reticulum," described by Boeke (1926 and later), has been questioned by S. Ramón y Cajal (1934; *see also* Heidenhain, Wilkinson). The anastomosing of the expansions of nerve cells frequently observed in cultures of living nerve tissue (Levi, Bauer, and others), and in the growing nerves of young animals (Speidel 1932, 1933, 1935) is a process not yet fully analyzed, whereas Hensen's hypothesis of the pre-existing connections of nerves with the peripheral organs and Schwann-Balfour-Schultze's syncytial or catenary hypothesis of the polyblastic origin of nerve fibers, as well as Held's hypothesis of the embryonic axons growing within the preformed protoplasmic bridges called "plasmodesms" or "neurodesms," all still defended by the reticularists (*see* Bielschowsky 1928, p. 131; Péterfi 1929, p. 131; Spielmeyer), after the brilliant experiments of Harrison (1908, 1910, 1912, 1924) and of Speidel (1932–35), have nothing positive to show in their favor.

Finally, the nervous system of primitive animals such as the Coelenterates had been shown by Bozler (1927) and by Woollard & Harpman (1939) to be synaptical in character rather than a continuous network, as the reticularists and many other writers under their influence had believed it to be for many decades (for Young's observation of the fusion of giant axons in Squid, *see* following section).

Even in the visceral organs, whose working would naturally require a more diffuse arrangement of the nerves, a supposedly continuous "terminal reticulum" described by Boeke (1926, 1936, etc.) had been revealed by Nonidez (1936–37) as largely nonnervous, of the nature of connective tissue. (*Cf.* also Kuntz 1953, p. 54.)

General histobiological considerations also militate against the "nerve net" as an organizational principle of the nervous system. If no barriers and boundaries separating the individual neuron territories existed, as they necessarily would not in a syncytium, a differentiation of diverse cell types from an original common form would hardly be possible. In an undifferentiated system neither dynamical polarity nor functional specificity of the nerve cells would have been developed. Such a nervous system would be histologically homogeneous, as are, for example, the striated muscle and the glands, where each of the many nuclei and myofibrils or agglomerations of cells appears to perform the same function.

In such a nervous system all elements would be of the same kind and would be connected with one another in a like way. Such a homogeneously built nervous system would not be capable of a locally differentiated activity, unless assisted by some unaccountable dynamical factors of a nonstructural nature, beyond the power of microscope to reveal and outside the judgment of a microscopist.

If, then, a neuroreticular syncytial nervous system contained some structures differentiated within the syncytium, these, in order to perform complex functions, would have to be endowed with exactly the same properties as those possessed by a multicellular synaptical nervous system. An imaginary nervous system containing "syncytial synaptical connections," proposed by Boeke (1926 and later), is therefore inconceivable, implying, as it does, two mutually exclusive principles—one, the syncytium, synonymous with continuity; and the other, the synapse, meaning contact barriers through which discrete nerve cells are related to one another.

This critical review may fittingly be terminated by the statement that not one single detail described in this book, mostly pertaining to highly differentiated nervous tissue of fully mature organs of Monkeys, Apes, Man, and other animal species, supports the contention of the neuroreticulum hypothesis as a general organizational principle (*see* sec. 4, this chapter).

References: On various shades of neuroreticularism, nervous continuum, neuroreticulum, neurencytium, and the like, *see* Abderhalden; Apáthy 1894, 1897, 1907, 1908; K. F. Bauer 1948; Beccari 1943; Beritoff-Beritashvili; Bethe 1895, 1897–98, 1903, 1910, 1931, 1933; Bielschowsky 1905, 1927, 1928, 1935; Boeke 1926, 1935, 1936, 1938, 1940, 1941–42, 1943–45, 1949; E. T. Brücke 1929; Dogiel 1893; Fortin 1930; J. Gerlach 1872; Glees 1939; Golgi 1891, 1901–3; A. Gurwitsch; B. Haller 1895, 1910–11; Held 1905, 1907, 1909, 1927, 1929; Heringa 1923; Hillarp 1946; S. J. Holmes 1944; Klarfeld 1925; Lawrentjew 1934; Marui 1918; S. Meyer; F. Nansen 1886–87; Nissl 1900, 1903; Péterfi 1929; S. Ramón y Cajal 1908, 1909–11, and later; O. Schultze 1905; Spatz; Spielmeyer 1932, 1935; Stöhr, Jr. 1928, 1937; Tartuferi 1887; Tiegs 1926; Uyama 1926, 1927, 1934; Uyama & Miyake 1934; J. Z. Young 1939.

SEC. 3. THE NEURON THEORY

1. THE ORIGINS OF THE NEURON THEORY.—A concept of a general organizational plan of the nervous system opposite to the idea of neuroreticulum is that of the *neuron*. It may be defined most simply as the "cell theory" of Schleiden, Schwann & Schultze applied to the nervous organs. It maintains that, like most other tissues and organs, the brain, spinal cord, and peripheral parts of the nervous system are made up of more or less independent cellular individuals, the "neurons."

Genetically, the young neurons arise at an early embryonic stage as structurally independent ectodermal cells of rather uniform appearance, the "neuroblasts" of W. His (1887, 1893; portrait, Fig. 343). During subsequent differentiation and adult existence they preserve a fair measure of trophic and functional independence and are to be considered as morphological and dynamical entities.

The idea of independent nerve cells was ar-

rived at toward the end of the nineteenth century, almost two decades after Gerlach (1872) promulgated his concept of nerve nets. Mention was made of Max Schultze (1871) and of T. Meynert (1872), who may be considered as its forerunners, to which also Hughlings Jackson (1869) may be added.

But the actual origin of the idea may be traced directly to the improved neurohistological technique, in particular to the discovery of special histoanalytical methods: Golgi's silver bichromate method (1878; Fig. 344) and Ehrlich's vital methylene blue method (1886). These two stains have contributed more to the advancement of neurology than any other single factor, not excluding even the improvements of microscopical optics by Abbé, mentioned in the preceding section.

It is an odd freak of history, however, that Golgi, whose method became such a mighty tool in the hands of S. Ramón y Cajal and others, persisted in his loyalty to Gerlach's reticularism. Ehrlich, however, because of the experience he gained with his newly discovered method, was among the first to abandon the concept of nervous continuity.

Soon after, as new observations with the silver bichromate technique began to accumulate, the idea of independent nerve cells gained ground. First promulgated by Kupffer (1872),

W. His (1886, 1887), and Forel (1887), it was molded into a theory by Waldeyer (1891, portrait, Fig. 345). After it was splendidly corroborated by R. T. Harrison (1908, 1910, 1912, 1924), who showed by in vitro cultures the sprouting of axis cylinders from the growing embryonic neuroblasts, it became widely accepted.

At last the goal, out of reach of the preceding

Fig. 343.—Wilhelm His, Sr. (1831–1904), professor of anatomy in Leipzig, Saxony, Germany. Pioneer student of the fetal nervous system. Discoverer of the "neuroblasts" or young, plastic nerve cells which make up the nervous tissue of the brain and of the spinal cord during early stages of embryonic development. The concept of "neuroblasts" as relatively independent structural units or "building stones," in turn, led to the "neuron theory" of Waldeyer (*see* portrait Fig. 345), S. Ramón y Cajal (*see* portrait Figs. 52, 131, 317), Van Gehuchten, and others. According to the neuron theory, the nervous organs are composed of structurally and functionally relatively independent nerve cells, the "neurons," related to one another by contact in multifarious ways, altogether making up the complex nervous tissue. The "neuron theory" is opposed to the "doctrine of *neuroreticulum*," or a continuous nerve net, championed by Gerlach, Apáthy, Bethe, Held, and some modern investigators. From a portrait at the University of Chicago, Department of Anatomy. Biography by Mall, Am. J. Anat., v. 4, p. 139, 1905, and Haymaker & Baer, *The Founders of Neurology*, 1953.

generation, which used older, inadequate "teasing" techniques and nonselective carmine stain, was sighted. The limitless variation in shape and size of the nerve cells and of their various expansions, their arrangement, termination of processes, and the manifold contacts—all details inexplicable on the basis of a neuroreticulum—began to make sense.

The neuron concept made it possible to understand in what way nerve cells, varying little in one or another detail, especially in their expansions and the manner of reciprocal contacts and probably also in biochemical and functional properties, were able to produce countless patterns of histological relationships that must have counterparts in distinct dynamical manifestations.

Altogether, in the opinion of its adherents, the new "neuron theory" gave a far more adequate picture of the intrinsic organization of the

FIG. 344.—Camillo G. Golgi (1844–1926), professor of general pathology at Pavia, Italy. Nobel Prize laureate for the year 1906 (with S. Ramón y Cajal). Discoverer of a staining method for nervous tissue, the silver dichromate stain known as the "Golgi method." The Golgi method shows individual nerve cells together with all their expansions, including the ultimate or terminal twigs, thus permitting the study of the character of each cell type and the exact topographic and functional relationship of each nerve cell with other nerve cells and other tissues (*cf.* corresponding figures in this book). The Golgi method and, to a lesser extent, Ehrlich's vital methylene blue stain, more than any other single histological method, in the hands of S. Ramón y Cajal and many other investigators has helped to unravel the complex structure of the nervous organs and laid the foundation of the modern concept of its organization. From München. med. Wchnschr., v. 54, 1907. *See also* W. Haymaker's *Guide*, 1948; Haymaker & Baer, *The Founders of Neurology*, 1953.

nervous system than the theory of neuroreticulum ever did. (*See,* for additional information, S. Ramón y Cajal 1909–11, v. 1, p. 1, esp. pp. 66, 80, and his articles published 1934 and 1935.)

2. TENETS OF THE NEURON THEORY.—The principal tenets of the "neuron theory" are as follows:

a) Specific nervous parenchyma and nonspecific nervous supporting constituents.—The tissue of the brain and spinal cord consists of nerve cells proper and of their expansions or processes. Together, these represent the nervous parenchyma or the constituent on which the specific function of the brain and spinal cord depends. The nerve cells originate from the ectodermal or outermost layer during the early period of embryonic development. The neuroglial cells and processes are also ectodermal in origin but form a supporting, nonspecific framework within which the nerve cells proper and their expansions are imbedded. The mesodermal blood vessels are a normal constituent of most nervous tissue, contributing to its growth and maintenance.

b) The neuroblasts.—The young multiplying nerve cells of the early stage of an embryo, the neuroblasts, at first appear alike and exhibit a considerable degree of independence from one another. Only by degrees, as they become further differentiated into mature neurons and develop numerous expansions, with which they become interlocked into sets of neurons in adult tissue, do they relinquish part of their original genetical independence. Yet even in the fully grown nervous organs the cellular boundaries of the adult neurons in most cases may easily be determined by an appropriate technique.

c) The neuron body with its expansions forms a physiologic and trophic unit.—Each nerve cell, including all its expansions, is a relatively independent unit, a "neuron" or "neurone," capable of individual existence within the tissue of which it is a part.

The neurons of Higher Vertebrates possess a cell body or perikaryon and processes of two kinds: protoplasmic dendrites, which usually are short, thick, and of which there are several to each cell, and a single long, smooth, and rather uniformly thick axon or axis cylinder (corrupted from "axis of the cylinder") or nerve fiber.

All expansions of a neuron, comprising both dendrites and axon with its terminal ramification or teledendron, grow from the cell body by sprouting during the process of maturation or regeneration: the "outgrowth theory" of Kupffer, W. His, S. Ramón y Cajal, and Speidel. They do not grow within the "plasmodesms" or preformed protoplasmatic bridges or along the *Leitzellen* or "conductor cells" of the German writers, exemplified by neuroglia and Schwann's cells, but follow intercellular spaces (*see* Harrison's experiments with living tissue, and S. Ramón y Cajal's experiments in 1920 on nerve regeneration).

The processes are nutritionally dependent upon the perikaryon containing the nucleus, which is, accordingly, the trophic center of a neuron. Cut off, the processes die or else regenerate by sprouting from the cell body, as is also the case with the axon, irrespective of length.

Each neuron leads an independent existence to a varying degree. Depending on whether a nerve cell suffers reparable or irreparable damage when injured, it shows signs of degeneration, or it may disappear completely, with the adjoining but synaptically unrelated neurons, if not directly affected, remaining normal. The synaptically related neurons, on the contrary, are trophically interdependent, this dependence varying in degree from case to case, being most pronounced in monosynaptically related neurons, exemplified in the lateral geniculate nucleus ("trans-synaptic degeneration").

d) Ramifications of neurons: dendrites, axon, and teledendron.—The more numerous and thicker "dendrites," with their terminal branches and button-like nodules or gemmules, improperly also called "spines," ordinarily remain within the confines of the gray substance, whose constituents, with the "body" or "perikaryon," they principally are. The single and usually longer "axon" or "nerve fiber" leaves the territory of the gray substance and, together with other axons, forms the white substance of the brain and spinal cord or, when leaving the central organs, forms the peripheral nerves. The sagittal strata of the parietotemporo-occipital regions of the cerebral hemispheres are an example of the white substance, the peripheral nerves being exemplified by the oculomotor and other cranial nerves. The optic nerves, chiasma, and optic tracts are drawn-out fiber bundles of the brain connecting the retina, a detached portion of the brain.

Whether relatively short and remaining within the gray substance or long and passing over into white substance or peripheral nerves, each axon fiber divides into a terminal arborization made up of a varying number of twigs, usually with spherical or irregularly shaped enlargements, swellings, buttons, or nodules at their ends, together called the "teledendron."

Some axons, usually while still within the gray substance, give off "collateral branches," spreading within the same substance. The teledendrons, both of the short axons belonging to neuron cells residing within the same gray substance and of the long axons whose cells of origin are in another part of the brain, spinal

Fig. 345.—Wilhelm Waldeyer (von Waldeyer-Hartz, 1836–1921), professor of anatomy at Strassburg and Berlin. Noted anatomist, creator of the modern concept of "neuron" as a structural and functional unit of the nervous system. From Waldeyer's *Lebenserinnerungen*, 1920.

cord, or a peripheral ganglion, usually terminate within the gray substance whose essential constituent they are. The axonal terminations in the muscles and glands are homologues of the teledendrons.

e) The functional polarity of the neurons.—The possession of two kinds of expansions, each usually with sharply defined morphological features, and the peculiar mode of attachment of these two categories of processes to other nerve cells, muscles, glands, and some other structures indicate that these processes also differ functionally. In particular, the dendrites and the surface of the cell body or perikaryon appear to be the only parts of the neuron capable under normal circumstances of receiving extraneous impulses or of being stimulated; these may, therefore, be considered the receptive end, or "ingress," of a neuron. Conversely, the axis cylinder and its terminal arborization or teledendron is the emissive or discharging end, the "egress," of a neuron, along which the excitation or impulse is carried away. The dendrites are somato- or cellulipetal, transmitting impulses toward the cell body, the axonal process being somato- or cellulifugal, carrying the impulses away from the body. In some cases, e.g., craniospinal ganglions, certain retinal bipolars, with the body attached sidewise, a direct transmission from a dendrite to an axon is probable. This is the axipetal conduction arrangement (S. Ramón y Cajal).

There are exceptions to the preceding rule, with an axon terminal attached directly to the initial portion of the other related axon fiber (Bartelmez & Hoerr, Bodian, Young) or to its terminal, such as the arrangement found in horizontal cells (*c*) and centrifugal bipolars (*i*); these require further inquiry.

Considering, however, these apparent exceptions also, the overwhelming evidence supports the view that the neurons of advanced animals are dynamically or functionally polarized, having parts specialized to react to extraneous impulses (dendrites and perikaryon) and other parts capable of inducing reactions in other related structures (axon and its teledendron). This functional polarity, or "one-way propagation of excitation" within each neuron, is another fundamental feature, in addition to the differentiation of neurons into various types or varieties, upon which the structural complexity of the nervous system, especially of the brain, is based.

f) Synapses.—The neurons do not merge or continue with one another by means of their processes or anastomatical bridges, as the "neuroreticular hypothesis" insists, but are interrelated through a more or less intimate contact (S. Ramón y Cajal). Usually, the slightly swollen terminal twigs, buds, or nodules of a teledendron of an axis cylinder of one neuron touch one or another dendrite or the surface of the body of a related neuron. The modes of contact vary practically endlessly in the complex nervous system of Higher Vertebrates, the contact in some cases being very slight, the terminal nodule of a teledendron barely touching the surface of a related neuron body or its dendrite, whereas in another extreme the ends of a teledendron firmly clasp or enwrap the body of a related neuron or are otherwise anchored to it.

In all cases, when appropriately studied, the barrier separating the substance of two related neurons can be outlined. In suitable cases the barrier appears as a distinct line, an optical cross-section of the area where the two surfaces are in contact (*see* Bartelmez & Hoerr 1933; Bodian 1937, 1940, 1942). This "synapse," as it was named by Sherrington at the suggestion of Verrall (*see* Fulton 1943, p. 52), has been interpreted by neurophysiologists as a "two-faced membrane," differently organized on both sides of the potential cleavage space or area of contact. How the details of this difference in ultramicroscopic organization of the two faces can ever be examined and defined is one of the remaining great problems.

Figuratively, the working of a synapse may be compared to a valve, under physiological conditions permitting a free flow of the excitation in one direction and hindering it in the opposite direction. It may be assumed that the dendritic or the somatic face of the synapse is of a receptive nature, facilitating the inflow of excitation into the substance of the dendrite or the cell body, while the teledendric face works as an emissive structure.

Since there is physiological evidence that the excitation within the body of a neuron and its processes, the axon and dendrites alike, may spread in any direction, it is necessary to look upon the synapses as the true cause of a dynamic or functional polarity of neurons by which the unidirectional flow of nervous excitations is determined and regulated.

g) The varieties of neurons.—In the highly differentiated nervous systems of advanced animals, the neurons are found in numerous varieties and types. They vary in many respects: in size and shape of cell body; in number, length, thickness, character of distribution, density, and place of spreading, and in many other subtle details both of dendritic expansions and of axons and axonal ramification or teledendrons; in the number, size, shape, and other features of terminal twigs and nodules; in the character of various cellular inclusions, such as

FIG. 346.—Gustaf Magnus Retzius (1842–1919), professor of anatomy at Stockholm, Sweden. Indefatigable investigator of the human and animal body, in particular of the nervous system, and of the sense organs. From Retzius' obituary by V. Ebner, in *Almanach der Akademie der Wissenschaften*, Wien, 1920. Courtesy Oesterreichische Akademie der Wissenschaften, Wien. *See also* Haymaker & Baer, *Founders of Neurology*, 1953.

the nucleus, nucleolus, and diverse granules, particularly of the chromophile substance of Nissl; and in numerous other cytological features demonstrable by various methods of histological staining technique.

In the fully differentiated nervous organs the features characteristic of a certain neuron variety are constant, the number of individuals deviating from the type or including features of two or more varieties being relatively small. This is in remarkable contrast with the uniform appearance of young nerve cells or neuroblasts in the early stages of a nascent embryonic nervous system. It likewise contrasts with the poorly differentiated nervous system of primitive animals close to the bottom of the phylogenetical scale.

In summary, the neuron concept epitomizes the morphological and functional diversity of the advanced nervous system as a climax of a long phylogenetical, and a shorter ontogenetical, process of differentiation from a simple and uniform original condition.

From this a logical deduction may be made that in the early phylogeny and ontogeny the individual nerve cells vary little in their functional capacities, as they vary little in their morphological appearance. As the biological situation of advancing animals becomes increasingly complex, the necessity arises for certain neurons to specialize gradually, to develop their innate potentialities to enable them to perform functions outside the scope of undifferentiated neurons or neurons differentiated in a different direction.

Otherwise expressed, the phylogenetical and ontogenetical differentiation of distinct neuron varieties, with the similar progressive differentiation of other tissues of the animal body, is the essence of progressive animal evolution. In this way new capacities are evolved, by means of which animals are able to utilize more of the physical factors of the world around them in ways which are increasingly favorable in their competitive existence. (*Cf.* chap. XIII, 2, 3.)

h) The physiological or functional specificity of neurons.—Closely related to the morphological differentiation into many varieties is the functional specificity of neurons. In early animal phylogenesis all nerve cells may have been adjusted to respond to a number of extrinsic and intrinsic stimuli, reacting more or less to all of them similarly (*see* chap. XIII, 2). With increasing functional specialization, of which morphological differentiation is but a visible manifestation, each neuron variety became dynamically responsive to a particular kind of stimulus, nervous or nonnervous, whereas the responsiveness to other kinds of stimulus decreased or vanished. In a highly differentiated nervous system a condition has been attained in which some or all specialized neurons have become responsive to one particular stimulation, different in each neuron variety, while at the same time becoming refractory to all other kinds of stimulating factors or reacting inadequately. Here each neuron variety is capable of reacting dynamically and within rather narrow limits of stimulation in its own specific way (*cf.*, e.g., Rushton 1949, 1950).

Similar ideas had been expressed as early as the end of the seventeenth century by Father Mariotte (1668) and again hinted at by Charles Bonnet (1759, 1770) and were subsequently elaborated upon during the early part of the nineteenth century by Charles Bell (1811) and thereafter by Johannes Müller in his concept of the "specificity of nervous energies."

"Functional neuronal specificity" presupposes the ability of each neuron variety to react to a relatively narrow range of extraneous stimuli and to react dynamically to them in its own peculiar way, conditioned by its own innate biochemical constitution. This may manifest itself, for example, in the size or amplitude and in the rate or number of individual impulses registered in a unit of time by a recording instrument in an electrophysiological experiment.

The evidence in support of the functional specificity of neurons is manifold: different physical and chemical constitution of cytoplasm and its inclusions, especially Nissl's chromophile granules; different character of expansions, both dendritic and axonal; dissimilar synaptical contacts and different interneuronal relationships; difference in normal and pathological reactions of different parts of the nervous system or different neurons or sets of neurons. Without the functional specificity of each neuron variety, a complex nervous system is difficult to conceive.

i) Interlocking of neurons, or interneuronal

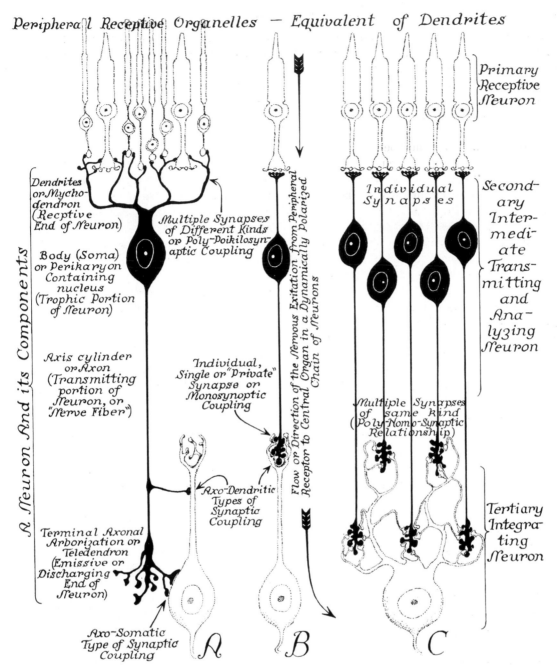

Peripheral Receptive Organelles — Equivalent of Dendrites

Primary Receptive Neuron

Individual Synapses

Second-ary Intermedi-ate Trans-mitting and Ana-lyzing Neuron

A Neuron And its Components

Dendrites or Mycho-dendron (Receptive End of Neuron)

Body (Soma) or Perikaryon Containing nucleus (Trophic Portion of Neuron)

Axis cylinder or Axon (Transmitting portion of Neuron, or "Nerve Fiber")

Terminal Axonal Arborization or Teledendron (Emissive or Discharging End of Neuron)

Multiple Synapses of Different Kinds or Poly-Poikilosyn-aptic Coupling

Individual, Single or "Private" Synapse or Monosynaptic Coupling

Axo-Dendritic Types of Synaptic Coupling

Flow or Direction of the Nervous Excitation from Peripheral Receptor to Central Organ in a Dynamically polarized Chain of Neurons

Multiple Synapses of same kind (Poly-Nomo-Synaptic Relationship)

Tertiary Integra-ting Neuron

Axo-Somatic Type of Synaptic Coupling

A   *B*   *C*

FIG. 347.—Diagram of various neuron types of human and simian retina, showing the essentials of the structural and functional organization of the nervous system. Each complete neuron cell usually has a body, one or several protoplasmic expansions or dendrites, and a single axis cylinder or axon, ending in a terminal ramification or tele-dendron. Neurons are believed to be polarized functionally or dynamically, each part having a specific function: the dendrites and body a receptive, the axon a transmitting, and the teledendron a discharging role. Each neuron is related by contact or concrescence to another or to several other neurons or to other structures, such as muscles or glands, whose activity it controls. The points of contact of a terminal teledendron of one neuron with the surface of the body or of a dendrite of the related neuron where the influencing takes place is called "synapse" or conjunc-tion. Each neuron variety is capable of reacting in its own specific way, different from the ways of other neuron varieties. The same dynamic specificity also applies to different kinds of synaptical relationships that various neuron types undergo with one another. In this diagram only a few of the many possible relationships are presented: *A*, common pathway for the rod and cone impulses; *B*, individualized or "private" cone synapses; *C*, several private cone synapses converging upon the same ganglion cell. These examples illustrate the possibility of changing in vari-ous ways the nervous impulses initiated in the rods and cones (*above*) as they pass through different bipolar varieties (*solid black*) to the ganglion cells (given below in outline).

relationships.—The structural and functional relationships or modes and ways in which countless neurons of various types may be interlocked in different groups or sets is the last, but perhaps the most important, single factor which makes possible the complex organization of the nervous system of advanced animals.

Whereas the factors discussed in the preceding paragraphs concern chiefly, or exclusively, the neurons as individual cellular or histological entities, the interrelationship of the neurons deals directly with the organization of tissue. To make this difference clear, the following comparison may be helpful. Assume that an architect is to design a building, using a single variety of bricks. If he is an admirer of classical styles, he may be able to build a very elaborate structure of Romanesque, Gothic, or Tudor type, using the same kind of bricks but differently arranged. He may very well be able to produce all the intricate decorative patterns of the walls, windows, doors, and chimneys, as required by the particular style, without changing the shape of a single brick. If several kinds of bricks—light red, dark red, blue, and black—are at his disposal, his task is made much easier, and the edifice may be more elaborate. If many more kinds of bricks and, in addition, several varieties of stone, plaster molds, and the like are available, the architect may well succeed in erecting an Alhambra or a Taj Mahal.

An elaborate nervous system, according to this example, would be feasible, even if all neurons were of the same variety. Unquestionably, however, an elaborate and more efficient structure is much more easy to attain if the "building stones," the neurons, vary in many particulars, in shape, size, arrangement, connections, and innate properties.

In practice, obviously, Nature, in creating the nervous system of Higher Vertebrates, considered by some "the most highly organized matter on the globe," has used all available means. The concatenation of the neurons into diverse patterns of cells variously related synaptically to one another is undoubtedly the most important architectural factor.

Differing from all other bodily organs that are more or less uniformly or homogeneously organized in their minute structure, the nervous system represents a huge aggregate of variously synaptically interrelated groups and sets of neurons woven into most intricate tissue patterns. Their synaptical connections indicate that these sets are capable of functioning not only as a part of the total tissue but, under special dynamical conditions, in their own way, more or less independently of other sets of the same tissue.

By disclosing the synaptical relationship of such sets of neurons with one another and with other related neurons of a given system—for example, the visual, auditory, somatomotor, and others—means may be found to understand the spreading of individual or complex excitations passing from the peripheral receptors through the intermediary stations to the cortical centers, or vice versa, their various changes traced therein and the ultimate fate of such excitations estimated.

j) Dynamical states of neurons and their mutual influencing.—In the analysis of various factors contributing to the building of a complex nervous system, still another angle needs to be considered: the nature of the excitation elicited in the individual neurons.

According to the reticularist concept, there are no true barriers between the individual nerve cells believed to be interconnected by the protoplasmic anastomoses or neurofibrils. The true substratum along which the nerve impulses spread are supposedly the neurofibrils. Since the neurofibrils are considered by reticularists to be continuous from cell to cell—in fact, Held claimed the continuity and unity of the entire bodily neuroreticulum—it is difficult to see how a nervous excitation arising anywhere within this network could be prevented from spreading anywhere within the system or be modified in any way. According to the neuroreticularist doctrine and like hypotheses, the regulation of the direction, intensity, division, merging, or fusion or any other modification of the currents of excitation within the nervous system remains unexplained.

The hypothesis of neuroreticulum takes into account neither the material nor the dynamical factors responsible for the immense local variation in function demonstrated by modern neurophysiology, especially electrophysiology, and by neuropathology. This adverse judgment must also be passed about any other similar hypothesis, such as the "resonance hypothesis" of P. Weiss, which pretends to disclaim the need for an elaborate structural relationship in the nervous system as a basis of functional diversity, a claim which is altogether in opposition to observable and measurable facts. Facts observable by the microscope and the innumerable indications from neurophysiological experimenting, clinical observations, and neuropathology overwhelmingly point toward the elaborate anatomical makeup of the nervous system as the principal factor responsible for its functional diversity.

We may put aside, for a while, the basic question of what are the factors which force Metazoans to build their bodies out of the countless minute morphophysiological entities called "cells," instead of letting them grow and prosper as single, huge, syncytial lumps. This apparently is predetermined by as yet unknown factors which initiate, regulate, and terminate the growth and the very life of animals. But, whatever these factors are, they indicate that there is a limit in tridimensional space and in the quantity of matter, as there is in time, beyond which animals cannot go. Hence the growth and perfection of animals must have recourse to the multiplicity and elaborate arrangement of their constituent elements. (*Cf.* chap. XIII, 2, 3.)

The nervous system, as we know it from modern investigations, is obviously an "aggregation," a "composite," or a "collective," made up of countless nerve cells varying almost ad infinitum, artfully put together into a complex whole. In it certain constituents, such as long axis cylinders or "nerve fibers" of the pyramidal tract, of the anterior or posterior spinal roots, and of many other systems, have the task of transmitting discrete nerve excitations from one particular point of the central organ (one or a few nerve cells of the cerebral cortex or of the spinal cord) to a particular restricted locality in the periphery of the body (a few muscle fibers, a small group of glandular cells, for example) or from a small area in the periphery (a small territory of the skin, or a few muscle fibers, or tendon fibers, and the like) to a narrow strip in the posterior gray columns of the spinal cord or to a minute cell nest in the nuclei of the posterior spinal columns, and so forth.

Here, obviously, the nerve fibers, their cells of origin, and their terminal arborizations, both in the periphery and in the central organ, have, to begin with, only one task to perform: to transmit quickly a particular discrete impulse generated in a small group of neurons, or even in a single neuron, to another small neuron nest. The insulation of axis cylinders by myelin sheaths is doubtless a means by which the loss of nervous current to the adjoining structures is minimized. At both ends of the conducting "nerve fibers" the arrangements differ. In the muscles each motor nerve fiber terminates with a group of end-plates attached to several muscle fibers, or a sensory nerve fiber is related to a number of muscle or tendon fibers, remaining entirely unrelated to other fibers of the same muscle. In the spinal cord and in the brain the terminals of the afferent fibers spread around one or several groups of cells of the various nuclei.

Up to this point the connections are adjusted merely to preserve the discreteness or individuality of the incoming nerve impulse and transmit it to the brain. Only in the complex mechanisms of the central organ may further processing of these impulses take place. The preservation of the impulses as discrete dynamical entities, accordingly, is the principal functional task of the nerve conductors. The individuality of dynamical entities remains preserved, however, only as far as the synaptical barriers of neurons. Beyond these, the character of excitation necessarily changes.

One may look upon each individual neuron as a cartridge shell filled with a definite, limited charge. The charges are the same in the same neuron variety and differ in different varieties. Each neuron is capable of developing one particular kind of energy only, which may vary somewhat, little, or not at all in "qualities" and more so in intensity. On the whole, then, there are as many possible elicitable "reactions" or "dynamical states" as there are individual neuron cells in a nervous system, the states in the same neuron variety being roughly potentially the same in quality and different in different neuron varieties.

Where two neurons are connected through a synaptical contact, the excitation of one may be capable of causing an excitation in its related companion. Because of the synaptical barrier, it is proper to consider the induced disturbance of the dynamical equilibrium in the related neuron as a separate event, even though caused by an excitation from the first neuron. The two excitations—that causing the disturbance and that

induced which follows—are not identical, even though they are causally related to each other. Each is determined principally by the innate properties developed during the ontogenetical differentiation based upon the preceding phylogenetical factors.

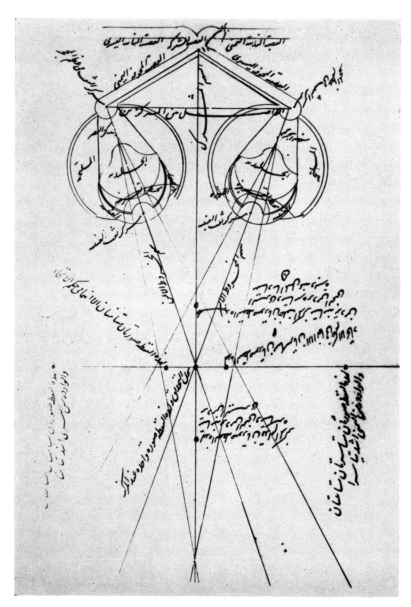

Fig. 348.—Explanation of binocular stereoscopic vision, according to Kamāl al-Dīn Abu'l-Ḥasan al-Fārisī, a Persian scholar of optics of the fifteenth century. Photo print of a diagram in an Arabic manuscript written A.D. 1433, entitled *Kitāb al-baṣa'ir fi 'ilm al-manāẓir*, or *Book of Reflexions on the Science of Optics*, now in possession of the Ayasofya Library, Istanbul, Turkey. The two eyeballs, connected to the brain through the optic nerves, chiasma, and tracts, converge with their axes, which meet in the common fixation point. The objects situated in front of this point along the common line of vision are depicted on the nasal sides of the two retinae and are therefore ipsilateral and do not overlap: "equilateral or corresponding images." The objects situated behind the common fixation point also produce two images, but these, being on the temporal sides of the two retinae, appear contralateral: "noncorresponding or crossed images." (For further details *see* Figs. 9, 56, 57, 58, 60.)

The direction and the mode of spreading or propagation of the excitations within a complex nervous system depend both on the innate or inherent factors and upon other circumstances, such as the kind or quality, intensity, and temporal duration of the initiating stimulus or excitation, on the condition of the related neurons owing to the preceding stimulation or rest, and the like. The principal factor in this remains the synaptical relationship of the neurons. An excitation from a given neuron may induce a secondary excitation only in that neuron or in those neurons with which it stands in synaptical contact. The other neurons, even those immediately adjoining the activated one, very likely remain entirely at rest, neutral. The elaborateness of the central nervous tissue postulates such a conclusion.

For the reciprocal influencing of the neurons, direct contact in the synapses seems to be a prime requisite. Other contacts, especially those mediated by the insulating myelin and apparently also those established by neuroglia, seem to be of no direct importance. Whether or not there are other relationships of neurons which could be called "distance synapses," there is no certain evidence, even though this remains a possibility that must be further explored. The excitations, then, spread, as far as we know, along the preformed channels represented by the concatenations or sets of neurons.

The initial impression of apparent structural and dynamical chaos reigning in the central nervous organs resolves itself into a firmly knit complexity of the highest order. In it each specialized structural unit performs its own functional role, assigned to it by its position in the synaptical tissue complex. And the function of a particular nervous tissue or locality is the sum total of the particular states of excitations that may be induced or elicited in its constituent neurons.

3. Summary of the neuron theory.—In summary, parts of the visual system, such as the retina, the subcortical visual centers, and the striate area, like the remainder of the nervous system, are composite organs made up of a great number of nerve cells put together according to a certain definite order. These "neurons" are present in numerous well-defined varieties, characterized by their own morphological, biochemical, and functional peculiarities or properties.

The neurons are functionally polarized. Because of this, the excitations normally are propagated from the dendrites or the body to the axon and its terminal ramification, the teledendron.

Each neuron variety possesses its own functional responsiveness or mode of reacting, predetermined partly by its own innate biochemical constitution and partly by its synaptical relationships with other nerve cells or other related structures (receptors, muscles, glands).

All these factors—the results of a long phylogenetical process of differentiation from the originally similar, neuroblast-like nerve cells into structurally and functionally dissimilar types—imply a great deal of structural stability. Even so, the gray nervous masses are not a mere mechanical agglomeration of static elements ruled by purely structural factors but are a living, adaptable, plastic substratum, whose dynamical reactions depend much upon varying extrinsic and intrinsic factors—condition of nutrition, kind and intensity of the external stimuli, the preceding activity, and other more or less fleeting and elusive factors.

This granted, neurodynamics nevertheless is largely governed by anatomical conditions. Whereas dynamical factors influence much of the spreading of the currents of nervous excitations, it is the structures that prescribe along what channels one or another dynamical change, called "nervous current," may or may not be propagated; how it may be subdivided into several secondary currents; or how several discrete currents may fuse into a single stream, as the case may be. If, therefore, no parts of the brain, such as a nucleus, a cortical area, and so forth, may be compared with a machine made up of artfully assembled gadgets, cogs, wheels, gears, or joints always responding in exactly the same way to the same stimulation applied to the same locality, they may respond with a dynamical change now in this way, now in another, only as their intrinsic organization permits.

The complex nervous system of advanced animals is made up of a great number and variety of "neurons" or nerve cells, structurally and functionally independent in varying degree, each variety attuned to respond in its own peculiar way to a particular external or internal stimulus. The nervous system is a "complex or composite whole," its complex structural make-up being the basis of its functional diversity, its unity being maintained by the synaptical connections of its constituent neurons. The nervous tissue may be compared to a "coat of mail," in which each link, a neuron, although a complete individual, has its own definite place in the whole fabric and may fulfil its functional role only as a part of the whole system.

The relative independence of the neurons, their differentiation into a multiplicity of forms, each reacting in its own way; the unidirectional regulation of the currents of excitation; and the diversity of reciprocal connections of the neurons appear as the prerequisites, principles, and tools of the histophysiological organization of the nervous tissue.

Lastly, the "factor of numbers" should be considered. From what has been said, it is clear that this factor alone could be considered irrelevant. Together with the other factors, however, the "factor of numbers" attains its full importance and makes sense of the increase of the number of nerve cells in the nervous system of the higher animal forms. It is one of the principal means by which its structural complexity is increased and hence its functional diversity and efficiency improved.

A complex nervous system is the result of its intricate structure and diverse biochemical and functional constitution. The numerous morphodynamically varying neurons, interlocked with one another in most varied ways through the synaptical connections that regulate the manifold reciprocal influencing, serve, on the one hand, as a substratum of specific, locally restricted functions and, on the other hand, in the aggregate, bring about and guarantee the unity of the entire nervous system of the individual organism.

4. Modifications of the neuron theory. —It is probable that, as our knowledge increases, the present definition of the neuron theory may have to be modified in many respects. Whether, for example, the neurons, as morphological and functional units, are sharply

defined in all parts of the human or animal body or whether in some parts the arrangement approaches a more or less syncytial character needs to be explored further.

Of all parts, the vegetative organs are most likely to show such an arrangement, since their working shows little local variation. However, there is, so far, no positive evidence in favor of such an assumption, and much against it (*see* Kuntz 1953; Fedorow 1935, 1937; Fedorow & Matwejewa 1935; Nonidez 1936–37; Herzog & Günther 1938).

A more "diffuse" nervous system, with the nerve cells retaining their supposedly unpolarized original character, may also more readily be expected in lowly forms than in the highly differentiated classes and orders close to the top of the animal scale. This view was formerly widely accepted under the influence of Apáthy and Bethe (*see* G. H. Parker 1919; Child 1921). Subsequently it has been seriously compromised by Bozler (1927) and by Woollard & Harpman (1939), who found the nervous system of Coelenterates to be synaptical.

The interesting observation made by J. Z. Young (1939) of the fusion of giant axons in the Squid and a similar observation by Glees (1939) of the fused ganglion cells in the selachian spinal cord may more easily be interpreted as an exception of adaptation of the synaptical nervous system to a special function. Both observations, however, require further study.

Other observations, in fact, show the nervous system of the "lower animals," as far as investigated, to be synaptical. In S. Ramón y Cajal's opinion, Insects have the most minutely differentiated nervous system of all animals (*see* Ramón y Cajal 1909, 1915, 1918, 1929–30; Ramón y Cajal & Sánchez 1915; Sánchez y Sánchez 1916, 1919, 1923). In other Invertebrates the nervous system is also synaptical (Sánchez y Sánchez 1909; S. Ramón y Cajal 1916, 1929–30; Droogleever Fortuyn 1920; Hanström 1928).

Even so, while a syncytial nervous system in the lower animals has not been demonstrated, this question must be left open. The work so far done, however, suffices to show the inadmissibility of a wholesale denial of the validity of the "neuron theory" for all nervous tissue, including the central nervous system of Man and of other Higher Vertebrates, as advanced by many reticularists upon questionable evidence obtained from the entrails of a Leech or an Earthworm (Apáthy), from the nervous system of a Crayfish (Bethe), or from the gut of an *Amphioxus* (Boeke).

References: H. W. Altmann 1952; Ariëns Kappers, Huber & Crosby 1936; Barker 1901; larp 1946; W. His 1886 and later; Hoessly 1947; Koelliker 1887, 1896, 1900; Kuntz 1953, p. 54; Lenhossék 1895, 1910, 1935; Levi & Meyer; Neal 1921; Nonidez 1936–37; Parker 1929; Polyak 1941–48; S. Ramón y Cajal 1888–1935; Ramón y Cajal & Sánchez 1915; Ranson & Clark; Retzius 1905, 1908; Rushton 1949, 1950; Sánchez y Sánchez 1909, 1916, 1919, 1923; E. A.

Fig. 349.—Galileo Galilei, the Florentine (1564–1642), the celebrated physicist and astronomer, native of Pisa, Italy, professor of mathematics at Padua and of astronomy at Florence, Italy. Originator of the concept of "force" as an agent of mechanical phenomena and a founder of "mechanics" as a branch of physical science. A forerunner of Newton in celestial mechanics (*see also* Kepler). Constructor of the refracting telescope, which he further improved and first used to study heavenly bodies. Discovered the moon's mountainous surface, the fact that the "Milky Way" is composed of individual stars, the satellites of the planet Jupiter, the rings of the planet Saturn, the seasonal phases of the planet Venus, the sun's spots, and the rotation of the sun around its axis. Investigated by the Inquisition for his adherence to the "heretical" Copernican view of the sun as the center of the solar system and for his opposition to the geocentric concept of Ptolemy. Painting by Subtermans at the Galleria degli Uffizi in Florence, Italy. From P. Capparoni, *Profili bio-bibliografici*, 1928. Courtesy Istituto nazionale medico farmacologico "Serono," Rome, Italy.

Barr 1940; Bartelmez 1915; Bartelmez & Hoerr 1933; Baumgardt 1952; Beccari 1943; Bodian 1937, 1940, 1942; Bozler 1927; Castro 1950, 1951; Chambers 1924; Edinger 1911; Fedorow 1935; Forel 1887; Glees 1939; Haggar & Barr 1950; Harrison 1908–24; Heidenhain 1911; Hilp; Schäfer 1893; Schiefferdecker 1906; Speidel 1932, 1933, 1935; Tello 1931; Tower 1935; Van Gehuchten 1900; Vermes 1905; Waldeyer 1891, 1895; Wilkinson 1930, 1931, 1934; Windle & Clark 1928; Woollard & Harpman 1939; J. Z. Young 1939.

SEC. 4. THE MINUTE ORGANIZATION OF THE NERVOUS CENTERS

1. Similarity and difference between the peripheral and central nervous systems.—The nervous system of advanced animals, such as Vertebrates, is customarily subdivided into two main divisions, peripheral and central.

The peripheral nervous system is made up of numerous, mostly small, accumulations of nerve cells called "ganglions" imbedded in various visceral organs, such as the heart, digestive tract, bladder, and so forth, the most prominent being the prevertebral chain of sympathetic ganglions. These ganglions are interconnected, with one another, with the organs which they supply, and with the brain and spinal cord, by various nerve strands of differing thickness. Other peripheral nerves, cranial and spinal, connect the brain and the spinal cord directly to the muscles, tendons, skin, and the various sense organs.

The central organ is represented by the bulky mass called "brain" or "cerebrum" and the spinal cord. In the peripheral system the conducting nerve fibers, or axons, predominate, whereas the brain and the spinal cord, especially the gray substance of the various nuclei and of the cortex, are largely made up of the bodies or perikarya of nerve cells, their dendritic processes, and the teledendrons or terminal ramifications of the axons.

The difference in intrinsic makeup indicates the difference in function. The peripheral nervous system serves largely to conduct impulses generated in the various internal organs and in the superficial receptors of the skin and of the sense organs to the brain and spinal cord, or from the latter to the peripheral organs of execution, e.g., muscles and glands. The central nervous system, on the contrary, is an organ in which the impulses from the periphery are "integrated" or "processed" into responses appropriate to a particular physiological or biological situation of the individual organism or part of it.

The distinction in the character of the two major subdivisions is only roughly accurate, each serving both conduction and integration to some extent. The numerous sympathetic ganglions of the visceral organs, for example, perform various local tasks by automatically regulating many functions which do not require central control or do so only occasionally and in slight measure. Their activity is largely independent of central control, that is, autonomic. The central organs, especially the brain, receive impulses generated within the body or elicited by the extrasomatic stimuli, out of which arise influences that, directly or indirectly, bring all parts of the organism under a single central authority, thus insuring the life and activity of the organism as a single biological entity.

2. Intrinsic organization of the nervous centers.—Since the basic biological task of the nervous system is to help an individual animal to adjust itself appropriately to its environment, both the conduction and the integration of the nerve impulses are necessary.

In the lowest forms of multicellular animals which possess a differentiated nervous system— the Coelenterates—this system, simple as it is, is nevertheless capable of performing the function of adjustment appropriate to the species. This is noteworthy, since there are no special centers in these primitive animals, their nervous system being made up of a rather uniform plexus of nerve fibers and cells. The cells are here represented by a few varieties only. Their expansions do not merge with one another into a continuous network, as was believed by the neuroreticularists, but are related to one another by true synapses (Bozler 1927; Hanström 1928; Woollard & Harpman 1939). Even in Coelenterates, then, the neurons are neither of a uniform kind nor without an individuality, nor are they put together haphazardly.

On higher levels of the animal scale, with an increased structural and functional complexity, the same basic functions of the nervous system —the conduction and integration of impulses— remain. In fact, the more the functional exigencies of an animal increase, the more complex becomes its nervous system. The most complex arrangement is found in the centers of most advanced animals, irrespective of whether they are Vertebrates, Insects, or Cephalopods. Here the tissue pattern is not only highly differentiated but varies much from place to place. Even in the same locality, several varieties of neurons intermingle and are synaptically tied to one another in different ways. The only general principle observed in all nervous centers is an arrangement permitting the passage of dynamical changes or influences from neuron to neuron.

The way in which the neurons of a nerve center are able to influence one another or other nonnervous tissues in most cases is by direct contact. An influencing by neurohumors secreted by some nerve cells and by other tissues or by the bioelectrical currents acting at a distance, while possible, requires further investigation (Parker 1930; Scharrer 1940, 1941; R. W. Gerard 1941).

It is obvious that the greatest number of orderly, well-organized contacts may be achieved in a synaptical nervous center where its neurons, especially their perikarya, are assembled in a small space and in compact groups. Such a concentration of nerve cells gives greater possibility of establishing numerous reciprocal relationships with the expenditure of the least quantity of matter. Limited space and therefore shortness of cellular processes by which such contact relationships are established likewise help the economy of time.

In a centralized nervous system, all other factors being equal, a greater number and variety of nervous influences may spread in less time to elicit responses more locally and qualitatively diversified than would be possible in a scattered arrangement, with fewer neurons and fewer neuron varieties and with greater distances between. The greater functional efficiency resulting from the economy of matter, space, and time is clearly the principal advantage in the phylogenetical creation and perfection of the centralized nervous system, especially of the nerve centers. (*See* S. Ramón y Cajal 1909–11, v. 1, pp. 1 ff.; *also* some of his other publications.)

A histological examination of the white substance of the brain and spinal cord shows it to be composed largely or entirely of the conducting nerve fibers or axons. Here no essential modification of the transmitted impulses takes place except such as may be due to a division of the axons into branches. But no change of "quality" or "intensity" and no "transformation" are possible. The gray matter, on the contrary, is organized in such a way as to permit precisely this kind of change in endless variety. Here take place the various subtle processes that may only inadequately be described as "selection," "division," "intensification," "transformation," "inhibition," and the like of the incoming peripheral impulses, and from here the elicited responses are sent back to the periphery. This greater activity of the gray matter is reflected also in its better blood supply, suggesting a higher rate of metabolism compared with the white substance.

The mode of the reciprocal relationships of neurons, according to the neuron theory, is determined by their dynamical polarity. The terminal axonal ramifications of one neuron variety are in contact with the surface of the body of one or several related neurons or are entangled with their dendrites in a definite way, quite specific for each particular neuron variety.

In routinely stained preparations, little may be seen or guessed of the abundance of the true relations of neurons. The gray substance of the cerebral cortex, for example, appears to be composed of a great number of nerve cells varying in shape, size, and distribution, arranged mostly in parallel layers. Between the layers and the individual cells the intercellular substance has a dotted or stippled look, and because of this it was given the name "punctate substance" (Leydig) and *neuropil* or *neuropilem* (W. His). Subsequently, this mysterious substance was revealed, with the help of the histoanalytical methods of Golgi, Ehrlich, Cajal, and others, to be an extremely complicated plexus or tangle, a plexiform substance (Heidenhain 1911) made up of countless, mostly unmyelinated, preterminal and terminal nervous branches and nodules, imbedded within the framework of neuroglial tissue.

The plexiform substance is one of the principal features of the gray matter. In localities where the segregation of cell bodies from the plexiform substance formed by their expansions is complete or almost so, as in the superficial plexiform layer of the cerebral and cerebellar cortex and, above all, in the outer and inner plexiform layers of the retina, these layers are composed practically exclusively of the naked, unmyelinated expansions of neurons. Since the synaptical contacts of the adjoining neurons take place in these plexiform layers, they have been quite appropriately named "synaptical fields," or layers, by C. J. Herrick (1934).

3. Dynamical factors responsible for the complex organization of nervous centers.—A complex intrinsic organization of nerv-

The situation would be improved but little if a dynamical change generated in one neuron were transmitted directly to other neurons, though these belonged to different varieties. In a nerve center thus organized, there would be little variation in dynamical change, called "excitation," spreading from cell to cell. It is more appropri-

Fig. 350.—Isaac Newton (1642–1727), celebrated English natural philosopher, mathematician, and physicist. Author of the *Principia* (1687) and of the *Opticks* (1704). Originator of the corpuscular or emission theory of light (in contrast with Huygens' wave theory of light *see* Fig. 351). Laid the foundation for the trichromatic theory of color perception (*see* Thomas Young and Helmholtz, Figs. 352, 356). Engraving by E. Scriven, from the original by Vanderbank in possession of the Royal Society of London. Courtesy Professor J. F. Fulton, of Yale University, New Haven, Conn. (*Cf. also* Fig. 76.)

ous centers is an indispensable condition for their functional diversity.

A center made up of a single neuron variety, with neurons whose individuality was largely or entirely suppressed, could do little in modulating a dynamical current "passing" through it.

ate, therefore, to assume that an excitation when reaching the point of contact does not pass over directly to the related neuron but merely "elicits" or "induces" in the latter a dynamical change that is not entirely identical with the eliciting stimulus.

Each elicited dynamical state is necessarily limited to the territory of a particular neuron. There are, at least potentially, as many elicitable dynamical states as there are individual neurons. These states may be similar in neurons of the same variety, and different in different varieties. The similarity of dynamical states of excitation may be compared with the similarity or identity of functional manifestations and is the expression of an innate organization of a particular neuron variety.

The "quality" of a dynamical response, accordingly, is an inherent "specific functional property" of a neuron variety, different from that of all other neuron varieties of a given nervous center.

The quantitative response or "intensity" may largely depend upon the intensity of the initiating stimulus and upon other extraneous factors, such as the duration of the stimulus, the number of related neurons, and so forth.

If the stimulating neuron is related to several neurons belonging to a single variety, as many new individual dynamical states may be released, even though all of them are of the same kind. If the stimulated neurons belong to different varieties, there are as many new states of dynamical change that vary from one another in their "qualities."

Figuratively, a complex nerve center may be compared to an electrical apparatus composed of many minute "closed circuits" related to one another according to the principle of primary and secondary induction coils. As in the secondary coils, so in the related neurons, the current does not derive directly from the primary neuron but is merely "elicited" by it. Likewise, as in the secondary coil, the current further depends in its properties upon such factors as material, thickness of wire, number of turns, distance between the primary and secondary coils, and so forth; so in a system of neurons the secondary, tertiary, and following chains of successively elicited states of excitation depend upon the number and variety of neurons, the way in which these are synaptically related to one another, their functional condition, the kind and intensity of the original stimulus, and probably other factors as yet little appreciated.

A complex nerve center made up of numerous individual neurons belonging to many different varieties related to one another by synapses implies innumerable potential combinations of states of excitation elicited either by external stimuli or by impulses originating within the organism itself. As the excitation spreads in such a center across the synaptical contacts from neuron to neuron, its nature changes with each new neuron variety activated, its path being determined partly by the pre-existing neuron relationships and partly by the various dynamical factors. In this way different sets of neurons are put into action. Translated into the language of neurophysiology, this may be interpreted as "analysis," or the opposite, as "merging," "combination," or "fusion" of excitations, or their "intensification," "facilitation," or "decrease in intensity," which, when complete, is called "blocking," "extinguishing," or "inhibition," and the like.

References: E. Baumgardt 1952; S. J. Holmes 1944; Lenhossék 1895, 1910; Polyak 1941–48; S. Ramón y Cajal 1909–11, 1934, 1935.

SEC. 5. THE STRUCTURE OF THE NEURON SYNAPSES AND THEIR PROBABLE FUNCTION

1. GENERAL REMARKS CONCERNING THE FACTORS INVOLVED IN THE WORKING OF THE SYNAPSES.—When the dynamical equilibrium of a neuron is disturbed by an outside stimulus, this "excitation" apparently spreads over all its parts, including its farthest ramifications. The spreading of an excitation within the neuron is a process requiring short, even though measurable, time (*see* Adrian 1935, esp. chap. V). The changed dynamical state is confined to the territory or substance of the stimulated neuron, leaving adjoining, but unrelated, neurons undisturbed. Roughly, such an excitation may be considered a uniform or homogeneous process, specific for the particular neuron variety and intrinsically independent of the possible or actual states of excitation of all other neurons.

The varying size, shape, number, distribution, and chemical composition of the chromophile granules, the different number, thickness, and arrangement of the dendrites and their "spines," and many other subtle features suggest that the parts of the same neuron are functionally not equivalent. The cytoplasmic core of the perikaryon containing the nucleus, the cortical zone of the perikaryon forming its superficial shell, the axon fiber with its collaterals, and the teledendron, all indicate different dynamical conditions, as already implied by the thesis of "dynamic polarity." Even more subtle local differences at the various points of the active surface of a neuron are indicated by the visible structures and their relationships: e.g., various terminal twigs and buttons in contrast with the main shaft of the same dendrite, and so forth. The neurofibrils again, where present, imply a specific functional differentiation.

The afore-mentioned differences in structural detail indicate dynamic diversity at the various synaptical points. The changes in the dynamical state of a neuron elicited through these points may, therefore, in considerable degree depend upon a particular surface point at which a synaptical contact is established (which in turn means that each particular dynamical state to be transmitted requires its own structural organelles and relationship with other neurons).

The synaptical contacts of the related neurons appear to be quite diversified and yet at the same time very stable. A particular neuron variety is found always to favor a particular mode of synapse with another particular neuron variety, its terminal branches touching it always at the same points, the few exceptions merely emphasizing the strictness of the rule. This evidence indicates, first, that different points of the active surface of a neuron are ultramicroscopically, and hence functionally, differently organized and, second, that homologous surface points in different individuals of the same neuron variety possess the same organization and functional affinities and hence exert the same or a similar influence upon the homologous points of the related neurons.

As an illustration of the foregoing statements, it suffices to call attention to the delicate dendritic filaments of a mop bipolar (*d*) of the primate retina which are always found adhering to the lateral sides of the cone pedicles (*b*), and never to the latter's vitreal faces; whereas a dendritic rosette or bouquet of a midget bipolar (*h*) exhibits precisely the opposite relationship (colored Figs. 177, 178, 179). Mechanical factors alone, quite obviously, would never have been able to enforce such strict structural conformity. The only recourse in explaining such subtle and precise structural differentiation is through an assumption of the working of some as yet wholly unknown forces upon which the phylogenetical evolution and ontogenetical development of all animals ultimately depend.

The surface of a neuron, accordingly, is not uniformly organized or dynamically equivalent. This is true not only of the global difference between the dendrites and the axon but also of the relative functional values of different points of each dendrite, of the surface of a perikaryon, and of a teledendron. The influences which are emitted through the various points of a teledendron or are received through different localities of the same dendrite are, accordingly, not of the same kind but vary in nature. Different dynamical states induced in different varieties of related neurons differ not only because of their varying innate properties but also because the influences through which they are elicited are received through differently organized synapses. This holds whether the source of the influence is different, in the retina, for example, whether it is represented by both the rods and the cones, or whether it is the same, e.g., represented by the cones alone.

2. THE NEURON, A COMPLEX FUNCTIONAL ORGANISM.—The structural features of the nerve cells and their functional properties indicate that each neuron is a complex microcosmic organism possessing differentiated organelles, each specialized to perform a distinct function.

In the particular instance of the retinal cones of Primates, where the synaptical relations are very clear, an accurate analysis of the situation may be made (*see* afore-mentioned colored figures). Anatomically each cone is related to every bipolar variety (*d, e, f, h*) and also to the horizontal cells (*c*). The synapses, all concentrated at the vitreal end or pedicle of the cone, homologous to a teledendron, are quite specific for each variety of related neurons. An examination of the possible spread of a dynamical disturbance elicited in the bacillary part of the cone cell by the action of physical light and of the possible ways by which the related neurons may be influenced shows the following possibilities.

First, if the disturbance under a given set of conditions, e.g., when the stimulating light is of single wave length, is imagined as a process spreading uniformly over the entire cone cell, to two particular synapses, e.g., to the mop bipolars (d), all types of synapses (c, d, e, f, h) are exposed to the influence of that particular cone process. The selection of a particular synaptical "exit" or "egress" along which the cone process influences one or perhaps two or more related neurons must, then, depend upon the organization of the particular synapse which makes it

CHRISTIANUS HUGENIUS
natus 14 Aprilis 1629.
denatus 8 Junii 1695.

FIG. 351.—Christiaan Huygens or Huyghens van Zulichem, of the Netherlands (1629–95), mathematician, physicist, and astronomer. Founder of the "wave theory of light" and discoverer of the basic laws of refraction upon which modern optics is built. Author of the *Treatise on Light* (1678–90). Improved construction of optical instruments, especially the telescope. First described construction of an artificial eye (1654) and declared the crystalline lens responsible for the accommodation of the eye for near vision. Frontispiece engraving by F. Ottens from Huygens' *Opera Varia*, v. 1, 1724.

including all parts of the pedicle and its barbules, it is necessary to postulate that it reaches all synaptical points unchanged. Unless there are within the cone itself certain preformed, discrete intraneuronal structures (so far not found), directing that particular process to only one or "passable" for that particular cone process, while the other synapses remain "closed" or "blocked."

It must further be assumed that the synaptical "permeability" or "impermeability" is also partly conditioned by the innate specific responsiveness, or lack of it, of the particular bipolar variety to a particular dynamical state of the cone, according to the principle of "functional neuron specificity." When the nature of a cone disturbance caused by the stimulus of a different wave length changes, it again spreads over the entire cone cell, potentially stimulating all synapses, but actually finding a free exit in only one or another differently organized from that synapse which was passable for the first monochromatic cone process. When the stimulus is a combination of several wave lengths acting simultaneously, a process within the cone is a combination of several simple, monochromatic excitations, or a compound process, in any case spreading over the entire cone; in this case most or all synapses may be passable for it, each "taking" from the common source that component to which it is attuned. Seen in this way, the nature of a nervous stimulus (e.g., a cone process), just like the nature of the original physical stimulus (e.g., wave length), is one factor upon which the elicited dynamic state depends, the other being the specific organization of the synapses at the discharging end of the cone cell and the specific responsiveness of the related neuron varieties.

Similar organizational principles are likely to be found in other parts of the nervous system, if due consideration is taken of the special functional requirements of particular local structures.

3. STRUCTURE OF THE SYNAPSE.—The precise structure of the minute surfaces through which the neurons are in contact remains unknown. There is, however, sufficient information, direct and circumstantial, to make it possible to form some idea of its organization.

The terminations of neuron expansions, by which they are functionally connected with one another, appear under the microscope in many forms. Usually they are shaped like minute swellings, buds, globules, or nodules at the very ends of the terminal twigs of teledendric ramifications or of dendrites. They vary considerably in size and shape, some being rather large, chunky, irregular varicosities with angular edges; others being minute, dainty, more or less regular, spherical nodules or buds, clearly visible only with the help of high-power Ultropak

oil-immersion objectives (giving a total magnification of 1,000×, 1,500×, and more). Still others appear as delicate terminal filaments, with their very ends barely perceptibly swollen. Their numbers also vary much in different neuron varieties or parts of these, some types being sparsely strung along the thicker branches, others hanging in clusters and bunches of various shapes, frequently assembled into bouquets, rosettes, compact or loose baskets, and the like. There is practically no end to the forms which these "synaptical organelles" may assume in the complex nervous system of an advanced animal, and an even greater variation is found in certain species of animals (*see* Bodian's figures). Even so, it is obvious that the synaptical organelles so far described are only a small fraction of the existing ones.

In this exceeding variability there is, however, one stable feature: each particular neuron variety is always distinguished by synaptical organelles specific for this variety. That is, the homologous organelles found in different individuals of a particular animal species, in identical parts of the nervous system, are always of precisely the same size, shape, number, and arrangement. The deviations from this rule seem to be fewer, the higher the phylogenetical status of a species and the higher the functional requirement of a particular organ or part of an organ. In the primate retina, for example, the highest conformity is found in the central area next to the foveal depression; less, away from it, with an increasing irregularity as the distant periphery closer to the ora serrata is examined. Again, the homologous neurons in kindred animal species possess organelles of similar types, even though these are not exactly identical—for example, in Man, Chimpanzee, Macaque, Sparrow, Pike, etc.

The impression gained from extensive study of various animal species suggests an extreme diversity of the synaptical organelles as one of the foremost factors of the functional organization of the nervous system. There is an extensive field open here for future research.

The synaptical organelles, no matter whether they are smaller or larger varicosities, irregular chunks, smooth spherules, or filamentous tendrils of various shapes and sizes, are practically always found in direct contact with the surface of a related neuron. The area of contact, however, varies much: it may be large in the voluminous varicosities and minute in delicate filaments. Sometimes a large preterminal varicosity, which otherwise may appear as a terminal swelling, sends off a minute twig or nodule which alone touches the surface of a related neuron.

The impression from such instances is that, while a direct contact, no matter how minute, is necessary, the larger preterminal swelling, even though not in direct contact, may nevertheless play a role in the transmission of influences, possibly through the surrounding liquid medium. In any case, in most synapses direct contact is found.

There is no clear evidence of the presence of a special "glue," a kind of undifferentiated intervening "synaptical membrane," a *ciment unitif* or *c. intercalaire*, formerly thought by S. Ramón y Cajal and some other investigators to separate the active surfaces of the two related neurons (on organization of protoplasmic surfaces *see* R. Chambers *et al.* 1950).

The absence of such a living or dead "membranous" sheet and the presence of a direct contact are quite favorable to the transmission of functional influences from neuron to neuron. This harmonizes well with the "neuron theory" and invalidates Boeke's claim, because of the absence of a *ciment unitif*, to dismiss the entire neuron concept or to mix it up into a self-contradictory hypothesis of a "synaptical syncytium."

The observation that an infinitesimal "dead interval" may not always block the passage of influences (Erlanger 1939) and the afore-mentioned participation of larger varicosities in a synaptical contact suggest that in certain instances an intervening space does not necessarily block the synaptical transmission.

In the overwhelming majority of the synaptical arrangements investigated, however, a direct contact of the surfaces of two living substances of the related neurons is found, with no space or extraneous structures intervening. Such points of contact are likewise bare of any neuroglial sheaths, shells, or encasings that otherwise envelop the perikarya and processes of neurons, as described elsewhere (chap. V, 8; chap. VIII, 7). At the points of synaptical contacts all obstacles are done away with, in order to facilitate free influencing of one neuron by another. This is in perfect harmony with complete insulation either by the neuroglial sheaths or by myelin of all other parts of the neurons, such as most of the perikarya and the larger dendrites and axons; without this, the neural energy would become dissipated, annulling the very purpose of an intricate structure of nervous organs.

The synaptical connections and relational arrangements in a complex nervous tissue point to an extremely delicate channeling of the nervous streams and influences, prevented by insulation where their passage would be harmful and permitted and facilitated at the synaptical points where their effect is useful and therefore desirable.

The exact place of contact where the substance of a teledendron of the influencing neuron meets the substance of a body or dendrite of another neuron that is to be influenced has been thought of as a "two-faced" or "interface membrane." Here the two neuron bodies are contiguous, closely pressed to each other, forming in many instances a true adhesion or concrescence. This locality may, in a sense, be considered a single film. The two sides of the film are biochemically and biophysically differently organized and are therefore dynamically polarized.

Something of this dissimilarity of the minute organization of the two sides of the synaptical membrane belonging to two related neurons has been well presented by Bartelmez (1915), Bartelmez & Hoerr (1933), and especially by Bodian (1937, 1939, 1940, 1942; *see also* Maximow & Bloom's *Textbook of Histology*, 3d ed.). Particularly instructive in these presentations are the colossal club endings of vestibular fibers in the fish brain, measuring up to 7 microns in diameter. In each club several distinct neurofibrils may be seen. They are sharply stained, discrete and parallel, nonanastomosing threads, each terminating with a slight swelling which ends abruptly very close to the synaptical surface of the club. The neurofibrils and their swollen terminations remain confined to the territory of their own club, that is, to their own neuron. They do not pass across the "synaptical membrane" over into the substance of the related neuron, as is claimed by the reticularist school, in spite of the intimacy of contact of the two related neurons. In the body of the related neuron to which the giant club endings adhere, the neurofibrils are much finer, have a different course, and are arranged differently. Clearly, the neurofibrils of the two related neurons rep-

All these details show that, at the point of a synaptical contact, the substances of two related neurons, precisely because of their dissimilarity, may be considered to be in a state of "unstable balance." This condition may easily be upset and transformed into a "state of disequilibrium," resulting in a transmission of in-

Fig. 352.—Thomas Young (1773–1829), founder of modern physiological optics, at the age of forty-nine. In the words of his biographer: "A physician, a linguist, an antiquary, a mathematician, scholar, and philosopher, in their most difficult and abstruse investigations, has added to almost every department of human knowledge that which will be remembered to aftertimes." Student of ocular dioptrics, discoverer of astigmatism of the eye. Made an attempt to explain accommodation of the eye for near and distant vision with the help of the changing form of the crystalline lens. Originator of the earliest consistent theory of color vision, later developed by Helmholtz into the "trichromatic theory of color perception." Discoverer of "interference of light" through which the wave theory of light, proposed by Hooke and Huygens, was advanced (against Newton's "corpuscular" or "emanation" concept). First measured the limits of the fields of view. Frontispiece from Peacock, *Life of Thomas Young*, engraved in copper by G. R. Ward, from a painting by Sir Thomas Lawrence, F.R.A.

resent two different, structurally discontinuous systems. The most superficial layer of the axoplasm of the club also stains somewhat differently, indicating a different chemical composition.

fluence or "excitation" across the synaptical membrane to the related neuron.

4. The nature of the influences transmitted across the synaptical "membrane."

—The precise nature of the physical and chemical processes and the identity of substances involved in the transmission of influences or "excitations" across the synaptical membrane still remain little known. According to one hypothesis, the synaptical membrane is semipermeable, permitting negative "ions" to pass over from one side to the other, while preventing similar passage to the positive "ions." Another opinion claims the secretion of a special chemical substance—acetylcholine—which would act as a stimulus for the related neuron. Whatever the actual process, it resembles catalytic surface phenomena essential to all life (J. Alexander 1948), which recalls Haeckel's "monera" or first living things proposed long ago, indicative of the "surface" as a basis of life's processes in general.

Speaking figuratively, it seems that there is not so much an actual passage of a material substratum or a direct transmission of nervous excitation as rather an emanation of a certain imponderable "influence" as yet to be precisely defined in terms of microdynamics. In support of this view an example of a relationship may be cited where a bulky neuron is under the influence of a neuron of diminutive size. If in this a principle similar to that valid in physical mechanics obtained, a minute rod cell (a) of the retina would hardly be expected to influence a large garland ganglion (p) or a parasol ganglion (m) through the equally diminutive bipolar cells (d, e, f).

Such examples indicate that a trans-synaptic influencing across a chain of neurons is not directly proportional to the initial stimulus and must be determined largely by other factors. One of these factors appears to be the kind and quantity of "latent energy" stored up in the related neuron. This again depends upon the inherent factors specific for each neuron variety. The "influence" passing through a synaptical membrane, then, acts as a suitable "fuse" or "trigger" which merely "releases" this energy, transforming it into a manifest, active process, or, in the language of modern neurophysiology, it "fires" the latent charge of the neuron.

The amount and kind of the response, accordingly, is greatly determined by the responsive capacity of the influenced neuron, in addition to the various qualities of the initiating stimulation. In other words, each neuron is capable of responding only within the limits of its own innate properties or inherent capacities.

Another determining synaptical factor is the size of the contact area. It appears probable that, if all other factors are equal, the volume of the influence ultimately manifested as "intensity" in an elicited response must be greater when the synaptical contact is more extensive. The very restricted contact between a rod spherule and a delicate dendritic filament of a mop bipolar (a & d synapse), for example, obviously represents a "bottleneck" offering greater resistance than does a relatively wider contact between a cone pedicle and a dendritic "rosette" or "bouquet" of its related midget bipolar (b & h synapse).

But the extent of the actual contact alone, undoubtedly, is not the whole story, as the last-mentioned synapse shows. In this, each "bouquet" represents a group of minute terminal buttons closely packed together and attached to the vitreal face of a cone pedicle. If the scleral expansion of a midget bipolar were a solid disk, as was held by S. Ramón y Cajal, its contact area with the cone pedicle would necessarily be somewhat larger. As it actually is, the tiny spherules making up the "bouquet" are in part separated by minute spaces within which the fluid content of the tissue may freely circulate.

The advantage accruing from this, expressed in terms of microdynamics, may only be guessed. Possibly, the surface of the terminal dendritic spherules not in direct contact with the pedicle also participates in some way in the transmission of synaptical influence. Thus the active surface of the synapse would, in fact, be made greater, provided that the minute gaps between the surfaces of the related neurons were not an obstacle for the passage of trans-neuronal influences, as already discussed. The quality of the influence a midget bipolar receives from the cone via the sides of the spherules of its "bouquet" may likewise in some way differ from the quality of the same influence passing through the minute areas where the spherules are firmly attached to the pedicle.

A further important factor in shaping the quality and quantity of influence transmitted across the synapses is the locality of the contacts. To use the preceding example, the vitreal face of a cone pedicle, obviously, is dynamically not equivalent with its sides. The only plausible interpretation, very clearly expressed in actual structures, is that the influence using the vitreal face of the pedicle as an exit is quite different from the influence emanating from the lateral sides.

Another similar instance is the synapse between the vitreal expansion of a midget bipolar and the basket-shaped dendritic termination of a midget ganglion (*h* & *s* synapse). This coupling represents dynamically quite a different route from the single-point contact between a teledendric twig of an *e* or *f* bipolar and the main dendritic stem of the same midget ganglion (*e* & *s* or *f* & *s* synapses). Similar contrasts among the synaptical arrangements are found everywhere and are the essence of the organization of the nervous system.

In conclusion, the kind and amount of response elicited in a related neuron depend upon several factors: the kind, intensity, duration, order of application, and so forth, of the initiating stimulus; the kind and amount of the latent charge of the influenced neuron; the condition of the influenced neuron, e.g., whether or not it was subjected to a previous stimulation; and last, but not least, the particular synaptical arrangement. (*Cf.* Lenhossék 1895, p. 81; S. Ramón y Cajal 1909–11.)

5. FUNCTIONAL POLARITY OF THE SYNAPSE.— According to Cajal's classical neuron theory, the body or perikaryon and its protoplasmic expansions or dendrites are functionally receptive parts of a neuron; the axis cylinder, with its collateral branches and terminal arborization or teledendron, is the emissive part. A neuron is a dynamically polarized functional unit capable of being influenced at one end and able to transmit its own influence at the other end. A neuron remains inert or refractory to the influences working in the opposite direction.

From physiological experiments it appears that the cause of this functional polarity is not a property of the cytoplasm of a perikaryon or of the substance of dendrites or of an axon but is conditioned by some ultramicroscopic organization of the synapses. It is the points of synaptical juncture that regulate the unidirectional

spreading of the dynamical disturbance called "excitation" from the teledendron of the influencing neuron to the dendrites and body of the influenced neuron.

The action of the synapses may be likened to the working of the valves in a system of pipes, permitting the flow in one direction and preventing it in another, the pipes themselves otherwise being passable for the circulating medium in any direction.

According to this view, the polarity of the synapses is the basis of functional neuron polarity and is thus one of the principal factors contributing to the complex organization of the nervous system. It is almost unnecessary to mention that the true causes of the functional polarity of a synapse, which could be expressed in terms of the basic sciences of microphysics, biochemistry, and electrophysiology, remain as yet unknown or are speculative.

An attentive study of the minute relationships of neurons, especially during their period of development, indicates that originally any point of the surface of a young neuron may possess potentialities for influencing both ways, out of which, by a process of "specialization," the final irreversible forms of fully differentiated one-way synapses evolve. The structural-functional differentiation and specialization, in turn, exert a profound influence upon the entire form and function of the neuron. From the young neuroblast cells in the early period of embryonic growth, which all appear similar in size and shape and are endowed with about equal universal potentialities, they produce an infinity of forms and relationships required by an infinity of special functions. The mature neurons of advanced animals, such as the Vertebrates, Insects, and higher Cephalopods, appear in this interpretation as the final product of phylogenetic and ontogenetic differentiation, under the influence of molding forces impossible as yet to define in terms of biochemistry and biophysics.

6. STABILITY OR PLASTICITY OF THE SYNAPSES.—The question of how stable or permanent the synaptical relationships are may be answered only conditionally. The fact that in the highly differentiated tissue of an advanced animal species, such as the primate retina or striate area, the various neurons are always found synaptically joined in precisely the same way, even though our technique of investigation may vary in detail, suggests practically a firm, permanent condition. The forces or dynamical factors which underlie the functional plasticity of such tissues are of an order beyond the resolving capacity of the ordinary optical apparatus.

The stable neuron relationships of a complex nervous tissue are a final result of the conditions

W. His, S. Ramón y Cajal, Harrison, and Speidel.

Whether anything of the original universal plasticity, comparable to the ameboid movement, is preserved in the mature nervous tissue, as had been suggested by Rabl-Rückhardt (1890) and by M. Duval (1895, 1900) and was contemplated by S. Ramón y Cajal is a matter for further research. In the retina of Lower Vertebrates, especially Fishes, the presence of

Fig. 353.—Immanuel Kant (1724–1804), professor of logic and metaphysics at Königsberg (now Kaliningrad), East Prussia. Metaphysician, transcendental philosopher, and naturalist. Author of the *Critique of Pure Reason* and founder of "critical philosophy." Sketch by Peché, from a painting by Doebler, 1791. From München. med. Wchnschr., v. 80, 1933. (*See also* Reichenbach in same volume.)

obtaining during embryonic growth. This presupposes a great deal of plasticity. Without freedom of the embryonic neuroblasts to move about, to send expansions in various directions, and to retract them, growth of the gray substance would not be possible. This view is uniformly supported by the histological evidence with fixed and stained tissue and by the observations of the living, growing nerves in tissue cultures and in the animal body furnished by

the "photomechanical response," discovered in the pigment epithelium by Boll (1877) and by Kühne (1877) and in the photoreceptor cells by Engelmann (1885), Van Genderen Stort (1887), and Lederer (1908), is a well-established fact (*see* Garten 1907; Arey 1915, 1916, 1919, 1928; Detwiler 1943). It is possible, therefore, that in the mature tissue in certain localities of the nervous system a modicum of the original plastic conditions remains. This question must be left open until more observations are gathered.

References: Adrian 1928 ff.; J. Alexander 1948; Ariëns Kappers 1917; Ariëns Kappers, Huber & Crosby 1936; Barnes & Beutner 1941; Barr 1940; Bartelmez & Hoerr 1933; Baumgardt 1952; Beutner & Barnes 1946; Bodian 1937 ff.; Bronk 1939; H. S. Burr 1943; F. de Castro 1950, 1951; Chambers 1924; Chambers *et al.* 1950; Eccles 1953; Erlanger 1939; Forbes 1936, 1939; Gasser 1939; R. W. Gerard 1931; Herzog & Günther 1938; R. S. Lillie 1932; Lorente de Nó 1938, 1939 ff.; Lucas & Adrian 1917; K. H. Meyer 1937; Monnier 1936; Muralt 1946; Polyak 1941–48; A. M. Shanes 1952; J. Z. Young 1937; Young & Coons 1945; also consult various papers in *Cold Spring Harbor Symposia*, v. 4, and in *Tr. Faraday Soc.*, v. 33, pp. 911 ff.

On the structure of synapse, synaptic organelles, etc., see numerous papers in *Trab. lab. invest. biol. Madrid*, published by S. Ramón y Cajal, and in *Biol. Untersuch.*, N.F., published by G. Retzius; see further S. Ramón y Cajal's *Histologie du système nerveux*, 1909–11; same author's papers 1934 and 1935; books and papers by Golgi, Dogiel, Gehuchten, Lenhossék, Bartelmez 1915, and C. J. Herrick's numerous publications.

SEC. 6. THE NEURON RELATIONSHIPS IN GENERAL

1. The synaptical grouping of the neurons.—The relative functional independence and functional specificity and the dynamic polarity of the nerve cells, according to the neuron theory, are essential for the organization of a complex nervous system and its working. These properties enable the neurons to associate in functional sets, synaptically interconnected among themselves and with other sets, in exceedingly varied systems. The study of the group relationships of neurons makes it possible to understand the functional significance of the elaborate structure of the various nervous organs, the functional role of the many neuron varieties, the significance of their varied relationships, the purpose of the agglomeration of nerve cells, and the very sense and purpose of the complex organization of the nerve centers in general.

In the case of a simple nervous system, e.g., of the Coelenterates, and probably in some reflex arcs of the Vertebrates, the pathway along which the nervous excitation is propagated from the peripheral receptors across the centers to the terminal effectors, such as the muscles or glands, can easily be outlined and the function of the whole mechanism understood: an immediate motor adjustment of the individual organism or a part of it to a particular biological situation through central integration (*see* Fig. 223 representing the pupillary reflex arc).

The problem becomes much more difficult in case of a complex peripheral receptor, such as the retina or cochlea, connected with an even more complex central organ, the brain. Here the tracing of an excitation is, for ordinary methods, soon lost in the labyrinth of structures. In order to unravel the functional significance of the structure of these organs, the first step to be made, obviously, is to examine the synaptical relationships of the peripheral receptors, the photoreceptors, or, in the cochlea, the hair cells.

2. Synaptical relationships of a peripheral photoreceptor. If, from a complex texture of the human or simian retina a cone cell is singled out, it becomes apparent that each cone is synaptically related to all three or four bipolar varieties (*b & d* and *e, f, h* synapses; cf. colored Fig. 179). If we further disregard the possibility that each cone may be related to several of each diffuse bipolar variety, this gives three or four distinct channels into which the excitation from a single cone may be diverted: *b & d, b & e, b & f, b & h* relationships.

Since each bipolar variety, according to the concept of the "functional specificity of the neuron," is capable of responding dynamically only in its own specific way, a cone excitation may in this way elicit three or four distinct dynamic reactions on the bipolar level. When, further, the connections of the same bipolars to the ganglion cells are examined, it is found that each midget ganglion is related to every bipolar variety, duplicating their cone relationships: *s & d, s & e, s & f, s & h* synapses. Here, then, the effect is reversed; the three or four distinct bipolar channels merge into a single midget ganglion cell channel (if other relationships are for the moment disregarded).

These are the actual anatomical facts. The puzzling question is: Why should a dynamical process, which on the cone level appears to be single, require on the bipolar level a separation into three or four distinct dynamical states, seemingly for no other purpose than to merge again into a single dynamical state on the ganglion level? This situation seems to make little sense. Neither on logical grounds nor considering a manifest tendency of the organism to economize with matter, space, and time is such useless luxury probable. Obviously, other factors qualifying the apparent situation are involved.

3. Functional significance of the intermediary neurons.

—Of the probable factors requiring an insertion of a triple or quadruple neuronal link between the cone and the midget ganglion, the first to be considered is the cone excitation. Under the action of light of different wave lengths the elicited cone reaction may vary. It is necessary to postulate this, irrespective of whether the assumption is made of several distinct photosensitive substances or of a single one; in the latter case the various cone excitations may be regarded as shadings of a single photochemical process. (The view of the identical responsiveness of the cones is based upon a conviction that all cones in any one particular restricted retinal area are of the same variety and possess identical function; see chap. V, 3 [3], 9 [5].)

Since the excitations of the cone are not transmitted directly to the brain, it is obvious that in a raw, unprocessed state they are not fit to evoke subjective color sensations according to different wave lengths of stimulating light. For this, co-operation of the bipolars is evidently necessary. It stands to reason that the interpolation of several varieties of bipolars between the cone and the midget ganglion imparts to the excitation certain attributes not possessed by the original cone process or processes. The "passage" through the bipolars must, in some way, make the cone process different. This transformation cannot possibly consist in a mere increase of intensity, since this could be as well achieved by an increase in the number of a

single bipolar variety. The specific attributes added to the cone excitations as they "pass" through the bipolar links of the chain of retinal neurons may be described as "qualities."

According to the concept of "functional neuron specificity," no cone excitation, in fact, is directly transmitted to the bipolars. What takes place is an eliciting or evoking of as many various excitations as there are varieties of bipolars. These bipolar states, even though in their quality, intensity, and duration they are causally strictly commensurate with the particular cone processes, are nevertheless distinct dynamical events dependent upon their inherent properties. Each bipolar, while reacting to a particular cone excitation, is capable of doing so only in the particular way prescribed by the limits of its own innate property. Each bipolar process, even though elicited by the cone, is an individual dynamical event. Briefly, each bipolar variety most closely specifically attuned to a particular dynamical state of the cone may respond to that particular stimulus either alone or with a minimum response of the other associated bipolar varieties.

The bipolar excitation, when "transmitted" to its related midget ganglion, passes to the brain as a disturbance of a particular kind. The brain messages originating in a single cone vary, then, according to which of its related bipolars was activated. If it was only one, the message has the character of that particular bipolar. In case of a combination of several or all bipolars, the message is a result of the activation of all bipolars.

Dynamical states elicited in the related midget ganglion vary among themselves and are distinct also from the cone processes by which they have been originated. Even when all bipolars have been simultaneously activated, the compound excitation in the related midget ganglion cell is a dynamical process different from the initiating cone process.

4. Modification of the nervous activity by the intermediary neuronal links.

—The preceding example shows how an excitation deriving from a common source (cone) elicits one or several distinct dynamical states in the intermediate link (bipolars), which, in turn, elicit an excitatory reaction in the final common pathway (midget ganglion).

Within the ganglion link, again, each state is a distinct dynamical event commensurate in quality or specificity, intensity, and duration with the particular bipolar excitation which initiated it, being either simple or compound, depending on whether it derived singly from d, e, f, h, or any combination of these. Altogether,

theoretically, a midget ganglion is capable of responding in either six or ten different modes (depending on whether three or four bipolar varieties are accepted), viz.: d, e, h, de, dh, eh, or d, e, f, h, de, df, dh, ef, eh, fh.

Here, then, several discrete dynamical processes may follow at different times along the same axon channel to the brain, either as simple or as compound excitations, a particular excita-

FIG. 354.—Johannes Evangelista Purkinje, or Yan E. Purkyně (1787–1869). Professor of physiology and pathology at Breslau (now Wroclaw), then Prussian Silesia, and at Prague, Bohemia. One of the foremost microscopists and physiologists of his time. The year 1832, when he acquired a new large microscope of Plössl, may be considered the beginning of the era of modern microscopy. Discovered the nerve cells of the brain and of the cerebellum, the latter known as "Purkinje cells," and correctly interpreted them (1837). He first described the principal expansion of the nerve cells, the "axis of the cylinder," now called "axis cylinder" or nerve fiber, and its medullary or myelin sheath (1839). Described "Purkinje's fibers," constituents of the conducting His-Tawara's bundle, or cardionector of the heart. Pioneer investigator in the physiology of vision. Discovered "Purkinje's figure" or shadows of the retinal blood vessels, a subjective phenomenon observable entoptically and first correctly interpreted by H. Müller (1854) (*see* Fig. 46). Determined the size of the field of view and the area of distinct central vision. Described the character of peripheral vision, poor in space and color perception but highly sensitive for movements. Discovered so-called "Purkinje-Sanson mirror images" of the eye, one reflected by the anterior surface of the cornea, two by the surfaces of the lens. Described "Purkinje's afterimage" and "Purkinje's phenomenon," the latter consisting of maximum brightness shifting in dark-adapted eye toward the short-wave end of the visible spectrum, out of which grew the modern concept of a duplex organization of the visual apparatus, photopic and scotopic. Sketch from a portrait painting by Jaroslav Čermák, 1856, published in O. V. Hykeš, *Přírodovědecké Prace J. E. P.*, Praha, 1928. For biography *see* Heidenhain in *Allgemeine Deutsche Biographie;* Purkinje's *Sebrane Spisy* (Collected Papers), Prague, 1928; Haymaker & Baer, *The Founders of Neurology*, 1953.

tion at a particular time. (Concretely, this may be accomplished by "frequency modulation," as suggested by Kohlrausch 1931, p. 1491.) In each case a dynamical change in the midget ganglion and in its axonal fiber terminating in the brain is somewhat different, even though merely a shading of basically the same process. A midget ganglion serves, accordingly, as a common pathway for excitations which, on the bipolar level, use different channels.

For reasons to be discussed later, the midget ganglions must be regarded as the most important neurons on the ganglion level both for color vision and for visual acuity.

The form or quality of excitation elicited in a midget ganglion as a result of an initial cone stimulation is a very different dynamical event from what it would be if there were no bipolars of different kinds acting as mediators. This excitation is modified, perhaps amplified, by additional or increased attributes or "qualities" and thus becomes more diverse in comparison with the original crude cone excitation. Possibly the differences in various shadings of the cone process initiated by light of many different wave lengths become more distinct through the action of bipolars, emphasized, differentiated, contrasting with one another more readily, than the slight nuances of a cone process alone would be. The photogenic messages carried to the brain thereby become more specific, more precise, and more diverse—in every way richer dynamical material to be utilized by the brain.

5. THE NEURONS AS FACTORS IN THE PHYLO-GENETICAL PERFECTION OF NERVOUS CENTERS.—From the preceding interpretation of certain neuron combinations an important fact becomes manifest: whenever one or more links are interpolated in a chain of neurons, the structural complexity of the chain increases, and so does its dynamical diversity. Each additional neuron variety means an added functional capacity of that set of neurons. Extended to the whole nervous system, this principle explains a tendency to create additional forms of neurons whenever a new functional demand appears. A functionally more diversified nervous tissue requires not only more neurons but also a greater variety of neuronal forms. (A similar idea had been expressed by Lenhossék 1895, p. 81, and by M. Heidenhain 1911, pp. 826, 927; *see also* Hering 1898 and Nissl 1898 on "functional neuron specificity.")

Considered from another point of view, the tendency of the nervous system, especially of the brain, to increase in bulk, manifested in the entire animal realm from early phylogenetical stages on toward more advanced forms, becomes understandable. Everywhere the nervous centers show not only a progressive differentiation of morphological details but also an augmentation of the number of cellular units or neurons. This urge is obvious, even though it works contrary to another tendency, that to economize in substance, space, and time. The cause is the narrow limits imposed by "functional neuron specificity."

The more specialized a nerve cell, the better it can perform its own specific task; conversely, the same cell is less able to substitute for other functions outside its own range. A more highly organized nerve center, precisely because it is made up of specialized neurons, requires many more of them to satisfy its need for greater functional diversity. A more elaborate organization of nervous tissue, composed of numerous functional units, where each additional nerve cell, each newly differentiated neuron, and each new synaptical relationship mean an increased combining ability, is the only way to make its function more varied and thus to satisfy the more varied conditions of advanced animal life. (*Cf.* S. Ramón y Cajal 1909–11, v. 1, p. 12.)

References: Ariëns Kappers, Huber & Crosby 1936; E. Baumgardt 1952; Heidenhain 1911; Hering 1898; Lenhossék 1895; Nissl 1898; Polyak 1941, 1948; S. Ramón y Cajal 1909–11.

SEC. 7. THE ELEMENTAL NEURONAL ASSOCIATIONS AND THEIR PROBABLE FUNCTION

1. GENERAL REMARKS.—In the entire nervous system there are probably only a few neurons, if any, which are synaptically connected with only one neuron. Such associations would add little to dynamical influencing and would be senseless, since they would defeat the purpose—integration—for which the nervous system appears to have been created.

In almost all cases which have been well investigated, each neuron is in contact with several other neurons and sometimes with many. A good example is the large motor nerve cells of the anterior gray columns of the spinal cord. Here one finds attached to their perikarya and dendrites numerous terminal nodules of teledendrons of many efferent neurons of a higher order located in the brain stem and cerebral cortex, as well as nodules of afferent posterior spinal root fibers and of integrating neurons of the spinal cord itself. (*Cf.* S. Ramón y Cajal 1909, Figs. 18 and 112; and especially D. Bodian 1937, 1940, 1942.)

The spinal motor cells, accordingly, collect nervous impulses of several kinds into one common channel. In this common outlet, termed "final common path" by Sherrington (1906), they meet several kinds of "excitations," varying in many respects. The resulting impulse is finally delivered by way of the anterior spinal roots to the peripheral organs of execution, such as the muscles and glands.

In an afferent system, such as the visual, the same principle of neuron coupling is found, even though applied in precisely the reverse order: one, two, or a few, of the peripheral receptors of the retina, for example, may represent a "common origin" or "common source" of the impulse. Here begins a synaptical concatenation of many increasingly complex neuronal links, which finally terminates in the cerebral cortex. The organization of such a system indicates that its function in the peripheral segment is chiefly analytical. That is, it splits an originally common peripheral excitation into a number of partial excitations. These, represented in the retina and in the intermediate segment by the lateral geniculate nucleus, are recombined and delivered to the "final integrator," the cerebral cortex, for further and final processing.

The preceding examples illustrate two principal functions of the synaptical relationships: one, which in a general way may be considered "combination," "fusion," or "merging," and the other, which may be considered "subdivision," "splitting," or "analysis" of nervous currents of excitation.

The organization of the advanced nervous centers goes beyond this, however. It may link together two or more sets of neurons into a compound mechanism. Neurons variously intimately related with one or more types of other neurons, serving now in one role, now in another, depending on the variation of dynamical conditions, illustrate such a mechanism (colored Fig. 179).

In the primate retina, for example, the cones are related to three or four distinct varieties of bipolars (b & d, b & e, b & f, b & h relationships) and to the horizontal cells (b & c relationship). The rods are also related to the same bipolars, with the exception of the midget bipolar (a & d, a & e, a & f relationships). Each bipolar variety, in turn, is related to each variety of ganglion cells, although in a somewhat different way. All bipolar varieties are used by the excitations arising both in the cones and in the rods, except the midget bipolar (h), which serves only the cones.

From this anatomical arrangement it is legitimate to conclude that both cone and rod excitations eventually pass to the brain by way of identical ganglion cells. However, since the neuron chain transmitting cone excitations is differently organized from that transmitting rod impulses, the effect in the central nervous organ must be different in each case.

The preceding example, incidentally, illustrates the economy of space and substance by which the same neurons are used to accomplish different purposes. It also shows how the central result in a complex system of neurons depends both on the kind of initial stimulation and on the synaptical pattern.

In the following are given a few samples of neuron relationships, with their tentative functional interpretation. Undoubtedly, many more such relationships will be found in different parts of the nervous organs.

2. ANALYTICAL NEURON MECHANISM.—A classical example of a nervous structure by means of which an originally single excitatory state is, as it were, divided into several different forms of excitation is the relationship between cones (b) and bipolars (d, e, f, h).

Each cone in the human and simian retina is synaptically related to the bipolar cells belonging to two, three, or four distinct varieties, as described in chapter V, 4, 11. (The number depends on whether e and f types are considered as one or two varieties; in the rodless area of the central fovea, e, f, and h varieties alone seem to be present; *cf.* colored Fig. 177.) The photochemical process elicited in the cone by the action of physical light probably varies according to the wave length of the stimulus. Even so, since each cone in the central area is equally

ificity" and its particular synaptical contact with the cone pedicle, as previously discussed (*see* secs. 3, 5, 6, this chapter, and par. 6, this section).

The states of excitation elicited in several bipolar varieties must, accordingly, differ in their intrinsic properties or qualities. The eliciting of these secondary excitations may take place either at different times in each bipolar

Fig. 355.—Johannes Peter Müller (1801–58), professor of anatomy and physiology at Bonn and Berlin, Prussia. One of the foremost biologists and physiologists of his time. Originator of the concept of "specific energy of nerves" and of the "theory of identical points" of two eyes in single binocular vision. An assiduous student of visual phenomena and of vision in general. (For biography *see* B. Chance 1944; U. Ebbecke 1951.)

responsive to all wave lengths, a cone must be looked upon as a common source of excitation for all bipolar varieties. From this common source each bipolar variety "takes" only that share of excitation to which it is specifically responsive by virtue of its innate "functional spec-

variety or simultaneously in combinations of two or more varieties at a time, or in all, depending upon the character of cone excitation, the condition of bipolars, and probably other factors.

In this or a similar way a single or global

original dynamical disturbance may be subdivided or analyzed by the cone-bipolar mechanism into several component excitations, to be further used by other groups of neurons. The relationship of the horizontal cells with the cones, not being in the path along which the excitations pass to the brain, may rather be labeled as a "diversion" used for a local purpose (*see* sec. 8 [5], this chapter).

3. Common pathway mechanism.—An example of a neuronal relationship serving a purpose precisely opposite to analysis is that of the rods (*a*) and cones (*b*) and the mop variety of bipolar (*d*); (*see* left sketch in Fig. 347). Throughout the primate retina the mop bipolar is related both to the cone pedicles and to rod spherules, each bipolar cell having synapses with a group of both photoreceptors (the minute central area of the fovea, where neither rods nor mop bipolars have been found, is an exception; *see* colored Fig. 177). The mop bipolar, accordingly, serves as a common passage for the excitations originating both in the rods and in the cones. It is therefore appropriate to call it the "common path," as the motor cell of the spinal cord is also called, for the same reason. It is a matter for further consideration how the working of this common pathway should be interpreted in detail.

First, the two different excitations originating in the rods and cones may elicit in the mop bipolar a dynamical change equivalent to a genuine "fusion" or a compound excitation embodying features of both ("spatial fusion"); the other and more likely possibility is that certain excitations arising under special conditions of stimulation both in the rods and in the cones are identical or nearly so, eliciting an identical response in the mop bipolar attuned to them. This may occur either simultaneously or at different times; in the latter case the mop bipolar serves only one kind of photoreceptor.

Such an interpretation would be in accord with the concept of "functional neuron specificity." It may, further, be interpreted in favor of an "identity" of subjective visual experiences caused by certain cone excitations and by those having origin in the rods, e.g., sensation of "white" or "gray."

The synaptical relationships of other diffuse bipolars (*e*, *f*) are similar, even though slightly different, and may be interpreted in a similar way, as slight shadings of the same process. This contrasts with the midget bipolar (*h*), which is related to the cones alone and hence is functionally much more specialized.

4. The mechanism of summation.—A combination of neurons by means of which impulses of the same or different kinds may be added and the resulting excitation concentrated or intensified is exemplified in the primate retina by the rod and mop bipolar synapses alone, or together with those of the cones (right and left sketches in Fig. 177, and left sketch in Fig. 347). Here each mop bipolar (*d*) is in contact with a compact group of rods (*a*) and cones (*b*), the groups being larger in the extra-areal periphery. It is legitimate to assume that if more rods are activated, the intensity of excitation elicited in the related bipolar becomes greater, the maximum being attained when the entire related rod group is stimulated: "spatial summation." Such a rod group may be stimulated either simultaneously by the application of a beam of light to the entire group: a "simultaneous spatial summation"; or the individual rods of the group may be stimulated in succession: a "successive spatial summation." In both instances all rods discharge upon the same mop bipolar, in the first in a "volley," in the second as "single shots." What difference in physiological effect this may make and how the phenomenon of summation could be reconciled with the refractory phase or period or state of unexcitability caused in the bipolar cell after its activation remain matters for further consideration. The same principle applies also to the cones, either alone (middle sketch) or in combination with the rods (lateral sketches, Fig. 177).

This anatomical summative mechanism contrasts with the "physiological or temporal summation," as, for example, when the same rods discharge upon the same bipolar cell but do so at different times in short succession. In the instance of different rods related to the same bipolar discharging in succession, the spatial and temporal summations really are combined, an added advantage from the latter being the bringing into play of fresh rods, whose charge, accumulated during a period of rest, is unexpended.

In this situation, while the first few activated rods alone may be unable, with their weak, subliminal impulses, to cause the discharge of a bipolar, they may "sensitize" it or "condition" it, in the sense of a decrease of its threshold, and thus "facilitate" its response to the influences originating in other related rods. In the same way a bipolar response, already taking place but of low intensity, may be intensified by the discharges from the additional related rods.

In the system of cones the retinal periphery may be cited as an example of a familiar mechanism of summation where several cones are synaptically connected to a simple polysynaptic type of midget bipolar (right sketch, Fig. 177).

The principle of anatomical spatial summation may be applied on a larger scale, in successive tiers or links of a neuron chain making up a system. In the initial portion of the vertebrate visual system, not only does each bipolar of the diffuse varieties (*d, e, f*) assemble into a common path influences arising from a group of rods and cones, or from the cones alone, but again on the ganglion level each cell unites influences from several—in the extra-areal periphery of the retina from hundreds—of bipolars into larger functional units. The size of these units varies, the smallest being that belonging to the midget ganglions (*s*) of the central area, the largest to the diffuse ganglion varieties (*m, n, o, p, r*) of the extra-areal periphery (Figs. 178, 179). Possibly such units may also vary among themselves in density, depending on the number of bipolars related to a given ganglion variety per surface area of the retina.

The probable effect of the "summative synaptical organization" is the increased intensity of influences passing through it.

5. The mechanism of avalanche.—A mechanism opposite to summation described by S. Ramón y Cajal (1909–11, v. 1, p. 137) in the afferent systems, under the label "avalanche of conduction," consists of terminations of each individual axon fiber around a group of nerve cells. An example of this is the teledendrons of optic nerve fibers in the lateral geniculate nucleus (*see* Fig. 220). As interpreted by Cajal, the functional effect of this arrangement is in the increase in intensity of stimulation as each successive link in a system made up of an increas-

ing number of neurons is activated. Similar arrangements had been described by Tello (1904) (*see* Fig. 216) and by O'Leary (1940). The terminations of the afferent visual fibers in the striate cortex are a good example of a mechanism of avalanche. More information on this subject is necessary (*see* chap. VIII, 7).

6. The mechanisms of facilitation or inhibition.—A structural arrangement whose function seems to be an interference with the synapses between other neurons is exemplified by the horizontal cells of the retina (*c*) and by the centrifugal bipolars (*i*) (*see* colored Fig. 179).

The synapses between the compact, short dendrites of the horizontal cells and the cone pedicles are obviously contacts through which the former are influenced by the latter. Termination of the axonal ramifications of the horizontals around the vitreal ends of a distant group of cones and rods that undoubtedly are emissive organelles of the photoreceptors, on the other hand, seems contrary to "functional polarity." The cone pedicles and rod spherules, according to the neuron theory, should be refractory to the influences arriving from other neurons. Yet the undoubted anatomical relationship mentioned demands an acceptance of some kind of influencing, most likely of the photoreceptor-bipolar relationship.

It is possible that through the action of horizontal cells the normal passage of rod and cone influences over to the bipolars is in some way interfered with, e.g., by a suppression of one or the other "quality" or by a change in intensity in the sense of an increased threshold, which, at its maximum, may amount to complete "inhibition" or "blocking." This effect may be attained, e.g., by the secretion of a chemical substance or by a counterionization, which, depending upon its concentration or composition, would work in the sense of a "selection," a "delay," or a "decrease in intensity," or even as a total "inhibition."

Another possibility is the blocking or inhibiting of the rods in daylight vision through the cone influences disseminated via the horizontal neurons, making the bipolars refractory to the rod stimuli. The opposite situation would probably not arise in scotopic conditions, owing to the high threshold of cones. There is yet another possibility to be considered: inhibition of regeneration of the visual purple in daylight conditions under the cone influence, and a similar inhibition of the substances in the cones not stimulated by light.

The centrifugal bipolar cells (i, in same figures) require a somewhat different interpretation. Their axon-like fibers teminate around the pedicles of a small group of cones located in the same territory of the retina. These alone, accordingly, are influenced either by excitations arising from a somewhat larger area via the ordinary centripetal bipolars (d, e, f, h) synapsing with dendrite-like expansions of i-bipolars, or possibly by the central influences arriving along the exogenous fibers (t). The physiological effect of this arrangement may be a lowering of the threshold or "facilitation" of the passage of influences from the related cones over to the bipolars, or vice versa.

7. THE TOPOGRAPHICAL RELATIONS OF THE NEURONS.—Whereas the mechanisms dealt with

FIG. 356.—Hermann Ludwig Ferdinand Helmholtz (1821–94), professor of physiology at Königsberg (now Kaliningrad), of anatomy and physiology at Bonn, of physiology at Heidelberg, and of physics at Berlin. Director of the Physico-technical Institute at Charlottenburg, Germany. One of the most encyclopedic and fertile minds in the field of science. Discovered the ophthalmoscope or "eye mirror," an instrument on which modern ophthalmology is built (Fig. 102). Developed, from Thomas Young's suggestion, the "trichromatic theory," still the most successful interpretation of color vision. Originator of the "resonance theory of hearing," again the most plausible explanation of the basic process underlying the auditory function. Classical investigator of physiological optics and of physics in general. Author of the *Treatise on Physiological Optics* and *On the Sensation of Tone as a Physiological Basis for the Theory of Music*. Portrait by F. von Lenbach, from Oswald's "Klassiker der exakten Wissenschaften," Nos. 1, 79, 80, 124. For biography *see* McKendrick 1899; Königsberger 1902–3; E. W. Melson 1938; Haymaker & Baer 1953; W. Schwagmeyer 1952. (*See also* Fig. 101.)

in the preceding paragraphs are concerned either with preservation or with change or modification of the qualities of excitations or with preservation or change of their intensity in the sense of an increase or decrease or inhibition of excitations, another widespread organizational principle obtains in the nervous organs whose obvious purpose is the preservation or maintenance of orderly topographical relations. Nowhere is this so clearly expressed as in the visual system, as may be expected in a mechanism serving an exquisitely spatial sense like sight. Here but a few salient facts may be recorded from a more extensive presentation given in chapters V, VI, VII, and VIII.

A very orderly arrangement, probably the most geometrical in the organism, is found in the bacillary layer of the retina (*see* Figs. 151–60). A similar orderly topography is maintained to the same or a lesser degree, link by link, along the entire chain of neurons in the visual system, including the striate area of the cortex. The functional significance of this is fairly evident: the preservation of topographical relations of synapses in the striate area nearly corresponding to those present in the photoreceptive bacillary layer of the eye. Whatever its detailed physiological motivation, the necessity of preserving such strict topography must be compelling.

A similar arrangement of neurons and their synapses is found in many other pathways and fiber systems: in the posterior gray columns of the spinal cord; in the inferior, and less so in the superior, olives; in the superior colliculi of the midbrain; in the fiber systems leading to and from the cerebral and cerebellar cortex, including the thalamic connections; and elsewhere.

Interpreted in a very general way, the principle of the topographical relations of the neurons indicates an inability of the nervous system—a mechanism made up of isolated conductors—to establish numerous contacts between its many divisions in any other way except upon factual initial and terminal contacts of its conducting structures, the nerve fibers. This automatically relegates to secondary importance in comparison with the principal factor—the preformed nervous structures—all other organizational factors, particularly the purely dynamical ones, that could bring parts of the nervous system into mutual relationship. Further, especially, embryological investigation is required to interpret the topography in the nervous system in terms of the basic functions.

References: Ariëns Kappers 1908, 1914, 1916–17, 1917, 1919, 1922, 1927, 1928; Ariëns Kappers, Huber & Crosby 1936; E. Baumgardt 1952; Bodian 1937, 1940, 1942; Lorente de Nó 1943; Polyak 1941, 1948; S. Ramón y Cajal 1909–11.

SEC. 8. THE FUNCTIONAL GROUPING OF NEURONS IN THE RETINA

1. Introductory remark.—In the preceding sections an attempt has been made to illustrate by means of a few samples the principal types of associations of neurons so far found in the nervous system and to indicate their probable function. It now remains to be seen whether the present knowledge of the minute structure of the visual system presented in chapters V, VI, and VIII allows us to determine into what physiological groups its constituent neurons are associated and what functions these groups or systems are most likely to perform in the complex process of vision. It is, however, necessary to admit that only a beginning can be made, the solution of this problem remaining the task of future research.

We may logically begin, first, with the photoreceptors of the retina and follow the paths along which the various excitations generated in the photoreceptors are transmitted to the brain. Thereafter, an attempt may be made to determine which of the particular numerous visual functions and phenomena may best be correlated with one or another of the several sets of neurons. This attempt, because of our fragmentary information, must necessarily remain unfinished until the neurons composing the entire visual system are completely revealed.

2. The systems of retinal neurons.—The neurons making up the nervous parenchyma of the retinal membrane may be roughly subdivided into two systems (*see* colored Figs. 177,

178, 179). One is the *receptor-conductor system*, represented by the rods (*a*) and cones (*b*), centripetal bipolars (*d, e, f, h*), and ganglion cells (*m, n, o, p, s*); its principal function is response to physical light stimulation and the transmission to the brain of excitations thus generated. The other is the *integrator system*, composed of the horizontal cells (*c*) and probably also of the various amacrine cells (*k, l*), including the centrifugal bipolars (*i*); its main role is to interconnect neurons of the first division and, by a mutual dynamical adjustment, to make a functional organ of the retina. Both divisions are synaptically intimately interconnected, indicating their continuous functional interdependence.

The receptor-conductor system may be further subdivided on the basis of photoreceptors into a *rod system* and a *cone system*. From the last-mentioned, a *pure or private cone system* may be separated out by elimination of those elements that are common to both categories of photoreceptors.

3. THE ROD SYSTEM OF NEURONS.—This system may be singled out of the complex retinal tissue pattern by following the synapses, beginning with the rods and along the subsequent links to where the excitations are passed to the brain.

The rods are related to all diffuse varieties of centripetal bipolars (*a* & *d, e, f* relationships), and through these to all ganglion cell varieties (*d, e, f* & *m, n, o, p, r, s* relationships). The midget bipolars (*h*) and, of course, the cones (*b*) are the only two units of the conductor division of neurons which are excluded from the rod system. Also, not all brush (*e*) and flat-top (*f*) bipolars, but only some, are a part of the rod system, the mop bipolar (*d*) apparently being the principal link on the bipolar level. Of the integrator group of neurons, the horizontal cells (*c*) have only emissive synapses with the rods, while the various amacrines (*k, l*) and the centrifugal bipolar (*i*) are related to the rod system only by similar efferent or emissive synapses of the diffuse centripetal bipolars.

The arrangement of the receptor and conductor units in the rod system is topical or spatial, with a fair preservation of topographical relations present in the bacillary rod layer. However, because of the relatively large dendritic expansions of diffuse bipolars, their reciprocal overlapping, the synapsing of each bipolar with a group of rods, and the synapsing of each of the diffuse ganglion varieties with many of the diffuse bipolars, the physiological units of the rod system are larger, its "grain" less fine, than in the cone system.

The course of currents of excitation generated in the rods, as reconstructed from their synaptical relationships, is, first, to the diffuse bipolars and from these to all ganglion cell varieties and, via the latter's axons, to the brain. The midget bipolars and the horizontal cells (and hence the cones) remain unaffected. The "local signatures" in the rod system are relatively crude and are not sharply separated from one another. The physiological units, because of a decrease in the number of rod cells synapsing with each bipolar from the central point toward the periphery of a given area, must be expected to show a functional gradient from the zone of the lowest threshold toward the zone where the threshold is highest. The area or zone of the lowest rod threshold will likely depend also on other than purely synaptical factors.

Since all rods are synaptically related to the mop bipolars and only some to the brush and flat-top bipolars, the first may be considered as most nearly the true rod bipolars, the latter two varieties as the auxiliary rod bipolars. It is also possible that the rod excitations may vary to some extent in quality, depending upon the bipolar variety used and on the retinal locality. However, the less complex synaptical relations of the rods and bipolars are indicative of a more uniform or simpler character of the rod excitations passed on to the brain by comparison with the composite nature of the cone excitations.

The third link in the neuron chain making up the rod system of the retina is represented by all ganglion cell varieties. The midget ganglions, because of their relatively slight synaptical connection with the diffuse bipolars, may play a somewhat subordinate role in the transmission of rod excitations. Conversely, the principal role in this task falls upon diffuse ganglions. These, owing to a great number of bipolars synapsing with each ganglion cell, increasing to several hundred and possibly to a few thousand in the extra-areal periphery, may be looked upon as huge collectors or summators of the rod currents of excitations manifested in an increased intensity. A possibility must also be considered of some additional shading in the quality of rod excitations, depending upon the ganglion variety by which they are transmitted and on the retinal locality.

The functional relation of the rod system to the cone system, judging from their synapses, is passive. That is, the cones are able to influence

while the responsiveness of rods attains its full value, in part possibly by the decrease or cessation of inhibitory influences emanating from the scotopic cones.

4. THE CONE SYSTEM OF NEURONS.—The cones are related to all varieties of centripetal bipolars (*b* & *d*, *e*, *f*, *h* relationships) and, through these, to all ganglion cell varieties (*d*, *e*,

FIG. 357.—Ewald H. Hering (1834–1918), professor of physiology at Prague, Bohemia, and at Leipzig, Saxony, Germany. Notable physiologist and psychologist. A lifelong student of visual functions. Author of the "theory of opponent colors," rivaling the "trichromatic theory" of Young & Helmholtz as an explanation of color perception. Originator of the concept of "cyclopean eye." From München. med. Wchnschr., v. 81, 1934.

the dynamical status of the rods, while the reverse cannot take place because of the absence of appropriate synaptical connections.

A rod system may be most nearly realized under physiological conditions of stimulation during scotopic or night vision, when the intensity of stimulus falls below the cone threshold,

f, *h* & *m*, *n*, *o*, *p*, *r*, *s* relationships), all belonging to the receptor-conductor division. In the small rodless area of the central fovea the mop bipolar (*d*) seems to be absent, however (Figs. 177, 178, 179).

The principal link on the bipolar level is the midget bipolar (*h*); on the ganglion level it is the midget ganglion (*s*). This mechanism may conveniently be called the *complete cone system*, in contrast to a more restricted monosynaptical system of cone neurons subsequently described. The integrator neurons are more intimately connected with the cone systems, the horizontal cells (*c*) synapsing with the cones both by the receptive dendrites and by the emissive teledendrons, the centrifugal bipolar (*i*) by its teledendron only, and the various amacrines (*k, l*) through the emissive synapses of the centripetal bipolars and probably also by direct synapses of an uncertain category with the bodies of ganglion cells.

The arrangement of receptor and conductor units in the complete cone system is topical or spatial, more so than in the rod system. As in the latter and for similar reasons, its physiological units are somewhat larger than the single cones, since each diffuse bipolar is related to a few cones, and so forth. However, with a great reduction in thickness of the cones, with a much reduced spread of both dendritic and teledendric expansions of the bipolars, and with a wholesale decrease in the foveal ganglion cells in both body size and dendritic expansions, together with the great increase of central cones, bipolars, and ganglions, the "grain" of the functional units of the complete cone system in the visual axis is, on the whole, much finer than that of the rod system.

There is still another factor that makes the cone a refined instrument serving maximal visual acuity: a strictly individual synaptical relationship between the cones, the midget bipolars, and the midget ganglions in the central area and fovea (*b & h & s* relationships). Here each functional unit of the cone system consists of a single cone, a small group of bipolars, including a single midget bipolar, and a small group of ganglion cells, including a single midget ganglion (*b & d, e, f, h & m, n, o, p, r, s* relationships).

It is, however, possible and probable that under certain conditions the *b-h-s* chain of neurons alone may be active. This makes it possible to isolate a receptor-conductor mechanism of superior performance: a *pure, monosynaptical or individual cone system* of the central area and fovea. In this system all diffuse neuron varieties, both on the bipolar and on the ganglion

levels, are eliminated. This leaves to the disposal of each individual cone a "monosynaptical" or "private" channel along which to send messages to the brain.

In the rodless area the size of the functional units in this private receptor-conductor system is determined by the diameter of individual cones; outside it, in the central area, by the interval separating the adjoining cones (outside the central area, owing to the replacement of monosynaptic by polysynaptic forms of midget bipolars, this system is very much roughened).

Each functional unit in the monosynaptical foveal cone system, if imagined free from any direct synaptical relations with the adjoining units of the same system, may under certain physiological conditions be capable of independent functioning. This contrasts both with the complete cone system, made up of all bipolars and ganglions, and with the rod system, where, because of diffuse synapses, an excitation originating in a single photoreceptor or a small group of photoreceptors is never strictly limited to a single conductor unit or entirely separated from the adjoining units, the more so, since in the rod system individual synapses are absent.

Because of the restricted size of its functional units and their isolation from one another, the monosynaptical cone system may be considered the chief instrument responsible for the highest degree of acuity corresponding to the center of the field of view.

The estimated course of the currents of excitations may vary according to which particular synaptical relations are considered. In the "complete cone system" of the central area of the retina an impulse generated in a cone may influence either one, two, or all bipolar varieties (in the rodless area, minus *d* bipolar, which here seems to be absent). The bipolars, in turn, elicit or may elicit dynamical changes in any one, in several, or in all related ganglion varieties. How to visualize such processes and what their physiological significance may be have been discussed in the preceding sections of this chapter and require further investigation.

The structural elements of a "complete cone system" and its functional units resemble those in the "rod system" except for the addition of the cones and midget bipolars. The "local signatures" are likely to be also about the same, except in the central fovea, where the cones predominate and are gradually reduced in thickness, principally in the central rodless area. Also, because of the overlapping of expansions, there must be some functional gradient from a central high responsiveness toward the periphery of a functional unit. There are, however, differences: a "complete cone system" is also related to the horizontal cells through which it may actively elicit dynamical responses both in the cones and in rods of the area surrounding the stimulated cone. The cones may likewise be influenced via the centrifugal bipolars either from other parts of the retina or from the brain.

The course of the excitations within the "monosynaptical cone system," owing to its simple synaptical composition, is easy to estimate. A cone disturbance elicits a response in its midget bipolar, which in turn influences its midget ganglion. In this connection the first may be considered a "private cone bipolar," the second a "private cone ganglion." There is no division or analysis or fusion of the transmitted influences, except as may be caused by an intrinsic dynamical modulation within the system itself in response to the variation of stimulus. The only qualification which this statement requires may concern the influences given to, and received from, the horizontal cells and those arriving via the centrifugal bipolars.

From the structural simplicity of the "monosynaptical cone system," however, it would not be warranted to conclude that its function is simple in terms of subjective sensations, already hinted at. Also, since the two receptor-conductor systems, that of the rods and that of the cones, are actually welded into a *common or duplex rod and cone system* in the entire retina except in the rodless area, it is possible that under certain conditions of stimulation the entire receptor-conductor mechanism functions as a unit, in which the same diffuse bipolars serve as a common channel for both rod and cone influences (as it could, for example, during the transitional period from photopic to scotopic vision, and vice versa). In different conditions, when the stimulation is below the cone threshold, the rod system alone would remain in action (thus probably in scotopic or night vision). Conversely, when there is an increase in intensity of stimulation above the cone threshold which may automatically inhibit the rods (hypothetically through the horizontal cells), the cone system would act alone (such a condition is probably realized during photopic, or daylight, vision). In either case the same bipolars and ganglions participate, with the single exception of the midget bipolars, which, under scotopic conditions, remain inactive (as presumably do the cones). (The possible identity of influences mediated by the diffuse bipolars, especially the mop variety, irrespective of whether originating from rods or from cones, e.g., of "gray" or "white" sensations, has been mentioned earlier.)

The third link of the "complete cone system" of the retina is represented by all ganglion varieties, precisely as in the "rod system." In spite of this similarity, the responses elicited therein, taking the cue from the synaptical relations which in the two systems are partly different, may not be identical or may be only partly so. In the "rod system" the stress of activity is upon the mop bipolar and the diffuse ganglions; in the "complete cone system" upon the midget bipolar and the midget ganglion.

There are several factors which should be considered here. First, in the "rod system," since the midget bipolar (h) is absent and no cone influences arrive through the diffuse bipolars (d, e, f), not only the responses of the diffuse ganglions (m, n, o, p, r) but also those of the midget ganglion (s) may differ from the responses elicited in the same ganglions when the cone influences are included. Second, within the "complete cone system" itself there may be further shadings of the responses on the ganglion level, each bipolar variety, or a combination of varieties, being capable of eliciting its own particular kind of response in each ganglion variety within the frame of its own particular functional specificity.

In this connection several points seem worthy of further attention. The shrub ganglion (n), for example, seems to be a suitable "collector," "summator," "accumulator," or "intensifier" of influences from a group of midget bipolars (right sketch, Fig. 347; also colored figures in chap. V). In this capacity the n ganglion is a polysynaptic counterpart of the monosynaptic midget ganglion. Undoubtedly also the responses of two such varieties as the parasol (*m*) and garland (*p*) ganglions, although related to the same bipolars, because of the great difference in their synaptical contacts, generate responses differing from each other in quality and intensity, as they differ from other ganglion varieties. The number of "qualities" of the ganglion messages from the retina to the brain must, therefore, be no less than the number of

ing of all retinal ganglion cells, pose a special problem. They are the principal conductors of the cone influences to the brain. In what way are they capable of transmitting the great variety of dynamical modulations necessary for perception of the hundreds of hues subjectively appreciated? It is a problem similar to that raised by the cone response to chromatic stimulation.

The great dynamic flexibility of the midget

FIG. 358.—Frans Cornelius Donders (1818–89), professor of physiology and ophthalmology at Utrecht, the Netherlands, at the age of seventy. Together with Helmholtz (*see* Figs. 101, 356), a founder of modern physiological optics, investigator of the accommodation and refraction of the eye. Portrait by Bramine Hubrecht, Donders' wife, painted 1888, now at Rijksmuseum in Amsterdam, Netherlands. Courtesy Rijksmuseum (Mr. A. M. Muntendam). (For biography *see* H. W. Williams 1889.)

morphologically distinguishable ganglion cell varieties and probably exceeds it considerably. In this count the finer modulations of each ganglion response, as well as the intensities, have not been taken into consideration.

The midget ganglions, these most interest-

ganglions may be considered especially in the condition when the "monosynaptical cone system" alone works, when all influences from the diffuse bipolars and the diffuse ganglion cells are eliminated.

The actual synaptical relationships of the

rodless central area, however, indicate that under ordinary daylight conditions all bipolars present (that is, probably without the mop bipolar) and all ganglions may participate, even though, because of their great numerical preponderance, the midget ganglions several times outnumber all diffuse varieties of this locality. Hence the midget ganglions are by far the most important factors in axial vision or visual acuity in general, as this function is usually defined. But whether acting independently or as a part of a neuronal team, the midget ganglions must be capable of a wide range of detailed qualitative grading of responses, in order to satisfy the functional demands of detailed spatial vision and, at the same time, to serve as a substratum of color vision in the region of the visual axis.

5. THE RETINAL INTEGRATORS.—This system of neurons, as far as revealed, is made up of the horizontal cells (*c*), centrifugal bipolars (*i*), some or all amacrine cells (*k*, *l*), and probably other structures. Judging from their synaptical relations, their role is to interconnect various points of the retina and to regulate the working of the receptor-conductor system.

The connections of the horizontal cells and of the centrifugal bipolars have been described in chapter V, 6, and in section 7, paragraph 6, in this chapter. A few more points may be added. The horizontal cells evidently represent a system of intraretinal associations through which each small area of the photoreceptor layer is functionally tied up with its immediate surroundings. In this way, like a coat of mail, the rods and cones of the entire retina are firmly knit into a functional whole. In particular, whenever a cone or a group of cones is stimulated, it automatically influences both rods and cones in the region surrounding it. The rods, however, since they have no synapses with the dendrites of the horizontal cells, are unable to do so. How to interpret this horizontal influencing by the cones in terms of subjective sensations is discussed in the passages referred to above. There, too, the probable function of the centrifugal bipolars was also mentioned.

The amacrine cells (*k*, *l*) still remain an unsolved enigma. Their great numbers are indicative of their importance in retinal responses. It will probably prove correct to consider their function in general as an intraretinal association, by means of which the neurons bordering on the inner plexiform layer, especially the ganglion cells, are in some way influenced. Their expansions, directly in contact with the bodies of ganglion cells, indicate this. But much more factual information is necessary before an attempt may be made at assigning to the amacrines any one of the known functions of vision.

The same is also true of the efferent or exogenous fibers (*t*) of the retina.

6. REVIEW OF THE RETINAL STRUCTURES AND THEIR PROBABLE DYNAMICS.—It may be useful to recapitulate briefly the neuron varieties of the vertebrate retina and their synaptical relations. From this, an attempt may be made to construct the probable course of excitations within the retinal tissue before the finished messages are sent to the brain. (*Cf.* colored Figs. 177, 178, 179.)

The initial photochemical reaction to visible physical light takes place in the bacillary layer (2), most probably in the outer segments of the rods (*a*) and cones (*b*), as first evidenced by Heinrich Müller (*see* chap. I, 7 [5]). From here the two categories of excitation pass to the inner rod and cone segments and their bodies and along their respective inner fibers to their vitreal terminations, the rod spherules and cone pedicles.

The rod excitations, in turn, elicit responses in the diffuse centripetal bipolars (*d*, *e*, *f*), always in groups not sharply separated from the inactive bipolars. These again influence any or all varieties of the ganglion cells (*m*, *n*, *o*, *p*, *r*, *s*). The localizing value of the rod messages to the brain, not so detailed as those of the cones, is nevertheless essential, especially because of the high summative effect of the rod system. Just how much the rod influences are propagated laterally is not known, since the amacrine associational system in the inner plexiform layer is still imperfectly known.

The cone influences pass over, actually or potentially, to all bipolar varieties (*d*, *e*, *f*, *h*) and also to the horizontal cells (*c*). The bipolars, in turn, activate all ganglion varieties (*m*, *n*, *o*, *p*, *r*, *s*), whence the messages are further dispatched to the brain. Both the qualities and the localizing value, the latter being much higher than in the rod system, vary according to which of the intermediate neurons are activated.

The most restricted in space and hence having the greatest localizing value are the messages that pass through the monosynaptical or through any bipolars over to diffuse ganglions of the same area (b & d, e, f, h & m, n, o, p, r) have considerably smaller localizing value. Of least value as a localizing factor are those cone influences that pass through the polysynaptic midget bipolars (h-h) and other bipolar varie-

Fig. 359.—Karl Spencer Lashley (1890), research professor of neuropsychology at Harvard University and director of Yerkes Laboratories of Primate Biology, Orange Park, Florida. One of the foremost experimental psychologists of modern times. A lifelong student of the visual functions and mechanisms of the visual behavior of animals. Courtesy Dr. Lashley, 1955.

"private" chain of neurons in the central area, especially in the fovea (b & h & s). Only a little less localized are the influences that use both the midget and the diffuse bipolars and the midget ganglions, also in the central area and fovea (b & d, e, f & s). Influences passing ties with a wide dendritic spread (d, e, f) to the large-sized diffuse bipolars and polysynaptic midget ganglions of the extra-areal periphery (m, n, o, p, r, s-s).

The cone influences that use any one particular bipolar variety as a channel must also vary in their dynamical qualities and hence are likely to be material for different psychophysiological correlates. But even those influences restricted to the monosynaptical chain of neurons (*b* & *h* & *s*) must be capable of a great range of shadings, for the reasons discussed in the preceding subsection. The most compelling reason to make such a conclusion is the fact that there is not a sufficient number either of neuron varieties or of synapses in the central area to account for the wealth of subjective color sensations in the region of the visual axis.

The cones, unlike the rods, are able to influence both the rods and the cones in the surrounding area through the horizontal cells (*c*) and are in turn influenced by other factors, possibly cerebral or from the surrounding retinal regions, through the centrifugal bipolars (*i*), exogenous or efferent fibers (*t*), and perhaps also by the amacrine cells (*k*, *l*).

From the mere description of its structure and the possible avenues it offers for the spreading of excitations generated in the photoreceptors, the retina is obviously not a simple peripheral receiver of stimuli but a true analyzer and integrator of a high order within which the photic excitations are processed, sorted, and rearranged, before they are dispatched to the brain for further elaboration and use. The accumulation of several million nerve cells belonging to a dozen neuron varieties representing more than fifty distinct kinds of synapses in the immediate proximity of the photoreceptor layers thus becomes understandable. It is an expression of the need for a prompt and speedy processing of the rod and cone excitations before they are passed on to the brain.

Phylogenetically a part of the brain, in the fully developed state the retina performs some functions otherwise reserved to the central organ (*see* chap. XIII, 2, 3). The complex processes of analysis, sorting, and integration, as the steps following the initial photochemical process in the sequence of events underlying the phenomenon of vision, cannot be performed satisfactorily, except by occurring immediately after, and in essentials duplicating, the initial photoreceptive process in the rods and cones.

7. CONCLUDING REMARKS.—In this chapter, first, the various opinions expressed by preceding investigators concerning the basic organization of the nervous system were examined. Next, an attempt was made to test these opinions with the help of our own observations. The concept of the "neuron" as a genetic, morphologic, and functional unit was found to fit the facts and to satisfy the requirements, whereas the doctrine of "neuroreticularism" or "nerve net," in all its modifications, was found wanting.

In further sections we have tried to interpret functionally the structures found in the vertebrate retina and in this way to test the neuron concept or to modify it. Our aim was, first, to understand the structure and significance of the synapse as a basic feature of the organization of the nervous system. Our second aim was to interpret in terms of the basic functions the synaptical grouping of the neurons making up the retina.

The next logical step should be a similar investigation and interpretation of the remainder of the visual system, in particular of the laminated lateral geniculate nucleus and the striate area. In this way, perhaps, the synaptical channels along which the impulses travel from the photoreceptors through the intermediate stations to the cortical centers of the brain could be traced. Such investigation, if successful, not only would give a hint about the devious channels along which the retinal impulses enter the cortex, and their fate therein, but would possibly provide a firmer foundation for our interpretation of the retinal structures themselves.

In chapter VI, 9, a few details of the finer structures of the laminated lateral geniculate nucleus were described. These show various terminal arborizations of axis cylinders arriving from outside. Some, because of their thick caliber and mode and place of spreading, are most likely of retinal origin. The others possibly belong to the neurons residing in the brain.

Since the ganglion cells of the retina represent several distinct varieties, as our study of Golgi-stained preparations shows, and since in other experiments with small lesions located in various parts of the retina the Marchi method of staining showed myelinated fibers entering all laminae of the nucleus in the corresponding segment, it is probable that all ganglion cells of the retina send their fibers into each lamina.

Hence it is probable that each minute territory of the retina is connected with its own particular minute segment of the nucleus by a multiple or composite cable made up of as many varieties of optic nerve fibers as there are varieties of retinal ganglion cells.

The exact number of component fiber varieties remains unknown. It stands to reason that they may be simpler. This we have expressed, hypothetically, in Figure 361, by triple cables leading from each point of the central area and fovea (b, c), by double cables from the binocular periphery (a), and by simple cables from the monocular crescentic portions of the retinae (x, y).

This further leads to the problem of types of

FIG. 360.—Dr. Ragnar Arthur Granit (1900), director of Medicinska Nobelinstitutet, Neurofysiologiska Avdelningen, Karolinska Institutet, in Stockholm, Sweden. The most accomplished modern investigator of the electrophysiology of the vertebrate retina. Courtesy Dr. Granit; photo by Benkow, Kgl. Hovfotograf, Stockholm, Sweden, 1947.

the individual conducting fiber units vary in different portions of the optic nerve. In the foveal and areal bundles they may be more complex; in the extra-areal periphery and even more so in the extreme monocular crescent, terminal arborizations of the optic nerve fibers in the laminated nucleus. It may be expected that the fibers that mediate a fine epicritic sense such as central acuity, belonging to small ganglions of the central fovea and area, would be

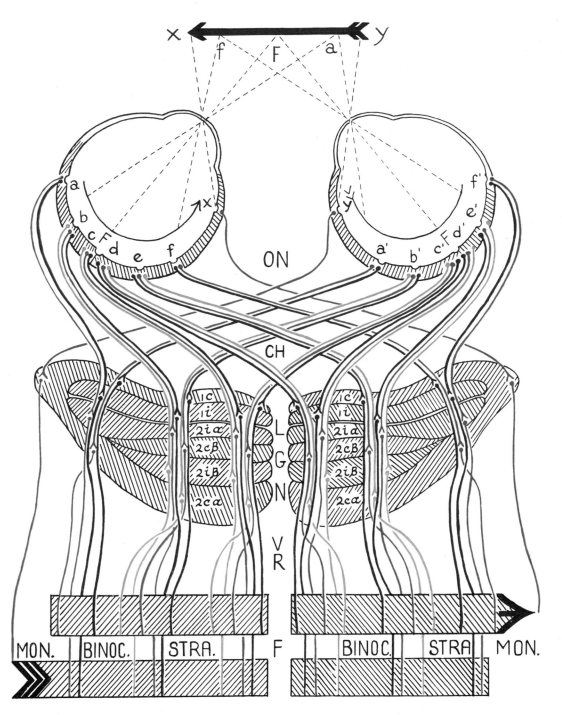

Fig. 361—Components of the primate visual system. Both eyes are focused on the centre *F* of an object *x-y*. The inverted retinal images partly coincide (*a-f, a'-f'*), and in part do not (*x-f, y-a'*). From each point of the images arise fiber bundles (*ON*) which, after partial decussation in chiasma (*CH*), enter laminated later. genic. nuclei (*LGN*). From here fibers of visual radiations (*VR*) continue to the right and left striate area where a single but two-fold cortical visual image is formed. *Note:* the point-to-point transmission of images along the entire visual system, the more complex components in and around foveae (*a, b, c, d, e, f; a', b', c', d', e', f'*) transmitting binocular portions (*BINOC-STRA*), the simpler temporal components (*x, y*) transmitting monocular portions of the images (*MON*). (*See* for further details text, and Figs. 401, 439.)

thin and within restricted terminals, whereas those of the large ganglions of the far periphery and of the monocular crescent, instrumental in crude peripheral vision, would be more robust and with wider terminal arborizations. Furthermore, it is likely that the terminal arborizations also vary in the same territory both in spread and in other features, according to the cell variety, the smallest being those of the midget ganglions and the larger belonging to the various diffuse ganglions, for example, those of the *m* and *n* varieties.

Is there a segregation of the optic terminals in different geniculate laminae, according to their origin in different ganglion varieties? This problem requires an unequivocal answer, necessary for the understanding of the intrinsic makeup and working of the visual apparatus. Unfortunately, only a few known observations give some hint as to what the answer may be. Such is the segregation of particular types of cells in distinct laminae. The two ventral laminae, for example, are composed of much more voluminous cells than those that fill the two or four dorsal laminae. It is, then, probable that the terminal arborizations of the giant retinal ganglion cells also spread principally, if perhaps not exclusively, in the two ventral magnocellular layers. But this may not mean that all larger ganglion cells send their axons only to the two ventral layers. The varying size of all ganglion varieties, each variety being present in all regions of the retina, makes this doubtful. The principal difference found is in the dimensions of the ganglions, those in the fovea and next to it being the most reduced in size, those in the far periphery the largest. Hence it is probable that several fiber categories, belonging to different varieties of retinal ganglion cells, terminate side by side in every part of the laminated lateral geniculate nucleus. This is most probable for the small-celled laminae, whereas the large-celled ventral laminae are more likely to contain only the more robust terminal arborization.

The preceding arrangements, still largely hypothetical, indicate a complex synaptical structure of the laminated lateral geniculate nucleus. The complexity of this internode further increases with the additional presence of the so-called "association" cells interspersed among the larger principal cells, as described in chapter VI, 9.

Are there in the lateral geniculate nucleus terminations of fibers arising from other parts of the brain, possibly from the cerebral cortex, as assumed by Brouwer and his co-workers? On the basis of our own examinations of Golgi-stained preparations, the presence of such fibers cannot be denied, even though this requires further study. Certain widespread teledendric arborizations, arriving from outside the nucleus, each fiber spreading over a large segment, most likely belong to this category, as pointed out in chapter VI, 9.

Concerning the visual radiations, the known observations also indicate a composite structure of these fiber systems. The experiments recorded in chapter VII, 7, showed each minute fiber bundle, or segment of the radiation, to be made up of several categories of fibers. First is the arrangement, caused by the semidecussation of optic nerves in the chiasma (*CH*, Fig. 361). Owing to this, fibers from each point of the binocular portions of the homonymous halves of both retinae meet in the same segment of the ipsilateral geniculate nucleus, although they terminate in different laminae, as described in the preceding chapters.

There is good reason to think, however, that each minute fiber bundle is not homogeneous but is made up of several categories of fibers. The evidence in support of this is found in the experiments described in the preceding pages, which showed minute zones of retrograde cell degeneration passing through all cellular laminae of the nucleus. This is the case whether the visual radiation is interrupted anywhere along its course or the striate area is damaged, provided that the ventral, infra-Gennarian layers are also involved. Since it is reasonable to consider different laminae of each homonymous laminar set of the nucleus, the right and the left, to be made up of distinct varieties of the principal nerve cells, each lamina of each set giving rise to its own category of fibers, each bundle of the visual radiation may then be expected to contain all fiber categories. The same postulation must be made for the terminal arborizations in the striate cortex.

The last and most difficult problem arises in tracing the further course and the final fate of the several distinct categories of impulses arriving in the striate cortex by way of the several categories of fibers of the visual radiation. Here, again, the first question is the identity and behavior of the ipsilateral and contralateral homonymous fibers in the striate cortex. The next is the problem of the varieties of neurons therein and their synaptical relationships. The final problem concerns the connections of the striate area within itself, with the para-peristriate areae of the same and the contralateral side, and with other parts of the brain, cortical and subcortical. These problems, as far as our knowledge permitted, have been discussed in the various sections of the preceding chapters, especially in chapter VIII, 7. There it was also shown how important and how vast this problem is—a great challenge to future research.

Chapter X

The Blood Supply of the Vertebrate Visual System

SEC. 1. GENERAL REMARKS ON THE BLOOD SUPPLY OF THE EYE
AND OF THE VISUAL PATHWAYS AND CENTERS

1. INTRODUCTION.—The normal function of the central and peripheral nervous organs, like that of any other living part of the body, depends upon several factors. The foremost is the kind, number, arrangement, and synaptical connections of its specific constituents—the nerve cells or neurons—and of the processes by means of which they are connected with one another and with other tissues of the body (*see* chap. I, 8 and 9; chap. V, 3–7; chap. VI, 8, 9, 10; chap. VIII, 5 and 7; and especially chap. IX). Another and almost equally essential factor is the blood supply. The smooth functioning of the intricately organized specific nervous parenchyma depends on the way the arteries that carry the nutritive fluid called "blood" are distributed to the various parts of the brain, the spinal cord, and the nerves.

The factors indispensable for a harmonious discharge of the normal functions are the place and the mode of distribution of the principal arterial stems and of the numerous secondary, tertiary, and other branches; the presence or absence of the anastomotical connections of the larger arterial stems; the character of the capillary network in a particular locality; and the proper vasomotor and other regulation of the amount of blood passing during a given unit of time through a given part of a nervous organ, depending upon its greater or lesser activity.

Of hardly less importance are the arrangements for free return of the venous blood through the veins of the brain and the venous sinuses of the cranium to the heart, at all times permitting replacement of used blood by fresh. Again such general factors as maintenance of normal blood pressure in the circulatory system; normal constitution of the blood by proper functioning of the blood-forming, respiratory, endo-crine, digestive, and excretory organs; normal condition of the blood vessels themselves; sufficient intake of nourishing food, including vitamins, salts, and water; avoidance of overworking the circulatory system; and avoidance of acute or chronic poisoning either by infection, by abuse of drugs, or by food poisons—all are necessary for preservation of the favorable conditions required. Any alteration of these factors may temporarily or permanently impair the function and the very life of the specific parenchyma of the nervous organs: the nerve cells proper, their expansions, and synaptical contacts.

It is reasonable to think that the general factors and agencies, when at fault, are more likely to cause diffuse or widespread pathological changes, the variation of the effect depending upon local factors and the innate histological and biochemical properties of the nervous tissue. The pathological processes confined to any one blood vessel, on the contrary, will most likely be of limited scope in space but more profound in degree, affecting only the part of the brain supplied by that particular vessel. The degree of the effect in the latter case may depend upon the degree of interference with normal circulation.

The most profound changes are caused by an occlusion or clogging of the larger blood vessels, especially the arteries, as exemplified by an embolism or thrombosis. In such an event the part of the brain or sense organ supplied by the obstructed vessel may undergo complete degeneration of its nervous parenchyma, with resulting permanent and irreparable loss of the particular function. The same effect may result from a prolonged vasospasm and probably also by a prolonged hemostasis.

The nervous system in general and the visual system in particular are exceedingly complex assemblies of agglomerations or systems of nerve cells, each agglomeration with its own entirely specific function (*see* preceding chapter). A serious localized impairment of any constituent of the visual system therefore impairs or abolishes its function. This function is irrevocably damaged and can at best be only inadequately compensated for by other parts of the nervous tissue.

Since the blood vessels alone provide the visual system with nutritive material and hence supply the food upon which the life of the elaborate neuronal organization of that system depends, an acquaintance with the organization of its blood supply and of vascular diseases in ophthalmic pathology, in neuropathology, and in general pathology is of paramount importance.

The role the vascular factor plays in vision is most dramatically illustrated in numerous types of visual field disturbances, and equally so in various forms of impairment of the higher or psychic functions of vision, in transient blindness, and in many other similar phenomena. From the study of the arrangement of the blood vessels supplying various parts of the visual system alone, the great importance of its vascular supply becomes quite apparent.

The several subdivisions of the visual system, the infranuclear, nuclear, and supranuclear, including the cortical centers, form a chain stretching the whole length of the base of the cranium (*see* chap. VI, 1; and chap. VII, 8). This chain begins with the two eyeballs and terminates with the two striate areae of the occipital lobes. Owing to the great length of the visual system, all principal subdivisions of the cerebral arterial tree participate in its supply. This fact again has an important bearing upon pathology, since each part of the system may be affected in its own way by a disease arising from a peculiar local character of the vascular supply.

In the following paragraphs a general outline of the sources of cerebral blood supply is first given. In the detailed description that follows, only the blood vessels directly related to the visual pathways and centers are presented, their source, course, distribution, connections

with one another (if any); their topographical relation to the sulci, gyri, cytoarchitectural areae and regions; and their relation to the localizable functions of the cerebral cortex. Special attention is paid to the blood supply of each of the several parts that make up the visual system. The pathophysiological significance of some of the vessels is also discussed, this subject being treated in some detail in Part III of this book.

It is perhaps not amiss to call attention to our present limited knowledge of the blood vessels and of the circulation in general, which is exceeded only by our ignorance of the intrinsic organization of the nervous system itself. The paramount importance which the vascular system assumes in the normal maintenance of the nervous organs and in their pathology makes additional work on the understanding of the vascular system one of the foremost tasks of modern research.

2. Sources and general character of the cerebral blood supply.—The brain, with the extra- and intracerebral parts of the visual system, is supplied by two pairs of arteries (Fig. 362): the internal carotids (*ica*) and the vertebral arteries (*va*).

At the base of the brain these four large blood vessels are connected by anastomoses or links, which, together, form the "arterial circle" of Willis (*acoa, acea, ica, mcea, pocoa, pocea, basa* in Figs. 366, 367, 368). From this circle emerge three pairs of arteries, one artery of each pair supplying a part of one cerebral hemisphere on its own side—the anterior (*acea*), the middle (*mcea*), and the posterior cerebral arteries (*pocea*). Each of these six arteries divides into several medium-sized branches, which, in turn, by repeated division, produce a great number of smaller preterminal and terminal arteries and arterioles (Figs. 369, 370).

The arteries spread over the surface of all parts of the brain, some exposed and others concealed in the sulci and fissures. In some regions, e.g., over the base of the brain and over the medial face of the frontal lobes close to the "knee" of the callosal body, the main stems remain on the surface (Fig. 369); over most of the inner face and over the entire outer or convex

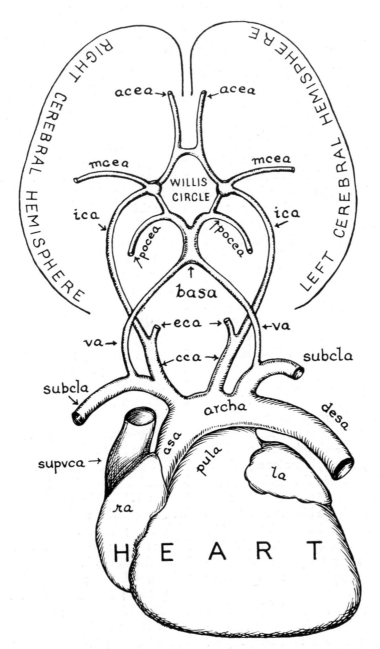

FIG. 362.—Sources of blood supply of the head and brain. The diagram represents the heart in a frontal view, together with the principal vessels arising from it—the superior vena cava, aorta, and pulmonary artery. From the
aortal arch arise arterial stems whose branches, the two vertebral and the two carotid arteries, form the arterial
circle of Willis. From this circle emerge three pairs of arteries, the right and the left anterior, middle, and posterior
cerebral arteries, which are distributed to the corresponding parts of the two hemispheres of the brain. *Labeling:*
acea, anterior cerebral artery; *archa*, arch of aorta; *asa*, ascending portion of aorta; *cca*, common carotid arteries;
desa, descending portion of aorta; *eca*, external carotid arteries; *ica*, internal carotid arteries; *la*, left auricle of heart;
mcea, middle cerebral artery; *pocea*, posterior cerebral artery; *pula*, pulmonary artery; *ra*, right auricle of heart;
subcla, subclavian artery; *supvca*, superior vena cava; *va*, vertebral artery.

face of the hemisphere, however, the arterial trunks, by preference, use the furrows that separate the convolutions from one another.

The principal arterial stems pursue the same direction which they assumed during the early fetal development (Fig. 370). This direction, roughly, radiates from Willis' "arterial circle" at the brain's base as a focal point toward the margins and poles of the hemisphere (*cf.* Fig. 375). Hence, while remaining buried as much as possible within the sulci, some arteries in places make bold short cuts across the free convexities of the gyri, only to dip again into the next convenient sulci, within which they continue in the same direction. Still other arteries may sweep across the sulci in the manner of bridges, while yet others, which remain buried during most of their course, may emerge for awhile on the surface in the form of longer or shorter loops.

The arteries, particularly the smaller ones, give off secondary, tertiary, and other branches. By further subdivision into minute twigs, the preterminal and terminal arterioles eventually dissolve into a capillary network that pervades all tissue.

All blood vessels, the arteries as well as the veins of the brain, irrespective of size, while on the surface of the brain, are imbedded within, or are enveloped by, the tissue of the two soft tunics or leptomeninges—the pia mater and the arachnoid membrane. The pia mater especially, whose delicate tissue coats the surface of the brain, filling all furrows, slits, and clefts, serves as a vehicle along which the blood vessels reach their place of destination, the substance of the brain. Most arteries penetrating into the brain's substance are small; in a few places larger arteries may be found pursuing a longer or shorter course.

The ultimate and smallest subdivisions of the arteries—the capillaries or hairlike vessels— may be seen only with the microscope (Fig. 364). They form a continuous network of varying density and pattern, especially rich in the gray matter, such as the cortex of the brain, and the various nuclei. The capillary network permeates all parts of the cerebral tissue, its meshes enveloping minute islands containing nerve cells and their expansions or, depending on the locality, only the nerve fibers and the supporting neuroglial tissue.

Through the capillary network, in the living organism fresh blood is carried along the arteries by the action of the heart and is brought into the closest contact with the living parenchyma of the brain, the nerve cells, and their processes. In this way the essential or specific structures of the brain are provided with the various nutrient constituents contained in the blood and are relieved of the used material, which is carried away by the veins.

Beyond the zone of capillaries, the vessels begin again to merge into larger stems of the venous system (blue in Fig. 364). These venules, by further uniting with their kind, produce larger veins, which reach the venous sinuses of the cranium in a more direct course over the cerebral surface and empty into the large veins of the neck, which eventually empty into the right half of the heart.

References: Alexander & Putnam 1938; Almeida Lima 1950; Bloom, Merz & Taylor 1946; Bostroem 1939; Brobeil 1950; Bronk 1938; A. C. P. Campbell 1938; Clark & Wentsler 1938; S. Cobb 1938; Cohnheim 1872; Collens & Wilensky 1953; Cone & Barrera 1931; Courville 1950; Craigie 1938, 1940, 1942, 1943; Davison, Goodhart & Needles 1934; Echlin 1942; Evans & McEachern 1938; Ferris 1941; Field *et al.* 1951; Finley 1938, 1940; H. Florey 1925; Foerster 1939; H. S. Forbes 1928; Forbes & Cobb 1938; Gellhorn 1925; R. W. Gerard 1938; Gibbs, Maxwell & Gibbs 1947; Gildea & Cobb 1930; Globus 1936, 1938; Gregg & Shipley 1944; W. R. Hess 1939; Hicks & Warren 1950; Himwich 1951; W. H. Hollinshead 1954; E. G. Holmes 1932; Houssay *et al.* 1950; Howe & McKinley 1927; A. Jakob 1927, 1929; Kabat & Schadewald 1941; Keller 1939; W. Kempner 1949, 1951; Kempner *et al.* 1949; Kennedy, Wortis & Wortis 1938; Knisely 1951; Knisely & Bloch 1948; Knisely, Bloch & Warner 1946; L. Krehl 1910; A. Krogh 1936; Kubie & Hetler 1928; Lazorthes 1949; Lennox, Gibbs & Gibbs 1938; J. Ley 1932; Livingston 1933; Lohr 1939; Lorente de Nó 1927; Märk 1944–45; Marchesani 1939; Marple & Wright 1950; L. R. Müller 1931; Pearce & Gerard 1942; R. A. Pfeifer 1928, 1930, 1931, 1939; Pfeiffer & Kunkle 1951; Putnam 1937; Putnam & Alexander 1938; Raab 1953; Ryder *et al.* 1951; Samuels 1950; Sánta & Cipriani 1938; Scharrer 1937, 1938, 1940, 1944;

C. F. Schmidt 1950; Schmidt & Hendrix 1938; Scholtz 1939; J. H. Schultz 1939; Sepp 1928; A. Šercer 1951; Shenkin & Harmel 1948; Spatz 1939; J. Stambul 1953; Starling 1949; G. W. Stavraky 1936; Sugar & Gerard 1938; *Symposium on Blood Supply* 1938; Thompson & Smith 1951; Tigerstedt 1921–23; Tureen 1938; Vander Eecken 1951; F. B. Walsh 1947; S. Weiss 1938; Wentsler 1936; Winterstein 1929; Wislocki 1940; H. G. Wolff 1936, 1938; Woollard & Weddell 1935; Youmans & Huchins 1951. *See also* numerous articles in *Zentralbl. f. d. ges. Neurol. u. Psychiat.*, v. 97, pp. 337–70, 1939 (*Symposium on Blood Supply*, German).

SEC. 2. THE BLOOD VESSELS OF THE EYE AND OF THE OPTIC NERVE

1. Sources of the blood supply of the orbital contents, including the optic nerve.—The various structures which fill the orbital cavity or the eye socket, including the eyeball, are supplied with blood principally through the ophthalmic artery (*opha; see also* sec. 3 [2], this chapter). This artery arises from the intracranial portion of the internal carotid artery (*ica*) and passes into the eye socket through the bony optic foramen closely attached to the optic nerve (Figs. 369, 370, 371).

The anterior continuation of the ophthalmic artery, the nasofrontal artery, emerges from the eye socket at the inner or nasal corner or canthus of the eye, where it is continuous with the dorsal-nasal and angular arteries, branches of the facial or external maxillary artery, which in turn originate in the external carotid artery (Fig. 362, *eca*). In this way an arterial circle is completed, its source being in the common carotid artery (*cca*). Other lesser sources supplying the orbital contents are the middle meningeal and the (internal) maxillary arteries.

The venous blood from the orbit and the eye empties principally through the superior and inferior ophthalmic veins by way of the superior orbital fissure, mostly into the cavernous sinus at the cranial floor, which in turn discharges through the superior petrosal sinus and the palatine vein and some other smaller outlets into the internal jugular vein. The anterior continuation of the superior ophthalmic vein, the nasofrontal vein, connecting with the anterior facial vein (in turn discharging into the common facial vein and through that into the internal jugular vein), completes the venous circle. (For details of illustrations not given in this book consult textbooks and atlases of anatomy and also the following monographs: Kronfeld, McHugh & Polyak, *The Human Eye in Anatomical Transparencies;* and Polyak, McHugh & Judd, *The Human Ear in Anatomical Transparencies.*)

2. The blood supply of the optic nerve and eyeball.—The eyeball and the optic nerve receive their blood supply from a number of small branches of the ophthalmic artery (Figs. 365, 371, *opha; see also* Figs. 369, 370): anterior (*anter. cil. art., acila*) and posterior (short and long) ciliary arteries (*mpcila, lpcila*), and by the central retinal artery (*cra.*).

The ciliary arteries, with the episcleral branches, supply the two outer tunics, the sclera and the uvea (Fig. 365). Of the three constituents of the uvea (chorioid, ciliary body, iris), the chorioid membrane is principally a vascular tunic made up of a dense network of blood vessels imbedded in a connective tissue stroma and of chromatophore cells filled with a dark pigment (Fig. 127). The locality where it is best developed corresponds to the central area and fovea (*A*, Fig. 129). The smallest and most numerous vessels of the chorioid are on its inner side facing the photoreceptor layer of the retina, the choriocapillary layer. The anterior transparent portion of the tough outer tunic, the cornea, and the crystalline lens normally do not contain blood vessels but receive nutritive fluids indirectly, principally from the aqueous and vitreous humors.

The intracranial portion of the optic nerve is supplied by the ophthalmic and anterior cerebral arteries (Fig. 371). The intraorbital portion is supplied by the branches of the ophthalmic artery above, chiefly by the external branches, and to a small extent by the central retinal artery, including a recurrent or postcentral artery.

The venous blood from the two outer tunics—the sclera and the uvea—is carried away principally by the four to six vortex veins, also by small veins on the surface of the sclera—the episcleral veins—and by the superficial veins of the optic nerve (Fig. 365). The retinal venous blood is returned by way of the central retinal vein. All this venous blood is finally emptied chiefly into the ophthalmic veins, the superior and inferior, and through these principally into the cavernous sinus in the sellar region of the cranial cavity and further into the superior petrosal sinus and internal jugular vein. (*See also* sec. 3 [2], this chapter.)

3. THE BLOOD SUPPLY OF THE RETINA.—The blood supply of the retinal membrane in Man and other Primates and to a greater or lesser degree also in other Mammals is double (Figs. 363, 365), directly from the central artery and indirectly from the ciliary arteries via the chorioid membrane.

In many Infraprimate Mammals the principal, and perhaps the only, supplier is the ciliary-chorioidal system. In the Inframammalian Vertebrates the retina receives its supply both from the chorioid and, osmotically, via the vitreal fluid from special vascular organs protruding from the head of the optic nerve into the vitreal cavity, the "vascular cone" of Lizards, the *pecten* or "comb" of Birds, and other similar organs (*cf.* Figs. 172–76).

The central retinal artery (*cra*), a branch of the ophthalmic artery (*opha*), accompanied by the central retinal vein (*crv*), enters the eyeball by way of the optic nerve (*see* sec. 3 [2], this chapter, and Figs. 148, 363). The bundle of these "central retinal blood vessels" penetrates into the optic nerve, in the adult and in the fetus from the third month on, in the center of the inferior aspect of the nerve or, at most, slightly nasal, at a distance individually varying from 6 to 15 mm., usually 10–11 mm., or from $\frac{1}{4}$ to almost $\frac{1}{2}$ inch, behind the eyeball (Figs. 201, *B;* 202). In the younger fetus the point of entry is in the middle of the lower nasal quadrant. Within the optic nerve the central blood vessels, surrounded by a moderate quantity of connective tissue, fill the so-called vascular channel, preserving a central location throughout their course as far as the papilla of the nerve (Fig. 185).

After passing through the cribriform lamina of the sclera, at the "head" or disk of the optic nerve, the central retinal vessels emerge at the inner vitreal face, whence, divided into branches, they spread over the expanse of the retinal membrane. They may be examined in the living person by means of an ophthalmoscope, or "eye mirror" (Figs. 148, 149, 165–70, 363).

During their passage through the initial portion of the optic nerve, the central retinal vessels, more the artery than the vein, are connected through the capillary and precapillary anastomoses with the ciliary system of the chorioid and scleral tunics, which system here forms the arterial circle of Zinn, Haller, and Leber surrounding the cribriform lamina of the optic nerve (Fig. 365). This connection, however, has been disputed by some (Beauvieux & Ristitch 1924) and reaffirmed by others (E. Wolff 1948). Beyond this point, the two vascular systems of the eye—the retinal and the ciliary-chorioidal—are normally separated. (*See* later in this subsection for Rucker and co-workers' experiments with monkeys.)

Both the central retinal artery and the vein, usually while passing through the cribriform lamina, divide, the vein a little sooner than the artery, into two principal branches, an upper and a lower papillary artery and vein. While still at the papilla, the four stems divide again dichotomically into a number of branches radiating in all directions. According to H. Magnus (1873), five pairs of larger, and two of smaller, arteries and veins may be distinguished (Fig. 363). These are: an upper and a lower temporal (*st, it*) and an upper and a lower nasal artery and vein (*sn, in*), oriented according to the four quadrants, and a single and somewhat smaller median artery and vein (*mn*) spreading in the middle zone on the nasal side.

Distinct from these five pairs of larger vessels are two minute pairs that partially supply the central area and fovea, or "macula": a superior and an inferior macular artery and vein. Ordinarily, however, this favored structure, both in Man and in other Higher Primates, is supplied by several smaller vessels branching from the larger stems and converging from all sides upon the foveal excavation (Figs. 148, 149, 165–69).

Occasionally the macular artery may arise from the arterial circle of Zinn, Haller, and Leber surrounding the initial portion of the optic nerve and formed, according to Leber, by the posterior ciliary arteries, whereas the macular vein may take its origin similarly from the chorioidal veins.

In two specimens of the Philippine Tarsier examined ophthalmoscopically, two distinct macular arteries of fair size and a single macular vein, upon which the supply of the central area and fovea in this species principally depends, were found in each eye (Fig. 149).

The division and distribution of the central retinal blood vessels shows much individual variation in detail (Gauss 1930; Bucciante 1933; Jensen 1936; Rucker 1946). Of the larger vessels, the temporal are thicker than the nasal. Also the temporal vessels pursue an arching course, circling above and below the central area and fovea, toward which smaller branches extend. In about one-fourth the cases there are no distinct macular arteries, and the entire foveal region is supplied by the twigs from the upper and lower temporal arteries.

In the central area, only small blood vessels are present. From these a few minute twigs normally slip over the brim, indicated by a circular or elliptical light reflex, into the foveal excavation (Fig. 363). Here they produce a fine capillary network, somewhat denser than in the extrafoveal periphery. In the deepest part of the foveal pit, where all vitreal layers including *6* and zone *5-c* are absent, in the foveal floor or foveola—and here alone—all blood vessels, including capillaries, are absent (*cf.* Fig. 364).

The extent of the avascular or vessel-free foveal area was much studied, especially by observing entoptically or subjectively the "vessel tree" or "figure" first described by Purkinje (portrait Fig. 354). Its diameter and shape vary individually from 0.13 to 0.75 mm., measuring, on the average, from 0.4 to 0.5 mm. across. According to the observation of Leber (1880), the diameter of the avascular center in one of his own eyes was 0.42 mm. on the retina, or 1°35′56″ of arc in his field of view (*see also* O. Becker 1881; Gescher 1925; Weale, quoted by Dartnall & Thomson 1949). The avascular area, accordingly, is practically coextensive with the central territory of the fovea, the so-called "outer" or "external" fovea, where cones alone are present, and is much smaller than the entire foveal excavation. (*See* chap. V, 9.)

The developmental factors which cause the archlike arrangement of the circumareal vessels in the temporal portion of the human and other primate retinae, including those of the pronouncedly nocturnal *Aotes* and *Tarsius* (*see* Fig. 149 and chap. XIV, 12), just like those responsible for a similar arrangement of the optic nerve fibers, remain unknown, precisely as do similar factors that form the foveal excavation. Whatever they are, the elimination of the vitreal layers *5-c* to *9* of the retina that contain blood vessels obviously serves to reduce a dioptrical impediment placed in front of the receptor layer *2*, thus increasing the resolving power and perhaps also the color perception of the retina in the line of direct vision (*cf.* chap. V, 10 [7]).

From the principal arterial branches, smaller twigs separate and, by further subdivision, produce a capillary network permeating the tissue of the vitreal layers throughout the entire expanse of the retinal membrane, excepting the very center of the foveal excavation—its floor, the central avascular area already mentioned. The vessels which compose the system of the central retinal artery and vein are imbedded in the retinal tissue as far as the inner limiting membrane. They supply the retina in its entire extent, from the optic papilla to the ora serrata. In Man, Monkey, and Ape and in some other Mammals there are, as a rule, no precapillary anastomotic connections between the individual larger and smaller arteries (Fig. 364). Nor are there any connections between the territories of the central retinal and the ciliary-chorioidal systems of the eyeball, except in the region of the optic papilla, where there is some connection with the scleral and chorioidal vessels of the ciliary system, as mentioned before (*see* later, this section).

The central retinal artery, accordingly, as a whole, and again each of its individual branches, including the precapillaries, fairly represent true "terminal arteries" or "end-arteries" as defined by Cohnheim (1872). The advantage of this arrangement, in the opinion of some, e.g., Magnus, is the relative independence of the retinal circulation, which keeps that all-important organ out of reach of the noxious influences arising from the pathology of the outer walls of the eyeball. The unavoidable disadvantage is the impossibility of establishing collateral circulation with the neighboring ciliary-chorioidal system in case the central artery or one of its branches is directly affected by a pathological process, such as thrombosis, embolism, atheroma, and the like. The branches of the central retinal vein are similarly arranged, except that they are united by anastomoses along the serrated margin.

Not the entire thickness of the retina, however, but only approximately the inner or vitreal three-fifths, in Man and his primate relatives, are supplied by the central retinal artery, or precisely all layers beginning with the inner zone of the outer plexiform layer, *5-c,* and inward as far as the inner limiting membrane, *10* (*cf.* Figs. 127, 128, with Fig. 365). The layers external to zone *5-c*—layer *1* to zone *5-b* inclusive—which practically correspond with the photoreceptors, do not contain any blood vessels. They are indirectly supplied with nutritive substances. In this, the major share is contributed by the vascular network of the chorioidal membrane and thus by the ciliary arterial system, particularly its innermost tier, the choriocapillary layer.

It appears probable that the nourishment of the entire bacillary layer, *2,* and also of the outer nuclear layer, *4,* is entirely chorioidal in most of the retinal expanse. This seems, in part, to be also true of the outer zone of the outer plexiform layer, *5-a,* especially where that zone is thick, as is the case in most of the central area (Henle's "outer fiber layer"). Zone *5-b,* however, may possibly receive its supply through the outermost loops of the capillary network of the central retinal system.

In the avascular center of the central foveal excavation, in the foveola, where there are no blood vessels of any kind, zone *5-a* or Henle's outer fiber layer, which here immediately borders on the vitreous—being separated from it only by the thin inner limiting membrane—and possibly also the outer nuclear layer may depend nutritionally, to some extent or entirely, upon the vitreous and thus indirectly upon the central retinal system. The indirect nutritional supply of the outer retinal layers and, in general, the exchange of metabolic substances are obviously of an osmotic nature, both in the avascular center and in the vascular extrafoveal periphery.

The intimate functional relationship between the chorioid membrane and the photoreceptor layer is attested by the exceptional thickness of the chorioid in the territory of the central area, particularly of the central fovea. And it is precisely this locality where the bacillary and other layers, made up of the rod and cone cells, are much thicker and where the nutritional requirement is undoubtedly much greater than in the extrafoveal regions (Man, Ape, Monkey, Tarsier, Golden Eagle). By contrast, it is exactly here that, owing to the absence of inner layers *5-c* to *9,* the vessels of the central retinal origin are also absent (Figs. 129, 161).

A double retinal blood supply, ciliary-chorioidal and central-retinal, is a feature characteristic of all Primates (Man, Ape, Monkey, Tarsier). However, it appears that in the Simians the two systems are not so completely separated as in Man, as the following observation indicates. In Man pressure on the eyeball, by which the central blood vessels in the cribriform lamina are strangulated, produces in a short time an ischemic edema of the retina, resulting in blindness. In the Macaque Monkey this type of visual loss could not be induced experimentally, according to unpublished experiments of Dr. C. W. Rucker, of the Mayo Clinic, Rochester, Minnesota, and his co-workers, indicating an incomplete separation of the ciliary and the central arterial systems.

In other Vertebrates either the ciliary-chorioidal or the central-retinal supply prevails more or less, in extreme types one to the almost complete exclusion of the other. In such a retina the vessels are either absent in the entire thickness of its tissue, the supply depending upon osmosis of the nutrient substances from the vitreous and chorioid; or in another extreme—rare to be sure—the entire thickness of the retina between the outer and the inner limiting membranes is permeated by the vessels belonging to the central system. (*Cf.* Kolmer & Lauber 1936.)

A blood supply of the retina similar to that of Man has been found in all Primates so far investigated, including the nocturnal *Aotes trivirga-*

tus and *Tarsius philippinensis* or *T. carbonarius* (*see* Figs. 149, 166–69, and chap. XIV, 12). In all of them the central vessels emerge on the vitreal face of the optic papilla, spreading in a typical way in all directions, in the temporal portion describing arches above and below the central area and fovea. Such an arrangement has been studied ophthalmoscopically and is easy to see in well-made specimens (Fig. 162). In Lemurs, judging from the plates published by G. L. Johnson (1901) and from his description, there is no true fovea; but the arrangement of vessels indicates an incipient avascularity of the locality homologous with the central area of Higher Primates, the vessels here being fewer and more delicate (so in *Lemur coronatus* and *Galago monteiri*). A similar incipient central avascular area is also present in the Philippine Tree Shrew (*Urogale everetti*), where it may be seen ophthalmoscopically. This seems to be of some interest, in view of the modern opinion, according to which the Tupaiidae, a suborder of Insectivora, are considered by some the phylogenetical precursors of the Primate Order (*see* chap. XIV, 10).

In most other Mammals and in the Inframammalian Vertebrates the source, distribution, and abundance of the blood supply of the retina vary extraordinarily. In the Carnivora, Pinnipedia, Squirrels, and some other Mammals the retina is well supplied with vessels, their source, however, being in part or entirely the chorioid-ciliary system. Also, in some, only the layer of the nerve fibers is permeated by the capillaries; in others, in addition, the ganglion cell layer; in still others the inner plexiform layer also (so in the Alpine Marmot). In the Horse, Tapir, Elephant, *Hyrax*, Insectivorous Bats, some Rodents, Edentates, and Marsupials the blood supply is restricted to the optic papilla or to the adjoining territory, while in the Rhinoceros, *Hystrix*, *Dasypus*, *Echidna*, and *Proechidna*, there are no blood vessels whatever in the retina. By contrast, in the Old World Dormice *Myoxus* and *Eliomys* and similarly in the Raccoon and Opossum, a dense capillary network has been found underneath the outer limiting membrane within the outer nuclear layer, whereas the choriocapillary layer is absent, according to Kolmer. Of all the other Inframammalian Vertebrates, the Eel Family or Anguilidae alone shows complete vascularization.

Other Vertebrates have either a completely or almost completely avascular retina. In these, as in the Higher Vertebrates, the outer retinal layers depend nutritionally upon the chorioid-ciliary system of blood vessels, while the inner layers receive their nutrient fluid by way of osmosis from special vascular structures, such as the pecten or comb of the Birds and the "cone" of Lizards, derivatives of the hyaloid artery protruding from the optic disk into the vitreous.

A remarkable and well-developed vascular system, entirely different from that of any other Vertebrate, is present in the Anuran Amphibians (Frogs, Tree Frogs, Toads). It consists of a "central vein," whose branches, imbedded within the hyaloid membrane of the vitreous, spread over the inner face of the retina. Morphologically and functionally this system closely simulates the system of the central retinal artery of the Higher Vertebrates. No less unique an arrangement was found by Kolmer in the Flying Foxes (*Macrochiroptera*): conical loops of chorioid vessels invading the retinal substance almost as far as the inner limiting membrane.

The Ruminants possess a rich and complex central retinal system, remarkable because of the presence of a long, horizontally placed central area supplied by serially arranged twigs arising from larger horizontal vessels (Fig. 170). (*See* Leber, Johnson, Franz, Kolmer, Kolmer & Lauber, Rochon-Duvigneaud, Rochon-Duvigneaud & Rode, Walls, and others, for additional information.)

The blood vessels of the retina, or "vascular retinal tree" of Purkinje, may be seen "entoptically," that is, introspectively, by looking toward a moderately bright surface in lateral illumination. Subjectively the vessels appear as grayish shadows, the principal upper and lower temporal arteries and veins arching above and below the foveal excavation or "fixation point," toward which smaller twigs spread without reaching it. When the source of light is moved, the "retinal vascular tree" executes a parallactic movement in the opposite direction, a phenomenon used by H. Müller to prove the photoreceptor function of the layer of rods and cones (*see* chap. I, 7 [5]). In hemianopia, only that portion of the vascular tree is seen entoptically which corresponds to the functional portion of the fields of view (self-observation).

References: Abelsdorff & Wessely 1909; F. H. Adler 1953; F. Arnold 1838–42; Ascher 1942, 1946; D. T. Atkinson 1937; Axenfeld 1923 (and later publications); Ayres 1884; Ballantyne 1941; E. H. Bárány 1947; Beauvieux & Ristitch 1924; O. Becker 1881; Bedell 1929; C. Behr 1935; H. Bloch 1906; Bucciante 1933; Burow 1863; Clerici 1943; Damel 1936; Davson 1949; Dedekind 1909; Denissenko 1880; Deyl 1896; Di Marzio 1937; Dimmer 1921; Dimmer & Pillat 1929; Duggan 1943; Duke-Elder 1932; Duke-Elder & Davson 1943, 1948, 1949; Duke-Elder, Quilliam & Davson 1940; Elias 1950; Elschnig 1888, 1897, 1898; Elwyn 1946; Erggelet 1929; J. N. Evans 1939; E. Fawcett 1896; F. P. Fischer 1925; R. Förster 1877; Fortin 1927, 1930; V. Franz 1934; Friedenwald 1944; Fuchs & Fuchs 1945; H. Gauss 1930; Gellhorn 1925; Gerlach 1881; Gescher 1925; Graefe & Saemisch 1874–1932; Granit 1947; Hartinger 1938; Henckel 1898; T. Henderson 1941; C. J. Herrick 1911; F. Hesse 1880; W. His 1880; Jensen 1936; Johannides 1880; G. L. Johnson 1896–97, 1901, 1927; Kapuściński 1948; W. Kempner; Kerschner 1943; Kinsey & Grant 1944; Kiss 1947; Köllner 1920; Koeppe 1918, 1920, 1937; Kolmer 1911, 1912, 1914, 1924, 1927, 1930, 1936 (with Lauber); Kolmer & Lauber 1936; Kraupa 1914; W. Krause 1875; Kronfeld, McHugh & Polyak 1943; Kümmell 1925; Kugelberg 1932, 1934, 1937; Kuhnt 1881; Lambert 1934; Th. Leber 1865, 1872, 1880, 1903; Magitot 1908, 1946; H. Magnus 1873; Marchesani 1939; E. Marx 1909; Mayerhausen 1883; Merkel 1875, 1885–90; Merkel & Kallius 1901; Michaelson 1948; Michaelson & Campbell 1940; Monnier & Streiff 1940; H. Müller 1854, 1872; Nettleship 1875; Nicholls 1938; Pavia 1936; Polyak 1941–48; Rados & Candian 1921; S. Ramón y Cajal 1909–11, 1928; Rea 1941; Rochon-Duvigneaud 1943; Rochon-Duvigneaud & Rode 1943; E. J. Ross 1949; Rucker & Keys 1950; St. Martin 1931; Salomonson 1921; Salzmann 1912; Scheerer 1925; Schieck & Brückner 1930–32; Seefelder 1909; G. F. Sleggs 1926; F. Smith 1917–18; Strahl 1898; Takahashi 1923, 1925; Tansley 1947; Traquair 1946; Uhtoff 1925; Usher 1906; D. Vail 1948; Versari 1909; Vidal & Damel 1944; H. Virchow 1881, 1882, 1901; A. Vogt 1918, 1919, 1921, 1937, 1947; A. Vossius 1882, 1883; Wagenmann 1890; Walls 1942; Wasmund 1948; Weale (quoted by Dartnall & Thomson 1949); Wegefahrt 1914; Wegefahrt & Weed 1914; Weinstein & Forgács 1947; Wilbrand & Saenger 1899–1927; W. H. Wilmer 1934; Wislocki 1940; E. Wolff 1948; Wolfrum 1908; C. A. Wood 1917; J. G. Zinn 1755; O. Zoth 1923.

SEC. 3. THE ARTERIAL CIRCLE OF WILLIS AND THE ORIGIN OF THE CEREBRAL ARTERIES

1. The base of the brain and its arteries.—The description of the cerebral arteries may conveniently begin with the base of the brain and the "arterial circle" of Willis, where the arteries of the neck meet and whence originate the principal arterial stems of the brain and many smaller vessels for the basal parts of the brain.

When the basal aspect of the brain is examined, the following parts and their topographical relationships are seen (Fig. 366): the two frontal lobes (*frl*) anteriorly, with the olfactory bulbs (*olfb*) and tracts (*olftr*) attached to them; the two temporal lobes (*tl*), flanking a deep central pit on both sides, the interpeduncular fossa

of Tarini, the latter limited posteriorly by a prominent central protuberance, the pons or "bridge" of Varoli (*po*), the more slender posterior extension of which is the oblong medulla (*om*) and spinal cord (*sc*). The pons, oblong medulla, and spinal cord are flanked laterally by the large hemispheres of the cerebellum or little brain (*cbl*).

Along the margins of the cord and medulla, between the latter and the pons, from the sides of the pons, and from the central pit, spinal and cranial nerves emerge, some as rows of delicate rootlets, others as more or less formidable trunks (*II, III, IV, V, VI, VII, VIII, otr,* etc.). In our figures, for the sake of clarity, most of these nerves were omitted (consult textbooks and atlases of anatomy and neuroanatomy).

In front of the pons, in the interpeduncular fossa, parts of the visual system lie exposed: the two optic nerves (*II*), joined in the chiasma (*ch*) and continuing as optic tracts (*otr*), and the two oculomotor nerves (*III*). Along the sides of the pons lie the much thinner trochlear nerves (*IV*), whereas the medium-thick abducent nerves (*VI*) originate from behind the posterior margin of the pons where that part is separated from the medulla by a deep transverse dent. The central structure in the interpeduncular pit just behind the optic chiasma is the infundibulum (*inf*), a funnel-shaped extension of the tuber cinereum or "gray hillock" of the hypothalamus, with the two round mammillary bodies behind. The pituitary gland or hypophysis, normally attached to the infundibulum, lodged in the depression of the "Turkish saddle" of the sphenoidal bone, is missing in the usual specimens.

In an intact specimen the interpeduncular fossa is bridged by a thin, smooth, translucent membrane—the arachnoid tunic—a continuation of the arachnoid meningeal cover of the brain. Through it, all nerves and blood vessels of this locality must pass on their way to and from the brain. Each nerve and vessel is here attached, though somewhat loosely, to the arachnoid, which is continuous with the epineurium of the nerves and the adventitial sheath of the blood vessels. Numerous threads and trabecules, partly forming bundles and sheets, pass into the fossa, in particular along its anterior, lateral, and posterior sides, to whose floor, formed by the inferior surface of the hypothalamus, they are firmly attached.

The nerves and the blood vessels, skirting the sides of the fossa, including the chiasma with the optic nerves and infundibulum, are all firmly imbedded in the arachnoid web and are thus securely held in place. The central space of the fossa is traversed by a few thin interconnected trabecules only. The described cavity, closed by a superficial arachnoid sheet, is the interpeduncular cistern. In the living, this cistern is filled with the cerebrospinal fluid and is continuous on all sides with the subarachnoid space of the brain.

The two internal carotid trunks (*ica*) emerge from their channels in the petrous temporal bones along the sides of the body of the sphenoidal bone—all parts that form the base of the skull. In the usual presentations of the basal aspect of the brain, these arteries appear to be lodged exactly in the two lateral crotches formed by the optic nerves and tracts (Figs. 366, 367). At a closer examination, however, this perspectival location is revealed to be an illusion, the actual distance between the carotid trunks and the chiasma in an anatomical specimen being not less than 6–8 mm. (Fig. 367). In the living, the distance may be somewhat less, owing to the turgor of the filled vessels, and probably varies depending on the conditions of circulation, as well as individually. A few minute blood vessels of the character of arterioles appear to arise from the carotid trunk before its further division and, imbedded in the lateral arachnoid partition of the fossa, pass to the tuber cinereum and infundibulum.

The topographical arrangement of the arteries at the base of the brain stem and in and around the interpeduncular fossa is as follows (same figures; *cf.* Fig. 362). The two *vertebral arteries* (*va*) course along the sides of the oblong medulla (*om*), gradually turning to its ventral side. Here the two vessels merge, to build a thick common stem, the *basilar artery* (*basa*). The point of juncture is almost at the upper limit of the medulla, although it may be a few millimeters below, or slightly above, the inferior margin of the pons. Before joining, each vertebral artery gives off a small branch—the *anterior spinal artery* (*asa*)—and one or more similar twigs that skirt the medulla as they pass to its lateral and dorsal sides and to the cerebellum—the *posterior spinal artery* (*posa*). One of these, a somewhat thicker blood vessel arising either from the vertebral or from the basilar artery, is the *inferior posterior cerebellar artery* (*ipocba*).

The trunk of the basilar artery (*basa*) is lodged in a shallow, central, longitudinal groove on the inferior face of the pons. From it a number of thicker and thinner arteries originate: medium-sized *inferior anterior* and *inferior posterior cerebellar arteries* (*iacba*, *ipocba*), one on each side; several minute branches that either enter the pontobulbar cleft or skirt it in order to reach the more dorsally situated parts, while others, branching off along the basilar trunk, the *pontine arteries* (*poa*), spread over the face of the pons or soon enter its substance.

In 60 per cent of the specimens, the auditory artery (*auda*) arises, according to Stopford (1916), from the inferior anterior cerebellar artery, and in the remaining 40 per cent, directly from the basilar artery, or, according to Lelli (1939), always from the inferior anterior cerebellar artery. According to our own observations, both situations may be present on different sides of the same specimen. Minute twigs of the auditory artery supply the common stem of the eighth cranial nerve, whereas the others enter the substance of the pons along the posterior margin.

Other similar small arteries are given off from the basilar stem for the remainder of the pons, including the anterior margin. Two of the thicker ones, unequal on both sides, arising from the intermediate basilar segment, spread partly over the pons in the direction of the crura or "limbs" of the brain, skirting the roots of the trigeminal nerve (*V*), and, if strong enough, may continue over the inferior face of the cerebellum—the *rostral inferior cerebellar arteries* (*ricba*).

Altogether, there are about a dozen arteries, mostly thin, arising directly from the basilar stem between the junction of the vertebral arteries at the caudal end of the trunk and its rostral end, where the two superior cerebellar arteries separate.

The two strong *superior cerebellar arteries* (*sucba*), a right and a left, arise close to the upper extremity of the basilar trunk at the anterior boundary of the pons (Fig. 368). They sweep in front and along the sides of that structure in an ascending course toward the dorsal face of the cerebellum and the midbrain. Initially they are, on the one hand, close to the oculomotor nerves (*III*), which they touch directly, and, on the other hand, to the trochlear nerves (*IV*), from which, however, they are separated by the tough superficial arachnoid laminae that stretch over from the pons to the adjoining temporal lobes (*un*, uncus). Along their further course upward on the lateral and dorsal sides of the midbrain, the artery and the trochlear nerve lie close together.

2. THE ARTERIAL CIRCLE OF WILLIS.—Two or 3 mm. rostrally from the origin of the superior cerebellar arteries, the basilar trunk finally divides into two thick *posterior cerebral arteries* (*pocea*), a right and a left, both located in the interpeduncular fossa. One, usually on the left side, is thicker (right side in Fig. 368). The posterior cerebrals are the principal subdivisions into which the basilar artery continues. Initially they deviate, respectively, toward the right and left pockets of the interpeduncular fossa, crossing the trunks of the oculomotor nerves in front and on the medial sides. They may give off a very fine twig or two to these nerves as they pass over them. Part of their more numerous branches, mostly thin and a few thick ones, sweep around the foot of the peduncle, the majority disappearing in the posterior perforated substance (*pps*), thus entering the midbrain and betweenbrain.

A thicker branch, one on each side, the *posterior chorioid artery* (*pocha*), supplies in part the chorioid plexus of the third cerebral ventricle (*see* Fig. 368; also Fig. 372), others supplying the nucleus of the oculomotor nerve.

Rostrally, each posterior cerebral artery gives off a medium or even a fairly thick vessel, the *posterior communicating artery* (*pocoa*), in this way linking up with the *internal carotid arteries* (*ica*).

Since the two *anterior cerebral arteries* (*acea*) that arise from the internal carotids are connected with each other either by one or by more distinct links, the *anterior communicating artery* or arteries (*acoa*), or by direct merging, the "arterial circle" of Willis is thus completed.

Occasionally, the posterior cerebral artery takes origin from the carotid of its own side, in which case it is connected with the basilar artery through a thin posterior communicating artery. This is, according to Duret, a more frequent occurrence on the right side (shown on left side in Fig. 368).

There are, altogether, seven arterial links that make up the circle of Willis: one anterior communicating (single or double), two anterior cerebrals, two posterior communicating, and two posterior cerebrals. If both internal carotids are included, the number of links increases to nine; if the basilar trunk is also added, there are ten constituents. The composition of the circle varies greatly in individual specimens.

The obvious function of the circle is to serve as a "general cerebral anastomosis" which equalizes the distribution of blood and blood pressure in all parts of the brain (Duret 1874)—that is, to permit the flow of blood in any direction, e.g., from the right to the left side or vice versa or from the anterior to the posterior parts or in any other combination, as the particular situation demands. Such a situation may arise when any one or two of the four principal arteries, the internal carotids or the vertebral arteries, alone or in combination, are obstructed, while the other two still function. (*See also* McDonald & Potter 1951.) A typical arterial circle is considered to be an arrangement characteristic of Man and of the majority of the Higher Primates, especially of the Anthropomorphous Apes, according to Grünbaum and Sherrington (1902).

3. Parts of the visual system supplied by the arterial circle.—The "arterial circle" of Willis and the adjoining arteries participating in it are topographically and functionally closely related to the infranuclear and nuclear divisions of the visual system (Figs. 366, 367, 368, 371). Topographically, the circle surrounds the terminal portions of the optic nerves joined by the chiasma and the initial portions of the tracts, the nerves slipping underneath the circle; the tracts, above. Concerning the functional relationship, each link of the circle or an artery contributing to it takes care of supplying one particular portion or segment of the visual pathways, besides other adjoining structures.

The *ophthalmic artery* (*opha*) arises from the anteromedial aspect of the stem of the internal carotid artery (*ica*) just before its division into anterior and middle cerebrals (Fig. 371). It accompanies the optic nerve, wrapped with it in the dural sheath, through the bony optic foramen or canal, on the lower side, into the orbit. It supplies most of the contents of the orbit, including the eyeball, with blood (*see* preceding section). The artery, as it arises from underneath along the lateral side of the nerve and passes over it to the medial side, gives off a branch, the *central retinal artery* (*cra*), which in

Man is the exclusive, and in other Primates the principal, source of blood supply for approximately the vitreal half of the retina (*see* sec. 2 [3], this chapter).

The intracranial and canalicular portions of the optic nerve are supplied partly by the twigs of the anterior cerebral and the ophthalmic arteries and partly by the central retinal artery (through its recurrent or postcentral branches as far as the optic foramen and through its deeper axial twig or twigs running along the central retinal artery and vein).

The layer of photoreceptors (*2*), the outer nuclei (*4*), and the outer and middle zones of the outer plexiform layer (*5-a, 5-b*) of the retina receive their nutrition via the innermost, choriocapillary, layer of the chorioid membrane, which is in turn supplied by the posterior ciliary arteries (short and long), which are branches of the ophthalmic artery (*see* preceding section).

The arterial supply of the optic chiasma is principally from the two anterior cerebral arteries (Figs. 368, 371). The most medial of the twigs, arising close to the mid-sagittal cerebral cleft, spread over the anterior and superior aspects of the middle, bridgelike portion and also over the terminal lamina of the diencephalon; several other branches arising from the more lateral points along the stems of the anterior cerebrals, closer to their carotid origin, spread over the lateral parts of the chiasma along its angles. A few delicate twigs of the anterior communicating arteries, spreading over the tuber cinereum, may possibly also contribute to the chiasmal supply along its posterior and inferior aspects. Whether other sources—the internal carotids, middle cerebrals, anterior chorioidals, and anterior communicating arteries—regularly participate in the supply of the chiasma, as believed by some (Abbie 1938), or do so only occasionally requires further investigation. The same is also true of the alleged anastomotical arterial network of the pia mater that lines the region of the chiasma.

The initial portions of the optic tracts receive their arterial twigs from the *anterior cerebral arteries*, the first to arise after the separation of the latter from the middle cerebrals (Fig. 368). The middle portions of the tracts are supplied by the twigs from the *posterior com-*

municating artery, which also supplies the *genu* or "knee" and the adjoining portion of the posterior limb of the internal capsule and the anterior third of the thalamus, except its anterior nucleus, which is supplied by the posterior cerebral, according to Abbie.

The principal source of supply of the middle and posterior portions of the optic tract, however, is the *anterior chorioid artery* (*acha*, Fig. 371; *see also* sec. 4 [2], this chapter). This vessel arises from the posterior aspect of the internal carotid artery at about the level of its division into the anterior and middle cerebral arteries, or sometimes from the stem of the middle cerebral artery. (Abbie [1938] considers such a middle cerebral origin very rare and as responsible for Duret's concept of a "lenticulo-optic artery.") The anterior chorioid is the first vessel to emerge along the middle cerebral stem, lateral to the posterior communicating artery. It crosses the anterior perforate substance in a posterior direction, coming to lie on the ventral face of the optic tract, between it and the uncus of the hippocampal gyrus (*unc*). Along its course in this locality it gives off several thin branches, some passing laterally, others medially, along the optic tract. One twig may penetrate the tract at its inferior aspect; still other numerous, very fine branchlets spread over the pial sheath, which covers the inferior surface of the tract and the adjoining portion of the hippocampal gyrus (uncus).

At the point where the anterior chorioid artery reaches the lateral geniculate nucleus, it enters the inferior chorioid plexus (*chpl*) of the inferior horn of the lateral ventricle, whose most oral portion it supplies. Before this, however, it gives off two or more small perforating branches for the lateral geniculate nucleus, one penetrating at the medial (*hilum*), the other at the lateral, contour of its posterior aspect.

Other very fine twigs spread in the pial sheath lining the free, inferior face of the lateral geniculate nucleus. Some of the deep twigs supply the lateral geniculate nucleus, the tail of the caudate nucleus, the roof of the inferior horn of the lateral ventricle, approximately the posterior two-thirds of the posterior limb and the whole of the infra- and retrolenticular portions of the internal capsule, and the adjoining portions of the thalamus and globus pallidus, ac-

cording to Abbie (1937)—this part of the capsule containing the auditory and visual radiations. Other branches spread over the lateral aspect of the cerebral peduncle adjacent to the optic tract.

In summary, the lateral geniculate nucleus is supplied by the anterior chorioid artery (*acha*) and also in part by the lateral chorioid artery (*lacha*), a branch of the posterior cerebral artery (*see* sec. 5 [2], this chapter; and also L. Chacko 1952).

4. The anterior cerebral artery.—This important vessel (*acea*) is the lesser of the two strong branches into which the trunk of the internal carotid artery (*ica*) subdivides (Figs. 368, 371). Its initial portion sweeps above the optic nerve and beneath the base of the frontal lobe toward the mid-sagittal cleft, which separates the two cerebral hemispheres. Along its arching course it gives off numerous small branches in the following order: most posteriorly, to the initial portion of the ipsilateral optic tract (*otr*) and the lateral aspect of the chiasma (*ch*), and also some branchlets to the proximal segment of the optic nerve (*on*), as well as branches that penetrate into the brain's base through the anterior perforate substance (*aps*); twigs arising closer to the mid-line, to the middle segment of the chiasma. Beyond this, there are no other known parts of the visual system to which this artery is related.

As soon as the mid-sagittal cleft is approached, the two anterior cerebral arteries are linked by one or more short, bridgelike anastomoses, the *anterior communicating artery* or *arteries* (*acoa*). Sometimes only a single anterior cerebral artery is found beyond the point of coalescence, which is reminiscent of conditions found regularly in the lower Mammals: an anterior azygos or unpaired cerebral artery (Critchley). On rare occasions the anterior communicating link is absent, the condition then resembling that normally found in the Lower Vertebrates.

The first branch of the anterior cerebral is the *medial striate artery* of Abbie (1937), formerly known as "Heubner's artery" (Aitken) and the "recurrent branch" (Shellshear). It is a medium-thick vessel originating from the anterior cerebral trunk opposite, or slightly peripheral

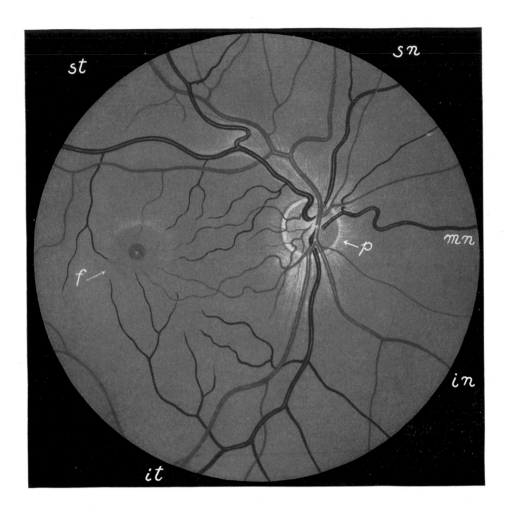

Fig. 363—Fundus or interior of a normal human eye as seen through an ophthalmoscope. Optic papilla (*p*) appears as a round disk, with a whitish, funnel-like physiological excavation in its center. Papilla is encircled by two rings, a white scleral one, and another grayish chorioidal ring on the outside, the latter more pronounced on temporal side (left). Nasal half of the papilla orange-red, left half pink. Central retinal blood vessels: arteries vermilion red, veins carmine red. After first dividing beyond the cribriform lamina, the vessels further subdivide into principal branches: the superior and inferior temporal (*st, it*), the superior, inferior, and a middle nasal (*sn, in, mn*), and the small arteries and veins for the central area and fovea ("macular vessels," unlabeled). Bundles of optic nerve fibers appear as whitish streaks radiating from the papilla, especially along the larger vessels (indication of perifoveal arching). Central foveal excavation (*f*) indicated by a faint grayish oval-shaped reflex ("Schirmer's phenomenon") about the size of papilla and two papillar diameters temporal from it. Fovea (*f*) encloses in its center a small, circular, dark-red area corresponding to the fundus or floor of the fovea, its deepest point, foveola, marked by a dot-like whitish foveolar reflex in the very center. Blood vessels on the nasal side (right) arranged radially, on the temporal side (left) arching above and below the fovea toward which many small twigs spread, with few terminals just slipping into it over its edge (*compare* Figs. 148, 149, 165, 365). Chorioidal vessels in this specimen remain invisible because of the retinal pigment (*compare* also Figs. 166 to 170). Approximate magnification 8x. (From Th. Axenfeld, *Lehrbuch der Augenheilkunde* 1910, with legend in part re-interpreted.)

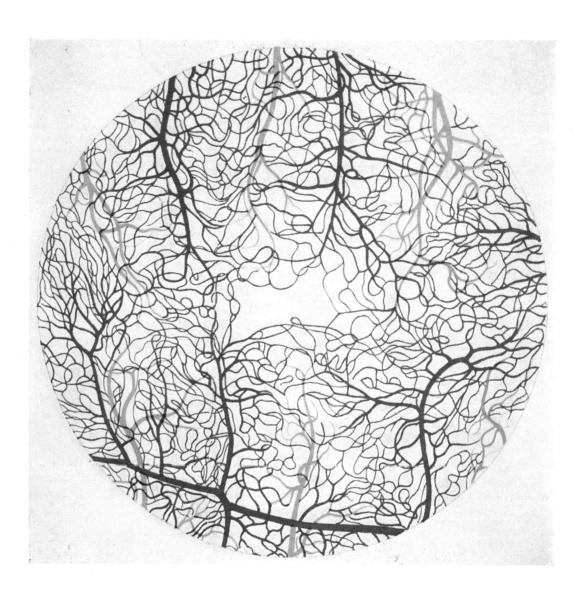

FIG. 364—Blood vessels of human central fovea of the retina, painted from an injection preparation of Heinrich Müller, pioneer investigator of the eye (portrait Fig. 46). The injection, including all capillaries, appears to be complete. Arteries (red), dividing into arterioles and finally into capillaries, are re-assembled into veins (blue) that carry the used-up blood away. In the very center of the foveal excavation all vessels, also capillaries, are absent: the central avascular or vessel-free area, roughly corresponding with the foveal floor (*see* Figs. 129, 161). Dimensions of the vessel-free area, according to original description, 0.31 x 0.41 mm. Position of the arteries relative to the veins is vitrealad. (From O. Becker, Graefe's *Archiv für Opthalmologie* vol. 27 [1], plates *I-II*, y. 1881).

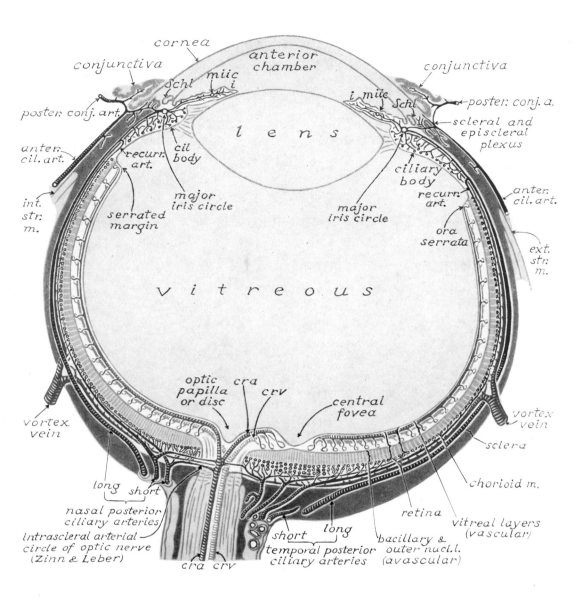

FIG. 365—Blood supply of the human eyeball schematically presented in a horizontal section, 5½x magnified. Retina and chorioid proportionally several times thicker than normal in order to show the arrangement of blood vessels; other structures including sclera, lens, and ciliary body drawn to scale. Partly adapted from Leber 1903 and others (*compare* Figs. 125, 363, 371). Central retinal system in orange (artery) and in light blue (vein), ciliary and conjunctival arteries in red, vortex and chorioidal veins in dark blue. *Note:* the presence of a communication between the central retinal and ciliary systems at the optic disk, and a complete separation of the two systems in the remainder of the eye; the presence of the vessels in the vitreal layers except in the foveal center, their absence in scleral layers (bacillary and outer nuclear layers) of the retina; increased thickness of the choriocapillary layer in the central area, especially fovea (small red circles); complete avascularity of the lens and cornea; rich blood supply of the ciliary body; anastomotical connections between ciliary and conjunctival vessels in the region of ciliary body. *Abbreviations: anter. cil. art.* anterior ciliary artery; *cra* central retinal artery; *crv* central retinal vein; *i* iris; *ext. str. m.* external straight muscle; *int. str. m.* internal straight muscle; *miic* minor arterial iris circle; *poster. conj. art.* posterior conjunctival artery; *recurr. art.* recurrent branch of long posterior ciliary artery; *Schl* Schlemm's canal.

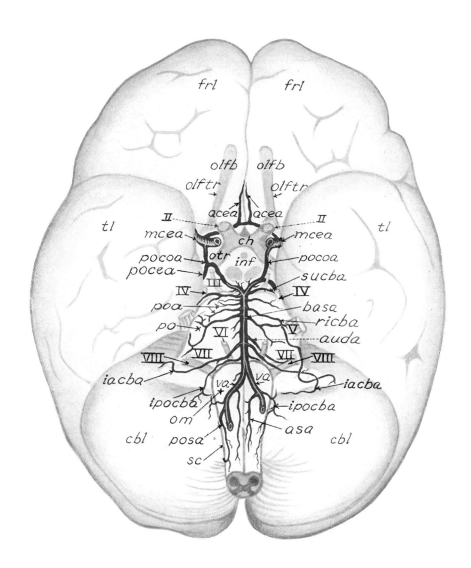

Fig. 366—Basal view of the human brain showing the sources of the arterial blood supply, and the arrangement of the principal vessels including the arterial circle of Willis. *Abbreviations: acea* anterior cerebral artery ; *asa* anterior spinal artery ; *auda* auditory artery ; *basa* basilar artery ; *cbl* cerebellum ; *ch* chiasma of optic nerves ; *frl* frontal lobe ; *iacba* inferior anterior cerebellar artery ; *inf* infundibulum of hypothalamus ; *ipocba* inferior posterior cerebellar artery ; *mcea* middle cerebral artery ; *olfb* olfactory bulb ; *olftr* olfactory tract ; *om* oblong medulla ; *otr* optic tract ; *po* pons or " bridge " ; *poa* pontine arteries ; *pocea* posterior cerebral artery ; *pocoa* posterior communicating artery ; *posa* posterior spinal artery ; *ricba* rostral inferior cerebellar artery ; *sc* spinal cord ; *sucba* superior cerebellar artery ; *tl* temporal lobe ; *va* vertebral artery ; *II* optic nerve ; *III* oculomotor nerve ; *IV* trochlear nerve ; *V* trigeminal nerve ; *VI* abducent nerve ; *VII* facial nerve ; *VIII* auditory nerve.

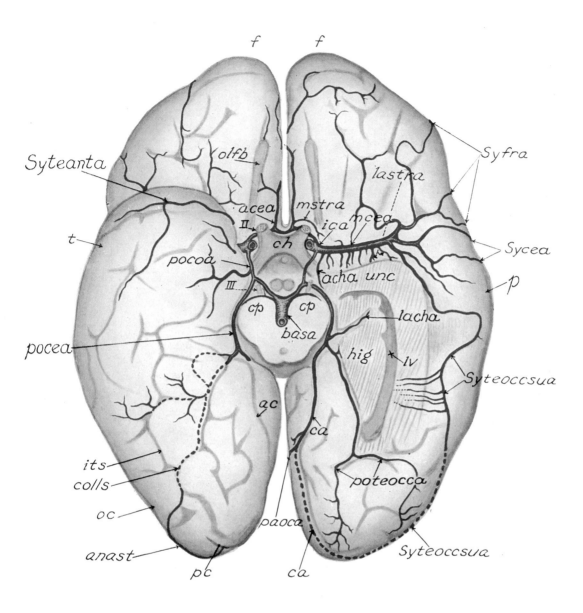

Fig. 367—Basal view of the human brain with ventral portion of the left temporal and occipital lobes removed in order to show the origin, course, distribution, and anastomosing of the deep arteries of the Sylvian pit. *Abbreviations: ac* anterior or medial calcarine sulcus ; *acea* anterior cerebral artery ; *anast* anastomotic connection between superior temporo-occipital Sylvian artery (*Syteoccsua*) and calcarine artery (*ca*) (*compare* Figs. 371, 374) ; *basa* basilar artery ; *ca* calcarine artery ; *ch* chiasma of optic nerves ; *cp* cerebral peduncle ; *acha* anterior chorioid artery ; *colls* collateral sulcus ; *f* frontal lobe ; *hig* hippocampal gyrus ; *ica* internal carotid artery ; *lacha* lateral chorioid artery ; *its* inferior temporal sulcus ; *lastra* lateral striate arteries ; *lv* lateral ventricle ; *mcea* middle cerebral artery ; *mstra* middle striate artery ; *oc* occipital lobe ; *olfb* olfactory bulb ; *p* parietal lobe ; *paoca* parieto-occipital artery ; *pc* posterior or lateral calcarine sulcus and posterior parietal artery ; *pocea* posterior cerebral artery ; *poteocca* posterior temporo-occipital artery ; *Sycea* central Sylvian arteries ; *Syfra* frontal Sylvian arteries ; *Syteoccsua* superior temporo-occipital Sylvian arteries ; *Syteanta* anterior temporal Sylvian arteries ; *t* temporal lobe ; *unc* uncus or " spur " of hippocampal gyrus ; *II* optic nerve ; *III* oculomotor nerve.   Note anastomotic connection : broken line in right lower portion of the figure, between superior temporo-occipital Sylvian artery (*Syteoccsua*) and calcarine artery (*ca*), and *compare* with Figs. 369, 370, 374.

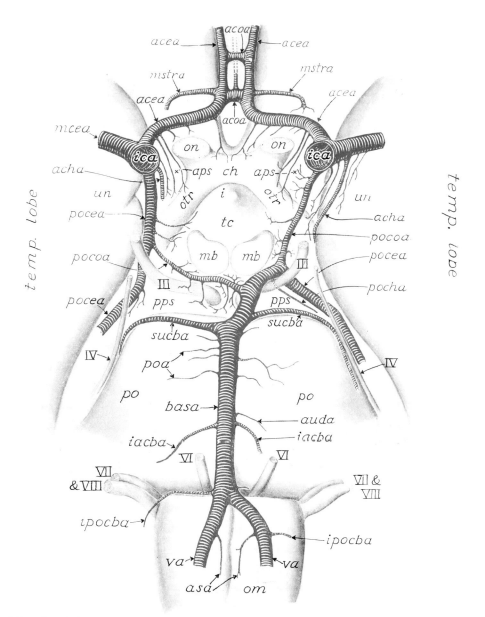

Fig. 368—Arterial circle of Willis of the human brain, and its topographical relations. Approximately 2x magnified, and slightly schematized. Special features in this specimen are a double anterior communicating artery, and on the right side (left in figure), the origin of the posterior cerebral artery (*pocea*) from the internal carotid (*ica*) instead of from the basilar (*basa*), with posterior communicating (*pocoa*) on that side much reduced in thickness and arising from the basilar. *Abbreviations:* *acea* anterior cerebral artery; *acha* anterior chorioid artery; *acoa* anterior communicating artery; *aps* anterior perforate spot or substance; *asa* anterior spinal artery; *auda* auditory artery; *ch* chiasma of optic nerves; *i* infundibulum or "funnel" of hypothalamus; *iacba* inferior anterior cerebellar artery; *ipocba* inferior posterior cerebellar artery; *mb* mammillary body; *mstra* middle striate artery of Abbie, "Heubner's artery" of Aitken, or "recurrent branch of anter. cerebr. artery" of Shellshear; *om* oblong medulla; *on* optic nerve (cut); *otr* optic tract; *po* pons or "bridge"; *poa* pontine arteries; *pocea* posterior cerebral artery; *pocha* posterior chorioid artery; *pocoa* posterior communicating artery; *pps* posterior perforate spot or substance; *sucba* superior cerebellar artery; *un* uncus of hippocampal gyrus; *va* vertebral artery; *III* oculomotor nerve; *IV* trochlear nerve; *VI* abducent nerve; *VII* facial nerve; *VIII* acoustico-vestibular nerve.

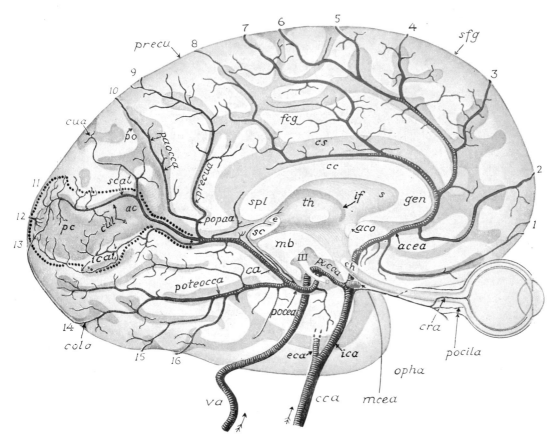

Fig. 369—Arteries of the human brain. Medial aspect of the left cerebral hemisphere with its principal sulci and fissures partly opened to show the concealed portions of vessels. The common carotid (*cca*) and vertebral (*va*) arteries, sources of blood supply of the cranium and brain, given in heliotrope color, are connected by the ipsilateral posterior communicating artery (*pocoa*), in this way forming the arterial circle (*see* Figs. 366, 367, 368, 371). From this circle arise the principal arteries which supply the hemisphere: anterior cerebral (*acea*, light blue), middle cerebral (*mcea*, green) and posterior cerebral (*pocea*, vermilion red). Of the middle cerebral only the initial portion is seen, its continuation and ramification is shown on the lateral face of the same hemisphere in Fig. 370. *Note :* even distribution and straight course of the principal branches of anterior cerebral, preserving their original fetal arrangement (*see* Fig. 375) ; calcarine sulcus (*ac* and *pc*) supplied by a superior (*scal*) and inferior calcarine artery (*ical*), not greatly differing in size, their separation following a horizontal line ; the region supplied by both almost coincides with the striate area marked by a dotted line ; posteriorly both calcarine arteries are linked by anastomosis, to which a long branch of the posterior temporo-occipital artery (*poteocca, 12*) also contributes ; additional supply is from extreme terminals of the superior temporo-occipital Sylvian artery (*Syteoccsua, 13*), a subsidiary of the middle cerebral (*see* Figs. 370, 371, 372, 374). *Abbreviations :* *ac* anterior or medial calcarine sulcus ; *acea* anterior cerebral artery ; *aco* anterior commissure ; *cc* corpus callosum ; *cca* common carotid artery ; *ch* chiasma of optic nerves ; *cola* collateral artery ; *cra* central retinal artery ; *cs* callosal or epicallosal sulcus ; *cua* cuneal artery ; *cul* cuneo-lingual gyri ; *e* epiphysis or pineal body ; *eca* external carotid artery ; *fcg* fornicate or cingular gyrus ; *gen* genu or " knee " of callosal body ; *ica* internal carotid artery ; *ical* inferior calcarine artery ; *if* interventricular foramen of Monro ; *mb* midbrain ; *mcea* middle cerebral artery ; *opha* ophthalmic artery ; *paocca* parieto-occipital artery ; *pc* posterior or lateral calcarine sulcus ; *po* parieto-occipital sulcus ; *pocea* posterior cerebral artery ; *popaa* posterior parietal artery ; *poteocca* posterior temporo-occipital artery ; *precu* precuneus ; *precua* precuneal artery ; *s* pellucid septum ; *sc* superior colliculus of midbrain ; *scal* superior calcarine artery ; *sfg* superior frontal gyrus ; *spl* splenium of callosal body ; *th* thalamus ; *va* vertebral artery ; *III* oculomotor nerve. Small Arabic numerals mark arteries which can be followed in Fig. 370.

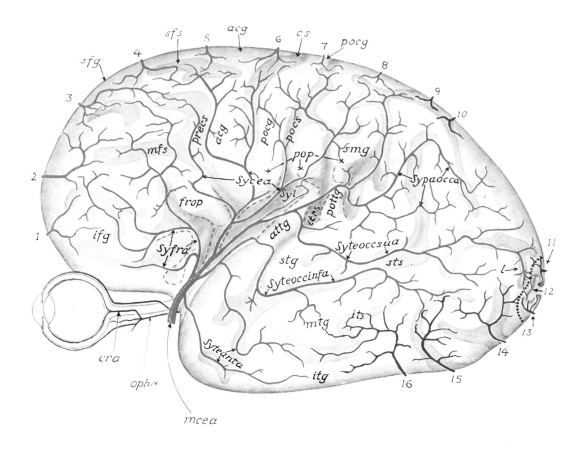

Fig. 370—Arteries of the human brain. Lateral aspect of the left cerebral hemisphere with the principal sulci and fissures represented partly opened to show portions of vessels concealed in the fissures. Middle cerebral artery (*mcea*, green), of which in the preceding figure only the initial stump is seen, spreading over most of the lateral face of the hemisphere, leaving to the anterior cerebral (*1-8*, light blue) and posterior cerebral (*9-11, 13-16*, vermilion) only a marginal zone. The number, division, topographical relations to the limiting sulci and gyri, and the course of principal branches of the middle cerebral artery are revealed by pulling apart the operculums of the frontal and parietal lobes from the temporal lobe, in this way exposing a deep and spacious pocket of the lateral fissure of Sylvius (*Syl*). Of special interest are posterior branches of the middle cerebral, whose deep twigs supply the visual radiation along a part of its course (*see* Figs. 367, 371). The longest of these, the superior temporo-occipital Sylvian artery (*Syteoccsua*), stretches as far as the occipital pole (*12*) where in this individual specimen, together with superior calcarine (*11*), inferior calcarine (*13*), and a branch of posterior temporo-occipital artery (*14*), it shares in supplying the posterior extremity of the striate area (marked by a dotted line). *Abbreviations : acg* anterior central gyrus ; *attg* anterior transverse temporal gyrus of Heschl ; *cra* central retinal artery ; *frop* frontal operculum ; *ifg* inferior frontal gyrus ; *itrs* intertransverse temporal sulcus ; *its* inferior temporal sulcus ; *l* lunate sulcus ; *mcea* middle cerebral artery ; *mfs* middle frontal sulcus ; *mtg* middle temporal gyrus ; *opha* ophthalmic artery ; *pocg* posterior central gyrus ; *pocs* postcentral sulcus ; *pottg* posterior transverse temporal gyrus of Heschl ; *precs* precentral sulcus ; *sfg* superior frontal gyrus ; *smg* supramarginal gyrus ; *stg* superior temporal gyrus ; *sts* superior temporal sulcus ; *Sycea* central Sylvian artery ; *Syfra* frontal Sylvian artery ; *Syl* Sylvian fossa or lateral cerebral fissure ; *Sypaocca* parieto-occipital Sylvian artery ; *Syteanta* anterior temporal Sylvian arteries ; *Syteoccinfa* inferior temporo-occipital Sylvian artery ; *Syteoccsua* superior temporo-occipital Sylvian artery. Small Arabic numerals mark terminals of arteries originating on the medial face of the hemisphere shown in the preceding figure.

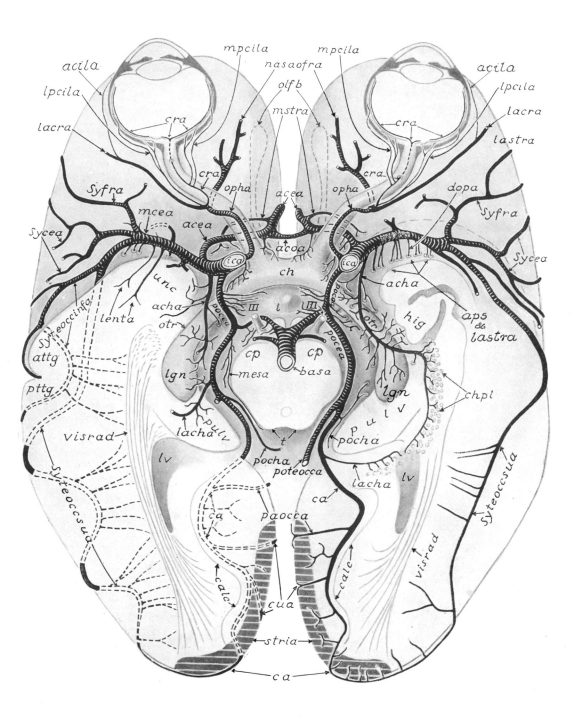

FIG. 371—Arterial blood supply of the human visual system presented in an ideal horizontal plane close to the base of the brain. Centrally located arterial circle of Willis made up of the anterior communicating (*acoa*), anterior cerebral (*acea*), posterior communicating (*pocoa*), and posterior cerebral (*pocea*) arteries interconnects the basilar (*basa*), and the two internal carotid arteries (*ica*). From it three pairs of arteries arise: anterior (*acea*), middle (*mcea*), and posterior cerebrals (*pocea*), spreading their branches over the brain and its dependencies, the optic tracts, chiasma, nerves, and eyeballs. *Note:* the supply of the retinae by central retinal arteries (*cra*), of the remainder of the eyeballs by the ciliary arteries (*acila, lpcila, mpcila*) arising from the ophthalmic artery (*opha*); multiple supply of the chiasma (*ch*), optic tracts (*otr*), lateral geniculate nuclei (*lgn*), visual radiations (*visrad*), and striate areae (*stria*). *For abbreviations see text.*

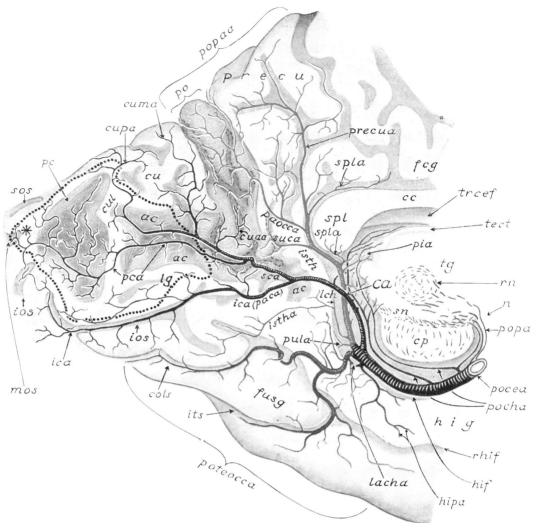

Fig. 372—Posterior cerebral artery. Medial aspect of left occipital lobe with sulci partly opened. Approximately natural size. The trunk of the posterior cerebral artery (*pocea*, heliotrope color) alongside of hippocampal fissure, between the hippocampal gyrus (*hig*) and cerebral peduncle (*cp*), divides in this particular specimen into three principal branches: calcarine artery (*ca*, vermilion red), posterior parietal artery (*popaa*, green), and posterior temporo-occipital artery (*potaocca*, light blue). Calcarine artery in turn produces two main divisions, a superior calcarine (*sca*), and an inferior (*ica*) or paracalcarine artery (*paca*). *Abbreviations: ac* anterior or medial calcarine sulcus; *ca* calcarine artery; *cc* corpus callosum; *cols* collateral sulcus; *cp* cerebral peduncle; *cu* cuneus; *cuaa* anterior cuneal artery; *cul* cuneo-lingual gyrus; *cuma* middle cuneal artery; *cupa* posterior cuneal artery; *fcg* fornicate-cingular gyrus; *fsg* fusiform gyrus; *hif* hippocampal fissure; *hig* hippocampal gyrus; *hipa* hippocampal artery; *ica (paca)* inferior calcarine or paracalcarine artery; *ios* inferior occipital sulcus; *isth* isthmus of fornicate and hippocampal gyri; *istha* isthmal artery; *its* inferior temporal sulcus; *lacha, lch* lateral chorioid arteries; *lg* lingual gyrus; *mos* middle occipital sulcus; *paca (ica)* paracalcarine artery; *paocca* parieto-occipital artery; *pc* posterior calcarine sulcus; *pca* principal calcarine artery; *pia* pial arteries; *po* parieto-occipital sulcus or fissure; *pocea* posterior cerebral artery; *pocha* posterior chorioid arteries; *popa* posterior perforate arteries; *popaa* posterior parietal artery; *poteocca* posterior temporo-occipital artery; *precu* precuneus; *precua* precuneal artery; *pula* artery for pulvinar of thalamus; *rhif* rhinal fissure; *rn* red nucleus; *sca* superior calcarine artery; *sn* substantia nigra of midbrain; *sos* superior occipital sulcus; *spl* splenium of corpus callosum; *spla* splenial artery; *suca* supracalcarine artery; *tect* midbrain tectum; *tg* midbrain tegmentum; *trcef* transverse cerebral fissure; * occipital pole.

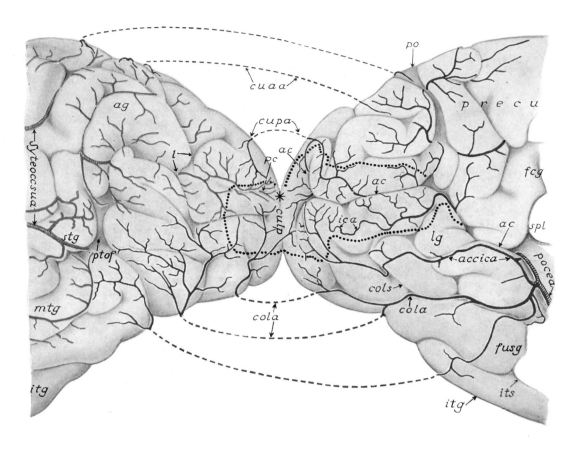

Fig. 373—Arteries of the left occipital lobe with sulci, gyri, and blood vessels left in their natural position. Right half of the figure shows the medial face, left half the lateral face of the same lobe. Middle cerebral artery green, posterior cerebral red. Approximately natural size. To be compared with the following figure. Boundary of the striate area marked by a dotted line. Shallow posterior or lateral calcarine sulcus (*pc*) separated from the anterior or medial c.s. (*ac*) by a posterior cuneo-lingual gyrus (*culp*). The latter, representing occipital pole marked by an asterisk (*), is used in this figure as a " hinge " on which the lateral face of the hemisphere was rotated to align it with the medial face (*compare* chap. VIII, secs. 2, 3, and Figs. 280 to 290). Only a few arteries may be followed in this figure for any considerable length along their course, their origin and relations, remaining mostly undisclosed, are revealed in the following figure. Some branches of the posterior cerebral turn above, the others below, the margins of the hemisphere to reach its lateral face, their identity being preserved by broken lines. Arterial anastomoses are merely indicated. *Abbreviations :* *ac* anterior or medial calcarine sulcus ; *accica* accessory inferior calcarine artery ; *ag* angular gyrus ; *cola* collateral artery ; *cols* collateral sulcus ; *cuaa* anterior cuneal artery ; *culp* posterior cuneo-lingual gyrus ; *cupa* posterior cuneal artery ; *fcg* fornicate-cingular gyrus ; *fusg* fusiform gyrus ; *ica* inferior calcarine artery ; *itg* inferior temporal gyrus ; *its* inferior temporal sulcus ; *l* lunate sulcus ; *lg* lingual gyrus ; *mtg* middle temporal gyrus ; *pc* posterior or lateral calcarine sulcus or fissure ; *po* parieto-occipital sulcus or fissure ; *pocea* posterior cerebral artery ; *precu* precuneus ; *ptof* parieto-temporo-occipital fossa or pit ; *spl* splenium of corpus callosum ; *stg* superior temporal gyrus ; *Syteoccsua* superior temporo-occipital Sylvian artery ; * occipital pole.

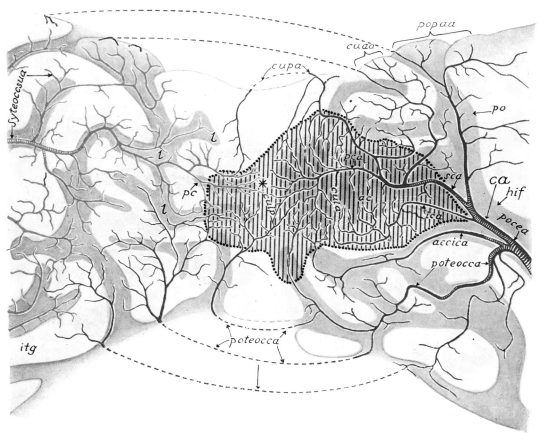

FIG. 374—Left occipital lobe of the same specimen shown in the preceding figure, with sulci and fissures partly opened in order to show arteries along their entire course. Right half of the figure represents the medial face, left half the lateral face, of the lobe. Occipital pole (*) used as a " hinge " on which the two sides were rotated in order to bring them into the same plane. Middle cerebral artery green, posterior cerebral artery red. Striate area vertically shaded. Approximately natural size. *Note :* spacious anterior calcarine sulcus (*ac*) opened wide reveals a low vertically oriented anterior cuneo-lingual gyrus (*cula*); distribution of arteries remarkably complex, showing calcarine arteries (*sca, ica*) to originate together as a common stem (*ca*) from the posterior parietal artery (*popaa*); superior calcarine (*sca*), much the stronger, gives origin to anterior (*cuaa*) and posterior (*cupa*) cuneal arteries; remaining vessel spreads fanwise as a principal or axial calcarine artery (*pca*) in the posterior half of the anterior calcarine sulcus (*ac*); upper lip of the calcarine sulcus supplied by numerous branches from both cuneal arteries, lower lip chiefly by inferior calcarine artery (*ica*), accessory inferior calcarine artery (*accica*), and by the terminals of posterior temporo-occipital artery (*poteocca*) pursuing a devious course below the inferior margin of the lobe; last-mentioned vessels also supply inferior half of the posterior segment of the striate area located on the lateral side of the lobe, resembling a simian " occipital operculum " (*see* this and Fig. 376); superior half of the opercular segment supplied by the terminal branches of a long superior temporo-occipital Sylvian artery (*Syteoccsua*), belonging to the middle cerebral system (*compare* Figs. 370, 373). To a multiple supply of the striate area in this case no less than seven arteries contribute, the two major systems (middle and posterior cerebral), meeting at the occipital pole (*). Several anastomotical connections unite various arterial territories. *Abbreviations :* *ac* anterior calcarine sulcus; *accica* accessory inferior calcarine artery; *cuaa* anterior cuneal artery; *cula* anterior cuneo-lingual gyrus; *culp* posterior cuneo-lingual gyrus; *cupa* posterior cuneal artery; *hif* hippocampal fissure; *ica* inferior calcarine artery; *itg* inferior temporal gyrus; *l* lunate sulcus; *pc* posterior calcarine sulcus; *pca* principal or axial calcarine artery; *po* parieto-occipital sulcus or fissure; *pocea* posterior cerebral artery; *popaa* posterior parietal artery; *poteocca* posterior temporo-occipital artery; *sca* superior calcarine artery; *Syteoccsua* superior temporo-occipital Sylvian artery; * occipital pole.

to, the point of origin of the anterior communicating artery (*mstr* in Figs. 367, 368, 371). It turns laterally, and, after crossing the olfactory trigone, it buries itself in the anterior perforate substance, supplying the anterior portions of the basal nuclei and the anterior limb of the internal capsule.

The further course of the anterior cerebral (*acea*, blue in Fig. 369) lies on the inner face of the frontal lobe, where it closely skirts the genu or "knee" of the callosal body (*gen*). From it, about half-a-dozen fairly thick, long branches are given off (*1–8*), which, partly buried in the sulci and partly by short cuts across the gyri, attain the upper margin of the cerebral hemisphere, beyond which they spread over a more or less narrow zone on the lateral face (*1–8* in Fig. 370).

Altogether, the entire medial and the innermost portion of the orbital surfaces and a narrow zone along the upper margin of the frontal lobe on the convex side are supplied by branches of the anterior cerebral artery, as are also the adjoining portions of the parietal lobe: the paracentral lobule, a portion of the precuneus (*precu*), and a corresponding zone on the lateral face of the hemisphere (*cf.* Figs. 182, 271). These branches have been labeled by Critchley (1930), from the lower surface of the brain upward, as follows: prefrontal (Foix's orbital), frontopolar, anterior internal frontal, middle internal frontal, posterior internal frontal, paracentral, superior parietal, and precuneal arteries. According to the classification of Kleiss (1944–45), four groups of the anterior cerebral branches are to be distinguished: an orbital, a precallosal, a supracallosal, and the pericallosal ramus or group.

References: See bibliography at the end of this chapter.

SEC. 4. THE MIDDLE CEREBRAL ARTERY AND ITS SUBSIDIARIES

1. General remarks.—The middle cerebral artery (*mcea*) is the largest of the three arteries supplying each cerebral hemisphere (green in Figs. 369, 370). It is the thicker of the two principal vessels into which the internal carotid artery (*ica*) subdivides (Figs. 368, 371). The territory supplied by it is likewise more extensive than that of either the anterior or the posterior cerebrals, comprising most of the lateral face of the hemisphere, including the lateral fissure or Sylvian fossa, the most roomy pocket of the cerebral depressions or infoldings (sulci and gyri). (*See* Moutier 1908 on various types or modes of ramification of the middle cerebral artery.)

Of the extensive arborizations of the middle cerebral artery, only a few branches are directly related to the visual system. Some of these, however, are of prime importance and are here described in detail, those of lesser interest are presented in the following only for the sake of completeness.

2. Short subcortical branches.—First to arise either from the internal carotid or more rarely from its continuation, the middle cerebral artery, after the separation of the anterior cerebral (*acea*) and the posterior communicating (*pocoa*) arteries, is the anterior chorioid artery (*acha*, Figs. 368, 371). Its origin and relationships are described in paragraph 3, in the preceding section. The anterior chorioid is the principal vessel that supplies the optic tract and, conjointly with the lateral chorioid artery (*lacha*, a branch of the posterior cerebral; *see* sec. 5 [2], this chapter), the lateral geniculate nucleus.

Next laterad to it, a series of small arteries arises from the middle cerebral stem; they immediately penetrate into the base of the brain along a line marking the juncture of the frontal and temporal lobes. This locality is the narrow lateral portion of the anterior perforate spot or substance (*aps*), so named because of a number of minute holes left after the afore-mentioned arteries have been torn out (*cf.* Fig. 181). This group of vessels was named *lateral striate arteries* (*lastra*) by Abbie (1937). They enter the substance of the brain, where, according to Abbie, they supply the larger portion of the striate body, including the lentiform nucleus (globus pallidus, putamen), caudate nucleus, and the entire internal capsule.

One of these vessels of medium size, the *deep optic artery* (*dopa*), in its backward course passes through the substance of the putamen to the infra- and retrolenticular parts of the internal capsule, where it supplies the initial portions of the visual and auditory radiations, according to Abbie (1937). From the actual dissections made by the author there may be, instead, one or two such deep optic arteries. These originate from the middle cerebral stem, 2 mm. apart, plunging at once into the cerebral substance. The course of these deep optic arteries ascends almost vertically, one artery behind the other, the more proximal being the more posterior. Both deep optic arteries enter the substance of the putamen, where they divide repeatedly. Some of their terminal twigs proceed farther up and may reach the subcortical fiber mass above the putamen. Possibly the more posterior artery may participate in supplying the initial portions both of the visual and of the auditory radiations, a point requiring further study. Both deep optic arteries are undoubtedly related to the putamen and possibly also to the external capsule and the claustrum. Because of this, the term *lenticular* or *lenticulocapsular arteries* would be justified (*lenta*, left side in Fig. 371).

3. LONG CORTICAL BRANCHES.—The stem of the middle cerebral artery (*mcea*, green in Fig. 370), beyond the lateral striate arteries, passes into the roomy pocket of the lateral fissure of the hemisphere, the Sylvian fossa or pit (*Syl*, Fig. 370). When the margins of this sunken region are pulled apart, about half-a-dozen thick branches, into which the middle cerebral artery subdivides, become visible. Their arrangement over the floor of the Sylvian pit may be compared with the handle of a fan oriented obliquely from the base of the frontal lobe toward the center of the parietal lobe, conforming with the position of the Sylvian pocket. From this locality branches radiate in various directions: anteriorly and dorsoanteriorly toward the frontal lobe, dorsally and posterodorsally toward the parietal lobe, with the central region in between; posteriorly across the back portions of the parietal and temporal regions toward the occipital lobe; and ventrally toward the temporal lobe. Briefly, the arrangement of the middle cerebral branches repeats in a more complicated way a similar, but simpler, radiating arrangement present in the human fetus

(Fig. 375) and a somewhat more complex arrangement found in an adult Rhesus Macaque.

In the Sylvian fossa the arteries pursue their course, on the whole, without much regard for the numerous gyri and sulci found here (Fig. 370). As egress from this locality, some use sulci that communicate with the fossa, e.g., at the frontal and parietal opercula (*frop*, *pop*): the postcentral (*pocs*) and intraparietal sulci and a sulcus by which the anterior and posterior transverse temporal gyri of Heschl (*attg*, *pottg*) are separated—the intertransverse temporal sulcus (*itrs*). In contrast with this, other arteries boldly climb out of the Sylvian fossa over the convexities of gyri that form its margins, e.g., those that supply the region around the central sulcus (*cs*) and others that spread over the anterior segment of the temporal lobe.

Altogether, about half-a-dozen Sylvian arteries may be distinguished in the Sylvian fossa: the *frontal Sylvian artery* or *arteries* (*Syfra*), supplying part of the orbital surface, the frontal operculum or inferior frontal gyrus, the inferior frontal sulcus, the middle frontal gyrus, and a part of the superior frontal sulcus; the *central Sylvian artery* or *arteries* (*Sycea*), spreading about four of its branches over the posterior part of the frontal operculum (*frop*), the middle frontal gyrus, and the back part of the superior frontal sulcus (*sfs*), as well as over most of the central sulcus (*cs*) and both the pre- and postcentral gyri (*acg*, *pocg*), except approximately the upper third adjoining the upper margin of the hemisphere, and the adjoining portion of the parietal lobe (*pop*, *smg*); the *parieto-occipital Sylvian artery* (*Sypaocca*), spreading over the posterior portion of the parietal and over the adjoining part of the occipital lobes; the *superior temporo-occipital Sylvian artery* (*Syteoccsua*), supplying the posterior half of the superior temporal gyrus (*stg*) and sulcus (*sts*), its ultimate terminals reaching as far back as the occipital pole (*see also* Figs. 373, 374); the *inferior temporo-occipital Sylvian artery* (*Syteoccinfa*), chiefly supplying the upper portion of the middle temporal gyrus (*mtg*) and the adjoining superior temporal gyrus (*stg*); and the *anterior temporal Sylvian arteries* (*Syteanta*), spreading over the anterior fourth of the temporal lobe, including its anterior pole.

Most of these arteries are in no way directly related to the visual pathways and centers. They supply extensive regions and areae of the cerebral cortex concerned with motor, somesthetic, and auditory functions, besides others as yet inadequately understood. Exceptions are foci of the frontal, temporal, and occipital lobes regulating the movements of the eyes, pupils, and accommodation of vision, and the cortical regions of the posterior extremities of the two hemispheres subserving psychic and associated functions of vision (*see* chap. VIII, 1 [4], and Figs. 274, 275).

The first of the Sylvian arteries related to the visual system is the *inferior temporo-occipital artery* (*Syteoccinfa*, Fig. 370). This vessel, after crossing the superior temporal gyrus, slips into the first temporal sulcus, where it assumes a posterior course. Here it gives off a number of branches which supply the cortical and subcortical substance of the temporal lobe. Some of these branches, especially those given off at the level of the lateral geniculate nucleus, very likely contribute to the blood supply of the initial portion of the visual and auditory radiations (*cf.* Fig. 371).

The superior temporo-occipital Sylvian artery is of great importance to both the normal and the pathological functions of vision (*Syteoccsua* in Fig. 370). It is an important source of blood supply both for the visual radiation and for the striate cortex. This artery is easily the longest of the middle cerebral branches. It separates from the parieto-occipital Sylvian artery (*Sypaocca*) within the Sylvian pit at about the level of the anterior transverse temporal gyrus of Heschl (*attg*). After crossing the superior temporal gyrus (*stg*), it plunges into the superior temporal sulcus (*sts*), within which, halfway between its floor and the surface, it courses toward the occipital lobe. In this locality, where it is topographically closest to the subcortical fiber substance, it gives off a succes-

sion of small branches which perforate the cortex of the sulcal floor and enter the sagittal fiber layers of the hemisphere containing the visual radiation and the occipital system of fibers for associated eye movements, besides various other not yet identified tracts and systems (Figs. 226–33, 235, 236). The clogging of this artery, e.g., in the superior temporal sulcus or posteriorly, may cause a part of the visual radiation, as well as other fiber systems, to degenerate (this is well illustrated by case MUNSON, described in chap. XII, 6).

In its further course backward, the superior temporo-occipital Sylvian artery divides into several branches spreading over the middle part of the convexity of the occipital lobe (Fig. 370). The most posterior terminals of this artery extend as far back as the occipital pole (*12*), where they meet the terminals of the calcarine artery (*11, 13*), especially its principal branch (*sca, scal*, or *pca* in Figs. 369, 372, 374; *see also* Figs. 367, 371). In this way an arterial contact is established between the territories of the middle and the posterior cerebral arteries.

The meeting line between the two arterial territories varies individually. It may coincide fairly well with the posterior limit of the striate area (thus in Fig. 372). In other cases a smaller or a wider strip of the striate cortex may be entirely supplied by the middle cerebral artery (thus in Figs. 369, 370, 373, 374), whereas by far the larger portion of this cortex remains supplied by the posterior cerebral artery. (For the pathophysiological significance of the foregoing relationship *see* secs. 6 and 8, this chapter, and chap. XI, 8 and 9.)

A double blood supply of the most posterior portion of the striate area is shown especially clearly in the Infrahuman Primates, the Monkeys and Apes, where it seems to be the rule (Figs. 286, 376; *cf.* sec. 7, this chapter).

References: See bibliography at the end of this chapter.

SEC. 5. THE POSTERIOR CEREBRAL ARTERY AND ITS SUBSIDIARIES

1. THE ORIGIN AND TOPOGRAPHY OF THE INITIAL PORTION OF THE POSTERIOR CEREBRAL ARTERY.—The posterior cerebral artery (*pocea*) originates from the basilar artery (*basa*), one for each hemisphere, at the frontal end of the pons

or "bridge" of the brain (Figs. 366, 367, 371). Occasionally the posterior cerebral takes origin from the internal carotid artery on its own side, in which case the much thinner posterior communicating artery of that side connects it with the basilar trunk (thus in Fig. 368, left side).

From approximately the point where it gives off the posterior communicating artery (*pocoa*), the posterior cerebral artery turns back around the pons, skirting the foot of the cerebral peduncle from underneath (*cp* in Figs. 367, 371, 372). Here, in the cleft between the pons and the arms of the cerebellum and the inner face of the temporal and occipital lobes (hippocampal gyrus, *hig*, and uncus, *unc*), it gives off several small branches, the *posterior perforate arteries* (*popa*), which supply the substantia nigra (*sn*), red nucleus (*rn*), and a part of the tegmentum (*tg*) of the midbrain.

Next, a series of small branches arises, closely attached to the inferior and lateral faces of the cerebral peduncle, which they in part supply, the larger and longer branches ascending as far as the optic tectum—the *mesencephalic branches* (*mesa*, Fig. 371, left).

2. The chorioid and hippocampal arteries.—One or two slightly thicker arteries, arising from the stem of the posterior cerebral artery, turn upward, closely attached to the cerebral peduncle—the *posterior chorioid arteries* (*pocha*, in Figs. 371, 372). These ascend along the sides of the midbrain to its roof (*tect*, *t*, also *sc* and *e*, in Fig. 369) and enter the meningeal fold filling the transverse cerebral fissure (*trcef*, in Fig. 372), a spacious cleft separating the midbrain and betweenbrain from the splenium (*spl*) of the corpus callosum (*cc*) of the telencephalon. Along their course they give off twigs for the midbrain, the medial geniculate nucleus, the dorsomedial nucleus of the thalamus, the region of the posterior commissure, and the chorioid tela of the third ventricle.

Just before the stem of the posterior cerebral artery divides into its principal branches (*see* below), it gives off from its posterior face a fair-sized twig, the *lateral chorioid artery* (*lacha*), which, after slipping into the hippocampal cleft, supplies a segment of the chorioid plexus of the inferior horn of the lateral cerebral ventricle next behind that supplied by the anterior chorioid artery (*see* Figs. 367, 371, 372, and sec. 4 [2], this chapter). Minute twigs of the lateral chorioid also participate in the supply of the pial plexus, which covers the exposed postero-

inferior face of the lateral geniculate nucleus. (*Cf. also* L. Chacko 1952.)

Another small branch of the posterior cerebral artery spreads over the surface of a portion of the hippocampal gyrus (*hig*), following the cleft for a short distance and extending on the medial inferior side as far as the rhinal fissure (*rhif*)—the *hippocampal artery* (*hipa*, in Fig. 372). Still other small arterial twigs, about half a dozen of them, enter the posterior aspect of the pulvinar of the thalamus.

3. The subdivisions of the posterior cerebral artery.—As soon as the posterior cerebral artery enters the hippocampal fissure (*hif*), still some distance from the isthmal portion of the fornicate-cingular gyrus (*isth*) that separates the hippocampal fissure from the rostral extremity of the anterior or medial calcarine sulcus (*ac*), its trunk branches into two or three principal subdivisions, depending on individual variation: two, if the calcarine (*ca*) and the posterior parietal (*popaa*) arteries have a common stem (Fig. 369); three if the posterior temporo-occipital (*poteocca*), the calcarine (*ca*), and the posterior parietal (*popaa*) arteries originate separately, in which case all three are of about the same thickness (Fig. 372). Occasionally one or two thicker vessels that supply the inner face of the temporal lobe may originate independently—the *medial temporal artery*.

4. The posterior temporo-occipital artery (*poteocca*).—This artery is the most inferior of the principal branches of the posterior cerebral artery (Fig. 369; blue in Fig. 372). Its course is directed posteriorly and downward. At first, it gives off a few small twigs for the near-by segment of the hippocampal gyrus below the isthmus and for the chorioid plexus of the lateral ventricle—the *lateral chorioid artery* (*lacha*). Its principal trunk soon divides into several larger branches, mostly concealed in the rhinal fissure and in the collateral and inferior temporal sulci.

The artery supplies an extensive region on the lower face of the temporal and occipital lobes as far as the occipital pole and beyond (*see also* Fig. 370). Its most posterior terminal branches pass below the inferior margin of the occipital lobe and, after bridging over the occipital pole, slip into the pocket of the posterior calcarine fissure, here undergoing direct anastomotical connections with the terminal arterioles of the principal calcarine artery (*pca* in Fig. 374; *also* Fig. 373). These anastomotical arterial links may measure, according to our own observations, about $\frac{1}{5}$ mm. in diameter (*see* following section).

According to Beauvieux & Ristich-Goelmino (1926), the terminal twigs of the posterior temporo-occipital artery always extend to the occipital pole, where, within the pial membrane, they connect with the calcarine artery by direct anastomoses up to 0.5 mm. thick. Within the cerebral substance there are, however, fewer connections of this size.

5. THE POSTERIOR PARIETAL ARTERY (*popaa*). —This vessel is the intermediate subdivision of the posterior cerebral artery (green in Fig. 372), unless it arises from a stem common both to it and to the calcarine artery (*ca* in Figs. 369, 374). If it arises independently, it plunges at first deep into the hippocampal fissure (*hif*), where it gives off several branches. Most of these are thin, with one somewhat thicker artery, all of them supplying the posterior aspect of the pulvinar (*pula*) and medial geniculate nucleus.

Another smaller branch, the *isthmal artery* (*istha*), emerges upon the hippocampal gyrus close to the isthmus and spreads over it and over a part of the isthmus and over the anterior portion of the lingual gyrus below the anterior or medial calcarine sulcus (*ac*).

Other branches arising in the hippocampal fissure are the lateral chorioid artery (*lch*), a twig for a segment of the chorioid plexus of the lateral ventricle in the rear of the pulvinar (*cf. also lacha*, Fig. 371); several delicate *pial* branchlets (*pia*) for the meningeal fold filling the transverse cerebral fissure beneath the callosal splenium; and a medium-sized *splenial artery* (*spla*).

6. THE SUPRACALCARINE AND PRECUNEAL ARTERIES.—The principal stem of the posterior parietal artery (*popaa*) eventually emerges upon the retrosplenial segment of the fornicate-cingular gyrus (*fcg*), where it divides into a number of branches which spread over the medial face of the parieto-occipital lobes (Figs. 369, 372): the *supracalcarine artery* (*suca*), supplying the upper lip of the rostral portion of the anterior calcarine sulcus (*ac*); the much larger *precuneal artery* (*precua*), supplying most of the precuneus (*precu*); and the equally sizable *parieto-occipital artery* (*paocca*), which supplies most of the deep and spacious parieto-occipital sulcus or fissure (*po*). The posterior parietal arteries may vary considerably individually; on occasion a single stem is present, buried in the parieto-occipital sulcus, from which branches arise to spread over the precuneal region (Fig. 369).

The origin, arrangement, course, and termination of all the above-described arteries, large and small, vary much individually. Especially is this the case when the calcarine and the posterior parietal arteries arise from a common stem, the smaller twigs for the mid- and betweenbrain then taking their origin from that stem (Fig. 369).

References: See the bibliography at the end of this chapter.

SEC. 6. THE CALCARINE ARTERY

1. ORIGIN AND DISTRIBUTION.—The *calcarine artery* (*ca*) either represents one of the three principal subdivisions of the posterior cerebral artery arising independently within the hippocampal fissure (red in Fig. 372) or forms a stem in that fissure common both to it and to the posterior parietal artery (*ca* in Figs. 369, 374). In both cases its initial portion lies within the hippocampal fissure (*hif*), imbedded between the cerebral peduncle (*cp*) medially and the isthmus (*isth*) of the fornicate-cingular (*fcg*) and hippocampal (*hig*) gyri laterally. Within this fissure it gives off a few smaller twigs for the lateral face of the midbrain (lemniscal trigone and lateral mesencephalic sulcus) and a somewhat thicker branch which penetrates into the posterior aspect of the medial geniculate nucleus.

After emerging from the hippocampal fissure, the calcarine artery or its common stem crosses the isthmus and enters the anterior or medial calcarine sulcus (*ac, cf.* chap. VIII, 2 [1], and *mc* in Fig. 273). Here it gives off a few twigs, one of them thicker than the others, which turns anteriorly toward the splenium of the callosal body (*spl*), which it supplies (Fig. 369).

The principal calcarine stem divides into two or three branches, two in case the calcarine artery originates independently from the posterior cerebral artery in the hippocampal fissure (Fig. 372); three if it has a common origin with the posterior parietal artery, in which case the latter separates from it in the anterior calcarine sulcus or close to it (Figs. 369, 374). In any case, in its further course the calcarine artery proper is represented by two principal branches, usually of more or less unequal thickness, the upper being the thicker.

2. The inferior calcarine artery (*ica*, also *ical*).

—This is the lower branch of the calcarine artery (*ca*). After a shorter or longer course within the anterior or medial calcarine sulcus (*ac*), it emerges over the lower lip of that sulcus, with which it runs more or less parallel in the occipital direction. Along part of its course it may be superficially imbedded either in the medial inferior paracalcarine sulcus (*mips*, Fig. 273) or in the inferior occipital sulcus (*ios; see* Fig. 372). Because of its location and character, this artery may also be called *paracalcarine artery* (*paca* in Fig. 372).

On occasion, as in the last-mentioned figure, it may extend backward as far as the inferior (*ios*) and the middle (*mos*) occipital sulci at the very tip of the occipital lobe in the rear of the posterior or lateral calcarine sulcus (*pc*). In other cases it barely touches the occipital pole or may fall considerably short of it (Fig. 374).

From it a number of small, deep branches are given off that enter into the anterior calcarine sulcus (*ac*), some supplying both lips and the fundus, the others supplying, in part or entirely, only the lower lip of that sulcus as far as the fundus.

If the inferior calcarine or paracalcarine artery is almost equal in thickness to the superior or principal calcarine artery (*sca, pca*), it sup-

plies the inferior calcarine lip along its entire longitudinal extent as far as the occipital extremity of the posterior calcarine sulcus (Fig. 372). If, on the contrary, this artery is poorly developed or is situated mostly outside the calcarine sulcus, the posterior portion of the anterior or medial calcarine sulcus (*ac*), the cuneo-lingual gyrus (*cula*), including its anterior slope, and the pocket of the posterior or lateral calcarine sulcus behind the posterior cuneolingual gyrus (*culp* in Fig. 374) remain outside its territory. In this case these and other adjoining parts of the occipital cortex on both the medial and the lateral faces of the occipital lobe are supplied in part by the superior or principal calcarine artery alone (*sca* or *pca* or *scal*) or, in addition, by the terminal branches of the posterior temporo-occipital artery (*poteocca*), slipping underneath the inferior margin of the cerebral hemisphere, and in part by other vessels, especially the posterior cuneal (*cupa*) and the superior temporo-occipital Sylvian artery (*Syteoccsua; see* Fig. 374).

3. The superior or principal calcarine artery (*sca*, also *scal*).

—This vessel is the upper and usually the thicker division of the calcarine artery. If it is much stronger than the inferior calcarine, most of the calcarine sulcus is supplied by it (Fig. 372). In this case, because of its course, location, and character, it may be considered the *principal* or *axial calcarine artery* (*pca*).

Close to the anterior end of the anterior or medial calcarine sulcus (*ac*) the principal calcarine artery dips into that sulcus and courses along its floor posteriorly. Its location is deep in the fundus, where it can be followed more or less as far as the posterior extremity of the posterior calcarine sulcus (*pc*). It gives off a succession of branches, supplying the upper or cuneal calcarine lip, including the adjoining portion of the cuneus.

One, two, or three fairly thick twigs—the *anterior, middle,* and *posterior cuneal arteries* (*cua, cuaa, cuma, cupa*), attached to the upper lip, emerge onto the medial surface of the cuneus. Here they spread as far as the upper margin of the hemisphere and beyond and also supply the posterior slope of the parieto-occipital sulcus (*po*). One or more cuneal arteries may arise from the posterior parietal artery instead of from the calcarine.

What is left of the trunk of the principal calcarine artery, now much reduced in thickness, emerges onto the exposed cuneolingual gyrus (*cul*), if such is present, and crosses this gyrus or meanders between the anterior and posterior cuneolingual gyri, if both are present and are submerged, and finally dips behind into the spacious pocket of the posterior or lateral calcarine sulcus (*pc*). Here the principal trunk continues more or less horizontally in the occipital direction, skirting along the deepest points of the floor of the pocket and again climbing up along the posterior wall of the pocket (Fig. 372). Its superficial terminal twigs emerge onto the surface of the very pole of the occipital lobe (indicated by *), spreading over it around the superior, middle, and inferior occipital sulci (*sos, mos, ios*), if such can be identified. In other cases the principal calcarine artery, as already mentioned, does not extend beyond the posterior cuneolingual gyrus, as described by Beauvieux & Ristich-Goelmino (1926). (*See* Fig. 374.)

Close to the posterior end of the principal calcarine artery, several terminal twigs arise in a successive series from the principal trunk in the posterior lateral calcarine sulcus (*pc*). In the specimen depicted in Figure 372, four twigs are given off above the main stem, and three below. The thicker and longer upper twigs supply the upper and much larger half; the thinner and shorter lower twigs supply the lower, smaller half of the posterior calcarine pocket behind the cuneolingual gyrus (*cul*), their terminals emerging somewhat upon the convex cortex around the pocket.

The twigs are arranged with their stems fairly vertical to the principal calcarine stem, being roughly parallel to one another. Each twig, with its system of arterioles, supplies a small strip of the striate cortex, the adjoining twigs supplying contiguous strips. An overlapping of the adjoining territories seems not to occur, nor is there usually found any mixing of the strips above with those below the principal trunk running horizontally. There are exceptions, however, where a single twig splits into minute terminals, some of which pass above,

the others below, the horizontal line indicated by the principal calcarine trunk.

Not all twigs of the principal calcarine artery at the occipital pole are terminal. Some, as a careful examination of specimens reveals, continue into branches which finally merge with the arteries whose principal spread is over the posteroinferior, posterolateral, or posterosuperior faces of the occipital lobe. Such are the posterior temporo-occipital artery (*poteocca*), a subsidiary of the posterior cerebral (*pocea*), and the superior temporo-occipital Sylvian artery (*Syteoccsua*), which belongs to the middle cerebral artery (*see* Figs. 369, 373, 374), and on occasion there may be other connections. Through these direct anastomotical bridges the system of the calcarine artery proper communicates with the adjoining arterial systems whose origins are at a greater or lesser distance from its own. Thus the long terminals of the posterior cuneal artery (*cupa*), on both the inner and the outer face of the occipital lobe, may descend as far as the calcarine sulcus and may approach, and also partly anastomose with, the circumpolar terminals of the principal calcarine artery. The latter artery (*pca*), in turn, may also be anastomotically linked with its mate, the inferior calcarine artery (*ica*), such linkage likewise taking place at the occipital pole (*).

The anastomosing vessels through which the linking of the calcarine artery is established are small, not exceeding $\frac{1}{5}$ mm. in diameter, or 200 microns, in a preserved specimen. They bear the character of preterminal arterioles. It is reasonable to assume that under physiological conditions these anastomotical bridges are wider, filled as they are with blood under steady pressure. Such anastomoses may help preserve nearly normal conditions of circulation in the cortex at the occipital pole whenever the intra-arterial pressure, owing to local pathological factors, decreases within the territory of one or another of the several arteries thus connected. However, because of their small size, these anastomoses may not be able to play the role of a vicarious passage to supply the whole, or even a major portion, of the cortical territory normally supplied by the obstructed vessel, or may do so only inadequately (except when small arterial twigs are affected). For example, in the case of the clogging of either the posterior cerebral artery or the calcarine artery alone, most of the striate area, together with the adjoining cortex lining the medial face of the cerebral hemisphere in its posterior portion, may degenerate, with the striate cortex around the occipital pole alone remaining spared.

The multiple arterial supply of the occipital pole, by which the foveal portion of the striate cortex is placed in a favored situation, is very well illustrated by one of our cases (chap. XII, MANTENO case No. 368). Here, owing to an arteriosclerotic occlusion of the common stem of the posterior temporo-occipital and calcarine arteries, almost the entire striate and nonstriate cortex of the calcarine sulcus, as well as almost all the cortex of the interior face of the temporo-occipital lobes, had wasted away, whereas the striate cortex at the very occipital pole, lining the most caudal portion of the calcarine sulcus, remained perfectly normal (Fig. 428). In this case not only the calcarine artery that normally supplies most of the striate area but also the posterior temporo-occipital artery that might have supplied it vicariously were completely eliminated, the supply being preserved entirely by the terminals of the most occipital branch of the middle cerebral artery (*Syteoccsua*). (*See* sec. 8, this chapter, for further details.*)

The distribution pattern of the calcarine artery exhibits considerable variation in detail in different brain specimens, and it also varies in each cerebral hemisphere. The two principal calcarine branches, the superior and inferior, may, for example, be almost equal in thickness, of the same length, pursuing a symmetrically similar course, and having a like territorial distribution. In the specimen depicted in Figure 372, the superior calcarine artery (*sca*), though completely concealed within the calcarine sulcus, closely follows the upper lip not far from the surface, sending twigs both into the sulcus and onto the cuneal surface. The inferior calcarine artery (*ica*), in like manner, follows the lower calcarine lip, but on the exposed medial surface, sending a series of branches into the sulcus for the supply of its lower lip. The line of separation or the "divide" between the two territories closely follows the deepest line or floor along the calcarine sulcus.

Again, the inferior lip of the calcarine sulcus may be supplied by two distinct arteries, one

arising from the principal calcarine stem within the fissure taking care of most of that lip, whereas the posterior segment of the same lip is supplied by the terminals of one, two, or more long vessels originating independently from the posterior cerebral artery within the hippocampal fissure (Fig. 374). In still other cases the principal calcarine artery, while fairly well developed and supplying the entire posterior calcarine sulcus, may leave a considerable portion of the striate area to be supplied by a circuitous route: the superior Sylvian temporo-occipital artery (*Syteoccsua*), the accessory inferior calcarine artery (*accica*,) and one or two terminal branches of the posterior temporo-occipital artery (*poteocca*). Finally, the terminal branches of the posterior cuneal artery may join with these vessels in supplying the caudalmost portion of the striate area.

These are but a few types observed in a limited number of specimens studied, upon which the present description is based. The impression gained is of an almost unlimited variation of the interlinking of the arteries by which the occipital lobe and pole are supplied, almost every brain and hemisphere differing from all other brains or hemispheres in some details.

On the basis of the preceding observations it is justifiable to conclude that a multiple linking of the arteries precisely at the occipital pole, where the central fovea and hence axial vision are localized, makes that locality arterially well supplied and functionally exceptionally well protected. That this may be the essential anatomical factor responsible for a most fortunate phenomenon frequently observed in the pathology of the cerebral visual mechanism—the "central sparing" or preservation of the foveal-macular parts of the fields of view in an incomplete homonymous hemianopia—is obvious.

Such an interpretation has been made on theoretical grounds and from clinical experience by R. Förster (1890) and was further substantiated by G. Holmes & Lister (1916), Igersheimer (1918), G. Holmes (1919), Monbrun (1919), Beauvieux & Ristich-Goelmino (1926), and Purves-Stewart (1945) in the study of the blood supply of the occipital lobe.

It is the conviction of the author that the phenomenon of the "sparing" of central portions of the fields of view in homonymous hemianopia is caused entirely by a peculiar organization of the central visual apparatus and by the multiple blood supply of the visual radiation and of the striate area, as further discussed in section 8 [4], this chapter, and in chapter XI, 8, 9.

References: See bibliography at the end of this chapter.

SEC. 7. NOTE ON THE BLOOD SUPPLY IN THE HUMAN FETUS AND IN THE MONKEYS AND APES

The understanding of the ontogenetical and phylogenetical origin of the multiple arterial supply of the foveal-areal, or "macular," portion of the striate area of the human brain is greatly facilitated by the study of the conditions found in the infrahuman species. This reveals that the pattern of a double or multiple blood supply of the occipital lobe is laid down far back in the ontogenesis and phylogenesis of the Primate Order.

In the human embryo, aged approximately six and one-half menstrual months (Fig. 375, upper sketches), the terminal branches of the middle cerebral artery (*mca*), spreading over the lateral face of the brain, closely approach the occipital pole. Here they meet the terminal branches of the posterior cerebral artery (*pca*) coming from the medial face and turning around the occipital pole. The meeting zone of the two arterial territories is, accordingly, on the lateral face of the occipital lobe, just in front of the occipital pole.

In a more advanced human fetus, where the conditions are more readily examined, it is found that the two territories, that of the middle and that of the posterior cerebral arteries, are in fact in this locality directly continuous (same figure, lower sketches). The connection is maintained by fair-sized anastomotical stems, producing, in the aggregate, a loose pial network. The meshes of this network in turn are filled in by a more delicate network of smaller arteries and capillaries, which together form a continuous pial netting. This arrangement indicates the possibility of an easy exchange of the blood in any direction.

The condition found in the adult human brain suggests, then, a condensation of this original pial network into definite larger and smaller stems, relatively little interconnected by the remaining anastomoses of the size of arterioles and larger (*cf.* Duret 1910).

In the Rhesus Macaque an arterial pattern is found in the posterior portion of the cerebral hemisphere which greatly resembles that of the younger human fetus mentioned. Here, too, the posterior branches of the middle cerebral arterial tree swing backward, dipping in and out of the first temporal and simian sulci, until the terminal twigs emerge over the anterior margin of the occipital operculum. The branches of the posterior cerebral artery in turn, after emerging from the deep calcarine sulcus, circle around the original "occipital pole" (which in Man becomes the posterior cuneolingual gyrus; *see* chap. VIII, 3). They spread onto the lateral face of the occipital operculum closer to the occipital pole. The zone where the two arterial territories meet runs a few millimeters behind and parallel to the simian sulcus.

In this way the anterior segment of the striate cortex along the simian sulcus (which in Man becomes the most posterior) falls within the middle cerebral arterial territory, and the segment next to the simian pole (which in Man forms the posterior cuneolingual gyrus) falls within the posterior cerebral, both being interconnected by a fine arterial network.

A double arterial supply of the foveal-areal portion of the striate area (stippled) is particularly conspicuous in the Anthropomorphous Apes. In the Chimpanzee, for example, a considerable portion of the striate area spreads over the posterolateral surface of the occipital lobe, extending almost to the lunate sulcus (*l*, in Fig. 376; *see also* Fig. 284). The branches of the middle cerebral artery, after emerging from the lunate sulcus, spread over the adjacent zone of the occipital operculum. Here they divide into smaller branches and finally into capillaries. From the medial face of the hemisphere arrive branches of the posterior cerebral artery by turning around the occipital pole. These also subdivide into smaller branches, which spread over the territory contiguous with the one supplied by the middle cerebral artery. A number of small arterial anastomoses of a size large enough to be noticed with the unaided eye bridge over from the territory of the middle to that of the posterior cerebral artery. Such direct anastomotic links in the Chimpanzee have not been seen by Shellshear (1931). In our opinion, however, it is fairly certain that in this Ape, as one or the other of the two principal arteries becomes obstructed.

A double or multiple arterial supply of the occipital operculum, with a rich anastomotical arterial network, with the extreme lateral or "posterior" segment of the striate cortex falling within the territory of the middle (*mca*) and

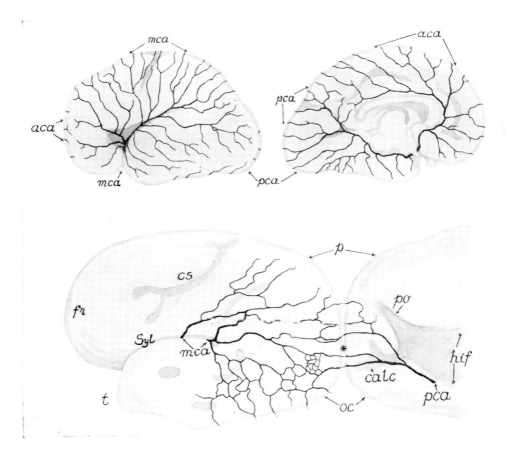

FIG. 375.—*Upper figures:* lateral and medial aspects of the left cerebral hemisphere of a human fetus of an estimated age of six and one-half menstrual months, showing the distribution of three principal arteries of the brain. *Lower figure:* left cerebral hemisphere of a human fetus of an approximate age of eight menstrual months, showing the lateral aspect and the posterior portion of the medial aspect, to demonstrate the anastomotical network by which the territories of the middle and posterior cerebral arteries are directly continuous. At this developmental stage of the complete vascular network of the pial membrane, only the larger vessels in the posterior region of the hemisphere, forming a loose meshwork, are present. One of the large meshes is filled in completely, to show the density of anastomotical connections, which in reality form a vast, continuous network, imbedded in the pial membrane, the larger vessels representing merely thicker ribs in it. *Labeling: aca,* anterior cerebral artery; *calc,* calcarine fissure; *fr,* frontal lobe; *hif,* hippocampal fissure; *mca,* middle cerebral artery; *oc,* occipital lobe; *p,* parietal lobe; *pca,* posterior cerebral artery; *po,* parieto-occipital sulcus; *Syl,* lateral or Sylvian fissure; *t,* temporal lobe; *,* occipital pole of cerebral hemisphere.

in Man, both sufficient precapillary and capillary connections and direct anastomotical links exist between the middle and the posterior arterial territories to establish a collateral circulation in the foveal or "macular" cortex if either with the posterior segment of the same area around the occipital pole, marked by asterisks (*), falling within the territory of the posterior cerebral artery (*poca*), is also present in the Gorilla (Fig. 286).

In the human brain an extensive anastomotical network of smaller venous branches is also present over the entire occipital operculum, duplicating a similar vascular network found in all other regions of the cerebral cortex.

The function of the anastomotical arterial network spreading over the occipital pole may be compared to that attributed to the arterial circle of Willis. This is to assure at all times an equal amount of blood delivered at the same pressure and speed to the foveal-areal or "macular" segment of the striate area, the anatomical substratum of the all-important epicritic vision. (*See* chap. VIII, 2, 3, for further information concerning the calcarine fissure and striate area.)

References: See bibliography at the end of this chapter.

SEC. 8. PHYSIOLOGICAL AND PATHOPHYSIOLOGIC IMPLICATIONS OF THE BLOOD SUPPLY OF THE VISUAL SYSTEM

1. GENERAL REMARKS.—The character of the cerebral blood supply in general and of the visual system in particular, described in the foregoing sections, lends itself to an important interpretation concerning both the normal conditions and the pathophysiological consequences in disease.

cerebral hemispheres or those that penetrate into their core (Fig. 362).

However, numerous minor arterial anastomoses are present, through which the territories or

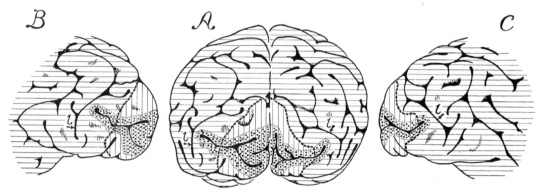

FIG. 376.—Blood supply of the occipital lobe in a newborn Chimpanzee and its relation to the striate area. *Labeling: A*, posterior aspect; *B*, lateral view of left, *C*, lateral view of right occipital lobe. Territories of middle cerebral arteries (*shaded horizontally*) are separated from territories of the posterior cerebral arteries (*shaded vertically*) by broken lines. Striate areae stippled. In both lobes the most lateral posterior portion of areae close to the lunate sulcus (*l*) falls within the middle cerebral territory, the larger portion remaining in the posterior cerebral territory. (*Cf.* Figs. 286, 369, 370, 372, 373, 374.)

The salient feature of the arterial supply of parts of the brain concerned with the visual function is a gradual division of the principal arteries into smaller branches, which eventually terminate in arterioles and capillaries that are visible only with the aid of a magnifying apparatus. Above the level of the arterial circle of Willis at the base of the brain, where all arteries are linked together before they are distributed to the brain, there are normally, in an adult human brain, no channels of considerable size which would link the individual arteries and branches spreading over the surface of the systems of the adjoining vessels are directly connected. Such connections are of great value in localities of great functional importance, as, for example, the posterior segment of the striate area, where the two hemifoveae are represented.

The other point of special interest is a multiple arterial supply found precisely in the foveal portion of the striate area. In many other parts of the brain—for example, over Broca's motor speech region, over the auditory center in the temporal gyri of Heschl, and elsewhere—similar arrangements may be present. This subject, however, has not yet been adequately investigated.

In the region of the central foveal cortex, as

is evident from the preceding section, a safe and abundant blood supply of that functionally important cortical locality is safeguarded, first, by a convergence of several arterial stems originating from different sources and, second, by linking the terminal twigs of these several arteries into a common terminal network.

This arrangement, on speculative grounds, not only permits at all times a uniform distribution of the amount of blood in the foveal area of the cortex but also provides for a certain amount of substitution by other arteries when one or another is shut off.

In the light of these facts and considerations it appears that all large and medium arteries of the brain, except those that make up the circle of Willis, physiologically and pathophysiologically act as "terminal arteries" in Cohnheim's sense. When any one of them is obstructed by a vascular event, such as an embolism, thrombosis, atheromatous narrowing of the arterial passage, or compression caused by an expanding pathological process (tumor, abscess, hemorrhage), its own territory receives a reduced amount of nutrient fluid—the blood—with complete stoppage if the obstruction becomes complete.

The specific tissue—the nervous parenchyma—thus deprived of the indispensable nutritive material, necessarily dies off or degenerates and is carried away. The capillary and precapillary and other slender anastomotical connections along the margins of the blocked-off territory are capable only of reducing the size of the damage in the marginal zones but can hardly prevent it entirely. This may be true of the shutting-off of the larger stems only, the small defects possibly being completely compensated for by a vicarious collateral circulation. Such may especially be the case in the processes affecting the foveal-areal cortex in the posterior segment of the striate area when a multiple anastomotical interlinkage is present. Minute transient, homonymous hemianopic scotomas close to the fixation points may be interpreted in this way (*see* chap. XI, 7).

Interference with free circulation in any artery of considerable size, accordingly, results in events identical with those which would occur if the artery were truly a "terminal artery" but of smaller territorial distribution than it theoretically has. The tissue loss in such cases is sharply defined, and the functional defect, if determinable—for example, a scotoma—is likewise well localized.

Contrasting with this are diffuse pathological processes, such as the effusion of blood within the brain tissue, compressing or directly destroying parts of the visual pathways and centers, and the hematomas and tumors exerting pressure upon parts of the system, which may possibly also be brought about by impeding the free outflow of venous blood.

Frequently the pathological process is a combination of several factors, often difficult to interpret correctly. The same is also true of the various traumas, since a localized lesion in part of the visual pathway will be complicated by an additional interference caused by the concomitant hemorrhage and stasis.

2. The character of the blood supply and the pathology of the constituent elements of the visual system.—In the following description the most important processes met with in the vascular affections of the visual system are briefly described.

An obstruction of the main stem of the *central artery* of the retina, irrespective of the agent, causes a degeneration of approximately the vitreal half of the retinal membrane, which comprises all bipolars, amacrines, and ganglion cells. The resulting complete blindness of the involved eye is not in the least alleviated by the preserved photoreceptors, which depend nutritionally upon the chorioid membrane (*see* Nicholls 1938; Tansley 1947).

If only one or a few arterioles are affected, only their particular retinal territories are eliminated, resulting in a scotoma, or partial blindness, of various shapes and locations. The layer of the photoreceptors seems to be more resistant; these, as is shown by the cases of partial detachment of the retina from the chorioid membrane, are again restored to normal or nearly normal function when they are brought into contact with that membrane.

The *optic nerve*, the most accessible part of the visual system, has been much studied, and the role that the vascular factor plays in its pathology has been fairly well represented in the literature.

The *optic chiasma*, having a multiple blood supply, possibly may not be appreciably interfered with by the clogging of any one of the several small arteries supplying it but may be affected when larger vessels, such as the anterior cerebral or internal carotid arteries, are obstructed. The same may be said of the *optic tracts*, largely depending on the anterior chorioid artery, where encephalomalacic foci have been described (Henschen 1911). The insufficient experimental and histopathological study of the pertinent cases, however, leaves this important question still largely unsettled.

A little more may, perhaps, be said on the vascular pathology of the *lateral geniculate nucleus*. In a partial affection of this internode, an inferior homonymous quadrantic hemianopia is produced by a focus in the medial segment (supplied by the posterior cerebral artery) and a superior homonymous quadrantic hemianopia by damage to the lateral segment (supplied by the anterior chorioid artery). The central vision represented in the intermediate segment of the nucleus is likely to remain preserved, owing to the supply of this segment by both arteries (Abbie 1933, 1938; Mackenzie, Meighan & Pollock). According to Chacko (1952), gross central visual defect results from the occlusion of the posterior cerebral artery, and an extracentral concentric contraction is caused if the anterior chorioid artery is blocked.

Since the blood supply of the *visual radiation* is also insufficiently known, few valid conclusions may be drawn concerning the vascular factor responsible in the pathology of each particular segment of this long fiber system. What the symptoms of vascular interference with the anterior portion of the visual radiation are, is not clear (Abbie 1938). It is possible that the superior homonymous quadrantic hemianopia caused by an obstruction of the anterior chorioid artery is, in reality, the result of damage to the lateral segment of the lateral geniculate nucleus. The possibility must be considered, however, that the same functional impairment may also be brought about by a compression or occlusion of the posterior temporo-occipital artery (*poteocca*) in the inferior temporal or in the collateral sulci, a branch of the posterior cerebral artery upon which depends the supply of the inferior segment of the sagittal fiber strata

through the whole length of the temporo-occipital lobes (Figs. 374, 377). Conversely, it is fair to expect a contralateral inferior homonymous quadrantic hemianopia when the main stem, or one of the posterior branches of the middle cerebral, especially the superior temporo-occipital Sylvian artery (*Syteoccsua*), is closed (*see* chap. XII, 6, case MUNSON).

The obstruction of the main stem of the calcarine artery (*ca*), which supplies most of the *striate area*, unavoidably produces a contralateral homonymous hemianopia. However, since the most posterior portion of the striate area, in which the homonymous halves of two hemifoveae are represented, is frequently supplied either by a circuitous route from the posterior cerebral stem other than the calcarine artery or by the middle cerebral artery via the superior temporo-occipital Sylvian artery, that portion of the striate cortex remains preserved to an individually varying extent when the calcarine artery proper becomes deficient.

Conversely, the posterior or foveal-macular portion of the striate cortex becomes affected, manifesting itself in a central scotoma, in the pathology of those individual cases where that portion depends upon a circuitous blood supply, if that supply is interfered with. This is more likely to happen if, as is probable, the intermediate foveal-macular segment of the visual radiation is damaged, in addition to a direct involvement of the foveal-macular cortex or that segment alone.

Ordinarily, however, it appears that such an event may be averted when the pathological process is confined to the territory of the principal calcarine (*pca*), the calcarine (*ca*), or even to the entire posterior cerebral artery (*pocea*), provided that the foveal-macular portion of the striate cortex receives its blood supply from the middle cerebral artery via the superior temporo-occipital Sylvian branch (*Syteoccsua*), the result being the preservation of the central portions of the fields of view. (*Cf.* Fig. 374; *see also* chap. XI, 9, esp. [3].)

To what extent central vision remains spared or may be restored may also depend upon the efficiency of the arterial anastomoses between the several arterial territories mentioned. Such vicarious vascular substitution is limited by the size and condition of the connecting links and by the condition of the terminal arterioles by which the blood passes to the nervous parenchyma. When the ultimate arterioles and capillaries have suffered from disease and a free passage of blood is mechanically obstructed or inhibited, no use or only inadequate use is made of the existing anastomotical links, even if these are present and are passable. The result is a relative or absolute ischemia, followed by encephalomalacia or degenerative softening of the brain tissue and an impairment of function or a permanent functional loss, depending on the degree of interference with circulation. Just how much the vicarious blood supply of the cortex is capable of restoring a function temporarily lost or impaired remains a problem to be dealt with by future investigation. (*See also* par. 4, this section.)

3. THE BLOOD SUPPLY OF THE STRIATE AREA AND THE SCINTILLATING SCOTOMA.—The peculiar character of the blood supply of the visual cortical centers may also be drawn upon to explain certain symptoms of visual pathology manifestly caused by a vascular factor. Such is the transient homonymous hemianopia frequently associated with migraine and with a subjective experience of scintillation, as in scintillating scotoma or scintillating blindness (for an excellent presentation, *see* Roger & Reboul-Lachaux 1921; Niessl von Mayendorf 1931, 1936; Rønne 1936; Lashley 1941; Donahue 1950; Patrikios 1950; Behrman 1951; Lieberman 1951; Somya; Weeks; *cf. also* chap. XII, 10).

In this phenomenon, in addition to the functional factors, such as the causative irritant followed by a spasm of part or all of the vascular tree of the calcarine artery, a purely anatomical factor plays an essential role (*cf.* Fig. 372). A spasm may begin with the circumpolar terminals and gradually spread along the larger branches and the trunk of the principal calcarine artery. The constriction automatically and effectively eliminates the utilization of the existing arterial anastomoses with the other related arteries (middle cerebral, for example). This interpretation harmonizes with the beginning of a subjective experience of photism at the fixation points and a gradual shifting of the "luminous scotoma" toward the periphery of

the fields of view, the initial central photoma gradually being replaced by a "shiny amblyopia," as the blood stream decreases in the arterial tree.

While in most cases this is apparently a transient process, permanent impairment may follow in consequence of irreparable damage to the nervous tissue in the territory of one of the calcarine arteries, resulting in variously shaped and located scotomas. The underlying causative pathology, too, may in each case be better understood if the topography of the retinal representation in the striate area and the distribution of the blood vessels supplying it are taken into consideration.

A contrary process, an inordinate dilatation of the calcarine vascular system and its engorgement, owing to an inhibition and slowing-down of circulation because of either mechanical obstacles or paresis of the vasoconstrictors, caused, for example, by abuse of such drugs as nitroglycerin or theocalcium, may conceivably bring about a similar subjective phenomenon of amblyopic scintillation and a temporary or even permanent decrease in, or destruction of, normal function in the homonymous fields.

Understanding the pertinent anatomical and physiological factors responsible for scintillating blindness is of great practical importance, since such phenomena may be the premonitory signs preceding a thrombotic or similar impairment or destruction of a part of the central visual apparatus, resulting in permanent functional field defect, unless immediate effective steps are taken to check the basic pathological process (atheromatosis, high blood pressure, etc.). (*See* chap. XI, 8, 9, for further discussion of the problem of "central sparing," especially in cases of complete unilateral destruction of the striate area or the interruption of one visual radiation; *see* chap. XII for the clinical and pathoanatomical analysis of cases; *see* especially the following paragraph.)

4. THE CEREBRAL BLOOD SUPPLY AND THE SPARING OF CENTRAL VISION IN HEMIANOPIA.— The problem of the "central sparing" or preservation of the foveal-areal-macular portions of the fields of view frequently observed in cases of incomplete homonymous hemianopia has been touched upon in sections 6 (3), 7, and 8 (2, 3) in

this chapter and is further discussed in chapter XI, 8 and 9. In view of the great practical importance of this phenomenon, an attempt is made here to link the relevant facts of the anatomy of the supranuclear division of the visual system with those of its blood supply, in order to find a plausible material basis of that phenomenon.

The supranuclear division of the visual system in each hemisphere of the brain is essentially made up of the fibers of the visual radiation (Fig. 377, *VR*), which conduct impulses, and the striate area of the cortex (given in solid black) lining the calcarine fissure of the occipital lobe, which is the terminal station (marked by an asterisk * in Fig. 377). As is shown by the sketches of the serial sections through the parietotemporo-occipital lobe in the same figure, different constituents of the central visual mechanism are supplied from different arterial sources at various levels.

At the occipital pole (Fig. 377, sketch *A*) the entire bulk of the hemisphere, including the striate cortex and the subcortical fiber substance, falls within the territory of the posterior cerebral artery (vertical shading). This extreme condition, however, must be qualified because in numerous cases the most posterior portion of the striate area may be supplied by the middle cerebral artery (as discussed in the preceding sections).

On the levels approximately corresponding to the tip of the posterior horn of the lateral ventricle (Fig. 377, *B*) the situation begins to change. Here the territory of the middle cerebral artery (horizontally shaded) not only has taken most of the lateral face (right side of the sketch) but has invaded the core of the hemisphere, spreading in the manner of a wedge as far as the posterior horn of the lateral ventricle (small oval).

On the next anterior level (*C*), the middle arterial territory spreads over the entire lateral face from the upper to the lower margin of the hemisphere. In the core it further expands along the lateral ventricle, where it includes the intermediate branch of the visual radiation (*VR*). The upper and lower margins of the radiation, including fibers that pass over to the upper and lower lips of the calcarine fissure, together with the entire striate area and its subcortical fibers

and the entire medial and inferior faces of the hemisphere, remain within the territory of the posterior cerebral artery.

On further anterior levels (*D*, *E*) the situation remains substantially the same, except for a relatively small displacement of the boundary line between the two arterial territories along the upper and lower margins of the hemisphere.

As the level of the splenium of corpus callosum (*CC*) is attained, the greater part of the visual radiation (*VR*) or, more correctly, of the sagittal fiber layers falls within the territory of the middle cerebral artery, the inferior segment of the same layers still being supplied by the posterior cerebral artery (sketches *F*, *G*).

Taking the above-described relationship as a basis, the following deductions seem permissible. When the pole of the occipital lobe is directly affected (*A*), it is probable that the central vision will be affected, since either the foveal-areal-macular fibers of the radiation close to their termination or the corresponding portion of the striate area, or both, are interfered with. The remainder of the fields of view may remain entirely free, provided that no damage has been done to any other part of the brain. The size, shape, and other features of the scotomatous defect will depend upon the size, shape, location, and kind of lesion.

If the lesion is located farther anteriorly from the occipital pole—for example, at the level of sketch *E*—an entirely different situation will arise. Assuming a massive elimination of the entire posterior cerebral territory, including parts of the striate cortex (black) and fibers of the radiation which depend entirely on the posterior cerebral artery, that is, the bundles streaming above and below the lateral ventricle (*V*), a functional defect will comprise the extra-areal-foveal periphery of the homonymous fields of view whose centers will be spared. The necessary condition for this is that the intermediate or axial segment of the radiation and the posterior or polar portion of the striate area, both related to the central fovea and area of both retinae, remain outside the pathological process. Such separation is possible, considering the territorial separation of the posterior and middle cerebral arteries at this level. The separation is further enhanced by the presence of the lateral ventricle, precisely in the line of separation, which serves as a vascular barrier.

The elimination of the extrafoveal-areal periphery by a pathological process in approximately the middle and anterior portions of the calcarine fissure is possible on anatomical grounds, with the sparing of the foveal-macular portion of the striate area at the occipital pole, provided that the foveal-macular fibers in the intermediate segment of the visual radiation also remain unaffected. How much of the periphery is eliminated and how much of the centers of the fields are spared will depend entirely on the location and extent of the lesion in the calcarine fissure. (*Cf.* case HOLT in chap. XII, 7.)

The final and least weighty argument

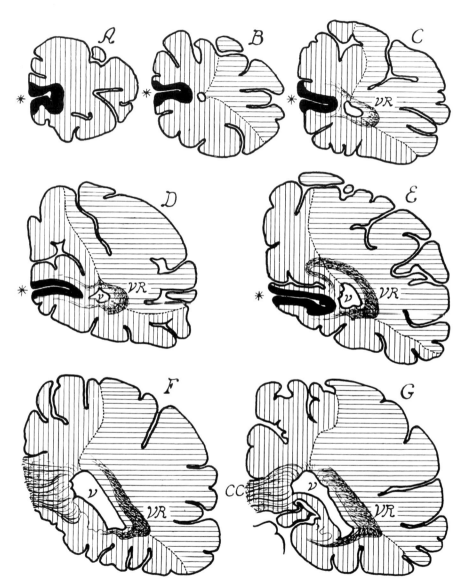

Fig. 377.—Coronal sections through human occipital lobe, beginning with the pole (*A*) and as far as the splenium of the corpus callosum (*G*), to show the variation of blood supply on different levels. The territory of the middle cerebral artery is shaded horizontally, that of the posterior cerebral artery is shaded vertically. Note the striate area (*solid black*), falling entirely in the posterior cerebral territory on all levels, whereas the bulk of the visual radiation (*VR*), in particular its intermediate branch, belongs to the middle cerebral territory, except at the pole (sketch *A*). In other cases the polar portion of the striate area is also supplied, partly or entirely, by the middle cerebral artery (*see* Figs. 373, 374). *Labeling: A*, caudal, *G*, oral levels through occipital lobe; *CC*, corpus callosum; *V*, posterior horn of lateral ventricle; *VR*, sagittal fiber layers containing visual radiation; *, calcarine fissure. (*Cf.* Figs. 231–33.)

brought in favor of the various speculations on the causes of central sparing are the minute central remnants recorded in cases where an entire striate area was removed, e.g., in occipital lobectomies. These central sparings are in-

variably very small, falling within the limits of error of the plotting technique, and are of no particular theoretical or practical significance.

References: See the bibliography at the end of this chapter.

SEC. 9. SUMMARY OF THE BLOOD SUPPLY OF THE VISUAL SYSTEM

1. SOURCES.—The blood supply of both the cerebral and the extracerebral parts of the visual system derives from the same sources as those which supply the brain—the two internal carotids and the two vertebral arteries, four in all.

2. THE EYEBALL, RETINA, AND OPTIC NERVE.—The eyeball receives its supply practically exclusively through the ophthalmic artery, which branches off from the upper end of the internal carotid.

The supply of the retina is twofold: through the central artery via the optic nerve, which provides the inner layers vitrealad to the outer plexiform layer, and osmotically from the chorioid membrane, which supplies the outer retinal layers, principally represented by the photoreceptors. The venous blood is carried away principally through the vorticose veins, which empty into the ophthalmic vein. The central artery is likewise the principal supplier of the optic nerve as far as its entry into the cranial cavity, the intracranial portion probably being supplied by the anterior cerebral artery.

3. CHIASMA.—The arterial supply of the optic chiasma is from several sources, principally from the anterior cerebral artery (anterior, superior, and lateral aspects). A few delicate branches of the anterior communicating artery may spread over the posterior and inferior aspects of the chiasma. Whether the internal carotid, middle cerebral, and anterior chorioid arteries also contribute to the anastomotical network in the pial sheath that envelops the chiasma remains to be investigated.

4. THE OPTIC TRACT.—The optic tract also has a multiple arterial supply: the anterior cerebral artery (initial portion), the anterior chorioid artery (middle and posterior portions), and,

according to Abbie (1938), also the internal carotid, posterior communicating, and middle and posterior cerebral arteries.

5. THE LATERAL GENICULATE NUCLEUS.—The lateral geniculate nucleus, according to Abbie (1938), is supplied by the anterior and posterior chorioid and by the posterior cerebral arteries. The anterior chorioid supplies principally the anterolateral aspect; the posterior cerebral artery supplies the posteromedial aspect; and both arteries supply the hilum of the nucleus. Some terminal twigs spread principally in the individual cell laminae, others pass through the nucleus to the initial portion of the visual radiation.

According to Alexander & Putnam (1938), the most abundant blood supply of all structures of the brain is found in the lateral geniculate nucleus, with the largest proportion of vessels of the fourth order, with a diameter measuring from 34 to 51 microns, and possessing the densest capillary network.

6. THE VISUAL RADIATION AND THE STRIATE AREA.—The blood supply of the supranuclear division of the visual system is intimately related to the blood supply of the cerebral hemisphere, particularly of the parietal, temporal, and occipital lobes, of which it is a part. Conversely, the blood supply of this division is largely independent of that of the infranuclear division of the visual system.

The visual radiation and the related cell and fiber systems receive their arteries from two sources, which, in addition, vary from level to level. The most anterior portion of the radiation, according to Abbie (1937, 1938), is supplied by the deep optic branch of the middle cerebral artery, which enters through the anterior perforate substance in association with the lateral striate arteries.

The arterial supply of the much larger posterior portion of the radiation in the parieto-temporal and occipital lobes is as follows (*see* Fig. 377). At the level of the splenium of the corpus callosum (*F, G*) a portion of the radiation (*VR*), principally its lower segment, as well as the corresponding segment of the tapetum, splenium, and the entire interhemispheric and cerebellar surfaces of the cortex, with their sulci and the subjacent white substance, is supplied by the posterior cerebral artery (Fig. 377, vertical shading). A portion of the sagittal fiber strata, corresponding to the intermediate segment of the visual radiation, however, belongs to the middle cerebral artery (horizontal shading). The upper segment of the external and internal sagittal strata is a boundary zone, where the territories of the posterior and the middle cerebral arteries meet.

From the level immediately behind the callosal splenium (*E*) to as far back as the posterior extremity of the posterior horn of the lateral ventricle (*B*), the vertical segment of all three sagittal fiber layers down to the ventricle (*V*) is completely taken over by the middle cerebral artery. The posterior cerebral artery here supplies the upper and the lower horizontal segments of the fiber layers, as well as the interhemispheric and cerebellar surfaces of the occipital lobe.

In approximately the middle of the occipital lobe the relative extent of the middle cerebral territory becomes larger, approaching, or even extending over, the superior and inferior temporal margins of the hemisphere. Behind the posterior horn of the lateral ventricle (*A*), most of the fiber mass immediately subjacent to the striate area (solid black) is again taken over by the posterior cerebral artery.

The striate area, the fibers of the visual radiation streaming from the upper and lower segments of the external stratum toward both lips of the calcarine fissure, and the fiber layer of the calcar avis, along their entire anteroposterior extent, are supplied by the posterior cerebral artery (*C, D, E*). The only exception is the tip or pole of the occipital lobe, where the middle and posterior cerebral arterial territories meet.

References: Abbie 1933, 1934, 1937, 1938; Aitken 1909; L. Alexander 1942; Alexander & Putnam 1938; Alezais & d'Astros 1892; Allers 1916; Almeida Lima 1950; Ariëns Kappers 1933; Ariëns Kappers, Huber & Crosby 1936; F. Arnold 1838; Ayer & Aitken 1907; H. L. Bair 1940; Bair & Harley 1940; Balado & Franke 1937; Batson 1944; Beauvieux 1930; Beauvieux, Piechaud & Rudeau 1929; Beauvieux & Ristich-Goelmino 1926; Beevor 1907, 1909; C. Behr 1931, 1935; Bethe, Bergmann, Embden & Ellinger, vols. 9, 10, 12, 1927–31; Bluntschli 1910; Bolton, Bramwell & Robinson 1915; Bostroem 1939; Bramwell 1915; Bronk 1938; Byron & Bramwell; A. C. P. Campbell 1938; L. Chacko 1952; Chauchard & Chauchard 1928; Clark & Wentsler 1938; Cobb 1938; Cobb & Lennox 1944; Cohn & Papez 1930; Cohnheim 1872, 1882, 1889; Cone & Barrera 1931; Corning 1909; Craigie 1920, 1938, 1940, 1942, 1945; Critchley 1930; D. J. Cunningham (G. E. Smith & W. E. Le Gros Clark) 1943; Dandy 1919, 1922, 1933, 1946; Dandy & Goetsch 1910–11; Davison, Goodhart & Needles 1934; B. H. Dawson 1950; Dendy 1909; Duret 1873, 1874, 1910; Echlin 1942; Eckstein 1935; Elvidge 1938; 'Espinasse 1934; Evans 1939; Evans & McEachern 1938; Favory 1926; Fawcett 1896; Fawcett & Blackford 1905; Fay & Grant 1923; E. B. Ferris 1941; Finley 1938, 1940; Florey 1925; O. Foerster 1929, 1939; Foerster & Penfield 1930; R. Förster 1877, 1890; Foix & Masson 1923; Foix & Schiff-Wertheimer 1925; Forbes 1928; Forbes & Cobb 1938; Franklin 1937; Freund 1916; Fulton 1928; R. W. Gerard 1938; Gildea & Cobb 1930; Globus 1936, 1938; Globus & Silverstone 1935; Godinov 1930; Graefe & Saemisch, v. 2, 1903; Gregg & Shipley 1944; Grünbaum & Sherrington 1902; Halstead, Walker & Bucy 1940; S. T. Harris 1928; Harvey 1950; Henschen 1911; C. J. Herrick 1935; W. R. Hess 1939; Heubner 1872, 1874; Hicks & Warren 1950; Hindzé 1930, 1933; W. His 1904; Hoff & Pötzl 1935; G. M. Holmes 1919, 1946; Holmes & Lister 1916; Hovelacque 1927; Howe & McKinley 1927; Igersheimer 1918; Janbon & Viallefont 1931; Kabat & Schadewald 1941; Kahler 1922; Kaplan, Rabiner & Browder 1953–54; Keller 1939; Kennedy, Wortis & Wortis 1938; Kerschner 1943; Kleiss 1944–45; Kleist 1934; Köbcke 1936; Kolisko 1891; Krehl 1910; Krogh 1936; Kubie & Hetler 1928; Lapinsky 1897; Lashley 1941; Leber 1903; Leblanc 1926, 1928; Lelli 1939; Lennox, Gibbs & Gibbs 1938; J. Ley

1932; Livingston 1933; Löhr 1939; Lorente de Nó 1927; McDonald & Potter 1951; Mackenzie, Meighan & Pollock 1933; McMullen 1926; McNaughton 1938; Magitot 1907, 1946; Mall 1905; Marchesani 1939; Marie 1936; Masson 1923; F. Merkel 1885–90; Monbrun 1924; Morax 1916, 1917, 1919; Morax, Moreaux & Castelain 1919; Moutier 1908; F. Müller 1930; L. R. Müller 1931; Pallarès 1931; Patrikios 1950; Penfield, Evans & McMillan 1935; Penfield & Rasmussen 1950; R. A. Pfeifer 1928, 1930, 1931; Pinkston & Rioch 1938; Poirier & Charpy 1901–4; Polyak, Judd & McHugh 1946; Popa & Fielding 1930, 1933; Poppi 1928; Purves-Stewart 1945; Putnam 1937; Putnam & Alexander 1928; Putnam & Liebman 1942; Quensel 1931; S. Ramón y Cajal 1928; Rea 1941; A. von Reuss 1876; Rønne (Roenne) 1919; Rubino 1933; Rucker 1946; Ryder *et al.* 1951; Saenger 1918, 1919; S. S. Samuels 1950; Scharrer 1937, 1940; Schieck & Brückner 1930–32; Schiff-Wertheimer 1926; Schiff-Wertheimer,

Foix, Chavany & Hillemand 1925; Schlesinger 1939, 1940–41; Schmidt 1950; Schmidt & Hendrix 1938; P. Schuster 1936, 1937; Sepp 1928; A. Šercer 1951; Shellshear 1920, 1927, 1931, 1933; Solnitzky 1939, 1940; Somya 1947; Spalteholtz 1926; Spatz 1939; Spielmeyer 1922; Stopford 1916–17; H. E. Story 1951; *Symposium on Blood Supply* 1938; Taboada 1927–28; Tanasesco 1905; Tandler 1898, 1926–29; Thompson & Smith 1951; Tigerstedt 1921–23; Toldt 1904; Traquair 1917, 1946; Traquair, Dott & Russell 1935; Tsang 1935, 1936; Tureen 1938; Uhthoff 1902, 1922, 1923; Vander Eecken *et al.* 1951; G. Voss 1917; Vossius 1896; F. B. Walsh 1947; Weil 1933; S. Weiss 1938; Wentsler 1936; Wilbrand & Saenger 1899–1927; S. A. K. Wilson 1917, 1940; E. Wolff 1948; H. G. Wolff 1936, 1938; Zander 1896; Zeeman 1925. *See also* numerous articles in *Zentralbl. f. d. ges. Neurol. u. Psychiat.*, v. 94, pp. 337–60, 1939 (*Symposium on Blood Supply*, German).

PART III

Pathology of the Retina and of the Visual Pathways and Centers of the Brain

Chapter XI

Disturbances of Vision and the Anatomical Organization of the Visual System

SEC. 1. INTRODUCTION

1. General remarks concerning the pathophysiology of the visual pathways and centers.—The disturbances of visual function caused by interference with the visual system are manifested in a great variety of symptoms. This is to be expected, since the visual pathway, from its beginning in the retinae of the eyes to its termination in the cortical visual centers in the occipital lobes, extends along the longer axis of the cranium, hence is either close to other important structures such as the cranial nerves or is, in fact, a constituent element of the brain itself during a part of its course.

The second and principal factor responsible for the variety of clinical symptoms, however, is the inherent elaborate organization of the visual system and of its blood supply, both of which vary at different levels. The third determining factor is the nature of the pathological agent, the locality where the pathological process applies, and the mode of its application.

The impairment of visual function depends, accordingly, upon several partly innate and partly accidental factors, such as the anatomical organization, the character of the blood supply, and the locality and nature of the pathogenic process. The latter, in turn, may differ greatly: a stationary or an expanding neoplasm or tumor, a slow or a sudden hemorrhage, an ischemic or encephalomalacic focus caused by an occlusion of a blood vessel by a spasm, embolism, thrombosis, or atheromatous constriction, an infectious focus, and, finally, a direct or indirect traumatic or mechanical injury of various kinds.

2. Fields of view and their relation to the retinal surface.—When either the retina or any portion of the visual pathway anywhere along its course is damaged or interrupted, a corresponding loss of the visual function occurs. Since the area seen by an eye, that is, a retina, called the *visual field* or *field of view*, may be subdivided by meridians or straight lines radiating from the points of fixation (f) into quadrants and sectors, and by concentric circles into belts or zones (Fig. 381), functional loss or blindness may be determined quantitatively by perimetric plotting.

Each field of view is customarily divided into four quadrants—an upper and a lower nasal and an upper and a lower temporal. The vertical dividing line coinciding with the vertical meridian and passing exactly through the point of fixation, or a point corresponding to the visual axis of the eye and thus corresponding with the center of the central fovea, divides each field into two unequal halves placed vertically. The larger temporal half of the field corresponds to the larger nasal half of the retinal surface; the smaller nasal half of the field corresponds to the smaller temporal half of the retina.

The reversed position of the homonymous retinal halves and of the four quadrants of the fields of view relative to their retinal halves and quadrants is a consequence of the "dark-chamber effect" and of the action of the dioptrical media of the eye. Because of this, the right retinal halves see the left halves of the fields of view, and the left retinal halves see the right ones (*cf.* chap. I, 5, and Fig. 33). The same principle holds for the upper and lower retinal halves, separated by the horizontal meridians, so that the former see the lower halves of the fields of view, and the latter see the upper.

3. Types of visual field defects.—The loss of visual function, a subjective defect, may be either total or partial. It may range all the way from a slight impairment, subjectively barely or not at all noticeable, to complete blindness to all visual stimuli (Figs. 382, 383).

Total loss is manifested in blindness of one whole field of view or of both, or of half of each of the two fields. In a partial field defect a portion or portions of one or of both fields of view are affected.

Blindness may be complete when it concerns the entire range of the visual perceptions, including simple light perception, together with

TEM.—The most important single factor on which the character of a visual field defect depends is the anatomical organization of the visual pathways and centers. Next in importance is the blood supply of the parts of the nervous system concerned in vision. The third factor is the locality of the lesion affecting the visual pathways and centers. The last, but not the least, important factor is the causative agency, its nature, mode of spreading, and extent. The character of a functional visual disturbance, in turn, helps us to learn about the anatomical and

FIG. 378.—Jean Cruveillier (1791–1874), distinguished professor of pathological anatomy in Paris. His fame rests upon a systematic correlation of clinical symptoms with post mortem examination of organic pathological changes, especially in the nervous system. A lithograph by François-Séraphin Delpech from a portrait by Maurin. (*See*, for biography, Haymaker & Baer, *The Founders of Neurology*, 1953.)

perception of color and form (amaurosis); blindness may be only relative either when light perception is preserved without perception of color and form (amblyopia) or when loss concerns perception of color alone, leaving perception of light and form more or less intact (achromatopia).

4. DEFECTS OF THE FIELDS OF VIEW AND THE ANATOMICAL ORGANIZATION OF THE VISUAL SYS-

functional organization of the central visual mechanisms. Using the character of the visual field defects as an indicator, it is possible to make a probable regional or topographical diagnosis, that is, to draw conclusions concerning the seat, extent, and nature of the lesion or process responsible for a functional visual disturbance.

According to the location, shape, size, and other features of the affected portion or portions of the fields of view, a number of types of field disturbance are distinguished in clinical ophthalmology and neurology (Figs. 382, 383). In the present chapter the principal types of disturbance are described, and their pathophysiological significance discussed. In the following chapter, as an illustration, a number of representative pathological cases is described, in the majority of which an attempt was made to correlate the gross and microscopic findings with the functional defects observed during life.

mors, because of their diffuse and expanding character, with pressure exerted upon more or less distant structures not directly affected, are least suitable for detailed analysis (e.g., cases AMES and STRAUSS). More useful are cases with multiple foci of softening, provided that each focus is well outlined and separated from the

FIG. 379.—Constantin von Monakow (1853–1930), encyclopedic investigator of the brain, in advanced age (*see* Fig. 118).

The value of human material as a source of information about the intrinsic organization of the visual system varies. The cases of brain tu-

other foci (cases HOLT, HOFFMANN). Of exceptional value, equaling or even surpassing the best animal experiments, are cases where there was only a single, well-outlined lesion (cases MUNSON, MALLORY). These cases may be a welcome addition to the well-analyzed cases, still too few, reported by Pötzl (1918, 1928),

Putnam (1926), Balado, Adrogue & Franke (1928), Brouwer (1930), R. A. Pfeifer (1930), G. Holmes (1931, 1934), Hoff & Pötzl (1934), and others. In contrast, the many purely clinical cases without anatomical control reported in the literature, especially since World War I, are of only auxiliary value (*see* terminal Bibliography).

The investigation of clinical manifestations of functional disturbances of vision and of the underlying pathology was and still remains the principal way to disclose the intrinsic organization of the visual system and its workings under normal and pathological conditions. It is an indispensable addition to the investigations carried out upon simian and other animal material, both being of material assistance in the clarification of the mechanisms serving the sense of sight. The review of this subject presented in this and in the following chapter considers chiefly the anatomical angle, physiology and pathology serving as the indispensable tools for

Fig. 380.—Otto Pötzl (1877), professor of psychiatry at the University of Vienna, Austria. A distinguished investigator of the pathology of vision. Few men penetrated as he did into the essential pathoanatomical and pathophysiological conditions and factors responsible for the manifestations of disturbed vision in cerebral disease.

the understanding of the organization of the visual mechanisms and their working under normal conditions.

5. Practical importance of testing the fields of view.—The importance of testing the fields of view, since its introduction into clinical practice almost a century ago by A. von Graefe and R. Förster, has been attested by its adoption as routine clinical practice. Clinical perimetry is now an indispensable method in the pathology of the eyes, optic nerves, and the

ties and professional ophthalmologists to regulate and supervise the means of modern communication and the working conditions of innumerable offices and factories.

Isn't it true that the sight of the millions of drivers, using high-speed modern automobiles, is under no control or under only the most perfunctory kind? What is known of the frequency of field defects, such as smaller and larger, absolute and relative, central, paracentral, and peripheral scotomas, or perhaps of the temporary reduction of perception among the driving pub-

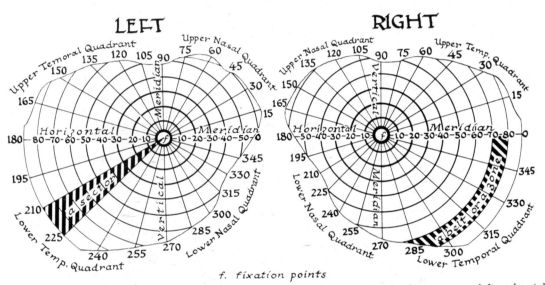

Fig. 381.—Fields of view and their landmarks. Each field represents a space seen by one eye, a left and a right visual field. Each field may be subdivided by a vertical meridian into a larger temporal half and a smaller nasal half, corresponding to the larger nasal and smaller temporal halves of the retina. The two halves of each field, in turn, may be subdivided into two quadrants, an upper and a lower, together making four quadrants in each field of view. Again, each quadrant may be subdivided into wedge-shaped sectors of different sizes, their pointed ends meeting at the fixation point. The circles inclosing beltlike zones are complete closer to the center and incomplete in the periphery. In the normal visual act the two single monocular fields largely overlap, with the fixation points coinciding, altogether forming a common binocular stereoscopic field of view. (*Cf.* Figs. 361, 401, 439.)

remainder of the visual pathways and centers, affected by the numerous diseases or by injuries, both in peacetime practice and in war. Great improvements have been made since its inception, and the theory is sound and well understood.

In contrast with this is the problem of a large-scale testing of the fields of view and of visual functions in general. In the conditions of modern life, vision is a prime factor, far surpassing the demand of the primitive conditions of the past. However, it is questionable whether enough is being done by the responsible authori-

lic, if it is not caused by an obvious defect, such as, e.g., hemianopia, large scotoma, or a reduction of central acuity? What effort, if any, is made to disclose the defects of which the drivers themselves under daylight conditions or good illumination may be entirely unaware or only dimly aware, but which, with decreasing illumination, increasing fatigue, or under the influence of tobacco and alcohol, may multiply many times the already great hazards of night driving, resulting in frightful slaughter along modern highways?

A more universally applied testing of the

fields of view by well-trained specialists for the actual or potential blind areas, including peripheral parts of the fields, seems the only means to use present knowledge and to increase it, for the prevention of accidents—a menacing cloud which threatens modern civilization.

References: F. H. Adler 1953; Aschoff 1939; Ashikaga 1934; Axenfeld 1910; Bab 1921; Bailey 1933; Bair 1940; Bair & Harley 1940; Balado, Adrogue & Franke 1928; Ballantyne 1943; Beauvieux 1916–17, 1930; Beauvieux, Piechaud & Rudeau 1929; Bellows 1921; Bender 1945; Bender & Furlow 1945; Bender & Krieger 1951; Bender & Nathanson 1950; Bender & Teuber 1946; Berger 1921; Best 1919, 1920; Bielschowsky 1915; Bing 1924, 1925; Bostroem 1939; Bramwell *et al.* 1915; Brobeil 1950; Brock 1949; Brouwer 1930, 1936; Bumke 1928–32;

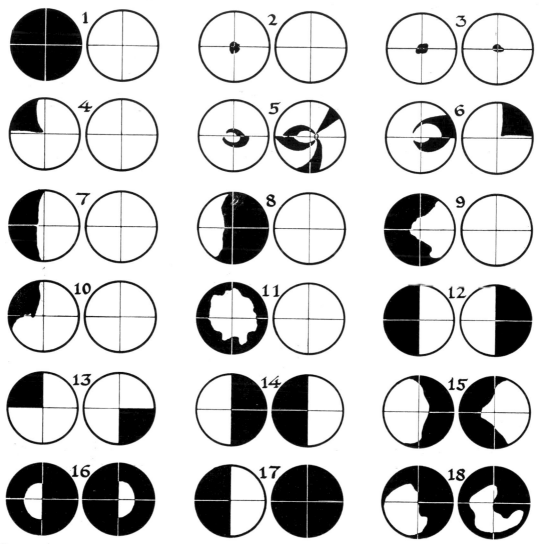

Fig. 382.—Principal types of visual field defects, given in solid black, in lesions of the peripheral portion of the visual system (retina, optic nerve, chiasma). *Labeling: 1*, amaurosis or blindness of one eye; *2*, central scotoma of one eye; *3*, central scotomas of both eyes; *4*, unilateral sector scotoma; *5*, annular or Bjerrum scotoma with central sparing and Roenne's "nasal step," sector scotomas extending to periphery; *6*, annular scotomas, one extending to periphery, also a quadrantic scotoma; *7*, monocular or unilateral hemianopia, temporal; *8*, same, nasal; *9*, same, temporal, with central sparing; *10*, unilateral quadrantic scotoma; *11*, concentric reduction; *12*, bitemporal hemianopia; *13*, bitemporal alternating or crossed quadrantic hemianopia; *14*, binasal hemianopia; *15*, incongruous binasal hemianopia in syphilitic chorioretinitis with central sparings; *16*, complete binasal, incomplete bitemporal, hemianopia; *17*, bitemporal chiasmal hemianopia associated with blindness of nasal half in one eye, same in lesion of optic tract or optic nerve and middle portion of chiasma; *18*, incongruous homonymous hemianopia.

Bumke & Foerster 1935–37; Busch 1918, 1921; Chamlin 1948, 1949; Chase 1938; Comberg 1920; C. B. Courville 1950; M. Critchley 1953; Dejerine 1926; Drews 1941, 1943; Dubois-Poulsen 1952; Duke-Elder 1932, 1947; Echlin 1942; Engel 1931; Evans 1929; Evans & Brow-der 1943; Feuchtwanger 1923; Field *et al.* 1951; O. Foerster 1929; Frey 1939; Fuchs & Fuchs 1945; Garcia Miranda 1944; Gerstmann & Kestenbaum 1930; Globus 1936, 1938; Godman 1949; Göpfert 1922; Göthlin 1943; Greear & McGavic 1946; R. Greeff 1927; Guy 1946;

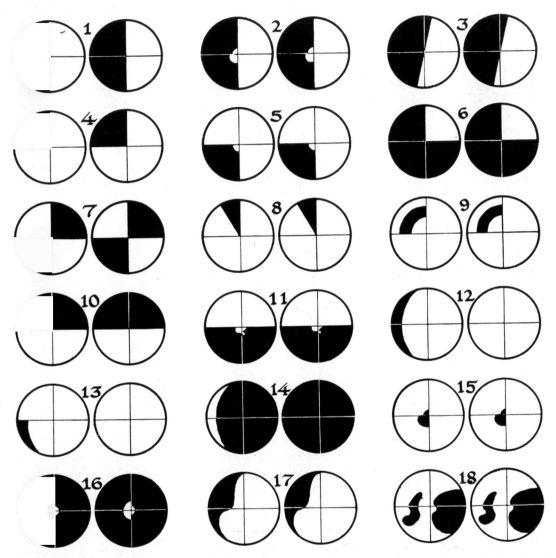

FIG. 383.—Principal types of visual field defects, given in solid black, in lesions affecting suprachiasmal portion of visual system (optic tract, lateral geniculate nucleus, visual radiation, striate area). *Labeling: 1*, homonymous hemianopia, complete (without central sparings); *2*, homonymous hemianopia, incomplete (with spared centers); *3*, homonymous hemianopia, complete, with oblique dividing meridians; *4*, superior quadrantic homonymous hemianopia, complete; *5*, inferior quadrantic homonymous hemianopia, incomplete (with spared centers); *6*, left homonymous hemianopia combined with right inferior quadrantic hemianopia, both without central sparings; *7*, alternating or crossed homonymous quadrantic hemianopia, complete; *8*, homonymous sector scotomas; *9*, belt-like homonymous quadrantic scotomas; *10*, bilateral superior quadrantic, altitudinal or horizontal homonymous hemianopia, complete (without central sparings); *11*, bilateral inferior quadrantic, altitudinal, or horizontal homonymous hemianopia, incomplete (with spared centers); *12*, temporal crescent hemianopia; *13*, inferior crescent hemianopia or scotoma; *14*, bilateral homonymous hemianopia with sparing of one temporal crescent; *15*, central homonymous scotomas; *16*, bilateral homonymous central rests; *17*, irregular peripheral homonymous hemianopic scotomas; *18*, multiple hemianopic scotomas with central sparings.

Hardy 1946; Hardy *et al.* 1951; Henschen 1890–1930; Herrmann 1929; C. Hess 1919; Hicks & Warren 1950; M. Hines 1942; G. Holmes 1918, 1919, 1920, 1930, 1931, 1934, 1946; Holmes & Lister 1916; Hughes 1943; Igersheimer 1918–20, 1920; Irvine 1950; Jakob 1927–29; Kekcheyev 1944; Keller 1939; Kempner 1949, 1951; Kempner *et al.* 1949; Kleist 1934; Klüver 1927; Laubenthal 1938; Lauber 1925, 1944; Lennox 1941; Lennox *et al.* 1938; Lenz 1927; Lhermitte & Ajuriaguerra 1942; Liepmann 1897; Livingston 1933; Lloyd 1926; Lutz 1921, 1923, 1925, 1926, 1928, 1930; Lyle 1947, 1949; McConnell 1933; McDonald & Potter 1951; Mandelbaum & Sloan 1947; P. Marie 1916; Marie & Chatelin 1914–15, 1915, 1916; Miles 1951; Monakow 1914; Oppenheim 1913; K. E. Pass 1939; Paterson & Zangwill 1944; R. H. Peckham 1947; R. A. Pfeifer 1926, 1930; Pötzl 1918, 1928; Putnam & Liebman 1942; S. Ramón y Cajal 1928; Rea 1941; Rønne (Roenne) 1921, 1924, 1927, 1944; C. W. Rucker 1946, 1950; Ruffin & Stein 1930; R. E. Ryan 1954; H. W. Ryder *et al.* 1951; Sabbadini 1923–24; Scholz 1939; A. Šercer 1951; L. L. Sloan 1942; Spielmeyer 1922, 1929; Stein & Weizsäcker 1927; J. Stambul 1953; Störring 1939; Szily 1918; Traquair 1939, 1946, 1948; Tschermak 1931, 1942; Uhthoff 1908, 1915, 1916, 1922, 1927; Wald & Burian 1945; C. B. Walker 1917, 1929; F. B. Walsh 1947; Weakley 1919; Weil 1933; Wichern 1911; Wiesly 1928; Wilbrand 1907, 1930; Wilbrand & Saenger 1917, 1918; J. Wilder 1928; D. Williams 1948; W. P. Williamson 1945; J. A. Wilson 1919; S. A. K. Wilson 1917, 1940; G. Worms 1923; Zentmayer 1912. *See also Symposium on Blood Supply* (American) 1938, and *Symposium on Blood Supply* (German) 1939.

SEC. 2. DISTURBANCES OF VISION CAUSED BY PATHOLOGY OF THE RETINA, OPTIC NERVES, AND CHIASMA

1. VISUAL FIELD DEFECTS CAUSED BY RETINAL LESIONS.—Interference with the function of vision caused by pathological processes localized in the eyeball, which includes the retina, is extremely varied. This subject is dealt with in detail in the numerous treatises of ophthalmology and neuro-ophthalmology. The following account is, therefore, limited to those defects of the fields of view which are directly related to the anatomical arrangement of the optic nerve fibers in the retina.

A lesion of the optic nerve fibers in the eye, like that of the optic nerve between the eye and the chiasma, is generally unilateral. A disturbance of vision in such cases is confined to the respective field of view (Fig. 382, sketches *1*, *2*). Or, if there are two field defects, one in each monocular field, each caused by a unilateral lesion, these defects most often differ in size, shape, and location (sketches *15*, *18*). This difference is termed "incongruity." In those cases where the field defects of both sides are equal or almost equal, as is often the case in axial retrobulbar tobacco and alcohol neuritis of the optic nerves, an ophthalmoscopically found partial atrophy of the optic papillae or disks makes possible a correct diagnosis (sketch *3*).

An exception to the rule that unilateral field defects are indicative of an infrachiasmal lesion is the unilateral affection of the monocular portion of the field of view, or "temporal crescent" (Fig. 383, sketches *12*, *13*). Such defect may be produced by a single, appropriately situated lesion anywhere in the visual pathways and centers, most readily in the occipital lobes. Other rare possibilities have been mentioned by Lutz (1923).

Partial damage to the retina of one eye causes an impairment of vision in the corresponding field commensurate with the size, shape, and location of the lesion or lesions. However, since the optic nerve fibers converge from all points of the retinal surface upon the papilla or disk, which is their exit (Fig. 162), retinal injuries of equal size and shape, if they involve the layer of optic nerve fibers, produce different results, depending upon their location, specifically their distance from the papilla.

If situated anywhere in the far periphery, close to the ora serrata, the field defect is likely to correspond more or less exactly to the extent, location, and size of the lesion. The closer the lesion is to the optic papilla, other factors being equal, the greater the number of fibers damaged, hence the larger the field defect. In the vicinity of the papilla, even small lesions may interrupt numerous bundles of optic nerve fibers arising from an extensive retinal territory. A small lesion situated in the immediate vicinity of the papillar margin may eliminate a large sector, possibly a quadrant or more, of one field of vision.

Still another local factor—the peculiar arrangement of the bundles of optic nerve fibers in the temporal half of the simian and human retina—must be considered. As described earlier (Fig. 162), the temporal bundles in the primate eye, on account of the formation of the central fovea, are not arranged radially, as they are in the nasal half (*see* chap. V, 10 [2], and chap. VI, 2 [2, 3, 4]). In order to avoid the foveal depression, the bundles circle above and below the foveal region.

This arrangement has several important consequences. First, the temporal bundles are assembled in greatest numbers at two points along the temporal margin of the papilla, approximately corresponding to between 7 and 8 and 10 and 11 o'clock, in an upright view, or between 4 and 5 and 1 and 2 o'clock, in an inverted view, in the right retina when seen ophthalmoscopically, for example. When interrupted by a block in one of these two localities, the entire or almost the entire upper or lower nasal quadrant of the corresponding field of vision may be affected. In such a case the blind and the unaffected quadrants may be accurately separated by the horizontal meridian. The reason is a cleavage line or "seam" (*raphé*) by which the optic nerve fibers, arising from the upper temporal quadrant of the retina, are separated from those originating in the lower temporal quadrant.

If a lesion is limited enough to interrupt only a small portion of fibers close to the optic papilla, corresponding to a sector of one quadrant, the field defect corresponds to a sector-shaped portion of a quadrant (Fig. 382, *5*, right side). The base of such a triangular field defect extends as far as the limit of the field of view. Since, however, the point of convergence of all retinal optic nerve fibers is not the central fovea but the optic papilla, the apex or pointed end of the blind sector is not at the fixation point, as in injuries to the supranuclear portion of the visual pathway, but a few degrees away from it (*cf. also* Figs. 392, 393).

This is true only of the lesions situated in the nasal portion of the retina and therefore of the cuneate field defects in the temporal half of the field of view. A different situation is found when a small focus along the temporal margin of the optic papilla interrupts a small fiber bundle or segment. In this locality the optic nerve fibers form arches above and below the foveal excavation in order to avoid it (*see* Fig. 162; and chap. VI, 2, 3). The fiber area eliminated here by a focus will necessarily resemble a curved wedge or sickle, and the resulting field defect will be an arcuate or sickle-shaped scotoma, mostly in the nasal half of the field of view (Fig. 382, sketches *5, 6*). The base of such an arcuate scotoma is either in the periphery of the upper or lower nasal field quadrant or somewhere along the horizontal meridian, depending on whether the interrupting lesion is farther away from, or closer to, the horizontal meridian at the papilla.

Only in the case of a minute focus placed in the horizontal meridian between the papilla and fovea, does the blind zone or belt extend to the fixation point, or even beyond it, and may also spread beyond the horizontal meridian. If a minute focus situated along the temporal edge of the papilla interrupts completely numerous fine fiber bundles arising from the fovea and its immediate vicinity, the central vision in the corresponding field alone is interfered with, producing a central scotoma.

The preceding schematic presentation of the various field defects caused by an interruption of small fiber bundles at the optic papilla needs to be further qualified. First, those lesions located close to the papilla, if nasal to the fovea, without, however, involving foveal fibers proper, are bound to produce arcuate field defects whose broader end terminates on the nasal side of the fixation point along the horizontal meridian, with or without extending to the field periphery. Also, and for the same reason, all larger defects on the nasal side of the field are bound to extend beyond the vertical meridian and may also involve the entire central portion of the field. Conversely, the analogous small lesions situated along the nasal edge of the papilla must produce wedge-shaped or cuneate field defects in the temporal quadrants, with their pointed extremity falling short of the fixation points (Fig. 382, sketches *5, 6*).

The quadrantic defects on the temporal side of the field of vision caused by lesions in the nasal half of the retina likewise will not necessarily extend to the vertical dividing meridian, if the zone of the retina between this meridian and the vertical line passing through the optic papilla remains intact. In other words, the wedge-shaped field defects of retinal origin tend to terminate with their sharp ends in the blind spot and not at the fixation point. In this respect the sector defects in the field of view caused by retinal pathology differ from those caused by partial damage to the striate area or cortical visual center, which, if complete, terminate at the fixation points, besides being hemianopic in character.

When several small lesions interrupt a number of separate fiber bundles in various localities of the retina in the same eye, the result is a combination of defects in the same field. When appropriately combined, this produces so-called annular or ring-shaped scotomas, often of bizarre shape, encircling the central portion of the field from all or almost all sides. Such scotomas are especially characteristic of glaucoma. The underlying pathological process in this disease interrupts more or less symmetrical fiber bundles encircling the fovea above and below the horizontal meridian. The ends of the resulting two small arcuate field defects merge, producing an annular, circular, or ring-shaped scotoma. (*Cf.* Traquair 1946; F. B. Walsh 1947.)

More extensive lesions of the retina, such as those found in luetic chorioretinitis, when limited to one nasal or one temporal half, may produce a field defect in either the temporal or the nasal half. When in the homonymous halves of both fields, they may approximate or simulate one of several forms of homonymous hemianopia, for example, a superior or an inferior quadrantic of a complete or incomplete type; or, when in the symmetrical halves of both fields, they may appear as a binasal or a bitemporal hemianopia (Fig. 382, sketch *15*). In such cases the field defects usually are incongruous (Wilbrand 1930).

2. VISUAL FIELD DEFECTS CAUSED BY LESIONS OF THE OPTIC NERVE.—The exact arrangement or location of functionally different fiber bundles on a cross-section through the optic papilla and optic nerve are even now only imperfectly known. Hence only a preliminary interpretation of visual field defects found in the pathology of optic nerves can be made at this time.

The first difficulty arises in the interpretation of the formation of the optic papilla. If the fibers from the various peripheral, intermediate, and central zones of the retina, as they converge upon the papilla, rigidly observed their relative topographical arrangement, bundles from the extreme retinal periphery would assume a position in the very center of the nerve, those arising from the region around the optic papilla would become most peripheral in the nerve, with fibers originating from the intermediate retinal belts filling seriatim the belts of the nerve between the central and the peripheral fibers. Such an arrangement in the nerve, with the ora serrata in the center and the fovea in the periphery, would reverse the zonal topography of the retina. This, however, as experiments and clinical cases with partial degeneration of optic nerve fibers—for example, of the foveal or "papillomacular" bundle—clearly show, is not the case. Only in the distal portion of the nerve, close to the eyeball, does this bundle preserve its original peripheral position, becoming gradually more central in the proximal portion of the nerve close to the chiasma. (*Cf.* chap. VI, 7, 11, and Figs. 201, 202.)

The foveal-macular fibers, in order to penetrate into the center of the optic nerve, have already assumed an advantageous position in the retina. They pour over the temporal brim of the papilla toward its center, pushing upward and downward those fibers that stream from more peripheral, extrafoveal portions of the temporal and the adjoining zone of the nasal retinal halves (Fig. 162). The foveal-areal fibers preserve this peripheral position along the temporal margin along most of the length of the optic nerve, becoming definitely central only in a section of the nerve close to the chiasma. The peripheral or extrafoveal fibers must also undergo certain rearrangements, in order to permit those from the more distant retinal zones to come to the surface and those from the zones closer to the papilla to assume a more central location. Since the fibers from the far periphery, while within the retinal fiber layer, are necessarily situated close to the vitreal surface of the retinal membrane, during their passage through the cribriform lamina or shortly before or behind it they probably intertwine with and cross the deeper fibers that arrive from the more centrally located retinal regions in order to reach the periphery of the optic nerve.

The result of all this shifting and changing is an arrangement of the foveal and extrafoveal quadrants on a cross-section of the initial segment of optic nerve next to the eyeball that closely corresponds to the topographical arrangement in the optic papilla, gradually resembling more and more the arrangement in the retina as the optic chiasma is approached. But in spite of the considerable displacement mentioned, there are reasons to think that the individual bundles of optic fibers that originate from small adjoining territories of the retina remain neighbors along the entire optic nerve, as well as in the chiasma and the optic tracts.

The relatively simple arrangement of the various bundles composing the optic nerves, because of their small size and compact structure, manifests itself in rather global symptoms in the pathology of the nerves. A complete severance of a nerve is, of course, followed by a loss of function, or amaurosis, of the corresponding eye (Fig. 382, sketch *1*). The inflammatory and toxic processes and also the infiltrating and enveloping tumors first affecting the superficial fibers of the nerve, provided that they are not located close to the eyeball, may initially manifest themselves by impairment in the peripheral zones or a more or less concentric contraction of the visual field (sketch *11*). When a process spreads into deeper layers of the nerve and also affects the foveal-areal or "macular" bundle, central vision suffers. In toxic degeneration of this bundle, central vision may be affected more or less independently (sketches *2*, *3*). Scotomas and hemianopic defects, in general rare, do not show regular boundaries typical of the lesions of parts of the visual system above the chiasma (sketches *7–10*).

3. Visual field defects in lesions of the optic chiasma: unilateral temporal or nasal and bitemporal or binasal or heteronymous hemianopia.—The most important

fact about the chiasma of the optic nerves is that it contains fibers originating from both the nasal and the temporal halves of the retinae of both eyes. The clinical and experimental evidence shows that the line of separation between the crossed nasal and the uncrossed temporal fibers follows the vertical dividing meridian, passing through the fixation points. This is as true of the fovea and of the rest of the central area as it is of the extra-areal periphery of the retina (*see* chap. VI, 6 [4]).

The details of how the crossing of the individual bundles is accomplished have been disclosed in different ways: indirectly with the help of clinical evidence and by direct anatomical investigation (*cf.* chap. VI, 6 [2]). The consensus is that the separation of the ipsilateral from the contralateral fibers is already beginning to take place in the optic nerve as it approaches the chiasma. The fibers from the nasal portion of the retina begin to separate from those coming from the temporal portion. It was further demonstrated that in the chiasma itself not all fibers take the shortest course to the contralateral optic tract but in the distal segment of the contralateral optic nerve form more or less extensive loops and detours, called the "anterior knee"; however, no detours, or only slight ones, are present in the initial portion of the contralateral optic tract (*see* Figs. 193, 194, 195, 198, 199).

The important problem of the identity, course, and location of the foveal-macular fibers in the chiasma has been variously answered. One view, based upon purely circumstantial clinical evidence, insists upon a central location both in the chiasma and in the optic tracts (Henschen 1910, and others; *see* chap. III, 9 [8, 9]). Another and a more recent view prevalent among modern clinical neurologists assumes that the foveal-macular fibers are located in the posterior margin of the chiasma, which would account for the frequent appearance of central and paracentral scotomas of a bitemporal type in chiasmal pathology (Cushing 1930; Traquair 1946; F. B. Walsh 1947).

The clear-cut evidence furnished by the experiments with monkeys presented in chapter VI, 7, shows both views to be at some variance with the experimentally determined facts. According to these facts, the foveal-macular fibers are in approximately the upper half of the chiasma, located immediately beneath the hypothalamus. The lower third of the chiasma next to the sphenoidal bone is entirely occupied by the extrafoveal peripheral fibers. In the longitudinal sense, the foveal-areal fibers occupy about the intermediate third of the chiasma, leaving free the anterior-oral and the posterior-caudal third of that structure. The monocular-crescentic fibers, as the same experiments with monkeys and the study of human pathological specimens show, are most ventral in the chiasma and, after crossing, form the inner, ventral margin of the contralateral optic tract. The extrafoveal or peripheral binocular fibers are arranged serial fashion between these two, also forming the anterior and posterior thirds of the longitudinal extent of the chiasma. (*Cf.* chap. VI, 6 [2], and especially 7 [2], and also the accompanying figures.)

The visual field changes caused by an interference with the chiasma play an important role in neurosurgery, since they are commonly caused by tumors of the pituitary gland or hypophysis and by pathology of the hypothalamus of the brain (*see* Walker & Cushing 1918; Cushing 1930; Bailey 1933; Traquair 1946). These have been extensively studied especially with respect to the progress and recession of the illness. The two types of field disturbances characteristic of the chiasma are temporal and nasal hemianopia and its variations.

Temporal or *bitemporal hemianopia* is blindness of both fields of view caused by an interruption of the two sets of decussating optic nerve fibers which form the connecting link between the two optic nerves or tracts, which is the intermediate, bridgelike portion of the chiasma proper (Fig. 382, sketch *12*). When an interruption is complete, the dividing lines separating the normal from the blind halves of the fields of view coincide with the vertical dividing meridians.

Since in the intermediate, bridgelike portion of the chiasma the decussating fibers alone are present, defects in the temporal halves of both fields may be complete without the nasal halves being appreciably affected. In such a case the two nondecussating systems of fibers may remain intact and are merely pushed aside. If, however, the causative factor, usually a tumor

of the hypophysis or pituitary gland, a gummatous infiltration and exudation, and the like, expands in one or in both directions and also compresses or interrupts the uncrossed or ipsilateral bundle of one or of both sides, blindness extends from the temporal halves beyond the vertical division line into one or both nasal halves of the fields (Fig. 382, sketch *17*).

If pressure is exerted first upon the basal bundles of the chiasma, compressing fibers related to the periphery of the inferior nasal retinal quadrants, a contraction of the fields may involve the upper temporal quadrants before the lower ones are affected, and the reverse order is observed in the process of recovery (Cushing & Walker 1915; Josefson 1915; Wilbrand 1930). If, on the contrary, a tumor presses from above, from the side of the optic recess, the first fibers to be affected are the foveal-areal or "macular" bundles, functionally manifested by an impairment of the central portions of the fields of view in their temporal halves.

Nasal or *binasal hemianopia* is blindness in one or both nasal halves of the two fields of view (Fig. 382, sketch *14;* Fig. 384). Such a defect is caused by an interruption of, pressure upon, or interference with, the blood supply of the ipsilateral or uncrossed optic nerve fibers of either the right or the left side in the region of the chiasma. The cause, usually a tumor, gumma, luetic basal meningitis, or atheroma of the arterial circle of Willis, initially compresses one set of the uncrossed fibers of the chiasma from the temporal side, producing a more or less pure unilateral nasal hemianopia. However, owing to the proximity of the nondecussating to the decussating fibers, a clean-cut nasal, unilateral or bilateral, hemianopia is hardly ever present. The reason is obvious: an expanding pathological process, in its further growth toward the center of the chiasma, gradually encroaches upon the crossed fibers from the ipsilateral and the contralateral nerves, impairing vision in the ipsilateral temporal and then in the contralateral temporal halves of the fields of view. If the process progresses to a point of interference with the contralateral nondecussating fibers of the opposite optic nerve, the nasal half of that field also becomes blind.

A bilateral lesion affecting the nondecussating bundles of both sides in a more or less symmetrical way and causing a binasal hemianopia, usually of an incongruous type, is a rare occurrence and therefore of small practical importance (Fig. 382, sketches *14, 15*). The reason is that on rare occasion only will there be two pathological processes impinging upon both lateral margins of the chiasma to the same extent. In this case, too, owing to the mingling of crossed fibers with uncrossed, there will be a partial loss in the temporal halves, in addition to the more or less complete blindness in both nasal halves of the fields of view.

It is remarkable that such a combination may be caused on occasion by apparently a lowermost plane of the chiasma and form the innermost margins of the optic tracts, it is possible that on occasion they may be interfered with on one or both sides separately, causing a unilateral or bilateral crescentic hemianopia (Fig. 383, sketch *12*). A crescentic defect may be an initial symptom, gradually spreading over the binocular temporal part of one or both fields, as the causative pathological process gradually involves crossed binocular fibers of the same side and finally those of the opposite side.

References: F. H. Adler 1953; Adler, Austin & Grant 1948; P. Bailey 1933; Bakker 1920; Beck-

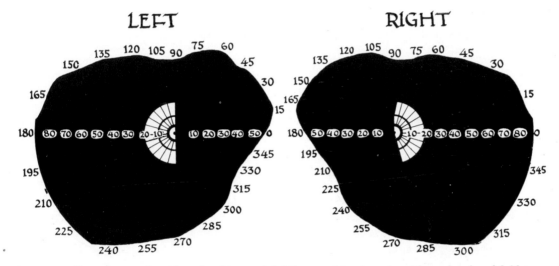

Fig. 384.—Case of a complete binasal and incomplete bitemporal hemianopia, with much reduced fields, caused by pressure on the chiasma due to an internal hydrocephalus, in consequence of a traumatically induced cerebral hemorrhage in and around the lateral ventricle, with an obstruction of the cerebral aqueduct by a blood clot. From K. H. Bouman, Monatsschr. f. Psychiat. u. Neurol., v. 25, p. 387, 1909.

single lesion, as, for example, an expanding internal hydrocephalus of the third cerebral ventricle (Bouman 1909; *see* Fig. 384). Other combinations may appear, depending on the location, spread, and multiplicity of the pathological process. Such is a tractus hemianopia associated with a contralateral temporal hemianopia caused by a compression of the uncrossed fibers on the opposite side of the chiasma (Fig. 382, sketch *17; see* Wilbrand 1930). A binasal hemianopia of an incongruous shape, such as that shown in sketch *15*, may be caused by a retinal pathology (see par. 1, this section).

Since the two decussating systems containing fibers from the monocular crescentic segments of the nasal retinal halves are located in the

mann & Kubie 1929; Bender & Teuber 1946; Benedict 1942; Berens 1936; Bertein 1926; Bilchick 1940; Bouman 1909; Brouwer 1931, 1936; Bruetsch 1948; Burnett 1887; Callahan 1941; Chambers 1951; Christiansen 1930; *Concil. Ophthalmolog. XIII* 1929–30; Critchley & Ironside 1926; Cushing 1922, 1930; Cushing & Eisenhardt 1929; Cushing & Heuren 1911; Cushing & Walker 1912, 1915, 1916, 1918; Dandy 1922; De Kleijn 1912; Delorme 1918–19; De Schweinitz 1923; De Schweinitz & Holloway 1912; Dickson *et al.* 1944; Dupuy-Dutemps *et al.* 1925; Elwyn 1946; Favory 1926; C. M. Fischer 1951; Fleischer 1914; Friedenwald 1929; Gallus 1902; Gartner 1951; Guttmann & Spatz 1929; Hancock 1906; Harms

1926; Harris 1928; Henschen 1911; Herrmann 1928; Hippel 1921, 1922–23; Hirsch 1921; G. Holmes 1920, 1930, 1946; Hughes 1943, 1945; Igersheimer 1918–20, 1920, 1940, 1947; G. Jefferson 1937; Josefson 1915; Jung 1928; Kahlmetter 1916; Kennedy 1911; King & Walsh 1949; Koby 1921; Kooy & De Kleijn 1910; F. Krause 1911, 1914; Kravitz 1948; Kuschel 1924; Landsberg 1869; Leber 1877; Lehmann 1926; Lillie 1927; Lillie & Lillie 1928; Lodge 1946; Lutz 1923, 1928, 1930; Lyle 1947; Malbrán 1939; Marlow 1947; Martin & Cushing 1923; Mathews 1946; May 1949; Meggendorfer 1916; Merritt & Aring 1938; Mooney 1948; D. E. Müller 1861; Niessl von Mayendorf 1936; Oppenheim 1913; Paterson 1944; Pennybacker 1943; Raiford 1949; Rea 1941; Rønne (Roenne) 1910, 1912, 1913, 1915, 1928, 1938, 1944; Schaeffer 1924; Schall 1926; Schlezinger, Alpers & Weiss 1945; Seidel 1919; A. Šercer 1951; Sisarić 1921; Sjaaff 1923; Sjaaff & Zeeman 1924; Stoll 1950; Szily 1918; Traquair 1917, 1931, 1944, 1946, 1948; Traquair *et al.* 1935; Uhthoff 1880, 1886–87, 1890, 1923, 1925; Van Bogaert 1930; Van der Hoeve 1919–20, 1922, 1928; C. B. Walker 1916, 1921, 1930; Walker & Cushing 1918; Wallis 1917; F. B. Walsh 1947; Walsh & Ford 1940; Wiesly 1928; Wilbrand 1878, 1926, 1929, 1930; Wilbrand & Behr 1927; Wilbrand & Saenger 1899–1927 (vols. 4 [1, 2], 5, 6), 1918; Zade 1916, 1919; Zander 1896; Zeeman 1925. (For additional references on the chiasma *see* chap. III, 9, and chap. VI, 6.)

SEC. 3. DISTURBANCES OF VISION CAUSED BY SUPRACHIASMAL PATHOLOGY OF THE VISUAL SYSTEM

1. GENERAL REMARKS ON HOMONYMOUS HEMIANOPIA.—The visual field disturbance called homonymous, vertical, or lateral hemianopia is a functional loss in either the right or the left homonymous halves of both monocular fields of view (Fig. 383, sketches *1, 2;* Figs. 385, 386, 387). It is a defect characteristic of unilateral lesions of the visual pathway anywhere from the chiasma of the optic nerves to and including the striate areae of the occipital lobes of the brain. (For uniocular hemianopias *see* Lutz 1923.)

Homonymous hemianopia is a pathophysiological manifestation of the partial decussation of the optic nerve fibers (chap. VI, 6, 7). In such a partial decussation, the fibers originating in the nasal half of the retina cross in the chiasma to join the contralateral optic tract, whereas those arising from the temporal retinal half proceed in the tract of the same side to the subcortical visual center. In other words, whereas, in the optic nerves, fibers both from the nasal and from the temporal halves of the respective retinae remain together, in the remainder of the visual system above the chiasma and as far as the visual centers in the occipital cortex, each cerebral hemisphere contains fibers conducting impulses both from the right and from the left homonymous halves of both retinae (*cf.* Fig. 259).

Because of this arrangement, the functional and pathophysiological character of the suprachiasmal portion of the visual pathway differs profoundly from that of the eyes and optic nerves. Whereas each optic nerve is anatomically and functionally related to its own eye and each retina to its own field of view, each tract, lateral geniculate nucleus, visual radiation, and striate area is related to the ipsilateral homonymous halves of both retinae.

In the fields of view, because of the "dark-chamber effect" of the eyes that makes the right retinal halves see to the left and vice versa, the relationship is reversed: whereas each eye or retina sees both halves of its own field of view, each optic tract, lateral geniculate nucleus, visual radiation, and striate area sees the contralateral halves, nasal and temporal, of both fields of view.

Concretely, the right tract, geniculate nucleus, radiation, and striate area see the nasal half of the right monocular field of view and the temporal half of the left, whereas the left tract, geniculate, radiation, and striate area see the nasal half of the left monocular field of view and the temporal half of the right. In the combined binocular visual act, the right side of the suprachiasmal portion of the visual system sees the left half of the common binocular field of view, the left side of the system sees the right half. (*See* Figs. 180, 225, 259, 260, 361, 439.)

The intrinsic organization of the visual system being as described, any massive unilateral lesion of the visual pathways and centers, from any point above the chiasma and as far as the striate areae, necessarily affects both monocular fields of view. The affected halves of the fields are either the right or the left ones and always on the contralateral side of the site of the lesion. A right homonymous hemianopia, for example, is caused by damage to either the optic tract, lateral geniculate nucleus, visual radiation, or striate area of the left side, and a left hemianopia by damage to the same structures of the right side.

Since the location, extent, and many other features of the causative process vary in each individual pathological case, the functional pathological manifestations also vary in a great many ways. The different types of hemianopia and the underlying pathological processes are discussed in more detail in subsequent paragraphs of this section and in the following sections of this chapter. In all cases one basic factor concerns anatomical mechanics: topographic organization of the visual pathways and the distribution of the blood vessels, both varying from level to level. The other essential factor is pathophysiological dynamics: the nature of the underlying pathological process which may be either a trauma, a nonexpanding encephalomalacia, a thrombosis or embolism, a temporarily expanding hemorrhage, or a progressively expanding tumor. In the first, dramatically exemplified by traumatic war injuries, the frequently observed outcome of an initial complete or almost complete amaurosis that gradually subsides is homonymous hemianopia as a residual symptom (Uhthoff 1915, 1916, 1922; Wilbrand & Saenger 1917; Szily 1918; Foerster 1929). In the latter cases the initial hemianopia may be gradually transformed into complete amaurosis.

The strictly unilateral lesions of the suprachiasmal portion of the visual system, owing to the fact that the two pathways of this system are at some distance from each other, produce strictly unilateral field defects. This simple situation may be complicated either by the presence of additional foci or by an expansion of a single focus. In the case of processes involving tracts, the most likely structures to suffer, because of proximity, are the chiasma and the

ipsilateral optic nerve, followed by the contralateral tract and nerve. In processes located in one occipital lobe, the most likely path of interference is by way of the splenium of the corpus callosum. The course largely depends on the nature of the pathological process. In case of a simple encephalomalacia, thrombosis, embolism, or arterial spasm, an initial unilateral hemianopia may become a complete or almost complete amaurosis when the unilateral process spreads to the opposite brain hemisphere, eventually interfering with the contralateral pathway.

2. LESIONS OF THE OPTIC TRACTS.—The constituent nerve fibers and nerve cells of the suprachiasmal portion of the visual pathway, unlike those of the optic nerves, are sufficiently spread out along the greater portion of their course to permit selective damage by lesions of limited size. This is least evident in the optic tracts, which are flat, compact bands attached to the base of the brain (Fig. 183). Unilateral interference with these structures may more likely be complete, hence causing a complete and absolute homonymous hemianopia on the side contralateral to the lesion.

In rare cases, however, superficial injury, such as a hemorrhage, encephalomalacia, superficial inflammation, abscess, edema, aneurysm, small tumor arising from the adjoining hippocampal gyrus, or a restricted traumatic lesion, may interrupt or exert an effect upon only a portion of the tract, affecting only a part of the opposite fields of vision. Also, for a short stretch next to the chiasma, the crossed contralateral and the ipsilateral fibers are partly segregated, permitting a selective injury.

In by far the longer portion of the tract, certainly close to the lateral geniculate nucleus, both sets of fibers intermingle, until in that nucleus the individual bundles, representing "corresponding points" of both retinae which in the binocular visual act are more or less simultaneously stimulated, come to lie very close together. The injuries in this part of the tract are likely, therefore, to produce disturbances in both fields of vision of a character congruous in shape, size, and location.

The segregation of the tractal fiber bundles according to quadrants and belts, in spite of a compact arrangement, is sufficient to make their separate damage possible. For example, a limited injury may independently interrupt fibers related to a part, or to a whole, of the monocular crescent or of the upper or lower binocular quadrants, of parts of these or of the central portions of the fields of view. The facilitating factor in producing congruity is the adjustment which the "corresponding bundles" undergo in order to assume their final place at the point of entry into the lateral geniculate nucleus. The most superficial fibers in the ventromedial corner of the optic tract, for example, are those conveying impulses from the monocular portion of the contralateral retina.

Conversely, the most dorsolateral on a cross-section through the tract are the foveal or "macular" fibers of both hemifoveae and central areae around the fixation point (*f*). The remaining fibers related to the greater intervening portion of the upper and lower binocular quadrants of the homonymous halves of the two retinae are placed in the dorsomedial and ventrolateral segments of the tract (*see* Fig. 225, *r. opt. tr., l. opt. tr.*; Fig. 259, *OT*).

The field defects, except in complete tract hemianopia, would rarely exhibit the straight linear boundaries encountered in deep lesions of the occipital lobes involving the radiations. The incongruity of the homonymous defects in the tractal lesions is also considered more frequent. Finally, the lesions which are low enough to affect the chiasma, complicate with their special features the simple picture of a unilateral tractal syndrome.

3. Lesions of the lateral geniculate nuclei.—In the lateral geniculate nucleus the "corresponding" or syndynamical retinal bundles have a location similar to that in the adjoining portion of the optic tract. The crossed monocular fibers enter into the ventralmost zones of the geniculate nucleus on both sides of the hilum; those related to the hemifoveae into the intermediate wedge-shaped segment; those from the upper homonymous retinal quadrants into the medial segment; those from the lower homonymous quadrants into the lateral segment (*see* chap. VI, 7, 11, and Figs. 225, 259, *LGN;* Fig. 260, *LLGN, RLGN*). An isolated injury to any of these segments, be-

cause of their small dimensions, however, may rarely occur. In such a case a functional defect would be confined to the corresponding quadrants and would bear a hemianopic character (thus in cases described by Henschen 1897–98; E. Vries 1913; and Winkler 1913). A hemianopic atrophy of both optic papillae has been described by Wilbrand (1930).

4. Lesions of the visual radiations and of the striate areae.—In the visual radiation the two sets of fibers, arising from the ipsilateral and contralateral layers of the lateral geniculate nucleus and carrying impulses from the homonymous halves of the right and left retinae, are so intimately intermingled that a selective injury seems unlikely (Fig. 259, *VR, LSA, RSA;* Fig. 260, *LVR, RVR, LSA, RSA*). This, as is assumed by some, is more probable when the initial portion of the radiation in the temporal lobe is affected, where a slight degree of anatomical discrepancy is believed to be present. In this way small incongruities of the right and left field defects may be explained (Harrington 1939; Sanford & Bair 1939). Outside of this, the unilateral lesions of the visual radiation or of the striate area, as a rule, produce hemianopic defects which are nearly absolutely congruous in shape, size, and location (an exception is, of course, the monocular portion).

The relatively large spread of the visual radiation on a cross-section through the posterior portion of the cerebral hemisphere and the large surface that the striate area represents offer the greatest chance in the entire visual system for partial damage and for an appearance of small defects in the corresponding homonymous fields of vision (*cf.* Figs. 228–33, 235, 236, 267, 269, 278, 289, etc.).

When a portion of the visual radiation is interrupted or a fraction of the striate area destroyed, field defects may be produced, ranging all the way from a complete quadrantic hemianopia to minute bilateral homonymous, or unilateral crescentic, scotomas or small blind islands or gaps in the visual fields. The size, shape, and location of the defects depend entirely on the size, shape, and location of the lesion. Extremely small lesions, especially multiple, affecting portions of the visual radiation or of the striate area, may produce such elusive impairment of vision that it cannot be determined by perimetric methods but is merely manifested in decreased function, such as lesser acuity, dim color vision, blurring of the shape of objects, and the like. If such zones or areae with a reduced function are situated in the periphery of the visual fields, they may cause no appreciable, or only slight, subjective discomfort. Conversely, even minute lesions, single or multiple, if close to, or in, the fixation points, may cause much subjective discomfort and reduction of vision.

The character of a hemianopic defect is either that of amblyopia or of amaurosis or absolute and permanent blindness for all vision in case of a complete interruption or destruction of one optic tract, lateral geniculate nucleus, visual radiation, or striate area. Or it is a temporary phenomenon when the impairment is indirect, as, for example, in a more or less distant pathological process such as compression by a slowly expanding tumor, thrombosis or embolism in an adjacent territory, a distant hemorrhage, an infectious focus surrounded by a collateral edema and infiltration, or a trauma to the adjoining parts of the brain. In such cases, after the removal or disappearance of the causative factor —e.g., collateral edema or compression or relaxation of a spastically contracted artery causing an ischemia—vision may be restored completely, sometimes dramatically, within minutes or hours, or else the rehabilitation of function may be incomplete. In the latter case portions of the hemianopic fields may remain permanently obscured in various degrees, with normal function returning to the remainder of the same fields. Or perception of light only, of light and cruder forms, or of finer details returns, leaving permanent impairment of color vision only.

A particular type—a transient hemianopia— appearing in brief attacks of only a few minutes' duration, often many times a day, and frequently terminating in absolute hemianopia or in scotomas of various shapes and location, was named by Hughlings Jackson "epileptic amaurosis." The basic underlying process appears to be the same as in scintillating scotoma (*see* chap. X, 8 [3]; *cf. also* sec. 7, this chapter).

The subjective experience in homonymous hemianopia, as in blindness of peripheral origin, is of the absence of visual perception, that is, the inability to see objects in the affected parts of the fields of view. It is contended by some observers that, in contrast to impaired vision caused by damage to the eye, retina, optic nerves, chiasma, tracts, and visual radiation, neither the loss of function in the blind parts nor the division lines separating the latter from the normal parts are subjectively noticed in blindness of central origin, where either the striate cortex or the near-by parts of the visual radiation are affected (Siegfried 1880; Anton 1898, 1899; Redlich 1907; Redlich & Bonvicini 1907, 1908; Wilbrand & Saenger 1918; Z. Bychowski 1920; Pick 1920; Pinéas 1926). The hemianopically blind halves, just like the space beyond the normal field limits, are simply nonexistent in subjective experience.

While this opinion is to some extent correct, the actual situation is much more complex. First, the boundary lines or, more correctly, zones are not absolutely sharp but have a certain width, wider in the periphery of the field and narrower when closer to the fixation points. Even quite close to the axis the transition from the amblyopic to the seeing territory is not quite sharp, amounting at an approximate distance of 5–6 degrees from the fixation point to as much as 1–2 degrees, and in the periphery to several times that much. This is hardly due entirely to diffraction and dispersion of light within the eye but must be caused to some extent by a margin along the defect separating the cortex still functioning in a normal or nearly normal way from the absolute cortical defect. In this transitional marginal zone there still remain enough functioning nervous structures to act as an anatomical substratum for a rough perception of light and movement ("protopathic vision" of Parsons) but not enough for an appreciation of finer details and of hues ("epicritic vision").

Subjectively, a reduced function of the zone adjoining the amblyopic parts of the fields of view is experienced as an uncomfortable "blur," especially felt in moving objects. In fact, the appreciation of "movement" in this zone is intensified during the first days and weeks after the insult and appears to be the essential factor underlying a subjective feeling of a "gelatinous transparency," especially marked in early stages and in smaller scotomas where the opposite borders are not far apart. And it is this zone wherein the "scintillation" or "flicker," often intermittent and of but a few seconds' duration, is subjectively experienced with gradually decreasing intensity, frequency, and duration in the early stages after a cerebral trauma. Hypothetically, these phenomena may be interpreted as an anatomical and physiological upset in the normal relations and function of the neuronal complexes populating the marginal zone along the focus of complete destruction of the nervous substance.

Another phenomenon much discussed and misrepresented is the "reorganization" of vision in hemianopia and a displacement of the "centers" or fixation points outside the anatomical fovea ("pseudo-fovea"). Unfortunately, there is, according to our own personal experience, nothing in support of the fantastic "gestaltist" or "configurationalist" concept assiduously propagated by Goldstein and his school (Goldstein, Gelb, W. Fuchs, *et al.*). In fact, no matter what part of the striate area and of the visual radiation is destroyed, the remainder, in our subjective appreciation, tries by will power to restore normal function in the remaining part, with the help of functional space values of the visual system inherent in it.

5. Basic types and complications in homonymous hemianopia.—There are two basic types from which other varieties of homonymous hemianopia may be derived. In complete hemianopia, blindness in the affected homonymous halves of the two fields of view extends to the vertical meridians (Fig. 383, sketch *1;* Fig. 385). In an incomplete hemianopia, more or less extensive territory around the fixation points in otherwise blind halves is spared (Fig. 383, sketch *2;* Fig. 386).

The character of the impairment in both types may be either that of an absolute scotoma, in which all perception is lost, or of a relative scotoma, in which some perception is still possible.

Homonymous hemianopia may be present either alone or associated with field defects in the opposite functioning halves, such as absolute or relative scotomas of different shapes, sizes, and locations.

In many cases there are at some time complications of various kinds—somesthetic, auditory, motor, and psychic—in addition to a field disturbance. These are related to the concomitant damage of the nervous system during or prior to the onset of visual disturbance, caused by the same basic factor. Such complications often appear during the initial or acute period; or they may appear any time in the course of the illness; or they emerge during the terminal phase.

At all events, these complications indicate a spread of the causative process to parts of the brain other than those strictly concerned with the perceptive functions of vision. Undoubtedly, such symptoms are a warning signal. Their appraisal, in the examination of a given case, requires a thorough clinical and pathophysiological experience in neuro-ophthalmology and a careful, balanced evaluation of many factors. In this evaluation, both a detailed examination and analysis of the visual disturbance and a careful appraisal of the general state of the case, including metabolism, are necessary to determine what further developments may reasonably be expected and, most important, what medical help can be offered.

Whereas in many cases extensive hemianopia is a threatening sign, much can be accomplished by expert medical care. An optimistic note is further introduced by such cases as the one reported in the following chapter of a dormant scotoma lasting for more than three decades, which in no appreciable measure interfered with the activity of a distinguished microscopist (*see* chap. XII, case Mallory).

The principal means of determining the presence and character of a homonymous hemianopia and of other forms of visual field defects is field plotting with the help of a perimeter, introduced by R. Förster (*see* chap. IV, 1 [2]). Subsidiary tests or signs by which a differential diagnosis between the infra- and supranuclear lesions may be aided in hemianopic disturbances, in addition to the presence or absence of an atrophic optic disk, are as follows. The first is the "hemianopic pupillary reaction," meaning an inability to elicit a pupillary light reflex in the hemianopic halves of the fields in case the seat of the injury is in the optic tract or lateral geniculate nucleus (*see* chap. VI, 10 [3]). Another indicator is "Lauber's symptom," consisting of the presence of optic nerve fibers observable ophthalmoscopically in infrared illumination in supranuclear lesions, and the absence of the same fibers in infranuclear ones, in the retinal halves corresponding to the affected hemianopic halves of the fields of view (Lauber 1927; Kolmer & Lauber 1936). For other symptomatology consult textbooks on ophthalmology and neuro-ophthalmology, especially R. L. Rea (1941) and F. B. Walsh (1947).

References: Adie 1930; F. H. Adler 1953; Airie; Allen 1930; Anton 1898, 1899; Austin, Lewey & Grant 1949; Bab 1921; Baracz 1916; Barbazon 1914; Behr 1916, 1931; Bender & Furlow 1945; Bender & Teuber 1947–48; Bender, Teuber & Battersby 1951; Bender & Wechsler 1942; Best 1919, 1920; Brock 1949; Brodal 1948; Bumke & Foerster 1935–37; Bunge 1928; Busch 1918, 1921; Cantonnet 1915; Coppez 1911; Cords 1925; Cosse & Délord 1917; Cross 1914; Cushing & Heuer 1911; Dandy 1933, 1948; Dejerine 1895–1901, 1926; De Schweinitz 1923; De Schweinitz & Holloway 1912; E. De Vries 1913; Dimmer 1915; Duke-Elder 1932; Economo *et al.* 1918; Falcao 1944; Fay & Grant 1932; Feigenbaum & Kornblueth 1946; Felix 1926; Feuchtwanger 1923; Fleischer & Ensinger 1920; O. Foerster 1929; Foix & Masson 1923; Forel 1919; Frazier & Ingham 1920; Freund 1916; W. Fuchs 1920; Gelb & Goldstein 1920, 1922, 1925; Globus & Silverstone 1935; Grignolo 1919; Harrington 1939; W. Harris 1897; Hawthorne 1914; Hegner 1915; Hegner & Naef 1923; Heinersdorf 1897; Henschen 1890–1930, 1897–98, 1900, 1911, 1912; Herrmann 1929; Hessberg 1915; Hine 1918; Hippel 1921; Hirschberg 1891; Hoff & Pötzl 1933, 1935; G. Holmes 1918, 1919, 1920, 1931, 1934, 1946; Holmes & Lister 1916; Igersheimer 1918–20; Inouye 1909; Jefferson 1919; T. H. Johnson 1935; Kennedy 1911; Kestenbaum 1932, 1946; Kleinberger 1921; Klüver 1927; F. Krause 1911, 1914; Kravitz 1931, 1938; Kronfeld 1932; Landau 1933; Lannois & Jaboulay 1896; Lauber 1927; Lemoine 1938; Lenz 1914, 1924, 1926, 1927; Levinsohn 1920; Lhermitte & Ajuriaguerra 1948; Lillie 1925, 1930; Linde 1900; Löwenstein & Borchardt 1918; Lohmann 1912; Lo Monaco & Canobio 1902; Lutz 1918, 1921, 1923, 1925, 1926; McConnell 1933; Macaskill 1945; Mahoney 1943; Manolesco 1928; P. Marie 1916; Marie & Chatelin 1914–15, 1915, 1916; Masson 1923; Meige 1904; Meyerhoff 1915; Monakow 1900, 1914; Monbrun 1916, 1917, 1920; Monbrun & Gautrand 1920; Mooney 1948; Moore & Stern 1928; Morax 1917, 1919; Morax *et al.* 1919; Munro 1938; A. Nessler 1891; Niessl von Mayendorf 1907; Oehming 1915; Oppenheim 1913; Pagenstecher 1916; Pallarès 1931; Pascheff 1922; Pennybacker 1943; Pesme 1931; Pick 1895, 1920; Pincus 1916; Pinéas 1926; Pötzl 1918, 1919; Possek 1915; Poulard & Sainton 1910; Raymond *et al.* 1906; Redlich 1907; Redlich & Bonvicini 1907, 1908; Redlich & Dorsey 1945; Rhighetti 1903; Rønne (Roenne) 1914, 1915, 1938, 1944; Rogalski 1946; Rossi & Roussy 1907; Rossolimo 1896; Rothfuchs 1915; Rübel 1913; Sabbadini 1923–24; E. Sachs 1946; H. Sachs 1895; T. Sachs 1888; Saenger 1918; Sanford & Bair 1939; K. Schaffer 1912; Schiff-Wertheimer 1926; Schiff-Wertheimer *et al.* 1925; P. Schirmer 1895; Segi 1923; Seppilli 1892; A. Šercer 1951; Serog 1910; Settlage 1939; Siegfried 1880; Sinkler 1898; Sjögren 1928; Smeesters 1921; R. Smith 1876; Souque 1917; Souque & Odier 1917; Stern & Lehmann 1929; Szily 1918; Terrien & Vinsonneau 1915, 1916; Throckmorton 1921; Tillmann 1915; Traquair 1946; Uhthoff 1902, 1908, 1915, 1916, 1922, 1927; Valière-Vialeix 1927; Velter 1916, 1918; Victor 1948; Voss 1917; Vossius 1896; Waddy 1915; F. B. Walsh 1947; Walsh & Ford 1940; Weakley 1919; Weber 1900; Wernicke 1893; Weve 1919; Wilbrand 1881, 1885, 1907, 1926; Wilbrand & Saenger 1917, 1918; J. A. Wilson 1919; S. A. K. Wilson 1917, 1940; Winkler 1910, 1913; Wood 1915; Worms 1923; Yaskin & Spaeth 1945; Yealland 1916; Zentmayer 1912.

SEC. 4. TYPES OF HOMONYMOUS HEMIANOPIA AND THEIR ANATOMICAL BASIS

1. COMPLETE HOMONYMOUS HEMIANOPIA WITH DIVISION LINES PASSING THROUGH THE FIXATION POINTS.—In this form of hemianopia the blind defects take the entire territory of the corresponding homonymous halves of the monocular fields of view, with the dividing lines

passing exactly through the points of fixation (Fig. 383, *1;* Fig. 385). The dividing lines are almost always straight and coincide with the vertical meridians. In rare cases the dividing lines are oblique or uneven or differently oriented in the two fields, producing incongruous, asymmetrical defects (Fig. 383, *3*). Whether this is caused by a genuinely faulty separation of the nerve fibers in the chiasma or rather by some inadequacy of testing or by other as yet unknown factors is not always clear. Another possible source of error is in the sector rests (the portions of sectors in which vision remains) on the blind side, caused by a peculiar localization of damage or damages, associated with blind

other cases; *also* case AMES in the following chapter). Since the pathological agent interfering with the tract is usually a tumor or a similar expanding process which before long affects the chiasma also, a tractal hemianopia is usually complicated by loss of vision in the ipsilateral homonymous half or in both halves of the fields of vision.

It is entirely possible and probable that the seemingly infrequent occurrence of complete homonymous hemianopia of occipital origin is merely the result of inadequate testing and that a more careful examination would eliminate some of the artificial sparing of central vision. (*See* secs. 8 and 9, this chapter.)

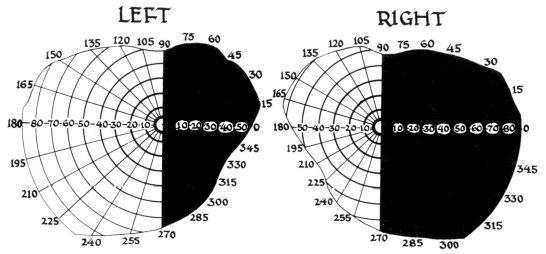

FIG. 385.—Typical complete homonymous hemianopia of the right side, with the dividing meridians passing through the points of fixation.

sectors in the opposite normal halves of the fields, the first decreasing the hemianopic loss on their own side of the vertical meridians, the latter expanding the hemianopic loss on the other side, and in this way merely simulating obliquity of the dividing lines.

A complete homonymous hemianopia is a rather frequent result in cases of a unilateral complete interruption of the optic tract or destruction of one lateral geniculate nucleus (somewhat less than half of all cases, according to Wilbrand 1930). It is more rare in unilateral injuries to the visual radiation and to the striate area of the occipital lobe (Bjerrum 1881; Dejerine 1892; Ziehl 1895; Wilbrand & Saenger 1917, p. 136; Foerster 1929, case *1,* even though his interpretation is inadequate; *see also* his

2. INCOMPLETE HOMONYMOUS HEMIANOPIA WITH PRESERVED CENTERS OF THE FIELDS OF VIEW.—This impairment is characterized sometimes by a slight, and in other cases by a large, sparing of the central or foveal-areal portions in the hemianopic halves of the two monocular fields of view: a "surplus hemianopia" (Fig. 383, *2;* Figs. 386, 387). Central sparing, in turn, is caused by a peculiar organization of the visual radiation and of the striate cortex and also by a multiple blood supply of the foveal-macular portion of the striate area, owing to which the foveal-macular portions of the visual apparatus are spared, while the extrafoveal portions are eliminated. (*See* chap. X, 8 [4]; and secs. 8, 9, this chapter.)

Whereas in a complete homonymous hemianopia the dividing lines, coinciding with the vertical meridians, pass exactly through the two fixation points, in the incomplete type the lines encircle the fixation points on the blind side. Since in clinical parlance the "central" and "macular" portions of the fields of view, or "central vision," are synonymous, it is customary in cases of an incomplete homonymous hemianopia to speak of "macular sparing" or "sparing of the macula" or of "central sparing" or of a "surplus or overshot field." The spared portions of the hemianopic fields, as discussed in sections 8 and 9 in this chapter, usually coincide more or less with the opposite homonymous halves of the two central foveae and areae.

In carefully tested cases the central surplus fields are usually of the same size and shape. Not infrequently, however, owing to inadequate testing or to fatigue of the tested person and possibly also to inaccurate apposition of the ipsilateral and contralateral fibers in the brain, an incongruity between the right and the left fields is found. True sparing, it is alleged by some investigators, is characterized by smooth outlines, whereas the "rests" of the visual fields tend to have uneven boundaries. Also, in the former, the boundaries for colors and for white are the same, or almost so.

In other cases more than small central areae around the fixation points are spared. Occa-

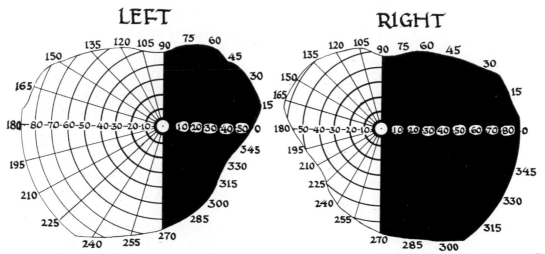

FIG. 386.—Typical incomplete homonymous hemianopia of the right side, with central foveal-areal, or so-called "macular," sparings of 5° around the points of fixation.

The extent of central sparing varies in individual cases and according to the investigators. Usually it does not exceed ½, 1, 1½, 2, or 3 degrees beyond the fixation points. In other cases it is much larger. In one case Heine (1900) computed the size of central sparing to be 2 mm. on the retinae and 7–8 degrees in the fields of view. Along the horizontal meridians central sparing measures from 5 to 10 degrees according to Morax (1919), and only 2 degrees according to Wilbrand (1930). Sparing is also more extensive along the horizontal than along the vertical meridians. In advanced age, sparing amounts to from 10 to 15 degrees, more rarely from 5 to 20 degrees, according to Schiff-Wertheimer (1926). In the first case the spared portions of the fields would approximately correspond to the central areae of the two hemiretinae.

sionally the spared or "surplus" portions of the fields are represented by narrow zones along the vertical meridians, either above or below the horizontal meridians. In still other rare cases such narrow zones of approximately equal width extend along the entire length of the vertical meridians. Again, on other occasions, the spared zones have the greatest width in the horizontal meridians, tapering along the division lines toward their upper and lower extremities (Wilbrand & Saenger 1917; *see also* cases STRAUSS, DYKSTRA, and HOLT, in chap. XII).

In still other cases considerable portions of the extrafoveal-areal homonymous field halves are spared, in addition to more or less well-preserved central or "foveal-macular" portions (thus in case DYKSTRA, early stage; *see* following chapter). Such field defects have been observed in most varied combinations, for example, in a quadrantic homonymous hemianopia associated with larger or smaller scotomas in the less affected quadrants of the same side, with sector or zonal defects of various shapes, sizes, and locations, some or all extending to the field periphery, with or without central sparing, though incomplete, damage to the visual system in one or both cerebral hemispheres (*cf.* Figs. 388, 389, 392).

Central acuity in the majority of cases of homonymous hemianopia, both complete and incomplete, is found to be normal. Where there is subnormal acuity, it is usually accounted for

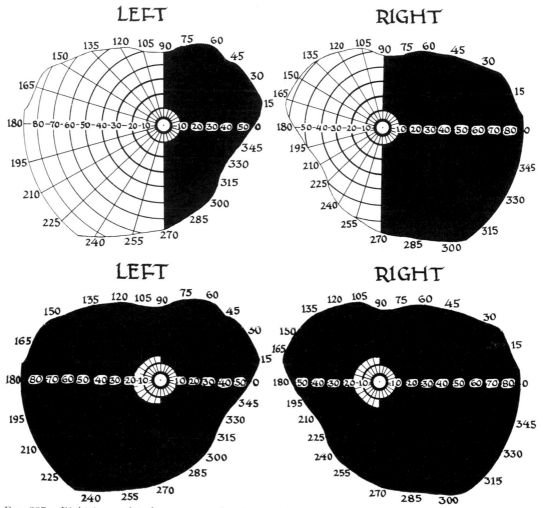

Fig. 387.—Right incomplete homonymous hemianopia (*upper fields*) transformed into a bilateral incomplete homonymous hemianopia, or field rests (*lower fields*). Case reported by R. A. Pfeifer in J. f. Psychol. u. Neurol., v. 40, 1930: a male patient, age sixty-two, interval between two plottings, six weeks; cause of visual disturbance, local defects induced by an obliterating endarteritis in the medial calcarine fissures, on right side less extensive; the right occipital pole was entirely spared, while the left pole was spared only slightly. Surrounding para-peristriate areae of both occipital lobes were not affected, nor were there any pronounced psychic symptoms registered.

or with only partial sparing in certain meridians. Such defects may be either absolute or relative or both, and may be combined with similar more or less complex defects in the opposite homonymous halves of the fields. It is only fair to say that such irregular, complex field disturbances are indicative of complex, even by secondary factors, such as pathology of the eye or optic nerve or damage to the spared foveal-macular portion of the striate area. Stereopsis usually is also found to be normal.

3. COMPLICATIONS IN HOMONYMOUS HEMIANOPIA.—An injury to the central visual mech-

anism may be either unilateral or bilateral. A lesion in one occipital lobe involving the visual radiation or striate area or lateral geniculate nucleus of one side always produces symptoms of a homonymous character, no matter what the extent and location of the lesion or what the particular quality of the disturbed visual func-

damage to the contralateral cerebral hemisphere. However, it may happen that a damaging agent in one hemisphere simultaneously damages the opposite hemisphere also, as is frequently observed in trauma, especially in war injuries.

A bilateral injury to the visual system may

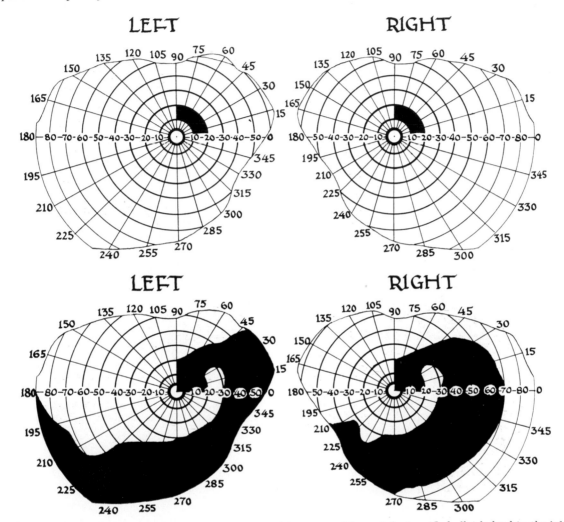

FIG. 388.—Visual field defects of a hemianopic zonal type caused by an infantry rifle bullet lodged in the left occipital lobe, verified radiographically. Point of the bullet (French type) facing anteriorly toward the sagittal plane and also 40° upward, probably beyond the mid-sagittal plane. No cerebral symptoms, except epilepsy. Operative removal of the bullet resulted in an extension of field defects on both sides of vertical meridians, especially in the upper field halves, corresponding to the operative approach. Note sparing of the right monocular temporal crescent, involvement of the lower half of the left temporal crescent, and destruction of the right upper quadrants as far as fixation points formerly preserved. B. Fleischer, Klin. Monatsbl. f. Augenh., v. 57, p. 140, case 2, 1916.

tion (an exception being the monocular temporal crescent). The loss of function is always confined to the homonymous fields opposite the site of the injury. An involvement of the ipsilateral homonymous fields necessarily indicates

most readily occur in those localities where the right and the left halves of that system are close together. Of all parts of the visual system, excepting the chiasma, the place where such an injury can most readily occur is the occipital lobes. Here the two striate areae lie close together, being separated by only a thin dural partition called *falx cerebri* or "sickle" (Fig. 228). A bilateral injury caused by a single lesion may occur here more easily than elsewhere. Such an injury, because of the toughness of the intervening dural partition or falx cerebri, takes place less frequently in peacetime activities, where the applying force of trauma is less violent or where the cause is a degenerative or other type of pathology. (*Cf.* R. Förster 1890; H. Sachs 1895; Laqueur & Schmidt 1899; Laqueur 1904; R. A. Pfeifer 1930; G. Holmes; *see also* Fig. 392.)

and partly to the accident of trauma or pathological process, the centers of both fields of view are preserved for a few degrees around the points of fixation alone, as in some of the above-quoted cases. This, especially in the war cases, may frequently be preceded by complete blindness, which, within a few days or weeks, gives way to partial restoration, almost always involving the centers of the fields of view, with a resultant "tubular vision" as a residual condition (Fig. 397).

The cases of bilateral injury are of special interest, since the symmetrically organized visual pathway, given favorable circumstances,

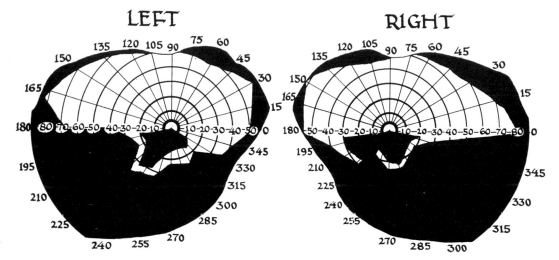

Fig. 389.—Inferior horizontal or altitudinal hemianopia of bizarre shape, with beltlike sparings, inclosing central scotomas spreading to horizontal meridians and points of fixation. Beltlike sparings apparently caused by spared strips of striate cortex lining deep secondary pockets of the calcarine fissures close to the occipital poles. A war case, Miert: rifle shot in the occiput at a level of occipital protuberance. From Wilbrand & Saenger, *Die homonyme Hemianopsie*, etc. (v. 7 of *Die Neurologie des Auges*), Fig. 134, 1917.

Bilateral damage, penetrating the dural partition is more frequent, however, in war injuries, where modern high-powered missiles easily pierce the dural falx, causing not only direct damage to the substance of the opposite hemisphere but also a complicating hemorrhage. Such bilateral lesions may cause a loss of visual function in a great many combinations (Figs. 388, 389, 390, 395).

The field defects in the right and left homonymous halves usually are not symmetrical, as they are caused by different damage to both striate areae and both visual radiations.

Occasionally, owing partly to a peculiar anatomical organization of the supranuclear portion of the visual system and its blood supply

produces symmetrical visual field defects on both sides when the causative agent impinges upon symmetrical portions of the visual system in both cerebral hemispheres. Asymmetric lesions, in turn, and for the same reason, when affecting both halves of the central visual apparatus, produce an infinite variety of visual field defects, depending upon their location, size, shape, intensity, individual anatomical peculiarities, and other factors. In particular, in war injuries the course of the channel made by the bullet in the two hemispheres is of importance, because it, together with the secondary factors such as hemorrhage, compression, and ischemia, is responsible for a particular form of disturbance in each individual case.

If the lesion is sufficiently large and if the destruction of the cerebral substance, including concussion, compression, and other interference by hemorrhage, edema, or thrombosis, damages and shuts off completely both occipital lobes, the result is complete blindness. This may be, however, merely an initial symptom, gradually receding within the first few days or weeks, with vision subsequently restored either completely or partially. Such a course of development was observed especially in traumatic injuries exemplified by the numerous war cases, where it almost seems to be the rule (Szily, Uhthoff, Wilbrand & Saenger, Morax *et al.*). In these cases intensive swelling and edema, associated with abundant hemorrhage, caused by laceration of the brain substance and very likely also by damage to the cerebral veins but especially to the arteries—primarily to the calcarine artery and its subsidiaries—often produce a general effect upon the entire brain, irrespective of the shock or commotion.

In some pertinent cases vision was eliminated completely and permanently. In other cases initial complete blindness was gradually relieved, giving way to incompletely restored function, with most variedly expressed residual partial field defects, to be discussed later. The reason for the relatively benign character of the traumatic injuries, especially in war, is the fact that the blood vessels are only a secondary cause of blindness, which, with the usually youthful and healthy state of the traumatized tissue, explains the speedy recovery of parts not directly destroyed by the trauma.

A considerably different situation is found in many cases met with in peacetime practice. Here the outcome is frequently not so favorable, because the underlying pathology is usually of a vascular, progressive character. Hence an incomplete right or left homonymous hemianopia may variously expand and sometimes become double or bilateral, occasionally leaving preserved only the centers of the fields of view, unless even these are engulfed in the general process of vascular degeneration, as may happen especially in advanced age. (*Cf.* case Hoffmann in chap. XII; *see also* Fig. 387.)

In a number of cases, homonymous hemianopia is the only clinical symptom that indicates an organic pathology of the brain. Such monosymptomatic hemianopia is especially characteristic of the nonexpanding processes confined to the occipital region (*cf.* cases Munson and Mallory in chap. XII). Contrasting with this are the lesions located in and close to the internal capsule, which directly or indirectly interfere with the lateral geniculate nucleus, optic tract, and the initial portion of the visual radiation. In such cases the clinical symptoms necessarily indicate an interference with one of the sensory or motor systems, including the cranial nerves.

In numerous other cases a simple sensory visual field defect may be accompanied by symptoms indicating disturbances of a "higher" order. Such are visual agnosia, or inability to recognize familiar objects and their use by sight; alexia, or inability to understand the meaning of written words which are otherwise seen; and especially disorientation in space, or the inability to find one's way about in formerly familiar territory (loss of mental formulas of space). Such "psychic" complications are symptomatic of more extensive organic damage to the cortex of the occipital lobes outside the striate area and to the near-by portions of the parietal and temporal cortex or to their association and projection fibers. (*Cf.* cases Ames, Dykstra, Holt, and Hoffmann in chap. XII; *see also* Figs. 274, 275.)

A rather frequent complication of right homonymous hemianopia is some form of impaired speech, sensory or motor. The underlying anatomical basis is the common blood supply of the cortical speech centers in the temporoparietal and frontal regions of the left hemisphere and, in particular, a common dependence of the visual radiation and other subcortical fiber systems upon deep branches of the middle cerebral artery (*cf.* chap. X). In some cases these symptoms may also be of a temporary nature, leaving a slight residue or none.

References: Adie 1930; Airie 1870; Allen 1930; Allers 1916; Ashikaga 1934; Axenfeld 1915; Balado & Malbrán 1932; Balado, Malbrán & Franke 1934; Baracz 1916; Barbazan 1914; Barletta 1930; Beauvieux 1916–17, 1930; Bellows 1921; Bender & Wechsler 1942; H. Berger 1921; Best 1919, 1920; Bielschowsky 1915; Bjerrum 1881; Bollack 1920; Bolton, Bramwell & Robinson 1915; Bramwell 1915; Bramwell &

Robinson 1915; Bumke & Foerster 1935–37; Bunge 1928; Busch 1918, 1921; Cantonnet 1915; Case 1903; Cérise 1916–17; Chatelin 1918; Coppez 1911; Cords 1925; Cosse & Délord 1917; Dejerine 1892, 1895–1901; O. Foerster 1929; Gonin 1911; Gowers 1876; Grignolo 1919; Harrington 1939; W. Harris 1897; Hegner 1915; Heine 1900; Hine 1918; G. Holmes 1918, 1919, 1931, 1934, 1946; Holmes & Lister 1916; Igersheimer 1918–20; Joukowsky 1901; Keen & Thomson 1871; Klüver 1927; Krainer 1936; Krainer & Suwa 1936; Kronfeld 1932; Landau 1933; Lenz 1905; Lohmann 1912; Longhi 1939; Lutz 1918, 1923, 1925, 1926; Manolesco 1928; P. Marie 1916; Marie & Chatelin 1914–15, 1915, 1916; Masson 1923; Monbrun & Gautrand 1920; Morax *et al.* 1919; Oehming 1915; Pallarès 1931; Penfield & Rasmussen 1950; R. A.

Pfeifer 1930; Piéron 1916; Pötzl 1918, 1919; Possek 1915; Poulard & Sainton 1910; Rønne (Roenne) 1914, 1915; Rogalski 1946; Rothfuchs 1915; Roussy 1907, 1909; Rowbotham 1949; Rübel 1913; Sabbadini 1923–24; H. Sachs 1895; T. Sachs 1888; Saenger 1918; Scarlett & Ingham 1922; Schiff-Wertheimer 1926; Segi 1923; A. Šercer 1951; R. Smith 1876; Strebel 1924; Szily 1918; Terrien & Vinsonneau 1915, 1916; Thomson 1897; Traquair 1946; Uhthoff 1902, 1908, 1915, 1916, 1922; Valière-Vialeix 1927; Vander Eecken *et al.* 1951; Valter 1916, 1918; Vossius 1896; Weakley 1919; Weber 1900; Weekers 1928; Weve 1919; Wilbrand 1881, 1885, 1890, 1907, 1926, 1930; Wilbrand & Saenger 1917, 1918; J. A. Wilson 1919; S. A. K. Wilson 1917; Winkler 1910; Wood 1915; Worms 1923; Ziehl 1895.

SEC. 5. PARTIAL HOMONYMOUS HEMIANOPIAS AND THEIR ANATOMICAL BASIS

1. QUADRANTIC HOMONYMOUS HEMIANOPIA, QUADRANTANOPIA, OR TETRANTANOPIA.—These terms designate a more or less complete loss of vision either in the upper or in the lower quadrants of the two homonymous fields of view (Fig. 383, sketches *4, 5*). Again, as in other field defects, loss may concern all functions, such as the perception of light, form, and color, resulting in an absolute quadrantic scotoma or amaurosis. Or perception of colors alone may be lost, resulting in a relative quadrantic hemianopia or achromatopsia. Or perception of forms may also suffer in various degrees, causing a quadrantic amblyopia.

The limits of the quadrantic defects usually coincide with the horizontal and vertical meridians, more or less (see case MUNSON, late phase, in chap. XII). The field defects may extend to the fixation points (Fig. 383, sketch *4*), or the central vision may be spared in a varying degree (sketch *5*). In some cases a zone along either the vertical or the horizontal meridians, or both, may also be spared (cases DYKSTRA and HOLT in chap. XII). Occasionally this zone may have the shape of a wedge or a sector, with its sharp end at the fixation points. Or the zone may extend more or less parallel to one or both meridians, or, finally, it may be of an irregular shape and location.

In an incomplete quadrantic hemianopia the field defects may be of various shapes and extent: wedge-shaped sectors or circular belts or a combination of both; or they may be irregular.

A quadrantic hemianopia may, in addition, be associated with defects in other quadrants of the same side (*see* cases MUNSON and DYKSTRA, early phases). These may disappear in the further course of the illness (case MUNSON, late phase); or, on the contrary, they may expand, producing as a final result an incomplete or complete homonymous hemianopia (case DYKSTRA, late phase).

An initial quadrantic homonymous hemianopia, on the other hand, may be temporary, improving later and even disappearing completely, with vision more or less restored to normal. Such changes depend on the nature of the causative process and on other concurrent factors.

Of the two possible types, the inferior quadrantic hemianopia is more frequent than the superior variety. The rarity of the latter, as of the upper altitudinal or horizontal hemianopia, particularly in war injuries, is to be explained by the small chance of survival because of the proximity of the vital centers in the brain stem and the damage to the large venous sinuses by a missile taking a course necessary to destroy the lower lip of one or of both calcarine fissures. (*Cf.* Figs. 228, 269; Fig. 383, sketch *10;* and *see* par. 9, this section; for an interesting case caused by an infantry bullet arrested by the cerebellar tentorium, illustrated with an X-ray figure, *see* Szily 1918, p. 87.)

2. THE ANATOMICAL BASIS OF QUADRANTIC HOMONYMOUS HEMIANOPIA.

—The anatomical cause of homonymous quadrantic hemianopia is a unilateral interruption of either the upper half of the visual pathway above, or the lower half below, the horizontal meridians anywhere above the chiasmal junction. Such a selective injury occurs more readily in a locality where the two quadrants are at some distance from each other, as they are in the visual radiation, than it does where they are close together, as in the tract and in the lateral geniculate nucleus.

In the visual radiation the fibers are arranged in a broad but thin lamina, each segment of that lamina representing a definite zone or belt of a quadrant in the two homonymous fields of view (Figs. 228–33, 235, 236). The most important single anatomical-mechanical factor that makes possible an elimination of one homonymous set of quadrants, the upper or the lower, by a single focus is the peculiar organization of the visual radiation. According to this, the extrafoveal-areal portions of the upper homonymous retinal quadrants are represented in the upper segment of the visual radiation, the lower quadrants in the lower segment or branch, with the foveal-areal, or "macular," fibers forming the intervening vertical segment of the radiation, filling the "gap" or "interval" of Gordon Holmes and Monbrun (*see* chap. IV, 7 [6]; chap. VII, 4, 5, 6; Figs. 259, 260).

This anatomical mechanism permits selective injury by a single agent of either the upper or the lower homonymous quadrants, without injury to the other quadrant on the other side of the "gap" (case MUNSON in chap. XII). The striate area, which also is potentially a favorable locality, owing to an individually varying blood supply, produces quadrantic hemianopias of its own that are less regular in shape.

The physiopathological agents responsible for the quadrantic hemianopia are as varied as those causing other visual field disturbances of central origin—trauma, hemorrhage, ischemia or thrombosis due to arteriosclerosis, embolism caused by a heart ailment or by one of the kidneys, the various tumors, syphilis, infectious foci, and so forth. In agreement with the prevalent vascular etiology, the onset is usually sudden (case MUNSON in chap. XII). In the further course the symptoms, after an initial period, may recede more or less, leaving as a residue a permanent, stationary defect (case MUNSON). This sometimes happens in pathology of vascular origin and in trauma. Frequently, however, the illness is progressive, and the field defects increase in size and intensity. This occurs in the vascular disturbances of advanced age and in expanding tumors (cases DYKSTRA and HOLT in chap. XII).

As in other visual field disturbances, a quadrantic homonymous hemianopia either may be the only cerebral symptom or may be associated with other signs indicating more or less widespread cerebral pathology. Such possible complications are hemianesthesia of the same side, Jacksonian epileptic seizures, hemiplegia, and various monoplegias. Manifestations of the higher order—e.g., visual agnosia, alexia, and agraphia; the various speech disturbances, such as aphasia, paraphasia, and so on—may also be present, frequently only temporarily. Spatial disorientation may likewise appear in benign cases, as a transient impairment. Visual hallucinations in the remaining fields of the same side have also been recorded. Scintillating scotomas and photisms of various kinds may be a prodromal or an initial symptom preceding partial or complete blindness. Or they may be residual manifestations persisting for a while after a cerebral insult. In still other cases a quadrantic homonymous hemianopia of an absolute character may be associated with a relative hemianopia in the other quadrants of the same side (case HOLT in chap. XII).

3. THEORETICAL INTERPRETATION OF QUADRANTIC HOMONYMOUS HEMIANOPIA.

—The importance of quadrantic homonymous hemianopia is great in understanding the intrinsic organization of the visual pathways. A functional field defect of such definite character must obviously be caused by some definite anatomical arrangement.

Of the several striking features deserving attention in a complete or almost complete quadrantic hemianopia, the first is the *straight boundary*, by which the affected quadrants are separated from the normal quadrants of the same side. This boundary coincides with the *horizontal meridian* and is a straight line, whether central vision is spared or not (Fig. 383, *4, 5*). A classical example is case Munson (chap. XII; *see also* case Holt). Strict observance of the horizontal boundaries is understandable only by assuming a mechanical-anatomical factor in the visual pathway, which, when involved, always manifests itself in precisely the same way. The straight boundary along the vertical me-

frequently reach. The sector-shaped remnants or rests found in cases of unilateral or bilateral incomplete homonymous hemianopia behave in exactly the same way (Fig. 392). This almost stereotypical mechanical repetition found in numerous cases, especially traumatic, again indicates an anatomical segmental arrangement in some part of the visual pathway, be it in the bundles of the visual radiation or in the visual cortex, a mechanism which permits individual interference with the sector-shaped portions of the visual fields.

There is still a third feature, the *zonal* or *belt-shaped defects* or *sparings*, not rarely found

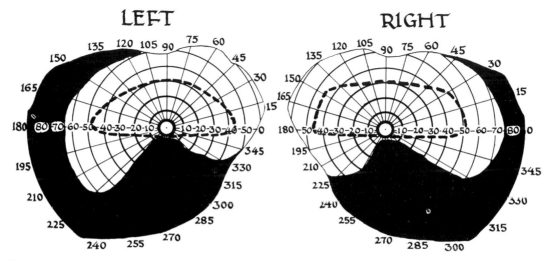

Fig. 390.—A wedge-shaped additive scotoma in lower halves of the fields of view along vertical meridians, of almost symmetrical shape, with central sparings, associated with blindness in both monocular temporal crescents. Lower relative horizontal hemianopia for colors. A war injury. Probable mechanism: partial destruction of both calcarine fissures along the cuneal margins, with additional damage, probably by thrombotic clotting, in both calcarine fissures in front of the two cunei. From A. von Szily, *Atlas der Kriegsaugenheilkunde*, etc., case 30, 1918.

ridians is, of course, caused by a separation in the chiasma of the nasal from the temporal fibers, which is responsible for the phenomenon of homonymous hemianopia in general.

The next noteworthy feature is the *sector defects* in cases where blindness does not extend to the vertical and horizontal meridians, or does so along only one of them (Fig. 383, *8;* Figs. 390, 391). Here the other boundary of the blind sector coincides with any one of the many possible meridians between the vertical and the horizontal meridians. The affected sectors always turn their broad base toward the periphery of the fields of view, while their pointed ends are directed toward the fixation points, which they

in cases of incomplete homonymous hemianopia, requiring an explanation (Fig. 383, *9;* Fig. 388). In such field defects or sparings the boundaries coincide with concentric circles whose centers are the fixation points. Such narrow or broad blind belts, or remnants, may stretch from the vertical to the horizontal meridians, or they may stop at any one of the intermediate meridians. Also, they may be bounded on one side by the periphery of the fields of view, or they may be located anywhere between the periphery and the fixation points.

The regularity of outline of these beltlike defects or sparings likewise indicates the presence of a special anatomical mechanism which permits an isolated interference with its constituent parts, corresponding to the beltlike zones of the hemiopic fields of view.

The necessity of explaining this triple mechanism, responsible for all varieties of quadrantic and partial quadrantic field defects, appears urgent in view of the fact that the sectorial and zonal defects especially appear to be mutually exclusive, in spite of their frequent occurrence in the same cases.

4. QUADRANTIC HEMIANOPIA AND THE ORGANIZATION OF THE VISUAL RADIATION.—A lesion that would cause more or less complete

produce almost mathematically accurate horizontal boundaries (in such a case the large intermediate foveal-areal segment would play the role of a "buffer").

The same argument is valid against the striate area also: its large, irregular surface in the calcarine fissure and at the tip of the occipital lobe would work against this. Its multifarious blood supply also varies from case to case and follows a different pattern in each hemisphere of the same brain (as pointed out in chap. X, 5–8; *see* Figs. 369, 370, 372, 373, 374).

These obstacles would hardly allow a single lesion to extend precisely along the crooked line

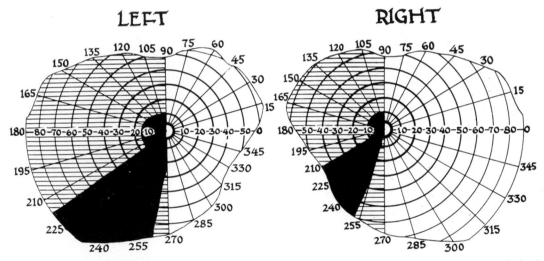

FIG. 391.—A combined left homonymous hemianopia without central sparings, consisting partly of absolute sector-shaped scotomas, but mostly of amblyopic reduction of vision (*shaded areas*). A war case, probably a combined cortical and subcortical injury. From Wilbrand & Saenger, *Die homonyme Hemianopsie*, etc. (v. 7 of *Die Neurologie des Auges*), Fig. 93, 1917.

homonymous quadrantic blindness bounded by the horizontal meridians could a priori be thought of as being anywhere between the optic chiasma and the visual cortex, or within the latter (*see* Fig. 180).

On closer examination it seems improbable, however, that it could be in the optic tracts or the lateral geniculate nuclei, because of the compact arrangement and proximity of their fiber bundles and cellular segments related to the upper and lower retinal quadrants. This is, of course, possible, although it would be difficult to imagine a lesion of such small size, precise form, and proper location as would be required to eliminate either the upper or the lower quadrants exactly in such a way as to

representing the straight horizontal meridians in the depth of the fissures. In cortical lesions it is more likely that a focus, limited, for example, to the upper calcarine lip, would partly spread over the lower lip of the calcarine fissure or that a part of the striate cortex in the upper lip would remain intact, resulting in an uneven boundary line either above or below the horizontal meridians or crossing the meridians at an angle (thus in the early phases of the cases DYKSTRA and MUNSON, in chap. XII).

By a process of elimination, the only probable structure of the visual system in which a single, relatively small lesion could readily produce homonymous quadrantic blindness appears to be the visual radiation. Here the fibers corresponding to either the upper or the lower homonymous retinal quadrants are close enough together to be interrupted by a single lesion. If the lesion destroys the upper segment of the radiation, it necessarily results in an inferior quadrantic hemianopia of the contralateral side (thus in case MUNSON, in chap. XII). The interruption of the lower horizontal branch or segment must produce a superior homonymous quadrantic hemianopia of the contralateral side (early phase of case HOLT, in chap. XII).

The spreading of the lesion either from the upper or from the lower "extrafoveal" or "extra-areal" segments into the "intermediate" segment of the radiation related to the fovea and central area ("macula") manifests itself in a definite way. The blindness spreads first toward the "fixation points" of the affected field quadrants, the defect being propagated along the horizontal meridians. In this process the wide intermediate "foveal-macular" segment acts as a "buffer" separating the two "extrafoveal-macular" segments from each other. Hence the blindness does not extend into the remaining homonymous upper or lower quadrants before all the "foveal-macular" fibers of the radiation are interrupted and the functional defect has reached and passed the fixation point. Consequently, the horizontal line of demarcation is respected until the quadrantic defects extend to the fixation points, provided that the lesion is single, strictly subcortical, and confined to the sagittal fiber layers of the occipital lobe (as illustrated by our case MUNSON, in chap. XII).

In the intermediate foveal or "macular" segment of the radiation the individual bundles represent decreasingly smaller territories in the fields of view, the closer they are to the "axial" segment representing the fixation points. Hence a spreading of the lesion toward the "axial" bundle only slightly increases the bulky quadrantic scotomas in the peripheral parts of the quadrants already caused by damage to either the upper or the lower peripheral segment of the radiation. Because of the compact arrangement of the fibers in the foveal segment of the radiation and because of the reduced size of its functional units in the field of view, a spreading of the lesion toward the "foveal" segment manifests itself in only a small additional central

blindness. The latter becomes progressively smaller in area as the centers of the fields of view are approached. The chief manifestation in such cases is that of a bulky loss of function in the "extrafoveal" portions of the affected quadrants.

Briefly, massive, though limited, damage in the white subcortical mass of the occipital lobe to either the upper or the lower extrafoveal segments of the visual radiation produces a contralateral homonymous quadrantic hemianopia with or without foveal sparing, depending on whether the intermediate foveal or "macular" segment of the radiation was spared or was affected. The inclusion of part or all of the striate cortex in the corresponding lip of the calcarine fissure does not add to the functional loss, as long as the cortical damage remains confined to the portion supplied by the afferent fibers from the interrupted segment of the radiation. However, inclusion of the cortex in the floor of the calcarine fissure, since there is no anatomical barrier here to separate the two quadrants, may interfere with the formation of clean-cut horizontal lines of demarcation in the fields of view (*cf.* Fig. 392).

5. LOCALIZATION OF THE HORIZONTAL MERIDIANS IN THE VISUAL RADIATION.—The homonymous quadrantic hemianopia caused by a strictly subcortical lesion in the occipital lobe may be helpful in localizing the horizontal meridians in the visual radiation. In case MUNSON described in the subsequent chapter, there was a lower homonymous quadrantic hemianopia caused by damage to approximately the upper half of the radiation serving the lower contralateral homonymous quadrants in the fields of view. Conversely, in case HOLT (chap. XII) an upper absolute homonymous quadrantic hemianopia was caused by destruction of the lower segment of the visual radiation and of the lower calcarine lip. These two cases, especially the first, show the horizontal meridians to be identical with the ideal "axial" rib or bundle in the fiber fan that is the visual radiation (at *f*, in Fig. 259, *VR;* Fig. 260, *LVR* and *RVR*).

This interpretation, however, needs to be further qualified. It is to be understood to exist only in the sense that an ideal "axial" rib separates the two fiber masses, the one above related to the upper quadrants of the ipsilateral homonymous hemiretinae, and the one below related to the lower quadrants. In fact, however, no "axial" segment of the external sagittal fiber lamina can be identified with a narrow stripe, which, in the homonymous fields, would coincide with the horizontal meridian, since every small fiber segment of the radiation represents a complete field belt curving between the vertical and the horizontal meridians in the respective homonymous quadrants.

Assigning to an "axial" segment of the radiation the role of representing the horizontal meridians means solely that a "virtual axis" separates the bulk of the fibers related to the upper quadrants from those related to the lower quadrants of the two ipsilateral hemiretinae or contralateral hemiopic fields of view.

6. THE REPRESENTATION OF THE WEDGE-SHAPED SEGMENTS AND BELTLIKE ZONES IN THE VISUAL RADIATION.—The representation of the homonymous sector defects in terms of anatomical arrangements is difficult to interpret (*see* Fig. 383, *8*). It would be necessary to assume that each small segment across the thickness of the radiation contained fibers corresponding to a narrow wedge-shaped sector in the ipsilateral homonymous retinal quadrants. This, however, is contrary to the concept of the organization of the visual radiation expounded in paragraphs 4 and 5 (this section), well founded upon experimental and pathological evidence (*cf.* chap. VII, 4, 5, 6; and Figs. 259, 260).

In order to explain homonymous sector defects and field rests, it would be necessary, in addition, to hypothesize that each small segment of the radiation comprises fibers of a particular field sector all the way from the fixation point to the periphery of the field. Such an organization alone would explain field defects and rests with a pointed end at the center and a blunt end at the field periphery, if a small segment of the radiation was interrupted.

This would also necessitate assuming that each small segment contains both "central" and "peripheral" fibers; for example, the axial segment would also contain extrafoveal fibers, and the upper and lower segments would also contain fibers representing the central fovea. Such an interpretation, however, cannot possibly harmonize with anatomical and clinical observations.

This forces one to the view that all hemianopic sector defects and field rests are strictly of cortical origin (thus Fig. 393). A corollary of this is the belief that the anatomical basis of sector defects and rests is essentially cortical-vascular. The uneven outlines of most of the sector defects and rests confirm this (Figs. 391, 393, and case HOFFMANN in chap. XII; *see* especially the case presented by G. Holmes 1934 and Fig. 392, this chapter).

The linear boundaries of the zonal or beltlike defects or sparings, on the other hand, coinciding with semicircles that may be drawn around the fixation points (Fig. 383, sketch *9*), agree well with the organization of the visual radiation, where each small segment on a cross-section corresponds to a quadrantic belt stretched between the vertical and horizontal meridians. According to this concept, each successive segment of the radiation, beginning with the axial-foveal and following seriatim toward the extremities of both upper and lower horizontal branches of the radiation, represents a parallel belt or zone encircling the adjoining zone closer to the fixation points, and so on as far as the periphery of the fields.

Each fiber segment of the radiation represents a complete belt or zone stretching from the vertical to the horizontal meridians in the contralateral homonymous field quadrants. The width of the blind or spared zones or belts would depend entirely on the size of the interrupted fiber segment of the radiation.

While this is easy to understand, the reason why in some cases the belts do not stretch from the vertical to the horizontal meridians, but stop short of these, must still be explained (thus in Fig. 388, lower fields; *also* Fig. 393). To assume the presence of a complicating cortical lesion is unsatisfactory for the reason already mentioned in connection with the sector defects: the difficulty of imagining lesions in the striate cortex with straight lines and a position exactly coinciding with a theoretically postulated zone or belt.

Considering the factors just mentioned, it may be assumed for the time being that most beltlike homonymous field defects or field rests of central origin are caused either by an interruption of, or by sparing, a small segment or bundle of the visual radiation. This may be especially plausible in instances of defects and sparings of equal width and regular, smooth outlines, stretching from the vertical to the horizontal meridians. The wedge-shaped sector defects and field rests and incomplete belts, on the contrary, may all have their origin in purely cortical lesions in the striate area of one side. This may be so in spite of the difficulty of visualizing such accurately outlined lesions. More careful plotting may yet show the outlines of the wedge-shaped defects and rests to be less straight than presented in the routine charts.

7. COMBINED CORTICAL AND SUBCORTICAL LESIONS AND COMPLEX FIELD DEFECTS PRODUCED BY THEM.—It is in the nature of the various pathological processes and equally in that of traumatic lesions to inflict irregular damage as they spread through the various brain structures serving vision. The same agent may, for example, destroy parts of the afferent fibers of the visual radiation and segments of the striate cortex. Since the bundles of the radiation and the striate cortex are spread in a tridimensional space, each in its own pattern, the resulting nonidentical or asymmetrical defects in the fields of view will equal the combined damage in the visual radiation and the striate area. It requires a thorough knowledge of the cerebral visual mechanism and a very detailed histopathological analysis of a given specimen, to interpret such complex cases in terms of anatomy and to understand the significance of each particular feature of the clinical visual disturbance in each particular case.

A good example of the difficulties is a case of incomplete hemianopia presented by G. Holmes (1931), here somewhat reinterpreted (Fig. 393). The conspicuous feature in this case was the shape of the scotomatous area. In the field periphery this area spread along almost the entire circumference, including in the left field most of the monocular temporal crescent. Toward the center it tapered along the horizontal meridian in the form of a wedge, terminating with a sharp end at the point of fixation.

According to what was said in the preceding paragraphs, the sector-shaped defect should be interpreted as of cortical origin. Instead, however, in sections through the occipital lobe (Holmes 1931, Figs. 3–6, in the original paper), the intermediate foveal-macular segment appeared completely destroyed, although, in reality, it may rather have been split and its bundles dislocated upward and downward, which may account for the small central area eliminated. The posterior extremity of the lesion undermining the striate cortex in the very pole of the occipital lobe may, perhaps, have been the very cause of the sharp salient of the scotomatous wedge resting at the fixation point (Fig. 3, in the original). The wide extent of the blind area along the periphery, on the contrary, may be squarely charged to an interference with the monocular crescentic fibers on anterior levels at their entry into the striate cortex along the middle stretch of the calcarine fissure (Fig. 6, in the original). (For additional pathophysiological analysis of cases *see* chap. XII.)

The homonymous field defects of an irregular, complex shape are, in general, attributable to cortical lesions, with or without partial involvement of the visual radiation (Fig. 393). This interpretation, with some reservations, is also applicable to the homonymous field disturbances, where small rests, e.g., in the central portions of the fields, are left intact ("central" rests, Figs. 392, 397), although a case may be imagined where a single lesion destroyed both lips of the calcarine fissure along its anterior portion ("medial calcarine") and, in addition, both horizontal branches of the radiation, without involving the intermediate "foveal-macular" segment of the radiation and the "foveal-macular" portion of the striate area at the tip of the occipital lobe (*cf.* cases STRAUSS and HOLT, in chap. XII). In such a case all but a small centrally located island of one or both sets of the homonymous fields may be included in the blind area (Fig. 383, *16;* Figs. 406, 413, 428, 432, 433). In a similar way homonymous rests in the periphery of the fields of view may be explained by the destruction of the entire striate area, including the polar segment, and of most of the radiation as well, but sparing a portion of the striate cortex along the medial calcarine fissure and a segment or segments of the radiation.

The narrow, wedge-shaped, beltlike, or irregularly shaped preserved rests of the fields of view located close to the normal field centers, often observed in a superior or inferior horizontal hemianopia, are also essentially of cortical origin. (Fig. 393; *see also case* HOFFMANN in chap. XII.) One factor responsible for the sparing of such narrow belts or islands in trauma is most probably the sheltered location of parts of the striate cortex in the sulci next to the tips of the occipital lobes (e.g., "lateral calcarine" pocket). While the more exposed portions suf-

In an attempt to interpret segmental and zonal hemianopic field defects in terms of anatomical arrangements, it is necessary to consider not only the nervous structures but equally the blood supply of the parietal, temporal, and occipital lobes (*cf.* chap. X). Many irregular field disturbances may well be caused by compression, thrombotic clogging, or an arteriosclerotic obliteration of one or another of

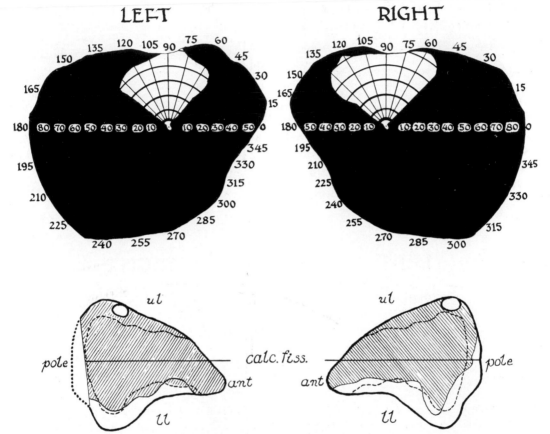

FIG. 392.—Wedge-shaped sector "rests" in both upper nasal and temporal quadrants in a bilateral homonymous hemianopia, caused by a superficial cortical softening. Preserved sectors along upper vertical meridians extend to the fixation points. Lower sketches show, by shading, the destroyed larger portions of both striate areae, with spared zones extending in an almost symmetrical way along the lower calcarine lips (*ll*) as far as the occipital poles (left pole largely missing). Floors of the fissures indicated by horizontal lines. This case demonstrates, first, a representation of sectors of homonymous hemiretinae along the vertical meridians in the fringes of calcarine fissures and, second, of the hemifoveae at the occipital poles. Age of the patient forty-seven, journalist, abuse of alcohol and tobacco. From G. Holmes, Jahrb. f. Psychiat. u. Neurol., v. 51, p. 39, 1934.

fer damage, by a bullet or a bone splinter, for example, other bands of cortex tucked into sulcal pockets may remain intact, producing belts or islands of bizarre shapes and location (Fig. 389). In vascular cases the different conditions of individual vessels supplying the striate area may account for the variety of sparings and defects (Fig. 392).

the arteries supplying the striate area, while not necessarily affecting in a marked degree, or affecting only slightly, the fibers of the visual radiation, even though these are in the immediate vicinity (good examples of this are cases HOFFMANN and MALLORY, in chap. XII). In this way a segmental or insular field defect close to the fixation point may be produced if one of the smaller branches of the posterior or middle cerebral arteries is interfered with and the supply of a segment of the foveal-macular cortex in the occipital pole is shut off. Conversely, only a segment of the peripheral portions of the fields may be affected, if one of several branches of the posterior cerebral artery is obstructed (*cf.* Figs. 369, 370, 372, 373, 374).

of the visual radiation in the temporal lobe. It was frequently observed that in tumors and other expanding processes in and next to the temporal lobe, the upper homonymous quadrants of the contralateral side are affected much earlier than would be expected from the site of the lesion. Since, according to Flechsig, the ventral bundles of the radiation do not take a

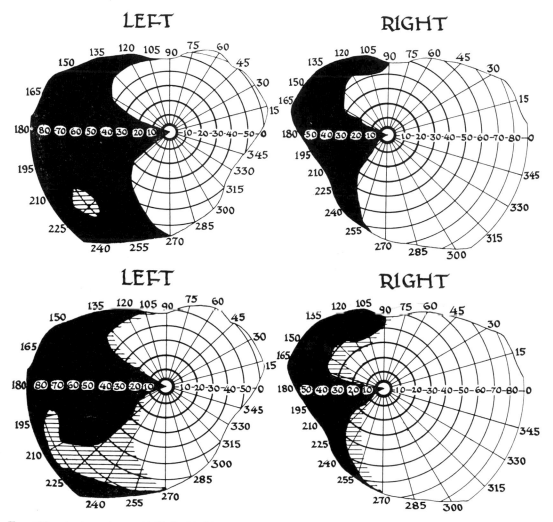

Fig. 393.—An irregular partial left-sided homonymous hemianopia extending in the shape of a wedge along the horizontal meridians as far as the points of fixation. Cause, a hemangioma with hemorrhage in the posterior portion of the right cerebral hemisphere, spreading almost to the tip of the occipital lobe, undermining the floor of the calcarine fissure, most extensively anteriorly, and gradually tapering toward the pole. Age of the patient thirty-two. Onset of illness 14 months before death, with influenza, headaches, vomiting, and photisms. Slight motor and somesthetic impairment. Onset of visual field disturbance 44 days before death. First field plotting 21 days, and second plotting 2 days preceding death. From G. Holmes, in Brain, v. 54, p. 470, 1931.

8. "TEMPORAL KNEE OR LOOP" OF THE VISUAL RADIATION AND SUPERIOR QUADRANTIC HOMONYMOUS HEMIANOPIA.—The anatomical interpretation of quadrantic hemianopia requires special consideration of the topography

straight course to the occipital lobe, as do the remaining and more dorsally situated bundles, but first turn down and forward, describing a "detour" or "loop" through the temporal lobe before turning sharply back and joining the rest of the radiation, it was claimed that this inferiormost portion of the radiation is necessarily the first to be interfered with by an expanding lesion of the temporal region (A.Meyer, 1912; H. Cushing 1922). On the other hand, the presence of a wide detour of a portion of the visual radiation was questioned (Traquair 1922).

In order to clarify this problem, the position of the lateral geniculate nucleus must, first, be correctly determined. This nucleus, as Figures 235, 236, and 269 show, even though not so far back or so dorsally situated as indicated in Meyer and Cushing's diagram, is approximately an inch behind the anterior point to

of the visual radiation and hence cause an upper contralateral quadrantic hemianopia.

One factor responsible for this is a mechanical compression of fibers. The other, and possibly primary, factor is an interference with the blood supply of the same radiation fibers by pressure upon the arteries and veins buried in the sulci of this region, particularly the posterior temporo-occipital (*poteocca*) and superior and inferior temporo-occipital Sylvian arteries (*Syteoccsua, Syteoccinfa*, in Figs. 369, 372, 373, 374). Such interference, by producing local ischemia, stasis, edematous infiltration, and the like, may interrupt the lower bundles of the

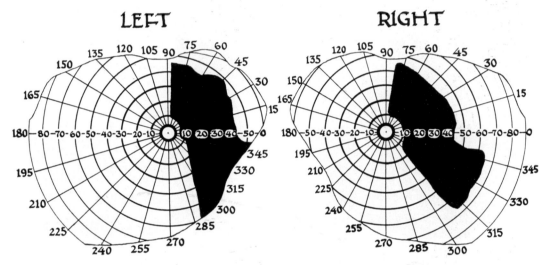

Fig. 394.—Irregular homonymous hemianopic scotomas of the right fields, probably of cortical origin. From Wilbrand & Saenger, *Die homonyme Hemianopsie*, etc. (v. 7 of *Die Neurologie des Auges*), Fig. 94, 1917.

which the detouring ventral fibers of the radiation extend. Furthermore, an examination of the serial sections through the temporal lobe shows the ventral margin of the radiation, formerly known as the "inferior longitudinal bundle" of Burdach, to be normally quite close to the cortex which lines deeper parts of the sulci on the ventral face of the temporal and occipital lobes—the inferior temporal and collateral sulci (*cf.* Figs. 228–33, 272, 273).

Projected upon the lateral surface of the brain, the lower margin of the radiation runs parallel to and only a few millimeters above the ventral outline of the temporo-occipital lobe (Figs. 235, 269). From this anatomical evidence it is safe to deduce that any process pressing upon the lateral and inferior face of the temporal lobe may first affect the lowermost bundles

radiation, as suggested by the study of pathological cases. (*Cf.* Cushing & Heuer 1911; Johnson 1935; Sanford & Bair 1939.)

In the Monkey the arrangement and the course of the ventral fibers of the visual radiation, as the experiments show, is similar (Fig. 93). Here the ventralmost fibers arise from the anterolateral segment of the lateral geniculate nucleus. Without describing much of a "temporal detour," however, these fibers turn outward and backward and, from underneath, join the other and more dorsal fiber bundles of the radiation that follow one another serially as they emerge from the successive medial segments of the nucleus. Here, too, the ventral fibers are first interrupted when, in an experiment, the temporal lobe is removed. (*Cf.* chap. VII, 4; Fig. 244.)

9. Horizontal or altitudinal hemianopia.
—This visual field defect is met with in cases
where either the superior or the inferior homonymous quadrants of both sides are affected
(Fig. 383, *10, 11;* Fig. 395; *also* case Hoffmann
in chap. XII). The effect of such bilateral quadrantic loss is blindness either in the upper or in
the lower halves of both visual fields, hence a
superior or inferior horizontal or altitudinal
hemianopia.

While an inferior type is not infrequent, a
superior horizontal hemianopia, especially in
traumatic war injuries, is rarely found. The reason is obvious. The anatomical prerequisite for

ever, that no case of a superior altitudinal
hemianopia was observed by the principal re-
porters during World War I. This is to be expected, since the course of the channel that a
bullet would have to take in order to interrupt
both visual radiations at their lower margins or
both inferior calcarine lips would have to be
close to the base of the skull. In this case direct
or indirect interference, by impact, pressure,
laceration, or hemorrhage, with the vital structures around the fourth ventricle could hardly
be avoided. (*See* chap. VII, 8 [6, 7]; and Fig.
269, for topographical relationships.)

As in other field disturbances, in altitudinal

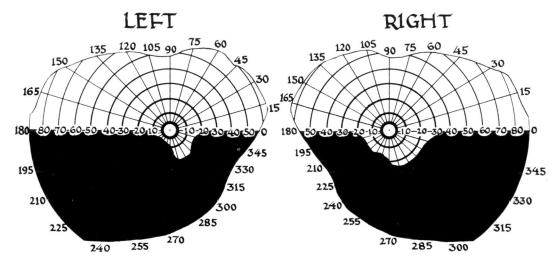

Fig. 395.—Inferior horizontal or altitudinal hemianopia with large, incongruous central sparings below the horizontal meridians. Bjerrum screen plotting. From A. von Szily, *Atlas der Kriegsaugenheilkunde,* case 39, 1918.

it would be either interruption of the ventral
bundles of both visual radiations or destruction
of the inferior lips of both calcarine fissures.
Such an injury, as is clear from the study of
Figures 228, 269, 369, and 370, would unavoidably involve other near-by structures of the
brain and skull, which would be likely to cause a
swift death. Such more or less vital parts of the
brain or those whose damage is likely to interfere with the vital parts are the near-by arteries
and veins, the venous sinuses, the cerebellum
with the fourth ventricle, but, above all, the
respiratory center in the medulla oblongata,
and the pons of the brain stem.

In peacetime practice such cases are also
rare, although it seems they had already been
observed in the early period of clinical perimetry (Schweigger 1876). It is significant, how-

or horizontal hemianopia also, either a functional defect may be complete, with blindness
extending to the fixation points (Fig. 383, *10*);
or the central or paracentral vision may be
more or less spared in one or both quadrants
(Fig. 383, *11;* Figs. 390, 395; *cf.* also case Hoffmann in chap. XII, and Fig. 417). Or the central portions of the normal halves of the fields
above or below the horizontal meridians may
also be included in the blind areas. Moreover,
the superior or inferior horizontal hemianopia
may be associated in the remaining halves of
the fields with absolute or relative scotomas
differing in size, shape, and location. Or the
horizontal hemianopic defects may not extend
over the entire upper or lower field halves but
may leave smaller or larger portions more or less
intact (thus in case Hoffmann, in chap. XII;

also Figs. 389, 390, 391). Again, if small enough and restricted to either the upper or the lower halves of both fields, such defects may appear as superior or inferior horizontal hemianopic scotomas: absolute or relative, central or peripheral, single or multiple, variously combined, and of various sizes, shapes, and location. (*Cf. also* case MALLORY, in chap. XII.)

The causative factors producing one or another form of horizontal hemianopia are as varied as those causing homonymous hemianopia in general. One of the frequent causes is the vascular and allied pathology of advanced age.

References: Allen 1930; Ask-Upmark 1932; Axenfeld 1915; Balado, Adrogue & Franke 1928; Barbazan 1914; Barletta 1930; Beauvieux 1930; Beevor & Collier 1904; Behr 1916, 1931; Berkley & Bussey 1950; Best 1919, 1920; Cords 1925; Cushing 1922; Cushing & Heuer 1911; Echlin 1942; L. Edinger 1902; Elsberg 1932; Felix 1926; Flechsig 1896, 1920, 1927; Fleischer 1916; Fleischer & Ensinger 1920; Gourfein-Welt & Redaillé 1921; Henschen 1890–1930, 1897–98, 1911; Hoche 1892; Hoff & Pötzl 1935; G. Holmes 1918, 1919, 1931, 1934; Horrax & Putnam 1932; Hun 1887; Johnson 1935; Klüver 1927; Kravitz 1931; Kronfeld 1932; Lannois & Jaboulay 1896; Lillie 1925; Linde 1900; Löwenstein 1911; Lutz 1921, 1923, 1926; Marie & Chatelin 1916; Martin 1925; A. Meyer 1907, 1912; Meyerhof 1915; Monbrun 1917, 1919; Morax *et al.* 1919; Pascheff 1922; Penfield & Rasmussen 1950; Polyak 1932, 1942; Railton 1892; Rasmussen 1943; Rønne (Roenne) 1916; Rübel 1913; Sabbadini 1923–24; Sanford & Bair 1939; Scarlett & Ingham 1922; A. E. Schultz 1949; Schwab 1925; Schweigger 1876; Szily 1918; A. Thomas 1928; Traquair 1922, 1946; Uhthoff 1927; Villaret & Rives 1916; Walsh 1947; Walsh & Ford 1940; Wilbrand 1926, 1930; Wilbrand & Behr 1927; Wilbrand & Saenger 1899–1927, v. 7, 1918; Zingerle 1911.

SEC. 6. HEMIACHROMATOPIA AND HEMIAMBLYOPIA

1. HOMONYMOUS IMPAIRMENT OF COLOR VISION AND OF VISUAL PERCEPTION OF FORMS AND OF LIGHT.—When the suprachiasmal portion of the visual pathways and centers is only moderately or indirectly interfered with, the functional disturbance is not necessarily a hemiamaurosis or homonymous blindness for all modes of vision, an absolute hemianopia, but an abolishment, a reduction, or a partial loss of some components or qualities which make up the function of vision. An example of such "relative" impairment is a reduction or loss of color vision of various kinds and degrees, with the perception of light and usually also of forms remaining more or less normal. This is hemianopic color dullness or blindness, or hemiachromatopia. A similar, but more intensive, disturbance, in which the colors and forms of objects are seen indistinctly or not at all and in which only a trace of light or "gray" is distinguished, is hemiamblyopia of various degrees, or "dullness of vision."

The manifestations of achromatopia or a selective impairment of color vision are as numerous as absolute forms of blindness. In a typical case of hemiachromatopia, colored objects appear to be different shades of gray. Perception of forms and visual acuity may be preserved (*see* Uhthoff 1899), or more often they also are reduced or are abolished altogether. In other cases colors are all distinctly perceived but appear subjectively duller. Or perception of some colors only may be lost, while others are perceived normally. First to suffer is the perception of green and red, followed later by the loss of blue and yellow. Complete destruction of chromatic vision is, however, usually associated with a measurable, or even considerable, impairment of the perception of light. In more severe cases the affected parts of the fields appear subjectively gray or dark, light assuming the quality of twilight. In such cases acuity and form perception are likewise, as a rule, reduced, although normal or almost normal acuity was described in cases with a total loss of chromatic vision in the respective portions of the hemiachromatopic fields. A peculiar subjective experience is dimness of vision in subdued illumination in the perception of light, form, and color resulting from certain cerebral lesions. It resembles the conditions in hemeralopia or night blindness, which makes finding one's way about in dim light extremely difficult, indicating a greater fragility of the scotopic component of the central mechanisms in comparison with the photopic.

Amblyopic or achromatopic disturbance either may be a temporary phenomenon gradually decreasing in intensity or even disappearing completely or may result in permanent loss. Often it is an initial or prodromal symptom, subsequently transforming into absolute blindness. The portions of the affected fields of view may be exactly the same as in absolute hemianopia and in the scotomas. The division lines may pass through the fixation points, or there may be "central sparing." The relative field defect may be confined either to the upper or to the lower homonymous quadrants, or there may be homonymous amblyopic or achromatopic scotomas of different shapes and sizes, located in different parts of the fields of view. Also, a relative field defect may accompany others where blindness is complete; for example, an inferior quadrantic achromatopia may accompany an absolute superior quadrantic hemianopia on the same side (thus in case HOLT, in chap. XII, and Fig. 413).

Color vision may be affected bilaterally and in varying degree and extent. In cases of an injury to both sides of the visual pathways and centers, color vision may be impaired bilaterally and is then usually associated with absolute field defects of various kinds (*see* par. 4, this section).

2. PATHOANATOMICAL BASIS OF HEMIACHRO-MATOPIA AND HEMIAMBLYOPIA.—A possible pathological cause of a partial qualitative impairment of visual function manifested in a hemianopic loss of color perception may be a unilateral trauma, a hemorrhage, a tumor, an abscess, a syphilitic process, or any other of the numerous pathological agents and processes already mentioned, which may interfere with, but may not completely destroy, normal conditions in the visual pathways and centers.

A hemorrhage or a thrombotic encephalomalacia which does not damage the visual pathway directly but exerts an effect from a distance seems to be the most frequent cause of impaired color vision of central origin. Both causative processes, in turn, may have their origin in an atheromatous change in the blood vessels, or a hemorrhage may complicate a trauma, as in gunshot injuries, and the like.

Such vascular etiology is suggested as a pathophysiological agent in hemiachromatopia characterized by a sudden onset. Gradual development and aggravation of symptoms that may eventually terminate in complete blindness point rather toward a slowly expanding process, such as a tumor. A scar, either in the cortex or in the subcortical fiber mass of the parietotemporo-occipital lobes, situated in the neighborhood of the visual pathway or visual cortical center, may have a similar effect because of its pulling action and the strangulation of blood vessels or of the fiber systems.

That an encephalomalacic ischemic focus may produce a disturbance of color vision is well illustrated by case HOLT described in the following chapter. At the time of plotting, this case also showed a combination of achromatopic disturbance in one quadrant with absolute blindness in the other quadrant of the same homonymous fields, both caused by a similar pathology present in a different degree in different localities (Figs. 413–16).

A temporary or transient hemiachromatopia may indicate a vascular functional origin—in any case, a reversible process—and hence may gradually give way to normal function. Or it may indicate the beginning of serious trouble which may eventually terminate in complete blindness.

To conclude, the prevalent opinion is that hemiachromatopia and hemiamblyopia and similar relative impairments of vision are distance phenomena caused by indirect action of the various pathogenetical factors and agents. Whereas in the field disturbances of an absolute and permanent character the underlying pathology is an interruption of fiber systems or destruction of the cortical substance, the interference responsible for the relative field disturbances is of a milder nature and lesser degree.

3. COMPLICATIONS IN HEMIACHROMATOPIA AND HEMIAMBLYOPIA.—A homonymous hemiachromatopia caused by damage to the occipital lobe and the adjoining portions of the cerebral hemisphere may be accompanied by disturbances of a higher order, localized on the same side as the field defect.

Of great theoretical interest is the visual hemiagnosia or inability to recognize or to identify by sight objects in the affected halves of the fields, although acuity and form and color perception may themselves be more or less preserved. On the other hand, visual hemiagnosia without hemiachromatopia, with or without absolute hemianopic scotomas, does not seem to occur (Schiff-Wertheimer 1926). This points to the presence in both hemispheres of a substratum in the cerebral cortex that is instrumental in higher visual functions, organized upon the same topographical principle as that by which the retinal surface is represented. (*Cf.* association connections of the striate area with the adjoining para-peristriate area, in chap. VII, 7, and Figs. 274, 275.)

Not infrequently a relative visual field disturbance is associated with other somatic motor and sensory symptoms of central origin, such as hemianesthesia, hemiparesis, or hemiplegia, and with symptoms indicating involvement of the cranial nerves. Other disturbances, such as the various forms of aphasia, agraphia, alexia, amnesia, and so forth, usually indicate a widespread organic cerebral pathology. Sometimes a homonymous achromatopia is preceded or accompanied by visual hallucinations of objects or colors that are localized on the side of the field defects.

4. BILATERAL HOMONYMOUS HEMIACHROMATOPIA (CEREBRAL ACHROMATOPIA) AND BILATERAL HEMIAMBLYOPIA (CEREBRAL AMBLYOPIA). —A bilateral impairment of color perception in both homonymous sets of fields of view was observed in a few cases where a cerebral seat of injury was either probable or practically certain. It is remarkable that in some cases there was a reduction neither of central or foveal acuity nor of the extent of the fields of view. Such a condition may last for several years without change, or a slight degree of color perception may be recovered. In other cases acuity is also impaired. A rather pronounced cerebral amblyopia, with achromatopia resulting from a brain injury incurred during the war, was described by Uhthoff (1915, 1916).

An achromatopia may be preceded or accompanied by hallucinations either of formed objects, scenes, and the like or by colored photisms. The hallucinated color may be the same in all attacks.

5. PATHOPHYSIOLOGICAL DEDUCTIONS FROM HEMIACHROMATOPIA.—The fact of separate impairment of color perception and in many cases of individual colors or of combinations of colors led to the assumption of the presence in the visual system of a specific material substratum underlying the perception of color. Incomplete dissociation of the chromatic from the achromatic visual functions, however, indicates a close anatomical and functional relationship between the several basic components of vision: those serving the perception of colorless light (achromatic vision), of color (chromatic vision), and of dimensions (acuity, perception of form and space).

Whereas, phenomenologically, these manifestations are separate, anatomically and in terms of underlying physical, chemical, and electrophysiological factors they have to be considered as closely related. In fact, the several functional components may be merely manifestations of basically the same material substratum reacting differently under different conditions. In other words, part of the structures serving all the functions of the visual apparatus are common to all, as discussed in the preceding chapters.

Nor is there unimpeachable anatomical evidence of a special region in the cerebral cortex concerned with the perception of color. Color vision appears, accordingly, to be a partial function of the same visual mechanism which otherwise serves the perception of white-light sensations and is a repository of the "local signatures" manifested in the perception of form, movement, acuity, and so forth.

How the higher susceptibility of the chromatic mechanisms to various noxious agents, in comparison with the more robust mechanisms instrumental in perception of colorless light, is to be interpreted in terms of anatomical structures and of physical and chemical processes cannot even now be answered except hypothetically. Possibly the chromatic mechanism of the visual afferent system all the way from the retina to and including the striate cortex is composed of more delicate neurons, as is indicated by the retinal structures that most likely serve color vision (chap. V, 3, 4, 5, 11).

In this connection one could point to the reduced synaptical contacts, their smaller numbers, and other subtle histological details as factors which possibly make the delicate "epicritic" cone mechanism less resistant to the noxious agents in conditions where the more crudely organized "protopathic" rod system, composed of much more robust neurons, thicker nerve fibers, and more numerous synaptical contacts, still functions satisfactorily, or does so in an exaggerated fashion, as the intensive photophobia in acute pathology of the striate cortex and visual radiation definitely suggests. Still other factors of an even subtler nature, such as a particular chemical composition of the cytoplasm, possibly make the cone mechanism susceptible to very slight noxious influences which remain inconsequential for the rod mechanism. How this can be made to harmonize with the greater fragility of the central scotopic apparatus in brain injuries, previously mentioned, remains to be explained.

Hemiamblyopic disturbances, where no detailed forms are perceived, but only simple light in contrast to darkness, are somewhat easier to interpret in terms of anatomy, physics, and other basic factors. It is possible to visualize a profound interference with the visual pathway where the more delicate and hence less resistant neurons—the majority—are gone, leaving an irregular array of scattered and more robust neurons and fibers through which it is still possible for impulses to pass from the retina to the cortex, and disseminate there. In such a defective central visual mechanism, most or all of the more delicate neurons, which are instrumental in refined spatial functions and in color vision, may have been destroyed, with all finer "local signatures" and hue perception abolished. The few surviving more robust elements, themselves vitally impaired, may nevertheless be sufficient to mediate crude, summary light perception. When the vitality of these *ultima morientia*, or "last-dying elements," is also undermined, all visual perception becomes impossible.

References: Akelaitis 1942; Best 1919, 1920; Cushing & Heuer 1911; Flesch 1908; Grant 1903; Henschen 1929, 1930, 1931; C. Hess 1890; G. Holmes 1918; Klüver 1927; Lenz 1921; Lewandowsky 1907; Liepmann 1897; Marie & Chatelin 1916; Monbrun 1919; Pesme 1931; R. W. Pickford; Pötzl 1949; Schiff-Wertheimer 1926; Seggern 1923; Shannon & Edgerton 1931; Sloan 1946; Steffan 1897; Szily 1918; Traquair 1946; Uhthoff 1899, 1900; Verrey 1888; Wilbrand & Behr 1927; Wilbrand & Saenger 1899–1927, v. 7, 1918.

SEC. 7. SCOTOMAS, FIELD RESTS, CRESCENTIC AND OTHER FIELD DEFECTS AND THEIR INTERPRETATION

1. CLASSIFICATION.—The term *scotoma* designates any relatively small defect in the field of view caused by a restricted injury to the visual system. The seat of the lesion may be anywhere in the visual system, from the retina to the striate area of the cerebral cortex.

The character of a scotoma varies considerably, depending upon the location of the lesion in the visual pathways and centers. In accordance with the general plan of the visual system, a single lesion in the retina or in the optic nerve produces a single scotomatous defect in the corresponding monocular field of view, whereas a single lesion in and above the chiasma results in a hemianopic defect in both fields of view (parts of the suprachiasmal pathways and centers related to the monocular temporal crescent are an exception).

According to the degree of the disturbance and the functions disturbed, three varieties of scotomas are distinguished. An *absolute scotoma* indicates a defect where all vision in the scotomatous area is abolished. Contrasting with this is a *relative scotoma*, where only color perception is impaired. Finally, in an *amblyopic scotoma* only dim vision remains.

Depending on the location in the field of view, two groups of scotomas are further distinguished. The *central* and *paracentral* scotomas are defects located in and around the fixation points, with or without involving these points. Defects located at some distance from the fixation points are the extrafoveal, extramacular or *extracentral* or *peripheral scotomas*.

2. NEUROANATOMICAL MECHANICS UNDERLYING THE SCOTOMAS.—A scotoma caused by a lesion below the optic chiasma residing in the retina or in the optic nerve differs in character from one caused by a suprachiasmal lesion. The first is often unilateral (Fig. 382, *2, 4, 5, 6, 10*); or, if there are two bilaterally situated scotomas, they usually are not congruous in form, size, and location (sketches *3, 15*). Circular, oval, arcuate, and annular scotomas are almost always caused by foci in the retina or in the optic nerve, on one or on both sides (Traquair 1946). The homonymous hemianopic scotomas are characterized by congruous shape, size, and location of defects in both fields (Fig. 383, *8, 9, 15, 17, 18*); they are most usually caused by a limited unilateral damage to the suprachiasmal portion of the visual pathway, including the striate area (Wilbrand & Saenger 1917).

Scotomas void of a hemianopic character, especially those restricted to central portions of the fields, are usually caused by either an infection or trauma or some other pathology of the eye. Such is glaucoma, or a degeneration of the "papillomacular" or, more properly, the "foveal-areal" bundle in the retina and in the optic nerve, caused by a toxic agent, usually tobacco or alcohol. Such scotomas, when present in both fields, are usually not congruous (Fig. 382, *3*).

Homonymous hemianopic scotomas are ordinarily caused by a vascular disturbance, such as hemorrhage, embolism, arteriosclerotic or spastic ischemia, or thrombosis, and less frequently by certain infectious diseases of the central nervous system, e.g., disseminate sclerosis, encephalitis, and syphilis. Tumors are, on the whole, of lesser account as an etiological factor because of their large size and usually expanding, progressive character. Trauma, on the contrary, is an important cause of scotomas, especially in war injuries, where bullets, shell fragments, and bone splinters may damage a portion of the visual pathway. Many such war-caused scotomas, especially if small in size, are liable to be overlooked, since they frequently do not cause subjective deficiency in function.

When, for one of these reasons, a small portion of one optic tract or a fraction of the lateral geniculate nucleus, a segment of the visual radiation or of the visual cortex—the striate area—is interrupted, destroyed, or otherwise affected, this manifests itself in a functional defect in the homonymous halves of both fields of view. For mechanical and anatomical reasons it is to be expected that, all other factors being equal, a small lesion may more readily produce a restricted functional field defect, if it applies to those parts of the visual system where its constituent fiber bundles and cells, or anatomical-functional units, are large and therefore widely spaced, than in those parts where they are crowded into compact tracts or nuclei. Damage to the optic tract or lateral geniculate nucleus is, therefore, less likely to produce a small scotoma.

More favorable in this respect are the visual radiation and, above all, the striate area. The latter offers a large surface which represents a mosaic made up of a great number of relatively large functional-anatomical units distributed over a wide area, as illustrated by our experiments (chap. VII, 5 [2]). A restricted mechanical injury such as that caused by a small instrument in an experiment, by Graefe's cataract knife, for example; or in trauma by a nail, a screw, a fragment of a shell, or a bone splinter; or in vascular pathology by a minute hemorrhage or an ischemic focus is likely to interfere with only a small group of functional units, producing a minute congruous hemianopic scotoma in both homonymous fields (Fig. 383, *15;* Figs. 388, 396; *see also* cases HOFFMANN, KRAFT, and MALLORY, in chap. XII).

Of special importance in understanding the intrinsic organization of the visual centers are small central, paracentral, and extracentral or peripheral homonymous hemianopic scotomas caused by an arteriosclerotic pathology or an arterial spasm restricted to the striate cortex, without any damage or with only insignificant damage to the subcortical fibrous substance, as illustrated by case MALLORY (*see* chap. XII, and Figs. 424–27). They may be satisfactorily explained by the size, shape, and location of the lesion limited to one of several arteries supplying the striate cortex or even to a single small arterial branch that may be shut off by a pathological process or agent.

When an ischemic or malacic focus is close to the anterior extremity of the striate area, the defects are located in the periphery (e.g., in the temporal crescent); when the lesion is at the occipital pole or close to it, the functional defects are central or paracentral scotomas; when either the upper or the lower calcarine lip is affected, the scotomas are located in the lower or upper field quadrants, etc. (*cf.* chap. X). When, as in some war cases, both occipital lobes are damaged, a complex injury is produced, manifested in variously combined defects, with or without impairment of the centers, of the periphery alone, or of the centers around the fixation points of both fields of view alone, in the latter case with acuity reduced to 1/100 or less.

§ 3. PATHOPHYSIOLOGY OF THE SCOTOMAS.— The onset of a scotoma, as of other field disturbances, is often associated with symptoms indicating an irritation of the cerebral substance, usually of a vascular nature: arterial spasm, sudden thrombosis, or venous stasis. Such symptoms are photisms of various kinds and frequently also visual hallucinations.

During the actual origin of even a small scotoma, if it occurs during full consciousness, the initial phase may be a violent one: an overwhelming display of brightly illuminated objects, blocks of buildings and mountains crumbling into a brilliant nothingness! This terrifying subjective experience only gradually subsides, within minutes or hours, as the underlying pathological process quiets down to the phase of repair setting in as soon as the destructive phase is over (a classical example of this is case MALLORY, in chap. XII).

Various subjective phenomena may follow the origins of a scotoma. Such is a brilliant display of fantastic photisms, stars, and whirligigs of different hues, still or in motion, localized along the edges of the final scotoma. This display sometimes lasts for several hours, and it may subsequently be replaced by outbursts of scintillation of gradually decreasing frequency and intensity during the following weeks and months (author's personal experience).

Obviously, the underlying pathological process responsible for this subjective experience is an irritation of the marginal zone of the remaining surviving striate cortex after the shutting-off of one of the arterial branches supplying that cortex. As a parallel, in a physiological experiment with an isolated portion of the cerebral cortex, such spontaneous "outbursts" of activity have been described as occurring at short intervals of 10–30 seconds, each lasting from 2 to 4 seconds, resembling the scintillation in the zone surrounding the scotomatous defect (Burns 1951).

Scotomas, especially central hemianopic, after an initial period of expansion lasting from a few seconds to at most a few minutes, followed by a period of recession, may become absolute and, after a relatively short time, may remain stationary until the end. More rarely, in scotomas of central origin, color perception alone is affected (thus in a case described by Wilbrand 1926). If small enough, especially if eccentric, a scotoma may not necessarily produce a subjective sensation of a defect, except in situations requiring greater use of vision, e.g., in reading fine print (cf. cases KRAFT and MALLORY, in chap. XII). Even more elusive subjectively are small scotomas located in the periphery of the fields of view (Wilbrand's and the writer's personal experience). This may especially be the case with scotomas caused by war injuries, requiring careful testing by the examiner.

The characteristic persistence of scotomas during long periods is a manifestation and evidence of their organic origin, that is, of their being caused by a definite and irreparable damage to the visual pathway (cf. case MALLORY, in chap. XII, where a central scotoma lasted more than three decades). Scotomas are sometimes the only disturbance, as is often the case with traumatic war injuries in young and otherwise healthy individuals. In other cases they are associated with other symptoms, such as a contraction of fields of various shapes, sizes, and locations (thus in case KRAFT, in chap. XII). They can, furthermore, be accompanied by other disturbances, such as somesthetic or motor disturbances, hemianesthesia, hemiplegia, aphasia, agnosia, agraphia, alexia, and other psychic manifestations indicating a more general cerebral pathology.

4. TRANSIENT SCOTOMAS.—The reaction of living structures, nervous and vascular, serving vision under pathological conditions is fortunately more pliable than it would appear from presentation in the literature. Especially is this true of the scotomatous phenomena in and close to the fixation points. A rigid, static concept of a scotoma as an absolutely or relatively blind area in the fields of view is true only for a residuum of a process corresponding to an irreparably damaged portion of the nervous struc-

tures. There are reasons to believe that during life, particularly in advanced age, or during an intercurrent illness, local impairments of tissue occur that are temporary and reversible, with a full or almost full return to normal function within a few hours or days after the onset.

In toxic conditions such as occur during treatment with dicumarol or in conditions of general disturbance of the cerebrovascular apparatus, as in hypertension, or after a cerebral vascular insult, as well as under the influence of caffeine, theobromine, or tobacco, and after prolonged administration of nitroglycerin or theocalcium, small scotomas may appear, which within a few minutes, hours, or days disappear without leaving a trace of a defect that can be determined with the usual methods. (In other cases the same drug poisons, widely used in vascular cardiac disease and as food, may have fatal consequences.) This is of extreme importance, both practically and in the theory of function of the central visual mechanism. A minute hemianopic scotoma a few degrees to the right or left of the common binocular fixation point is highly bothersome, as it interferes with reading, even though it may not be a serious impediment to distance vision or orientation in space. Such a scotoma, when caused by a passing disturbance, e.g., an arterial spasm, possibly also by a reversible thrombosis, may be almost entirely erased by relaxation of the spasm, resolution of the causative clot, or establishment of collateral circulation. A multiple blood supply found in the occipital pole of the cerebral hemisphere, as described in chapter X, 6, 7, 8, is a powerful factor in the process of repair. (*See also* Wilbrand 1907.)

There are indications that in large scotomas caused by massive destruction of the brain substance a certain amount of repair also takes place along the fringes of the defect, as a slow, gradual reduction of the scotomatous territory is noticeable, even after a lapse of many months. (*Cf. also* following sections in this chapter.)

5. Theoretical significance of scotomas. —From the beginning of modern clinical research much attention has been paid to the minute defects of the fields of view, especially to central scotomas. The theoretical importance of such defects is evident (*see* Wilbrand 1926).

Such minute defects are possible only if the conducting fiber bundles and nerve cells making up the visual system are arranged so that the original topographical relationships present in the retina are preserved all the way along that system and as far as the visual cortex, the striate area (as presented in chaps. VI, VII). Only in systems thus organized is it conceivable that a small injury could destroy a small cell nest or interrupt a small, individual fiber bundle, which would produce a single small functional defect in one monocular field, if the injury was below the chiasma, and in each homonymous half of both fields one of an almost absolute congruity, if the location of injury was above the chiasma. (For the historical background *see* Part I in this book, especially chap. III, 8, 9, and chap. IV, 4, 5.)

Several inferences, each of basic importance to knowledge of the organization and function of the visual system, may be drawn from the foregoing proposition. The first is anatomical. The presence of scotomas measuring 1 degree of arc or less in diameter postulates a parallel course of fibers in the optic nerves, tracts, and visual radiations. Minute bundles arising from the adjoining minute territories of the retina remain close together in the optic nerve and also preserve in a high degree the same position relative to one another. If it were otherwise, if the bundles were in any considerable degree to deviate from one another and were to intermingle with the bundles originating from more or less distant points of the retinal surface, the outlines of a scotoma would not be sharp, but fuzzy and indefinite, with more or less wide transition zones of decreased function between completely blind and entirely normal territories of the fields of view. Or, if the mixing or overlapping of individual bundles of nerve fibers were to go beyond a certain degree, a small injury could never produce an absolute scotoma but only one where vision was reduced or in some way altered, as is the case in relative scotomas.

Furthermore, the fact that small injuries to the visual apparatus above the optic chiasma produce minute scotomas of an almost mathematically congruous shape, size, and location (except in the monocular temporal crescents) shows that the ipsilateral and contralateral fibers and cells related to the "corresponding" or "syndynamical" points of two homonymous retinal halves in most of the visual pathway are very accurately aligned or apposited. This deduction is in complete accord with the results obtained by experiment (*cf.* chap. VI, 7, 9; chap. VII, 4, 5, 6).

Moreover, an absolute loss of all components of visual function in the scotomatous area (perception of light, color, and shape and acuity) indicates that if some or all of these particular functions are using special nerve fibers as conductors of their own, these different fiber categories must be uniformly distributed on a cross-section through the visual pathway. This view alone is consistent with the fact that, in absolute central scotomas, boundaries for white and those for several colors, even though not absolutely identical, differ only a little.

Finally, the persistence of minute scotomas in any part of the fields of view, especially in the very centers, indicates a high degree of anatomical and perceptive functional independence of each of the countless receptor-conductor units making up the visual system. This independence, in turn, is a prerequisite for the detailed function of the visual system. This same independence, unfortunately, prevents any substantial "vicarious" functional substitution for a loss by the adjoining units. Hence functional recovery in cerebral injury is entirely the result of rehabilitation of the structures that do not suffer irreparable or irreversible damage.

The indicated organization is to be accepted in the entire visual system from the retina to the occipital cortex. Anywhere along its course a small injury may produce a small scotoma of a particular type, subject to certain local variations. A small defect in one optic nerve or retina results in a scotoma in one monocular field only. A lesion above the optic chiasma, in the tract, lateral geniculate nucleus, visual radiation, and the striate cortex, produces defects of a hemianopic character in the corresponding territories of both fields. There are two localities which are exceptions. First is the chiasma, where a single monocular field defect may be produced, depending on the seat of the lesion, if, for example, one of the nondecussating fiber bundles is interrupted. The other localities above the chiasma are those segments of the

visual pathways and centers where the monocular temporal crescents are represented; here a unilateral lesion produces a single, monocular scotoma in the contralateral field of view (Fig. 383, *13*).

While the basic principle upon which the visual system is organized remains essentially preserved in its entire extent, the relatively gross anatomical features vary much, as described in chapters VI and VII. Hence limited damage necessarily produces a different result, depending on the injured part or segment. In the optic nerve and tract and in the chiasma, because of their small size and compact structure, only lesions of very restricted size may produce defects smaller than one-fourth of a field that may be classified as scotomas.

Scotomas caused by a mechanical or toxic agent acting selectively are an exception (Fig. 382, *2, 3, 5, 6*). Almost the same is true, because of its small size, of agents damaging the lateral geniculate nucleus.

The visual radiation provides more favorable conditions for the production of a small scotoma by a restricted lesion. Here the fibers are distributed in a relatively thin lamina of considerable spread, requiring a much larger lesion to produce the same effect. Since the intermediate segment containing foveal or "macular" fibers is a relatively large portion of the radiation, even a sizable injury localized here may cause only a small hemianopic defect in the central portions of the fields of view. The responsible factors are the small size of the central fovea, the compact arrangement of its receptor-conductor units, and the minute dimensions of these units.

Conversely, a lesion in the upper or lower horizontal segments of the radiation, even though it may be restricted, produces a large scotoma, which may easily expand over one whole quadrant. Here, in contrast to the foveal segment, each receptor-conductor unit controls a relatively large territory in the extra-areal retinal periphery.

The same reasoning applies also to the lesions confined to the striate cortex. Damage to that cortex in the anterior or medial portion of the calcarine fissure may more readily result in a large field defect, whereas the same lesion in the posterior or lateral calcarine fissure around the occipital pole would produce a minute homonymous hemianopic defect close to the fixation points.

The fact that minute central scotomas, especially of an absolute variety, are found in many shapes, sizes, and locations shows further that the retina, especially the fovea, has a very detailed representation in the entire visual pathway, including the striate cortex. This representation or "projection" is carried out according to the principle of a cable composed of numerous individual, insulated, parallel conductors. In this way the original topographical relationships, present in the retina and indispensable to the normal functioning of the visual mechanism, are maintained throughout that entire mechanism. This accounts for the great similarity in pattern on a cross-section at the beginning of the pathway, in the retina, and at its termination in the striate area. There is no confusion or any considerable mixing of the heterodynamical conductor units, the preservation of the original pattern being carried out with the greatest fidelity and most detail precisely where one would expect it: in the part conducting impulses from the central fovea-area ("macula"). The small size and sharp outlines of the central and paracentral scotomas are evidence of this. This interpretation of clinical observations fully agrees with the results obtained from experiments with monkeys (chap. VII, 4, 5, 6).

The detailed organization of the visual system discussed in the preceding paragraphs needs to be qualified in one point only. This concerns the important changes in the course of the fibers in the chiasma, in the optic tracts, and in the lateral geniculate nuclei. In the first the two nasal sets of fibers temporarily intermingle with each other, without coming into any functional relationship, however. In the tracts and geniculate nuclei the homonymous ipsilateral and contralateral fibers undergo an intimate relationship, which is fully achieved in the striate cortex. But all these changes are carried out without detriment to the fundamental requirement for the preservation of original topographical relationships, as found in the photoreceptor retina, throughout the whole system.

The preceding views on the intrinsic organization of the visual system may appear rather dogmatic. They will, however, appear less so if one realizes the uncompromisingly severe functional demands on the sense of sight exacted by biological and physiological conditions, as discussed in chapter XV. Slight individual departures from the prescribed principle of organization, e.g., a genuine hemianopic asymmetry, are, of course, possible but need to be documented by further observation (*see* par. 8, this section).

6. Scotomas and the cortical representation of the central fovea.—Small hemianopic scotomas close to the fixation points are, in general, of value in the problem of cortical representation or localization of the central fovea or "macula." A sufficient number of cases has been reported to serve as evidence that the posterior portion of the striate area is related to the centers of the homonymous fields, the anterior portion closer to the splenium of the corpus callosum, to the periphery and to the monocular crescent. This agrees with the results derived from experiments.

The number of cases with small central or peripheral scotomas or with equally significant small field rests which have been carefully examined anatomically is still extremely small. Even so, sufficient clues have been collected to aid in devising a map of the topographic organization of the "cortical retina." Such is case Eggerz (Fig. 396) reported by Henschen (1911), which indicates the position of the horizontal meridians in the floor of the calcarine fissure. Other valuable modern cases which help solve the question of precise topographical representation of the retina in the striate area are those published by Pötzl (1918, 1919, 1928), G. Holmes (1918, 1919, 1931, 1934), Brouwer (1930), R. A. Pfeifer (1930), Polyak & Hayashi (1936), and also case Mallory, described in chapter XII.

The study of scotomas proves to be of great value in the controversy about the representation of each complete "macula" in both cerebral hemispheres (the term *macula*, unfortunately, was accepted in the clinical jargon as synonymous with *central fovea*). This hypothesis was devised in order to explain the sparing of central vision frequently found in homonymous hemianopia of central origin. Because some of the most notable investigators have adhered to it, as, for example, Wilbrand, Henschen, and Brouwer, and because of the many discussions connected with it, this problem is dealt with in detail in the following sections of this chapter.

7. HEMIANOPIC "RESTS" OR "REMNANTS" OF THE FIELDS OF VIEW.—This term designates small remaining portions or "leftovers" in otherwise amaurotic homonymous fields of view. Such normally functioning field rests are "positive" counterparts of the "negative" hemianopic scotomas which represent blind defects

that is left of the two fields of view are two minute central territories extending in various directions from one degree or less to several degrees from the fixation points (Fig. 397). Their shape usually is strictly congruous. Acuity, form, and color perception within such minute central field rests may be more or less impaired, or, on the contrary, some or all of these functions may remain normal. Other visual functions, such as orientation in space, judgment of size, position, and direction of stationary or moving objects, direction of the gaze, and similar complex functions, may in some, although

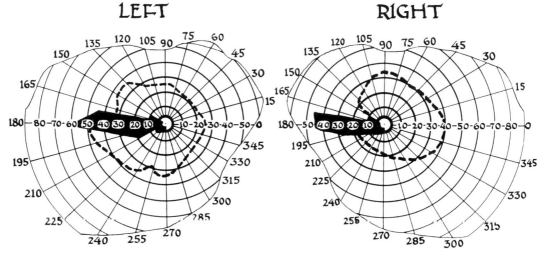

FIG. 396.—Homonymous hemianopic scotomas of left side oriented along the horizontal meridians, with minute central sparings around the points of fixation on that side. The case, perimetrically examined by Wilbrand, represents an injury in the floor of the right calcarine fissure. It indicates the position of the horizontal meridians in the striate area. From S. E. Henschen, *Pathologie des Gehirns*, Part 4, p. 94, case Eggerz, 1911. (*See also* Wilbrand 1907.)

in the normal visual fields (*see* preceding paragraphs in this section).

Depending on their location, two types—*central* and *peripheral field rests*—are distinguished. The first are located in or around the fixation points and are usually restricted in size (Fig. 383, *16;* Fig. 397). These may be interpreted as bilateral homonymous hemianopia with central sparing (*see* sec. 4 [2], this chapter). The peripheral rests often are of considerable size and may extend as far as the normal field limits. Occasionally a homonymous hemianopia may be present, with a monocular crescent in the extreme temporal periphery of one field alone spared (Fig. 383, *14; cf.* par. 7, this section).

Central rests of a restricted size are of special theoretical interest. In the extreme cases, all

not in all, cases be considerably disturbed because of the extreme contraction or absence of the peripheral portions of the fields of view instrumental in these functions. The responsible factor is the presence and extent or the absence of an injury to the parts of the cortex surrounding the striate area and to the various fiber systems of the occipital lobes.

Frequently the past history of a "rest" case records an initial complete blindness which was subsequently modified by the reappearance of smaller or larger islands in the central or peripheral portions of the fields where function returned more or less to normal. Such field disturbances with partially restored rests may remain as a permanent condition. Conversely, an initial homonymous hemianopia of one side may be completed on the contralateral side, with a central or paracentral rest as a final, permanent condition. The affected portions of the fields surrounding a rest may be absolutely blind for all qualities of vision, or a trace of function may still be preserved in the form of amblyopia. Sometimes signs of irritation, such as photisms or photopsias and visual hallucinations, may be an aggravating complication.

The pathology underlying the visual field rests is as varied as in other field disturbances of central origin. Among frequent causes are brain tumors and trauma, including war injuries,

plete destruction of the central visual apparatus and, second, the characteristic intrinsic organization of that system, described in chapters VI and VII, which makes possible the elimination of most of that mechanism while leaving the remainder more or less intact. The bilateral field rests caused by a pathology applying to the visual system below the chiasmal junction are rarely congruous, since they are necessarily caused by a double or a single asymmetric process. The minute field rests of a homonymous hemianopic character are caused by extensive destruction of the visual pathway above the

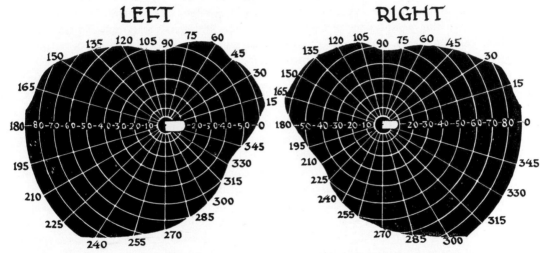

LEFT RIGHT

F<small>IG</small>. 397.—Minute hemianopic central rests (*white*) extending for a few degrees along the horizontal meridians into the right halves, surrounded by blindness enveloping by far the greatest parts of fields of view (*solid black*). Otherwise defined, this case represents a bilateral homonymous hemianopia made up of a left complete hemianopia, combined with a right incomplete hemianopia with central sparing. A war injury, fields carefully plotted with a 2-square-mm. target. Boundaries for red color same as for white (*see*, however, chap. XII, 7 [4]). From Wilbrand & Saenger, *Die homonyme Hemianopsie*, etc. (v. 7 of *Die Neurologie des Auges*), Fig. 172, 1917.

vascular disturbances, such as hemorrhage, but especially the encephalomalacia following vascular changes in connection with kidney and heart troubles, a post partum embolism, and other similar etiology.

Like the other field disturbances, the central rests may also be accompanied by other cerebral symptoms, such as hemiplegia, hemianesthesia, speech disturbances, disorientation in space, impairment of memory, and the like, indicating an involvement of other parts of the cerebrum by the same pathology, besides the visual mechanisms proper.

The underlying anatomical factors responsible for the appearance of visual field rests of restricted size are, first, a widespread but incom-

chiasma. Small central field rests extending approximately equally on both sides of the fixation points indicate symmetrical damage to the right and left halves of the suprachiasmal central visual mechanism.

In case of softening in the territories of both posterior cerebral arteries or of the calcarine arteries, the two polar segments of the striate areae related to the foveae or "maculae" and perhaps also their immediate vicinity, supplied by the middle cerebral artery, may remain intact. There is little likelihood that such selective destruction with central sparing, because of the compact arrangement of the cells and fibers, could take place in either the optic tracts, lateral geniculate nuclei, or visual radiations close to their origin. This is more likely to occur in massive lesions caused by a hemorrhage or encephalomalacia along the calcarine fissure.

It is possible to visualize a case with a rather symmetrical destruction of most of the striate cortex in both calcarine fissures, leaving, however, both occipital poles intact (e.g., case reported by R. Förster 1890, and by H. Sachs 1895). Since the poles may preserve sufficient collateral blood supply via the middle cerebral arteries, as discussed in chapter X, and since the intermediate foveal-macular branches of the visual radiations, separated as they are from the calcarine fissure by the posterior horn of the lateral ventricle, would not be affected by a process confined to the medial sides of the occipital lobes, central vision, mediated by the spared parts, would remain more or less preserved. (*Cf.* chap. X, 8 [2]; and case HOLT, in chap. XII.)

An interference with the visual radiations and the striate areae which produces small field rests may vary in a great many ways. Such destruction may, e.g., be complete on one side and incomplete on the other side, leaving the foveal or "macular" segment of the opposite radiation and the polar portion of the striate area intact. In such a case small hemianopic rests, one side of which is formed by the vertical meridians, would remain in the centers of the hemianopic fields (thus in Fig. 397).

The observation that in many "rest" cases the appreciation of color, form, and acuity either remains normal or is restored after an initial decrease and that these particular functions extend close to the boundary of the spared field rest indicates an intimate and uniform intermingling of structures instrumental in the transmission of color impulses with those structures which mediate the perception of "white," of form, and of acuity; or that the identical structures may perform, in part at least, all these functions. (*See also* Wilbrand & Saenger 1917, p. 132.)

The theoretical significance of the minute central rests of the visual fields for the understanding of the organization of the visual system is as great as that of the minute central scotomas (*cf.* par. 4, this section). Both indicate a collective organization of that system made up of a great number of minute anatomical-physiological units capable of independent existence and action, besides being able to influence, and being influenced by, one another.

8. CRESCENTIC HEMIANOPIA.—This term is applied to an absolute or relative blindness in the unpaired sickle- or crescent-shaped temporal monocular portion of the field of view (Fig. 383, *12;* Figs. 398, 399; *cf. also* Figs. 225, 259, 260). In the horizontal meridian this area extends from 60 to 95, 100, or even more degrees (depending on the extent of the field). A crescentic defect may be the only symptom, or it may accompany an impairment of other, binocular portions of the fields of view (Fig. 383, *17;* Fig. 399; cases STRAUSS, DYKSTRA, MUNSON, and HOFFMANN, in chap. XII; also Fig. 417).

A crescentic hemianopia may be present on both sides in bilateral lesions. It may be partial or incomplete, affecting either the upper or the lower quadrant, either completely or partially, in the latter case producing monocular crescentic scotomas of various sizes, shapes, and locations (Fig. 383, *13*). Often a crescentic hemianopia in one quadrant is merely an extension of more or less complete blindness in the adjoining upper or lower binocular quadrants of the same side. It may be either an initial symptom which gradually disappears (Fig. 383, *17;* case MUNSON, in chap. XII); or it may indicate the beginning of a process culminating in a typical homonymous hemianopia (case DYKSTRA, in chap. XII).

In general uniform depression of function in the entire homonymous halves of the fields, called *homonymous hemiamblyopia,* the blindness in the monocular crescent is usually more complete and may appear first (Fig. 399). This lesser resistance of the anterior monocular crescentic portion of the striate area to pathological agents, especially vascular, is probably caused by its blood supply, which, unlike that of the posterior foveal-areal portion, is more dependent on a single vascular source; if this one breaks down, because of local damage to the particular artery, for example, the entire crescentic area is eliminated, since vicarious substitution is insufficient here (*see* Figs. 369, 372, 374; *see also* the end of this subsection).

The cause of an impairment of function in

the monocular field crescent is a destruction of the crescentic portion of the visual pathway or center (*cf.* Figs. 225, 259, 260). It is self-evident that such selective damage is less likely in the infranuclear portion, on account of the compact arrangement of its fibers and cells, than above the chiasma, where the fibers and cells are farther apart.

In the optic nerves the crescentic fibers occupy a narrow zone along the inner or nasal margin. In the chiasma the crescentic fibers form its ventrolateral margin and may be affected alone, or first, by a pathological process man 1926; Henschen 1926; Wilbrand 1926; Kronfeld 1932; Polyak 1932; *see also* chap. VI, 6, 7.)

Selective damage to the crescentic fibers may more easily occur in the visual radiation and in the striate area, where they are better segregated from the rest of the visual apparatus (*see* chap. VII, 3, 4, 5, 6). The belief that the most ventral bundles of this portion of the radiation are related to the entire monocular crescent disagrees with the absence of an isolated crescentic blindness in the temporal lobe tumor (Kronfeld). Another possibility, viz., that these fibers

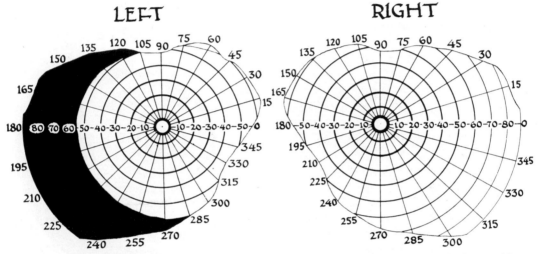

Fig. 398.—Left temporal crescentic hemianopia limited to monocular portion of the left field, caused by an artillery splinter (mine shell), lodged about 1 inch in front of the occipital protuberance, verified by X-rays. There were no other cerebral symptoms. Repeated checking during four months gave same results. Removal of the splinter, because of persistent headaches, resulted in complete permanent left homonymous hemianopia. From B. Fleischer, Klin. Monatsbl. f. Augenh., v. 57, case No. 1, 1916.

spreading from underneath—for example, by an aneurysm of the internal carotid artery and its branches or by an atypical tumor, an inflammatory process, or the like.

In the optic tract the crescentic fibers are assembled in and along its ventromedial margin, preserving this position as far as the lateral geniculate nucleus. In the latter the crescent fibers spread over the ventromedial and ventrolateral segments on both sides of the hilum in approximately the anterior half of the nucleus.

Any pathological process of limited extent at the base of the brain may, under favorable circumstances, affect these fibers in a more or less selective way. However, the pertinent clinical observations need to be further verified by careful post mortem studies. (*See* Brouwer & Zee- may be the most lateral in the radiation, is likewise ill founded.

The crescentic fibers, as they emerge from the ventrolateral and ventromedial segments of the lateral geniculate nucleus, sweep partly downward and partly upward, closely attached to the rest of the radiation, and soon turn medially to the calcarine fissure (*cf.* Figs. 235, 236, 259, 260). In the radiation close to the lateral geniculate nucleus the crescentic fibers are probably only imperfectly segregated from the remainder. The segregation is more complete farther back, until, on the level of the oral extremity of the striate area, they sweep above and below the posterior horn of the lateral ventricle and in this way enter the calcarine fissure.

In this respect the bundles of the radiation

related to the upper and the lower halves of the temporal crescent behave in exactly the same way as do those related to the upper and lower binocular quadrants of the visual fields. Since the most anterior portion of the striate cortex is usually confined to the lower calcarine lip, the dorsal crescentic fibers have to describe a longer detour in order to reach this cortex than do the ventral fibers. Hence there is no evidence in support of the opinion advocating a lateral position of the crescentic fibers in the radiation. Numerous cases of quadrantic homonymous hemianopias, where the crescentic portion was included in the affected quadrant, are opposed

is possible to calculate the position that a lesion must have in order to produce a selective crescentic defect. This may take place most easily and completely in approximately the middle third of the calcarine fissure, corresponding to the anterior point of the cuneus and just in front of it (Figs. 182, 235, 269, 271, 273, 274, 278). The prerequisite is a limited and nonexpanding pathology, such as, for example, an embolic infarction, an ischemic or encephalomalacic focus, or a local hemorrhage or trauma. Such a lesion may, in a single "episode," eliminate the entire anterior extremity of the striate area, with or without simultaneous damage to the

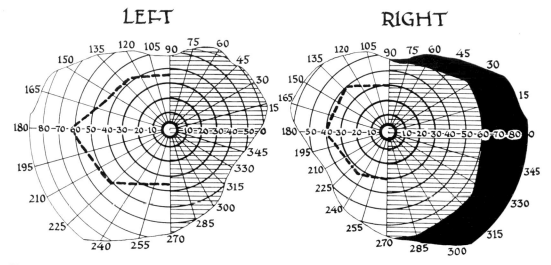

Fig. 399.—Right homonymous hemiamblyopia for colors (*shaded*), combined with an absolute scotoma in the monocular temporal crescent of the same side (*solid black*). From C. Behr, Klin. Monatsbl. f. Augenh., v. 56, p. 161, 1916 (*see* Wilbrand & Saenger, *Die homonyme Hemianopsie*, Fig. 193, 1917).

to such an assumption (*cf.* case MUNSON, in chap. XII).

The representation of the monocular crescent of the retina in the most anterior portion of the contralateral striate area was confirmed by Foerster (1929) in a human experiment. In a patient suffering from an inferior crescentic defect he found a focus of softening in the upper calcarine lip close to its juncture with the parieto-occipital sulcus. Electrical stimulation of this locality produced a subjective sensation of a scintillating scotoma, corresponding to the affected portion of the field of view. (*See* chap. X, 8 [3], on scintillating scotoma.)

From the course and location of the crescentic fibers in the upper and lower segments of the visual radiation and in the visual cortex, it

upper and lower crescentic fibers of the visual radiation.

In other cases either the upper or the lower crescentic fiber bundles of the radiation may alone be interrupted, producing an inferior or a superior quadrantic crescentic hemianopia on the contralateral side. In still other cases the retrocrescentic binocular portion of the striate area, with or without its afferent fibers, may be damaged, producing a homonymous hemianopia with crescentic sparing.

If such a lesion is bilateral and symmetrical, the result is complete blindness, including the field centers, with a sparing of both temporal crescents flanking the blind central parts of the binocular field of view. Other complex cases of field defects involving the unilateral or bilateral crescentic scotomas or sparings may be caused by irregular damage to the central visual mechanism. (*See* Fleischer 1916, 1920; Wilbrand & Saenger 1918; Balado, Adrogue & Franke 1928; Foerster 1929; Kronfeld 1932.)

The cases where unilateral crescentic blindness is caused by unilateral damage to the outward or lateral face of the parietal region of the cerebral hemisphere require special consideration. This, in the first place, may simply mean a general reduction of function in the entire extent of the homonymous fields, most pronounced in the temporal crescent. Possibly, a crescentic impairment is an expression of a lesser resistance or a greater vulnerability of the crescentic fibers of the visual radiation, perhaps caused by their unfavorable or exposed location or, more likely, by their less favorable blood supply (*see* above).

It may well be that the most anterior bundles of the radiation or the rostral segment of the striate area, both related to the monocular crescent, first become compressed or have their blood supply interfered with in case of pressure arising in one cerebral hemisphere. This may easily occur in parietal or temporal hemorrhages and tumors with chiefly a local effect. The responsible mechanism may be a compression of the hemisphere against the juncture of the falx cerebri and tentorium, in which way the crescentic fibers or the blood vessels supplying them first become compressed or strangulated. More light may be brought to this particular problem by an additional careful post mortem study of suitable cases. (*Cf.* case DYKSTRA in chap. XII.)

9. GENUINE ASYMMETRY AND INCONGRUITY IN HEMIANOPIC DEFECTS.—Unequal shape, size, and location of hemianopic defects in the right and left fields of view indicate a localization of a lesion in a section of the visual pathways where the right and left syndynamical or "corresponding" elemental units are not accurately aligned.

In the retinae and optic nerves, where the units are anatomically separated, it is only on rare occasions that two discrete bilateral lesions are sufficiently alike in their size, shape, and location to result in congruous defects in the two homonymous halves of the fields of view. This, owing to a partial decussation in the chiasma,

becomes basically different in the suprachiasmal portion of the visual system. Here the crossed and uncrossed fibrous and cellular elements, working together in the binocular visual act, approach very closely. Hence a unilateral injury, small or large, produces field defects in the two homonymous halves that in appearance, extent, and location are practically alike.

This statement, however, requires some qualification. The first concerns the monocular temporal crescent which does not have a "corresponding" counterpart in the contralateral field (Figs. 225, 259, 260, 398, 399). The other cases are those of incongruous defects in strictly binocular parts of the two monocular fields. Such smaller or larger discrepancies may be simply the result of inaccurate plotting, found in almost every routine chart (Figs. 388, 389, etc.). However, a number of investigators have described in carefully plotted cases what is termed a "genuine incongruity."

It appears that certain levels of the suprachiasmal pathway more readily cause such a discrepancy of the two sides than others. One such locality, according to Wilbrand (1926, 1929, 1930), is the initial portion of the optic tract, where the two sets of fibers, the crossed and the uncrossed, are supposed to be still somewhat separated. Another locality, according to Harrington (1939), is the initial portion of the visual radiation, next to the lateral geniculate nucleus. Here the two sets of fibers are believed to be not accurately juxtaposed, permitting a certain degree of isolated injury to only one set. (*See also* Sanford & Bair 1939.)

Closer to the occipital pole, the adjustment of the ipsilateral and contralateral fibers becomes more accurate, and the lesions of this portion of the radiation result in almost mathematically congruous field defects: Wilbrand's "absolute congruity." The most perfect union of the crossed and uncrossed sets of conductor elements, it appears, is achieved in the striate cortex itself. Therefore, the unilateral lesions, although they may be very limited in size, if confined to the striate cortex are bound to produce hemianopic disturbances which appear practically alike in every respect.

Whether this indicates the mathematical accuracy of the union of the crossed and uncrossed conductors or whether, nevertheless, there is a certain minute latitude, an overlapping, or the like, of the terminal ramifications is as yet uncertain. The alleged independent termination of the two fiber sets in the two sublayers of the inner granular layer of the striate cortex, improbable in itself and unproved, remains irrelevant to this problem (*cf.* chap. VIII, 7).

References: Abelsdorff 1916; Allen & Carman 1938; Austin, Lewey & Grant 1949; Balado, Adrogue & Franke 1928; Barkan & Barkan 1930; Behr 1916, 1931; Brouwer 1930; Brouwer & Zeeman 1926; Burnett 1887; Burns 1951; J. N. Evans 1941; Field *et al.* 1951; Chamlin 1949; Feigenbaum & Kornblueth 1946; Fleischer 1916, 1920; O. Foerster 1929; R. Förster 1890; Frenkel 1916–17; Fuchs & Pötzl 1917; Garcia Miranda 1944; Harrington 1939; Henschen 1903, 1909, 1911, 1926; Hoff & Pötzl 1935; G. Holmes 1918, 1919, 1931, 1934; Holmes & Lister 1916; Irvine 1950; Klüver 1927; Kronfeld 1932; Lenz 1927; Lutz 1925, 1926; Marie & Chatelin 1914–15, 1916; Monbrun 1917; Morax 1919; Morax *et al.* 1919; Moreau 1918; Münzer 1928; Pallarès 1923; Pesme 1931; Pötzl 1928; Pötzl & Urban 1935; Polyak (Poliak) 1932; Polyak & Hayashi 1936; Rønne (Roenne) 1915; H. Sachs 1895; Samelsohn 1882; Schlesinger *et al.* 1945; A. Šercer 1951; Shenkin & Leopold 1945; O. Sittig 1923; Traquair 1923, 1946; M. Treitel; Vorster 1893; F. B. Walsh 1947; Walsh & Ford 1940; Wilbrand 1907, 1925, 1925–26, 1926, 1930; Wilbrand & Behr 1927; Wilbrand & Saenger 1899–1927 (v. 7 and suppl., 1927), 1918.

SEC. 8. CENTRAL SPARING IN HOMONYMOUS HEMIANOPIA: THE HYPOTHESES AND SPECULATIONS

1. The origin of the concept of "central sparing" in hemianopia.—Even before the introduction of perimetry or plotting of the fields of view in clinical neuro-ophthalmology by R. Förster (1867), A. Graefe (1865) noticed a frequent "sparing" of the central portions of the fields of view around the fixation points in some cases of homonymous hemianopia, while in other cases the lines separating the blind from the normal halves of the fields were straight (*cf.* chap. IV, 1 [2]). This remarkable phenomenon, the frequent preservation of central, foveal, or "macular" vision, precisely that which makes sight the most important sensory instrument of Man's mind, could not fail to challenge many investigators to find an anatomical explanation for it, although Keen & Thomson (1871) assumed that central sparing was merely a product of an eccentric fixation (*see* Goldstein).

It was only natural that, since the exact organization of the visual mechanisms was not yet known, the early suggestions made were hypothetical. On general grounds it was assumed that the basis of "central sparing" was some particular pre-existing anatomical arrangement that makes central or "macular" vision less vulnerable in comparison with the less important "peripheral" or "extramacular" portions of the fields of view. Upon this speculative ground arose the "hypothesis of bilateral representation of the macula" (Wilbrand 1881, 1895; Marchand 1882; and others).

According to this, each complete or total "macula" or, more correctly, central fovea was represented in each occipital lobe. Thus defined, the hypothesis had been adhered to and propagated by numerous investigators until the present time, some of them most prominent in the investigation of the central visual mechanisms (Wilbrand; Henschen; P. Marie; Monbrun; O. Foerster; Penfield, Evans & McMillan; Halstead, Walker & Bucy; Penfield & Rasmussen 1950; and others). The emergence from time to time of other and quite different explanations, however, is the best evidence of the unsatisfactory nature of Wilbrand's concept.

2. The hypothesis of intraretinal decussation of foveal-macular fibers.—The earliest explanations of "central sparing" put stress on the peripheral portion of the visual system. Unlike the extrafoveal regions of the retina that are represented according to the principle of division along the vertical meridian, the foveal-macular fibers were supposed to pass to both halves of the brain.

The earliest suggestion, that of partial intercrossing of fibers in the retina, made, according to Seguin (1886), by Hannover (Fig. 400, upper sketch), was easily refuted on the evidence of frequent complete homonymous hemianopias caused by an interruption of one optic tract: in these there was neither a contralateral central sparing nor a reduction of acuity in the ipsilateral halves of the centers, both necessary postulates of the hypothesis.

The same argument was also applicable to a bitemporal hemianopia, e.g., caused by an interruption of decussating fibers in the chiasma. Also, minute injuries either to the nasal or to the temporal half of the central fovea cause scotomas restricted to only half of the field of view, an observation in full accord with the author's experiments with monkeys (Figs. 202–5; *also* chap. VI, 1 [2], 6 [4], 7).

Finally, the hypothesis of an intraretinal crossing of the foveal-macular fibers suffers from an inherent weakness, in that it would force the assumption of two sets of fibers, one passing from the right half of the fovea to the

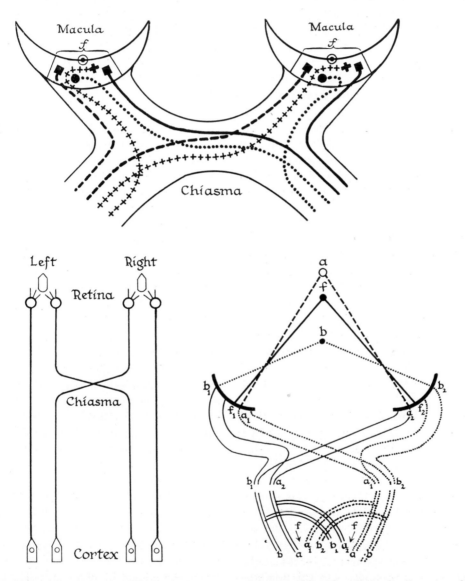

Fig. 400.—Diagrams illustrating various attempts to explain central foveal, or "macular," sparing often found in cases of homonymous hemianopia. *Upper diagram:* hypothetical partial crossing of fibers in the retina, resulting in a connection of both "macular" halves with each cerebral hemisphere. *Left lower diagram:* connection of each foveal cone with two ganglion cells in the retina, the axon of one of them passing over to the opposite cerebral hemisphere (Wilbrand & Saenger 1917). *Right lower diagram:* partial decussation of "macular" fibers in the corpus callosum (Heine 1900).

left half, and the other set passing in the opposite direction. This is required, since central sparing is found in unilateral lesions whether of the right or of the left side. A two-way crossing has not been observed in experiments referred to, nor is the visual acuity necessarily reduced in the functioning half of the field of view where there is a central scotoma in the other half. The same reasoning applies to a suggestion made by Morax (1919), according to which only the very center of the fovea, corresponding to the fixation point, is supplied with mixed crossed and uncrossed fibers (*cf.* chap. VI, 7).

3. The hypothesis of bilateral connections of the foveal photoreceptors with the brain.—This hypothesis assumes a connection of each foveal-macular cone with both hemispheres of the brain. Each cone, according to this, would be related to only one ganglion cell, but the axons or fibers of the ganglion cells would divide dichotomically into two branches, one proceeding to the ipsilateral hemisphere, the other passing over to the contralateral by way of the chiasma, as found by S. Ramón y Cajal and by Koelliker (*see* below).

Another variant of this idea suggested by Wilbrand could be that there would be two sets of the foveal cones, one set connected with the ipsilateral half of the brain, the other with the contralateral. Still a third possibility was suggested by Wilbrand (1930): that each foveal cone might be connected with two different ganglion cells, the axon of one of them proceeding to the opposite hemisphere (Fig. 400, left lower sketch).

The effect of any of the suggested hypothetical arrangements would be the preservation of function in the entire fovea or "macula," since the impulses, in unilateral suprachiasmal injuries, would still be able to pass over from the affected halves of the foveae to the cerebral hemisphere contralateral to the seat of injury (Wilbrand & Saenger 1917, v. 7, p. 19; Wilbrand 1930). The bilateral central connections of each complete fovea-macula, it was further assumed by some proponents of this hypothesis, would vary individually in extent and in some cases would be entirely absent (Wilbrand 1930).

All these speculations break down on close scrutiny because of a lack of concrete evidence. It is true that S. Ramón y Cajal (1899, 1899–1904, 1909–11) and Koelliker (1899) demonstrated the presence of bifurcating fibers in the chiasma of the Rat, Rabbit, Cat, Dog, and Ox. However, such bifurcations have never been discovered in Man and in other Primates. In fact, the experimental evidence shows fibers, originating from the nasal and temporal halves of the fovea, separating in the chiasma along a cleavage line coinciding with the vertical meridian passing through the foveal centers (chap. VI, 6 [4], 7).

The pathophysiological evidence is also against the bilateral concept. The cases of complete homonymous hemianopia or of a central hemianopic scotoma with a "splitting" of the centers of the fields of view are not necessarily associated with a reduction of visual acuity, as it would be legitimate to expect if, according to the hypothesis, half of the foveal photoreceptors and conductors were eliminated in the entire territory of the two foveae by a unilateral lesion. (*See* cases Kraft and Mallory, in chap. XII; *also* experiments by Le Gros Clark & Penman 1934 on detailed retinal representation in the lateral geniculate nucleus; and the experiments described in chap. VI, 6 [4], 7, and chap. VII, 3 [4], 4, 5, 6.)

The experimental evidence of a separation of the right from the left retinal fibers strictly along the vertical meridian referred to agrees with the clinical cases of a complete homonymous hemianopia caused by a complete interruption of one optic tract (Heine 1900; Rønne or Roenne 1911, 1914; Lenz 1914). In other similar cases the preserved central vision could be explained satisfactorily through a sparing of the foveal-macular bundle by the responsible pathological process.

The histoanalytical evidence is also opposed to the preceding hypothesis. The actual conditions of the structures found in the primate fovea show only individual synapses between the cones and midget bipolars (*b* & *h*) and between the midget bipolars and midget ganglion cells (*h* & *s*). These synaptical relations, obviously, are instrumental in the highest degree of visual acuity (*cf.* chap. V, 4 [10–14], 11).

4. The hypothesis of a midbrain decussa- tion of the "macular" fibers.—Since, ac- cording to the preceding review, there was no good reason to put the burden for central spar- ing upon the retina and the chiasma, Landolt (1875), Charcot (1876–80), and Ferrier (1886) suggested that the foveal-macular fibers that do not decussate in the chiasma may do so in the tectum or "roof" of the midbrain and, in par- ticular, in the quadrigeminal commissure (*cf.* chap. III, 7 [4], 9 [6]). This hypothesis, without any concrete foundation to support it, also had no success. It is likewise clearly contradicted by the experiments of Barris, Ingram & Ranson (1935) and by those described in chapter VI, 4 [5], 5, esp. [7]. (*See* Figs. 186, 187, 191, 192.)

5. The hypothesis of bilateral repre- sentation of the complete fovea in the cortex.—In the course of the further evolu- tion of Landolt and Charcot's idea of a partial crossing of the foveal-macular fibers in the mid- brain arose the concept of bilateral representa- tion of each complete fovea-macula in the cere- bral cortex, which has been much discussed in modern controversies concerning the organiza- tion of the central visual apparatus. Ferrier (1886) devised a scheme of the visual pathways where only fibers belonging to the centers of the fields of view would cross in the supranuclear di- vision and would terminate in the angular gyrus, which, in his opinion, was a center of "clear vision," that is, of the foveae (chap. III, 7). Elaborating upon this speculation, Heine (1900) and Lenz (1909, 1914) believed that the locality where the decussation took place was in the posterior segment or splenium of the corpus callosum (Fig. 400, lower right-hand sketch).

In Heine's view a portion of the fibers (a_1, b_2) of the visual radiation originating from the lat- eral geniculate nucleus, instead of proceeding to the striate area of the same side, crosses in the corpus callosum to the contralateral hemi- sphere, where it joins the opposite radiation (*a*, *b*). In this way the two foveal-macular halves of the retinae, separated by partial decussation in the chiasma, rejoin in the visual radiations and in the striate areae. (*Cf. also* O. Foerster 1929, Fig. 1.) When one of the occipital lobes is inter- fered with, impulses from both complete foveae would still be able to pass over to the other nor- mal lobe, partly via the chiasma and partly by way of the corpus callosum.

For a number of years Heine's hypothesis was a convenient way of explaining "central sparing" in homonymous hemianopia, a phe- nomenon frequently observed in clinical prac- tice. It remained a hypothesis, even though Niessl von Mayendorf (1914, 1926) made an effort to furnish anatomical evidence for it in a *fasciculus corporis callosi cruciatus*, or "crossed callosal macular bundle." The presence of this "bundle" seemed to become more certain when R. A. Pfeifer (1925) believed that he had dem- onstrated it with the help of Flechsig's myelo- genetical method. This appeared to be so, even though the evidence produced was not convinc- ing and the correctness of Pfeifer's interpreta- tion was questioned by no less an authority than Flechsig (1927; *see also* Polyak 1932, 1933). A similar fiber connection, an "inter- tractal commissure," supposed to relate both lateral geniculate nuclei, was suggested by Klossowski (1930), without any substantial evi- dence.

More impressive evidence against the hypo- thetical callosal fibers is the preservation of cen- ters in operations where the callosum was sec- tioned (Hyndman 1934). Maison, Settlage & Grether (1938) and again German & Brody (1940) also disproved the presence of a decus- sating tract.

However, in spite of the lack of positive evi- dence, Wilbrand's and Heine's concept of a "bi- lateral representation of a complete macula" in the cerebral cortex enjoyed and still does enjoy wide popularity among the clinicians (O. Foer- ster, 1929; Juba 1934; Penfield, Evans & McMil- lan 1935; Halstead, Walker & Bucy 1940; Pen- field & Rasmussen 1950; and others).

Wilbrand & Saenger (1917, p. 9) went even further in expressing their opinion that central sparing must be present in every case of a ho- monymous hemianopia, correctly thinking that a mechanism of such importance would hardly permit any latitude in individual variation, i.e., the presence of a bilateral arrangement in some and the absence of it in others, as was light- heartedly assumed by many ophthalmologists and neurologists. In those cases where a dividing line was seemingly passing through the fixation points, central sparing, according to Wilbrand & Saenger, would remain undisclosed because of the difficulties of exact plotting.

Since in a number of cases of central sparing a biopsy or a post mortem examination showed complete unilateral destruction of the visual radiation, either alone or with that of the striate area, the opinion was expressed that a "splitting" of the centers took place only in those cases where the lesion was close to the lateral geniculate nucleus whence the "decussating callosal macular bundle" was supposed to branch off. In foci farther back in the occipital lobe, since these would spare the decussating macular fibers, the central vision would remain preserved (Lenz 1914; *also* Penfield & Rasmussen 1950).

In support of this thesis, reference was made to statistical studies. In a collection published by Wilbrand (1930) there were, in pathology involving the cerebral hemispheres, 37 cases of hemianopia with central sparing and only 5 cases where there was no such sparing, a proportion of almost 8 to 1, whereas in tractus hemianopia there were 13 cases with, and 7 without, sparing, or a proportion of 2 to 1. Also, in 200 cases collected by Sanford & Bair (1939) where vision was involved, central sparing was present in approximately one-third of the temporal lobe cases (30.5 per cent), whereas the centers were spared in more than half of the occipital lobe cases (57.1 per cent). Such statistical studies are impressive and are undoubtedly in many respects valuable. However, the evidence which they furnish, in spite of its apparently objective character, may prove to be quite misleading unless carefully checked by other criteria, primarily by anatomical study.

The final verdict on Wilbrand's hypothesis of central sparing, in spite of all efforts, including modern ones, to sustain it, is negative: its anatomical, experimental, pathological, and theoretical foundations are all unsound. It certainly does not have any theoretical basis (*see* 9 [2], this chapter). In this connection, as a curiosity, may be quoted the opinion of no other than Monakow, a principal opponent of the concept of a detailed representation of the retina in the cerebral cortex advocated by Wilbrand and by Henschen. On logical grounds, and very correctly so, Monakow (1914, p. 408) considered Wilbrand's hypothesis "rather dangerous than useful" to his and Henschen's idea of a point-to-point representation of the retina in the cortex, since such organization would, in unilateral injuries, altogether preclude the appearance of hemianopic macular scotomas. (*Cf.* chap. IV, 5, 6.)

6. THE HYPOTHESIS OF ASYMMETRIC DIVISION OF DECUSSATING AND NONDECUSSATING FIBERS IN THE CHIASMA.—As a further possible cause of central sparing in hemianopia, a suggestion was made of an irregular or asymmetrical cleavage of the nasal and temporal fibers in the fovea-macula. In some individuals the line of separation would not coincide with the vertical meridians but would deviate to a greater or lesser extent toward one or the other side, hence making an asymmetric division of the foveal-macular fibers in the chiasma (Wilbrand 1881; Lenz 1915). In such individuals one occipital lobe would, accordingly, represent more, the other less, than half the foveae-maculae, or retinae. The amount and direction of deviation would vary individually.

This speculation is invalidated by the following considerations. First, if an unequal division of the foveal fibers were the anatomical basis of central sparing, one would expect, on the basis of statistical probability, the number of cases with and those without central sparing to be approximately equal, both in the infranuclear (chiasma, tract, lateral geniculate nucleus), and in the supranuclear or temporo-occipital lesions. This, however, is not borne out by Wilbrand's statistics, already quoted.

Furthermore, on the basis of the same law of probability, approximately as many cases of homonymous hemianopia with a central scotoma in the functioning halves of the fields should be expected as those with a central sparing in the blind halves. In any event, in some cases, instead of a central sparing, there would be at least a central amblyopia in addition to the usual hemianopia of the contralateral side. This is, however, not supported by the available evidence.

Finally, the experiments on the cerebral representation of the simian fovea made by Le Gros Clark & Penman (1934) and those described in chapter VI, 6 (4) and 7, demonstrate the identity of the vertical meridian and the line in the fovea by which the uncrossed temporal fibers remaining on the same side are separated from the nasal fibers that decussate to the contralateral side by way of the chiasma.

7. CENTRAL SPARING CAUSED BY A MULTIPLE ARTERIAL SUPPLY OF THE OCCIPITAL POLE.—A hypothesis less spectacular than Wilbrand's but closer to reality was the explanation of central sparing by a multiple arterial supply of the occipital pole suggested by R. Förster, inventor of the perimeter (chap. IV, 1 [2]).

Describing a case of incomplete bilateral homonymous hemianopia or "central field rests," the first of its type on record, in considering the multiple vascular supply of the retinal "macula," he interpreted the minimal central rests as sparings of the macular cortex made possible by the anastomotical connections of two or more arterial territories in the occipital lobes. He wrote: "In case the principal vessel of the occipital lobe is obstructed, and an extensive area of the cortex is shut off, precisely that portion of the cortex which corresponds to the most acute vision may be spared" (Förster, 1890, p. 106).

Förster's view was shared by a number of reliable authorities, some with a firsthand knowledge of the cerebral blood supply (G. Holmes & Lister 1916; Igersheimer 1918; G. Holmes 1919; Monbrun 1919; Traquair 1925; Beauvieux & Ristich-Goelmino 1926; *cf. also* Beevor 1909; a very different and, according to our opinion, erroneous interpretation of Förster's case was given by Wilbrand [1895] in the sense of a bilateral representation of each complete fovea-macula).

Holmes & Lister, for example, found the pole of the occipital lobe to be at the "watershed" area of the posterior and middle cerebral arteries, and hence "it may under normal conditions draw blood from both, and if one is blocked, the other may suffice to maintain its nutrition"; and again "the presence or absence of macular escape in hemianopia due to vascular lesion may be explained by the varying degree of anastomosis between, and the relative extent in the distribution of, the posterior and the middle cerebral arteries at the occipital pole of the hemisphere. The frequent persistence of central vision in bilateral hemianopia due to bilateral cortical lesions may be possibly explained by this same fact."

Igersheimer and others, based partly on their own study of the vascular supply of the occipital lobe, also considered multiple blood supply as the true cause of central sparing. (*Cf. also* cases MARTIN P. and ANONYMUS, Figs. 428, 432, 433.)

In spite of the above-quoted opinion, however, the "magic" of the hypothesis of a bilateral representation of the complete fovea-macula in the cerebral cortex, supported by weighty authorities, even now prevails, as against Förster's concept, which requires a substantial knowledge of the cerebral vascular anatomy. (*Cf.* chap. X, 6 [3], 8 [4], and sec. 9, this chapter.)

8. CENTRAL SPARING: A SPECIAL FORM OF HEMIAMBLYOPIA.—An interpretation of central sparing as a variety of hemiamblyopia was advanced by Rønne (Roenne 1911). In many cases which appear as an incomplete homonymous hemianopia there was, in reality, only extensive reduction of function in the larger peripheral portions of the affected fields. This peripheral hemiamblyopia, when tested with ordinary perimetric methods, would escape notice, leaving only the central parts of the fields intact on account of their "functional superiority" (a concept itself in need of explanation).

Briefly, in Rønne's opinion an incomplete homonymous hemianopia was only a special form of homonymous hemiamblyopia. A similar view, assuming greater sensitiveness for the "macular region" and therefore greater resistance in comparison with the periphery of the fields of view, was also advocated by Sanford & Bair (1939).

9. PROTECTED LOCATION OF THE FOVEAL-MACULAR FIBERS IN THE VISUAL RADIATION THE CAUSE OF CENTRAL SPARING IN HEMIANOPIA.—In his further attempts to find a plausible explanation of the frequent sparing of the visual field centers in homonymous hemianopia, Rønne (1919) called attention to the protected location of the foveal-macular fibers in the visual radiation. The exact location of these fibers was not known at that time (*see* chap. IV, 7 [6]). However, Rønne compared them with the arrangement in the retina, where the so-called papillomacular bundle is flanked above and below by the arching extrafoveal fibers from the upper and lower temporal quadrants (*cf.* Figs. 162, 207, 208). He believed that in some cases the "peripheral" fibers of the radiation would suffer more easily, while the centrally located "macular bundle" would remain intact more readily, with the resulting sparing of central vision.

This ingenious hypothesis of Rønne, like a similar concept of an "anatomical interval" filled by the foveal-macular fibers—a suggestion made by G. Holmes at about the same time—both closely approaching the truth, had no chance of being accepted by contemporary writers and was dismissed as "artificial" and "far-fetched." One reason for this was a lack of suitable pathological or experimental evidence to document it. But the most weighty deterrent was the confusion in the anatomical concepts of the organization of the visual radiation. (*Cf.* chap. IV, 7 [6]; chap. VII, esp. 4, 5, and 6; *see also* Figs. 235, 236, 259, 260, 269.)

10. RECENT ATTEMPTS TO INTERPRET CENTRAL SPARING IN HEMIANOPIA.—The various attempts of many investigators of the past hundred years to explain the remarkable and teleologically extremely useful phenomenon of the sparing of central portions of the fields of view in homonymous hemianopia were obviously not satisfactory. Even the most popular hypothesis, that of a bilateral cortical representation of each complete fovea-macula in both cerebral hemispheres, suggested by Wilbrand, was accepted as a mere stopgap expedient until a better theory could be formed.

The unsatisfactory character of all explanations so far suggested is proved by further attempts made from time to time to devise a better solution. Unfortunately, none of the recent suggestions is any more convincing, some possessing even less ingenuity and logical appeal than the old ones. The obvious reason is their purely speculative character. None of the modern suggestions is based on an earnest effort to turn to the only reliable source of information: detailed study of the anatomical organization of the visual system and of its blood supply. The

unavoidable result is "turning in circles" and perpetuation, one might almost say "in desperation," of fantastic concepts which should have been put to rest long ago.

Brouwer (1917), for example, discussing the cases where there was central sparing, even though the occipital pole was destroyed, believed that the "macular" cortex might stretch along the floor of the calcarine fissure as far as the anterior extremity of the striate area, reverting in this respect to Monakow's idea of a multiple or "diffuse" cortical representation of the retina (*see* chap. IV, 5). In the case of damage to the pole there would still remain enough of the "macular" cortex to account for the preserved central vision. Brower's speculation, while a priori possible, loses ground against contrary evidence represented by a case reported by R. A. Pfeifer (1930), in which there was central sparing and where careful histological examination revealed that more than the rostral half of the striate area was destroyed.

In a similar case with central sparing, published by Brouwer (1930) himself, the anterior portion of the striate area, corresponding to the wedge of the cuneus, was destroyed, while the occipital pole was preserved, a counterpart to a case of Holmes & Lister (1916), in which a central scotoma was caused by the destruction of the occipital pole.

To complete this account, reference may also be made to case MALLORY described in chapter XII. Here a central scotoma was caused by a lesion localized in the posterior extremity of the striate area, with the anterior extremity of the same area, including the floor of the calcarine fissure, practically normal (Fig. 426). The various experiments upon monkeys, described in chapter VII, 4, 5, 6, also decidedly disprove a localization of the fovea in the anterior segment of the striate area. The same evidence likewise invalidates other similar attempts to localize the fovea-macula anywhere in the cortex except in the posterior, polar extremity of the striate cortex (Halstead, Walker & Bucy 1940; and others).

Another suggestion, equally without foundation, was of a second, additional representation of the fovea-macula outside the striate area or occipital lobe, to substitute in case of the destruction of the "regular" foveal representation in the occipital pole. This suggestion was made by Balado, Adrogue & Franke (1928), Brouwer (1930), German & Fox (1934), and Hyndman (1939). Such a concept of double or multiple foveal representation would be tantamount to a reversion to Monakow's ill-founded idea of diffuse retinal projection in an extensive area of the cerebral cortex, which has been refuted with all desired clarity by modern experimental evidence, including that presented in this book (*see* chap. VII, 3, 4, 6).

In the same category of unsubstantiated hypotheses belongs the suggestion made by Monbrun (1919), according to which each complete fovea-macula would be represented not only in each striate area, as Wilbrand and his supporters insist, but also in the upper and lower half of each striate area. This, in his opinion, would account for the surplus areae above or below the horizontal meridians, or an altitudinal sparing, occasionally observed in homonymous central scotomas (*see also* Wilbrand 1930).

But the questionable honors for what appears to be a classical example of undisciplined pseudo-scientific speculation of modern times belong unqualifiedly to the noted neurologist and neurosurgeon, Otfried Foerster, late professor at Breslau (now Wroclaw). According to his opinion, not only the fovea-macula but also the remainder of the retina are represented in full in each cerebral hemisphere. His evidence was a case (case *3*) of a large dural meningioma of the parietal region in a young man manifesting itself in an incomplete hemianopia. Bioptically, "the entire left occipital lobe, except for the insignificant rests, was compressed in an anterior direction as far as the *cella media* of the lateral ventricle." After successful elimination of the tumor, the function in the entire hemianopic field was restored, which, in Foerster's interpretation, was caused by a substitution by the contralateral striate area. No autopsy control, unfortunately, was possible.

Foerster's conclusion, we may say, is contradicted by all evidence at our command. It is not in any way borne out by the facts laboriously collected during a continuous study of three decades, now presented in this volume. It is also unwelcome, since it is supported by the great authority of a respected scientific worker, hence the more liable to bring confusion into a delicate problem requiring, above all, sober facts and clear thinking. (*Cf. also* Horrax & Putnam 1932.)

The preceding review may suffice to show the difficulties and the existing confusion in the problem of central sparing in hemianopia, a subject that had a great deal to do with the understanding of the anatomical and functional organization of the cerebral visual mechanism. In the following section an attempt is made to marshal all available information to clarify this problem.

References: Balado, Adrogue & Franke 1928; Balado & Malbrán 1932; Balado, Malbrán & Franke 1934; Barris, Ingram & Ranson 1935; Best 1919, 1920; Brouwer 1917, 1930; Charcot 1876–80; Clark & Penman 1934; Ferrier 1886; Flechsig 1927; O. Foerster 1929; R. Förster 1869, 1890; Fox & German 1936; German & Brody 1940; German & Fox 1934; Graefe 1865; Halstead, Walker & Bucy 1940; Hannover (quoted by Seguin 1886); Heine 1900; Hyndman 1939; Igersheimer 1918; Juba 1934; Klossowski 1930; Klüver 1927; Koelliker 1899; Krainer & Suwa 1936; Landolt 1875; Lenz 1905, 1909, 1914, 1915; Lutz 1926; Maison, Settlage & Grether 1938; Marchand 1882; P. Marie 1916; Marie & Chatelin 1916; Monakow 1914; Monbrun 1919; Morax 1919; Morax *et al.* 1919; Niessl von Mayendorf 1914, 1920, 1921, 1926, 1932; Penfield, Evans & McMillan 1935; Penfield & Rasmussen 1950; R. A. Pfeifer 1925, 1930; Putnam 1934; Putnam & Liebman 1942; S. Ramón y Cajal 1899, 1899–1904, 1909–11; Rønne (Roenne) 1911, 1919; Sanford & Bair 1939; Seguin 1886; Sjögren 1928; Traquair 1925, 1946; F. B. Walsh 1947; Wilbrand 1881, 1895, 1930; Wilbrand & Saenger 1917; Yoshimura 1909.

SEC. 9. CENTRAL SPARING IN HEMIANOPIA: THE UNDERLYING FUNCTIONAL AND ANATOMICAL FACTORS

1. TESTING OF THE FIELDS OF VIEW AND THEIR INTERPRETATION.—Plotting of the fields of view is essentially a subjective reaction of the person examined. If not done with great care and repeatedly, small defects, such as minute scotomas, may easily be missed (Wilbrand &

Saenger 1917, p. 22; Traquair 1925, 1946; Wilbrand 1926, 1930; Putnam & Liebman 1942; *see also* G. Holmes 1946).

Conversely, it is possible that minute central rests may be found where there are none. Improperly tested cases, therefore, are not evidence for or against the hypothesis of bilateral representation of a complete fovea-macula in the brain. The flicker-campimeter method in a case where there may be, for example, sizable initial central sparing, after the condition becomes stabilized, may show the same sparing gradually receding to a vanishing point. Such striking reduction of an initially extensive central sparing cannot be attributed to the spreading of the underlying pathological process long after all pertinent symptoms have disappeared. It rather demonstrates the presence of a "functional factor" that simulates sparing where there is none (*see*, e.g., case KRAFT, in chap. XII).

Such a decrease or elimination of artificial central sparing in the course of prolonged testing shows the working of some innate tendency of the sensory-motor mechanism to make the contralateral functioning halves of the hemiretinae oscillate beyond the mid-line to the other side, precisely when the centers are tested, in this way producing a "pseudo-sparing."

This factor may in some cases be responsible also for the narrow surplus zones of the fields extending along the vertical meridians in the blind fields. Here, too, the oculomotor balance may have been "reorganized," but actually "disorganized," in a way to dislocate the points of fixation away from the centers of the anatomical foveae in the direction of the periphery of the normal halves of the fields.

The central "pseudo-sparing" appears to fall in the same category of phenomena as the "pseudo-fovea" of W. Fuchs (1920, 1922). This brings closer to our understanding those intriguing cases where, in spite of a complete removal or destruction of one striate area, an irreducible "central sparing" was found (Foerster 1929, case *2;* German & Fox 1934; Penfield & Evans 1934; Halstead, Walker & Bucy 1940; Penfield & Rasmussen 1950).

The factor responsible for the tendency to produce a "central pseudo-sparing" in an anatomically complete homonymous hemianopia may be designated as a disturbed dynamical oculomotor balance of the two cerebral hemispheres in the case of damage to the posterior extremity of one hemisphere. Probably it is essentially the same sensory-motor oculogyric mechanism, the slight physiological imbalance of which manifests itself in the oscillation of the points of fixation under normal conditions recorded by Marx & Trendelenburg (1911) and others. In pathological conditions such imbalance may be expected to be considerable.

From the preceding considerations it appears that many "macular sparings" recorded in clinical practice will be eliminated when refined testing methods are developed and regularly used (as applied, e.g., by Austin, Lewey & Grant 1949). For there is no doubt that much which is designated "central sparing" in present clinical routine is nothing more than "pseudo-sparing." However, even with this qualification, the fact of true central sparing is too well founded to need further discussion. Hence the problem posed is: What anatomical arrangements are responsible for the frequent sparing of the central parts of the fields of view in homonymous hemianopia?

Before trying to examine various factors, however, it will be useful—for the sake of clearing the atmosphere—to analyze the theoretical aspect, which has been the core of the problem: Is a bilateral representation of each complete central fovea or "macula" possible, without interfering with the very principle by which the visual system works?

2. VISUAL SYSTEM: HOW IT CAN FUNCTION AND HOW IT CANNOT.—In the modern way of thinking there are certain ideas and concepts gained from numerous observations, experiments, and tests which must be considered basic. These concepts must fully agree with the innumerable manifestations of nature, or else they must be modified accordingly.

One such basic revelation that has gradually emerged is a strict parallel between the functional organization of the eye as a reacting sense organ and the inherent properties of physical light as its adequate physiological stimulus (*cf.* chap. XIII, 2). A similar parallel between the intrinsic organization of the visual pathways and centers of the brain, on the one hand, and the structure of the eye and physical properties of light, on the other, is only now beginning to be comprehended (*see* chaps. V and VII).

Even so, sufficient knowledge is at hand to indicate just what functional organization may be expected in the vertebrate visual system and what can safely be ruled out as improbable. This will give a general answer to the problem of "central sparing" in hemianopia, particularly to the controversial hypothesis of cortical representation of each complete fovea-macula in both cerebral hemispheres.

For this purpose several anatomical and physiological possibilities may be examined with the help of a diagram (Fig. 401). This diagram shows the essentials of the organization of the human and simian visual system. Uppermost in the figure is the object to be viewed, symbolized by an arrow (A–B), whose images are depicted in a reversed order on the retinae of both eyes focused on the center of the object ($f\phi$). The two sets of the impulses generated in the two retinae are propagated along the preformed pathways, represented by the optic nerves, chiasma, tracts, lateral geniculate nuclei, and visual radiations, to the two visual cortical centers or striate areae of the occipital lobes of the brain. The intrinsic organization of the visual pathways is assumed to be known from the description in chapters VI and VII and from Figures 225, 259, 260.

The two images (a-b and a-β) are transmitted to the two lateral geniculate nuclei in such a way that their right halves (a-f and a-ϕ, black) coincide in the right nucleus, and their left halves (b-f and β-ϕ, white) coincide in the left nucleus. This is a necessary deduction, first, from the partial crossing of fibers in the chiasma and, second, from the fact of a joint representation of the right and the left syndynamical or "corresponding" points of both retinae in the same minute segments of the optic nerves, chiasma, tracts, and geniculates (thus a and a; f and ϕ; b and β). The points f and ϕ on the retinae are the two points of fixation, or centers of two foveae, through which the two dividing vertical meridians pass, separating each retinal image into two halves—a black, pointed one and a white one with a blunt end.

From each lateral geniculate nucleus a double half-image is further transmitted along the vis-

ual radiations to the visual cortical centers, the striate areae of their own sides (for the sake of simplicity, only a single image is drawn: solid black on the right side, and in outline on the left side). Since each geniculate nucleus is represented in its own striate area strictly according to a one-to-one plan (as documented in chap. VII, 5, 6), the transmission of the double retinal half-images to the areae is also strictly preserved with all topographical relations. The two cortical half-images—the solid black one with the pointed end on the right side and the white one with the blunt end on the left side—together produce a complete cortical image. (*Cf. also* Figs. 361, 439; *see also* S. Ramón y Cajal 1898, 1899, and 1909–11, v. 2, p. 376; Jacobsohn-Lask 1924, 1928; Best 1930; *cf. also* chap. XIII, 3.)

The hypothesis of a bilateral cortical representation of each complete fovea-macula in both cerebral hemispheres, in addition to the homonymous mechanism just described, forces one to presuppose the coexistence of another heteronymous connection maintained by way of the hypothetical macular bundles decussating in the corpus callosum—crossed "macular" bundles. This also necessarily implies a connection of each "corresponding point" of both homonymous hemiretinae, for example, of a and a, not only in the homonymous cortical visual center (at aa) but also with another symmetrical point in the contralateral heteronymous cortical visual center (at $b\beta$), a point in turn related to the "corresponding points" of its own contralateral retinal halves (b and β).

In order to analyze the consequences which must logically follow from the preceding exposition, certain facts evidenced by modern experience, both anatomical and clinical, have to be kept in mind. The first such fact is the separation of the central representation of each retina along a vertical meridian into two halves, a nasal and a temporal. Hence each cortical visual center or striate area represents homonymous halves of both retinae. The periphery of both halves along the ora serrata (a and a, b and β) is represented at the anterior extremity, the points of fixation (f and ϕ) are represented at the posterior polar extremity of the cortical center. All the other numerous "corresponding points" of the two homonymous retinal halves

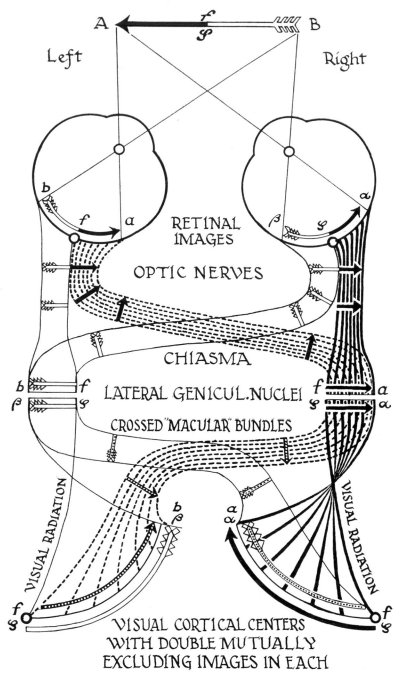

FIG. 401.—A diagram to illustrate the physiological impossibility of the conventional concept of the projection of each complete fovea, or "macula," upon both halves of the brain, as advocated by Wilbrand and by Heine. Such an arrangement, in particular the decussation of a portion of "macular" fibers in the corpus callosum, would reverse the retinal image in the cortex and hence would annul the physiological sense and aim of the topographical representation of retinal surfaces in the cortical visual centers of the brain. (For details *see* text and Figs. 361, 439.)

between the serrated margins and the dividing vertical meridians are evenly represented according to the same topographical principle between the points of fixation ($f\phi$) and the far peripheries ($a\alpha$ and $b\beta$). The cortical representation of, for example, point a of the nasal half of the left retina is the same as its "corresponding point" α, of the temporal half of the right retina (if, for the sake of simplicity, we disregard the surplus monocular crescent). In this way each two "corresponding points" of both retinae, which work in unison in the binocular visual act, merge in the cortical center into a single point.

If there were heteronymous connections in the foveal-macular portions of the visual system, as implied by the hypothetical "crossed macular bundles," both the point-to-point principle and that of a symmetrical representation must also be postulated for the retinal points that are at an equal distance from the fixation points. The "corresponding points" a and α, for example, would be represented not only in $a\alpha$ of the right cortical center but also in $b\beta$ of the left center, where the two heteronymous symmetrical "corresponding points" b and β of the contralateral retinal halves are already represented. In no case could a and α be represented asymmetrically, for example, at $f\phi$ of the contralateral center, precisely as they could not be represented at $f\phi$ of the ipsilateral cortical center; likewise a simultaneous representation of several "corresponding points," for example, of a and α and of f and ϕ, in a single cortical point, e.g., in $f\phi$, is unthinkable, since such a chaotic arrangement would obliterate all topographical retinocortical relationships whose presence has been demonstrated by experiment.

From the preceding analysis it is plain that in a quadruple projection of the retinal images upon the cerebral cortex—a necessary effect of a hypothetical "decussating callosal macular bundle"—the antagonistic or disparate retinal points would be represented in the same cortical points. For example, the "corresponding retinal points" a and α would be represented at $a\alpha$ of the right cortical center, but also at $b\beta$ of the left center, where the "corresponding retinal points" b and β are already represented. In other words, the same cortical locality would receive messages from more than a single object

point, for example, the right cortical point $a\alpha$ from the object points A and B, the same from which the left cortical point $b\beta$ would receive its messages. The cortical fixation points of both sides, $f\phi$, alone would remain simple.

In the visual system thus organized, the action of the "dark-chamber effect" and of the dioptrical apparatus of both eyes would be annulled. The two cerebral images created in each visual cortical center would be superimposed in reversed positions, with nonmatching ends together. In the right center, for example, at $a\alpha$, the pointed end of the black arrow and the blunt end of the white arrow would be simultaneously depicted in one image.

The effect of this arrangement would be the same as taking a picture with a photographic camera of the same object on the same film twice—the second time with the film inverted. It is difficult, indeed, to imagine a more absurd, and biologically less purposeful, result of the creative forces of nature. (*Cf.* chap. XIII, 2, 3.)

From the preceding analysis of the known organization of the vertebrate visual apparatus and its mechanics, the concept of the representation of each complete fovea-macula in the cortical visual centers of both cerebral hemispheres is unthinkable on theoretical grounds alone. The explanation of central sparing in homonymous hemianopia is not to be found from nebulous concepts but is to be sought in a realistic way.

3. ANATOMICAL FACTORS RESPONSIBLE FOR THE SPARING OF CENTRAL VISION IN HEMIANOPIA.—The anatomical factors responsible for the phenomenon of sparing of central vision in homonymous hemianopia are several. The first and most important is the intrinsic organization of the visual system which makes possible an isolated injury to the parts of that system related to extrafoveal portions of the retinae, while leaving foveal-macular parts intact. The other, and in cerebral pathology equally important, factor is the multiple blood supply of the posterior portion of the cerebral hemisphere, especially of the occipital pole where the fovea is represented. This makes possible the preservation of a normal or nearly normal blood supply to the pole, even though other parts of the striate cortex serving the extrafoveal vision may be suppressed or destroyed. The third and apparently less weighty factor is the nature of the underlying pathological process or injury, which becomes important only in connection with the first two factors.

In the preceding subsection certain anatomical and physiological reasons were advanced to show why, on these grounds alone, the hypothesis of bilateral representation of each complete fovea in both cerebral hemispheres is not defensible and hence cannot be accepted as a valid explanation of central sparing in homonymous hemianopia. In the following, other anatomical factors are discussed that make such sparing possible.

The fiber bundles that make up the visual radiation, at the point of their emergence from the lateral geniculate nucleus, form a compact system (Figs. 235, 236, 269). Here they may easily be interrupted by a single lesion, for example, in the posterior portion of the internal capsule or immediately behind it in the fiber mass of the parietotemporal lobes. Such a lesion, if of any considerable size, is likely to interrupt the entire radiation, including the foveal or "macular" fibers. The resulting functional defect is a complete homonymous hemianopia of the contralateral halves of the fields of view without central sparing.

Such an outcome is further facilitated by the fact that in this locality the bulk of the radiation is supplied by the middle cerebral artery (*mcea*) and the inferior branches of the posterior cerebral artery (*poteocca*, in Figs. 370, 371, 374; *cf. also* Figs. 226, 227, 230, 233). Any interference with the radiation in this locality must necessarily have a global effect. This, together with the other pertinent experimental and clinical facts (complete degeneration of the ipsilateral geniculate nucleus when one striate area is completely removed, and preponderantly a complete homonymous hemianopia in processes localized in the temporal lobe), effectively disposes of the hypothetical "crossed callosal macular bundle."

Farther back in the hemisphere the fibers of the visual radiation spread apart, forming the outer sagittal fiber lamina, curved on cross-section to resemble a horseshoe (Figs. 228–32). The inner curve of this horseshoe envelops from above, from below, and laterally the posterior horn of the lateral ventricle, which, in turn, separates it from the calcarine fissure. A limited lesion, such as may, for example, be caused by a thrombosis of one branch of the middle or posterior cerebral arteries, may interfere with only one segment or branch of the radiation (Fig. 377).

In one case, for example, a branch of the middle cerebral artery may be clogged, causing an encephalomalacic destruction of the upper segment of the radiation, manifested by an inferior quadrantic hemianopia (case MUNSON, Fig. 412). In another case lower branches of the posterior cerebral artery may be put out of commission, causing smaller or larger defects in the lower segment of the radiation and producing a superior quadrantic hemianopia (initial stage in case HOLT, Fig. 415).

The centers of the fields of view may or may not be spared, depending on whether the intermediate segment of the radiation and the posterior segment of the striate area were or were not spared. In case MALLORY, for example, the extreme polar segment of the right striate area was damaged, resulting in central hemianopic scotomas extending to the vertical meridians (Figs. 424–27).

Since in many individuals, possibly in the majority, most of the anterior portion of the striate area serving the periphery of the fields of view is supplied by the posterior cerebral artery, while the posterior segment of this area is, in part at least, supplied by the middle cerebral artery, an obstruction to the posterior cerebral eliminates only the extrafoveal-macular parts of the fields and spares the centers. The exact mechanism responsible for such "dissociation" is described in detail in chapter X, 8 [2, 4].

The medial or anterior portion of the calcarine fissure, accordingly, behaves in regard to its blood supply and its vascular pathology as a unit, largely separated from the lateral or posterior portion of the fissure at the pole, which depends largely or entirely on the middle cerebral artery for its vascular supply (as described in chap. X, 6). This fact is well illustrated by the later stage of case HOLT (Fig. 415). In this case a limited encephalomalacia destroyed most of the cortex along the medial calcarine fissure, leaving the pole of the occipital lobe intact (Fig. 414). Owing to this, most of the fibers of the radiation degenerated in the retrograde sense except the axial segment passing to the spared occipital pole (*vr*), and in the lateral geniculate nucleus the posterior foveal extremity alone remained normal (Fig. 416), both parts being related to the spared central vision (Fig. 260). In two other cases examined, the situation was even more drastic, since here much or almost all cortex on the medial and inferior faces of the occipital and temporal lobes, supplied by the posterior cerebral, was wasted away, except the polar segment of the striate area (Figs. 428, 432, 433). This was the more remarkable, since in one case the axial segment of the radiation supplied by the middle cerebral artery was also interrupted. Here, unlike case Holt, the posterior horn of the lateral ventricle broke down in its role as a vascular barrier, owing to the extensiveness of the lesion.

Simultaneous destruction of both lips of the calcarine fissure along its medial or anterior stretch, with or without damage to the incoming upper and lower radiation fibers, may easily follow a thrombotic occlusion of the principal calcarine artery (*pca* in Figs. 372, 374). The striate cortex lining the medial calcarine fissure, especially along its floor, is eliminated in this way. The fringes of this cortex in both lips of the fissure may be spared if they are supplied by the branches arising from the main stem of the calcarine artery (*ca*) below the obstructed locality—for example, by the paracalcarine or inferior calcarine artery (*paca, ica, ical*) and by other arteries (*cuaa, cuma, cupa, poteocca*).

In the fields of view this results in variously formed sparings along the vertical dividing meridians (Fig. 392; a typical example is the case published by G. Holmes 1934). An involvement of the field centers takes place only if the lesion spreads into the polar segment of the striate area (as it did in the same figure).

In traumatic cases, e.g., war injuries, a fairly isolated damage to the medial "peripheral" striate cortex may be made, depending on the course or direction of the missile. Another factor is the presence or absence of concomitant hemorrhage, which, in turn, depends on whether or not one of the larger arterial vessels was injured.

Infiltrating and even expanding tumors arising from the medial calcarine fissure may, in their bizarre spread, on occasion selectively eliminate the portion of the striate area related to the extrafoveal periphery of the fields and leave their centers spared (cases Ames and Strauss; *see* Figs. 403, 406). In these, the protecting mechanism is the lateral ventricle and the circuitous blood supply of the polar striate cortex from the middle cerebral artery.

A good example of this is a case published by Lenz (1914, Frau M. G.), which is, however, reinterpreted here in our sense. Clinically a visual disturbance began as a relative impairment of the peripheral, extrafoveal vision, eventually terminating in complete hemianopia. The cause was a tumor originating from the ventricular endothelium at the meeting of the calcarine and parieto-occipital sulci. During the initial period, moderate pressure interfered with the extramacular cortex. In the further course, with expansion of the tumor and compression not only of the calcarine blood vessels but also of those belonging to the middle cerebral artery and strangulation of the foveal segment of the visual radiation laterad to the posterior horn of the ventricle, the centers of the fields of view also were eliminated. (*Cf. also* Morax 1919.)

In many gunshot injuries during the war, where a hemianopia with central sparing was observed, hemorrhage into the medial calcarine fissure as a complicating factor is a plausible interpretation. Here there was frequently an initial complete and absolute homonymous hemianopia, or amaurosis, caused partly by direct destruction and partly by an expanding hematoma or a calcarine hematocele exerting pressure and causing a collateral edema in the entire striate area, including its polar segment. The visual radiation, especially the segment situated laterad to the ventricle, may or may not have been substantially affected, but this was of no great account during the initial phase. As the hematoma gradually became resorbed and the edema receded, central vision became restored to a greater or lesser extent, leaving, as a temporary or permanent residue, a hemianopia with spared central vision.

In such cases it is necessary to assume that terminal recovery of central vision was made possible through rehabilitation of the foveal-macular cortex at the occipital pole and of the intermediate foveal-macular segment of the visual radiation sheltered behind the lateral ventricle. In other cases where an initial central sparing disappeared in the course of the illness, it must be assumed that this was caused by a further spread of the pathological process, engulfing the polar cortex and the foveal fibers in the intermediate segment of the radiation.

In some unfortunate cases, such a fatal outcome was caused by inexpert surgical interference to remove a foreign body, e.g., a bullet lodged in the calcarine region; with the removal of the bullet, the foveal-macular cortex and its afferent fibers were also destroyed, and central vision irrecoverably lost (thus in Fig. 388).

For the reasons hinted at, even though as yet little understood, the above-described vascular process in the territory of the posterior cerebral artery may take place in both occipital lobes, occasionally simultaneously and symmetrically (*see* case HOFFMANN, Figs. 417, 418, 419). In the resulting impairment, both fields of view may be eliminated with the exception of both centers around the fixation points (resembling Fig. 397). Such are the notable cases described by R. Förster (1890), H. Sachs (1895), Laqueur & Schmidt (1899), Laqueur (1904), and R. A. Pfeifer (1930). Other similar cases have been reported off and on in the literature, even though usually they have been poorly utilized and their underlying mechanism misunderstood.

From the older cases collected by Monakow (1914), such may be those of Anton (1886), Schmidt-Rimpler (1893), Peters (1896), Vossius (1896), O. Meyer (1900), Raymond, Lejonne & Galezowski (1906), and Poulard & Sainton (1910); among the newer cases are those of Rønne (Roenne 1914), Bolton, Bramwell & Robinson (1915), Bramwell (1915), Monbrun & Gautrand (1920), Segi (1923), Foix & Schiff-Wertheimer (1925), Manolesco (1928), Weekers (1928), and Pallarès (1931). (*Cf. also* Oulmont 1889; Neukirchen 1900; Toulouse & Marchand 1907.)

In conclusion, the several positive factors—neuroanatomical, physiological, vascular, pathoanatomical, and mechanical—discussed in the preceding paragraphs entirely suffice, in all their individual variety, to account for the preservation, or the absence of preservation, of the field centers in homonymous hemianopia.

References: Adler & Fliegelman 1943; Adler & Meyer 1935; Akelaitis 1942; Anton 1886; Austin, Lewey & Grant 1949; Bair 1940; Bair & Harley 1940; Beauvieux 1930; Beauvieux & Ristich-Goelmino 1926; Beevor 1909; Best 1930; Courville 1950; Cushing 1921; Dandy 1933, 1948; Echlin 1942; O. Foerster 1929; R. Förster 1890 (*see also* H. Sachs 1895); Foix & Schiff-Wertheimer 1925; Fox & German 1936; Gardner 1933; German & Brody 1940; Globus 1936, 1938; Globus & Silverstone 1935; Halstead, Walker & Bucy 1940; Himwich 1951; M. Hines 1942; G. Holmes 1919, 1945; Holmes & Lister 1916; Igersheimer 1918–20, 1920; Jacobsohn-Lask 1924, 1928; Karnosh & Gardner 1941; Kestenbaum 1946; Klüver 1927; Laqueur & Schmidt 1900; Lenz 1914; R. Lindenberg 1939; W. K. Livingston 1933; Longhi 1939; Maison, Settlage & Grether 1938; Manolesco 1928; Marx & Trendelenburg 1911; O. Meyer 1900; Moench 1951; Monakow 1914; Monbrun 1917, 1919; Monbrun & Gautrand 1920; Morax 1919; Morax, Moreau & Castelain 1919; Moreau 1918; Neukirchen 1900; Niessl von Mayendorf 1932; Oulmont 1889; Pallarès 1931; Partridge 1950; Penfield & Evans 1934; Penfield, Evans & McMillan 1935; Penfield & Rasmussen 1950; Peters 1896; Pfeifer 1930; Poulard & Sainton 1910; Purves-Stewart 1945; Putnam 1934; Putnam & Liebman 1942; S. Ramón y Cajal 1898, 1899, 1909–11; Raymond, Lejonne & Galezowski 1906; Rønne (Roenne) 1911, 1914, 1919, 1921, 1924, 1927, 1944; Rucker 1946; Sabbadini 1923–24; H. Sachs 1895; Sanford & Bair 1939; Schiff-Wertheimer 1926; Schmidt-Rimpler 1893; Segi 1923; Sjögren 1928; Souque 1917; Souque & Odier 1917; Toulouse & Marchand 1907; Traquair 1925, 1931, 1939, 1946; Uhthoff 1902, 1908, 1927; Valière-Vialeix 1927; Van Wagonen & Herren 1940; Verhoeff 1943; Vesey 1950; Vinsonneau 1916; Vossius 1896; C. B. Walker 1917, 1929; F. B. Walsh 1947; Weekers 1928; Wilbrand 1930; Wilbrand & Saenger 1917; Youmans & Huckins 1951; Zeeman 1925; Zollinger 1935.

Chapter XII

Clinical and Pathoanatomical Observations of Cases with Disturbances of the Visual Fields

SEC. 1. MATERIALS AND METHODS

1. GENERAL REMARKS.—An investigation of the visual mechanisms and their functioning in normal and pathological conditions would remain incomplete if it were limited to animal material and to normal human specimens. No matter how convincing the deductions obtained from a normal anatomical study and from experiments on animals, the true sense of the reality is obtained only by a study of patients suffering from disturbed vision.

Two reasons are obvious. The first is the general interest in human welfare and the factors which endanger it. The other is the ease with which visual disturbances in Man may be accurately tested and their particular features correlated with the underlying pathoanatomic changes. Well-analyzed human cases, therefore, not only are interesting in themselves but are necessary to complete the information gained from the study of animal and normal human material and from experiments.

2. CLINICAL OBSERVATIONS AND PATHOLOGICAL SPECIMENS.—The clinical observations and the pathoanatomical material presented in this chapter were collected during twenty years from various sources, mostly from friendly ophthalmologists interested in the problem of vision. In some the clinical observations are very sketchy, almost nonexistent; in others they are rather complete. Fortunately, in almost all cases the brain specimens were in a satisfactory state of preservation.

The plan followed in each case was, first, to give as exact a description as possible of the functional disturbance, followed by a gross and microscopic analysis of the specimens and stained sections, upon which a plausible interpretation of visual disturbances observed during life was made. In this way, by further comparing the results with the observations recorded in chapters VI, VII, and VIII, the concept of the anatomical and functional organization of the visual mechanisms, gained largely from the study of normal human and animal material, was amplified and completed.

In the functional manifestations of the pathoanatomical causation, special attention was paid to the course of illness or the temporal sequence of clinical symptoms and the histopathological findings. In this way it was possible to interpret correctly the sequence of pathological processes underlying the visual disturbance and to correlate these processes with clinical manifestations as they occurred in the course of each case.

References: Alpers, Forster & Herbut 1948; Austin, Lewey & Grant 1949; Ballantyne 1943; Bender & Teuber 1947–48; Birge 1945; Bloom, Merz & Taylor 1946; Bostroem 1939; Bumke 1928–32; Bumke & Foerster 1935–37; C. B. Courville 1950; M. Critchley 1953; Dejerine 1926; Garcia Miranda 1944; Goodman 1949; Hegner 1915; S. E. Henschen 1890–1930; G. Holmes 1945, 1946; Himwich 1951; Hyland 1950; Jakob 1927–29; Joy 1947, 1948; Keller 1939; Kendall 1948; Kestenbaum 1946; Kleist 1934; Laubenthal 1938; Lawless 1941; Lindenberg 1939; Livingston 1933; Longhi 1939; McMullen 1926; Macaskill 1945; Mooney 1947; Niessl von Mayendorf 1930, 1931, 1936; Oppenheim 1913; Patrikios 1950; C. von Rad 1931; S. Ramón y Cajal 1928; Rea 1941; Riddoch 1917, 1935; Riley 1932; H. Rønne (Roenne) 1936, 1944; Roger & Reboul-Lachaux 1921;

Rowbotham 1949; Ruffin & Stein 1930; Ryder *et al.* 1951; Scheinker 1945; H. J. Scherer 1944; Scholz 1939; Spatz 1939; Spielmeyer 1922, 1929; J. Stambul 1953; Szily 1918; S. A. K. Wilson 1917, 1940; Uhthoff 1927; Vogt & Vogt 1926, 1936; F. B. Walsh 1947; Walshe 1947; Wybar 1945. For additional references *see* chapter XI and *Symposium on Blood Supply* (American) 1938 and *Symposium on Blood Supply* (German) 1939.

SEC. 2. CASE OF THE CHIASMA DISPLACED BY A PITUITARY TUMOR WITHOUT INTERRUPTION OF CHIASMA

1. HISTORY.—POPJOY, Rose, forty-two years of age, Billings Hospital, University of Chicago, UNo. 2654.

Diagnosis: Adenoma of the hypophysis without interruption of the chiasma of the optic nerves; cancer of the breast with metastases in various internal organs; no clinical diagnosis of disturbed vision.

Six years previous to admittance, patient hurt her left foot in a fall. Five years previously she was knocked unconscious in an auto accident. Four years and five months previously she suffered from a severe "cold," accompanied by a general involvement of the joints. After several months of medication, was cured but was left with a firm fibrous ankylosis of the left ankle joint.

Approximately five and one-half months prior to death she noticed a lump in the left cheek, accompanied by intermittent lancinating pains in the same region, and had a severe vomiting spell. At about the same time another lump appeared in her right breast. Six weeks and five days before death this was diagnosed as a cancer with a metastasis in the right axilla, and probably also in the left parotid gland. A radical mastectomy was performed the following day.

Thereafter the general condition gradually worsened, the patient at times becoming irrational, maniacal, suffering from continuous severe pains and vomiting, with metastases and complications of various internal organs, terminating in death. No ophthalmological or neurological examination was made.

2. PATHOANATOMICAL EXAMINATION.—The brain, in fresh condition, appeared grossly normal except for a 1.5 × 2-cm. incapsulated carcinomatous nodule on the convex face of the left frontal lobe at a distance of about 2 cm. from its pole.

In the sella turcica a large incapsulated tumor was found, protruding upward. Microscopically, the tumor was diagnosed as a chromophobe hypophyseal adenoma. The tumor compressed from underneath the tuber cinereum of the betweenbrain, which was found pushed up, the excavation formed in this way being at least $\frac{1}{2}$ cm. deep. The chiasma of the optic nerves appeared to be completely interrupted in the middle, the lateral vestiges of it adhering to the respective nerves. The two optic nerves and tracts, if reduced in size, seemed to be so to only a small degree.

A careful inspection of the specimen, however, disclosed that the middle, bridgelike portion of the chiasma was not actually severed, but only flattened and expanded, appearing much wider and longer than normal, with ipsilateral nondecussating bundles spaced far apart. Hence the middle portion of the chiasma was pushed up, forming, with the betweenbrain, the dome or roof of a smooth cavity in which the enlarged hypophysis was lodged.

The examination of the continuous serial sections through the chiasma in a horizontal plane confirmed the gross inspection. On the lowermost levels the gap separating the two lateral parts of the chiasma was no less than 9 mm. wide (Fig. 402, upper sketch). On intermediate levels the gap gradually narrowed (middle sketch) until on the highest level, next to the betweenbrain, the middle portion or "bridge" of the chiasma alone remained as an island (lower sketch). This portion was made up entirely of crossed or decussating fibers. All portions of the chiasma appeared to contain normal fibers. A further comparison of the sections revealed certain features indicative of an interplay of several mechanical factors responsible for the conditions found.

3. COMMENT.—The initial condition in this case was necessarily that found in a normal chiasma (*cf.* Figs. 196, 197). How long prior to death the hypophysis began to increase beyond its normal size, there is no way of telling. A severe vomiting spell suffered by the patient five and a half months preceding death probably indicates a tumorous increase of the gland at that time. Hence we may conclude that the pituitary tumor grew slowly for a considerable period of time. This would be in fair agreement with the absence of obvious ocular symptoms. Dislodgment of the chiasma in this case was an accidental anatomical finding, made during the autopsy.

The course of the chiasmal changes, as reconstructed from the anatomical findings, may have been as follows (Fig. 402): In the early period, during the initial slow increase in the size of the gland, the middle bridgelike portion of the chiasma was gradually pushed upward. With further growth of the pituitary tumor, this portion was pushed deeper into the betweenbrain, which was the direction of least resistance. Under continuous pressure from below, this portion became deformed into a broad but thin band, which formed the concave ceiling of the cavity in which the hypophyseal tumor was lodged. Simultaneously, the right and the left portions of the chiasma, made up principally of nondecussating fibers, as well as the adjoining portions of both tracts, became displaced laterally. This lateral displacement was also accompanied by some rotation along the longitudinal axes of the tracts and lateral parts of the chiasma, owing to a pull on the optic nerves fixed in their bony channels, the rotation being clockwise on the right side and counterclockwise on the left side when viewed from the back.

The result of these changes was that the two nondecussating systems of chiasmal fibers remained on a lower horizontal level (upper sketch), while the intermediate portion, made up of decussating fibers, was pressed high up into the vaultlike ceiling of the cavity formed in the betweenbrain (lower sketch). The central portions of the supraoptic commissures, it may be noted, were also pushed into the ceiling of the cavity, closely following the decussating chiasmal optic nerve fibers (*cf.* Fig. 402).

The appearance of the nerve fibers in the chiasma did not show any gross pathological changes beyond a beadlike arrangement of myelin usually found in routine specimens. From this it is probable that there was no gross interference with vision, albeit no fields were taken to make this certain. The good condition of the lateral geniculate nuclei agrees with this assumption. This indicates considerable adapt-

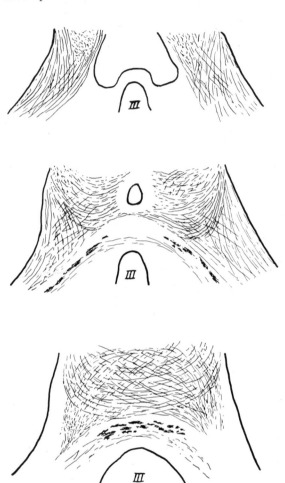

Fig. 402.—Case Popjoy: dislodgement of the chiasma of optic nerves caused by a tumor of hypophyseal gland. Upper sketch shows a complete separation of optic nerves and tracts, corresponding to the lower levels, while on the higher levels the intermediate bridgelike portion of the chiasma, shown in lower sketch, is still continuous. (For further details *see* textual description.)

ability in the chiasmal structures to deformation, pull, and pressure. Had the illness continued until the middle portion of the chiasma was severed, the eventual outcome would have been a bitemporal hemianopia (Fig. 382, *12*).

References: See chapter XI, 2.

SEC. 3. CASE OF COMPLETE HOMONYMOUS HEMIANOPIA

1. History.—Ames, Walter, age forty-four years, Billings Hospital, University of Chicago, UNo. 18231.

Diagnosis: Right homonymous hemianopia without sparing of central vision, caused by a brain tumor (multiform glioblastoma) of the left temporal lobe (Fig. 403).

History indicates six months of "eye strain," one and one-half months of intermittent headaches with inability to concentrate, one month difficulty with vision, three weeks inability to read, one month increasing irritability, three weeks loss of memory and disorientation, two weeks crying spells, apparent blindness to objects on the right side, one week nausea and vomiting, ten days steady frontal headaches, one week bad taste in the mouth, intermittent periods of complete disorientation, incoherent talk, inability to recognize friends, inability to remember words or to grasp their meaning.

In summary, the clinical picture, composed of numerous symptoms, comprising sensory defects, such as blindness of a hemianopic character, and disturbances of a psychic character, falling into the category of visual agnosia, sensory aphasia, etc., and a steady, relentless, progressive course, all pointed toward an organic, malignant brain disease.

2. Neurological examination.—Ophthalmoscopic examination revealed choked disks of from 2 to 3 diopters on both sides, slight facial weakness on the right side, no obvious paresis, although the muscular tonus was increased on the right side, increased deep reflexes, ankle and patellar clonus, and also probably the presence of the sign of Babinski on the right side, no sensory disturbance of the head, both pupils dilated and fixed, aphasia, disorientation, and confusion. Blood pressure 140/80.

Operation, craniotomy-decompression, revealed a subcortical glioma in the left parietal region. After the operation and X-ray therapy the psychic disturbances improved very rapidly, the disks receded to normal, but the reaction of the pupils remained poor.

3. Ophthalmological examination.—A week after the cranial decompression, exam-

ination revealed the blurred margin of the right disk, which, however, was of normal size and red in color, being surrounded by a grayish-white zone half as wide as the diameter of the disk. There was a group of hemorrhages in the disk and in its margin at approximately four o'clock. The veins were not dilated, but most arteries were contracted, with an exudative patch in the disk at three o'clock. The margin of the left disk was also blurred, but its size was apparently normal. The disk was surrounded by an areola of half its diameter, grayish-white in color. The excavation was visible. There was a linear exudation area along the superior nasal artery for a short distance. The veins were not dilated. The majority of the arteries were slightly contracted, and there were no hemorrhages. *Diagnosis:* a completely receded papilledema.

Eight months after the onset of the illness, a right homonymous hemianopia, with central vision involved (no "macular sparing"), was determined by stereo-campimetry, with a white target of 1°. The fields plotted with a routine perimeter, however, showed a small central sparing in the right upper quadrants (Fig. 403).

4. Pathoanatomical examination.—The gross macroscopic examination of the brain showed a glioma in the splenium of the corpus callosum spreading along the medial sides of the posterior horns of the lateral ventricles into both occipital lobes. The microscopic examination of sections through the brain, stained according to the Weigert-Kultschitzky method, revealed the following changes from the norm.

In the *left parieto-occipital* lobe the tumorous mass occupied a portion of the corpus callosum and penetrated far into the temporal lobe. The sagittal fiber layers were displaced down and outward. They showed a great loss of fibers, those still remaining being in an advanced state of degeneration. In the left occipital lobe the tumor gradually decreased to an irregular, round mass, $1\frac{1}{2}$ cm. in diameter, inward to the posterior horn of the lateral ventricle, not quite reaching the subcortical fiber layer of the lower lip of the calcarine fissure.

The caudal end of the tumor was approximately at the middle of the longitudinal extent of the occipital lobe. At this level and in the tip of the occipital lobe the ring of the sagittal strata still retained its usual, normal appearance, surrounding the posterior ventricular horn, which was somewhat dilated, even though its fibers were mostly gone. The fibers of the tapetum (callosal) and of the internal sagittal stratum (efferent) were also greatly reduced in number, the rest being in a process of degeneration.

The external sagittal stratum, containing the visual radiation, was still well preserved in shape and position, but its constituent fibers were mostly gone. Its remaining fibers all exhibited unmistakable signs of an advanced degeneration, such as beadlike varicosities and disintegration, and these disintegrated fibers could

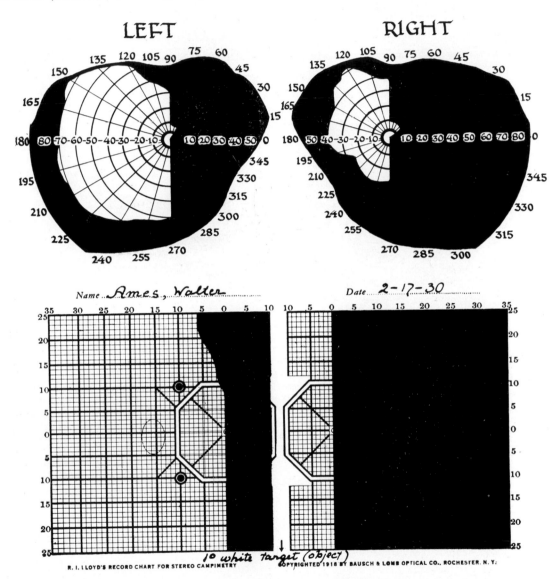

FIG. 403.—Case W. Ames: a complete homonymous hemianopia of the right halves of the fields of view, caused by a glioblastomatous tumor of the left temporal lobe of the brain (*see* following figure). Upper fields, plotted with an arc perimeter, show small central sparings in upper quadrants of the blind halves, while lower fields, taken with a stereocampimeter, show a splitting along the vertical meridians, with a slight encroachment of blindness upon the left upper temporal quadrants outside the central area. A slight sparing in the upper fields was possibly caused by an incomplete interruption of the intermediate foveal fibers of the radiation, while a surplus scotoma in the left lower field may be explained by the general condition of the patient.

be followed into the striate cortex. Practically all other fibers of the left occipital lobe—the callosal, associational, and efferent—were also degenerated.

A noteworthy observation concerns the intracortical stripe of Gennari or Vicq-d'Azyr. This stripe, in contrast with the much depleted supra- and infra-Gennarian layers of the striate cortex, was found to be practically normal. This observation, like the other similar observations, indicates a preponderantly intracortical origin and termination of this fiber layer (*cf.* chap. VIII, 6, 7).

clusters of which appeared more or less normal. Other cells had disappeared or showed signs of the intermediate stages of degeneration. On the anterior levels, represented in sketches *4* and *5*, cells of a more normal appearance were more frequent among the degenerated ones also found along the upper margin of the nucleus. In summary, the upper or dorsal layers of the nucleus suffered more. The lateral segment related to the upper field quadrants was most completely degenerated.

In the *right parieto-occipital lobe* (Fig. 404) the tumor mass in an almost identical way en-

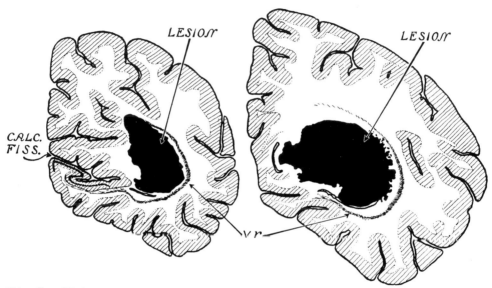

Fig. 404.—Case W. Ames: coronal sections through the right parieto-occipital lobe at two levels, the right one closer to, the left one farther away from, the callosal splenium. The lesion, a glioblastomatous tumor (*solid black*), originated from the splenium of the corpus callosum, spreading backward in both hemispheres in an almost symmetrical way. The growth in the left hemisphere was of an earlier date, destroying the visual radiation on that side completely, causing at the time of the plotting of the fields a practically complete hemianopia with split centers (Fig. 403). In the right hemisphere the tumorous growth at that time had not yet advanced enough to destroy the radiation *vr*, but merely pushed it aside and down, hence making vision still possible in the left halves of the fields. *Labeling: CALC.FISS.*, calcarine fissure; *vr*, visual radiation. Note in left-hand diagram fibers of the lower segment of radiation streaming into lower calcarine lip, which alone at this level contained striate cortex, as indicated by a stippled intracortical line of Gennari.

The *left lateral geniculate nucleus* (Fig. 405), examined in sections stained by the Nissl method, likewise showed profound degenerative changes. The caudal tip (sketches *1* and *2*), related to the fovea-macula and normally composed of small nerve cells, was completely depleted. In it only a few "shadows" of nerve cells remained. These and the increased number of glial cells showed the approximate outlines of the layers, which were blurred. The ventral layers still contained numerous nerve cells,

tered from the splenium of the corpus callosum into the subcortical fiber substance and penetrated far back into the occipital lobe. At the anterior limit of that lobe the tumor was the size of a pigeon's egg (left sketch). It was located inward and above the posterior horn of the lateral ventricle, which was dislocated down and outward (narrow slit below the tumor given in solid black, *lesion*). The sagittal fiber layers were also displaced down and outward. The upper horizontal segment of the visual radiation (*vr*), normally related to the upper calcarine lip, was interrupted by a tumor mass pushing toward that lip. In the same way the fibers coating the calcar avis were destroyed, and the lateral ventricle obliterated. The tumor also infiltrated the tapetum and the internal sagittal layer and pushed through the destroyed dorsal horizontal branch of the visual radiation absent, while others showed signs of degeneration. The lower horizontal segment of the radiation was still well preserved and compact, and the fiber plexus in the striate cortex lining the lower calcarine lip was still almost intact. In particular, the thick, obliquely coursing terminals of the afferent visual fibers were abundant here and well stained. What the condition

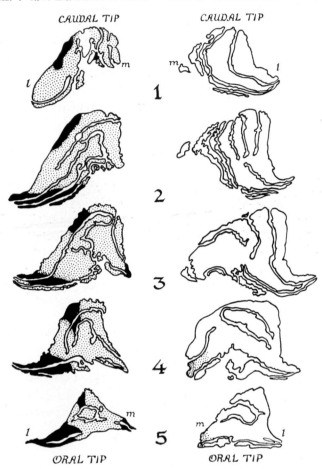

FIG. 405.—Case W. Ames: lateral geniculate nuclei, *left*, in an advanced state of degeneration, *right*, almost normal. Areae of complete cell degeneration in solid black; areae where only partial degeneration was present given in stippling; areae where cells still appeared fairly normal given in white. Medial sides of nuclei facing thalamus at *m*, lateral sides at *l*.

into the upper portion of the subcortical fiber mass of the occipital lobe.

The external sagittal fiber layer, or the visual radiation proper, showed no fibers in its upper horizontal segment and no intracortical fiber plexus in the upper calcarine lip (*CALC. FISS.*, Fig. 404). In the intermediate or vertical segment, displaced outward, numerous fibers were of the cortex and of the afferent fibers was in the occipital pole it was not possible to determine.

The *right lateral geniculate nucleus*, in contrast with the nucleus of the left side, proved to be almost normal (Fig. 405). It was of normal size, with layers well filled with apparently normal nerve cells. Here and there the cells seemed, however, somewhat decreased in numbers or slightly changed in appearance, but nowhere could there be found a clearly degenerated zone. The only exception was the inner or medial tip in the oral fourth of the nucleus, which was somewhat degenerated (stippled in sketches *4*, *5*). The contrast between the right and the left nucleus was especially apparent in the posterior extremities concerned with foveal-macular or "central vision" (sketches *1* and *2*). Whereas in the left nucleus this portion was found almost completely degenerated, in the right nucleus the appearance and number of nerve cells were found to be almost normal.

5. Correlation of functional disturb-ance and pathoanatomical findings.—In analyzing this case, the following points appear to be of interest. The tumor, causing an extensive cerebral destruction and eventually death, had its origin in the corpus callosum or close to it. In its expansive growth it spread in an almost symmetrical way into both hemispheres, sooner or more rapidly into the left one. Here it had completely interrupted the visual radiation, causing a complete right homonymous hemianopia (Fig. 403). In agreement with this, the left lateral geniculate nucleus degenerated almost completely. The only exception was a small cluster of cells in the foveal-macular tip of the nucleus, where the nerve cells were fairly normal (sketch *1*, in left column, in Fig. 405). This cluster may have been responsible for a small central sparing in the right upper blind quadrants. With this questionable exception, the completeness of degeneration both in the left radiation and in the left geniculate nucleus and also in the visual cortex of the left hemisphere agrees well with a complete hemianopia of the opposite, left side.

The symmetrical spreading of the tumor in both hemispheres is another remarkable feature. The anatomical factor responsible for it is the arrangement of the callosal fiber bundles, possibly also the vascular distribution, both

similar in the two hemispheres, which may have served as a preformed pathway.

Another noteworthy feature, observed also in the preceding case, was the "plasticity" or resistance of the brain structures, especially of the nerve fibers. This is especially evident in the visual radiation of the right hemisphere (Fig. 404). Although displaced from its normal position, this system of fibers caused no marked disturbance in the function of the left homonymous fields as long as these could be tested, in view of the patient's mental state toward the end. This interpretation agrees well with the fairly normal condition of the right lateral geniculate nucleus (Fig. 405). It further indicates that the absence of a gross left hemianopic disturbance manifested itself in spite of the bad preterminal condition of the patient. However, there may have been a slight contraction of the left lower quadrants, indicated in the right perimetric field, in Figure 403, caused by partial damage to the upper horizontal segment of the right radiation and also evidenced by a limited retrograde degeneration in the medial tip of the right lateral geniculate nucleus (sketches *4* and *5*). The good condition of most of the right geniculate nucleus, including its posterior foveal-macular extremity, on the other hand, speaks against the hypothesis of "macular fibers" decussating in the corpus callosum to the left hemisphere, since on that side all sagittal fiber layers were completely interrupted. This again fully agrees with the experiment, described in chapter VII, 4, in which one occipital lobe was removed completely without causing any degeneration in the contralateral geniculate nucleus. (*Cf.* chap. XI, 8, 9.)

Finally, the extensive destruction of the association and callosal fiber systems in the left parieto-occipital lobes and similar, even though less extensive, degeneration of the same systems in the upper right lobes are sufficient to account for the disturbance of visual memory, disorientation, and other psychotic symptoms.

References: See chapter XI, especially 3 and 4.

SEC. 4. CASE OF AN INCOMPLETE HOMONYMOUS HEMIANOPIA

1. History.—Strauss, Louis, forty-eight years of age, Billings Hospital, University of Chicago, UNo. 19828.

Diagnosis: Left homonymous hemianopia

with central sparing, caused by a brain tumor (multiform glioblastoma) of the right occipito-temporal lobes.

The illness began five months prior to admission, with weakness, convulsions, headaches, vomiting, paresthesiac, and difficulty in walking. Visual symptoms had appeared two months earlier, with a blurring of vision.

2. NEUROLOGICAL EXAMINATION.—The inspection of the eyes showed the left pupil to be somewhat larger, with both pupils reacting poorly to light. Ophthalmoscopically, there were choked disks with some hemorrhage. The conjugate eye movements were synchronous, but not full, and were jerky; notably incomplete was the movement to the right, which also had a tendency to relapse to the mid-line. The ventricle was punctured in the right hemisphere, and a decompression was made on the right side, with much discharge of fluid and pus. A slight hemiplegia and hemianesthesia on the right side were noticed.

3. OPHTHALMOLOGICAL EXAMINATION.—Both disks showed moderate choking, with some hemorrhage, with the physiological excavations still present, while the remaining portions of the retinae were normal. Two months later the choking disappeared. Perimetrically, an incomplete left homonymous hemianopia was found, with perhaps a slight contraction of the right halves (Fig. 406). This condition persisted for one month, which was approximately three months preceding death. Owing to the patient's bad general condition, especially mental, further plotting was not done, but the impression was that the left hemianopia persisted to the end.

4. PATHOANATOMICAL EXAMINATION.—Gross macroscopic examination of the brain showed the tumor to occupy the lateral face of the entire right temporal lobe. The tumor also invaded the lower portion of the right parietal lobe and extended backward to the preoccipital incisure. On coronal sections grossly examined, a vascular tumorous mass was revealed, diffusely infiltrating the entire right temporal lobe and the lower portion of the right parietal lobe. Medially, the tumor also involved the internal capsule and entered the thalamus. Posteriorly, it extended to 4 cm. from the tip of the right occipital lobe.

The *right cerebral hemisphere*, examined on sections stained according to the method of Weigert-Kultschitzky, revealed a tumorous mass at the level of the pulvinar, occupying approximately the lateral two-thirds of the hemisphere and penetrating through the subcortical fiber substance as far as the lateral ventricle (Fig. 407, *E*). The three sagittal fiber layers—the external, internal, and tapetum—were all partly interrupted and degenerated. Of the external stratum or the visual radiation proper, the lower horizontal segment alone appeared fairly well preserved (*vr*). On subsequent caudal sections this branch could be followed to the lower lip of the calcarine fissure (*D, C, B*).

Of the intermediate or vertical segment, only its lower portion was preserved, with its fibers considerably depleted. The remainder of the visual radiation, that is, the upper half of the intermediate segment and the entire upper horizontal segment, had degenerated completely.

On anterior sections the preserved portions of the radiation were seen slipping just underneath the tumorous mass and entering the posterior portion of the internal capsule (*F*). On sections through the anterior portion of the occipital lobe, the tumorous mass extended as far as the floor, or the deepest portion, of the calcarine fissure, but its two lips remained intact (*B, C*). So also remained the posterior portion of the calcarine fissure close to the pole of the occipital lobe (*A*).

The course of the preserved lower segment of the radiation and its entering into the cortex of the lower calcarine lip were clearly visible as far as the tip of the occipital lobe. In this portion of the striate cortex the oblique, irregular fibers in the lower half beneath the stripe of Gennari or Vicq-d'Azyr, identified in experiments as the exogenous afferent visual fibers, were present, although in reduced numbers (*cf.* Figs. 315, 316, 327, 328, 334). In the upper calcarine lip and in the upper half of the striate cortex which lined the tip of the occipital lobe, these characteristic slanting fibers were almost gone.

The *right lateral geniculate nucleus*, stained with thionin blue, was found partially degenerated (Fig. 408, right sketches). The loss of the nerve cells was more pronounced in its anterior or oral part (*3, 4*) than in its posterior or caudal portion (*1, 2*). The lateral segment was, on the whole, better preserved. On anterior levels all nerve cells showed more or less pronounced signs of degeneration. On caudal levels most of the cells of the lateral segment were in a fair shape. Most completely degenerated was the inner or medial segment through the greater anterior portion of the nucleus (solid black in

varying degrees, least advanced in its posterior extremity serving the foveal-macular or central vision and in the outward segment related to the upper homonymous quadrants. The *left lateral geniculate nucleus* was found to be normal (left column in the same figure).

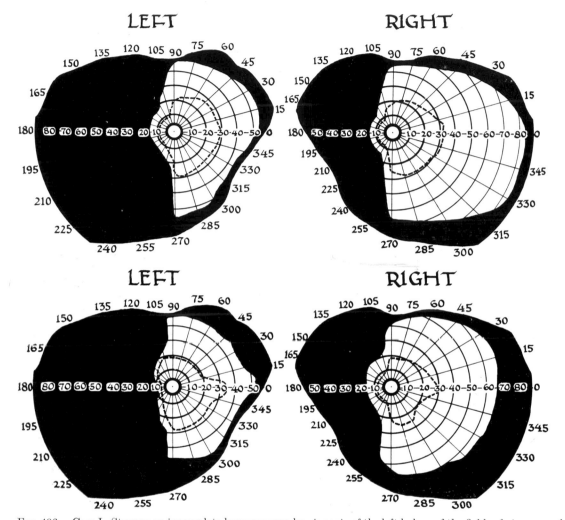

Fig. 406.—Case L. Strauss: an incomplete homonymous hemianopia of the left halves of the fields of view caused by a glioblastomatous tumor of the right occipitotemporal lobe of the brain (*see* following figure). Upper fields plotted approximately four months, lower fields three months, before death. In both fields, in the affected left halves, there are large central sparings tapering along the vertical dividing meridians toward the field limits. The only substantial change between the two plottings was a marked temporal restriction in the right halves, in the second plotting, amounting to a right monocular temporal crescentic hemianopia.

sketches *2, 3, 4*). The same was also true of the intermediate segment, except farther back, where many nerve cells were still present, although these, too, were considerably affected (white and stippled portions in sketches *1, 2*). In fact, the entire lateral geniculate nucleus of the right side showed signs of degeneration in

5. Correlation of functional disturbance and pathoanatomical findings.—In analyzing this case, the clinical course must be considered, especially the development of the visual field disturbance.

First, on two occasions a left homonymous hemianopia was found, both times with central sparing. The last plotting was made three months prior to death. Whether the same condition remained until the end or whether subsequently a complete hemianopia without central sparing, or almost so, developed, the history does not tell. Judging from the pathoanatomical

have been as follows: The tumorous mass, approaching from the region of the parietal lobe, at first pushed toward the dorsal or upper portion of the sagittal fiber layers. By breaking through these, it entered into the posterior horn of the lateral ventricle not far from the spleni-

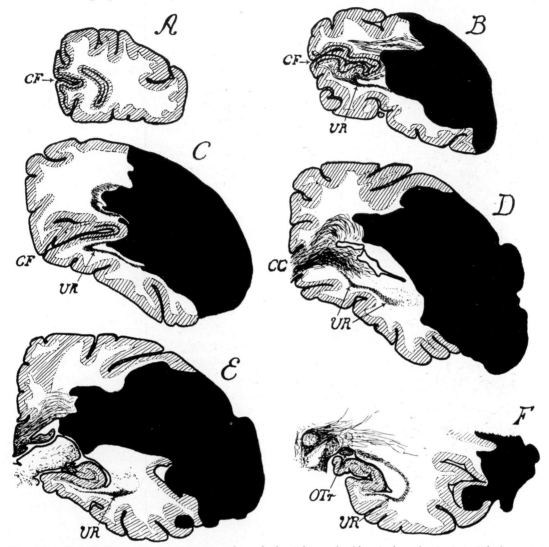

Fig. 407.—Case L. Strauss: coronal sections through the right cerebral hemisphere, beginning with the occipital pole (*A*) and extending as far as the posterior level of the thalamus (*F*), showing the tumorous mass in solid black which had destroyed and replaced the brain substance. In spite of the extensive destruction, the visual radiation (*vr*) in part remained preserved, which together with the preserved striate area, marked by an intracortical stippled stripe of Gennari in the polar calcarine fissure, may account for the large central sparings in the fields of view. This anatomical fact agrees well with the preserved posterior foveal-macular tip of the lateral geniculate nucleus of the same side (*see* Fig. 408).

findings, it is likely that some sparing may have persisted until the end, particularly in the upper half of the central vision.

The probable terminal stage, as it can be reconstructed from the anatomical facts, seems to

um of the corpus callosum. Finally, spreading backward and at the same time medially, the farthest portion of the tumor entered the anterior portion of the calcarine fissure. The interruption of the dorsal segment of the sagittal strata and damage to the anterior calcarine fissure must have caused, first, a peripheral contraction of the homonymous fields of the left side, principally in the lower quadrants. The foveal-macular or central vision remained at first unimpaired, since the intermediate segment of the visual radiation was at first not interrupted but merely displaced downward and medially and also since the foveal-macular portion of the

LEFT LAT. GENIC. NUCL.   **RIGHT LAT. GENIC. NUCL.**

CAUDAL TIP   CAUDAL TIP

ORAL TIP   ORAL TIP

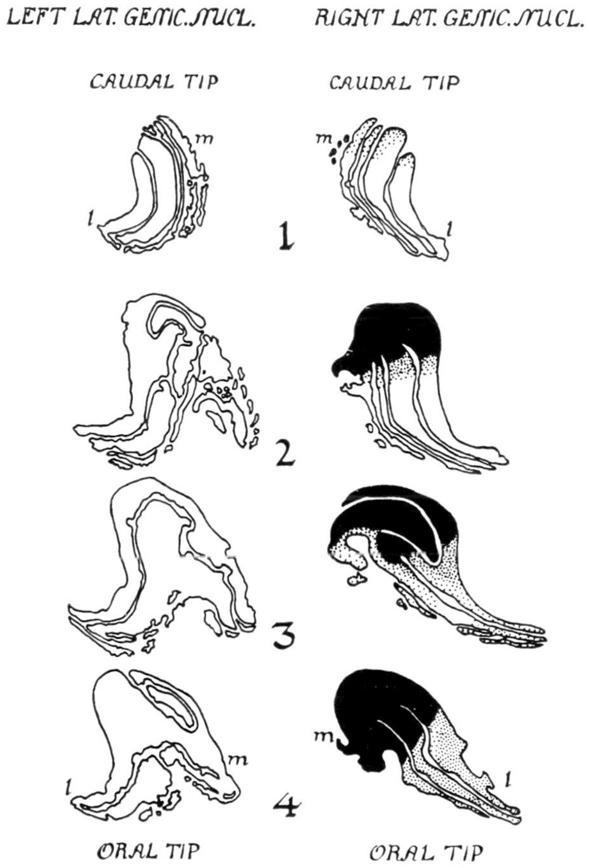

Fig. 408.—Case L. Strauss: lateral geniculate nuclei, left normal (*white*), right largely degenerated (*solid black and stippled*), except in the posterior foveal-macular extremity (sketches *1* and *2*). Most advanced degeneration was found in the medial half of the nucleus, corresponding with a complete interruption of the upper segment of the visual radiation shown in Fig. 407.

striate area around the tip of the occipital lobe remained out of reach of the tumor.

The subsequent course can only be surmised from the study of the lateral geniculate nucleus of the right side. Here practically all the nerve cells were more or less degenerated. However, there were important differences concerning the

degree, that is, the advancement, of the degenerative process in different portions of the nucleus. Obviously, most completely degenerated and hence probably first affected were the inner and the intermediate segments of the nucleus on its more anterior levels. This agrees well with the fact that the tumor had apparently first interrupted the dorsal bundles of the radiation. The lateral or outward tip of the nucleus showed degenerative changes somewhat less advanced, again agreeing with the later involvement of the anterior portion of the calcarine fissure and its afferent fibers (which include both horizontal branches) and the sparing of the intermediate foveal branch.

Since both lips were involved, the extramacular portions of the upper homonymous field quadrants must have been affected during the preterminal phase of the illness, in addition to the lower extramacular quadrants, which were eliminated previously by reason of the interruption of dorsal bundles of the radiation.

The last to go was evidently the intermediate foveal-macular segment of the radiation, since the signs of the retrograde degeneration were least advanced in the posterior tip of the lateral geniculate nucleus concerned with central vision (Fig. 408, right-hand sketch *1*). This indicates that the foveal-macular fibers, at first only displaced downward, became interrupted, compressed, or infiltrated in their further course by the advancing tumor, eventually possibly producing a complete homonymous hemianopia on the left side without any central sparing. This, however, since the general condition of the patient did not permit further testing, remained unrecognized.

Several points in this analysis need to be emphasized. First is the fact that the opposite lateral geniculate nucleus, corresponding with the intact left cerebral hemisphere, remained completely unaffected (Fig. 408, left-hand sketches). This is interesting in connection with the hypothesis of bilateral representation of each total "macula" discussed previously (chap. XI, 8 and 9). It is fair to assume that if a part of the visual radiation were to decussate in the corpus callosum (splenium), as assumed by some, the left geniculate nucleus would have shown some degeneration, at any rate in its posterior foveal-macular extremity. It is necessary to postulate this, not so much because of the probable ultimate complete impairment of the sagittal strata in the right occipital lobe, as chiefly because the tumor interrupted the callosal fibers of the splenium, exactly where, according to R. A. Pfeifer (1925), the decussating fibers are supposed to be located.

Another noteworthy fact to consider is the presence of an incomplete initial hemianopia, although it has been claimed that, in the pathology of the temporal lobe localized close to the lateral geniculate nucleus, the most usual type of field disturbance is a complete hemianopia. This, it was alleged, is caused by the interruption of the hypothetical decussating "macular" fibers as they arise from the lateral geniculate nucleus. Our case furnishes contrary evidence and disproves this hypothesis.

Of further interest is the course of the ventral segment of the visual radiation, easily followed all the way from its origin in the incompletely affected lateral segment of the lateral geniculate nucleus (*VR* in sketch *E*) to its termination in the lower calcarine lip (sketches *D, C, B*, in Fig. 407). The case shows that in Man this branch has an origin, course, and termination similar to that found experimentally in the Monkey, except that in the human brain it is longer and has a long detour, which it does not have in the Monkey (*cf.* chap. VII, 3, esp. [6], and Figs. 93, 235, 236).

Finally, this and the preceding case, AMES, both alike with respect to the pathophysiological process and clinical symptoms, well illustrate the limitations that human pathological material, especially the neoplasms, has for the finer analysis of the visual pathways. Such material may be utilized only with circumspection and by taking into account the knowledge obtained from other pathological cases caused by the nonexpansive and noninfiltrating processes and from experiments with monkeys and apes.

References: See chapter XI, especially 3, 4, and 9.

SEC. 5. CASE OF A QUADRANTIC HOMONYMOUS HEMIANOPIA TRANSFORMED INTO A BILATERAL INCOMPLETE HEMIANOPIA

1. HISTORY.—DYKSTRA, Mike, Billings Hospital, University of Chicago, UNo. 10950.

Diagnosis: Right upper quadrantic homonymous hemianopia, expanding into a bilateral incomplete hemianopia with large central sparings, caused by a cystic multiform glioblastoma.

The illness began a year previous to admission, with spells of dizziness and "noise" associated with vertigo, uncinate attacks ("peculiar odors"), headaches, and weakness of memory. Six weeks before admission there had been a spell of complete blindness, lasting four hours, with subsequent improvement. Vision at the time of admission was below par. The fields of view, examined grossly, suggested a notching of the upper quadrants in the right homonymous halves. Both disks were well defined but were choked, on the right side for 3.5 diopters, on the left side for 5 diopters. There were also minute hemorrhages in the disks. A few months later a subtemporal decompression craniotomy was made on the left side in order to relieve the intracranial pressure. The tumor, on inspection during the operation, was found to occupy the anterior three-fourths of the left temporal lobe.

2. OPHTHALMOLOGICAL EXAMINATION.—Nine months after the onset of the illness the plotting of the fields revealed an incomplete right homonymous hemianopia in the upper quadrants (Fig. 409, upper fields). Ten days after the operation both disks were found to have subsided to a normal level. The visual fields, plotted on several occasions later, approximately eight weeks and again ten weeks after the operation, showed a progressive increase of the blindness from a right upper quadrantic to an incomplete homonymous hemianopia in the entire right halves of the fields, with a sparing of the central regions. There was also a concentric loss in the periphery of the left halves of the fields and, in general, a marked reduction of visual acuity (Fig. 409, lower fields). A few days later a recurrent papilledema was found, the right disk being swollen up to 3 diopters, the left one up to 2.5 diopters.

3. PATHOANATOMICAL EXAMINATION.—The anatomical inspection of the brain showed hemorrhages around the base and in the ventricular cavities, including the fourth ventricle. The

ventral half of the left temporal lobe was replaced by a tumorous cavity spreading almost
as far as the thalamus. The left lateral ventricle
was found compressed. The tumor also invaded
the left frontal lobe.

Since much of the *left hemisphere* was destroyed by the pathological process and by a
surgical intervention that followed, this hemi-

nous stasis. The spaces around the base of the
brain were completely filled with extravasated
blood and distended veins, which further filled
the hippocampal fissure, extending backward in
a decreasing amount into the medial or anterior
calcarine fissure and into the collateral sulcus.
These fissures, especially the calcarine, were
filled with clotted blood as far posteriorly as the

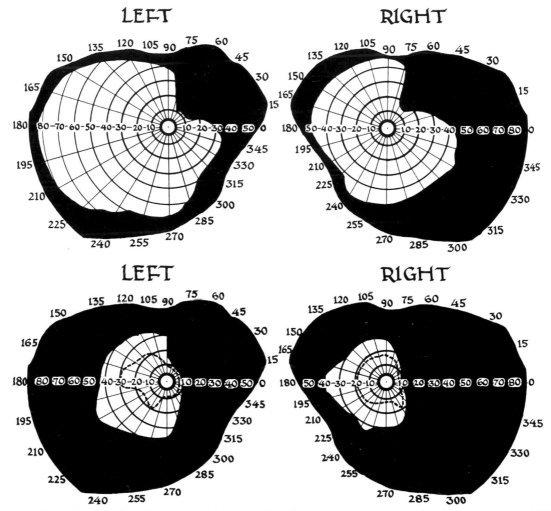

Fig. 409.—Case M. Dykstra: upper right incomplete homonymous quadrantic hemianopia (*upper fields*),
subsequently expanding into a bilateral hemianopia, or field rests, more restricted in the right halves. Upper
fields taken seven months and three weeks, lower fields taken twenty-seven days, preceding death. Cause: brain
tumor in the ventral half of the left temporal lobe.

sphere was not examined histologically. The
right hemisphere, on the contrary, was found to
be free from tumorous growth. It was by no
means free from pathology, however. This was
manifested by an engorgement of all venous
passages belonging to the system of the great
vein of Galen, indicating a high degree of ve-

anterior segment of the striate area in the lower
calcarine lip.

Almost the entire extent of the *left lateral geniculate nucleus* contained rarefied nerve cells,
mostly showing an advanced stage of retrograde
irritation and degeneration (Fig. 410, sketches
1–7). Most advanced and most completely de-

generated was the outward or lateral segment, comprising approximately one-fourth to one-third of the nucleus (marked by letter *l*). Here all nerve cells were either greatly decreased in numbers and size or had disappeared. The medial segment was less affected (marked with letter *m*). The intermediate segment was also less changed, especially in the posterior foveal-

matolysis, with a swelling of the bodies and with peripherally dislocated nuclei.

The posterior extremities (sketches *1, 2,* and *8*) related to the foveal-areal or central parts of the fields were somewhat better preserved in both nuclei than the oral portions related to the extrafoveal-areal portions of the fields (*3–7, 9, 10*).

LEFT LATERAL GENICULATE NUCLEUS

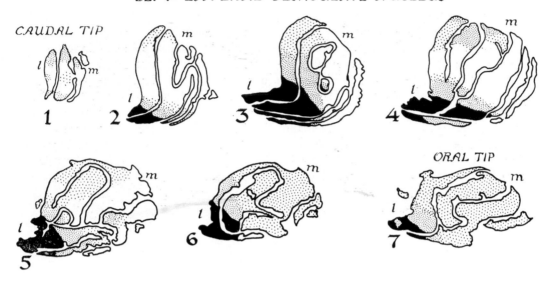

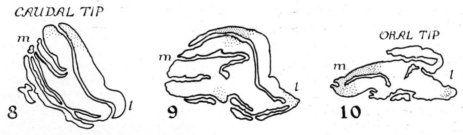

RIGHT LATERAL GENICULATE NUCLEUS

FIG. 410.—Case M. Dykstra: left and right lateral geniculate nuclei, showing variously advanced retrograde cell degeneration. The most intensive loss was found in the lateral segment of the left nucleus (*solid black*). This agrees with the most complete destruction of the lower segment of the visual radiation which had first abolished the right upper quadrants of the fields of view.

macular extremity of the nucleus (sketches *1, 2*).

The *right lateral geniculate nucleus* was found to be, on the whole, in a much better condition (sketches *8–10*). But even here many scattered nerve cells showed signs of slight irritation. In the medial segment (*m*) and in the very tip of the lateral segment (*l*) the loss of nerve cells was most pronounced. In these localities some of the cells also showed unmistakable signs of chro-

4. CORRELATION OF FUNCTIONAL DISTURBANCE AND PATHOANATOMICAL FINDINGS.—On the basis of the clinical symptoms, especially the notching of the upper right homonymous quadrants of the fields of view and "uncinate attacks," it is apparent that the tumor originated in the left temporal lobe. The focus of the tumor, as determined by pathoanatomical examination, also proved to be in that lobe.

As the tumor expanded in the occipital direction, first the lower calcarine lip was separated from the visual radiation, whose lower segment was interrupted. This must have increased further the scotomatous area in the right upper quadrants.

The next step was an interference with all afferent fibers of the anterior portion of the striate area, resulting in an elimination of the entire right monocular temporal crescent, illustrated by the upper fields in Figure 409.

In the course of further expansion of the tumor, the upper calcarine lip was also undermined, which caused the blindness to extend into most of the right lower quadrants. This phase is illustrated in the lower fields in the same figure. The centers of the right homonymous halves and the adjoining zones in the same halves about 10° wide, extending along the vertical meridians as far as 30° in the lower quadrants, were spared. The quality of vision in the spared parts, owing to the general intracranial conditions, deteriorated also. To this is also to be attributed a reduction of the left

halves of the fields, there being a compression of the anterior segment of the right calcarine fissure and of its afferent fibers, for which hemorrhage and thrombosis along the base of the brain, including the right hippocampal and calcarine fissures, must be blamed.

The principal feature of this case is central sparing during an advanced phase of the illness. This can be entirely explained by the elimination of the anterior portion of the striate area and its afferent fibers because of the location of a tumor medial from the lateral ventricle. The lateral salient of the visual radiation containing foveal-macular fibers, located on the lateral side of the ventricular barrier, escaped. This is of special interest, as it shows that the same protective mechanism responsible for central sparing in vascular cases may also function as a protective barrier in some cases of brain tumor. The remarkable fact is the long duration of this protection.

References: See chapter XI, especially 3, 4, and 5.

SEC. 6. CASE OF A PURE INCOMPLETE QUADRANTIC HOMONYMOUS HEMIANOPIA

1. History.—Munson, Le Roy, age twenty two years, student.

Diagnosis: Left incomplete inferior quadrantic homonymous hemianopia, caused by an endocarditic embolic infarct in the right occipital lobe. Specimen kindly given by Dr. C. W. Rucker, then of the Department of Ophthalmology of the University of Minnesota Medical School at Minneapolis (now of the Mayo Clinic, Rochester, Minn.), through the initiative of Dr. F. Burch, of the same institution.

Since childhood the patient had suffered from "rheumatism" and an indefinite heart trouble. The terminal illness began fifty-eight days preceding death, with a sudden headache in the right frontoparietal region, associated with "double vision in the right eye, and blindness in the temporal half of the left eye." Fifteen minutes after the onset the patient felt nauseated and vomited. A tentative diagnosis was that of a subacute bacterial endocarditis with bacteremia. This was confirmed by cultures made from blood, which showed the presence of *Streptococcus viridans*.

2. Ophthalmological examination.—The plotting of the fields revealed the presence of a left-sided incomplete inferior quadrantic homonymous hemianopia (Fig. 411, upper fields). The visual fields were plotted for the first time thirteen days after the onset, which was forty-five days before death. The blindness extended also into the periphery of the left upper quadrants, eliminating the upper half of the left monocular crescent, together with the adjoining segment of the binocular portions of the same quadrants. The central portions of the affected quadrants were spared, up to 3° or 4° from the fixation points. In addition, there was a cotton-wool exudate in the right retina at the first branching of the superior temporal vein about 1.5 × 3 times the diameter of the vein.

A second plotting was made eleven days after the first, or thirty-four days before death (Fig. 411, lower fields). This time the left upper crescentic field was found to be restored, and the blindness limited to the left inferior homonymous quadrants. As before, central vision was spared. This situation remained substantially the same until death. The target used in the plotting was 3 mm., white, at 33 cm. distance, by daylight. On both occasions the patient was ill because of the high fever which persisted until the last, but he was co-operative.

3. PATHOANATOMICAL EXAMINATION.—A post mortem examination corroborated and amplified the clinical diagnosis by the presence of a chronic endocarditis. Infarcts were found in the spleen, kidneys, and brain. The brain had a cyst

in the right occipital lobe but appeared otherwise normal. There were no signs of meningitis.

The *right occipital lobe*, grossly examined, showed on the lateral face, near its dorsal margin, a small focus of softening, whose extent could not be determined macroscopically. The serial sections stained by the methods of Weigert-Kultschitzky, Van Gieson, and hematoxylin and eosin revealed the presence of a single cystically degenerated, crescent-shaped, vertically placed cavity (Fig. 412, solid black marked with * in sketches *A–F*). This focus ex-

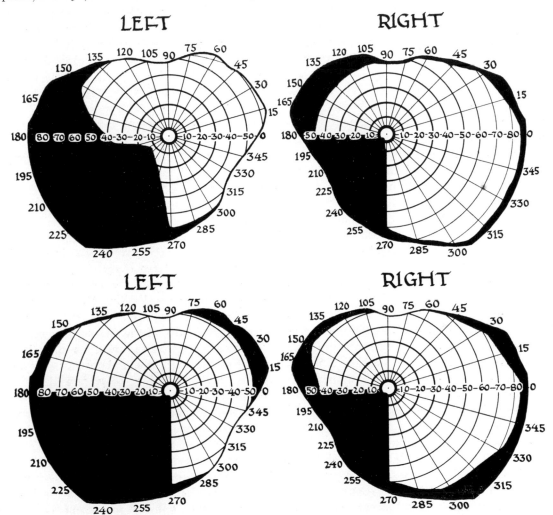

FIG. 411.—Case LeRoy Munson: left lower incomplete homonymous quadrantic hemianopia, caused by an endocarditic embolism of a branch of the middle cerebral artery in the right occipital lobe. Upper fields taken thirteen days after the cerebral insult, or forty-five days before death; lower fields taken twenty-four days after the cerebral insult, or thirty-four days before death. Cause of the visual defect a purely subcortical interruption of the upper segment of the right visual radiation (*see* following Fig. 412). Note the extension of blindness into the upper half of the left monocular temporal crescent, becoming entirely restored at the second plotting; the central sparings of about 4° in the affected quadrants, except in the left field at the first plotting, where the sparing was more extensive, extending also as a wedge along the vertical meridian, very likely caused by the poor condition of the patient during the plotting (headache, fever, fatigue).

tended from the surface of the brain through the white subcortical fiber mass, down to the ependyma of the posterior horn of the lateral ventricle (*lv*), through almost the entire longitudinal extent of the lobe. The cavity was lined by a reactive membrane that was even and smooth, without diffuse zones of transition or inflammatory infiltration. Obviously, the cavity was caused by an embolic obstruction of a branch of the middle cerebral artery, most likely the parieto-occipital Sylvian or superior temporo-occipital Sylvian artery (*Sypaocca, Syteoccsua,* in Figs. 370, 374). The ultimate etiology of the lesion was an infectious chronic endocarditis which produced the embolism.

An examination of the serial sections through the brain showed approximately the upper half of the sagittal fiber layers of the right occipital lobe to be absent and replaced by the cystic cavity. In particular, the upper segment or horizontal branch of the *visual radiation*, indicated by shading in the solid black lesion in sketches *B–F* in Figure 412, was found to be missing, with the exception of its innermost portion, made up of fibers entering the upper lip of the calcarine fissure (*fc*). The adjoining dorsal portion of the intermediate segment or vertical branch of the radiation was also interrupted (thus in *C, D,* and *F*).

On levels closer to the tip of the occipital lobe, the lesion destroyed almost the entire upper or dorsal half of the radiation, just sparing its "lateral salient," where the upper and lower segments join (*B, C*). In the occipital pole the posteriormost bundles of the radiation that supply it were just barely missed (*vr* in sketch *A*).

In the striate cortex lining the calcarine fissure, the following situation was found. In the anterior third of the longitudinal extent of the fissure the intracortical afferent visual fibers, distinguished by their slanting course, appeared normal in both lips (*cf.* Figs. 315, 316, 327, 328, 334). The immediately subjacent subcortical fibers, including those that line the calcar avis in the lateral ventricle, were likewise normal in this locality. In the middle third of the calcarine fissure, in its upper lip, beginning with the deepest point of this fissure, the subcortical fibers were considerably depleted. In the same locality the slanting infra-Gennarian intracortical af-

ferent visual fibers were also almost entirely absent. In the occipital or posterior third of the calcarine fissure and in the pole of the lobe, the subcortical and intracortical infra-Gennarian afferent visual fibers in the entire striate area again appeared normal.

In the *right lateral geniculate nucleus,* stained with the modified Nissl-Lenhossék's toluidine blue method, a single well-defined zone was found, where the nerve cells were in various stages of retrograde degeneration, beginning with "primary irritation," but mostly far advanced, including complete disappearance (Fig. 412, solid black marked with * in sketches *2–4*). The zone was wedge-shaped, with its broad base at the upper convex extremity and its sharp end turned toward the hilum of the nucleus, exactly as in the experiments with monkeys described in chapter VII, 4 [5], 5 [2]. (*See* Figs. 247, 250, 251, photo *2; cf.* a different type of degeneration in Fig. 200, but similar in Figs. 202–8.)

The second fourth was completely degenerated, if the nucleus be divided on a cross-section in the coronal plane into four segments. In the innermost segment, coinciding with the inner tip of the nucleus, a number of nerve cells appeared less affected. The degeneration passed through all six cellular layers, including the ventral layers with large elements. In the outward or lateral half of the nucleus the nerve cells appeared normal, filling the compact cellular layers in great numbers, except in the immediate vicinity of the degenerated zone.

The cell depletion was most complete in the center of the zone, where almost all cells were altered to a point where they were difficult to recognize. The neuroglia, as usual in such retrograde foci, was greatly increased in numbers in the entire degenerated territory, in comparison with the normal parts of the nucleus.

The position of the degenerated wedge, limited to the medial half of the nucleus, changed along its longitudinal extent. Closer to the anterior or oral extremity, the wedge extended to the mid-line or slightly beyond it (sketch *4*). On the middle levels the zone, together with the most medial and less affected portion, occupied almost exactly the inner half of the nucleus (sketch *3*). In the posterior or caudal third of the nucleus the zone of degeneration was gradually reduced to the inner third of the nucleus or less (sketch *2*). In the posterior sixth (sketch *1*), where the nucleus is composed of four cell layers only—two dorsal ones made up of small cells and two ventral ones composed of larger cells—almost all cells preserved a normal appearance (lower photo in Fig. 213). The few scattered cells that were discolored or shrunken were an exception, probably in consequence of general factors such as toxic agents and fever.

In addition to a single large zone of retrograde degeneration caused by a single distant lesion that interrupted a compact portion of the visual radiation, there were a few small, scattered, primary infectious foci represented by an agglomeration of nonnervous cells, either in or outside the degenerated zone described. These minute, fresh, inflammatory nests, similar to those found here and there in other parts of the

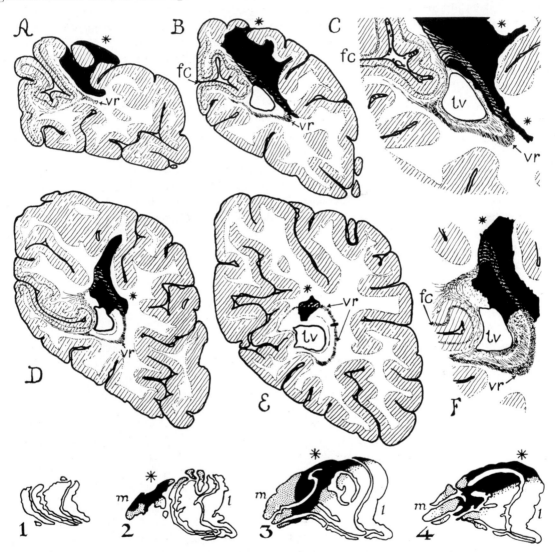

FIG. 412.—Case LeRoy Munson: right occipital lobe (*upper sketches*) and right lateral geniculate nucleus (*lower sketches*), showing the anatomical cause of the left lower homonymous quadrantic hemianopia (*see* Fig. 411). Sketches *A–F* represent coronal sections through the lobe at approximately equal intervals, beginning with the occipital pole; sketches *C* and *F* are slightly magnified details of *B* and *D*. Sketches *1–4* represent coronal sections through the right geniculate nucleus at approximately equal intervals, beginning with its posterior extremity (*1*) and terminating at its anterior extremity (*4*). Solid black in upper sketches indicates the brain lesion, in lower sketches the zone of advanced retrograde cell degeneration, surrounded by partial degeneration, indicated by stippling. Striate area shown by a stippled intracortical line of Gennari or Vicq-d'Azyr. *Labeling: fc*, calcarine fissure; *l*, lateral side of lateral geniculate nucleus; *lv*, lateral ventricle; *m*, medial side of lateral geniculate nucleus; *vr*, visual radiation; *, lesion (*upper sketches*) or core of degenerated zone in lateral geniculate nucleus.

brain, were obviously caused by a recent slight widespread encephalitic process, in turn caused by bacteremia of endocarditic origin. Such foci could easily be dissociated from the large, solid retrograde degeneration, the more so since the nerve cells located in the immediate vicinity of, or even imbedded in, these foci showed only slight degenerative changes or none at all.

The left lateral geniculate nucleus, in contrast with the right nucleus, was found to be normal. Here no noticeable zone of retrograde degeneration or scattered degenerated cells were found which could in any way be brought into connection with a partially interrupted visual radiation in the right occipital lobe.

4. CORRELATION OF FUNCTIONAL DISTURB-ANCE AND PATHOANATOMICAL FINDINGS.—Owing to a remarkably clear pathoanatomical situation in this unique case, equal to the best experiment, its analysis and correlation of functional disturbance with the changes in the central visual mechanism were easily made.

First, since the cortical lesion was slight and was located outside the striate area, it was to be ruled out as a possible cause of the homonymous quadrantic visual field defect (Fig. 412, *A* and *B*, marked with an asterisk [*]). The striate cortex itself was also entirely undamaged. Hence the functional field defect must be entirely attributed to the lesion in the subcortical fiber substance. Here again the destruction of the fibers outside the sagittal layers, since these are not instrumental in the conduction of impulses from the retinae to the striate area, was irrelevant. Thus, by exclusion, a partial interruption of the external sagittal layer, which, as indicated by the previous evidence, contains the afferent fibers of the visual radiation (*vr*, in corresponding figures), must be considered the cause of the visual field defect.

The next fact of consequence is an almost complete interruption of the upper horizontal segment of the radiation on the anterior levels through the occipital lobe (Fig. 412, *D, E, F*). This segment terminates in the upper calcarine lip, as clearly evidenced by the experiments with monkeys and other anatomical procedures described in chapter VII. This agrees well with the functional defect, which was limited to the contralateral inferior homonymous quadrants

of the fields of view (Fig. 411, lower fields). A single lesion had in this case interrupted fibers that carry impulses from the right upper homonymous halves of both retinae, with the exception of the foveae-maculae.

This is evidenced, first, by the clinically observed defect, an incomplete left-sided inferior quadrantic hemianopia, contralateral to the side of the lesion. In the first plotting, this defect extended into the upper crescentic territory also (upper fields). This initial extension was likely caused by an indirect, probably edematous, interference with the normal blood supply of the lower lip in the anterior extremity of the calcarine fissure, caused by the same focus (exemplified by sketches *D* and *F*). The left upper crescentic blindness, as was made fairly certain by the second plotting, was merely an initial symptom, disappearing afterward and leaving as a permanent residue a defect strictly limited to the inferior left quadrants.

The second evidence is the position of the degenerated zone in approximately the inner third to half of the lateral geniculate nucleus, the same locality where, according to experimental evidence, optic fibers from the upper extramacular homonymous retinal quadrants terminate (*see* chap. VI, 7, 11, and corresponding figures).

The final evidence is the absence of afferent nerve fibers in the striate cortex in the upper calcarine lip, in the middle third of this fissure, a locality related to the upper retinal, or lower opposite, field quadrants (*see* chap. VII, 4, 6, and corresponding figures).

The analysis of this case points decidedly toward a vertical division of the visual radiation, with the upper and lower extrafoveal or "peripheral" retinal quadrants represented in the upper and lower segments, respectively, and the foveal-macular or "central" vision represented in the intermediate or axial segment of the radiation placed between the first two. This possibility was suggested by G. Holmes (1918) and advocated by Rønne (Roenne 1919) and in a somewhat different way by Monbrun (1919), and was experimentally demonstrated in the Monkey by Heuven (1929) and by the author (1932, 1933). (*See* chap. IV, 7 [6].)

The case MUNSON further shows that the assumption that the "foveal-macular bundle" is located either in the dorsal segment (Pfeifer, Niessl von Mayendorf) or in the ventral segment of the visual radiation (Niessl von Mayendorf) or that the "foveal-macular fibers" may be scattered all over the visual radiation (Monakow) is not borne out by the evidence. For, in spite of the almost complete destruction of the dorsal segment of the radiation, in our case the central fields of the affected inferior left homonymous quadrants remained spared to the extent of from 3° to 4° around the points of fixation. It is therefore apparent that the fibers which carried impulses from the preserved central portions of these quadrants must have been in the segment of the radiation that escaped destruction.

Since the origin of the interrupted upper segment of the radiation in the lateral geniculate nucleus is contiguous with the intermediate foveal-macular segment and is separated by the latter from the lateral "peripheral" segment of the nucleus and since the inferior segment of the radiation, remaining intact in this case, terminates in the inferior calcarine lip, the chain of evidence is complete in favor of the intermediate location of the foveal or "macular" bundle in the visual radiation, that is, in its intermediate or axial segment.

In sections through the anterior part of the occipital lobe, the radiation somewhat resembles a horseshoe, with an upper and a lower segment, both linked by an intermediate segment, as described (Fig. 412, *D, E, F;* compare with Figs. 228, 229, and 231–33). The upper segment, together with the adjoining portion of the intermediate segment with which it is continuous, was destroyed in this case. Accordingly, it is this vertical segment which, if one looks upon the radiation as a fan composed of rather parallel bundles of fibers, forms its axial or central rib (*cf.* Figs. 259, 260). Here are located fibers that represent both homonymous halves of the central areae of the two retinae, including the foveae-maculae, measuring up to 3° or 4° on both sides of the horizontal meridians.

On levels closer to the pole of the occipital lobe the radiation changes its shape somewhat, the vertical branch becoming transformed into an obtuse angle pointing down and outward, with its concavity facing the calcarine fissure (Fig. 412, *B, C;* also Fig. 231, *B*). Here it is

more proper to speak of an upper and a lower segment and of a lateral angle or salient of the radiation. In our case the fibers of this salient just escaped the injury (at *vr* in sketches *B, C*).

Farther back, in the tip of the lobe, these fibers slip behind the posterior horn of the lateral ventricle and turn inward, to reach the most posterior portion of the striate cortex at the occipital pole (*A,* in Fig. 412). In this way the "central," "axial," or foveal segment of the radiation (at *vr*) remained preserved all the way from its origin in the caudal tip of the lateral geniculate nucleus of the same side (*1*) to its terminal station in the tip of the occipital lobe (*A,* in same figure).

The preservation of the axial foveal or "macular" fibers, in turn, explains the sparing of the central portions of the affected quadrants of the visual fields. The position of the foveal or "macular" bundle in the radiation thus determined agrees well with the one found in case HOLT (Fig. 415) and is essentially the same as that found in the experiments with monkeys (Figs. 259, 260).

Case MUNSON also illustrates the position of the horizontal meridians in the visual radiation. It shows that if the upper segment, on anterior levels through the occipital lobe, is completely interrupted or almost so, the extrafoveal portions of the blind homonymous quadrants are separated from the seeing ones of the same side by straight horizontal lines, which are the horizontal meridians (Fig. 381; *also* Fig. 383, *5*).

The exceptions are the small areae, corresponding to the central portions of the respective quadrants, around the fixation points, which remain normal when the foveal or "macular" fibers are spared. The only possible explanation of this remarkable feature—a straight linear delimitation of the quadrantic hemianopia—is the assumption of a sizable "gap" between those fibers of the radiation that represent the extrafoveal periphery of the upper homonymous quadrants and fibers representing the extrafoveal periphery of the lower, as suggested long ago on the basis of analysis of clinical cases by Gordon Holmes (1918), Monbrun (1919), and Rønne (Roenne 1919). Hence it is this mechanism whose partial destruction is responsible for the strictly quadrantic hemianopic defects in purely subcortical lesions. The "gap" of

G. Holmes, however, is not void but is filled with the foveal or "macular" fibers, which, as pointed out, lie between the two "peripheral" or "extrafoveal" branches of the radiation. The foveal or "macular" fibers form, accordingly, a central or axial rib of the fiber fan that is the visual radiation. (*Cf.* chap. XI, 5; and Figs. 235, 236, 259, 260, 269.)

In accepting this arrangement, one has to assume further that, beginning with the most peripheral bundles at the upper and lower margins of the radiation, those closest to the upper and the lower calcarine lip, respectively, each narrow subsequent segment of the outer sagittal fiber layer closer to the axial bundle represents a narrow concentric quadricircular belt or zone of the corresponding homonymous quadrants. These belts are necessarily longer in the extreme field periphery, becoming gradually shorter, the closer they are to the points of fixation.

Each fiber segment is to be imagined as made up of minute bundles of homonymous fibers representing individual functional visual units, each capable of functioning independently. Such a series of the respective functional units makes up each of the quadricircular belts in the corresponding homonymous visual quadrants. In the far periphery of the fields the functional units are relatively large and few, and hence few fibers in the visual radiation represent a relatively large territory. Closer to the fixation points, the units gradually decrease in size and increase in number. This again requires an increasing number of fibers, although the respective belts in the fields of view rapidly decrease in territory.

The uppermost and lowermost and, at the same time, the most medial bundles in both upper and lower segments of the radiation, passing, on anterior levels of the occipital lobe, to the upper and lower calcarine lips, respectively, are related to the extreme nasal segment, or monocular crescent, of the contralateral retina. In case MUNSON these crescentic fibers in the upper segment of radiation were interrupted with the binocular fibers of the same quadrant, showing that both are arranged on the same principle, the upper crescentic fibers adjoining the upper binocular quadrantic fibers, the lower crescentic fibers adjoining the lower binocular fibers.

A logical corollary to the expounded concept of visual radiation is that, in purely subcortical lesions, caused by a single focus, interrupting a smaller or larger portion of the radiation, the field defect should always comprise a belt-shaped quadricircular zone (Fig. 383, sketch *9*). Such a scotomatous zone will be either narrow, if a small segment of the radiation is damaged, or wide, if a broad segment is interrupted. The blindness may eventually spread over the entire upper or lower homonymous quadrants, if exactly half the radiation is interrupted. The central vision may or may not be preserved, depending on whether or not the adjoining intermediate foveal-macular segment of the radiation was preserved or destroyed (*see* chap. X, 8).

In other words, any small, purely subcortical, damage to the radiation may produce a visual field defect in the shape of a more or less narrow belt extending concentrically around the fixation point from the horizontal to the vertical meridian. The same should be expected in the case of a field "rest" caused by extensive subcortical damage that spares a segment of the radiation. The width of a scotomatous belt or a single spared rest may vary, depending upon whether a smaller or larger portion of the radiation is interrupted or preserved.

The wedge-shaped defects, or field "rests," of a more or less triangular shape, with a broad base at the periphery of the fields and a pointed end at the fixation points, are present only in purely cortical cases, where the striate cortex alone is involved, if the lesion is of suitable shape and location.

Irregular homonymous field defects likewise cannot be explained by means of purely subcortical lesions. They must be referred to the lesions where the striate cortex is damaged alone or is damaged in addition to the radiation. Nor can small lesions in the "axial" segment of the radiation produce narrow, homonymous, wedge-shaped or stripelike field defects extending more or less along the horizontal meridians, since each such lesion is bound to produce central or paracentral scotomas in any case, extending from the vertical to the horizontal meridians, with or without sparing the area around the fixation points.

No mention is made in the history of case MUNSON of visual disturbances of a complex or psychic order, such as alexia, visual agnosia, or disorientation in space. The absence of these symptoms is best explained by the location of the lesion in the right occipital lobe and by the sparing of the right parietal lobe, although the examiners may have failed to test for such disturbances.

Attention should also be called to the accurate lateral subjective localization of the sudden headache as an initial symptom by the patient in the right frontoparietal region of the head and the absence of such subjective sensation in the right occipital region. This is of interest because of the modern interpretation of the causes

underlying headaches (Moench 1951; Pickering 1951). This again may have been merely an omission on the part of the attending physician, since in vascular pathology, especially acute, involving the calcarine region, an intensive, dull, prolonged headache accurately localized in the affected lobe is a very marked subjective symptom. Finally, the absence of a subjective experience of symptoms of irritation (photopsia, photophobia, etc.) may be merely the result of the confusion which is not surprising in a severe cerebral insult.

References: See chapter XI, especially 5.

SEC. 7. CASE OF A SUPERIOR QUADRANTIC HOMONYMOUS HEMIANOPIA ASSOCIATED WITH QUADRANTIC HEMIACHROMATOPIA

1. History.—Holt, George H., age fifty-eight years, vocal teacher.

Diagnosis: Left incomplete homonymous hemianopia, absolute in the upper quadrants

seven years earlier. Five years previous to admission some mental irregularity and forgetfulness had been noticed. The present examination revealed general symptoms of senility, right

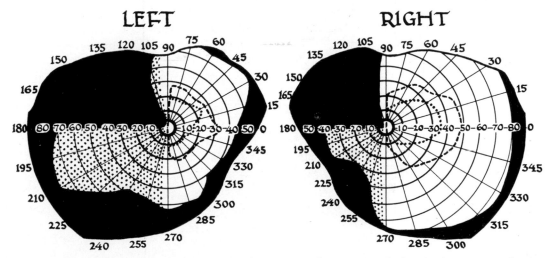

Fig. 413.—Case G. H. Holt: an incomplete left homonymous hemianopia, absolute in the upper quadrants and relative for colors in the lower quadrants, with central sparings and an overshot zone along vertical meridians. Cause: a thrombotic encephalomalacia of the calcarine sulcus of the right occipital lobe, developed on an arteriosclerotic basis (*see* Fig. 414).

and relative in the lower, caused by a thrombotic encephalomalacia of the right occipital lobe, of approximately six months' duration, situated along the medial calcarine sulcus, developed on the basis of general arteriosclerosis and hypertension. Specimen received from Dr. E. F. Hirsch, of St. Luke's Hospital, Chicago; clinical information and field chart received from Dr. T. Allen, Chicago.

The patient had suffered from hyperthyroidism (goiter), for which he had been operated on

hemiplegia, aphasia, and irrationality. On two occasions the patient showed signs of a cerebral "stroke," the last, one month before death, caused by a thrombotic softening in the left internal capsule. A few days preceding the last stroke he was lifting timbers. After the second stroke his vision became disturbed ("blindness"). He also had difficulty with hearing, more on the left side, and became paralyzed on the right side of the face, in the right arm and the right leg. He was able to speak, however.

2. Ophthalmological examination.—The fundi of the eyes, examined approximately six months before death, revealed a marked arteriosclerosis of the retinal blood vessels. At the time when the fields were tested first with the hand, and when again two days later perimetrically, which was forty-eight days before death, a left homonymous hemianopia was discovered (Fig. 413). The upper quadrants were found to be absolutely blind, with the exception of a narrow zone along the vertical meridians, where

ried from the blind to the seeing portions of the fields. The target not only was brought from the periphery to the center but was likewise held at a certain meridian on the arc, which itself was rotated. The patient was fairly co-operative, although perhaps not so much as would have been desirable.

General arteriosclerosis with arterial hypertension, followed by cerebral hemorrhage from the lenticulostriate artery of the right side, was diagnosed.

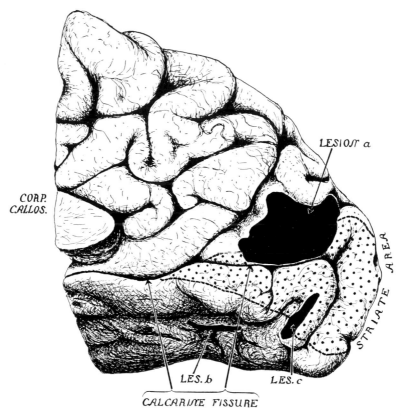

Fig. 414.—Case G. H. Holt: medial aspect of the right occipital lobe, showing the three foci of softening visible at a gross examination, a large one (*Lesion a*) spreading over much of the cuneus, and the two smaller ones (*Les. b* and *Les. c*) below the calcarine fissure (*cf.* Fig. 415). Striate area stippled. *CORP. CALLOS.*, corpus callosum.

only a relative scotoma for colors was found. The left lower quadrants were relatively blind for red and blue and were contracted in the periphery. The central vision was spared between 2° and 3°.

The light during the examination was good, although the day was overcast (December). A simple arc perimeter, with a radius of 33 cm., and a target of 1 cm. were used. To determine the edge of the blind areas, the target was car-

3. Pathoanatomical examination.—Examined grossly, three encephalomalacic foci were found *in the right occipital lobe* (Fig. 414, lesions *a, b, c*). The larger lesion (*a*) was on the inner face of the hemisphere, where it spread over the greater part of the cuneus. It extended to the calcarine fissure, destroying its upper lip. The other two malacic foci, located ventral to the calcarine fissure, appeared much smaller on the surface The anterior focus (*b*) was at the level of the anterior tip of the cuneus; the posterior focus (c) was closer to the posterior curved end of the calcarine fissure next to the occipital pole.

Microscopic examination of the serial sections, stained according to Weigert-Kultschitzky technique, showed that all three superficially visible foci were, in reality, but one single large focus, located between the posterior horn of the lateral ventricle (lv) laterally and the inner face of the hemisphere medially (Fig. 415). This focus, essentially of a thrombotic ischemic nature arising on the basis of arteriosclerosis of the brain, had destroyed a substantial portion of the cortex of the calcarine fissure and parts of the cortex and of the subcortical fiber mass immediately adjoining this fissure.

In particular, on the most anterior levels through the occipital lobe, the lower calcarine lip was either destroyed or undermined to such an extent as to become separated from its afferent fibers streaming to it from the lower horizontal segment of the visual radiation (sketches D, F). Here the lesion corresponded with the anterior small superficial focus (b). The fibers arriving from the upper horizontal segment of the radiation just missed the damage. Farther posteriorly, where the malacic focus approached the upper calcarine lip, these also must have been affected (sketch C).

In sections through the middle of the occipital lobe the destruction expanded to the upper lip of the calcarine fissure (sketch B). Here a portion of the striate and extrastriate cortex, with all subjacent fibrous substance, was destroyed (at *). In all sections through the occipital lobe the lesion was strictly confined to the medial half of the hemisphere inward to the lateral ventricle (lv), hence limited to the territory of the posterior cerebral artery.

Farther back toward the occipital pole, the lesion decreased (sketch A) and finally disappeared, leaving the pole of the occipital lobe and its fiber mass intact. Lateral to the ventricle, only two small lesions were present in sections passing through the parietal and temporal lobes (small, black, triangular area and a gap in vr, in sketch E). These lesions interrupted portions of the intermediate segment of the visual radiation.

In summary, in this case, in spite of its superficial appearance, a single malacic focus directly destroyed or undermined the lower, lingual lip along the entire main body of the calcarine fissure; the upper, cuneal lip, however, was destroyed only along the posterior third of the fissure. A considerable segment of the upper lip, with its afferent radiation fibers, was fairly well preserved (sketch D), as was also the tip of the occipital lobe. In consequence, the lower segment of the visual radiation degenerated because of the complete destruction of the lower calcarine lip and its afferent fibers. The upper segment of the radiation degenerated only partially, owing to partial destruction of the upper lip and its fibers and also because of a small primary vascular focus in the medial half of the lateral geniculate nucleus of the right side (small coarsely shaded area in Fig. 416).

In the intermediate segment of the radiation, even though depleted, many fibers remained, being best preserved in a single solid bundle in the "lateral salient" (thus at vr in sketches B and E).

Most striking was the contrast between the upper and the lower calcarine lips at the level of the sketches D and F: whereas in the former a fair number of the afferent geniculostriate fibers was found in the infra-Gennarian half of the cortex, in the latter they were practically absent.

The *lateral geniculate nucleus* of the right side (Fig. 416), stained with Lenhossék's modified Nissl-toluidine method, was found reduced in all dimensions, its layers poorly defined, with its nerve cells in the anterior half mostly gone (4-7). In approximately the middle third (3, 4) the intermediate segment alone showed a considerable number of cells still somewhat preserved, although these, too, exhibited clear signs of degeneration. Farther back in the same intermediate segment, the number of normal nerve cells increased, until close to the caudal extremity of the nucleus the cells seemed to differ little from the normal (1, 2). On the anterior levels both the medial and the lateral tips of the nucleus also remained less affected.

In addition, there was a small, narrow, primary vascular focus located in the inner segment, extending slightly into the intermediate segment. This focus was present in the middle third of the longitudinal extent of the nucleus (oblong, coarsely shaded area in *3, 4, 5*). The glial cells, as usual in a retrograde process, were considerably increased in those parts of the nucleus where the nerve cells degenerated.

The lateral geniculate nucleus of the opposite, left, side proved normal in all respects, except for such changes as were compatible with the general pathophysiological makeup of the case (*8–14*).

4. CORRELATION OF FUNCTIONAL DISTURBANCE WITH THE PATHOANATOMICAL FINDINGS.—

The analysis of this rare case must, first, take into consideration the fields of view (Fig. 413). Concerning these, it is probable that, in spite of only one plotting, the observation of absolute blindness in the left upper homonymous quadrants and of relative blindness for colors in the left lower quadrants was roughly correct. The questionable points concern spared zones along the vertical meridians above and below the fixation points and the central sparings. In an attempt to correlate the functional loss with the lesion, the time factor must also be considered.

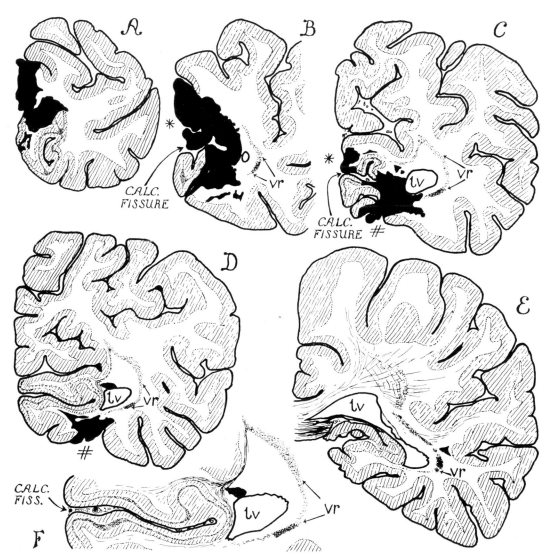

FIG. 415.—Case G. H. Holt: coronal sections through the right occipital lobe, beginning with the most posterior, closest to the occipital pole (*A*), and terminating with the section passing through the posterior extremity of the corpus callosum (*E*). Sketch *F* is an enlargement of a portion of sketch *D*. Foci of softening given in solid black. *Labeling: lv,* lateral ventricle; *vr,* visual radiation; asterisk (*) indicates focus *a* in the cuneus; double cross (#) indicates foci *b* and *c* in the lingual gyrus.

To begin with, the partial escape of the upper calcarine lip and its afferent fibers streaming from the upper horizontal segment of the radiation may indicate that the lesion started at the lower face of the occipitotemporal lobes (focus marked with # in Fig. 415, corresponding to *Les. b* and *Les. c* in Fig. 414). The most likely responsible factor was thrombosis of a branch of the

The elimination of the lower lip must have taken place at a time prior to the field plotting, forty-eight days before death, at which occasion absolute blindness in the upper quadrants and relative blindness for colors in the lower quadrants were found. At the time of the plotting of the fields, the upper calcarine lip was still functioning as a "protopathic" visual organ capable

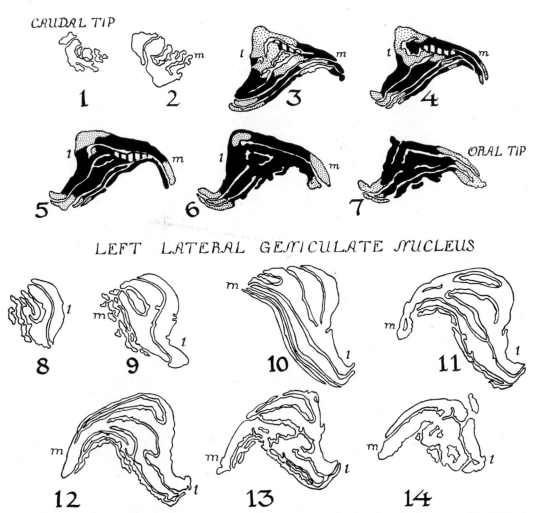

FIG. 416.—Case G. H. Holt: the right and left lateral geniculate nuclei, first heavily degenerated (*solid black and variously shaded*), the latter normal, corresponding with the normal left hemisphere of the brain.

posterior temporo-occipital artery (*poteocca*, Fig. 369) or of some other subsidiary artery supplying, in this individual case, the root and the core of the lower calcarine lip, e.g., the inferior calcarine artery (*ica*, *ical*, Figs. 369, 372) or the inferior accessory calcarine artery (*accica*, Fig. 374).

of appreciating crude photic stimuli, but no hues and no finer spatial details. This agrees very well with the fair preservation of finer structures in the upper lip, especially of the terminals of the geniculostriate fibers, which were practically absent in the lower lip.

During the terminal phase of the illness, the

thrombotic occlusion spread farther, probably by way of anastomotic connections with the principal calcarine artery (*pca*, Fig. 372), over the upper calcarine lip along its middle, cuneal stretch, transforming it into lesion *a* of Figure 414, identical with the focus marked by * in Figure 415.

A pathophysiological factor responsible for the spreading of the thrombosis may have been a hemodynamical imbalance in the common anastomotical territory. This, in turn, by eliminating the accessory or collateral arteries, placed a greater burden on the principal calcarine artery than this artery, itself diseased, could carry. Thrombotic softening of the upper calcarine lip, again, transformed a relative inferior quadrantic scotoma into absolute or near-absolute blindness, which, owing to the absence of further field testing during the six preterminal weeks, remained unrecorded.

Whether the centers of the fields of view remained spared until the end or were also affected remains uncertain also. However, considering that the "axial" lateral salient of the radiation (*vr*, in Fig. 415), the posterior extremity of the geniculate nucleus (*1, 2*, in Fig. 416), and the polar segment of the striate area (Fig. 414) all remained fairly well preserved, it is probable that the field centers were somewhat preserved to the end, the total result being an incomplete left homonymous hemianopia with central sparing.

From the preceding evaluation of the pathoanatomical facts and the probable course of the terminal phase of the illness, several valuable conclusions may be drawn about the anatomical organization of the supranuclear division of the visual system.

The first and least questionable inference is the relationship of the lower calcarine lip to the lower segment of the radiation and hence to the upper contralateral field quadrants, including the upper half of the temporal monocular crescent, but excluding the foveal or central vision.

The second point concerns the qualitative impairment of vision manifested in relative blindness for colors in the lower homonymous quadrants. Without hesitation, this can be accounted for by incomplete impairment of the upper calcarine lip and of the afferent fibers from the upper segment of the radiation by which it is supplied; judging from sketches *C, D,* and *F* in Figure 415, this lip was preserved on anterior, cuneal levels until death, even though a small malacic focus in the upper wall of the ventricle was dangerously close to the fibers streaming into it. A considerable number of oblique afferent fibers, experimentally identified as terminals of the visual radiation, found in the upper lip and missing in the lower calcarine lip, is direct evidence of this. (*Cf.* chap. VIII, 6, 7.)

The third point to be considered is the single preserved compact bundle in the "lateral salient" of the visual radiation (*vr*, in Fig. 415). This bundle could be followed along the lateral side of the lateral ventricle to the pole of the occipital lobe, which also remained in good condition. Since in our experiments described in chapter VII, 4, 5, 6, the intermediate segment of the radiation was found to be related to the polar portion of the striate area and to the intermediate segment of the lateral geniculate nucleus, where the foveal-areal fibers of the retinae terminate, the preservation of the central vision in case HOLT is made understandable in this way. The lesion here largely eliminated those parts which are related to the extrafoveal or extramacular vision, while it spared the segments of the radiation and of the striate cortex related to the centers or to the "macula" of the fields of view (*cf.* chap. X, 8 [4]; chap. XI, 9). The preceding evidence shows the preserved "lateral salient" of the radiation to be the much-debated foveal or "macular" bundle.

The upper and lower segments of the radiation, flanking the foveal-macular bundle, are related to the extrafoveal or peripheral parts of the upper and lower homonymous retinal quadrants, as found in experiments and pathological cases described previously. The location of the foveal-macular bundle thus revealed is not exactly "axial" but a little below the center of symmetry on a cross-section, more radiation belonging to the upper peripheral segment than to the lower one. This, in turn, indicates that there is more striate cortex above than below the horizontal meridians, which agrees with the somewhat larger inferior quadrants in the field of view.

In the lateral geniculate nucleus the horizontal meridians are also a little off-center, being more lateral, that is, closer to the lower retinal, or upper field periphery, as might be expected from the smaller size of the upper quadrants in comparison with the lower quadrants of the fields of view (Fig. 381). All this agrees well with the information gained from other cases, especially from case MUNSON (Figs. 411, 412), and from experiments (Figs. 259, 260).

The fourth point deserving attention is the fact that practically the entire pathological process involving the central visual apparatus in case HOLT was confined to the inner portion of the occipital lobe, inward to the posterior horn of the lateral ventricle. The pathophysiological factor which determined this is the peculiar vascular supply, or distribution of blood vessels, described in chapter X, 6, 7, 8, 9. This case demonstrates in the manner of a pathological experiment the relative vascular independence of the greater medial portion of the striate area and of its subjacent fiber systems from the cortical and subcortical regions on the lateral side of the occipital lobe supplied by the middle cerebral artery. When either one of the principal arterial territories is obstructed, the other, if in fair condition, may preserve the polar region by way of anastomotical connections and hence save the central vision, provided that the foveal-macular fibers in the radiation are also spared.

In case HOLT, in spite of extensive destruction of the calcarine cortex, the nutrition of the polar striate cortex was upheld via the middle cerebral artery. The posterior horn of the lateral ventricle, in this mechanism, played the role of a barrier preventing a pathological process from spreading to the other arterial territory. The region of the calcarine fissure, except for its caudal portion around the pole, acts as a pathophysiological unit largely independent of the region of the lobe lateral to the "watershed" represented by the lateral ventricle. (*See* chap. X, 8, and Fig. 377 for further details.)

The fifth point of interest is how far in the polar striate area the representation of the central fovea or "macula" extends. Since in our case the portion of the area behind the curved posterior end of the calcarine fissure was found

intact, it would seem that this rather large segment of striate cortex was related to the central vision measuring no more than 2° or 3° from the fixation points. It might be easier to accept this if one considers the tremendous demand on the central vision as the principal instrument of the "epicritic" or "gnostic" visual functions. The central fovea of the retina—the main "gateway" of the human intellect—requires and is also well provided with a great number of individual anatomical-functional units, as the great number of the foveal cones and the large area in the lateral geniculate nucleus indicate. An extensive foveal cortex in the occipital pole would seem plausible.

At any rate, it is fair to assume that the polar cortex behind the curved calcarine fissure does represent homonymous halves of both central areae, corresponding to from 8° to 10° from the fixation point in the field of view, and that a substantial portion of the polar cortex belongs to the central hemifoveae (2°30′), much of it belonging to the homonymous halves of the outer foveae (from 40′ to 1° of arc) best supplied with the cones. (*Cf.* chap. V, 10 [4, 5], and case MALLORY, sec. 10, this chapter; *see*, for phylogenesis of foveal cortex, chap. VIII, 3 [6].)

The last point requiring consideration is a separation of the upper amaurotic quadrants from the lower amblyopic quadrants along the horizontal meridians. This is of special interest, since, unlike case MUNSON, where the responsible lesion was subcortical, in case HOLT it was a combination of cortical and subcortical softening. The most logical interpretation is the preservation of the foveal-macular bundle and of the polar cortex, the central vision acting as a barrier between the upper and the lower extrafoveal quadrants, as discussed in chapter XI, 9.

It may be noted that a boundary separating the striate cortex in the upper lip containing afferent fibers from the cortex in the lower lip devoid of such fibers was exactly in the floor of the calcarine fissure, indicating the position of the horizontal meridians.

References: See chapter XI, especially 5, 6.

SEC. 8. CASE OF HORIZONTAL OR ALTITUDINAL HEMIANOPIA AND MENTAL BLINDNESS

1. HISTORY.—HOFFMANN, Mary, sixty-six years old, schoolteacher.

Diagnosis: Inferior horizontal or altitudinal hemianopia caused by a cerebral softening or encephalomalacia on an arteriosclerotic basis. Specimen received from Dr. D. T. Vail, of Cincinnati, Ohio, through the courtesy of Dr. P. Bailey, of the University of Illinois Medical School, Chicago.

Four years previous to admittance the patient had fallen, probably collapsed, and had had to be led to a chair. During this incident she did not become unconsious, however. After this the left side of her face had been drawn up for several hours. Since that time the patient had become easily exhausted. She did not notice weakness of her left leg or arm, however. For six months prior to hospitalization the patient had suffered from blurred vision while reading, which gradually became worse. Changing glasses one month previously had not improved vision.

Four months earlier she had suffered from bronchitis, after which she had periodic severe headaches, reaching their peaks at noon each day. Lately the headaches had lessened. For a number of years she had had high blood pressure.

During the preceding two weeks the patient had felt that if she were away from home, she would be unable to find her way back. Even in her house she could not locate familiar articles from memory. Thus, for example, in trying to recall the furnishings of her dining-room, she could not remember where the radio was placed. She felt certain that she would have a great deal of difficulty in finding her home, even if she were only a few blocks away. Her memory was good for present and recent events, and she was well oriented as to time and place. There was no complaint of a motor or sensory disturbance other than the blurring of vision, which was gradually getting worse. In the past there had been no major illness, injury, or operation.

2. CIRCULATION AND NEUROLOGICAL EXAMINATION.—The examination revealed blood pressure of 184/160, on two other occasions 185/90 and 170/90. There were a few casts in the urine,

later no casts but only albumen. Neurologically, there was a paresis of the left side involving the face, arm, and leg. Abdominal reflexes were absent, left knee-jerk was increased, and there was a tendency toward falling to the left when walking. The somatic sensation was normal. There was no ataxia, adiadochokinesis, or astereognosis.

3. OPHTHALMOLOGICAL EXAMINATION.—With the right eye the patient saw fingers at 15 feet, corrected to 20/40 with a 4.50 + 2.75 cyl. ax. 130, add +2.75 read J. #2 slowly. With the left eye the patient saw fingers at 15 feet, corrected to 20/25 with +4.25 + 1.0 cyl. ax. 65, add +2.75 read J. #2 nicely. She could not read the finest print (J #1) with the left eye with any correction at any distance.

A congenital muscle defect had persisted through her whole life in the form of a bizarre alternating divergent strabismus, so that, in fixing with the right eye, the left eye deviated outward and down, and, in fixing with the left eye, the right eye deviated up and out.

The optic papillae were entirely normal and remained so throughout her illness. At no time did they show any sign of increased intracranial pressure. The retinal blood vessels in each eye showed a moderate degree of vascular sclerosis, and there were no hemorrhages or exudates. The pupils were equal and responded promptly.

4. FIELDS OF VIEW.—A perimetric plotting of the fields of vision showed a lower horizontal or altitudinal hemianopia (Fig. 417). Twenty-one days later, the patient complained about her vision dropping considerably. Ophthalmological examination showed the right vision 20/50, the left 20/50, with a correction. She was unable to read any print. The fields of vision showed the same horizontal inferior hemianopia, with the beginning of a right homonymous hemianopia as well. This remained so until approximately six days before death. A provisional diagnosis was a vascular lesion, changed later into that of a small tumor situated in the cunei of both occipital lobes, more on the left side. The inferior hemianopia also involved the macular region (?).

The preceding information obtained from the treating physician is to be amplified by the following considerations. Both mappings of the fields, the first made approximately four weeks before death and the second made one week before death, showed somewhat incongruous de-

along the horizontal meridians up to 40 or less degrees in the right homonymous halves, and up to 50 degrees or more in the left halves. In the upper periphery, along the vertical meridians, the fields were contracted only a little. The lower quadrants of both sides were blind, with the exception of wedge-shaped sectors along the horizontal meridians. These triangular rests

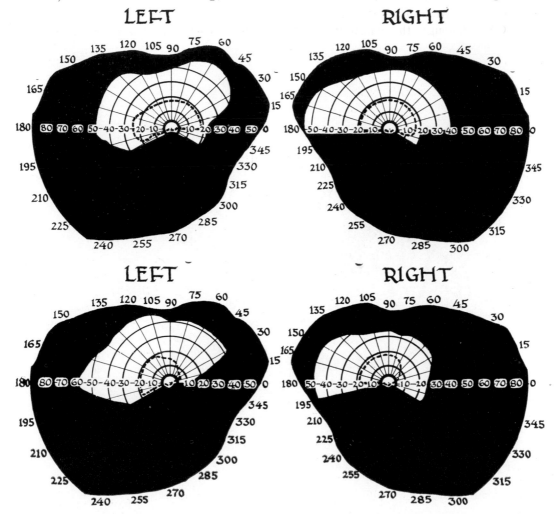

Fig. 417.—Case M. Hoffmann: inferior horizontal or altitudinal hemianopia expanding into a bilateral homonymous hemianopia and mental blindness. Cause: encephalomalacia developing on an arteriosclerotic basis (*cf.* Figs. 418–22). Upper fields taken four weeks, lower fields taken one week, before death.

fects in all blind parts. Only taken together do they permit a judgment as to the probable course of the underlying pathological process.

First, it appears fairly certain that the temporal monocular crescents of both fields of view were put out of function prior to the first plotting. In addition, the blindness extended into binocular portions of the upper quadrants,

were turned with their wide bases toward the periphery, their sharp ends toward the fixation points. At the second plotting, substantially the same situation was found, except that the scotomatous areas expanded in the right upper temporal quadrant to approximately 25° and in the left upper nasal quadrant along the horizontal meridian as much as 15°. The incongruity found in both fields can be most easily explained by reduced central acuity, which made fixation difficult, and by the generally poor condition of the patient.

Concerning the central vision, the accompanying note expressly states that the lower parts of the "macular" areas were also included in blind portions enveloping the lower field halves. However, both field charts show sparings of about 3° below the horizontal meridians

calcarine fissure close to the occipital pole (lesion *b*). Other similar foci were found outside the territory of the striate area (stippled).

Serial sections through the left occipital lobe, stained for myelin sheaths, revealed numerous small and large softenings throughout its substance, some quite irregular and spreading through both the subcortical core and the cortex, others again being principally or entirely confined to the cortex (Fig. 420, solid black).

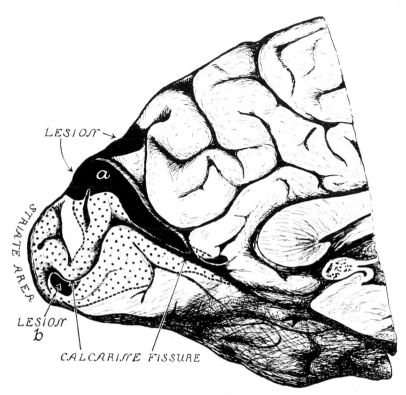

Fig. 418.—Case M. Hoffmann: medial aspect of the left occipital lobe, showing a large, principal focus of softening in the cuneus (*a*) and a smaller focus (*b*), just below the curved end of the calcarine fissure at the occipital pole. Striate area stippled. (For cross-sections *see* Fig. 420.)

and possibly more, equal for a white target and for hues.

5. LEFT OCCIPITAL LOBE.—Grossly examined, this lobe showed a narrow encephalomalacic focus in the anterior portion of the cuneus, located between the parieto-occipital sulcus and the calcarine fissure (Fig. 418, lesion *a*). The lesion destroyed the anterior extremity of the upper lip of the fissure and extended to the dorsal margin of the lobe along the parieto-occipital sulcus. Another and superficially smaller focus was found in the lower lip of the

The larger stripelike lesion, visible on the inner face of the lobe (*a*, in Fig. 418), directly destroyed a portion of the upper calcarine lip, including the peripheral fringe of the striate area in that lip (*a*, in Fig. 420). On the intermediate levels (*4*, *5*, *6*) this lesion penetrated but little into the subcortical substance, except on level 4, and hence damaged only a small number of fibers streaming from the upper segment of the visual radiation (*vr*) into the striate cortex. On the anterior levels (*7*) this lesion enveloped the entire upper calcarine lip and interrupted all fibers streaming into that lip from the upper segment of the radiation. Now entirely concealed from the surface and becoming quite irregular, lesion *a* extended anteriorly in several directions, undermining and partly destroying much of the striate cortex at its anterior extremity and finally reaching the splenium of the corpus callosum (*8*). The conspicuous feature of this focus was its symmetrical extent and location with a similar lesion in the contralateral hemisphere (*cf. 7* and *8* in Fig. 420 with *6, 7, 8* in Fig. 421).

entirely or almost entirely confined to the cortex. A nest (*c* in sketch *8*) arising from the tentorial surface of the lobe, a replica of a similar focus in the contralateral hemisphere, interrupted with its two prongs two small fiber segments in the "lateral salient" of the visual radiation (*x, y* in sketches *6, 7, 8*).

The occipital pole, as in the opposite hemisphere, was almost entirely spared (sketch *1*). Considerable segments of the striate area in the posterior portion of the calcarine fissure (*C.F.*)

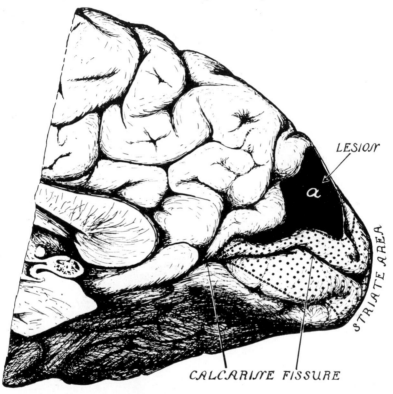

FIG. 419.—Case M. Hoffmann: medial aspect of the right occipital lobe, showing a single, large focus of softening taking up much of the cuneus. Striate area stippled. (For cross-sections *see* Fig. 421.)

The posterior and superficially quite insignificant focus in the lower calcarine lip close to the occipital pole (lesion *b* in Fig. 418) extended in serial sections through the entire length of the striate area as far as its anterior limit (*b* in sketches *1–7*, in Fig. 420). In most sections this lesion remained strictly limited to the cortex, or almost so. Its effect, because of extensive destruction of the cortex itself, was equally devastating.

Besides these two principal lesions, other independent and much smaller foci were scattered throughout the left occipital lobe, many of them

and close to it were also spared (sketches *2, 3, 4, 5*).

6. RIGHT OCCIPITAL LOBE.—The gross examination of the right occipital lobe revealed a single encephalomalacic focus with an irregular, depressed surface on the medial face (lesion *a*, solid black in Fig. 419). Its shape was roughly that of a triangle, fairly congruous with the shape of the cuneus. Its horizontal side extended for a short distance along the calcarine fissure, its anterior side running along the parieto-occipital sulcus. The upper extremity of the focus just touched the dorsal margin of the occipital lobe. The inferior calcarine lip and the pole of the occipital lobe appeared superficially normal.

The examination of sections stained with Weigert-Kultschitzky technique revealed two large and several smaller malacic foci (Fig. 421). Other numerous larger and smaller foci, not directly affecting the visual system, were scattered throughout the brain substance. Of all foci, the most conspicuous was the cuneal focus visible on the surface (*a* in sketches *2, 3, 4, 5*). It was wedge-shaped, with the base at the surface and an irregular, lacerated point penetrating deep into the subcortical core of the cuneus. In part, this focus directly affected the upper lip of the calcarine fissure (*Calc. Fiss.* or *C.F.*) and destroyed the marginal zone of the striate cortex in it, and in part it may have interrupted fibers of the upper segment of the visual radia-

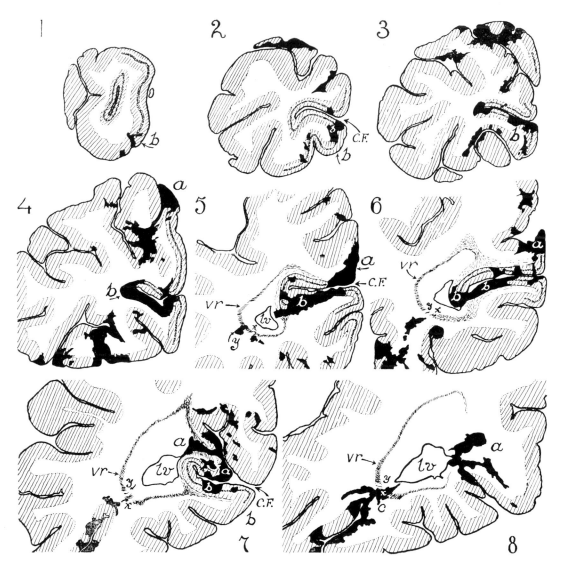

FIG. 420.—Case M. Hoffmann: coronal sections through the left occipital lobe, beginning with occipital pole (*1*) and ending with a level not far from the callosal splenium (*8*). (For description *see* text.) *Labeling: a,* large cuneal focus which destroyed a portion of the upper calcarine lip; *b,* focus, little seen from the surface, which destroyed much of the lower calcarine lip; *c,* focus in the tentorial surface of the temporal lobe which interrupted a bundle in the lateral salient of the visual radiation at *x; C.F.,* calcarine fissure; *lv,* lateral ventricle (posterior horn); *vr,* visual radiation; *y,* gap in the visual radiation caused by a small focus of softening. Striate area marked by a stippled intracortical stripe of Gennari. (*Cf.* Fig. 421.)

tion streaming into the upper lip (*vr*). Several small foci in the cortex of the upper lip further added to the injury of this lip. The floor of the calcarine fissure and the adjoining parts of the striate cortex, as well as the lower lip on the levels described, did not show any damage.

On intermediate levels the small foci in the upper lip and in its subcortical substance increased in extent and interrupted fibers of the upper segment of radiation at the point of entry into that lip (sketch 5). One of these foci (*c*), placed at the deepest point in the floor of the calcarine fissure, interrupted fibers in the calcar avis next to the posterior horn of the ventricle (*lv*). A noteworthy feature of some of the smaller foci was their restriction to the striate cortex itself, formerly a point of dispute between Henschen and Monakow; our evidence, supporting Henschen's viewpoint, shows the possibility of strictly cortical lesions besides

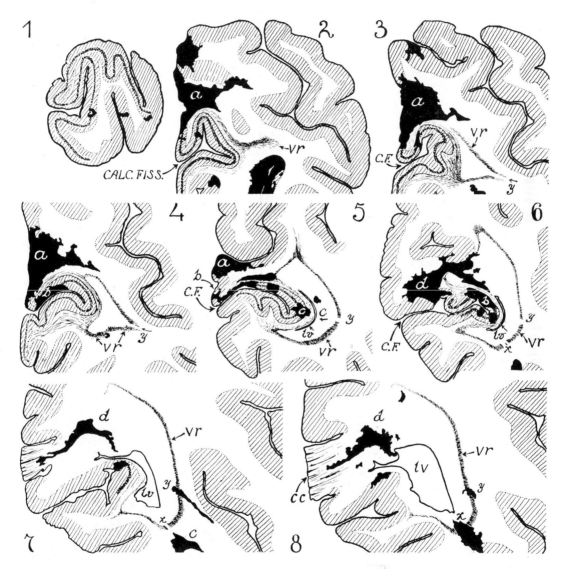

FIG. 421.—Case M. Hoffmann: coronal sections through the right occipital lobe, beginning with the occipital pole (*1*) and ending with a level in the splenium of the corpus callosum (*8*). (For description *see* text.) *Labeling: a*, large cuneal focus visible on the medial face of the occipital lobe in Fig. 419; *b*, series of small, mostly strictly cortical, foci in upper calcarine lip; *c*, small focus in *calcar avis* opposite the floor of the calcarine fissure; *C.F.* and *CALC. FISS.*, calcarine fissure; *lv*, posterior horn of lateral ventricle; *vr*, visual radiation; *y*, gap in the visual radiation caused by a small focus visible in sketches *7* and *8*; *x*, another similar gap in the lateral salient of the visual radiation. Striate area indicated by a stippled intracortical line of Gennari and Vicq-d'Azyr. (*Cf.* Fig. 420.)

other, larger ones that destroy both the cortex and the subcortical fiber substance.

The series of small foci just described, which on intermediate levels practically eliminated the upper calcarine lip, formed a bridge to a large and quite irregularly shaped focus (*d*), extending from the upper calcarine lip (sketch *6*) into the fibrous core and farther anteriorly into the splenium of the corpus callosum (*7, 8*). This focus interrupted the most anterior fibers in the upper segment of the visual radiation (*vr*) supplying the upper calcarine lip. Because of this and because of the several small foci located in the most anterior portion of the striate cortex, this cortex must have been put entirely out of function (*6, 7*).

The polar portion of the striate area in the right occipital lobe remained fairly well preserved except for the presence of a few minute malacic foci, strictly confined to the cortex (sketch *1*). The subcortical fibrous core of this lobe was also mostly spared. In spite of this, it is probable that many afferent fibers supplying the foveal-macular cortex of the pole must have been interrupted by smaller and medium-sized malacic foci in the core of the hemisphere. A fairly large focus, located in the ventrolateral "salient" of the radiation, made a breach at *x* (sketch *8*), while another similar but smaller focus made a breach at another point in the radiation (*y*). Such gaps made in the solid formation of the sagittal fiber strata, measuring approximately 1 mm., could be followed posteriorly on many sections through the hemisphere, retaining the same relative distance from one another; this agrees with the composition of the radiation of individual, parallel bundles as revealed by dissection (*see* Figs. 235, 236). Farther back toward the occipital pole, where the fibers of the radiation begin to deviate from a sagittal direction, these gaps became obliterated.

In summary, in the right occipital lobe a series of foci, beginning anteriorly with the splenium of the corpus callosum and extending backward through the upper calcarine lip close to, but not quite reaching, the occipital pole partially destroyed or separated this lip from its afferent fibers. On anterior levels the striate cortex was almost completely eliminated. The pole of the lobe was largely spared. A number of

fiber bundles in the visual radiation, particularly in the "lateral salient," were interrupted. The lower calcarine lip was spared throughout its entire length except in its most anterior portion. The same was also the case with most of the fibers of the radiation supplying that lip.

7. RIGHT LATERAL GENICULATE NUCLEUS.— Along its entire length from its oral to its caudal extremity (*1–10*), this nucleus showed an irregular zone of retrograde cell degeneration in all sections (Fig. 422). The zone was almost entirely restricted to the inner half of the nucleus, closer to the thalamus (*cf.* Figs. 205, 206, 208).

On most posterior levels where there are only four cell layers, the degeneration was represented by two narrow stripes confined to the inner or medial third of the nucleus (sketch *1*). The stripes passed through all four layers, resembling similar stripes in experiments involving minute lesions in the foveal segment of the striate cortex (thus in Figs. 254, 258). These stripes were probably caused by an interruption of two separate fiber bundles in the intermediate foveal-macular segment of the visual radiation by two small softenings (*x* and *y*, in Fig. 421, sketches *7, 8*). Toward the middle levels these two small zones merged with the others (*2–7* in Fig. 422) until on the anterior levels the entire medial half of the nucleus was found degenerated (*8, 9*), the zone again decreasing in the rostral tip of the nucleus (*10*).

The left lateral geniculate nucleus, because of inexpert handling, was unfortunately lost.

8. CORRELATION OF FUNCTIONAL DISTURBANCE AND PATHOANATOMICAL FINDINGS.—The analysis and correlation of clinical symptoms and of pathoanatomical findings in this case, in spite of the complex situation caused by bilateral lesions and by a great number of foci, did not offer insurmountable difficulties.

The striking feature was the presence of almost identical and symmetrically located foci, spreading from the callosal splenium along its forceps major into the anterior portions of both calcarine fissures. In a very similar way they partly destroyed and partly separated the most anterior segments of the striate areae from the upper segments of both visual radiations (Fig. 420, *7;* Fig. 421, *6*). This destruction, in accordance with our functional scheme of the radiation, satisfactorily accounts for the complete elimination of the temporal monocular crescents of both fields of view (Fig. 259).

The long, but narrow and less penetrating, lesion, *a*, in the left cuneus (Fig. 418; sketches *4–6* in Fig. 420), spreading over the upper lip along its middle and anterior extent, with several small foci in this lip, may help explain the

sizable loss in the right upper binocular quadrants, must have made more complete a functional loss in the right lower quadrants, caused by an incomplete damage to the left upper calcarine lip. The spared segments of the cortex in the upper lip (sketches *1* and *2* in Fig. 420), in turn, may account for the sparing of the central parts of the right lower quadrants.

The large wedge-shaped lesion *a* in the right

RIGHT LATERAL GENICULATE NUCLEUS

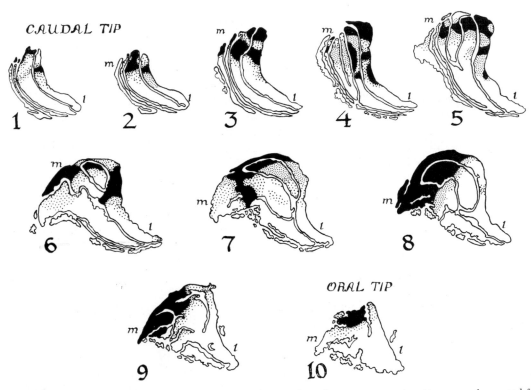

FIG. 422.—Case M. Hoffmann: right lateral geniculate nucleus shown on coronal sections, evenly spaced from the caudal extremity (*1*) to the anterior end of the nucleus (*10*). Zones of retrograde cell degeneration given in solid black and stippled; normal parts of the nucleus in white. Note that almost entire degeneration is found in the inner, or medial, half of the nucleus next to the thalamus (*m*), the lateral half (*l*) remaining normal. This degeneration was caused by a large wedge-shaped focus *a* and by smaller foci *b* in the cuneal lip of the right occipital lobe (Figs. 419, 421). It caused blindness in the left lower homonymous quadrants of both fields of view, including the lower half of the contralateral monocular temporal crescent (Fig. 417).

loss of the binocular portion of the right lower quadrants, even though fair-sized segments of the striate cortex and of the incoming fibers of the upper segment of the visual radiation were spared on the same levels. This aggravation was probably caused by the almost complete destruction of the lower lip by lesion *b* on the same levels. This destruction, besides causing a

cuneus (Fig. 419; sketches *2–4* in Fig. 421), together with the several smaller foci (*b*) in the upper calcarine lip of the same right side (Fig. 421, sketches *4–6*), must be held responsible for a loss in the binocular portions of the left lower field quadrants. Moreover, the sparing of a wedge-shaped sector in the same left lower quadrants along the horizontal meridians is to be explained by a sparing of the striate cortex in the upper lip of the right calcarine fissure on posterior levels, as far as the occipital pole (sketches *1, 2, 3* in same figure). The sparing of the lower lip of the right calcarine fissure along practically its entire length (sketches *1–5*), except on its most anterior levels (sketch *6*), agrees well with the preserved left upper binocular quadrants and a loss of the upper half of the left monocular crescent. A degeneration found in the right lateral geniculate nucleus is an accurate copy of the supranuclear lesions found in the right occipital lobe just described (Fig. 422).

The sparing of a small wedge-shaped sector in the left lower quadrants extending along the horizontal meridians to approximately 60° is to be interpreted by the integrity of the striate cortex in the deeper portion of the right upper calcarine lip on levels closer to the occipital pole (sketches *2–5* in Fig. 421). The position along the horizontal meridian and the varying width of the sector, especially its tapering in the peripheral direction, are understandable when the location of the spared cortex, close to the deepest point of the fissure, and its decreased extent from posterior to anterior levels are taken into consideration.

The poles of both occipital lobes were not grossly damaged (Fig. 420, *1;* Fig. 421, *1*). This merits special attention, since the perimetric notes expressly state that the blindness included the inferior halves of the field centers also, even though the charts show a small sparing below the horizontal meridians, both for white and for colors. A functional test with reading about three weeks before death revealed a marked decrease in visual acuity, making the patient unable to read any print. Obviously, the few minute malacic foci in the two polar cortices are insufficient to account for this rapid preterminal impairment of the fine spatial sense of the central foveal apparatus. For this the blame must be placed directly upon the malacic foci in the core of both hemispheres, especially the foci $c, c,$ or x and $y,$ arising from the inferior face of both temporal lobes (Fig. 420, *8;* Fig. 421, *8*). These foci, in a bilaterally remarkably symmetrical way, have damaged precisely those portions of both visual radiations which, according to our scheme of the visual pathways,

are instrumental in the transmission of impulses from the central areae and foveae, or "maculae" of the clinicians, to the polar portions of the striate areae (*see* Figs. 225, 259, 260; *cf. also* cases MUNSON and HOLT, in this chapter).

The last-mentioned observation poses an important question that concerns the very foundations of cerebral vascular organization: Why, in a decaying brain, should precisely those parts of the transmitting visual fibers which are related to the centers of the fields of view most intensively used suffer a degenerative vascular insult in both hemispheres of the brain, at precisely the same moment, and in almost exactly the same manner, because of the degeneration of small vessels which do not seem to be directly interconnected anatomically? It is a further elaboration of the problem of the functional symmetry of both hemispheres, strikingly demonstrated in our case by symmetrical lesions in the anterior segments of the striate areae and of the visual radiations (Fig. 420, *7;* Fig. 421, *6; cf. also* chap. XI, 9[3, last paragraph]).

Another important topic on which case HOFFMANN sheds light is the controversial problem of bilateral representation of each complete fovea-macula in both cerebral hemispheres. This problem is dealt with in detail in chapter XI, 8, 9. Here only the most concrete arguments against this hypothesis, emanating from our case, may be pointed out.

As is clear from the history of this case and from the field charts, the monocular temporal crescents of both sides with a goodly portion of the adjoining binocular fields, as well as the inferior quadrants, were eliminated prior to the plotting of the first charts of the fields of view (Fig. 417). In spite of this extensive loss, our patient still had fair central acuity at that time, although it dropped abruptly a few weeks later (*see* pars. 3, 4, this section).

The loss of the peripheral portions of both fields during the early period was accordingly compatible with good central acuity. Since the loss of the peripheral portions of the two fields is fully accounted for by the destruction of the anterior portions of both striate areae, the hypothesis of a foveal-macular localization in the oral-rostral portion of the striate area becomes untenable. This, in turn, makes localization of central vision in the polar portion of the striate areae mandatory. A preterminal reduction of central acuity in this case, explainable by an impairment of the foveal-macular fibers in both radiations, harmonizes well with this view.

9. Summary.—In case Hoffmann, far-reaching destruction of the anterior portions of both striate areae fully accounts for the loss of both monocular temporal crescents, while partial destruction and undermining of the upper calcarine lip of both sides account for the loss of

the binocular portions of the inferior field quadrants of both sides. Preterminal reduction of the central acuity, in spite of the sparing of both occipital poles, was caused by symmetrical malacic damage to the foveal-macular fibers in both visual radiations. The psychotic symptoms, especially disorientation in space, are explainable by disseminate damage to the extra-striate parts of the parietotemporal-occipital lobes and their fiber systems.

References: See chapter XI, 3, 4, 5, 9.

SEC. 9. CASE OF CENTRAL HOMONYMOUS HEMIANOPIC SCOTOMA

1. History.—Kraft (Crofts), Harry, age fifty-four years, Billings Hospital, University of Chicago, UNo. 83289.

Diagnosis: Right central homonymous hemianopic scotomas caused by a local vascular spasm developed on the basis of primary vascular hypertension.

Until three or four months before admission the patient had been in rather good health. The trouble began with gradually increasing persistent headaches behind the eyes, radiating to the occiput, particularly on the left side. The headaches were more pronounced during the morning. Two months before admission, the blood pressure was 174/100. Two days before admission, there was a rather sudden development of a right central homonymous scotoma. The patient noticed that "things looked queer." While reading, he could see only the first half of a word (a symptom described by Wilbrand 1907 as a "hemianopic disturbance of reading"). Similarly, he could see only half of a person's face, while at the same time he was able to see the objects in the periphery of the affected side.

2. Ophthalmological examination.—An ophthalmoscopic examination showed a very slight arteriosclerosis in the retinal fundi, which were otherwise normal. The fields taken with an ordinary perimeter revealed right homonymous central scotomas of an approximate extent up to 6° along the horizontal meridians and up to 4° along the vertical (upper fields, in Fig. 423). According to a stereoscopic field plotting, the horizontal extent of the scotomas was up to 7 degrees, the vertical from 3 to 4 degrees below, and up to 5 degrees above, the horizontal meridians (lower fields in the same figure). In the

stereoscopic charts, remarkably, there was also a minute sparing of less than 1 degree around the fixation point, but only in the right field. This slight incongruity may be of less significance than it appears, since the patient was fatigued from the preceding examination and had a severe headache. (*See* chap. XI, 9 [1].)

3. Somatic examination.—There were very few indications of general arteriosclerosis. Nor was there any enlargement of the heart, although numerous extrasystoles were present. The blood pressure was 185/110. Hyaline casts and traces of albumen were found in the urine. The neurological examination was negative.

4. Subsequent development.—As far as the available information goes, the above-described "episode" terminated in an incomplete recovery, which remained stationary for several years. Gross visual disturbance disappeared within three days or so after onset. Seven months later the patient still occasionally saw "black spots" in the right fields, but otherwise saw well. Four years after the beginning, there was no recurrence of the central scotoma. During this time he was treated for hypertension, and the blood pressure decreased to 146/86. Five years after the beginning of the trouble, however, the field examination showed a contraction up to 40°, although at intervals the patient seemed to be able to see in the periphery as well. The contraction was bilateral but was more marked in the right field. There was, besides, some reversal of the limits for the red and blue hues. A central scotoma at that time was not mentioned.

5. COMMENT.—In view of the absence of autopsy, only circumstantial evidence can be used to determine the probable seat and nature of the injury responsible for the scotomas. Since these scotomas had a hemianopic character and were fairly congruous in size and shape, it is practically certain that they were caused by a

duces the possible location of the injury either to the visual cortex or to the visual radiation.

A single, small transient thrombotic or spastic ischemic focus either at the left occipital pole next to the posterior boundary of the striate area or in the intermediate foveal-macular segment of the visual radiation at its "lateral

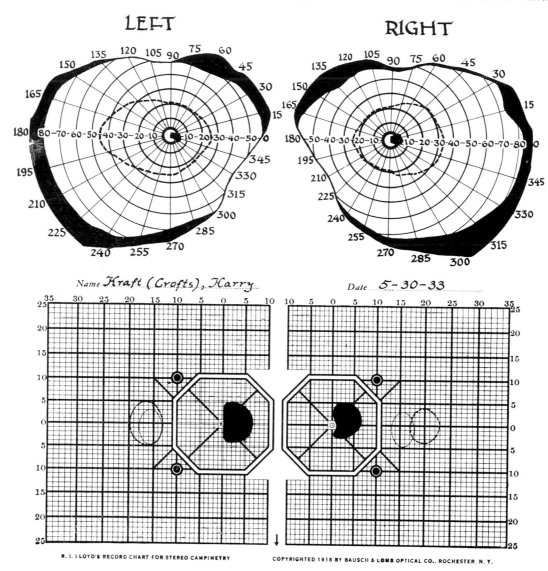

FIG. 423.—Case H. Kraft: right central homonymous hemianopic scotoma, presumably caused either by a local "vascular spasm" or rather hemorrhage, developing on the basis of a primary vascular hypertension.

single lesion and that the seat of the lesion was above the chiasma.

In a further attempt to determine the locality of the injury, the optic tract and the lateral geniculate nucleus may safely be ruled out, for the reasons discussed in chapter XI, 3. This re-

salient" could have caused a comparable disturbance (latter alternative illustrated by lesions *x* and *y* in case HOFFMANN, in Figs. 420, 421). In both localities the anatomical-functional units are widely spaced, making it possible for a small focus to produce a restricted injury, which, in the centers of the fields of view, manifests itself in a minute field defect. The most likely underlying pathoanatomical mechanism was vascular, probably spastic.

The noteworthy features in this case were the rapid initial improvement and the long duration of the residual symptoms. The first may be partly explained by the multiple blood supply of the occipital pole discussed in chapter X, 6, 7, 8. The long duration, as well as a gradual contraction of both fields, was most likely caused by a gradual spread of the basic deficiency of the cerebral blood vessels, by an essentially less efficient blood supply of the anterior calcarine fissure, and by the vascular interdependence of the occipital lobes discussed in case HOFF-MANN.

References: Anders & Eicke 1939; Beauvieux 1930; Beauvieux *et al.* 1929; Rea 1941; Uhthoff 1927; Traquair 1923, 1946; C. B. Walsh 1947; Walsh & Ford 1940; Wilbrand 1907, 1926; *see also* chap. XI, 7; *Symposium on Blood Supply* (American) 1938; and *Symposium on Blood Supply* (German) 1939.

SEC. 10. CASE OF CENTRAL HOMONYMOUS HEMIANOPIC SCOTOMA WITH POST MORTEM EXAMINATION

1. HISTORY.—MALLORY, Dr. Frank B., noted American pathologist, age seventy-eight years, of Boston, Massachusetts.

Diagnosis: Homonymous hemianopic scotomas in the upper quadrants of the left fields of view caused by an old brain softening of the inferior lip of the calcarine fissure in the right occipital lobe. The brain specimen received from Dr. G. A. Bennett, of the Department of Pathology, Harvard University Medical School, UNo. H-41-530, on November 27, 1941, thanks to Professor K. S. Lashley, of Harvard University and of Yerkes Laboratories of Primate Biology, at Orange Park, Florida.

At the age of eighteen the patient suffered from a streptococcal infection of the right side of the face and of the right eye. The cornea of that eye was affected by an ulcer which left a scar and impaired vision. Similar trouble apparently developed forty years later.

From his late twenties on, the patient began to suffer from recurrent attacks of an "ophthalmic migraine," regularly accompanied by a scintillating scotoma in the left fields of view, sometimes also by nausea.

At the approximate age of forty-seven, on a Sunday in the summer of 1910 while at dinner, immediately after the reflection from a white surface of bright sunlight into the patient's eyes, he began to complain of brilliant flashes recurring at very frequent intervals, leaving within a few hours—at any rate in less than a day—a visual field defect. The defect, according to the patient's estimate, was at first large, but subsequently it "cleared up." The duration of this attack was approximately from 20 to 40 minutes. Whether or not the subjectively experienced "light" was colored and whether or not the photism had a definite shape it was not possible to ascertain by questioning the patient's associates.

After this attack the patient remained for the rest of his life very sensitive to brilliant white light, and flashes of sun on a window in a neighboring building would often bring on a transitory attack of scintillating scotoma. The spontaneous attacks of scintillating scotoma, off and on during the subsequent years, were of short duration, none lasting more than a minute or two, and without further restricting the fields of view.

At the age of fifty-six the patient's right hand became infected at autopsy, followed by erysipelas and high fever. At the age of sixty-one the patient began to suffer from attacks of syncope, with a lapse of consciousness for periods up to 30 minutes. These attacks did not have the character of epilepsy and were diagnosed as cerebral ischemia caused by a spasm of the arteries. At the age of seventy-one bothersome pains appeared in the lower parts of the legs, developing into an intermittent claudication. At the age of seventy-two the patient's memory for recent events began to fail, and he occasionaly became disoriented. With advancing age the mental symptoms grew more pronounced.

In February, 1941, six or seven months prior to his death, the patient appears to have suffered a fall, thereafter experiencing difficulty in moving his legs. After this accident he lost interest in his laboratory, where, until then, he had been doing a certain amount of work. He also ceased reading and listening to the radio. Whether this was because of his eye trouble or because he lost interest, his consulting physician could not determine but was inclined to attribute the condition to cerebral pathology. Pains in the lower parts of his legs, attributed by the patient to "rheumatism," induced him to seek relief in Florida. A blood examination at that time showed moderate anemia, with 85 per cent hemoglobin and 3 million red blood corpuscles.

His physical and mental condition gradually deteriorated. On September 17, 1941, he fell down a flight of stairs and was found unconscious. The right side of his face and skull were bruised, and five ribs on the right side were fractured. Subsequent to this accident the patient contracted pneumonia, from which he died on September 27, 1941 (for obituary *see Science,* v. 94, p. 430).

2. Ophthalmological examination.—In 1911, or one year after the dramatic attack of photisms resulting in a defect of the fields of view, the patient consulted an ophthalmologist (Dr. F. H. Verhoeff, of Boston, Mass.), in order to have a foreign body removed from his right cornea. On this occasion a superficial examination showed a large hemianopic scotoma in the left upper fields, "too far from the macula to cause him any disturbances in microscopic work." No accurate plotting of the fields was done on that occasion, however. The patient was conscious of the defects in the fields of view, although ordinarily this did not annoy him except when playing tennis. The central acuity was 20/15 in each eye.

In March, 1934, seven years and six months prior to his death, at the age of seventy-one, the patient was examined by an ophthalmologist for an undisclosed reason (Dr. J. H. Waite, of Boston, Mass.). On this occasion the only plotting of the fields of view was made. The testing with a Ferree & Rand 330-mm. arc perimeter showed normal peripheral limits of the fields of view (Fig. 424, upper fields). The examination with a tangent screen at 1,000 mm. disclosed absolute homonymous hemianopic defects in

the upper left quadrants, extending from the fixation points along the vertical meridians for 10° and along the horizontal meridians for 20°, "predicting a lesion in the occipital cortex on the right side and below the calcarine fissure" (lower fields).

In the right eye an old posterior synechia, binding the iris to the lens, and a centrally located nebula of the cornea were found, sufficient to explain the maximum acuity of 20/40 with a correction. In the retina of this eye there was a moderate sclerosis of the blood vessels, but no retinopathy was found. The left eye was normal except for sclerosis of the retinal vessels and astigmatism of $\frac{1}{2}$ diopter, its acuity with a correction being 20/10. The ocular muscles were well balanced by the Maddox test, but the stereopsis was faulty.

The additional information obtained from the patient's son, Dr. Tracy B. Mallory, revealed his father as a conscientious, hardworking scientist, always intent upon his work, never communicating his symptoms to his associates, and visiting physicians only rarely. In his microscopic work he always used a monocular microscope, using his left eye, and preferred daylight illumination. His detailed discrimination or visual acuity and his appreciation of minute shades of color were both extraordinary. His consulting ophthalmologist, who was also one of his staff, "never knew a man who could see more detail in a microscopic section of tissue within a short time than Dr. Mallory."

Until a year or two prior to his death his visual acuity and form vision were at a supernormal level. In a microscopic slide he was able to see more than other competent histopathologists. Despite a visual field defect and a scarring of the right cornea, he was able to play tennis until he was well into his seventies, and his judgment of the speed and distance of the ball was surprisingly good. When reading, the patient apparently experienced no difficulty in following the lines and in scanning the page from left to right, the field defect being on the left side of the points of fixation. The patient knew of his defect, although it is doubtful whether in the circumstances of daily life he was conscious of it. He never complained of visual hallucinations.

3. GENERAL PATHOANATOMICAL EXAMINATION.—The autopsy, made 12 hours post mortem, revealed the following changes: marked generalized arteriosclerosis; marked coronary arteriosclerosis; a large, old infarct of the left ventricle of the heart, likewise small irregular areas of fibrous replacement just visible to the unaided eye; aneurysm of the abdominal aorta, with an organized mural thrombus; arteriosclerosis of the cerebral arteries; an old infarct in the right occipital lobe of the brain; bronchopneumonia of the inferior lobes of both lungs;

etc. A dominant feature was the extreme degree of arteriosclerosis. The cause of death was bronchial pneumonia in consequence of a recent fall and trauma associated with it.

4. GROSS EXAMINATION OF THE BRAIN.—Both cerebral hemispheres, grossly examined, appeared symmetrical and showed no discoloration from hemorrhage or other causes. No areas of softening could be detected by palpation. The total brain weight was 1,400 gm. The carotid arteries were extremely tortuous and mark

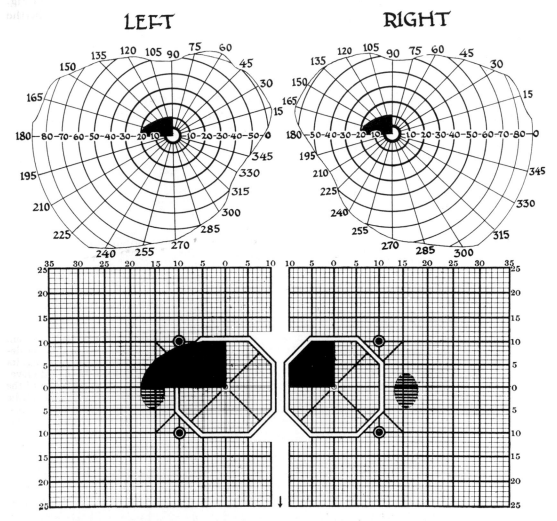

FIG. 424.—Case F. B. Mallory: centroparacentral homonymous hemianopic scotoma, strictly limited to the left upper quadrants, extending to the points of fixation, persisting without change for more than thirty years. Upper fields plotted with Ferree & Rand arc perimeter, lower fields taken with Bjerrum's tangent screen, then transferred to Lloyd's stereocampimetric chart of Bausch & Lomb. Cause: a limited softening of the lingual lip of the calcarine fissure of the right occipital lobe, caused by a transient arterial spasm. Note linear boundaries of the field defects accurately outlined by vertical and horizontal meridians as far as their intersection. Mariotte's blind spots in lower charts indicated by horizontal shading. Courtesy Dr. J. H. Waite, of Boston, Mass. (*Cf.* Figs. 425–27.)

edly thickened, with small calcified areas in their walls. Evidence of arteriosclerosis in isolated patches for a considerable distance was found in the larger vessels at the base of the brain.

The sectioning of the brain into thin parallel slabs revealed a single long and narrow scar on the inner face of the right occipital lobe, located in the lower lip of the calcarine fissure (solid black, including white shading, in Fig. 425).

The configuration of the right occipital lobe showed a calcarine fissure (*mc, lci, lcs*) entirely

beyond which it proceeded in a fairly straight course in the direction of the occipital pole. This it did not reach but divided into an ascending and a descending prong running parallel to the contour of the pole (*lcs, lci*).

The striate area, projected onto the inner face of the occipital lobe, formed a narrow wedge asymmetrically divided by the calcarine fissure, with a shorter and wider stripe in the upper calcarine lip and a longer and more narrow stripe in the lower one (stippled area in Fig. 425). As in the majority of specimens, in the

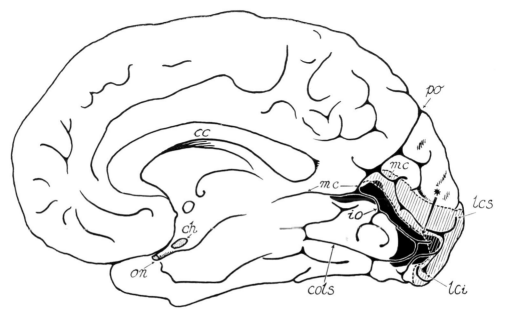

FIG. 425.—Case F. B. Mallory: right cerebral hemisphere, showing the size, shape, and location of the lesion, caused by a large ischemic softening. The lesion (*solid black*), largely outside the striate area, undermined or destroyed the striate cortex in the lower calcarine lip. The striate area is indicated by black or white shading, its boundaries indicated by black or white broken lines. The arrow, marked with an asterisk (*), indicates the leve behind which, right to the arrow, a portion of the striate cortex was destroyed, whereas in front, to the left of the arrow, little or no direct damage to the striate cortex or its afferent fibers was done. Note a strict limitation of the lesion to the lower calcarine lip. *Labeling: cc*, corpus callosum; *ch*, chiasma of optic nerves; *cols*, collateral sulcus; *io*, inferior occipital sulcus; *lci*, lower prong of lateral or posterior calcarine sulcus; *lcs*, upper prong of the same sulcus; *mc*, medial or anterior calcarine sulcus; *on*, optic nerve; *po*, parieto-occipital sulcus.

located on the inner face of the lobe (*cf.* chap. VIII, 3 [5]). The lateral or posterior calcarine sulci (*lci, lcs*) at the occipital pole were superficially continuous with the medial or anterior calcarine sulcus (*mc*), but the basic sulcal arrangement probably resembled the type shown in Figure 293, middle sketch (no detailed macroscopic inspection was made for the sake of further microscopic study). Just anterior to the point of branching of the occipitoparietal sulcus (*po*), the calcarine fissure made a sharp bend,

lower lip the striate area extended farther anteriorly than in the upper lip, where it was present only as far as the occipitoparietal sulcus (*cf.* Figs. 289, 290, etc.). Posteriorly the striate area enveloped the occipital pole (*cf.* Figs. 288, 293).

Upon superficial examination, the lesion—a smooth, narrow scar caused by an old malacic infarct thirty-one years earlier—was found to be situated in the lower or lingual lip of the calcarine fissure, corresponding to the narrow, black zone below *mc* and in front of *lci*, in Figure 425. Its anterior extremity was midway between the callosal splenium and the junction of the parieto-occipital and calcarine fissures. Posteriorly the superficial scar extended as far as the descending prong of the calcarine fissure. At its posterior extremity the lesion fanned out, extending over the posterior end of the fusiform gyrus and also a little beyond the collateral sulcus (*cols*). On cross-section the scar appeared in part as a narrow, shrunken lingual gyrus, yellowish in color, just ventral to the calcarine fissure. At the posterior end of the lesion the gray matter was largely destroyed, but the white matter appeared to be quite well preserved throughout the extent of the lesion.

The striate area, based on macroscopic examination, appeared to be affected only in its posterior segment along the calcarine fissure and in front of its descending prong (*lci*), while the polar striate area behind the prong did not appear to have been directly damaged.

5. Microscopic examination of the brain. —The preceding description of the extent of the lesion is to be somewhat qualified by the examination of sections through the right occipital lobe stained with the Weigert-Kultschitzky method for myelin fibers and with the Nissl-Lenhossék toluidine blue stain for nerve cells (Figs. 426, 427).

The microscopic examination showed the lesion to be somewhat more extensive than at an inspection of the intact specimen (solid black area, including parts shaded by white lines, in Fig. 425). Briefly, all along the inferior calcarine lip the extreme margin of the striate area was damaged by the malacic process. Just how much of the striate area was destroyed here could only be guessed, but it appears that it was merely a narrow zone along most of the inferior fringe of the striate area. One exception was the anterior extremity of the striate area at the cuneal lip, the other at the posterior extremity next to the inferior calcarine prong. In the first locality the extent of damage at best was small (marked by white dots at *l*, sketch *D*, Fig. 426). In the posterior locality, close to the occipital pole, the lesion definitely destroyed a portion of the lower calcarine lip (*l*, sketch *A*, same figure). This appeared to be the principal damage that must be blamed for the clinically found scoto-

mas. Here most of the cortex lining the inferior calcarine prong (*lci*) stained poorly and contained but few of the obliquely coursing intracortical fibers, elsewhere identified as the terminals of the visual radiation. The anterior limit of the polar focus was at a point indicated by an arrow marked by an asterisk (*) in Figure 425.

Along most of the calcarine fissure (*mc*) between these two localities, the lesion partly un-

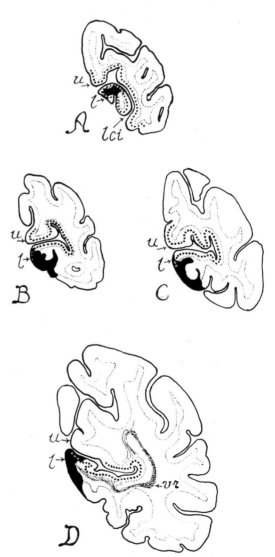

Fig. 426.—Case F. B. Mallory: coronal sections through successive levels of the right occipital lobe shown in Fig. 425, beginning with the occipital pole (*A*) and ending with a level through the anterior portion of the cuneus (*D*). The striate area indicated by dotted lines, the lesion by solid black. Visual radiation *vr*. Note that the lesion on all levels is strictly confined to the lower calcarine lip. (*Cf.* sketch *B* in Fig. 427.)

dermined the lower calcarine lip, as shown in sketches *B* and *C*, in Figure 426, with little direct damage done to the fringe of the striate cortex in that lip (marked by a few white dots). This was remarkable, since the lesion (solid black in same sketches) undermined that lip for at least half its extent. Another noteworthy observation was the preservation of the incoming afferent fibers streaming from the lower segment of the visual radiation into the lower calcarine lip (*vr*, in Fig. 427). These fibers hugged the inferior boundary of the cortex very closely and gradually passed into it, where they could

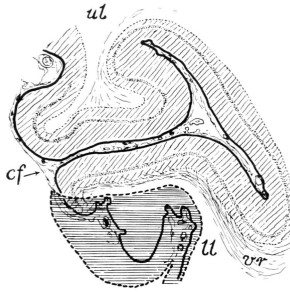

Fig. 427.—Case F. B. Mallory: slightly magnified detail of sketch *B* in Fig. 426. The horizontally shaded area indicates the probable size and shape of the normal lower calcarine lip, *ll*, shown here much reduced. The extent of the striate cortex indicated by an intracortical stippled stripe, the line of Gennari or Vicq-d'Azyr. Note fibers of the lower segment of the visual radiation, supplying the lower calcarine lip, well preserved, in spite of the proximity of the focus. *Labeling: cf,* calcarine fissure; *ll,* lower calcarine lip; *ul,* upper calcarine lip; *vr,* visual radiation.

be identified as terminals in the infra-Gennarian half of the cortex. In fiber stains the number of these slanting afferent fibers, as well as those of other categories such as radial, and the fine fuzz in and below the stripe of Gennari, belonging to the various association and callosal systems, were but little less abundant than those found in the upper calcarine lip on the same level, which remained at a considerable distance from the lesion.

In the sections stained for cells, other and even more marked changes from the norm than those in the sections stained for fibers were found in the undermined lower lip. Here all cells were a little paler, less numerous, and smaller in size than in the normal upper lip. In this process of general depletion and devitalization there were marked gradations in different layers. In general, the infra-Gennarian half of the cortex suffered most. Here the cells were markedly reduced in numbers, layer *6* being almost absent. In layer *5* the normally conspicuous Meynert's giant "solitary cells" were still recognizable but were much shrunken. In the inner granular layer the larger elements of sublayer *4-b* were quite atrophic, the process of atrophy having also affected sublayers *4-a* and *4-c*. In the supra-Gennarian layers the process of atrophy was less pronounced, even though noticeable, not excluding layer *1*. The atrophy had affected not only the cell bodies but also the intercellular substance, made up of the expansions of nerve cells and fibers.

The total reduction of the cortex in the lower calcarine lip may be guessed at one-tenth or more of its normal size. The intensity of the atrophic process decreased from the fringe of the lower lip, where it was most pronounced, toward the floor of the fissure, where it gradually faded away. The calcarine floor and the upper lip were entirely free from any recognizable pathological changes.

In summary, microscopic study of sections through the right occipital lobe confirmed and somewhat extended that obtained from gross macroscopic inspection. There was a single ancient malacic scar which undermined the lower calcarine lip along its entire length, encroaching upon the lower fringe of the striate area but little except at its anterior end, and more especially next to the lower calcarine prong. The afferent fibers of the visual radiation were found substantially spared, but the fiber connections with other cortical regions must have been largely severed. The cell and fiber content of the lower lip was found much depleted.

Whereas the principal pathological features of the right striate area were in good accord with the visual field defect, only a slight depletion of fibers was noticeable in the lower segment of the visual radiation—the external sagittal fiber stratum of the occipital lobe. In the "lateral salient" of the radiation, especially, there was no gap to be found, as could be expected from the site of the principal lesion in the occipital pole. A possible explanation may be the closing of the gap during the three decades following the vascular "episode."

The lateral geniculate nucleus, however, produced more positive clues. In the lateral fourth or less, in the so-called lateral spur, the cells were clearly atrophic, which would agree with the location of the lesion in the lower calcarine lip. In the posterior extremity of the nucleus, precisely where, from our experiments with monkeys described in chapter VII, 4, 5, one would expect them to be, clear signs of localized degeneration were found in all four cell layers on this level. The process bore the signs of retrograde degeneration, including local proliferation of the neuroglia. The location of the retrograde zone of degeneration in the most posterior extremity of the nucleus and its intensity agreed well with the principal lesion next to the inferior prong of the calcarine fissure.

6. Correlation between functional disturbance and the pathoanatomical findings.—The task in this, as in other similar cases, was to furnish a plausible explanation of the visual defect, observed during life, by means of the abnormal changes found in the brain.

A rough correlation, in the light of information about the organization of the central visual apparatus presented in chapters VI, VII, VIII, and X, was relatively easily made. A much more difficult problem was to give an exhaustive account of a long process of decay of a living, working, central nervous organ stretching over a period of almost five decades, beginning with the initial manifestations in the late twenties, down to the concluding phase of a long, laborious, and fruitful life. Hence the insistent queries as to the why, how, and when of the particular underlying process can be answered only conditionally. The somewhat sketchy clinical information on the visual disturbance recorded during life is also a hindrance, precluding any adequate interpretation.

The principal facts, in spite of the difficulties mentioned, are plain. Clinically, approximately thirty years prior to death, during a single cerebral vascular event or "episode" lasting only a few minutes, a homonymous hemianopic central scotoma in the left upper quadrants developed, which, after a relatively short initial period, apparently remained unchanged for the rest of the patient's life. As anatomical evidence of the cause of this scotoma, a shrunken malacic scar in the lower calcarine lip in the right occipital lobe was found. The underlying anatomical cause of the scotoma was a malacic focus in the lower lip, just in front of the inferior prong of the calcarine fissure (*lci*, in Fig. 425; *l* in Fig. 426). The affected territory, its anterior limit indicated by an arrow in the first figure, was situated along the lateral or posterior calcarine fissure, which is the later phylogenetic addition to the original calcarine fissural complex of the Primates (*cf.* chap. VIII, 3, and *lc* in accompanying illustrations). The much less extensive portion of the lesion in front of the level, indicated by an arrow marked by *, stretching along most of the calcarine fissure, whose lower lip it undermined, must be absolved from direct responsibility for the central scotoma.

The probable course of the pathophysiological process may have been as follows. In his early thirties, possibly even before, a state of cerebral vascular irritability developed, manifesting itself in recurrent attacks of an "ophthalmic migraine," regularly accompanied by a scintillating scotoma, sometimes also by headache and nausea. The eliciting factor or factors remain unknown and may only be surmised as any one or a combination of infections or toxins, including coffee, tea, tobacco, medical drugs, and, perhaps the most important, overexertion in eyework to be expected in an assiduous and eager microscopist ("dynamic factor").

During the fourth and fifth decades of life the same recurrent attacks of scintillating scotoma may have continued with increasing frequency and intensity, even though no mention was made of this in the scanty report. At one time, at the age of forty-seven, at mealtime, a particularly violent attack, apparently elicited by bright light stimulation, occurred, which left in its wake a permanent defect in the fields of view. During the subsequent years, milder attacks of scintillation took place without, however, further impairing the vision. While this indicated that the state of cerebrovascular irritability continued, the focal visual attacks ceased, ending in partial destruction of the central visual apparatus.

What the extent and quality of visual function was in the period just preceding the fateful attack remains unknown. It is possible that a careful testing would have disclosed some reduction of acuity or color vision in the territory later permanently affected, indicative of the wearing-out of the responsible artery. Equally beyond discovery is the actual condition of vision during the period immediately following the fateful attack. However, the fact that, according to the patient's own estimate, the defect was at first large and that it subsequently "cleared up" indicated a considerable reduction in the initial disturbance. Hence it is fairly certain that after the fateful attack not only the central but also the peripheral or extrafoveal-areal vision in the left upper quadrants was impaired.

This assumption is corroborated by the finding of a hemianopic scotoma "far up in the left corner of each eye," whereas a central scotoma on the same occasion was overlooked by the examining ophthalmologist. Slender as this evidence is, it nevertheless indicates that the peripheral or extrafoveal portions of the upper left quadrants may also have been initially impaired.

The peripheral fields subsequently improved to a degree subjectively appreciated as "normal." This restoration agrees well with the histological findings in the lower calcarine lip anterior to the point indicated by the arrow (*). Even though its structure was found below par when compared with the upper lip, it still preserved a majority, possibly most, of its cells and afferent fibers and some of the association fibers, permitting it to function in a fairly normal way. A slight retraction of the useful area along the periphery of the left upper quadrants—for example, up to 60° or 50° or less—which must be postulated from the actual destruction of the extreme margin of the lower lip, could also have been easily "absorbed" or disregarded in the patient's subjective experience.

As a final, residual state the only defect that mattered and the only one found during the plotting of the fields remained a central scotoma up to 20° in the horizontal meridian. But this, too, was so well psychophysiologically compensated for that the scotoma ordinarily did not inconvenience the patient except in certain difficult situations. Undoubtedly, the scotoma was no serious impediment to the patient's activity, including microscopy, during the thirty remaining years of his life. This is noteworthy, since his occupation certainly required a high degree of "epicritic vision" (one of the patient's co-workers "never knew a man who could see more detail in a microscopic section of tissue within a short time than Dr. Mallory").

In the evaluation of the patient's defect, the completeness of the pathoanatomical destruction in the affected portion of the striate cortex and the degree of functional impairment to be expected in the scotomatous territory are also to be considered. It is possible that while finer discrimination was here abolished, or at least made more difficult, not all vision was destroyed. A "hard" scotoma, difficult to crack, or a high-threshold condition may perhaps be a more adequate description. Hence, under the ordinary conditions of clinical testing, an impenetrable or "absolute" scotoma would be found, while under favorable conditions some stimuli would still be appreciated.

This interpretation would agree better with a sparing of segments of fairly well-preserved striate cortex and its afferent fibers adjoining the malacic focus along the lower calcarine, especially along the lower calcarine prong and probably behind it, in the occipital pole (thus in sketch A, Fig. 426). This would also fit the presence of some crisscrossing infra-Gennarian fibers experimentally identified as the terminals of the geniculo-calcarine visual radiation, entirely absent only in the localities where the striate cortex was completely undermined. A territorially discontinuous lesion in the polar cortex, varying in degree at different points, and its diffuse character and long duration reflected in a patchy appearance in the zone of retrograde degeneration in the posterior extremity of the lateral geniculate nucleus, with a few scattered nests of relatively preserved cells, would also harmonize with this view.

The preceding considerations logically lead to a question of the genesis of the entire pathological process. From the clinical symptoms, consisting in the recurrent attacks of scintillating scotomas for many years preceding the fateful "episode," and from the sudden onset and short duration of the principal event that had left in its wake a scotomatous defect, it is beyond doubt that the anatomical basis of the responsible underlying process was vascular. Less certain is the identity of the vessel, owing to individual variations in blood supply of the occipital lobe, as pointed out in chapter X.

A careful study of the serial sections showed that the main stem of the calcarine artery (*ca*) and its continuation—termed in this book *principal calcarine artery* (*pca*)—were in no way to be blamed, since the vessels in the calcarine fissure were all of normal appearance and were patent. The only vessels that would come into consideration were those supplying the lingual gyrus on the inner face of the hemisphere. These, in our own specimens used for the study of blood supply in chapter X, have been termed *posterior temporo-occipital artery* (*poteocca*), *inferior calcarine* or *paracalcarine artery* (*ica* or *ical*, or *paca*), and *accessory inferior calcarine artery* (*accica*).

Since in case MALLORY the lesion did not extend laterally beyond the inferior occipital sulcus (*io*), as it did in case MANTENO (*see* Fig. 428), the stem of the posterior temporo-occipital artery must be ruled out. This leaves as an alternative either the *ica* (*paca*), the *accica*, or the posterior branch of *poteocca*. Closest to the required type would come *ica* (*paca*) or *ical*, depicted in Figures 369, 372. Its secondary branches, however, in case MALLORY did not enter the calcarine fissure, which appears to have depended entirely on the calcarine artery. (*Cf. also* Fig. 374.)

Microscopic examination of sections surprisingly revealed no obstructed, sclerosed vessels (as, e.g., in the MANTENO case). Most vessels, including those in the degenerated territory, were found patent, some filled with formed blood elements, the erythrocytes. The very artery responsible for the necrosis, deeply sunk in the pial fold of the inferior medial paracalcarine sulcus, surrounded by its bared walls caused by a necrotic colliquation and removal of the cortical tissue, was found wide open and of normal size.

This observation forces one to conclude that the essence of the fateful vascular event occurring thirty years earlier was not an occlusion of the blood vessel in the sense of a permanent thrombosis or embolism, as is usually implied by such a definition in clinical diagnosis. Rather, the pathophysiological cause may be visualized as a temporary occlusion owing to an arterial spasm or angiospasm, lasting long enough to cut off the necessary flow of blood, hence primarily an anoxemia or hypoxemia. An unavoidable consequence was the suffocation of the sensitive nervous parenchyma, varying in intensity or degree in different parts of the vascular tree, all the way from a slight impairment to complete death of the nerve cells. A further process was merely a sequence of the histopathological changes induced by suffocation of the neurons, resulting in the picture found in the post mortem conditions. (On the extreme sensitiveness of the nerve cells of deep cortical layers to anoxia *see* Adrian in *J. Physiol.*, v. 88, quoted by Burns 1951; *see also* R. W. Gerard 1937, 1938, 1941.)

In the final analysis, the same factors that had induced a transient scintillating scotoma on other numerous preceding occasions, from the patient's late twenties to his forty-seventh year, on that particular summer afternoon culminated in a complete temporary spasm in a branch of the right posterior cerebral artery. The spasm lasted long enough to cause an irreversible, and hence irreparable, injury to the delicate structures of the lingual gyrus, including parts of the right striate area.

From the state of the vessels thirty years later, it is certain that, after the termination of the attack a few minutes later, almost normal circulation was restored. This restored circulation, owing to the irreparable character of the injury in the core of the affected vascular territory, had but little effect. Only along the periphery of the affected territory, which included most of the lower calcarine lip and most of the afferent fibers of that lip, the circulation was not completely shut off. Here a normal flow of blood soon permitted true rehabilitation of the nervous parenchyma, manifesting itself subjectively in a "clearing-up" of much of the initially large functional defect. In this process of restoration the anastomotical connections of the affected vascular territory with other adjoining and less affected territories had certainly played an important role, as discussed elsewhere. (*See* chap X, 8; *cf. also* following MANTENO case.)

In the light of the views, expressed in the preceding paragraphs, it is plain that a purely static anatomical concept of a pathovascular process, termed "cerebral thrombosis," needs to be replaced, at least in many cases, by one in which all pertinent factors, such as anatomical-mechanical, physiological-dynamical, and pathological in the narrow sense, receive due consideration. Of these much remains obscure.

The foremost problem of what causes an arterial spasm that so completely shuts off the lifegiving blood from the delicate brain tissue as to kill it cannot be answered. Is it a lowering of the threshold in the sympathetic constrictor nerves and centers regulating the arteries of the brain, or in the smooth muscles themselves?

What agents—dynamic or functional, chemical, metabolic, toxic, nutritional, or others, including medical poisons—are instrumental in such a lowering of the sympathetic threshold or increased irritability?

Are there any physical factors to point at—for example, increased blood pressure, perhaps temporary and localized to a particular vascular territory? Could such a localized rise of blood pressure be caused or induced by a preceding localized stimulation of vasodilators, in turn stimulated by a greater demand upon parts of the nervous organs under greater functional stress ("overwork"; *cf.* Field *et al.* 1951)?

Could an unusual demand upon a part of the nervous system, in our case the visual cortex, bring on a state of greater irritability of the supplying vascular sympathetic apparatus, with all its dangerous potentialities, including an arterial spasm capable of killing off the nervous parenchyma?

Is not a scintillating scotoma, then, essentially a premonitory sign signaling a state of functional unrest or lability of the central visual apparatus, preceding its "breakdown," with an outcome of irreparable damage? Hence, could not such a signaling be interpreted as essentially a defense mechanism intended to prevent a condition of intolerance, and thus avoid an injury?

Is it not logical to look upon physical light, normally an "adequate physiological stimulus," in one way as an agent necessary for maintenance of normal physiological conditions in its "adequate nervous substance" that makes up the visual system, and in another way as a "destroyer" or "decomposer" of the same substance, which is the essence of the process of vision (by analogy with the synthesis and decomposition of the retinal visual purple)?

In this connection the organic or anatomical angle of the genesis of hemianopic scotomas must not be overlooked. It is probable that both factors, the "organic" and the "functional," may work hand-in-hand. The first, for example, as an incipient local atheromatosis of a particular blood vessel, may be the anatomical basis upon which the "functional," "dynamic," "toxic," etc., factor, in the form of a local spastic constriction elicited by any one of the above-mentioned agents, may be superimposed, the result manifesting itself in a narrowing or constriction of an artery varying in time and hence in intensity of the subsequent organic damage. (*Cf.* experiments by Echlin 1942.)

7. GENERAL DEDUCTIONS CONCERNING THE VISUAL SYSTEM.—As few of the cases in our collection, case MALLORY is eminently suitable to shed full light upon the basic facts of the intrinsic organization of the human visual system and some on its behavior in pathological conditions.

The first point concerns the cortical representation of the central fovea ("macula"). Here the focal question is: Is the central fovea represented according to the same plan as the remainder of the binocular portions of the retina, that is, by a projection of each two homonymous foveal halves upon one single striate area, or is each complete fovea represented in both striate areae?

The answer is unequivocally in favor of the first concept. Making a legitimate assumption that the field charts in Figure 424 are reasonably accurate, case MALLORY shows the homonymous halves of both hemifoveae to be exclusively and entirely represented in one particular striate area. Just as the lesion extended close to the posterior limit of the affected right striate area at the occipital pole, so the central scotomas extended to the very fixation points, or dividing meridians, in the contralateral halves of the fields of view. The contralateral, or left, occipital pole, as the serial sections stained with toluidine blue showed, was normal, just as the central vision to the right sides of the dividing meridians was entirely normal. Hence the thesis, supported by other evidence presented in this book, notably the experiments upon monkeys and upon other human pathological cases, is corroborated in this human experiment: each retinal fovea or "macula," like the remainder of the binocular portions of the retina, is divided through its center by a vertical meridian, its temporal half being projected upon the ipsilateral hemisphere, its nasal half upon the contralateral. (*Cf.* chap. X, 8; and chap. XI, 8, 9.)

The other closely related question which received a clear-cut answer is: Where, precisely, are the homonymous halves of the two foveae represented in the striate area? Since the lesion responsible for a central scotoma in case MALLORY was found in the occipital pole, the polar segment of the striate area—and that alone— must be regarded as representing the fovea (sketch *A*, in Fig. 426). The remainder of the striate area, the portion situated in front of the arrow marked in Figure 425 with an asterisk (*), in particular its floor, is not related to central vision. Especially is this true also of the anterior segment of the striate area, which, as well as its afferent fibers, remained almost entirely outside the lesion (sketch *D*, in Fig. 426). A sparing of the central vision found in many cases of homonymous hemianopia cannot, therefore, be explained by an assumption of a sparing of the anterior segment of the striate area, as has been suggested by some, but is in all cases caused by a sparing of the polar, foveal segment of the striate area and of its afferent fibers (*see* chap. X, 8; and chap. XI, 8, 9).

How far anteriorly does the representation of the central vision in the striate area extend? The answer will depend on where the limit to the central vision is set in the field of view. If anatomical criteria are applied, and half the diameter of the human fovea is set at 750 microns, then, roughly, $3°$ in the field of view from the fixation point or $6°$ in diameter would correspond to it. Again, if half the central area is set at 2,750 microns, in the field of view this

would correspond to $11°$ for one half or to $22°$ for its total diameter.

On this basis, in case MALLORY, where the scotoma extended along the horizontal meridians up to $20°$ and along the vertical meridians up to $10°$, one may say that the destroyed segment of the striate cortex in the dorsovertical sense, parallel to the inferior calcarine prong, corresponded approximately to the central area, while in the longitudinal sense, from the polar extremity to the arrow marked with *, the destroyed cortex represented twice the extent of the central area.

The fovea in the strict sense or, more correctly, the two superimposed homonymous hemifoveae would have a correspondingly smaller representation, roughly corresponding to the area back of the two prongs of the calcarine fissure at the very occipital pole (Fig. 425). This approaches fairly closely the estimate made more than thirty years ago by Gordon Holmes, shown in Figure 124, and is in fair agreement with other cases of our own and those found in the literature (Holmes & Lister 1916; Brouwer 1930; R. A. Pfeifer 1930).

Another item clearly illuminated by our case is the one that has caused much debate between the localist viewpoint advocating a firm and stable representation of the retinal surface in the cerebral cortex and the opposing, more or less "omnivalent," concept of an ill-defined, diffuse, vague, unstable, or floating representation of the specific functions, with the possibility of a "vicarious" substitution or compensation, also expressed in such concepts as the "functional fovea" or "pseudo-fovea," and the like (*cf.* chap. IV, 4, 5). From the patient's own words it is obvious that after the onset of the visual "episode" the considerable initial disturbance subsided (the defect "cleared up"). In the further course the disturbance improved so much that, even though the patient was conscious of it, it did not interfere with his ordinary occupation except in conditions requiring perfect vision, as, for example, when playing tennis. In the words of his eye doctor and associate, it is doubtful whether he was conscious at all of his defect in the circumstances of daily life.

A marked improvement in the patient's vision indicated that the defect became largely eliminated from his consciousness, or was "psychically compensated." What a "psychic compensation" means in concrete terms of anatomy and physiology remains unknown, the more so, since the entire question of a "psychophysical" correlation still remains in a nebulous state. The reality of the scotomas in the patient's fields of view, of their hemianopic character, of their definite shape, size, and location, however, cannot be disputed. Hence, even though in ordinary circumstances the visual defect in the patient's conscious awareness was nonexistent or practically so, the same defect could easily be measured by even so gross a procedure as routine perimetry. Undoubtedly, a defect was present all the time, even though subjectively it was not felt. This makes it resemble a physiological scotoma caused by an absence of retinal structures in the region of the optic papilla, the so-called Mariotte's blind spot. Hence, a "psychic compensation" was at work, even though we do not know what it is.

One factor contributing to the emergence of the defect to the level of conscious awareness of the visual defect was the suddenness of change. This was especially apparent during the onset of the disturbance and the period after it, when the patient was most keenly aware of his trouble. During the further course the awareness of a scotoma gradually "faded away" and sank to almost a vanishing point, at least temporarily or periodically.

Besides the "psychic factor," a purely histo-anatomical process of repair was also at work in our case. This factor, in the final analysis, may have been entirely responsible for the improvement and for a "psychic compensation" of the functional defect. The traces of this palpable, material process of repair were very clearly distinguishable in the microscopic sections. They were histological signs of a restitution in much of the lower calcarine lip adjoining the lesion.

It is probable that during the initial period, immediately following the vascular insult, much and perhaps most of the lower calcarine lip, together with the entire striate cortex in and around the inferior calcarine prong at the occipital pole, was impaired, resulting in a scotoma enveloping practically the entire left upper quadrants. Soon, probably within the next few minutes following the relaxation of the spasm of the paracalcarine artery, the process of rehabili-

tation set in. In this, in so far as the striate area and visual radiation were concerned, the major share was contributed by the calcarine artery proper, buried in the calcarine fissure. This artery evidently was not subjected to the spastic occlusion that had temporarily knocked out its neighbor, the paracalcarine artery. The evidence of this is the good condition of the upper calcarine lip and of its incoming fibers. Since both calcarine lips were largely supplied by the calcarine artery, only the nutrition of the lower lip was partly affected by the subtraction of that share of blood contributed by the paracalcarine artery—just enough to put it temporarily out of commission but not enough for complete anoxemic suffocation and necrosis.

In the further course of the process of "repair" and "restitution," several factors worked hand-in-hand: anatomical, physiological, hemodynamical, and nutritional, besides direct histological processes of degeneration and regeneration. With cessation of the spasm in the affected vascular territory, the circulation was resumed, possibly in increased volume, into the partly suffocated tissue of the lower lip, thus speeding up the process of repair (as in the inflammatory processes). In this way most of the gross quadrantic hemianopia was erased in a matter of minutes or, at the most, hours or days. The rehabilitation of the finer structures and hence of the subtle qualities of vision in the left upper quadrants, however, required a longer time, extending probably over many weeks and possibly months, never to reach the normal level possessed before the insult. Of this we have no knowledge, owing to an absence of detailed testing. The depletion of the cells and fibers in the lower calcarine lip alone remained an unmistakable indication of permanent damage. Even so, since the majority of cells in the lower lip escaped destruction, enough of "function" was left in that lip for vision in the affected quadrants to be felt subjectively as "normal."

The foregoing set of anatomical and physiological factors in case MALLORY appears to represent the essence of the process of "rehabilitation" or "restitution," fully accounting for the observed functional disturbance: a central scotoma in the left upper quadrants, found in the perimetric testing of the fields of view. There is, therefore, no place here to invoke other unaccountable factors, such as "psychic," "functional," "plastic," and what not, that have so largely confused and obscured the problem of rehabilitation in modern discussions of this item.

Together with the other evidence adduced in this book, case MALLORY puts a question mark upon some modern concepts of the normal working and rehabilitation of the impaired functions of the nervous system, for example, of the "pseudo-fovea" of Fuchs (1921) and of the "reorganization" of the cerebral mechanism in general, championed by Goldstein (1923, 1925, 1931). In fact, all factual evidence at our command, in opposition to these and similar modern attempts at resuscitation of the antistructuralist functional equipotentialism of the nervous system, points toward a strict parallel between the anatomical structures and functional performance: the first being the material basis, the second a working manifestation of the same thing. (*Cf.* chap. III, 3, 4; and chap. IV, 5.)

Briefly summarized, the following are the results that may safely be drawn from case MALLORY concerning the organization of the human visual system: the central foveae are represented in the posteriormost segments of the striate areae in exactly the same way as are the extrafoveal portions of the retinae, each two homonymous hemifoveae in the right or left halves of the brain, with the upper homonymous quadrants in the upper half and the lower homonymous hemifoveal quadrants represented in the lower half of the foveal portion of the respective striate area.

The topographic representation of the retinae in the cortex is permanent and immutable, putting a functional displacement of any retinal point outside the realm of concrete possibility. Hence the migrating "pseudo-fovea" of Fuchs, Goldstein, and others, appears to be a product of undisciplined, pseudo-scientific faddism.

In fact, the cortical representation of the fovea and, in general, of the retina is the very antithesis of the idea of "cerebral plasticity" championed by the modern opponents of cerebral functional localization. In the light of all available information, the foveal portions of the vertebrate visual apparatus appear as the very culmination of the most exquisitely organized sensory instrument, created during the incalculably long vertebrate evolution, and a basis upon which the ascendancy of the Primate Order was built and is maintained. (*Cf.* chap. XIII, 2 and 3; and chap. XV.)

References: Adrian 1936 (quoted by Burns 1951); Aschoff 1939; Beauvieux 1930; Beauvieux, Piechaud & Rudeau 1929; Beauvieux & Ristich-Goelmino 1926; Cantilo 1929; Chase 1938; Critchley 1953; Echlin 1942; Evans & McEachern 1938; Field *et al.* 1951; Frey 1939; Fuchs 1921; Goldstein 1923, 1925, 1931; Goodman 1949; Hine 1918; Igersheimer 1918–20; Jakob 1927–29; Keller 1939; Kleist 1934; Lange & Wagner 1938; K. S. Lashley 1941; Lennox 1941; Lennox *et al.* 1938; Livingston 1933; Lohr 1939; McMullen 1926; Marchesani 1939; Merritt & Aring 1938; Mayer-Gross 1928; Morax 1919; Morax, Moreau & Castelain 1919; Moreau 1918; Niessl von Mayendorf 1930, 1931, 1936; Putnam & Alexander 1928; S. Ramón y Cajal 1928; A. von Reuss 1876; H. A. Riley 1932; H. Rønne 1936; Roger & Reboul-Lachaux 1921; Ruffin & Stein 1930; Sabbadini 1923–24; Sántha & Cipriani 1938; Scholz 1939; Spatz 1939; Spielmeyer 1922, 1929; J. Stambul 1953; Störring 1939; Traquair 1923, 1925, 1946; Tureen 1938; Uhthoff 1927; Vorster 1893; Walsh 1947; Walsh & Ford 1940; Wilbrand 1907, 1925; Wilson 1917; Young 1942. *See* references in chapter XI, especially 7. *See also* numerous articles in *Symposium on Blood Supply* (American) 1938, and in *Symposium on Blood Supply* (German) 1939.

SEC. 11. CASE OF INCOMPLETE HOMONYMOUS HEMIANOPIA WITH CENTRAL SPARINGS

1. HISTORY.—PAGLIERO, Martin (MANTENO case), age fifty-three, Manteno State Hospital, UNo. 1029 (1944), Manteno, Illinois.

Diagnosis: Left homonymous hemianopia with central sparings, caused either by cerebral thrombosis or embolism of cardiac origin.

From the scanty information one learns that the patient suffered from a coronary disease. Three years previously (1941) he had suffered a stroke. He died of an acute cardiac complication, presumably of coronary nature. During life the patient had no noticeable psychic symptoms, particularly none of the visual kind. However, the clinical examination was rather casual, and the fields of view were not tested except with the hand. In this way a left homonymous hemianopia was found, with a central sparing. The specimen and information were received from Dr. W. R. Kirschbaum, then affiliated with Manteno State Hospital, Manteno, Illinois.

2. Pathoanatomical examination.—A gross inspection of the brain revealed, as a prominent feature, general arteriosclerosis of the cerebral vessels, most noticeable in the large arteries at the base of the brain. The pathological change which makes this specimen of special interest was a single, large area of softening on the medial and inferior faces of the right cerebral hemisphere (Fig. 428, shaded). This area comprised the entire lower face of the occipital lobe and much of the temporal. Another area of softening, measuring $1 \times 1\frac{1}{2}$ inches, located in the center of the right parietal lobe, was presumably of less concern for the problem of vision and will not be considered here.

The temporo-occipital softening appears as a shallow depression lined with a smooth, glistening, opaque membrane continuous with the pial membrane covering the preserved parts of the brain which formed a frame of the depression. In places this membranous lining was in folds, oriented mostly longitudinally. Through this membrane and imbedded in it, the principal arterial stems were visible, pursuing their tortuous course. These were the various branches of the posterior cerebral artery. They could be followed across the defect as far as the normal cortex, which formed the rim of the defect.

The rim formed by the normal cortex surrounding the defect was represented in the temporal lobe by the inferior margin of the second temporal gyrus (*t2*). The rim passed over on the inferior face of the hemisphere into the uncus (*u*). Behind the uncus most of the hippocampal gyrus was missing as far as and including the isthmus of the hippocampal and cingular convolutions.

The upper boundary of the defect was represented by the precuneus and the cuneus, of which, however, the lowermost zone was either missing or atrophic. The lower calcarine lip

(*lcl*) was mostly gone. Of the upper calcarine lip (*ucl*), only a vestige remained. The occipital pole (at *), upon superficial inspection, alone seemed to be in a fairly good state of preservation. This pole was formed by the posterior cuneolingual gyrus, which in this case remained on the surface.

Of the medial or anterior calcarine sulcus, as defined in chapter VIII, 2 [2], the most caudal portion remained as a forked end: the original primate termination exemplified by the Lower Monkeys (*mc* in Figs. 280, 284, 289). The lateral or posterior calcarine sulcus (*lc*) was found entirely separated from the medial calcarine by an interposed polar posterior cuneolingual gyrus; it ran obliquely across the posterolateral face of the occipital lobe. Its identity was ascertained by the presence of a whitish intracortical stripe of Gennari, visible on a smooth cut surface through the striate cortex. The lateral calcarine sulcus was approximately 1 inch long. Laterally, it was surrounded at a distance of $\frac{1}{3}$—$\frac{1}{2}$ inch by a typical curved lunate sulcus (*l*) marking off a small occipital operculum (*cf.* Figs. 290, etc.).

In summary, in this case, almost the entire striate area of the right side, with much other cortex of the inferior and medial faces of the temporo-occipital lobes, was wasted away, except for a small segment in the upper lip and in the occipital pole, the latter, as evidenced by experiments and other pertinent pathological cases described in this book, being related to the foveae or centers of the homonymous fields of view.

Owing to a wasting of the nervous parenchyma, almost the entire inferior face of the occipitotemporal region was found to be nothing but a pial-arachnoid membrane, covered on the inside by a smooth ependyma of the lateral ventricle. The ventricle, in turn, was considerably enlarged *e vacuo*, and so also was the chorioid plexus, which otherwise did not show any gross abnormality.

3. Arteries in and around the area of softening.—The blood vessel responsible for a single large focus in the right temporo-occipital lobe found in the Manteno case was the posterior cerebral artery (Fig. 428, *pocca*), including all its subdivisions—the superior and inferior calcarine arteries (*scal, ical*), the posterior temporo-occipital artery (*poteocca*), and the hippocampal artery (*hipa*). The upper branches —the anterior and posterior cuneal arteries (*cua, cup*) and the posterior parietal artery (*popaa*)—escaped (for comparison *see* figures in chap. X, esp. Fig. 372). The preservation of the occipital pole apparently was accomplished cir-

clogged by an atheromatous process. The superior calcarine artery (*scal*) was free, even though it was found to be diseased. Just what were the connections of that artery that permitted a backward flow of the blood in this case it was not possible to make absolutely certain. Such circulation could have been established,

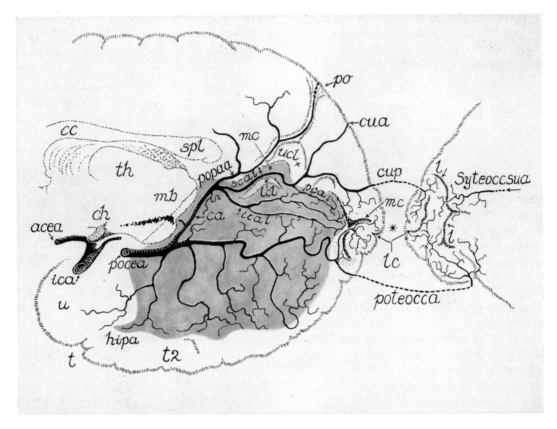

FIG. 428.—Case M. Pagliero (Manteno case): right cerebral hemisphere showing a large temporo-occipital area of softening (*shaded*), responsible for a left incomplete homonymous hemianopia with central sparings observed during life. Left diagram shows the inner face of the hemisphere; right diagram shows the posterolateral face of the occipital lobe of the same hemisphere. System of posterior cerebral artery (*pocea*) presented to show all principal branches involved in the pathology of this case. Note a sparing of the occipital pole, marked with an asterisk (*), and its circuitous vascular supply both from the posterior cerebral artery (*cup, poteocca*) and from the middle cerebral artery (*Syteoccsua*), responsible for that sparing. *Labeling: acea,* anterior cerebral artery; *ca,* calcarine artery; *cc,* corpus callosum; *ch,* chiasma of optic nerves; *cua,* anterior cuneal artery; *cup,* posterior cuneal artery; *hipa,* hippocampal artery; *ica,* internal carotid artery; *ical,* inferior calcarine artery; *l,* lunate sulcus; *lc,* lateral or posterior calcarine sulcus; *lcl,* lower calcarine lip; *mb,* midbrain with substantia nigra; *mc,* medial or anterior calcarine sulcus; *pca,* principal calcarine artery; *po,* parieto-occipital sulcus; *popaa,* posterior parietal artery; *poteocca,* posterior temporo-occipital artery; *scal,* superior calcarine artery; *spl,* splenium of corpus callosum; *Syteoccsua,* superior temporo-occipital Sylvian artery; *t,* temporal lobe; *t2,* second temporal gyrus; *th,* thalamus; *u,* uncus of hippocampal gyrus; *ucl,* upper calcarine lip.

cuitously: reverse circulation via the preserved branches above the obstructed locality.

Careful dissection revealed the stem of the posterior cerebral artery (*pocea*), close to its origin at the basilar artery, to be completely

e.g., through the posterior parietal artery (*popaa*) from the convexity of the hemisphere, since this artery was found in fairly good condition. The two branches of the inferior calcarine artery (*ical*) were also found in fair condition and communicating with the patent calcarine artery (*ca*) above the point of its obstruction. The principal trunk of the posterior temporo-occipital artery (*poteocca*) was also found patent everywhere, even though its passage was reduced in diameter.

A tentative diagnosis of the state of the posterior cerebral arterial system as found at the time of death was an obstruction of its principal stem close to its origin, with the compensatory collateral circulation re-established above the point of obstruction by way of the anastomotic backflow from the surrounding preserved arteries.

4. Correlation of functional disturbance and the pathoanatomical findings.—The occipital lobe examined in a cut specimen showed an encephalomalacic defect penetrating deep into the hemisphere. In the occipital pole and close to it, only the cortex and the short subcortical association fibers of Meynert, connecting the adjoining gyri in the manner of the letter U, were found, the longer fibers having altogether disappeared. In the temporal lobe the sagittal fiber layers were present in their upper and intermediate segments as far as the "lateral salient"; their appearance, however, indicated an abnormal condition that could have been confirmed only by stained sections. Of the striate area a segment in the upper calcarine lip (*ucl*), directly continuous with the remaining mass of the subcortical fiber substance of the hemisphere, showing a line of Gennari, may have preserved a modicum of normal func-

tion. The occipital pole, in spite of its sparing, undoubtedly was functionally dead, since the afferent fibers from the visual radiation were gone. The central sparing recorded in the sketchy history must therefore be considered as a typical "pseudo-sparing" frequently found in carelessly plotted cases of homonymous hemianopia.

The question concerning the primary etiology of this case, whether thrombosis on an arteriosclerotic basis or embolism of cardiac origin, must remain unanswered. The numerous signs of advanced atheromatosis suggest the first; definite obstruction in the principal stem and heart trouble rather indicate the latter pathology.

In either case, the circuitous, multiple arterial blood supply of the occipital pole, the very locality where the foveal-macular or central region of the retina is represented, has been demonstrated in a practical way, and its importance as a mechanism by which central vision may be preserved in homonymous hemianopia shown. (*Cf.* chap. X, 8 [2, 4]; chap. XI, 8 and 9.)

Anatomical sparing of the occipital pole, in spite of a complete malacia of the afferent fibers, is of interest, since it shows that an extensive malacia caused by an occlusion of the posterior cerebral artery may destroy foveal-macular fibers, even though the foveal-macular cortex may be spared. In a less extensive injury both the foveal fibers and the foveal cortex may be saved and central vision preserved.

References: See chapter XI, especially 8 and 9.

SEC. 12. CASE OF A LESION IN THE LOWER CALCARINE LIP AND OCCIPITAL POLE

1. History.—St. Luke's case No. 101 (1940), unidentified patient of unknown age and sex.

Diagnosis: Limited encephalomalacic lesion of the lower lip of the calcarine fissure in the left occipital lobe; encephalomalacia of the lateral side in the right parieto-occipital lobes of the brain. Specimen received from St. Luke's Hospital, Chicago, 1940.

Eleven days before death, weakness of the face on left side, paralysis of the left arm, and a Babinski sign of the left foot were noticed, indi-

cating a lesion of the pyramidal tract in the right half of the cerebrum. No neurological examination was made, or fields of view taken. *Streptococcus viridans* was cultured from the heart blood. Kahn test was negative. Pathoanatomical diagnosis was of a thrombo-ulcerative endocarditis of the mitral valve and of the left auricle. Other findings: multiple infarcts of the spleen and kidneys (as well as the brain); cholecystitis and cholelithiasis; general arteriosclerosis and hyperemia; multiple fibrous and fibroplastic scars and fatty degeneration of myocardium; fatty degeneration of the liver; chronic fibrous interacinar pancreatitis; general hyperemia and edema of the brain; moderate arteriosclerosis of the cerebral blood vessels.

According to the preceding pathoanatomical report, it may be accepted that the specimen belonged to an individual in later middle life or in advanced age. It is also fairly obvious that the essential etiology was of cardiac origin, ap-

tion of the brain. Such *tentative diagnosis* would be: homonymous hemianopic scotoma in the right upper quadrants, extending as far as the fixation points, but probably affecting little, if at all, the periphery beyond 20° or 30°. In this respect, St. Luke's case is almost a copy of case Mallory, with the essential difference that, while in the latter the scotoma was "mono-symptomatic," apparently caused by a vascular

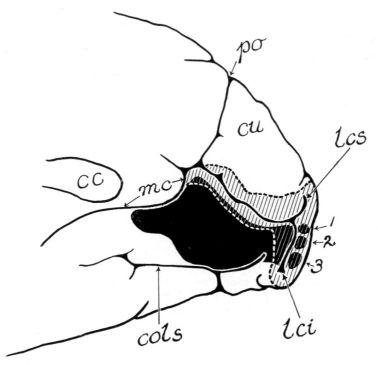

Fig. 429.—Case St. Luke's Hospital No. 101 (1940), drawn into the outlines of case Mallory, hence transposed from the left to the right occipital lobe. The diagram represents the inner face of the right occipital lobe, showing the location of the lesion below the calcarine fissure. Solid black indicates the destroyed portions of the extrastriate cortex lining the lingual and fusiform gyri. Black area shaded with white lines indicates the destroyed portions of the striate area. Undamaged striate area white, shaded with black lines. Boundaries of the striate area marked by black or white interrupted lines. In spite of the large size of the lesion and the undermining of the lower calcarine lip along its entire length, as shown in Fig. 430, only a narrow strip of the striate area was directly destroyed, the principal damage being in front and behind the lower calcarine prong (*lci*), making this case an enlarged copy of case Mallory (*cf.* Fig. 425). *Labeling: cc*, splenium of corpus callosum; *cols*, collateral sulcus; *cu*, cuneus; *lci, lcs*, lower and upper prongs of lateral calcarine sulcus; *mc*, medial calcarine sulcus; *po*, parieto-occipital sulcus; *1, 2, 3*, polar lesions. (*Cf.* Fig. 431.)

parently of an infectious nature. Upon this basis, in the course of illness, a vascular degenerative process in various parts of the body gradually developed, including the brain. The involvement of the visual system was incidental.

Since no information was available concerning the visual disturbance, the only recourse was to venture a probable diagnosis from the facts found on gross and microscopic examina-

spasm during the fifth decade of life and continued for about thirty years, in St. Luke's case the visual defect developed during the terminal phase of a general organic vascular decay originating from an infectious endocardial process.

2. Pathoanatomical examination.—The gross examination of the brain showed an encephalomalacic lesion in the lower lip of the

calcarine fissure of the left occipital lobe (Fig. 429; in this figure, in order to facilitate comparison, the lesion was drawn into the outlines of the right occipital lobe of case MALLORY; see Fig. 425). Superficially, the lesion was strictly limited to the lingual and fusiform gyri below the calcarine fissure. A narrow zone along that fissure seemed to have been spared. Downward, the lesion at its widest extent just reached the collateral sulcus (*cols*). The anterior limit of the lesion was slightly in front of a point midway between the callosal splenium (*cc*) and the juncture of the calcarine (*mc*) and parieto-occipital sulci (*po*). The posterior extremity of the macroscopically visible lesion was 1 cm., or a little less than $\frac{1}{2}$ inch, in front of the occipital pole. The surface of the lesion showed rather normal contours.

Microscopically the lesion extended antero-posteriorly beyond the indicated limits. This was especially apparent in the occipital pole, where a series of ischemic foci was present in the very tip of the lobe behind the lower prong of the calcarine fissure (*lci*). The exact extent of the lesion, given in solid black, is illustrated in sketches *A* and *B*, in Figure 430. These show that, in accord with the macroscopic examination, the lesion was limited throughout its longitudinal extent to the region below the lower lip of the calcarine fissure, the upper lip of that fissure being entirely free from any pathology determinable in the usual way.

The next fact of interest was the limited extent to which the central visual apparatus in the restricted sense—the visual radiation (*vr*) and the striate cortex (indicated by a dotted or stippled line)—was damaged, in spite of extensive total destruction of the occipital lobe. On most anterior levels in front of the striate area there were only a few diffuse ischemic foci, confined to the cortex of the lingual gyrus. Through the anterior segment of the striate area, corresponding to the widest extent of the lesion, only the fringe of the striate cortex was directly destroyed, while by far the greater portion of that cortex in the lower lip was only undermined (*cf.* sketches *B* and *C*, Fig. 430).

The most noteworthy observation was the escape of the bulk of the afferent fibers, which, closely skirting that lip, streamed from the lower segment of the visual radiation (*vr*) into the lower calcarine lip. These fibers could be followed underneath and into the striate cortex, where, according to our own previous experiments, they spread in the infra-Gennarian half, pursuing a slanting course (*see* Fig. 315). However, many of these fibers in the ST. LUKE'S case had undoubtedly perished. This was evidenced by their gradual numerical decrease from the floor of the calcarine fissure, where they appeared normal, toward the fringe of the lower lip, where they were practically bleached out. The same must be assumed also for the other categories such as the in- and outgoing callosal and associational fibers.

An instructive indication of the partial disappearance of fibers was found in the Gennari fiber layer itself; here the bleaching kept pace with that of the subcortical fibers of the lower calcarine lip. Thus, while Gennari's layer was approximately normal in and close to the calcarine floor, that layer almost vanished toward the margin of the lower lip. This partial loss of Gennari's autochthonous fibers may be attributable partly to an actual loss of those terminal ramifications that belong to the afferent geniculo-cortical and perhaps to other fibers, while in part it may be an expression of impaired vitality of the neurons and their expansions caused by their proximity to the ischemic focus. This latter factor was especially obvious in the margin of the lower lip.

In the occipital pole more definite changes appeared in the form of minute malacic foci, strictly limited to the cortex (Fig. 430, sketch *A*; and Fig. 431). These were located in the floor of the lower prong of the calcarine fissure (*lci*) and in the portion of the striate cortex in the very pole just behind that prong. The three larger foci (*1, 2, 3*) in the last-mentioned figure were from 2 to 3 mm. wide and were fairly evenly spaced, being separated by segments of less affected cortex, each 2 mm. wide. Focus *1* spread almost entirely in the infra-Gennarian half of the cortex. Focus *2* was principally located in the supra-Gennarian half, with its tentacles passing into the infra-Gennarian half. Focus *3*, in turn, spread through almost the entire thickness of the cortex. In all foci the innermost zone, closest to the subcortical fiber layer, roughly corresponding to layer *6*, was spared.

There were other features of interest from the viewpoint of the organization of the striate cortex. Such was especially the intracortical fiber layer of Gennari, from which the striate area received its name (*see* G. Elliot Smith in chap. VIII, 4). This layer remained visible almost everywhere in the foci, although it was reduced to roughly a fourth of its density outside the foci. Only in places where the causative process was most intense was the visibility of Gennari's layer reduced to almost the vanishing point. Hence the layer could be followed as a continuous formation throughout the cortex, irrespective of the gaps represented by the foci (strippled stripe in Fig. 431). Another noteworthy feature was a more intensive staining of that layer next to the margins of the foci, instead of a reduction in staining, as one would expect, when a focus crossed that layer. This, with the experimental evidence given in chapter

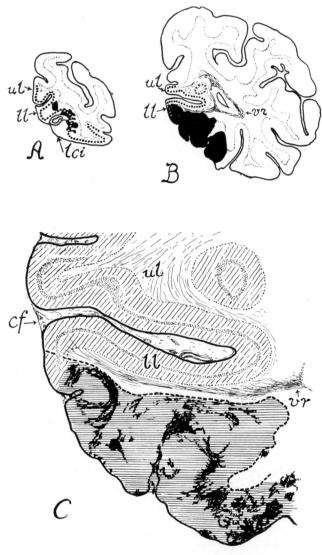

Fig. 430.—Case St. Luke's Hospital No. 101 (1940), showing the lesion in the lower calcarine lip, in sketch *A* through the occipital pole, in sketch *B* through the middle stretch of the calcarine fissure; *C*, slightly magnified detail of sketch *B*. In upper sketches lesions given in solid black, striate area marked by a dotted line. In lower sketch the lesion indicated by horizontal shading, the striate area by oblique shading and a stippled stripe (Gennari), the hemorrhages in the lesion by solid black. Note the sparing of the incoming fibers of the visual radiation (*vr*), in spite of the proximity of the lesion. *Labeling: cf*, calcarine fissure; *lci*, lower calcarine prong; *ll*, lower calcarine lip; *ul*, upper calcarine lip; *vr*, visual radiation. (*Cf.* Figs. 429, 431.)

VII, 7 [2], indicates Gennari's layer to be made up largely of short association fibers, this being in harmony with the observations on Marchi-stained material and with the study of Golgi-stained structures of the striate cortex (*see* chap. VII, 7; and chap. VIII, 7).

In the visual radiation, however, no clear gap

rograde sense whose terminal arborizations had been destroyed in the infra-Gennarian half of the striate cortex or in the Gennarian layer itself (*cf.* experiments in chap. VII, 5). Another possible factor may be the short lapse of time since the "episode" which caused the infarct in the left occipital lobe.

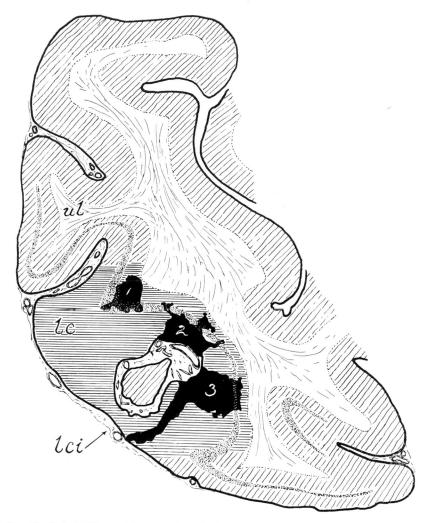

Fig. 431.—Case St. Luke's Hospital No. 101 (1940), figure representing medium magnification of sketch *A* of Fig. 430. The extent of the striate area indicated by a stippled intracortical stripe of Gennari. The horizontally shaded area shows the total extent of the damaged cortex, the solid black areas *1, 2, 3,* indicating the ischemic foci along the lower prong of the calcarine fissure *lci* in the occipital pole (*cf.* Fig. 429, foci *1, 2, 3;* and Fig. 430, sketch *A*). Gennari or Vicq-d'Azyr stripe in the normal or slightly affected striate cortex given in black stippling, in severely damaged foci by white stippling. The striate area along the upper calcarine lip (*ul*) and along the lower end of the inferior calcarine prong was found to be normal or only slightly affected.

interrupted its course. This observation, as in case MALLORY, may be interpreted as being caused by the diffuse character and incompleteness of the malacic process in the cortex, owing to which only those fibers degenerated in a ret-

Somewhat clearer were the signs of retrograde cell degeneration in the left lateral geniculate nucleus, where a scattered loss of cells was found in its posterior tip and in its lateral segment along much of its length.

3. COMMENT.—The distinguishing feature of ST. LUKE'S case was the limited damage to the striate cortex, even though the causative lesion destroyed a large portion of the cortex on the inferior, tentorial surface of the occipital lobe. In this respect ST. LUKE'S case resembles case MALLORY.

There are further similarities because of the underlying pathological factors acting in a like way in both cases. The artery responsible for the infarct was apparently the terminal branch of the posterior temporo-occipital artery (*poteocca*) or a similar vessel with a comparable spread. The lesion, even though it undermined

the lower calcarine fissure, spared the bulk of its fibers, which, with its cortex, depended upon the calcarine artery. The lower half of the polar portion of the striate cortex was also affected, the same that was spared in the MANTENO case in spite of a much larger lesion there (Fig. 428). The responsible factors may have been either greater dependence of the polar cortex on the mentioned artery in ST. LUKE'S case or an underdevelopment or a shutting-off of the anastomotical connections with the adjoining arterial territories by the underlying pathological process in the responsible vessel.

References: See chapter XI.

SEC. 13. CASE WITH AN ENCEPHALOMALACIC FOCUS ALONG THE CALCARINE AND PARIETO-OCCIPITAL SULCI

1. HISTORY.—Case ANONYMOUS, of whom very little is known except that the patient was a male, of advanced age, probably a luetic and a drunkard, and had impaired vision, possibly caused by a cerebral stroke. Because of the mental symptoms which followed, the patient was confined to the State Hospital at Manteno, Illinois. No examination of vision was made.

2. PATHOANATOMICAL EXAMINATION.—Gross inspection of the brain revealed pronounced brachycephaly and general opacity of the entire soft covering of the cerebral hemispheres, indicative of chronic leptomeningitis (possibly specific luetic, or of some other infectious origin). The principal arteries, surprisingly, showed hardly any rigidity, and there were no macroscopically visible atheromatous changes in their walls. A single focus of softening found in the right occipital lobe was the reason for including this specimen in our collection.

The encephalomalacic area was roughly of a triangular shape (Fig. 432). Its upper and anterior boundaries were formed by the anterior lip of the parieto-occipital sulcus (*po*) and the upper lip of the medial calcarine fissure (*mc*). The lower boundary roughly followed the collateral sulcus (*cols*), which was posteriorly obliterated. The anterior fourth of the cuneus (*cu*) was destroyed. On the inferior face of the hemisphere the lingual gyrus was entirely erased. The occipital pole was formed by a superficially located cuneolingual gyrus (*cul gyr*). The lateral

calcarine sulcs (*lc*) was 1⅓ inches long and followed a horizontal course, turning around the pole onto the exposed face of the hemisphere directly posteriorly (a position caused by extreme brachycephaly). A long and flat lunate sulcus (*l*) encircled the posterior extremity of the lateral calcarine sulcus.

The malacic focus, solid black in the figure, just reached the lower branch of the lunate sulcus (*see* right diagram). As a result of the malacic softening, a **V**-shaped defect was formed, roughly following the parieto-occipital and collateral sulci, its concavity facing backward. This concavity was filled in by the posterior spared portion of the cuneus (*cu*). The loss of substance, even though limited, was considerable, the depth of the defect where most pronounced being no less than 8–10 mm. below the level of the surrounding normal cortex.

Superficially, the entire lower lip (*ll*) of the medial calcarine fissure, with the exception of a narrow strip at its posterior end (shaded in the figure), and much of the upper lip (*ul*), which normally forms the anterior point of the cuneus, were gone. The cavity was covered by a smooth, but thickened and slightly opaque, arachnoid-pial membrane, through which the principal blood vessels and some smaller ones were visible.

3. BLOOD VESSELS IN AND AROUND THE MALACIC FOCUS.—The posterior cerebral artery (*pocea*), in this particular hemisphere, divided in the following order into several principal arteries (Fig. 433): a smaller and a larger medial temporal artery (*mta*), followed by a posterior temporo-occipital artery (*poteocca*), and a calcarine artery (*ca*). The latter, in turn, gave rise to a single long and rather thin principal calcarine artery (*pca*), as well as a posterior parietal artery (*popaa*). The *pca*, following the upper calcarine lip in its posterior course, dipped into the medial calcarine fissure; and, after giving off fine branches to both lips and again emerging upon the surface of the cuneolingual gyrus, it

shriveled arachnoid-pial membrane, turned around the inferior posterior margin of the occipital lobe and, after emerging upon it, dipped into the lower section of the lunate sulcus (*l*); then, after crossing the lower lip of the lateral calcarine sulcus (*lc*), it spread in that sulcus. The lateral division of the *poteocca* spread in and around the more lateral portion of the lunate sulcus (*l*) in a similar fashion.

Hence the principal supplier of the foveal-macular cortex in this hemisphere was the posterior temporo-occipital artery. In addition, the

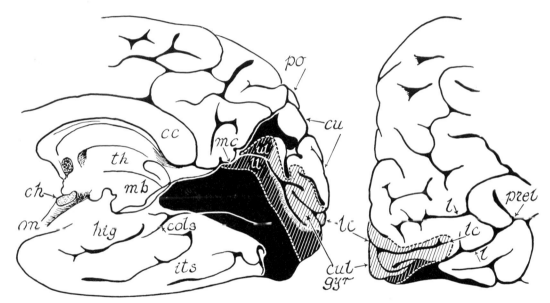

Fig. 432.—Case Anonymous, showing the inner (*left*) and posterolateral (*right*) views of the right occipital lobe, with a focus of softening, given in solid black, in relation to the sulci and to the striate area. Boundaries of the striate area marked by broken lines. White portions shaded with black lines indicate spared parts; black portions shaded with white lines indicate malacic parts of the striate area. Note spared posterior portion of the striate area around the occipital pole (*cul gyr*). For pathophysiological analysis *see* text and the following figure. *Labeling: cc*, corpus callosum; *ch*, optic chiasma; *cols*, collateral sulcus; *cu*, cuneus; *cul gyr*, cuneolingual gyrus; *hig*, hippocampal gyrus; *its*, inferior temporal sulcus; *l*, lunate sulcus; *lc*, lateral calcarine sulcus; *ll*, lower calcarine lip; *mb*, midbrain; *mc*, medial calcarine sulcus; *on*, optic nerve; *po*, parieto-occipital sulcus; *prel*, prelunate sulcus; *th*, thalamus; *ul*, upper calcarine lip.

ended in the polar portion of the lateral calcarine sulcus (*lc*).

The much thicker stem of the calcarine artery (*ca*) continued as a posterior parietal artery (*popaa*). The posterior temporo-occipital artery (*poteocca*) spread its several smaller and larger branches in the arachnoid-pial membrane in the area that was the lingual gyrus, its principal branch reaching the posterior inferior margin of the hemisphere, where it divided into two divisions of fair size (right diagram, Fig. 433).

The medial division, still enveloped in the

edge of the foveal cortex along the upper section of the lunate sulcus and the surrounding area were supplied by the superior temporo-occipital Sylvian artery (*Syteoccsua*).

A small contributor to the visual cortex was also the cuneal artery (*cua*), which in this case was single. It originated from the common stem of the posterior parieto-occipital artery (*popaa*). It was easily followed in the floor of the malacic parieto-occipital sulcus (*po*) and over the surface of the spared posterior portion of the cuneus not far from the occipital pole.

4. Relation of the occipital arteries to the malacic focus and to the striate area. —The problem of why in this case a vascular insult damaged some parts of the occipital lobe, while sparing others, after a careful dissection of the specimen, appeared far more difficult to solve than it would seem at first sight. The questions arising concern the state of the particular artery in each of its divisions, as well as the

Examined on coronal sections through the occipital lobe, in accordance with the examination of the uncut specimen, the focus on the anterior levels through the calcarine fissure destroyed both lips and the floor of that fissure medially to the posterior horn of the lateral ventricle. The territory eliminated from circulation belonged entirely to the posterior cerebral artery, while the territory lateral to the

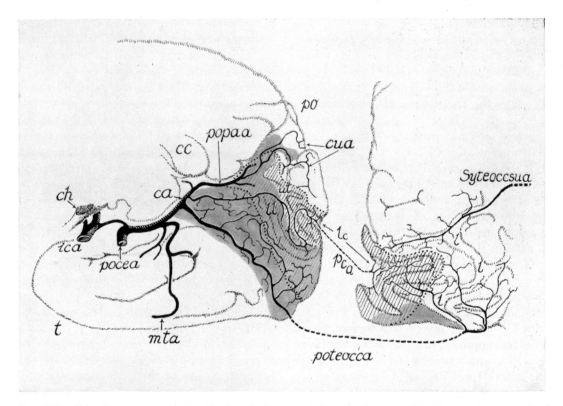

Fig. 433.—Case Anonymous, showing the distribution of arteries in and around the extensive focus of softening in the right occipital lobe. Left-hand diagram represents the inner face of the lobe, right-hand diagram represents the posterolateral face. Uniformly shaded area, including the white shading, represents the malacic territory. Striate area given in black or white shading, the latter indicating the destroyed parts of the same area. Boundaries of the striate area indicated by dotted lines. Arteries which continue from the inner to the posterolateral face of the hemisphere indicated by broken lines. Note a multiple blood supply of the occipital pole to which several arteries contribute, belonging partly to the middle cerebral and partly to the posterior cerebral artery, resulting in an almost complete sparing of the foveal-macular cortex. *Labeling: ca*, calcarine artery; *cc*, corpus callosum; *ch*, optic chiasma; *cua*, cuneal artery; *ica*, internal carotid artery; *l*, lunate sulcus (opened, to show arterial distribution); *lc*, lateral calcarine sulcus (opened, to show arterial distribution); *ll*, lower calcarine lip; *mta*, medial temporal artery; *pca*, principal calcarine artery; *po*, parieto-occipital sulcus; *pocea*, posterior cerebral artery; *popaa*, posterior parietal artery; *poteocca*, posterior temporo-occipital artery; *Syteoccsua*, superior temporo-occipital Sylvian artery; *ul*, upper calcarine lip. (*Cf.* Figs. 428, 432, and colored figures in chap. X.)

arterial distribution, and the state of each particular territory of the brain substance, both spared and destroyed. Only after this could an attempt have been made to interpret the final post mortem condition in terms of pathological cause and effect.

lateral ventricle, supplied by the middle cerebral artery, was spared.

Of the fibrous core of the occipital lobe, both the upper and the lower segments of the sagittal strata related to both calcarine lips were gone or appeared seriously affected. Closer to the occipital pole, back of the posterior extremity of the lateral ventricle, the malacic process affected only the lower calcarine lip, both at the back end of the medial calcarine fissure and along the inferior limb of the lunate sulcus. The striate cortex in the upper calcarine lip, both along the back end of the medial calcarine sulcus (*mc*) and along the lateral calcarine sulcus (*lc*), and the underlying fibrous core of the lobe remained preserved.

Special mention is to be made of the sparing of the cortex in and around the lateral calcarine sulcus (*lc*) and in the lunate sulcus (*l*) surrounding the first and its subcortical fibrous core, except along the lower margin of the occipital pole, where the fiber substance underlying the lower lip of the lateral calcarine fissure was partly gone and was partly undermined.

Examination of the blood vessels, carried out with a dissecting magnifier, showed little that could explain the encephalomalacia. All principal arteries—the anterior, middle, and posterior cerebrals—were of normal size. Their walls were surprisingly elastic and translucent, with none of the atheromatous patches usually found in places of predilection in advanced age. This was also true of all medium and smaller branches visible at the magnification employed. All lumens of the arteries of all sizes were free, no clogging having been found in any vessel. The nearest approach to a narrowing was found in a deep medium branch of the principal calcarine artery (*pca*) imbedded in the most advanced locality of the malacic focus (in Fig. 433 terminating with a broken line next to *ll*). But even this vessel was not found obliterated and contained some blood.

5. COMMENT.—From the state of the arteries it is obvious that the etiological background of encephalomalacia in this case was not an atheroma. No signs were found which would justify a diagnosis of arteriosclerosis. The only questionable exception referred to in the preceding paragraph, that of a narrowed branch of the principal calcarine artery, could be explained by a secondary influence caused by encephalomalacia rather than vice versa.

Even if a doubtful admission were made that a primary thrombosis took place in that particular instance on an atheromatous basis, this would still in no way explain the huge loss of nervous parenchyma in most of the medial calcarine sulcus, in the parieto-occipital sulcus, and along the collateral sulcus on the cerebellar face of the occipital lobe. For this, no concrete anatomical cause was found. Unlike the MANTENO case, where, in addition to widespread atheroma, complete plugging of the stem of the posterior cerebral artery was found, in case ANONYMOUS all arteries, even those imbedded in the necrotic tissue or enveloped in the empty leptomeninges, were found without visible pathological changes. It is, however, possible that some such changes of a subtle character could be discovered by a careful microscopic examination.

With the exception of the doubtful qualification just mentioned, the absence of concrete pathoanatomical evidence in the arteries of the affected area forces one to assume that the cause of the defect of the nervous parenchyma was purely functional. As in case MALLORY, discussed in detail, in the present case, too, the destruction must have been produced by a spasm of a sufficient intensity and duration to kill off the sensitive neurons by anoxemia.

The artery responsible for the suffocation of nervous parenchyma, according to the spread and location of the focus, was obviously the posterior cerebral from the point just in front of the separation of the posterior temporo-occipital artery (*poteocca*). This is indicated by the sharp demarcation line of the focus along the collateral and parieto-occipital sulci. The barrier that prevented further spread of the destruction to the temporal and parietal lobes was the normal circulation in those lobes, maintained by the medial temporal artery (*mta*) and the vessels supplying the precuneus. The spasm that had killed off nervous tissue in much of the occipital lobe was, accordingly, an entirely local affair, limited to the posterior territory of the posterior cerebral artery.

Not the entire territory of the posterior cerebral artery described was affected by the spasm, however; nor was it affected uniformly. The spared portion of the cuneus on the inner face of the occipital lobe was continuous with the preserved cortex on the posterior and lateral faces of the hemisphere. In the preservation of the cuneus the terminal branches of the middle cerebral artery, in particular the superior temporo-occipital Sylvian artery (*Syteoccsua*), must have played an important part. This alone, however, does not seem to have been sufficient. The large size of the spared territory must be considered against the assumption of the middle cerebral as the only alleviating factor. But, above all, against this interpretation one may point to the distribution of the terminal branches of the cuneal (*cua*), the principal calcarine (*pca*), and the posterior temporo-occipital (*poteocca*) arteries. Even assuming an abundant anastomotical connection of all these arteries with the adjoining arterial territories, it is unlikely that a backflow from these alone would have sufficed.

One is, then, further forced to hypothesize that the shutting-off of circulation in the posterior cerebral territory was not complete but was merely partial. In the area of the focus, especially where the loss of substance was greatest, the circulation slowed down below the level of tolerance compatible with the survival of neuronal parenchyma. This was the case in the zone between the collateral (*cols*) and medial calcarine (*mc*) sulci and also along the parieto-occipital sulcus (*po*). These two belts, farthest away from the unaffected arterial territories, represented the core of the ischemic area that was most severely affected. A little less severely affected was the lower calcarine lip (*ll*), where the colliquation and the removal of the necrotic tissue was not complete. In the medial calcarine sulcus (*mc*) the zone of demarcation followed its floor, with a sparing of the upper lip (*ul*) along most of its length.

On the back face of the occipital lobe, shown in the right sketch in Figure 433, the merging of the terminals of the three contributing arteries: *pca*, *poteocca*, and *Syteoccsua*, was particularly evident. The sparing of the foveal-macular cortex in the lateral calcarine sulcus (*lc*) and next to it was probably accomplished by both of the following factors. One was the reduced flow in the spastically constricted posterior cerebral territory, which alone, being subliminal, did not prevent anoxemia in most of its territory; the other factor was the additional flow from the middle cerebral, that, taken with the first factor, was sufficient to keep conditions within the normal range and the tissue alive.

Concerning the basic cause—the factor or factors which had elicited the spastic condition—one may refer to the discussion of this topic in the section dealing with case MALLORY. Perhaps it will not be amiss here to emphasize again our present ignorance of the many functional factors by which the normal conditions of circulation are maintained, which factors are in many ways responsible for the reaction of the cerebral mechanisms in pathological conditions and in the processes of repair.

A tentative diagnosis of a functional defect in the fields of view, in this case, deduced from the anatomical findings, would be a left-sided incomplete homonymous hemianopia with a large central sparing, the spared parts of the fields being almost entirely in the lower parts of the fields below the horizontal meridians.

References: See chapter XI; *see also* case MALLORY, section 10, this chapter.

PART IV

Origin, Development, Comparative Anatomy, Physiology, and Biology of the Vertebrate Organs of Sight

Chapter XIII

Origin and Development of the Vertebrate Eye and Visual System

SEC. 1. ONTOGENESIS OF THE VERTEBRATE EYE

1. INCEPTION OF THE VERTEBRATE EYE IN THE ECTODERMAL LAYER OF THE EMBRYO.—Our knowledge of the development of the vertebrate eye during ontogenesis, or the early period of individual life, derives from embryological research. It is the product of investigations which began more than a century ago with the notable work of K. E. von Baer (1828) and his contemporaries. Through it the principal facts and innumerable details of the development of the eye, of the optic nerves, of the visual centers, and of the brain in general became known. Of these, the most important disclosure is the intimate genetical relationship of the eye and the brain.

The earliest differentiation of that part of the ectoderm of the human embryo which subsequently develops into retinal membranes around which the eyes are formed is represented by two thickened localities, the retinal primordia, at the rostral end of the neural or medullary plate, which in that early stage is still wide open (shaded parts in Fig. 434, *A*). At still earlier and as yet little known stages the retinal primordium is possibly a single patch (*see* Mangold 1931).

The remarkable fact shown in Figure 434 is that during its earliest known period of development most of the neural plate at its rostral and most differentiated end is taken by the retinal primordia. At the stage indicated by eight somites, approximately corresponding to 21 days of intrauterine life, the human embryo is essentially a tiny sac of ectoderm containing the primordia of the endodermal viscera, e.g., the pharynx (*ph*), and of the mesoderm. The incipient invagination along the mid-sagittal axis of the neural plate into a neural groove is indicated by a shallow, centrally located primitive groove or furrow (*pg*), flanked on cross-section by two thickened wings. Two barely noticeable dents, one in each wing, mark the beginnings of the optical grooves or sulci (*os*). In the center, in the primitive groove, and on both sides where the neural plate is continuous with the general integument (*int*), the ectodermal cover is much thinner.

2. FORMATION OF A TUBELIKE EMBRYONIC BRAIN, WITH OPTICAL PRIMORDIA DOMINANT.— When the twelve-somite stage is reached, the primitive groove (*pg*) deepens further, and the optic sulci (*os*) become more marked (Fig. 434, *B*). The total transverse expanse of the neural plate is also somewhat increased. The thickened portions of the plate, still entirely optical at this stage, indicated by single and double shading, do not extend beyond the lateral corners, where the general integument begins. The optic sulci, further deepened into optic *foveolae* or pits, are the earliest indication of an incipient invagination of the two optic primordia, which are later to develop into primary optic vesicles.

The process of deepening the neural groove and the optic foveolae proceeds further until, at the stage of fourteen to sixteen somites, the lateral parts of the two wings of the neural plate are raised into folds (*f*, in sketch *C*), and their margins finally merge (sketch *D*). In this way the neural groove is transformed into a neural tube or, more correctly, into a primitive neural or cerebral vesicle (*cv*) at the rostral end of the tube.

By far the largest part of the wall of the neural vesicle is represented by the two thickened retinal primordia, together forming the primitive eye-brain. Both primordia (shaded parts) almost meet at the anterior end, only a minute vestige remaining between, the raphé or seam, which is nonoptical (*r*, solid black). The caudal portion of the cerebral vesicle given in solid black, where the vesicle is continuous with the neural tube (*nt*), also does not contribute to the formation of the eyes. At this early stage the orimental or incipient brain, clearly, is still mostly an *ophthalmencephalon* or "visual brain."

3. Beginnings of the preponderance of the nonoptical over the optical parts of the embryonic brain.—During the subsequent stages of development, from sixteen to twenty-seven somites (up to 4 mm. in length), important changes take place (Fig. 435, *A*). These are brought about by rapid expansion of the nonoptical bridge (*C*, *C*, solid black) separating the two optic primordia (shaded segments). Within this period this intervening bridge increases to such an extent that the optic

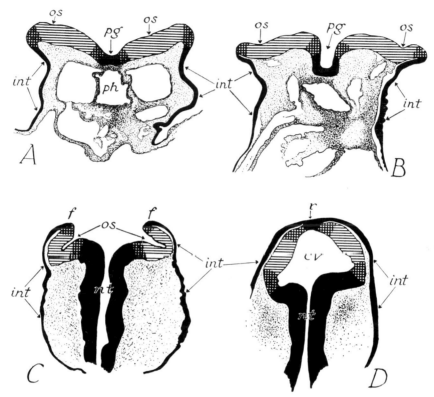

Fig. 434.—Early stages of human embryos showing successive steps in the development of the eye and brain. *A*, eight-somite stage with thickened neural plate wide open, with a shallow median sulcus, the primitive groove (*pg*), flanked by two optic primordia from which future retinae develop, each primordium dented by a slight nick, the optic sulcus (*os*) (from the University of Chicago collection, H87). *B*, twelve-somite stage with widely opened optic primordia, separated by a deepened primitive groove (*pg*), with optic sulci (*os*) more pronounced and optic primordia sharply marked off by lateral folds against general integument (*int*), rendered in solid black (University of Chicago collection, H197). *C*, fourteen-somite stage with advanced folding of optic primordia around greatly deepened optic sulci (*os*), forming open primary optic cups (Carnegie embryological collection, No. 4529; *see* Heuser 1930). *D*, seventeen-somite stage, showing fusion of two lateral folds (*f*, *f*, in sketch *C*) of primary optic cups in a median *raphé* or "seam" (*r*), by which the primitive cerebral vesicle (*cv*) is closed (University of Chicago collection, H951; *see* Wen 1929). Note that throughout their further development, shown in Fig. 435, the nervous optic vesicles remain close to the nonnervous general integumental layer (*int*) or its derivative, the lens primordium (*l*) and the lens (*lv*), in this way continuing the exposed location of peripheral photoreceptors characteristic of the Vertebrates from the earliest ontogenetical stage to full development. Optic primordia shaded, simple shading indicating the inner or nervous sheet, double or crossed shading indicating the outer sheet or pigment layer, of fully developed retina. *Other labeling: nt*, neural tube, into which cerebral vesicle continues; *ph*, primitive pharynx with surrounding entodermal and mesodermal tissue, out of which viscera, skeleton, muscles, and all other organs develop, except the nervous system and nervous constituents of the sense organs. Preparations used by courtesy of Professor G. W. Bartelmez, of the University of Chicago. (*Cf.* following figure.)

primordia come to lie far apart. These two primordia, in turn, also begin to expand and form vesicular protrusions. The entire anterior portion of the primitive brain now consists, on cross-section, of three vesicles, a bulky central one representing the brain proper (*cv*) and two lateral smaller ones—the primary optic vesicles (*ov*), as the future retinae are now called.

The intermediate cerebral vesicle already has much thicker walls (*c*) and is larger, suggesting a preponderance in bulk of the brain proper over the optic primordia. This eventual preponderance of a part of the original cerebral mechanism destined to serve the integration of the incoming impulses and their co-ordination into effector channels over the chiefly receptor ophthalmencephalon, or future retinae, becomes even more accentuated as the subsequent stages of thirty-three somites or 5.7 mm. (sketch *B*) and 11 mm. in length (sketch *C*) are attained. Finally, the two primitive optic vesicles, with their hollow stalks (*ost*), and the future optic nerves appear as mere appendages of a huge cerebrum (*c*), at least in the advanced Vertebrates such as Birds and Mammals.

4. Differentiation of the vertebrate retina.—Coincident with these changes goes a detailed histological differentiation of the optic primordia into retinae and, with the addition of other ectodermal and mesodermal tissues, their elaboration into eyeballs. First, the two primary optic vesicles (Fig. 435, *A*, *B*) become gradually invaginated in the center, forming at the end double-walled secondary optic vesicles or optic cups (*C*, same figure). The thicker inner leaf of the wall, by a complex process of differentiation, develops into nervous layers (*2–10*, Figs. 127, 128), the thinner outer wall becoming the pigment layer of the retina (*1*, same figures). The inner space or ventricle of the optic vesicle, toward the middle of the second fetal month in Man, communicating with the cerebral ventricles through the tubelike, hollow optic stalk —the future optic nerve—becomes reduced to an intraretinal slit or cleft (*ov*, in Fig. 435, *C*), which eventually also disappears in the finished organ.

On the ventricular face of that slit the thicker inner leaf of the retina at a later stage becomes coated with photoreceptors—the rods and cones—their "outward" or ventricular location being easily explained by the afore-mentioned facts of developmental mechanics. The ventricular position of the mature photoreceptors shows that, in the final, fully differentiated retina of modern Vertebrates, the photoreceptors preserve exactly the same "outward" position, facing outside space (which the cerebral ventricle and its derivatives in the optic cups, actually or potentially, are) which they had at the very inception of individual embryogenesis. This may be considered, in the light of Haeckel's concept, an ontogenetical recapitulation of the phylogenetical conditions present at the very inception of vertebrate evolution, with the neural plate wide open and the surface of the optic primordia bathed by the circumambient liquid medium in which the Vertebrate Ancestor, the primitive Prevertebrate, lived (Fig. 436, *A*, *B*; *cf.* following section).

In order to complete the description of the principal points of development of the vertebrate eye, it suffices to mention that from the thickened locality of the integument closest to the optic vesicle—the *lens placode* (*l*, in Fig. 435, *B*)—the crystalline lens develops by a process of invagination and separation and is eventually included in the "hollow" of the optic cup (*C*). Most other parts of the eye develop from the surrounding mesodermal tissue (*m*). This forms the two outer coats of the eyeball, the scleral and the chorioid membranes. By invading the interior of the cup either through the chorioid fissure (*chf*) of the secondary optic cup or through the primitive "pupil" of the cup, the mesodermal tissue provides the blood vessels for the retina.

The ciliary body and the iris, including the dilator and sphincter muscles of the pupil, are derivatives of the retina; and so the vitreous (*vi*, in *C*), which is chiefly a product of the supporting retinal structures, also appears to be. The nerves (*n*) which supply the ocular muscles, blood vessels, and other tissues have a peripheral character and reach their destination during the period of development.

5. The interdependence of the ontogeny and phylogeny of the eye.— The evaluation of the afore-mentioned facts established by embryology leads to the following important de-

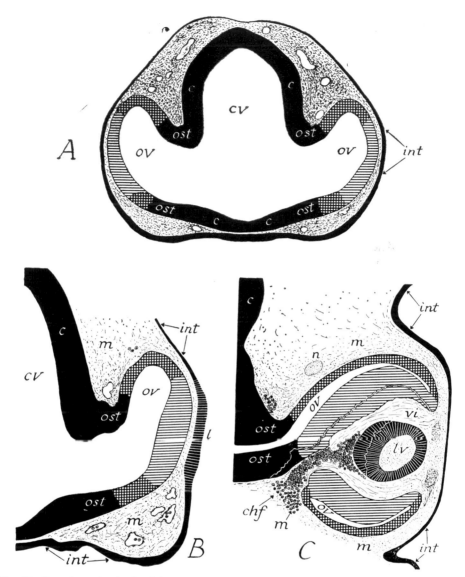

Fig. 435.—Further stages in the fetal development of the human eye. *A*, twenty-seven-somite stage, 4 mm. in length (University of Chicago collection, H1261), showing optic primordia transformed into primary optic vesicles, inclosing optic ventricles (*ov*), which freely communicate through hollow optic stalks (*ost*) with central cavity or cerebral ventricle (*cv*) of brain vesicle *c. B*, thirty-three-somite stage, or 5.7 mm. in length, approximate age four menstrual weeks (University of Chicago collection, H1426), showing a local thickening of the general integument or lens placode (*l*), opposite primary optic vesicle, from which the lens develops. *C*, 11 mm. in length, age six menstrual weeks (University of Chicago collection, H566), showing a double-walled secondary optic vesicle, or optic cup, with an outer leaf (crosshatched) containing granules of incipient retinal pigment epithelium (future layer *1* in Figs. 127, 128), and a much thicker inner leaf (*simply shaded*) which subsequently develops into the inner or vitreal portions of the retina containing photoreceptor rods and cones, bipolars, horizontals, amacrines, and ganglion cells (layers *2–10*, in same figures). Parts surrounding primitive pupillary opening gradually transform into pigment-containing nonnervous retina that lines the ciliary body and the interior of the iris. The lens vesicle (*lv*), formed by the invagination of the lens placode (*l*) and separated from the general integument (*int*) where it originates, becomes lodged in the optic cup, which is also invaded by mesenchymal tissue (*m*) by way of the chorioidal fissure (*chf*) and primitive pupil, to form a system of central artery and vein and in part the vitreous body (*vi*). Simple shading indicates the inner, nervous leaf of optic primordia, double shading the outer leaf. Preparations used by courtesy of Professor G. W. Bartelmez, of the University of Chicago. (*Cf.* preceding figure.)

ductions concerning the probable course of the evolution of the veretebrate eye and the factors by which it was brought about (for details see following sections).

The retina, ontogenetically the earliest, and in the developed state the most important, part around which, like a core, the eye is formed, was the start not only of the vertebrate organs of sight in the process of evolution but also of the brain itself.

Ordinarily, the origin of the vertebrate eye-retina, following the original description by von Baer, is presented as if it were an evagination, or outpocketing, of the primitive cerebral vesicle. In truth, however, as the course of ontogeny followed step by step clearly demonstrates, the retinal oriments, or optic primordia, are the principal and dominant parts of the neural plate, being the earliest and most advanced differentiations of the ectoderm or "outer skin" of a vertebrate embryo.

The brain develops from the nonoptical parts of the neural plate at a later stage. The eyes, therefore, do not appear as subordinate appendages "sprouting out of the cerebral vesicle," but rather the reverse is the embryological truth: the eyes, that is, the optic primordia, are the ontogenetical germ or "initial agent" from which the impulse for the development of the brain originates.

Ontogenetically and very probably also phylogenetically, the eyes are first to appear, the brain being a subsequent outgrowth. When in the further course of evolution the brain is largely taken over by other systems: the somesthetic and its derivative, the auditory, the motor, olfactory, and gustatory systems, the dominance of the eye is reduced, according to the species, to a varying degree, even though it is rarely eliminated.

Keeping the preceding in view, other facts of ontogenesis become understandable. The eyes-retinae never develop as outpocketings of the brain, sprouting from the central organ toward the integumental periphery in order to become accessible to the action of light (as the hypotheses of T. Boveri, Studnička, Walls, and others maintain). Vertebrate eyes, as embryology unequivocally shows, originate, from the very first, on the surface of the body and uninterruptedly, throughout ontogenesis, preserve their original peripheral location into the fully developed state (*see* following section).

Very likely vertebrate eyes originated during phylogenesis as superficial organs and have remained on the surface during all evolutionary stages, being always accessible to the maximum action of physical light and with minimum interference by intervening impediments, including parts of the body itself. Only in biological conditions where the stimulation of light is reduced in intensity or totally absent do the eyes recede from their favored position on the surface of the body and become immersed in the bodily tissues and reduced to insignificance, as exemplified by cave-dwelling, burrowing, nocturnal, and abyssal Vertebrates.

Migration of the eyes from a central location in the head or brain to the surface of the body, as the "ependymal hypothesis" insists, never took place, because it was unnecessary. Such a migration—if such it may be called—was carried out, instead, by the brain, which became central instead of retaining its originally superficial location as a medullary plate. As the brain was gradually freed from its original role of peripheral receptor and became an organ of integration, it was incapsulated by the other organs and tissues which formed the "head," leaving on the surface as its outposts the receptors, of which the foremost and most ancient are the eyes.

References: Adelmann 1929, 1930, 1934, 1936, 1937; Ammon 1832, 1858; Arey 1946; F. Arnold 1832, 1845–51; Babuchin 1863, 1864; Bach & Seefelder 1914; K. E. von Baer 1829–37–88; Balfour 1885; Bartelmez 1922, 1923; Bartelmez & Blount 1954; Bartelmez & Evans 1926; Bischoff 1842; Th. Boveri 1904; Brachet, Dalcq & Gérard 1935; Da Costa 1947; Detwiler 1936; De Beer 1940; M. Duval 1889; Eycleshymer 1893, 1895; V. Franz 1923, 1934; Heape 1887; Heuser 1930; W. His 1888, 1893, 1904; Huschke 1835; Jokl 1918–19, 1923; Keibel 1906; Koelliker 1861; Leplat 1912, 1932; Magitot 1910; Mangold 1931; I. Mann 1950; Meckel 1815; Nowikoff 1944–45; Nussbaum 1908; Petersen 1923; Rabl 1917; S. Ramón y Cajal 1909–11, 1919; Rugh 1948; Seefelder 1930; W. Shumway 1942; G. F. Sleggs 1926; Spemann 1927, 1938; Strahl 1898; Studnička 1900, 1912, 1913, 1918; Szily 1912; Takahashi 1930; Tello 1922; Walls 1922, 1939, 1943; Wen 1929.

SEC. 2. THE PHYLOGENESIS OF THE VERTEBRATE EYE

1. GENERAL CONSIDERATION OF THE PROB-
ABLE FACTORS RESPONSIBLE FOR THE EMER-
GENCE OF THE VERTEBRATE EYE.—The way in
which the vertebrate eye came into being is unknown, in spite of some of the best efforts in biology to find the answer. Numerous more or less
ingenious hypotheses have been made, without
any of them being sufficiently convincing (for
modern summary *see* W. K. Gregory 1951, p.
83). The reason for this failure is the complete
absence of concrete information about the dawn
of vertebrate evolution. Therefore, our speculations must be limited at present to an evaluation of the probable factors which may have
been instrumental in the creation of the vertebrate eye and of Vertebrates in general.

The most remarkable feature of the eye of
now living Vertebrates is its uniformly high
state of structural and functional perfection.
This is noteworthy, especially in view of an almost endless variation in detail. The vertebrate
eye, as we know it, is a finished product, a perfect apparatus, even in the phylogenetically
lowest representatives, the Cyclostomes and
Fishes. This fact is further demonstrated by the
well-developed orbits and channels for the optic
nerves found in fossil Ostracoderms, the most
ancient Fishes known, which lived during the
early Paleozoic Era, approximately 400 million
years ago.

In the case of the vertebrate eye, one gets the
impression of an organ which, from the beginning, was well conceived and logically manufactured to serve its specific purpose. Truly, it is
difficult to visualize an eye more perfectly devised than that found even among the most
primitive of the modern Vertebrates, the Cyclostomes (Lamprey, Hagfish). A less perfect
eye, it seems, would not have satisfied even a
minimum of the biological needs of the Vertebrate Phylum.

The impression of the vertebrate eye as a
perfect, finished organ appearing as if from nowhere, at an unknown time in the dim phylogenetical past, is well expressed in the words of
Froriep (1906, p. 140): "A finished product, like
Athena from the head of Zeus, the vertebrate
eye appears on the scene, and both comparative anatomy and embryology are powerless to
explain how it came about." A similar negative
attitude, tracing the origin of the vertebrate
eye back to the simpler photoreceptors of more
primitive forms of life which preceded the Vertebrates, was recently announced by Walls, one
of the best-informed of modern authorities on
the eye: "The vertebrate eye owes nothing
whatever to the visual organ of any invertebrate animal" (*Ciba Symp.*, v. 5, p. 1586, 1943).

And yet, difficult though the problem of the
phylogenetical origin of the vertebrate eye may
be, a roundabout way to its solution may be indicated. For this, it is necessary to reach far
into the past of life on earth. For we are entitled to believe that just as the Vertebrates
may have evolved from some more simple creatures, so the vertebrate eye must have been
preceded by more primitive photoreceptors.

To trace the probable history of this remarkable organ, we may profitably begin with the
well-established paleontological fact that the
entire Phylum of Vertebrates or rather Chordates is a rather late newcomer among living
beings. The vertebrate period does not represent more than a fraction of the estimated
time since the beginning of life, roughly calculated at 3 billion years (Zeuner; Church, quoted
by Schuchert 1931). By comparison, the "age of
the earth" has been estimated at from 7 to 10
billion years (Bock & Watson, quoted by
Zeuner), and the time since the formation of
its crust at 6–7 billion years. It is probable that
these estimates, as knowledge progresses, will
have to be revised upward, as was done on several occasions during the last hundred years,
and that the figure of 30 billion years for the
duration of life and of 65 billion years for the
age of the earth, given by V. Franz (1924), will
appear less fantastic.

In any case, long ages must have passed before living creatures had sufficiently advanced
to be considered as immediate precursors of the
Vertebrates (the earliest Fishes appeared during the Paleozoic Era or about 360–400 million
years ago, according to Zeuner). It is, therefore,
permissible to speculate that the preliminary
period during which the Vertebrate Ancestors
were evolved must have been a long one, probably not less than the entire known span of the

Vertebrates and possibly several times that much.

What the Vertebrate Ancestors were and what their external appearance was we do not know. Most likely they were small, soft-bodied animals living in the water, somewhat resembling young embryos of the Ascidians and of *Amphioxus* (*see* Parker & Haswell, v. 2, 1940). Since they had no bony skeleton, they have left no known petrifacts which would indicate the intervening steps by which the vertebrate eye was evolved. There is little hope, therefore, of tracing the history of living forms from their inception through the Archeozoic (825–1,550 million years ago), Proterozoic (500–825 million years), and the early period of the Paleozoic Eras (450–500 million years), down to the time when the true Vertebrates appeared. Obviously, any attempt at present to explain the phylogenesis of the vertebrate eye factually is futile.

Again, the information one gains from the eyes found in many modern Invertebrates (Worms, Arthropods, Mollusks) is highly unreliable. Interesting as such study is, it helps little except as an illustration of the various possibilities of which animals availed themselves in developing the organs of sight (*cf.* R. Hesse 1896–1932; Taliaferro 1917, 1920; Plate 1924; Ovio 1927; Buddenbrock 1932; Hagedoorn 1936; Nowikoff 1944–45; Verrier 1945; Buchsbaum 1948; and others). The suspicion is justified that all living Invertebrates have in some way gone too far in specialization to be acceptable as samples of the original conditions.

This is equally true of the borderline forms between the Invertebrates and Vertebrates, the primitive Chordates (Hemichorda, Urochorda, Acrania). All these subphyla have undergone a greater or lesser degree of degeneration. The *Amphioxus* or *Branchiostoma*, for example, this most interesting of the living Higher Chordates and probably most akin to the actual Vertebrate Ancestor, is a disappointment (Fig. 445). In this Acranian there is nothing that could be considered an incipient eye or retina and little that could be looked upon as a primordium, or residue, of the "brain" or "head," as found in the true Vertebrates. The photosensory cells or optic cups discovered by R. Hesse and by Joseph, scattered through its spinal cord, in both shape and distribution are of a kind difficult to use in any hypothesis without undue stretching of the imagination (*see* Ariëns Kappers, Huber & Crosby, v. 1; *see also* Joseph, Parker, Franz, Crozier, Lönneberg).

Almost the same negative verdict must be given about other representatives of the Chordates: *Balanoglossus*, Ascidians, and *Salpa*. In fact, none of the living creatures more or less related to the early Vertebrates is particularly helpful in the attempt to find some clue to the preceding history or in determining the factors which ultimately fashioned the perfect photoreceptor organ, the vertebrate eye.

2. The probable photic environment of primitive animals.—It is by now generally accepted that life originated in water. Whether it was the fresh water of the swamps, rivers, and lakes or the salty water of the seas and oceans, even if at that remote period there were two such categories of water, is essentially immaterial. Also it is of only secondary importance whether the nursery of life was the shallow shore waters or the wide pelagic bodies of the seas.

The abundance of dissolved and formed potential nutritive substances seems to have been of greater importance. All other factors being equal, the shore waters may have offered more favorable conditions. In the first place, oxygen was more abundant near the shore and surface than in the deeper zones. (*Cf.* Sverdrup, Johnson & Fleming 1942.)

Besides water and its contents, the other and equally essential factor for the rise of life was the radiant energy emitted by the sun—light and heat. The complete dependence of all plants and indirectly of all animals upon solar radiant energy illustrates how fundamental this was.

Exactly how the process occurred of putting together the inorganic molecules into the first organic matter still remains to be explained (*cf.* Lichtig 1938; Alexander 1948; Bertalanffy 1949; Bernal 1951; Oparin 1953; Shapley 1953). The process of "photosynthesis," beyond doubt the most fundamental of all biochemical reactions, according to Rabinowitch (1945), is being repeated every day in the action of chlorophyll in the green, red, and yellow leaves of terrestrial plants and of seaweeds and takes place on an even more gigantic scale in the unicellular algae that populate both fresh and salt waters in uncounted quantities. Light, then, which created life, has always been and still remains the essential factor in its maintenance.

Since light and heat are absorbed by water, the surface layers of this transparent fluid medium are most accessible to its penetration and contain most of it. Reflection of light and heat from the bottom, where it is possible because of the shallowness or great transparency of the water, is an added factor increasing the amount of radiant energy it stores up. Shallow waters are likely to be better illuminated and warmer and thus eventually contain more nutritive material, including oxygen. Shallow waters may well have been as advantageous to the creation of life as they are to its maintenance. Here both plants and animals found the most light and heat and food which the plants could assimilate with the help of light.

The sensitiveness to light or the ability of living protoplasm to respond to photic stimuli may not be a universal property of all modern living beings, particularly of animals. However, this may not always have been so. Especially during the initial period, all living substance must have been photosensitive. This must be positively assumed for the forms which gradually evolved into "plants," which otherwise would not have been brought into existence. The "animals" in due course of time could have become largely emancipated from direct dependence upon light, as they became converted into "parasites" living upon the plants. Photochemical and, above all, photosynthetic processes must be viewed as the source from which life on earth took its origin.

The "animals," even though proceeding along their own independent evolutionary course, have nevertheless retained a great deal of their original universal photoirritability, as certainly for a long time they were entirely dependent upon solar heat and still largely remain so. The fundamental similarity in the modes of reaction to light of all animals, from the most primitive to the most complex, as far as they have been investigated, is remarkable. It is evidence of the essential identity of the basic photochemical reactions of all living beings (*see* experiments by Hecht, Crozier, Hartline, Wald, *et al.*).

With the emancipation of the "animals" from direct dependence upon light as a food producer, one property of light—its ability to initiate organic photosynthesis—receded to a second place or was eliminated. For the initiation of protoplasmic reactions, a photolytic phase of light's action, dissimilation—that is, the breaking-up of chemical compounds and the release of stored-up energy—sufficed. This ability, in turn, could now have been further perfected, differentiated, and refined to render protoplasm specifically responsive to various aspects of light, in particular, to wave lengths or "colors," and to increase its sensitiveness to weak stimuli.

Still another fundamental quality of light—its rectilinear propagation—could now have been made use of. With the abandonment of photosynthesis and a sedentary mode of life and with the assumption of active hunting habits by the now mobile animals, this became of paramount importance. The form of energy which is universally present and potentially connects along straight lines every point with all other points in an illuminated habitat is of such superior biological significance that it could not have been left unused. Most animals, and certainly all higher forms, would be unthinkable without this medium of orientation. Higher animal life, in fact, is synonymous with photobiotic existence, or "life in the light."

3. The Vertebrate Ancestors and their utilization of light.—The question of how the ancestors of the Vertebrates looked, what their living habits were, and how they utilized light may be answered in the present state of our ignorance, if at all, only hypothetically. Their soft bodies have disappeared without leaving discoverable traces in the rocks formed during primeval times.

Again, the living representatives of the various Invertebrates or animals without backbones—for example, the Jellyfish; Worms (e.g., Planaria, Leech, Earthworm); Arthropods such as Crustaceans, Insects, and Spiders; Mollusks; Echinoderms; and to hardly a lesser extent the Lower Chordates (*Balanoglossus*, Ascidians), including the nearest relatives of Vertebrates, the Acranians or Cephalochordates (*Branchiostoma, Amphioxus*)—all seem to have gone far along the road of specialization, or retrogression and degeneration, as the case may be. They may therefore be used only with discretion to illustrate in one way or another the past history of Vertebrates (Fishes, Amphibians, Reptiles, Birds, Mammals).

The problem of the probable origin of the vertebrate eye must, accordingly, be treated upon its own merits rather than upon analogy to modern Invertebrates. One may cautiously obtain glimpses from the early embryonic stages of Craniates or Vertebrates. In doing so, however, it must be borne in mind that there is no way of telling to what extent Haeckel's "first law of biogenesis"—which assumes ontogenesis to be an abridged recapitulation of phylogenesis—is correct. Some, if not all, features of an embryo may be merely adaptations to the necessity of a practical task—to grow a body of a new being from scant material, within a limited space, and in a restricted period of time.

General reflection suggests that there must be a firm causal relationship between the present form and function of the vertebrate eye and the photoreceptors of the ancient creatures from which the Vertebrates have evolved. The vertebrate eye, in all its present complexity and perfection, could not possibly have arisen from a phylogenetical vacuum. Like all other parts of a Vertebrate's body, the eye, too, must have evolved out of an original animal matrix, endowed with the properties characteristic of all early organic matter. Only those fundamental evolutionary potentialities present in the original living substance and possessed by the early animals could have developed fully into the complex structures of vertebrate organization and, in the long course of evolution, have produced the vertebrate eye.

At the beginning of animal life, sometime during the Archeozoic Era, variously estimated at from 825 to 1,550 million years ago or even earlier, it is possible to assume that there were creatures later to become Vertebrates that had not yet developed any organs that could justly be called "eyes." One may imagine them as minute, soft-bodied animals, almost without any differentiated parts. They were almost nothing more than clumps or aggregates of cells, as yet poorly integrated into a whole organism.

At a slightly advanced stage of evolution their bodily tissues had differentiated into three layers: an outer ectodermal, an inner endodermal, and a third, the mesodermal, between. At the outset, their body form probably more or less resembled a sphere. In advancing further, they became cylindrical, with a bilaterally symmetrical arrangement of parts somewhat resembling the embryo of a modern *Amphioxus* or an Ascidian.

Whatever were the unknown factors that initiated this particular evolutionary trend, they had a compelling urgency. The result was a body with a wide opening, the "mouth," at one end, leading into the "gut." Food, consisting of minute plants and animals floating in the water, was brought into the gut by means of cilia or flagella, the whiplike processes of cells coating the mouth and gut.

At some time after its inception, this early "Prevertebrate" or "Protovertebrate," as the creature may be called, developed limited locomotion, attained by means of lateral movements of its body carried out by the groups of contractile cells of the middle, mesodermal, layer. The integration of the action of these motor cell groups, it may be imagined, was extremely primitive. It probably was achieved by short expansions of cells of the outer, ectodermal layer arranged in a longitudinal chain with partial overlapping of the links.

The fact that the outer cell layer eventually became an integrator was logical. It came most frequently into contact with the environment. The ectoderm had to stand the impact of small bodies carried by the currents of the water in which the Prevertebrate lived. The other and almost synonymous role of the ectoderm was to protect the entire individual against the attacks of small, predaceous animals. By developing sensitiveness, an ability to react to any physical or chemical attempt to disrupt its integrity as an "individual," and to communicate this reaction to the locomotor mesoderm, the Prevertebrate became able to move itself from place to place and thus escape damage.

The fundamental properties of living substance as formulated by Albrecht von Haller in the second part of the eighteenth century, universally possessed by all living beings including the unicellular—irritability, or sensitiveness of the outer skin to outside agents; conductivity, or ability to transmit impulses to the middle layer; and contractility of the middle layer, with the help of which the body was moved— all developed simultaneously in the Prevertebrate, for the development of any one alone would have had no effect and would have made no sense. Indeed, there is good reason to assume that all three properties were already present in the unicellular ancestors and were merely segregated and accentuated in the particular layers when this ancestor progressed to the point of becoming a multicellular Metazoön.

In the transformation of the ectoderm into a sensory receptor and integrator layer, small noxious agents, repeating their attacks innumerable times during untold ages, even though each agent represented but a slight potential injury, probably played by far the most important role. Larger, more powerful, and more perfectly organized predatory animals could have been only a negative factor in the evolutionary game at that early period. From attacks of such adversaries, the small and as yet poorly organized Prevertebrate had no chance of escape; and, with every individual perishing, there was no accumulation of phylogenetical experience and no resulting perfection. This became possible only when the Prevertebrate attained a higher level of organization.

Since the locomotion of the Prevertebrate was still limited, the creature is to be imagined as one of rather sluggish habits, spending its life mostly at the bottom of shallow waters. In several respects this was an advantage. Such a habitat offered shelter in the nooks and recesses between the grains of sand and gravel. Again, since all the minute microörganisms that died or were otherwise incapacitated tended to fall to the ground, there were good prospects for an abundant food supply.

Life on, or close to, the bottom had other consequences. For just as all food came from above, so also did most of the enemies. These, having necessarily a more advanced organization, not only possessing distinct sense organs with a fair range but also being able to move about at a fair speed, populated the watery habitat above the floor. In this world in which the primitive Prevertebrate lived, its principal interest, therefore, was "above." The part of the ectodermal layer facing up, the "back" of the Prevertebrate, received by far the greatest number of relevant, diversified stimuli, whereas the part facing down, the "underbelly," remained in a relatively sheltered, neutral position.

In due time the cells along the back of the Prevertebrate became more responsive, that is, more ready to react quickly to appropriate stimuli. Accordingly, they developed phylogenetically into the earliest "neurosensory cells" of the budding Vertebrate Phylum. When this stage of development was attained, the specialized receptor-conductor cells of this newly differentiated "neural or medullary plate" spread their processes farther up and down the longitudinal axis of the animal. Gradually they became more like the nerve cells or "neurons" of modern animals, capable of some limited integration of groups of the contractile mesodermal cells into a now faster-responding locomotor "muscular" system.

Briefly, at that stage of phylogenesis the Prevertebrate attained a level of organization above that of a mere "gastrula" and could be compared with the "neurula" of modern vertebrate embryology.

4. The inception of the vertebrate photoreceptors.—In the earliest period of prevertebrate evolution the outer ectodermal cell layer necessarily was barely sensitive. It responded but little at first and probably chiefly to directly applied physical and chemical stimuli. Light at this stage probably had only a small effect. However, a trace of the original, inherent responsiveness to light, as well as to heat, possessed by all living matter must also have been retained by the bodily tissues of the Prevertebrate, in particular by the ectoderm, the first tissue to be exposed to such stimuli. This photosensitiveness must have increased further in the neural plate—the streak of thickened ectoderm along the "back" of the animal.

At a certain slightly advanced phylogenetical stage, this stripe facing toward the ceiling of the water, whence light and enemies came, became in a sense an "eye" in its entire extent. It became more definitely so when the integrative ability of the neural plate and the locomotor ability of the mesodermal layer had progressed further and were able to move the Prevertebrate from place to place more efficiently. For only now was the utilization of the advantage of an extended exteroceptive range possible.

Heretofore, with the responsiveness of the ectoderm, including the neural plate, restricted to immediate touch and chemical action, the protective role of this specialized locality was limited to stimuli caused by the attacks of small creatures and the action of various chemicals dissolved in water. When, in addition to being a "tangoceptor" and "chemoceptor," the neural plate also became a "photoceptor" or "eye," a real opportunity was given the Prevertebrate to survive against the attacks of bigger, better-organized, and faster predators. Now these could be detected at a distance which, no matter how small originally, was greater than immediate contact, which, when established, must usually have been identical with the lost battle for survival. The conversion of the neural plate into a photoreceptor meant an immeasurable achievement, an advantage upon which the entire future of the incipient vertebrate development was built.

5. Prevertebrate optic primordia, their utilization and gradual perfection.—It is intriguing to speculate further upon what use the Prevertebrate, now in the possession of definite, even though as yet very primitive, photoreceptors, could have made of these wonderful new sense organs which widened its "world" from immediate surroundings to a radius of, perhaps, a few inches and later to a few feet.

The question is: Was the hypothetical creature positively or negatively phototactic or phototropic? To answer this, the only guide is the possible biological usefulness of either of the two properties. To an almost helpless creature, living on the floor of a world of water where most light came from above, any unusual change in illumination may have signaled the approach of a potential foe. Mostly it may have been a shadow, a dark patch moving on the bright ceiling, where the intensity of illumination was suddenly reduced in comparison with its "background." It was a sign of a prowling predator looking for a victim. Any shadow moving about, therefore, was likely to be avoided. Practically the same would be true of any

bright spot, such as might be caused by a reflection of light from the smooth, glistening surface of the body of an animal of prey suddenly appearing on the uniformly illuminated ceiling. Briefly, any unusual condition of light from the "viewpoint" of a Prevertebrate was a suspicious thing, to be avoided as rapidly as possible. The creature, accordingly, must have been attuned to an avoidance of all unusual positive and negative photic stimuli.

The next step in the development of prevertebrate photoreceptors was to concentrate and to increase sensitivity to photic stimulation, or to a sudden absence of it, at the cephalic, or front, end of the neural plate. As the Prevertebrate became more efficient in moving about, it was apt to develop a preferential use of either of the two ends of its elongated body. Moreover, it is probable that the entire process of elongation of the body consisted in a simultaneous and complex interaction of several factors—in the advantage of moving the body with one end ahead; in the elongation and bisymmetry of the body, facilitating locomotion by a reduction of resistance to water; and in an increase of sensitivity at the front end of the neural plate, which thus became a refined exploratory receptor organ. The increase of photosensitivity at the front end of the neural plate was, then, merely a continuation and intensification of the same tendency toward greater locomotive efficiency and thus toward greater safety, better food supply, and perhaps other advantages.

The various steps of a hypothetical evolutionary process of the incipient vertebrate photoreceptors may be understood if two things are constantly borne in mind. First, of a general character, is that each of the subsequent phylogenetical steps in the perfection of the photoreceptors was a goal in itself, serving particular biological needs of their possessors in particular circumstances. No matter how primitive the photoreceptors were at a particular evolutionary stage, they must have served their possessors fairly well and would have continued to do so, even if there had been no further "progress" (as countless primitive "eyes" of modern Invertebrates show).

That in the particular case of the Vertebrates the whole long-lasting evolutionary process eventually culminated in the creation of an elaborate chamber eye is a consequence both of evolutionary mechanics and of the inherent properties of light and of physical environment rather than the result of some preordained supernatural wisdom. Or, to speak in harmony with modern times, the creation of the vertebrate eye, as of other parts of the body, cannot be looked upon as a result of purposeful planning by some omniscient "brain truster," "commissar," or "Führer" of the universe. That the vertebrate eye is what it is, instead of still being a simple patch of thickened ectoderm coating the "back" of a primitive creature crawling over the bottom of the ocean, is solely the result of its limitless original plastic potentialities and of the slight discrepancy between what the organ at a certain phylogenetical stage could do and what was required from it—just enough difference to push it toward further perfection.

A second consideration is the inseparable organic and functional dependence of the photoreceptor upon the remainder of the organism and, in particular, upon the neuromotor system (and to some extent vice versa). While it is possible to imagine a motor system of an animal without photoreceptors (since the former may be associated with other receptors, particularly those of touch), a reverse situation is unthinkable. An eye without nerves and centers and without a locomotor system would be an absurdity, without biological purpose.

The vertebrate eye, from its very inception and through all subsequent steps of its phylogenesis, must have had its appropriate nervous and motor counterparts to work with. For a simple photoreceptor, capable of utilizing light stimuli only a little, a poorly organized neuromotor apparatus sufficed, and vice versa. When the capabilities of photoreceptors expanded, more complex and more efficient nervous and locomotor systems developed, this in turn being a stimulus for the continuous perfection of photoreceptors. The separation of the stimulus-perceiving "photoderm" and its co-ordinated motor "mesoderm" is, in fact, an artificial procedure, at least in the early period of vertebrate phylogenesis, justified merely to facilitate an analytical understanding and interpretation of the factors and forces at work. The true process of the phylogenesis of the vertebrate eye may be likened to a continuous chain of actions and re-actions, with mutual interdependence of various factors and with ultimate consequences for all. It is for this reason that the various attempts to explain the origin of the vertebrate eye by twisting and molding of parts of the embryonic ectoderm and neural tube alone, touching, as they do, merely upon a superficial phenomenon, must remain unsatisfactory (Balfour, Boveri, Froriep, Hesse, and others; *see* Walls 1939, 1942, 1943).

6. PROBABLE STAGES IN THE EVOLUTION OF THE VERTEBRATE EYE.—The various stages in the phylogenetical development of the vertebrate eye, one after another, and the external and internal factors responsible for them may be imagined in the following way (Fig. 436; *cf. also* Fig. 434, and sec. 1, this chapter).

The earliest stage (sketch *A*) would show, on a vertical section, the body of a Prevertebrate with a somewhat round or oval shape, with, perhaps, its dorsal extremity or "back" somewhat expanded. The ectoderm in this locality may have contained sensory cells not necessarily in a compact arrangement and not greatly differing in shape and properties from the other adjoining ectodermal cells. Such an only slightly differentiated patch, because of its general, nonspecific functional character, could be called a primitive sensory "omniceptor." It extended about equally down both sides of the body. It may be considered the phylogenetical inception of the "neural plate" of a modern vertebrate embryo from which the nervous system and the eyes develop.

As far as this ectodermal patch also responded to photic stimuli, it could be regarded as a primordial "cyclopean eye." Optically and therefore functionally, such an "eye," even though extremely primitive, was not in all points equivalent. The reason is obvious: with every change in position of the body or of the optic stimulus, a different group of photosensory cells of the curved surface was stimulated, and stimulated differently. If, for any considerable length of time, the creature was capable of maintaining an upright position, with its midsagittal plane of symmetry oriented vertically, a unilateral photic stimulus must have affected the side closer to the stimulus more than the opposite side. If, for example, of the two sources

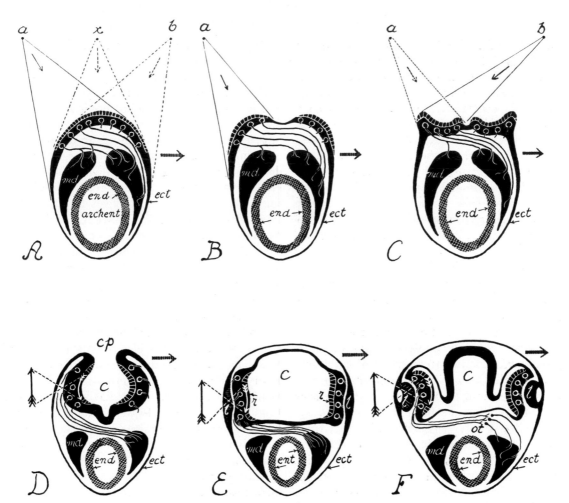

FIG. 436.—Probable stages in the phylogenetic origin of vertebrate eye and visual system, illustrated on cross-sections through the cephalic end of a hypothetical Prevertebrate or Vertebrate Ancestor. *A*, open neural-plate stage, with a single common everted integumental photoreceptor patch on "back," facing light stimuli (as in Earthworm), permitting crude local differentiation of intensity, and hence of direction, without image formation, with efferent fibers partly mixed but mostly decussated (a photophobic arrangement); *B*, neural-groove stage with photoepithelium concentrated in two lateral patches, with an incipient median invagination, with accentuated functional differentiation of "right" and "left," or of "direction," with efferent fibers largely decussated (a photophobic arrangement); *C*, incipient invagination of optic sulci of optic primordia into primitive optic cups, their incipient rotation under prevalence of contralateral stimuli (e.g., left primordium influenced from *b*), with each primordium facing opposite half of field of view, with a preponderant decussation of efferent fibers (a photophilic or photopositive arrangement subsequently compensated by a complete inversion of optoneural plate and restoration of original photophobic arrangement, as illustrated by next stage); *D*, complete invagination of optoneural plate, with inversion of photoepithelium and inception of tubular nervous system, approaching closure of neural groove or "cerebral pupil" (*cp*) into cerebral vesicle (*c*), rotation of primitive optic cups, and eversion of efferent connections, their convex face acting as a primitive collecting lens, with a lateral position of primordia and a complete decussation of efferent fibers, the effect of these changes being restoration of original photophobic arrangement ("turning of evolutionary corner"); *E*, closing of the cerebral pupil in a median *raphé* and completion of primitive cerebral vesicle (*c*), complete inversion of photoepithelium (*r*), lateral position of optic primordia, inception of nonnervous ectodermal dioptrical apparatus (*l*, lens placode) with early image formation, complete decussation of efferent fibers (a secondary photophobic arrangement); *F*, formation of essential parts of final vertebrate visual system, with "eyes" or secondary optic cups consisting of a nonnervous outer pigment layer (eliminating all light stimuli except those coming through pupil and lens) and an inner nervous or photosensitive layer or retina proper, with a cornea and lens at some distance from the retina, hence forming an image-producing dioptrical apparatus; nutrition of retina by a mesodermal chorioid, hence permitting the unobstructed passage of image-forming rays, and with completely decussated optic nerve fibers, resulting in the preservation of the original photophobic arrangement. (*Cf.* Figs. 434, 435.) *Labeling: a, x, b*, left, central, and right viewed points or source of stimulating rays of light; *archent*, archenteron or primitive gut; *c*, primitive cerebral vesicle; *cp*, cerebral pupil or passage before closure of cerebral vesicle; *ect*, ectoderm; *end, ent*, endoderm or entoderm; *l*, lens primordium, later lens vesicle; *md*, mesoderm; *r*, retina. Shaded arrows indicate direction of response or body movement (e.g., to right when left half or left optic primordium is stimulated by stimulus *a*).

of light, *a* and *b*, situated at two symmetrically opposite points, one—e.g., point *a*—sent a greater number of light rays, more rays would be arrested by the ipsilateral half of the body than by the contralateral half. This, for reasons of geometrical optics, must have taken place even if the transparency of the body was great, which was likely. In the modern *Amphioxus*, with its highly transparent body, such a lateralizing effect is absent because of the location of photosensitive cells in the center of its spinal cord and their particular orientation; hence the creature customarily lies on its side when at rest.

The effect of unilateral photic stimulation of the Prevertebrate must, necessarily, have been preponderantly unilateral: right, when the stimulus came from the right side, and vice versa. The total effect upon the creature, however, depended upon its internal organization— the efferent structures or organs of execution along which the excitation spread from the stimulated groups of photosensory cells to the locomotor or muscle cells of the mesoderm.

Initially, it is possible to imagine that each photosensory cell had a tendency to contact, by its short expansions, the nearest group of the mesodermal muscle cells. The connections and the effect of visual systems thus organized were essentially ipsilateral, the photic stimulation of the right half of the neural plate activating the muscles of the right side and vice versa.

Biologically, this would make sense only if the consequence was beneficial. Since at the earliest evolutionary stage a rather passive way of feeding or, at most, by means of cilia was probable, and considering an as yet poorly developed intrinsic organization of the Prevertebrate, which prevented it from embarking upon an active, hunting mode of life, it is most likely that a negative optokinetic response was far more advantageous—activation of the contralateral set of mesodermal muscle cells. When a threatening shadow or an ominous bright spot appeared on one side within its effective range, the activation of the contralateral musculature effected a contralateral deviation and a flight in the opposite direction from the approaching potential danger. The way to accomplish such contralateral response was by making the efferent connections of each half of the neural

plate cross to the musculature of the contralateral half of the body.

Such partial or preponderant decussation, a "primordial chiasma," was advantageous in yet another respect: it offered a simple mechanism for an alternating activation of the right- and left-side myotomes, a prerequisite for rectilinear, unidirectional movement of the body. In order to achieve this, the other addition required was a "central integrator" to regulate the alternating activity and keep it up for some time. This, too, could easily have taken place by making some efferent fibers of one side establish contact with the sensory cells of the other half of the medullary plate, instead of directly with the contralateral muscle cells. Once this stage of differentiation was achieved, a foundation was laid for the development of the future complex central nervous system of Vertebrates.

The visuosensory and visuomotor mechanisms, in the light of the preceding speculation, seem like two sides or aspects of a basically identical apparatus. Both have contributed equally, or almost so, to the rise of the central nervous organ, the brain. The phylogenetical inception of both components must have been practically simultaneous. Photosensory cells without effectors would have had no influence upon the behavior and welfare of the Prevertebrate and would never have developed; the effector structures alone would likewise never have arisen, nor could they have existed independently (unless served by other receptors). This assumption is self-evident, even though it is plausible that both constituents of the incipient visual system—the receptive-sensory and the effector-motor—have evolved out of the same primitive tactile-motor or possibly chemoceptor system which preceded them.

The next stage in the evolution and perfection of the eye—or rather visual system—was attained with a segregation of photosensory cells into two patches, each facing up and somewhat laterally (sketch *B* in Fig. 436). That this should have been the case was logical and unavoidable. With a vast majority of visual impulses coming from the lateral direction, in a creature now capable of moving about, the lateral impulses prevailed in the long run (since in an aquatic habitat, limited by two horizontal levels, a ceiling above and a floor below, there is vastly more "biological space" laterally than "above" or "below"). In consequence, the dorsolateral parts of the originally uniform photosensitive neural plate became thicker. In early human embryos these two localities appear as two "optic primordia" or "retinal oriments," from which and around which the two definitive eyes develop (Fig. 434, sketch *A*).

The third stage (sketch *C*, in Fig. 436) was characterized by dents or depressions in the two optic primordia (*cf.* sketch *B*, in Fig. 434). First to appear were shallow primitive optic sulci or grooves (*os*). These sulci gradually deepened until each primordium resembled a cup. The deepening of the two primordial optic cups was coincident with another remarkable change—rotation of the cups from the original position, in which their concavities faced up to one where they faced each other (Fig. 436, *D*).

The functional factors which have necessitated such profound changes are difficult to fathom. Heretofore the relation of cause and effect was rather clear: at first, a single photosensory area covering the more or less convex "back" of the body, with superficially located photosensory cells first to meet the light rays coming from above (sketch *A*); then, when the creature became more active, a concentration of the photoreceptors at its anterior end and their segregation into two somewhat laterally placed patches partly facing up, and preponderantly stimulated by the rays coming from either the right or the left side (sketches *B* and *C*). Such an arrangement appears advantageous, since the majority of photic stimuli arrived from the sides. Why, at this point in evolution, should this arrangement be abandoned, and a new one adopted that amounted to a veritable revolution (sketch *D*)?

The factors responsible for this reversal remain, for the time being, hidden. Whatever they were, the urge must have been compelling. The turning point may have been reached when, at stage *C*, the stimulation of the contralateral primordial optic cup gradually increased until it finally threatened to prevail—that is, stimulation of the left cup by rays coming from the right side (point *b*), and vice versa. With the efferent fibers largely or completely crossed, no biologically useful purpose would have been served by this, unless the Prevertebrate funda-

mentally changed its life habits at this stage and frankly became positively optotactic.

Since the creature still must have been a small and rather sluggish animal, with its sensory and motor apparatus precluding the great mobility necessary for a predator, this was unlikely. In this situation any unilateral stimulation would have brought it directly into the path of its foe rather than away from it, as heretofore. Here a complete inversion of the two optic cups may have restored the former advantageous situation, provided that the decussation of the efferent pathway also was complete, as indicated in sketch *D*. Now, by a relative shading-off of the contralateral optic cup, made more effective by inside pigmentation (*see* Eycleshymer), the normal negative optotactic situation was again restored, or, since the change was gradually accomplished, the original situation was preserved, and stimulation was again chiefly concentrated upon the optic cup ipsilateral to the stimulus. With the efferent fibers crossed, the beneficial photofugal reaction, leading away from the danger, could again be effectuated (indicated by horizontal arrows in our sketches *D*, *E*, *F*).

A complete inversion of the primitive optic pits had other important advantages. From now on, the stimulating rays of light, instead of reaching the primordial photosensory epithelium directly, had to penetrate through the whole thickness of the overlying ectoderm and the tissue between. While this may appear to be an impediment to effective penetration of light, in the subsequent evolutionary stages it became manifestly transformed into an advantage. In the phase represented by sketch *D*, the bulging convex face of the body, inclosing the optic primordia, may already have acted as a collecting lens, by which the intensity of stimuli focused upon photosensory cells behind was increased.

This situation remained basically unchanged in the entire further phylogenetical perfection of the vertebrate eye. When at the following stage (*E*) the two localities of the ectodermal integument contiguous to the retinal primordia thickened into the lens primordia (*l*), as illustrated by the ontogenetical phase *B* in Figure 435, and the formation of double-walled secondary optic cups was initiated (sketch *F*, in Fig. 436), the integumental ectodermal lens, increasing in size and structural homogeneity and probably located at a distance from the photosensory layer equal to its focal length, was a much more efficient dioptrical apparatus than the outside curvature of the optic primordium and its integumental covering alone (as in sketch *D*).

There are a few more phylogenetical deductions of special interest, which, without any undue stretching of the imagination, one may read into the ontogenetical record registered in the early stages of vertebrate embryology. During the earliest phylogenetical period the photoreceptor organs were located dorsally, at the "back" of the Prevertebrate's body, facing upward (sketches *A*, *B*, and *C*), as exemplified by the ontogenetical stages *A*, *B*, and *C*, in Figure 434. In the subsequent stages the optic primordia, simultaneously with their inversion (*D*), moved downward, eventually to assume a frankly lateral or ventrolateral position (sketches *E*, *F*, in same figure).

At its inception the Chordate Phylum was probably represented by bottom dwellers, as already mentioned. From this lowly and restricted habitat the somewhat advanced forms gradually worked themselves into the upper reaches of their fluid world, eventually becoming frankly pelagic. This they achieved after developing more perfect eyes and more efficient motor and central regulating mechanisms. When they began to move freely through the upper regions of the water, the direction of their visual interest also changed. Whereas in the beginning the "visual world" of the Prevertebrate was "above," at a later period it became "lateral." For this, laterally situated eyes were appropriately placed sensory organs.

The road from the floor to the upper regions of the water and toward higher evolutionary possibilities was the road toward the source of light. The means which alone permitted this was the perfection of the visual organs. The alternative, without this improvement, was to remain on the ground or partly buried in it, a habit still practiced by the contemporary eyeless *Amphioxus*. The advantages and consequences of this "visualization," or increasing dependence upon visual organs of the chamber-eye type, are clear.

Once more casting a glance upon embryology as a clue to the phylogeny of the vertebrate visual system, one cannot help being impressed by the precociousness and relative size of the visual primordia. In the earliest embryo, more than at any other period of the subsequent development and maturity of the individual, the visual organs dominate. Here they represent a substantial part of the central nervous system (later to become brain and spinal cord), wherein most of what is to be the brain belongs to the visual primordia.

Does this indicate that in the Vertebrate Ancestor most of the "brain" consisted of the eyes? That the huge nervous organ called the brain, so characteristic of the advanced Vertebrates, received its first and most potent impetus from visual stimuli? That, accordingly, the Vertebrates from their inception were principally "visual animals," "creatures of light and sight"? That the "visualization" of Vertebrates or a biologically almost complete dependence upon sight adopted by them was the magic formula by which they climbed from the twilight of the ocean's floor into the upper reaches of the water and finally out of it into the unlimited photic freedom of the air?

References: E. D. Adrian 1943; Agar 1943; J. Alexander 1948; Ariëns Kappers 1929; Ariëns Kappers, Huber & Crosby 1936; Arrol *et al.* 1942; K. E. von Baer 1828; Balfour 1885, v. 3, p. 470; Bartelmez 1922, 1923; Bartelmez & Blount 1954; Bartelmez & Evans 1926; Beadle 1948; Beebe 1931, 1932, 1934; Th. Beer 1901; Béraneck 1890; J. D. Bernal 1951; Bertalanffy 1949; Bethe *et al.*, v. 12 (1, 2), 1929–31; Birge & Juday 1931; A. F. Bliss; Boeke 1902, 1934; Boell *et al.* 1948; N. Bohr 1933; Bok & Watson 1940; Bounoure 1949; Th. Boveri 1904; Bozler 1927; Brehm's *Tierleben*, 4th ed., v. 1, 1918; Bronn 1924 (Lönnberg *et al.*); E. W. Brown 1931; E. T. Brücke 1929; Buchsbaum 1948; Buddenbrock 1921, 1932, 1937–39, 1952; Burckhardt 1902; Buxton 1912; Carrière 1885; Chamberlain 1900; Child 1921; Chun 1903; Le Gros Clark 1947; Clark & Medawar; G. L. Clarke 1936; Clasing 1923; Clements & Long 1950; Cloud 1949; Coghill 1929, 1930, 1933, 1936, 1943; Colman 1950; Creed 1930; Crosby 1949 and later; Crozier 1917; Da Costa 1947; Dakin 1928; C. G. Darwin 1932; Chas. R. Darwin 1859, 1871, and later eds.; De Beer 1940; Deevey 1951; Demoll 1914; Dohrn 1885;

Eddington 1933; L. Edinger 1906; *Encyclopaedia Britannica*, 14th ed. (articles "Distribution of Animals," "Plankton," "Sight," "Zoöl. Regions"); Erickson 1933; Eycleshymer 1893, 1895; Fischer 1931, 1932; Florkin 1948; Fraenkel & Gunn 1940; Fraisse 1881; V. Franz 1923, 1924, 1927, 1934, 1935; Franz & Steche 1914; K. Frisch 1924; Froriep 1906; Garbowski 1902; Gaskell 1908; Gladstone & Wakely 1940; Goerttler 1950; W. K. Gregory 1936, 1951; Grenacher 1874, 1879, 1880, 1886, 1892; Gundersen & Hastings 1944; E. Haeckel 1866, 1870, 1875, 1891, 1894–96, 1895, 1908, 1916; Hagedoorn 1930, 1936; Haldane 1929, 1932, 1944; Hanström 1928; E. N. Harvey 1940, 1948; H. W. Harvey 1928, 1945; Hasse 1876; Haug 1933; Hausmann 1923; Havet 1922; Heberer 1943; Hecht 1926, 1928; Hedinger 1937; Heidermann 1928, 1933; Heintz 1935; Hempelmann 1926; Hensen 1865, 1866; C. J. Herrick 1925, 1938, 1939, 1949; Herrick & Coghill 1915; O. Hertwig 1906; R. Hertwig 1907; Hescheler & Boveri 1923; C. Hess 1913, 1914; W. N. Hess 1924, 1925, 1937, 1938; R. Hesse 1896–1902, 1898, 1902, 1908, 1929, 1932, 1935; Hesse, Allee & Schmidt 1937; Hesse & Doflein 1935–43; Heuser 1930; Heyl 1929; Hogben 1930; A. Holmes 1931, 1937; S. J. Holmes 1944; Horowitz 1945; Howell 1939; Huettner 1949; J. Huxley 1942; Jeans 1942; Jelgersma 1906; Jennings 1906; Johnstone 1932; Joseph 1904, 1928; Keibel 1906, 1928; Kennel 1891; Kepner & Foshee 1917; Kessler 1871, 1877; Klinckowström 1895; A. Knopf 1931, 1949; A. Knopf *et al.* 1931; O. Köhler 1924; Koehring 1950; Kohl 1890; Kolmer 1928; Korschelt (& Heider) 1936; Kovarik 1931; Kowalewsky 1871; Kraatz 1950; Krabbe 1947; W. Krause 1897, 1898; Krisch 1933; A. Kühn 1929; Kupffer 1872; O. Lange 1908; Langerhans 1876; Lankester 1875, 1880; Lehmann 1945; Lemke 1935; Leydig 1861; Lichtig 1938; Lillie 1945; Locy 1894; Loeb 1891; Lönnberg *et al.* 1924; Lubosch 1909; Lukin 1936; Lull 1947; Luntz 1936; Magnus & De Kleyn 1932; Mangold 1931; I. C. Mann 1928, 1950; Manten 1948; Mast 1910, 1911, 1922, 1926, 1927; Matisse 1947–49; Merker 1937; Merton 1905; Metcalf 1906; Minnich 1939; T. H. Morgan 1932; Murray & Nagel 1894, 1896; *Nat. Research Counc. Washington*, v. 80, 1931; W. A. Nagel 1894, 1896; Neal & Rand 1936, 1939; Newman 1939; Nowikoff 1932, 1944–45; Nuëll 1887; Olson 1932; Oparin 1953; Orton 1951; Osborn 1918; Ovio 1927; Pantin 1941; G. H. Parker 1908, 1909, 1919, 1923; T. J. Parker & W. A. Haswell 1940; J. Parsons 1943; B. M. Patten 1917; W. Patten 1886; Peter 1920; Pietschmann 1929; F. H. Pike 1944, 1946; Plate 1924; Popovskij 1949; Prince 1949; Prosser 1934; Pütter 1908–12; Rabinowitch 1945, 1951; E. Rádl 1910; S. Ramón y Cajal 1898, 1899, 1909–11, 1915, 1917; Ramón y Cajal & Sánchez 1915; Rand 1950; Redikorzew 1905; Reinöhl 1940; Rensch 1947; Roaf 1930; Romer 1943, 1945, 1946, 1949; Romer & Grove 1935; E. Rüchardt 1952; Sánchez 1909–12; Schanz 1918; Schimkewitch 1921; Schuchert 1931; Schultz 1948; Segall 1933; Semper 1877; Sewertzoff 1929, 1931; H. Shapley; Simpson 1947, 1949; Sleggs 1926; G. E. Smith 1926, 1932; J. P. Smith 1900; Spemann 1927, 1936, 1938; H. Spencer 1867; Spitzer 1910; Spratt 1940; Stebbin 1950; Steiner 1898–1900; Studnička 1900, 1912, 1913, 1918; Studnitz 1940; Sverdrup, Johnson & Fleming 1942; *Symposium on Hydrobiology;* Szütz 1915; Taliaferro 1917, 1920; Thienemann 1925; Thompson 1944; Torrey 1946; Tracy 1926; Tretjakoff 1909; Triepel 1920; L. Th. Troland 1924, 1929; Uexküll 1921; Vandel 1949; Van der Horst 1933; Veit 1926–27; Verrier 1945; Viaud; Voronikhin 1945; Waddington 1947; Wald 1945–46; Walls 1939, 1942, 1943; D. M. S. Watson 1919, 1926, 1932; Weel 1937; A. L. Wegener 1941; W. C. Wells 1792; Wesenberg-Lund 1939; H. Weyl 1934; Whitman 1892, 1893, 1899; Wiemann 1949; Willey 1894, 1895; Wollenhaupt 1934–35; R. Woltereck 1940; Yerkes 1903; Yonge 1949; Zeuner 1946.

SEC. 3. THE PHYLOGENETICAL ORIGIN AND FUNCTIONAL SIGNIFICANCE OF DECUSSATION OF THE VERTEBRATE VISUAL SYSTEM

1. Introduction.—One of the most remarkable and at the same time most baffling features of the vertebrate visual system is the decussation of the optic nerves. In the lower classes, the Fishes, Amphibians, Reptiles, and Birds, the decussation is considered to be complete (Figs.

188–90). In the Mammals a smaller or larger portion of the fibers remains on the same side, thus producing a partial decussation. The proportion of the nondecussating to decussating fibers increases from a small fraction found in the Rodents (Fig. 191) to approximately one-third or more in the Carnivores (Fig. 192) and the Primates (Figs. 186, 193–99; *see also* chap. VI, 5, and chap. XIV, and corresponding figures).

From its universal occurrence it is obvious that this anatomical feature must be of fundamental importance in the bodily organization and in the physiology and biology of the Vertebrate Phylum. Hence its phylogenetical inception must be sought in those factors and circumstances that gave rise to the Vertebrates.

In order to determine what factors, in what way and for what biological purpose, created the crossing of the optic nerves, various hypotheses have been proposed. Of these, the most plausible is the one by S. Ramón y Cajal (1899, 1909–11). Briefly, it is as follows. The total decussation of the optic nerves found in the Inframammalian Vertebrates represents a phylogenetical phase preceding a partial decussation. It is related to the centralization of the nervous system, culminating in the creation of the brain. The decussation appears first in the afferent or centripetal visual pathway and is followed by a decussation of the efferent or motor pathways correlated with the first.

In the Inframammalian Vertebrates, e.g., in a Fish, a Frog, a Lizard, or a Bird, each optic nerve terminates in the contralateral optic lobe or tectum of the midbrain (Fig. 437, right-hand sketch). The right eye, accordingly, sees to the right with the left optic lobe, and the left eye sees to the left with the right optic lobe. The two monocular fields of view are separate, with no overlapping in the center. Such an arrangement may be called "panoramic." In it, owing to an assumed absence of binocular convergence and of superimposable "corresponding retinal points," a third dimension or stereopsis would be absent in a subjective experience (this and other similar statements must be qualified in view of our own observations to the contrary, made on a Golden Eagle, Barn Swallow, Anole Lizard, and Pike; *see* chap. XIV).

Even without binocular overlapping, which

S. Ramón y Cajal assumed was absent, in a panoramic system the two eyes always work together. Since the retinal images, because of the action of the chamber eyes, are inverted, they are necessarily projected in an inverted way upon the optic lobes (*C*). However, because of complete decussation, the natural or logical order of the central images is again restored.

Just as the two monocular fields of view are spread in one plane, alongside each other, and are natural extensions of each other, so the two visual centers, the optic lobes, are placed side by side, the details of the visual fields represented therein being arranged in a logical way, corresponding to the details of the panoramic view of the two eyes. The only difference is the reverse order, caused by the inversion of retinal images, the right end of the common panoramic field of view being represented at the left end of the left visual center, and the left end of the field at the right end of the right visual center. In this way a single "mental image" of the entire panoramic field of view is created.

This arrangement is possible because of complete decussation of the optic nerves. If there were no decussation and each nerve terminated in the optic lobe of its own side, the two halves of the "mental image" would be arranged illogically, that is, would be incongruous or incompatible with each other (as shown in the left-hand sketch, Fig. 437). As it is, the "mental image" is always complete, each half of it representing one half, the contralateral, of the external, visible reality. In a panoramic visual system thus organized, the "symmetrical points" in both optic lobes represent two different localities in visual space, and there is no "functional duplexity." Putting it into a single phrase, "the decussation of the optic nerves is motivated by a necessity to restore the lateral inversion of the two images caused by the action of the lenses" (that is, chamber eyes).

In the mammalian visual system, S. Ramón y Cajal assumed that there is a common binocular field of view caused by the "parallel" position of the two visual axes (Fig. 438). Here a portion of the optic nerve fibers does not decussate, and parts of both retinae, working together, send their fibers to the same cerebral hemisphere. Hence each cerebral hemisphere is related to the homonymous parts of both retinae or to the contralateral parts of both monocular fields of view. Each point of a visual object, depicted at the "corresponding points" of both retinae, is projected on a single point in either the right or the left cortical center, depending on its position in the viewed object.

Partial decussation, accordingly, permits the formation of a single "mental image," *Rv*, comparable to that in the Inframammalian Vertebrates, made up of a right and a left half, representing the left and right halves of the viewed object. The important difference is that, whereas in a panoramic system each half of the

viewed object is seen with only one eye monocularly, in a stereoscopic system each half of the object is viewed to a greater or lesser extent with both eyes, even though the impressions from both eyes come together in the same half of the brain, the contralateral relative to the viewed object. In this way the advantage of decussation is fully preserved, owing to which

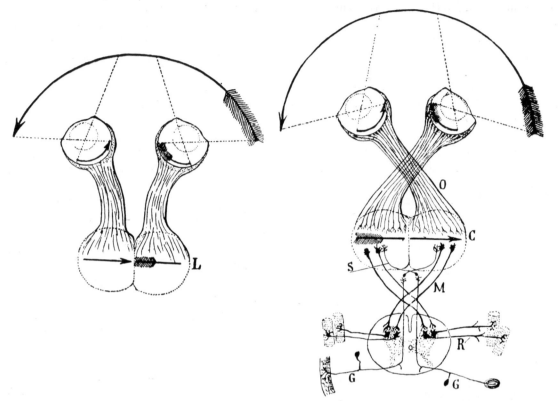

Fig. 437.—Ramón y Cajal's diagrams purporting to explain the phylogenetical origin of the decussation of the optic chiasma and of the functional organization of the vertebrate visual system. Left-hand sketch illustrates the misplacement of two central images formed in optic lobes (*L*) of the brain received by two retinae, in a hypothetical case where optic nerves remain uncrossed (no such case is on record among Vertebrates). Right-hand sketch shows the effect of total decussation found in all lower Vertebrates such as Fishes, Amphibians, Reptiles, and Birds and the almost total decussation in Lower Mammals possessing panoramic vision. In each case each retinal image represents half of the viewed object, each image being inverted in the same sense, as against the particular half of the object (owing to the dark-chamber action of the eye). In the first case, where there is no decussation, the two single central images are projected ipsilaterally, hence incongruously, not forming a single harmonious central representation of the total object. In the second case the ocular inversion of two retinal images is compensated by a chiasmal decussation, which makes the two central images (in *C*) assume a logical order, with the right retinal image projected upon the left center, and the left image upon the right center, both fitting together and forming a single harmonious central image. The optic decussation in turn has inforced a secondary decussation of the motor and somesthetic pathways, making possible co-operation of these systems with the visual system. From S. Ramón y Cajal, *Die Struktur des Chiasma opticum*, etc., 1899; also *Histologie du système nerveux*, v. 2, Figs. 242, 243, 244, 245, 1909–11. (*Cf.* following figure.)

parable to that in the Inframammalian Vertebrates, made up of a right and a left half, representing the left and right halves of the viewed object. The important difference is that, whereas in a panoramic system each half of the

the two halves of a "mental image" remain congruous, each being a natural or logical extension of the other half (but for the lateral inversion, which is immaterial). The two visual centers in the brain of a Mammal may be looked upon as a single cerebral retina made up of two halves, one half in each cerebral hemisphere, each half representing one half of the common field of view.

Both types of visual system—the one with complete decussation, and the other with partial—require a crossing of motor fibers in the brain. This is necessary to preserve the original functional relationship between the sensory and the motor mechanisms of the body working to-

Wundt and Spitzer objected to the assumption of the accurate projection of retinal images upon the cortex.

Wundt's objections to an accurate adaptation of the ipsilateral and contralateral fibers in the cortex along which the impulses from the "corresponding retinal points" arrive are invalid, since precisely this was proved by our experiments (*see* chap. VI, 7; chap. VII, 5, 6). Both Wundt's and Spitzer's opposition to an

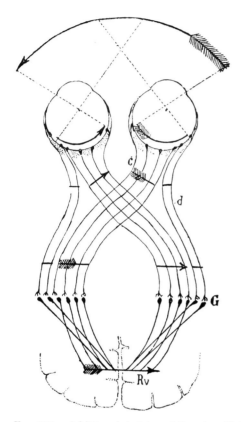
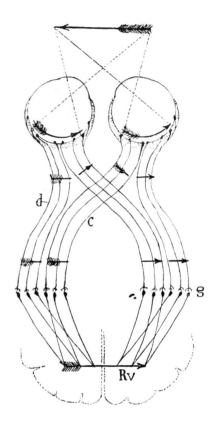

Fig. 438.—Additional sketches of Ramón y Cajal illustrating the formation of a single cerebral image in Man and in Higher Mammals which have partial decussation in optic chiasma and binocular vision. Left-hand sketch represents the visual system of a Mammal with mixed panoramic and binocular vision, the right-hand sketch that of Man and Higher Mammals with a common binocular field of view where a single central image is formed. Note that in Man the visual system also belongs to a mixed type (*see* Fig. 439). *Labeling: c*, crossed, *d*, uncrossed fibers; *g*, lateral geniculate nucleus and pulvinar of the thalamus; *Rv*, visual area of cerebral cortex with a "psychic image."

gether, e.g., between the right monocular field, or right halves of both monocular fields of view, and the limbs of the right side; and vice versa, as illustrated in the right sketch in Figure 437.

S. Ramón y Cajal's hypothesis of the visual decussation, brilliant and effective though it appears to be, did not become popular or was rejected outright. The blame for this was chiefly the general aversion to a new idea.

accurate, quasi-photographic reproduction of retinal images in the striate cortices, like other similar objections, was also nullified by modern research, including electrophysiological experiments (Talbot; Talbot & Marshall 1941; Marshall & Talbot 1942; Köhler). Wundt's demand for a vertical chiasma in order to compensate for the vertical inversion of the retinal images in the brain is positively naïve.

The objection to S. Ramón y Cajal's emphasis upon the "lens" of the eye as a factor responsible for the inversion of the retinal image and a consequent optic decussation made by Jacobsohn-Lask belongs in the same category, since making the effect of a *camera obscura* or "dark chamber" responsible for it would have been more accurate, even though it is probable, as will be discussed subsequently, that the chamber eye may have been merely a factor in the perfection, and not in the origin, of the decussating arrangement of the visual mechanism.

Spitzer's attempt to explain visual decussation by purely mechanical factors is highly artificial, improbable, and mechanically and logically impossible. Whereas a torsion may conceivably be invoked to explain a decussation of a single system, such as the visual, it could not account for the other numerous decussating systems scattered over the entire length of the neuraxis. Rádl's idea that "the optic nerves of Vertebrates decussate because of the inversion of the retina" lacks any basis.

Perhaps the most detailed study of the problem of nervous decussations in general is that of Jacobsohn-Lask. His conclusion is that the following factors are involved: (1) the basic form of the primitive nervous system, which is a plexus; (2) the basic form of the animal body, which is that of a tube; (3) the functional and structural adaptation of the nervous system to the tube-shaped animal body and to the bilaterally arranged inner and outer parts of the body. Besides these, there are, according to Spitzer, probably many additional factors whose interplay has produced decussations of the particular systems, varying from a total crossing to one where numerous fibers remain ipsilateral.

2. PROBABLE CAUSES OF DECUSSATION OF THE VERTEBRATE VISUAL SYSTEM.—What microdynamical factors working in the growing nervous tissue of an embryo have brought about the decussation of the vertebrate visual system, and do so during the ontogeny of every Vertebrate, remain unknown. This is a problem which should rightfully be dealt with by developmental mechanics and, in general, by embryology. Whatever these factors are, it is apparent that they are identical with, or similar to, the as yet unknown "forces of growth" responsible for the development and differentiation of the nervous system in general. An attempt to describe the working of these forces was made in the hypothesis of "neurobiotaxis" and the like (Ariëns Kappers 1908, 1916–17, 1922, 1929, 1941; Ariëns Kappers, Huber & Crosby 1936).

The functional effect of the crossing of the visual pathways is more understandable than its causes. An attempt may therefore be made to explain teleologically or in terms of a functional "purpose" what the incipient and subsequent factors may have been which caused a complete crossing of the optic nerves in the inframammalian vertebrate classes, a phylogenetical process that eventually culminated in the partial crossing that is characteristic of the Order of Primates: Tree Shrew, Lemur, Tarsier, Monkey, Ape, and Man.

It is remarkable that in all classes of Vertebrates below the Mammals the decussation in the chiasma, as far as is known, is complete (for a slight qualification of this statement *see* data on the Pigeon, chap. VI, 5 [3]). Whether or not this was an original condition present in the earliest stages of the nascent Craniate-Vertebrate Phylum or in their immediate Prevertebrate Ancestors cannot be answered, owing to an absence of information (*see* sec. 2, this chapter). However, from the above-mentioned fact it is permissible to hypothesize that, after an initial chaotic condition with a diffuse or irregular arrangement somewhat exemplified by an Earthworm (W. N. Hess 1924, 1925), at an early stage of vertebrate phylogenesis the photosensory epithelial cells tended to gather into two lateral patches at the rostral end of the body (Fig. 436, *B*).

The next permissible assumption, after what was said in the preceding section, is that, before any central nervous system was organized, the photosensory cells of the ectodermal layer may have been directly related to the muscle fibers of the mesoderm. If the primitive Prevertebrate was a creature inclined to react to any sudden photic change, be it light or shadow, negatively, as was likely, the connections had to be mostly crossed. The functional effect of such an arrangement would be a turning of the rostral end of the body away from the stimulus. Such a reaction, while better than an entirely passive immobility, was a poor way to avoid extinction by prowling predators. For this, the development of a more efficient receptor-effector system, capable of initiating not a single or a few discordant optofugal aversion reactions but a sequence of well-co-ordinated avoidance movements, was required.

A well-organized avoidance reaction, followed by a flight from any sudden photic stimulus that indicated a potential danger, was biologically most useful. Such could be carried out if the Vertebrate Ancestor, the Prevertebrate or Protovertebrate, developed an elongated, frankly bilaterally symmetrical body, supported by a stiff axial notochord to give a hold to the segmentally arranged muscles. The anatomical requisite for the working of such a locomotor mechanism was a concentration of the nervous system into a spinal cord.

In due course of time the leading segments of the cord became condensed into an incipient brain—a *protencephalon*—to initiate and maintain a proper sequence of laterally alternating movements of the body. The brain, too, in a bilaterally symmetrical animal also had to consist of two halves, each concerned preponderantly with one half of the body. The final step would be a differentiation of a central co-ordinator regulating the activation of the right and left bodily muscles alternately.

If one imagines a Prevertebrate as resembling a Fish, the following would be its basic optomotor mechanism. First, the optic nerve fibers originating in either patch of the photosensory epithelium would have to decussate completely in order to terminate in the contralateral half of the brain. This could be considered merely as a further differentiation of the original condition, where the optic fibers terminated directly in the contralateral muscles. It certainly appears the most economical way to elicit a simple avoidance reaction, such as a turning of the head away from the stimulus, by twisting the body as the result of a contraction of the contralateral muscles.

In order to give the body a forward propelling thrust, however, activation of the ipsilateral musculature is also necessary, with the tail pressing against the inertia of the ipsilateral mass of water, again resulting in a turning of the head end of the body away from the stimulus. This appears to be a more effective response, since, in addition to a simple aversion, it gives the body an initial propelling motion in the rostral direction. In order to accomplish active, purposeful flight, the same kind of activation, alternating in time on both sides, is required, with a resulting propelling of the body in the desired direction, away from the noxious stimulating object.

The anatomical condition making possible, first, an activation of the contralateral musculature in response to an ipsilateral stimulation was a decussation of the optic nerve fibers. When a bilaterally symmetrical brain developed, the optic fibers, assembled into optic nerves, continued to be decussated, terminating in the contralateral half of the brain. The motor fiber systems originating in the two cerebral halves may, at first, have remained uncrossed, or preponderantly so, thus preserving for a while the original completely decussated optomotor arrangement.

A partial recrossing of the motor system may have taken place as the next phase, as the necessity arose for the development of alternating body movements capable of propelling the Vertebrate Ancestor forward. Eventually, as the recrossing of the motor system prevailed over the original nondecussating arrangement, with a development of alternating forward movement over the simple unco-ordinated twisting, an evolutionary change was attained which further increased the bilaterally symmetrical organization of the Prevertebrate.

In summary, the decussation of the vertebrate visual system and a preponderantly crossed arrangement of the correlated motor system may be looked upon as a mechanism originally created, first, for the inducement of a simple negative response and, subsequently, for the initiation and carrying-out of sustained escape movements.

3. Phylogenesis of the decussation of the visual system.—The development of a decussated visual pathway through which a co-ordinated motor response could be elicited apparently took place during a remote period of prevertebrate evolution, long before a dioptrical apparatus was added to the eye—in fact, before

a peripheral photoreceptor built upon the principle of a *camera obscura* or "dark chamber" was created. The decussation of the visual system may, at first, have been entirely motivated by the need for wholesale activation of the contralateral musculature, preceding a biological necessity for the perception of a detailed "figure" of stimuli "painted" on a peripheral photoreceptor surface, such as a retina.

In producing the completely decussated visual system found in most vertebrate classes, neither a narrowing of the photosensitive epithelial surfaces into hollow chamber eyes nor a closing of the latter by a refringent cornea nor an addition of a crystalline lens could have played any role, as was assumed by S. Ramón y Cajal (1899, 1909–11) and by Flechsig (1899). As a glance at Figure 436 shows, the effect of the chamber eye, with or without a dioptrical apparatus, is merely an inversion of the image, both on the retinae and in the visual centers of the brain, which by itself could not have been a factor in the creation of visual decussation. The decussation of the visual system of Vertebrates and probably of all other animal phyla wherever such an arrangement is found, especially of the Arthropods and Mollusks, appears to have been a primary or original condition caused by the bilateral symmetry of the bodily organization already present at the very inception of vertebrate phylogenesis, as discussed in the preceding section.

The bilaterally symmetrical vertebrate organization, in turn, was a result of molding forces and factors active over a long period of time. The crucial point in this process of phylogenetical trial and error may have been reached when a primitive Metazoön had evolved a tendency to move in one particular direction in preference to others. This stage may be roughly illustrated by the "gastrula" of a young developing Lancelet (*see* Parker & Haswell 1940). The next stage in vertebrate evolution was a further elongation of the body similar to that of an early embryo of the same Acranian. Such an animal obviously requires an alternate activation of the contractile structures of the two halves of its body. A regulating mechanism capable of bringing about such a sequence of alternating contractions must be arranged crosswise.

In this way the contralateral muscle fibers could be influenced by the ipsilateral stimuli. As an activating agent, any stimulus capable of eliciting a response would do, the most likely in the earliest phylogenetical stage being mechanical-tactile stimuli. The alternating activation of the two halves, in turn, was the means by which locomotion was achieved. This stage was attained as soon as the tissue became sufficiently differentiated, part of it becoming responsive to the external stimuli and part capable of conducting impulses to yet other structures that developed contractility.

When out of an initial chaos of diffusely propagated impulses and haphazard motor responses, more definitely unidirectional movements gradually developed in consequence of the differentiation of the simple sensory-motor system, a foundation was laid upon which a more efficient machine could be built. Some, possibly the majority, of the conducting nerve fibers of this sensory-motor apparatus must have been crossed, since only in this way could the physical obstacles encountered in unidirectional locomotion have been efficiently avoided.

When, as a further step in organizational perfection, the ectoderm of the rostral extremity of a Prevertebrate became photosensitive, it already had an efferent tangomotor system to use, with the help of which it could further differentiate its own optomotor system. Almost simultaneously, an integrating mechanism must have been differentiated next to the principal tangoreceptors and photoreceptors, by which the rostral extremity became the leading end of the now functionally polarized animal body.

At its phylogenetical inception the Vertebrate Ancestor was but a minute clump of loosely associated cells, a *morula*, which subsequently developed into a minute sac inclosing a cavity, a *blastula*, which in the course of further evolution, by a process of invagination, became transformed into a *gastrula*, a double-walled sac. At this stage the feeding of the creature later to become a Vertebrate was probably by some type of ciliary motion of the epithelium. By this motion, solid food particles, in addition to dissolved nutrients, were brought into its *archenteron*, or primitive gut, without the animal's need for active locomotion.

When, in consequence of an increased demand for nourishment, the creature became more active, it had to develop some sort of locomotion to hunt for its food supply. This, in turn, seems to have been the prime cause of the functional polarization or differentiation of its body into a sensitive frontal end with a *prostoma*, or primitive mouth, and the rest of the body trailing behind. A Lancelet larva at the gastrulation stage may serve as an illustration (*see* Parker & Haswell).

Whether in this phase of vertebrate evolution photic stimulation contributed to a functional polarization of the sensitive front end, or whether this significant modification was wholly a product of tactile and chemical stimulation, there is no way of telling. At the least, however, photosensitiveness must have stepped in at a very early period of phylogenesis. The precociousness and the bulk of the retinal oriments in the earliest stages of a developing vertebrate embryo seem to support this view (*see* Fig. 434).

As soon as a photosensitive region developed in the Prevertebrate, its influence began to be felt. Here again, assuming a photonegative responsiveness, a decussating efferent connection seems most useful biologically. The two major influences—the sensorimotor and the optomotor—worked concurrently. Subsequently, the sense of vision and the visual system became of paramount importance.

During the remainder of vertebrate evolution, including its latest stage, the Mammals, the decussation of the visual pathways remained a fundamental factor influencing the architectural plan of the entire central nervous apparatus, as suggested by S. Ramón y Cajal (1899).

4. The chamber eye and the organization of the vertebrate visual system.— The creation of the chamber eye equipped with a dioptrical apparatus must be looked upon as the next important phase in the evolution of visual mechanisms after the differentiation of the photoepithelium. It was the most important single step in the perfection of visual discrimination, particularly of epicritic vision, requiring high visual acuity.

The chamber eye and the complex organization of the visual system of modern Vertebrates appear to be the terminal phase of a long evolutionary process, of which there is no record. It must have taken place very early in phylogenesis and must have been concluded early, since the chamber eye is standard equipment in all Vertebrates, including the most primitive, in this respect resembling the early appearance and universal presence of visual decussation.

The formation of the chamber eye must have been preceded by a whole series of intermediary stages (Fig. 441). To illustrate this, one may point, first, to the simple epithelial patches or eyespots of a Medusa or a Starfish. As the next step, the cup-shaped eyes resembling those found in some Gastropods, e.g., *Patella*, may have followed. The subsequent and more elaborate stages may have resembled the vesicular eyes provided with a dioptrical apparatus found in varying degrees of complexity in some Flatworms (*Platyhelminthes*), certain Annelids (*Nereis*), Onychophors (*Peripatus*), many Mollusks (*Chiton;* Gastropod Snails, *Triton, Helix, Trochus, Turbo, Murex, Limax,* and others; certain Mussels, such as *Pecten*), the ocelli of Arthropods (Crustaceans, Insects, Arachnids), the eyes of Chaetognates (*Sagitta*), the remarkably simple pinhole chamber eye lacking a dioptrical system found in the primitive Cephalopod, Pearly Nautilus (*Nautilus pompilius, N. macromphalus,* and others), and, finally, the advanced eyes of the Cuttlefish, Squid, and Octopus, equipped with a cornea, lens, vitreous, iris, retina, and other detailed structures, making them closely resemble vertebrate eyes. From this comparison the compound eyes of the Arthropods and others are omitted, since they follow a different pattern. (For illustrations and other details *see* Hesse, Willey, Buddenbrock, Plate, Hagedoorn, Parker & Haswell, R. Hertwig, Van der Horst.)

The preceding examples may illustrate the phylogenetical transformation of the peripheral photoreceptors from the simple epithelial patches or "dimple eyes" into efficient dioptrical instruments, "chamber eyes." These were capable of better utilization of light stimuli, manifesting itself in greater acuity, and in this way made possible further perfection of the visual system, as subsequently discussed. The fact that the eyes in most animals below the Vertebrates are close together and in a definite position at the rostral end of the body, closely related to the cephalic accumulation of nerve cells called the brain or cerebral ganglions, indicates a certain degree of co-operation of the two sides in response to light stimulation (*see* Rochon-Duvigneaud 1933, 1943).

In the Vertebrates the tendency of both eyes to work together is manifest. In most Fishes the two monocular fields seem to approach or partly to overlap. A similar arrangement with two fields contiguous or overlapping only slightly seems to be present in most Vertebrates below the rank of Mammals and in most Infraprimate Mammals with limited sight.

In this "panoramic visual system" the two single fields of view are more or less contiguous, usually at the front end. The two laterally inverted ocular images projected in the two visual centers, the optic lobes of the midbrain, which function as "projection screens" of the brain, are oriented homonymously or in the same way and together form a single complete cerebral image. Each cerebral half-image is a natural continuation or extension of the other half, precisely as are the two halves of the visual object toward which the view is directed. A complete cerebral image, accordingly, is a fairly accurate replica of a viewed object. The only essential difference is an inversion, especially lateral, in the brain, the right end of the cerebral image corresponding to the left end of the viewed object, and vice versa.

The inversion of each of the two half-images in the two cerebral visual centers, the right and the left, and of both when looked upon as a single complete cerebral image is caused by two factors: one, the effect of the eyes acting as "dark chambers," owing to which only certain rays coming from a viewed object are permitted to enter and thus to form the retinal image, and, second, the decussation of the optic nerves in the chiasma, by which the natural order of the two half-images, disturbed by the inversion of the two retinal images, is re-established in the brain.

Obviously, without decussation of the optic nerves, each half-image of the viewed object would be projected inverted in the ipsilateral visual center, the two cerebral half-images would thus be placed in the wrong order or sequence, and the objective situation would be falsified. The effect of total decussation of the optic nerves is the preservation of a natural sequence of details of a topographical order in the visual centers of the brain as existing in the objective external world.

In a strictly panoramic visual system, with total decussation and no overlapping of the monocular fields of view, each point on the cerebral screen represents only one point in either of the two retinae or in each monocular field of view (Fig. 437, right-hand sketch). How often a strictly panoramic visual system is realized among the Vertebrates and animals in general, except in the lowliest forms (e.g., Flatworms), remains a problem for future investigation to solve. It appears that in most living Vertebrates, including the Fishes, there is some overlapping of the two single ocular fields, even though it is restricted, usually in front of the head.

Extensive binocular overlapping of both fields of view in front of the snout and great mobility of the eyeballs are found, according to our own observations, in species largely depending upon vision, as, for example, the Pike and the Trout (*see* following chapter and Figs. 450–55). The macrosmatic and macrogeusic species, e.g., Carp, principally depending upon smell and taste, have an overlapping of but a few degrees, according to Tschermak (1915). A surprisingly extensive binocular field, amounting in a vertical coronal plane to not less than 120°, is found in the Northern Brown Bullhead (Fig. 457). The minute dimensions of the eyeballs and poorly differentiated retina in this species and its nocturnal habits, however, indicate the absence of high acuity and the use of sight chiefly as a photophobic warning sense, and also probably for a rough orientation in space. (*Cf.* chap. XIV.)

In numerous Inframammalian Vertebrates entirely dependent upon sight, such as the diurnal Birds of Prey (Hawks, Eagles, etc.) and the Swallows, with eyeballs highly mobile in the horizontal plane and consequently with an extensive active and adjustable convergence of the two visual axes, there is wide overlapping of the two monocular fields of view (*see* chap. XIV). A similar situation obtains in the nocturnal Owls, except that the eyes here are permanently fixed in their sockets, with a resulting stable forward direction of the visual axes, which are not adjustable or very little so. By what central mechanism the fusion of the "corresponding retinal points" and a stereopsis far superior to the human are here achieved and whether or not there is complete visual decussation in the mentioned species are intriguing problems yet to be solved.

In the Tarsier, a strictly nocturnal Primate, even though the chiasma is partially decussated, the eyes are almost as immobile as in the Owls. The presence of a central fovea, however, is indicative of high acuity and stereopsis, similar to that in the diurnal Primates (*see* chap. XIV, 12).

5. The origin and functional organization of the stereoscopic visual system.— While from a wider biological viewpoint the idea of certain investigators—Uexküll, for example—that each animal species is best equipped for its own mode of living may be correct, it would be untrue to deny a manifest phylogenetical tendency of certain phyla, classes, and orders of animals to excel over other phyla, classes, and orders in organization and many types of functional performance. The same verdict is applicable with as much justice to many bodily systems, e.g., to the locomotor apparatus, the organs of generation, the circulatory system, and, above all, the nervous sytem and the sense organs.

The visual system, too, is one of the clearest examples of a gradual perfection, beginning with the simplest kind of structure—for example, the photosensory cells scattered over a part of the body surface of an Earthworm— through the various stages of simple photoreceptors in the primitive animals, culminating in the extremely complex eyes of the Higher Vertebrates, the Mammals and the Birds.

What is true of the peripheral photoreceptors is equally true of the visual system as a whole. Here, too, graded series of stages of increasing complexity may be imagined, beginning with the very simple nervous connections of primitive animals and culminating in the quite elaborate mechanisms found in Higher Mammals and Birds.

The function of such systems may also be expected to vary within wide limits. The final

stage of phylogenetical perfection in the vertebrate visual apparatus, especially when appraised from our own anthropomorphous viewpoint, has been attained by the Primates, terminating in the extremely delicately adjusted stereoscopic visual system of Man.

The foremost single factor responsible for the development of primate stereopsis is the rearrangement or phylogenetical reorganization of the entire visual pathway. Whereas in all submammalian classes of Vertebrates, the infranuclear division of the visual pathway, with some slight exception in the Birds, is completely crossed, in the Mammals some optic fibers originating in the temporal segments of the retina do not decussate in the chiasma but pass to the lateral geniculate nucleus of the same side.

In the lowest ranks of Mammals, e.g., Rodents, with laterally placed eyes and little more than panoramic vision, the nondecussating portion of fibers originating in the most temporal segment of the retina represents only a fraction of the total number, accounting for a small overlapping of the most nasal segments of the monocular fields of view. In the higher orders, with more frontally placed eyes and a frankly stereoscopic vision, exemplified by the Carnivores and Primates, the proportion of the nondecussating to decussating fibers increases from approximately 30 per cent in the Cat to 40 per cent and possibly more in the Monkey and in Man (for details *see* chap. VI, 3, 4, 5). The central overlapping of the two fields of view is here correspondingly larger.

The partial crossing of the optic nerve fibers in Man amounts almost to a semidecussation. It is the basic anatomical arrangement of the primate visual system. For its proper functional employment, however, it requires the co-operation of a delicately adjusted oculomotor mechanism: the accurate converging of both visual axes upon the same point of the viewed object— the common fixation point; the influencing of the ciliary muscles to change the refractive power of the lenses and thus to accommodate the focal plane to varying distance; and, lastly, the regulation of the amount and composition of light entering the eyes through an appropriate change in the size of the pupils, in this way improving the definition of the retinal image. All three additional factors are indispensable for bringing identical details of the two sharply defined retinal images upon the syndynamical or isodynamical localities of both retinae and for transferring these to the brain, where they are appreciated as a single mental experience.

An almost equal division of the retinal nerve fibers in the chiasma, with a resulting similar division of each field of view into two homonymous halves, and an aiming of the two visual axes at a common fixation point are two essential factors resulting in an extensive overlapping or superposition of the two monocular fields of view, which is characteristic of the Primates. The impulses from each two paired points of the homonymous halves of the binocular portions of both retinae situated at an equal distance from the dividing vertical meridians in the horizontal plane must perforce meet in the visual centers—the lateral geniculate nuclei and the striate areae—of the same side (Figs. 361, 439).

An observed object, e.g., a vertical pillar, viewed simultaneously by each eye from its own side, is seen somewhat differently, depending on the angle or distance from the common vertical meridian: parts of the mid-line of the pillar, being closest to the common vertical meridian, are seen nearer; its two sides, being at some distance from the dividing meridian, since being more distant, are seen farther away. The total effect is vision in three dimensions or in space: right-and-left and fore-and-aft, producing in our subjective or mental experience a stereoscopic impression. The two monocular wings flanking the binocular central portion of the common binocular or cyclopean field of view, by their greater dissimilarity in the horizontal sense, help further to increase the binocular stereopsis. (This observation was made and accurately described by Galen eighteen centuries ago in his book *De Usu Partium Corporis Humani; see* chap. II, 2–5.)

The phylogenetical reorganization of the afferent visual pathway and a readjustment of the accessory oculomotor mechanism have transformed the original panoramic or largely panoramic visual system of the Lower Mammals into the stereoscopic mechanism of the Monkeys, Apes, and Man. In this reorganization the eyes have been deprived of their former functional independence, in so far as they possessed any. They have been integrated into a complex machinery of a higher order, working as a single unit or team. They may be compared to a two-pronged tentacle or to two hands with their thumbs crossed, grasping a single object.

From the panoramic condition present in the Lower Vertebrates, with its two halves—two separate fields of view, two eyes, and a right and left brain center of vision, to some extent or temporarily independent—the visual system of the Primates has developed. In it both eyes and fields of view, with the two sets of centers in both halves of the brain, became intimately welded into a single mechanism working as a complex unit—a cyclopean stereoscopic visual system.

A further development of this principle is found in the sharp-eyed birds of prey, such as the Eagles and Swallows, and in some Lizards (Chameleon, Anole). Here each individual eye may be used at will; or both eyes may be directed simultaneously, as a team, at one single object in a typical binocular act of vision. The facultative independence of each eye, lost in Primates for the sake of permanent binocular teamwork, has been fully preserved in these species. (*See* chap. XIV, 7, 8.)

6. The functional plan of the primate visual system.—The central stereoscopic visual apparatus of Man and of the Higher Primates is organized upon the principle of a single cerebral screen instead of two—the two optic lobes—more or less apposited along their margins, as in the Inframammalian Fishes, Amphibians, Reptiles, and supposedly also Birds (Fig. 439).

Each retinal receptor screen (LE, RE) is cut along the vertical dividing meridian passing through the foveal center (f_1f_1 and f_2f_2) into two unequal halves, owing to a separation in the chiasma (ch) of decussating fibers from those that do not decussate. The smaller temporal parts of the ocular screens (f_1-x_1 and f_2-y_2) are represented in the two halves of the visual center ipsilaterally (F_1-X_1 and F_2-Y_2); the larger nasal parts (f_1-y_1-b_1 and f_2-x_2-a_2) are represented in the visual center contralaterally (F_1-Y_1-B_1 and F_2-X_2-A_2). In each half of the brain the two homonymous halves of both ocular screens—the hemiretinae—somewhat dissimilar in size and shape, are represented together, the right halves

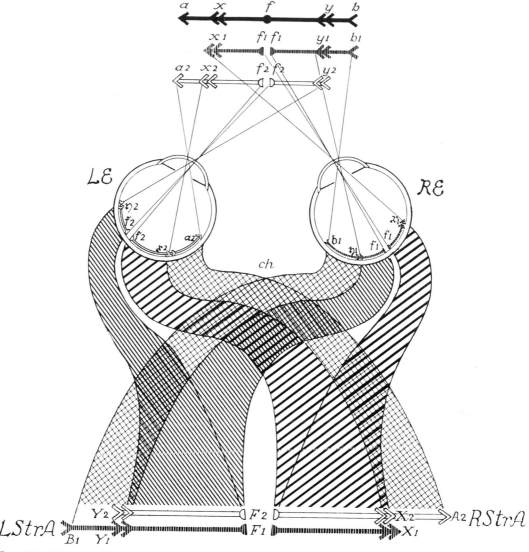

Fig. 439.—Diagram showing the intrinsic makeup and functional effect of the primate visual system, projected upon a horizontal plane (Man, Ape, Monkey). A single object a—b is focused by both the right (RE) and the left eye (LE), the right (f_1f_1) and left fovea (f_2f_2) aiming simultaneously at a common fixation point (f). A portion of an object seen by the right eye (x_1—b_1) partly coincides with (x_1—y_1), and partly differs (y_1—b_1), from that seen by the left eye (x_2—y_2, a_2—x_2, respectively). The two retinal images also partly coincide (x_1—y_1 and x_2—y_2) and partly differ (y_1—b_1, a_2—x_2). Every detail of each retinal image is transmitted along central pathways to the striate area in such manner as to preserve the original topographic relationships. Owing to a partial decussation in the chiasma (ch), each retinal image is split along vertical meridians passing through fixation points. The nasal portion of the right retinal image (f_1—b_1) is transmitted to left striate area ($LStrA$), which also receives an image from the homonymous temporal portion of the left retina (y_2—f_2). A doubling-up, however, comprises only the portion closer to fixation points (F_1F_2—Y_1Y_2), while the portion at the opposite end (Y_1—B_1) has no counterpart in the left retina. The left striate area, accordingly, sees the right half of a common field of view partly with both eyes and partly with the contralateral, right, eye alone. The temporal portion of the right retinal image (f_1—x_1) is transmitted to the right striate area closer to the fixation points (F_1F_2), where the homonymous portion of the left retinal image is also deposited (F_1F_2—X_1X_2), leaving the peripheral flank (X_2—A_2) to serve the extreme nasal segment of left retina (x_2—a_2). The right striate area, accordingly, sees the left half of a common field of view, binocularly in the portion closer to the fixation points (F_1F_2—X_1X_2), and at its flank monocularly (X_2—A_2). As a total result, each striate area sees the contralateral half of a common binocular field of view: the right area, the left half; the left area, the right half. Together, both striate areae see the entire field of view as a unit (a—b), the central portion around a common fixation point binocularly (x—y) and both flanks monocularly (a—x, y—b). The process of a cerebral fusion of two separate homonymous images into a single mental experience is prepared in the lateral geniculate nuclei and is consummated in the striate areae. An indispensable prerequisite for this is the correct working of the delicately balanced oculomotor apparatus, directing visual axes of both eyes to a common fixation point, irrespective of the distance of the observed object. The result is a union within the cerebral cortex of two slightly differing retinal images of a single object, a single subjective experience, which, in addition, possesses a three-dimensional character. (Cf. Figs. 361, 401.)

of the retinae (f_1-x_1 and f_2-x_2-a_2) being represented in the right cerebral hemisphere (F_1F_2-X_1X_2-A_2), the left halves of the retinae (f_2-y_2 and f_1-y_1-b_1) being represented in the left cerebral hemisphere (F_1F_2-Y_1Y_2-B_1).

Since the retina of each eye is represented partly in the ipsilateral hemisphere and partly in the contralateral one or, in other words, since each cerebral hemisphere represents ipsilateral halves of both retinae, the visual centers or striate areae of both hemispheres taken together represent both retinae or both eyes. The two striate areae, one in each cerebral hemisphere, must, accordingly, be looked upon as two halves of a single cerebral cortical center spread out in a single plane, like a screen upon which the two retinal images formed separately in the two eyes are projected as a single unit.

The portions of the cortical visual screen closer to the vertical dividing meridians and fixation points (F_1F_2-X_1X_2 and F_1F_2-Y_1Y_2) represent binocular portions of both retinae (x_1-y_1 and x_2-y_2); the two flanks of the cortical screen represent the monocular portions of only one, the contralateral, retina, the right flank (X_2-A_2) representing the left nasal monocular retinal segment (x_2-a_2), the left flank of the common cortical visual screen (Y_1-B_1) representing the nasal monocular segment of the right-side retina (y_1-b_1).

The complete cortical visual screen (*LStrA* and *RStrA*) is formed by pairs of the "corresponding cortical units" or "identical points," representing the "corresponding points" of the binocular portions of both homonymous retinal halves (thus the X_1X_2 point represents the x_1 and x_2 points, and the Y_1Y_2 point represents the y_1 and y_2 retinal points), and by the single "nonidentical cortical points or units," representing points of the monocular portion of either one or the other retina (thus the A_2 cortical point represents the a_2 retinal point, and the B_1 cortical point represents the b_1 retinal point).

In this way, in the brain of Man and his primate relatives, Monkeys and Apes, is created a single stereoscopic cerebral visual screen, corresponding in all details with the entire field of view as a unit (a-x-f-y-b) except that, owing to a dark-chamber effect of the eyes, the correspondence is inverted, both in the horizontal and in the vertical sense; thus the left end of the viewed object at a is depicted at A_2 in the periphery of the right striate area, and the right end of the object b is shown in the periphery of the left striate area at B_1.

There are other differences also. The center of the binocular field of view around the common visual axis (f), corresponding to both central foveae of the retina when focusing at the common fixation point, relatively and absolutely representing but a small fraction of the total area of the field of view (roughly 2°, as compared with 180° in the horizontal meridian), is relatively magnified or inflated to roughly one-fourth of the total extent of the combined striate areae in the horizontal meridian. Conversely, the cortical representation of portions of the field of view away from the axis, especially the two flanks, representing the large monocular segments of the fields of view, are shrunken or diminished in size—facts of no immediate consequence for the present theme. (*Cf.* Figs. 225, 259, 260.)

In comparing the panoramic visual system of the Inframammalian Vertebrates, such as Fishes, Amphibians, Reptiles, and Birds which have a completely decussated chiasma (Fig. 437, right-hand sketch) with a partially decussated stereoscopic visual system of Primates (Fig. 439), the following features merit attention. In a panoramic visual system each point of the cerebral visual projection screen or "mental image" (C), made up of two apposited centers, represents but one point in either the right or the left retina, corresponding to one locality in one or the other monocular field of view (Fig. 437, right sketch). In a stereoscopic visual system (Fig. 439), in the greater binocular portion (Y_1Y_2-X_1X_2) around the points of fixation (F_1F_2), each single point of the cerebral screen represents pair-wise the corresponding or syndynamical points of both retinae, which under normal circumstances receive similar impulses from the same point of the viewed object (thus X_1X_2 from x through two corresponding retinal points x_1x_2). The flanking monocular portions of the cerebral screen of the stereoscopic visual system (Y_1-B_1 and X_2-A_2) alone, having no corresponding area in the ipsilateral retina, still preserve the panoramic character which is believed to be present exclusively in the Lower Vertebrates, or almost so.

Functionally, the middle binocular portion of the stereoscopic visual apparatus acts as a double screen made up of superimposed right and left "corresponding units" receiving more or less identical stimuli from the same point of the viewed object via the corresponding points of both retinae, and tests them with regard to their similarity or dissimilarity (intensity, hue, etc.). Conversely, the monocular flanks are to be compared with lateral guards, acting only with reference to the binocular center in the horizontal plane.

The vertebrate binocular stereoscopic apparatus is organized upon a horizontal plane, with two eyes capable of directing their visual axes to a common fixation point at any distance in that plane. The retinal fibers are therefore separated in the chiasma along the principal vertical meridians, and the stereoptic effect naturally concerns vision in the horizontal plane alone. A visual system which would be required to accomplish the same in the vertical plane would have to have two eyes placed one above the other, with fibers separated in a chiasma along the horizontal meridians of both retinae.

Since, because of the force of gravitation, the bodies of all advanced animals, certainly of all Vertebrates, are oriented vertically with respect to the horizontal plane, this plane is the principal or exclusive dimension in which such animals move, act, use, or refer to their visual apparatus—the horizontal plane of sight. A visual system which combined both horizontal and vertical stereopsis in a Vertebrate would be nothing short of a monstrosity whose problematical usefulness could, perhaps, be measured by a "fourth dimension" of the "theory of relativity" but could not be expressed in terms of present-day anatomy and physiology of vision.

Since the binocular stereoscopic visual system normally functions as a unit, it was compared by Hering and Helmholtz to the single median eye of the Cyclops, the fabled giants of ancient Homeric mythology: the *Deckauge* or "superposed eye" of Hering; and *Cyclopenauge* or "cyclopean eye" of Helmholtz. This comparison, however, is only a figure of speech, and for the following reason. A truly cyclopean visual system, containing a single median eye, it is obvious, would not be equal in its functional performance—above all, in stereopsis, that is,

in tridimensional visual space perception—to the primate system as it is, even though a single cyclopean eye was imagined to have been large. The inherent defect of a true cyclopean system, with a median chamber eye, would be the single image of each point of an observed object, which, owing to the principle of the "dark chamber," would alone be formed, no matter how large the eye. Consequently, there would be only one single image projected upon the brain. There would be no central fusion of *two* similar or slightly different retinal impressions of the same object point observed from two different "viewpoints," as in binocular vision. The term "cyclopean eye" is, therefore, at best useful only as a figure of speech to indicate a unified sensory-motor apparatus possessed by Man and his primate relatives, where both eyes perforce act as a team and where the stimulation of identical or corresponding retinal points necessarily elicits a response in a single locality of the cortical visual center.

7. Ultimate causes and consequences of decussation of the vertebrate visual system.—A tentative explanation which may be given at present for the phylogenetical origin and physiobiological motivation of decussation of the vertebrate visual system may be summarized as follows.

At the very inception of Vertebrates a decussation of the visual system may have been forced upon them by the general character of the visual system as a nociceptor. This visual decussation may have had its parallel in a similar thigmotactic, tangofugal habit of the Vertebrate Ancestor, if, indeed, the tactile system had not preceded it. At that early stage the visual decussation may have been an instrument of a global optofugal reaction of the incipient eyes, even before these developed into chamber eyes. (*Cf.* Coghill's experiments.)

With improved visual discrimination, owing to the creation of the chamber eyes, and with the visual system changing into a positive, phototropic, analytical instrument, the same causes continued to preserve total decussation. However, its motivation now became more complex. The two retinal images required such decussation even more, since in this way alone could a normal arrangement or sequence of the details of the total image projected in the two apposited visual centers, right and left, be established and maintained. In such a panoramic visual system, details of a central image preserve their congruous arrangement when compared with those of the observed object.

Since very early in vertebrate phylogeny a decided urge became manifest to use both eyes simultaneously as a team, a good illustration of which is the Silversides and Minnows hunting gnats above the surface of the water (*see* sec. 2, the following chapter), a gradual reorganization of the visual pathway was initiated. Of this and of the following stage, however, we still know very little. Just what the central mechanisms underlying binocular vision are in the inframammalian classes, such as the Fishes, Amphibians, Reptiles, and Birds, remains as yet imperfectly known (*see* chap. VI, 5, and the following chapter).

In the Mammals, however, the process of a gradual change from a totally or almost totally decussated panoramic or largely panoramic to a partly decussated and now frankly stereoscopic binocular arrangement may be traced step by step from the lowest orders, such as the Rodents, to the visually most progressive, the Primates (*see* chap. VI, 3–5). In the first the eyes are mounted laterally or almost so, with only small segments of the two fields of view overlapping, if at all, and with only a fraction of the optic nerve fibers, if any, originating from the most temporal retinal segments remaining on the same side.

In the higher orders the relative size of the overlapping or common binocular field increases, as does the portion of fibers that does not decussate, until in Man about 40 per cent of the fibers or more remain uncrossed. In this way a mechanism is created by which the impulses arising from practically identical points of both homonymous retinal halves are brought to the same locality of the visual cortex, the right or the left striate area, and are welded into a single histodynamical process, which is the material basis of the singleness or unity of vision. Just what the particular structures in the striate cortex are that are instrumental in this binocular fusion still remains a problem. (*See* chap. VIII, 7.)

References: E. D. Adrian 1943; Ariëns Kappers 1927, 1929; Ariëns Kappers, Huber & Crosby 1936; R. Bárány 1924; Bartels 1925; Beccari 1943; Best 1930; Bethe, Bergmann, Embden & Ellinger, v. 12, 1929–31; Buddenbrock; Le Gros Clark 1947; Cloud 1949; Coghill 1914–43; Colson 1951; Creed 1930; De Beer 1940; Demoll 1917; Droogleever Fortuyn 1920; Fischer 1931, 1932; Flechsig (*see* preface to S. Ramón y Cajal's paper, 1899); I. Franklin 1942; V. Franz 1923; French 1926; M. S. Gilbert 1935; Goldschmidt; E. Haeckel 1894–96; Hagedoorn; Hanström 1928; W. Harris 1904; Havet 1899; Helmholtz 1924–25; E. Hering 1868, etc.; C. J. Herrick 1925, 1938, 1939, 1941, 1948; Herrick & Coghill 1915; Hesse 1924, 1925; S. J. Holmes 1944; Ch. D. Howell 1939; Jacobsohn-Lask 1924, 1928; Jansen 1929, 1930; Johnson 1901; K. Kato 1934; J. J. Kollros 1947, 1948; Lugaro 1899; M. Marquez 1900; May 1945; Miskolczy 1926; Ogle, Mussey & Prangen 1949; Oppenheimer 1942, 1950; Ovio 1927; Parker & Haswell; F. H. Pike 1944, 1946; Prosser 1934; Rádl 1912; S. Ramón y Cajal 1899, 1909–11, 1915, 1917, 1918; Ramón y Cajal & Sánchez 1815; G. Retzius 1891, 1892, 1898; Roaf 1930; Rochon-Duvigneaud 1933, 1943; Sánchez y Sánchez 1909–12, 1919; Southall 1937; Sperry (all papers); Spitzer 1910; W. Steinitz (MS); L. S. Stone 1944, 1946, 1947; Stone *et al.* 1933–34, 1940, 1945; Suttie 1926; Szily 1927; Tretjakoff 1909; Tschermak 1902, 1915; Tschermak-Seysenegg 1942; C. J. Van der Horst 1933; O. Veit 1924, 1926–27; R. Volkmann 1936; Walls 1939, 1942, 1943; W. C. Wells 1792; Ch. Wheatstone 1838; K. Wollenhaupt 1934–35; R. Woltereck 1940; Wundt 1908; Zawarzin 1912–14.

NOTE: At this point the attention of the reader should be called to the fact that the numbers of cones or rods counted on a "stretch of 500 microns" in the retinae of various species in the following chapter (chap. XIV) are apparently correct, as indicated by recounts done on sections made available to me after Dr. Polyak's death. There appear to be some arithmetical errors, however, made by Dr. Polyak in a few instances when computing the total number of cones or rods in a circular area measuring 500 microns in diameter. I have not changed these values for various reasons, but the reader, who wishes to make use of them, may want to recompute them for the Northern Brook Silverside, Trout, and Bullhead.—HEINRICH KLÜVER.

Chapter XIV

Biology of the Organs of Sight and of the Visual System of Vertebrates

SEC. 1. THE ROLE OF VISION IN THE MAINTENANCE OF ANIMAL FORMS OF LIFE

1. GENERAL CONSIDERATIONS OF VERTE-BRATE LIFE.—The essential problems with which every living being is confronted are those of being born, of successfully preserving its individual integrity, and of reproducing other beings similar to itself. If the first and the third problems, properly belonging to reproduction, are eliminated, the remaining task may be briefly defined as that of the preservation of individual integrity and welfare. Thus broadly stated, the definition of the essential problems of life applies to all living things, whether they are animals or plants.

In further limiting our theme to animals, we observe that the latter maintain themselves through two processes or acts. The first is intake of material which can be assimilated and incorporated into their bodies. The other is avoidance of being taken by other animals as food or, broadly speaking, the avoidance of annihilation. Both these biological tasks are related, being, in fact, two aspects, positive and negative processes of life. In other words, animals, unless plant-eaters, either act as predators subsisting on other animals or serve as food to other animals, the two roles being interchangeable in different situations in many cases.

The acquisition by animals of suitable food, both plant and animal, requires locomotion. This may be passive, as when the food particles are brought by currents of water or air; or food is acquired through active pursuit. The first method does not require any sense organs responding to distant stimuli and only primitive organs of locomotion. This method is widespread among lowly organisms, such as the Protozoa and Lower Invertebrates. The active method of food procurement requires sense organs capable of recognizing and locating objects of food at a distance, as well as organs of locomotion to reach and capture them. This is the standard arrangement in the Higher Invertebrates and in all Vertebrates.

The avoidance of various harmful factors may also be a passive or defensive one, as, for example, through the production of a protective armor and other means of defense, mechanical or chemical, or by various forms of camouflage or mimicry. Or it may be achieved by locomotion, that is, by active escape. Or, as in many cases, it is accomplished by a combination of passive defense and flight. A purely passive mode of defense does not necessarily require any sensory and locomotor organs. In the more advanced animals, however, efficient sense organs capable of responding to distant stimuli and a co-ordinating nervous and locomotor equipment are indispensable for executing the reaction of avoidance of the harmful factors.

In advanced animals the satisfaction of the two basic tasks of life, that of acquiring food and the avoidance of annihilation, is intrusted to two sets of bodily organs. First are the higher sense organs, those called by Sherrington "distance receptors," that is, organs of sight, hearing, and smell, while the organs of taste are of lesser importance. The other sense organs concerned with exteroceptive or superficial touch, pain, and temperature, the proprioceptive qualities of deep sensibility and sense of balance, are all also involved in various degrees. The other complementary sets of organs are an efficient locomotor equipment and a central nervous organ to sift the messages received from the peripheral receptors and to initiate, co-ordinate, and carry out purposeful actions.

Since in their multifarious relationships all animals compete with one another in their struggle for existence, the success or failure of each particular form will depend on successful satisfaction of the basic instincts of life. This again depends directly upon the acquisition by each form of the minimum of bodily equipment essential for the procurement of food and avoidance of annihilation.

its properties, for this particular purpose, to all other factors. Its foremost properties: rectilinear propagation and great speed, its spreading in all directions from any luminous or illuminated point, its property of being reflected from evenly outlined, smooth surfaces, and, above all, refrangibility when passing through trans-

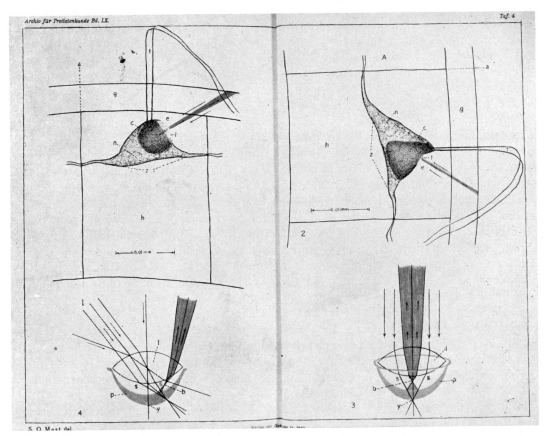

FIG. 440.—Zoöids or individual cells of a primitive colonial organism, *Volvox globator*, showing the structure of its ocelli or eyespots and their optical action, as described by S. O. Mast (Arch. f. Protistenk., v. 60, p. 197, 1927). Upper sketches represent two individual cells, each provided with one eyespot from which a narrow beam of light is reflected, with a pair of long flagella or locomotor "whips" (*f*) and with lateral expansions by means of which each cell is held in the colony. Lower sketches show schematically the respective eyespots, each made up of a shallow pigmented cup filled with a photosensitive substance and provided with a transparent biconvex lens whose presence is indirectly disclosed by the light refraction. When light enters the concavity of the cup, the yellow and the red components of the rays pass through without eliciting further biological action, whereas the bluish-green component is selectively reflected as a small beam, its direction depending on that of the entering light. This results in an altered direction of the strokes of the flagella, influencing the movement of the entire colony. The eyespots, accordingly, play the role of "directional eyes" in unicellular and colonial organisms, as they do in multicellular animals, such as the Flatworms, Leeches, and others.

2. LIGHT AND THE ORIENTATION OF ANIMALS IN SPACE.—Of the several physical factors, such as gravitation, inertia, touch, heat, and cold, the chemical stimuli, and the luminous radiation called "light," the last is the most useful orientating factor in space for the more advanced forms of animal life. Light is superior in

parent optical bodies, and none the less its composite nature, made up of a series of colored constituents which may in various ways be separated from one another and again combined—all make light the most versatile tool which Nature has given animals.

The segment of luminous radiant energy capable of being utilized by both animals and plants is rather narrow. It includes "visible light" and the "infrared" and "ultraviolet" parts of the spectrum. It represents but a small portion of the total solar radiation or energy emanated by our sun. (*See* Th. Preston 1928; C. G. Darwin 1932; R. W. Wood 1943; E. Rüchardt 1952.)

The basic qualities of visible light used by animals are rectilinear propagation, wave length, intensity, and chemical activity. It may logically be expected that living beings have developed the ability to utilize one or another or all of these properties in various combinations and degrees.

A remarkable phenomenon is the selectivity with which living beings restrict their responsiveness to one or to a few properties of photic stimuli, while remaining refractory to the others. This again is a part of a more basic phenomenon, that is, the responsiveness of all living things to only a narrow band of the solar spectrum, which, in turn, may be a proper theme for a more profound philosophic-scientific inquiry into the origins of life, into the nature of living matter, and the physical factors responsible for the creation of living substance in general. Whatever the final answer, the available knowledge points toward a basic identity of the organization and photic responsiveness of all living substances. (*Cf.* A. I. Oparin, *The Origin of Life*, 1938; also I. Lichtig 1938; J. Alexander 1948; Bertalanffy 1949; J. D. Bernal 1951; H. Shapley 1953.)

In the world of Plants the properties of light largely utilized appear to be wave length and intensity. Rectilinear propagation seems to remain little utilized. Future research may possibly qualify this statement to a much greater degree than now suspected, as indicated by the work of G. Haberlandt (*see* Naturwiss., v. 12, p. 1087). In contrast to mostly sedentary Plants, the mobile Animals have concentrated greatly upon utilization of this particular property, while not neglecting, and in some respects further developing, utilization of other qualities of light.

The beginning of the utilization of the rectilinearity of light, developed to perfection by advanced animals, especially Insects, some Cephalopods, and all Vertebrates, is already found in certain unicellular and colonial organisms. The *ocelli* or "eyespots" found in the Dinoflagellates, according to most authorities, are organs sensitive to photic stimulation, as evidenced by experiment. The individual zoöids or constituent cells of the colonies of *Volvox globator*, as described by S. O. Mast (1927), are each provided with a complex *ocellus* or a minute "eye," consisting of a hemispherical pigmented cup filled with a photosensitive substance and a biconvex lens (Fig. 440). Through the action of this eyespot, green and blue light is subjected to reflection, while red and yellow light passes through it. (*See* Pavillard 1952, on *Volvox globator*.)

Mast found similar, although somewhat simpler, eyespots in unicellular organisms which do not form colonies: *Chlamidomonas, Euglena, Leptocinclis, Phagus, Trachelomonas*, and others. In all these primitive beings the eyespots serve for orientation in space, utilizing green light, the maximum of stimulating efficiency being at the wave length of 500 millimicrons. In *Volvox*, Mast assumes the presence of a photosensitive substance and a "neuromotor apparatus," along which the generated impulses are transmitted upon the *flagella*, or whiplike locomotor organs, whose response results in the orientation of the entire colony. "The eyespots in these organisms therefore function as direction eyes, and in this respect they are similar to the eyes in Flatworms, Leeches, and many other animals," according to Mast.

It is revealing to find, from this account of Mast, already existing, on the lowest level of organismic life, complex photoreceptors, consisting not merely of an accumulation of photosensitive substances and pigment but also of a structurally differentiated dioptrical apparatus. This agrees well with the hypothesis expressed earlier, that light is to be considered the major, possibly the only, factor in the origin of life (*see* chap. XIII, 2).

Still another point in Mast's presentation appears noteworthy: the minute size of the lens of the *Volvox* zoöid, measuring only 1 micron, or one twenty-five thousandth of an inch, in diameter. The fact that even so small a lens is capable of concentrating the rays of light makes doubtful the insistence of the physicists that the smallest diameter of a lens capable of doing so cannot be less than 20 microns (which, in turn, reminds one of the doubts raised about the possibility of individual stimulation of outer cone segments of less than 1 micron in thickness, as discussed in chapter V, 3 [5]).

In summary, the available evidence shows the great influence that physical light exerts upon organisms down to the most primitive ones, especially in their orientation in tridimensional space. A preliminary conclusion may, therefore, be permissible that, from this universal responsiveness of primitive animals to light, more complex visual organs developed in the

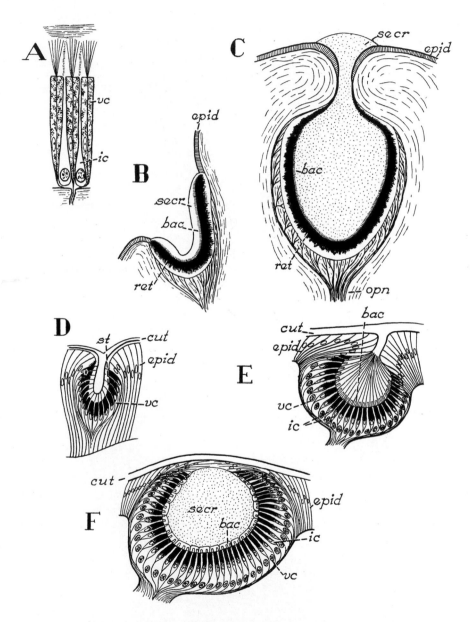

Fig. 441.—Phylogenetical stages of the eyes of Snails: *A*, visual epithelium of *Patella* at higher magnification; *B*, dimple eye of *Patella* and of *Haliotis* (*see* also *G* in the following figure). Phylogenetical stages of Annelide Worms: *D*, dimple eye of *Ranzania; E*, vesicular eye of *Syllis; F*, same of *Nereis. Labeling: bac*, bacilli or rods; *cut*, cuticle; *epid*, epidermis; *ic*, indifferent epithelial cells; *opn*, optic nerve; *ret*, retina; *secr*, secretion; *vc*, visual cells. Note the simplest eyes made up of epithelium that first becomes invaginated, then closes to form a vesicle; the latter, in turn, becomes filled with secretion, which, together with a transparent cuticle and epidermis forms a dioptrical apparatus of the eye. Redrawn from R. Hesse & F. Doflein, *Tierbau und Tierleben*, v. 1, 1935.

course of progressive evolution, when more advanced forms of animal life emerged which became the faunal population of the earth.

3. Types of eyes and visual systems and their use.—The organs of sight, peripheral and central, evolved by the animals, beginning with the unicellular and including those found in the multicellular Metazoa, are bewildering in variety. Many are very simple in structure and presumably also in function, whereas others are extremely complex in organization and per-

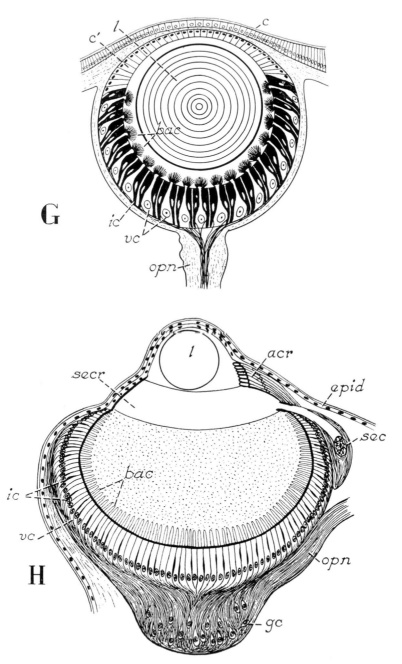

Fig. 442.—Eyes provided with a lens: *G*, of a Snail *Helix*, and *H*, of an Annelide Worm *Alciopa. Labeling: acr*, accessory retina; *bac*, bacilli or rods; *c*, cornea; *c'*, external epithelium of eye vesicle; *epid*, epidermis; *gc*, ganglion cells; *ic*, indifferent cells; *l*, lens; *opn*, optic nerve; *sec*, secretory cell; *secr*, secretion of same; *vc*, visual cells. Redrawn from R. Hesse & F. Doflein, *Tierbau und Tierleben*, v. 1, 1935.

formance. Between these two extremes is an unevenly graded series of an endless variety of forms.

On general biological grounds the assumption is justified that each type or special form of peripheral visual photoreceptor and its co-ordinated visual pathways and centers were evolved to satisfy the life-requirements of each particular animal form. In fact, we may be justified in assuming that each animal form is adapted to its particular habitat and mode of life in every detail of its organization.

All peripheral visual organs have certain features in common. These are a photosensitive surface, or epithelium, accessible to the direct action of light stimuli, within which the incipient photic reaction takes place. There are also structures of some sort along which the generated impulse is propagated and transmitted to the organs or structures of execution.

In many lowly animal forms, for example in the Earthworm, the photosensitive cells are rather diffusely scattered over the surface, with the greatest accumulation in the rostral segments. In others they are arranged in groups, rows, or clusters, either in the integumental epithelium or in deeper parts of the body, which remain transparent.

Photoreceptors which have the photoepithelium spread out to form a screen upon which the incident rays of light are arrested are of a slightly advanced type. In most such organs the opposite side of the photoepithelium is coated by an opaque layer of dark pigment, permitting free access only to some rays, while barring those coming from other directions. This early appearance of distinctive structures capable of responding to and of regulating the rectilinearity of light is indicative of the inherent necessity of animals to respond to this particular property of light.

Eyes resembling those possessed by Man and his nearest relatives, the Monkeys and the Apes, are present in all Vertebrates from Fishes through the Amphibians, Reptiles, Birds, and in all the Infraprimate Orders of Mammals. The structure and function of the vertebrate eye has been the object of intensive investigation during modern times by a great number of students, of whom the most prominent are Leuckart, Pütter, Plate, V. Franz, R. Hesse,

Buddenbrock, Kolmer, Walls, Rochon-Duvigneaud, and Verrier. The result of these many efforts shows that, in spite of great variation in detail, the vertebrate eye in all classes is built according to the same plan.

In other animals the eyes are made according to a more or less different pattern. A notable exception are the eyes of Cephalopods (*Nautilus*, Squid, *Octopus*), animals that stand in no phylogenetical relation to the Vertebrates but whose eyes are similar to the eyes of Vertebrates in structure.

The intriguing problem of the origin of the vertebrate eye from some earlier and more primitive form, even though much debated, remains unsolved; the possible factors that have brought about the creation of the vertebrate eye are discussed in chapter XIII, 2.

The numerous types of eyes of Invertebrates described by many investigators, interesting in themselves and showing how countless animal forms have solved the problem of utilizing light as an instrument of orientation in space, are of little use in solving the question of the origin of the vertebrate eye. Some of them, however, illustrate one or another intermediate stage through which the Vertebrate Ancestors may have passed during the preceding evolutionary process.

In many of the lowermost animals the photoepithelium is accumulated at the front end of the body in patches or clusters, sometimes in rows or groups of patches, occasionally along the margins or other exposed parts of the body. The next step in the phylogenetical advancement of the photoreceptors toward the vertebrate eye is the invagination of an originally flat photoepithelium to form a dimple, as illustrated in sketches B and D, in Figure 441. A further step still is the closing of the margins of the invaginated cavity to form a vesicle (C, E, F). The latter is filled with a secretion, and on the outside it is coated with dark pigment, except at the transparent front end or "cornea" through which the light passes into the interior. In this way a primitive "pinhole camera" or a "dark chamber" (*camera obscura*) is created, where some sort of image is formed. Such an eye, even though producing a poor image, is somewhat more useful than an open dimple eye, and decidedly so when compared with a patch of photoepithelium spread diffusely over the surface of the body.

Even more useful in forming an image is the eye of a *Nautilus*, an ancient Cephalopod. It is, in fact, a living "dark chamber" filled with sea water, which freely communicates through an open pupil, without any dioptrical structures but provided with a photosensitive retina which lines its interior.

crease in intensity of stimulus but also localization of the rays upon a small area of the photo-epithelium lining the inside of the vesicular eye, the effect being greater brightness and better definition of the image.

The final step in the perfection of the eye in the Higher Vertebrates is the addition of minute muscles supplied with nerves and other accessory structures, by which the shape of the lens

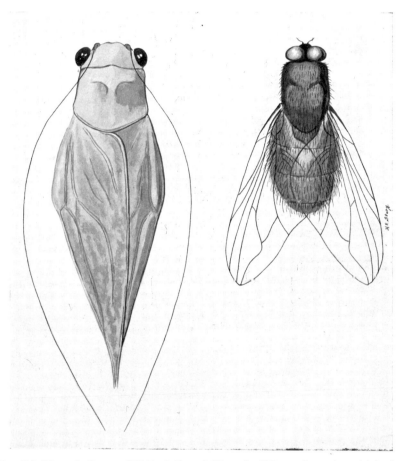

FIG. 443.—Katydid (*Pterophylla camellifolia, left*) and Housefly (*Musca domestica, right*), showing the shape, size, and position of the eyes in the two insect species. The Katydid is a large insect native to eastern North America, whose sound, made by the male rubbing its wings against each other, is frequently heard from the trees late in summer and early fall; its eyes are rather small compared with its body size and are mounted on the corners of the broad head. In the Fly, a much smaller insect, the relatively large eyes make up most of the head and are placed close together, more so in the male than in the female. Magnification 4.5×.

A further evolutionary step is represented by the addition of a transparent dioptrical body, more or less resembling a lens. In some cases there is also a vitreal body, presumably possessing a higher index of refraction, hence capable of further concentrating rays of light upon the photoepithelium (Fig. 442, *G, H*). This arrangement, in connection with the dark-chamber effect, makes possible not only an in-

is changed and the pupillary opening regulated. These improvements not only increase the sharpness of the retinal image in a given situation, by accommodation of the lens to the distance of the viewed object, but also make possible adjustment of the eye to varying intensities of illumination.

The perfection of the vertebrate chamber eye is one way by which the photoreceptor organ became more efficient. Another and quite different principle is realized in the composite or musivic eyes of the Arthropods, such as the Crustaceans, Insects, and Spiders. This is a special problem to be dealt with independently (*see* Autrum, Exner, Hesse & Doflein, Horst, Fingerman & Brown, H. Stumpf, K. von Frisch; *cf*. Figs. 443, 444). The principles and detailed organization of the central visual mechanisms of Invertebrates, unfortunately, are but little known. Especially is this true of the very delicately organized cerebral ganglions of the

Insects, as the studies by S. Ramón y Cajal, Sánchez, Hanström, Horst, and Fingerman indicate.

The organization of the vertebrate eye and of the remainder of the visual pathways and centers, in their main outlines, is by now fairly well known. A great task still remains, however. The first problem concerns the finer synaptical structures of the subcortical and cortical visual centers and their functional interpretation (*cf*. chap. VI, 9 and 10; and chap. VIII, 7). The other problem, as vast as the Vertebrate Class

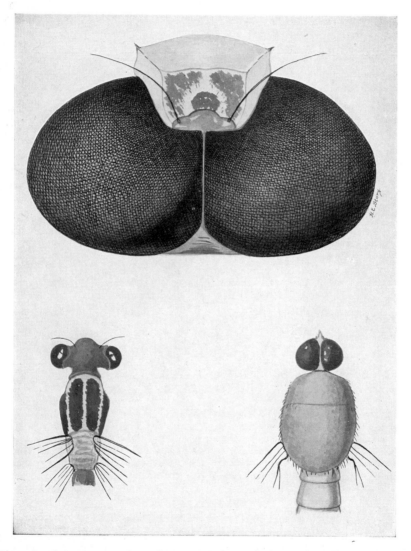

FIG. 444.—Upper sketch represents a frontal view of the head of the Big Green Darner (*Anax junius*), a large native Dragonfly, showing the huge composite eyes made up of several thousands of separate ommatidia of locally varying size. The left lower sketch represents a Damselfly of undetermined native species, showing relatively small, semiglobular eyes mounted on short stalks, hence separated by a considerable interval. The right lower sketch is that of a Mosquito of undetermined species, probably belonging to the Family Culicidae, showing the semiglobular eyes closely apposited to each other and making up most of the head. Magnification, in the same order, approximately 9×, 3½×, and 20×.

itself, is the investigation of the principal vertebrate subdivisions and noteworthy individual species in their adaptation to their particular habitats, their specific habits, and the individual and general changes that such adaptations have imposed upon their bodily organization, especially the visual apparatus, peripheral and central.

chapters an attempt is made to investigate in a few selected vertebrate species, including Man, the ways and means through which they have mastered their particular problems through bodily adaptation, especially the use they have made of their visual apparatus, and its biological consequences.

References: E. D. Adrian 1943; J. Alexander

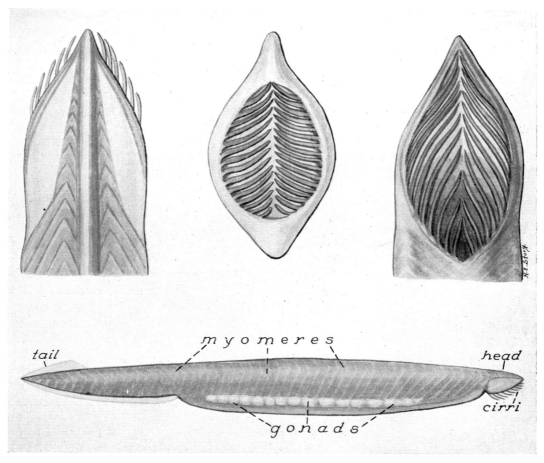

Fig. 445.—*Amphioxus* or Lancelet of an undetermined Atlantic species, the eyeless and brainless Acranian, possibly resembling one of the ancestral evolutionary stages of the Vertebrates. The lower sketch shows the general appearance of the segmented body and the eyeless head, with its oral hood and tentacles, called cirri, surrounding the mouth. The body is made up of V-shaped muscular myomeres, containing a row of reproductive organs of gonads, and terminates in a propelling tail bordered by a fin. The upper sketches show at greater magnification, from left to right, a dorsal, anterior, and ventral view of the head, with the oral hood and the arrangement of cirri encircling the mouth. Magnification of the upper sketches 18×, of the lower sketch 3½×.

Since the noteworthy writings of Charles R. Darwin and numerous other investigators that followed, it became increasingly clear that the choice of habitat and habit were the principal factors which molded the plastic animal substratum in its "struggle for existence." In the following sections of this and the concluding

1938; H. Autrum 1952; Autrum & Stumpf 1950, 1953; L. F. de Beauford 1951; Beer 1901; Béraneck 1890; Bernal 1951; Bertalanffy; Bethe *et al., Hdb. norm. u. path. Physiol.*, v. 12 (*Receptionsorgane*) 1929–31; Brown's *Classen*, v. 6, Part I, Book 1 (*Leptocardier*); Buchsbaum 1948; Buddenbrock 1937–39, 1952; Carr 1952;

Carrière 1885; Clasing 1923; Colas-Pelletier 1940; Cuénot 1952; C. G. Darwin; C. R. Darwin 1859, 1871; D. D. Davis 1942; Dean 1901; Dice 1952; Eigenman 1903, 1909; Exner 1876, 1891; Fingerman & Brown 1952; V. Franz 1923, 1924, 1927, 1934; Frisch 1950, 1951; R. B. Goldschmidt 1940; P.-P. Grassé 1952; W. K. Gregory 1952; Grenacher 1879, 1880, 1886; K. Guenther 1931; Gundersen & Hastings 1944; Hagedoorn 1936; B. Haller, in Semon's *Zoologische Forschungsreisen*, v. 5; Hanström 1928; Heidermann 1928; Hensen 1865, 1866; R. Hertwig 1907; W. N. Hess 1924, 1925, 1937, 1938, 1943; R. Hesse 1892–1902, 1898, 1902, 1908, 1929, 1935, 1951; Hesse & Doflein 1935–43; Horst 1933; Ch. D. Howell 1939; Jahn & Wulff 1943; H. S. Jennings 1906; O. Koehler 1924; M. Küpfer 1916; K. Lemke 1935; Leuckart 1876; I. Lichtig 1938; S. O. Mast 1927; E. Merker 1926; Merton 1905; H. H. Meyer 1934; W. A. Nagel 1894, 1896; A. F. Oparin 1953; Ostoya 1951; Parker & Haswell 1940; Patten 1886; Pavillard 1952; Piveteau 1951, also *Traité de Paléontologie*, vols. 4, 5, 6, 7; Plate 1924; A. W. Porter 1928; Pütter 1908–12; S. Ramón y Cajal & Sánchez 1915; Rochon-Duvigneaud 1943; E. Rüchardt 1952; Sánchez 1909–12, 1916, 1918, 1919, 1920, 1940; Serres 1826; Shapley 1953; G. G. Simpson 1949; Studnitz 1940; H. Stumpf 1952; Taliaferro 1917; N. Tinbergen 1953; J. V. Uexküll 1921; C. J. Van der Horst 1933; Vayssière 1896; Verrier 1945; G. Viaud 1938; Walls 1942; Walter 1949; Warden, Jenkins & Warner 1934, 1935–40; M. F. Washburn 1936; Weichert 1951; Whitman 1892, 1899; Wigglesworth 1938; Willey 1895; A. Winchester 1947; R. H. Wolcott 1946; E. Wolf 1943; R. Woltereck 1940; R. W. Wood 1906; R. M. Yerkes 1903; Yerkes & Watson 1911–12; Zawarzin 1912–14.

SEC. 2. NORTHERN BROOK SILVERSIDE

1. Taxonomy and habits.—The Northern Brook Silverside (*Labidesthes sicculus*), also called Glassfish because of its transparency, is a small, slender, and delicate fish of clear, quiet, fresh waters of the Middle West of North America. Superficially it resembles a typical "minnow" (Fig. 447). It is, however, not related to the true Minnows of the Carp or Cyprinide Family, belonging instead to the almost exclusively marine family of Atherinidae, and a subfamily Atherinopsidae, of which it is the only representative in the Great Lakes Region of North America.

The Brook Silverside or simply Silverside, as it may briefly be called, assembles in large schools, feeding extensively close to the surface on planktonic crustaceans and small insects, according to Eddy & Surber (1947).

According to Hubbs & Lagler (1949), the Brook Silverside is a surface swimmer, found in the lakes and quieter streams, and is popularly named "Skipjack" because of its habit of skipping into the air for short distances. These authors also present a good figure of the fish in color.

In the opinion of A. R. Cahn (1924), who made a special study of the habits of this fish, its life history is more complex than that of most other fishes of the Great Lakes Region.

The Brook Silverside, as Hubbs (1921) observed, is very active by day and quiescent at night. During bright, moonlit nights, however, Cahn observed frenzied activity among the fish as they darted hither and thither, skipping over the surface of the water, producing a characteristic noisy commotion that might last throughout the whole night.

The Brook Silversides, according to Cahn, inhabit the upper stratum of the water during all ages. The young subsist exclusively on plankton life, such as Entomostracans and Rotifers, gradually shifting to insect-eating as they grow older. They eventually become entirely insectivorous as they attain maturity, at which time they are 7.62 cm., or about 3 inches, long. During their babyhood they are pelagic, living in the uppermost stratum over deep water, where they are best protected against their enemies. They show daily migrations, in the morning offshore, in the evening toward shore. When adult, they settle permanently in warm, shallow shore waters and in the shoals. The Brook Silverside is strongly positively phototropic.

2. Comparison of Northern Brook Silverside with true Cyprinide Minnows.— The Brook Silverside, because of its small size, slender, streamlined shape, habits, and food, resembles in many respects the true Minnows, with which it may be confused. "In common parlance," according to Hubbs & Lagler (1949), "all young fish regardless of kind are called 'minnows.' Technically, however, minnows are fishes belonging to the family Cyprinidae. These are all soft-rayed fishes, which, like the suckers,

temperate zone and throughout Africa, the greatest diversity being found in southeastern Asia and China. Most North American forms, represented by a large number of genera and species, are built on essentially the same pattern. In the Great Lakes Region the Minnow Family is the most numerous in species and individuals. It is of considerable economic sig-

Fig. 446.—Ludwig Edinger (1855–1918), professor and director of the Neurological Institute at Frankfort on the Main, Germany, at the age of fifty-four. One of the foremost authorities of his time on the comparative anatomy of the brain (*cf.* G. Retzius; and Ariëns Kappers, Figs. 346, 467). Courtesy Dr. R. M. Strong, professor emeritus of anatomy at Loyola University School of Medicine, Chicago. (*See* for biography Neurol. Centralbl., 1915; K. Goldstein 1919; Haymaker & Baer, *The Founders of Neurology*, 1953.)

have toothless jaws and bear teeth in the throat only. . . ."

The Minnow Family, according to the same authors, is probably the largest of the recognized fish families, populating, in hundreds of species, almost all fresh waters of the north

nificance, even discounting the Carp transplanted from the Old World, because of its abundance, owing to which the Minnows form an important food chain for the predaceous fishes and are therefore extensively used as a bait in fishing.

The Minnow Family, on the whole, is omnivorous in diet, the various species, however, showing considerable difference in the selection of food from the general available supply, according to Eddy & Surber (1947). The Minnows of the Great Lakes Region are mostly carnivorous, feeding principally, because of their small size, on Insects and Crustaceans, a few subsisting largely on vegetation, some wholly on the highly organic mud of the bottom of the ponds and streams.

In the words of Forbes & Richardson (1908, quoted from Eddy & Surber 1947, p. 139):

In the general scheme of aquatic life, the native members of this family, taken together as a group, play a multiple role. They operate, to some extent, as a check on the increase of the aquatic insects, from which they draw a large part of their food supply; they make indirectly available, as food for their own most destructive enemies, these aquatic insects, many terrestrial insects also, which fall into the water and are greedily devoured by them, and the mere mud and slime and confervoid algae gathered up from the bottom of the waters they inhabit; and they rival the young to a great degree, of all larger fishes, their own worst enemies included, by living continuously, to a great degree on the *Entomostraca* and insect life which these fishes must have, at one period of their lives, in order to get their growth. They also offer a considerable means of subsistence to certain aquatic birds . . . and, through their contributions to the support of the best food fishes, they form an important link in the chain of agencies by which our waters are made productive in the interest of man. . . . From the standpoint of the predaceous species, minnows are young fishes which never grow up, and thus keep the supply of edible fishes of a size to make them available to the smaller carnivorous kinds when the young of the larger species have grown too large to be captured or eaten. . . . Moreover, by their great numbers, by their various adaptations and correspondingly general ecological distribution, and by their permanently small size, the minnows must distract in great measure the attention of carnivorous fishes from the young of the larger species, upon which, without them, the adults of these larger species would fall with the full force of their voracious appetites. By offering themselves, no doubt as unconscious, but sufficient, substitutes, they thus help to preserve—for their own future destruction, however, be it noticed—the young of many species which would otherwise be forced to feed on each other's progeny. It is not too much to say, consequently, that the number of game fishes which any waters can

maintain is largely conditioned upon its permanent stock of minnows.

In summary, the Minnows and the Silversides represent the indispensable ecological link between the small aquatic life, principally insects, which they consume, and the larger predaceous fishes, which feed upon them. In general character, in adaptation to the principal biological molding factors, in feeding habits, and in the type of enemy they must avoid, the Minnows and Silversides reflect faithfully the conditions under which they live.

3. CHARACTER OF THE NORTHERN BROOK SILVERSIDE AND ITS VISUAL APPARATUS.—Examined under natural conditions and freshly caught, the Northern Brook Silverside appears as a small, frisky, and very alert fish about 75 mm., or 3 inches, long, sometimes attaining the length of $4\frac{1}{2}$ inches. The head is short, measuring 12 mm., or $\frac{1}{2}$ inch, in length, the narrow, upturned muzzle having a protractile maxillary (*see* accompanying figure). The long, greenish, and laterally compressed transparent body is streamlined relatively even more than that of the Pike (sec. 4, this chapter). On each side of it runs a composite dark-pigmented horizontal stripe along the middle, from the head to the forked tail fin, continuous over the head and across the eye and as far as the muzzle just below the nostrils. The stripe is made up of numerous minute specks of dark pigment. Similar specks, even though fewer in number, are present along the back, and fewer still along the belly. Below runs a brilliant silvery stripe which is lost in preserved specimens (hence not shown in our figure). There are two dorsal fins, the anterior fin being quite small (*dfI, dfII*), and a long anal fin (*anf*).

The brain, which, because of the translucency of the surrounding tissues, is clearly visible, is completely enveloped by the meningeal membranes containing similar dark pigment. The optic tecta of the mesencephalon, or visual centers, are a dominant feature in the brain.

The oversize eyes are placed laterally, with the ventral margins much closer than the dorsal margins (*cf.* three upper sketches). The optical axes, accordingly, are directed slightly downward from the horizontal plane. What the position of the actual lines of view is must be determined by further investigation.

The corneae of the eyes shown in an optical cross-section have a slant or lopsided curve, the "corneal bulge," facing anteriorly and downward. This curvature is increased in a living fish when the upper conjunctival fold sweeps down over at least a part of the cornea in a way similar to that of the upper lid of the Advanced Vertebrates. This movement occurs rather in-

frequently and does so simultaneously on both sides.

In observing the head of a living fish from the front, with the fish kept freely moving in a glass jar, both pupils are clearly visible from a vantage point directly in front of the muzzle from a distance as close as 2 or 3 inches and possibly less (middle sketch). When an eye converges toward the median sagittal plane, more of its pupil becomes visible from the frontal as-

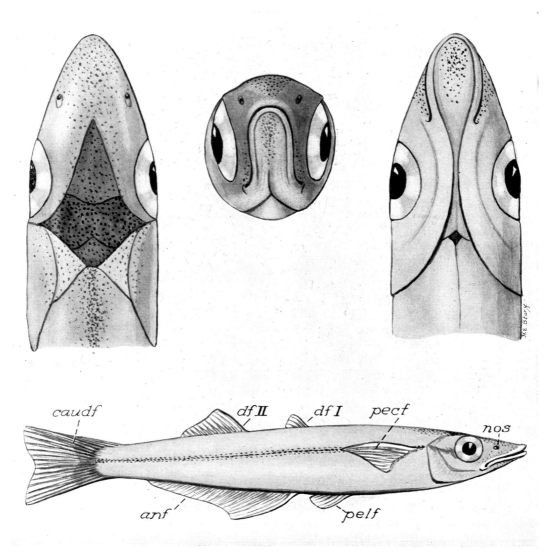

FIG. 447.—Northern Brook Silverside (*Labidesthes sicculus*), a small, slender fish of quiet fresh waters of North America, resembling the Minnows, without belonging to their family. It is noted for its habit of hunting for small insects by leaping out of the water. Upper sketches give, from left to right, an upper, anterior, and lower view of the head, showing the relatively large eyes and their slanting position, with the lower corneal margins closer and upper margins farther apart. *Labeling: anf,* anal fin; *caudf,* caudal fin; *dfI,* diminutive anterior dorsal fin; *dfII,* larger posterior dorsal fin; *nos,* nostril; *pecf,* pectoral fin; *pelf,* pelvic fin. Magnification: upper sketches, 6×; lower sketch, 2¼×.

pect. Whether both eyes ever converge simultaneously, as would be advantageous for binocular vision, it was not possible to ascertain, since both eyes could not be observed at the same time. It is certain, however, that a converging movement of one eye is possible, while the other eye remains motionless, in a way similar to that sometimes observed in the Anole Lizard and in the Barn Swallow (*see* secs. 7, 8, this chapter).

4. OBSERVATION OF THE EYE MOVEMENTS IN CONFINEMENT.—When kept in a glass jar in full light, the Silverside is continually on the move, chiefly turning round and round, occasionally sinking to the floor, and again climbing to the surface, as it tries to find a way out of its confinement. The eyes repeatedly make short, jerky movements, mostly in the horizontal plane, once or twice back, and again converging toward the point of the muzzle. The eye movements are not synchronous but alternate with similar jerky lateral movements of the head.

A change of water has an unexpected effect: the fish becomes quite frisky, the lateral eye movements become much less pronounced and difficult to observe, as if the fish were more in command of its bodily movements than before the change and hence was relying more on the movements of its head and body than on those of the eyes. The movements of the eyes are, however, present as before, but their excursions are reduced in amplitude.

5. OBSERVATION OF THE BEHAVIOR IN NATURE.—To describe the living habits of a small and largely crepuscular fish such as the Northern Brook Silverside in any detail would obviously require a prolonged study. In the following is given a description of the insect hunting by this fish observed on several occasions at Spirit Lake, near Frederic, in northwestern Wisconsin, during the months of July and August, 1949, 1950, and 1951.

The first note reads: As the dusk slowly descended upon the lake, its smooth surface showed small circular ripples here and there. At first my impression was that this was caused by the Sunfish in which the lake abounds. Close observation, however, revealed the cause to be the little Silversides hunting for the "gnats" which were performing their "nuptial dance" close to the lake's surface.

The disturbances appeared in the form of little blobs at the surface, soon spreading into little circles increasing in size from the disturbed center. The circular disturbances were at first few, their number increasing with the setting dusk, until at last the surface of the water was fairly boiling. Occasionally a tiny fish would emerge a little from the water, only to disappear in the next moment into its own element. In other cases the diminutive piscine hunter would make a somersault, while a few venturesome daredevils would make a clear leap out of the water and back again into it. The leaps were in each case different, some straight and vertical, others with a long and flat trajectory, or in any other possible manner. The leaps apparently depended upon the distance and the location of the hunted insects.

The second note reads: On the wooded shore of Spirit Lake it is pitch dark (August 12, 8:30 P.M. standard time). The surface of the water, however, still reflects a faint bluish light. Observed at a slant the surface appears unexpectedly alive, with silently expanding circles appearing here and there. In fact, the surface was teeming with ripples.

If one looks closely, one sees for a split second dark little objects emerging halfway into the air, to disappear again almost as quickly in the glossy water. The little Silversides are having a hunting feast. Occasionally a diminutive geyser leaps out of the water as a little body falls back into it. The air reveals to an attentive ear a fine continuous musical hum of rather low pitch, as if a swarm of bees at some distance was collecting honey from a tree in bloom. The hum is caused by a nuptial dance of uncounted "gnats" resembling minute Caddisflies or perhaps Microlepidopteran Moths of the size of Mosquitoes which are attracted to the water for the obvious purpose of depositing their eggs as soon as the wedding ceremony is over.

This up-and-down jumping of the crepuscular insects begins at about 5:00 to 6:00 P.M. and continues for quite a while into the night. As uninvited guests the little Silversides participate in it, in this way getting their protein. The feeding continues late into the night, even though there is, by human standards, little light to be utilized. At 9:30 P.M. the surface of the water is hardly visible to the human eye, even after a prolonged adjustment to the scotopic condition, but the noise proves that the Silversides are still busy. A flashlight, confirming this, reveals the water literally swarming with tiny fish, leaping after their diminutive prey.

That, in addition to the Silversides, some other uninvited guests participated in this nocturnal free-for-all feast was indicated by certain extraneous noises probably caused by the Aquatic Birds, but, above all, by the nocturnal Bullheads: the Silversides feasting on moths, the larger fish and birds devouring the Silversides (*see* sec. 6, on Bullhead, this chapter).

The question of whether crepuscular insect hunting is a habit specific to the Northern Brook Silverside or is also practiced by other species, such as the various Minnows, as is probable, must be answered by future investigation.

6. Visual equipment of the Silverside.— Macroscopic examination of the Silverside and its behavior indicates that the visual apparatus of this fish plays the major role in its life. Following are a few points which may be of special interest.

The eye in general conforms to the organization of a fish eye. The retina is relatively thick, with all layers, including the layer of optic nerve fibers, well developed. The regular stratification of the retina is remarkable, few ectopic elements being found outside their own layers.

The layer of optic nerve fibers is, for a Fish, unusually well developed close to the optic papilla and amounts to almost half the thickness of the entire retina.

Another remarkable feature is the accumulation of the ganglion cells in the most caudal corner of the retina, next to where it adjoins the iris membrane, in two or three closely packed tiers. This zone gradually fades to a single continuous tier in the larger portion, or *fundus*, of the eye closer to the optic papilla. A similar, even though somewhat smaller, accumulation of ganglion cells is found in the anterior or rostral corner. Hence there is, in the Silverside, a "ring-shaped area" in the periphery of the retina, encompassing the more centrally placed territory, where the ganglion cells are fewer.

The inner plexiform layer is thick and regular. It is faintly, although quite distinctly, stratified, indicating a very even, regular arrangement of the bipolar and ganglion synapses, as found in other well-organized retinae.

The inner nuclear layer, equally regularly stratified, consists of two somewhat larger and paler ventral rows of cells (which may be in part amacrine cells and in part displaced ganglion cells), and three or more rows of much smaller and more darkly stained and closely packed nuclei, which, according to their location, are bipolar cells and nuclei belonging to Müller's radial fibers. The outermost somewhat larger and paler nuclei, slightly separated from the remainder, apparently are those of the horizontal cells.

The outer plexiform layer has three zones, with zone 5-b made up of the lower swollen ends of photoreceptors. The outer nuclear layer contains rather dark nuclei, smaller than those in the inner nuclear layer. They are very closely packed together, and their stain varies but little. Hence a certain distinction cannot be made as to which nuclei belong to the rods and which to the cones.

The bacillary layer is made up of both kinds of photoreceptors. All the cones appear to be of the principal variety subjected to the photomechanical changes. In a scotopic retina they are found about midway between the outer limiting membrane and the upper limit of the pigment epithelium. The numerical proportion of the two kinds of photoreceptors, in vertical sections, is, on the average, three rods filling the space between each two cones.

The diameter of the individual rods is about 3 microns, that of the cones slightly less. Since, according to this, the number of rods exceeds that of the cones and the total mass of the rod substance does so even more, the Silverside retina must be considered to be principally adjusted for vision in dim light, even though it is not entirely scotopic.

The number of cones counted on a stretch of 500 microns in the posterior "area," most likely used in frontal binocular vision, is 30; that of the rods and cones together, 133. The total number of the cones, computed on this basis, in a circular area measuring 500 microns in diameter, is from 2,800 to 3,000; that of both kinds of photoreceptors taken together, from 18,000 to 20,000. This number of potentially individually stimulable units compares rather favorably with 35,000 cones counted in the rodless center of the human fovea having approximately the same areal extent (*see* chap. V, 10 [5]).

If the cones alone are considered as mediating distinct vision or acuity, the number of individually stimulable units is much less, being comparable to that in the same area of the Pike and is only about one-fourth of that found in the Trout (*cf.* sec. 5, this chapter). This is a low degree of acuity, which, however, may suffice at the close range at which the Silverside hunts insects. Whether in this it also uses the scotopic rods, as is probable, can be answered only by the application of the Golgi method. This alone may show the presence of individual bipolar synapses not only in the cones but also in the rods; hence their use in distinct vision (*cf.* sec. 12, on Tarsier, this chapter).

7. PHYSIOLOGICAL CONSIDERATIONS.—The item of particular interest in the above-described mode of catching insects by the Silversides is the use of their eyes. This, of course, can be solved with certainty only by direct observation and by experiment. For the present, the following considerations may be of some use.

It is probable that in hunting prey as mobile as the flying Moths, the Silversides would have small success unless they used both eyes simultaneously in stereoscopic vision, as a binocular team. It is, of course, possible that the fish use one eye at a time to observe the prey, as is the case with certain birds, e.g., the Robin. However, the act of aiming at the insect and the actual seizing are most likely accomplished under the guidance of both eyes, as is the case with the Robin when seizing an Earthworm (*see* sec. 13 [5], this chapter).

From the regularity of the phenomenon and the number of hunters observed every calm evening and night, one judges that the fish must be quite successful. A habit as regularly observed must be well intrenched within the inherent organization of the fish, going back to the early days of Fish and Insect phylogenesis. Hence the employment of stereopsis, where both eyes are used as a functional team, must be very old.

The other related problem is that of physiological optics. The fish undoubtedly see the insects while still completely submerged in the water; hence the hunting is done in quiet weather when the surface of the water is smooth. How the fish can correctly judge not only the position of the insects but also their distance, in spite of their constant and rapid movement, can be only guessed. Whatever future detailed investigation may disclose, the preceding observation shows that the urge of the fish to get the needed supply of protein is compelling and must be old, as the fact of complete mastery of the hunting technique proves. A preliminary conclusion must therefore be made that the Silversides use both eyes, as a binocular team, in hunting insects.

The example of the Brook Silverside shows why many, perhaps most, of the Fishes must have vision good for daylight and also for at least part of the night. It explains their possession of both types of photoreceptors—rods and cones. It shows also that even in a visual apparatus preponderantly organized for scotopic use a fair degree of visual acuity is present (*cf.* sec. 12, on Tarsier).

The puzzling problem of piscine vision concerns both its dioptrics and its psychology: How do the fish compensate for the cheating rays of light, passing from a rarer medium, the air, into the denser water, which shows them the desired prey in the wrong place? To the eye of a fisherman observing the Silversides leaping above the water and actually catching the insects, the oar appears broken at the point below which it is submerged in the water, as it did to the ancient Greek and Arab naturalists, a puzzle that remained unexplained until Willebrord Snell formulated the laws of refraction (*see* chap. I, 5 [6]).

While this phenomenon is now understood by the informed, how can the Silversides, with their diminutive mentality, allow for the changed direction of the rays of light as they pass from the air into water, gauge the exact position of the jumping insects, and catch them? And all without ever having heard of Snell and of the laws of refraction and without any cerebral cortex whatsoever, with a complete decussation of the optic nerves in the chiasma, and with a physiological myopia, all factors supposedly detrimental to acute distant vision, to binocular stereopsis, and to "psychic compensation" of errors of geometrical optics?

These problems can be only outlined here, since their working out and their solution require modern scientific technique.

References: Cahn 1924; Curtis 1938; Eddy 1945; Eddy & Surber 1947; Forbes & Richardson 1908 (1920); M. Gaffron 1934; Gobrecht & Oertel 1953; Greene 1935; Hineline 1927; Hora

1932; Hubbs 1921; Hubbs & Cooper 1936; Hubbs & Lagler 1949; Jarmer 1928; Jordan, Evermann & Clark 1930; Karsten 1923; Kolmer & Lauber 1936; La Gorce 1952; Lyle 1926; Macan & Worthington 1951; Markus 1934; Moore, Pollock & Lima 1950; H. Müller 1952; W. Nolte 1932; Parker & Haswell 1940; C. D. Reeves 1919; Reighard 1920; Rochon-Duvigneaud 1943; Russell & Bull 1932; A. Sand 1935; Schiemenz 1924; Schrenkeisen 1938; Surber 1949; A. Thienemann 1939; Traver 1929; Van Cleave & Markus 1929; W. Volz 1905; Walls 1942; Ward & Whipple 1918; Washburn & Bentley 1906; Wesenberg-Lund 1939; G. M. White 1919; H. Wolff 1925; Zolotnitski 1901.

SEC. 3. SUNFISH

1. TAXONOMY.—The Sunfish is one of the commonest fresh-water fishes of North America. However, in spite of this, some species, e.g., the Pumpkinseed, rival in appearance many gaudy fishes of the Tropics (*see* colored figure in Eddy & Surber 1947).

The Sunfishes populate most of the lakes and rivers in great numbers and hence are popular game for every angling schoolboy. The physiological and biological interest in the Sunfish in the present study derives from its representing the food upon which the Pike Family feeds, thus affording an insight into the relationship of a predator and its prey (*see* sec. 4, this chapter).

In the book on Northern Fishes by S. Eddy & Th. Surber (1947) the following species are described: Green Sunfish (*Lepomis cyanellus*), Orangespot Sunfish (*Lepomis humilis*), Great Lakes Longear Sunfish (*Lepomis megalotis peltastes*), Pumpkinseed or Common Sunfish (*Lepomis gibbosus*), and Common Bluegill or Redbreasted Sunfish (*Lepomis macrochirus macrochirus;* Fig. 448; *see* for other illustrations, in part colored, Eddy & Surber 1947; and Hubbs & Lagler 1949).

2. CHARACTER.—The Sunfish Family, according to C. L. Hubbs & K. F. Lagler (1949), is a diverse group of spiny-rayed fishes which have the spinous and soft-rayed portions united into a single dorsal fin (*df*), rather than separated into two distinct fins, as in the Perch Family. The Sunfishes are essentially carnivorous, feeding upon animals they can master, mostly those of

small size. The dimensions of a good-sized Bluegill or Pumpkinseed, for example, may be from 7 to 8 inches and as much as 12 inches in length.

The characteristic feature of all Sunfishes is a relatively short but deep body, much compressed sidewise. The dimensions of a fully grown Pumpkinseed, for example, were found to be: length 8 inches, height 4 inches, and width, or thickness, only slightly more than 1 inch.

The head is relatively small (compared with that of a Northern Pike; *cf.* Fig. 450). The mouth in a large specimen is just wide enough to permit entry of the small finger. The teeth in both jaws and other bones of the mouth are numerous but very short. There are no barbels. The tail fin is relatively small. The dorsal fin in its anterior half contains ten stout and sharp spines. In the anal fin there are three similar spines at the anterior end, and in the abdominal fins one spine in each. The fins may be raised with the spines, making it difficult for a predator to swallow a Sunfish grabbed by its tail.

The Sunfishes are good swimmers for a short distance but are not capable of a sustained effort at great speed, and hence may be classified as rather sluggish. In summary, the Sunfishes are rather passive in character, their bodily equipment indicating an adjustment rather for defense than for offense.

3. VISUAL APPARATUS.—The eyes of the Sunfish are well developed, even though they are smaller than those of a Northern Pike of

equal size. The transparent part, or cornea, represents almost the entire visible portion of the eyeball. It has a pronounced "anterior bulge" (lower sketches in Fig. 449). This bulge, however, is flatter than in the Pike (*cf.* Figs. 450–52). The pupil is somewhat ovoid in shape, with a narrow, pointed anterior coloboma or gap; it is not certain whether another, posterior but narrower, coloboma is also present. The spherical lens, in a living specimen, protrudes into the anterior chamber, seemingly touching the inner corneal surface.

anterior corneal bulge. The lens protrudes into the anterior chamber almost as far as its equator. Normally the two eyes are held slightly turned inward with their anterior margins, the two anterior lines of vision thus being set for close vision in binocular use.

The eyes make occasional horizontal jerking movements either as a team or individually. The labyrinthine eye reflexes are pronounced and prompt. The protective visual reflexes are automatic and prompt. When a threatening movement with a hand is made over a fish lying

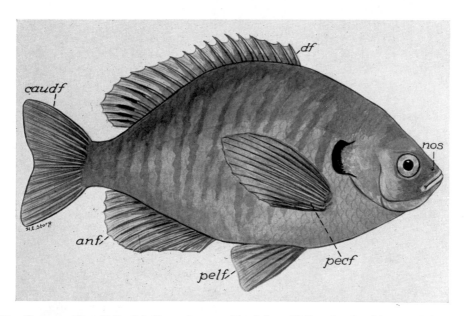

FIG. 448.—Common Bluegill Sunfish (*Lepomis macrochirus*), beautifully colored and largest of the North American Sunfishes. It is a popular "panfish," and it, together with other Sunfishes, constitutes an important food for larger game fishes, such as the Northern Pike and Bass. The Sunfishes are moderately good swimmers, with well-developed visual organs and of rather strict diurnal habit. They are somewhat inferior in their vision to their principal enemy, the Northern Pike, which defect is compensated for by their habit of swimming in schools and by the sharp, stiff spines with which their fins are reinforced. Two-thirds natural size. *Labeling: anf*, anal fin; *caudf*, caudal fin; *df*, dorsal fin; *nos*, nostril; *pecf*, pectoral fin; *pelf*, pelvic fin. (*Cf.* following figure and section on Pike.)

The "sighting grooves," described in more detail in the Pike, are present but are short, wide, and shallow and are either partly pigmented or unpigmented. They run, as usual, from the anterior margins of the eyes horizontally beneath or across the olfactory pits toward the point of the muzzle. Their extension lines converge toward a common meeting point from 1 to 2 inches in front. The anterior lines of vision from the summits of the lenses and the anterior corneal bulges seemingly fit into the "sighting grooves." The point where the lens touches the cornea seems a little posterior to the

still in a basin, the dorsal find spines are promptly raised, and the pectoral and caudal fins agitated. Whether the abdominal and anal fins are also set into motion, it was not possible to ascertain; however, when the fish is taken out of the water, these fins are also erected and the spines stiffened.

The eyeballs show great passive mobility: in the horizontal meridian for approximately 90°, in the vertical-transverse meridians almost as much. In a living fish in good condition, the eyeballs are constantly moved around the vertical axes, that is, in the horizontal plane, for approximately 10°–30°, either simultaneously as a team or singly.

In a specimen carefully dissected so that both retinal images could be seen on the caudal faces of the two eyeballs, after removing that portion of the sclera and chorioid (in a way similar to that suggested by Rochon-Duvigneaud 1922, an experiment first performed by Scheiner more

Sunfish a common binocular field of vision at least 40° wide. It is probable that, in the forming of the binocular image, the "anterior corneal bulge," even though not so pronounced as in the Pike, plays the chief role. This may indicate the ability of the cornea to collect rays passing through its marginal zone and to transmit these to the lens, approximately half of which pro-

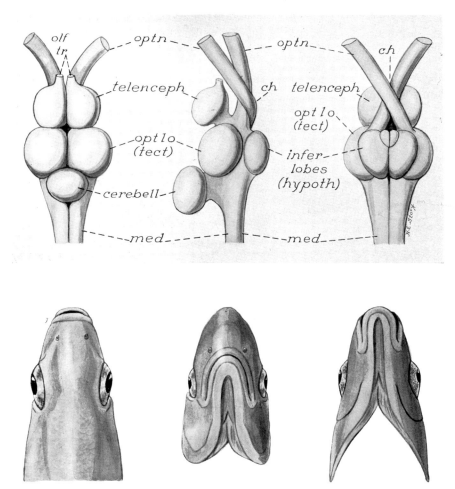

FIG. 449.—Brain and head of a Bluegill Sunfish in various views (*cf* preceding figure). Upper sketches show the brain, from left to right, in an upper, lateral, and lower view; lower sketches show, in the same order, the upper, frontal, and lower view of the head. Note the large visual centers (*optlo*) which, in fact, are the largest parts of the brain (*cf.* same in the Northern Pike); the thick optic nerves (*optn*) which are completely crossed; large eyes, their pupils visible from several aspects, best from the dorsal. *Labeling: cerebell*, cerebellum; *ch*, optic chiasma; *infer lobes* (*hypoth*), inferior lobes of hypothalamus; *med*, oblong medulla; *olf tr*, olfactory tract; *optlo* (*tect*), optic lobe or tectum; *optn*, optic nerve; *telenceph*, telencephalon or forebrain. Upper sketches 4× magnified; lower sketches slightly enlarged.

than three centuries ago), it was a surprise to find the images of a single, small object held in front of the muzzle formed for approximately 20° or more on the opposite sides of both retinae beyond the mid-sagittal plane. This gives the

trudes into the anterior eye chamber—an unexpected finding in a fish in which the eyes in a relaxed condition face laterally.

The optic nerve on cross-section appears as a folded ribbon, the same as, for example, in the kindred Black Crappie (*Pomotis nigromaculatus*). It is composed of at least 100,000 nerve fibers of mostly fine and medium caliber (1–2 microns), with a few up to 8 microns in diameter.

4. Physiological and biological considerations.—In the natural habitat in which Sunfish live, in addition to the physical conditions, the principal factors to be taken into account in order to evaluate their anatomical equipment and its use are feeding habits and the enemies to be avoided.

The physical condition of the native waters indicates plenty of light and fair to good transparency, except after a heavy rainfall and during the turbidity in late summer caused by an increase in animal and plant life of microscopic and almost microscopic size. Hence the Sunfish, with only moderately developed olfactory organs, depend for food detection on vision as a distance receptor. They are good daylight animals, and, from our own personal experience, there is no indication that their vision extends much beyond the morning and evening twilight periods.

The food of Sunfishes consists of various insects, grubs, snails, slugs, worms, and other small aquatic animals, as well as frogs and small species of fish and the fry of larger fishes. Precisely how this food is acquired remains a problem that can be solved only by careful observation and experimenting. For the time being, the only guide—and a very inadequate one—is the experience gained from fishing. This suggests vision as the principal sense acting at a distance, and that the senses of smell, taste, and touch play the role of final discriminators.

When an unbaited hook is thrown into water, even though provided with a shiny or colored "spinner," there is usually no response, although there may be many Sunfish milling around. The situation changes at once when a bit of fresh earthworm is attached to the hook, which soon results in some nibbling, possibly in a lively response. However, that sight may play an important role in noticing and locating food is illustrated by the small response to a baited hook held close to or at the bottom, and in the weeds, exactly the situation where one has the

best chance of catching the scotopic Bullhead (*see* sec. 6, this chapter).

The best response is induced when the bait is suspended from 2 to 4 feet below the surface of the water, provided that there is plenty of light and the bait is clearly visible. In this situation both the photic and the chemical senses are stimulated in quick succession. In very turbid or deep water and after nightfall the Sunfish usually cease to be interested in any bait, precisely when the nocturnal or scotopic Bullheads, relying on the chemical senses alone, begin to show a lively interest (*see* sec. 6, on Bullhead, this chapter).

In clear water, on the contrary, if hungry, the Sunfish pay attention to a hook and float or "bobber" from a distance of several dozen feet, beginning to flock to the center of disturbance long before any chemical sense could have had a chance to act. Also, in clear water the Sunfish prefer to keep a distance of at least 30 feet from an object of suspicion, especially if it is in motion.

Briefly, in acquiring food, Sunfish use all their senses, sight at long range, smell at close range, closely followed by the tactile and the proprioceptive senses, and taste, which require close approach or contact with the prospective food. If it is a desirable object, it is swallowed; otherwise it is spat out or disregarded. The sense of sight in the life of a Sunfish acts as a distance explorer and initiator of the alimentary function, the other senses continuing the function of feeding as the subsequent processors.

The other problem of a Sunfish, that of avoiding extinction by predators, is practically entirely intrusted to the sense of sight. Here, too, much remains unknown. If the adult individuals of the larger species, such as a Pumpkinseed and a Bluegill, alone are considered, the Northern Pike and the Muskellunge and perhaps some other fish that grow to a large size, e.g., Bass, are the only ones that come into the picture. They alone grow big enough and have sufficiently wide mouths provided with formidable teeth to be capable of mastering and swallowing a fully grown Sunfish.

The members of the Pike Family are especially to be considered the archenemies of the Sunfishes. The relationship between these two links of what amounts to a biological circle or chain probably became established in a long evolutionary process of mutual adjustment. Under natural conditions, where there is no appreciable interference by Man or by any violent natural factors, it may be assumed that the balance is neat and even.

The principal medium by which this balance is maintained is the sense of sight of both the pursuing predator and the pursued prey. Since both are strictly diurnal fishes, the visual systems of both must be similarly organized, a slight advantage perhaps being on the side of the Pike, represented in larger eyes and in their more definite adjustment for binocular stereoscopic vision, with a more pronounced anterior corneal bulge (*see* sec. 4, on Pike, this chapter).

The same may be said about the brain in the Sunfish as in the Pike, the optic lobes being the largest single structures, each lobe as large as the entire portion of the brain in front of the midbrain (*optlo* in Figs. 449 and 454).

This fairly even balance between the pursuing Pike and the pursued Sunfish may indicate a visual competition between both in the struggle for survival. In this struggle, in each individual contest, the victory varies, the total net result being a status quo, at least in so far as the conditions now in existence can be appraised, guaranteeing a survival of both categories of fish.

It is probable that this simple relationship is, in fact, much more complicated by additional factors to be further determined. One such factor may be the habit of the Pike of preying as a solitary, freelance hunter, while the Sunfish developed a herd instinct that keeps them in "schools," representing additional protection provided by many watchful eyes. This again seems a compensation for a slight inferiority of the visual and locomotor equipment of the Sunfish as compared with the superior performance of the Pike's visual and locomotor apparatus.

References: Ariëns Kappers, Huber & Crosby 1936; V. Bauer 1909, 1910, 1911; Beaufort 1951; Bellonci 1888; Breder 1932; Brunner 1934; H. O. Bull 1935; Burkamp 1923; Canella 1937; Carter 1948; Colas-Pelletier 1940; Contino 1939; Curtis 1938; Dean 1916–23; Eddy & Surber 1947; Fischer & Löwenbach 1935; V. Franz 1934; K. von Frisch 1912, 1913, 1923, 1924, 1925; Gaffron 1934; Grundfest 1931, 1932; E. B. Hale 1949; Hamburger 1926; C. J. Herrick 1922; C. L. Herrick 1891; C. Hess 1909, 1913, 1914, 1919; Hora 1938; Horio 1938; Hubbs & Lagler 1949; Jarmer 1928; Lagler 1949; La Gorce 1952; Macan & Worthington 1951; Meader 1934; Merker 1937–38, 1939; Mirto 1895; Moore, Pollock & Lima 1950; H. Müller 1952; Joh. Müller 1826; W. Nolte 1932; Norman 1936; Parker & Haswell 1940; J. H. Parsons 1924; Perkins & Wheeler 1931; Pütter 1908–12; Rádl 1915; C. D. Reeves 1919; Rochon-Duvigneaud 1922, 1943; W. Roth 1911; Russell & Bull 1932; Sand 1935; Schiemenz 1924; Schiller 1934; Schneider-Orelli 1907; Schnurmann 1920; Sperry & Clark 1949; Schreitmüller & Relinghaus 1926; Schrenkeisen 1938; Streuli 1925; Ströer 1939; Sumner 1940; Szepsenwol 1938; A. Thienemann 1939; Verrier 1928, 1938, 1945; Verrier & Escher-Desrivières 1937; Walls 1942; Ward & Whipple 1918; L. H. Warner 1931; Washburn & Bentley 1906; Weed 1927; Wesenberg-Lund 1939; G. M. White 1919; H. Wolff 1925; R. W. Wood 1906; Wunder 1925, 1926, 1927, 1930; Zolotnitski 1901.

SEC. 4. PIKE

1. Taxonomy.—The Northern Pike (*Esox lucius*) is a classical example of a carnivorous fish subsisting entirely on animal food mostly represented by other fish. Its other native names are Pickerel and Great Northern Pike.

The Pike is a native of the northern waters of North America. It is generally held that it is identical with the Pike of northern Europe and of Asia; it is akin to other members of its genus, such as the spectacular Northern Mus-kellunge or "muskie" (*Esox masquinongy*), the Eastern Common or Chain Pickerel or Green Pike (*Esox niger*), the Bulldog or Barred Pickerel (*Esox americanus*), and the Mud Pickerel (*Esox vermiculatus*). (Fig. 450; *see also* Weed 1927; Eddy & Surber 1947; Hubbs & Lagler 1949.)

2. Character.—The external appearance and internal organization of the Pike are indicative of highly successful adaptation to its predatory mode of life.

Its sleek body is several times as long as it is deep or wide. On cross-section the body is almost cylindrical and varies little in diameter along its length. Anteriorly the body begins with the pointed head, the broad muzzle of

mounted far back, increase the propulsive action of the caudal fin. The two pairs of pectoral and abdominal fins are relatively small and, like all other fins, are soft, that is, have no sharp bony spines affording passive protection (compare with those of the Sunfishes, Perches, and Bullheads). Altogether, the shape and loco-

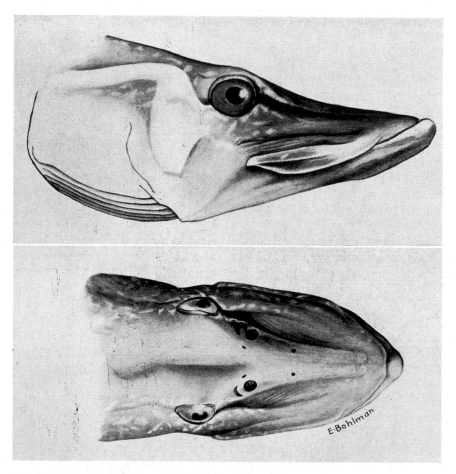

FIG. 450.—Northern Pike (*Esox lucius* or *E. estor*), upper figure lateral view of the head, lower figure upper view. A predaceous, fresh-water Fish, native of North America, Europe, and Asia. Like other members of the Family Esocidae, which also includes the giant Muskellunge, the Pike is a strictly diurnal species, subsisting by preying on other fish. Hence all parts of its bodily organization—its keen visual organs, powerful propelling muscles, strong jaws armed with formidable teeth, spacious, expansible mouth and gullet, and aggressive character—are minutely adjusted to its predaceous habit. Of all equipment possessed by the Pike, vision is paramount. Indications are that the superiority of this sense is based not alone upon its keenness or acuity but as much upon binocular use or stereopsis. On anatomical grounds both ocular axes may readily converge upon a single point fixed in front of the muzzle. This is made possible by the presence of pigmented "sighting grooves" extending from the anterior margins of the eyes, in a converging direction, toward the muzzle. In the economy of nature, the Pike and its congeners play the role of a mighty factor which influences the course of evolution and adaptation of all life within its range. Structurally and biologically the Pike is the reverse of the Bullhead (*see* Figs. 456–58). (*Cf.* following two figures.)

which is flattened in the manner of a "duckbill." Posteriorly the body terminates with a formidable tail provided with a broad, forked, propellent fin. The dorsal and anal fins,

motor equipment of the Pike indicate great ability to overcome the resistance of water.

That a Pike makes the best use of its equipment is dramatically illustrated by the behavior of the kindred small "muskies" only 2 months old and not more than 6 inches long: "They would stalk their prey, poise, and then dart faster than the eye could follow and swallow their prey with one gulp. If the victim happened to be a large fish one slash was sufficient to sever the tail of the unlucky victim" (Eddy & Surber 1947).

The spacious mouth of the Pike, its jaws as well as the palatal bones, and even its stiff tongue are armed with numerous sharp teeth, set with the points turned toward the throat, some of them of imposing size. Any prey seized has, therefore, little chance to escape. Such chance is further reduced, according to Eddy & Surber, by the habit of the Pike and Muskellunge of swallowing the prey, usually head first.

If the prey is caught by the tail, the predator shifts it into proper position before swallowing it, according to these authors. In this way the protection offered to such species as the Sunfish and Perch by the sharp, bony, and erectile rays or "spines," especially of the frontal parts of the dorsal and anal fins, is eliminated, as the spines are pressed against the body of the prey by the jaws of the Pike: in this position the spines rather facilitate the swallowing, whereas with the tail first, the spines would stick in the mouth of the Pike and would make the process of swallowing difficult or impossible. (All species of Sunfishes and the Perch have developed a protective reflex habit of erecting and holding in such position their spiny fins when threatened or when taken out of water; *see* preceding section.)

In the habit of turning the prey head first, the Pike and Muskellunge, curiously, resemble the primate Tarsier, who does precisely the same when eating a lizard, and probably for a like utilitarian purpose. The only difference is that a Pike does the turning with its mouth, while the Tarsier accomplishes this with his hands (*see* sec. 12, on Tarsier, this chapter; a similar habit is described in the Common Shrew: *see* sec. 9, on Shrew, this chapter).

3. Habits.—The Pike is a persistent hunter, slinking from early morning until late evening along the weedy aquatic groves, always on the lookout for suitable prey, usually a Minnow, Sucker, Perch, or Sunfish. Its activity is restricted to daylight. With increasing dusk, it slows down and ceases its search for food altogether, even though a fisherman may get an occasional "bite" after the sun is gone.

The movements of the Pike, as far as they are known, are made up of a number of straight lines, each corresponding to a short and differently oriented dart. The length of a single dart in a grown-up Pike may average 20, 25, or 30 feet, judging from the stretch along which the hunted small fry scatter on the surface of the water in order to evade their foe.

When the Pike notices an object of interest within the range of a single dart (which, in turn, may be equivalent to the average range of its sight within given optical conditions), it "freezes" for a moment, adjusts its sensory-motor apparatus to the precise location and distance of the object, and reaches it and seizes it with a single swoop. Such swift and precise action implies excellent co-ordination of the entire bodily machine: it requires, above all, keen sight to notice the potential prey and to recognize its size, shape, color, and movement—the essential qualities that elicit an attacking response.

At what distance the Pike and other fish can notice a visual object is known only imperfectly. Visibility in water depends much on its chemical composition and on the number, size, shape, and other qualities of the formed particles suspended in it, as well as on the amount, quality, and direction of light entering the water. In the fairly clear waters found in the northern lakes of North America, the object may well be seen at noontime, in summer, at from 20 to 40 feet and, under favorable circumstances, several times that distance; in turbid conditions less. On the average, it may be assumed that a fish should be able to see in good light at least 50 feet or more in the lateral direction (*cf.* Erickson 1933; G. L. Clarke 1935).

The visual acuity required to utilize in full the physical conditions of the water, accordingly, may be far below the acuity found in the keen-sighted air-living terrestrial Vertebrates, such as the Birds and some Mammals, e.g., the Primates. The true measure, however, is the average acuity found in most Fishes, the competitors among and upon which the Pike lives. Sight good enough to see objects at 50 feet under water and under exceptional conditions at a much greater distance must be recognized as the maximum in the aquatic element. Even though there are no precise data dealing with the particular features of the Pike's sight, the available information is sufficient to warrant the assumption that its vision is fairly close to the limit imposed by the physical conditions of its aquatic habitat.

A feature characteristic of a quick-acting fish is the Pike's behavior in a basin filled with water, where for a while it keeps perfectly still and then, suddenly, for no apparent reason, becomes violently active.

4. EYEBALL.—The study of the Pike's eyes and of the rest of its visual system tends to confirm the foregoing assumption about the excellence of its sight. Its eyeball is large. In a specimen 18 inches long, the horizontal rostrocaudal diameter amounts to almost 22 mm., the horizontal transverse diameter to 12.5 mm. (*cf.* diameter of human and simian eyeballs in chap. V, 1 [2]).

In a freshly caught specimen the eyeballs are quite mobile. They may easily be moved in any direction: up or down, forward or backward, or in any intermediate meridian. This is possible, in spite of a superficial impression that the eyeball is tightly fitted in the orbit. Passively the eyeball may easily be rotated around its vertical axis for approximately 45° and somewhat forcibly to as much as 100°. How much it may be rotated under physiological conditions is a problem yet to be solved. In the specimens preserved in fixing fluids, such as formalin and alcohol, the eyeball entirely loses its natural mobility.

The few observations so far made in a living specimen under conditions far from natural indicate an exceptional ocular alertness, quickness, and extent or amplitude of the eye movements as a response to both visual and labyrinthine stimulation. For example, an eye may be rotated medially or inward so that its pupillary plane makes an angle of approximately 30° with the mid-sagittal plane. In this movement the posterior margin of the cornea is turned for a few degrees anteriorly, and the inferior margin slightly lifted, which makes the posterior retinal segment face anteriorly and the inferior segment face a little upward. Spontaneous eye

movements may also be noticed in a living specimen. When the body of a Pike is moved passively, lively labyrinthine reflexes of the eyeballs in the horizontal and vertical planes, and as extensive as in a Trout, may promptly be elicited. (*Cf.* following section.)

The great mobility of the Pike's eyes is possible because of several factors: a deep conjunctival pocket surrounding the eyeball on all sides, great flexibility of the conjunctiva, well-developed and long extrinsic eye muscles, and particularly a loose, watery tissue in which the principal organs filling the orbit, such as the muscles, nerves, blood vessels, etc., are imbedded. The Pike's eyeball literally floats on a "fluid cushion," permitting easy displacement of all these structures in any direction.

5. CORNEA, LENS, AND THE SIGHTING GROOVE. —The cornea of the Pike's eye is almost as large as the visible portion of the eyeball (Fig. 450). It is pear-shaped, with its longer axis horizontal and its pointed end facing anteriorly. In a horizontal section or in an optical section in a living or preserved specimen looked upon from above, the cornea appears asymmetrically curved, the radius of curvature of the anterior portion closer to the muzzle being considerably shorter than that of the posterior portion (Fig. 451).

The anterior portion of the cornea is, accordingly, much more curved, producing an anterior or rostral protrusion or bulge. The anterior corneal bulge must, accordingly, be a more potent refractive medium than the flatter, posterior part. The rays of light coming from the front are therefore more strongly bent and more easily directed to the lens. But even if the refractive index of the Pike's cornea and that of the surrounding water were identical or almost so (an identity in Fishes now generally assumed but requiring further testing) and if no considerable refraction in the cornea were present, its anterior bulge would still be of pre-eminent importance, since it would permit a goodly portion of the lens to protrude beyond the body surface and in this way make possible collection of the anterior rays coming from the direction of the muzzle (Fig. 452).

From the anterior rim of each orbit a darkly pigmented groove extends between the nostrils of the olfactory sac and the upper jaw along the head in a horizontal direction toward the frontal end of the duck-billed muzzle (Fig. 450). Superficially, the two grooves appear to be no more than "decorations," or elements fitting into the mottled pattern of the Pike's exterior, possibly serving as a useful and effective decoy to the finny predator.

A closer examination, however, while not dis-

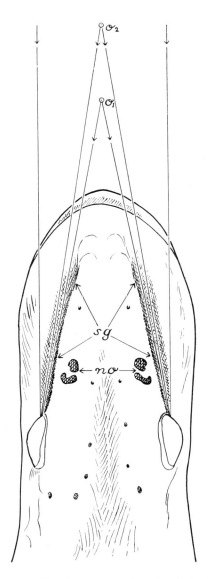

Fig. 451.—View from above of the head of a Northern Pike (*Esox lucius*) showing the position of the eyes and sighting grooves, with the anterior pencils of light rays used in binocular stereoscopic vision drawn at different angles of convergence, depending on the distance of the viewed object, beginning from approximately 5–6 inches (O_1, O_2) to infinity (*parallel lines*). *Labeling: no*, nostrils; *o*, viewed object; *sg*, sighting grooves. (*Cf.* preceding and following figures.)

proving this interpretation, indicates that these two grooves may have another and more important function, that of sighting or aiming at the prey. Their extension lines converge anteriorly toward a point approximately 1 inch in front of the muzzle, more or less depending on the age and size of the specimen (O_1, O_2, in Fig. 451).

It appears, therefore, that these grooves are chiefly used as channels along which the two principal lines of vision, the right and the left, have an unobstructed passage. This is made possible, in particular, when the eyes are turned slightly inward and the pupillary planes are inclined with the front ends toward the mid-sagittal plane. In this position the principal lines of vision hit the surface of the corneal bulge at a greater angle and are thus more easily inflected by refraction toward the lens, or simply pass through the cornea into the lens without refraction (Fig. 452).

The anterior pupillary notch, or "coloboma," also facilitates the passage of the frontal rays into the eye. This notch (*apn*), as observed in a living specimen, is exactly in line with the sighting groove, being, in fact, a little inward when the eye is maximally rotated inward toward the sagittal plane. In this position the notch permits the clear passage of rays passing through the caudal portion of the sighting groove into the interior of the eye.

It should also be of some interest to note that similar grooves or depressions are present in other fresh-water species of fish that depend largely on good vision, as, for example, the Trout and the Bass, and many other Vertebrates, including Mammals (*see* sec. 7, on Anole Lizard, this chapter).

6. INTERNAL EYE STRUCTURES.—The lens of the Pike's eye, as in other fishes, is spherical in shape and is only loosely fitted into the pupillary aperture (Fig. 452). It protrudes about a third into the spacious anterior chamber and almost touches the inner surface of the cornea (in the living fish the apparent interval between the cornea and the lens, when observed from above, measures 0.3–0.4 mm.).

This optical arrangement, with the considerable protrusion of the lens beyond the surface of the body, is especially favorable for the collection of the rays that pass through the marginal

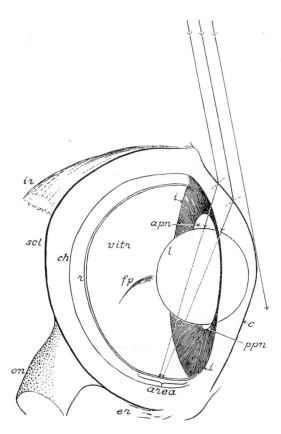

zone of the cornea. Such are all rays that are more or less parallel with the Pike's body. Of these, however, only those that are biologically most useful are maximally utilized: the rays coming from the front. In order to permit free passage of these frontal rays into the eye's interior, the lens is pushed somewhat toward the posterior blunt margin of the oversized pupil, leaving unobstructed in front, toward the muzzle and pigmented sighting groove, a wide aphakic gap of a semilunar shape—the anterior pupillary notch or coloboma.

The shape of the Pike's pupil is oval, with the narrower end facing the muzzle and the longer axis horizontal, precisely as in the cornea. A posterior coloboma or notch is also present but is less wide. When the rostral end of the eye is turned inward for about 30° in comparison with the position at rest, the notched anterior pupillary margin is pushed inward, which brings it to lie about 1 mm. behind the back end of the pigmented sighting groove. In this position the frontal pencil of rays, after its refraction in the anterior corneal bulge, easily slips through the anterior pupillary notch and, after a further refraction in the lens, is projected as a sharp image upon the caudal or posterior segment of the retina tucked in the posterior corner of the eye near the back end of the iris.

This particular locality contains an especially differentiated "area" with an increased number of photoreceptors in the bacillary layer and the ganglion cells accumulated in greater numbers, instead of in a single and rather discontinuous tier found elsewhere in the retinal membrane. This "area" of the Pike's retina is not central but temporal, lateral, or posterior, comparable to a similar area in the Swallow, Swift, and Owl. It is the locality where a higher degree of neuroreceptive resolution of physical light stimulation takes place. (*Cf.* following subsection, and section on Northern Brook Silverside.)

Fig. 452.—Horizontal view of the right eyeball of a Northern Pike (*Esox lucius* or *E. estor*), with upper portions of coats removed, in order to show refractive media and other structures regulating the passage of frontal rays of light used in binocular stereoscopic vision: two that hit the surface of cornea at obtuse angles, refracted into eye where they are focused by the lens (*l*) at a temporoposterior "area" of clear vision, whereas the tangential rays pass by without being inflected into the eye. Broken lines at points of contact of the rays with the corneal surface indicate verticals or "normals" to the surface with which various rays form varying angles of refraction. Note spherical lens, held in suspension by ligament and accommodating muscle, the anterior half of which protrudes through the much larger opening of the iris into the anterior chamber, where it almost touches the cornea; the latter, viewed in a horizontal optical section, appears lopsided or asymmetrically curved, its radii of curvature being shorter in the anterior segment facing the snout (*upper half* in drawing). Lens does not fill in the oval-shaped aperture of the iris (*see* Fig. 450), leaving a wider anterior and a smaller posterior pupillary cleft, through which the anterior and vitreal chambers communicate. Frontal pencils of rays, coming from the direction of the muzzle, pass through the more strongly curved anterior corneal segment and through the anterior pupillary notch (*apn*) into the lens (*l*), by which they are focused on the retinal "area" in the posterior eye corner through which distinct vision is mediated. Since the eyeballs are easily and extensively rotated in the horizontal plane, both axes of acute vision may be brought to converge toward a common fixation point, hence creating conditions necessary for binocular stereoscopic vision. Magnification $3\frac{1}{2} \times$. For other details *see* Fig. 451. *Labeling: apn,* anterior pupillary iris notch or cleft; *c,* cornea; *ch,* chorioid; *er,* attachment of external rectus or straight muscle; *fp,* falciform process; *i,* iris; *ir,* attachment of internal rectus muscle; *l,* lens; *on,* optic nerve, partly pigmented; *ppn,* posterior pupillary notch; *r,* retina; *scl,* sclera; *vitr,* vitreous.

7. RETINA.—The general character of the Pike's photoreceptor membrane is that of a "duplex retina," fit to function under both diurnal and nocturnal conditions of illumination. However, the impression one gains from the microscopic study is of an emphasis upon the structures instrumental in daylight vision, whereas those used in dim-light vision appear less developed. (*Cf.* the opposite arrangement in the Northern Brook Silverside and Bullhead.)

The pigment layer, packed with granules, needles, and threads of a dark-brown color, amounts to no less than one-fifth of the entire thickness of the retina. In the photopic condition it envelops the outer segments and a part of the inner cone segments.

The principal structures of the bacillary photoreceptor layer are huge cones. Their slightly bottle-shaped inner segments fill most of the space as a solid formation, leaving little between for the more numerous but much thinner rods. The long and much more attenuated outer cone segments, similar in shape to those found in the periphery of the human and simian retina, extend toward the pigment epithelium to as far as two-thirds or more of the bacillary layer.

The thickness or diameter of individual cones measured at the level of inner segments varies only a little. In the "posterior area" it is from 6 to 7.5 microns, their intercenter distance being from 9 to 10. In the extra-areal periphery the cones are 9 microns thick, their intercenter distances from 12 to 13.

The number of cones counted on a stretch of 500 microns in the "posterior area" is 30–40; in the center of the fundus it is 24–25. Computed for a circular area measuring 500 microns in diameter (same as the average diameter of the human central territory free from rods), in the "posterior area" this would give roughly 1,500 individually stimulable units (provided that each areal cone has its own midget bipolar). This number, representing less than one-twentieth of 35,000 cones found in the rodless area of the human central fovea, is still a respectable number, providing the Pike with a degree of visual acuity apparently sufficient in its aquatic habitat. (*Cf.* chap. V, 10 [5].)

The number of cones in the far more extensive extra-areal fundus of the eye was found to be about 600 in the same circular area measuring 500 microns across. This represents a rather rough "grain," in comparison with the highly efficient aerial vision of the Primates, Birds, and Lizards, but still indicates a fair degree of acuity. In this estimate the fact that the entire retina is provided with at least that many cones, hence affording a fair degree of visual resolution in the entire wide field of view of the Pike, must also be taken into consideration.

In comparison, then, the Pike's visual resolution in most of its field of view is no less than that in the extracentral parts of the human fields. The degree of visual acuity possessed by the Pike in most of its field of view appears even more serviceable to the fish in its short-range aquatic environment than the same low peripheral acuity appears to Man in his aerial vision.

Whether or not the Pike has accessory cones comparable to those found in the Trout (sec. 5, this chapter) requires further study. In routinely stained preparations none were found. According to Reich (1874), all cones are double cones; but according to our own examination, all of them appear to be single cones.

The approximate numerical ratio of cones and rods is 1:3 or 1:4, and possibly as small as 1:10. This ratio, however, is deceptive, since it does not express the relation of the total mass or substance of the two categories of photoreceptors, which may be 1:1 or even more in favor of the cones. The situation in the Pike, in this respect, is the opposite of what was found in the Northern Brook Silverside, in which the quantitative ratio of the cone and rod substances is approximately 1:10 and approximates the arrangement found in the diurnal Primates. (*See* sections on Northern Brook Silverside and on Tree Shrew, sec. 10, this chapter.)

The outer nuclear layer is quite thin, being made up of an upper row of large, pale, angular, or elliptical cone nuclei with delicate inner framework, located just below the outer limiting membrane, and of a double row of much smaller, elliptical, and vertically arranged rod nuclei. In hematoxylin-eosin or phloxin-stained preparations the rod nuclei appear almost black; in toluidine preparations, stained according to Nissl-Lenhossék's method, the cone nuclei can easily be identified by their clear, purplish hue, very different from the dark-blue color of the rod nuclei (remarkably, the inner rod segments above the outer limiting membrane have the same purplish hue, while the inner cone segments remain unstained by this method, staining in a pink color with eosin or phloxin).

The outer plexiform layer is also thin. In spite of this, its three zones 5-a, 5-b, and 5-c are easily seen. In the middle zone, as in all diurnal retinae, the row of evenly spaced so-called "granular clods" is conspicuous. These are synaptical contacts between the lower swollen ends of the cones and the upper ends of midget bipolars and horizontal cells. In hematoxylin- and eosin-stained sections these synaptical contacts are arranged in a very regular horizontal line, with small intervals separating each two adjoining contacts. Hence the number of such contacts may be used as an indication of the number of cones in a particular locality of the retina. With this as a criterion, the number of the cones in the "posterior area" was found to be fifteen, and in the extra-areal periphery about twelve, to a distance of 150 microns. This is about the number of cones found in the two localities by direct count, as mentioned earlier.

The inner nuclear layer is rather thick. It is made up of several varieties of cells, differing greatly in appearance. The bulk in the middle zones 6-b and 6-c is represented by small, dark, and unevenly spaced nuclei, which belong to the radial fibers and bipolar cells. In the lowermost zone are larger and paler cells, closely packed together, with a few smaller and darker nuclei interspaced. These are the classical amacrine cells, some of which, however, may be ganglion cells and Müller's "radial fibers." The uppermost tier 6-a, next to the outer plexiform layer, belongs to the so-called horizontal cells. These are remarkable because of the extraordinary size of their bodies and horizontal expansions, with cytoplasm completely lacking a chromophile substance and inclosing a very large spherical nucleus containing a large nucleolus.

The inner plexiform layer is thick and has a granulated appearance, finer in its upper half and coarser in its lower half. Conspicuous in it are the thick, vertically arranged, and evenly spaced radial fibers of Müller, and also an even, horizontal striation.

The layer of the ganglion cells everywhere contains a single, often discontinuous, row of smaller and medium cells, with an occasional cell of giant size. The exception is the "posterior area" next to the iris in the posterior corner, where the cells form a single, solid, continuous row with an occasional tendency to accumulate into two tiers, as mentioned.

A similar but less dense increase of ganglion cells is found in the anterior segment of the retina, both "areae" together forming a ring-shaped "area" resembling that found in the Northern Brook Silverside and in the Trout (*see* corresponding sections).

The cytoplasm of the ganglion cells contains either diffuse or finely granulated chromophile substance of Nissl. In this the ganglion cells exactly resemble those in the innermost tier of the inner nuclear layer. The few smaller and darker nuclei found here may belong to the neuroglia.

The layer of optic nerve fibers is thick and horizontally striated, with thick, conically expanded, and evenly spaced lower ends of Müller's supporting radial fibers, which together form the inner limiting membrane.

In summary, the Pike's retina, with its great number of giant cones representing the bulk of the photoreceptor structures and with the diminutive, although more numerous, rods, appears to be an organ chiefly adjusted for photopic or daylight vision. Its acuity, owing to the great thickness of individual cones, must be rated as inferior to that of Vertebrates possessing a differentiated fovea, such as many Lizards, Birds, and Primates, including Man.

In appraising functionally the structures of the Pike's retina, several factors must be taken into consideration. The great number of cones, the considerable thickness of the layer of optic nerve fibers, and the exceptional thickness of optic nerves indicate that a number of optic nerve fibers may originate from the ganglion cells displaced into the inner nuclear layer. Such are present in small numbers in the primate retina and have been found in the Frog, Lizard, and Birds (*see* chap. V, 5 [1]; and S. Ramón Cajal 1911). Investigation with the Golgi method should clarify this particular point.

The giant cells found in the inner nuclear layer, located where the horizontal cells are found in other Vertebrates, appear to belong essentially to a system of neurons whose function is a lateral or horizontal association, or functional integration, of the adjacent and more distant territories of the retina. The horizontal course of the thick expansions of these cells lends itself to such an interpretation. The Golgi method should also clarify this point.

Even though the synaptical relations of the Pike's retina still remain unknown, it appears that this membrane is essentially an organ adjusted to respond with relatively low acuity but with great speed and intensity to rather feeble photic and chromatic stimuli over the entire range of its wide field of view. A locality sufficiently differentiated to act as a "posterior area," comparable to the "central area" of other Vertebrates, is present in the posterior-caudal corner, precisely where an anterior pencil of rays strikes, used in stereoscopic binocular vision. The large dimensions of the cones, furthermore, may be interpreted in terms of low threshold or high responsiveness to chromatic stimuli, which this predator certainly needs in order to notice its multicolored prey. Briefly, the Pike's retina faithfully reflects the predatory habits of this diurnal fish.

8. Binocular vision. From the preceding there is not much doubt that the Pike's eye is well organized for its special task. This and other arrangements connected with it permit the frontal rays of light to pass along the pigmented sighting groove through the frontal bulge of the cornea and the anterior notch of the pupil to the lens, and through it to the posterior area of the retina. Here these rays are most completely utilized for detailed vision and are therefore biologically most useful for this species.

The next inference to be drawn from the foregoing fact is the likelihood of a simultaneous use of the principal lines of vision of both eyes. With the position of both lines in a relaxed specimen as stated, a relatively slight inward turn of the two eyeballs will suffice to make them meet in a single point in front of the muzzle (Fig. 451). The great mobility of the eyes described in the preceding paragraphs certainly permits this. The two eyes may, accordingly, be used simultaneously for binocular stereoscopic vision.

The organization of the peripheral parts of the Pike's visual system indicates its use in binocular convergence and stereopsis, similar to that present in the Swallow. (*See* sec. 8, on Swallow, this chapter.) However, actual observation of the use of the Pike's visual apparatus during life, particularly in catching prey, is required to confirm and to amplify, or to modify, the deductions made from the anatomical investigations.

If the answer is positive, as may be expected on the basis of some observations of the living fish, in analogy with similar observations upon Fishes made by Rochon-Duvigneaud (1933), it will be shown that the Pike has the ability to converge both eyes toward an object situated at varying distances in front of its muzzle. Likewise, a comparable range of accommodation of its dioptrical apparatus may be postulated. This, at any rate, is what one would expect in a fish depending entirely on living, moving food.

9. Nervous system.—The optic nerves and centers of the Pike are no less remarkable and characteristic of this "visual animal." The optic nerves, in comparison with the small size of the entire brain, are disproportionately huge, cylindrical trunks. Each optic nerve is almost as thick as the spinal cord just behind the brain. This is the more unexpected, since certainly the somatomuscular system, whose centers are in the spinal cord, is very well developed, and its swift and powerful action of paramount importance in this species; the Pike's body, except for the relatively small internal organs, is mostly solid musculature. The ribbon-like arrangement of fibers, found in the optic nerve of other fishes, is not noticeable.

The diameter of the optic nerve of a rather small specimen is from 1.8 to 2.2 mm. In larger individuals the diameter is much larger. A cross-section shows it to be more or less round or slightly deformed. The microscopic appearance is rather uniform, thus duplicating the rather uniform size of the ganglion cells in the entire expanse of the retina. The caliber of the fibers is also rather uniform and moderate in size, the far greater majority being thin fibers of about 2–3 microns, with many smaller ones, and also a few large ones of 4, 5, and 6 microns in diameter. In this way the cross-section of the optic nerve reflects the rather uniform organization of the retina. The number of fibers may amount to 400,000 or more.

In the chiasma the two optic nerves inter-cross in bulk, either the right or the left nerve being the upper one in different individuals.

The optic nerves apparently terminate chiefly in the midbrain, each nerve in the contralateral lobe. The optic lobes (*opl, optlo*), representing the optic tectum (*tect*), are of in-front of the huge optic lobes (*forebr, telenceph,* in same figures).

The entire brain of a Pike may be said to be a composite of the lower vital centers of the medulla oblongata (*med*), of a small cerebellum (*cbl, cerebell*), and of the relatively large mammillary bodies, upon all of which is superimposed a huge visual mechanism which dominates the whole.

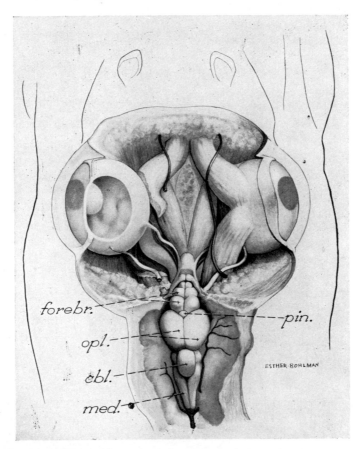

Fig. 453.—Dissected head of the Northern Pike, to demonstrate the brain (*cf.* Fig. 454), eye muscles, and nerves connected with the eyeballs. The two largest paired structures of the brain are the optic lobes (*opl*). The three other and much smaller paired structures in front of the optic lobes represent the diminutive forebrain (*forebr*). The single small structure in the mid-line, just in front of the optic lobes, is the pineal gland (*pin*). Behind the optic lobes is the cerebellum (*cbl*) and oblong medulla (*med*). Note the large eyeballs and giant extrinsic eye muscles, compared with same parts in the Northern Brown Bullhead, a Fish with small eyes and a well-developed olfactory apparatus. (*See* Fig. 456.)

ordinate size and dominate the external appearance of the brain (Figs. 453, 454; *see also* Beccari 1943, Fig. 182). They are its largest single structures. The mass of each optic lobe is roughly double that of the entire telencephalon, comprising the striate bodies, thalami, and olfactory apparatus, all these parts together giving the appearance of a small appendage in

The topographical relations of the retinal quadrants to the various fiber bundles of the optic nerve and their representation in the visual centers of the brain remain a problem for future investigation.

The highest level, or centers, of the Pike's visual system are the two optic lobes, principally made up of a cortex-like structure, poor in

824   *The Vertebrate Visual System*

cells and rather simple in structure. Here the most important processes take place, including those that may be described as "mental" or "psychic." These comprise visual orientation in space, detailed visual discrimination, visual memory, recognition of the symbolical meaning of the visual impressions of shapes and colors, and judgment and making of decisions whether, when, and how to act or not to act.

From examination of the brain alone it is obvious that the Pike is practically exclusively a visual animal. Visual impressions are of over-

smell and taste are stimulated, the condition being that the lure moves.

The role the chromatic stimuli play in the biology of the Pike, believed important by many fishermen, remains another problem that must be solved by careful experimenting. The numerous and voluminous cones may seem to be evidence of the essential function of color vision in the life of this predator (*cf.* Carter 1948). The summating apparatus, in turn, may be interpreted in terms of the extreme sensitiveness of this fish to objects in motion.

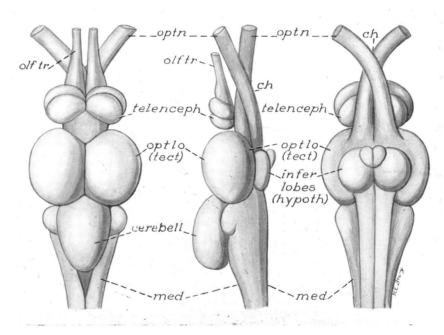

FIG. 454.—Brain of the Northern Pike in three views (from left to right): an upper, lateral, and lower aspect. Note the large size of the visual centers (*optlo*), which from every angle appear as the largest parts of the brain. The optic centers, together with the posterior parts of the brain, in this species far outweigh the diminutive telencephalon or forebrain (*telenceph*) which serves olfactory and other nonoptic functions. *Labeling: cerebell*, cerebellum; *ch*, chiasma of optic nerves; *infer lobes* (*hypoth*), inferior lobes of hypothalamus; *med*, oblong medulla; *olf tr*, olfactory tract; *optlo* (*tect*), optic lobe or midbrain tectum; *optn*, optic nerve; *telenceph*, telencephalon or forebrain. Magnification 3×.

whelming importance in its life. The Pike, speaking in terms of human psychology, "thinks" through its sight, almost to the point of exclusion of all other senses. This may account for the fact that a Pike strikes at any shiny lure, such as an artificial minnow, if it only approximates the size, shape, and brilliance of a fish upon which it customarily preys. And it does so, irrespective of whether or not the hook is baited with some animal lure, hence without regard to whether or not its senses of

10. BIOLOGICAL CONSIDERATIONS.—From the study of its anatomical organization, its habits, and other factors of its biology, one becomes convinced that the Pike, the "wolf of the waters," or rather the "tiger of the lakes," is what it is because of its superior sight.

The visual apparatus of this predator fish has undergone remarkable increase, perfection, and specialization to serve as a daylight distance receptor. That it is precisely the sight that became specialized is accounted for by the fact that, even in the water, light is a more certain medium of communication for a predator than any other physical or chemical form of stimulus used by the Vertebrates, such as those to which the senses of taste and smell respond.

Light, measured in terms of biological processes and events, is instantaneous, whereas the chemical substances capable of stimulating the senses of taste and smell require measurable time, even when working at close range. The fact that physical light propagates rectilinearly even in water, greatly though it is restricted and modified by absorption, dispersion, and other factors, still makes it a more dependable guide to a diurnal predator than any other external stimulus.

The sense of sight, however, had to be perfected to the limit allowable by the physical conditions of the water, particularly by its transparency, in order to be of great use. This seemingly was accomplished by the Pike and its relatives, the Esocidae. This, in turn, forced a comparable perfection of sight in other species upon which the Pike Family preys, such as the Sunfishes, Minnows, and Suckers. Without such an adjustment, they would have been exterminated, which would likewise have meant the disappearance of the Pikes.

The biological relation between the Pike and its prey may be crudely described as a perpetual, neatly balanced, war, wherein the perfection of sight of the eaten prey always closely follows that of the eating predator—a delicate relationship that in natural conditions safeguards the perpetuation of both categories of these species.

References: Ariëns Kappers, Huber & Crosby 1936; Atkins & Poole 1934; Bauer 1911 *etc.*; Beccari 1943; Beer 1894; Bellonci 1888; Beniuc 1933; R. Berlin 1893; Birge & Juday 1931–32; Brehm's *Tierleben*, v. 3, 1914; Brunner 1934; H. O. Bull 1935; Burkamp 1923; Butcher 1938; Cahn 1924; Canella 1937; Carlander 1950; Carter 1948; Charlton 1933; G. L. Clarke 1936; Colas-Pelletier 1940; Contino 1939; B. Curtis 1938; Dean 1916–23; Eddy & Surber 1947; Eizenmann & Schaffer 1900; Erickson 1933; Fischer & Löwenbach 1935; V. Franz 1905, 1906, 1912, 1913, 1931, 1934; Franz & Steche 1914; K. von Frisch 1912, 1913, 1923, 1924, 1925; Gaffron 1934; W. K. Gregory 1941; Grundfest 1931, 1932; Hale 1949; Hamburger 1926; Harris 1904; Hein 1913; C. J. Herrick 1922; C. L. Herrick 1891; C. Hess 1909, 1912, 1913, 1914, 1919, 1922; Hesse & Doflein 1935–43; Hineline 1927; Holmgren 1922; Hora 1938; Horio 1938; Hubbs & Lagler 1949; Huber & Crosby 1934; Jarmer 1928; R. E. Johnson 1946; Kahmann 1934; Karsten 1923; Kendall 1917; Kühn 1919; Lagler 1949; La Gorce 1939, 1952; La Monte 1945; Langlands 1926–27; Le Danois 1949; Macan & Worthington 1951; Matthews 1933; Meader 1934, 1936, 1938; Merker 1937–38, 1939; Mirto 1895; Moore, Pollock & Lima 1950; A. H. Morgan 1930; H. Müller 1952; Johannes Müller 1826; McEwan 1938; Needham *et al.* 1941; Needham & Lloyd 1937; Needham & Needham 1941; Neumeyer 1895; Nolte 1932; Norman 1936; Ovio 1927; G. H. Parker 1903, 1922, 1932; Parker & Haswell 1940; Parker & Van Hensen; Parsons 1924; Perkins & Wheeler 1931; Piša 1939; Pütter 1908–12; Rádl 1915; P. Ramón y Cajal 1890, 1899; S. Ramón y Cajal 1892–93 (1933), 1894, 1896, 1898, 1899, 1909–11; Reeves 1919; M. Reich 1874; Riese 1924; Rochon-Duvigneaud 1922, 1933, 1934, 1943; W. Roth 1911; Russell & Bull 1932; Sand 1935; Scheuring 1921; Schiemenz 1924; Schiller 1934; Schneider-Orelli 1907; Schnurmann 1920; Schreitmüller & Relinghaus 1926; Schrenkeisen 1938; Sgonina 1933; Sperry & Clark 1949; Streuli 1925; Ströer 1939; Studnička 1898; Sumner 1940; Szepsenwol 1938; Trautmann & Hubbs 1935; Tschermak 1902, 1915; Uexküll 1921; Van Oosten 1946; Verrier 1927, 1928, 1934, 1938, 1940, 1945; Verrier *et al.*; Wallenberg 1913; Walls 1942; Ward & Whipple 1918; L. H. Warner 1931; M. F. Washburn 1936; Washburn & Bentley 1906; Weed 1927; Wesenberg-Lund 1939; G. M. White 1919; H. Wolff 1925; R. W. Wood 1906; Wunder 1925, 1926, 1927, 1930; Zolotnitski 1901.

SEC. 5. TROUT

1. TAXONOMY.—The Trout is mostly a small to medium-sized fish, of slender, graceful build, subsisting exclusively on small animal life, mostly insects. It is a resident of cold running streams and lakes of elevated regions of the Northern Hemisphere. It belongs to the Family

Salmonidae of which the other representatives are the salt-water Salmons.

The Trout is a popular game fish, being, in the opinion of many, a personification of all that is noble and ideal in a fish: beauty, fighting qualities, and an exquisite taste.

There are several native Trouts, the most widely distributed being the Common Brook Trout (*Salvelinus fontinalis*, Fig. 455) and other

2. CHARACTER.—As a fish subsisting on small, mobile prey, the Trout embodies all features one would expect from it: a slender body form, with a pointed and laterally flattened head, a spacious mouth well provided with medium-sized teeth, and a powerful musculature, which, with a large tail fin, represents an efficient locomotor equipment.

Of its senses, sight is superior and obviously

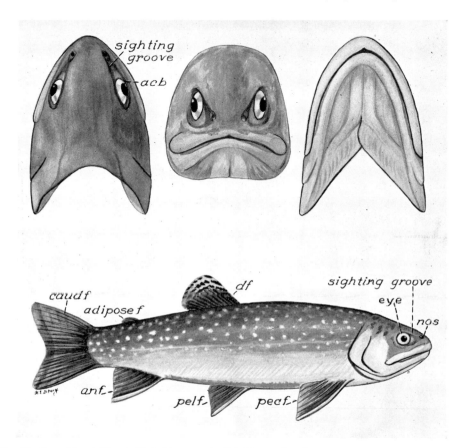

FIG. 455.—Northern Brook Trout (*Salvelinus fontinalis*). Upper sketches represent, from left to right, an upper, anterior, and lower view of the head, the lower sketch showing the full side view of the fish. Note the well-developed eyes, easily seen, including both pupils, from above and from the front, but not from below; the "sighting grooves," along which the two visual axes converge toward the common fixation point when both eyes are used together (*see* same details and interpretation in the preceding section on Northern Pike). *Labeling: acb*, anterior or rostral bulge of cornea; *adipose f*, adipose fin; *anf*, anal fin; *caudf*, caudal fin; *df*, dorsal fin; *nos*, nostril; *pecf*, pectoral fin; *pelf*, pelvic fin.

more local varieties, such as the Coast Rainbow Trout (*Salmo gairdnerii irideus*), Common Lake Trout (*Christivomer namaycush*), and the Brown Trout (*Salmo trutta fario*), the latter transplanted from Europe. (For other illustrations, some in color, *see* Schultz & Murayama 1939; Eddy & Surber 1947; Hubbs & Lagler 1949; Sisson 1950.)

the leading and dominant sense. This, with an alert nature, makes the Trout an eminently "visual animal." According to the practically unanimous testimony of anglers, its vision is exceedingly acute, the fish being quite wary, especially in much-fished waters.

The Trout's color sense also seems well developed, which harmonizes with its gaudy appearance, especially during the spawning season.

In fishing, the Trout is especially responsive if the lure is moving, simulating a moving insect, its natural food. Because of this, "fly casting" is the preferred mode of angling. As to fishing for the Common Trout, Eddy & Surber remark: "Like most other trout they are exceedingly wary, and the angler must exercise great caution, keeping out of sight as much as possible."

3. Visual apparatus and behavior.—A living specimen of a Common Brook Trout, $12\frac{1}{2}$ inches long, examined in a basin filled with water, shows the following noteworthy features: The eye is relatively large, with a definite "anterior" or "rostral bulge," even though much less pronounced than in the Pike (*see* sec. 4, this chapter). When the cornea is viewed directly from above, with the fish in its "normal" horizontal position, in optical cross-section it appears not to be a portion of a circle or a spheroid (as in Flying Squirrel, Tarsier, or Owl) or of an ellipse or ellipsoid, a parabola, or paraboloid (as in most Primates, including Man), but more nearly resembles the outlines of a longitudinal section of a chicken egg, with its blunt end turned toward the muzzle of the fish (left upper sketch in Fig. 455). Otherwise expressed, the radii of curvature in the horizontal plane become gradually shorter as the anterior extremity of the cornea is approached. (*Cf.* Fig. 452.)

The effect of this lopsided corneal curving must be a stronger refraction at the rostral end of the cornea than at the caudal end (which observation is at variance with the generally accepted belief that in aquatic animals corneal refraction is of little or no importance). The stronger refraction in the anterior segment of the cornea is useful in turning the rays, coming from the direction of the muzzle, into the eye, which in a flatter cornea, with a tangential incidence of incoming rays, would be deflected and would pass by without entering the eye (*see* Fig. 451).

The described arrangement indicates the importance of the frontal rays, coinciding with the direction in which the fish moves and hunts. These frontal rays are of importance only if both eyes are used simultaneously, that is, as

instruments in binocular stereoscopic vision. Hence the "frontal corneal bulge" is an indicator of stereopsis wherever it is present in a fish provided with laterally placed eyes, as found in all species with well-developed sight, as, for example, the Northern Brook Silverside, Sunfish, Bass, Trout, and, more so than in all species so far examined, the Pike.

Harmonizing with this interpretation are the "sighting grooves" or shallow furrows, one on each side of the head. As in the Pike, in the Brook Trout these grooves begin at the anterior corners of the eyes and run between the upper jaw and the olfactory pits. Their extension lines converge in front of the muzzle at a distance which varies with the size of the fish.

The plane of the iris membrane roughly coincides with the equator of the spherical lens. It is inclined anteriorly about 5° toward the mid-sagittal plane. The iris has an anterior angular notchlike coloboma or pupillary "cutout" in the anterior margin of the iris, precisely in the direction of the "sighting groove." As in the Pike, a posterior, but much narrower, semilunar coloboma or notch is also present.

In the living fish the eyes appear to be quite mobile. Spontaneous movements are present, but in narrow confinement their direction could not be made certain. The eye movements elicited by a visual stimulus, e.g., a hand suddenly approaching from the front, consist of a quick move inward in the horizontal plane, hence of a convergence. There are spontaneous movements in the horizontal plane from time to time.

When the fish, while in water, is passively moved to one side, both eyes promptly and in unison respond with compensatory movements in the opposite direction. Labyrinthine compensatory responses of the eyes, elicited by the rotation of the fish around its longitudinal axis, are also quite pronounced.

Passively, with the forceps, the eyeball can be easily moved in the horizontal plane as follows: backward or toward the tail for approximately 30°, and forward-inward, that is, toward the muzzle, for at least 45°. This makes possible total movement of the eyeball in the horizontal plane of not less than 70°–80°, which approximates the active mobility of the human eyeball.

Both pupils when observed from above are

fully visible, while they cannot be seen at all when viewed from below. This indicates an upward direction of both principal lines of vision, and in binocular vision toward a common fixation point above the horizontal plane. This would hardly be the case if the planes of both iris membranes were vertical or if they were inclined with their lower ends toward the horizontal plane, as in the bottom-gazing Perch. (*See also* Northern Brook Silverside, sec. 2, this chapter.)

The position of the theoretically disclosed lines of vision says nothing, of course, of the actual principal lines of gaze utilized by the Trout in pursuit of its usual prey, the flying insects. This must be determined by carefully planned experiments. The calculated arrangement, however, makes it at least probable that one pair of lines of view—those touching the lower extremities of both retinae in the posterior corners of the eyes—converge and meet somewhere above the head and at some distance in front of the muzzle.

The preceding description and observation were obtained from living, fresh, and preserved specimens of the Common Brook Trout, kindly provided by the Fish Hatchery in Spooner, Wisconsin. The results of the study of the Rainbow Trout, also obtained from the same hatchery, are practically a duplication. Like other Trouts, this fish, too, is exceedingly wary. The slightest move of the hand toward its head within its visibility range elicits a violent reaction of escape movements. The eyes, even when the fish is at rest, constantly make slight jerky movements in the horizontal plane, either to or from the sagittal plane, each eye being capable of an inward deviation of at least 20° or 30°. Whether both eyes make simultaneous movements of convergence, by turning inward (as observed in the Swallow), as they certainly do singly, it was unfortunately not possible to ascertain by simple observation. When the fish is passively rotated around its longitudinal axis, the eyeballs describe compensatory rolling movements in the vertical plane of almost 45° around their longitudinal axes.

The fish frequently pushes its muzzle out of the water, probably in search of oxygen. Occasionally there are periods when the fish remains unresponsive to visual stimuli, alternating with other periods when it reacts violently. As in the Brook Trout, we find a slight anterior corneal bulge, shallow sighting grooves, and a wider angular anterior pupillary notch or coloboma of the iris, together with a narrower semilunar posterior notch. In both species the lens is yellowish in color and practically touches the cornea on the inside.

4. EYE AND RETINA.—The eye of the Trout is quite as remarkable as that of the Pike and quite as characteristic of a "visual animal." In the following paragraphs are described the most important features found in the Brown Trout and the Rainbow Trout, two species closely related to the Common Brook Trout.

The shape of the eye resembles half of a sphere whose dividing side, the cornea, is slightly curved to accommodate the lens. The outer coats also deviate from a circle in the anterior and posterior extremities. Here they are flattened, to form even surfaces on which the retinal images are formed. (*Cf.* sec. 4 and illustrations of Northern Pike.)

The retina is of a pronounced diurnal type. In a photopic specimen the pigment layer represents about one-fifth the entire retinal thickness or the outer half of the combined first and second layers. In this way both outer and inner cone segments are exposed to the action of light, whereas the longer outer rod segments are entirely enveloped by the pigment.

The bacillary layer is made up of rods and cones. The rods, much longer and more numerous than the cones, hardly equal in their total mass, much less exceed, the total cone mass.

The cones are of two varieties: the much more spectacular *principal cones*, and another more slender variety which may be called *accessory cones*. The principal cones are much thicker in the inner segments, which have the shape of a champagne bottle. Their upper ends extend to the level separating the upper from the middle third of the bacillary layer. The accessory cones, on the contrary, are much thinner and shorter. Their bases rest on the outer limiting membrane, their inner segments being only about half the length of the inner segments of the principal cones.

The cones, examined on a horizontal cross-section of the eyeball, are found to be more numerous and thinner in two localities. One is close to the anterior margin of the retina, the other close to the posterior. In the more extensive, centrally located territory or *fundus*, around the papilla of the optic nerve, the cones are less dense but are thicker.

In the anterior and posterior "areae," the diameter of the inner segments of the principal cones is from 6 to 7.5 microns; of the accessory cones, from 4 to 5 microns, the intercenter distance of the first being from 12 to 15 microns. The number of the principal cones counted on a stretch of 500 microns in these two areae of greatest density was from 40 to 50. This or a little less may also have been the number of the accessory cones. However, in places, two principal cones seem to alternate with one accessory cone.

In the fundus the principal cones are about 10 microns thick and the accessory cones from 6 to 7, with the intercenter distances of the first measuring 25 microns. The number of principal cones found on a stretch of 500 microns was 22; of the accessory cones, 14.

Taking the preceding numbers as a basis, the following was the total number of cones computed for a circular area measuring 500 microns in diameter: in the anterior and posterior areae, 11,000 cones; in the fundus, 4,000 cones.

This result is noteworthy in two respects. It shows, on the one hand, the number of cones in localities of greatest density to be, in the Trout, about four times that found in the Pike. This number also favorably compares with the 35,000 cones found in the rodless area of the human central fovea measuring 500 microns in diameter. (*See* chap. V, 10 [5].)

It is most likely that the anterior and posterior areae are but sections of a ring-shaped area which encircles the larger central territory containing fewer cones. This would duplicate a similar ring-shaped area found in the Northern Brook Silverside and in the Northern Pike, where, however, it is much less noticeable.

To complete this account, two other features must be mentioned. First, the ganglion cells are also found in greater numbers in the anterior and posterior areae than in the fundus. Especially in the anterior area, the ganglion cells form a closely packed row, with a tendency in many places to form two tiers. In the fundus no

such tendency, but rather its opposite, was observed in occasional gaps, making the layer of the ganglion cells appear discontinuous. Second, the layer of the optic nerve fibers is conspicuous because of its thickness. Close to the optic papilla, the thickness of this layer increases to no less than half the entire thickness of the retina. The number of fibers in the optic nerve is 350,000 and may be as much as half a million.

The preceding observations, interpreted functionally, indicate a great number of individually stimulable units, beginning with the photoreceptive cones, through the optic nerves, to as far as the optic lobes of the midbrain. The number of the units in the retinal periphery is about three times their number in the larger central territory around the optic papilla. Also, the size of the receptor units in the periphery is somewhat smaller than the size of the units in the fundus. This again indicates greater visual acuity in the periphery than in the central territory of the retina.

The great thickness of the inner segments of the principal cones may be interpreted as indicating a lower threshold or greater responsiveness to visual stimuli. This greater sensitiveness of the diurnal cones most likely also includes the perception of hues.

What the presence of two different kinds of cones means functionally it is not possible to answer at present except hypothetically. It may indicate two maxima of responsiveness in the visible spectrum, possibly utilized in two different dioptrical conditions. Or it may be a device to increase sharpness of the retinal image at a distance, and again at close range; hence it may indicate the ability to accommodate.

5. PHYSIOLOGICAL CONSIDERATIONS.—A correlation of the anatomical equipment and physiological performance with the living habits of the Trout, on the basis of the preceding sketchy information, must necessarily remain incomplete. It may, therefore, suffice to consider only a few items of special interest for the understanding of vertebrate vision.

If our deduction concerning the convergence of the two principal anterior lines of view toward a common binocular fixation point situated somewhere above and in front of the head proves correct, this certainly would disclose a very useful arrangement by which the Trout could notice an insect flying above the water or floating on its surface. In the Pike a somewhat different arrangement is present, with a fixation point straight ahead, since this fish feeds almost exclusively on other fish caught in the water, hence aimed in the direction of the Pike's body.

The use of the superior or "ceiling point of fixation," as it may be called, would represent only the initial phase of the act of insect hunting by the Trout. This would be immediately followed by a switching of the gaze of both eyes to another, the "frontal common fixation point" directly in front of the head, requiring an adjustment of the body, a binocular focusing in the frontal direction, and a propelling attack directly ahead. In this second phase the binocular use of both eyes, the fixing of the prey in a common fixation point directly in front of the head and in continuation of the bodily axis, would be the position for the best utilization of the propelling apparatus of the fish for the seizure of a flying insect by a leap out of the water, the usual way by which the Trout captures its prey.

A very much more detailed observation of a Trout in action, preferably also by using a good movie camera, combined with laboratory experimenting and careful anatomical examination, would not fail to reveal further elements of the basic activity of this interesting fish. But even with our present limited knowledge, it is justifiable to say that the perfection of the Trout's visual apparatus is the principal factor in the life of this fish. Microscopic examination of its retina showed two areae, an anterior and a posterior, where the number of cones is almost three times that in the fundus of the eye. Here the density of the cones is close to one-third of the central foveal cones of the human eye. This indicates a high degree of acuity in an animal whose biologically required usefulness of vision cannot extend more than a few dozen yards. The high acuity is made even more useful with the help of the tridimensional binocular stereoscopic vision, the existence of which seems probable, at least by circumstantial evidence.

A related problem requiring further study concerns the ring-shaped "area" and its use. If our interpretation proves to be correct and the existence of this area is demonstrated beyond doubt, it will show that the Trout is in possession of a ring in the periphery of its field of view where it sees details best. In the horizontal plane this ring would have two distinct points of higher visual acuity, an anterior and a posterior. In the vertical plane there would be a superior and an inferior point of distinct vision. Or, as might be expected from the position of the eyes, there would be no inferior point in the Trout, a fish principally subsisting on surface insects, since such would not be necessary.

References: Ariëns Kappers, Huber & Crosby 1936; Atkinson & Poole 1934; V. Bauer 1909, 1910, 1911; R. Berlin 1893; A. E. Brehm's *Tierleben*, v. 3 (fishes); Brunner 1934; H. O. Bull 1935; Burkamp 1923; Canella 1937; Carter 1948; Colas-Pelletier 1940; Contino 1939; B. Curtis 1938; H. S. Davis 1937; B. Dean 1916–23; Dymond & Vladykov 1934; Eddy & Surber 1947; Fischer & Löwenbach 1935; V. Franz 1913, 1934; Franz & Steche 1914; K. von Frisch 1912, 1913, 1923, 1924, 1925; Gaffron 1934; Grundfest 1931, 1932; Hale 1949; Hamburger 1926; Hankinson 1924; Hein 1913; C. J. Herrick 1922; C. L. Herrick 1891; Hora 1938; Hubbs & Lagler 1949; Jarmer 1928; Jordan, Evermann & Warren 1930; Lagler 1949, La Gorce 1952; La Monte 1945; Macan & Worthington 1951; McEwan 1938; Meader 1934; Merker 1937–38, 1939; Mirto 1895; A. H. Morgan 1930; H. Müller 1952; Joh. Müller 1826; Needham 1938; Nolte 1932; Norman 1931; Parker & Haswell 1940; Parker & Van Hensen 1917; Parsons 1924; Perkins & Wheeler 1931; Pütter 1908–12; Rádl 1915; P. Ramón y Cajal 1899; C. D. Reeves 1919; Rochon-Duvigneaud 1943; W. Roth 1911; Russell & Bull 1932; Sand 1935; Scheuring 1921; Schiemenz 1924; Schiller 1934; Schneider-Orelli 1907; Schnurmann 1920; Schreitmüller & Relinghaus 1926; Schrenkeisen 1938; Schultz & Murayama 1939; Sgonina 1933; J. R. Simon 1946; Sperry & Clark 1949; Sumner 1940; Szepsenwol 1938; A. Thienemann 1939; Verrier 1927, 1928, 1938, 1945; Verrier & Escher-Desrivières 1937; Walls 1942; Ward & Whipple 1918; L. H. Warner 1931; M. F. Washburn 1936; Wesenberg-Lund 1939; G. M. White 1919; H. Wolff 1925; R. W. Wood 1906; Wunder 1925, 1926, 1927, 1930; Zolotnitski 1901. (*See also* references on Pike.)

SEC. 6. BULLHEAD

1. TAXONOMY.—The Bullhead or Horned Pout is a fish that is an opposite of the Pike and Trout in its anatomical and physiological organization and its biological behavior (Fig. 456). It is a member of the North American Catfish Family or Ameiuridae, closely related to the Siluridae or Catfish Family of Europe and Asia and to other Catfishes of Central and South America and of Africa. The Northern Brown or Speckled Bullhead (*Ameiurus nebulosus*) may serve as a representative; its other North American relatives are the Northern Black Bullhead (*Ameiurus melas*), the Northern Yellow Bullhead (*Ameiurus natalis*), and others. (*See*, for additional information and illustrations, Hubbs & Lagler 1949; Eddy 1945; Eddy & Surber 1947.)

2. CHARACTER.—In common with other Catfishes, the Northern Bullhead has a stout, truncated body, with a broad, flattened head decorated with one pair of shorter, and one of longer, barbels or "whiskers," partly stiff and sticking up (hence the name "Horned Pout"). Each of its pectoral and dorsal fins is armed with a strong bony spine connected with poison glands.

The mouth of the Bullhead is wide and spacious, though less so than that of the Pike. The upper and lower jaws and the gullet are armed with numerous short teeth arranged in "pads," sufficient to seize small prey and other particles of food but not fit to serve as offensive weapons against a formidable adversary.

3. HABITS.—The external appearance of a Bullhead is not that of an aquatic beauty or of a fast swimmer but rather of a fish of lowly, sluggish habits, living close to the bottom, often in muddy waters. Its food consists of anything that can be had without much effort: worms, insect larvae, snails, crayfish, frogs, and an occasional small fish, but principally decaying vegetable and animal matter. The Bullhead is no aristocrat: the sluggish, shallow, turbid waters, often poor in oxygen, and as food all kinds of detritus, both shunned by the more sensitive fish, are just right for the smaller species of Catfishes. They have been well described as scavengers.

In disposition the Bullhead is a peacefully inclined creature, not looking for the exploits of a sneaky aquatic gladiator, such as the Northern Pike, or for dainty acrobatic stunts such as those performed by a Brook or Rainbow Trout. However, when cornered or on the hook, a Bullhead is a determined fighter, well provided, as he is, with a powerful locomotor apparatus and with three long, sharp, and stout erectile poisonous spines. A Bullhead has a tenacious life: with its head almost severed, it still tries to inflict a painful wound as it wiggles in order to regain the water.

4. SIGHT.—In procuring food the Bullhead depends little on sight, and that only indirectly. Most of what it eats it finds by smell and taste, and it would not see well, even if it had better visual organs: the lower reaches of its usually weedy and turbid aquatic habitat are but little illuminated.

It is true that Bullheads may be caught on a hook and line at any hour of the day, especially if the hook is placed close to the bottom. However, they bite most readily when the traces of the setting sun have died down and dusk has descended upon the waters.

The Bullheads are pronounced nocturnal, or rather scotopic, animals. Sight, it seems, serves only a negative role in their life: to warn them during the day to hide and in this way to avoid potential enemies, particularly diurnal predators like the Pike. The sense of hearing, however, seems to be of considerable importance (*see* D. Poggendorf 1952).

Bullheads do not need illumination for the gathering of food. In the conditions of an aquarium, according to Eddy & Surber, "Bullheads become very much excited when food is thrown to them; they swim and gyrate about the food, trying to locate it. They must come close or touch it before they can seize it, and there is no evidence that they see it even then." (*See also* experiments by Schiemenz 1924.)

5. EYEBALL AND RETINA.—The Bullhead's eyes are small for a fish, both in comparison with the size of its body and when compared with the eyes of such diurnal hunters as the Pike and the Trout. (*See* corresponding sections

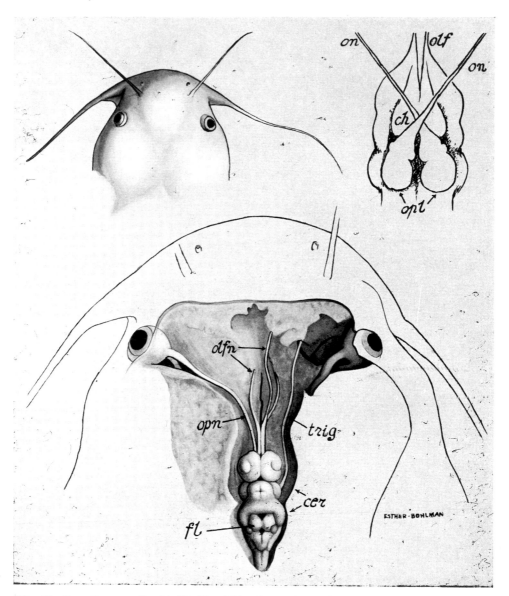

Fig. 456.—Northern Brown or Speckled Bullhead (*Ameiurus nebulosus*), a representative of the Family Ameiuridae, or North American Catfishes, closely related to Siluridae or Catfishes of Europe and Asia. A species with relatively small eyes adjusted to a life in subdued light, crepuscular and nocturnal in habit, depending practically entirely for its livelihood on the senses of smell and taste. Left upper sketch shows an intact head, lower sketch a slightly enlarged head with brain and some cranial nerves exposed. Right upper sketch shows a ventral view of the brain, together with long and slender optic nerves, decussating in the chiasma and terminating in diminutive optic lobes (*cf.* Fig. 458). Note the diminutive size of the optic lobes, in comparison with the nonoptic parts of the brain, where the olfactory nerves terminate, a situation opposite from that present in the Northern Pike, a pronounced diurnal, visual animal. Note also the two pairs of barbels, one large and one smaller, provided with taste buds, responsible for the popular name "horned pout" given to the Bullhead. Structurally and biologically the Bullhead is the reverse of the Pike. *Labeling: cer,* brain; *ch,* chiasma; *olf, olfn,* olfactory nerves; *on, opn,* optic nerves; *opl,* optic lobes; *trig,* branch of trigeminal nerve.

in this chapter.) In a well-built mature specimen 12 inches long, the average diameter of the eyeball is from 6 to 7 mm. Its shape is almost spherical. The pupil is nearly circular, and there is only an indication of a frontal and caudal pupillary notch. The extrinsic eye muscles are long but slender and poorly developed. Passively the eyeball can easily be moved in any direction.

The eye movements seen in a living specimen are of several varieties: a slight inward pull, synchronous with the action of gill musculature; an occasional slight scanning movement in the horizontal plane; and an infrequent pulling in

The field of vision of each eye is quite wide, apparently no less than 200°, judging from the shape, size, and position of the cornea (Fig. 457). The curvature of the cornea, in both the horizontal and the vertical meridians, is slightly paraboloidal. There is, however, no indication of an asymmetrical bulge, characteristic of the corneae of the Pike, Sunfish, Trout, Bass, and Silverside.

The shape of the head makes possible a slight expansion of each individual field of vision in particular directions. Dorsally above each eye a shallow depression permits the cornea to be seen from the opposite side along a straight line

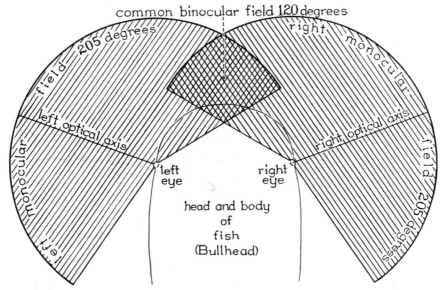

Fig. 457.—Fields of view of the Northern Brown Bullhead, a diagram showing the direction of the optical axis and the position of the monocular field of each eye and the overlapping of the two fields in front of the head, producing a common binocular field of view.

and turning down, as if compensating for the nictitating membrane which is not present in the described species. What other eye movements there are under physiological conditions remains to be determined by future investigation.

The eyes are set far apart, almost at the periphery of the broad, squat head. The distance between the vertices of the two corneae amounts to no less than 52 mm. in the same specimen. (For comparison, the interpupillary distance in Man measures 65 mm.) In the living fish the optical axis of the eye is deflected anteriorly, and it includes an angle of about 70° with the vertical sagittal plane.

that makes an angle of 60° with the sagittal vertical plane. This produces a common binocular field of view of as much as 120° above the head in the transverse-vertical plane. The two fields of view, including their monocular portions, may extend here to approximately 300°. In front of the snout, the common binocular field of both eyes is still considerable, even though it is reduced to about 60°.

The retina of the Bullhead contains all layers and elements found in other Vertebrates, but in much changed form and proportion. The pigment layer, including the bacillary layer, represents more than half the thickness of the entire retina, to which the much reduced and modified layers *4–10* are attached below. In a photopic retina the pigment so completely permeates the entire bacillary layer as far as the outer limiting membrane that no details can be seen in ordinary, unbleached preparations.

The frame of the pigment layer in bleached preparations is revealed as a single row of epithelial cells containing large, spherical nuclei.

The photoreceptors are represented by both the rods and the cones. The rods have an outer, smooth, cylindrical segment of regular shape, with a great affinity for hematoxylin. The outer segment is linked by means of a very nar-

ward the light, the rods away from it, opposite to the movement of the pigment.

The diameter of the outer rod segments is from 2 to 3 microns; that of the cones at their widest point, from 3 to 4. The average length of the outer rod segments is 35 microns; that of the outer cone segments, from 7 to 10. The mass of each outer cone segment, accordingly, is much smaller and is contained in the outer rod segment probably not less than ten times and possibly more.

The number of the cones, counted on a stretch of 500 microns, was found to be 60; that

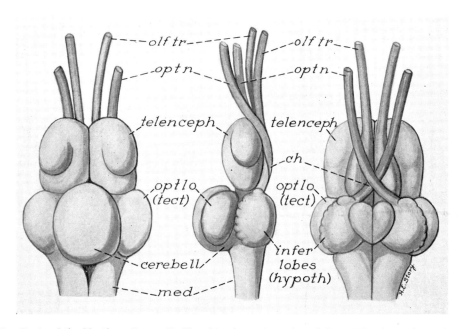

FIG. 458.—Brain of the Northern Brown Bullhead in three views, from left to right: from above, from the side, and from below. Note the relatively small size of the optic lobes (*optlo*) in this pronounced nocturnal Catfish, in comparison with the same parts in the diurnal Bluegill Sunfish, and Northern Pike (*see* preceding figures). The telencephalon, or forebrain, mainly olfactory in function, in the Catfish, on the contrary, is better developed than in the above-mentioned species. For gustatory centers *see* Fig. 456. *Labeling: ch*, chiasma of optic nerves; *cerebell*, cerebellum; *infer lobes (hypoth)*, inferior lobes of hypothalamus; *med*, oblong medulla; *olftr*, olfactory tract; *optn*, optic nerve; *optlo (tect)*, optic lobe or tectum of mesencephalon; *telenceph*, telencephalon or forebrain.

row middle zone, entirely refractory to stain, to the inner segment, whose expanded outer end, which stains well, tapers into a very narrow, long, and fiber-like portion, entirely refractory to stain. The cones are small, with a short conical outer segment attached to a relatively large and well-staining middle segment, continuing into an unstained inner segment.

Both rods and cones, as is well known, exhibit lively and prompt photomechanical movements in opposite directions: the cones to-

of the rods, from 80 to 100. Computed for a circular area of the same diameter, the number of the cones was 11,000; that of the rods, 20,000 or more. While the number of rods is comparatively small and is compensated for by their large size, the number of the cones is quite respectable, when compared with other investigated species of fish: 2,800–3,000 of the Silverside; 1,500 of the Pike; and from 4,000 to 11,000 of the Trout. The number of the cones in the Bullhead's retina, however, expresses only a part of the role they may play in the visual act. This is indicated by the poor condition of the remaining layers of the retina.

The layers below the outer limiting membrane can be considered disorganized, in comparison with the well-developed and spatially well-organized ventral layers in sharp-sighted species, such as the Northern Pike, Trout, and even the Silverside. Of these layers, the best developed is the outer nuclear layer, which contains two or so rows of unevenly arranged nuclei. The outer plexiform layer is very thin and contains swollen lower ends of rods and cones. The inner nuclear layer cannot be well defined. Certain large, widely spaced polygonal cells are possibly the horizontal cells, whereas a row of rather large, darkly stained nuclei are probably those of the bipolar cells. Whether other large scattered cells are amacrines or displaced ganglions cannot be determined. The inner plexiform layer has the usual granular appearance but is much thinner than in other species. The ganglions are few, separated by long gaps. The layer of optic nerve fibers cannot be made out.

The optic nerve is thin, its diameter being 0.7 mm. The composing fibers are from 1.5 to 8 microns thick, with thicker ones predominating. The total number of fibers found is 15,000 or more. (Bruesch & Arey [1942] found 26,000; *see* chap. VI, 3 [4].)

In summary, the Bullhead's eyes and retina are poorly equipped to form anything but crude images and to analyze them in the crudest way. They are well equipped to react as a sensitive instrument of protopathic vision, responding to low intensities of light positively and to strong light negatively. But they can hardly mediate any but the crudest sort of spatial or epicritic vision, a defect which is to some extent compensated by their wide and overlapping fields of view. (*Cf.* Rochon-Duvigneaud 1925.)

6. NERVOUS SYSTEM.—The optic nerves are quite thin and flattened along part of their course. Because of the location of the eyes on the far periphery of the broad head, they are quite long (about 30 mm. in the same specimen). The optic lobes (*optlo* in Fig. 458) are absolutely and relatively small in comparison with those of a Pike of comparable size, each lobe amounting to about half the mass of one lobe of

the telencephalon, or the part of the brain in front of the optic lobes, mainly concerned with smell and locomotion. The taste centers, on the contrary, are inordinately developed, being represented by four round eminences on the upper face of the medulla oblongata, the anterior

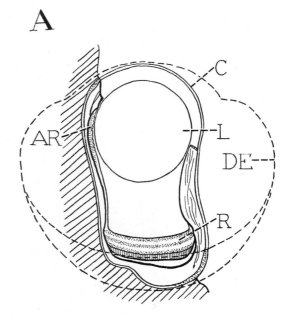

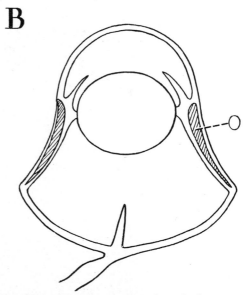

FIG. 459.—*A*, median section through the so-called telescopic eye of *Argyropelecus affinis*, an abyssal fish, drawn into an outline of a normal fish eye, to be compared with *B*, Owl's eye, somewhat similar in shape. *Labeling: AR*, accessory retina; *C*, cornea; *DE*, outline of a normal fish eye; *L*, lens; *O*, scleral ring; *R*, principal retina. Redrawn from R. Hesse & F. Doflein, *Tierbau und Tierleben*, v. 1, 1935.

being known as "facial lobes" (Fig. 456, *fl* in lower sketch).

7. BIOLOGY.—In summarizing the available information on the Bullhead, it is apparent that the anatomical organization of this fish agrees perfectly with its physiology and its behavior, and vice versa.

It is understandable that a fish which hides during the day close to the bottom of the water among the weeds and begins to forage for food only with the falling dusk is found to possess small and poorly developed eyes, degenerate retinae, thin optic nerves, and small visual centers in the brain. Sight is apparently an unimportant factor in the procurement of food. For this, the olfactory and gustatory senses are employed. These work efficiently even when a very small amount of light enters the water, either because of its depth or turbidity or because there is little light, during the night, for example, or on overcast days.

FIG. 460.—Charles Judson Herrick (1868), professor of neuroanatomy at the University of Chicago, at approximate age fifty-five. America's most assiduous student of the minute structure of the nervous system of the Primitive Vertebrates. A prolific writer on general biological and philosophical problems. Co-founder (with his brother Clarence Luther Herrick) of the Journal of Comparative Neurology. Courtesy Professor Charles J. Herrick, November 1, 1947. (For biography *see* Ariëns Kappers, Nederl. tijdschr. v. geneesk., v. 85, p. 1362, 1941.)

The Bullheads have renounced active competition with the photopic or daylight species. They retired into the darkness of the deeper reaches, where the superiority of sight of the diurnal predators is eliminated, precisely as it is in the upper layers of the water during the night. That, in doing so, they have chosen a less spectacular but nevertheless successful mode of life is proved by the fact that the representatives of the Bullhead tribe are found in every water, be it a broad river or an obscure

1928; C. Kohl 1892; Kolmer & Lauber 1936; Lagler 1949; La Gorce 1952; Le Danois 1949; Macan & Worthington 1951; A. H. Morgan 1930; H. Müller 1952; Needham *et al.* 1941; Needham & Lloyd 1937; Needham & Needham 1941; Nolte 1932; Norman 1936; Ovio 1927; Parker & Haswell 1940; Parker & Hensen 1917; D. Poggendorf 1952; Pütter 1908–12; P. Ramón y Cajal 1899; S. Ramón y Cajal 1892–93 (1933), 1894, 1909–11; C. D. Reeves 1919; Russell & Bull 1932; Sand 1935; Scheuring 1921; Schie-

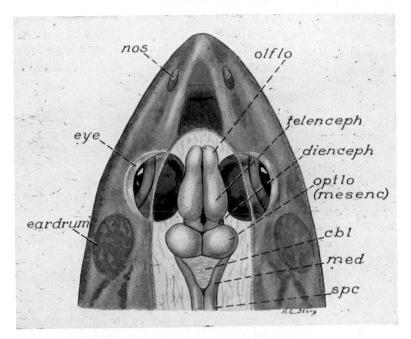

Fig. 461.—Head of a Meadow, or Leopard, Frog (*Rana pipiens*), with superficial parts dissected to show the brain and the eyes in their natural position. Note the size of the visual centers (*optlo*), which is approximately equal in mass to the telencephalon. Compare same structures in various species of Fish, in the Anole Lizard, and in the Painted Turtle. *Labeling: cbl*, cerebellum; *dienceph*, diencephalon or betweenbrain; *med*, oblong medulla; *nos*, nostril; *olflo*, olfactory lobe; *optlo (mesenc)*, optic lobe of mesencephalon or midbrain; *spc*, spinal cord; *telenceph*, telencephalon or forebrain.

creek, a large lake or a mudhole, within all inhabitable regions of the earth.

References: Birukow & Knoll 1952; A. Brehm's *Tierleben*, v. 3, 1914; Cable 1928; Carlander 1950; Charlton 1933; G. L. Clarke 1936; B. Curtis 1938; S. R. Detwiler; Eddy 1945; Eddy & Surber 1947; Erickson 1933; V. Franz 1934; K. von Frisch 1912, 1913, 1924; Gobrecht & Oertel 1953; W. Harms 1914; C. J. Herrick 1899, 1904, 1922, 1941; Hesse & Doflein 1935–43; Horio; Hubbs & Lagler 1949; Jarmer

menz 1924; Schiller 1934; Schnurmann 1920; Schrenkeisen 1938; Sumner 1940; A. Thienemann 1939; Tschermak 1945; Uexküll 1921; Verrier 1928, 1938, 1945; Verrier & Escher-Desrivières 1937; Walls 1942; Ward & Whipple 1918; L. H. Warner 1931; Welsh 1938; Welsh & Osborn 1937; Wesenberg-Lund 1939; C. D. Whitman 1899; R. W. Wood 1906; Wunder 1926, 1927. (*See also* references appended to section on Pike.)

SEC. 7. ANOLE OR "AMERICAN CHAMELEON"

1. TAXONOMY.—The Anolis or Anole is a small lizard, native of the southeastern region of the United States. It subsists on insects and possibly on other small animals it can catch. Because of its ability to change color, it is popularly known as the "American Chameleon," even though it belongs to the Family Iguanidae, characteristic of the Western Hemisphere, a subdivision quite different from the true Chameleons of Europe, Africa, and Asia, the Chamaeleontidae. As a type, the Carolina Anole (*Anolis carolinensis*), native of Louisiana, Florida, and other southern parts of the United States, is described in the following paragraphs (Figs. 462, 463, 464, 465).

2. CHARACTER AND HABITS.—The general appearance of the Anole Lizard and its anatomical equipment are similar to that of other Iguanidae. The average length, when fully grown, is from 5 to 6 inches. Its graceful build makes it admirably adapted to insect hunting, which contrasts with the more robust appearance and sluggish habits of its larger relatives of Central and South America.

Following are notes that portray the functional versatility of the visual apparatus and the behavior of the Anole, observed in captivity.

November 9, 1947, at 3:30 P.M. The day was overcast, the room warm. In the terrarium, whose floor was covered with sand and scattered twigs and leaves of a southern shrub, all seemed quiet. Only the eyes of one or another Anole moved from time to time in a jerky way.

The mobility of the eyes was amazing (Figs. 463, 464): each eye could be moved independently of the other eye, and again, on occasion, both eyes could be moved in unison as a team. According to a rough estimate, the maximum excursion of an eyeball in the vertical meridian was not less than 90°, in the horizontal meridian probably somewhat less.

Occasionally both eyes converged toward the same object in front of the head. In this case the visual axes of both eyes met in a common fixation point situated somewhere in front and not far from the snout. The convergence was facilitated by the two pigmented "sighting grooves" running on both sides of the head, each in continuation of the line of view of its own eye, passing below the nostril, duplicating the arrangement described in the Pike (sec. 4, this chapter).

The way an Anole feeds, particularly how it uses its eyes in feeding, is as follows: When hungry, it first sizes up one of the meal worms, then it moves toward it a little, and then in a flash it "shoots" at it and grabs it with its teeth. An insect, for example, a fly, is attacked even more speedily, if within reach. The fly, an alert creature, always intent on a quick getaway, is not always caught. The initial phase, a prelude to an attack, is an attentive eyeing of the fly, even if it is as much as a foot or more away. The appearance of a fly within "shooting range" does not always arouse action, the inattention being even more frequent in the case of the meal worms. This happens when the activity of the animals declines and they appear drowsy toward the close of the day.

The movements of the eyes in various situations are easily studied at close range. The separate or independent movements of each eyeball are especially apparent when the head is viewed directly from the front, since in this position both eyes are seen simultaneously. This situation is represented in the right lower sketch in Figure 463. In this position the occasional direction of both eyes toward the same object, which is viewed binocularly, becomes quite apparent. In this case the two corneae and pupils are not directed forward, as in the Primates, but at a slant of about 45°. Even so, owing to a refraction in the cornea and lens, the principal frontal pencil of light passes into the eyes in such a way as to meet the central foveae, which in this lizard are quite well developed.

On November 10, 1947, a large fly was put into the terrarium. Before long, possibly because of too great heat and stuffiness in the box, the fly crawled down the side, stopping here and there, and finally coming close to a group of the lizards. Several at once tried their luck, but missed. Finally, a daring half-grown Anole launched a straight attack, shooting like an arrow, and in a split second the fly was caught, chewed up, and swallowed.

The alertness of the lizards when watching

the fly contrasted remarkably with their almost complete indifference to a number of fat meal worms crawling about in a small Petri dish in the terrarium. Hence it appears that the flies and similar moving insects probably represent the "adequate stimulus," which is wholly visual, and are the principal food.

November 17, 1947. A fresh package of

since they had been captured and shipped from Louisiana.

First they were given plenty of water in a flat dish (which they mostly disregarded), and more water was sprinkled over the leaves of a native shrub with which they arrived. They at once began eagerly to lick the moisture from the leaves with their tongues, and after a while

Fig. 462.—Anole Lizard, or American Chameleon (*Anolis carolinensis*), a native of southeastern United States. A representative of the Iguanid Family (Iguanidae), characteristic of the Western Hemisphere. Member of the Genus Anolis, largest, most complex, and most widely distributed of the genera on this side of the globe, according to H. M. Smith (1946). A small, vivacious, alert, and intelligent Lizard of strictly diurnal and arboreal habit. An excellent climber, keen of sight, distinguished for its ability to change color under the influence of its eyes and nerves (hence its popular name "Chameleon," even though it is not related to the true Chameleons or Chamaeleontidae of Asia, Africa, and Madagascar). Anole is remarkable because of the extraordinary mobility and versatility of its eye movements, matching in this respect, and perhaps exceeding, the true Chameleons. Compare the following two figures showing Anole's ability to use each eye independently or both eyes together in a binocular visual act, as the situation requires. (*Cf. also* section on Barn Swallow.)

Anoles arrived to be used as food for the Tarsiers, described subsequently in this chapter. The animals appeared dejected, dazed, skinny, emaciated. Evidently they had been neither fed nor watered during the many hours

seemed to be in better condition. Then half-a-dozen rather small meal worms were placed in a dish on the floor of the terrarium. For some time these also remained unnoticed.

Before long, however, possibly by accident,

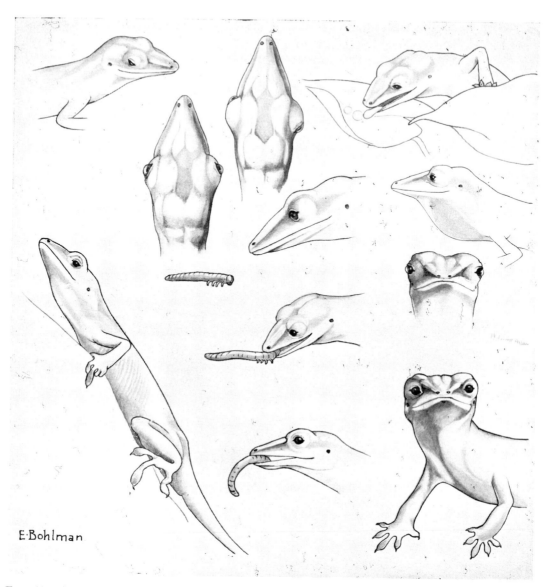

E·Bohlman

Fɪɢ. 463.—A composite figure of the Anole Lizard or American Chameleon, showing the use of visual apparatus (*see* preceding and following figures). *Upper left corner:* watching with its right eye a meal worm approaching from behind; *upper right corner:* lapping drops of water from a plant leaf, eyes directed forward; *upper center:* two views of the head from above, left view with both eyes directed laterally and slightly anteriorly ("normal" or "rest" position), right view watching other lizards, with left eye turned straight forward, and right eye turned backward; *center:* three views, upper fixing and evaluating a meal worm, middle seizing it and fixing it with both eyes, lower eating it, with eyes in an indifferent position; *lower left corner:* quiet siesta on a leaf, with left eye observing the artist; *upper right center:* expressing anger or fear, with a chin-lap, orange-red in color, expanded, as before a fight with another of its kind, with eyes attentively observing; *right middle center facing observer:* alert, watching a fly buzzing in the cage, both eyes only slightly converged (indicating use of its panoramic vision); *right lower corner:* intently watching a fly crawling on the glass pane directly between lizard and the observer, with both eyes glued on the prospective meal just before leaping to catch it (binocular stereoscopic vision). Note in last two views, pigmented "sighting grooves" converging toward the point of muzzle and nostrils, useful in binocular stereoscopic vision (*cf.* section on Pike, and Figs. 450, 451). Observed and drawn by Esther Bohlman.

or rather driven by hunger, one of the smaller Anoles cautiously sneaked toward the dish filled with unaccustomed food. After some time it finally took cognizance of the worms crawling in the dish. It slowly turned its head toward one of them and made a halfhearted attempt to nibble at it, without seizing it. Then, as if making up its mind, it resolutely tried again and seized one meal worm with its mouth. Little by little, as the Anole chewed, the worm disappeared, the deglutition movement along its throat being clearly visible. This done, possibly after 10 seconds or so, the little Anole again turned its head toward another meal worm. This time there was a shorter period of hesitation before another worm was seized, chewed up, and swallowed. Before long, a third worm was also eaten in the same way. The appetite of the little glutton seemed to grow as the feast progressed, as if to illustrate the well-known proverb. The remaining worms were devoured in the same way before the lapse of as many minutes.

This observation revealed the Anoles to be different from what one would expect from their appearance on arrival. They were not delicate and meek little animals, but voracious miniature monsters, well representing their Jurassic and Cretaceous forefathers that once held sway over the earth, and against which the humble ancestors of Mammals had to struggle to save themselves from extinction. (*See* sections on Common Shrew and on Tree Shrew, secs. 9, 10, this chapter.)

3. Eye, retina, and the visual centers of the brain.—The eyeballs of the Anole are noteworthy because of their relatively large size and great mobility. In this, as in their finer structure and use, they show a degree of perfection rarely matched and hardly ever exceeded among the Lizards and among other Vertebrates, not excluding the true Chameleons, Birds, and Primates.

The diameter of the eyeball of a fair-sized adult specimen is 5 mm., or about $\frac{1}{5}$ inch. Small as this is, however, it amounts to one-fifth of the human eyeball. The two eyes together in such a small animal make up almost the entire width of the head, which measures about 12 mm. or $\frac{1}{2}$ inch across. (*See* Figs. 463, 464.)

Each eye is provided with a relatively deep and spacious central fovea. The diameter of the foveal excavation in a large specimen measures from 0.6 to 0.7 mm., which is half the foveal diameter of the much larger human eye. In other structures—the photoreceptors, bipolars, and ganglion cells—the eye of the Anole, in spite of its small size and because of its delicate build, is also capable of forming sharp images, of analyzing them, and of conveying them to the brain. Hence the eyes and the remainder of the Anole's visual system serve the species excellently as a refined instrument of sharp sight and stereopsis. (*Cf.* Rochon-Duvigneaud 1925.)

The examination of several series of sections of the retina and of the brain of the Anole stained with modified Golgi stain (*see* Technical Note at beginning of book) shows the extraordinary complexity and perfection of these organs, approaching in this respect the delicate organization described in Insects by S. Ramón y Cajal and Sánchez. Prolonged investigation would be required to do full justice to this absorbing subject. The following few observations must, therefore, suffice here.

The photoreceptor layer is made up of both rods and cones. In the extrafoveal periphery the individual cones are from $2\frac{1}{2}$ to $3\frac{1}{2}$ microns thick, their intercenter distances measuring 7 microns. At a distance of 350 microns from the foveal center, the cones decrease to a diameter of from $1\frac{1}{2}$ to 2 microns, their intercenter distance diminishing to from $3\frac{1}{2}$ to 4 microns.

The rods in this locality have a diameter of 1 micron or less and are few in number. From a point 280–300 microns from the very center, the rods are entirely absent. The rodless central territory, accordingly, measures no less than from 560 to 600 microns, which is equal to the diameter of the human central rodless area. (*See* chap. V, 10 [5].)

At a distance of 250 microns from the center, the cones are $1\frac{1}{2}$ microns thick, and their intercenter distance is from 3 to $3\frac{1}{2}$ microns. The closest cones to the center which could be measured were $1\frac{1}{2}$ microns thick, but these were still 150 microns away from the very center. The cones in the very center which were measured had a thickness of less than 1 micron. In refinement the cone apparatus of the Anole's retina appears to be as good as the human, if not better. (*Cf.* chap. V, 10 [5].)

The remainder of the retina of the Anole is equal in refinement to its photoreceptors. The central area is conspicuous because of the great accumulation of nerve cells in layers *4, 6,* and *8.* In the ganglion layer there are several tiers, which in the central fovea gradually decrease to four, three, two, and one tier, and in the very center, measuring about 240 microns in diameter, they disappear entirely.

There are several varieties of ganglion cells, with bodies 10 microns in diameter or less. Their delicate dendritic arborizations spread along several horizontal lines noticeable in routinely stained preparations in the inner plexiform layer. These lines indicate synapses with the lower ends of the bipolar cells. The upper delicate expansions of the bipolar cells in turn spread in the upper plexiform layer, measuring hardly 3–4 microns across. The bipolars are apparently present in several varieties whose exact classification and functional interpretation require further study.

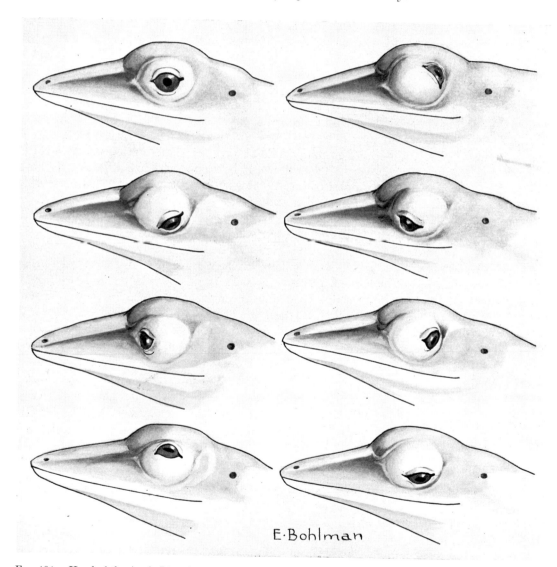

E·Bohlman

FIG. 464.—Head of the Anole Lizard or American Chameleon in left profile, approximately 3× magnified, showing relatively large eyes, their extreme mobility and the extent of their movements. Beginning with the upper left corner and terminating with the lower right corner: looking at the observer, looking down and backward, looking straight ahead as in binocular vision, looking upward, looking back and up, looking forward and down, looking straight back, looking down. Observed and drawn by Esther Bohlman. (*Cf.* preceding figure.)

The structures making up the brain are also extremely complex, delicate, and unbelievably abundant in detail. This subject may easily supply material enough to fill a series of papers matching the life-work of Santiago and Pedro Ramón y Cajal and of C. J. Herrick. Figure 465 gives magnified views of the brain of the Anole, showing the large optic lobes found in this species.

4. PHYSIOLOGICAL CONSIDERATIONS.—In the life of the Anole Lizard, primarily in the pro-

pages is its ability to use either each eye independently or both eyes together as a binocular stereoptic team in essentially the same way as do the Higher Mammals, particularly the Primates. Whereas the visual stereopsis in visually advanced Fishes, such as the Trout and Pike, was disclosed by circumstantial evidence such as the anatomical structures and organization of the visual apparatus, in the Anole the facultative binocular use of the eyes could actually be observed at work. This brings closer to our understanding the basic importance of the bin-

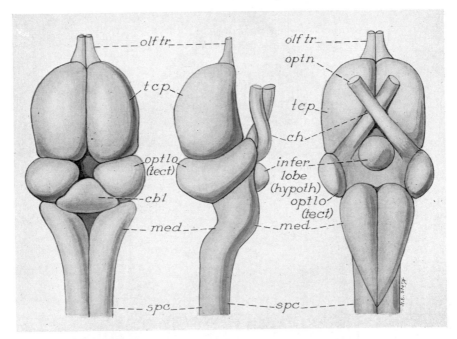

FIG. 465.—Brain of the Caroline Anole or American Chameleon, possessing a versatile visual apparatus and a large central fovea instrumental in acute vision (*cf.* preceding figures). The optic lobes of the brain are well developed, and the completely crossed optic nerves are thick. The forebrain (*tcp*), as in all Lizards, is much increased in size, in comparison with phylogenetically lower classes, the Fishes and Amphibians (*see* figures of Bluegill Sunfish, Northern Pike, and Meadow Frog). The olfactory tracts, however, are thin, owing to the lesser biological importance of the sense of smell in this pronounced diurnal visual species. *Labeling: cbl*, cerebellum; *ch*, chiasma of optic nerves; *infer lobe* (*hypoth*), inferior lobe of hypothalamus; *med*, oblong medulla; *olftr*, olfactory tract; *optlo* (*tect*), optic lobe or midbrain tectum; *optn*, optic nerve; *spc*, spinal cord; *tcp*, telencephalon or forebrain. Magnification 9 ×.

curement of food, the sense of vision and the visual apparatus appear dominant, almost to the exclusion of the other distance receptors, smell and hearing. Just what particular role each of these two senses plays in the acquisition of food and of mates, in the avoidance of enemies, and in other ways remains a task for further investigation.

The principal phenomenon observed in the behavior of the Anole described in the preceding

ocular team in all advanced animals, and especially the Vertebrate Phylum and the Prevertebrate Ancestors which preceded it (*see* chap. XIII, 2). The importance of stereopsis, at least as a facultative arrangement, already found in the Reptiles, phylogenetically midway between the lowest vertebrate class, the Fishes, and the highest class, the Mammals, is thus demonstrated.

In the Anole, however, the binocular use of

the two eyes is apparently resorted to only when needed. At other times each eye is used independently; or, if used as a part of the team, it is not necessarily in the stereoptic sense. We may, then, tentatively until further and more thorough investigation of this problem is carried out, indicate three particular uses of the two eyes in an Anole and many other Lizards.

First would be a static use of both eyes as constituents of a panoramic system, with both

The second is the employment of each eye as an independent instrument, not related functionally to the other eye. This use is obviously of a higher order, since it presupposes a structural differentiation of a particular locality capable of a finer, more detailed resolution of the optical image of the retina. Mobility of the eye makes sense only when there is a differentiated area or fovea to be directed at a viewed object of particular interest.

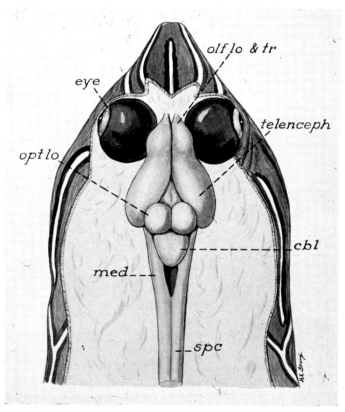

Fig. 466.—Head of a Painted Turtle (*Chrysemis picta*), with upper parts dissected to show the brain and the eyes in their natural position. The optic lobes are well developed but are much smaller in comparison with the much increased forebrain (*telenceph*). (*Cf.* preceding figures.) *Labeling: cbl*, cerebellum; *med*, oblong medulla; *olflo & tr*, olfactory lobe and tract; *optlo*, optic lobe; *spc*, spinal cord; *telenceph*, telencephalon or forebrain. Magnification 2.5×·

eyes functionally interrelated in a stable way, in which the two monocular fields of view do not overlap or do so only a little or are perhaps separated by an interocular gap. This produces basically panoramic vision. Its advantage is its wide scope or extent, which in certain situations or species may amount practically to a complete circle, or, in fact, to a complete sphere. The advantage of this arrangement is obvious: it permits the animal to notice any object that may concern it anywhere in its surroundings.

The third use requires both a basically panoramic adjustment of the two single eyes to each other and a differentiation of areal or foveal vision, the first serving as a binocular functional background upon which the refined binocular stereoscopic areal and foveal vision are superimposed.

The advantage of this third use of the eyes is not only a wide scope of panoramic vision and a refinement of areal or foveal vision but, in addition, the working of both eyes, including both areae or foveae, as a single functional team directed at a common viewed object. This is the anatomical and functional basis of stereopsis or single tridimensional vision, in so far as the peripheral organs, the eyes and their mechanics, are concerned. That this is not the entire story of stereopsis and that, in addition to these peripheral arrangements, the central factor or factors play an essential role is probable and is further discussed in several places in this book.

In the visual apparatus of an Anole, all three potentialities are skilfully realized. This apparatus permits the animal to employ at will, according to the situation, any of these three uses. Concretely, when the animal is at rest, with its visual apparatus relaxed, both eyes look in opposite directions, giving it a wide panoramic vision. Any stirring of a small object, such as a fly or a bug, or the appearance of a potential enemy, whether on the right or the left side or above, will be noticed. This is but the first phase in a process of satisfying the biological service which the visual apparatus has to render, which is to acquire food and avoid destruction.

The next step is to locate the object of attention. This is done by searching movements of one eye, that facing the object. The fly must be exactly located. This task is performed by the superior resolution of the areal-foveal vision. This is essentially an epicritic or visuo-gnosic performance. In it the entire visual mechanism of the particular side participates: the visuomotor directing the eyeball; the visuosensory controlling the retinal receptor surface in the desired position, where the foveal center corresponds exactly with the tested object, while the crude protopathic periphery "holds" it like a ring or a vise. The third and final phase consists of the employment of the visuo-gnosic substratum of the brain, which evaluates the impulses according to phylogenetically and individually acquired standards, requiring further action, if positive, and disregarding it, if negative.

If the "adequate" physiobiological impulse initiates further trains of action, the chain of events may be as follows: while the active eye fixes the prospective prey, the contralateral eye is now likewise set in motion, the motor machinery adjusting the head, possibly including also a part or all of the body, for the final action. The task of the other eye is to add that component of the subjective visual experience that underlies stereopsis or the "third dimension." This added quality, obviously, is of great importance for success, since it is paramount in estimating distance; for this a single eye, capable only of judging the two-dimensional or projectional location of the prospective prey, would be an inferior instrument.

Once the "third dimension" or distance is determined, the impetus is given to the entire locomotor machinery of the animal for the execution of the attack and the capture of the prey. The fulfilment of this depends on the balanced co-ordination and speed of all parts concerned. In this concluding act, one may judge, the visual apparatus also plays an important role as a controller of the organs of execution.

The various parts of the central co-ordinating machinery in Lizards and other Lower Vertebrates are known only in a descriptive way. So far, only a few attempts have been made to analyze it and to interpret it functionally, e.g., by Santiago and Pedro Ramón y Cajal, Coghill, C. J. Herrick, Ariëns Kappers, and some other investigators. For the most part, this problem still awaits solution.

5. The CHAMELEON AND ITS EYE.—It is here appropriate to give a brief summary of Rochon-Duvigneaud's description of the visual apparatus of the Old World Chameleon, an animal that has attracted much attention since ancient times. (*See* Ann. d'ocul., v. 170, 1933.) Even though taxonomically not closely related, the true Chameleon of Europe, Africa, and India, in its anatomical equipment and physiological performance, closely resembles the American Anole, its New World counterpart.

The Chameleon, according to M. F. Angel, in *La Terre et la Vie* (1931), summarized from Rochon-Duvigneaud, is an animal which avoids light. It does not like sunshine, especially when the temperature is high. It lives mostly in dense tropical forests of Africa, where the light is quite subdued by the foliage, with moderately elevated temperature and the necessary humidity. This is its ideal habitat, in which its coloring is most brilliant. (For an excellent account of the Chameleon's life *see also* Brehm's *Tierleben*, v. 5, 1913.)

According to Rochon-Duvigneaud's investigation, the Chameleon has a deep fovea (also studied by S. Ramón y Cajal and others). Its field of view is probably restricted, owing to a small cornea and retina, which is perhaps the reason for the unusual mobility of its eyes.

other. The eye movements appear to be volitional and not of a reflex nature. In their movements ordinarily "they are neither synchronous nor symmetrical, each eye moving on its own account, exploring its own space independently." A synchronous asymmetric movement is possible, however, with one eye moving forward and the other backward (*see* sketch in

Fig. 467.—Cornelius Ubbo Ariëns Kappers (1877–1946), director of the Institute for Brain Research in Amsterdam, Netherlands, at the age of sixty-three. One of the foremost modern comparative neuroanatomists (*cf.* Edinger, Fig. 446, and Herrick, Fig. 460). Author of *The Comparative Anatomy of the Nervous System of Vertebrates*, 2d ed., enlarged and edited by G. Carl Huber & Elizabeth Caroline Crosby, 1936. (For biography *see* Psychiat. en neurol. bl., v. 38, p. 265, 1934, and Haymaker & Baer, *The Founders of Neurology*, 1953.)

"The Chameleon's retina is, in a sense, reduced to an extremely developed central fovea." The compass of its eye movements in the horizontal plane amounts to 180°, in the vertical meridian almost that (a little less upward than downward). One or the other of its eyes is constantly on the move, the eyes being independent of each

the upper center in Fig. 463). When a prospective prey is within 15–20 cm., that is, within shooting range, both eyes converge toward it, the mouth opens, and the fly disappears so quickly that the movements of the tongue are barely visible.

It is probable that the convergence of the

eyes is accompanied by accommodation and certainly by constriction of the pupils (the pupillary constrictor muscle being also partly responsible for accommodation, there being no pupillary light reflex). The Chameleon has, in Rochon-Duvigneaud's opinion, according to circumstances, either double monocular or panoramic vision or associated single binocular vision. In both, the central foveae are involved, a fact difficult to comprehend, in view of the diplopia present in human vision when the two foveae are not focused upon the same object.

The central fovea of a Chameleon, according to the quoted authority, is as deep as that of the Birds. In the foveal center the retina is 280 microns thick, in its next vicinity as much as 600 microns. The cones in the fovea are 100 microns long; outside the fovea, they are 140 microns long. The nuclei of the foveal cones are displaced laterally, so none are present in the very center. As in all diurnal Lizards, in the Chameleon all photoreceptors are cones (in this respect differing from the Anole). The cone cells and their oil globules are of a yellow color, which, apparently depending upon illumination, is either clear yellow or greenish. In the foveal center, even the bodies of the cone cells are yellow, the pigmentation being most intense here. The oil droplets are present also in the foveal center. The central region, where the cones are extremely thin, is quite extensive, the cone thickness increasing only gradually toward the extrafoveal periphery. This, in Rochon-Duvigneaud's opinion, makes it probable that the minute central territory in which the acuity

is highest is less pointlike than in Man. He estimated the diameter of the cones in the very center at less than 2 microns, in the extrafoveal periphery at 8 microns. (Compare much smaller values of the Anole and of the simian and human cones given in chap. V, 10 [5].)

References: F. Angel 1931; Ariëns Kappers, Huber & Crosby 1936; J. A. Armstrong 1950; Bagley & Langworthy 1926; Beccari 1943; Bellonci 1888; A. E. Brehm's *Tierleben*, 4th ed., v. 5; Clausen & Mofshin 1939; H. E. Colbert 1949; De Lange 1913; Del Duca 1930; Detwiler 1916, 1923, 1940, 1943; Detwiler & Laurens 1921; Detwiler & Lewis 1926; Ditmars 1935, 1946; Dursy (quoted in Brehm's *Tierleben*, v. 5, p. 231, 1913); Durward 1930; Ehrenhardt 1937; Engelhardt 1924; V. Franz 1913, 1934; Frederikse 1931; J. Gross 1903; W. Harris 1904; C. J. Herrick 1910, 1948; C. Hess 1910, 1912, 1913, 1914; Huber & Crosby 1926, 1933, 1934; G. L. Johnson 1927; Kahmann 1933, 1934; Klinkowström 1894; Kuroda 1923; Leblanc 1925; Milne & Milne 1948; Joh. Müller 1826; Noll 1935; Parker & Haswell 1940; Pope 1944; Pütter 1908–12; P. Ramón y Cajal 1890, 1891, 1894, 1896, 1897, 1917, 1923, 1943; S. Ramón y Cajal 1892–93 (1933), 1894, 1909–11; Rochon-Duvigneaud 1933, 1943; A. Sand 1935; Shanklin 1930, 1933; D. A. Simpson 1949; H. M. Smith 1946; W. B. Spencer 1887; Verrier 1930, 1932, 1933, 1935, 1938, 1940, 1945; H. Wagner 1932; Walls 1942; J. Warren 1910–11; Watkinson 1906; W. A. Willard 1915; S. W. Williston 1914; F. H. Wilson 1939; Wojtusiak 1933; Zoond & Bokenham 1935; Zoond & Eyre 1934.

SEC. 8. SWALLOW

1. TAXONOMY.—The common Barn Swallow (*Hirundo* or *Chelidon rustica erythrogastra*) is a small, insectivorous bird, entirely subsisting upon prey it catches in flight (Fig. 468). It and its cousin of the Old World, the Chimney Swallow (*Hirundo* or *Chelidon rustica*), in appearance and behavior are the most typical, even though they are among the smallest members of the Swallow Family (Hirundinidae) of the Order Passeres, and Suborder Oscines.

Other American representatives of the family are the well-known Purple Martin (*Progne subis purpurea:* see sec. 13, "Miscellaneous Notes," in this chapter), Cliff or Eave Swallow (*Petrocheli-* don *pyrrhonota albifrons*), Tree Swallow (*Iridoprocne bicolor*), Northern Violet-green Swallow (*Tachycineta thalassina lepida*), Bank Swallow (*Riparia riparia r.*), and the Rough-winged Swallow (*Stelgidopteryx ruficollis serripennis*). Their better-known counterparts of the Old World are the Cave Swallow of southern Europe and Africa (*Chelidon rufula*), Cliff or Rock Swallow (*Riparia rupestris*), and Town Swallow (*Hirundo urbica*). Numerous other species populate all habitable parts of the world.

2. CHARACTER.—The Barn Swallow is a highly specialized bird, living exclusively on

flying insects which it catches "on the wing." It is an excellent flier, better than its larger relative, the Purple Martin, though somewhat inferior to the still smaller masters of the air, the American Chimney Swift (*Chaetura pelagica*), the Cliff Swift (*Cypselus melba*), and the Common Swift or Black Martin (*Cypselus apus*) of the Old World, which, however, all belong to the Family Apodidae or Micropodidae (Order Macrochires, Suborder Cypseli).

In every part of its build the Barn Swallow shows a close adaptation to its peculiar mode of living. Its body is relatively light and slender; its pectoral muscles, the source of the power that moves its wings, are comparatively huge; the wings are long, narrow, and pointed; the tail well developed, its outside feathers longer than the middle ones, making up the typical forked "swallow tail"—all features considered characteristic of a good flier. The beak of the Barn Swallow is short and as wide as the head at the root, so that the aperture of the gullet is as spacious as possible in a bird of so small a size, facilitating the capture of prey. Altogether, the anatomical equipment of the Barn Swallow is admirably suited to its particular way of living. (*See* A. A. Allen, Nat. Geog. Mag., v. 93, p. 790, and his book *Stalking Birds with Color Camera*, 1951.)

3. HABITS.—The principal features of the Swallow's living habits have been well known since time immemorial. The reason is its close association with Man, its preference for human habitations, where it builds nests of mud, and no less its gentle nature, through which it endeared itself to the people, especially to the country folk (as, for example, in my native Croatia). Its excellence in flying is appreciated even by the casual observer.

Somewhat more detailed observation reveals that the Barn Swallow spends many minutes on the wing, with occasional brief periods of rest in between. Its flight is graceful, swift, and enduring. The beats of its long wings, alternating with sailing or gliding, carry its light weight with great speed. Obstacles, be they close to the ground, near the surface of the water, or high in the air, are expertly avoided.

Conspicuous in its flight are quick turns, which make it appear irregular and zigzagging.

This is understandable when one considers the purpose of the flight, which is the capture of flying insects. If the flight were along more or less straight lines, much of the prey would not be captured, even if noticed, because momentum would cause the bird to overshoot its goal. Quick, sudden turns are therefore indispensable.

How the Swallow does the trick remains a problem that has not yet been properly formulated in the minds of naturalists and aeronautical physicists and engineers. Nothing short of systematic investigation with modern technical means will solve this problem. For the time being, therefore, let it suffice to mention a few details gleaned from observation and such other facts as can be obtained from anatomy and from simple physiological tests. These indicate that the way the Swallow earns its living by means of its wings is a strenuous and complicated process.

Aside from the problem of keeping the body afloat in a medium specifically as light as air, the following questions require elucidation: determination of the leading sense by which the Swallow notices its prey; the way the leading sense reacts to the stimulus; and the way the body in general, and in particular the locomotor system, responds to make the capture of the prey a success.

4. FOOD.—Flying insects: Moths and Butterflies (Lepidoptera), Flies (Diptera), Beetles (Coleoptera), and Ant-Lions (Neuroptera) are the principal food source, evidently presenting an adequate visual stimulus, which promptly arouses the hunting instinct. The Bees and Wasps (Hymenoptera) armed with a sting, according to Brehm (O. zu Strassen), are shunned, but these and the Locusts are caught by other species of Swallows, e.g., by the Cliff Swallow, according to L. N. Nichols.

When I held in my hand a young Swallow that had never left its nest, it was alert enough to follow the insects flying around. When a big fly suddenly arrived and buzzed around, the bird made several snapping moves with the open beak in the direction of the fly, indicating the intention of catching it. This was particularly noteworthy, as only one eye was used, the other apparently having been hurt during a lengthy transportation on the preceding day.

Fig. 468.—Barn Swallow (*Hirundo* or *Chelidon rustica erythrogastra*), one of the smallest and swiftest flyers of the Northern Hemisphere. Its visual apparatus, little known as yet, is marvelously developed, its sight among the best among Vertebrates. Composite plate from A. Brehm (1913), H. Harrison (1948), and others, showing an adult bird perching and in flight and various views of its physiognomy, also a nest full of young, with an adult bird clinging to the nest. (*Cf.* Figs. 469, 470.)

5. SENSE OF SIGHT.—The observation of the behavior of the Barn Swallow in nature, as well as its anatomical organization, speaks in favor of the sight as the most important, if possibly not the only, sense used.

The Barn Swallow and its relatives are diurnal animals in the sense that their activity extends throughout the light period of the day. However, they are early risers, and toward the close of the day they hunt in the evening twilight, when their twitter is still heard, while to the human eye they are almost invisible. In their intensive preoccupation with insect hunting, they remain aloft until the falling night forces them to depart, when their place is taken by their mammalian counterparts, the small, insectivorous Flying Bats (Microchiroptera).

Whether hearing and possibly smell are of any use in their hunting is not known. If this were the case, especially with hearing, it would not be astonishing, in view of the known role that audition plays in the life of the Bats and, according to Kellogg & Kohler (1952), of the Porpoises.

The available evidence favors the view that the overwhelming, almost exclusive, share in the biology of the Barn Swallow belongs to vision, while other senses play a subordinate role. The diurnality of the Swallows is also attested by the fact that they move on their annual migrations only during daylight and rest at night.

6. EYE MOVEMENTS.—In the living bird the expression of its "physiognomy" indicates a visually alert, intelligent animal. The nictitating membranes of both eyes contract either simultaneously or separately in quick moves. The pupil is of an elliptical shape, with the long axis almost vertical to the palpebral fissure. When the lids are shut, it is chiefly the lower one that covers the cornea.

When the bird is at rest, either the one or the other eye makes short, jerky motions from time to time. These are interspersed at irregular intervals with more extensive scanning movements, as if trying to fixate various visual objects. The lids, principally the lower ones, in quick winking moves, shut the eyes alternately.

Occasionally both eyes make a similar quick movement, both simultaneously converging upon a single fixation point in front of the beak. Such movements are either short and jerky or extensive, proportionately not less than in Man, amounting in the horizontal plane to at least 30°.

Such eye movements may or may not be associated with short, synchronous, ipsidirectional movements of the head. Again, the head alone may move spontaneously to the right or to the left, apparently without eye movements. On occasion, both eyes execute a quick simultaneous move toward the beak, definitely converging upon a single binocular visual object or fixation point. At other times similar movements toward the beak are made by only one eye.

When an object comes into view, that particular eye makes a quick move to fixate it, with the opposite eye remaining still. When an object that has been in view for some time is removed, that eye likewise makes a quick move as if to follow it. When the eye fixates an object turning quickly toward it, its pupil contracts, the movement of the iris apparently accompanying the accommodation (as in binocular fixation in human vision).

Unilateral fixation by one eye is often accompanied by one or two minute, jerky, ipsidirectional movements of the head, as if to assist the fixation. When the bird is drowsy, the eye in shade, away from the light, is kept shut, or its palpebral fissure is narrowed, with the other eye half-opened, executing slight exploratory moves, some definitely toward the beak, similar to those visible during binocular fixation. When after a period of dozing, the bird awakens, both palpebral fissures are suddenly opened wide, and the eyes for a while make scanning movements. These are mostly in the horizontal plane, but less extensive movements up and down as well as in any other meridian are also possible.

The two eyes of the Barn Swallow are normally placed in the head in such a way as to permit the observer viewing them from straight in front to see most of both corneae and of both pupils (Fig. 468, right upper sketch). When a visual object is offered to the bird from the front in the mid-sagittal plane, both eyes sometimes turn toward it in unison, converging upon it. Again, after a while, with the relaxation of the convergence upon the binocular fixation point, a definite diverging movement of the two eyes toward the initial, resting "normal" position is noticed. When an object, e.g., a hand with still or wiggling fingers moves rapidly in front of the beak at an approximate distance of from 6 to 8 inches from side to side in the horizontal plane, both eyes converge upon it and

the bird tries to keep the stimulating visual object in its binocular fixation point, may be elicited a dozen or more times in succession. Similar binocular eye movements, accompanied by the synchronous ipsidirectional head movements, may be induced not only in the horizontal plane but also in the vertical and in any other inter-

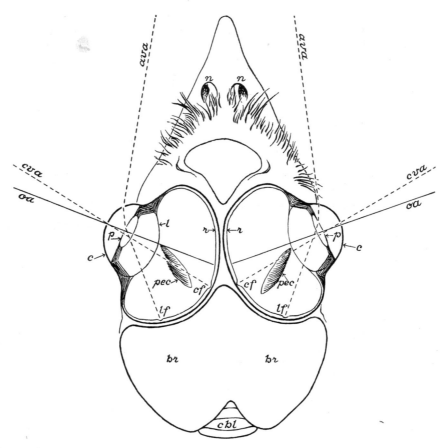

Fig. 469.—Horizontal section through the head of a Barn Swallow, with eyes and their dioptrical apparatus left in place. In each eye there are two foveae, a central, nasal or anterior (*cf*) and a lateral, temporal or posterior fovea (*lf*). A central visual axis (*cva*) incloses with the optic axis (*oa*) an angle smaller than that inclosed by the anterior or frontal axis (*ava*). The central axes of both eyes diverge from each other, forming an obtuse angle facing anteriorly; the two anterior or frontal axes, when the eyes are at rest, converge toward a common fixation point at some distance in front of the beak. This angle can be changed at will by the bird, making possible focusing at different distances when both eyes are used as instruments in binocular stereoscopic vision. In this, the two lateral foveae are used simultaneously, precisely as in human vision. However, the Swallow is also able to use each eye independently when it wishes, focusing objects with one central fovea alone, leaving the other eye at rest, exactly as does the Anole Lizard, a functional flexibility superior to that of Man and other Primates. Note considerable distance between the points at which the two anterior visual axes hit the cornea of the eyes in so small an animal. Figure drawn at 6.7×, reproduced at 4×. *Labeling: br*, brain; *c*, cornea; *cbl*, cerebellum; *l*, lens; *n*, nostrils; *p*, pupil; *pec*, pecten or "comb"; *r*, retina. (*Cf.* Figs. 468, 470.)

follow it regularly and in unison from right to left and back again.

The eye movements are automatically associated with the synchronous ipsidirectional movements of the head. These movements, by which

mediate planes or meridians as well, depending on the movements of the visual object.

The fixation movements up and down are executed principally with the head, assisted only a little by corresponding movements of the eyes. The associated eye and head movements in the horizontal plane may amount to from 30° to 40° and possibly more but are usually less (depending on the movement of the stimulating object).

7. PUPILLARY MOVEMENT.—When the bird is at rest, it shows lively spontaneous pupillary movements. Tests for direct pupillary light reaction show that the pupil responds very promptly to the stimulus, much faster than the

The nictitating membrane normally closes at irregular intervals of from 2 to 5 seconds, either simultaneously on both sides or, more often, on each side independently. The membrane does not close when the pupil constricts on light stimulation, except accidentally.

8. THE EYEBALL.—In agreement with the practically exclusive dependence of the Barn Swallow upon its sight is the relatively extraordinary development of its eyes (Rochon-Duvi-

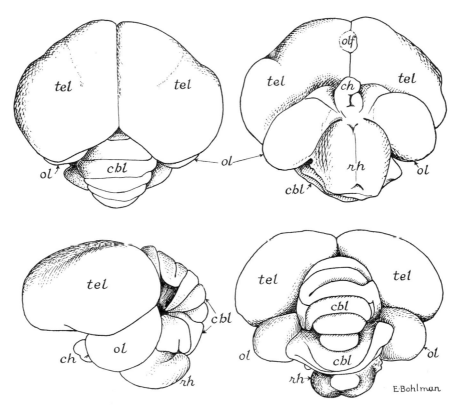

FIG. 470.—Brain of a Barn Swallow viewed from above (*upper left*), below (*upper right*), from the side (*lower left*), and from the rear (*lower right*). Drawn 9×, reproduced 5× magnified. Note relatively large size of optic lobes. *Labeling: cbl*, cerebellum; *ch*, chiasma of optic nerves; *ol*, optic lobes; *olf*, olfactory bulbs; *rh*, rhombencephalon or oblong medulla; *tel*, telencephalon. (*Cf.* Figs. 468, 469.)

human pupil does. A consensual reaction of the pupil on the side opposite to the eye stimulated by direct light, however, was not noticed. The pupils are regularly constricted whenever the bird makes an attempt to fixate an object binocularly and to follow its motions by corresponding movements of the head. Sometimes the pupil remains wide open, even though light falls into it after shading it off, as if kept open by a volitional inhibitory impulse.

gneaud [1943] calls them a model of structural and functional refinement).

The eyeballs of an almost fully grown young bird ready to leave the nest measure in diameter, in the vertical meridian, 7.5 mm. The central visual axis is approximately 7 mm. long, the temporal or lateral axis 7.5–8 mm. Each eyeball approximates in size one cerebral hemisphere (Fig. 469; *cf. also* Fig. 470).

The eyeballs are placed very close together,

back-to-back, almost touching in the mid-line, the central foveae being less than 4 mm. apart. The distance between the two lateral foveae is greater, amounting to 8.7 mm. However, the poles or summits of the two corneae are no less than 15.5 mm. from each other, a respectable distance in so small an animal. (For comparison, the interpupillary distance in Man measures about 60 mm.)

The two central lines of vision or central visual axes (*cva*), lines passing through the summits of the corneae and the central foveae (*cf*), diverge considerably, inclosing an angle of about 120° or somewhat more. Also the central visual axis (*cva*) diverges considerably more from the optical axis (*oa*), the line of rotation symmetry of the optical surfaces of the cornea and the lens, than in the human eye, the angle inclosed by them amounting to from 13° to 15°.

The two anterior or frontal lines of vision or visual axes (*ava*), lines connecting each lateral or posterior fovea (*lf*) with the anterior or nasal margin of the iris in the pupillary aperture, in a fixed specimen are approximately parallel. Slight nasal deflection of the two eyeballs, owing to their great mobility, as in the act of convergence, as described before, therefore, may suffice to make the anterior visual axes meet in a single common fixation point in front of the beak.

Such binocular convergence and fixation are further assisted in several ways. One is the position of the corneae, which face, as in the half-profile, in the anterolateral direction, conforming with the position of the central visual axes, each of which in a fixed specimen incloses, with the mid-sagittal plane, an angle of approximately 70°, or, together, 140°. The other factor is a slight distortion of the corneal curvature similar to the "anterior bulge" of the Fishes, because of which the more sharply curved anterior segment of the cornea is more favorable to the passage of rays coming from the direction of the beak. (*Cf.* sec. 4, on Pike.)

The visual behavior and anatomical arrangements of the Swallow described in the preceding paragraphs indicate the use of the lateral or posterior foveae for the simultaneous fixation of single visual objects necessary for binocular stereopsis, similar to that of Man and other Primates. In this respect the visual apparatus

of the Swallow is comparable with that of the Birds of Prey (such as the Eagle, Hawk, Falcon), Gull, Cormorant, Crow, Raven, Pelican, and some Parrots (see M. Bartels). It differs from other Birds, for example, Sparrows and Pigeons, whose eyes face more laterally and have no lateral or posterior fovea.

The Swifts and the Owls represent a further step in the development of binocularity, with the exclusive employment of the lateral foveae used binocularly and an abandonment of the central foveae instrumental in single, monocular vision. (On eye movements in various Birds, *see* Bartels 1920, 1931.)

9. Cornea, lens, sclera, and retina.—The cornea of the Swallow in comparison with the size of the eye is small, its diameter being only 4 mm. It is strongly curved, its radius of curvature being 1.5 mm., and it represents about half a sphere, with perhaps a slight anterior "bulge." The crystalline lens is relatively large. The scleral ring with the bulging cornea fitted into it, the small, hemispherical cornea asymmetrically deflected in the direction of the beak, the presence of two foveae in each eye—all make the eye of a Barn Swallow resemble the "telescopic" eyes of the Diurnal Birds of Prey (Eagle, Hawk, etc.).

The retina lines the much larger posterior portion of the eye, amounting to somewhat more than half the corresponding sphere. It is remarkable because of its regular structure. Its histological elements—photoreceptors, nuclear and ganglion layers, and the two plexiform layers—are very even in their outlines.

The pigment layer is rather thin but is dense in its structure. The outer segments of the photoreceptors in the examined specimen are mostly enveloped by the pigment. There are indications of photomechanical changes which depend on the condition of illumination.

The bacillary layer is very regular in its structure. It is apparently made up of both rods and cones in the entire expanse of the retina, including both foveal depressions. In the central fovea, however, the cones seem to prevail.

The outer nuclear layer contains both rod and cone nuclei in the entire retinal expanse, including both foveae. The cone nuclei are larger, elliptical in shape, with longer axes vertical to the outer limiting membrane. They form one continuous, thickly packed tier, close to the outer limiting membrane, increasing to two tiers in the central area and to three tiers in the central fovea. The spherical rod nuclei, which in mass seem paler but, in fact, are darker, are found in three or more tiers, except in the floor of the central fovea, where they appear to be in only one or two tiers.

The outer plexiform layer is relatively thick.

In routinely stained preparations it appears finely granulated. In Golgi preparations it is very accurately differentiated into three subzones, zone *5-b* being formed by filamentous cone pedicles and rod spherules.

The inner nuclear layer is remarkable because of its regularity and other features. The general arrangement of nuclei is in oblique columns, slanting from the central fovea away and down toward the inner plexiform layer. This

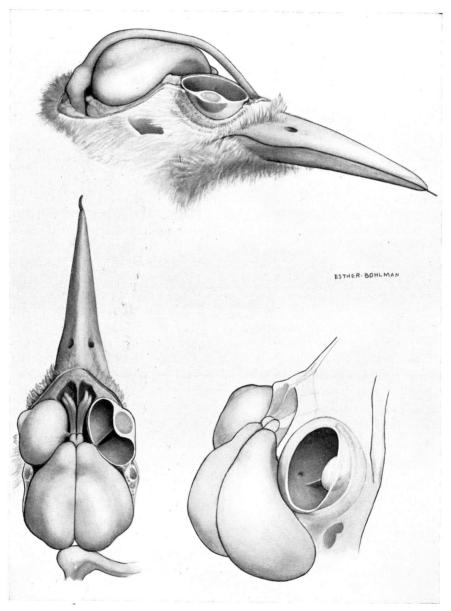

ESTHER·BOHLMAN

Fig. 471.—Flicker (*Colaptes auratus*), a pretty-colored, sharp-sighted member of the Family Picidae or Woodpeckers. This figure shows the dissected head in various views: *above*, lateral aspect; *left*, view from above; *right*, half-profile. Note the central fovea, a small dimple next to the upper margin of the pecten, visible in the right eye, whose upper segment was removed.

Fig. 472.—Yellow-billed Cuckoo (*Coccyzus americanus*), a sharp-sighted insectivorous bird of high intelligence, living in thickets and dense groves of eastern and middle North America. The plate portrays various views, including slightly magnified closeups of the left eye. *Left upper corner:* examining new items of food, using binocular vision; *upper center:* fixing down an object with left eye without moving head; *right upper corner:* looking backward with both eyes at a source of unexpected noise, before turning around; *just above artist's signature:* with both eyes at rest while taking a bit chilly, though comfortable, siesta after a rather soaking bath; *left center:* playing with a piece of art-gum eraser given it to observe the use of its stringlike tongue in "manipulating." Lower two rows show the left eye, beginning at the left end of the first row: expression of fear; looking up to satisfy its curiosity; looking slightly down at food when not very hungry; looking forward, using binocular vision, at a slowly moving meal worm; interest without fear; unaccounted for, probably rather indifferent; nictitating membrane drawn over cornea while killing a wiggling meal worm, this being done by running it repeatedly crosswise between its mandibles in a sort of chewing movement; slightly squinting or reducing the palpebral fissure in an affectionate mood (same observed in a Blue Jay). Observations and drawings by Esther Bohlman. Note remarkable versatility of ocular movements, depending on situation, in this bird that possesses a well-developed central fovea.

arrangement is evidently caused by the slanting bipolar cells and supporting "radial fibers" of Müller, typical of the avian retina. (*See* S. Ramón y Cajal on the fovea of Birds, in his book 1909–11, or in Trav. du lab. de recherches biol. Madrid, v. 28, Pl. VI, Fig. 16.)

The other and also quite apparent feature is the segregation of the inner nuclei into parallel zones, more conspicuous in the Swallow than in other investigated species. The nuclei of the upper and slightly thicker half are markedly different from those of the lesser vitreal half. The first are somewhat smaller and darker, while the latter are a little larger, spherical, paler, and less closely packed. This difference indicates here, as in the outer nuclear layer, a segregation of various bipolar types from one another, possibly the individual midget or cone bipolars from the common cone and rod bipolars.

The single uppermost tier of the sixth layer, made up of somewhat larger and paler nuclei evidently belonging to the horizontal cells, is again somewhat separated from the bulk by a less compact arrangement. The lowermost tier, in the same way, is somewhat separated from the rest, its nuclei belonging to the amacrine cells and possibly also to the displaced ganglions.

The inner plexiform layer is thick. It is conspicuous because of its several thicker and thinner and remarkably evenly arranged horizontal streaks. Golgi-stained preparations show that these streaks are made up of long, horizontally running expansions of "amacrine" cells and may also indicate synaptical couplings of the adjacent neurons.

The ganglion cells are very numerous and found in almost the entire expanse of the retina in at least two tiers. In the two areae their number increases to four tiers, and in the margin of the central foveal excavation to five and possibly six tiers. In the very center—the floor—of the central fovea, measuring approximately 40 microns in diameter, all ganglion cells have been displaced in a lateral direction; this ganglion-free area coincides with the minute territory where the photoreceptors are thinnest. In a narrow, peripheral belt along the ora terminalis, only a single tier of closely packed ganglion cells is present.

10. THE CENTRAL AND LATERAL FOVEAE.— Of the various features of the Swallow's retina, the most remarkable are the foveal formations, two in each eye (Figs. 173, 469). They may be observed in freshly fixed specimens, both in the enucleated eyes and in those left *in situ* or in their normal place in the head, appropriately dissected. Even though small, they may be noticed macroscopically, and even better at slight magnification (6–10×).

One is the central fovea (*cf.* Fig. 469). It is a minute, well-formed circular depression situated 1.5 mm. above the posterior extremity of the pecten or "comb" (a vascular structure protruding into the interior of the eye, conveniently displaced downward, thus leaving the spacious vitreal cavity almost free from the obstacle which would otherwise interfere with the passage of light rays). The diameter of the central fovea is roughly 0.5 mm., which is no less than a third of the human foveal depression (*cf.* chap. V, 10 [4, 5]).

The other, also circular but smaller and more shallow, is the lateral, temporal, or posterior fovea, located approximately on the same horizontal level but about 3 mm. posteriorly, behind the first, and about 2 mm. from the posterior limit of the retina.

Examined microscopically, the central fovea appears as a deep, funnel-shaped excavation, whose sides inclose an angle of approximately 40°. It is conspicuous because of its centralmost photoreceptors, whose diameter in the available preparations unfortunately could not be measured. In the zone next to the very center the inner cone segments are approximately 2 microns in diameter or less. From this a guess may be ventured that the thickness of the centralmost cones may be 1 micron or less (*cf.* sec. 7 on Anole, this chapter).

The lateral fovea is much smaller and more shallow, with all layers continuous and with only a slight thinning of the inner nuclear and ganglion layers. The grain of its photoreceptors also seems to be rougher than that in the central fovea.

The analysis of the minute structure of the Swallow's retina, with the help of Golgi staining, remains a worthy object for future research. The few glimpses we were able to obtain indicate a rich differentiation of the constituent

Fig. 473.—Saw-Whet Owl (*Cryptoglaux acadica*), a "little clown," smallest of the Strigide Family, inhabitant of dense evergreen woods of northern North America. (*Cf.* following figure.) A typical nocturnal bird of prey, with eyes adapted to its way of living. This and the following plate, made from personal observations by the artist, show the versatile use of observable parts of the visual apparatus in different situations. *Upper left:* attentively watching a live mouse, by directing both eyes straight ahead, with iris membranes moderately constricted; *upper right:* sleepily turning the head directly backward, with one eye closed; *below:* at ease, a pose often taken expressing affection or expectation of a titbit.

neurons. The problem here is not only to determine the types of neurons but most of all their synaptical relationships also. This alone may help interpret the visual functions of the Birds and of the Vertebrates in general.

Summarizing the few facts so far known, it is apparent that the Swallow's eye, in spite of its small size, is eminently capable of forming accurate images of external objects because of its delicate construction. It is further able, because of the refinement of the retina, to analyze retinal images in a most efficient way and to transmit detailed nervous messages to the brain. In its wealth of photoreceptors and other nerve cells, the Swallow's eye may be compared with the fovea and central area of the human or simian eye, surrounded by a very narrow and less efficient extra-areal periphery. In its perfection the Swallow's eye and retina may closely approach the limitations imposed by the vertebrate organization. (*Cf.* Rochon-Duvigneaud 1943.)

11. Nervous system.—The brain of the Swallow conforms to the general type of avian brain (Fig. 470). The telencephalon (*tel*) is of a squat shape and smooth in appearance. What its function is, unfortunately, still remains largely a mystery. The optic lobes (*ol*) are relatively large. They protrude on both sides from under the telencephalon. The cerebellum (*cbl*), especially its *vermis* or middle portion, is also well developed for a bird, with small, stumplike cerebellar hemispheres attached to the sides.

Concerning finer structures, a glance at a few microscopic sections, variously stained with hematoxylin and eosin, Weigert, Nissl, Golgi, and Golgi-Cox methods, shows an extremely rich differentiation of the finer structures into various nuclei and layers. Nothing short of a thorough monographic study could disclose the innumerable details and interpret them functionally. This is especially true of the optic lobes, which exhibit stratification of cells and fibers in no way less elaborate than the striate area of the Primates. (*See* chap. VIII, 5–7.)

Finally, special mention must be made of the optic nerves. These were found to be no less than from 770 to 850 microns in diameter, comparing favorably with the optic nerves of Monkey and Man. This comparison becomes even more favorable when the caliber of individual fibers, generally thin, is considered. The thickest fibers, as our measurements show, have a caliber of only 3 microns, while the majority are 2 microns thick, with many being 1 micron or less. This provides the Swallow with a great number of individual conductors from the retina to the brain. Our tentative estimate of the number of fibers in the Swallow's optic nerve would be at least 500,000 and possibly as many as 1,000,000. (*Cf.* optic nerve in Man and Monkey.)

12. Biological considerations.—The visual system of the Barn Swallow is characterized by features common to all Birds, besides others peculiar to the species. The first are the large size of the eyeballs and their peculiar shape, with completely crossed optic nerves, terminating in the large visual centers of the midbrain. The special features are: position of the eyeballs in the head and their extreme mobility; the ability of the Swallow to use its eyes either independently or together, which again may be either in panoramic vision or as a binocular stereoscopic team; the extraordinary wealth of photoreceptors and other nerve cells, which make most of the retina resemble the "central area" of the Primates; the presence of both rods and cones everywhere, probably even in the very center of the central fovea; the presence of two specially differentiated foveae, a central and a lateral or posterior; relatively thick optic nerves, made up of a great number of fine and very fine fibers; huge optic lobes of the midbrain, showing an elaborate structural makeup. These features undoubtedly indicate the dominant role of vision in this species. What the importance of smell is, as indicated by the unexpectedly large and contorted turbinates, and of hearing remains an object for further investigation.

The manner in which the Swallow probably gets food, which almost certainly consists exclusively of flying insects caught on the wing, is somewhat as follows. It is apparent that the entire visual mechanism, beginning with the rods and cones of the retina and terminating in the brain, and minutely co-ordinated with the entire remaining bodily machine, is organized in its gross and detailed structures and properties to respond instantly to the minute visual stimuli characteristic of particular species of insects.

It is likely that most prey is first noticed monocularly by any part of the extrafoveal retina. The next phase is the fixation of the object by the central fovea of that particular eye, permitting a more detailed, even though extremely rapid, critical examination. This impression is

or a negative urge. In the first case the two eyes, assisted by the appropriate movements of the head and neck, converge upon the prey, which is sharply focused binocularly; its position is appraised tridimensionally and stereoscopically by means of the two lateral or posterior foveae and their parts of the visual cen-

Fig. 474.—Saw-Whet Owl, showing various manifestations of the observable visual behavior. (*Cf.* preceding figure.) *Upper left:* awkwardly and slowly leaning away, with eyes and pupils wide open, distrustfully avoiding the hand attempting to pet it, until it seemed it would topple over; *upper right:* looking at the ceiling in a drowsy, contemplative mood; *lower figures:* two attitudes taken while being admired by the visitors.

at once "mentally" digested on the basis of inherent instincts and past experience.

The third step in the process of hunting, also practically instantaneous and automatic, is a "decision" which is colored as either a positive

ters. In this act the binocular convergence must be conceived as extremely rapid and, at the same time, elastic, capable of following the insect in its erratic movement, accurate focusing being essential for the success of the capture,

The accurate binocular stereoscopic appraisal and tridimensional judgment of the prey's position and distance in space, itself constantly on the move, facilitates proper regulation of the locomotor mechanism in pursuit and in the final capture of the prey. In all this exceedingly rapid process, there is little left to chance, invoked by some students of this problem (*arabesques du vol* of Rochon-Duvigneaud). It is an exceedingly fast and precise co-ordination of many systems for the single biological purpose of feeding.

It is hardly necessary to add that all these acts have to be performed in a definite order, according to a definite formula, almost mechanically, even though permitting great variation in detail, in order to adapt the pursuit and capture of the prey to the conditions of each particular instance. In this way alone is the biological demand satisfied and the survival of the species and of the whole family guaranteed.

How the details of the entire process are carried out and how the exceedingly complex retinal, cerebral, and neuromuscular apparatus works in performing the necessary functions is a worthy subject of investigation with modern scientific methods and technical means.

Of special interest is the visual system of the Barn Swallow and similar Birds in possession of two foveae in each eye, in comparison with the arrangement in Man and other Primates with but a single central fovea. The problem which arises here is both anatomophysiological and psychological. How does a Swallow, Hawk, or Eagle utilize the two foveae of each eye for the purpose of single vision, and how must their central visual apparatus be organized in comparison with the human, in which the slightest discrepancy in the "correspondence" of the two homonymous halves of the visual system causes most acute discomfort in Man, owing to diplopia?

References: G. Abelsdorff 1907; Alaerts 1935; A. A. Allen 1951; G. M. Allen 1939; Ariëns Kappers, Huber & Crosby 1936; Bartels; Beal *et al.* 1941; Beccari 1943; Beebe 1949; Th. Beer 1892; Bellonci 1888; Benner 1938; Beritov & Chichinadze 1937; Bingham 1922; R. Blake 1953; A. Brehm's *Tierleben*, v. 9 (Vögel, v. 4), p. 42; Chard 1939; Chard & Gundlach 1938; Chievitz 1891; Colas-Pelletier 1940; Craigie 1928, 1931, 1932, 1940; Cruickshank 1947; Davis 1945; Delage 1926; Demoll 1917; Detwiler 1940; Dunlap 1934; Dursy (quoted by Brehm, v. 5, p. 231, 1913); Eck 1939; Edgerton *et al.* 1951; Edinger & Wallenberg 1899; Ehrhard 1924; V. Franz 1934; H. Friedmann 1946; Grassé 1950, v. 15; Grinnell 1921; Groebbels 1932–37; Gudger 1944; Gundlach 1933; Gundlach *et al.* 1945; E. Hahn 1916; W. F. Hamilton & Coleman; W. F. Hamilton & Goldstein 1933; Harris 1904; Hausman 1946; Hesse & Doflein 1935–43; Honigmann 1921; Huber & Crosby 1929, 1933, 1934; Igersheimer & Hahn-Haslinger 1926; Kahmann 1936; Kajikawa 1923; Koelliker 1896; Kosaka & Hiraiwa 1915; Kolmer (& Lauber) 1936; A. Kühn 1919; Kükenthal & Krumbach 1934; Lack 1949; Langlands 1929; Lashley 1916; Lassell 1948; Layman 1936; Leuckart 1876; J. Levine 1945; Mayr 1942, 1949; A. & S. Menaboni 1950; R. E. Moreau 1930; H. Müller 1863–64; Joh. Müller 1826; Münzer & Wiener 1892; L. J. J. Muskens 1914, 1927, 1929, 1930, 1934, 1936; Noll 1915, 1922, 1935; O'Day 1940; Ovio 1927; Palmar 1954; Parker & Haswell 1940; T. G. Pearson 1936; Pearson *et al.* 1936; Perlia 1889; R. T. Peterson 1947; Piša 1939; Plate 1922–24; Plath 1935; Porsch 1931; Portier 1923; Pütter 1908–12; P. Ramón y Cajal 1890, 1898, 1943; S. Ramón y Cajal 1891, 1892, 1893 (1933), 1894, 1898 (1899), 1909–11; Rendahl 1924; Ridgway & Friedmann 1901–50; Ris 1899; Rochon-Duvigneaud 1922, 1933, 1934, 1943; Rochon-Duvigneaud & Veil 1936; Sälzle 1933; Singer & Münzer 1889; Steiner 1891; Storer 1943; Streuli 1925; Tschermak (Tsch.-Seysenegg) 1902, 1914, 1927, 1942; Verrier 1936, 1938, 1940, 1945; R. Wagner 1837; Wallenberg 1898, 1904, 1934; Walls 1942; J. B. Watson 1915; A. Wetmore 1933; Yerkes 1915.

SEC. 9. COMMON SHREW

1. Taxonomy.—The Shrews that form the Family Soricidae, among the smallest of the Mammals, are spread over most of the inhabitable earth (Figs. 475, 476). They are akin to the subterranean Moles or Talpidae, and the flying Bats or Chiroptera, in particular to the insectivorous suborder of Microchiroptera or Small Bats.

Scientific interest in the Shrews derives from a realization that they closely resemble the primitive, generalized animals of past ages, the Pantotherians, from which all Mammals, past and present, originated, and that the earliest linear ancestors of the Primates, including Man, were shrewlike. The purpose of this section, accordingly, is briefly to summarize available information on the anatomical characteristics of the Shrews and their habits and to consider to

Northern Hemisphere, both in the Old and in the New World, including all of India and the island of Ceylon. In the Southern Hemisphere the Shrews are present as far as South Africa, being absent from the southern portion of South America and from the entire Australian continent.

Of the Old World species, A. Brehm (L. Heck) mentions as the most common the Forest Shrew (*Sorex araneus* or *vulgaris*), further the Alpine Shrew (*Sorex alpinus*), Pigmy Shrew (*Sorex minutus* or *pigmaeus*), the aquatic or Water

Fig. 475.—*Pachyura etrusca*, smallest terrestrial Shrew, insectivorous, nocturnal, body length 4 cm., tail 2.5 cm., inhabitant of countries adjacent to the Mediterranean and Black Seas. A type of primitive, generalized Mammal, resembling the Early Insectivores of the Cretaceous Period of the earth's prehistory, which lived from sixty to one hundred and twenty-seven million years ago. From A. Brehm's *Tierleben*, 4th ed., *Säugetiere*, v. 1, p. 291, 1912, with special permission of the Bibliographisches Institut A.G. (Dr. E. List), Mannheim, Germany. (*Cf.* Figs. 476–79, 482–88.)

what extent these characteristics, especially the senses, and under what influencing circumstances, could have served as a starting point for the rise of the Primates. (*See* sections 10 and 12 on the Tree Shrew and the Tarsier.)

The now living Shrews are grouped by systematic zoölogy into numerous genera, in turn subdivided into hundreds of species and subspecies, variously adapted to their particular habitats, including the aquatic. As far as is known, the Shrews seem to inhabit most of the

Shrew (*Neomys fodiens*), House Shrew (*Crocidura russulus*), Mediterranean or Ciliated Shrew (*Pachyura etrusca*), and others. (*See*, for additional illustrations, Brehm 1912; English; and Lydekker 1916.)

The North American Shrews are subdivided, according to H. E. Anthony, into the following genera: Shrew (*Sorex personatus* or *S. cinereus*), Water Shrew (*Neosorex palustris*), Pigmy Shrew (*Microsorex*), Little Shrew (*Cryptotis*), Short-tailed Shrew (*Blarina*), and Gray Shrew

(*Notiosorex*). (*See*, for illustrations, H. E. Anthony 1928; H. H. T. Jackson 1928; and T. Surber 1946.)

2. CHARACTER.—The external appearance of the Shrews, their anatomical organization, physiological performance, and biology are remarkably similar, no matter what their particular mode of life. They are small in size, externally resembling small Rodents, with a pointed muzzle and small eyes and ears. Their metabolic rate is high, requiring great quantities of food. The Shrews eat various small ani-

tail 2.7; *Microsorex*, total 3.3, including tail 1.3; *Cryptotis*, total 3.1, including tail 0.64; *Blarina*, total 5, including tail 1; *Notiosorex*, total 3.6, including tail 1.24.

The measurements of the smallest species of Shrew, also one of the smallest Mammals in existence, that of the Mediterranean Shrew (*Pachyura etrusca*, *see* Fig. 475), inhabiting southern Europe and North Africa, are: body length $1\frac{1}{2}$ inches, and tail length 1 inch, according to L. Heck (*see* A. Brehm's *Tierleben*, 4th ed., v. 10, p. 292, 1912). Several African species, thus the Giant Shrew (*Prazsorex goliath*), of the

FIG. 476.—*Sorex araneus* (*above*) and *Crocidura russulus* (*below*), two somewhat larger representatives of the terrestrial and nocturnal Shrews of Europe. Approximate body length $6\frac{1}{2}$ cm., tail length $4\frac{1}{2}$ cm. Note minute eyes and pointed snout, shriveled ears and long bristles, indicating poor vision and well-developed tactile and olfactory senses. From A. Brehm's *Tierleben*, 4th ed., *Säugetiere*, v. 1, p. 276, 1912, with special permission of the Bibliographisches Institut A.G. (Dr. E. List), Mannheim, Germany. (*Cf.* preceding and following figures.)

mals, including insects. They are rather nocturnal and secretive in habit and do not hibernate. Their dentition is of a primitive, little-differentiated, sectorial type, resembling that of the Inframammalian Vertebrates, from which the dentition of the more advanced Mammals has differentiated in the course of evolution.

The length of the representative domestic species in inches, given by H. E. Anthony (1928), is as follows: *Sorex personatus*, total 4, including tail 1.6; *Neosorex*, total 6.4, including

size of a Rat, are mentioned by Malbrant & Maclatchy (1949).

The diameter of the eyeball, both in *Crocidura russulus* and in *Sorex araneus*, measures 1.5 mm. in the sagittal axis and a little less in the transverse, according to Rochon-Duvigneaud, and in the *Sorex minutus* a little more than 1 mm., according to the same investigator. In comparison, the eye of *Pipistrellus*, a small European Bat, is a little larger, measuring 1.75 mm. across, whereas that of the European Mole and the European Hedgehog, both much larger animals, measures from 0.8 to 0.9 mm., and from 5 to 6 mm. across, respectively.

Small as the eyes of the Shrews are, they are nevertheless in all particulars fully developed, possessing all usual structures: a transparent cornea, iris, biconvex lens, chorioid, retina, and blood vessels. Of the photoreceptor cells, in *Crocidura* both rods and cones are present, in *Sorex araneus* only the rods. In comparison, in the Mole both categories have been found by the same investigator, and in the Hedgehog and in the Bat only the rods.

The eyes of the Shrew, because of their small size, do not form images with sharp details and must be considered as largely lucifugal, directional organs of sight adjusted to respond chiefly to the varying intensities of light stimuli (*see* Rochon-Duvigneaud 1925, 1943; *see also* Verrier 1935; Walls 1942).

The eyes of the European Shrews *Sorex* and *Crossopus* have been examined by Kolmer, with the following results: diameter 1.5 mm., well-developed retina, photoreceptor layer made up of rods and cones in the ratio of 3 to 1, numerous ganglion cells, rich supply of blood vessels belonging to the central arterial system, and an optic nerve containing approximately 2,000 fibers (*see* Kolmer & Lauber 1936).

3. HABITS.—The habits of the Shrews, even though the animals are widespread and important in the origin and phylogenesis of Mammals and have been much investigated, unfortunately still remain in many respects little known because of the animals' secretive habits. In the following paragraphs is given a digest, first, from the important older publications, followed by the more recent ones, based on first-hand observation.

Perhaps the best presentation of the biology of the Shrews in general, especially those of Europe and near-by parts of the Old World, even though largely based on older sources, is found in the celebrated work on the life of animals by A. Brehm (*Tierleben*, 4th ed., v. 10, revised by L. Heck 1912). In it are recorded the observations not only of the German and other European investigators but also of some earlier American writers.

The Shrews, according to Brehm, inhabit both the lowlands and the elevated regions, climbing high into the Alps. They prefer dense woods and thickets, meadows, gardens, and buildings. Most of them love damp places, some taking to an aquatic life, a few burrowing into soil in which they dig passages or use those made by other animals, such as Mice and Moles, which they may have chased away. They prefer darkness and shade, avoiding dryness, heat, and light, being quite sensitive to sunlight, of which many perish. Their movements are exceedingly quick. In their behavior the Shrews resemble the Martens among the beasts of prey: like the latter, they also are adapted to various conditions of life and exhibit a daring, ferocity, and cruelty quite out of proportion to their diminutive size.

Among their senses, smell seems to be foremost, the next being hearing, whereas sight is poorly developed. Their intelligence is rather modest. Toward small animals they are merciless killers, while from more powerful adversaries they run as fast as they can.

The Shrews subsist almost exclusively on animal food: insects and their larvae, worms, mollusks, young birds and mammals, occasionally fish and their eggs, crayfish, and the like; they do not eat fruits, seeds, and other vegetable matter.

Immensely voracious, they daily consume food equal in amount to their own body weight; hence they cannot stand long hunger and, because of this, are unable to hibernate. In an experiment made by Rorig, a Shrew (*Sorex vulgaris*) weighing only 12 gm. had consumed, during 88 days, 3,733 meal worms (614.6 gm.), 4 grubs, 3 frogs, and 1 mouse. The dry weight of the substance was 200.58 gm., the daily ratio being one-fifth of the body weight of the living Shrew. There are, however, other experiments that make it doubtful whether the Shrews must eat continuously to remain alive. (*See*, for a modern study of the Shrew's physiology, Morrison *et al.* 1946, 1953.) The Shrews are able to produce a high-pitched, chirping twitter.

The archenemies of the Shrews are the Owls, against which their musky odor is no protection. The Storks and the Snakes, whose sense of smell is also poor, eat them with relish. Cats, Dogs, Foxes, and other Mammals who live by preying, on the contrary, avoid them.

While most of the observers emphasize the terrestrial habits of the Shrews, except of the aquatic species, a few mention having seen them climb low tree trunks to collect insect eggs or even build a nest.

There are few animals that are so unsociable toward their kind as the Shrews, except perhaps the Moles. Not even the opposite sexes live with each other in peace except during the mating time. Wherever two Shrews meet on their rambles, a duel is inevitable. However, even among the Shrews, there are occasionally peaceful relations, as the one reported of a gathering of about one hundred of them which were seen merrily scampering around.

The Water Shrews, as could be expected, are adapted to their peculiar mode of life: their fur is thick and impervious to moisture; their toes are provided with special hairs that are used as the web is used by the aquatic birds; their external ears can be folded, and the external auditory meatus may be closed; and the hairs along the underside of the tail are arranged in a ridge which possibly makes this limb usable as a propelling organ.

The Water Shrew is described as an extremely vivacious, clever, and agile creature, swimming and diving exquisitely, and with a remarkable ability to float either with the head alone above the surface or with the entire body. When swimming, its body appears flattened and usually also covered with a layer of minute, brilliant air bubbles which act as an insulator (possibly also adding to its buoyancy).

C. H. Merriam, in his book *The Mammals of the Adirondack Region* (1884 or 1886), has given us an interesting record of his personal observations on the habits of the American Shrews, of which the following excerpts are quoted from his description of the Cooper's Shrew:

Like its congeners, it manifests a predilection for the immediate vicinage of old logs and stumps, and its holes can frequently be found, both in summer and winter, in these places, and about the roots of trees. Underground life does not appear as attractive to it as to its relatives, the moles, yet it avoids too much exposure and commonly moves, by night and by day, under cover of the fallen leaves, twigs, and other *debris* that always cover the ground in our northern forests. . . .

Its ceaseless activity, and the rapidity with which it darts from place to place, is truly astonishing, and rarely permits the observer a correct impression of its form.

Whenever a tree or a large limb falls to the ground, these Shrews soon find it, examining every part with great care, and if a knot-hole or crevice is detected, leading to a cavity within, they are pretty sure to enter, carry in materials for a nest, and take formal possession. Hence their homes are not infrequently discovered and destroyed by the wood-chopper. . . .

Not only are these agile and restless little Shrews voracious and almost insatiable, consuming incredible quantities of raw meat and insects with great eagerness, but they are veritable cannibals withal, and will even slay and devour their own kind. I once confined three of them under an ordinary tumbler. Almost immediately they commenced fighting, and in a few minutes one was slaughtered and eaten by the other two. Before night one of these killed and ate its only surviving companion, and its abdomen was much distended by the meal. Hence in less than eight hours one of these tiny wild beasts had attacked, overcome, and ravenously consumed two of its own species, each as large and heavy as itself!

Merriam found the weight of a grown-up Shrew to be hardly more than half a dram, or not quite 2 gm., the largest specimen weighing 2.85 gm.

Further interesting observations of the habits of the Short-tailed Shrew in Michigan have been reported by A. F. Shull in the *American Naturalist* (1907). He found it catching Meadow Voles, mostly at night. It stores up piles of snails of the genus *Polygyra* and, with ease, like a miniature athlete, digs burrows and underground nests. Its food consists of Snails, Voles, House Mice, May Beetles and their grubs, Moth larvae and other insects and their pupae, Earthworms and Sow Bugs. Vegetable food, such as carrots, crackers, and grass roots, it never touched, which contrasts with the Common Shrew (*Sorex personatus*), which apparently also eats plant material (*see* Merriam's experience below). Its appetite is prodigious: a day's fare, for example, consisted either of two-thirds of a Meadow Vole, 1 Mouse, 15 May Beetles, 13 larvae of the same beetle, or 35 small Earthworms. It eats many other insects, the Ground Beetles and Sow Bugs being preferred. Beef was eaten by it readily. The method by which it captured its prey was to grab it by the ears and hold it until tired, then to pierce its skull with a quick bite. It ate the brain and the cranium first, then the neck and the shoulders, while the snout, skin, legs, and tail were left unconsumed.

Of the senses of the Short-tailed Shrew, Shull found touch to be very fine, but sight poor, its principal role being to distinguish light from shadow. Its sense of smell is acute: "When the shrew was above ground, it was always going about with its nose slightly elevated and its nostrils dilating and contracting rapidly in unison with movements of the sides of the body, as if sniffing the air."

Hearing is also very well developed. A loud noise repeated often, however, would not elicit any response, but a response was obtained from slight sounds heard for the first time. Most persistent response was obtained from the flutter of the wings of a Pigeon, which "always sent the shrew scurrying into its burrows." "This particular sound must have been heard hundreds of times during that period [five weeks], yet even at the last could not be heard with equanimity by the shrew"—which may indicate an instinctive reaction to the noise of an owl.

"Sufficient evidence has been offered that most of the shrew's work on snails is done at night." The Shrews, it appears, are physiologically intolerant of bright light and of considerable heat. This seems to be the reason for their being active chiefly during the night, even though they are not entirely nocturnal, as evidenced by their capture by the Hawks. This last observation by Shull was substantiated by V. Bailey (1926), who was able to catch the Short-tailed Shrews as often during the day as during the night, even though the animals are not seen except when trapped.

The Short-tailed Shrew is universally present and in great numbers, the ratio in its range being four Shrews to one acre. The Shrew is well protected against the predators, Hawks and Owls, by its constitution and habits; compared with Mice, few Shrews are caught by Snakes, Foxes, Minks, Skunks, or Red Squirrels.

On the Common and other species of Shrews, much interesting observation, including that from the older literature, was gathered by Seton (1909). In the words of Cope (1873): ". . . the strength, ferocity, activity, and courage of the Blarina are such that if it were increased to half

the size of a tiger it might quite logically make tigers its habitual prey." As it is, its preferred food, according to the same writer, was Field Mice. According to Morden (1884), *Blarina* eats about twice or three times its own weight of food every twenty-four hours.

From Seton's own experience, the Common Shrew (*Sorex personatus*) is not capable of climbing. It is never found far from the water, even though it is not aquatic. In character it is unsociable to the point of ferocity. "Whenever two of them fell into one of the pitfalls that I used for their capture, the stronger one invariably attacked and devoured his weaker brother." However, he quotes Herrick (1892), who found the Shrews to be sociable among themselves.

The mating of the Shrews, in Seton's experience, takes place during any season except the winter. Their voice is high pitched, at the limit of audibility. They are active during both day and night. Their eyes are useful only "to tell them when they are emerging from safe shadow into the open light with its great increase of danger." The Shrews are active during the whole winter, running in minute tunnels just under the surface of the snow.

The food of the Common Shrew consists chiefly of insects and worms and of flesh of any kind. It is extremely voracious and even cannibalistic. It needs an enormous quantity of food, and, to satisfy its appetite, Merriam and Seton believe that it may also eat vegetable products such as beechnuts, seeds, and roots.

Its enemies are Hawks and Owls. The Weasel, Cat, and Mink, even though they will kill it, do not eat it on account of the repugnant "musky" odor emanating from its glands.

Seton reports that the Short-tailed or Mole Shrew (*Blarina brevicauda*) preys under conditions where eyes are of little use, as in brush, moss, and among fallen leaves. Its home is in woodlands, among the tangles of brush and sedgy grass, under log piles, along streams, and in hardwood bush. In general, it prefers conditions similar to those favored by the Field Mouse, but it also digs tunnels in a way that recalls the Moles. It also digs beneath the leaves. Referring to *Blarina*'s way of life, Seton says that "this little inter-world betwixt floor and carpet was for him; and thus I learned why he had bartered his eyesight for keener powers of smell and touch."

The Short-tailed Shrew, according to Seton, lives very close to water, in fact, "on the water's edge." It subsists chiefly on insects, worms, and any other living food, and prays largely on the Field Mice, equal to it or larger in size. In a pinch, it also eats beechnuts, corn, and oats. Merriam (1884) reported about one which he fed for a whole week with beechnuts, which it liked very much and on which it thrived. According to Eadie (1944), Field Mice, however, form a large part of its diet, possibly to some extent those weakened by disease or dead.

All Shrews, in Seton's opinion, are heavy drinkers, which is the reason why they live close to the water. This close attachment to the water is even more pronounced in the Water or Marsh Shrew (*Neosorex palustris*), which, according to Herrick (1892), resembles "a miniature otter."

The senses of the Shrews, in Seton's experience, vary much. While hearing is extremely acute, their eyesight is reduced to the point where the animals are practically blind. Sight apparently is useful only to distinguish light from shade. The sense of touch is exquisite. Smell, in his opinion, strangely enough, seems not to be well developed. *Blarina*'s motor functions also seem not to be out of the ordinary, the animal not being capable of climbing or running fast. In Seton's words, *Blarina* "offsets all its shortcomings by a superlative development of hearing and touch, and a restless energy combined with indomitable courage, great muscular powers, and tireless activity, an equipment that makes it a fearsome beast of prey, a terror to all wild creatures of its small world, that are less than double its weight."

The Shrews, according to H. E. Anthony's *Field Book of North American Mammals* (1928), may be quite abundant in a given region but, for all that, are rather infrequently observed.

Their small size, quick movements, and habit of working under cover do not give one much opportunity to see these least of all mammals. Although these tiny creatures seem to be most active at night, they are often abroad in full daylight. . . . When one does see a Shrew it is usually but a glimpse as the animal rustles among fallen leaves or darts from under one log to another. . . . They are such highly organized, nervous creatures that they give instant response to any stimulation. Live Shrews which I have trapped have started violently when I have attempted to give an imitation, rather crudely I fear, of their fine, high-pitched squeak, and I have actually had one die in my hand from nervous shock.

Anthony, together with other observers, emphasizes their predatory, courageous nature, not hesitating to attack animals several times larger, even though hunting mostly for insects that are not able to put up much resistance.

Mice put into cages with Shrews are dispatched with a celerity that indicates this is by no means a new experience for the Shrew at least; and as a further index to the Shrew character there are accounts to tell us that a cage can not contain more than one Shrew at a time for one will kill and eat the other if two are confined.

Shrews require an abundance of food and consume a surprising amount because of a very rapid rate of digestion. Deprived of food for even a few hours they starve to death.

For their abode Shrews choose humid localities on the banks of small streams overgrown by rank vegetation and shrubbery, except the Pigmy and Gray Shrews, which prefer dry clearings instead of dark woods or damp, marshy places. "Shrews are active throughout the year and do not hibernate. Cold has no terrors for them and they range north of the Arctic Circle." Of their home life, very little is known.

The genus *Neosorex* or Water Shrew is well adapted to its aquatic mode of life, with its close pelage, partly webbed hind feet, and long tail. This Shrew lives along small streams and on the shores of marshes.

The activity of the Shrews apparently extends over twenty-four hours a day, with a decided preference for the night. *Blarina*, for example, is about during the daylight hours, even though it is seldom seen.

"The Short-tailed Shrew usually has five young in a litter and the nest is in an underground den or under rocks or stumps. The female makes a warm nest and lines it with shredded material such as grass and leaves. The young may be born from April to fall or even later."

Thaddeus Surber, of the Minnesota Department of Conservation, gave additional valuable information on the habits of the Shrews (*Con-*

servation Volunteer, v. 9 [July–August], p. 20, 1946). According to him, the Shrews

are largely nocturnal in habit and live just beneath the surface debris of the earth, the leaves, the moss and the wild grasses, so they are usually unobserved unless one is versed in their habits and has acquired the patience to watch for their occasional appearance above the surface. While they utilize the runways of the voles to a certain extent, in the damp cold sphagnum bogs they form tiny runways of their own and in the hardpacked snow often form tunnels just beneath its surface, from which it must be inferred they are active throughout the year. . . . Gifted with an insatiable appetite and a powerful digestion, they are extremely active in their endless search for food and it requires an enormous amount of insects and their larvae, earthworms and flesh to sustain them. As they occur in considerable numbers throughout the state, it can be readily seen they perform an important part in the economy of nature in holding in check myriads of insects. With the exception of owls, their enemies are few as these tiny beasts are provided with a peculiar nauseating odor that no doubt repels most animals. . . .

The largest species . . . , the water shrew, about equals the house mouse in size. It is almost as aquatic in habits as the muskrat and inhabits the same character of surroundings—peaty marshlands—as the star-nosed mole.

While all the shrews are very active, vicious and quarrelsome, the long-tailed species are the most pronounced in this respect. Savage and unsociable in disposition, they seldom encounter each other without engaging in a fight. Where two or more are taken alive and placed in confinement it means a fight to the death. Individually they do not hesitate to attack woods mice several times their weight.

The water shrews are the only mammals actually capable of running on the surface of still waters. Living as they do in the vicinity of ponds and small brooks, they play and search for their food with all the activity of the otter, even catching small minnows. Speaking of their ability to traverse water surfaces, Jackson (*N. A. Fauna*, No. 51, page 9) relates the following: "They can swim, dive, float, run along the bottom of a pool or creek, or actually run on the surface of the water with the greatest ease. In a bog near Rhinelander . . . the author saw one run a distance of about five feet across a small pond, the surface of which was glassy smooth. The body and head of the animal were entirely out of water, the surface tension of the water supporting the shrew, and at each step the animal took there appeared to be held by the fibrillae on the foot a little globule of air, which was also discernible in the shadow at the bottom of the pool, exactly as one might notice in the case of the water strider (*Gerris remigis*)."

On the Little Short-tailed Shrew (*Cryptotis parva*) there are several informative papers published in the past few years. This species, studied by W. J. Hamilton (1944) in northern Indiana, lives in leaf-mold tunnels in damp woods but also in the open grassy clearings along the forest margins. Its diet consists of Insects, Earthworms, Centipedes, Mollusks, and a small amount of vegetable matter. It is a glutton, consuming more than its weight of food in 24 hours, also eating Amphibians, Lizards, and Mice. In captivity it eats almost any animal food, but also cooked vegetables in the amount of three-fourths of its weight a day. Under natural conditions it probably consumes less. It is fond of apples. Its digestion is exceedingly rapid: the time required for the food to pass through the alimentary canal is, on the average, from 3 to 4 hours, sometimes as little as 114 or even 95 minutes. It likes water and drinks it freely. Under these circumstances, it is not surprising that it becomes fully grown at the age of one month. Sight appears to play a minor role in the life of this Shrew, the movements of the animal apparently not being under the guidance of the eyes. The sense of smell also seems not to be particularly well developed, the animal seemingly relying chiefly upon the tactile sense of the snout and the vibrissae (Edinger's "oral sense"). Its hearing is likewise not very acute, unless for the ultrasonic sounds. The animal sleeps well but is active at all hours, more during the night.

Additional information was gathered on the Texas variety of the same Little Short-tailed Shrew (*Cryptotis parva Texas*) by Davis & Joeris (1945). This Shrew is proficient in digging burrows in soil and making nests of shredded blades of grass in them. It is sociable, never fighting with its kind, except when given a single morsel of food. A prominent trait of this Shrew is meticulous personal cleanliness, which it keeps up by "washing" and combing its fur with its forepaws. It sometimes uses a special locality for defecation. The animal is active at all times, but the peak is attained during the night, with most of the day hours spent sleeping or resting in its nest, curled up on its side. Most of the specimens were caught during the early winter, when the natural food was reduced. Its preferred food was the softer kinds of insects, such as Sow Bugs, Grasshoppers, and Crickets, while the hard-shelled Beetles were avoided. It

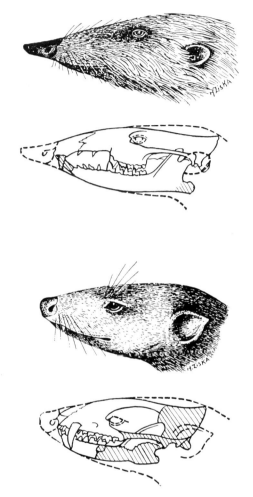

FIG. 477.—Skulls and restored heads of the ancient Cretaceous Placental Mammals which lived approximately one hundred million years ago and are believed to have resembled generalized types from which modern Orders of Mammals have developed: *above,* "insectivore" *Zalambdalestes lechei,* or an ancient Hedgehog; *below,* the "little carnivore" *Deltatheridium pretrituberculare,* a generalized type "not far removed from the base of the entire placental stock," according to Romer (1945). Discovered by Walter Granger, of the Third Asiatic Expedition of the American Museum of Natural History, near the Flaming Cliffs at Shabarakh Usu, in the Gobi Desert, in Mongolia. The petrifacts represent, according to W. K. Gregory, the "veritable missing links in the story of mammalian evolution." From W. K. Gregory, "Mongolian Mammals of the 'Age of Reptiles,'" Scient. Month., v. 24, p. 225, 1927. Slightly reduced. (*Cf. also* R. C. Andrews, W. Granger, *et al., The New Conquest of Central Asia; Natural History of Central Asia,* v. 1, pp. 271–74, 1932.)

also was fond of hamburgers, and it relished skinned Mice, while it was afraid of a live Mouse. On occasion it proved cannibalistic, as when confined with a dead comrade or when two found themselves in a trap.

Concerning the sense of smell, the importance of which Hamilton questioned, Schorger (1947) relates his own recent observation in the field, which showed that, in situations where vision was practically eliminated, the sense of smell was used very well to find food, concluding that the Shrew's sense of smell is much better than it has been considered to be by recent observers.

Whereas observers are unanimous about the poorly developed sense of vision in the terrestrial Shrews, in the aquatic genus of *Neosorex* this may be different. There is the observation of a Rocky Mountain Water Shrew (*Neosorex palustris navigator*) catching small fry of Salmon parr, $2\frac{1}{2}$ inches long, in the water, reported by Ben Hur Lampman (1947).

4. SHREWS AND THE ORIGIN OF PRIMATES.— The modern Shrews and other living Insectivores, exemplified by *Centetes* or *Tenrec,* aquatic *Potamogale, Solenodon, Chrysochloris,* Mole, Hedgehog, *Gymnura,* and Elephant Shrew, are the most ancient of living Placental Mammals (*see* description in Brehm, v. 10, 1912). Even though they are in many respects modified from the ancestral placental type, the Shrews are the best living example of how the ancient Placental Mammals of the early Jurassic Period of roughly 125 million years ago looked before they became differentiated into various orders of Modern Mammals. (*See* Fig. 468 in Parker & Haswell, *A Text-Book of Zoölogy,* v. 2, 1940, for the appearance in time and probable relationship of mammalian subclasses and orders; *see* Fig. 83, in Zeuner, *Dating the Past,* 1946, for a table of subdivisions of the past geological epochs; *cf. also* Fig. 257, in Romer, *Vertebrate Paleontology,* 1945.)

In anatomical features and living habits, the Shrews may be characterized as the most primitive living Placental Mammals of small to diminutive size, of principally terrestrial habits, with subterranean and nocturnal leanings, largely carnivorous in diet. In order to gauge the early phase of primate evolution, it is necessary, first, to examine the character of the shrewlike animals in their role as the ancestors of Primates and to fit together the results with the subsequent phases, of which the Tree Shrew and the Tarsier may be an illustration. (*Cf.* Figs. 475, 476, 478, 479, with Figs. 482–85, and Figs. 497–500; *see also* figures in subsequent sections, this chapter.)

If the Primates developed from forms roughly resembling present Shrews, these ancestors must have possessed anatomical and biological characteristics sufficiently pliable to develop into features characteristic of the Primate Order. Of these features, the most salient are the dominance of diurnal vision, grasping hands, omnivorous diet, and superior intelligence. On general, speculative grounds, it may be hypothesized that these features have a common genetical basis, caused by common conditions that created them.

The first characteristic—superior vision, with an emphasis on diurnality—is a far cry from the micropic and scotopic type of vision found in practically all terrestrial Shrews. There are few cues to indicate whether this is an inherited or a secondarily acquired characteristic. It would be easy to take refuge in a general thesis that, under the influence of changing conditions of life, almost any feature could be modified, even to its extreme. But this explanation, applied to the nocturnal habits of the Shrews, may appear somewhat strained. For this the nocturnalism of the Shrews is too universal and has been in existence at least since the Eocene Epoch or during the last 50–60 million years. Hence it is more likely that this nocturnalism is a characteristic closely related to the very origin of the Mammals.

Among the modern Insectivores, small eyes, poor vision, and terrestrial and nocturnal habits are practically universal (*see* Brehm 1912). From this fact it is legitimate to hypothesize that similar features may have been the original condition of the incipient Mammalian Phylum, during which some Vertebrates began to differentiate into forms eventually terminating as Placental Mammals. This time may very crudely be identified with the Triassic Period, the first of the three periods that make up the Mesozoic Era, dating roughly 175 million years in the past, according to Zeuner (1946).

The causes that imposed nocturnalism with its consequences continued during the following and much longer Jurassic and Cretaceous Periods. These two periods were coextensive with the climax of the Flying Reptiles and Dinosaurs. It is apparent that during these long periods the lowly ancestors of the Mammals passed through a severe testing, during which they were transformed from reptile-like diurnal animals with good vision into true Mammals.

In this critical "bottle-neck" time of trial and error, compelling factors must have worked to bring about a radical transformation and, with it, survival. Extinction was always threatened by the Dinosaurs or Dominant Reptiles, endowed with good sight. The only way for weak creatures to survive and become Mammals was to hide in darkness and behind camouflage. In doing this, the ancestors of the Mammals lost the precision of diurnal vision. (In the absence of light, the development of photopic vision is suppressed, as experiments by Birukow & Knoll [1952] showed.)

To compensate for reduced sight, other senses had to develop. In the case of terrestrial Shrews, the senses of smell, hearing, and touch competed for priority. In the Insectivorous Bats the sense of hearing combined with touch became dominant, at the expense of both smell and sight (*see* Polyak, J. f. Psychol. u. Neurol., v. 32). For the ancestors of the Mammals, including those of the Shrews, this meant a flight into darkness, a realm dominated by odors and sounds. This, in turn, imposed other profound changes: reduced body size, an increased demand for animal food in order to maintain high metabolism, and so forth.

Of these changes, macrosmia or dependence upon the sense of smell may have been most fraught with consequence. It was a keen nose that led the primitive Mammals to food, which, of necessity, was the "small life" that lives close to and in the ground: insects, grubs, earthworms, and other creatures of small size and their eggs. In fact, any "flesh" was very welcome to them. Eggs of all sorts were a delicacy, since they represent the best combination of nutritive material. The Ancient Mammals must have been especially eager to locate this prize. The facilitating factor was the poor protection of reptilian eggs afforded by their soft

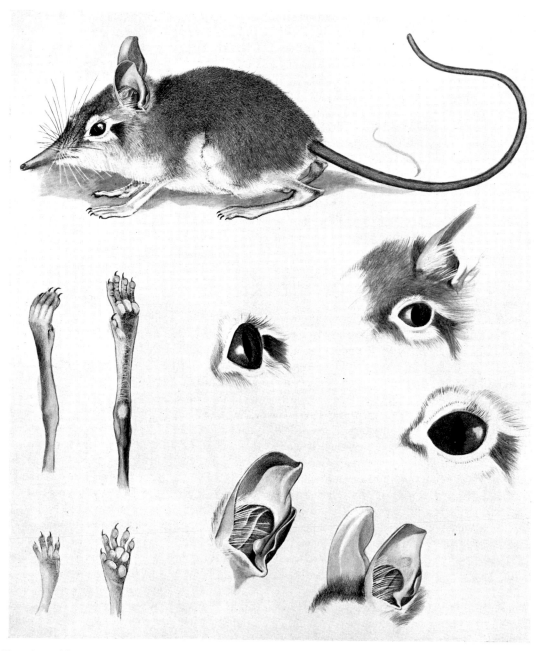

Fig. 478.—African Elephant Shrew (*Elephantulus rufescens*), one of the Jumping Shrews or Macroscelidae of the African Sudan, a suborder of Insectivora. A terrestrial relative of the Tree Shrews or Tupaiidae of Asia (*see* subsequent figures), the modern representatives of the ancient Mammals from which the ancestors of Primates have developed. This and the following plate have been prepared from a preserved specimen with the help of A. Brehm's *Tierleben*, 4th ed., *Säugetiere*, v. 1, 1912. Details show, in addition to a restored animal, views of the hind and front foot, of the eyes in plain view and in half-profile, and of the auricles. (*Cf.* Figs. 479–81.)

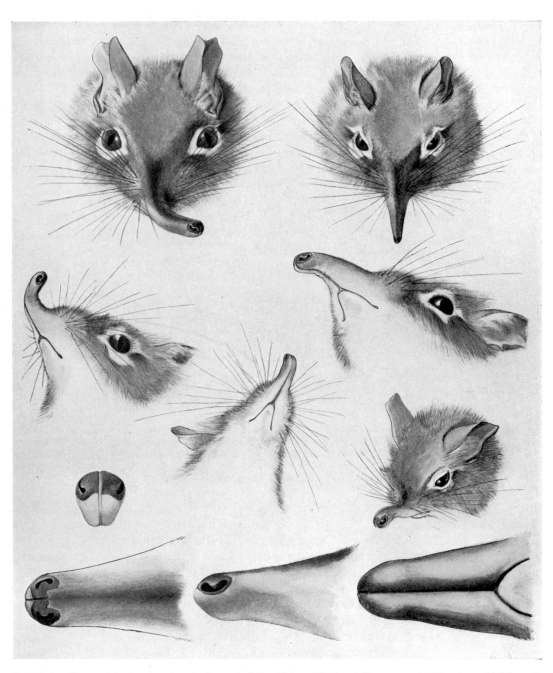

FIG. 479.—Views of the head and parts thereof of the African Elephant Shrew, a primitive terrestrial insectivorous relative of the Tree Shrews of Southeast Asia, the *Tupaia* (Figs. 482, 483), *Ptilocercus* (Fig. 484), and *Urogale* (Fig. 485). The eyes, even though quite laterally placed, indicate by their position some slight overlapping of both fields of view in front of the head. The pupils, when contracted, form vertical slits, the iris providing a protective screen against excessive insolation, an arrangement useful in a tropical habitat with scanty vegetation. Large, delicate, and movable auricles, a long flexible snout, and numerous long vibrissae all bespeak the great importance that hearing, smell, and the "oral sense" of touch have in the life of the Elephant Shrews. This contrasts with the small auricles and well-developed eyes of the Tree Shrews, which, from the viewpoint of primate phylogenesis, appear to be a more advanced division of menotyphlous suborder of Insectivora. (*Cf.* Fig. 478.)

envelope. When a clutch of these was destroyed, another chance for survival of the mighty Dinosaurs was lost.

It is obvious, however, that this presentation of cause and effect—the rise of the Mammals and the downfall of the Reptiles—is too simple to do justice to a very complex process of factors and circumstances that extended over many millions of years. Of these, nothing now remains but the final historical result, which we see in the disappearance of practically all large Reptiles and their replacement by Mammals. It is an outcome of the "struggle for existence," where the lowly, but not weak, and better-

adaptation to a secretive, mostly nocturnal, mode of life. Their scotopic obscurity, evidently, must be advantageous to them, even in present conditions, and they may continue in this way indefinitely. In their way, they are as successful as are the subterranean Moles or *Chrysochloris*, even though they do occasionally use daylight, mostly negatively, by shunning it and consequently are not able to respond to colors, which play a large part in the lives of the diurnal Fishes, Lizards, many Mammals, and most Birds.

The Shrews continue their existence in the darkness into which they were driven by bio-

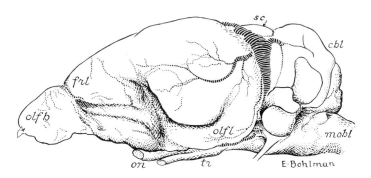

FIG. 480.—Brain of the Elephant Shrew in side view, 4× magnified. Note the large olfactory bulb and lobe and absence of the occipital lobe, indicative of the dependence of this insectivore animal chiefly on the olfactory sense and on hearing (as the long snout and large, flexible auricles in the preceding figures show). (*Cf.* following figure.) *Labeling: cbl*, cerebellum; *frl*, frontal lobe; *mobl*, oblong medulla; *olfb*, olfactory bulb; *olfl*, olfactory lobe; *on*, optic nerve; *tr*, trigeminal nerve. Venous sinuses and a few other blood vessels also shown.

equipped Shrews won over the mighty, but less adaptable, Dinosaurs.

The rise of the Placental Mammals from their Jurassic and Cretaceous obscurity into a Cenozoic luxuriance did not appreciably affect the modern Shrews. They may have changed somewhat, retaining, however, the essential organization and habits which we may assume their ancestors possessed at the end of the Jurassic Period: small size, short limbs, clawed feet, small brain, large olfactory bulbs and lobes, small eyes and poor vision, and little differentiated dentition. For this the blame may be put upon the larger Mammals and Birds, which meanwhile developed and replaced the Dominant Reptiles.

According to the competent observers quoted in the preceding pages, Shrews populate most of the globe in great abundance, contrary to the superficial appearance caused by their perfect

logical necessity more than 100 million years ago and in which they have been kept ever since. In their adaptation to obscurity they parallel the Microchiroptera or Insect-eating Bats, depending, however, principally upon a combination of senses: smell, touch, taste, and hearing, instead of upon hearing alone, as their flying relatives do.

During the Cretaceous Period, when the downfall of the large Reptiles was initiated, very likely assisted by the rising Shrewlike Mammals, many of the latter took the opportunity to emerge from obscurity. From these, almost like an explosion, developed practically all now living orders of Mammals, which very soon spread over most of the earth. This was a "Sturm und Drang period" for the Class of Mammals (*see* Fig. 257 in Romer's *Vertebrate Paleontology*, 1945; also Parker & Haswell, *A Text-Book of Zoölogy*, v. 2, Fig. 468, 1940).

This period may be described as the unshackling of a class, hitherto living in darkness under perpetual terror and threat of extinction, to new freedom and opportunity. This miracle was mediated by a return to the full diurnal vision of their reptilian ancestors, a vision far superior, in its precision and reactions to radiant stimuli, to any nocturnal adaptation, no matter how superlatively utilized (*cf.* sec. 12, Tarsier). In its significance for the further advancement of Mammals, this rebirth was on a par with the transformation the sense of vision made the major contribution. We have a glimpse of this in a few insectivorous representatives whose vision seems definitely improved over the blindness of the Moles and the extremely poor vision of most of the Shrews. Such examples are the Hedgehog, *Gymnura*, probably *Potamogale*, and our native Water Shrews. Except for the well-observed Hedgehog (*see* Herter & Sgonina 1933), the record on these, unfortunately, is less than meager. This is also true of the many exotic

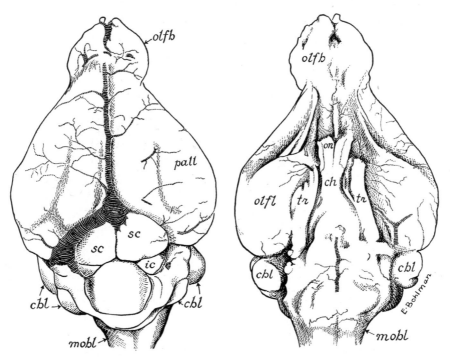

FIG. 481.—Brain of the Elephant Shrew, left figure a dorsal view, right figure a ventral view, 4× magnified. Note the large superior colliculi (*sc*) of the midbrain or primitive mesencephalic centers of sight entirely uncovered by the still undeveloped occipital parts of the great hemispheres; prominent olfactory bulbs and lobes interconnected with marked striae; optic nerves which are much thinner than the trigeminal nerves; asymmetry of venous sinuses, the left sigmoid sinus much larger than the right one. (*Cf.* preceding figure.) *Labeling: cbl*, cerebellum; *ch*, chiasma of optic nerves; *ic*, inferior midbrain colliculus; *mobl*, medulla oblongata; *olfb*, olfactory bulb; *olfl*, olfactory lobe; *on*, optic nerve; *pall*, pallium or forebrain cortex; *sc*, superior midbrain colliculus; *tr*, trigeminal nerve.

"invention" of photoreceptors by the early Prevertebrate, the change that made possible the initial rise of the Vertebrate or Chordate Phylum, as described in section 2, in the preceding chapter.

How from this evolutionary stage and under what influencing factors the grasping hands and superior intelligence of the Primate Order gradually evolved is a theme treated in the following sections of this chapter and in the final chapter. However, it may be mentioned here that in this

little-observed and poorly described Shrews of Asia and Africa.

The next step, that represented by the Elephant Shrews (Figs. 478, 479) and the Tree Shrews (Figs. 482–86), is a great advancement over the soricide Shrews. It may illustrate the real beginning of the emancipation of the Mammals from their inherited nocturnality and their readoption of daylight habits, an absolute requisite for the rise of Primates.

Other habits occasionally noticed in the

Shrews, such as adding plant products to their diet and making short excursions up trees, may also have been the first timid attempts which, in favorable circumstances and in due course of time, developed into the arboreal life of the Tree Shrews, from which the true Primates eventually evolved.

References: Ärnbäck-Christie-Linde 1900, 1907; Alcock 1898; G. Alexander 1905; G. M. Allen 1939; Andrews, Granger, *et al.* 1932 (esp. p. 272); Anonymous 1943, 1946; A. Anthony & H. Valois 1913; H. E. Anthony 1928; Arvey & Glass 1950; Babcock 1914; V. Bailey 1888, 1925, 1926; G. Ballou 1953; Barbour 1944; Beddard 1901, 1923; Beidelman 1950; Birukow & Knoll 1952; E. Bischoff 1900; Bobrinskoy *et al.* 1944; A. E. Brehm's *Tierleben*, 4th ed., v. 10 (*Säugetiere*, v. 1), p. 272; Bryant 1945; Cade 1952; Cahalane 1947; Carlsson 1909, 1922; Christian 1950; Christie 1943; E. H. Colbert 1949; Cope 1873, 1885; Crandall 1946; Crowcroft 1951; Chas. R. Darwin 1859, 1871, and later editions; Davis & Joeris 1945; Dobson 1883–90; Dollman 1932; Dräsecke 1903; Dusi 1951; Eadie 1944, 1952; D. English; Flores 1911; Fürbringer 1904; Gagnebin 1947; Ganser 1880, 1882; Ghosh 1945; Gregory 1916, 1927, 1951; Gregory & Simpson 1926; Hamilton 1930, 1937, 1939, 1940, 1941, 1944; Harrison & Traub 1950; Heller 1910, 1912; Heppenstall 1946; C. L. Herrick 1892; Herter & Sgonina 1933; R. Hertwig 1907; C. Hess 1889; Hesse (Allee & Schmidt) 1951; Hesse & Doflein 1935–43; C. E. Hope 1944; Hornsey 1944; Hunt 1951; W. M. Ingram 1942; H. H. T. Jackson 1926, 1928; Jerdon 1867; Kennicott 1857–59; Kilham 1951; Kriszat 1940; Lack 1949; Lampman 1947; K. Z. Lorenz 1952; Lydekker 1916; Malbrant & Maclatchy 1949; Marshall 1951; W. D. Matthew 1943; Maynard 1889; Mayr 1949; C. H. Merriam 1884, 1886; Merzbacher 1903; Merzbacher & Spielmeyer 1903; R. G. Miller 1945; R. F. Morris 1943; Morrison & Pearson 1946; Morrison & Ryser 1946; Morrison, Ryser & Dawe 1953; Munn 1934, 1950; Munn & Collins 1936; S. I. Ognev; R. S. Palmer 1947; G. H. Parker 1922; Parker & Haswell 1940; O. P. Pearson 1942, 1946, 1950; Pearson & Pearson 1947; Piveteau 1951, and *Traité de paléontologie*, vols. 4–7; F. H. Pike 1943; Polyak 1925; Rand 1935; Romer 1943, 1945, 1949; Rochon-Duvigneaud 1928, 1934, 1943; M. Rose 1912; Rudd 1953; Ryser & Morrison 1953; Sawyer 1944; Schorger 1947; S. Schwarz 1935; Seton 1909, v. 2; Shull 1907; Simpson 1928, 1931, 1947, 1949; Slonaker 1902; Smokey 1944; Soper 1944; Surber 1946; Tate 1935; Troucaart 1898–99, 1922; Tryon 1943; Van der Horst 1946; Verrier 1935; Walls 1942; H. G. Watson 1907; M. Weber 1927–28; G. Wilcke 1938.

SEC. 10. TREE SHREW

1. TAXONOMY.—The Tree Shrews are Mammals the size of a good-sized Rat, which they superficially resemble (Figs. 482–86). In their anatomical organization and living habits they closely emulate the primitive, generalized type of Mammals of the Cretaceous Period of the earth's prehistory, roughly estimated as having started 127 million years ago and terminated 58 million years ago.

The Tree Shrews at present are found in India and Assam, in Farther India (Burma, Siam, Indo-China, the Malay Peninsula), southern China, Malaysia west of Wallace's line (Sumatra, Java, Borneo), and in part of the Philippines (Mindanao).

At least seventy-five species have been described so far (Lyon 1913). Best known in the literature are the Dusky Tree Shrew (*Tupaia ferruginea*), Tana (*Tupaia tana*), Anathana (*Anathana ellioti*), Midget Tree Shrew (*Tupaia minor*), the Philippine Tree Shrew (*Urogale everetti*, "Tarra-Bahbooey" of the natives), and the Pen-tailed Shrew (*Ptilocercus lowii*).

Systematically, the Tree Shrews belong to the Family Tupaiidae, which, together with the closely related African Elephant Shrews or Macroscelidae (Figs. 478, 479), form the suborder Menotyphla or Tupaioidea, one of the subdivisions of the Order Insectivora. Other suborders representing the Lipotyphla are: the extinct Deltatheroidea (Cretaceous *Deltatheridium*, Fig. 477, Eocene *Didelphodus*), Centetoidea (Tenrecs of Madagascar, *Solenodon* of Cuba and Haiti, the African Otter Shrew or *Potamogale*), Chrysochloroidea (Golden Moles of South Africa), Erinaceoidea (Zalambdalestidae of Upper Cretaceous, Leptictidae of Upper Cretaceous to Oligocene, the still living Erinaceidae or Hedgehog Family of the Old World, represented by the Hedgehogs and *Gymnurae*), the Soricoidea or the common terrestrial and aquatic Shrews (Soricidae) and the Moles (Talpidae).

2. Character.—In its general appearance and in its size and behavior, the Tree Shrew somewhat resembles the Squirrel, for example, the native Red Squirrel or Chickaree (*Sciurus*

(Soricidae). A row of fine eyelashes sticks out from each eyelid, especially the upper, an additional protection being a few long, stiff bristles growing above and below the eyes (Figs. 488, 489). Similar bristles adorn both the upper and lower jaws and the snout.

The external ears are unlike those of almost any other Mammal. They are reduced in size, and, instead of having the usual shovel shape, they appear shriveled, markedly resembling the auricles of the higher Primates: Monkeys, Apes,

Fig. 482.—Long-nosed Tree Shrew (*Tupaia tana*), a native of Sumatra and Borneo, representative of advanced Insectivorous Mammals or Tupaiidae. Measurements: head and body 25 cm. long. Habit partly arboreal, diurnal, insectivorous, and probably also fructivorous. From A. Brehm's *Tierleben*, 2d ed., v. 2, p. 224, 1880, with special permission of the Bibliographisches Institut A.G. (Dr. E. List), Mannheim, Germany.

hudsonicus, Fig. 494). However, when more closely observed, the Philippine *Urogale* seems more like a typical soricide Shrew, such as the Old World House Shrew (*Crocidura russulus*, Fig. 476), except for its larger size and eyes which are relatively much larger.

The fairly stout body of the Tree Shrew rests upon shorter forelimbs and longer hind limbs, all provided with five toes armed with curved claws. The elongated head terminates in a pointed snout covered with naked, moist skin. The eyes are moderately large, relatively much larger than in the small terrestrial Shrews

and Man. As in the latter, they are almost immobile. (*Cf.* Polyak *et al.*, *The Human Ear in Anatomical Transparencies*, 1946.)

The tail is fairly long and is covered with rather scanty hair; it usually is carried half-raised, often with its tip curled to one side or the other (Fig. 486).

3. Specific features.—The preceding description is that of the Philippine Tree Shrew observed during life and studied in detail by the author. While it may in general be true of the entire family, greater or lesser deviations from it are seen in numerous species scattered over many lands of southern and southeastern Asia and the near-by islands. In *Tana* (Fig. 482), e.g., the snout is longer than in *Anathana* (Fig. 483), which makes the latter approach some of the Lemurs in appearance (Figs. 524, 525). On the other hand, because of the abundance of hair, the tail in both species resembles rather more that of the Squirrels, whereas in the Pen-tailed Tree Shrew (Fig. 484) the hairs are limited to somewhat less than the distal half of the tail, with the hairs of the tuft arranged distichously or in two rows, one on each side.

4. HABITS.—There are many notes about the living habits and character of the Tree Shrews, scattered in the observations of numerous travelers and explorers since their discovery. They were first mentioned by Ellis, one of the surgeons of Captain Cook's expedition (1780), and thereafter by Leschenault de la Tour (1807), Diard (1820), Raffles (1822), Schlegel & Müller (1841), Gray (1848), W. Elliot (*ca.* 1849), Whitehead (*ca.* 1879), and O. Thomas (1892). However, all of them are casual or sketchy, none giving a sufficiently complete picture of the animal.

There is general agreement that, except for *Ptilocercus*, which is nocturnal, all Tree Shrews are diurnal in habit, arboreal, and rather omnivorous in diet, with a preference for insects, such as ladybirds and other small beetles, flies, crickets, grasshoppers, ants, earthworms, and cockroaches. They are also reputed to be partial to birds' eggs, small birds, mice, lizards, and the like. In all species fruits, seeds, and buds form part of the diet, while some species seem to be almost entirely frugivorous. Food is taken both from the ground and from trees.

According to Wharton (1948), who gathered his information from the natives of Mindanao, the Philippine *Urogale* lives in holes in the ground or under rock cliffs and bears about five young in a leaf-lined nest. It is strictly a diurnal animal and sleeps all night, curled into a tight ball. It feeds in the morning hours, regularly visiting certain fruit-bearing trees growing on steep, moist hillsides along river gorges.

About the Dusky Tupaia, Cantor (1846) wrote that at times it sits on its haunches, holding its food between its forelegs; and, after feed-ing, it smoothes its head and face with both forepaws and licks its lips and palms.

According to some observers, the Tree Shrews are alert, fast animals, climbing almost with the agility of a Monkey. Others, on the contrary, question this, since Tree Shrews are often caught by cats and dogs. Young ones are easily tamed, and many live in and around the huts of the native villages in semidomestication, which strangely contrasts with their alleged inclination to quarrel with their own kind.

Tree Shrews live under widely differing conditions, in dense jungle, as well as in bamboo thickets, among scattered trees and bushes in human settlements, and in Burma also as house pets. They are found both in flat country and in mountains, where they climb to 6,000 feet and more, for example, in the Himalayas in India and in Assam, and on Mount Apo, on the Philippine island of Mindanao.

What proportion of time the Tree Shrews spend in the trees and how much on the ground is not quite clear from the scanty information. It seems that in this respect there are considerable differences in various species and genera. The Dusky Tree Shrew and *Anathana* may be more arboreal, the Pen-tailed Tree Shrew entirely so (Le Gros Clark 1926, 1927), whereas *Tana* and *Urogale* possibly are more ground dwellers, although *Tana* and *Urogale* may also frequently climb small trees and bushes. According to Ridley (1895), the Dusky Tree Shrew is more terrestrial in its habits than a squirrel.

According to Robinson & Kloss (1909) and Kloss (1911), only a few species of Tree Shrews are truly arboreal, the majority of them living and feeding mostly on the ground and only occasionally climbing low bushes. Some species, e.g., *Tupaia* of the Nicobar Islands, according to Abbott & Kloss (1902) and Kloss (1903), are undoubtedly arboreal. They are common in the heavy jungle and are found only in the treetops, where they are "as active as squirrels in running along branches, or climbing about amongst smaller twigs in search of insects." Their voice is a sort of trilling squeak.

5. OBSERVATION OF TREE SHREWS IN CAPTIVITY.—Until recently, Tree Shrews have on very few occasions been observed alive under more or less civilized conditions (Brehm, v. 10;

FIG. 483—Anathana (*A. ellioti*), a Tree Shrew native of India south of the river Ganges. The figure represents an adult male specimen. Dimensions: from the tip of the nose to the root of the tail about 8 in., tail 9 in., from the nose to the ear 1½ in. Note relative shortness of the head and larger eyes compared with most other species of the same genus. (From G. R. Waterhouse, in the *Proceedings of the Zoological Society of London, Mammals*, plate XIII, y. 1849.)

FIG. 484—Pen-Tailed Tree Shrew (*Ptilocercus lowii*), the most arboreal of the genus, native of the Malay Peninsula and nearby islands (Sumatra, Borneo, etc.). (From J. E. Gray, in the *Proceedings of the Zoological Society of London, Mammals*, pl. II, y. 1848).

Le Gros Clark 1926, 1927). The following notes were made by the author from observations of a pair of Philippine Tree Shrews, acquired in the summer of 1947 and held in captivity for many months. Additional valuable information was obtained from observing several living animals of the same species in the Brookfield Zoölogical Garden, Brookfield, Illinois. All these Shrews ing the day, the Shrews run about their cages, jumping here and there, constantly examining everything, even when not hungry, climbing up and down the sides, and occasionally hanging for a moment from the ceiling, pushing under the cardboard box given them as a hideout, and poking their long noses everywhere—in short, born busybodies.

Fig. 485.—Philippine Tree Shrew (*Urogale everetti*), a native of the island of Mindanao, Philippines. A Graflex camera flash photo, reduced to two-thirds natural size. The primitive Mammal from which, or from a similar form, the Primate Order, including Man, originated. Note the well-formed eye and the auricle not unlike that of the Monkeys and Apes. (*Cf.* Fig. 477 and following figures.)

came from the slopes of the 9,690-foot-high Mount Apo, the highest elevation in the Philippines, along the river Sibulan.

The Tree Shrew, according to our own observation, is an active, nervous, fussy, intelligent, and inquisitive creature. Most of the time dur-

They are omnivorous. They eat oranges, bananas, apples; like lettuce; nibble at carrots, peanuts, and other vegetables; and love fresh, soft white bread. They have a "sweet tooth." Fresh fruit, such as grapes, is relished by them, while sour oranges and carrots are only nibbled

Fig. 486.—Freehand sketches of the Philippine Tree Shrew. Upper sketch shows its usual appearance when running around the cage investigating, with the characteristic posture of its tail; middle sketch with a raised and bushed-up tail, observing with its left eye (an expression of mild curiosity or slight apprehension); lower sketch shows a characteristic attitude when scratching its fur with one of its forepaws and often "combing" it with the teeth of the upper jaw at the same time.

at. However, they do not care much about dry raisins. Fresh milk they like, but there are individual differences: while one Shrew drinks it by lapping it up to the last drop, another Shrew takes but little.

They are very fond of fresh and frozen meat and, in general, animal food. Any part of a rabbit, guinea pig, or rat they eat avidly, be it

first, the Tree Shrew usually gives the lizard a quick poke with one of its forepaws, always ready to run away if the situation appears dangerous. If the repetition of the trick finally convinces it that the prospective meal can be conquered, it quickly snatches it and carries it away to devour it.

The tidbit these living Cretaceous gourmets

Fig. 487.—Sleeping and resting postures of the Philippine Tree Shrew. Upper figure alone, sound asleep. Lower figure represents a typical pose during an afternoon nap, taken regularly as a matter of daily routine, with one of the pair soundly asleep, the other dozing and keeping vigil.

muscles, internal organs, brain, or fat. Softer bones, cartilage, and tendons are also all consumed.

Anole Lizards are devoured whole with relish, although they are apparently afraid to tackle them alive. When a live lizard is offered to them, it rarely is attacked with a rush, as by the Tarsiers, but rather approached timidly. At

prefer to every other food, however, is meal worms. Two dozen of these given them at each meal are gobbled up in no time. When the meal worms are put in the same dish with fruit and vegetables, the first thing the greedy Shrew does is dig for the worms. In this process the pieces of fruit are disdainfully scattered over the floor of the cage and are partly eaten only after the more tasty morsels have been consumed. Other insects, such as cockroaches, are also eaten with gusto.

One day a fresh pigeon egg was placed for the first time on a dish in the cage. After taking a look at it from some distance and without any preliminary olfactory exploration, in a surprisingly quick rush, the Tree Shrew attacked it and, with a single bite, opened the shell and eagerly lapped its contents, which were running over the floor, and finally it licked off its front paws which had been soiled. In a very short time nothing remained except empty pieces of the shell. Whether or not the animal had had a previous similar experience with eggs in its native jungle, the display indicated that in the wild state bird and lizard eggs may be a frequent fare eagerly sought by the Tree Shrews.

Judging from the greed with which animal food is eaten, Tree Shrews seem to be more carnivores than fructivores or omnivores. On the other hand, considering their timidity when attacking living prey and their liking for certain vegetable products, such as sweet grapes, the foregoing statement must be qualified: Tree Shrews, while partial to animal food, cannot be rated as true, aggressive, bloodthirsty carnivores, such as members of the Weasel, Dog, and Cat tribes, or even like the Tarsier, not to speak of ordinary Shrews (Soricidae), whose greed for animal food in captivity sometimes culminates in cannibalism. (*See* preceding sec. 9, on Common Shrew.)

The principal animal food of the Tree Shrews in the state of nature, it seems, is a variety of insects, grubs, worms, slugs, snails, and other small animals, including vertebrates which, because of their helplessness, can be easily captured, as, for example, young birds, lizards, frogs, and the like, as well as their eggs. For the rest, they have to be satisfied with whatever else nature provides for them in the form of various fruits, which they also like, the sweeter the better, their taste in this respect being substantially not different from our own.

In eating, being no altruists, each Tree Shrew had to look after its own interests. This naturally caused a reaction, which in German is succinctly called *Futterneid* or "competition at the fodder trough." Such rivalry erupted especially at the offering of meal worms. On this occasion the difference in individual character was clearly manifested. The more aggressive and more agile Shrew usually got the better part of the bargain, whereas the other more clumsy and more timid Shrew, which perhaps had been hurt by rough handling when it was caught, had to be satisfied with the leftovers. In a scramble for tidbits, the slighted Shrew was driven off or frightened away, giving expression to its offended feelings by squealing in protest as it ran around the cage.

Outright squabbles or fights, however, were not observed, possibly owing to the abundance of food which the animals had at all times. The squealing was occasionally also elicited on teasing the animals by offering them a desired morsel, and then taking it away.

6. BEHAVIOR.—The captive Tree Shrews became fairly tame very shortly after their arrival. In the course of a few weeks, they were quite confident and could be easily handled, if a certain amount of circumspection was used. However, even after many months of gentle treatment, they still maintained a certain reserve and could not be taken with an unprotected hand. Whenever anything unusual happened in the animal room, they became alarmed and ran quickly behind their cardboard hideout.

Their daily cycle showed two maxima of activity, one early in the morning, the other higher one in the late afternoon. During these two periods they were most active, ate most, ran about, and did exploring. Toward the end of the afternoon period, with the falling dusk, their activity reached its peak: for a few minutes and without an apparent cause, they ran about their cage in confusion, squealing aloud at the same time, gradually quieting down with the coming of night. During the noon hours they usually were quiet, partly resting curled up, one dozing while the other kept watch (Fig. 487). It is interesting to note that the two maxima of activity are the same as those when, according to Ridley (1895), the animals in the Malayan jungle also are "brisk and on the alert."

7. USE OF THE LIMBS.—Throughout many months of captivity special attention was paid to the use of the forelimbs. Ordinarily, the Tree

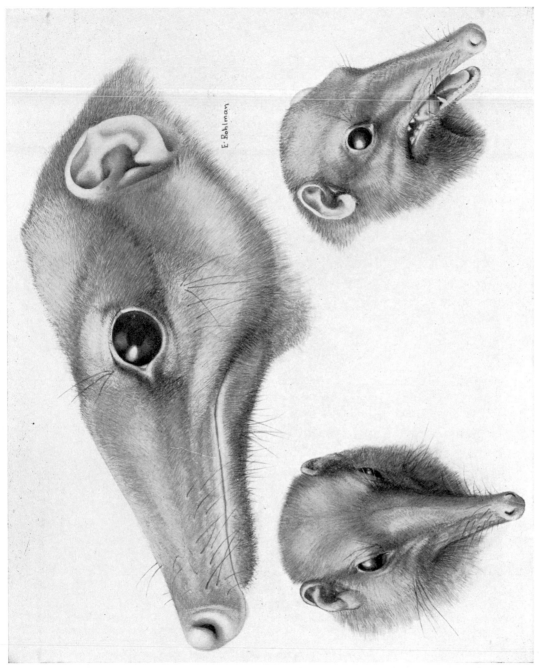

E. Bohlman

FIG. 488.—Philippine Tree Shrew, close-up views of the head and of the physiognomic expression. Upper sketch, left profile magnified almost two times normal size, shows details of the eye, auricle, muzzle with nostrils, etc. Note the long protective vibrissae above and below the eye and under the chin; tiny lashes along both lids; circular, centrally placed pupil; remarkably human shape of the external ear, with an indication of a "Darwin's tubercle." Left lower sketch is almost a frontal view, slightly from above, of the head, a pose induced by rattling the cage, showing both eyes, ears, and nostrils, together with the protective bristles. Right lower sketch shows animal chewing a small Tokay grape, of which, as of other sweet fruit, it is very fond. Lower sketches of approximately three-fourths normal size.

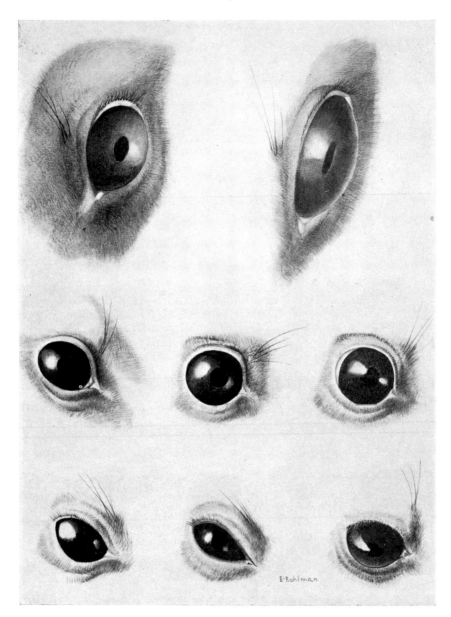

Fig. 489.—The eyes and the surrounding parts of the head of the Philippine Tree Shrew at varying magnifications, expressing different moods and uses. *Upper left*, left eye in three-quarters view, listening to an unfamiliar noise; *upper right*, same, viewed directly from the front. The smaller sketches show the right eye, beginning with the left end of the second row, as follows: animal at rest, looking slightly backward; expression of curiosity, smelling something new, gaze of both eyes directed down the nose toward the explored object; puzzled at an unfamiliar object close to and directly in front of it, with the inner canthus almost out of sight, a part of sclera visible as a semilunar zone along the blunter outer canthus, and with the lashes of the maximally drawn-up upper lid mingling with the fur of that lid, hence indistinguishable from it; dozing in sunshine; very sleepy and unafraid; resting and looking at something at the far end of the cage. Note the varying size and shape of the palpebral fissure, the varying position of the lids, hair, and pupil, indicating unexpected variety of movements of which the eyeball and other parts of the eye are capable. Upper sketches approximately 3× magnified, lower sketches almost twice natural size.

Shrews seized morsels of food with their teeth. Even then, however, they frequently assisted the chewing process by holding the morsel or by pushing it into the mouth with one forepaw. Occasionally they assumed a squirrel-like posture, sitting on their haunches while manipulating a piece of food.

Probably the clearest demonstration of manual dexterity was exhibited when catching a meal worm offered to them with a forceps a few inches outside the cage. This was accomplished usually with a single, quick, and well-aimed stroke of a forepaw. If one attempt failed, it was repeated until the desired morsel was secured.

When a meal worm accidentally fell through the screen floor of the cage into the tray, 3 inches below, even this difficult problem of recapturing the worm was usually mastered with a single forepaw after two or three attempts. The crawling meal worm was clutched with the claws and fingers and carried nimbly, by the same hand that had seized it, to the mouth.

The peak of the performance was reached, on rare occasions, when a fly carelessly sat close to a Tree Shrew and was caught by a flashlike movement of one forepaw and carried with it to the mouth. (*See* for similar actions by the Baboons, chap. XV, 5 [2].)

8. CLIMBING.—The climbing ability of the Philippine Tree Shrew was another item of special interest, as much as it could be observed in the limits of confinement. The general impression was that, while the animals were on the ground most of the time, they climbed the sides of the cage and the ceiling frequently and easily, seemingly for the fun of it, out of sheer exuberance, often remaining for a few seconds suspended from the ceiling before jumping down again. The incessant climbing seemed to be part of their "nature," just as when on the ground they rarely rested but ran around, or at least turned their heads one way or another, looking and observing.

All movements of the head, body, and limbs were quick, including scratching the exact spot that itched with one paw (parasites? *see* Fig. 486, lower sketch). In its vivaciousness the *Urogale* may approach or equal the Red Squirrel or Chickaree and seems more frisky than the Eastern Gray Squirrel. There may, however, be individual differences in disposition or other influences that may make one a better climber than the others.

In the Brookfield Zoo the male, living in his own fairly large compartment, with a branched tree mounted in it, was quite active, whereas the female and the baby were more restrained. Time and time again he climbed up the stem and, like a squirrel, hopped from branch to branch and jumped back again to the ground, 2 or 3 feet below. Occasionally he would squat for a while in the crotch of a branch, then start again on his climbing tour from branch to branch, down and up again. The almost ceaseless activity, the ease with which he climbed the smooth stem and the branches, the way he clutched the thinner twigs with his digits and claws, and the easy leaps he made, all gave the impression that the Tree Shrew feels at home in the trees, being in this respect not much inferior to the Red Squirrel. Whether it compares to the latter in negotiating large gaps in the treetops, observation in its native habitat alone could determine.

The claws apparently are principally used for climbing the stem. When holding small twigs, both the claws and the phalanges of the paws were employed. When on the ground, the animal stepped on the entire palm, both of fore and hind extremities, thus exhibiting a typically plantigrade gait, never digitigrade. Concerning the opposability of the big toe and thumb to other toes and fingers, more observation is required; the impression, however, is that, if present, it is rather limited.

9. VISION.—Judging from the observation of their behavior, the leading sense of Tree Shrews in all activities is undoubtedly sight. They watched attentively the activities about them and got excited when their food was prepared. They recognized, located, and to some extent selected at a distance, by sight, food offered them, whether it was fruit, a lizard, meal worms, or milk.

In puzzling situations, such as when they had to tackle a live lizard, their vision was the only criterion on which they acted. The same was true in locomotion, where the direction of the course, the distance of the jumps, and so forth were principally or exclusively judged by sight.

The sense of smell and Edinger's "oral sense," however, definitely seemed of importance, since the Shrews often "nosed" the morsels before eating them (which the Tarsiers never did), except in the case of meal worms, which they grabbed at once. Their pointed muzzle seemed to be quite an instrument of exploration, its naked, moist tip and delicately shaped nostrils always being in motion when searching about.

They often drank water after meals, and likewise fresh milk, lapping it up by rapidly dipping in and pulling out the tongue.

Last but certainly not the least of their outstanding traits was their cleanliness: as a rule, they performed their natural functions in a restricted locality, in this way keeping most of the cage clean.

10. FIELD OF VISION.—The position of the eyes of the Tree Shrew in the head is lateral, with, however, a slight deviation of the anterior margin of the cornea toward the mid-sagittal plane. In certain situations, for example, when the animal expected a tidbit, it turned its head straight forward, both eyes facing a common fixation point in the mid-sagittal plane in front of the muzzle. Obviously, both eyes were then used together, binocularly, the two corresponding ocular images being depicted on the posterior temporal segments of the two retinae. A rough estimate of the common binocular overlapping of the two fields of vision is from 50° to 60°, in this respect practically duplicating the condition in the Red Squirrel. (*See* sec. 11, on Squirrel.)

11. EYEBALL AND THE RETINA.—The eyeball of the Philippine Tree Shrew is remarkably similar in shape to, but is slightly smaller than, that of the native Red Squirrel (*Sciurus hudsonicus*). Its optical axis is 8.5 mm. long, its transverse horizontal axis 9.3 mm.; in the Squirrel the same dimensions are 9 mm. and 10 mm.

The diameter of the cornea in the horizontal meridian is 7 mm., both in the Tree Shrew and in the Squirrel. In the first, accordingly, the cornea is relatively larger. The corneal curvature in the horizontal plane in the Tree Shrew is paraboloidal and is considerably flatter than in the Squirrel.

The shape of the pupil is fairly circular in both. The lens, both in the Tree Shrew and in the Red Squirrel, is relatively larger and much thicker than in diurnal avian eyes of comparable size, as found, for example, in the Barn Swallow. In both Mammals the anterior lens surface is much flatter than the posterior, the latter in the Tree Shrew being almost hemispherical, in the Squirrel slightly paraboloidal. Both lenses are clearly colored with yellow pigment, less intensively in the Tree Shrew. The optic nerve of the latter is about 1.5 mm. thick, while that of the Squirrel is slightly more.

Ophthalmoscopic examination of the eyes of the Philippine Tree Shrew did not reveal much. No certain sign of a central area—much less of a foveal depression—was found in the locality temporal to the disk, where they could be expected. The only visible feature was a delicate striation radiating from the disk, indicating bundles of nerve fibers, and possibly a slight difference in coloring. Larger blood vessels seem to avoid this area, however, which may be suggestive of an early stage in the phylogenetical differentiation of the central fovea.

A noteworthy feature is a long, thin "cone," similar to that found in the Lizards. It is a residual formation, left after obliteration of the embryonic hyaloid artery. The wider base rests in the optic papilla, the sharp point protrudes into the vitreal cavity. The "cone" consists almost entirely of neuroglial tissue.

The iris, including the stroma, is heavily pigmented, the constrictor well developed, the dilator muscles discernible. The ciliary body, both the muscular part and the folds, is well developed. The chorioid membrane is heavily pigmented.

The retinal membrane lines almost the entire and larger posterior portion of the eyeball. The bacillary layer is made up almost exclusively of cones. The inner cone segments, measuring about 6 microns in thickness, make up a continuous formation as far as the ora terminalis, with hardly any intervening spaces between the adjoining cones. The number of the cones varies little in different localities, being almost uniformly from 20 to 23 cones to a stretch of 150 microns, or from 65 to 75 cones to a stretch of 500 microns (the diameter of the rodless central area of the human eye).

The outer nuclear layer is also remarkable, in that it is composed of a single continuous row of pale, oval nuclei, arranged with their long axes vertical. These nuclei undoubtedly belong to the cone cells, with which they agree in number and arrangement. There are, however, a few rod nuclei, as the employment of oil-immersion objectives shows. These stain much darker and are but a fraction of the cone nuclei, the numerical proportion being about 1 rod nucleus to 5 or 10 cone nuclei.

Still another notable feature is the "granular clods" of Dogiel (*cf.* chap. V, 4 [10, 11, 15]). These are found in the middle zone or *5-b* of the outer plexiform layer as a single, discontinuous row, corresponding exactly with the cone nuclei and the cones. These "clods," as elsewhere, may indicate individual synapses of the cones with midget bipolars (*b & h* synapses), besides those of the cones with the horizontal cells (*b & c*) and other bipolars.

A further notable feature is the thick inner nuclear layer made up of six or seven tiers. The ganglion cell layer is remarkable, since it is continuous in the entire retina, including the extreme periphery. In places, in particular in the posterior segment of the eye, there are, contrary to the statement of Woollard (1926), two or three tiers of ganglion cells. In accordance with this, the layer of the optic fibers is also thick, especially on the temporal side of the papilla. Here fibers collect from the posterior or temporal segment, which is smaller but richer in ganglion cells, owing to which the fiber layer next to the optic papilla increases to no less than half the total thickness of the retina.

In an attempt to appraise the functional efficiency of the eye and retina of the Tree Shrew, the following points must be considered. The first is an almost exclusive presence of cones (an anticipation made by Walls 1942). Interpreted according to the "duplexity theory," the Tree Shrew must be considered as specialized almost exclusively for photopic conditions or daylight vision. The rods, while not entirely absent, are found in only insignificant numbers. This is a reversal of the conditions found in the nocturnal

Vertebrates, even more extreme than in the Northern Brook Silverside or Bullhead, and, above all, in the Tarsier (sec. 12, this chapter). It resembles the conditions found in the Pike, but even more to the detriment of scotopic vision. The observation of the behavior of the Tree Shrew in nature, especially during nocturnal illumination, should be of great interest.

The other point of interest is the practically uniform size of the cones in the entire retina. There are no significant differences in this respect between the posterior parts, where ganglion cells are accumulated in two or three tiers, and other localities, where they are found partly in a single tier. If the functional "grain" varies, it does so because of the synaptical arrangements, for example, the presence or absence of the polysynaptical variety of midget bipolars and midget ganglion cells. Only the application of the Golgi method of staining to the retina could answer this question.

The computation of the functional receptor "grain," on the basis of the number of cones, gives from 4,000 to 5,000 units in a circular area measuring 500 microns in diameter. This is only about one-eighth of the number of cones found in the rodless area of the human central fovea (chap. V, 10 [5]), but is three or four times greater than the number of cones found in the posterior area of the Pike (*cf.* sec. 4 [7], this chapter).

The visual acuity of the Tree Shrew, accordingly, is much below the acuity of human vision. It must, in the biological sense, also be rated as inferior in an arboreal Mammal in comparison with the Pike, considering the much shorter effective distances at which a fish must be able to see in its aquatic habitat. This inferiority of acuity, however, is much compensated by the fact that in the Tree Shrew practically the entire retina, with its huge number of cones, acts as a crude "central area," superior as it is to the extra-areal periphery of the human retina.

In addition, if the good structural development of the cones in the entire expanse of the retina is interpreted physiologically, one is forced to concede that the Tree Shrew has good color vision in the entire field of view, compared with the color perception restricted to the central portion of the human field. This, in a diurnal and arboreal Mammal living in a brightly illuminated tropical habitat and largely subsisting on fruits, is understandable. (*Cf.* K. Guenther 1931; *see* chap. XV.)

12. Comparison of the retina of the Tree Shrew with that of the Red Squirrel and other Mammals.—Since the Tree Shrew in its arboreal habit is similar to the arboreal Rodents, it is of great interest to compare the ocular structures of these two taxonomically so widely different species. (*See also* sec. 11, on Squirrels, this chapter.)

In the Red Squirrel the cones are somewhat smaller, but more numerous, and are found in similarly close formation as far as the ora terminalis. In the extreme periphery, the number is from 22 to 25 cones, in the temporoposterior area 30–35 cones to a stretch of 150 microns, with a very gradual variation. No morphologically discernible rods in the bacillary layer are present. However, in the outer nuclear layer there are two tiers, the upper consisting of larger nuclei and the lower tier of smaller, rounder, but darker nuclei, which may possibly belong to the rods, in a ratio of about 2 to 1.

There is a very definite areal formation in the lateral posterior segment of the eye. Its features are a greater number of smaller cones, a thick inner nuclear layer made up of ten tiers, and an accumulation of ganglion cells in four tiers, instead of two, as in the remainder of the retina.

The "grain" of the cones is surprisingly high. Computed for a circular area 500 microns in diameter, there are at least 10,000 cones in the lateral posterior area, the cone diameter here being from 3 to 4 microns. This is almost one-third of the entire cone population of the rodless territory of the human central fovea, which has the same areal extent. It is about twice the number of the cones found in the posterolateral area of the Tree Shrew, as mentioned in the preceding subsection.

Since the cone apparatus is so well developed, with the cones spreading in close formation as far as the ora terminalis, it is fair to assume good color vision in the entire extent of the field of view, both in the Squirrel and in the Tree Shrew. Both species are examples of strong diurnal adaptation. In contrast, in the Tarsier,

Cat, and Guinea Pig no cones can be found in the bacillary layer or assumed on the basis of the cone nuclei in the outer nuclear layer. Hence it is necessary to assume that these largely nocturnal species are color-blind. (*See,* however, Locher 1933; Walls 1942.)

13. The optic nerves.—The optic nerve of the Tree Shrew is a round and relatively thick cylinder (*on* in Fig. 492). It is made up of bundles of various sizes, held together by neuroglial septa in a way similar to that found in the Monkeys, Apes, and Man. In Weigert-stained sections it measures from 1.2 to 1.5 mm. without the dural sheath. On cross-section it is circular, whereas the optic nerve of the Red Squirrel is more elliptical (*see* following section).

The fibers appear to be well provided with myelin sheaths. Their caliber varies from approximately 1 to 2.5 microns, with a few as much as 3 microns or a little more in thickness. The coarser fibers are absent.

The number of fibers is quite considerable. According to a rough count, it amounts to 300,000 and probably more. Their caliber must be rated as thin. The total number of cones in the retina, according to a rough count, is 2 million, making the cone-fiber ratio 7:1. This indicates that in less favored regions of the retina many cones are synaptically related to a single optic nerve fiber, in order to reduce the functional units to the 1:1 ratio in the region with the greatest visual acuity.

The comparable numbers in the Red Squirrel are: the total number of fibers in the optic nerve, 200,000 or more; the total number of cones in the entire retina, roughly 3 million; the cone to fiber ratio, 15:1. Since the same ratio in the Tree Shrew is only 7:1, the slightly smaller eyes of the latter are better supplied with optic nerve fibers than those of the Squirrel.

In the Elephant Shrew (*Elephantulus rufescens*), a native of the Sudan in Africa, the number of cones is but a fraction of the rods, at least five of the latter filling the space between the two adjoining cones. The numerical ratio of the cones to rods, roughly estimated, may be 1:25. The total cone number in the retina is approximately 1 million. Since the optic nerves in this Insectivore are much thinner than in either the

Tree Shrew or the Red Squirrel, the number of the optic nerve fibers is also much smaller. There are apparently coarser, well-myelinated fibers and possibly also thinner and poorly myelinated ones in the optic nerve. The total number of coarse fibers is approximately 15,000. The cone to fiber ratio, computed on this basis, is 70:1. This indicates a coarse photoreceptor and conductor "grain."

How the biological requirements of the Elephant Shrew are satisfied must remain a problem for future investigation. The good development of the cones agrees well with the diurnal habits and great affinity for light and strong sunshine, emphasized in this species by ob-

In shape and dimensions it may well stand comparison with that of the Red Squirrel, being, however, both in the great hemispheres and in the brain stem, rather more slender, less full and rounded, and hence containing less substance. It is a typical lissencephalous brain, with few faint dents and depressions on the external surface of the neopallium, except for the marked ectorhinal fissures (*rhfiss*) and sulci separating the olfactory bulbs (*olfb*), tracts, and lobes (*olfl*) from the rest of the hemisphere.

There are certain features in which the brain of the Tree Shrew differs strikingly from that of the Red Squirrel. The olfactory bulbs (*olfb*) are roughly three times in volume, and the olfac-

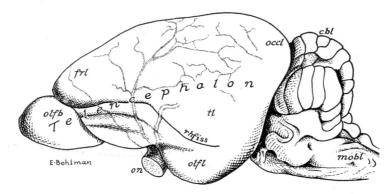

FIG. 490.—Brain of the Philippine Tree Shrew, lateral view, magnification 3×. Note the beginning of a posterior expansion, or occipital lobe (*occl*), which, even though small, is quite noticeable when compared with the blunt end in the Elephant Shrew (Fig. 480), while the olfactory parts are about equally well developed in both. *Labeling: cbl*, cerebellum; *frl*, frontal lobe; *mobl*, oblong medulla; *occl*, occipital lobe; *olfb*, olfactory bulb; *olfl*, olfactory lobe; *on*, optic nerve; *rhfiss*, rhinal fissure; *Telencephalon*, forebrain.

servers (*see* Brehm's *Tierleben*, v. 10, p. 349, 1912). The great number of rods in the retina, on the other hand, indicates that the animal must be equally at home in scotopic and semi-scotopic conditions, in contrast with the *Urogale*, which, judging from the latter's poorly developed rod system, must be expected to be almost entirely photopic.

14. The brain.—The brain of the Philippine Tree Shrew, in all essential details, is identical with that of the Midget Tree Shrew (*Tupaia minor; see* Le Gros Clark 1924, 1933). Like the latter, it has the appearance of the brain of a small Placental Mammal (Figs. 490–92). From the tips of the frontal lobes to the back of the oblong medulla it measures 28 mm., of which 19 mm. is the length of the cerebral hemispheres. At the widest, its diameter measures 18.5 mm.

tory striae much broader, passing over to the slightly larger olfactory gyri or tubercles and the piriform areae, amygdaloid nuclei, and hippocampal gyri that are of about the same volume.

Another marked difference is found in the cerebellum (*cbl*). In the Tree Shrew this organ amounts to barely half the volume or mass of that of the Red Squirrel. Its configuration is much simpler, the hemispheres much less prominent, the elemental *folia* thicker but numbering hardly one-third, altogether giving the impression of a structurally and functionally more primitive, less elaborate, and less efficient organ.

The distribution of the blood vessels over the lateral face of the hemispheres in both species is roughly the same. The exception is the meeting line between the territories of the middle and posterior cerebral arteries, which is more rostrally located in the Tree Shrew, about 5 mm. in front of the occipital poles. (*Cf.* similar arrangement in the human fetus and in the Monkey; *see* chap. X, 7.)

15. Optic pathways and centers of the brain.—Like the eyes and optic nerves, so the highly developed central parts of the visual system betray the Tree Shrew as a "visual animal."

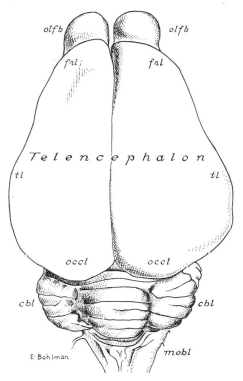

Fig. 491.—Brain of the Philippine Tree Shrew, dorsal view, magnification 3×. Note the complete covering of the midbrain colliculi by the posteriorly expanded occipital lobes, the same colliculi remaining still uncovered in phylogenetically less advanced Elephant Shrew (*see* Figs. 480, 481). This change indicates further "migration," in the *Urogale,* of gnostic visual functions from the superior colliculus of the midbrain to the cerebral cortex of the telencephalon. *Labeling: cbl,* cerebellum; *frl,* frontal lobe; *mobl,* oblong medulla; *occl,* occipital lobe; *olfb,* olfactory bulb; *tl,* temporal lobe; *Telencephalon,* forebrain.

The chiasma or intercrossing of the optic nerves is quite thick and is made up of numerous small intertwining bundles. Unfortunately, it was not possible to determine, in our Weigert-stained series, whether all fibers decussate or whether a part does not and, if it does not, what proportion of the total it represents. This can be

determined only in suitable experiments, e.g., by the application of the Marchi stain after enucleation of one eye.

From the upper margin of the chiasma, a great number of less intensively stained fibers ascend into the ventralmost part of the hypothalamus, entering the floor of the third ventricle and the near-by portions, in the way found in other species of Mammals of low phylogenetical standing (Figs. 191, 192).

There are at least two other and, according to size, more important subcortical visual centers, where the greater majority of optic fibers terminate. One is the superior colliculi of the midbrain, the other the lateral geniculate nuclei of the betweenbrain.

The superior colliculi are exceptionally large and elaborate in structure. They form huge caps surmounting the ventral portion of the midbrain, being almost equal to it in the quantity of substance. Laterally, each colliculus overhangs the sides of the midbrain to the middle. In substance it contains about four times the volume of both subdivisions of the lateral geniculate nucleus. The large size is an indication of the relative preponderance of the mesencephalic over the diencephalic and cortical centers of the visual apparatus of the Tree Shrew.

The internal organization of the superior colliculi also indicates their great functional importance. The optic tract fibers enter from the side in great numbers, forming a thick medullary layer. The upper cortex-like gray cap is rich in nerve cells, except the superficial zonal stratum, where there are but few of them. Just beneath this stratum numerous small nerve cells are condensed in such a way that they resemble the outer granular layer in the striate cortex (chap. VIII, 5–7). Following this is a zone with fewer cells and again, just above the medullary stratum, a layer of more numerous and larger cells, with many cell clusters in the latter. In the ventral layers of the cap appear large cells, as well as smaller ones. The large size and elaborate organization of the superior colliculi are indicative of the important role these mesencephalic centers play in vision in this species. As in the Inframammals, they probably are of greater importance than the striate areae of the cerebral cortex.

The lateral geniculate nucleus, in general, resembles that of the Lower Mammals (*cf.* Fig. 191). As in these, it is made up of two subdivisions—a dorsal and a ventral—attached to the lateral side of the thalamus. The slightly larger dorsal nucleus consists of two thicker laminae and a thin medial one, separated by thin sheets of fibers entering from the optic tract. In some sections there are four laminae, with two slightly thicker lateral and two thinner medial laminae, arranged like the skin of an onion, parallel to the lateral contour of the thalamus. In other sections the laminae are not exactly parallel, resembling the somewhat twisted laminae found in the Higher Primates.

The smaller ventral nucleus is of roughly triangular shape, with many thinner fibers from the tract entering and undoubtedly terminating here (as was found to be the case in the Rat and Cat; *see* chap. VI, 4, 5). The bulk of the fibers of the tract, as in all Lower Mammals, on the lateral side proceeds to the superior colliculus. These also are thin.

Both subdivisions of the lateral geniculate nucleus are filled with closely packed nerve cells, those in the dorsal nucleus being slightly larger. Whether the cells are arranged in laminae in the dorsal nucleus must be examined in well-stained Nissl series of sections. The vascular supply, especially the capillary network, is somewhat denser in both subdivisions of the nucleus than in the adjacent thalamus.

The striate area in our series was difficult to identify. Its exact boundaries can be determined only with a series of well-stained Nissl sections. According to Le Gros Clark (1931), this area is located in the posterior extremity of the occipital lobe. It extends on both the lateral and the medial faces (Fig. 279, *C*).

In our own Weigert-stained sections this area appears to extend on the lateral face of the lobe down as far as the boundary of the second and third fifth, indicated by a slight dent and a blood vessel. On the medial side, the striate area extends over the interhemispheric surface and a little over the so-called cerebellar surface, which, however, faces the superior colliculus.

The medial geniculate nucleus is much less developed. In volume it represents only approximately one-eighth or one-tenth of the lateral geniculate nucleus. This difference indicates the

lesser importance of hearing for the Tree Shrew, as do also the reduced and deformed external ears (*see* Figs. 485, 488).

The oculomotor apparatus of the brain stem is very well developed. The oculomotor nerve is quite thick, and its nuclei, both somatic and vegetative, are large nests of cells. This is also true of the trochlear and abducent nerves and nuclei.

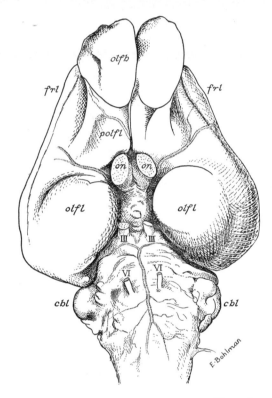

Fig. 492.—Brain of the Philippine Tree Shrew, basal view, magnification 3×. Note the thick optic nerves (*on*) which make possible high visual acuity in this diurnal species, which is in agreement with the numerous cones found in its retina. Well-developed oculomotor nerves (*III*) and the abducent nerves (*VI*) also indicate good motility of the visual apparatus, while the large olfactory centers (*olfb, olfl*) indicate that smell is an essential sense still relied upon by this species. *Labeling: cbl,* cerebellum; *frl,* frontal lobe; *olfb,* olfactory bulb; *olfl,* olfactory lobe; *on,* optic nerve; *polfl,* parolfactory lobe; *III,* oculomotor nerve; *VI,* abducent nerve.

16. THE PHYLOGENETICAL AFFINITIES OF THE TREE SHREWS.—The habits and anatomical peculiarities of the Tree Shrew described in the preceding paragraphs offer an opportunity to appraise the biological importance of their several faculties, to speculate how they could have evolved in the past, to compare them with those of the Rodents similarly adapted to an arboreal life, and to make tentative deductions concerning the role of the Mammals similar to the Tree Shrews in the origin of the Primates.

The eye of the modern Tree Shrew, especially the retina, is that of a Mammal strongly, almost exclusively, specialized for photopic conditions or daylight vision. Since in it the overwhelming majority of photoreceptors are cones, its retina, by no stretch of the imagination, can be considered to represent a "generalized type" from which, on the one hand, the photoreceptors of Monkey, Ape, and Man have evolved and, on the other, those of the preponderantly nocturnal Lemurs. (Such assumption was made by Woollard 1926, 1927, and others.)

It is, then, more appropriate to hypothesize that the original generalized condition, developed by the Vertebrate Ancestors and inherited through the Fishes, Amphibians, and Reptilians by the Early Mammals, was taken over directly by the Primate Ancestors which subsequently gave rise to Monkeys, Apes, and Man. Such a duplex retina and visual system may be somewhat exemplified by the Elephant Shrews. The Tree Shrews, strongly adapted for photopic conditions, almost opposite to the entirely scotopic Tarsiers, illustrate only in a general way the stage just preceding the coming of the true Primates after their ancestors had successfully squeezed through the "phylogenetical bottleneck" during the early mammalian "struggle for existence," as discussed in the preceding section. But the Tree Shrews represent a good argument for the assumption that a modicum of duplex visual apparatus may have been salvaged by the Primate Ancestors even during times of stress, a condition keeping balance between the photopic Tree Shrews and the scotopic Soricide Shrews.

Other features of the anatomical equipment also necessitate caution in accepting the Tree Shrew as an illustration of the beginning of primate phylogenesis. Its lateral geniculate nucleus, with a larger dorsal and apparently laminated division, appears advanced beyond the condition found in the Rat and Guinea Pig, approaching one found in the Lemurs and Lower Simians. But, again, this advancement is qualified by the huge superior colliculi of the midbrain, which rather recall Inframammalian Vertebrates, where this visual center preponderates or is definitely supreme. It is a feature altogether characteristic of all lowly Mammals except those in which, as in the Mole and Bat, vision has receded in importance or is abolished.

From its well-developed olfactory centers, it would appear that the Tree Shrew depends greatly upon the sense of smell, more so than do the arboreal Squirrels. As compensation, one would logically expect a lesser development of other senses, especially vision. The behavior of the Tree Shrew, while definitely showing the importance of smell, however, indicates vision to be superior.

Another puzzle is the much inferior development of the cerebellum, the part principally concerned with the delicate regulation of postural movements, especially important in a tree-dwelling animal. While this would agree with the observations of some naturalists, it does not harmonize with the testimony of other travelers or with our own observation of the captive animals, even though some inferiority of the Tree Shrew to the best climbers among the Squirrels, such as the Chickaree, may be conceded (*see* following section).

A tentative interpretation may be suggested, that the relatively underdeveloped cerebellum of the Tree Shrew is compensated for by better development and working of its sight. A similar situation is found in the Barn Swallow, certainly an excellent flier, in which the relatively small cerebellar mechanism is compensated for by an exquisite visual apparatus (*see* sec. 8, on Swallow, this chapter). Obviously, more observation of the behavior of the Tree Shrews in their native habitat is required, with a careful comparative evaluation of the arboreal habits of the different species, correlated with a systematic study of their sense organs and brain, and all compared with that of other arboreal and terrestrial animals.

Whereas the comparison of the brain of the Tree Shrew with that of the Red Squirrel is useful, since it concerns species of similar arboreal habits belonging to different orders of Mammals, a comparison with such ground-dwelling representatives of the order of Insectivora as the Old World Hedgehog, Mole, and Common Shrew is likewise of interest. This may give some indication of the hypothetical initial form and function of the visual equipment of the brain, and hence the habits, of the original ancestors of the Tree Shrews or Tupaiidae, from which have evolved the Primates: the Lemurs, Monkeys, Apes, and Man.

The first striking feature noticeable in the brains of the now living primitive Insectivores is the extraordinary development of their olfactory apparatus: olfactory bulbs, tubercles, piriform lobes, and the rest. In the brain of *Centetes*, *Solenodon*, *Microgale*, Hedgehog (*Erinaceus*), *Gymnura*, *Blarina*, *Crocidura*, *Scalops*, *Talpa*, *Chrysochloris*, and *Macroscelides* not less than half of the whole organ, judging from the surface aspect, is olfactory (*see* Le Gros Clark 1932).

In the Jumping Shrew, for example, the neopallium or "new cortex" concerned with nonolfactory functions, such as vision, hearing, and skilled movements, is represented by a minute cap mounted over the huge olfactory parts (Fig. 279, *A*). Since most of these species are highly specialized for a particular mode of life, e.g., subterranean in the case of the Moles, where the senses of smell, touch, taste, and hearing, are the only ones that matter, the excessive development of the olfactory system must be considered as a secondary adaptation.

The original condition of the early mammalian ancestors may be more truly represented by the terrestrial Shrews, such as the native *Blarina* and the Old World *Crocidura*, in which the neopallial cortex is somewhat better developed. Compared with the brain of the Short-tailed Shrew (*Blarina brevicauda*), the brain of the Philippine Tree Shrew is far advanced. In it the entire mass of the olfactory parts amounts to hardly more than one-third, the neopallium to two-thirds. The small extent of the neopallium in *Blarina* and the large olfactory apparatus agree well with the small eyes, poor sight, and principal dependence upon smell. The recession of the olfactory apparatus and the sizable development of the neopallial cortex in *Urogale* again fit well the greater role that vision plays in its life, whereas audition may have remained on the same level or receded somewhat.

The increased size of the neopallium in *Urogale* compared with *Blarina* is noticeable in three directions: frontal, temporal, and occipital. Whereas in *Blarina* there are hardly more

than the beginnings of the frontal and occipital expansions and none of the temporal, in *Urogale* the three poles of the hemisphere, in particular the frontal, are well formed (Figs. 490–92). In the development of adequate cortical centers for the higher senses: sight (*occl*, occipital lobe), hearing (*tl*, temporal lobe and Sylvian region), and the more elaborate sensory-motor functions (*frl*, frontal lobe), the Tree Shrews excel all other Insectivores. It is because of this that they are regarded as the "progressive" representatives of an insectivorous stock from which the Primate Order may have evolved. (*Cf.* Figs. 274, 275.)

The objections made to this interpretation, because of the presence of claws on the hands and feet of the Tree Shrews (Lorenz 1927), seem of less weight when one considers, first, that all primitive Insectivores possess claws, even though the assumption must be made that the Primates must have arisen from similar forms; and, second, that in certain species which are unquestionably Primates, the nails still either resemble rudimentary claws or actually are claws (e.g., *Hapale*, Tarsier; *see* following section).

Altogether, most of the available evidence points in the direction of some insectivorous Mammals, more or less resembling modern Tree Shrews, as the probable form from which the Primates originated. In Le Gros Clark's words (1932): "It may be deemed appropriate that special emphasis should be laid on the highly developed condition of the cerebral mechanisms of vision in *Tupaia*, for it evidently indicates that in this animal the visual sense exerts a predominating influence over its behavioural reactions, and this is precisely what Elliot Smith has held to be fundamentally characteristic of the Primate phylum as contrasted with other mammalian groups."

In support of his thesis Le Gros Clark points out the following features in which *Tupaia* approximates the Primates: large brain size, the presence of an incipient calcarine sulcus, a distinct temporal pole, a richly differentiated and laminated cerebral cortex, differentiation of cortical areae, thick optic nerves, large lateral geniculate nuclei with incipient lamination, large and well-laminated striate areae, well-differentiated oculomotor nuclei which also include a distinct median group of cells, and a nuclear differentiation of the thalami.

All these distinct anatomical features indicate that the Tree Shrew has made at least the first evolutionary step beyond the undoubtedly more primitive Soricide Shrews toward the true Primates—the Lemurs, Tarsiers, Monkeys, and Apes—irrespective of whether or not it is to be classified in the technical sense as a Primate. "Many of the features of the brain of *Tupaia* are remarkably 'progressive' and certainly confirm the opinion of those authors who are disposed to regard the *Tupaioidea* as representatives of an insectivorous stock which may well have given rise in Palaeocene times to the early Primates." Hence, "the Tree Shrews," in Le Gros Clark's opinion, "should logically be classified as primitive Primates and grouped with them," even though "they are still much more primitive than any recent member of this order. . . ."

In summary, the modern Tree Shrews, in the light of past and present investigations, are revealed as strongly diurnal Mammals, with an acute sense of vision and a structurally well-differentiated visual system that has definitely assumed the leading role in their life. This is a far cry from the nocturnal Soricides, largely depending on olfaction, audition, and the tactile sense.

However, because of their excessive photopic specialization, a doubt must be raised whether modern Tree Shrews represent more than a general example of the actual forms which gave rise to the Monkeys, Apes, and Humans, most of which possess a more balanced duplex visual mechanism. In any case, the Tree Shrews may illustrate the first decisive step in the emancipation from the lowly olfactory level of the terrestrial existence which led toward the arboreal life and intellectual development of the Primates. (*See* following sections in this chapter and chap. XV.)

17. Prehistory of the Tree Shrews.— The reason for the great scientific interest in the Tree Shrews is their kinship with the Early Insectivores that lived during the Cretaceous Period of the prehistory of the earth. Such was the *Deltatheridium*, which lived from 80 to 100 million years ago and which is considered to be the ancestor of all extinct and modern orders of the Placental Mammals, including the Primates (Fig. 477). These Early Insectivores, in turn, developed from still older and more primitive Mammals, the Pantotheria or Pantotheres of the Jurassic Period, which lived approximately 127 to 152 million years ago, from whom they inherited many anatomical features.

The modern Tree Shrews apparently derived from forms whose scant and somewhat archaic remnants are represented by *Anagale* of the Asiatic Oligocene Epoch of 35 million years ago. They may not be identical with their predecessors in all anatomical details. However, they retain the essential characteristics of their bodily organization and presumably also of their living habits: small body size, sharp-cusped insectivorous dentition, five toes on all four extremities, which are short, a plantigrade gait, diurnal vision, omnivorous taste, and numerous other features reminiscent of their reptilian ancestors. Together with other Insectivores, therefore, the Tree Shrews represent the most primitive living Eutherians (Le Gros Clark 1933).

Even so, the Tree Shrews or Tupaiidae definitely represent an evolutionary upgrade, perhaps tied by an intermediate stage of Gymnurae to ancestors which resembled the modern Ground Shrews or Soricidae, which subsist almost exclusively on animal food and depend chiefly upon the sense of smell and not on vision (*see* preceding section on Common Shrew, this chapter).

In fact, in anatomical makeup—the skeleton, muscles, intestinal tract, and other parts—the Tree Shrews have been found by some to be closer to the Lemurs than to the typical Insectivores, such as, for example, the Hedgehog. Hence they are regarded by a number of authorities as "forms transitional between the primitive insectivore ancestors and more typical primates," and are included by them in the "primate stock" as its "basal members," the Tupaioidea (Gregory 1910; Carlsson 1922; Wood-Jones 1929; Le Gros Clark 1934; Romer 1945).

Other investigators, however, basing their opinion particularly upon cranial development, continue to adhere to "the classical inclusion of the Tupaioidea with the Insectivora," especially the Macroscelidae or Elephant Shrews (Henckel 1928; Klaauw 1929), and deny the possibility of development of the Primates from the Tree Shrews assuming the latter became separated from the Primitive Insectivores long after the differentiation of the Primates (Roux 1947).

18. ARBOREAL LIFE AND THE ORIGIN OF PRIMATES.—In the speculations concerning the origin of Primates from the early generalized Mammals, the arboreal mode of life has been the center of attention. The necessity of adaptation from the original terrestrial existence to the very different and more exacting conditions of life in the trees, according to this view, was the compelling factor that, in a long course of evolution, created the advanced types out of the humble forms of Mammals, a process that eventually culminated in the arrival of *Homo sapiens*, or Modern Man. Thus, broadly stated, the foregoing thesis may at present not meet with much opposition. The difficulty, however, arises when it comes to identifying and evaluating all the probable factors that were at work and to link these in a causal chain of events. (*Cf.* chap. XV.)

The first question is: Why should there have been any need for some of the early Mammals to leave the ground and to climb the trees? Keeping in mind the familiar picture of a cat taking to the tree when it meets a dog, as the better part of valor, one may think of the relative safety the trees offered against ground-dwelling marauders. From what we know of conditions during the Jurassic and Cretaceous Periods, the time called the "Age of Reptiles," there certainly was no lack of rapacious beasts to make life miserable for the small and weak ancestors of the Mammals.

Granting that the factor of safety played its role, it could hardly have been decisive. This is demonstrated by the success of the modern terrestrial Shrews or Soricidae, smallest among the Mammals, which, since their appearance at least 50 million years ago, have not only held their own but managed to spread over the greater part of the habitable globe. And this they achieved in spite of remaining strictly ground dwellers, while some have also taken to the water. Most other Insectivora likewise are ground dwellers, and somehow or other have survived. The only exception is the Flying Bats or Chiroptera, which alone of the Mammals had developed the ability to fly, through which they acquired an abundant source of food and comparative safety.

In their ground-dwelling mode of life, most modern Insectivora resemble the early land Vertebrates, which, of necessity, must have been terrestrial. Paleontological studies show that the treelike plants were still in their evolutionary infancy during the emergence of these land Vertebrates approximately 300 million years ago, during the Devonian Period. During the subsequent Triassic Period, dating 175 million years ago, when the Ferns, Cycads, Ginkgos, and Conifers already had a long history, the nonplacental Mammals appeared.

Much later, by the time the Placentals had already arrived, during the Paleocene and Eocene Epochs of the early Tertiary Period, from approximately 30 to 60 million years ago, the modern Angiosperms, with their abundance of blossoms and fruits, attained their full development. This appears to have been an opportune time for some of the early terrestrial Insectivores to make more frequent excursions up into the trees. In this light, the thesis that the ancestors of the Mammals, the ancient Pantotheres, which flourished principally during the late Jurassic Period (*ca.* 120 million years ago), were originally arboreal and that the Tree Shrews and the true Primates merely continued their ancestral pattern by keeping to the trees does not look plausible, in spite of such anatomical evidence as the insectivorous dentition and the divergence of the thumb and the big toe found in the Pantotheres.

The next task is to identify the compelling factors which brought about the change from a terrestrial to an arboreal life, with its concomitant reorganization of the body, in particular of limbs, sense organs, and the brain. There seem to have been several of such factors at work in a complex cause-and-effect relationship.

An abundance of fruit in the trees does not seem to have been a direct inducement, at least not during the early phases of arboreal adaptation. The principal lure appears to have been the teeming insect and other small life subsisting on and from the trees. To a venturesome ground-dwelling Insectivore the bugs, slugs, and grubs picked from the trees merely represented a welcome extension of a diet to which it was already accustomed.

An additional and largely new factor was the improvement in the quality of fruit brought about by the co-operation of the winged insects and birds (*cf.* H. N. Ridley 1930). The winged insects appeared during the late Carboniferous Period (225 million years ago), and the birds toward the end of the Jurassic Period (127 million years ago).

Fruits and seeds, as well as animal food, may have been an additional lure that influenced the transformation of the original insectivorous ground dwellers into omnivorous semiarboreal or entirely arboreal Tree Shrews. These, in turn, may have contributed their share to the selective improvement of their own diet and thus prepared the way for some of their members to evolve into fructivorous, tree-dwelling Primates—the Lemurs, Monkeys, and Apes.

For life in the trees an animal requires efficient grasping limbs, good sight, and well-developed brain centers. The first may be obtained by developing either claws that can dig into bark or pads capable of adhering to the surface or digits for clasping twigs. Any of these may be quite efficient, as the examples of the Squirrels, Tree Frogs, Birds, and Primates show.

The Tree Shrews obviously must originally have used claws and still chiefly use them. Only gradually, as some of them became transformed into Lemurs, much bigger in size and with considerably longer digits capable of clasping smaller branches and boughs, did claws become of less importance and, in the Tarsiers and Monkeys, with few exceptions, were transformed into flat nails, giving a better hold. The grasping quadrumanous extremities of the Higher Primates, in turn, helped to establish them firmly in their arboreal habitat.

The present Tree Shrews have not yet achieved this stage. Their grasping ability is rather limited. In climbing they mostly use their claws. Their hands and digits have not become, as yet, grasping instruments with finely diversified movements of tentacles, fit to hold small objects and examine them by vision, smell, and taste, useful though they already are for carrying morsels of food to the mouth. In this respect, the Tree Shrews are but little above some Rodents, particularly Mice, Squir-

rels, and Chipmunks, distinguished by their ability to manipulate food with their forepaws (*see* sec. 11, on Squirrel).

The other requisite—well-developed sight—is also indispensable for a successful life in the trees. This concerns not only visual acuity but also correct space perception, especially distance judgment. The large central area found in the eyes of Tree Shrews indicates the beginning of a differentiation of the locality of acute sight instrumental in epicritic vision and in binocular stereopsis. Stereopsis, or good tridimensional vision with both eyes, seems to be a prime necessity in such a life. This requires at least some overlapping of the two monocular fields of view, creating permanent binocularity. This may not be entirely absent in the Tree Shrews but seems to be inferior to that found in Monkeys.

The third factor necessary to a successful arboreal existence—the brain—is still primitive in size and organization in the Tree Shrews. Nevertheless, it is superior to that of the Soricide and Elephant Shrews, in that it is relatively much bigger, with large, elaborately organized visual centers of the midbrain and between-brain, and with a better-developed cortex, larger striate area, and relatively reduced olfactory apparatus. Altogether, it is a more efficient regulating central organ, though less so than in any of the true Monkeys, or even in the Lemurs.

In the evaluation of the importance of arboreal adaptation for primate evolution, many other factors must also be considered. The arboreal habit alone, obviously, is not a magic formula guaranteeing phylogenetical progress. The proof of this is the Sloth (*Bradypus*), probably one of the most arboreally adapted animals in existence. By restricting its diet to the foliage of the trees, in which it spends its lazy, immobile life, it reduced its senses and intellect to one of the lowest levels in the entire realm of Mammals. The strictly arboreal adaptation in this case was a potent deterrent directly responsible for the low sensory and mental abilities, and it also exerted a deleterious influence upon the entire organization of this Mammal. The arboreal habit alone, therefore, could never have sufficed to start some of the early Mammals toward becoming Primates, which eventually culminated in Man. (*See* for the continuation of this subject the following sections in this chapter, and chap. XV.)

References: Abbott & Kloss 1902; Ärenbäck-Christie-Linde 1900, 1907; J. Anderson 1878; Andrews, Granger, *et al.* 1932; H. E. Anthony 1928; R. Anthony 1912; Anthony & Vallois 1913; Ariëns Kappers, Huber & Crosby 1936; Banks 1931; Barbour 1944; Beattie 1927; Beddard 1901, 1923; Beebe 1949; Belanger 1834; Bellonci 1888; Blanford 1881–91; Blyth 1875; A. Brehm's *Tierleben*, v. 10 (*Säugetiere*, v. 1, p. 354, 1912); Bryant 1945; T. Cantor 1846; Carlsson 1909, 1922; H. C. Chapman 1904; Le Gros Clark 1924, 1925, 1926, 1927, 1928, 1929, 1931, 1932, 1934; E. T. Collins 1921; N. Cook 1939; Cope 1885; Chas. R. Darwin 1859, 1871; Diard 1820; Dobson 1882–83; Dollman 1932; Dunbar-Brander 1923; W. Elliot 1849; W. Ellis 1782; Flatau & Jacobsohn 1899; Flores 1911; V. Franz 1913, 1934, 1935; Gagnebin 1947; Ganser 1880, 1882; Garrod 1879; Ghiselli 1937; Ghosh 1945; J. E. Gray 1850; W. K. Gregory 1910, 1916, 1927, 1930, 1932, 1933, 1935, 1936, 1943, 1951; Grossmann & Mayerhausen 1877; A. Günther 1876; K. Guenther 1931; W. J. Hamilton, Jr. 1930, 1937, 1939, 1940, 1941, 1944; Hardwicke 1822; P. J. Harman 1946; Harrison & Traub 1950; Heller 1910, 1912; K. O. Henckel 1928; Herter & Sgonina 1933–35; Hesse 1951; Hesse & Doflein 1935–43; Horsfield 1851; Hose 1893, 1927; Kloss 1903, 1911; Knopf 1949; Krzywanek & Glaub; Lack 1949; Leche 1905; Leschenault de la Tour 1807 (*see* Belanger); Locher 1933; Lorenz 1927; Lowther 1939; M. W. Lyon 1913; P. F. Mason 1850; W. D. Matthew 1915, 1943; Mayr 1949; Mearns 1905; Merriam 1884; Midlo 1935; G. S. Miller 1902, 1911; R. A. Miller 1935, 1943; Mott 1905, 1907; Mott & Halliburton 1908; Mott & Kelley 1908; Mott *et al.* 1910; Osborn 1929; Ossenkopp 1925; Ovio 1927; Parker & Haswell 1940; A. D. Parker 1941; Piša 1939; Piveteau 1951 and *Traité de paléontologie*, vols. 4–7; Pocock 1939–41; Raffles 1822; Regan 1930; H. N. Ridley 1894, 1895, 1930; Robinson & Kloss (*see* Thomas & Wroughton); Rochon-Duvigneaud 1943; Romer 1943, 1945, 1949; Rose 1912; G. H. Roux 1947; T. C. Ruch 1941; K. Sälzle 1936; Scherzer 1861–63; Schlegel & Müller 1843; G. Schneider 1905; A. H. Schultz 1936, 1940, 1941; S. Schwarz 1935; Sclater & Sclater 1899; Sewerzoff 1929; Shull 1907; O. Sickenberg 1934; G. G. Simpson 1928, 1931, 1937, 1947, 1949; G. Elliot Smith 1900, 1909, 1911, 1925, 1926, 1927, 1928, 1930, 1932; Sonntag 1924; W. L. Straus, Jr. 1940, 1949; Tate 1944, 1947; O. Thomas 1892; Thomas & Wroughton 1909; Van der Horst 1946; Van der Klaauw 1929; Verrier 1935, 1938, 1945; K. Vogt (quoted by Brehm 1912); Walls 1942; G. R. Waterhouse 1849; G. H. Watson 1907; M. Weber 1927–28; C. H. Wharton 1948, 1950; Whithead 1879 (*see* O. Thomas 1892); Woollard 1926, 1927; Ziehen 1903, 1903–34.

SEC. 11. SQUIRREL

1. Taxonomy.—The Squirrels are mostly small Mammals of terrestrial, semiarboreal, or entirely arboreal habit, belonging to the Order of Rodents (Rodentia). In common with other Rodents, such as Mice, Rats, and Beavers, they are distinguished by a dentition adapted for cutting and grinding hard vegetable substances, such as wood and nutshells, with two prominent, sharp, chisel-like upper and lower incisor teeth, one pair in each jaw, and with molar teeth with flat crowns adapted for grinding. In anatomical and physiological constitution, they are, of all native Mammals, best adapted to life in the trees and bushes.

In the following, only the semiarboreal and arboreal genera, the Chipmunks (*Eutamias*) and the Tree Squirrels (*Sciurus*) are considered, in particular the Western Chipmunk (*Eutamias quadrivittatus*) and the Red Squirrel (*Sciurus hudsonicus*), or Chickaree.

The paleontological age of the Sciurides is much more recent than that of the Tree Shrews described in the preceding section, which they emulate in habit and appearance. The earliest record, which is doubtful, according to Bryant (1945), is from the Upper Eocene, dating roughly 30 million years ago, becoming definite in the Lower Eocene of approximately 25 million years ago, the family becoming more numerous only in the Upper Miocene and later, estimated at 20 to 25 million years ago. The ancestral prototype of the Squirrels has not yet been determined, being probably most closely related to the Family Paramyidae.

The first animal whose behavior was observed by this writer in its native habitat was identified, with the help of the authoritative description given by H. E. Anthony in his *Field Book of North American Mammals* (1928), as the Western Chipmunk (Fig. 493). It is a smaller and more slender species than the Eastern Chipmunk (*Tamias striatus*). It is conspicuously striped with five dark and four buff-

lowing is either the Least Chipmunk (*Eutamias minimus*) or the Timber-Line Chipmunk (*Eutamias minimus oreocetes*).

The other animal observed was probably either Bangs Red Squirrel (*Sciurus hudsonicus gymnicus*) or Minnesota Red Squirrel (*Sciurus hudsonicus minnesota*). According to H. E. Anthony, it is the smallest of the North American diurnal arboreal Squirrels (Figs. 494, 495). In summer its upper parts are pale rusty red, its underparts clear white, with a moderately

FIG. 493.—Western Chipmunk (*Eutamias quadrivittatus*), a small terrestrial and semiarboreal Squirrel. Inhabitant of western North America, differentiated into many species, especially numerous in the Rocky Mountain Region. A keensighted, alert, intelligent little Rodent of diurnal habits. It subsists on a variety of fruits, seeds, nuts, and buds and on some insects, grubs, slugs, and bird eggs. It frequently rests on its haunches when consuming food, which leaves its forepaws free to pick fruit or to carry it to its mouth. Redrawn from A. H. Howell, *Revision of the American Chipmunks*, etc. ("North American Fauna," No. 52, 1929).

colored narrow longitudinal stripes, is of an alert, active disposition, and is semiarboreal in habit. Its total length is from 8.5 to 9.5 inches, more than one-third of this belonging to the bushy tail. Its food is seeds, nuts, buds, fruit of many varieties, some insects, and occasionally birds' eggs. Its enemies are Snakes, Hawks, Weasels, Foxes, Coyotes, Badgers, and Wildcats. The genus *Eutamias* is very large and diversified into no less than fifty-seven forms inhabiting western North America. The probable species observed and described in the fol-

bushy tail. Its total length is 12.5 inches, the tail accounting for 4.6 inches. It is strictly diurnal and arboreal. It is alert and inquisitive in disposition, feeding on plant and tree products and occasionally on animal food. It inhabits the coniferous forests of North America. Its enemies are Hawks, Owls, Pine Martens, Foxes, Wildcats, and others.

2. HABITS.—Both the Chipmunk and the Red Squirrel, in their bodily equipment, appear to be admirably adapted to their particular

modes of life, which in the first may be characterized as semiarboreal, in the second as completely arboreal.

The western or *Eutamias* genus of Chipmunks are of more slender form and more agile than the eastern *Tamias* genus and are far more "plastic" in their adaption to the many locally varying conditions of the Rocky Mountain Region. In the words of H. E. Anthony, they are

ground nests, to be consumed during the winter. Their habit is terrestrial, although they climb readily when pursued by an enemy or to get fruit or nuts from the shrubs. The Eastern Chipmunk, on occasion, climbs trees of considerable height, though not so well as the Red Squirrel.

The Red Squirrel or Chickaree, the commonest Tree Squirrel, is essentially a denizen of the

FIG. 494.—Red Squirrel or Chickaree (*Sciurus hudsonicus*), a small, strictly arboreal Squirrel, alert, intelligent, and vivacious, an inhabitant of the coniferous forests of North America. It is the smallest of the native arboreal Squirrels, strictly diurnal in habit, and the best climber of them all. It subsists on various fruits and buds, seeds and nuts, especially pine cones. It has the reputation of being a robber of birds' nests and is considered "the most carnivorous of our Squirrels." Its character is bold and daring, its curiosity insatiable. The arboreal Squirrels, even more than the semiarboreal Chipmunks, have the ability to manipulate objects in a way similar to that of the Monkeys. In this, however, the Squirrels are greatly handicapped by the absence of thumbs, which forces them to use both of their hands together (as in this figure). This, in spite of their dexterity, is a disadvantage, contrasting with the ability of the higher Primates, including Man, to oppose the thumb to other fingers of the hand, which makes it possible to use each hand independently for delicate grasping movements (the exception is the Primates, which have secondarily lost their thumbs). Redrawn from A. B. Klugh, "Ecology of the Red Squirrel," J. Mammal., v. 8, p. 1, Pl. 1, 1927.

bright, alert, active, and inquisitive creatures, moving about during most of the daylight hours. Those living in the open plains are shyest, since most exposed, whereas the well-protected forest-dwelling species, with avenues of escape at every turn, are bold and curious and are often heard calling, chattering, or scolding the intruder. They store up food in under-

evergreen forests, not being found out of the timbered areas. It is active throughout the year, taking only temporarily to a shelter during inclement winter weather. It subsists on a plant diet of nuts, seeds, and buds and stores up food for winter. This practice makes it an important reforestation agent.

Chickarees "have gained an unsavory reputation as robbers of birds' nests, suckers of eggs, and eaters of fledglings, and many naturalists have written accounts of how the animals were caught in the act. They appear to be the most carnivorous of our Squirrels," according to Anthony.

"The unquenchable curiosity of these Squirrels makes them a conspicuous mammal. Upon the appearance of a man or a Dog they begin a violent harangue and scold and chatter for long

comys volans, which, even though the most arboreal of all Squirrels and also forest dwellers, are strictly nocturnal in habit (Fig. 496).

The "Chickarees," according to Anthony, "are good swimmers and have been known to cross bodies of water a mile in extent." In this respect they resemble their larger relatives, the Eastern Gray Squirrels, which also do not hesitate to take to the water during their migrations across the country.

Fig. 495.—Red Squirrel, a young, not fully grown animal, in a pose expressing intense curiosity. The Red Squirrel represents, in its climbing dexterity, the keenness of its higher senses, and its supple sensory-motor co-ordination, a high degree of adaptation of a pure quadruped to an arboreal mode of life. Redrawn from A. B. Klugh, "Ecology of the Red Squirrel," J. Mammal., v. 8, p. 1, Pl. 2, 1927.

periods of time. Instead of being shy and secretive, like most wild mammals, they attract attention and seem to feel that nothing on the ground will be able to catch them in the trees."

The most important characteristic of the Chickaree is its strict diurnality. In this respect it is like the rest of the Arboreal Squirrels, the Eastern Gray Squirrel (*Sciurus carolinensis*), the Tuft-eared Squirrel (*Sciurus aberti aberti*), and the Fox Squirrel (*Sciurus niger*). It differs from the Flying Squirrels of the genus *Glau-*

3. NOTE ON THE BEHAVIOR OF WESTERN CHIPMUNK.—The observation of the behavior of the Western Chipmunk recorded in the following was made on August 12, 1950, in Jackson Hole, in Grand Teton National Park, in the western part of Wyoming, just south of Yellowstone National Park. The time was about 8:00 A.M., along Cottonwood Creek, a tributary of the Snake River. The window of the cabin overlooked a little patch extending to the arm of the creek, overgrown by tall grass, with a few

trees and shrubs in it. The campers were mostly gone, and the camp was quiet.

There was a slight stir among the vegetation only a few feet from the cabin window. A little Chipmunk appeared along one of the slender stems of a berry bush whose fruit was just beginning to turn red. This shrub was later identified as Shadbush or Juneberry (*Amelanchier*

ripening at that high elevation, from 5,000 to 6,000 feet, as late as the second half of the month of August.

Observing the striped, rusty, and alert little Rodent, it was difficult to imagine a Mammal more nimble and better adapted to an arboreal way of life. The manner in which it climbed and fed may well illustrate the beginnings of the

Fig. 496.—Flying Squirrel (*Glaucomys volans*), a native North American, strictly arboreal rodent of nocturnal habit, possessing lateral skin folds extending between the fore and hind legs, by means of which it can glide from one tree to another. Phylogenetically, this mode of locomotion may be considered the first step in the evolution of flight, fully developed by the Birds, Bats, and the extinct Flying Lizards. The picture shows two young squirrels peeking from a hole in a dead branch of a tree, their usual home. Note the large, spherically curved corneae of the eyes and the long whiskers, both characteristic of the nocturnal Mammals. Courtesy R. C. Hermes, Buffalo, New York.

canadensis), or a kindred western species (*see* F. S. Mathews, *Field Book of American Trees and Shrubs*). Its fruit is described as "a dry, edible berry, lacking distinct flavor, resembling a huckleberry, varying in color from crimson through magenta to dark or black purple, according to the stages of development," and

arboreal adaptation of the early insectivorous ancestors of the Primates. Since the clusters of berries hung at the ends of the branches, the animal had to reach for them with its forepaws, sometimes stretching itself as far as its body and limbs would permit. The principal instruments to secure its hold on the twig were its hind limbs. This freed its forelimbs for "manipulation," to gather the terminal berry-bearing twigs, to pluck one berry, to retreat to a stronger limb in order to assume a more comfortable position on its haunches, and to nibble on the fruit which it dexterously held and turned in both "hands."

The process of picking a berry and consuming it was repeated about a dozen times until hunger was satisfied. In order to get to the fruit, the Chipmunk had to reach for different branches, always holding its bushy tail in a certain position, indicating that this part may be used less as an "organ of balance" than as a "tactile organ" in order to maintain precise orientation in space by means of the tactile rather than the vestibular sense. When it wanted to climb another stem of the bush, the Chipmunk would easily leap a foot or so, commensurate for his size with the average leap of two or three feet that the Red Squirrel usually makes when not hard pressed.

The Western Chipmunk appears to be as perfectly adapted to life in the shrubs as is the Red Squirrel to life in larger trees. If measured by an absolute standard, the Chipmunk appears hardly less arboreal than the Philippine Tree Shrew or *Urogale* described in the preceding section of this chapter, at least as far as it is possible to judge by observing the latter in captivity.

The Chipmunk is adapted to a semiarboreal way of life, that is, in shrubs, because it gathers food from smaller plants, whence an important part of its sustenance derives, instead of in tall trees, as is the case with the Sciuride Squirrels. The Chipmunk seems to be an earlier, more primitive type, less emancipated from terrestrial habit, hence representing an earlier, less advanced phase of arborealization than do the Sciuride Squirrels.

In locating and recognizing the fruit on the shrubs and in gathering it, it is fair to assume that the Chipmunk's eyesight is not only the most important, but the only, guiding sense. The fruit of the Juneberry and of similar shrubs does not make a noise, nor does it produce an odor that would be effective at any considerable distance. It acts upon the sense of sight alone before it is selected and put into the mouth, after which other senses, those of smell, touch, and taste, are used to determine edibility.

Hearing plays no direct role in the procurement of plant food, even though it performs a biologically important role as an active and passive warning sense. Hearing is of capital importance as a distant warning sense to so small an animal, living mostly in tall and dense vegetation, which restricts or eliminates sight. In these circumstances hearing is the only sense through which the animal is alerted to an approaching, invisible predator. Only when a Chipmunk climbs up a shrub or a tree, as it often does, does sight become useful as an important distance receptor, warning of approaching danger, which makes the ability to climb an important avenue of escape and eventual survival.

In this appraisal of the factors which make the Chipmunk's "world," the diurnal Birds of Prey, moving about above the level of the obstructing vegetation, are an exception; these can easily be noticed both by sight and by hearing. On the other hand, the diurnality of the Chipmunk and its instinct to retire at nightfall to the relative safety of its underground burrow appear to be sufficient protection against the silent nocturnal Owls. As a means of survival, sight is of capital importance to a diurnal animal like the Chipmunk in view of its role in acquiring food and, in open country, also as a warning sense.

4. NOTE ON THE BEHAVIOR OF TREE SQUIRRELS.—The Squirrels, both the Eastern Gray Squirrel and the Red Squirrel or Chickaree, especially the latter, become very excited when they notice a potential source of danger, for example, a human intruder. From a safe vantage point, such as a high branch, they chatter loudly, scolding at the intruder for quite a while, shaking body and tail violently, and occasionally pounding on the branch on which they stand. All the while they attentively observe the object of their ill will, using only one eye, and shifting occasionally from one side to the other.

Or, when sensing danger or when perplexed, they "freeze," that is, remain perfectly still while looking at the object of their suspicion with one eye only. In this they behave just as other Rodents, such as the Guinea Pig, Gopher, Chipmunk, and Woodchuck, do in similar situations. Monocular vision alone is used as an epicritic sense.

When, however, the Chickaree becomes truly inquisitive about an object, it quiets down and turns toward it, facing it squarely with both eyes, binocularly (as does the Tree Shrew). It also uses both eyes when it climbs a tree trunk or runs along the limb or branch of a tree to the very end and leaps to the opposite branch of an adjoining tree.

Crossing the gap from the tip of a branch to the opposite branch of another tree is the most dangerous of the many superb antics which these accomplished acrobats are capable of performing. The reason is obvious. The twig is thinnest at the end. It is least able to support the weight of the heavy body of a running animal. It bends just at the moment when it receives the additional push necessary to give a sufficient momentum to the leaping animal, which, in turn, increases even more the gap between the terminal twig and the opposite tree it wishes to climb onto. The unsteadiness of the support and the obscuring of the opposite branch by leaves make a leap from one tree to another perilous. A miss in grabbing the opposite twig by the forepaws would result either in a serious injury or death, depending on the distance from the ground. Frequent near-misses may be observed, especially when the animal is frightened by a pursuer.

In ordinary circumstances a Squirrel does not seem to pay much detailed visual attention to the surface of the bark of a trunk or limb as it climbs or runs. Its head is carried rather high, and its eyes are directed straight ahead. Even though it does not seem to examine the path carefully, it is certain that its eyes are directed upon the course along which it runs so that it is able to modify its movements according to need. For this purpose the numerous cones, in close formation extending almost as far as the ora terminalis of the retina, are most useful to the Squirrel, as they are to the Tree Shrew.

In difficult situations, such as negotiating a long gap between the opposite branches of two neighboring trees, the Squirrel must use all its superb powers of vision to measure the distance and the position of both takeoff and point of landing and probably other matters, such as the thickness and the position of the twig on which it is to land, as well. Binocular stereoscopic vision must then be utilized to its full capacity if it is to render satisfactory service and accomplish its biological purpose, which in most cases is either the saving of individual life, the acquisition of a mate, or the procurement of necessary food.

The Red Squirrel shows inherent and unmatched powers of co-ordination of stereopsis and motility, especially when hotly pursued. Then it runs with amazing speed up or down a tree trunk or along a crooked limb to the very end or makes, without the slightest hesitation or miss, an astonishing leap of 3–4 feet or more, as recorded by Klugh (1927).

The performance of the Red Squirrel may be close to the peak of arboreal locomotion of any Mammal of its size. In its way it is comparable to the performance of the best climbers among the Monkeys. A thorough functional analysis of its movements by means of modern photographic techniques would undoubtedly furnish the basis for an objective scientific appraisal of the arboreal mode of life, and what it meant in the evolution of Primates. (*Cf.* sections on Tree Shrew and on Tarsier, this chapter, and also chap. XV.)

5. Squirrels, arboreal habit, and the origin of Primates.—The factors responsible for the phylogenetical emergence and molding of the Primates, in spite of profuse literature on this subject beginning with the classical writings of Charles R. Darwin, are difficult to understand even now.

Two factors especially have been prominently discussed. One is the pre-eminence of primate vision, which is of diurnal type; the other is the arboreal way of life adhered to by most of the Primates, with the notable exception of Man. But although both these factors have been much analyzed, the way in which they have worked together to produce Primates remains unexplained. Above all, the initial phylogenetical stimulus which transformed some of the early insectivorous Mammals into Primate Ancestors remains still unknown.

If arboreal life and the pre-eminence of vision it imposed were the prime factors in the rise of Primates, one may well ask: Why have not the Sciuridae and even more the modern Tupaioidea progressed beyond their present state, which they attained long ago?

With respect to the Squirrels, the basic difference between the presumable insectivorous ancestors of the Primates and the early Rodents in anatomical equipment, diet, and probably other more elusive factors may be emphasized. This difference may have been sufficient to allow further perfection in one, while limiting the progress in the other. Such difference may have been essentially dietary. The Primates, as far as our knowledge goes, originated in the tropics, the arboreal Squirrels in colder climates. Their food, even though grown on trees, was markedly different. For the Primates it was soft, succulent fruits, varied in appearance, especially in color, while for the Squirrels it was nuts and seeds, rather uniform in their dull coloring and incased in hard shells. In their nutritive value, fruits rich in carbohydrates also differed substantially from the seeds of the north, filled with proteins and fats.

Both diets, even though imposing an arboreal adaptation, must have had a different effect. The primate ancestors, in order to exist, had to develop manipulative ability and good color vision, whereas the ancient Squirrels had to specialize in gnawing shells and husks and in extracting the seeds with their teeth, while developing but little their manipulative ability and color vision. The Primates had, therefore, to develop the grasping hand with an opposable thumb, capable of holding objects without the use of the other hand, while their dentition remained fundamentally archaic. The Squirrels in turn, relying on their rodent dentition in feeding, went so far as to abandon their thumb. This loss, although detrimental to feeding, made their hands more useful for their mode of climbing by digging with claws into bark, instead of grasping the boughs with the fingers

and the opposable thumb, as the Primates do.

In the retardation of the Squirrels, their late appearance during the Miocene, or 25 million years ago, may also have been some factor, compared with Primates, which had already begun their evolutionary ascent from a generalized stock during the Eocene and Paleocene Epochs, or from 40 to 58 million years ago.

There is no such phylogenetical excuse, however, that could be cited in favor of the Tree Shrews, which have had plenty of time since the origin of Mammals, during which they seem to have remained practically stationary. A thorough appraisal of past and present factors alone may answer this question. (*Cf.* Bryant 1945; Romer 1945.)

In conclusion, while one must accept arboreal life and superior vision as factors responsible for the rise of Primates, the complete story of their origin and of all major factors responsible for it still remains to be told. (*See* chap. XV.)

References: H. E. Anthony 1928; Bobrinskoy *et al.* 1944; A. E. Brehm's *Tierleben*, 4th ed., v. 11 (*Säugetiere*, v. 2), pp. 517, 536, 1914; Bryant 1945; Burroughs 1900, 1923, 1926; Cade 1951; Cahalane 1947; E. T. Collins 1921, Da Cruz Lima 1945; Ellerman 1940–49; F. C. Evans 1951; O. W. Geist 1951, p. 358; Ghosh 1945; W. K. Gregory 1951; Grossmann & Mayerhausen 1877; Hatt 1929; D. O. Hebb 1938; Hesse & Doflein 1935–43; W. E. Howard 1951; A. H. Howell 1929; A. B. Klugh 1927; D. Lack 1949; G. Kolosváry 1934; C. J. S. Locher 1933; Lorente de Nó 1922, 1933, 1934; Malbrant & Maclatchy 1949; E. Mayr 1942, 1949; C. H. Merriam 1884 or 1886; R. A. Miller 1943; A. H. Morgan 1930; O. J. Murie 1927; W. J. C. Murray 1944; W. O. Nagel 1944; Ognev 1947–48; A. D. Packer 1941; Parker & Haswell 1940; Piša 1939; Piveteau 1951 and *Traité de paléontologie*, vols. 4–7; S. Ramón y Cajal 1922, 1924; H. N. Ridley 1930; Rochon-Duvigneaud 1943; Romer 1945; M. Rose 1912; K. Sälzle 1936; G. G. Simpson 1931, 1949; Volkmann 1926; Walls 1942; Walton & Bornemeier 1938, 1939; Watson & Watson 1913; M. Weber 1927–28.

SEC. 12. TARSIER

1. TAXONOMY.—The Tarsier was first described by the noted French naturalist G. L. L. de Buffon in the year 1769. Ever since, because of its unique zoölogical position, it has been an object of scientific interest. According to G. Elliot Smith, the Tarsier is "the most primitive living primate" which undoubtedly represents a definite advancement toward the Higher Primates, the Monkeys and the Apes, in comparison with the Tree Shrews and Lemurs. The Tarsier is considered to be the residue of a side branch of the Early Primates which was wide-

FIG. 497.—Philippine Tarsier (*Tarsius philippinensis* or *T. carbonarius*), a strictly nocturnal and carnivorous Primate from Mount Apo, of the island of Mindanao, Philippines. A Graflex camera flashlight photo, slightly reduced, of an adult animal showing the normal resting posture on flat ground, in the attitude of alertness. The characteristic features are the huge, almost circular eyes, set in a large head, which, together with the soft, fluffy, mottled, grayish-colored fur and the retiring habit, make it markedly resemble its avian counterparts, the Owls. Note the slight difference in the size of the two palpebral openings; the "mongoloid" or oblique position of the lines connecting the inner and outer canthi; the horizontally oval, miotically constricted pupils in daylight, which become widely distended during the night; and the "platyrrhine position" of the nostrils facing laterally, resembling the New World Primates. (*Cf.* following figures.)

spread over Eurasia and North America during the Paleocene and Eocene Epochs, which cover a period from 58 to 20 million years ago.

The Tarsiers (Tarsiidae, Tarsioidea) are at present restricted to the islands bordering on southeastern Asia and near-by regions. One species, the Spectral Tarsier (*Tarsius spectrum*), inhabits the Malay Peninsula, Java, Sumatra, Celebes, and Borneo; the other species, the Philippine Tarsier (*Tarsius carbonarius* or *philippinensis*), is found on the islands of Min-

culiar appearance (Fig. 497). It has a relatively large, round head, with a short muzzle and a pug nose, the nostrils facing laterally, as in the South American platyrrhine Monkeys.

The dentition of the Tarsier is essentially that of an Insectivore. Conspicuous is the sharp **V**-shaped angle formed by the two branches of the lower jaw, characteristic of the Lower Monkeys and only slightly so of Man, whereas in the large Apes the two branches become parallel (*see* Fig. 499).

Fig. 498.—Philippine Tarsier, a primitive Primate, of predaceous habit, survival of an ancient epoch of earth's prehistory, remarkable for its overdeveloped vision strictly adapted to nocturnal life. A resting attitude. Graflex photo.

danao and Bohol. These and perhaps some other less-known species, e.g., *Tarsius fischeri*, represent the Tarsioidea, which systematically are the second suborder of the Order of Primates (Primata), the first and older suborder being the Lemurs (Lemuroidea), the third and more advanced being the Monkeys, Apes, and Man (Pithecoidea or Anthropoidea). (*Cf.* Woollard 1925; Gregory 1951, p. 464.)

2. GENERAL CHARACTER.—The Tarsier is a small, shy, retiring, monkey-like animal of pe-

The Tarsier's large, bulging eyes and big ears are conspicuous and, together with its solemn expression, soft, fluffy fur, and nocturnal habits, make it resemble, especially when in a sitting position, a native Screech Owl (*Otus asio*).

The other conspicuous parts of the anatomical equipment of the Tarsier are its long hind legs, adapted for leaping, and a long, almost naked, tail that likewise assists in locomotion (Fig. 503).

When it is wide awake, its huge eyes are wide open, with the palpebral fissures widened to almost full circles. When the animal is at rest, the large corneae are all that is visible of the eyes, a narrow pericorneal margin of the sclera becoming visible only when the attention of the animal is aroused (Figs. 503, 505).

In ordinary daylight the pupils usually are reduced to small elliptical openings whose longer axes are horizontal (Figs. 497–99). In darkness the pupils expand to the corneal margins. Fine lashes are attached to the palpebral margins, especially those of the upper lid. A bunch of long bristle-like hairs sticks out from each eyebrow. Similar bristles protrude lateral to the eyes from the cheeks and from the upper lips not far from the base of the nose.

The auricles are large, shovel-shaped, and very flexible in shape, resembling those of some Lemurs, such as the African Galagos, the Aye-Aye (*Daubentonia* or *Chiromys madagascariensis*), and some insectivorous Flying Bats. Horizontal wrinkles on the inner face of the auricles are a characteristic feature (*see* Polyak *et al.*,

Fig. 499.—Philippine Tarsier (*Tarsius philippinensis*), a Graflex camera snapshot at rather close range, showing a typical reaction of moderate fright: palpebral fissures maximally open, eyebrows drawn up, mouth half-opened showing typical "insectivorous" sectorial teeth, with auricles widely distended and turned frontally, all features indicating a high degree of preparedness to receive a maximum of visual and auditory stimuli and a readiness for self-defense. Other numerous anatomical details may also be noticed, such as the horizontally elliptical shape of the pupils, here miotically reduced because of the photopic conditions; iris structure when expanded; well-marked lashes on upper lids; platyrrhine position of the nostrils; and the marked foldings of the auricular surfaces. (*Cf.* Figs. 497, 498.)

The Human Ear in Anatomical Transparencies,
1946).

The hands and the feet are perhaps the most
remarkable features of the anatomical equipment of the Tarsier. Whereas the ears and the
eyes, even though of an uncommon appearance,
are duplicated in some other Mammals, the terminal parts of the four extremities are truly
those of a full-fledged Primate. Even though

typical grasping organs. Even though there is
not, as yet, as much diversity in their use as is
found in the true Monkeys, they already approach simian hands and feet.

The usefulness of the Tarsier's hands, however, is still largely limited to crude prehension
and locomotion. To this end the tips of the fingers and, far more, the tips of the toes have
spread into flat, soft pads which can adhere

Fig. 500.—Slender Loris (*Loris* or *Stenops gracilis*), native of South India and Ceylon, one of two small, nocturnal, slow-moving Lemurs of Asia. Inhabitant of the forests, feeding on fruits, insects, birds, and other small life.
Note perfectly apposited eyes oriented in a frontal plane; large, round corneae, and almost vertical pupils, indicative
of a nocturnal habit; small interval separating the inner margins of the corneae caused by the large size and approximation of the eyeballs; perfect binocular fixation, making for a large overlapping of both monocular fields of view,
a sure sign of excellent stereopsis. *Cf.* preceding photos of the Tarsier. With the permission of Wide World Photo,
1951. (*See* Fig. 524.)

specially adapted to the Tarsier's peculiar mode
of living, they retain their original, primitive
features, most important, the five digits. While
the "hand" and "foot" of a Tree Shrew are still
essentially the "paws" of the Infraprimate
Mammals, of limited use as prehensile organs
(Figs. 485–87), in the Tarsier they have become

firmly to the surface of the grasped object,
such as the upright bamboo stems, which is
especially useful in the Tarsier's rainy habitat.

The nails of almost all fingers still are definitely narrow, pointed claws, closely adhering
to, and about the same length as, the terminal
phalanges, except in the second and third toes,

where the claws are long and turn up. The big toes alone possess flat nails resembling those found in most other Primates (Figs. 513, 514).

The root of the long tail is stiff, being a continuation of the spine, and affords support to the body when the animal hangs suspended from a stem. The greater part of the tail, however, is flexible. The hairs on the tip of the tail are slightly longer, thus making up a scanty tuft.

habitat little or almost nothing was known until modern times. But even after the recent reports by Hoogstraal (1947) and Wharton (1948), much remains obscure. A thorough scientific study of the Tarsier, just as of the Tree Shrews, in their native country, considering every angle of habit and habitat, still remains to be done.

From the early travelers Raffles (1822), H. Cuming (1838), S. Muller (1855, 1857),

FIG. 501.—Philippine Tarsier eyeing a meal worm, immediately before making a leap to snatch it. Insects, lizards, and other small animals are the food of this carnivorous Primate, which entirely disdains fruits and other plant products.

The entire bodily organization of the Tarsier is closely adapted to its hopping locomotion in dense undergrowth, probably mostly represented by the bamboo thickets of its tropical home, and to its nocturnal habit.

The anatomy of the Tarsier has attracted a great deal of interest since the early period of modern research and has been worked out in great detail, first by Burmeister (1846) and again by Woollard (1925).

3. HABITS.—About the living habits of the Tarsier and, indeed, about the character of its

Jagor (1873), and H. Rosenberg (1878), one learns that the Tarsiers inhabit dense forests in flat parts of their native countries. By daytime they hide in the dark, humid recesses, in thick foliage, or in the holes of trees. Or they are found between the roots and brambles in the densest bamboo thickets, usually a male and a female together. They make leaps of 3 feet easily.

Their food consists mainly of insects or of lizards, although in need they eat shrimps and cockroaches. The information about vegetable food is contradictory. According to S. Müller, the Tarsier eats various fruits as well as insects, but in Jagor's opinion, it dislikes plant food but eagerly eats grasshoppers. The animal is nocturnal, drowsy during the day and lively during the night, leaping noiselessly here and there, its pupils wide open. The young, carried on its mother's belly, clings to her fur with its hands.

its, all observations made on the Island of Borneo. The taxonomic affinity of this primate suborder to Man is not clearly revealed by blood serum precipitin reactions.

Raven (*see* Tilney 1928, p. 90) found the Tarsier extremely active during the night, "probably the quickest jumper of all mam-

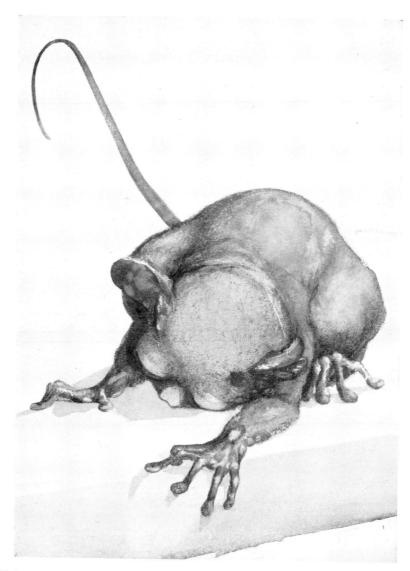

Fig. 502.—Philippine Tarsier, in the typical act of seizing a meal worm, by mouth alone or by mouth and both hands, after a quick leap toward it, during which both eyes are closed, with one ear folded up, and an upraised tail.

The information obtained during the past few years is more abundant and reliable, even though some gaps and contradictions still remain. Le Gros Clark (1924) presented quite an exhaustive report about the Tarsier's habitat, locomotion, use of limbs, food, and eating hab-

mals." According to G. C. Lewis (1939), the Tarsier's eyes possess great mobility and roll extensively sidewise and vertically in their sockets, "exposing great expanses of white eye ball in the faint light in a way reminiscent of a southern pickaninny hearing a ghost story." In the experience of N. Cook (1939), the sight of the Tarsier in daytime is very poor, the pupils of the eyes reduced to mere pinpoints. The sense of smell is little developed, while hearing is more acute. The animals begin to move "about the time chickens go to roost."

The first successful attempt to bring living Tarsiers to the United States was made by Eckman, and the first scientific study of the living animals was undertaken by Catchpole & Fulton (1939).

A much richer picture of the life of the Philippine Tarsier and its native country is obtained from the firsthand observation of Hoogstraal (1947). While hunting with a headlight at night, he several times saw Tarsiers hopping from branch to branch in the thick second-growth forest in the lowlands of Mindanao, occasionally making long jumps on the ground. The animal apparently is much more abundant than heretofore believed. During the daytime it is usually found in dense, deeply shaded thickets, tightly clutching slender trunks or branches from 4 to 10 feet above the ground. When the animal notices an intruder, it usually moves its head slightly, with a fanlike opening, closing, and twitching of the ears.

Not infrequently a pair, a male and a female, is found in the same tree, sometimes a baby with its mother. During the day they apparently rest, and jump only when the tree in which they sit is cut or violently disturbed. When picked up, they are ready to defend themselves with their sharp, needle-like teeth.

In crowded cages the Tarsiers may fight among themselves, uttering a single, loud, shrill-pitched trill, whereas when they are surprised in the forest they are always silent. Instead of being a scourge of the forest, for which they have been decried by ignorant, sensationalist publicity-seeking writers, they are, in fact, timid little creatures, easily frightened, and Hoogstraal saw some topple over and die of fright. According to his experience, Tarsiers are never found under the roots but always on the branches or slender trunks of the trees.

The Tarsiers search for food only during the night. This consists largely of lizards, insects (mostly orthopterous), beetles, and spiders. Small rodents such as mice are not natural food, at least not for the Philippine Tarsier, these animals not being present in Mindanao. The epithet *carbonarius* or "coal-eater" in its scientific name is, of course, founded upon a baseless myth believed by the local natives, refuted long ago by Jagor (1873).

The manner in which the Tarsier secures its food by leaping upon it and reaching for it with one or both hands is peculiar. The morsel is held in the hand while the Tarsier eats it. The head of the prey is always eaten first, and the remainder gradually pushed into the mouth.

The female Tarsier gives birth to a single baby that arrives fully formed, with open eyes. The baby clings to its mother's belly until quite large. (*Cf.* Fig. 515.)

The latest and equally valuable information about the living habits of the Tarsier is from Charles H. Wharton (1948). He found this "exceedingly specialized" little Primate in the region surrounding the Davao Gulf at the southern end of the Philippine island of Mindanao. The animal thrives best in the second- and third-growth, vine-tangled thickets, along the coast and in the valleys, and sometimes in the gardens of native settlements.

Its favored haunts are thickets of small trees, where it clings to the upright limbs with its long fingers which are equipped with little, round, tenacious pads, especially advantageous in the rainy country where it lives. As night falls, the Tarsier leaves its hideout in a series of rapid leaps from branch to branch. Some of these leaps measure as much as 6 feet. When jumping, it holds its ears extended, hands and feet drawn to the body, with the tail trailing behind. "An instant before landing, the tail swings upward, and the long hind legs come forward to touch first and break the impact."

Its large eyes "can be moved only slightly in their sockets," owing to which "the tarsier must pivot its head about, even to inspect something a few inches to its right or left." Just how good the sight of this entirely nocturnal animal is during the night is not clear from the report.

The large and extremely mobile ears can be folded, betraying an acute sense of hearing, apparently adjusted to the sounds produced by the various insects upon which the Tarsier preys. When its sharpened ears catch a faint noise made by the potential prey, e.g., a large

FIG. 503.—Philippine Tarsier scrambling up a twig or a branch, holding on to it with both hands, the right foot fastened to a stem, the left leg maximally extended, the head turned backward (in the manner of an owl), with its eyes fixing the object of suspicion, its lids maximally drawn back, making the huge eyes appear even larger, and with its pupils reduced to minute, horizontally placed elliptical openings

910

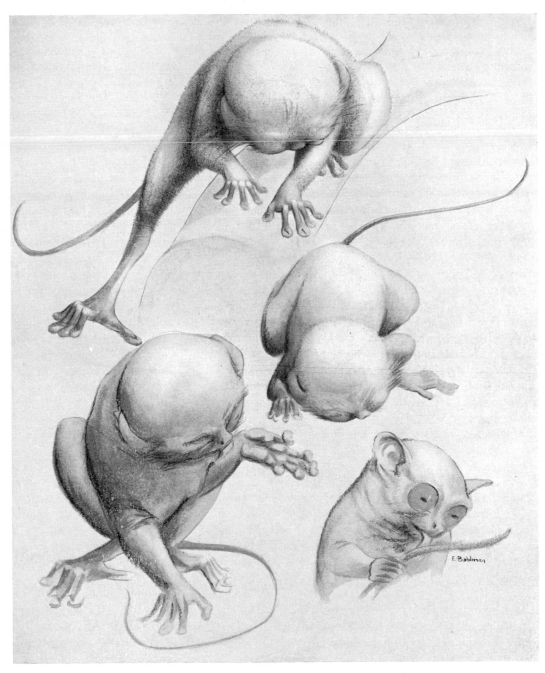

FIG. 504.—A female Philippine Tarsier in various characteristic attitudes of grooming: *above and at left below,* licking fur of her left forearm; *center,* rubbing face against the floor; *right lower corner,* preening and licking the tip of her tail which she holds with her right hand, while gazing at it attentively and with great interest. The Tarsier's preoccupation with its own appearance is interesting in a nocturnal Mammal, the instinct and manipulations resembling those of the true Monkeys.

beetle crawling not far behind, its head slowly turns around until it looks backward, the large eyes widen to the maximum, the pupils expand to the corneal rim, the ears move back and forth until the source of the noise is located, the eyes turning toward the prey. An instant after the eyes have detected the slight stir of the beetle, the Tarsier leaps "across the intervening space faster than the eye can follow," and lands on a near-by branch. The next moment it catches the beetle in its hands and eats it, head first.

How the Tarsier likes the final phase of the hunting drama just described, repeated many times every night in its native jungle, it shows by closing its eyes, now for a while out of action, down to the size of "mere furry slits, completely covered by the russet eyelids."

The food of the Tarsier in the wild state, according to Wharton, consists of insects, lizards, and probably mice(?); in captivity, of grasshoppers, lizards, raw meat, wild birds, beef, liver, meal worms, crabs, mice, June beetles, all to be furnished in abundance to this most carnivorous of the Primates.

The Tarsier's voice, when at peace, is a "beautiful birdlike trill or twittering," resembling "a series of locustlike chirps," or a loud shrill when alarmed.

The pairs like to sit together and hold each other for hours when they are not hunting.

The fable of Tarsiers eating charcoal, which is believed by the natives, apparently has its source in the fact that the animal is frequently found in burned-over places. Connected with this is the story told by the natives that the *amas*, or the "Old Man of the Mountains," in the native language, is attracted by fire and lamp "in order to warm himself."

4. Behavior in captivity.—The two living specimens bought from Mr. Wharton arrived in Chicago via airplane in good shape in July, 1947. They were a pair, a male and a female. In order to give them enough room for exercise, they were placed in a large cage, about $2\frac{1}{2} \times 3 \times 3$ feet. A shelf was put in the back, 18 inches above the floor, together with several fresh leafy oak branches to climb on and to hide in. A small cardboard box was also placed in the cage to serve as a hiding place and as sleeping quarters. The floor tray was covered with dry

sand, and care was taken to have fresh water at all times. Following are a few notes from my personal observations (*see also* accompanying figures).

During the day the animals, when undisturbed, were usually found sitting on their haunches, hiding behind the leaves, either on the shelf or perching on a branch. They were like two fluffy, round, brown little balls, almost perfectly motionless except for an occasional, barely perceptible, twitching of the tips of the auricles and a slight rotation of the head.

The female in particular, as she clung to a twig, resembled a little owl more than a mammal. The two pairs of big, round, bulging, brown eyes were motionless, intently glued on the intruder. The pupils were small ovals, 1×2 mm. in diameter, with the longer axis horizontal. No movement of the lids was observed for a long while. When a pencil was moved behind the back of the male as he sat on the shelf, he slowly rotated his head until he faced directly backward, and fixed the object with his protruding eyes, as if puzzled, also moving both auricles in the direction of the gaze. After the pencil was withdrawn, he again resumed his former statue-like pose. A similar experiment with the female sitting on a branch a few inches above her companion produced the same effect. Otherwise, when unmolested, both animals were motionless, as if drowsy or asleep, their eyes kept wide open, their gaze directed past the observer, as if oblivious of his presence. In this frozen pose they continued after the observer moved away.

One October afternoon when the room was filled with sunlight, both Tarsiers were found concealed behind the leafy branches. The female was facing the door of the room, quietly watching in that direction. Her pupils were reduced to minute horizontal slits. A live Anole lizard was placed on a branch in front of her, about a foot distant. The lizard, evidently not recognizing danger, leaped toward her, landing close in front of her on the shelf. First she slowly turned her gaze toward the lizard and watched it for a little while, then, her eyes popping out a bit as the lids retracted, holding both hands close to her face she threw herself at the lizard but missed it. She apparently misjudged the distance, possibly because daylight conditions were unnatural to her. On a second attempt the lizard was caught, crushed, and left on the shelf.

Remarkably, the female did not take further notice of the dead lizard. Possibly she was not hungry or, more likely, she was in a state of drowsy stupor, as might be expected in a

her right hand, and occasionally stopped chewing for quite a while. In holding it, all five fingers of the hand, including the thumb, were in apposition (Fig. 511). On this occasion she began chewing the tail, an exception to the usual procedure, which is quickly to bring the head of the live prey into the mouth and crush it. Both

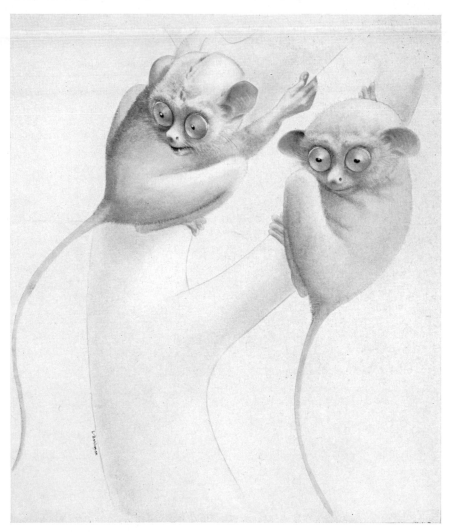

Fig. 505.—A pair of Philippine Tarsiers showing a male (*left*) and a female (*right*) the moment after both scrambled up a limb when the door of their cage was suddenly opened. Their physiognomies, turned toward the source of trouble, reflect fear, their eyes intently fixing the object of their apprehension, their lids maximally pulled back, baring part of the sclera normally not visible, with the mouth of the male slightly opened.

strongly nocturnal animal during the daytime. Only when the lizard was moved by a long forceps did she repeat the attack and grab it. For a while she held it in her mouth without eating it, as if absent-minded, then she retired into a corner and began to munch on it.

While eating the lizard, the female held it in

hands are used in this action, and they move too fast for the observer to analyze precisely how the manipulation is carried out. This is especially true when the prey is caught by the tail and must be turned quickly.

During all this activity the male Tarsier remained perfectly motionless behind the leaves.

A live lizard was placed where he could see it. As soon as he noticed it, he began to shake off his drowsiness. He soon became very attentive and slowly stretched his head toward the prospective meal, retracting his lids and popping out his eyes. Then in a flash, he rushed in the same way, headlong at the lizard. He promptly caught it and quickly put it into normal position, head first, into his mouth, and began to chew, while both hands worked very fast in helping the jaws.

Thereafter he began the slow, deliberate, measured process of chewing his meal, stopping periodically, the left hand holding the lizard,

Fɪɢ. 506.—Male Philippine Tarsier impersonating human attitudes. Left-hand sketch depicts the animal in the act of "chinning" or raising himself by the strength of his arms alone until his chin was above the level of the limb. Right-hand sketch shows the same animal resting on a limb, in a pose not unlike that of "a cowboy on a corral fence," with his right hand and right foot firmly gripping the limb, his left upper arm partly supporting the body weight, his left forearm and hand nonchalantly crossed, his left leg and foot dangling in midair, his face expressing the perfect equanimity of a person "gazing out of the window."

while the right was used as a prop. During the slow process of chewing he would occasionally turn his head to one side or the other, while his large auricles made scanning motions, apparently caused by the constant racket made by the Tree Shrews in a near-by cage. As he chewed, with part of the lizard's body still hanging out of his mouth, he would occasionally push it farther into his mouth with the back of one hand.

Even after the tip of the tail disappeared, he went on chewing for a few more minutes. All the while he was enjoying his repast, he continued to stare into space. Only rarely did he shut his eyes, "winking" by slowly pulling his upper lids over his bulging eye globes. Sometimes this did not occur in both eyes simultaneously, one lid occasionally closing, while the other eye was still completely or partly held open, in the manner observed occasionally in Cats and Owls

Fig. 507.—A male Philippine Tarsier in a characteristic pose and facial expression, indicating a mild emotional dilemma between apprehension from a possible danger and interest in a meal worm offered to him and held between the thumb and index finger. Note the wide-opened eyes, with the mouth opened only slightly, the legs, feet, and body facing away, as if making ready for a quick leap in the opposite direction.

(Fig. 509). After finishing his meal, the male again retired behind the foliage, keeping a watchful eye, however, for another possible tidbit.

Fights between the two little animals were not observed. At the most, when one was served a lizard the other would try to grab it away, usually unsuccessfully if the first Tarsier already had it securely in his mouth. Most of the time they showed themselves to be gentle, peaceful creatures, glad to be left alone. Frequently they were found huddled together.

Only once could the voice of the Tarsier have been identified for certain. Late one afternoon the animals were in the little cardboard box in a corner of the large cage in which they usually spent the day. Suddenly there was a somewhat shrill and extremely high-pitched sound heard, not intensive or loud, and sustained for 3 or 4 seconds; it began with a somewhat lower pitch and terminated on a higher note. Its acoustic quality was decidedly that of a "reed" (that is, not of a "flute"), resembling the song of a Hooded Nun Finch of India, the so-called "Java" or "Love Bird." The sound was repeated two or three times.

5. Food and eating habits.—The diet of the Tarsier, as observation in captivity shows, is entirely animal. The Tarsiers are, in fact, the only truly carnivorous Primates in existence. They never touched vegetable products and fruits, such as bread, carrots, peas, lettuce, bananas, oranges, grapes, raisins, apples, peanuts, and the like—all things which the Tree Shrews ate well or fairly well.

During the day they were given one or two Anole lizards each, in the morning and the afternoon, depending upon the size. Other meat, such as fresh or frozen parts of a rat, guinea pig, pigeon, and the like, they ate only during the night, this food apparently not representing a sufficient stimulus to attract them in the daytime. Usually much of this meat was found on the next morning untouched and dried.

The preferred food, to which they responded at any time, as did the Tree Shrews, was meal worms. No matter when it was offered, and even after they had eaten a sizable lizard, the sight of a dish full of crawling worms placed in the farthest corner of the cage was a potent visual stimulus which aroused interest and action. This happened even when the animals were dozing, concealed among the leaves, and seemed to be uninterested.

Sometimes the reaction would come after a considerable lapse of time, during which it was doubtful whether the dish had been noticed. The fleeting image of the dish, always the same size and shape, that meant great enjoyment for them, however, must have registered on their minds. At last the leaves would be pushed aside, and their large eyes would appear, looking about. After the dish was located, there was usually a meditative pause. But the sight of crawling meal worms evidently was too much to resist.

At long last, one of the Tarsiers would finally come out of his lair and jump down to the floor of the cage close to the dish. After another brief moment of scanning the dish, one of the fat worms was selected and a quick attack made on it. This was always done in a particular way, by precipitated, headlong "diving" in such a way that both the hands and mouth touched the prey at the same time. This manner of eating was maintained even while, from the human viewpoint, there was no need for a double assurance of success and the hands were not needed and not used. Actually, most meal worms were seized with the mouth alone, or the hands were used only to assist in the capture. In any case, the mouth was the principal, usually the only, instrument used in picking up the worms (Fig. 502).

6. Eye, ear, and head movements.—The process of catching and eating meal worms offered a favorable opportunity to observe in some detail the behavior of the eyes. When the animal sat quietly and there was nothing to attract its attention, the eyes seemed absolutely immobile. No movements either of the lids, eyeballs, or iris could be detected for long periods of time.

As soon as a dish with the meal worms was offered, the Tarsier turned his head toward it and retracted his eyelids, which made the eyes seem to pop out. A slight convergence of both eyes, to bring both lines of vision toward the common binocular fixation point, seemed to take place (Fig. 501). When making searching movements with the eyes, in either the horizontal or the vertical plane, definite but slight jerking movements, simultaneous in both eyeballs, were noticeable. They were, however, very small, these movements amounting to hardly more than 1 mm.

A counterpart to an almost complete immobility of the eyes was the ability of the Tarsier to rotate his head almost 180°, as if it were on a pivot. This enables the Tarsier, as it does the Owls, to look behind him without turning his body (Figs. 503, 508).

In contrast to the rigidity of the eyes was the extreme mobility of the ears, which could be moved in almost any direction and changed in size and shape in an almost infinite variety of

FIG. 508.—A male Philippine Tarsier, showing characteristic poses when observing and examining his surroundings: *upper left*, looking to his left, showing the face in profile, with his body weight chiefly resting on his left foot and leg; *upper right*, the body turned away from the observer, the head turned toward the same, with his eyes wide open, expressing a mixture of inquisitiveness and doubt; *lower left*, quietly and attentively observing something, possibly the noisy Tree Shrews in the adjoining cage; *lower right*, with his face turned away, his body weight entirely supported by the legs, his hands barely touching the ground. The great flexibility of the neck and the ability to turn the head backward strikingly resemble the same trait in the Owls.

ways. Such auricular mobility undoubtedly indicates a refined hearing, that evidently plays an important role in the life of the Tarsier (Fig. 514).

7. USE OF LIMBS.—The use of the extremities is definitely more advanced toward the condi-

digits longer and more flexible than in the Tree Shrews. The upper extremities are true hands with differentiated fingers and thumbs; the lower extremities, in spite of the inordinately elongated tarsal bones, exhibit the essential features of the prehensile hind feet of the Monkeys. Such extremities represent a great ad-

FIG. 509.—Facial expressions and body posture of a male Philippine Tarsier when in a good mood. Upper figure portrays rapt attention under the spell of quiet, gentle, friendly talk. Lower sketches show the effect apparently caused by continuous, friendly talk made in order to hold his attention while somewhat tired, during which he occasionally shut either one or both eyes, as if in hypnosis. The closing of only one eye occasionally takes place when the animal rests, as is the habit of his avian counterparts, the Owls.

tion found in the Pithecoid Primates in the Tarsier than is the case in the Tree Shrew (Figs. 498, 503, 504, 506, 510, 511, and esp. 513, 514).

To begin with, the palms of the hands and the soles of the feet are much larger and the

vance from the more primitive conditions in the Tree Shrews.

An object of great interest was the opposability of the thumb and the big toe. In the Tarsier this movement could more accurately be defined as an abductibility and adductibility of these two digits from, or to, the rest of the fingers and toes than as true opposability. The big toe was usually found about 45° abducted from the axis of the second toe. It was more difficult to ascertain the rotation of the big toe, which became apparent only in certain situa-

aligned with, the rest of the fingers (Figs. 497, 504, 506, 511, 514). When the hand rested on flat ground, with the fingers sprawled, the thumb usually was kept farther away from its neighbor than the average distance between the remaining fingers (thus in right lower sketch in Fig. 510, and in right upper sketch in Fig. 513).

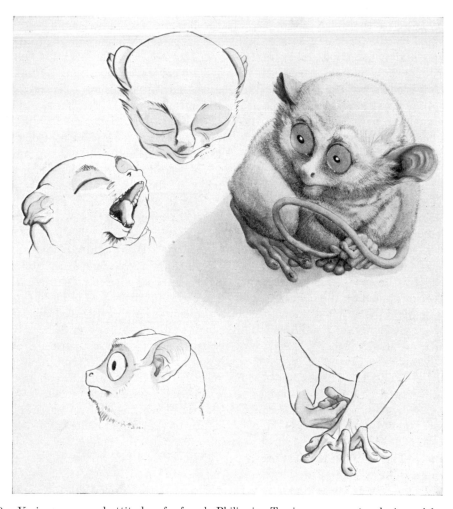

Fig. 510.—Various poses and attitudes of a female Philippine Tarsier: *upper center*, dozing; *right upper sketch*, just wakened from sleep; *left upper sketch*, yawning; *left lower sketch*, showing full profile after turning the head to right on slight sound from that direction, with both ears cocked; *right lower sketch*, showing a peculiar position of the hands, left hand broadly spread, resting on the ground, and supporting a part of the body weight, right hand curled up as in "embarrassment."

tions. There was a certain amount of true opposability of the big toe to other toes.

The evidence in favor of the opposability of the thumb was much more difficult to obtain. Most usually, when holding an object or a piece of food—for example, a lizard—or clutching a branch or holding the tail during the process of grooming, the thumb was apposited to, or

This may indicate a certain amount of rotation of the thumb around its axis and the ability to use it in opposition to other fingers. But the opportunity of securing positive evidence of this was given only rarely, as, for example, when the thumb was adducted to the index finger and at the same time rotated around its axis for about 90°, practically duplicating the condition present in the human hand (right middle sketch in Fig. 513).

How frequently the Tarsier uses his thumb in this fashion and whether it is capable of true opposition of the thumb to all fingers of the hand remain to be further investigated. In any case, the squatting position, with partial or complete release of the upper extremities from the task of supporting the weight of the body, readily assumed by the Tarsier; the flexibility of the fingers and some opposability of the thumb; and the ease of pronation and supination of the forearm and of rotation and other movements of the upper arm—all these contribute to the emancipation of the upper extremities from the exclusive or principal function of locomotion, making them available to a greater degree as instruments of feeding and of manipulation in general.

The hind extremities are the principal instruments of locomotion and are adapted to a hopping gait. This adaptation has been achieved by the general strengthening and lengthening of the legs. This lengthening has been accomplished chiefly by the inordinate prolongation of the tarsal or ankle bones, the calcaneus and navicular or scaphoid (hence the name "Tarsier"), greatly resembling the conditions found in Birds, but not in the Kangaroo, in spite of a superficial resemblance. Nevertheless, true to the arboreal habit and the inherent pithecoid organization, the hind limb has been developed into a grasping organ, with padded terminal phalanges and opposable big toe.

8. EYEBALL.—The eyes of the Tarsier are remarkable. In absolute size they are large, and in proportion to the size of the animal they can hardly be matched anywhere among the Mammals. In order to meet a like relationship, one must look among the Birds and Fishes with the best-developed sight.

The eyelashes, arranged along the margins of both lids, up to 5 mm. long and bent away from the palpebral fissure, at close view give the eye a human appearance. Each eye is protected above by a matted brow, a part of the general pelage, with a few 15-mm.-long vibrissae or bristles arising in a bunch above the inner canthus. The outer canthus is sharp, the inner one blunt, and there is a relatively large third lid.

The length of the palpebral fissure is about 12 mm. The fundi of the upper and lower conjunctival pockets run just behind the corneal margin, but, because of the great expanse of the lids, the pockets are roomy.

The transverse axis of the eyeball measures about 18 mm., the longitudinal axis about 17.5 mm., which approaches the 24-mm. diameter of the human eye, all strangely contrasting with the enormous difference in weight of the Tarsier (*ca.* 150–200 gm.) and Man (75,000 gm.).

The cornea is spherically curved and, as in most nocturnal animals, is relatively large, measuring about 18 mm. from margin to margin, which is nearly equal to one-third of the ocular circumference. The root of the iris is attached to the cornea along the margin and is visible through it as a dark-brown, 0.7-mm.-wide circular stripe.

The lens is very large and proportionately thick, its diameter being 10 mm., its longitudinal axis or thickness in the center 6.5 mm., compared with the 8-mm. diameter and 3-mm. thickness of the human lens. Both surfaces of the lens are spherically curved, the anterior having a shorter radius of curvature.

The anterior chamber in the axis is relatively shallow, the distance from the lens to the cornea measuring only 3 mm. However, owing to the great expanse of the cornea, amounting to almost half the corresponding sphere, the anterior chamber is quite roomy, since its main extension is along the sides of the huge lens. The depth of the vitreal chamber in the axis is 6.5 mm.

The ciliary body is well developed, being made up of 1.5-mm.-long, and 1-mm.-high ridges that are thinner but more numerous than in the human eye. The iris is a brown and thin curtain inclosing a pupillary aperture and pressing upon the anterior lens surface. It and the chorioid membrane are heavily pigmented.

The optic nerve with its sheaths is only 1.3 mm. in diameter; without the sheaths, barely 1 mm. From the point of its implantation slightly nasal to the posterior pole, it runs closely along the eyeball for a short distance before it turns nasally, making an angle of almost 45° with the sagittal plane.

The six extrinsic eye muscles, four straight and two oblique, are relatively little developed.

Together they form a small cone around the optic nerve. The four straight muscles are quite short and are attached to the eyeball well behind the equator, a factor that further reduces their effectiveness as an oculomotor agent. The levator muscle of the upper lid is a thin, broad slip, whose bundles spread fanwise before mingling with the orbicular muscle; these bundles are partly attached to the aponeurosis of the eyeball.

the bundles arranged meridionally (Brücke's muscle) and radially. These are all attached, on the one hand, to the well-developed scleral roll at the root of the iris and, on the other hand, to the chorioid membrane. In meridional sections, almost all ciliary muscle bundles show a straight or slightly curved course, only a few, close to the inner corner of the body transversally cut, representing the circular portion (Müller's muscle).

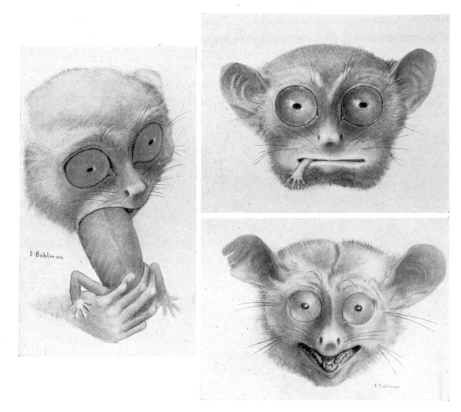

Fig. 511.—Various expressions of the physiognomy and of the eyes of a Philippine Tarsier: *left sketch*, contentedly munching on the tail of an Anole Lizard, a reverse situation from the usual procedure of starting with the head, since in this instance a decapitated specimen was offered; *upper right sketch*, showing a startled expression caused by observer's loud laughter; *lower right sketch*, an expression of fear rather than ferocity, with the mouth half-opened, the baring of the teeth, and the tip of the tongue just visible.

A study of microscopic preparations of the eye reveals further noteworthy details. The cornea is relatively thin, its structure very homogeneous, its two surfaces very even and smooth. The ciliary body, directly continuous with the chorioid membrane, is well developed. It contains, besides the smooth-muscle fibers, numerous chromatophore cells filled with brown pigment.

Best developed of the ciliary muscles are

The fibers of the ciliary zonule of Zinn are numerous; some are thin; others, formed by the merging of several thin ones, are quite thick. Peripherally they are attached directly to the ciliary processes and body and in this way to the chorioid membrane and also to the hyaloid membrane and through it to the retina. Inwardly, they merge with the lens capsule along the equator.

The iris contains blood vessels and heavily

pigmented stromal cells of a light-brown color. This color contrasts with the dark-brown, almost black, color of the pigment filling the cells of the iridial portion of the retinal epithelium that lines the inner face of the iris, while the pigment filling the ciliary portion of the blind, nonnervous portion of the retina, as well as that in the ciliary chromatophores, is of an intermediate-brown intensity.

The sphincter muscle is a well-developed layer close to the pupillary margin. The dilator muscle may be identified as a thin, distinct layer next to the pigment epithelium, best seen in the outer half of the iris closer to its root.

The hyaloid membrane is a thick, structureless sheet, distinct and separate from the actual inner limiting membrane, from which it can be easily detached without tearing off the lower ends of Müller's radial fibers.

The nervous or functioning portion of the retina extends almost to the ciliary body. There is no ora serrata or serrated margin, since the line along which the nervous part of the retina terminates is quite even, representing the ora terminalis. Small cystic cavities along the terminal margin are a reminder of similar, but much larger and more numerous, cavities in the human ora serrata. A small neuroglial "cone" filled with nuclei, a remnant of the hyaloid artery that functions during embryonic life, protrudes from the vitreal face of the disk. The chorioid membrane is well developed, being especially thick in the territory of the central area, and is rich in heavily pigmented chromatophores.

To summarize, the eye of the Tarsier appears to be an organ highly adapted to its nocturnal life. The cornea and lens are huge dioptrical light collectors, and the large iris is an efficient regulator of the amount of light to be admitted into the eye: as much as possible during the night and very little during the day.

The well-developed ciliary muscle is necessary to counteract the strong pull by the thick fibers of the ciliary zonule and thus permit the huge crystalline lens to accommodate for close range through an increase in its sphericity. Such accommodative mechanism can be fully utilized only in an eye whose retina allows for a high degree of visual acuity. This is possible in the Tarsier, in spite of the subdued

nocturnal illumination during which it is active, in virtue of a good development of the central area and fovea of the retina, as described in the following subsection. The most economical utilization of nocturnal illumination is further assisted by the heavy pigmentation by which most of the interfering stray light is eliminated.

Finally, in view of the poorly developed extrinsic eye muscles, whose effect in turning the eyeball is small, as shown by observation, the question may be raised as to whether in some way these muscles may not assist in accommodation, a function obviously of great biological importance for the survival of the species.

9. Retina.—The retina of the Tarsier is as remarkable in its structure as is the rest of the eyeball. For this, above all, two factors are responsible. While, in general, it conforms in its makeup to the structure found in other Primates, it stands apart from most species of this order in the absence of cones.

The bacillary layer is made up entirely of rodlike photoreceptors (Fig. 512). In this respect it is homologous with the rod-bearing retina of the Cat and of the prosimian *Galago* and *Nycticebus* (Detwiler 1938, 1939, 1940, 1943). But unlike the prosimian species, the Tarsier is remarkable in its possession of both a central area and a fovea (whereas a central area alone is found in the Cat). Hence the Tarsier breaks the rule by which these two specially differentiated structures are found only where cones are present. In this respect the Tarsier agrees with the South American Night Monkey (*Nyctipithecus* or *Aotes trivirgatus*), in which a central area and fovea are also present.

The Tarsier's retina is relatively thin. In the axial region it measures 220 microns or slightly more, being gradually reduced to 35 microns along its terminal margin. Its layers, for a Mammal, are regular, the boundaries being mostly quite sharp and even, with very few ectopic or displaced nuclei found in the two plexiform layers and none in the bacillary layer.

The absolute and relative thickness of the layers varies markedly from the periphery toward the axial region, where it is most pronounced in the formation of the central area. Taking as a criterion the increase in the ganglion layer to more than a single tier of cells, the diameter of the central area measures 2,000 microns or 2 mm. across. Its center is little more than 2 mm. distant from the temporal margin of the disk; hence the central area is relatively smaller in extent than, for example, in a Rhesus Macaque. However, the increase in the number of ganglion cells and other refine-

are brown. This contrasts with the chorioid pigment, which, although also brown, appears almost black because of its abundance. The granules in the specimen examined were confined to the pigment layer.

The thickness of the bacillary layer increases from about 40 microns at the equator to 70 in

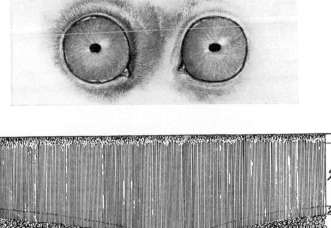

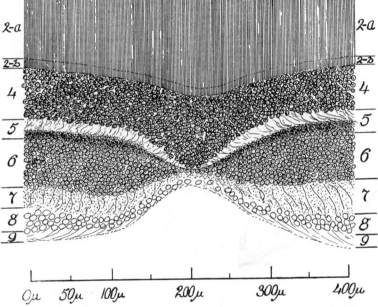

FIG. 512.—Tarsier's eyes and structure of central fovea. Upper sketch represents a close view of the eyes, showing the huge corneae in the almost maximally extended palpebral fissures, which are oriented with a "mongoloid" slant, the horizontally elliptical pupils almost maximally contracted, as in full illumination. The lower sketch represents, at medium magnification, a vertical section through the center of the Tarsier's central fovea, showing the layers described in detail in the text. Note the extraordinary length and thinness of the foveal photoreceptors, longest in the very center and resembling the rods (layers *2-a* and *2-b*); swollen outer nuclear layer *4* in the very center and attenuation of all layers from *5* to *9* in the same locality. These features are in harmony with the strictly nocturnal habit of the Tarsier, which, in spite of this, preserved the central fovea, a common heritage of all Monkeys, Apes, and Man. It is the possession of the central fovea that, in spite of the Tarsier's nocturnalism, affords this Primate a high degree of visual acuity. The layers of the retina indicated along the sides, the actual magnification in microns indicated on the scale below. (*Cf.* Figs. 129, 161.)

ments in a zone immediately surrounding the central area proper indicate that the pericentral zone is also on a higher functional level than the periphery.

The pigment granules of the pigment layer

the periphery of the central area and to as much as 140 in its center (Fig. 512). The arrangement of its structural elements is remarkably smooth and even, just as the underlying outer limiting membrane is smooth. There are no "convolutions" or "plications," as described by Woollard (1926); these artifacts, where found, are caused by an inadequate technique of fixation.

The photoreceptors making up the bacillary layer, both in the extra-areal periphery and in the central area, including its very center, are exclusively rods. They are very thin in diameter, all alike, arranged remarkably uniformly, and vertical to the limiting membrane. Where they are found bent or otherwise displaced, the

original vertical arrangement can easily be restored.

The caliber of the individual rods differs little in the central fovea and area and in the extra-areal periphery. In the first it is 0.5 micron, in the latter about 1 micron. The inter-center distance between the adjoining rods measures from 1 to 1.5 microns.

Whereas the difference in thickness is insignificant, the rods vary considerably in length,

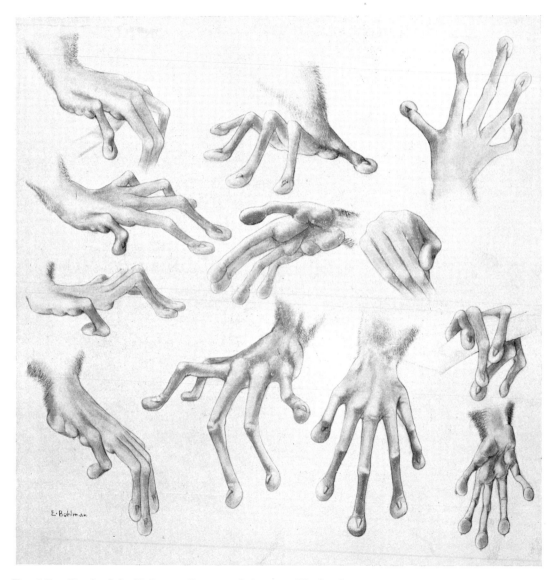

Fig. 513.—Hands of the Philippine Tarsier and their use. The hands are typical, even though somewhat modified, primate hands, the figure showing the form and relative size of the fingers, thumb, and palm and their various employment. The two sketches in the right lower corner are drawn on a slightly smaller scale. The sketch under the one in the right upper corner depicts the right hand with its fingers bent and the thumb held adducted to the index and middle fingers. The sketch in the center of the upper row and the one in the right upper corner show the thumb abducted from the other figures. (*Cf.* following figure.)

as expressed by the increased thickness of the bacillary layer. They are shortest in the periphery and gradually lengthen toward the center, where they are longest. The greater length of the central rods is caused entirely by the relatively greater lengthening of the outer segments, especially apparent in the center of the outer fovea (Fig. 512, layer *2-a*).

The outer nuclear layer is thick and is made up of a great number of closely packed nuclei. This layer attains its maximum thickness in the areal periphery and just outside the area, where up to sixteen tiers of nuclei may be counted. In the very center of the fovea the number of nuclei increases to eighteen or more tiers. The nuclei are all of the same appearance; they are small, dark, containing coarse framework and granules—in other words, they appear as typical rod nuclei found in the human and simian retinae, where both rods and cones are present.

A row of larger and paler nuclei stained in a different hue, located just underneath the outer limiting membrane, found in the cone-containing retinae, is absent in the Tarsier. However, the uppermost tier of the nuclei, while of the same hue as the rest, contains slightly larger elements, which, however, is an insufficient criterion by which to consider them true cones. It is therefore possible that, with the adoption of a strict nocturnal mode of life by the Tarsier, the original primate cones were transformed into rods, while their nuclei still retained their former location below the outer limiting membrane and remain slightly larger. Hence, if there are cones in the Tarsier's retina, they cannot be demonstrated with the hematoxylin and phloxin stain or with the toluidine blue stain of Nissl & Lenhossék. Other methods, such as Golgi and perhaps modifications of Klüver's Luxol fast blue cell-fiber stain, may furnish a decisive answer to this particular question.

The outer plexiform layer attains almost half the thickness of the outer nuclear layer. As in other Mammals, it is made up of three zones: *5-a*, fibrous; *5-b*, inner swollen ends of photoreceptors; and *5-c*, outer expansions of the bipolars and horizontal cells. In the Tarsier this layer is more uniform, chiefly consisting of photoreceptor fibers in the upper half and, in the lower half, an ill-defined granular mass,

identified in other species as made up of rod spherules and outer expansions of various bipolars and horizontal cells. A continuous line of "granular clods," especially prominent in the central area and fovea of the Macaque and Man, identified with the outer dendritic expansions of midget bipolars individually attached to the lower faces of the cone pedicles, is missing in the Tarsier. This again harmonizes with the absence of true cones. (*Cf.* Figs. 512 and 128, 129.)

The inner nuclear layer contrasts with the outer nuclear layer by its paler stain and larger nuclei. A discontinuous row of slightly larger nuclei surrounded by a fair amount of cytoplasm immediately adjoining the outer plexiform layer, apparently belonging to the horizontal cells, is conspicuous here. Another zone where larger nuclei are present is close to the inner plexiform layer. Other nuclei of a more or less angular shape and slightly darker in color, belonging to the radial fibers of Müller, are present in the vitreal half of the layer.

The inner plexiform layer contains numerous fibers arranged vertically, the space between being filled with a granular mass. Owing to a condensation of the granules, several parallel horizontal zones may be distinguished.

The ganglion layer is composed of cells varying considerably in size but, in general, being larger than in either of the two nuclear layers. Their nuclei, as usual, are of a spherical shape, with a delicate chromophile framework in which a number of smaller and a few larger granules are inclosed, one of which, the largest and of a round shape, occasionally appears as a nucleolus. Chromophile Nissl substance either is present as minute granules or is more diffusely distributed over the cytoplasm of the body and larger dendrites. Outside the central area the ganglion cells form a single, almost continuous row; in the central area they gradually accumulate in several rows until, close to the fovea, they form five or six tiers. The size of the ganglion cells does not vary much, only a few somewhat larger cells being found in the extra-areal periphery scattered among the smaller ones.

The layer of optic nerve fibers in most of the retina is thin but distinct. Close to the disk it increases in thickness, amounting to as much as

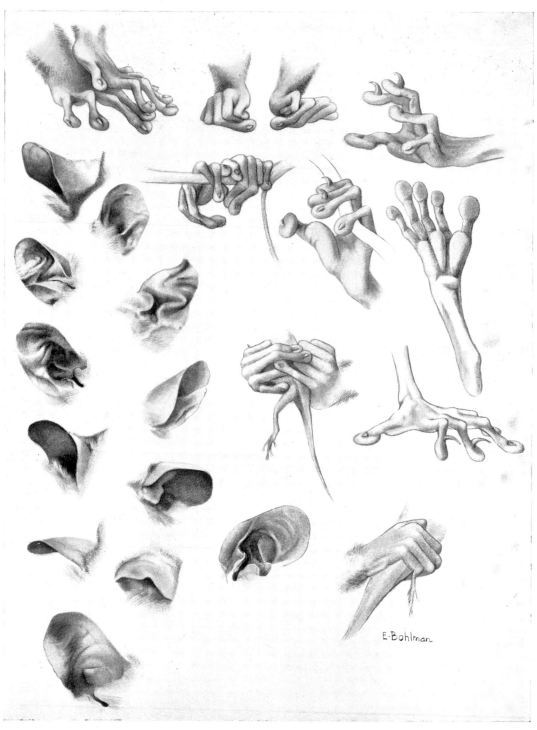

Fig. 514.—Hands, feet, and auricles of a Philippine Tarsier expressive of various moods, acts, or manipulations. Hands and feet, beginning with the left upper corner: both hands as the animal sits intent and alert, while talked to; typical position of both hands when the animal is about to pounce upon a meal worm; both hands resting on a twig when the animal is at ease, though alert and interested; both hands firmly gripping the body of an Anole Lizard whose head is being held in the mouth; right hand holding a lizard during the meal; two views of the left foot, as the animal in a leisurely way climbs the side of the cage; plantar view of the left foot and its long "hock"; left foot sprawling on the ground, with its big toe abducted. Ears, from the top: right ear seen in front view while the animal was asleep; left ear while listening to gentle talk; right ear at a moment of catching a meal worm; left ear while the animal was getting ready to pounce on a meal worm; right ear expressing fear, with the head in profile; left ear while preening his fur; right ear when the animal was at rest; left and right ear as the animal pounces on a meal worm; left and right ear while eating; left ear while the animal rests, with his head in profile.

one-fourth or more of the thickness of the retinal membrane.

The neuroglia is well developed. Radial fibers of Müller are present everywhere, including the foveal depression. They are particularly conspicuous in the inner plexiform layer, whence many of them can be followed through the ganglion and fiber layers to the inner limiting membrane formed by the joining of the widened vitreal ends.

The central retinal artery and vein enter through the optic disk, whence, imbedded in the retinal substance, their branches spread over this membrane. The endothelial nuclei of the capillaries are met with in layers ventral to the outer plexiform layer. Abundant capillaries, but no large vessels, are present throughout the central area, including the fovea. In the areal periphery an occasional medium-sized vessel is found.

The chorioid membrane in the central area and fovea is thicker than outside, a feature found in all primate eyes where area and fovea are present.

Ophthalmoscopic examinations of the eyes of the living Tarsier made in our laboratory by Dr. F. S. Ryerson, of Detroit, in both ordinary and red-free light, revealed the presence of a well-developed yellow spot or "macula" temporal to the disk (*see* color Fig. 149, and *cf.* with color Figs. 148 and 165–70). This locality is distinguished by an arrangement of blood vessels typical in other primate species in which a central area and fovea are present. That is, the larger arteries and veins follow an arching course above and below the central area, in this way avoiding the locality of the retina instrumental in central vision. A small macular artery or vein may pass over, either directly from the disk or, branching off from one of the larger vessels, toward the center of the yellow spot.

The territory containing yellow pigment is large and somewhat pear-shaped, beginning almost immediately temporal to the disk and spreading laterally for about 4 disk diameters. The pigmentation is most intensive in a small, circular, approximately centrally located area about the size of the disk and $2\frac{1}{2}$–3 disk diameters temporal. Small blood vessels converge from all sides toward this area, but only the

terminals enter it, without, however, reaching the center, which appears to be free of all blood vessels. The pigmentation in this circular area appears to be much finer in grain than that outside it. In the very center a minute, faint, foveal light reflex was seen occasionally.

The presence of a central fovea, found ophthalmoscopically, was confirmed by the ex-

Fig. 515.—Fetus of a Philippine Tarsier during a late stage of development. Note the large size of the eyes, whereas the external auricles are still some distance from their full development.

amination of preserved specimens at slight magnification (2, 4, 8×). It was, however, the microscopic study that finally corroborated its presence and gave detailed information.

The fovea of a Tarsier is small in comparison with that found in other Primates. Its diameter is about 250–300 microns. Its small size and shallowness may be the reason that it was not found by the preceding investigator (Woollard 1925, 1926). Small though it is, it exhibits all the principal features characteristic of a primate fovea: lengthening of the photoreceptors in the center and a greater or lesser reduction of other layers (Fig. 512).

In particular, the outer limiting membrane shows a dip, or "outer fovea," in the very center, to accommodate the rods, which attain their greatest length in this locality. The outer nuclear layer is increased in the very center for about half its thickness in the immediately adjoining region, whereas the outer plexiform and the inner nuclear layers barely remain continuous. The inner plexiform layer is reduced to almost half, and in the ganglion layer a single discontinuous row of cells remains. In all three cellular layers the arrangement of the nuclei shows a slant down and away from the center. A similar slant is maintained by the fibrous constituents wherever visible, this being most conspicuous in the two plexiform and the optic fiber layers.

The arrangement of the cellular and fibrous elements indicates the process of lateral displacement, least advanced in the outer nuclear and most in the ganglion and optic fiber layers. From this it is apparent that the factors which form the Tarsier's fovea are the same as those responsible for the formation of the fovea in all other Primates and in Vertebrates in general. The only difference is the degree of the lateral displacement, which, in the Tarsier, amounts only to approximately half or less of the displacement found in the diurnal Primates and is most pronounced in the center of the human fovea, where practically all layers in front of the photoreceptors have been removed (*see* chap. V, 10, and accompanying figures).

In evaluating the physiological significance of the Tarsier's central fovea, we must first consider the photoreceptors. This layer, according to accepted histological criteria, is made up exclusively of rods. All the nuclei of the outer nuclear layer also possess features characteristic of rod nuclei of such definitely duplex retinae as those of the Rhesus Macaque, Chimpanzee, and Man. A continuous zone *5-b*, made up of relatively large chromophobe cone pedicles with the more numerous and smaller chromophile rod spherules squeezed in between, is absent in the outer plexiform layer, and zones *5-a* and *5-c* have a more uniform fibrous or granular aspect. A discontinuous row of "granular clods" of

Dogiel, indicating synapses of midget bipolars with the cone pedicles, or *h* & *b* synapses, is absent in the Tarsier.

The available evidence favors the view that the only photoreceptors in the Tarsier's fovea are the rods. True to the functional purpose of the fovea, the centralmost rods in it are as thin as the building factors could have created them. Thus individual stimulability of the rods, through the reduction of rod diameter in the foveal center, and consequently acuity in night vision are increased. On the other hand, the great lengthening of the outer rod segments, hence the increase in the mass of the photosensitive substance, may be interpreted as meaning a greater increase in functional responsiveness or a lowering of the threshold in the very center. In the Tarsier's fovea we have, then, the same factors contributing to maximal visual acuity as in the diurnal Primates, but adapted to nocturnal vision.

The synapses are the next object in the functional histoanalysis. This problem cannot be solved except through well-stained Golgi preparations. Until this is done, a few general remarks must suffice. What the synaptical relationships of cells making up the inner nuclear layer are, may only be guessed. If the true cones are absent, it is probable that the well-differentiated midget bipolars are also absent. The true midget ganglions, which form such a conspicuous feature in the diurnal Primates (Macaque, Chimpanzee, Man), are likely to be absent also. But whatever the particular variety of the ganglions in the Tarsier's fovea, their synapses must be considerably restricted in space, almost individualized, in order that their great numbers may be used adequately.

The great number of ganglion cells in the fovea and its immediate vicinity permits the assumption of the presence of at least 10,000 functional units in this locality. These, together with the units in the remainder of the central area, represent a formidable apparatus making for a high degree of visual acuity. In any case, the number of ganglion cells, if the majority of these are capable of an independent response (as they are in the fovea of the diurnal Primates), would permit a high degree of physiological resolution probably approaching the maximum possible under conditions imposed by scotopic vision. That this is somewhat below the maximum of the most developed photopic vision of Primates is understandable. The dimensions of the Tarsier's fovea, smaller than those in a Rhesus Macaque, would indicate this.

Another Primate adapted to a nocturnal life, in which a central area and fovea have been found, is the South American Night Monkey (*Nyctipithecus* or *Aotes trivirgatus*). According to reliable unpublished investigations of Dr. H. Klüver, visual acuity and form vision in this species are not much below human. It was, therefore, of special interest to compare the dimensions and structure of the fovea of the Night Monkey, on the one hand, with those of the nocturnal Tarsier and, on the other hand, with those of the diurnal Primates, Man, Rhesus Macaque, and Chimpanzee.

The central fovea and area of the Night Monkey show features essentially similar to those in the Tarsier, with, however, certain peculiarities. The area is larger, the fovea shallower, the bacillary layer thinner. The diameter of the area measures about 2,500 microns, or 2.5 mm. across; that of the fovea, 600–700 microns, or 0.6–0.7 mm. The thickness of the photoreceptor layer in the fovea is from 63 to 70 microns, with a slight dip of the outer limiting membrane in the very center. Other peculiarities are: the bacillary layer, as in the Tarsier, is composed exclusively of rods, the outer nuclear layer showing ten tiers in the center, and twelve tiers outside the fovea, with all nuclei exhibiting characteristic rod appearance and uniform arrangement, while the typical cone nuclei are absent; the outer plexiform layer in the very center is very thin, increasing outside it to 40 microns and showing three well-differentiated zones in the central area—*5-a* (fibrous, with a slant away from the center), *5-b* (dark, granular, but with cone-pedicles absent), and a thin and poorly structurally differentiated zone *5-c;* the thick inner nuclear layer, measuring 100 microns outside the fovea, is reduced to 30 microns in the very center; the inner plexiform layer, finely granulated, is 35–40 microns thick outside the fovea and in the very center is reduced to 20 microns; the ganglion layer, consisting of three tiers outside the fovea, is reduced to a single continuous tier in the foveal center.

The rods of the Night Monkey, as of the Tarsier, are thinnest in the foveal center, their thickness being reduced here to 1 micron or less, with the intercenter distances measuring 1.5 microns. Approximately 400 rods could be counted along the foveal diameter of 600 microns. The total number of the foveal rods, computed on this basis, would be from 150,000 to 200,000.

The general conclusion which may be drawn from the preceding structural peculiarities and considerations is that a Primate, in adapting himself to a nocturnal mode of life, may achieve a degree of visual acuity and over-all utilization of the visual stimuli comparable with the best achieved by the members of the same order adapted to the photopic habit. The limitations of scotopic vision appear to be chiefly in hue discrimination, whereas visual space perception, notably acuity, seems to be less affected.

10. The optic nerves and the visual pathways and centers of the brain.—The optic nerve of the Tarsier is a symmetrical cylinder, circular in shape on cross-section and 1.5 mm. in diameter. It is relatively rich in fine and very fine fibers, with only a few coarser ones interspersed, while very coarse ones are entirely absent. The caliber of most fibers measures from 1 to 2 microns only, a few even less, with some 3 microns thick and almost none thicker. The total estimated number of fibers is at least 150,000, approaching 200,000. Even this figure, because of the difficulty of counting, may fall far short of the actual number.

The chiasma is remarkable because of the great number of fibers which do not decussate. The nondecussating fibers, according to a rough estimate, may amount to at least one-fourth, and possibly to as much as one-third, of the total. Any certainty of this, however, can be had only through experimental evidence, preferably by the employment of the Marchi method of staining.

The brain of the Tarsier, primitive though it is, definitely bears marks common to all Primates (Figs. 516–18; *cf.* Figs. 270, 279, 280, 282, 284, 306, 307). These marks are the three distinct lobes of the great cerebral hemispheres: frontal, temporal, and occipital.

For the size of the animal, the brain is relatively large. Its dimensions are: total length from the frontal to the occipital poles, 16 mm.; from the frontal poles to the summit of the cerebellum, 17.5 mm.; and across the two great hemispheres in the widest place, 17.5 mm.

The squat shape and the location of the brain in the posterior half of the head are caused by the inordinate size of the eyeballs. Because of this, the brain is pushed back and compressed, just as the facial part of the skull is squeezed and pushed down by the huge orbits. These changes have been made by the same

temporal lobe is much the thicker. The occipital lobe has the shape of a broad, curved, but quite attenuated, spoonlike plate. A sharp, deep dent —the primordium of the lateral fissure of Sylvius—separating the frontal from the temporal lobes, provides enough space to accommodate the fundus of the huge orbits.

The external surface of the brain is typically lissencephalous or smooth, except for a delicate filigree of shallow furrows in which the blood vessels are lodged. On the inner face of the occipital lobe, overhanging the midbrain and cere-

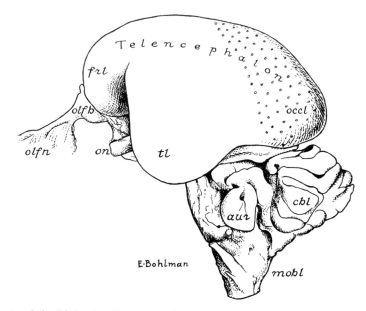

Fig. 516.—Brain of the Philippine Tarsier in a lateral view, 4× magnified. Note the relatively enormous development of the temporal (*tl*) and occipital lobes (*occl*), which is in line with the extraordinary development of the auricles and eyes, both being indicative of a highly specialized mode of living, with nocturnal adaptation of sight and hearing. The olfactory apparatus, becoming of secondary importance, is reduced. The striate area stippled with circles. *Labeling: aur,* cerebellar auricle; *cbl,* cerebellum; *frl,* frontal lobe; *mobl,* oblong medulla; *occl,* occipital lobe; *olfb,* olfactory bulb; *olfn,* olfactory nerves; *on,* optic nerve; *tl,* temporal lobe.

mechanical factor that determines the configuration of the head and brain of the Birds, most of which also have large eyes (*see* Figs. 469, 470, 471). Another contributory factor may have been the center of gravity of the body and of the head, important in a leaping animal. It is the same factor which caused the shortening of the brain of the Insectivorous Bats (Microchiroptera), in spite of their diminutive eyes.

The cerebral hemispheres can be roughly subdivided into three lobes, with little substance to spare. The beak-shaped frontal lobe (*frl*) is the smallest, the larger temporal (*tl*) and occipital lobes (*occl*) representing the bulk. The

bellum, is a deep furrow resembling the letter Y. The posterior limb of that furrow is the orimental or incipient calcarine fissure, the principal landmark indicating the visual cortex of the Monkeys, Apes, and Man (*c* in sketch *E*, Fig. 279; *cf. also* Figs. 306 and 307; *see also* Woollard 1925). The two frontal limbs facing the corpus callosum are the arcuate or hippocampal sulci. Along the lower face of the temporal lobe an irregular furrow is found that has yet to be identified. The corpus callosum reaches back only as far as midway of the longitudinal extent of the hemispheres.

The olfactory bulbs (*olfb*) are small and are

almost completely overhung by the frontal lobes. They resemble small, triangular, flattened seed kernels standing vertically, side by side, along the mid-sagittal plane. From the anterior angle of each bulb a single, thin, flattened olfactory nerve arises (*olfn*). The two nerves, closely attached to one another, coursing between the two orbits, enter into the posterior upper corners of the small nasal cavities whence they take their origin. The inferior-posterior extremity of each olfactory bulb gradually attenuates to become the olfactory tract that connects with the rest of the brain.

The principal parts of the brain concerned in vision are the same as in the Monkeys, Apes, and Man: the lateral geniculate nuclei, the superior colliculi, and the striate areae of the cerebral cortex. Whether there are any hypothalamic connections remains a problem to be further investigated.

Both geniculate nuclei—the lateral and the medial—are proportionately quite large. The lateral geniculate, where it is best developed, on coronal sections represents at least one-fifth and perhaps as much as one-fourth of the area of the entire betweenbrain. It is made up of a larger dorsal laminated nucleus and a smaller ventral or "pregeniculate" nucleus. The dorsal nucleus is composed of somewhat larger cells of various sizes arranged in contorted laminae resembling the superior olive, whereas no distinct lamination is recognizable in the ventral nucleus. The lamination pattern is complicated, requiring further careful study and interpretation. This is especially necessary in determining which of the laminae belong to the ipsilateral homonymous halves of the fields of view, and which to the contralateral. This problem may best be investigated experimentally, with the removal of one eye and a subsequent examination of Nissl-stained sections through both geniculate nuclei. The exact number of the laminae also remains to be determined. It appears probable, however, that there are at least two, and probably as many as four, cell laminae.

The ventral geniculate nucleus consists of slightly smaller and paler cells when stained by the Nissl method. It is best developed on anterior oral levels. Its cells and fibers are continuous with the subthalamus, the subthalamic connections apparently predominating. This, in

view of the nocturnal habit of the Tarsier and, in this connection, of the importance of the pupillary function and accommodation, may be of significance. (*See* chap. VI, 10.)

The medial geniculate nucleus is also quite well developed. Its cells and fibers are very clearly organized into laminae and groups, according to a special pattern to be further worked out. In view of the acute sense of hearing in the Tarsier, this is understandable.

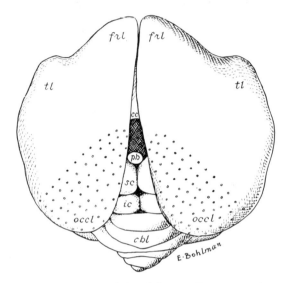

FIG. 517.—Brain of the Philippine Tarsier seen from above, with both hemispheres slightly separated in order to show the midbrain colliculi and other parts normally not visible, since they are overhung by enormously expanded occipital lobes. The striate areae marked with small circles. *Labeling: cbl*, cerebellum; *cc*, corpus callosum; *frl*, frontal lobes; *ic*, inferior colliculi; *pb*, pineal body or gland; *sc*, superior colliculi; *tl*, temporal lobes.

The colliculi of the midbrain are likewise well developed (Figs. 517, 518). However, the gray cap of the superior colliculus is much thinner and structurally less elaborate than in the species where the midbrain predominates (Rodents, also Tree Shrews). In agreement with this, the number of optic nerve fibers terminating here is but a fraction of those entering the lateral geniculate nucleus.

The inferior colliculus is proportionately large and rich in nerve cells. These in part are arranged into layers, indicating an elaborate organization of this internode of the auditory system.

The oculomotor nerve and nucleus are surprisingly large. In fact, the entire gray sub-

stance lining the Sylvian aqueduct of the midbrain is thick and elaborately differentiated
into numerous cell nests, made up of nerve cells
of various sizes, shapes, and staining properties.
Whether this is because of the well-developed
parasympathetic functions of the eye, indicated
by a large iris, and probably also because of accommodation, as might be expected with such
strongly adapted nocturnal vision, or because
of the presence of the central area and fovea
remains a problem to be solved by future investigations.

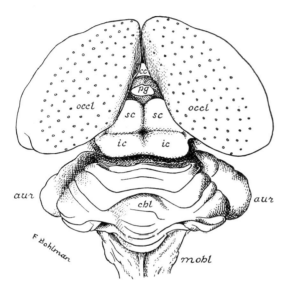

Fig. 518.—Brain of the Philippine Tarsier in back
view, showing also the midbrain colliculi between the
separated hemispheres. The striate areae marked with
small circles. *Labeling: aur,* cerebellar auricle; *cbl,* cerebellum; *cc,* corpus callosum; *ic,* inferior colliculus of
midbrain; *mobl,* oblong medulla; *occl,* occipital lobe; *pg,*
pineal gland; *sc,* superior colliculi of midbrain.

The lower auditory centers, represented by
the dorsal and ventral nuclei of the acoustic
nerve, were found to be large, their cells indicating stratification and folding of the layers—
all testimony to the excellence of the sense of
hearing. (*Cf.* S. Poljak, J. f. Psychol. u. Neurol., v. 32, p. 170, 1926.)

The cerebellum (*cbl*) is fairly well developed,
although it has perhaps a more primitive aspect
than in the Tree Shrew (*cf.* Figs. 490, 491). Its
two hemispheres extend considerably in the lateral direction, though less so than the auricular
portions. As in the Higher Primates, the occipital lobes of the great brain, extending far back-

ward, almost completely cover the cerebellum
from above.

The striate areae of the occipital lobes or
those parts of the cerebral cortex in which fibers
of the visual radiation conducting impulses
from the homonymous halves of both retinae
terminate are relatively very large.

The location and the general structural
makeup of the striate area are similar to those
of the other Primates. There are, however, features peculiar to the Tarsier. Possibly the most
outstanding is its relatively enormous extent.
Examined in a continuous series of Nissl-
stained coronal sections, the area stretches from
the occipital pole to midway between the latter
and the frontal pole. However, it is oriented
somewhat differently than shown in Woollard's
diagram (*see* Fig. 279, sketch *E*).

The striate area, on the basis of our own
study, resembles a long flat cap, similar to, but
proportionately larger than, that in the Tree
Shrew, determined by Le Gros Clark (sketch *C*
in same figure). Its ventrolateral boundary, instead of being vertical, however, slants. Hence
the area extends anteriorly much farther along
the dorsal margin of the hemisphere than posteriorly, where it envelops the entire occipital
lobe only as its pole is approached. Most of the
lateral face of the hemisphere above the temporal lobe, accordingly, does not belong to the
striate area (stippled in Figs. 516, 517, 518).
Even so, a substantial portion of the pallium or
cerebral cortex, roughly amounting to one-
fifth or more, is visual.

The boundaries of the striate area where it
passes over into surrounding areae are, in histological sections stained with Nissl–toluidine
blue, quite sharp, the transition abrupt. It is an
area richer in nerve cells than the extrastriate
areae. It is elaborately differentiated into layers
and sublayers in the same way as in the Monkeys, Apes, and Man. The notable feature is the
splitting of the inner nuclear layer into three
sublayers, the thinner outer *4-a* and the much
thicker inner sublayer *4-c,* both filled with numerous "granules," and an intermediate zone
4-b, less rich in cells, in which a few outer solitary cells of Meynert are found. The inner and
larger solitary cells are located in layer *5,*
which, as in other Higher Primates, is less rich
in cells. Even finer distinctions may be identi-

fied as, e.g., *4cα* and *4cβ*, suggesting an advanced structural and functional differentiation. The details, as well as the synaptical organization, must remain a problem for future research.

In summary of the most important facts of the visual system of the Tarsier, it is no exaggeration to say that it is relatively more indicative of the supremacy of the sense of sight than in any other Primate of which we have sufficient knowledge. The Tarsier's huge eyeballs and extraordinarily developed subcortical and cortical centers of vision indicate this. The retina, with its multitude of extremely delicate rods and absence of cones, indicates complete adaptation to the nocturnal mode of life in which color vision is abolished. In spite of this, the visual acuity of the Tarsier, because of its possession of a small, but well-organized, fovea and yellow spot and a fairly thick optic nerve, may be assumed to be rather high. The partial decussation in the chiasma, in turn, may indicate an organization of the visual pathways and centers of the brain which, together with the frontal position of almost immobile eyes, indicates a high degree of tridimensional binocular stereopsis. Finally, the extraordinary size of the striate areae, together with the relatively small size of the superior colliculi, may be interpreted in the sense of a preponderance of cortex over the lower, mesencephalic, centers in the visual apparatus. Briefly, more than any other Primate, the Tarsier is a "visual animal."

11. RELATIVE IMPORTANCE OF THE TARSIER'S SENSES.—The comparison of the brain of the Tarsier (Figs. 516, 517, 518) with that of the Elephant Shrew (Figs. 480, 481), the Philippine Tree Shrew (Figs. 490, 491, 492), and the native Short-tailed Shrew demonstrates the extent of the reduction of the olfactory system in the Tarsier. The olfactory bulbs of the Tarsier represent hardly more than a fraction of the mass or volume of the same bulbs in the Tree Shrew, perhaps 5 per cent. Even in comparison with the *Blarina*, a much smaller animal, the Tarsier's olfactory bulbs may amount to hardly more than one-fifth. The great difference in the size of the olfactory centers in these species is related to the varying size of the nasal cavities. In the *Blarina* the length and width of

the cavities is double the nasal cavities in the Tarsier, a much larger animal.

These anatomical facts merely confirm the extent of the reduction that the olfactory sense suffered in the Tarsier. This reduction is caused by the extraordinary development of the Tarsier's vision, which in the micropic Soricide Shrews, with their keen sense of smell, plays but a minor role. The Elephant Shrews and the Tree Shrews maintain an intermediate position in this respect. The behavior of the Tarsier and of the Tree Shrew confirms this, in that the Tarsier was never seen to use its sense of smell in testing food, whereas the Tree Shrew used it regularly.

The deductions concerning the faculties of the Tarsier that can be made from the study of its brain and sense organs are almost self-evident. From the diminutive size of the olfactory centers it is safe to conclude that the sense of smell in this suborder plays an insignificant role, apparently even more so than in other advanced Primates: Monkeys, Apes, and Man. The well-developed subcortical centers of sight and hearing, the fact that at least one-fifth of the pallium or cortex of the cerebral hemispheres is directly related to vision and probably as much to audition, are all self-explanatory. This all agrees with the inordinate development of the externally visible peripheral organs of these two senses—the eyeballs and the auricles.

The only question that could reasonably be raised concerns the supremacy of sight over hearing. Obviously, an answer could be given only after a thorough observation of the Tarsier in its native habitat and upon valid experimental evidence. The presence of a large yellow spot and a well-developed central area, with a well-formed, though small, central fovea; converging lines of vision; and a partially decussated chiasma, in opposition to the opinion of some recent investigators (Elliot Smith, Woollard, Tilney), favor the view that the tridimensional stereoscopic sense in the Tarsier is not absent but is, in fact, quite well developed. This is the more remarkable, since its retina is that of an entirely nocturnal animal.

The stereopsis of the Tarsier shows that this sense is not necessarily restricted to the diurnal animals but is also compatible with a nocturnal mode of life, depending on the degree of perfection of vision (the Cats and the Owls are a good example of this).

The behavior of the Tarsier observed during life shows that it possesses a keen sense of sight, good visual memory, accuracy in gauging the distance and direction of its leaps when catching its prey; that its various motor actions, such as moving the head, eyes, auricles, and upper extremities in perfect harmony with the movements of the trunk and of the hind extremities are well co-ordinated, and all guided by sight, as described in subsections 4–7 of this section. All this favors the view that the sense of vision in all its manifestations, except color perception, has apparently been brought to the highest state of perfection compatible with the nocturnal mode of life in this suborder.

In its dependence upon the two higher senses, especially sight, the Tarsier is like the rest of the true Primates, whether they are chiefly nocturnal, as are the Lemurs, or almost entirely diurnal, as are the Monkeys, Apes, and Man.

12. The Tarsier and the problem of the origin of Primates.—In the attempts to answer the following questions Which of the Early Mammals first showed bodily features characteristic of the true Primates? What were the external factors influencing the evolution of the Primate Ancestors? And how and why did their organism react in the particular way that resulted in primate evolution?—the Tarsier has played a conspicuous role.

The reason for the intensive interest in this suborder is the fact that even superficial observation reveals the true primate nature of the Tarsier. Its numerous other characteristics, on the other hand, link it with the phylogenetically older Order of Insectivora. Again, while it resembles the more primitive Lemuroidea in many ways, in others the Tarsier appears close to true Monkeys and Apes (Pithecoidea or Anthropoidea), owing to which an intermediary suborder, Tarsioidea, has been established. Finally, in paleontological chronology, the Tarsiers and the Lemurs appeared as early as the Paleocene (*ca.* 50–60 million years ago) and Eocene (*ca.* 35–50 million years in the past). This indicates that the Tarsiers preceded the true Monkeys, which developed, probably from a primitive, nonspecialized tarsioid stock, by the beginning of the Oligocene Epoch, 30 million years ago.

The Tarsier, in the words of G. Elliot Smith, "is a remarkably generalised creature which in many respects is akin to the Menotyphlous Insectivora [Tree Shrews], and has persisted with extraordinarily little change from the beginning of the Eocene period," or about 45 million years ago. Yet every part of its anatomy, according to Smith, "reveals its affinity to the higher Primates and affords evidence of its differentiation from the Lemuroidea."

Some of the extinct Tarsioids, known as Anaptomorphidae, particularly *Tetonius* of the American Lower Eocene (*ca.* 45 million years ago), had a skull whose general structure was "quite similar to that of the living *Tarsius*, with a very short face and huge, forwardly turned orbits . . ." while the older forms, e.g., *Necrolemur* of the Upper Eocene of Europe (30–35 million years ago), quite properly, "appear to have been rather more lemur-like, with a somewhat less reduced snout" (Romer 1945).

The brain of the Tarsier, according to Cope (1885), also resembles that of the extinct Anaptomorphidae, which he believed were the most simian Lemurs yet discovered, and probably represented the family from which the Higher Monkeys, Apes, and Men derived. Notable authorities, such as Gregory (1922) and Simpson (1950), however, have raised a voice of dissension in the chorus glorifying the Tarsier as a close kin of Man, and admit at most a very remote common ancestry of both.

The intermediate position of the Tarsier in primate evolution, according to Woollard (1925), is manifested by the following anatomical peculiarities: (1) Primitive—smooth brain, small corpus callosum, large ventral commissure, simple subdivision of cerebellum resembling that found in the Marsupials, a large third eyelid containing a plate of cartilage, a well-developed Harderian gland, and alimentary viscera that are of the simplest among the Mammals, approaching in this respect those of the Reptiles and Amphibians. (2) Lemurine—arrangement of the cortical areas, absence of a pigmented macula, "specialisation of vision, the nocturnal habits, and a general retinal pattern of the nocturnal type" (the second statement concerning the absence of a "macula" and of a foveal excavation is obviously an error; *see* par. 9, this section). (3) Anthropoid—reduction of the face, eyes directed forward, erect posture, orbits almost completely separated from the temporal fossa, facial muscles highly differentiated. "With all the evidence of its anatomy marshalled," Woollard somewhat incongruously concluded, "there can be no doubt that *Tarsius* is a Lemur of the Lemurs and is annectant to the early Eocene primitive placentals, and that standing at the base of the Primate stem it reaches forth to the Simian forms and is annectant to the Anthropoidea."

The information so far mentioned indicates the great antiquity of the Tarsiers. This view, in the light of available evidence, seems reasonable, whether or not the Tarsier is to be regarded as "the oldest mammal inhabiting the earth, since no other mammalian form of the Eocene period is now extant" (Fulton 1939). As soon, however, as an attempt is made to evaluate definite anatomical features of the Tarsier and to try to estimate the probable factors that have been in play in primate evolution, the difficulties and contradictions become apparent.

"*Tarsius*," according to G. Elliot Smith (1919), "represents the phylum whose progress was brought to a sudden stop in Eocene times by an over-development of, and an exaggerated reliance upon, those specialisations of vision and its cerebral instruments which were responsible for the differentiation of the Tarsioidea from the Lemuroidea, and gave impetus to those developments which produced the Anthropoidea from one of the Tarsioid families. But *Tarsius* was able to escape extinction only by adopting the safe nocturnal habits which also played a part in sparing the Lemuroidea." In other words, the Tarsier is the result of a scotopic specialization of sight beyond the level reached by the Lemurs, which, in turn, had precluded any further progress, although by this specialization it saved itself from extermination. Other members of the Tarsioid suborder were more fortunate in remaining diurnal. By doing so, they became modern Monkeys, Apes, and Men.

13. Adverse effect of nocturnal adaptation on further evolution of the Tarsier.—The thesis of an adverse effect of nocturnality upon the evolutionary progress intended eventually to lead toward the anthropoid stage is quite plausible. Unquestionably, the wealth of information about the external world gained under scotopic conditions in all respects—acuity, color, stereopsis, and range or distance—is much poorer, being partly or entirely abolished, compared with daylight vision. What remains doubtful is the course of the phylogenesis. The incompleteness of our information about the visual apparatus of the Lemurs does not permit us to speculate logically about this, however.

To judge from G. Elliot Smith's statement, both the Lemurs and the Tarsiers were originally diurnal and became nocturnal when competition by the diurnal animals of prey exceeded the limits of their tolerance. Whether or not this was so there is no way of judging. If, however, a well-developed central area and fovea are instruments of diurnality, both the Asiatic Tarsier and *Aotes* of South America would have to be considered forms of originally diurnal animals, since both possess a well-developed fovea, which secondarily became adapted to the nocturnal way of living.

This view is supported by the pronounced diurnality of all Tree Shrews (with the exception of the Pen-tailed Shrew), which preceded all these suborders of the Primates, the Lemurs, Tarsiers, and Monkeys. The presence in *Urogale* of an orimental or incipient central area agrees with this.

Important as the inherent phylogenetical tendency is, however, functional requirements and adaptations are also to be considered. In many cases the functional demand may have exerted pressure upon the plastic potentialities of bodily organization greater than the long-range factors inherited from the past. The visual apparatus of the Owls and Swifts may serve as an example. Here a new posterior or temporal fovea was created in response to the emphasis on high acuity and binocular vision. This structure is functionally motivated exactly in the same way as is the similar posterior or temporal fovea of the diurnal Hawks, Eagles, and Swallows, whereas an anterior or central fovea, important in all diurnal species, was abolished as useless in the Owls. Again, in the Domestic

Cat—an animal of pronounced nocturnal habit, but with both eyes almost facing anteriorly and obviously used stereoscopically—a well-formed central area is found, even though no certain fovea is present.

To conclude, the nocturnality of the Tarsier appears as a secondary adaptation, a "flight into the night," of an originally diurnal form. In its striving to adapt itself to the new mode of life, the Tarsier has gone as far as circumstances permitted by preserving its original diurnal central area and fovea and by adapting it and itself to the nocturnal habit.

14. PROBABLE FACTORS RESPONSIBLE FOR THE TARSIER'S NOCTURNAL ADAPTATION AND ITS EVOLUTIONARY STAGNATION.—What the actual biological factors were which exerted the phylogenetical pressure that brought about a change in the mode of the Tarsier's life during the Paleocene (60 million years ago) and Eocene (40 million years ago) can only be guessed. The Pterosauria or Flying Reptiles of the Jurassic and Cretaceous Periods, lasting from 60 to 150 million years in the past, and the Dinosaurs had died out by that time. But the large-toothed Birds of those times, some of formidable size, as, for example, *Hesperornis*, armed with a beak 10 inches long, and the smaller *Archaeornis*, and *Archaeopteryx*, and their kin, may still have lingered during the early part of the Tertiary Period to make life miserable for the small and largely helpless Early Primates.

There were, in addition, numerous predaceous terrestrial Reptiles in the Late Cretaceous Period, contributing to the complex scene. From what can be judged from the size and position of the orbits and scleral rings of the Early Birds, it appears that they were diurnal predators. When, during the Cretaceous and early part of the Tertiary Period, more modern birds began to appear, many of them retained the predatory habits of their predecessors. They, too, seem to have been largely diurnal in their habits. Most conspicuous among them were the giant flightless *Phororhacos* of the Miocene Epoch of South America (from 10 to 25 million years ago) and the *Diatryma* of the Eocene Epoch of North America and Europe (from *ca.* 25 to 40 million years ago).

The Falconiform Order, which includes well-flying diurnal Birds of Prey such as the Falcons, Hawks, Eagles, Ospreys, Buzzards, and Vultures, appeared later on the phylogenetical scene. This order may therefore have exerted a powerful influence upon the nascent Primates and may have been partly responsible for their complete disappearance from North America by the end of the Oligocene Epoch (*ca.* 30 million years ago).

Even more important may have been the early terrestrial carnivorous Mammals, such as the Creodonts, some of giant size, which lived during the Paleocene and Eocene Epochs (from 30 to 60 million years ago) and the more modern Miacids of the Late Eocene and Oligocene Epochs (from 25 to 35 million years ago). These subsequently became transformed into extinct and living Fissipedes: Civets, Weasels, Dogs, and Cats. Themselves partly arboreal, these ancient Carnivores may have been a potent inducement to some of the Insectivores to take refuge in the trees.

In the further course of evolution these arboreal Insectivores either became Primates or, in the Paleocene (from 50 to 60 million years ago), took an additional and final step in their striving to emancipate themselves from the burdens and deprivations of terrestrial existence and found safety and abundance in the air as Flying Foxes (Megachiroptera) and Bats (Microchiroptera). The Strigiform Order of Birds, the Owls, present during the entire Tertiary Epoch (since 60 million years ago), may have been another important factor in the ecological pressure that resulted in primate evolution.

15. TERRESTRIAL INCEPTION OF THE INSECTIVOROUS PHASE OF PRIMATE EVOLUTION.—The picture that one may draw of the probable beginnings and course of evolution of the Primates is necessarily tentative. The initial stage was represented by the terrestrial Insectivorous Mammals of the Upper Cretaceous Period, which lived from approximately 60 to 90 million years or more ago. They may have resembled in size and appearance some Soricide Shrews (Figs. 475, 476) or even more the Malayan Gymnurinae (*see* Brehm's *Tierleben*, v. 10, p. 347). Living almost exclusively on the ground, in shady undergrowth and in dense vegetation, they subsisted on low forms of life, such as worms, insects, slugs, and the like which they were able to master. In their obscure habitat they found not only an abundance of food but also shelter from the big carnivorous beasts that ruled the world during that epoch.

Their most important distance receptor in such circumstances was the sense of smell, closely collaborating with the senses of touch and gustation. Sight, in general well developed in the Reptiles, of small use in a life close to the ground, where the view is obstructed by a mass of vegetation, receded to a poorly differentiated, though not meaningless, photophobic "warning sense." The other distance receptor, hearing, was retained and further developed. The reason was that hearing reacted to sound waves, which, unlike the rays of light propagated in straight lines, are capable of "turning around the corner."

Thus adapted for a life in obscurity, the Early Insectivores were admirably equipped for the "struggle for survival." Of this their little-changed modern descendants are a living testimony (*see* section on Common Shrew, this chapter). They and their kin, without glory or glamour, have existed these past hundred million years or so, while the mighty Dinosaurs of the Cretaceous Period have vanished. (One may pertinently ask whether the Early Insectivores were, perhaps, a prime agent in bringing about the downfall of the big beasts upon whose unprotected eggs and young, led by their efficient sense of smell, they may have preyed.)

Thus the Insectivores would have gone on without change for untold ages. Following the tendency of all living beings to expand, however, the various strains of the Insectivores embarked upon a conquest of other realms. Of these, several possibilities offered themselves: an underground, an aquatic, an arboreal, and an aerial existence. Each of these habitats was successfully invaded. The Talpidae or Moles and to a lesser degree some Soricidae went underground, with the resulting further reduction of sight and the overdevelopment of senses which work at close range. The Potamogalidae, or African Otter Shrews, and some of the Soricidae, such as the American Water or Marsh Shrew (*Neosorex palustris*) and its Old World

counterpart (*Neomys fodiens*), and the curious Desman or Výchuchol (*Myogale* or *Desmana moschata*) of southeastern Europe and Central Asia have become aquatic.

16. Arboreal life and the origin of Primates.—The adaptation to the arboreal life of those Insectivores later to become either Primates or Chiropterans must have occurred prior to the earliest Tertiary Epoch, the Paleocene, that is, sometime during the later part of the Cretaceous Period of the Mesozoic Era (about 60–80 million years ago or earlier). The reason for thinking so is the paleontological discovery, according to Romer (1945), of skeletons of Insect-eating Bats with well-developed wings in the Middle Eocene deposits both in Europe and in North America whose approximate age is 40 million years. The ability to fly, accordingly, must have developed sometime during the Paleocene Epoch, 50–60 million years ago, and must have been preceded by an adaptation to arboreal life. This again agrees well with the appearance of both Lemurs and Tarsiers as early as the Paleocene (from 50 to 60 million years ago) and certainly during the Eocene Period (estimated to have lasted from 40 to 50 million years ago).

The arboreal habit developed by the Late Cretaceous Tree Shrews was one of the two possible ways to leave the obscurity and semi-nocturnality of the underbrush and to acquire a freer view of the surrounding habitat. The other way was to increase in size and strength, to develop offensive and defensive weapons, to perfect terrestrial locomotion, to widen the range and improve the quality of distance receptors—sight and hearing—and to add all other possible anatomical equipment for eluding or fighting aggressors or to overcome the resistance of prey, as the case may be. This road was taken by the majority of the Orders of Mammals. A classical example is the Horse, which evolved from a diminutive ancestor not larger than a fox terrier, the *Eohippus* of the American Lower Eocene (roughly 40 million years ago), gradually increasing in size to a giant *Megahippus*, approximating a Rhinoceros, a species which lived during the Pliocene Epoch, which lasted from 1 to 10 million years ago.

17. Changes in bodily equipment of the Primates caused by arboreal life.—Arboreal life, except for flying, was the only way to rise above the ground and thus to increase the range of view, to survey the surrounding territory better, to escape powerful enemies, and to reach the source of more abundant food. It required the adaptation of the limbs to climbing, the reorientation of the senses to new conditions, and a corresponding change in the integrating central organ—the brain.

Efficient claws were already present and were used first. This mode of progression has been retained until the present by the modern Tree Shrews and was developed to perfection by another group of arboreal Mammals, the Squirrels, which appeared during the Miocene Epoch (from 12 to 25 million years ago; *see* preceding section).

During this process of adaptation and apparently within a relatively short space of time, some of the arboreal Insect-Eaters developed the habit of grasping boughs or twigs with their digits, instead of digging with their claws into the bark (such incipient use of fingers to grasp objects is already observable in the Squirrels). The fingers and toes lengthened, they became more flexible, and their neuromuscular use more supple and varied, especially by the development of opposability of the thumb and the big toe. In this way, one must assume, efficient prehensile digital instruments developed. At the same time the original claws gradually flattened into shields protecting the terminal phalanges, thus giving better support to their pads when an object was being held.

Of all these changes, the opposability of the thumb to the remaining digits of the hand was of first importance. It not only increased and diversified the grasping ability of the hand but emancipated one hand from the assistance of the other. The thumbless Squirrels, for example, can use their hands very well to hold and efficiently manipulate a walnut or an acorn, but they are not able to do so except by the use of both hands. With an opposable thumb, however, a Primate has acquired a pincer- or tong-like hand which can hold objects unassisted by the other hand, thus increasing many times the usefulness of the hands. The Tarsier in this respect has advanced little beyond the Squirrel,

while many Monkeys have again reduced the usefulness of the thumb or have lost it altogether.

The foregoing basic changes in the anatomy and function of the limbs must have occurred quite early in primate evolution, apparently not later than during the Paleocene Epoch (from 50 to 60 million years in the past). It was at that time that the true Lemurs and Tarsioids appeared, followed later by the Monkeys during the Oligocene Epoch (from 25 to 45 million years ago).

Simultaneously with these changes in the limbs, a veritable revolution must have taken place in the senses during the early phase of adaptation to arboreal life. Whereas the insectivorous Soricide Shrews are largely scotopic, the omnivorous tupaiide Tree Shrews have developed a pronounced diurnal habit, of paramount importance in an arboreal existence which requires the sense of sight to be fully developed and utilized. A diurnal habit was the prime factor, then, in enabling one branch of the early Insectivores to assume an arboreal existence, and as such it remained important until the present.

Evidence of this is found in the fact that most Primates, extinct and modern, except Humans, live in the trees. In the past, as now, trees meant safety, relative, if not absolute. This must have been true in spite of the many Birds of Prey, which included such forms as the modern Monkey-eating Eagle of the Philippines (*Pithecophaga jefferyi*), and in spite of the fact that the Strigidae, or Owls, have been making the nights unsafe at least since the beginning of the Tertiary Epoch. But, more important, trees were the source of food, especially in the tropics, which appear to be the real homeland of the Primates.

18. Diurnality, the prime factor in progressive primate evolution.—The fact that all Primates, from the earliest of which there is a paleontological record to the modern ones, show either a pronounced adaptation to arboreal life or derive from arboreal forms is evidence that the arboreal habit was a prime factor in their origin. Diurnality also was of equal importance in progressive primate evolution. Of the now living Primates, the advanced Pithecoidea, or true Monkeys, with few exceptions are expressly diurnal, whereas nocturnality has been retained—or rather redeveloped—only by the backward Lemurs and the conservative Tarsiers.

The flight of the Lemurs into night's darkness, evidently as a means of preventing their extinction, even in their principal home, the Island of Madagascar, where they are confronted with relatively inefficient competition, is rather remarkable (*cf.* J. Sibree 1915). In other parts of the world, as in Africa and on the mainland of southeastern Asia, where the competition is stiff, the few remaining forms, such as the Galagos, Pottos, and Lorises, exist only by sufferance.

The same may be said of the Tarsiers: they, too, have survived only on the secluded islands of the East Indies and in the Malayan Peninsula, which may well be compared zoögeographically with an island. Both the existing Lemurs and the Tarsiers appear as evolutionary flotsam left along the outskirts of the great regions where a dynamic, progressive primate evolution took place and where in the past the Lemurs and the Tarsiers had lived: almost the entire great Eurasian continent, most of Africa except Madagascar, and both Americas. (Australia, never in prehistory invaded by the terrestrial Placental Mammals, remained outside the sphere of primate evolution.)

The nocturnal habit assumed by the Tarsier merely indicates an attempt to postpone the complete elimination of this "debris" of a formerly much more abundant life. It is therefore improbable that, beyond the insectivorous stage, the main stream of primate evolution ever again passed through a nocturnal phase. Neither the nocturnal Lemurs nor the nocturnal Tarsiers of the Paleocene and Eocene Epochs, therefore, could have been the links in the evolutionary chain that led to the overwhelmingly diurnal Pithecoids. Otherwise, it would be necessary to assume, first, a transformation of the diurnal Tree Shrews into nocturnal Lemurs and Tarsiers and their dedifferentiation again into diurnal Pithecoids.

It is more probable that the inception of the Primates was in fair-sized terrestrial Insectivores of a preponderantly diurnal habit, somewhat resembling modern Malayan Gymnurines.

The further phylogenetical stages may have been represented by the ancient, but less strictly photopic, Tree Shrews, followed by diurnal forms of the Lemurs and Tarsiers, and continued by the almost exclusively diurnal Monkeys, Apes, and Man.

The nocturnal genera, such as the Pen-tailed Tree Shrew (*Ptilocercus*), Lemurs, Tarsiers, Night Monkey (*Aotes* or *Nyctipithecus*), are all side lines, biologically motivated by their incapacity to compete successfully with their diurnal rivals, especially animals of prey. They took an easier, defensive way of self-preservation, paying for it by renouncing a further progress precluded by nocturnal conditions. Most of their diurnal cousins of past epochs, the Lemurs, Tarsiers, and Monkeys, with the exception of modern Tree Shrews, have left the scene not so much because they have been exterminated as because they have been transformed into more advanced diurnal Monkeys, Apes, and Humans.

The same idea is equally applicable to the Lower Insectivores, e.g., the Shrews and other Soricoids, such as the Moles (Talpidae), Solenodontids, Chrysochlorids, Erinaceoids, and possibly also the present Gymnurines and Macroscelidids. Most of them are remnants from past ages. They were able to preserve themselves only by the adoption of secretive habits, either by going underground, by becoming aquatic, or, if remaining above the ground, by strictly observing nocturnal habits (Bats, Soricide Shrews), by growing a more or less effective coat of sharp spines (Hedgehog, Tenrec), or in some other way. All these surviving members of the Orders of Insectivora and Chiroptera, as well as the nocturnal Primates, have followed the principle that "discretion is the better part of valor" and got out of the way of the well-armed, mighty, and bold aggressors which took possession of the earth.

Briefly, diurnality and arboreal habit appear to have been the main instruments of early Primate evolution during the Mesozoic Period of the earth's prehistory.

19. THE PROBLEM OF INTELLECTUAL PRE-EMINENCE IN PRIMATE EVOLUTION.—In the preceding subsection the thesis that arboreal habit and diurnality are the principal factors responsible for the progressive evolution of Primates was discussed. The remaining and even more difficult subject is concerned with the inordinate development of the brain and mental faculties in which the Order of Primates surpasses all other animals.

The theme of Man's intellectual superiority has been a favorite topic of philosophers and students of nature since ancient times. With the increased knowledge of Man's bodily organization and his kinship to other Mammals, especially his near relatives, the Monkeys and the Apes, the answer was sought in the comparative study of the brain, sense organs, and behavior.

Among modern students G. Elliot Smith, in the words of Woollard (1927), has brought forward the concept of "the acquirement of skilled movements and the correlation of these with vision" as a causal factor in primate evolution. "The Tarsioidea," in the opinion of Smith (1919), "seem to have become differentiated from the Lemuroidea by a reduction of the face, which permitted the much fuller development of stereoscopic vision." But how exactly these and other relevant factors have co-operated in stimulating the growth of the brain and, with this, the development of mental faculties—properties to which, in the final analysis, Man owes his pre-eminence in nature—still remains one of the greatest problems of science. (*See* chap. XV for continuation of this topic.)

20. Uncertainties concerning the true causes of the primate evolution.—It is amazing how many details are known about primate evolution without the core of the problem, the true causes of the whole process, being found. It is necessary to recognize the fact that we do not know either the exact phylogenetical origin of Man or the precise phylogenetical process which led to it. We are not able to point to some specific and exclusive external and internal factors responsible for the phylogenetical appearance of the Primate Order in general and for the coming of Man in particular. The available explanations all are descriptive, logical, roundabout constructions instead of clear demonstrations of evidence.

First, the exact causes of the development of the subsequent higher primate suborders from the lower ones are not clear: the Lemurs from the Tree Shrews, the Tarsiers from the Lemurs, the Monkeys from the Tarsiers, the Apes from the Monkeys, Men from the apelike ancestors— if this was the phylogenetical sequence. We know, or rather are convinced, on the strength of a very obvious anatomical, physiological, and biological kinship, that some such chain of events must have taken place in the past. But just what the stimulating factors were and how the individual links in this long process were causally interconnected still remain largely guesswork.

A few critical questions are: Why, above all, was the adoption of an arboreal mode of life necessary in order to make Primates from the generalized ground-dwelling insectivorous ancestors, whereas, obviously, to make Man out of the apelike ancestor, the creature had again to come down from the trees and rely entirely upon bipedal gait, thus freeing its hands and arms from the duty of locomotion (since otherwise Man would have reverted to the largely quadrupedal habit exemplified by the Baboons)?

And how was the sense of vision responsible for this "anthropogeny," if at all, since, obviously, the Monkeys have developed this faculty practically to perfection, even though (or, should we say, because?) they went up into the trees and stayed there?

And, if vision was the only, or the principal, responsible factor, why did it not work in the preponderantly ground-dwelling Monkeys, such as the Baboons, where certainly there were enough compelling reasons for this: few trees to be used as a source of food and refuge, lots of "social life," and plenty of game animals to prey on?

And while it is plausible that the arboreal phase in primatogenesis may have been necessary for the rise of that order, is it not just as apparent that staying in the trees would have prevented further progress and that it is therefore likely that Man's direct ancestors were among the early simian-like Primates to come back to the ground, or that they never were as completely adapted to the life in the trees as are most other Primates?

But just what was the impelling cause that made Man's ancestors rise on their hind legs, leaving their arms and hands completely free for use as manipulators, thus making possible the development of the brainiest creature of the globe, Man?

These and similar questions have been advanced by a great number of naturalists and thinkers ever since Charles R. Darwin made the principle of evolution a recognized factor in modern scientific thinking. In the final chapter of this book an attempt is made, on the basis of facts and logic, to understand the origin of Man in his physical and mental characters from the infrahuman forms that preceded him.

References: R. Anthony 1912; Ariëns Kappers, Huber & Crosby 1936; Beattie 1927; Bierens de Haan & Frima 1930; A. Brehm's *Tierleben,* v. 13 (*Säugetiere,* v. 4), p. 417, 1916; Burmeister 1846; D. Campbell 1947; Carlsson 1922; Carter 1938; Catchpole & Fulton 1939; Le Gros Clark 1924, 1930, 1931, 1934, 1935, 1945; E. T. Collins 1921; N. Cook 1939; E. D. Cope 1885; H. Cuming 1838; J. T. Cunningham 1919–20; C. R. Darwin 1859, 1871; Detwiler 1938, 1939, 1941, 1943; Earle 1897; D. G. Elliot 1910, 1912; I. Franklin 1942; V. Franz 1934; J. F. Fulton 1939; W. K. Gagnebin 1947; Ghiselli 1937; Gobrecht & Oertel 1953; Gregory 1910, 1916, 1920, 1922, 1930, 1932, 1933, 1935, 1943, 1951; R. Gunter 1951; W. Harris 1904; S. Hecht *et al.* 1948; Hennig 1950; Hesse & Doflein 1935–43; J. P. Hill 1919, 1932; W. C. O. Hill 1953; Hoogstraal 1947; Hooton 1942, 1947; C. Hose 1893, 1927; A. B. Howell 1944; Hubrecht 1897; Hubrecht & Keibel 1907; Hunter 1923; Jagor 1873; F. Wood Jones 1918, 1919, 1926, 1929, 1942; Kindahl 1944; A. Knopf 1949; A. Lawson *et al.* 1943; G. C. Lewis 1939; P. C. Livingston 1943; Lowther 1939; Marcy 1943; W. D. Matthew 1915, 1939, 1943; Matthew & Granger 1915; A. B. Meyer 1915; G. S. Miller 1911; R. A. Miller 1943; P. C. Mitchell 1919; Montagu 1944; Morton 1922, 1924; Mott 1905, 1907; Mott *et al.* 1910; Mott & Halliburton 1908; Mott & Kelley 1908; Joh. Müller 1826; S. Mueller 1855, 1857; K. N. Ogle *et al.* 1949; Orione 1950; H. F. Osborn 1896; Ossenkopp 1925; Ovio 1927; Packer 1941; Parker & Haswell 1940; J. Parsons 1943; F. H. Pike 1943; Piveteau 1951 and *Traité de paléontologie,* vols. 4–7; Pocock 1918, 1919, 1920, 1925, 1939–41; A. Posner 1945; Raffles 1822; Regan 1930; W. J. B. Riddle 1943; Rochon-Duvigneaud 1943; Romer 1943, 1945; H. Rosenberg 1878; T. C. Ruch 1941; K. Schmidt 1947; A. H. Schultz 1936; Sclater & Sclater 1899; Sewertzoff 1929; J. Sibree 1915; O. Sickenberg 1934; G. G. Simpson 1931, 1947, 1949; G. E. Smith 1907, 1909, 1919, 1921, 1925, 1926, 1927, 1930, 1932; Sonntag 1924; W. L. Straus, Jr. 1940, 1949; K. C. Swan 1948; Symposium on the *Origin and Evolution of Man* 1950; Teilhard de Chardin 1921; O. Thomas 1896; A. R. Thompson 1933; Tilney 1927, 1928; E.-L. Trouessart 1898–99, 1922; Tschermak 1902, 1914, 1927; Vandel 1949; Verrier 1938, 1945; E. P. Walker 1954; A. R. Wallace 1894; Walls 1942; M. Weber 1927–28; H. Werner 1942; C. H. Wharton 1948, 1950 (2 papers); H. Wheatstone 1838; Woodward *et al.* 1919; Woollard 1925, 1926, 1927; Zeuner 1946; Ziehen 1903, 1903–34, 1904; Zuckerman 1933; Zuckerman & Fulton 1934, 1940–41.

SEC. 13. MISCELLANEOUS NOTES ON THE VISUAL BEHAVIOR OF THE ANIMALS IN NATURE

1. TREE FROGS AND THEIR VISUAL BEHAVIOR.—The Tree Frogs, by definition, are anuran or tailless Amphibians of arboreal habits, inhabiting in numerous species many parts of the world. With other Frogs and Toads they form the Order of Anura, which, with the tailed Newts and Salamanders or Urodela and the limbless or wormlike Apoda, forms the Class of Amphibia. The Amphibians are phylogenetically the oldest land vertebrates which developed from fishlike ancestors. In external and internal makeup they are closely related to the latter, and their early development takes place in the water.

Since the Tree Frogs are well adapted to arboreal living, it was of considerable interest to observe them in their natural habitat, in order to determine, if possible, why and how these water-dwelling creatures took to the trees, and how they and their visual organs became adapted to the arboreal habit.

These observations of the behavior of Tree

Frogs were made in the woods of northern Wisconsin in late August. In some years Tree Frogs are quite numerous here, and the trees and bushes team with them. In other years, however, few of them are seen.

During the night there were long periods without any sounds that could be attributed to Tree Frogs, in spite of fairly good illumination, for the quartermoon was shining brightly and parts of the forest were full of light (1:00 A.M. in late August, 1948, and 1949). Only occasionally a brief sound, shorter than during the day, was heard, but there was no "chorus." During the early morning hours the Tree Frogs were still quiet. Even as late as 8:00 A.M. hardly a sound was heard from the trees. Thereafter, the Tree Frogs were heard more frequently, until, toward late afternoon, their voices multiplied and finally increased to a "chorus." This observation would indicate that the indigenous Tree Frogs are largely diurnal in habit.

There were two kinds of sounds: a peeping, high-pitched note and another soft, smooth, sonorous rattle. The latter especially was heard more frequently in something like a "chorus" started by one individual and kept up alternatively by the others on the neighboring trees. Unfortunately, in spite of all efforts, it was not possible to locate and identify the species with the character of the sound. According to A. H. Morgan's *Field Book of Ponds and Streams*, however, the first sound was to be attributed to the Spring Peeper (*Hyla crucifer*), the other to the Common Tree Frog (*Hyla versicolor*). (*See also* Brehm, v. 4, 1912; K. P. Schmidt 1929; Wright & Wright 1949; for figures in color *see* A. A. Allen in Nat. Geog. Mag., v. 97, 1950.)

The Common Tree Frog is an alert, vivacious animal, with a physiognomy indicating a flicker of batrachian intelligence. Its eyes are relatively large and bulging, as they are in all its congeners, and are mounted in such a way that almost the whole cornea and pupil are visible when observed directly from the front. The pupils are oblong horizontally, with pointed angles. The binocular overlapping of the two fields of view, roughly estimated from the position of the corneae, may be as much as 60°.

When the Frog is held quietly, small, jerky, horizontal movements of the eyeballs are seen from time to time, as well as inward-pulling movements. The horizontal movements are executed in the horizontal plane, in short jerks, as if the Frog were trying to hold in view an object of interest. Similar slight jerks of the head may also be seen, as if the animal were trying to fixate a visual object. The compensatory movements of the eyes in the horizontal plane are automatic. Whether these are labyrinthine or optical it was not possible to determine. The vertical movements of the eyes induced by the rotation of the animal around its axis may, with more certainty, be considered labyrinthine.

The pupil of the side exposed to light was smaller, the one kept in the shade larger. Sometimes the reverse was true, with the shaded pupil smaller, which, however, was opened wide when the animal was excited or when the eye was mechanically stimulated. The pupil exposed to light became smaller only after a considerable time, a half-minute or longer. A prompt, direct pupillary light reflex, comparable to that found in the higher Vertebrates, was absent. The nictitating membrane sweeps from below over the entire cornea at rare intervals. After decapitation the pupils were at once reduced to minute horizontal slits, while the protective reflexes of the nictitating membranes and the pulling-in of the eyeballs still persisted for some time.

The preceding sketch of the Tree Frog, with the exception of the sounds, indicates rather general organization of the visual system with few signs of specific diurnal adaptation. Other equipment, such as suction pads on the terminal phalanges, shows the advanced adaptation of this genus to arboreal habit and habitat. Whether there are any other detailed characteristics indicative of arboreal habit and diurnal adaptation, especially of the visual system, such as the preponderance of cones and the presence of a central area or fovea of the retina, must remain a problem for future investigation. (*Cf. also* Fig. 461).

2. Painted Turtle.—The Genus of Painted Turtle (*Chrysemys picta*) is representative of several of the beautifully decorated Turtles of eastern North America. These Turtles have a more elaborately organized visual apparatus than do the Amphibians. Observation showed that their visual behavior was comparable with that of the Anole Lizard and the Swallow, described earlier in this chapter. The feature common to all three species is an elaborate organization of the oculomotor apparatus, permitting the use of each eye individually or of both together as a binocular stereoscopic team (*cf.* Fig. 466).

The appearance of the Painted Turtle fully justifies its name. While most of the upper surface of its carapace or shield is more or less uniformly dark green and brown, its margins and those of the lower plastron are elaborately decorated with orange patches shading into yellow, and with dark-green and yellow stripes on the head, neck, tail, and limbs. (*See* for figures, partly in color, Brehm, v. 4, p. 403, 1912; K. P. Schmidt 1938; R. L. Ditmars 1946; C. H. Pope 1946.)

Observation in captivity showed the Turtle to be an alert visual animal. Its eyes are mounted at a slant, so that the two optical axes are directed forward and downward. The angle that each axis incloses with the mid-sagittal plane is approximately 60°, with the horizontal plane about 70°. The iris membrane, in turn, incloses an angle of 45° with the sagittal plane, the two iris membranes together making an angle of about 90° to the rear. The pupil is almost a perfect circle and is set a bit anteriorly from the exact center of the iris. There is a slight dent in the posterior pupillary margin. Occasionally a minute, but quick, spontaneous movement of the pupillary margin is noticed, which is probably an indication of the action of accommodation.

From the position of the eyes, one may conclude that the locality of principal interest to the Turtle is in the anterior direction and downward. This would agree with the habitual attitude, in which the head is held at an angle of 45° to the horizontal plane. In this attitude the two visual axes are directed to some extent forward, instead of only downward, as they would be if the head were held horizontally.

When the animal was alerted, its head was raised so that its axis formed an angle of at least 75°, and possibly more, with the horizontal plane. In this position, when the Turtle is in water, with its head above the surface, the dark pigmented streaks passing across the head and eyes, including iris and pupil, become perfectly

parallel with the surface of the water. This again may indicate the probable role of these streaks as arrangements for absorbing the rays of light reflected from the surface of the water which would otherwise interfere with visual acuity (*cf.* "sighting grooves" of the Pike).

In the normal swimming position of the Turtle, both eyes deviate from the strictly lateral position for about 45°, as indicated by the position of the iris membranes. This is an indication of the deviation of the theoretical optical axes of the eyes toward the chin, with the lines of vision probably directed straight ahead and parallel to the surface of the water. The two lines of vision may well be used in binocular stereoscopic vision, as discussed in the sections on the Anole Lizard and the Swallow. To a Turtle swimming with its body just submerged, this attitude would afford a sweeping view over the entire expanse of the water of a lake or pond, so that it could see at once any object that might be of particular interest to it, such as a floating dead fish or other potential food.

The eyes of the Turtle, when the animal was quiet, gave an impression of alert watchfulness. They continuously scanned the field of view, being directed from one object to another. When both eyes moved, they frequently did not act as a perfect team, one occasionally lagging or standing still. The movements were short, quick jerks in a more or less horizontal plane only, or associated with up-and-down movements. The scanning movements were accompanied by those of the head and neck, especially lively when the animal tried to free itself from the grip of the examiner's hand. Hence the great mobility of the head and neck further assisted the movements of the eyes. Spontaneous movements of an individual eye in the horizontal plane may amount to at least 40°. If the eyeball was suddenly illuminated, it very promptly turned toward the stimulus.

When making scanning movements, the eyes moved easily in their sockets. When an object moved so that it fell within the Turtle's field of view, the head and eyes promptly turned toward it. Even a slight move of the examiner's hand at some distance elicited an immediate turning reflex of one or both eyes. However, when the hand was moved quickly or suddenly toward the Turtle, the head and neck were promptly drawn into the shell.

The convergence of both eyes was more difficult to determine. Binocular convergence was easily obtained by moving fingers toward the eyes directly from the front. Repeated testing, however, definitely showed a converging downward, toward the mouth, when the Turtle had its head upraised—its usual attitude. Similar converging movements were also made anteriorly, toward the muzzle, when the animal wished to look upward. In this case, movements of the eyes were accompanied by those of the head and neck.

Occasionally one eye made a similar movement alone, sometimes followed by the other. Again, after fixing an object for a while binocularly, both eyes would relax and return to the initial resting position, clearly showing the presence of a divergent movement.

When an object was brought near one side, that eye alone quickly turned toward it, to fix it for a while, whereas the other eye sometimes remained shut. The stimulated eye was "cocked" at the visual object in the manner of a Robin looking for an earthworm. Occasionally both eyes moved together when an object was approached from only one side. Whether one eye or both as a team were used to fix an object, they again returned to the initial position after the object had disappeared or the stimulus ceased to attract.

The lids and the nictitating membrane may be shut either individually or both simultaneously. The corneal reflex, consisting of moving the lower lid upward and pulling the eyeball inward, was very promptly elicited from the corneal center and less promptly from the corneal periphery. It has not been possible to determine the presence of a pupillary reflex to direct illumination, however.

Compensatory movements of the eyeballs to a changed position in the sagittal plane may amount to about 35° or 40°.

When placed in a basin filled with water, the Turtle promptly sank to the bottom, pulling in its head and neck. However, the eyes made scanning movements all the time. After a while there was a general scramble of all four limbs, as if trying to escape, followed by a period of complete quiescence, with only scanning eye movements persisting.

While the Turtle was being held quietly for some time in a horizontal position, it became rather adjusted to this situation, showing more enterprise by its greater activity. When turned so that it saw the lake before it, it scrambled as if trying to regain its freedom. A buzzing bee aroused quite an interest and caused it to stretch its head and neck and follow the flying insect with its eyes.

When a visual object appeared on one side, so that its image fell on a point in the periphery of the retina—for example, in the horizontal plane —that eye promptly turned to a position where its center faced it. This visual reflex may be termed a fixing movement of the eye, indicating the presence of a differentiated locality of the retina—a central area found by Detwiler (1940) —and a corresponding organization of the entire visual apparatus, including the neuromuscular parts serving the purpose of fixation. The "fixing movement" could be elicited several times in succession, provided that sufficiently long intervals intervened between the tests.

The preceding observation, sketchy though it is, shows the Turtle to be in possession of a visual apparatus more advanced in its functional elaboration, and hence in its efficiency, than that of the native Batrachians. However, a more detailed study, together with correlation of various structures with their functions, would undoubtedly give a fuller picture of the role that visual and other sensory and motor systems perform in the life of the Turtle.

3. Purple Martin.—The Purple Martin (*Progne subis*) is the largest of the North American Swallows. In its bodily organization and its habits it resembles its smaller, more delicately built, and more nimble relative, the Barn Swallow, described elsewhere in this chapter. (*See* illustrations in Pearson & Burroughs 1936; Pough 1946; Peterson 1947; A. A. Allen 1951, p. 31.)

The objects of the observation recorded on the following pages were young birds fairly advanced in development, even though not yet fully grown, and adults. The young birds were convenient subjects for the study of their eye movements when squatting on the perch of their birdhouse in a neighbor's garden. This they unwillingly shared with several families of House Sparrows, which insolently managed to take possession of part of it.

The young Martins, while waiting for their parents to bring them, alternatively and at frequent intervals, food which they caught on the wing, had to be constantly on guard against the Sparrows. When one of the Sparrows came uncomfortably close, the young Martin faced it suspiciously, and on some occasions it opened its beak, indicating its willingness to fight rather than to yield any further ground to the intruders.

The belligerent intention of the young was unmistakable: their feet were firmly planted on the ground to preserve balance, their grim countenances resembled the determined expression of large Birds of Prey such as Hawks and Eagles, with "brows" lowered, and eyes "hurling darts" against their potential foes. In this situation, on several occasions, it was possible to see, with the help of powerful binoculars, both eyes executing converging movements toward the object of their hatred, the Sparrows, with the convergence relaxing when their foes moved away. The movements of convergence were similar to those observed in the young Barn Swallow when binocularly focusing on an insect or some other object to which it paid attention (*see* section on the Swallow, this chapter).

The observation of the adult Purple Martins with 7× binoculars at a distance of 15 feet showed their eyes to be remarkably mobile. The birds, when on the perch of their house where they rested between flights, were constantly examining the world around them with either one eye or the other. The eye movements in their sockets were clearly visible and were often combined with short movements of the head and neck. The converging eye movements, however, could only rarely be seen, owing to the extreme alertness of the birds, the quickness of their movements, which only rarely offered the chance of a good frontal view of the head, and their dusky coloring. The black stripes around and in front of their eyes, especially visible in the female bird because of its lighter coloring

and resembling the "sighting grooves" described in the Pike (sec. 1, this chapter), may be useful here, as in the fish, in reducing the stray light entering the eye and thus increasing acuity in binocular vision.

In flight, especially when soaring, the Purple Martin resembles the larger predaceous birds, such as Eagles and Hawks. Its distinguishing feature is long stretches of gentle gliding without much change of direction. Only occasionally may the soaring be interrupted by the flapping of wings, which is followed by a change of direction in the form of a turn or loop. If the flapping periods and change of direction are indications of a successful hunt, it is a puzzle how the bird is able to catch enough insects to sustain itself, even though it may cover a large area in order to satisfy its needs.

This may explain why Martins must fly such long distances, which is also to some extent true of the other Swallows and the Night Hawks. The Swifts, smaller birds, apparently subsist upon smaller insects, which are more abundant, and so they must make more frequent turns.

In any case, the hunting method of all these birds is an active pursuit, guided and controlled by sight, and is in no way the hit-or-miss affair suggested by Rochon-Duvigneaud (1943). The same is to be said of the small insectivorous Flying Bats or Microchiropterans, except that these are directed in their hunting by their superior ultrasonic hearing and possibly also to some extent by touch.

An observation of a Purple Martin, without leaving its perch, occasionally catching an insect that accidentally flies close to it may be mentioned as a curiosity and exhibition of constant visual vigilance.

By comparison with the Swallows and Swifts, the larger Birds of Prey, living upon larger animals harder to locate, with the chances of making a catch much less frequent, are forced to cover even more extensive hunting grounds than those of the Swallows. Hence their flight is almost entirely of the soaring type, which requires the smallest expenditure of energy during their prolonged hunting periods.

4. Dragonflies, Damselflies, and Insectivorous Bats.—It is interesting to compare the hunting habits of the Dragonflies (Odonata) with the habits of the Swallows, Swifts, and Bats.

The Damselflies and Dragonflies, just like their avian and mammalian counterparts, catch their prey on the wing. They are rated as perhaps the best fliers in the insect world, and, of the two, the Dragonflies are superior. In their life, which is mostly spent in catching flying insects such as Mosquitoes, they are guided exclusively by their sight.

They are visually extremely alert animals. Their eyes are enormously developed, especially in the Dragonflies, where they make up most of the head. Each eye is made of a great number of ommatidia or individually stimulable units. The smallest ommatidia face forward, in the direction of flight, where they are most useful in binocular focusing on the prey (Fig. 444).

The entire head, when the Dragonfly rests, is frequently moved in various directions from the neutral position, which is mostly in the horizontal plane (to right or left), up or down, or in any one of the oblique meridians. The movements are very minutely adjusted in their speed and excursions, altogether indicating superior visual performance. The single moves may amount to more than 30° or 40°, with many very small moves possible. Whether the eyes are firmly fixed in their relative position or may also be moved individually must be further investigated.

The Odonates are preponderantly daylight hunters, some being crepuscular. Their flight, as could be expected, has much in common with the flight of the Swallows and Swifts. Its particular feature is a zigzagging course, as they dart here and there after their diminutive prey. This flight, as easily observed in the early hours during warm, quiet August and September evenings, is much more zigzag than that of any flying Vertebrate, a Swallow, Swift, or Bat. It greatly resembles the fluttering of the small Bats, reduced to much smaller proportions. Long straight stretches do occur, but they alternate with series of short darts, each measuring from 2 to 3 feet, more or less.

As in the Swallows, Swifts, and Bats, the hunting method of the Dragonflies is active pursuit, under the guidance of a superior sense of sight, where the element of chance, Rochon-Duvigneaud's "arabesques of flight," is practically eliminated. In this pursuit the excellence of their vision is their principal instrument.

Their photoreceptors are highly differentiated, with the smallest elemental ommatidia in the frontal parts of their huge composite eyes, and the larger ones in the peripheral parts. This affords them both high acuity and tridimensional stereopsis.

Their very flexible legs are adjusted not only for locomotion but even more to catch and "manipulate" the prey in the process of feeding.

5. BIRDS WITH PREPONDERANTLY PANORAMIC VISION.—In hunting for prey, different species of Birds use their visual apparatus in different ways, as has been well described by their lifelong student, Rochon-Duvigneaud (1943, and earlier). One way is to use one eye at a time, individually; the other is binocular. The two may alternate, according to the situation; or they may be variously combined. (*Cf.* also section on the Swallow, this chapter.)

According to my observation, the House Sparrow (*Passer domesticus*) and the Domestic Pigeon (*Columba livia*), with their laterally placed eyeballs, ordinarily use their eyes monocularly for observation, as do the American Robin (*Turdus migratorius*) and numerous other birds. In pecking grain or aiming at an angleworm just prior to seizing it, the final act that follows the critical examination, however, these birds use both eyes simultaneously in a binocular stereoscopic way.

In the Pigeon, for example, there is nothing one would call a "frozen eye," as one would be inclined to judge on the basis of a superficial observation. When I observed the Pigeon as it squatted on the sill just in front of my window, about 40–50 feet above ground, the eye facing me moved all the time, as probably also did the eye looking in the other direction toward the buildings opposite and the court below where people were moving about.

Observation with powerful binoculars revealed surprisingly extensive movements of the visible parts of the eye in a more or less horizontal meridian, as well as up and down and in any other intermediate way. The impression gained was that of a sharp and constant vigilance, the animal using and mentally digesting all the available cues, ever ready to fly away, if need be.

The bird, as I observed it, was somewhat suspicious of me, even though I was inside, behind windowpanes, and in relative shade. Every once in a while it would stop as it slowly paced the sill and focus its gaze for a second or two in order to examine me intently, although I kept quiet and although it had seen me in a similar position on many previous occasions.

The Pigeon would sometimes make a quick, short movement with its head backward and forward, along a line vertical to its line of gaze, in order to utilize the visual parallax to view me from another point. (Monkeys do the same when watching a suspicious object or person, except that they use both eyes and move the head sidewise; similar action is observed in many other animals.) The entire behavior of the Pigeon betrayed a high degree of visual alertness short of manifest alarm, the visual apparatus being used continuously to gain useful information which the curious bird was eager to obtain.

One had here a good demonstration of the tremendous advantage of a wide field of view, as the Pigeon has. The same is true of other Vertebrates which have panoramic, or rather largely panoramic, vision, practically amounting to a complete circle. It permits them to see simultaneously most of the horizon and to see it with about the same high acuity as that possessed by Man, as other observations of the Pigeons and Sparrows indicate. (*See* Fig. 457.)

This leaves the old and deeply absorbing question still unanswered: how to explain the superb tridimensional quality of the Pigeon's vision which, beyond doubt, this and many other birds have, in spite of their almost completely decussated optic tracts, as shown by experiment (*cf.* chap. VI, 5 [3]).

6. Monocular and binocular-stereoscopic use of vision in Birds.—The diurnal species of large Birds of Prey, such as Hawks and Eagles, have very excellent vision in both stereoscopy and acuity. This is confirmed by the fact that they possess two foveae in each eye, one lateral and one central (*see* Figs. 171, 172).

A Harlan's or a Red-shouldered Hawk or an Eagle, for example, when cruising over forests and glades and scanning for hidden prey, moves its head frequently from side to side. It is probable that they do so in order to bring the landscape into the range of their central foveae for a detailed examination, even though, because of the great distance, it was not possible to ascertain whether the head was actually inclined laterally and downward in the way the Robin does when "cocking" one of its eyes in looking for an earthworm in the lawn.

The behavior of a Flycatcher, Kingbird, and other Tyrannidae is a duplicate of the Robin's when examining details. The utilization of only one eye when intently fixing an object is also especially characteristic of Domestic Chickens when they notice a predator in the skies, which they follow with one eye, keeping their heads tilted at a slant. Yet all these birds when picking up their food—for example, a Robin in the moment when it tries to seize an earthworm; a Chicken and a Sparrow when picking grain from the floor—use both eyes simultaneously, that is, binocularly and apparently stereoscopically.

Stereoscopic use of vision in all those species that on other occasions are inclined to use each eye separately is especially in evidence during flight. When the Sparrows, for example, chase one another through the branches of a tree and most expertly dodge the twigs without touching a leaf, they use both their eyes simultaneously. The same may easily be observed in other small, alert birds, such as the Finches, Flycatchers, Titmice, or Chickadees. In this respect they perform a highly complex visuosensory-motor act. They almost equal the performance of the Swallows, skimming over the lake without ever touching the surface of the water with the tips of their wings, when hunting at evening for minute insects that congregate for their nuptial dance. In both locomotor functions the guidance is entirely intrusted to the stereoscopic sense of vision. In the Swallow the major share is apparently contributed by the two lateral or posterior foveae, in the Sparrow and Pigeon by the central foveae; in other birds the responsible structures are yet to be found.

Unilateral use of the visual apparatus, with a quick shifting to binocular stereoscopic use, when the need arises, is seen in numerous other birds. A Redstart (*Setophaga ruticilla*), for example, systematically examines branches and leaves of a tree for insects, using exclusively one eye or the other, but probably both when aiming with its beak to pick the prey. A similar technique may be observed in various Warblers (Parulidae), House Wren (*Troglodytes aëdon*), and Nuthatch (*Sitta carolinensis*).

The Hairy Woodpecker (*Dendrocopus villosus*) exhibits interesting and somewhat different behavior. It fixes both eyes firmly on the point at which it aims the blows of its beak. Possibly it uses one eye or the other individually when quickly running up or down a branch or when hopping from twig to twig and looking for peeled bark or a dead branch, localities in which its prey may hide. It is duplicated in this behavior by the Chickadees (Paridae), which, in fact, appear to be miniature Woodpeckers.

Binocular use of the eyes may definitely be seen in the Downy Woodpecker (*Dendrocopus pubescens*). In this bird both eyes may converge toward a single fixation point a short distance in front of its beak when examining a dead branch for a bug, and not only when pulling it out of a crevice of the bark. During this occupation the gaze of both eyes is directed straight ahead, each line of vision passing along a black streak running toward the beak, the streaks resembling the "sighting grooves" described in the Northern Pike (sec. 4, this chapter).

In the female Mallard (*Anas platyrhynchos*), in the male of the same after a summer molting or the "eclipse," and in the young, the "sighting grooves" or rather pigmented "sighting streaks" meet in imaginary prolongations at a point situated some distance in front of the beak. The plane of these streaks is parallel to the surface of the water when the duck assumes its normal swimming position, during which its beak is inclined toward the horizontal at an angle of approximately 30°. This position appears favorable for binocular vision in the normal habitat of the bird, the marshes and swamps. It may also be advantageous to it during flight. When pursuing its peaceful occupation, the Duck seems, however, to rely principally on its panoramic vision.

7. Visual behavior of Lower Mammals. —A Woodchuck or Ground Hog (*Marmota monax*), one of the largest native American Ground Squirrels (Sciurinae), observed on a shady forest road during daylight, sees a man at 50 feet quite well, but, when one is still, it does not recognize a person at that distance as a potential enemy.

The road, where this observation was made, was frequented but little by humans (Iowa State Park at McGregor, overlooking the Mississippi River). Even though the observer, the author, was motionless during the entire time the animal was in sight, the Woodchuck remained suspicious, rising on its haunches from time to time and lifting its head as high as possible above the vegetation to have a better look, first with one eye, then with the other. Only after quietly and intently observing the object of its suspicion for some time did it feel assured, and proceeded, lumbering on all four legs, about the business of eating. However, again and again it would rise to look over the strange object until it finally decided to disappear in the tall weeds and shrubs.

In its exclusive use of monocular vision for a gnosic or "psychic" appreciation of visual impressions, the Woodchuck behaves in exactly the same way as do the smaller Rodents, such as Ground Squirrels or Gophers, Chipmunks, Rats, and Guinea Pigs. The Arboreal Squirrels deviate in this respect: while ordinarily they use their eyes panoramically, in circumstances which require greater attention they use them as a binocular stereoscopic team (*see* section on Squirrel, this chapter).

The preceding observation of the Woodchuck may indicate rather moderate acuity and visual resolution, which undoubtedly would have been greater in better light. The degree of caution exhibited by the animal shows a fair amount of mental capacity, considering the small previous experience the animal could have acquired in its secluded habitat.

8. Visual behavior of the Vertebrates during twenty-four-hour activity in summertime.—The activity and visual behavior of numerous species and larger groups of Vertebrates show great variation, depending upon the particular period of the twenty-four-hour day. That some animals are mainly or exclusively active during the day and rest during the night, while others manifest the opposite behavior, is common knowledge. Obviously, such variation is caused and regulated chiefly by the intensity, and to some extent also by the quality, of the light, which also varies during the twenty-four-hour cycle.

More attentive observation discloses subtler gradings of daily activity, indicating a finer adjustment of the senses according to the specific period of the day. In brief, just as the animals are in various ways adapted to a great number of habitats spread over the globe and to the larger cyclic changes of each particular habitat, called seasons of the year, so they are also, in a more subtle way, attuned to the twenty-four-hour cycle of a solar day.

By observing the animals during their daily activity and rest, the impression is gained that the twenty-four-hour period of time is comparably subdivided, in the economy of living beings, as is the space in which they live and the two principal elements within which they live, water and air. This daily temporal diversification of behavior, in turn, points toward a similar diverse structural organization of various animal forms. Hence the anatomical basis of diverse animal behavior is a reflection of the daily cycle caused by the molding forces of nature.

In the following are described the habits of a few representative Vertebrates gained through rather casual observation in the American Middle West, during late summer.

The first riser in the morning, in cities and in smaller towns, is the Robin (*Turdus migratorius*, also *Planesticus migratorius*). This bird is, in fact, a Thrush, much larger than its original namesake of the Old World (*Erithacus rubecula*), with which it was mistakenly identified by the early settlers of America. Its merry morning song resounds first in the early dawn before any of the other diurnal birds begin their daily work. In this respect it resembles its black relative of the Old World (*Turdus merula*).

From the moment the first Robin's fluting calls are heard until the earliest timid chirpings of the House Sparrow (*Passer domesticus*) begin to be perceived from under the eaves of the town's dwellings, it takes fully thirty minutes. During the following quarter of an hour, Sparrows' voices gradually increase in intensity, sometimes to a very babble, frequently degenerating into lively disputes and formal quarrels. In another thirty minutes or so the Sparrows' voices have considerably subsided, as the birds settle down to the serious business of gathering food.

The Robin not only rises early, it also retires late. In the evening when the Sparrows have long since been still, the Robins continue for a while to hunt for the earthworms on the shady lawns. This is the more remarkable, since single blades of grass have at that time become largely indistinguishable to the less sensitive human eye.

The conclusion must be drawn that the Robins' eyes, while not as capable of perfect nocturnal vision as those of the truly scotopic Owls and probably also less than those of the Nighthawks and other Caprimulgidae, are superior in their adaptability to scotopic conditions to those of the Sparrow and Man. Undoubtedly, such graded visual behavior must be related to a somewhat different organization of basically similar visual apparatus in each of these species.

In small communities, in isolated groves around farms, and in the forests, the first to announce the day are the Blue Jay (*Cyanocitta cristata*) and the Mourning Dove (*Zenaidura macroura*). The first usually appear all of a sudden, in small, noisy flocks, raucously calling from the treetops and excitedly flying about, making a great commotion and fuss. The timid Doves, on the contrary, seem to make every effort to render their presence as inconspicuous and unobtrusive as possible. The very character of their cooing, which sounds as if it came from a distance, camouflages the true whereabouts of the birds, which, in fact, may be very near.

In the more extensive woods the conspicuous early risers are the Crows (*Corvus brachyrhynchos*). Their loud cawing sounds over great distances, as the birds excitedly fly from place to place in search of food, which may be the carcass of a rabbit or the nest of some smaller and helpless bird which they plunder, or when in great numbers they mob a luckless Owl which selected a wrong hideout for the day. In their behavior they greatly resemble their smaller congeners, the Blue Jays. Their keen-sighted eyes are good enough to detect anything suitable for consumption on the forest floor or in the tops of the trees, whether a heap of garbage or a Squirrel on a branch, which is lucky if it can slip into a hole in a tree.

Nor is this a matter of simple perception, since all objects are quickly scrutinized whether useful, neutral, or a source of potential danger. Of this the best example is the appearance of a man. To the Crows, Man is most acceptable when kept at a safe distance. The closest tolerated approach may be guessed at no less than one hundred yards, provided that there is sufficient cover in between, e.g., the bushes in a forest. Silent and invisible to a human intruder, the Crows may continue their plundering for some time, all the while keeping a sharp eye on the suspect newcomer. When the latter, unknowingly, comes too uncomfortably close, one of the lookout guards gives a signal, and the entire flock flies away. Or, as frequent experience shows, a few stragglers may continue their doings behind the camouflage, trusting that the dangerous visitor was fooled by the flight of some of them. However, if a hunter appears with a gun or a person with a stick held like a gun, no chance whatever is taken, and all the Crows fly away as soon as the limit of safety is reached, which in this case is a much greater distance.

The appearance and behavior of the diurnal Birds of Prey is always a fascinating sight. The little Sparrow Hawk (*Falco sparverius*), as it perches on a telephone wire, seems to rely chiefly on its patience and on its keen, bifoveal eyes to help it discover a grasshopper or a mouse hiding in the weeds. Its larger congener, the Red-tailed Hawk (*Buteo jamaicensis*), pursues the same policy of watchful waiting, as it sits on a high limb of a tree, overlooking the farm lands, hoping that chance may bring it a gopher or some other acceptable meal.

A flock of Bald Eagles (*Haliaeetus leucocephalus*), numbering on occasion as many as a dozen birds, is a magnificent sight. As the birds sail above the hills and marshes along the swinging shore line of the great lake, with more experienced older ones in the lead and on the far flanks, every wooded slope and grassy dale and every turn of the sandy beaches of the dunes are scanned for potential food. This "food," if still alive, takes pains to stay under cover of large

trees and bushes, as the ominous shadows glide by, as do the various smaller birds, or, better yet, slips into the hole of a tree or a burrow in the ground, as the Squirrels and Gophers prefer. It is the competition and matching of the keenness of sight of the pursuer against that of the prey and of wits against wits that decide the biological outcome.

An easier way for the Eagles, then, to procure sustenance is to be on the lookout for dead fish which the water of the lake may have washed up on the beach. But again, it is more likely that the Gulls, always busy along the beach, will have been there first. It is this difficulty of procuring food that appears to be the principal reason for the long, sustained flights that the Eagles and other large Birds of Prey make, in order to cover huge areas with relatively small expenditure of energy.

During daylight hours enormous numbers of smaller Birds, amounting to many billions on the North American continent alone, are busy performing their daily duties, procuring food, building nests, and rearing their young. The bulk of these is represented by the Warblers (Parulidae), Vireos (Vireonidae), Titmice (Paridae), and Flycatchers (Tyrannidae), mostly migratory.

The remarkable feature of the small bird life is that, unlike most other Vertebrates, Birds have developed several subtle talents which to the human mind appear rather an expression of pleasure than a utilitarian necessity. These are complex auditory harmonics and refined color sense, manifested by singing and body coloring. These two talents indicate a correspondingly refined differentiation of their auditory and visual organs, including cerebral centers. A long and systematic investigation of this phase of Bird life is required to give account of it and to make it useful for the understanding of the same faculties found in the Primates, including Man. (*See* Charles R. Darwin's *The Descent of Man;* cf. also A. E. Brehm's *Tierleben* 1911–18; F. S. Mathews 1921; Pearson & Burroughs 1936; J. J. Audubon 1941; A. A. Allen 1951; E. T. Gilliard 1953.)

In their daily occupation, the small diurnal Birds show two rather distinct periods of increased activity. One is during the somewhat advanced morning hours, the other during the late afternoon. The time in between, corresponding to the noon hours, the period of greatest heat during the summer, is a recess, or at least the birds are less active then.

As the day declines, the behavior of the Birds also changes in a way characteristic of each species. At a certain moment of reduced intensity of illumination prior to nightfall, objects still remain as bright as during the noon hours to human vision. It is then that the Sparrows, after a brief period of heightened activity, manifested by an excited fussing for better roosting places, gradually settle down for the night in some cover where they are tolerably safe from the sharp scotopic eyes of the Screech Owl (*Otus asio*). If they are disturbed and fly away, the Sparrows again try to locate their hideouts, but obviously, owing to their poor adjustability to scotopic conditions, have difficulty in finding them. And when the dusk thickens, they all become silent. At night, even when closely approached, the Sparrows remain perfectly still, as if in a trance, apparently not able to see anything in the darkness, when to human vision larger objects are still discernible.

Even more striking is the behavior exhibited by Domestic Chickens (*Gallus domesticus*) at a time when objects still remain tolerably distinguishable to human vision. This happens during late afternoon, when to subjective human appreciation the "photosphere" appears just as intensively illuminated as during high noon, although the composition of the light has definitely shifted toward the red, or long, end of the spectrum. At that period of the day one sees some of the Chickens already beginning to flock slowly toward the henhouse, illustrating the well-known proverb.

During the following half-hour or so, most of the chickens are gathered on their roosts. Thereafter, when the dusk thickens further, even though the human eye still sees most of the objects as clearly as before, there are still a few stragglers that strayed too far into distant fields. These, being less familiar with the details of the chicken yard and because of the increasing darkness, have difficulty in recognizing objects and finding their way home. One sees such late-comers slowly plodding through the tall weeds and over the lawn, often hesitating and making false turns, before finding their roosts.

The behavior of these Chickens is reminiscent of amblyopics or persons suffering from hemeralopia or night blindness, who, because of their organically or functionally reduced acuity, have difficulty in finding their way about at night.

The behavior of Sparrows and Chickens at nightfall is in sharp contrast with that of other Birds, which, even though they are not nocturnal, continue their activity late into the dusk. The Robin, the early riser, is an example. Long after all Sparrows and Chickens have retired and the human eye has difficulty in distinguishing single blades of grass on the lawn, one occasionally sees the Robin cocking one eye to search for an angleworm or nightcrawler, which, fooled by decreased light, imprudently sticks its "head" out of the ground. The feat is perhaps somewhat less remarkable when one considers the short distance at which the Robin hunts, not exceeding 6 or 8 inches, in this way compensating somewhat for the decreased intensity of illumination. In any case, the Robin's day is considerably longer than that of the more strictly diurnal Sparrows and Chickens and partly overlaps the nocturnal activity of the Owls (Strigidae) and Nighthawks (*Chordeiles minor*) and also the Domestic Cat (*Felis domestica*).

Among the late hunters, the Purple Martin (*Progne subis*), Chimney Swift (*Chaetura pelagica*), and Barn Swallow (*Hirundo rustica erythrogastra*) are conspicuous. The last-mentioned bird, one of the best flyers, may frequently be seen sailing over the treetops late in the evening. In lake regions it may skim at high speed close to the surface of the water, rarely touching it, considerably after the sun has set and there is just enough light left to make objects fairly distinguishable to the human eye.

The Swallows apparently are attracted not only by the night moths which perform their nuptial dance just above the water but also by little fish, evidently Northern Brook Silversides and other fry, which, in turn, attracted by the moths, leap out of the water to hunt for the insects. These fish evidently represent richer food which the Swallows eagerly catch by diving, resembling diminutive Sea Gulls. (*See* sections on the Northern Brook Silverside and on the Swallow, this chapter.)

However, a moment comes in the gathering

dusk beyond which the insufficiently developed scotopic apparatus of the Swallow does not serve. It is at this moment, when the darkness of night is almost complete, that one hears the twittering of the last departing flock of Swallows as the first insectivorous Flying Bats (Microchiroptera) appear to fill the gap left by the Swallows. The fact that the Swallows continue hunting until late into evening dusk may to some extent be explained by the physical conditions, viz., sufficient remaining light reflected from the surface of the water, as frequently happens on calm nights. During this phase of the day, or a little earlier, there also appear the Nighthawks (*Chordeiles minor*) and other Goatsuckers or Caprimulgidae, to fill the transition from the daylight to the night.

As night deepens, the pronounced diurnal animals, in particular the Birds, disappear, and the nocturnal prowlers become supreme. The transformation in the life of a high northern forest, for example, is amazing. For long minutes there is not a twitter to break the silence, and a still, impenetrable darkness alone fills the space between the shrubs and trees. Only occasionally will the high-pitched or soft rattle of a Tree Frog interrupt the stillness. Then, all of a sudden, a single, deep, powerful, booming hoot spreads through the dark timber, the voice of a Great Gray Owl (*Strix nebulosa*).

After a while, other, different hoots sound through the darkness. They are in groups, strictly measured, and in orderly sequence, according to a definite pattern, characteristic of a Barred Owl (*Strix varia*). Some individuals, apparently the younger ones, repeat the same pattern but in a higher key, and others of the same species vary the same basic rhythm in minor ways.

Again, if the Great Horned Owls (*Bubo virginianus*) congregate in a particular locality and begin a dispute among themselves, a strange nightly serenade may take place in one or another corner of the dark woods. At another time, in late dusk, there may be a sudden violent swish along the shore trees, as a giant nocturnal robber shoots upon one of the Mallards browsing in the reeds, followed by a desperate squawk indicating either the end of a victim or a lucky escape with a bad fright.

And all this drama of the forest and lake enveloped in night, filled with primeval cunning, remains in the darkness, beyond the power of Man's visual apparatus to discern, even though some participants in it are obviously fully equipped by nature for it and now feel in their own element. It is the "struggle for existence," for life and against annihilation, as cruel as the one whose brightly colored battleground is illuminated by the shining rays of the sun. It is a contest between one set of the senses against the other set, against the cerebral performance of one and the other, and the many large and small details that differentiate one animal machine from another.

Difficult though it is to follow the nightly doings of the nocturnal Birds, it is even more difficult to follow during the night the creatures that crawl over the ground and hide between the roots of the trees and bushes and among the vegetation. On the surface all may appear unruffled. Yet attentive observation discloses surprising, though silent, activity in the fields and gardens and in the meadows and forests. Where during the bright day there seems to be nothing but clumps of grass and dead leaves, every step now appears to stir some object to life. Here a clod of earth hops away as a Toad, there a dead leaf is transformed into a Frog, leaping into a pond, or a broken twig becomes alive as a Snake wriggles away into a patch of weeds.

The number of living creatures in some localities is truly astonishing, especially toward the close of the summer, when a new generation of tiny arboreal Batrachians is on the march. Then the ground and the trees and bushes fairly swarm with them. All these creatures, each in its own way, are regulated by the night's low intensity of illumination, during which they are active.

On quiet evenings the surface of the lake, reflecting the last traces of the sun's light long since gone, at first sight resembling a perfect mirror, appears to be slightly disturbed by little pinpricks which expand into circles. They are caused by little fish of many kinds, commonly called Minnows, especially the Northern Brook Silverside (*Labidesthes sicculus*), hunting for "gnats." In this activity vision is the only sense used. How their eyes are employed as a binocular instrument has already been discussed.

In the early evening, while there is still some light to make objects fairly visible to the human eye, the Insectivorous Bats (Microchiroptera) come out from their diurnal hideouts. They are seen fluttering between the tall trees of the forest, being especially attracted to the little glades and clearings where the crepuscular and nocturnal insects abound. In the cities, especially in the South, and for the same reason, they fly around the street lamps which attract the night moths.

The Bats are unique among the Mammals, since they alone have developed a true ability to fly. The flight of the native midwestern Bats, e.g., the Little Brown Bat (*Myotis lucifugus*), Pipistrelle (*Pipistrellus subflavus*), Brown Bat (*Eptesicus fuscus*), Red Bat (*Nycteris borealis*), Hoary Bat (*Nycteris cinerea*), and others, markedly resembles that of the Chimney Swift among the Birds and of the Dragonflies among the Insects. (*See* for details A. E. Brehm, v. 10, 1912; H. E. Anthony's *Field Book of North American Mammals*, 1928; and G. M. Allen 1939.)

The characteristic feature of the flight of Bats is the frequent sudden turns, sometimes amounting to aerial somersaults. The component turns of the flight are quite short, the impression of the entire performance being that of a constantly changing zigzag line, hence called erratic. By comparison, the turns of a Barn Swallow and even more those of the Purple Martin are gentle. There is also some slight resemblance to the flight of a Nighthawk, which also makes occasional sudden turns.

The Bats depend largely on their hearing, which is extraordinarily developed. In fact, it is capable of responding not only to high-pitched tones audible to the human ear but also to the ultra- or supersonic stimuli to which the human ear does not respond (Galambos 1942, 1943; Galambos & Griffin 1942; Griffin 1944, 1946, 1950).

Whether hearing is the only long-range or distance sense in the Bats, as it undoubtedly is the leading one, is a problem to be dealt with in the future. The excrescences over the muzzle which many species possess, richly supplied by the terminals of the trigeminal nerve, may be structures of a refined vibratory or tactile sense co-ordinated with the auditory sense proper. (*Cf.* F. P. Möhres 1952.)

In any case, the Bats appear biologically to be a mammalian counterpart of other aerial insect hunters, the Swallows, Swifts, and Dragonflies, whose leading sense is vision. All of them have a similar mode of life and subsist upon a similar diet. The only difference is the form of physical energy used for orientation and the sense organs by which they detect their flying food: in Birds and Dragonflies light and the eyes, in the Bats sound vibrations and the ear, and possibly the trigeminal sense. Hence one group of animals is practically entirely adapted to diurnal conditions, the other to nocturnal. The period of activity also determines what their enemies are: diurnal Birds and Insects hunted largely by diurnal Birds of Prey; Bats, mostly by Owls. (*See* on ultrasonic perception of Porpoises, Kellogg & Kohler 1952.)

The Owls (Tytonidae and Strigidae) are of special interest as a comparison. Like the Bats, they, too, are practically entirely adapted to the nocturnal way of life. Their two principal problems—the procurement of food and the avoidance of annihilation—they have solved differently, by an overdevelopment and scotopic specialization of vision, although the auditory sense is not neglected.

While the Owls reign supreme over the smaller Vertebrates that populate the forests, fields, and barnyards, the Bats dominate the hosts of nocturnal insects in the fields and forests. Both take advantage of the numerous creatures that use the nocturnal reduction of light as a means of escaping from their pursuers. In the case of the Owls and Goatsuckers, this seems to be an adaptation of the original sauropsidan diurnality to the nocturnal adaptation of their prey, mostly small Mammals and Insects. In the case of the Insectivorous Bats, it is rather a continuation of a nocturnal habit inherited from their ancestors, the Early Mammals, as discussed in the section on the Common Shrew.

Another ecological relationship is between the Owls and Bats, which is that of predator and prey. Both are adjusted to nocturnal life, even though in different ways. The fact that, although using different leading senses, both remain a thriving part of the faunal community indicates their complete and successful biological adjustment to each other.

(For a description of twenty-four-hour activity of animals in tropical Africa *see* Martin Johnson, *Camera Trails in Africa*, 1924, chap. XIII: "Seeing Africa from a Blind.")

9. Photopic and scotopic modes of vision and their antagonism as a molding factor in vertebrate evolution.—The two modes of vision, diurnal and nocturnal, may be considered two opposite, alternative habits used for the same biological purpose, which is the maintenance of life. If one does not work, the other still remains to be tried. When conditions become unbearable in full light, there is darkness to escape into; and when, after a period of trial and error, this does not work, a species, a family, or an order may try to save itself by switching back to habits long since abandoned. If this succeeds, fine; if it fails, the unsuccessful species perishes. It is a deadly game of biological hide-and-seek, where the forms and methods of making a living constantly change and the "formalities" are abandoned for the sake of saving the "substance," the life.

In this game, which Charles R. Darwin appropriately called the "struggle for existence," as in a complex duel, partners change positions, or they change partners; or they abandon the contest altogether, by retiring into quieter recesses of nature. They may do so either forever, or temporarily, for longer or shorter periods. When they are found again by their ever searching pursuers, they may be forced to join the battle, even though in different circumstances and with new weapons and new protective equipment.

The original conditions from which the Early Vertebrates emerged and how they began to use vision as an instrument of their phylogenetical advancement remain unknown. Even so, it is legitimate to speculate that at a certain stage of its phylogenetical perfection the Vertebrate Ancestor came into possession of a bodily organization which in the further course of evolution caused it to become a true Vertebrate. (*See* chap. XIII, 2.)

The Vertebrate Ancestor, we may assume, almost from its inception, must have been organized along a vertical-sagittal plane, with a leading cephalic extremity at one end and the formation of a principal locomotor apparatus at the other. The creature, furthermore, must have been photosensitive, a faculty that became gradually centered in the cephalic end of the body.

In fact, the photosensitiveness must have been the very factor that gave impetus to vertebrate origin, as already discussed. Also, the nature of the circumstances that shaped the Vertebrate Ancestor makes it probable that its photosensitiveness was at first negative. But it was just as imperative in the subsequent phase of its evolution that the same Ancestor became positively photosensitive, since only thus could it have evolved into a true Vertebrate. The result was an animal dominated by its photoreceptors.

When the Vertebrate Ancestor evolved into an early Fish, its photoreceptors assumed the form of eyes resembling those possessed by the modern Fishes. These eyes were capable of forming images of external objects, to which the brain and the locomotor apparatus responded in a purposeful way. This was the case, irrespective of whether the result was a phobic reaction, flight, as when avoiding a pursuer, or a positive reaction, as when attracted by a prey to be pursued. In both cases the sense of sight was a decisive factor.

It must, then, be assumed that the early Fishes were strongly diurnal, just as most modern Fishes still are (notable exceptions being elasmobranch Sharks and Rays, chondrostean Sturgeons, siluride and ameiuride Catfish, and some other forms). The reason for this assumption is the necessity of procuring food, which in most cases consisted of moving animals which had to be captured by active pursuit. The few species of Fishes that have rudimentary visual organs or have lost them altogether are those that became trapped by conditions where the sense of sight, because of the absence or extreme reduction of light, had lost its usefulness, as in the cave-dwelling species (*see*, e.g., Ramsay 1901).

The fact of the almost universal dependence of Fishes on vision is, in another way, demonstrated by the abyssal forms living at great depth in the oceans, where little or no light penetrates (*see* Beebe 1930, 1931, 1932, 1934). These have developed various modes of artificial illumination as a substitute for the absent natural light which permit them to use their organs of sight in a more or less normal manner. (*See also* La Gorce & Marden 1952.)

When the first Amphibians evolved from their piscine ancestors, they were able to continue their customary way of life in full light. This was natural for them because daylight vision is superior to vision in reduced illumination. And this was possible because no important terrestrial animals, including Arthropoda, of which the Winged Insects, for example, were just beginning to emerge, had as yet appeared. The paleontological record of the Carboniferous Period of the prehistory of the earth, dating approximately 205 to 255 million years in the past, indicates this.

It was just during this period that the Amphibian Class reached its climax. But soon, owing to the very fact that some Amphibians developed in such a way that they were able to prey upon their weaker congeners, the remainder were forced to adapt themselves secondarily to a secretive or nocturnal way of life as a means of survival.

When subsequently more highly organized Vertebrates evolved, first, the Reptiles, and from these the Birds and the Mammals, the situation became even less favorable, pushing the surviving Amphibians even deeper into a nocturnal way of life. As a reminiscence of their phylogenetical transformation from diurnal aquatic animals into nocturnal or seminocturnal terrestrial dwellers, even now most modern Amphibians, after passing through the initial aquatic phase, remain for the rest of their life dependent on water as a permanent refuge.

In their adulthood, according to competent authorities, most Amphibians are rather attracted to poorly illuminated, damp localities and, in general, shun strong light. The reasons for this amphibian nocturnalism and scotopia are not difficult to find: their small size, inefficient organization, and general helplessness, which make it difficult for them to compete with more highly organized and more efficient rivals. These circumstances, then, must be considered the principal factor which imposed upon

the Amphibians the largely scotopic way of life.

The result of the adaptation of the aquatic Vertebrates to terrestrial conditions, in so far as vision is concerned, was a change from the overwhelmingly photopic vision of the Fishes to the preponderantly scotopic vision found in the Amphibians. The impetus for the change from the aquatic to the terrestrial environment, it seems, was not only a search for food but also the necessity of escaping predators among the fish. Yet the Amphibians, since their development takes place in the water, had to continue their close attachment to it, even though they could return to it safely only when the photopic vision of most of their finny pursuers was put out of action during the night. It was the first major period of stress, the "amphibian bottleneck," which the evolving Vertebrates had to pass through in their conquest of a new environment.

When during subsequent periods predaceous Reptiles evolved, and from these predaceous Birds, both largely diurnal in habit, the nocturnal habit of the Amphibians continued not only to serve them well but also to keep them perpetually under its influence.

The luxuriant development of the Vertebrates at the reptilian stage became possible through a complete emancipation from their former aquatic habitat and through continuation of their ancestral piscine diurnality, which is especially pronounced in the Lizards.

When the first Mammals developed during the age of Dinosaurs or Dominant Reptiles, they were again pushed into nocturnality as the only means of avoiding extinction. This second depression, the "mammalian bottleneck," may have been more severe and exacting than the first, the amphibian, since the Mammals were entirely emancipated from their ancestral refuge, the water, and there were now many more diurnal predators, both the Reptiles and the Birds. This bottleneck left a deep imprint upon the entire mammalian class which has lasted until the present (*see* section on Common Shrew, this chapter).

Only relatively few of the mammalian orders have been able to emancipate themselves from nocturnality and return to their habit of good, clear daylight vision possessed by their aquatic ancestors, the overwhelmingly diurnal Fishes.

The most successful in this reorganization of visual apparatus were the Higher Primates, the Monkeys, Apes, and Humans. But among the Primates also there are some notable exceptions. The Lemurs, as a rule, are overwhelmingly nocturnal (Hooton 1942), apparently a secondary adaptation of the originally diurnal Tree Shrews and the Early Primates which succeeded them.

The climax of nocturnality, finally, was attained by the Tarsiers, which among the Higher Mammals are the most completely adjusted to nocturnal life (*see* section on Tarsier, this chapter). The Bats went even further in their adjustment to life in darkness, in that they, to a great extent, eliminated vision as an active epicritic sense, relying entirely on hearing as their leading distance receptor.

The widespread adaptation to the nocturnal way of life among the now living Mammals is worthy of note. Most Dogs, Bears, and especially Cats are more or less nocturnal, and, if duplex or arrhythmic, the emphasis is on night habit. Whether this is a continuation of the primitive mammalian nocturnality exhibited by the Soricide Shrews and most other Insectivorans or a secondary adaptation to the nocturnality of the animals upon which they prey is difficult to decide.

The nocturnalism of the Mammals appears to be a "vicious circle," in which the prey tries to escape into darkness, where it is again followed by the predator, which also becomes nocturnal or arrhythmic. The pursued prey may again try to find salvation in readapting itself to daylight conditions, with a concomitant increase of visual acuity and color perception, improved audition, better locomotion, and increased intelligence. It is a perpetual process, whose success is measured by survival.

A number of vertebrate species and larger taxonomic subdivisions have adopted a mode of life where vision is of little or no use. Such are fossorial, or burrowing, speleal, or cave-dwelling, some aquatic, and many nocturnal animals, e.g., *Proteus*, *Amphiuma*, *Necturus*, Caecilians or Gymnophiona, *Sphenodon*, *Notoryctes*, *Chrysochloris*, *Urotrichus*, *Myogale* or Desman, the Moles, Soricide Shrews, Insectivorous Bats, *Spalax*, Opossum, Sirenians, and many others. Here again several reasons may have worked together to bring about the result: an inherent habit, the search for food, avoidance of extinction, small use of vision in poor illumination, and so on. The fact that most of these animals have persisted for long geological periods is an evidence of their life's success. (*See* for an able presentation of this subject G. L. Walls's book, *The Vertebrate Eye*, 1942; *see also* Plate 1922–24; Hesse & Doflein 1935–43.)

References: A. A. Allen 1950, 1951; G. M. Allen 1939; H. E. Anthony 1928; Arey & Mundt 1941; E. A. Armstrong 1947; J. J. Audubon 1941 and other editions; W. Beebe; Benedetti 1933; S. C. Bishop 1943; A. E. Brehm 1911–18; Cahalane 1947; A. F. Carr 1952; Casteel 1911; Cochran 1952; C. R. Darwin 1859, 1871, and later editions; S. R. Detwiler; M. C. Dickerson 1907; Ditmars 1946; Frisch 1950; Galambos 1942, 1943; Galambos & Griffin 1942; Grassé, v. 15, 1950; D. R. Griffin; W. K. Gregory 1951; F. Groebbels 1925; K. Guenther 1931; Hamilton & Goldstein 1933; L. A. Hausman 1946; R. Hertwig 1907; C. Hesse 1889; Hesse & Doflein 1935–43; C. L. Hubbs 1938; Jahn & Wulff 1943; Kellogg & Kohler 1952; Kriszat 1940; Lack 1949; Lee 1870; Lorenz 1952; Lydekker 1916; Mayr 1942, 1949; Milne & Milne 1943; F. P. Möhres 1952; A. H. Morgan 1930; H. J. Müller 1949; G. K. Noble 1931; Parker & Haswell 1940; T. G. Pearson 1936; Pearson & Burroughs 1936; Petersen 1947; F. H. Pike 1943; Piveteau (*see Traité de paléontologie*, vols. 4–7); Pope 1944, 1946; Pough 1946; Quaranta & Evans 1949; Ramsay 1901; Rochon-Duvigneaud 1943; Romer 1943, 1945, 1949; K. P. Schmidt 1929, 1938, 1945; Schmidt & Davis 1941; J. Sibree 1915; G. G. Simpson 1949; H. M. Smith 1946; W. T. Stille 1950; A. Thienemann 1939; A. R. Thompson 1933; Tryon 1943; Uexküll 1921; C. J. Van der Horst 1933; Walls 1942; M. Weber 1927–28; J. H. Welsh 1938; Wendt & Dodge 1938; Wheeler 1918; Wojtusiak 1933; E. Wolf 1942; Wright & Wright 1949; R. M. Yerkes 1903, 1905–6; Zeuner 1946; Zipse 1953.

Chapter XV

Vision and Its Role in the Origin of Man

SEC. 1. THE ROLE OF VISION IN THE EVOLUTION OF VERTEBRATES

1. PHYLOGENETICAL ROLE OF VERTEBRATE VISUAL SYSTEM.—The most advanced of the animals, the Vertebrates, rely more than other living creatures upon the information they receive from their environment through their organs of sight to satisfy their principal needs, viz., the acquisition of food, self-preservation, and reproduction. This dependence is so complete that we can say that without the visual organs and the visual system there would be no Vertebrates. In this sense vision and the Vertebrates are one. Without the sense of vision, the vertebrate forms of animal life would never have developed (*see* chap. XIII, 2). Nor would the Vertebrates have differentiated into countless forms during the preceding geologic periods.

The few exceptions, such as the cave-dwelling species, all of whom derive from ancestors with well-developed visual organs, are aberrations which merely underline the rule. The same statement is equally applicable to the nocturnal forms, such as the Bats and other Insectivores and some Rodents, where vision became unimportant or was abolished altogether.

2. VISION AND THE VISUAL ORGANS IN THE ECONOMY OF VERTEBRATES.—In appraising the relative importance of vision in the life of Vertebrates in comparison with the other senses and faculties, it is necessary to avoid both exaggeration and oversimplification, faults which the obvious importance of the sense of sight might induce. A balanced view is obtained only through the study of all pertinent factors: the visual organs and centers themselves, their minute organization, physiological performance in normal and pathological conditions and in experiment, and not least through observation of the behavior of living animals and of the biological conditions under which each larger group or individual species lives.

Such investigations may reveal many of the numerous factors that make up the "external world" of each particular group or species, to which it is adjusted in internal organization, habits, temperament, and all other respects. This may show unsuspected adaptations undergone by one species or another and many deviations from the original plan. As a result, such study may reveal each animal species to be a true reflection of all those numerous factors which are summed up in the concept of habitat or environment.

The exact role played by vision in the phylogenetic advancement of the Vertebrates, in particular of the Mammals, and in the rise of the Primates is exceedingly difficult to determine. Superficial examination gives the impression that vision was the major, and probably the decisive, factor in primate evolution, culminating in the advent of Man and in the development of human intelligence. However, other important factors unquestionably contributed their share to this outcome. The difficulties in the way of an objective appraisal are formidable, because of the long course and fluctuations of the evolutionary process, with the shifting of emphasis from one factor to another and with some factors working at cross-purposes. The major difficulty remains the insufficient record of life during past ages.

It is obvious that a study of the role of vision in the various Vertebrates, to remain within the bounds of the practicable, must be limited to a few representative cases. Hence vast material must remain untouched. In the preceding chapter, therefore, we described and analyzed a few representative Vertebrates, beginning with the Fishes and terminating with the Mammals. These phylogenetically graded portraits, even though few, may nevertheless give a glimpse of the forces and factors, including vision, that have molded the Vertebrates into their various shapes and given them their many diverse roles.

In this chapter the probable factors responsible for the advancement of the Primates and the probable role of vision in this advancement are discussed. In particular, an attempt is made, by a careful analysis of known and some hypothetical factors, to identify the circumstances responsible for the rise of Man to his present pre-eminent status in the world.

3. CLASSIFICATION OF THE VERTEBRATES ACCORDING TO THEIR DEPENDENCE ON VISION.—The earliest Vertebrates were the Fishes, living in the aquatic habitat in which they originated. They were followed by the transitional Amphibians, from which arose the terrestrial Reptiles, which, in turn, gave rise to the Birds and the Mammals.

Together with other animals, such as the unicellular Protozoa, the multicellular Coelenterates, the various more or less wormlike animals, the Arthropods, Mollusks, and others, the Vertebrates are assembled in numerous diverse communities whose members depend upon one another to a greater or lesser degree. This is equally true of plant life, without which animal life would not be possible. All these factors contributed in one way or another to the rise of Vertebrates and their multifarious differentiation and are indispensable to their maintenance.

The phylogenetical perfection of the visual function of the Vertebrates, as far as the available evidence permits us to judge, was not a straight line ascending from the lowest to the highest levels. Among the fishlike classes, especially among the many Teleosteans, there are some with structurally highly organized eyes, including a differentiated fovea, and sight which is among the keenest of all Vertebrates. Contrasting with these are Fishes, with small, poorly developed eyes and vision which biologically plays a subsidiary role at best. The extreme is the cave-dwelling species, where the organs of sight have become atrophic or have disappeared altogether. Except for these qualifications, the Fishes, even though phylogenetically the most primitive Vertebrates, are among the most advanced visually.

The Amphibians, even though as a class they have progressed further, are, on the whole, in-ferior to the Fishes in visual equipment and performance. In comparison, the level of the visual attainment of the Reptiles is above that of the Amphibians, many being equipped with a highly differentiated retina and fovea, an efficient oculomotor apparatus, and elaborate centers. In functional accomplishment and versatility some Lizards—for example, the Chameleon and Anole—equal and in some respects exceed most other Vertebrates (*see* preceding chapter). Many other Lizards—for example, the large *Anolis equestris* of Cuba and the Rhinoceros Iguana (*Cyclura cornuta*) of Haiti and Puerto Rico—judging from their extensive eye movements, may also have an efficient visual apparatus.

The Birds, with their relatively enormous eyes and minutely differentiated retina, which has one and sometimes two or more differentiated foveae or areae, are the visual animals par excellence, in which this faculty by far predominates. Many Birds also excel in ocular movements and are certainly in this respect superior to all Mammals, including Man and other Primates, contrary to the opposite statements on this subject by the foremost authorities. This is well illustrated by the Swallow and the Eagle, as described in the preceding chapter. The observations on other species, as, for example, the Rhinoceros Hornbill (*Buceros rhinoceros*) of Java, which can easily perform extensive eye movements, also indicate the presence of a highly differentiated visual apparatus. (For details on the eye of Fishes, Amphibians, Reptiles, and Birds *see* chap. V, 11; for the visual pathway *see* chap. VI, 5.)

The Mammalian Class is quite diversified in the structural development of its visual organs and their function. It contains orders, families, and species, such as the Primates, including Man, which, in the organization of their visual apparatus, are fairly close to the top of all Vertebrates, while the Orders of Insectivora and Chiroptera are characterized by a pronounced microphthalmia and poor sight. In a few extreme cases vision is abolished altogether. The remaining orders, with respect to vision, range themselves between these two extremes. Each order, family, and often each particular species of Mammal, in the adaptation of sight, is an exact reflection of its particular mode of life and the requirements of that life. Each Mammal, in other words, is the product of a particular combination of evolutionary factors. However, whereas each particular smaller or larger taxonomic group of Mammals reacted in the manner and degree of development of its vision to its particular mode of life, other and more basic factors have put a general imprint upon its visual behavior.

4. VISION AND THE ORIGIN OF MAMMALS.— The most primitive of living Mammals, the Insectivores or Bug-Eaters, are of special interest in the phylogeny of primate vision. In their bodily organization they are at the bottom of the mammalian scale. Phylogenetically they are closest to their reptilian ancestors. This contention is further corroborated by paleontology, which shows the most ancient Mammals to have been insectivorous in character (*see* Fig. 477).

This poses the following alternatives: first, since the Early Mammals may have evolved from large-eyed and keen-sighted Reptiles, they probably had inherited good vision. In this case the reduced sight of the Insectivores would be a secondary phenomenon imposed by their special mode of living. The other alternative would be a reduction of vision in the earliest Mammals, or possibly such reduction had already occurred in their reptilian ancestors during the evolutionary process of becoming Mammals. In either case, differing only in time, the Mammalian Ancestors or the Early Mammals must have reduced their dependence on vision and compensated for it by increasing their reliance on other senses, especially those of smell and hearing, as the only means of survival.

An enforced adaptation to optically unfavorable circumstances may be described as an "evolutionary bottleneck." Those Reptiles that were to become Mammals had to squeeze through it. While undergoing this long and painful process of severe reorganization, the vision of the Early Mammals was lost, in some largely, in others entirely. When, at the end, a Reptile was transformed into a Mammal, it is plausible that little remained of the original good reptilian vision, barely enough to form a nucleus from which a fresh start could be made. Such a nucleus was preserved in those forms

that did not undergo an extreme degree of adaptive specialization. Such may have been some tropical Shrews and possibly forms similar to the Gymnurinae of India. Others, exemplified by burrowing forms like the Moles, in which the eyes became reduced to insignificance, apparently had no role in the further evolution of Vertebrates.

5. IMPEDIMENTS TO A PROGRESSIVE EVOLUTION OF MAMMALS.— The factors which constituted the "evolutionary bottleneck" mentioned earlier can be identified only by circumstantial evidence. One factor may have been the Dinosaurs or Dominant Saurians, who at that time were at the zenith of their development, preying on weaker inhabitants of the dry lands. Another may have been the Pterosaurs or Flying Reptiles, which infested the air. However, these may have been merely the most palpable "enforcers" of an emerging new order, while there were probably many other more subtle and elusive factors which are now impossible for us to determine or appraise. Whatever these factors were, their discipline was extremely severe, and their influence lasted many millions of years.

The result was that for many weak animals there were but few avenues of escape from certain annihilation. One was flight into the twilight of dense vegetation; the other was subterranean retirement; and the third was to take to the trees and thence, for some, to the air. The ancient Mammals followed all three evolutionary avenues. In all cases they had to adjust themselves to different living conditions. The common feature of the first two was to decrease or abandon vision, while in the arboreal and aerial way of life, on the contrary, the sense of vision became dominant.

The nascent Class of Mammals, in order to squeeze through the "biological bottleneck," had to undergo numerous adaptations in habits, functions, and anatomical organization. The Early Mammals had to follow specific rules of life. Their body size had to remain small. As compensation for their reduced or lost sight, they had to overdevelop their senses of smell, touch, hearing, and gustation and, in general, remodel their characters and temperaments to a high degree of alertness, boldness, persistence, and endurance. They had, in addition, to reorganize their entire bodily machine, which required an increase of fuel for a greatly stepped-up metabolism to cope with the increased expenditure of energy imposed by their small size and greater activity. In most essential changes the terrestrial and subterranean Insectivores were emulated by their winged relatives, the Insectivorous Bats or Microchiroptera, with the important qualification that the latter became entirely dependent upon hearing and possibly upon touch and vibration, as the guiding senses in the procurement of their insect food, which they caught exclusively in flight.

6. POSSIBLE EXCEPTIONS IN THE EVOLUTIONARY MAMMALIAN BOTTLENECK.—The evolutionary process sketched here, which resulted in a transformation of some Reptiles into Early Mammals or Protomammals, still remains

FIG. 519.—Charles Robert Darwin (1809–82) at the approximate age of forty-five. One of the most influential naturalists of all time. In Haeckel's opinion, "a Newton of the organic world." Author of the book *On the Origin of Species by Means of Natural Selection, or the Preservation of Favoured Races in the Struggle for Life*, 1859; *The Descent of Man, and Selection in Relation to Sex*, 1871; etc. Elaborated the idea of "evolution" of animals and plants, by proposing the theory of the origin of species from lower forms under the influence of "natural selection" and of "sexual selection," as the molding factors which in the continuous "struggle for existence" have produced all forms of life which have existed during the past ages and presently populate our globe. Darwin's ideas, as few in the history of mankind, profoundly influenced biological thinking and have affected the entire concept of nature, of life in general, and of Man's relation to nature and the world in particular. An engraving made in 1884 for *Harper's Magazine* from a photograph taken by Messrs. Maull & Fox, 1854, and published as a Frontispiece to v. 1 of *The Life and Letters of Charles Darwin, Including an Autobiographical Chapter, Edited by His Son, Francis Darwin*, by John Murray, 3 vols. London, 1888. (For additional biographies *see* O. Hertwig 1909; W. Waldeyer 1909; Bradford 1926; M. C. Lloyd 1928; J. Rostand 1947; and an autobiography edited by Sir Francis Darwin, 1950.) *See* following figure.

largely obscure. We must very inadequately substitute hypothesis for knowledge of most of the factors which were involved and their interplay.

It is certain that those species which had adapted themselves to subterranean and aerial modes of life did not contribute to the rise of the

It is not at all improbable that some strains of the Early Mammals now extinct did not sink to the point of visual dissolution found in most of the modern Shrews and Moles. Their "biological bottleneck" may have been a little less narrow than that through which the ancestors of the Soricidae and Talpidae went.

Fig. 520.—Charles Robert Darwin (1809–82) in advanced age. Courtesy British Information Service. *See* preceding figure.

Primates. It must have been different with those Early Insectivores or Protoinsectivora which remained on the ground. They were able to retain their general features, such as dentition, proportionate limbs, some omnivorous taste, and, most important, a modicum of the original good vision inherited from their reptilian ancestors.

The living testimony of this contention possibly is found in some modern Insectivora such as the Hedgehogs, whose vision, even though not excellent, is better than that found in most of the terrestrial Shrews (as Herter & Sgonina 1933 found in their experiments). Other examples may also be cited: the Water Shrews, the African *Potamogale*, and perhaps most of all the Indian Gymnurinae and the African Elephant Shrews or Macroscelidae (*see* Figs. 478, 479). All these, according to the scanty information available, have fair vision, even though some are nocturnal (Brehm). Enough similar well-seeing forms of the Early Mammals may have persisted during the "dark ages" of early mammalian evolution, to form a start from which more advanced Mammals have subsequently developed.

7. Probable factors responsible for the evolutionary progress of Early Mammals. —What were the probable biological factors that initiated and continued transformation of the Early Insectivores into more advanced Mammals?

If living Insectivora are at all representative, some of their Triassic ancestors may not have been exclusively "insect-eaters," that is, depending solely upon Arthropods, Snails,

Ernst Haeckel

Fig. 521.—Ernst Heinrich Haeckel (1834–1919), biologist and philosopher, at the age of eighty. Professor of zoology at Jena, Germany. Protagonist of the idea of organic evolution. Formulated the "first law of biogenesis" or an abridged embryonic recapitulation of the historic evolution through which the particular animal species passed during its phylogenetical past. One of the chief defenders of Darwinism. Author of *Allgemeine Anatomie (generelle Morphologie) der Organismen* (1866), *Natürliche Schöpfungsgeschichte* (1868), *Anthropogenie oder Entwicklungsgeschichte des Menschen* (1874), *Studien zur Gastræatheorie* (1877), *Die Welträtsel* (1899), *Die Lebenswunder* (1904), etc. Portrait from Haeckel's *Die Natur als Künstlerin*, Vita Deutsches Verlagshaus, Berlin-Charlottenburg, 1914. Biography *ibid.*; another by Bölsche 1906.

Slugs, Centipedes, Earthworms, and other small creatures easily procured through olfaction, audition, and gustation. Their diet must also have included some of the fruits, such as various berries and nuts and also buds. Small Rodents, such as Mice, Rats, Chipmunks, and Squirrels, are a good illustration of this. Fruits, to be sure, may also have been procured principally through smell. But the fact that much of this plant food grew above the ground and had to be noticed at a distance and reached by climbing implies the necessity of at least some adaptation to an arboreal mode of life. Moderately fair vision was a necessary requisite for this. The desire to gather fruits which grew on bushes and trees may have been the inducement to take the first step away from a strictly terrestrial manner of life and to embark upon a more venturesome career above the ground.

An additional inducement may have been the appearance of winged insects and their larvae and pupae during the late phase of the Carboniferous Period, long before the first Nonplacental Mammals of the late Triassic Period

emerged. A subsequent inducement may have been fruits growing on angiosperm plants during the Jurassic and Cretaceous Periods of earth's prehistory (from 152 to 58 million years ago, according to Zeuner 1952).

All these factors and probably others may have provided sufficient stimulus for some of the Early Insectivores to take to the trees, to embark upon an arboreal mode of life, eventually terminating in the development of Primates—the Lemurs, Tarsiers, Monkeys, Apes, and Humans, and, as a side line, the Flying Bats.

Other and more numerous Early Mammals pursued their divergent evolution, forming numerous extinct and living modern orders: Carnivores, Cetaceans, Ungulates, Rodents, and others. Each of these followed its own evolutionary line, including its own mode of vision, whose past history, specific biological motivation, structural equipment, and physiological performance are at most sketchily known, or are not known at all. (*See* G. G. Simpson 1949, 1953; W. K. Gregory 1951.)

SEC. 2. THE ROLE OF VISION IN THE ORIGIN OF PRIMATES

1. THE FOUNDATIONS OF PRIMATE VISION.— The foundations upon which primate vision, including Man's, are built are at least as old as the entire Chordate or Vertebrate Phylum. (This theme is dealt with in chap. XIII, 2.)

This still leaves the question: What were the particular factors, and how did they work together, which shaped the specific character of primate and human vision, whose salient features are diurnalism associated with high visual acuity; well-differentiated color sense; strictly binocular stereopsis; and richly developed mental attributes?

The first requisite in finding the answer to this question would be to know the various ways in which other Vertebrates have solved their particular problems of vision. Unfortunately, we do not have this knowledge. There is, therefore, little with which primate vision can be compared. The few samples given in the preceding chapter, especially the Anole and the Swallow, at best merely indicate the solution of this problem, emphasizing at the same time its great complexity.

2. CHARACTER OF PRIMATE VISION AND THE ORIGIN OF THE PRIMATES.—The first important feature of primate vision is the obligatory or permanent binocular stereopsis in which both eyes work in unison, with the larger parts of the two monocular fields in common. In this way each eye receives a slightly different image from the same object. In the visual centers of the brain the two slightly discrepant images are fused into a single subjective experience, of which the tridimensional character, or perception of depth, is the distinguishing feature.

Two other essential features are diurnalism and high central acuity, made possible by the formation of a specially differentiated central fovea. The fourth feature, also associated with the diurnal habit, is color vision, best developed in and around the fixation points. To these four, a fifth essential feature, more highly developed in Man than in any other species, must be added—the faculty to discriminate, that is, to see intelligently, to memorize, to reproduce subjectively, and to utilize past visual experiences in many practical ways, alone and in combination with experiences received through other senses and memorized, all of which forms the specific "human mind." This is a subject which from Aristotle to our own times has inspired a profuse literature (*see* Part I, in this book, especially chaps. II, III, and IV; on physiological optics *see* especially H. von Helmholtz' *Treatise*, 1924, and others; and Bethe *et al.*, Handb. d. norm. u. path. Physiol., 1929–31).

3. ELLIOT SMITH'S HYPOTHESIS OF VISION AS THE CAUSE RESPONSIBLE FOR THE RISE OF PRIMATES.—The problem of the origins of primate vision has been in the focus of scientific interest for the past few decades. G. Elliot Smith and his associates and followers did most to keep it alive. In his essays on *The Evolution of Man* (1927), in which he plotted the probable course that led to the rise of Man and the factors that contributed to it, he wrote (p. 44):

Increased reliance upon the guidance of the sense of sight awakened in the creature [Tarsier] the curiosity to examine the objects around it with closer minuteness and supplied guidance to the hands in executing more precise and more skilled movements than the Tree Shrew attempts. Such habits not only promoted the development of the motor cortex itself, and cultivated the discriminative powers of the tactile and kinaesthetic senses, but they linked up their cortical areas in bonds of more intimate associations with the visual cortex.

In the process of the rise of the Primates from the Infraprimate Ancestors, the increase in size and functional elaboration of the great prefrontal areae, "concerned with attention and the general orderly co-ordination of psychic processes," and the further evolution of cortical centers of conjugate eye movements were the prerequisite milestones, a goal not yet attained by the Tarsiers but only by the true Monkeys. In Elliot Smith's words:

The Primates at first were a small and humble folk, who led a quiet life, unobtrusive and safe in the branches of trees, taking small part in the fierce competition for size and supremacy that was being waged upon the earth beneath them by their carnivorous, ungulate, and other brethren. But all the time they were cultivating the equable development of all their senses and limbs, and the special development of the more intellectually useful faculties of the mind that, in the long run, were to make them the progenitors of the dominant mammal—the mam-

mal destined to obtain the supremacy over all others, while still retaining much of the primitive structure of limb that his competitors had sacrificed.

The foregoing paradisaical picture of the conditions in which the Primates were reared during their infancy may be essentially true, even though our information is too scanty to pass an objective judgment on it. The point that raises our doubts is the aggressive character of the shrewlike ancestors of the Primates, so much emphasized by most observers (as described in chap. XIV, 9), and a similar trait characterizing practically all terrestrial Monkeys of the Old World and likewise the Apes and Man (*see* secs. 4 and 5, this chapter). As presented by one of the competent observers, S. Zuckerman (1932), incidentally verified on many occasions by the writer of these lines, the character of many Simians is far from peaceful innocence; in fact, it often verges on demoniacal sadism and cruel despotism. The possible importance of this trait in human evolution is further discussed in subsequent sections of this chapter. (*Cf. also* Hooton 1942.)

4. THE PHYLOGENY OF VERTEBRATE STEREOSCOPIC VISION.—The development of stereoscopic vision appears to have been one of the essential factors in the evolution of the human intellect. Just how primate stereopsis evolved and just how it, in turn, became instrumental in the rise of Man's intellect—the core of the problem of anthropogenesis—is not as yet clear. The views expressed on this subject are not precise and not well documented. The following remarks are intended to help solve this problem at some future time when more positive information becomes available.

Let us begin with the definition of stereoscopy, which simply means single, tridimensional vision with two eyes. However, before analyzing its conditions and possible causes, it is important to point out the magnitude and complexity of this problem, the solution of which will require concerted action along many lines of approach: physical-optical, anatomical, physiological, and psychological. Also it must be borne in mind that human stereopsis is only a special case, one of the many ways in which the problem of tridimensional single vision was solved by the various Vertebrates and Invertebrates. (*See* interesting comparative study of vertebrate stereopsis by J. Orione 1950.)

Binocular stereoscopic vision is already clearly expressed in the lowest Vertebrates, the Fishes. According to Rochon-Duvigneaud (1922, 1925, 1933, 1934, 1943), Verrier (1927, 1938, 1945), and my own studies, in almost all Fishes so far examined the frontal portions of the monocular fields of view overlap, producing a common binocular field comparable with that of Man (*see* sections on Sunfish, Trout, Pike, and Bullhead, in chap. XIV).

In Man, it is assumed, single stereoscopic vision is accomplished through the fusion of two homonymous sets of fibers above the chiasma, carrying similar or identical impulses from both retinae (*cf.* chap. VI, 4, 5, 6; *also* Fig. 361). In the Inframammalian Vertebrates, in which chiasmal decussation is believed to be complete, Rochon-Duvigneaud assumed a different arrangement within the cerebrum to compensate for such total crossing. In my own experiment with the Pigeon the optic fibers were found to be completely crossed in the chiasma (chap. VI, 5 [3]). However, two small bundles were found to recross above the chiasma, to terminate in the ipsilateral half of the diencephalon (*see* Fig. 190). That this arrangement must have some function, even though we remain ignorant of it, is obvious. On the other hand, this ipsilateral connection is too scanty to serve as the basis of stereopsis. Additional anatomical and physiological experimental investigations upon keensighted Birds, such as the Eagle, Hawk, Swallow, Swift, and others, are required to clarify this and related points (*see* sections on Anole Lizard and Swallow, chap. XIV, 7, 8).

Whereas there is the possibility of an arrangement in the visual system of Birds and Reptiles which would effectively duplicate the partial decussation in the chiasma of Mammals, even though this is unlikely because of the absence of commissural connections of both neopallia by way of the corpus callosum, such compensatory partial recrossing of the optic fibers above the chiasma in the brain of Fishes is even less likely. Hence the problem of vertebrate stereopsis must be sought in a different direction.

In the Inframammalian Vertebrates, according to Rochon-Duvigneaud, a lifelong investiga-

tor of vision in all classes, the two eyes are mostly used independently. On special occasions both eyes are used simultaneously, as a conjugate team, aiming at a single object. The binocular association, then, in all Vertebrates below the Mammals is a facultative arrangement. In the Mammals, definitely so in the Primates, on the contrary, the two eyes have lost their independence, becoming permanently coupled into a team always working in unison.

5. This author's view on the probable origin of primate vision from that of Inframprimate Vertebrates.—A tentative view that I formed gradually on this subject may be stated as follows: The vertebrate visual system, including its sensory and motor components, gradually evolved from the Prevertebrate Ancestors, through the Fishes, to the Mammals, according to essentially the same bilateral plan (even though the earliest optic primordia may, or may not, have originated from a single *Anlage* or orimental nucleus). This bilateral plan is the same that is manifested in all bilaterally organized animals. It is visible in the early vertebrate embryo as soon as the optic primordia are recognizable and is present without exception in the entire Vertebrate Phylum (*see* Fig. 434).

A principle of so universal an occurrence indicates an original and basic functional interdependence of the two peripheral photoreceptors, the eyes. The binocular association may undergo change, and the bond tying the two eyes may weaken, sometimes to a point of complete dissolution, but in most Vertebrates it is clearly indicated. The two eyes exert a reciprocal influence, mostly positive, occasionally negative.

In all Vertebrates, including Inframammals, the two eyes, when at rest or in their initial position, are firmly related to each other. This arrangement must be considered both anatomical and functional. It is maintained by the size, shape, and position of the two eyeballs in the orbits, by the organs and tissues filling the orbits, by the tension in these tissues sustained by circulation, by the fasciae and the common integument, and especially by the extrinsic eye muscles when at rest. This may be considered the neutral position, the position of balance. In it the two monocular fields of view have a definitive position in relation to the head and are definitely related to each other.

In the majority of Vertebrates, Rochon-Duvigneaud and others and especially J. Orione found that the two fields partly overlap in front. This neutral, inactive, balanced arrangement may be changed by a number of factors, most obviously by the action of extrinsic eye muscles and their nerve centers. Consequently, the two monocular fields of view may vary in relation to each other and relative to the head.

In the Primates, owing to the coupling of both eyes into a conjugate team, the two lines of view are always focused on a single point, a common fixation point, whose distance alone may vary.

In the Inframammals there are several possibilities: both eyes may remain permanently in the neutral position; or one eye only may maintain a neutral position, while the other eye may go on exploring its own visual space as far as the anatomical limits set by the orbit, etc., which may be further increased by the movement of the head and neck, of the body, or of both; or both eyes may temporarily team up in pursuing a single, commonly viewed object, which again may be carried out with the eyes alone, with the assistance of the movements of the head and neck and/or also of the body, or of the body alone. The various movements, or combinations of movements, are specific for the animal to which they are biologically appropriate.

Only that act of vision in which both eyes are directed toward a single object should be considered a binocular visual act. In Man and in all other Primates, according to this definition, all vision is perforce binocular and stereoptic. In many other Mammals a similar situation obtains, even though it is apparent that further detailed investigation, especially in various Carnivores and other sharp-sighted orders, is necessary.

In the low-ranking Mammals, according to Rochon-Duvigneaud, the two eyes are also coupled into a functional team. This problem, however, requires further study. According to our own observations, most Rodents, such as the Mouse, Rat, Rabbit, Guinea Pig, Gopher, and Woodchuck, focus with only one eye, alternately first with one and then with the other. The Red and the Gray Squirrels also use a

unilateral fixation by preference. However, on occasion, when especially aroused, they squarely face the object of their attention, focusing it with both eyes. Similar behavior was noticed in the Philippine Tree Shrew (*see* sec. 10, in the preceding chapter).

In the Guinea Pig there are no ipsilateral, noncrossed optic nerve fibers above the chiasma, and very few in the Rat, according to our own experiments (*see* chap. VI, 5 [4, 5]). Stereopsis in the sense of human vision, accordingly, must be denied to the Guinea Pig, and almost entirely to the Rat.

An incipient stereopsis, however, must be admitted both in the Squirrel and in the Tree Shrew. In both species binocularity, that is, simultaneous use of both eyes, is apparently present. Automatic stereopsis on all occasions is quite evident in some Dog varieties, in the Cat, Leopard, Lion, Bear, Monkey, Ape, and Man whose eyes face forward and whose lines of vision are directed toward the common point of fixation. In all these species, as far as investigated, almost half the optic nerve fibers remain uncrossed in the chiasma. This again harmonizes with the generally current view, according to which a partial crossing in the chiasma is an indicator of the anatomical arrangements serving stereoscopic vision. (*See* chap. VI, 4, 5 [6, 7], 6.)

6. Problem of inframammalian stereoscopic vision.—The vision of many Inframammalian Vertebrates, measured by human standards, is unquestionably far superior to that found in most Rodents, definitely so in comparison with the Guinea Pig, Rat, and Rabbit.

The binocular convergence observed in the Golden Eagle, Barn Swallow, and Anole Lizard resembles exactly that which is standard in the Primates. There is no justification for denying these species binocular stereopsis, which in some cases is possibly superior to that of the Primates. The fact that they do not have partial decussation in the chiasma, as do the Primates, is no evidence against this, since their visual apparatus has not yet been adequately investigated. Hence the possibility must be left open that in the Birds of Prey, Owls, Swallows, Swifts, the Anole Lizard, the Chameleon, and probably many other Vertebrates, including some Fishes such as the Trout and Pike, central arrangements are present which make possible a facultative use of their visual apparatus in stereoscopic binocular vision. In fact, in some, as, for example, in the Swallow and the Anole, a central visual mechanism more pliable than the human must be postulated which permits them an easy change from purely panoramic, or largely panoramic, vision to binocular stereoscopic vision, and back again, as the functional situation demands from time to time. Such rapid switching from one visuomotor mechanism to another may be compared with a quick accommodation of dioptrical apparatus from an aerial to an aquatic condition observed in those Birds that gain their livelihood by diving.

7. THE ROLE OF ACUITY IN THE PHYLOGENY OF PRIMATE VISION.—Visual acuity is the ability to distinguish fine details of the viewed object. It is the faculty which, in addition to the ability of the visual organs to react to the photic impulses in general, may be considered basic, that is, the very essence of vision.

Visual acuity may be defined as the responsiveness of the visual organs to light stimulation, or its absence, limited in space. Its anatomical prerequisites are a photoreceptor mosaic made up of a sufficient number of individually stimulable elements, and a system of conductor units to the central organ which permits separate transmission of impulses generated from small groups or even from individual photoreceptors. Such "spatial organization" appears indispensable, indicating an inability of a diffusely organized visual system to respond spatially.

The degree of acuity of vision is a function as varied as the biological tasks it serves in the diverse animal species. It ranges from a condition that is only a little above complete lack of response to light stimuli arranged in space, through the various intermediate stages to the highest possible degrees permissible by the fineness of the organic structures and the analytical properties of the physical mediator, light. The first is exemplified among the Fishes by the Bullhead, and among the placental, eutherian animals by the terrestrial Shrews, Moles, and Bats (*cf.* preceding chapter). It is characteristic of the Order of Insectivora, typified by the terrestrial or Soricide Shrews, all animals of pronounced nocturnal habit. At the other end of the scale are types active in full daylight and possessing rapid locomotion, such as the Birds and the higher Primates, including Man, whose behavior is largely regulated by sight.

The habit of an animal, whether photopic or scotopic, is obviously decisive in determining the minimum of visual acuity each given species requires. The particular factors determining visual acuity may be imperfectly described as the "way of life," mode of locomotion, food habits, and habitat.

In the case of the Swallow, for example, a very high degree of visual acuity, associated with quick binocular convergence and instantaneous accommodation, alone satisfies the biological task of vision, which is to catch small insects on the wing at high speeds (*see* section on Swallow in the preceding chapter). Yet an equally high degree of acuity and binocular convergence and stereopsis is required by a Chickadee or Titmouse, a bird that flutters from twig to twig, instead of crossing long distances at high speeds, as the Swallow does. Even though the conditions in which these two species hunt for their prey appear on the surface quite dissimilar, in both cases they put a high premium upon sharp discrimination of fine details: the Swallow must notice and locate a minute flying insect at a great distance against the usually uniform background of the sky; the Chickadee must discover small bugs and their eggs among the leaves and in the crevices of the bark of the trees, which offer as a background a confusing variety of minute details. In such conditions only a visual apparatus capable of quick testing of minute shades of illumination and quick appraisal of shapes and sizes, transformed into a tridimensional judgment of minute distances, is good enough. A similar rapid appraisal of a bewildering number of minute details, differing little in size, shape, and color, must be made by the visual apparatus of a flying Eagle when scanning the landscape at high speeds in search of prey.

The high performance of primate vision with respect to acuity is based on numerous observations and experiments with monkeys and on innumerable tests of normal human individuals and pathological cases, as well as on practical experience. This high degree of acuity in human vision is apparently the most important single faculty upon which Man's intelligence is based. So refined a tool is undoubtedly the product of a long evolutionary process.

By reversing our argument, it is probable that at some time in the distant past Man's Ancestors did not possess a high degree of visual acuity. The probable phylogenetical stages and the probable factors which, starting from insignificant beginnings, have produced the visual apparatus with the help of which Man rose to his present pre-eminent status, may have been as follows.

8. PROBABLE LIVING HABITS, AND THE VISUAL ACUITY OF EARLY MAMMALS.—The early shrew-like Mammals, ancestors of all subsequent Mammals, were probably humble creatures, spending their lives in subdued light in places thickly overgrown with vegetation, as do the present Shrews and many small Rodents (*see* section on Shrew in the preceding chapter; *cf.* Weinstein & Grether 1940). When some of them embarked upon a more definitely arboreal life, becoming early Prosimians, they continued their nocturnal habit, as do their descendants even now. Why many modern Lemurs persist in their nocturnalism and arboreal habit is quite difficult to explain, notably so for the bulk of the Prosimians inhabiting Madagascar, the remnant of the hypothetical ancient Lemuria, or Gondwana. There are no palpable factors in Madagascar, such as powerful carnivores, acting as "enforcers" of nocturnality. (*Cf.* J. Sibree, *A Naturalist in Madagascar*, 1915.) The explanation of the prevalent prosimian nocturnalism as being caused by an atavistic inertia is even less appealing. More easily explained is the nocturnalism of the African Galagos and Pottos and the Asiatic Lorises and Tarsiers as imposed by fierce competition from the more advanced members of the local fauna, in particular by animals of prey, such as Snakes, Birds, and Mammals, including the more advanced Primates, the Monkeys (*cf.* F. Barth 1950).

Whether or not the almost universal nocturnalism of modern Prosimians, the pure rod retina, and the color blindness which accompany it are inherited or enforced by some spe-

cial factors, future investigation should be able to reveal. Contrasting with the prosimian nocturnalism is the pronounced diurnalism of most living Tree Shrews, or Tupaiidae (*cf.* section on Tree Shrew in the preceding chapter). Unquestionably, they are phylogenetically older than the Prosimians. They successfully managed to survive, in spite of their diurnalism—and, in fact, because of it—in ecologically similar conditions, while the Prosimians had to escape into darkness. What complex interplay of the various factors is responsible for this difference in habit, only a thorough study of conditions on the spot may explain. But the very fact of the presence of strongly diurnal Tree Shrews permits one to hypothesize that the evolutionary stream of Early Vertebrates which evolved into true Monkeys or Anthropoidea, almost entirely diurnal, must have by-passed the forms which became differentiated into largely nocturnal Prosimians.

In summary, just as some Insectivores may have passed through a less narrow "evolutionary bottleneck" and saved much of the diurnality inherited from their sharp-sighted reptilian ancestors, subsequently to become diurnal Tree Shrews, so the latter, or some of them, may have embarked upon an arboreal way of life, to become primitive Primates and subsequently true Monkeys, without sacrificing much, if any, of their original diurnality. The evolutionary road along which moved those Vertebrates eventually to become Higher Primates, that is, the Monkeys, Apes, and Humans, may have been less devious than is commonly assumed. The diurnality of the piscine and reptilian ancestors of the Mammals may have continued uninterruptedly, without too profound modifications, through the Early Mammals into Tree Shrews and finally into higher stages of Primates and Humans. (*Cf.* Le Gros Clark, *History of the Primates*, 1953.)

9. DIURNAL HABIT AND VISUAL ACUITY OF ADVANCED VERTEBRATES.—The diurnal habit of the majority of modern Monkeys, as of the other diurnal Mammals and Vertebrates, if not an absolute yardstick by which to measure acuity of vision, is at any rate a fairly good indicator of it. In subdued light, all other factors remaining equal, details must be larger to be noticeable than is necessary in good light. In other words, finer details may be seen in good light than are seen in poor illumination. High acuity demands good illumination, such as full daylight usually provides. Hence only the diurnal habit could have furnished the necessary phylogenetical basis upon which the vision of the Monkeys, Apes, and Humans could have evolved. For this reason the Prosimians must be excluded from the course of anthropogenesis or the process culminating in the emergence of Man. Almost the same applies to the Tarsiers, except for the very early, nonspecialized forms of the suborder of Tarsioidea, which, judging from their smaller orbits, were very likely diurnal.

In short, a more or less pronounced diurnalism, associated with a fair to high degree of visual acuity, must be considered the essential condition obtaining during the entire long course of evolutionary changes and intervening stages, beginning with the Fishes, Amphibians, Reptiles, and through the Early Mammals, which eventually terminated in the rise of Higher Primates and the advent of Man.

10. Diurnality, arboreal habit, and the high acuity of primate vision.—The high degree of visual acuity possessed by most Monkeys, all Apes, and Man, in comparison with most other Mammals, is well attested by numerous observations, experiments, and tests. In fact, as far as investigated, only the keen-sighted Birds and some Lizards may possess acuity equal or superior to some Monkeys and to Man. (*See especially* Weinstein & Grether 1940; Grether 1941.)

The need for a type of vision capable of analyzing the minute details and objects that constitute the natural habitat is obvious in the Monkeys. They must, because of their arboreal and semiarboreal mode of life, be able to see clearly the branches on which they climb or onto which they leap. They must, further, recognize by sight at considerable distances the fruits upon which they subsist and must notice the enemies which threaten them both from the air and on the ground, to which most of them occasionally descend. But, above all, they require good acuity for the location and recognition of their food at a distance, like the Birds and unlike most other Mammals, which they finally test by taste and smell only after they have picked it with their hands.

Careful, detailed examination of objects by sight is a characteristic of the Monkeys. Small concealed objects, such as fruit, grain, or insects, they find by pushing aside the vegetation, grass, straw, foliage, shavings, or fur either with one hand or with both. A good illustration of such use of both hands under the guidance of eyes is the so-called "grooming," or "fur-picking," a frequent mutual favor the Monkeys give and receive. In this visuo-manipulation both hands are used to search systematically over the fur for possible parasites, the eyes being used entirely binocularly, the stereoptic quality of vision, as well as acuity, being basically utilized (Fig. 526, sketch *16*).

Most Monkeys and Apes are agile, mobile, alert animals. They are constantly on the move, ever doing something, except during periods of rest, which in most species is during the night. Such activity puts a premium on the visual apparatus, which for them is by far the most important sense. The highly perfected primate vision is, then, the matrix out of which developed human vision.

11. The role of color vision in the evolution of Primates.—The specific subjective reaction to the hues of the visible color spectrum of light is a further perfection or refinement of the basic function of vision, which is responsiveness to light in general. It may be looked on as a subsidiary quality secondary to the original or primary function of responding to light and to the visual acuity or discrimination of details of the viewed objects arranged in space or dimensionally.

How general color vision is in the Vertebrates is even now not well known. Opinions vary from those who would admit it in most species to those denying all or most color vision in by far the majority of the Vertebrates, including most Mammals.

Observation of the animals and their behavior in experiments suggests that many Vertebrates, beginning with the Fishes, especially the Teleosts, on through the Amphibians, Reptiles, Birds, and including the Mammals, possess some degree of specific hue discrimination, with numerous species having a highly developed ability to discriminate hues. In a respectable number of species of all vertebrate classes, color vision must be rather well developed and may not differ substantially from that in Man. In some of them, particularly in Birds, color vision may be superior to Man's. The Prosimians appear to be color blind, according to experiments of Bierens de Haan & Frima (1930), which agrees with their mostly pure rod retina (Kolmer & Lauber 1936; Detwiler 1939, 1940, 1943; Rochon-Duvigneaud 1943). Good color vision, on the contrary, is practically certain in most Higher Primates, the Monkeys, Apes, and Man. In some, e.g., the Cebus Monkey, however, color vision is comparable to that of a protanopic dichromate with defective red vision (Grether 1940).

The ability to perceive hues specifically, next to superior acuity and binocular stereopsis, may have been one of the principal factors contributing to Man's rise to his pre-eminent status. The need to utilize all potential visual cues present in nature, including chromatic cues, in addition to the bi- and tridimensional, may have been the basic condition for the perfection of primate vision. The increase in quality and quantity of information conveyed by chromatic vision compared with achromatic plainly provided the stimulus to develop it, as was well presented by G. L. Walls in chapter XII of his book *The Vertebrate Eye* (1942). Once developed, it greatly increased the usefulness of the sense of sight to the ancestors of Man in their "struggle for survival."

It is true that color vision may be defective under the conditions of civilized life, without interfering with most normal pursuits. This may, however, be quite different under natural conditions, where an appreciation of hues, or lack of it, may mean success or failure in the severe struggle for survival and in the sexual competition for mates, that is, for posterity. Color vision must have been especially important in the female progenitors of mankind, to whom the principal task of procuring vegetable food was intrusted (as indicated by a tenfold frequency of the major red-green color defect in men, according to R. W. Pickford 1947). Color vision in the phylogenetical sense must, therefore, be considered as one of the principal pillars upon which Man's vision was built.

(*See* for physical, physiological, and pathological aspects of color vision: A. Bethe *et al.* 1929–31, *Photoreceptoren;* P. J. Bouma 1947; *The Science of Color*, published by the Optical Society of America, 1953; H. von Helmholtz' *Treatise*, 1924–25; J. B. Judd 1952; J. H. Parsons 1924; R. W. Pickford; T. Preston 1928; J. P. C. Southall 1937; R. W. Wood 1934; G. W. Walls 1942; W. D. Wright 1947; Symposium on Color Vision in *Documenta ophthalmologica*, v. 3, 1949; for the commercial aspects of colors *see* D. H. Taylor *et al.* 1950; for psychological aspects *see* F. Birren 1950.)

12. THE ROLE OF COLOR VISION IN THE STRUGGLE OF ANIMALS FOR SURVIVAL.—Under illumination of less than a certain minimum of intensity, all visible objects appear to be different shades of gray, ranging from a lighter gray to a saturated gray which appears black. Above a certain intensity of illumination and increasingly so toward full daylight conditions, in addition to the quality of "whiteness," other qualities emerge which are called "hues." This addition of many varieties of color shades or hues greatly increases the number of potential cues, of which many animals avail themselves. It is the difference between the so-called "achromatic vision" obtaining in Man in scotopic conditions when the visual apparatus is adjusted for night life, and the so-called "chromatic vision" characteristic of adjustment for daylight activity.

The addition of numerous spectral or chromatic qualities to the intensities, localities, shapes, sizes, tridimensional character or depth perception, and the temporal sequence of sensations greatly improves the sense of sight as a tool with which to test the viewed objects. Biologically, this must be of small or no importance for many animals, whereas for others it appears to be essential.

In many species, for example, those of nocturnal habits, hence in most Mammals, color vision is of small value or none. Here the various shades of gray or of brightness and forms suffice to distinguish one object from another; the lowering of the threshold or the increased sensitiveness to weak stimuli is more important here. This is realized under the scotopic conditions under which Cats and other members of the Feline Family, for example, hunt. Almost the same seems to be true of the Canines. To the totally color-blind Cat, therefore, the far more essential quality is a summation of stimuli in the visual apparatus through which the slightest movement of a Mouse, for example, is detected.

Co-operation of the auditory sense in locating the source whence the rustling caused by a Mouse comes is yet another help to the hunting Cat. In the largely amblyopic Soricide Shrew or a Bullhead, living in obscurity, discrimination of the spectral hues would be an unnecessary luxury, capable as these species are of locating their food by their superior olfactory sense, assisted, in the Shrews, by a fine auditory sense and touch, mediated by the vibrissae or "whiskers," and in the Bullhead by the gustatory sense. A situation similar to that in the Cats obtains in the Tarsiers and Owls and probably also in most Prosimians, where, in contrast to the macrosmatic and micropic Shrews, the principal role is assigned to the greatly increased achromatic sense of sight, assisted by the auditory sense. In the Insectivorous Bats, finally, the ultrasonic auditory sense became supreme.

In the case of the Tarsier, a strictly carnivorous Primate, the dependence for its livelihood is divided between the senses of sight and hearing, with an even greater emphasis upon nocturnal vision; the Tarsier resembles the Owl in this respect as in others, for example, the dull-mottled grayish and brownish coloration and the fluffy, noise-deadening texture of its fur. It is, then, no surprise to find, as in the Cat and Night Monkey, no photoreceptors in the Tarsier's retina which could with certainty be called cones, the rodlike structures being found here, as in the Night Monkey, also in the very center of its small fovea. It must be assumed, then, that, as in the Cat and Night Monkey, color vision plays no role in the Tarsier's life, even though this species and the Night Monkey did their utmost to preserve their central acuity in scotopic conditions, as the presence of a fovea shows. (*Cf.* section on Tarsier in the preceding chapter.)

Whereas color vision plays no important role or none at all in the life of nocturnal animals, particularly Mammals such as the Cat, Dog, Raccoon, Mink, Marten, Polecat, Rat, Mouse, Civet, and questionably also the Squirrel, a quite different situation obtains in most animals active during daylight. These are found in all vertebrate classes, with only the Amphibians and many Nonprimate Mammals in addition to most Prosimians on a doubtful list (e.g., *Lemur mongoz*).

Of the Fishes described in the preceding chapter, three are of a pronounced diurnal habit (Trout, Sunfish, and Pike), one is pronouncedly nocturnal (Bullhead), and one diurnal, with an extension of activity into crepuscular and nocturnal conditions (Northern Brook Silverside). These habits for each particular Fish agree with the kind, quality, and quantity of photoreceptors that each of them possesses. This close agreement between the behavior and the structure is fully borne out by other species described in the preceding chapter: the Anole Lizard, Swallow, Tree Shrew, and probably also the Squirrel, which are diurnal, and the Soricide Shrew and the Tarsier, which are scotopic or nocturnal. This, in connection with other modern investigations and observations, permits one to conclude that the presence of structural cones, whenever found, is fair evidence of at least some degree of color vision. On the basis of this criterion, widespread discrimination of hues among most Vertebrates must be claimed. Such a deduction harmonizes with physiological experiments on Monkeys and with human physiology.

13. Color perception a basic quality of vertebrate vision.—The preceding evidence points to color perception as one of the basic qualities of vision in most Vertebrates. The varied colors found adorning the bodies of many Fishes may not be an idle decoration, even though in many instances we are not able to explain their biological usefulness. Almost the same is to be said about the many varied colors found in the numerous Amphibians and Reptiles, although the evidence for color vision in the first is mostly negative so far. We are on safer ground in trying to appraise the frequently brilliant coloring of many male Birds whose behavior often indicates appreciation of their colors by their mates. From our own observation, such are the Parrots, including Lories, Parakeets, Macaws, Cockatoos, Pheasants, Rhinoceros Hornbill, Peruvian Cock, Quetzal, Motmot, Scarlet Ibis, Weaverbirds, Tanagers,

Finches, Peacocks, Birds of Paradise, and Hummingbirds. The significance of the brightly colored plumage of these and other Birds in "sexual selection" has been discussed in detail by Charles R. Darwin in his book *The Descent of Man* and has been touched upon again by F. Kipp (1939) and others (*cf.* A. A. Allen, A. Brehm, Chute, Gilliard, Ripley & Weber, W. J. Schmidt, and Zahl). In comparison, the coloring of most Mammals is dull. But even here there is reason to suspect more appreciation of color than is commonly assumed.

And should good hue discrimination be denied to the Primates (except the nocturnal Prosimians, Tarsier, and Night Monkey), which in many species show gaudy coloring no less brilliant than the multicolored adornment of many Fishes, Frogs, Toads, Salamanders, Lizards, Snakes, Turtles, and Birds? Examples are the male Mandrill, whose scarlet-colored nose, blue cheeks, yellow goatee and sideburns, and equally vividly colored posterior may not appeal to civilized aesthetic feeling but may be a potent stimulus to the opposite sex of its own species. Other bizarre color compositions are the vivid blue and green of the penis and scrotum in some Cercopithecs, which contrasts with the red color of the hind part of the body. Many other Monkeys, as for instance the Mangabeys, Rhesus Macaques, and certain Baboons during the ovulation period, may also be mentioned. What the true biological significance of such odd decoration is we do not know, but we must assume that it is essential. (*Cf.* Darwin, *The Descent of Man*, 1871, chaps. IX–XVIII.)

If hue discrimination is not to be denied to numerous Vertebrates as a means of recognizing their mates and also their enemies, color vision must also be admitted to be an important means in their acquisition of food and, in general, in their orientation in the environment.

14. Color of fruits, and its relation to the color sense of animals.—The role of color, especially of red and of black, as a means of attracting frugivorous birds to the many kinds of fruits, is well known, just as is the power of attraction of the flowers for certain birds and many insects; the fondness of the Ruby-throated Hummingbird for the red-flowering Scarlet Sage or Salvia, *Salvia splen-*

dens, for example, is notorious (F. Knoll, 1921–22, 1924, 1925; A. Kühn & Dora Ilse 1925; Porsch 1924, 1931; K. Guenther 1931; and especially H. N. Ridley 1930). The same must be true of those Mammals which subsist on fruits and other produce of plants. Especially is this likely in the case of the microsmatic Monkeys, whose acquisition of food under natural conditions depends primarily on colors, less on shape and size, and only slightly on the senses of smell and taste.

In most instances fruit would not be easily noticed by animals if it were not for its color. The green, unripe fruits, for example, blend with the green foliage and remain unnoticed until they become ripe and change color. The many various red, scarlet, purple, orange, yellow, brownish-yellow, bluish-yellow, and green-yellow berries, grapes, and pods, especially the brightly colored fruit of numerous members of the Rosaceae or Rose Family, when ripe, contrast vividly with the surrounding green foliage. Without such hue contrast, for example, the small red-colored Hawthorn apples would be difficult to notice at biologically effective distances by size, shape, and brightness alone, concealed as they are in a dense foliage (see Fig. 518-*A*).

Among the numerous fruits common in the North American Middle West and distinguished by bright colors may be mentioned such well-known species as the wild red cherry, pimbina or highbush cranberry (*see* same figure), shadbush (juneberry or serviceberry), chokecherry, barberry, many varieties of hawthorn (*see* same figure), fever bush, checkerberry, cranberry, raspberry, strawberry, bunchberry, dogwood, currant, hips of the wild rose bush, berries of the American holly, bittersweet, and, among the cultivated fruits, the sweet and sour cherry, pear, apple, and grape. The great attraction these fruits have for the Robins, Thrushes, and Blackbirds is shown by the latter's persistent interest and the quick consumption of berries during the time of ripening.

That other less vivid colors, mostly purple, blue, or black, have a similar effect upon some fruit-eating birds, even though for us their coloring is subdued, is shown by their speedy disappearance after they become ripe. Such somber-colored fruits are those of the blackberry, mulberry, elderberry, various huckleberries and blueberries, gooseberry, wild black cherry, wild plum, black cherry, arrow-wood, porter's plum, fruit of the sour gum tree, sassafras, buckthorn, wild grapes, and many other similar products of our orchards, gardens, fields, meadows, bogs, hedges, and forests (*cf.* Fig. 518-*A;* and R. S. Lemmon 1947).

In summary, the coloring of all these fruits seems to have the definitely utilitarian purpose of attracting birds, for which they supply food and by which their seeds are propagated and dispersed. However, this interesting problem still remains to be investigated by modern scientific methods.

15. EVOLUTIONARY INTERDEPENDENCE OF COLORED FRUITS AND PRIMATE COLOR SENSE.— Since it is probable that the evolution of the Primates took place in the tropical regions of the world, it would be of great importance to learn something about the coloring of the fruits of those regions and of its biological effect. Of this, unfortunately, little is known. H. N. Ridley (1930) describes them as "dull-coloured and not very showy." From other scanty information recently published on this subject, for example, from the beautifully colored illustrations in the article by J. R. Magness (Nat. Geog. Mag., v. 100, p. 325, 1951), however, the many fruits of the citrus family, mango, banana, persimmons, papaya, and possibly also of durian indicate the coloring of the tropical fruits, if anything, is even more varied and vivid than that of the fruits of the temperate regions of the world. We are therefore entitled to hypothesize that fruit coloring, wherever present, was evolved for the direct purpose of attracting, by its specific hues, the attention of the animals, including Primates, which feed upon it.

The evolution of colored fruits, of course, was a process parallel to the evolution of the color sense in the animals to be attracted. It indicates a close biological interdependence of the fruit-eating animals and the fruit-bearing plants. This relationship became beneficial to both partners, which profited from it: the animals in getting food, the plants in perpetuating themselves and spreading into new regions. It is a relationship similar to that found in the flowering plants depending for pollination upon In-

sects, except that in the latter the sense of smell and taste, besides vision, is an essential factor. (*See* detailed presentation of this subject in H. N. Ridley, *The Dispersal of Plants throughout the World,* 1930.)

16. EVOLUTION OF COLORED FRUITS AND THE ARBOREAL HABIT.—In the evolution of colored fruits, still another factor is worthy of consideration. It does not appear to be mere coincidence that the fruit-bearing plants are the trees and shrubs and not the low-growing herbs, weeds, and gramineous or grasslike plants (Graminaceae), certainly so in the tropical regions (*see* K. Guenther 1931). This fact harmonizes with the arboreal habits both of the Primates and of the Birds. Naïvely expressed, colored fruits began to grow on shrubs and trees when there were animals capable of noticing them by sight and able to get to them by climbing and flying. Inversely, the Primates began to evolve from the terrestrial Shrews through the semi-arboreal Tree Shrews, and likewise the Birds began to become formed out of the terrestrial Dinosaurs when the fruits began to grow above the ground. But the origin both of the fruit-bearing trees and of the fruit-eating Birds and arboreal Mammals must have started "from the ground," beginning with the low-growing plants and the terrestrial animals.

Still another factor was the urge of many plants to decrease competition for solar energy —light—by growing tall and hence forming lofty treetops. In this way the elevation above the ground of the leafy and fruiting parts of the trees may have been the prime incentive for the ancestors of Birds and Primates to embark upon their arboreal way of life, rather than to take to the arboreal "refuge area," as believed by some (Barth 1950). The lofty canopy of the primeval Brazilian forests described by A. von Humboldt (1805–23, etc.), A. R. Wallace (1853), H. W. Bates (1863), and others, full of light and fruit-bearing trees, according to K. Guenther (1931), illustrates this condition well (*see also* R. Spruce 1908; R. R. Gates 1927; M. L. Jobe Akeley 1950; and W. R. Philipson 1952, esp. p. 38).

One may develop this idea further in various directions. One is the growing of the fruits on shrubs and trees above the ground, out of reach of the strictly terrestrial animals, such as the

Soricide Shrews and most of the Rodents and likewise most terrestrial Insects. In this way, useless destruction during the optimum period of ripening, the time most useful for attracting the arboreal Mammals and flying Birds, and the competition which would largely interfere with the prime purpose of the colored fruits—the distribution of seeds at some distance from the parent-tree—are reduced.

The picture of a functional interdependence of the colored fruits and the color sense, as sketched, is obviously too simple to do justice to the immensely complex and in many ways overlapping spheres of life of many animal and plant species living in the same natural community, and the many factors involved. A more detailed investigation may disclose similar relationships of other species, in particular of the various Mammals, occasionally, periodically, or regularly subsisting on fruits, of which just a few may be mentioned here: Bears, Raccoons and Squirrels, and in the tropical countries Coatis, Viverrines, fruit-eating Bats or Flying Foxes, but especially Monkeys, Apes, and Lemurs. Many of these, as much as their habits are known, contribute to the very purpose for which the colored fruits were evolved rather than interfere with it, fostering the spreading of the fruit-growing plants and in this way further augmenting the source of their own food supply. (*Cf.* Dice 1952.)

In summary, there is sufficient evidence in favor of the hypothesis of the origin of colored fruits and of color vision as mutually interdependent phenomena, caused by the general urge of the plants and animals alike for a more abundant life.

The color sense of animals when it is well developed may not be very different from, and in many cases may be superior to, the human color sense. An example of this is the gorgeously colored plumage of the Hummingbirds (Trochilidae) and of the Birds of Paradise (Paradiseidae) developed through sexual selection. The delicate shadings of their various colors and the many patterns are exquisite, pointing not only to an excellent color vision by itself but also to a highly developed aesthetic color sense, or appreciation of color harmonies and contrasts. How much superior this sense of the Birds may be to the color sense and color aesthetics of primitive, untrained humans is shown by the use the natives of New Guinea and of other parts of the world make of the gaudy feathers of the same birds for their own adornment, which, together with their garishly painted faces and bodies, rather recalls the bizarre coloring of the lesser Primates, for example, Mandrill and Rhesus Macaque, already mentioned. (*Cf.* E. T. Gilliard, "New Guinea's Rare Birds and Stone Age Men," Nat. Geog. Mag., v. 103, p. 421, 1953; and Ripley & Weber, "Strange Courtship of Birds of Paradise," Nat. Geog. Mag., v. 97, p. 247, 1950; for the biological role of color vision *see* C. R. Darwin, *The Descent of Man*, 1871 or later editions; and E. A. Armstrong, *Bird Display and Behaviour*, 1947; for the fruits eaten by the Tree Shrews *see* chap. XIV, 10; for the food of the Monkeys and Apes in their native habitat and in captivity *see* secs. 4 and 5, this chapter.)

SEC. 3. THE ORIGIN OF MAN

1. Introduction.—The principal features of Man's bodily and mental organization are similar to the features characterizing other Primates, of which the most obvious are manipulative ability, visual acuity, and stereoscopic vision. Other human peculiarities, such as erect posture, with the characteristic poise of the head, and bipedal gait, are in vivid contrast to the quadrumanous posture and locomotion of all Monkeys and Apes. This similarity and contrast have been, since Darwin's and Wallace's inauguration of the concept of evolution, the object of much speculation on the origin of Man from some infrahuman species, as well as why and how such a change could have been accomplished. In these speculations special attention was paid to the locomotor apparatus, viz., the foot, leg, pelvis, spine, and poise of the head, the arrangement of the muscles of the extremities, as well as to the skull and the brain, including the visual apparatus, and their uses.

In appraising these changes, opinions have fluctuated from the assumption of a close phylogenetical relationship of Man with the large Anthropomorphous Apes to that of an early separation of Man's linear ancestors from the common primate stock and their abandonment of an arboreal habit, if, indeed, they ever were as completely adapted to it as are the majority of the now living Monkeys and Apes.

An attempt is now made to appraise the bipedal gait of the various classes and orders of the Vertebrates, beginning with the Birds, on through the lower orders of Mammals, and terminating with the Infrahuman Primates, to find out what effect this mode of locomotion may have had upon manipulation, posture, gait, development of the brain, and vision. In this way it may be possible to determine, perhaps, what stages in vertebrate organization preceded, and which functional factors were responsible for, the reorganization of the body characteristic of Man.

2. Bipedal gait of the Birds and its effect.—The most universally bipedal Vertebrates, aside from Humans and certain extinct Lizards, are the Birds. Avian bipedalism most certainly evolved from that of their ancestors, the Dinosaurs. By intrusting the task of terrestrial locomotion exclusively to the hind limbs, it enabled the Birds to concentrate completely upon the use of the upper or anterior extremities for aerial locomotion, or flight.

This was an immense advantage, since it opened a new frontier to this class. For this mode of life a parallel perfection of the sense of sight was a necessary prerequisite and a consequence. But avian bipedalism, associated with flight, had a drawback in completely adapting the arms and hands for the use of locomotion, albeit of a nonterrestrial kind. Hence it in itself precluded the development of extremities which could be used for manipulation, capable of close co-operation with visual control. And it was the visual control of detailed motor acts which was the key to a further elaboration of the so-called "mental faculties," eventually terminating in the rise of Man.

Even so, the "handling" abilities of many Birds, for example, Parrots and Weaverbirds, are nothing short of astonishing, especially since for the making of their artfully constructed nests, for example, they are forced to use their feet and beak, at best clumsy instruments, compared with primate hands. (The gorgeously colored Leadbeater's Cockatoo, for example, uses one foot to carry a morsel of food to his beak, exactly as do Man and Monkeys in the same situation, except that they use hands.)

The superior power of vision possessed by the Birds, absolutely necessary for their life, because of the lack of adequate "handling extremities," remained therefore largely unused for the development of mental faculties specific for the Primates.

3. Bipedal gait of Mammals an exception.—The bipedal posture and progression in Mammals is rather an exception, and, when present, it is used facultatively, on special occasions only.

There is, however, one group of Mammals in which bipedalism is firmly intrenched, viz., the marsupial Kangaroos. Here the powerful hind legs, assisted by an equally stout tail, are the exclusive supporting and propelling limbs, the progression being by leaping. The diminutive front limbs have practically no part in locomotion in these Mammals. They are used to some degree in "handling" objects, even though this handling is of a rather simple, summary kind. The weak, short fingers are here provided with long, hooklike claws, which, because of their poorly diversified movements, precludes their use as primate fingers. This, in turn, harmonizes with the herbivorous habit, relying upon taking food by means of a long muzzle, long neck, and flexible body. The situation in this respect in Kangaroos is essentially the same as in other herbivorous animals, as exemplified by Horses, Antelopes, Deer, Giraffes, and others, hence making the need for detailed visual control of manipulations unnecessary.

4. The use of the forelimbs for manipulation in Infraprimate Mammals.—More use of the forelimbs in "handling" objects is found in small Rodents, for example, in Mice, Rats, Chipmunks, and Squirrels. These habitually take and hold the kernels of grain with their front paws when eating. At other times, when running around, they use all four extremities.

The use of the front paws and toes as "hands" and "fingers" in the Mice is rather well diversified. This is even more manifest in the Squirrels, including the Chipmunks, as described in one of the sections of the preceding chapter (Figs. 493–96). The manipulation of objects—for example, nuts and acorns, when gnawing the outer, hard shell, or pine cones, when extracting the kernels—is quite a dexterous act, even though it remains relatively below the performance of primate fingers. The Squirrel's hands and fingers are used only to

in a way which is only a little more elaborate, as described in the preceding chapter. Here, too, the fingers are employed in a wholesale manner, no diversified use being apparent. The relatively long, curved claws would, in any case, be a hindrance to an individualized use of fingers and are, instead, cleverly used as a hooked

FIG. 522.—John James Audubon (1785–1851), French-American naturalist and painter of wildlife. An acute observer of nature, in particular that of early North America. Author of a monumental book, *The Birds of America.* From a painting by F. Cruickshank. Courtesy National Audubon Society, 1006 Fifth Avenue, New York. For biography *see* F. H. Herrick, *Audubon the Naturalist,* 1938.

hold the nut or a cone and to turn it, always bimanually, as in a flexible vise, whereas the extracting of the kernels is done with the teeth, unlike the method of most Simians, which always pick up the morsels with the fingers, together with the opposable thumb (Figs. 526, 531, 532, 534, 537, 539).

The Tree Shrews use their hands and fingers

"poker" or a grabbing tool. However, the hands are more frequently used individually in taking and holding morsels of food and carrying them to the mouth.

5. BIPEDALISM AND MANIPULATIVE ABILITY OF THE TARSIER.—In the Tarsier the specialization of its hind limbs for locomotion and of the

front limbs for handling, as in Man, is complete (*see* section on Tarsier in the preceding chapter, and Figs. 513, 514). In spite of this, there are so many qualifications here that a comparison suffers a great deal. The long, relatively powerful legs of the Tarsier are used not for walking but for leaping across long distances. The hands, provided, as originally in all Primates, with five fingers, are used as quick prehensile graspers and in a wholesale way, with all fingers, including the thumb, lumped more or less together.

in seizing food and in eating. The character again is wholesale rather than diversified, as described in detail in the section on the Tarsier. The seizing of food, in particular a live animal, is a formal attack in which the entire body is employed, after locating and sizing up the prey by means of sight and hearing. In this assault both hands are used simultaneously, and the prey is seized almost simultaneously with the mouth.

FIG. 522*A*.—Heinrich Klüver (1897), professor of experimental psychology at the University of Chicago, at the approximate age of forty-two. A lifelong investigator of the mental capacities and behavior of the Infrahuman Primates. Author of *Behavior Mechanisms in Monkeys* and of many other publications, including those on the pathology of vision. Courtesy Professor H. Klüver, Chicago.

ing the thumb, lumped more or less together. Also, while the hands are not exactly the propelling organs, they do assist in the process of locomotion in their role as organs of attachment which hold the body in position just before leaping, and to arrest the shock at the end of the jump. In certain situations, as in "chinning," the hands and the arms are actively used in assisting the legs or are used alone (Fig. 506).

The Tarsier's hands are used in a special way

More variation in the use of the hands and fingers is seen when the Tarsier chews his morsel, but even here the hand is merely assisting the chewing apparatus (Fig. 511). On rare occasions the thumb is seen opposed to the other fingers, perhaps by accident, as shown by another illustration (Fig. 513). The use of the thumb and fingers in the human way and in that of most Simians, especially by opposing the tip of the thumb to the tips of other fingers, was never noticed during our observations. (*Cf.* Figs. 526, 531, 532, 534, 539, 540.)

The verdict about the Tarsier must be rather negative. This Primate strayed far from the course along which Man's Ancestors must have traveled—in its nocturnalism, its special type of bipedalism, and its poorly diversified use of hands and fingers. The nucleus from which Man took origin, on the preceding evidence, must be sought in some primitive primate forms of long ago, before the present Tarsiers began to differentiate along their special evolutionary lines.

FIG. 523.—Carl Ethan Akeley (1864–1926), naturalist and sculptor, originator of the modern art and science of taxidermy, which, as exemplified in the American Museum of Natural History in New York and in the Chicago Natural History Museum, has preserved and re-created true animal life as much as any textual description and illustrations have done. In the words of Henry Fairfield Osborn, in the Preface to Akeley's book on Africa (1923), Akeley was a sculptor and biographer of the vanishing life of that continent, who used taxidermy in recording the vanishing greatness of the natural world, which he immortalized in the museums. Akeley's greatest achievement was, perhaps, the stimulus he gave for the establishment of Gorillas' sanctuaries in the Belgian Congo, around Mount Karisimby, in his "Gorilla Country," where his body rests. Portrait from C. Fisher, "Carl Akeley and His Work," Scient. Month., v. 24, p. 97, 1927. *See* Akeley's book *In Brightest Africa*, 1923. For additional biographical information *see* Mary L. J. Akeley, *Congo Eden*, 1950.

6. SIMIAN BIPEDALISM AND MANIPULATIVE ABILITIES, AND THEIR ROLE IN HUMAN EVOLUTION.—The change from the quadrumanous, that is, modified quadrupedal, way of locomotion to complete separation of the locomotor function of the hind limbs from the manipulative, exploratory role of the forelimbs must have been a very gradual process of adaptation and reorganization extending over a vast stretch of time, difficult now to estimate. To trace this momentous process, it is necessary to begin with the condition which may be considered generally simian, gradually coming to a critical point where the two ways separated, one continuing along the customary way characteristic of all Infrahuman Primates, the other taken by Man.

The initial condition may be considered that found in many Marsupials and in the majority of Mammals, in which all four limbs are used for locomotion. In these a more definite tendency to use the forelimbs as manipulative instruments is noticeable in all those species which habitually climb trees and bushes for food. Such are the Opossum, Raccoon, Mustelids, Cats, and most small Rodents, for example, Mice, Chipmunks, and Squirrels. Good manipulative use of the forepaws is seen in the Cat when it "washes" its face or catches a mouse.

The Tree Shrew also occasionally uses one of its forepaws to pull a morsel of food, instead of both hands simultaneously in the way the Squirrels, Chipmunks, and Mice do. Beginning from this, perhaps, as a starting point, it is possible that, with increased adaptation to the arboreal mode of life, some ancient Tree Shrews developed an opposable thumb and long fingers, in this way initiating a transformation of their forepaws into typical prosimian and simian forehands (Figs. 524–40).

In the Monkeys, with complete adaptation to the arboreal way of life, the hind limbs became also transformed into supplementary grasping hands (Fig. 540); hence the designation of this order as Quadrumana or "four-handers." But the forehands and hindhands of the Monkeys are never exactly equivalent in anatomical structure and performance, the manipulative ability of the forehands always being superior to that of the hindhands. The first are able to perform more delicate motor acts, while the latter, more robustly built, give better support to body weight and function as the propelling limbs, assisted by the grasping pull of the forehands. In the brachiating Apes the locomotor function of the arms and hands more or less prevailed (Figs. 528, 535, 536).

The division of labor between the forehands and hindhands of the Primates is, in fact, merely a modified continuation of the same physiological division between the front and hind extremities found in practically all quadrupedal animals, which, in turn, is a reflection of the orientation of their bodies, with one pair of limbs leading, the other propelling, in pro-

tions, some of the Primates, later to develop into Human Ancestors, began to spend more time on the ground, they already had more robustly built hind limbs, which could gradually be converted into typical human "legs" and "feet." This change to a more emphatic use of the hind limbs for standing and walking may have taken place more easily in those Primates which were originally not so completely adapted to the arboreal way of life, or in those which, because of their habits and the character of their habitat, with few trees and more open country, had less incentive to keep to the trees

FIG. 524.—Slender Loris (*Loris* or *Stenops gracilis*), a small nocturnal Lemur of South Asia. From A. Brehm' *Tierleben*, 2d ed., v. 1, p. 258, 1876, with special permission of the Bibliographisches Institut A.G. (Dr. E. List) Mannheim, Germany. (*Cf.* Fig. 500.)

gressive locomotion. The leading extremities naturally need to be more delicately organized than those whose task is more a passive support. This is the consequence of the bisymmetric organization of the body along the midsagittal vertical plane, with concentration of the principal sensory organs and the brain in the leading segments of the body, which form the head during ontogenesis and phylogenesis.

A different anatomical organization and functional specialization of the forehands and hindhands persisted throughout the entire course of primate history. When, for reasons discussed in the following subsections and sec-

The initiation into human erect posture and bipedalism is well illustrated by the terrestrial Macaques and Baboons and other Simians, which spend much or most of their time on the ground (Figs. 526, 527; *see also* secs. 4, 5, this chapter). Their use of the forehands in locomotion resembles that of other quadrupeds although it has its peculiarities, such as the shambling or shuffling gait of the Baboons. However, when resting or feeding, their habitual posture is sitting on the buttocks, with the body and head more or less upraised. This leaves their arms and hands temporarily entirely free for "handling" objects in many ways and for various purposes, such as the close visual scrutiny of objects, and bringing them close to the organs of taste and smell. In this complex control, it must be assumed, the superficial sense of touch, very highly developed precisely in the hands and fingers and very elaborately represented in the cerebral cortex, and the deep proprioceptive muscle sense are constantly used, together producing complex ideational and sensomotor formulas in the brain (*cf.* P. Bard 1938; Woolsey, Marshall & Bard 1942; Critchley 1953).

all Infrahuman Primates. The other was the development of obligatory bipedalism, with the emancipation of forehands from locomotion, now entirely taken care of by the hind "legs" and "feet," with the concomitant erect posture of the body as the result.

The first possibility is exemplified by the largely ground-dwelling Baboons and Hamadryads, or Dog-faced Monkeys (Cynocephali, or Cynomorphous or Cynocephalous Monkeys), which greatly resemble dogs not only in their elongated snout but also in their quad-

Fig. 525.—Large nocturnal Galagos or Lemurs of the island of Madagascar. From A. Brehm's *Tierleben*, 2d ed., v. 1, p. 272, 1876, with special permission of the Bibliographisches Institut A.G. (Dr. E. List), Mannheim, Germany.

7. Abandonment of arboreal habit by terrestrial Primates and Man's Ancestors, and the parting of their evolutionary ways.—When the phase of primate evolution in which differentiation between the use of fore and hind extremities became more accentuated, two possibilities opened. One was conservative, that is, to continue, despite prehensile hands and feet, the ancestral mode of progression on all four limbs, which is essentially modified quadrupedal. This is the case with practically

rupedal posture and habit (Figs. 526, 527). This solution of the problem of readaptation to the terrestrial mode of life may have been the easier way out. In it not a great deal of reorganization of the body and limbs was necessary. The limbs, especially since in the original moderate arboreal adaptation they did not become greatly different in length and structure, could have remained little changed. The length and arrangement of the fingers and toes may have remained almost the same. The delicate prehensile power of all four extremities, especially of the fore-hands as instruments of the well-developed simian intellect, representing a definite advantage, was largely retained. Obviously for this reason, the Dog-faced Primates never developed the speed of locomotion possessed by the Canines, Horses, Antelopes, and some Cats, which would have made a radical reorganization of their limbs mandatory (as exemplified by the Patas Monkey). Viewed from another angle, the retaining of all four prehensile hands by the Cynocephalous Monkeys from the viewpoint of human phylogeny had its evil consequences, in that it had precluded obligatory bipedalism and erect posture, the two conditions absolutely indispensable for the use of arms and hands as delicate instruments of mind and, in turn, necessary for the rise of higher intelligence.

The other road open to the semiterrestrial Primates, for the reasons discussed earlier, was a radical change to a bipedal terrestrial life. This change could not have occurred abruptly, but only over a long stretch of time. There may have been many trials and failures, some prehominid Primates again retreating to the arboreal conditions they were accustomed to, the others readopting a quadrumanous terrestrial locomotion.

It is, in fact, difficult to visualize conditions for which one of the two modes of locomotion would not have been satisfactory, and certainly they seem to have been an easier way out, as illustrated by the modern Monkeys and Apes (Figs. 526–40).

At this point along the evolutionary road, which terminated in the coming of Hominidae, the veritable crossroads of humanity, the Primates had three choices: one, to turn back into the primeval jungle; another, to become terrestrial Cynocephali; and the third and most difficult, to become human.

8. PHYSIOLOGICAL AND BIOLOGICAL MOTIVATION OF THE BIPEDAL GAIT AND OF ERECT POSTURE IN MAN'S ANCESTORS.—The probable factors which may have been especially responsible for the adoption of bipedal gait and erect posture in Man's Ancestors are lost in the impenetrable evolutionary past. There are as yet few concrete facts in available paleontological information which would shed light on this crucial

problem. There certainly are no particular anatomical or physiological factors which alone could be held responsible for human bipedalism. The senses of the living Primates, the Monkeys and the Apes, with few exceptions, are fairly close to those possessed by Man. Acuity, color vision, and stereopsis appear to be about equal in many, in some slightly superior, in others not greatly inferior, to that of Man. Manual organization and dexterity, even though not equal to the human in many Monkeys, approaches it; in some it may surpass it. Hence the best hypothesis at present is to put the emphasis on the *specific manner* and *degree of collaboration* of the original primate senses and motility, particularly manual dexterity and vision, which eventually resulted in the coming of Man. (*Cf.* following subsection.)

The types of Primates from which the development of the specific human organization started may be imagined as rather small in size, possessing acute senses, of an alert, inquisitive disposition, and of largely terrestrial habits. They may have resembled somewhat the smaller and medium-sized monkeys, such as the Macaques, and less so the more specialized Cynocephali (Figs. 526, 527). The proportions of limbs were more harmonious in both than in the large Apes. Their hands had an opposable and not too drastically reduced thumb (Fig. 540, sketches *16, 19*). Their feet, even though typically prehensile, were straight plantigrade, with the sole and heel resting flat on the ground (Fig. 540, sketches *15, 17, 18, 20*). Hence they were favorable material from which, after further perfection, more efficient human hands could have evolved and from which, by elimination of unnecessary detailed movements, more compact arrangement of tarsal and metatarsal bones, and strengthening of the musculature, the human leg and foot could have been formed.

Whether or not the now living large Anthropomorphous Apes and those of the past that resembled them could have furnished material sufficiently pliable to lend itself to such a radical reorganization, is doubtful (*cf.* secs. 4, 5, this chapter). The least suitable would be the types resembling the Orangutan, whose legs and feet are completely adjusted to the arboreal habit. The next would be the Chimpanzee, whereas the Gorilla and the Gibbon appear to be more advanced toward pronounced bipedalism. But all now living Apes appear in a greater or lesser degree to be highly specialized for arboreal life. Admirably adapted for it as they are, if they were forced to undergo such radical reorganizations as would be required for life exclusively on the ground, they would be doomed to certain failure. Only a primate type, nimble, elastic, and not too far removed from the original quadrupedal mode of progression of its shrewlike ancestors, could have been the stock from which Man emerged. This form may, perhaps, be typified by one or several extinct Simians discovered in India and in East Africa (*see* Leakey; Le Gros Clark & Leakey; and Le Gros Clark 1953; *cf.* sec. 8, this chapter).

Whichever the simian-like ancestors of Man were, they must be visualized as having attained the stage—through their previous history, inclination, and circumstances—where they began to use their hind extremities for locomotion by preference. In the course of time, their hind limbs became powerful, better attached to the pelvis, itself changed in shape, and straightened so they could carry their bodies swiftly and without undue effort for long distances. In this way the arms and hands were largely emancipated from locomotor duties and were employed for the exploration of the immediate surroundings and for the manipulation of objects under visual control.

The other consequence of emancipation of the arms and hands was the freedom of the senses, first that of vision, which was now able to concentrate upon problems other than the immediate control of locomotion. The sight was now free to roam over the territory between the immediate surroundings and the distant horizon and mentally to digest countless impressions from objects and events, and to adjust conduct in the best possible way.

With this, the terminal phase of human evolution was initiated. The outcome was the formation of a strong, powerfully built, bipedal animal, swift of pace, equipped with efficient exploratory limbs, under balanced control of the senses and motility, the most important being vision. The Human Ancestors finally embarked upon a strictly terrestrial career, to become, in Homer's expression, the true *epigeoi* or "earthly dwellers."

Bipedal gait and upright body posture appear to have been the principal factors which molded Man. Yet they were not the initiators, but only the potent levers applied to human evolution. The prime factor, as in all animal motivation, was the need to acquire food by means of the arms and hands, to ward off danger, and to secure progeny, or, in other words, "the struggle for existence."

9. The "struggle for existence" the prime factor responsible for the rise of Man.—The motivating stimulus for the reorganization of a quadrumanous into the bimanous-bipedal body of Man's Ancestors, in the final analysis, must have been purely functional. At one particular phylogenetical stage, it must be presupposed, these ancestors developed a tendency to rise and stand on their hind limbs more often and for longer periods of time than do any now living Simians. A special stimulus may have been peculiar dietetic habits and a peculiar habitat.

In a largely open, grassy, savanna-like prairie much vegetation consists of gramineous grasses. The average height of these grasses when mature is from 4 to 6 feet. At this level the hands must be used for long stretches of time in gathering the kernel-bearing ears. The most favorable and least fatiguing posture for this occupation is bipedal standing and walking. The same is true also of a habitat containing low-growing, fruit-bearing shrubs and bushes, where the position of the gathering arms and hands is most comfortable and efficient in an upright position.

In contrast, in the high forest the fruit-bearing treetops are easy of access only to the arboreal Primates and to Birds. Here Man's Ancestors would have been greatly handicapped, forced as they would have been to gather fruit by time- and energy-consuming climbing. Another extreme would have been a diet of low-growing herbs, roots, and tubers, requiring a stooping attitude comparable to that of the Gorilla (*see* secs. 4 and 5, this chapter). The dependence upon either tall fruiting trees or low-growing herbs would have worked against a strictly bipedal gait and upright posture.

The obvious reason would have been the small chance that an incipient biped would have had to survive during phylogenetically available time. Hence the more profitable way would have been a reversion either to an outright arboreal or to a quadrumanous terrestrial habit, whichever would best fit the circumstances.

Another and perhaps equally decisive reason for the cultivation of prehominid bipedalism and upright posture was the deficiency of the tree-grown fruits in proteins and fats, in contrast to carbohydrates, salts, and vitamins. The need for proteins especially may have been caused by the active, roaming habit. During the incipient stage this need may have been satisfied by the gathering of small animals, such as snails, slugs, some insects, shells, frogs, lizards, birds' eggs, and their young, and the like. With an increase in body size and an active, roaming habit, this omnivorous inclination, present, even though little exercised, in many of the Primates (e.g., the Chimpanzee and Baboons), may have been the prelude to more pronounced hunting for game animals, more plentiful in a diverse habitat and open savanna than in a dense forest. (*Cf.* sec. 8, this chapter.)

Additional factors may have contributed to the tendency toward exclusive bipedalism. The basic one may have been the scarcity of food, both plant and animal, in most regions at any given time. This made it necessary to cover wide spaces of territory, many repeatedly, as the seasons of differently ripening fruits, supply of eggs, or abundance of game demanded. This migratory struggle of nascent humanity for survival could have become more successful with the developing upright posture and bipedal walk, requiring a modified pelvis, elastically acting vertebral column, and long muscular legs able to be fully extended and thus to support the body weight with a minimum of expenditure of muscular energy. All these changes developed for the express purpose of transporting the body swiftly and without much fatigue over long distances and many varieties of ground and obstacles.

10. PROBABLE PHYSICAL CHARACTER, HABITS, AND THE HABITAT OF PRIMEVAL MAN.—Many more factors besides those enumerated must be imagined to have worked together in the complex process through which one or more types of Simians became gradually transformed into primitive Humans. In speculations along this line it is necessary to take into consideration every scrap of evidence from paleontology, paleobotany, and geographic and geological conditions of past ages, as well as climatic changes. In this way, perhaps, it will be possible to determine roughly the likely regions and the probable conditions in which primeval humanity was finally molded. In this process the flora and fauna of the likely homelands of Man and other external circumstances contributed a substantial share, in addition to the inherent potentialities of Man's Ancestors carried over from the past.

From what is at present known, especially from the paleontological researches of Leakey and of Le Gros Clark (1950, 1951, 1954), it now appears that a separation of the human line from the other Primates took place farther back in the past than had formerly been assumed. Man's upright posture and bipedal gait, even though evolved from the common primate organization, represent a substantial deviation from the locomotion of the Monkeys and Apes, which is quadrumanous, that is, essentially modified quadrupedal. This substantial bodily reorganization, assuming all other factors reasonably equal, must have required a very long stretch of time, its roots possibly reaching as far back as the early period of primate phylogenesis. During all that time other subdivisions of the Primate Order continued to cultivate quadrumanous locomotion and to perfect it in various special directions, usually with emphasis either upon the hind or the fore limbs. One notable exception in this respect, among all nonhuman Primates, is the Tarsier, where, as in Man, the hind limbs are used practically alone for the leaping gait, with the almost complete emancipation of the arms and hands from locomotion (*cf.* chap. XIV, 12). The other is the Gibbon, with his frequent bipedal walk but brachiating arms (sec. 5 [3], this chapter).

The upright posture and bipedal gait of primeval Man almost certainly indicate that his home was neither an impenetrable jungle nor a pronounced mountainous country nor swamps nor deserts. It must have been instead a flat or gently rolling savanna and prairie or low hills, mostly overgrown with grass and interspersed with shrubs and wooded patches. The climate was warm or subtropical, with sufficient and well-distributed rainfall.

Primeval humanity, accordingly, must have shunned extreme conditions and preferred milder parts of the world with a variety of natural conditions and products. Its habit was rather mobile, strolling over the wooded hills and grassy plains. As the long, muscular legs carried the body, the hands were busy examining objects, gathering fruits and carrying them to the mouth, collecting various small animals and birds' eggs or catching larger prey. During the long ages since the first definite use of the legs as the principal carriers and the hands as the exclusive manipulators of objects under visual guidance, this division of two physiological tasks gradually became firmly intrenched in human nature. Locomotion became the sole duty of the legs and feet, perfectly adjusted to balance the weight either at a slow, measured walk or at physiologically high speeds. The arms and hands, in turn, became the most versatile grasping organs that nature had devised. The entire bodily machine became reorganized, including the senses and the regulating and directing mechanisms of the brain. From an originally largely quadrumanous, that is, essentially quadrupedal creature, capable of a short leaping gait, with limited intellectual capacities, Man became, in the course of a long evolutionary process, a high-speed biped and an enduring walker, with hands which serve his intellect and a mind which encompasses the universe.

11. Contribution of vision to Man's rise to his pre-eminent status in the world.— On the argument of the preceding subsections the following thesis concerning the rise of Man from obscure origins to his dominant place in nature may be advanced.

Human vision developed from more simple conditions found in Man's Ancestors. It is the dominant sense upon which, phylogenetically and ontogenetically, human intellect principally rests. Not vision alone, however, but a concurrence of several fortunate circumstances is responsible for the growth of Man's superior intellect. The principal factors were the erect posture of the body and the bipedal gait, initiated by the terrestrial habits of Infrahuman Primates and developed to perfection by Man's

Ancestors. The long-range influence was the omnivorous diet working under the impetus of the "struggle for existence."

The arms and hands, emancipated from the task of locomotion taken over entirely by the legs and feet, became transformed into delicate tentacles capable of handling objects in the most varied ways. Manipulation, or the use of hands, is mostly under the control of vision, with the assistance of the somesthetic senses of touch, muscular sense, temperature, pain, and the sense of balance. These sensory qualities help regulate the actions of the muscles of the hands and arms and other co-ordinated groups of muscles to perform purposeful acts of the will.

The arms and hands, chiefly under the close guidance of vision, are Man's principal organs of exploration of his immediate environment. They are his anatomical instruments by means of which he acquires food, feeds himself, takes care of himself and his kin, and in many other ways adjusts himself to his immediate environment. With his hands, too, he defends himself and commits acts of aggression. By means of his hands, mostly guided by vision, Man fashions and uses various tools and instruments through which his capacities and physical powers are magnified many times. In this way Man sets himself in relation to his distant environment, seemingly as far as the limits of the universe and the confines of time. (*Cf.* H. Petersen 1924.)

The possession of such versatile organs of mechanical accomplishment has tremendously enlarged the influx of knowledge, which in turn necessitated a many-sided development of the brain as a repository of past experiences and an integrator or inventor of new combinations of numerous complex skills. The most important of these is speech or language, the instrument of crystallized thinking, and human intellectual intercourse.

Without the kind of vision possessed by Man, he would not be the supreme intellectual being on this globe. But without the locomotor and handling extremities he has, he would never have developed the kind of vision he has, nor would he have been able to make practical use of it, as he did and does. Many other peculiarities of human organization, such as the upright position of the head and the flexible neck on which the head pivots, contributed their share in making Man what he is.

It is doubtful whether a similar statement could be made concerning any other part of the human organism, not excluding the brain itself. Marvelously organized as the human brain is and working as a superefficient integrator and arbiter, it never would have become that without the quasi-mechanical tools, the arms and hands, and the legs and feet. No other organ can compare with them in importance in the rise of human intellect. The task of the heart and the vascular system, of the organs of digestion, respiration, generation, and the rest, as in other animals, is to maintain the physical integrity of the body and of the human race, irrespective of the intellectual level and accomplishment of its possessor, whether it be an Aristotle or an *Australopithecus*.

The three principal factors upon which Man's physical character and intellect rest are vision, manipulative ability of the arms and hands, and the locomotor ability of the legs and feet and other adaptations that make the upright gait possible. The sense of hearing, closest in its "spiritual" or "intellectual" quality to the sense of sight and the basis of human speech, must itself take second rank in comparison with the superb performance of vision in the kind and variety of information that it supplies to Man's intellect. Much lower in the scale must be ranked all other senses, such as taste and smell, whose roles in the building of the human mind are relatively modest. Of greater importance are the various modalities of the somesthetic sense, of equilibrium, of motility in particular as the indispensable components of the manipulative and locomotor functions of the extremities, and of speech. Each, according to its particular role, contributes to the harmonious working of the perfect human machine.

Human vision, that is, the organs that perform it, like vision in other animals, developed to serve the particular purposes of human life. Human vision had to be good to notice in a rough, summary way large and medium objects at long and medium distances, still or in motion, colored or without color, in good light or in the semidarkness of twilight. But it also had to be good enough to analyze the minutest objects within the manipulative range of the arms and hands, as well as to discern moving Humans and larger animals several miles away.

The arms and hands, working under the close binocular guidance of the eyes, became Man's universal instruments, easily and quickly carried by sturdy legs anywhere over the accessible parts of the globe. Largely with their co-operation, vision became the funnel through which an immense wealth of impressions poured into the brain, which expanded into a huge repository of past experiences of the most varied kinds which could be integrated with other senses and motility, recombined, and put to new uses. In this way the foundations of the superior human intelligence were created.

In summary, the adaptations of the legs and feet for locomotion and of the arms and hands for manipulation in Man's Ancestors and the subsequent development of human intelligence may be, in a larger sense, viewed as a special case of adaptation to a new, terrestrial habit and habitat. Just as a Fish had to undergo fundamental reorganization in order to become an Amphibian, the latter to be transformed into a Reptile, thereafter to become a Mammal or a Bird, so the originally arboreal Primate had to pass through very many changes in order to become a Human. In each case the cerebral development did not precede but apparently followed the reorganization of the body for the new way of life. In the origin of Man, too, the primary stimulus was the change of habit and habitat, which, under the general urge of life, was followed by the transformation of the anatomical mechanisms, including the brain, resulting in the intellectualization of Mankind. (*Cf.* secs. 7, 8, 9, this chapter.)

SEC. 4. INFRAHUMAN PRIMATES AS AN ILLUSTRATION OF MAN'S ANCESTORS BEFORE THEY ASSUMED AN ERECT POSTURE AND BIPEDAL GAIT

1. INTRODUCTORY REMARKS.—In the preceding chapter various representative Vertebrates were portrayed, in an attempt to discover just what role vision played, and in what way, in the formation of their characters. For this, we had necessarily to delve into their environment, habits, and anatomical organization. These sketches, of necessity, had to be brief. Even so, they showed each animal species to be quite well adapted in habits and organization to the particular conditions in which it lives. Expressed differently, each particular set of environmental factors and their particular use, given the opportunity, produced their own particular type of animal. In all species investigated, vision was found to play its own special role.

The evidence so far adduced in the present chapter indicates that the process by which Man was formed was no exception. Unfortunately, however, our knowledge of the early stages of human evolution is quite meager. One is therefore forced to resort to speculation, inference, and deduction to re-create the picture of Man's infrahuman ancestors, their physical and physiological character, sensory and mental faculties, probable behavior in their natural habitat, and, finally, the principal environmental factors which probably initiated and influenced the course of human evolution. (*Cf.* secs. 8 and 9, this chapter.)

2. Man's derivation from infrahuman ancestors.—From what was said in the preceding section, it is apparent that at some time in the distant past Man's Ancestors probably resembled more or less one or another of the present species of Infrahuman Primates. The first association in this connection is the large, so-called Anthropomorphous, or Manlike, Apes. An idea of close kinship between Apes and Man seems to have been entertained by many. However, in spite of the obvious similarities, objection may be raised to this view on several points mentioned below. Hence all that may be accepted as certain is the derivation of Man from some early infrahuman primate ancestor, whether an early Tarsioid, an early Cercopithecoid, or even an early Prosimian.

The question of whether the linear ancestors of Man resembled one of the now living forms or some extinct and perhaps not yet discovered species, what the intervening stages of human evolution were, what the probable living habits of Man's Ancestors and the physical and climatic conditions of their successive habitats were cannot be answered except on the basis of well-documented evidence. Here we shall merely call attention to a few bodily and psychic features which make the thesis of a close phylogenetical relationship with the Great Apes difficult to accept. These are (*cf.* Figs. 528–40): disproportionately long arms and short legs in Apes, the reverse of those found in Man and in the terrestrial Monkeys; disfigured feet in some, unfit for a straight plantigrade gait on flat ground (Orangutan, Chimpanzee); excessively short neck, restricting the mobility of the head, especially in the adults; excessive shortness and relative weakness of the thumb, making it and the fingers less fit for delicate "picking" prehensions; all-around crudity, robustness, and clumsiness of the entire body build; the peculiar curvature of the spine, different from the S-like shape of the human spine, and the large canine teeth, all of which, without considering further details, make the so-called Manlike Apes difficult to bring into close ancestral relationship with Man. In contrast, the even proportions of the limbs of the smaller Monkeys and their use and the structure and use of the feet compare rather favorably with those of Man (Figs. 526, 527).

Other features of the Apes, such as their practically exclusive vegetarianism, their relative unsociability or solitary, hermit-like way of living in their primeval arboreal home, tend to underline their isolation from the main primate stream, to which direct ancestors of Man appear to have been much closer. For these reasons some of the smaller Monkeys seem more fit, at any rate, to illustrate the physical appearance, the character, and the habits of that phase of nascent humanity in which its basic mental and bodily organization and its social instincts, which represent one of Man's most prominent features, were formed. (*Cf.* W. L. Straus, Jr. 1949.) Such are some of the Macaques and the so-called Dog-faced Monkeys or Baboons, in spite of the beastlike appearance of the last-mentioned species, which seems to be an adaptation to the conditions of their quadrumanous terrestrial mode of life. (*See* A. Brehm's *Tierleben*, 4th ed., v. 13, 1916: *Die Säugetiere*, v. 4; also Zuckerman, Carpenter, Klüver, Hooton, Malbrant & Maclatchy, C. Akeley, and Mrs. Mary L. Jobe Akeley; *see also* following section.)

3. Character, habitat, and behavior of the Rhesus Macaque.—The Java Macaque (*Macacus cynomolgus, Macaca cynomolga*), and the Indian Rhesus or Red Macaque (*Macacus rhesus, Macaca mulatta*), the *bandar* or *markat* of the Hindus, may be taken as typical of the Macaques. These and other kindred species inhabit all of southern and southeastern Asia and North Africa, including the Rock of Gibraltar in Europe.

The Rhesus, in a number of local species, inhabits central and northern India, Kashmir, Nepal, Sikkim, much of China, part of Tibet, and most of Japan, here being the northernmost living subhuman Primate in the world.

Physically the Macaques are well built, being huskier than the African Cercopithecs but lighter than the Baboons. Climatically, they are quite hardy. In the Himalayan Mountains they prosper at an altitude of 9,000 feet, where they prance about in winter under snow-covered pine trees. Others live in the dry and hot Gujarat, while still others find it comfortable in the hot, steamy bamboo thickets of flat Bengal.

The habitat of the Macaques is almost anywhere: in forests and orchards, in jungles and next to cultivated fields, and also in rough, rocky country. Water is a necessity for them, and they swim and dive excellently, especially when pursued. Even though they are arboreal and capable climbers, easily making leaps of from 12 to 15 feet, they spend much of their time on the ground in search of food. Ridley (1895) frequently observed in the jungle large Macaques walking erect for short distances.

The male Macaques are formidable fighters, well armed with powerful canine teeth, strong enough to ward off a Leopard, their chief enemy.

They are not especially choosy about food, even though they have a "sweet tooth," eating many kinds of fruits, seeds, kernels, leaves, buds, insects, and eggs. Some observers saw them eating crabs and shells. In my own long experience the Rhesus Macaques hardly ever touch any meat, either raw or cooked. In captivity, with this exception, most other human food is readily taken by them, especially bread and milk and sweet fruits, such as bananas, apples, pears, and grapes.

The senses of the Macaques are acute. They seem to love colored objects. Their vision and visual attention are of superior quality, brightness discrimination and color vision, visual acuity and form vision being little inferior to, or as good as, that of Man (*see* experiments by Shepherd, Klüver, Brecher, Bierens de Haan, Révész, and Grether).

The Macaque's brain and other parts of the nervous system, like the remainder of the body, are organized according to the same general primate plan as in Man (*cf.* Fig. 280). The visual system in particular has all the elements of Man's: eyes, optic nerves, chiasma, subcortical centers, visual radiations, cortical visual centers or striate areae, albeit they are simplified and of sketchy configuration, as could be expected from a phylogenetically less advanced Primate (Fig. 186). Even in its minute histological structure, as, for example, that of the retinal nerve cells, their arrangement, and synaptic relationships, in the minute structure of the lateral geniculate nucleus and of the striate cortex, all details are very similar to the human, even though they are not exactly the same (*cf.* Polyak, *The Main Afferent Fiber Systems*, 1932; *The Retina*, 1941 or 1948; and chaps. V–IX in this book; for other data *see* Hartman & Straus 1933).

The Macaques are pronouncedly social animals. They are found in bands of from 10 to 50. They are very active, much of the time being busy with the gathering of food or playing and squabbling with their companions. Occasionally such squabbles degenerate into more serious fights. Much of the time the whole company is on the move, examining every bush or clump of grass for something to eat, always on the alert for a possible enemy.

In character the Macaques may be described as highly intelligent, alert, bold, clever, tricky, saucy, inquisitive, tough guys, capable and ready to defend themselves and their own, when need be, to the utmost; occasionally wicked, treacherous, unreliable, and again, when treated well or when not molested, tolerant but moody; in youth gentle and full of "monkeyshines," in advanced age irritable and of morose disposition.

In their family affairs they are full of tender love for their young, exhibiting a high degree of social unity (principle of "all for one, one for all"), sometimes to the point of utter disregard of personal danger. They are capable of heroic self-sacrifice but are also extremely greedy, avaricious, and jealous in matters of food. On still other occasions, for example, in the presence of a snake, true or artificial, they show themselves to be abject cowards.

The mental abilities of the Macaques, much investigated during the past few decades, are of a high order, on that score alone fully justifying their rank of primate mammals. Their powers of observation of whole situations and minute details are very good. Their memory is excellent and long lasting. They can easily be trained to perform complex acts in the laboratory and in the circus, where they can be great "showmen."

In laboratory experiments the ability to acquire visuo-mental ideas of a practical kind, a degree of abstraction and some reasoning power, the presence of "practical memory," and a good degree of mental retention were found. Even though only the rudiments of the highest mental powers are present, the Macaques have been found, on the whole, far superior mentally to most other experimental animals, such as the Dog, Cat, and Elephant. Whether Macaques ever use objects as tools, as do the Cebus Monkeys, has not been found out and is questionable (W. T. Shepherd 1910; H. Klüver 1933). In intelligence the Rhesus Macaques have been found, however, to be outranked by both the Cebus Monkey and the Gibbon (W. E. Galt 1939).

Contrasting with the many creditable features of the Macaque's character are those of an adverse kind. In accord with their moody, irritable, and unpredictable disposition, they are easily provoked and offended, their reaction quickly becoming stormy rage, an eruption of violent emotions expressed by loud, angry voices and other signs of ill will. On a few occasions they have been observed throwing stones, sand, or water at their molesters. The outburst of anger may be accompanied by a reddening of the face and of the hind part of the body. When thoroughly aroused, they are little devils, ready to attack anyone, including humans. (For similar behavior of the Spider Monkey observed in nature *see* W. R. Philipson 1952, p. 35.)

Toward the weaker members of their community they sometimes become malicious, sadistic tyrants. They bite, pummel, and otherwise torment their unfortunate victims with pleasure, even preventing them from getting food, drink, and rest. Briefly, the Macaques, especially the old males, are unstable, inscrutable, evil fellows, ready to commit every malicious trick that springs to their minds and is within the limits of their physical power. As a counterpart, the female Macaques, when in sexual heat, are described as veritable nymphomaniacs.

The Macaques have a definite sense of the "rights" due them, and of "injustice" done to them, as the following episode convincingly shows. Among the half-dozen or more of these monkeys held in several large cages for experimental purposes, there was "Peter," a large male with long canines, and a gruff character. He was accepted by the younger males and the females as a recognized overlord. One morning the experimenter wished to examine the pupils of the eyes of one of his females to compare their size after an experiment made some time earlier. In order to have a good look at the eyes the experimenter had to entice the female to come quite close to the wire wall of the cage, and himself had to approach it closely. This was difficult with the timid female, who had the big "boss" at her side always ready to snatch away the morsel of food offered her. Several times the experimenter almost succeeded, but each time Peter almost got the food. Little by little, by occasionally threatening Peter with a dirty look, and in between intently peering at the pupils of the female slowly approaching, the experimenter thought he had almost achieved his object when suddenly he was given a severe blow on the head by the cunning Peter, who in no time had retreated to the opposite corner of the cage.

Translated into human psychology, Peter's act was a punishment of the experimenter for having fooled him repeatedly on that occasion. It is difficult to deny that the big male had "understanding" or "insight" into the situation, and deliberately intended to revenge himself for "unjust" treatment. It was clearly a demand for at least equal, if not preferential, treatment, commensurate with his superior rank, maintained through his greater strength and cunning. Unpleasant as this interpretation may be to civilized human feelings, Peter's action, in the light of phylogeny, appears as an early spark of an emerging "morality," upon which the social order of the primate world, including Man's, is based. It gives us a glimpse of the primitive primate mind from which the immensely increased and complicated human mind itself developed! (*Cf.* Epilogue.)

The following observations may further round out the portrayal of the Macaque's character. They are, above all, greedy, incorrigible egotists. Their greed, to be sure, exhibits all the gradations from the highest to the lowest. This greed is especially manifested in relation to food. The crassest greed is, naturally, exhibited by the hungry animals, for example, during the morning feeding if they were poorly fed during the preceding day or two and no food was left overnight. On this occasion one sees the Monkeys not only avidly gulping the morsels and stuffing their cheek pouches, but also holding as many pieces of food in each hand and foot as they possibly can. The limit of what appears to be legitimate greed, finally, is attained when a Macaque drops one or more pieces of food in order to rob another Monkey, even though that morsel may be smaller and of poorer quality.

But the greed of the Macaques has a transient quality. They have never been seen by this observer to hoard food or to accumulate a cache. The other extreme—the offering of food by one individual to another, not excepting parents and their children—has never been seen by this observer either. The greatest unselfishness they demonstrated, which by a long stretch of the imagination could be interpreted as an expression of altruism, was a benevolent abstention from interfering with other, usually weaker and meeker, members of the group, which happened only when there was an abundance of food and physiological hunger was completely satisfied.

Another feature of the Macaque's character, in particular of the weaker individuals, such as the females and the young, is a frantic effort to escape from some terrifying experience, at the expense of other members of the same group. In this situation, as soon as the keeper approaches, e.g., with the net the monkeys learned to know from previous experience (one such experience is quite enough!), they all move to the opposite corner of the cage. As the dreaded net

comes closer, all the monkeys crowd together, and each tries as hard as he can to squeeze into the mass of bodies, heads, and limbs, in order to hide behind this living shield.

This act and its purpose are exactly the same as the tactics employed by human criminals when they grab an innocent bystander and use him as a living shield. There is, however, a significant difference between the wicked humans and the frightened monkeys: the former intently watch both victim and adversary during the fracas, while the monkeys, in contrast, hide their faces as much as possible from their pursuer, and seem to be afraid even of his appearance, and try to avoid their fate by closing their eyes to it. The proverbial "ostrich diplomacy," much practiced by modern nations, may have had an early start in primate evolution.

Only occasionally do the monkeys throw furtive glances at the dreaded figure, just enough to determine his whereabouts and his intentions. In this situation, all the manifestations of fear that the primate organism is capable of are seen, evacuation of the bladder and rectum being prominent. On other occasions, when a little monkey finds himself in an entirely helpless situation, the reaction is a silent stupor accompanied by an intermittent clonic shiver, such as may be experienced by unfortunate humans in a condition of paralyzing fear.

Still another feature of the Macaque's character occasionally observed may be worthy of recording: a ganging-up on one or another of the group, constantly harassing him, until he is in an extremely nervous state. What the occasion eliciting this attitude is, it is not possible to determine except, perhaps, by prolonged observation. On the surface, the cause is, as in human life, unaccountable "dislike" or "incompatibility of character."

A positive feature of the Macaques' character is their gregarious instinct to stick together. Even after a squabble, sometimes resulting in the injury of one or several members of the group, they peacefully huddle together, friend and foe alike, nursing their wounds as best they can.

4. CHARACTER, HABITAT, AND BEHAVIOR OF THE DOG-FACED MONKEYS OR BABOONS.—The physical, mental, and social features so char-

FIG. 526.—Baboons of the species Guinea Baboon (*Cynocephalus sphinx*) observed on "Monkey Island" in the Zoölogical Park at Brookfield, Illinois, in conditions similar to those in which they normally live in their natural habitat. *1*, picking up candy with right hand; *2*, turning to left, facing a possible competitor; *3*, testing candy by smell before eating it; *4*, scratching right arm with index finger of left hand, guided by sight; *5*, walking on slightly flexed hind limbs, while balancing with forelimbs; *6*, rear view in an upright walking posture, beginning of the next step with the left foot, with additional support afforded by resting the left arm on a rock; *7*, leaning over to drink; *8*, young, fishing for peanuts; *9A*, sitting and using hands to open a sack of popcorn by holding one upper corner with the thumb of left hand opposed to other fingers and tearing off the top with the thumb of right hand opposed to other fingers; *9B*, similar manipulation, continuing to tear off the top; *9C*, left corner held by left hand, in a fashion typical of Higher Primates, with the extended fingers of right hand reaching for popcorn; *10A*, right hand, with thumb and third digit opposed, carrying half of the candy bar to the mouth, the other half held by the thumb opposed to other fingers of the left hand; *10B*, first act of unwrapping of candy bar—both hands holding opposite ends of bar, with thumbs opposed by other fingers; *10C*, second act—right index finger and left thumb sliding under the wrapper in order to remove it; *11*, adult walking on all four limbs, with fingers and toes, when resting on ground, extended flat or overextended when progressing (unlike the Apes, especially Orangutan); *12A*, thumbs of both hands opposed to index fingers holding a peanut, just before breaking its husk; *12B*, fingers of right hand holding a part of peanut, fingers of left hand extended to drop broken shell; *13A, B, C, D*, left hand fishing for peanuts, fingers and thumb first extended, then locating one peanut by touching it with extended fourth and fifth fingers, then moving it with the tip of index finger, and finally seizing peanut by the opposed index finger and thumb; *14*, position of left hand in walking: *A* and *B*, back and side views, tips of overextended fingers alone touching ground; *C*, further extension of fingers, with two terminal phalanges resting on ground; *D*, overextended terminal phalanges still resting flat on the ground in forward progression, with thumb clearly off the ground, with palm in no phase touching the ground; *15*, movements of the foot in walking: *A*, foot squarely placed on the ground, including ex

acteristic of the Macaques are further accentuated in the more powerful and fiercer Cynocephali, Cynopithecidae, or Dog-faced Monkeys (Figs. 526, 527). Of these, several species have been studied either in their native habitat or in captivity. The older but still quite useful observations have been collected by Alfred Brehm in his encyclopedic *Tierleben* or *The Life of the Animals*. Especially worthy are his presentations of the Gelada Baboon (*Theropithecus gelada*) and of the Hamadryas (*Papio hamadryas*), both natives of the middle parts of Africa and the latter also of a part of Arabia, and of the Chacma Baboon (*Papio porcarius*) of South Africa. Other observers, such as L. Heck and S. Zuckerman, have further enriched our knowledge of these and other related species. (*See* S. Zuckerman 1932 and 1933.) Other large allied species, Drill (*Papio* or *Mandrillus leucophaeus*), and Mandrill (*Papio mormon, Papio* or *Mandrillus sphinx*), live in low tropical forests of African Guinea.

The Baboons, even more than the Macaques, give the impression of being tough, determined animals, supplied with powerful dentition, including long canine teeth for defense, always ready to take care of themselves in any conceivable situation.

They inhabit the entire wide territory of Africa south of the Sahara Desert and, in Asia, a part of the Arabian Peninsula. The country they live in is mostly mountainous and rocky, Hamadryads preferring medium altitudes, from 3,000 to 6,000 feet, while Chacmas are found in a higher zone, from 9,000 to 12,000 feet. They shun dry desert, preferring regions with good plant growth. The vicinity of water is an absolute necessity for them, to which they cling tenaciously, and they know how to find it, if need be, by digging.

The diet of the Baboons is quite mixed. It consists of various roots, tubers, bulbs, herbs, leaves and buds, grasses and grain. Native fruits such as wild figs, tamarind, *Cissus* grapes,

and berries of the *Khetam* shrub are eagerly eaten. In many regions their favorite food is the "prickly pear" or fruit of the *Opuntia* cactus, which, incidentally, they have helped to spread over a wide territory. Their staple food is *Ixia*, a variety of iris, whose roots they dig from the soil with their hands.

Whenever opportunity offers itself, the Baboons are quick to plunder fruit orchards, vineyards, and fields of Indian corn and millet. They are said to be especially partial to Durra or Dhurah, a cultivated variety of *Sorghum vulgare*, a tropical cereal widely grown in Africa and southern Asia.

The Baboons also eagerly hunt for every kind of small life, such as insects, especially grasshoppers, centipedes and millipedes, scorpions, worms, snails, lizards, mice, shells, crabs, young of birds and their eggs. In order to find insects and other small animals, they turn over loose stones, several of the Baboons applying their concerted effort to the larger boulders. They are bold and tricky enough to take an earth bee's comb filled with honey, a delicacy to them, from its burrow.

Whenever they can, the Baboons satisfy their craving for protein-rich food by attacking game animals, also hunting larger animals like antelopes and the young of sheep and goats, and in this way occasionally becoming partly carnivorous. This report, based on native belief, was questioned by Zuckerman (1932). However, that there may be more than a kernel of truth in it was shown by Klüver's Baboons, which eagerly caught stray rats in his laboratory and devoured them.

Baboons congregate in troops whose size varies according to the species, being usually larger than the bands of Macaques. The average size may be from 150 or 250, to 300; but much larger congregations numbering several thousands are mentioned by some observers. Only one-tenth of the bands are fully grown males, whereas the fully grown females are

tended phalanges of toes, but with the heel slightly off; *B*, heel further raised, toes slightly flexed; *C*, entire sole lifted clear off the ground, with flexed toes alone supporting the weight; *D*, entire foot off the ground, except the tips of toes, the foot at right angles with the ground ("ballerina stance"); *16*, adult sitting with his head thrown back in a typical posture, allowing inspection of his fur by a companion using both hands, the left holding the hair aside, the right picking dandruff and "lice" with index finger and thumb, all minute objects closely scrutinized, and all delicate movements carefully guided by vision. (*Cf.* following figure.)

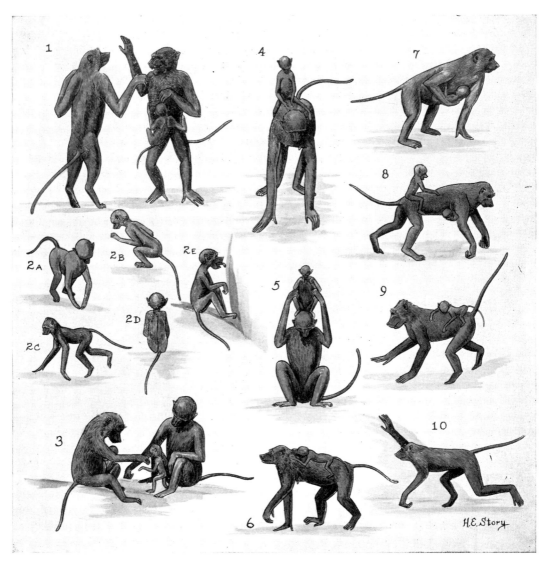

FIG. 527.—Guinea Baboons observed in their daily activity on "Monkey Island" of the Zoölogical Park at Brookfield, Illinois, in conditions resembling their natural habitat. *1*, two females apparently in an argument about a baby belonging to one, to whose abdomen it firmly clings, both females standing on their hind extremities in human fashion, probably either for greater emphasis or in preparation for a fight (note left female standing on tiptoes slightly flexed, affording a firmer grip on the ground, right female with feet flat and toes, including big toe, extended to increase supporting surface, the hind limbs of both females slightly flexed); *2*, young in *A* walking on all fours, half-profile; *B*, hind limbs flexed before jumping; *C*, walking on all fours in lateral view; *D*, rear view of a sitting posture, human fashion; *E*, licking surface of the rock while sitting in side view; *3*, two mothers with young babies, in a friendly chat, watching one of the babies attempting an upright walk; *4*, baby taking a ride on the back of its mother walking on all fours, front view; *5*, baby having fun sitting on the top of the head of its mother which holds it by its knees, front view; *6*, side view of a mother walking on all fours, with a baby napping on her back, firmly gripping her fur; *7*, mother limping on three limbs while holding a baby to her chest with the right hand, in side view; *8*, mother in side view walking on all fours with fingers of both hands flexed to form "knuckles," the newborn infant hanging to her chest, with the older youngster riding upright on her far back; *9*, side view of a mother walking on all fours, with an infant clinging almost crosswise to her lower back; *10*, side view of an adult walking on a ledge, holding to the rock with his right hand, with left fingers flexed. (*Cf.* preceding figure.)

about twice that number. Hence the number of individuals of reproductive age amounts to approximately one-third of the total, the remaining two-thirds being young and adolescents. Each troop is said to inhabit its own territory, approximately 1½–2 miles in diameter, even though they are much on the move about the country to find better feeding grounds.

Much of the time during the day hours the animals are on the move, particularly in the morning and afternoon, gathering food or going to or from the watering places or night shelters. When on a plundering expedition, they exercise the greatest caution. Most Baboons rarely climb trees, usually only when hard pressed. There are, however, exceptions, such as the Babuin (*Papio cynocephalus*) of Sudan and adjoining regions, which customarily spends nights in the trees high above the ground.

In rocky country, the true home of the Baboons, they scale the most difficult cliffs with unsurpassed skill, ease, and speed. For the night, each band selects a protected, favorably located shelter difficult of access by a marauder, usually in cracks and caves along the steep walls or under overhanging cliffs. Here they are protected from inclement weather and are relatively safe from the depredations of Hyenas and, in particular, Leopards, their principal enemies.

In posture and movement the Baboons betray their true quadrumanous terrestrial nature (Figs. 526, 527). Even when they rise on hind legs, they often support their body on one of their hands. Their gait, when slow, appears clumsy. When pursued, they fall into a shunting gallop unlike that of any other animal. It is said that they can easily be overtaken by a dog. But in the broken country where they live, with their climbing ability, formidable weapons, numbers, and habit of acting as a team, and their courage, they are more than a match for almost any of their natural enemies. Their great numbers in their home countries testify to their success and to their adaptability to various conditions of life, including resistance to the encroachment of human civilization.

The disposition and mental character of the Baboons form a kaleidoscopic picture. These qualities depend largely on age, sex, and species and to some extent on individuality, as

well as on the various accidents of life. Age is an essential factor. The youngsters are generally playful, amiable, and full of spirit. The females usually treat their babies with great love and concern during the first few weeks or months of life. Thereafter their affection gradually cools to a state of indifference or outright animosity. Toward the males whose sexual mates they are, the females practice a tricky submissiveness or trade their charms for the favors of their overlords in true courtesan fashion.

The fully grown males are powerful, well armed, hard-boiled, and tough, usually suspicious, ill disposed, and difficult to please. They are always ready to pick a quarrel with other grown males, usually on the basis of sex rivalry. The older they get, the more ugly their dispositions become. On small provocation, for a "cross look" for instance, they may take offense, their fury erupting with an elemental force. They have a long memory for wrongs done to them, real or imaginary, and do not forget to take revenge at an opportune time. Physically, too, they are tough animals, difficult to kill with buckshot. When hit, unless in the head or chest, they just rub the spot and run away as if nothing had happened.

The males, especially in confinement, are very jealous of one another, and fight for the females, sometimes to the point of the females' and their own destruction. Toward the females they are exacting, sadistic tyrants.

There is, however, another side to this offensive character of the Baboons. They are described as highly intelligent, quick-witted, resourceful, sure of themselves, never embarrassed to find a way out of a situation, no matter how difficult. They are pronounced "herd animals," sticking together, in their family and their band, and most unselfishly protecting them against enemies.

Their instinct of self-sacrifice becomes especially evident on the approach of a dangerous enemy, such as a Leopard or a party of hunters. In such a situation the entire troop becomes "mobilized" for common defense, expressed by the assumption of a defensive position, by a loud growling, barking, and howling, and by a general uproar and hubbub. In an actual attack against an enemy, the entire band works as a concerted team, the powerful males being in the forefront of the battle line and in the rear guard.

In their natural habitat the Baboons are described as being ordinarily tolerant of other animals and of native humans, for example, at the watering places where they often wait patiently until the others have satisfied their thirst. Toward humans, if not molested, they exhibit a high degree of indifference. On a few occasions, possibly when hunted, they are said to have attacked people, sometimes using stones for that purpose.

On one occasion an old Baboon, hit by a hunter's bullet, was helped by two young ones to get away, and even in that desperate situation he found opportunity to castigate his helpers for not having performed their samaritan job quite to his liking.

A remarkable episode, showing a high degree of cool determination and astuteness, is described by Brehm. In a hunting drive in Abyssinia in which two experienced greyhounds were also used, a troop of the Hamadryas Baboons crossed a ravine, leaving a young animal behind, which, in order to escape its pursuers, leaped upon a rock. "We were already congratulating ourselves," says Brehm, "that we would get hold of that one; yet it happened otherwise. There appeared from the other bank one of the largest males. Gravely and with great dignity, without the least hurry, and without paying attention to us, he fearlessly marched toward the dogs, throwing at them dagger-like glances, and in this way keeping them in perfect check; then he climbed the rock slowly, comforted the little one, and retreated with it close to the dogs, which were so nonplussed that they let him and his protégé quietly pass by." A somewhat similar episode was observed among the Chacma Baboons by Zuckerman.

On another occasion a troop of Baboons tried to prevent people from coming to a watering place, by throwing stones, pieces of wood, and mud at them. In order to shoo them away, a shot was fired, severely wounding a young Baboon. Quickly it was picked up by its mother and carried away. On the next slope the entire troop stopped and gathered around the luckless animal, which continued to wail. With anxious eyes it looked at its wound and tried to stop the blood with its hands. Its mother plucked leaves from the next shrub and tried to plug the wound. But the horrible wailing continued for another quarter of an hour until, after a last sigh, the stillness of death set in. Thereafter the entire band disappeared into a thorny thicket carrying away the body of the victim. Similar experiences, where Baboons carried away their dead and wounded, have been reported by other observers, according to Brehm. No such experiences or the use of stones as weapons have been reported during recent times. (*See also* Charles R. Darwin's *Descent of Man*.)

The intellectual abilities of the Baboons are rated quite high by those who have observed them in nature and their tricks in captivity, in the circus, or in experiments. The Babuin especially is reported as being intelligent and docile. However, most of the observers emphasize their unpredictable emotionalism, the sudden flaring-up of their anger, its quick rise to a climactic rage, and its long duration.

In their natural condition the Baboons have only a few serious enemies, such as the Lion, Hyena, and Leopard, of which the latter appears to be the principal. Snakes, Lizards, and Frogs are highly respected by them, as by the other Monkeys and Apes. Yet in spite of the terror these animals hold for them, their curiosity may get the upper hand of them and force them, for example, to open the boxes in which snakes are kept to have a good look at the dreaded things.

The interesting observation made by De Beaux, reported by Brehm, on the way the Gelada Baboons communicate among themselves by voice, may be of importance in understanding the origin of human speech. According to this:

The voice of the Gelada is extraordinarily flexible, and unusually mellow; even his loud call does not sound as harsh as the barking of a Hamadryas. And Martin talks directly of a speech. During the noon siesta, when the menagerie had few visitors, the family used apparently to entertain themselves by chatting, in the most lively way, when it sensed itself alone. The modulation and accentuation of the tones was so varied that one was forced to think oneself to be in the presence of creatures endowed with the power of speech: The sounds recalled somewhat the inarticulate voices made by people hampered in their speech by an organic defect.

In the following, as a comparison, are a few notes from my own observation on the vocal and bodily expressions of the Rhesus Macaques. These are of several kinds, each sound having a distinct semantic value, and each is promptly understood by all members of the community. The sound "Oh!" brief and sharp, given once or several times in succession, is an expression of astonishment or surprise, its meaning being exactly the same as that of the same sound pronounced in a like situation by Man, Baboons, and other Monkeys. Other sounds and actions have also specific meanings: the call for food and during lonely hours, sounding like a prolonged, somewhat high-pitched, plaintive *oooo!* pronounced as in the word *true;* a high-pitched squealing, when molested or threatened, for example, by a more powerful monkey; a quiet chattering accompanied by a quick succession of smacking of the lips and tongue, sometimes without smacking, with baring of the teeth, and grimacing, as an expression of friendliness or subservience or as an invitation to be nice; a turning of the back part of the body toward a monkey or a person, with or without a few short grunts, used as a friendly gesture or a sign of subservience; a quick motion of the head down and up, somewhat resembling a Chinese nod, with or without a short grunt and with or without an opening of the mouth, while intently fixing the eyes on a person or another monkey, meaning an interrogation complex, as if saying "What is the matter?" "What do you have up your sleeve?" Many other sounds and signs, variously combined and modulated, may be distinguished; altogether, this is a subject worthy of a thorough study. (*See* the vocal expressions of *Macacus cynomolgus* observed in the Malayan jungle by Ridley 1895; *see also* C. Darwin, *The Expressions of the Emotions in Man and Animals*, 1873; and K. Lorenz 1951.)

In conclusion, even though the above-mentioned simian expressions of thoughts and feelings are few and primitive, they may well have served as a nucleus from which human speech, the pride of mankind, originated.

5. COMPARISON OF HUMAN CHARACTER AND THAT OF THE LESSER PRIMATES.—Both the Macaques and the Baboons, in physical equipment, in sensory, mental, and emotional faculties, and in habits, may roughly illustrate the early Infrahuman Primates directly ancestral to the present human race or races, before they assumed a bipedal gait and erect posture and before their hands became entirely emancipated from the task of locomotion. In their basic characteristics they represent the germ from which Man developed. If the comparison is not in all respects flattering to Man's self-esteem, this is not the fault of the Monkeys or of Man, but is due to the common catarrhine inheritance.

In comparison, Man's superiority in intellect, emotions, and morals appears to be only in degree and not in kind. Universal human selfishness, ruthless cruelty in internecine struggles of the human races, creeds, nations, and classes, sexual promiscuity, and individual and collective greed are, in fact, only feebly emulated by Man's infrahuman relatives. (*Cf.* chap. XII on primate sociology in Hooton's book, *Man's Poor Relations*, 1942; and subsequent sections, this chapter.)

This adverse picture, on the other hand, is equally balanced, if not overcompensated, by the tremendous powers of human intellect, Man's ever searching, inventive genius for technical accomplishment, his merciful compassion for the sufferings of his own kind and even for those of his lesser brethren, by his artistic abilities, and by his superior ability to organize his life, which has, by and large, incomparably improved his own lot since the prehistoric dark ages and through historic times.

It may be of interest to mention here diseases similar to human diseases from which the lesser members of the Primate Order suffer. These are apparently many, including cancer, observed in several cases by Klüver, but they are naturally less well known than human pathology (*see* A. H. Schultz 1936; and H. J. Scherer 1944). It stands to reason that, under natural conditions, as an illness attains a degree which interferes with the essential activities, the animal is eliminated by death, usually through beasts of prey. This is also true of advancing age. Nature, cruel in its ways, does not tolerate a biological ballast, a factor which has become of increasing importance in advanced human society.

In artificial conditions such as in confinement, where a defective individual remains protected, conditions develop not unlike those found in Man. An illness may develop in an aged Macaque, resembling, for example, a primary optic atrophy, with a substantial impairment of vision, interfering with feeding and other normal activities, as observed by myself. (On a similar effect of old age in Mountain Sheep *cf.* A. Murie's book, *The Wolves of Mt. McKinley*, 1944.)

6. Behavior of the Monkeys under natural conditions.—The following story related to W. Horst by a native of Nepal, and published by F. W. Champion in his book *The Jungle in Sunlight and Shadow* (1934), describing a Leopard catching an Indian Bandar or Rhesus Macaque, illustrates vividly not only the extreme curiosity by which the Monkeys are dominated but also the cunning of their principal enemies, the Leopard and the Tiger.

The native's story, translated into English, was as follows:

"Yes, Sahib, panthers [i.e., Leopards] are very bold and very cunning. Have you ever seen one catch a monkey? No. Well, I will tell you what four or five men of my village and I saw in the patch of jungle you beat through yesterday. We had been ploughing since dawn and sat down to rest under the big mango tree. There were some brown monkeys feeding quietly in the trees near by, and suddenly one of them gave the usual sharp alarm call. We then heard the grunt of a charging panther, and saw a big one rush half-way up one of the smaller trees and then down again as the monkeys left it for the safety of the large *jamun*. He then charged over to the foot of the *jamun* and scratched up the grass and leaves round its roots. The excitement among the monkeys was now tremendous and they leapt about the branches in an agitated way, which was just what the panther expected and wanted. Had a monkey missed his hold or had a branch broken under one of them, the panther would have had his meal. But his luck was out and in a short time we saw him stretch himself out on the ground a few feet away from the tree and apparently go to sleep. The monkeys soon quieted down and we could see them looking down at the panther with the greatest interest. After a little while one of the bigger ones climbed right over him and began to drop leaves and twigs onto him; but still there was no sign of movement. The other monkeys then began collecting closer and closer above him, and it was obvious that they couldn't understand what had happened. One then climbed down a tree a

short distance away and took a few steps towards the panther, but his nerve failed him and he dashed back to safety. There was still no movement from the panther, however, and soon three or four monkeys were on the ground, taking good care to keep well out of reach of claws and teeth. This continued for nearly half-an-hour, the monkeys drawing nearer and nearer, until at last one, bolder than the rest, actually touched the panther with his hand. This was what the patient hunter had been waiting for; he struck immediately and, seizing the inquisitive monkey, he quietly carried his victim away to the patch of thick thorn out of which the pig broke yesterday. That, Sahib, shows the cunning and the patience of a panther when he is hungry, and how the inquisitiveness of monkeys can lead them to their destruction."

This story also illustrates well the extreme importance of the arboreal habit, the excellent sense of vision, and the high intelligence of the Rhesus Monkeys, even though in this particular instance the mental powers of the too inquisitive leader of the band were outwitted by those of the tricky feline. The related episode also shows the phylogenetical pressure that the big beasts of prey exert as the enforcers of the jungle's "law of tooth and claw," matched only by the Primates' combination of quadrumanous arboreal adjustment, keen vision, and superior intelligence. The use of leaves and twigs as "tools" by the Monkeys in testing the Leopard's reactions also agrees with a similar use of objects by the Baboons (*see* preceding section).

Other useful hints on jungle life may be quoted from the rich experience of Champion, in particular on the alertness and acuity of senses of various animals under natural conditions, especially of the Monkeys, and the way they react to the presence of the "law enforcers," the Tiger and the Leopard:

Some creatures will stand perfectly motionless when frightened, others will rush away without a sound, birds will frequently hurl themselves into the air with a scream, and many animals have special cries that denote anger or terror. The tiger and the leopard are the two animals above all others that cause alarm among other creatures of the wilds, and on sighting or scenting either of these great felines the many and varied inhabitants of the jungle will behave in a number of different ways. The elephant will probably stand perfectly motionless and watch, possibly occasionally striking the ground with his trunk; the sloth-bear, who is in the jungle but not of it, fearing nobody, will pay not the slightest attention; the wild-pig will bolt as fast as he can go; the deer will generally stand and stamp their fore-legs, frequently uttering their calls of alarm; the jackal will fill the jungle with his cries of "pheaou"; the peacock will fly rapidly away with raucous shrieks of fear; and the monkeys, comparatively safe in the branches of the trees, will hurl abuse at these great disturbers of the peace of the jungle.

It is the alarm cries made by the two common species of monkeys of India—the langoor and the common *bandar*—that are generally considered to be the most useful sign to the sportsman of the presence of a tiger or a leopard. In my previous book I expressed the opinion that the harsh guttural alarm cry of the black-faced langoor was the most valuable of all jungle signs. . . . I know that langoors are individuals and all do not behave in quite the same manner. In some places langoors are much more jumpy than others, and . . . may occasionally be caught napping. . . . langoors rely upon eyesight only for detecting enemies. . . .

The continued and agitated alarm cries of langoors in a jungle in most cases is the most valuable sign available that indicates the presence of a tiger or a leopard. Some langoors in some places will call, although not to the same extent, for other animals and very occasionally langoors will not call when a tiger or a leopard is close to them—because they haven't seen it, or just possibly, because they recognise that it is not in a hunting mood.

Brown monkeys [that is, Rhesus Macaques] are also very useful indicators in the same way, but, in the jungles with which I am acquainted, they are possibly not so alert or quick-sighted as langoors—or at least so it seems to me. I have several times heard them call for a dead leopard or a leopard-skin and for crocodiles, but I have not yet heard langoors do this.

Similar observation of the behavior of the Rhesus and Java Macaque and Langur Monkey is found in the book by J. Corbett (1953) and in the paper by H. N. Ridley (1895).

7. CHARACTER, HABITAT, AND BEHAVIOR OF THE MANDRILL, DRILL, CHIMPANZEE, AND GORILLA.—The natural conditions under which live the large Manlike Apes and the larger Cynocephalous Monkeys, which in many respects resemble them, and their behavior in free nature are but little known. The present scanty knowledge was mostly deduced from circumstantial evidence and is largely obtained from biologically untrained observers, such as hunt-

ers and natives. This is apparently due to the small effort made by experienced naturalists to investigate these animals in their natural habitat, despite the importance they represent for the phylogeny of Man. This is the more unfortunate since the great problem of Man's origin could obviously be better understood if the conditions in which these animals live were thoroughly known. The following description chiefly summarizes the report by R. Malbrant & A. Maclatchy (1949), based on prolonged personal observation in French Equatorial Africa, with additions taken from a few other sources.

The Mandrill (*Papio* or *Mandrillus sphinx*) seems to be mostly of a terrestrial habit and inhabits forests which have little developed underbrush. It rarely climbs small trees, either for food or to sleep. It congregates in bands numbering sometimes as many as 100 individuals. Its food consists of grain, insects, and fruits, including bunches of *Elaeis*, terminal twigs and seeds of the sunflowers, and the various mushrooms. During the rainy season it lives in brushwood, where it finds an abundance of fruit. Later it invades the natives' *manioc* cultures, to which it is very destructive. In character it is considered inoffensive.

The smaller Drill (*Papio* or *Mandrillus leucophaeus*), like his larger congener, lives in the forests and is also exclusively terrestrial. It climbs the low limbs of the trees, but only for the night. It congregates in large bands, vagabonding everywhere. There is nothing said about food, nor is any other information given.

The Chimpanzee (*Pan troglodytes*, of which two varieties are mentioned—*P. t. troglodytes*, and *P. t. paniscus*)—lives in thick secondary forests, never in the open savanna. It forms small groups or families, which occasionally may include as many as 60–80 individuals. In comparison with the more powerful, taciturn, and reserved Gorilla, it is boisterous and expansive in character. The bands are always on the move, covering large territories very rapidly. The loquacity of the Chimpanzee is expressed in frequent loud shouts and may be heard whether the band is on the move or at rest. Even during the night the Chimpanzees are sometimes active, as indicated by their "nightly concerts," which may be interpreted as a partial nocturnalism. In habit they may be considered partly arboreal and partly terrestrial. They spend their nights in the trees, where the females make large nests, whereas the large males sleep next to the tree trunks. When pursued, they escape to the ground.

The food of the Chimpanzee varies: fruits growing on the trees, red fruit of *mayombo*, palm nuts, peanuts, bananas, sugar cane from the plantations, and the like. The following plants are mentioned specifically: *Staudtia gabonensis*, *Poga oleosa*, *Pachypodanthium confine*, and *Irvingia gabonensis*. Chimpanzees, like all other Primates, have a "sweet tooth" and cleverly pillage hives of wild bees to get honey. They are also fond of large white grubs found in the stems of certain trees.

The Lowland Gorilla (*Gorilla gorilla*), by far the largest of the Manlike Apes, is a denizen of dense, primeval jungle. Along the middle Congo River and the Gaboon River it is found only occasionally in the so-called "gallery forests" and in the open savanna. In the Oka region and near to Aboundji it is, however, found in wooded patches dotting the sandy savanna. Even though it has an affinity for the thick forest, it apparently is easily adapted to the thick, brushy growth along the margins of human cultivations. As a rare exception, perhaps, single individuals may penetrate through the gallery forests into plain savanna.

The Gorilla's retiring character makes him a subject difficult to observe in nature. As soon as he notices danger, he becomes silent.

The band is a family consisting of a male, a female, and the young. In some localities bands made up of 15, 20, and 25 are assembled around a single old and a young male, with several females and their young. It is not certain whether the Gorilla is monogamous or polygamous, although the latter seems to be probable. (In one instance Akeley observed three, possibly four adult males, and perhaps a dozen females and youngsters; in another band there was but one male and several females; *see also* Reichenow 1921; Bingham 1932.)

The Gorillas do not move about as much as do the Chimpanzees. But, like the latter, they appear to incline to a partially nocturnal habit, making mysterious nightly visits to plantations in search of food. Some of them, more courageous, dare in plain daylight to invade gardens of the native villages, where they pillage bananas, and are bold enough even to attack the natives.

The families spend the night in low trees, the female with the young ones on the limbs, the husky male at the base of the tree trunk. According to Bingham, the nesting habit varies according to circumstances, the nests being built either all on the ground, part on the ground, or part in the trees, some as high as 40, 50, and 60 feet; Reichenow (1921) found Gorillas' nests in some regions always on the ground or close to it; in other regions, where there are many Leopards, the nests are partly in the trees, like those of Chimpanzees.

The Gorilla habitually walks on all four extremities, the hands resting on the ground upon "knuckles." Sometimes only the impression of the thumb, index, and middle finger is found in the track, indicating the major part of the body weight is carried by the hind extremities, while the arms and hands are used merely as an auxiliary support. (This harmonizes with C. Akeley's observation of an imprint in mud of a Gorilla's foot with a heel, "which no other living thing in the world but the gorilla and man has.")

In its movements the Gorilla is clumsy, and it does not get aroused except when on the ground. The male becomes especially aggressive when the female is to give birth to young, attacking everyone approaching his domain. (*See* description of an unprovoked attack by C. Akeley 1923, and by H. C. Bingham 1932.)

Because of his weight, the Gorilla shuns acrobatics such as are practiced by the lighter Chimpanzee. When climbing, it exercises caution and climbs only trees of small diameter. Large, bulky males dislike climbing and dare to ascend only lower limbs. Even so, accidents occur, such as one where a Gorilla fell from a tree and broke his spine. Hence a Gorilla ventures into higher branches only when hard pressed.

In choosing his food the Gorilla is an eclectic. He eats terminal shoots of young *parasoliers*, a variety of forest fruits, especially *atanga* and wild *mango*, wild sorrel, banana, the red fruit of *mayombo*, sweet *manioc* or *cassava*, peanuts, palm nuts, a kind of *kola* nut, and the like. The mentioned plants are apparently representative of only the investigated regions, while the products of many more regions remain unexplored (*cf.* sec. 5, this chapter).

Both Chimpanzee and Gorilla, according to Reichenow, are exclusively vegetarians, subsisting mostly on leaves, buds, and the soft pith of stems, while fruits are merely an accessory food. Much preferred by them is *Musanga smithi*, whose large leaf, buds, and sweet fruit are especially attractive to them.

8. Observations of the habitat and habits of the Mountain Gorilla.—The natural conditions in which the Mountain Gorilla (*Gorilla beringei*) lives and how he is adapted to them are equally little known. Nobody qualified by scientific training and experience in the field, except Bingham (1932), has studied them. This is the more deplorable, since in the opinion of C. E. Akeley and R. M. Yerkes this Ape appears to be on the verge of extinction (Yerkes 1951). This gap may be filled in only inadequately by the following information from C. Akeley's and M. J. Akeley's books (*see* for the original report on the Gorilla, and for the first description, by T. S. Savage 1847, and by P. Du Chaillu 1855, respectively, C. E. Akeley's book 1923, pp. 191, 193, 237; *see also* A. Brehm's *Tierleben;* for the illustrations of brain, hands, and feet *see* F. Tilney, *The Brain from Apes to Man*, 1928; and Figs. 286, 536–40 in this book).

Carl E. Akeley, the originator of modern scientific taxidermy, imbued with true scientific zeal, made the first and almost the only attempt to study the Mountain Gorilla and to photograph him in his native habitat on the high slopes of the mountains Mikeno and Karisimbi, around Lake Kivu in the Belgian Congo.

The Gorilla, according to Akeley, appears to be a silent creature. Only when aroused does he emit a terrific roar, and the powerful male may rush against the invader of his sanctuary in defense of his band.

The Gorilla does not travel either far or fast, and an average man probably could outrun him. The country he lives in is mountainous, intersected by deep chasms with steep slopes. The vegetation consists of a thick growth of trees and bushes.

In Akeley's opinion "the gorilla is not a ferocious beast, although I was gaining the utmost respect for his size and power." And again:

"When I came up with the old male that I had killed first, he had run back and forth on the hillside barking in protest or surprise at my intrusion just as I have seen little monkeys run back and forth on a limb and bark; but of his having savage intentions against me I saw no sign. Of the two I was the savage and the aggressor. In the case of the female I had just shot, the same was true, even though she was accompanied by her baby. She evidently preferred to get away if possible. Cornered, I think and hope she would fight for her young." This young Gorilla, about four years old, Akeley met: "a half hour later when we were trying to find a way down we came across him and, as he ran about, one of the guides speared him. I came up before he was dead. There was a heartbreaking expression of piteous pleading on his face. He would have come to my arms for comfort."

Another interesting scene, which Akeley caught with his movie camera, practically the first and only one taken in the natural habitat, he described as follows:

Ten minutes later the guides ducked, and crouching, came back and fell in behind me. I took the gun from the bearer, and looking over the tops of the greenery of a little rise in front of us I saw a spot of black fur perhaps fifty yards ahead. As I crouched, waiting for a better view, the animal I was watching climbed up on a nearly horizontal branch of a tree looking back in my direction. In the meantime, the motion-picture camera had been brought to my side. I raised it carefully, put it in position, and all this time another larger gorilla was making the ascent of the horizontal branch of the tree. It was apparently an old mother and her two-year-old baby. Almost before I knew it I was turning the crank of the camera on two gorillas in full view with a beautiful setting behind them. I do not think at the time that I appreciated the fact that I was doing a thing that had never been done before. As I ground away, a second baby came scrambling up a near-by tree. The baby seemed very much interested in the operation. The mother professed indifference and a certain amount of boredom and after a bit pretended to lie down on one arm and go to sleep. The babies, one of them at least, seemed to be amused. He would stand up, fold his arms and slap them against his breast, which suggested uproarious laughter on his part. . . .

There were probably ten or twelve in the band; but never again [after the band bolted away when Akeley, in order to change the scene and make a close-up view, showed himself in full view] did I get the opportunity to photograph them—just little glimpses of black fur dodging about through the greenery. At one time with my glasses I watched them across a ravine for a considerable time. The old female was lying down on her back yawning and stretching, but she was too far away for a photograph. So finally, feeling that I had about all I could expect from that band, I picked out one that I thought to be an immature male. I shot and killed it and found, much to my regret, that it was a female. As it turned out, however, she was such a splendid large specimen that the feeling of regret was considerably lessened. This female had a baby which was hustled off by the rest of the band. The baby was crying piteously as it went.

This was the first film taken with a movie camera perfected by Akeley, and first of any photographs, still or moving, taken of the Gorilla in his native habitat.

Up to a certain time Akeley had not seen more than one male Gorilla in a band. Later, however, he changed his opinion, as the following experience shows:

We were near the edge of a ravine the opposite slope of which was cleared of bamboo and bush. I suggested to him [Akeley's gun-bearer] that if we could possibly see them in a place like that, it would enable us to do the things that we wanted to do. Not that I actually hoped for any such luck; but as a matter of fact, fifteen minutes later we heard the bark of a gorilla. Peeping through the bush we saw the entire band on that opposite slope, all of them in full view. There were at least three old males, I think four, and perhaps a dozen females and youngsters. They, of course, had seen us. They were making off toward the crest of the opposite slope as fast as possible. [A similar scene was described by Bingham 1932.]

My first thought was along these lines: "Here is a perfectly peaceful family group including three or four males. I could use my two males [previously collected for the museum] without apologies. There is really no necessity for killing another animal." So the guns were put behind and the camera pushed forward and we had the extreme satisfaction of seeing that band of gorillas disappear over the crest of the opposite ridge none the worse for having met with white men that morning. It was a wonderful finish to a wonderful gorilla hunt.

Such was Akeley's work and its scientific motivation, which finally resulted in the creation of the "Gorilla sanctuaries" around Lake Kivu and elsewhere.

Even though the Gorilla is partial to deep woods, he is not arboreal. Akeley believed that the Gorilla "has nearly passed out of the arboreal phase of life and is perhaps entering the upright phase and that he is the only animal except man that has achieved this distinction." To stand erect and balance, an animal needs heels. The plaster cast of the Gorilla's foot shows that the gorilla has "developed a heel." (My own observation in zoölogical parks shows, however, that the Chimpanzee also has a "heel," and uses it and steps on the sole in a way similar to, but slightly differing from, that of the Gorilla and Man; *see* sec. 5, this chapter.)

The gorillas I saw in Africa always touched both their feet and hands to the ground in running but most of the weight was on their feet. Their legs are short, their arms long, and they carry the body at an angle of 45 degrees forward. They do not, however, put their hands down flat and rest their full weight on them. They seem to be evolving toward a two-legged animal. And if they spent most of their time in trees they would not have developed heels and leg muscles for walking upright on the ground.

Not only has the gorilla developed a heel, but his big toe is much nearer like man's than that of any other animal. This may seem a small matter, but a big toe that turns out from the foot as a thumb . . . is useful in climbing. A big toe that is parallel with the other toes is useful for walking but not for climbing.

But the gorilla has not lost all his arboreal characteristics by any means. The length, size, and strength of his arms are evidence of the tree-climbing habits of his ancestors. I know that a gorilla can now climb with more ease than the average man. But I only once saw gorillas in trees and that was when I was taking the moving picture of a mother and two youngsters, and an active man could have walked up the inclined trees these gorillas were on about as easily as they did. Nor did I see any evidence of their having been in trees.

In this observation Akeley concurs with E. Reichenow that "the gorilla is much more a stranger to tree living than the chimpanzee."

The hand of the gorilla is as interesting to me as his foot. If you look at the illustration of the plaster cast you will see that it looks much like a man's, finger-nails and all. You will see that the fingers are bent over. When running he puts his knuckles on the ground. It is a peculiarity of the gorilla that when his arms are extended his fingers are always bent over. He can't straighten them out except when his wrist is bent. [*Cf.* Fig. 536, sketch *4;* Fig. 538, sketch *2; cf. also* Fig. 540, *1, 2.*]

This peculiar feature Akeley believed to be a legacy of the Gorilla's arboreal habit, "which has not left him even in all the years he has been developing heels, muscles, and toes which are good for ground work only." Hence Akeley was certain that the Central African Gorillas have practically abandoned the arboreal habit.

That the Gorilla makes a hammock-like nest in the trees to sleep in Akeley denies. In this Akeley agrees with Reichenow, who found them also mostly, if not always, on the ground. Bingham's observation, however, provides evidence for such tree nests.

I cannot help believing that this report arises from a confusion with the chimpanzee habits [continues Akeley]. The chimpanzee is not strong enough to fight a leopard. Consequently, he has to sleep out of reach of this foe. The gorilla, on the other hand, has no foe but man. No flesh-eating animal in his territory is large enough to harm him. The gorilla is a vegetarian, so he kills no animals for food. . . .

Altogether, then, as the gorilla has no enemies, he has no need to fashion himself a bed out of harm's way. All the gorilla beds I saw were on the ground. They consisted of a pile of leaves, about what the long arms of a gorilla could pull together without moving. I saw no signs of their occupying these hastily constructed sleeping places more than once.

As to whether the Gorilla is monogamous or polygamous, Akeley honestly confessed his limitations: "The truth is that people know little about the habits of the gorilla." In spite of much work, little is known about the Gorilla's bodily organization.

And even less of study has been given the gorilla's living habits than has been devoted to his dead body and bones. Most of the information which man can get of and from this nearest relative in the animal kingdom is still to be had . . .

As I travelled down from Mikeno toward the White Friars' Mission the fascinating possibilities of the study of the gorilla and its immense scientific importance filled my mind along with the fear that his extinction would come before adequate study was made. These considerations materially led my mind to the idea of a gorilla sanctuary; and I realized that a better place than the one I had just left could hardly be hoped for.

Meanwhile, Akeley's dream materialized when the Belgians, beginning in 1925, established a system of wildlife refuges in Central Africa for the preservation and study of the Gorilla.

Since the publication of C. Akeley's book, knowledge of the Gorilla's habits and habitat has increased somewhat through the efforts of Yerkes (1927–29), Bingham (1932), and Gregory & Raven (1937). The most useful observations of the food habits, manipulation, and locomotion, nest-building, and social behavior are by Bingham (1932) and by Malbrant & Maclatchy (1949; *see* preceding subsection). The attempts by Mrs. M. L. Jobe Akeley (1950), partly summarized in the following, were unfortunately largely frustrated because of insurmountable difficulties.

The Gorilla country along Lake Kivu, in the experience of Mrs. Jobe Akeley, is not free of Lions, as Carl Akeley believed, since these have been seen on one occasion on the slopes of Mount Karisimbi at an altitude of 12,000 feet and higher. The powerful arms and long canine teeth of the Gorilla seem, therefore, quite indispensable for the survival of this Ape.

But the omnipresent menace, especially to the babies and young Gorillas, are the numerous Leopards infesting the jungle, the more so as they are the largest and most formidable of all African Leopards. Other Carnivores, such as the Hunting or Wild Dog, Jackal, Civet Cat, Genet, Mongoose, and Ratel or Honey Badger could normally represent hardly any danger for the powerful Ape.

The Mountain Gorilla inhabits mostly the dense forests of the slopes of the extinct volcanoes of the Albert National Park and a few scattered sanctuaries outside the park in the Tshabirimu and Tshabinda Mountains, at Walikale, Baraka, and other places where he is protected.

His range is from 8,500 feet altitude and up, as far as his favorite food is obtainable (12,000 feet and more). In this mountainous climate he is well protected from the heavy rainfall and icy winds by his thick coat of hair.

When excited, the Gorilla assumes a human-like bipedal attitude; his normal mode of locomotion, however, is quadrumanous, with feet placed flat on the ground and hands supported by the knuckles. The span of the outstretched arms may be more than 8 feet, the length of the arms contrasting with the short legs. In the quadrupedal posture the head and shoulders necessarily are higher, the back sloping down toward the pelvic region.

The footprints of the Gorilla resemble those of the natives to a surprising extent. The distinguishing mark is the imprint of the abducted big toe, this feature not differing greatly in every case, since many native toes are very short, partially webbed, and somewhat prehensile.

The procurement of food by the Gorilla is not a great problem, since there is plenty of it in his native habitat. He is almost exclusively a vegetarian and a heavy eater. His ordinary fare in the lower altitudes is succulent shoots of young bamboo, and in the higher regions sorrel, blackberries and wild celery, including its large, knobby roots. The occasional additions to the herbaceous diet are large white larvae, which he, as does the Chimpanzee, gets by breaking up decaying logs.

The only serious enemy of the Gorilla seems to be the Leopard, by which not a few young ones apparently are destroyed. The evidence is the small number of immature animals in the Gorilla family and their remains found in the Leopard's excrements. The protection against the wily cat is parental care, the mother holding the baby in her arms during the night and carrying it on her back during the daytime when feeding on the ground. The adolescent Gorillas make their beds high up in the trees, where some of them may yet perish, since the Leopard is an excellent climber.

The beds of the young are close to those of the grownups, who spend their night on the ground, next to some protecting tree trunk and under a canopy of vines. But the most potent defense is the grown-up male:

With one grip of his powerful hands, the gorilla can break the leopard's back or twist his head from the torso. It is only when the young gorillas stray beyond their parents' watchful eyes or fail to make their beds far enough above the ground that the silent sneaking leopard can seize and destroy them. Otherwise there is peace in the great woodlands. Elephant, buffalo and gorilla—all herbivorous animals—have plenty of food to spare, hence there is no conflict between them, no struggle for survival.

Of special interest was the "bedroom" of a band of twenty-two Gorillas, in which two pairs of "beds" consisted of a big bed and a little one beside it, on each side of a large *Hagenia* tree. The beds were used each night for about a week, during which time the band was feasting in a large celery field. The two pairs of nests apparently were used by two females and their babies, indicating their friendly relationships. Most of the beds were clean, although some were used more than once, in which case they usually had a fresh "sheet" of vines over the old, soiled "bedding." The Gorillas seem to have no external parasites.

The Gorillas, except when in danger, are very silent in their behavior. During many nights of observation of their camping grounds not a sound was heard from them by Mrs. Akeley. During feeding time, if they were unaware of the presence of Man, Derscheid heard mothers cooing to their little ones in a succession of highly pitched and pleasant, sweet, and melodious tones, "not unlike some silvery though monotonous bird song."

The Gorilla seems to be rather peacefully inclined, except when attacked, or in any way interfered with.

But harmless as a gorilla may be when undisturbed, yet few men, unless armed or else expert in tree climbing, would care to meet a gorilla unexpectedly and face to face in the midst of the dark jungle. . . . When a gorilla's family is threatened he will charge with a terrific speed. A lion or a leopard with its "nine lives," as has been said, would have only small likelihood to survive the attack of an infuriated gorilla. Never might he achieve victory. A man would have no chance at all. [*Cf.* Bingham 1932 on the suddenness of the Gorilla's attack.]

The Gorilla is the most elusive of wild creatures living in the deepest jungle. In the "Gorilla sanctuary," after the period of indiscriminate pursuit, it is now fairly safe from destruction. But it seems that this most manlike Ape is now so well protected as to become a sealed enigma even to science. It seems unwise, therefore, to put such a complete prohibition upon any legitimate scientific study of the Gorilla. Time seems to be running low, and the present favorable opportunity may not last forever.

SEC. 5. OBSERVATION OF THE MONKEYS AND APES IN CAPTIVITY

1. Introduction.—The best way to learn about the habits of Infrahuman Primates is to observe them in their native habitat (*cf.* preceding section). The next best way is observation in large, well-organized zoölogical parks, where the animals are kept under conditions approximating those in nature. Here the Monkeys and Apes are little hampered in satisfying their natural instincts and in exercising their native talents. It is here, then, that one may get an answer to many a question concerning the behavior of the individuals, groups, or sexes toward each other, to learn about their postures and movements, the use of their hands and fingers in various manipulations, the employment of their limbs in progression and in climbing, the reaction and acuity of their senses, the varied expressions of their physiognomy and its meaning, their vocal utterances and their significance, the associations they form with their kind and possibly with other animals and humans, and other numerous acts so abundantly developed in this highest category of Mammals.

These observations and impressions may go a long way to help form an opinion about the probable course of human evolution. Especially they may show the role that vision played in the rise of the Primate Order from its ancestral origins and the way the coming of Man was probably prepared for and accomplished.

In the following are a few observations which I made during the past few years at Brookfield Zoo and at Lincoln Park Zoo in Chicago, partly undertaken under the stimulus of the ideas expounded by W. L. Straus, Jr., on the origin of Man.

2. Macaques and Baboons.—In the Indian Rhesus Macaque (*Macaca mulatta*), in the African Chacma Baboon (*Papio porcarius*), Hamadryas Baboon (*Papio hamadryas*), Guinea Baboon (*Cynocephalus sphinx; see* Figs. 526, 527), Drill (*Papio* or *Mandrillus leucophaeus*), and Mandrill (*Papio* or *Mandrillus sphinx*) the four extremities do not differ greatly, the legs being only a little longer and the toes being relatively short. The fingers (Fig. 540, sketches *16* and *19*) are somewhat stubby, their length

not so disproportionate in comparison with the thumb as in the Anthropomorphous Apes, especially in the Orangutan (sketch *9*) and in the Gibbon (sketch *11*). The opposition of the thumb to the fingers is therefore relatively more effective than in the Apes, where the thumb is much shorter and weaker than the fingers (sketches *1, 3, 6, 7, 9* in same figure). In the proportion of their fingers and thumb the Baboons resemble the Macaques and Man. Hence in all of them the hands form more efficient grasping instruments, better fit for delicate manipulations such as picking seeds, small fruits, and insects, and "grooming." The picking of small objects, made exclusively under the guidance of vision, is excellent and is frequently practiced (Fig. 526, sketches *1, 4, 9A, 9B, 9C, 10A, 10B, 10C, 12A, 12B, 13A–D, 16*; *cf.* Figs. 531, 532, 534, 539).

The feet of the Macaques and of many other Monkeys, especially of the various Baboons, Drill, and Mandrill are long and narrow (Fig. 540, sketches *15, 17, 18*). In this respect they approach human conditions more than those of the large Apes (*2, 4, 5*), even though they still are essentially prehensile, with abducted big toes. The feet of the Hamadryas or Chacma Baboons, for example, are narrow and long, with flat soles, the entire surface of which is placed on the ground. The toes are provided with nails somewhat resembling claws, useful for digging.

The fingers and toes, including the thumb and the big toe, can easily be stretched out, or dorsoflexed, as in Man, or better (Fig. 526, especially sketches *14* and *15;* Fig. 540, sketches *15, 18*). In the Drill the fingers can be easily dorsoflexed or overstretched, to make an angle of 90° relative to the plane of the palm. The fingers and hands in the macaque-like and Dog-faced Monkeys are delicate and flexible, easily used for all kinds of fine manipulations.

In walking, the Macaques, Baboons, Drill, and Mandrill habitually use all four extremities. They place their feet with the entire sole, or almost so, flat on the ground, in the way Man does (Fig. 526, sketches *4, 6, 7, 9A, 10A;* Fig. 527, sketches *5, 7*). In progression the heel end of the foot is lifted first, while the distal end, together with the toes, remains last on the ground, exactly as in the human walk (Fig. 526, sketches *11, 15A–D;* Fig. 527, sketches *2C, 6, 8, 10*). In this movement the toes are over-extended, or dorsoflexed, forming not only a support for the body weight but also a pro-pelling fulcrum for forward progression. In the quadrupedal, or rather quadrumanous, walk mostly practiced, the palms of the hands, to-gether with the outstretched fingers, are placed flat on the ground, the fingers remaining last on the ground in the forward movement. Both the fingers and the toes are nicely lifted off the ground in preparation for the next step. (*Cf. also* F. W. Jones 1942, chap. XXV; and W. L. Straus, Jr.)

Frequently, especially in the Baboons, only the fingers touch the ground, with the palm off (Fig. 526, sketch *11*). Sometimes only their ex-tremities, approximately the two terminal pha-langes, are put down lightly, sharing the sup-port of the body weight but little. In this way the principal portion of the body weight in the Baboons and Macaques, in progression, rests on the hind extremities, in contrast to the thor-oughly arboreal Orangutan, for example, in which much of the body weight in quadrupedal progression rests on the arms (Fig. 532, *6, 7;* Fig. 535, *10*). The condition present in the Gorilla may, perhaps, be considered intermedi-ary (Fig. 536, *2, 4;* Fig. 538, *2*).

When not walking, both the Macaques and the Baboons sit on their buttocks, where they have developed callosities. The body is main-tained and secured in an upright position by the legs and feet sprawling on the ground. In this way the arms and hands are temporarily freed from locomotion and are employed for manipu-lations, such as examination of objects under visual control. The locomotion, then, is com-posed usually of short quadrumanous walks or leaps from one to the next sitting posture. No stretching of the imagination is required to vis-ualize this habit further increased by the human ancestors by lengthening the walking periods until true bipedalism developed.

The Macaques, Baboons, Drill, Mandrill, and similar Monkeys are alert, quick-witted, vigorous, and intelligent animals, which show all essential human traits in appearance and be-havior. Even in such grotesque and gaudily col-ored species as the Drill and Mandrill, this simi-larity is no less apparent. The behavior and mannerisms of the Monkeys impress one even more with their "human"—or shall we say their fundamental "primate"?—quality. Not only do the Drill's fingers resemble human fingers, but the manner in which he casually wipes his mouth with the back of his right hand is identi-cal with that of an unsophisticated country lad. And the way he deftly catches a fly is a vir-tuosity itself, which could be duplicated by a human artist only after long training. It gives evidence not only of acute sight and alert atten-tion but also of exceedingly quick co-ordination of binocular movements of the eyes with the muscles of the neck, shoulder, arm, hand, and fingers. (*See* similar action observed in the Tree Shrew, chap. XIV, 10 [7].)

Finally, in their emotions, their excitability, and their tender love, the Monkeys have been recognized since time immemorial as the reflec-tion, sometimes advantageous, of Man. The sight of the family of Bonnet Monkeys, with a very young baby lovingly huddled to his mother while she "grooms" an adolescent, with the father contentedly watching them, or that of a Hamadryas mother holding her baby in her arms and observing it with eyes full of love, could hardly be better duplicated in human life.

3. GIBBONS.—The smallest of the so-called Apes, the Gibbon Lar (*Hylobates lar*), has a thumb only half the length of his fingers (Figs. 528–31, and Fig. 540, sketches *11, 13*). In spite of its shortness in comparison with the extraor-dinarily long fingers, the thumb is well used in opposition with the index finger when picking small morsels of food. However, the impression is that the long fingers are more fit to grasp the limbs in brachiation than to be employed for continuous, delicate manipulations as they are by the Macaques, Baboons, and Man. (*See* C. R. Carpenter in *Psychol. Monog.,* No. 84, 1940, for an excellent presentation of the Gib-bon's behavior in nature.)

The Gibbons, both Lar and Siamang (*Sym-phalangus syndactylus*), probably practice a bipedal gait more often than any other Ape or Monkey (Fig. 528, *5;* Fig. 530, *2, 4*). When walking, they do so exclusively on their legs and feet, resembling Man in this respect. Never during our observations have we seen a Gibbon resorting to the quadrupedal gait intermittently or preponderantly practiced by all other Infrahuman Primates, the Monkeys and the Apes. This is true in spite of the arboreal adaptation of feet which makes it impossible to place the toes flat on the ground, but always slightly bent (the toes with the well-opposable big toe are made good use of for grasping).

Nor does the Gibbon use his arms and hands to support himself when walking, as, for example, the Gorilla, Chimpanzee, and Orangutan do when attempting a bipedal gait. The only use the Gibbon makes of his arms and hands is

Fig. 528.—Gibbons of the species Lar (*Hylobates lar*), dark and white phases, observed in Lincoln Park Zoo, Chicago. *1*, walking erect, with slightly flexed lower limbs or legs, toes of right foot slightly flexed, toes of left foot extended and resting flat on the ground, arms semiflexed and used for balancing; *2*, two friends separated by a partition, listening to each other and watching through the cracks, feet resting flat; *3*, portrait of a Gibbon, with protruding and compressed lips uttering call "woot-wootoooo . . ."; *4*, Gibbon hanging from a horizontal bar, left leg slightly flexed, with left foot in midair, right foot grasping a vertical bar of the cage; *5*, side view of the Gibbon walking in bipedal fashion, right sole and toes resting flat on the ground; of the left foot, the toes alone resting on the ground, with the sole lifted up as in human progression, and the arms and hands balancing; *6*, sitting posture of a light color phase, human fashion.

to maintain his balance by freely moving them in control of his upright posture (Fig. 528, sketches *1, 5*).

When a Gibbon stands upright or walks, he holds his heels turned in and his toes out, the two diverging feet inclosing an angle of roughly 90° (Fig. 528, *1*). This is advantageous in walking along the more or less horizontally placed limbs of the trees. It places the soles at about 45° to the long axis of the limb, thus minimizing possible misses, while still permitting the use of much of the sole and the toes for support. This mode of bipedal progression, however, appears less advantageous for walking on flat ground.

In standing or walking upright, the Gibbon holds his legs slightly bent at the knee joints, exactly as do the Gorilla and Chimpanzee, and never straightened, as Man does. This gives the body an elastic support easily adjusted to the crooked surface of the limbs. This sort of bipedal gait appears advantageous for life in the trees but would not be the most efficient for walking on level ground in human fashion.

It appears that in the Gibbon's bipedal progression the springiness of the legs is more effective as a shock absorber, while in human gait a portion of the task is assigned to the specific human curvature of the spine. In a species with an arboreal habit, with its frequent leaps, the first is more of an advantage, while the opposite is true in Man, with his strictly upright posture, walking on stable, mostly level ground.

The Gibbon's walk consists ordinarily of short tripping runs between climbing and other acrobatics. The steps are made in human fashion, as they are made by a fast-running child, interspersed with light, springy hops. All movements of the Gibbon indicate great muscular power, elasticity of locomotor apparatus, and extraordinarily delicately measured central neuromotor control.

The Gibbons are accomplished acrobats in brachiation or progression by the use of long, powerful arms. This is accomplished by swinging on the arms, giving the body a calculated impetus, which throws it in the desired direction, usually another branch of the tree or a swing on a rope, which is reached with unfailing accuracy. The apparently effortless ease with which the body is propelled through the air is truly astonishing. The strength of the muscles may be judged by the frequent habit of the Gibbon of hanging suspended by the fingertips of one or of both hands. (On the acrobatic performance of the South American Spider Monkeys observed in nature *see* W. R. Philipson 1952, p. 35.)

The sitting posture of the Gibbon duplicates the human, the small area around the anus, devoid of hair, supporting the body weight.

A remarkable accomplishment of Gibbons such as the Lar is vocalization. It has no equal among the Primates except Man and possibly one of the Tamarin Marmosets (*Leontocebus oedipus*), according to Brehm, and none among all other Mammals; even though the roar of a Lion and the voice of a Howler Monkey are more powerful. (On Singing Mice *see* C. R. Darwin's *The Descent of Man*, chap. XIX, "Voice and Musical Powers.") But unlike the sounds produced by other Mammals, the Gibbon's vocalization more truly deserves to be called "singing." It is performed equally well by both sexes. When fully presented, it is an extraordinary performance. The sounds are entirely made up of clear, resonant tones of the quality of the sound of long *ooo* (as in the word *soon*). The tones are powerful, varied, and richly modulated, and the entire display on occasion is prolonged and quite elaborately constructed. The singing ascends up and down the scale and may terminate in a high-pitched crescendo. It may continue in briefly uttered vowels of low and medium pitch, interspersed with short staccatos of all kinds, extending into long-drawn-out powerful legatos of various pitch.

The "singing" of the Gibbons is a remarkable vocal display, contrasting with the shrill screaming, howling, and grunting utterances of most other Mammals, including other Primates, except human singing. Such vocal display may either be given as a long solo or alternate with a duet or a concert in which several individuals participate. In the native jungle many adult individuals of one or of several neighboring groups may contribute to such a primeval "concert" or "opera." (*See* Benchley 1942 for the description of a similar vocal display of the Siamang; C. R. Carpenter describes "vocal battles" staged by the free-ranging Gibbon Lar in Siam or Thailand.)

What the biological purpose of the Gibbon's musical display may be is difficult to fathom.

The impression gained from observation in captivity is the same as from other high-quality musical displays, e.g., the Nightingale, Brown Thrasher, and Mocking Bird: enjoyment of the senses, the exuberance of life, and, in the Gibbons, an apparent entertainment. In this, perhaps, the Gibbon is an example of the human ancestors whose vocal propensities finally cul-

The Gibbons are at times very active for long periods, performing acrobatics on ropes and swings, or rolling or playing together on the ground, then again resting. In this respect there are marked individual differences. Visually they are very alert, all their locomotion and manipulations being carried out under strict visual guidance.

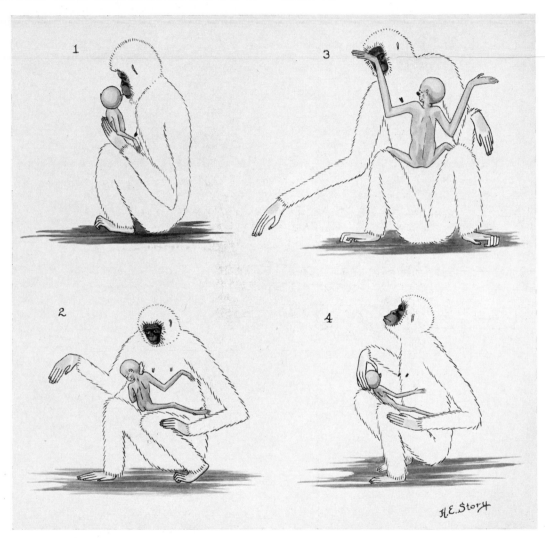

FIG. 529.—A female Gibbon Lar (white phase), nursing her newborn infant, observed in the Zoölogical Park at Brookfield, Illinois. *1*, female holding her two-day-old infant, lateral view; *2*, infant holding the fur of its mother with lower extremities, its long arms free; *3*, infant in nursing position, holding to its mother with lower limbs, while waving its arms in the air; *4*, mother picking up her infant with right hand, its head held by the thumb of the right hand opposed to other slightly flexed fingers.

minated in singing and in human speech. Whether some utilitarian purpose, such as the sex life, is involved in this, as Darwin assumed, remains to be investigated. (*Cf.* C. R. Darwin, *The Descent of Man*, chap. XIX.)

4. CHIMPANZEE.—The smaller of the two Anthropomorphous Apes inhabiting Africa, the Chimpanzee, is lighter, more agile, and more definitely arboreal than the Gorilla (Figs. 532, 533). However, in limbs and their use it is simi-

larly equipped, but with added characteristics of its own (*see* following subsection on Gorilla).

The walk of the Chimpanzee on even ground resembles that of the Gorilla, in that almost the entire sole is placed flat on the ground. There is, perhaps, a slight emphasis on the outer edge,

his hands and fingers flat on the ground, resembling the Gorilla in this respect (Fig. 532, sketches *6* and *7*). In spite of this handicap, he is able to peel the skin of a banana with the index finger and thumb of one hand or of both, sometimes assisted by the teeth. He is not able

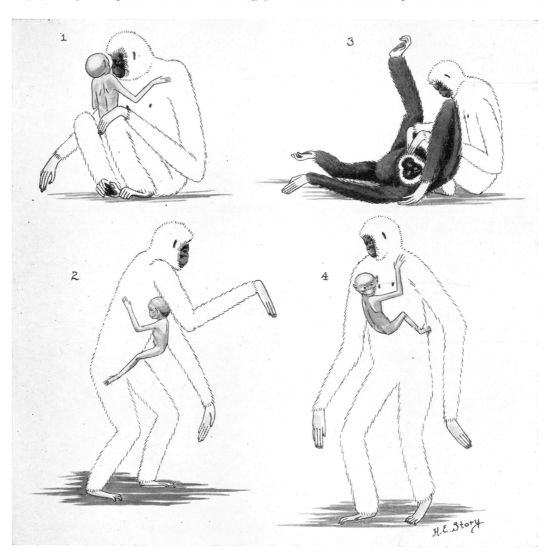

Fig. 530.—Female Gibbon Lar nursing a newborn infant, and a pair of the same species grooming, observed in Zoölogical Park at Brookfield, Illinois. *1*, female in a sitting position, with the infant clinging to her fur in an elevated position; *2*, female walking in human fashion, with her legs, however, slightly flexed, infant clinging with all its four extremities to her in a nursing position; *3*, two Gibbons enjoying siesta, the white female grooming the fur of her relaxed black mate, under control of vision; *4*, female walking human fashion, with slightly bent legs and loosely hanging arms, infant clinging in a nursing position.

and the toes are not entirely straightened, but are slightly bent at their joints (Fig. 532, sketches *2* and *4*).

Unlike the Macaques, Baboons, and Man, the Chimpanzee is not able to place the palm of

to pick up a peanut from a flat floor in the way of the Macaques, Baboons, and Man, however, and uses for this purpose the middle and index fingers of a hand placed with its back downward.

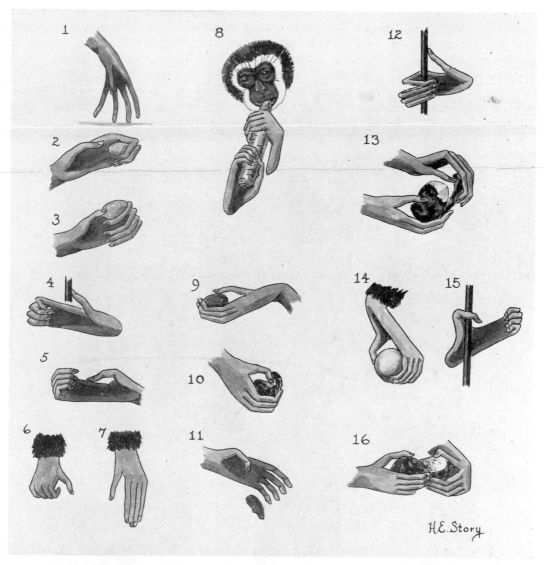

Fig. 531.—Use of the hands and feet by Gibbon Lar, observed in the Zoölogical Park at Brookfield, Illinois. 1, left hand with fingers extended and spread out, touching an object, the thumb weaker and shorter than in the human hand; 2, volar view of left hand clutching a sweet potato with fingers alone, without the assistance of the thumb; 3, volar view of left hand holding a sweet potato between the thumb opposed to index finger; 4, plantar view of right foot, with long toes flexed and short thumb pushing against a bar; 5, plantar view of right foot with all toes flexed, showing disproportionately short "big" toe; 6, dorsal view of right foot with all toes more or less flexed in standing pose; 7, dorsal view of left foot with all toes extended and body swinging in midair; 8, nibbling a raw carrot while holding it with left hand at the root end and with right foot at the top end; 9, left hand holding a sweet potato between opposed index finger and thumb; 10, right hand, with the thumb pushing against the peeling of a sweet potato to remove it; 11, volar view of left hand opened in order to drop the sweet potato; 12, volar view of right hand, with fingers clutching an upright bar and thumb pressing against it in the opposite direction; 13, use of both hands in removing the skin of a white potato by holding it in the right hand and peeling off the skin by taking it between the opposed thumb and principally the index finger of the left hand; 14, right foot holding a ball between the flexed toes and the big toe, hand-fashion; 15, palmar view of left foot, with big toe hooked around an upright bar and other toes flexed in midair; 16, both hands used in human fashion to break a white potato into halves, with fingers flexed around outer surface and opposing thumbs pressing against inner surface of each half.

Nor does the Chimpanzee easily notice small objects quickly detected by the Macaques and Baboons, but he notices larger objects, especially if they are brightly colored. This reduced visual alertness and acuity are probably caused by the less refined organization of the retina, where many more bi- and polysynaptic midget bipolars are present in the central area than in the Macaque.

The intellectual abilities and the habits of the Chimpanzee, more than of any other Ape, have been repeatedly studied by numerous investigators (Köhler, Bingham, Klüver, Benchley, Nissen, Yerkes, Kohts).

5. ORANGUTAN.—This largest of the Infra-human Primates inhabiting Asia, the "Man of the Jungle" of the Europeans, the "Mias" or

FIG. 532.—Chimpanzee (*Anthropopithecus troglodytes*), observed in his daily activities, in the Zoölogical Parks at Chicago, and at Brookfield, Illinois. *1*, an adolescent in half-erect posture, holding with his right hand a bar of the cage; *2*, an adult walking erect, with arms held against chest, legs slightly bent, soles planted flat on the ground, but with toes flexed; *3*, adult eating lettuce by holding it between fingers and thumbs (not seen in the picture); *4*, an adult walking erect, with legs bent, his body supported by arms, and hands holding his thighs above the knees, impersonating an old man, or actually suffering from rheumatism; *5*, gobbling grapes from a strand held rigid by the stem, between index fingers and thumbs of both hands, picking each grape separately with his lips; *6*, walking on all four limbs, using "knuckles" of his hands and with his toes bent (front view); *7*, lateral view of the same in quadrupedal walk, showing incapacity of Chimpanzee to extend his fingers and toes fully and place them flat on the ground, in the way usually done by the Macaques, Baboons, and Man. (*See* preceding figures.)

"Mayas" of the Malays, is noteworthy for his advanced adaptation to life in the trees, which, conversely, makes him least fit for terrestrial existence (Figs. 534, 535). His arms are proportionately very long, touching the ground when the much shorter legs are fully extended (Fig. 535, sketch *10*). The legs and feet, however, are entirely unfit for walking on even ground.

Neither the foot nor the toes can be stretched out, hence the sole cannot be placed flat on the ground.

When standing or walking, the toes are bent under the sole, which in turn is not parallel with the ground, but incloses with it an angle facing inward (Fig. 535, sketches *1, 2, 6, 7, 8*). The toes are bent toward the sole, filling the angle,

Fig. 533.—Chimpanzees observed in the Zoölogical Park at Brookfield, Illinois. *1*, adult Chimpanzee walking on a horizontal bar and keeping balance by holding another bar with the terminal phalanges of the fingers of his left hand, the left foot and flexed leg supporting most of his weight; *2*, elderly Chimp in a sitting posture, amusing himself by clapping his hands in response to the audience, with his right fingers fully extended, his left fingers partly flexed, his right toes extended, his left toes flexed in their terminal joints, except the big toe, which is fully extended; *3, 5*, and *6*, an adolescent having fun by making himself into a ball, then rolling over and over again, but taking care to protect his face and eyes with his hands; *4*, apparently a mated pair of older Chimps sitting together, the female examining the fur of the male and picking "lice" or dandruff with the index finger opposed to the thumb, assisted with the fingers of the other hand, every act controlled by vision.

the outer side of the bent toes being also used as additional support. This arrangement forces the Orangutan to step on the outer margin of his foot. Altogether, the Orangutan's feet in terrestrial locomotion resemble human fists, which give to the body only unstable support.

Since the structure of the foot forms merely an insecure base for the entire body weight in walking, the arms are used as additional support. But the arms also represent only an awkward buttress, since the hands and fingers cannot be stretched out and the palms and fingers

cannot be placed flat on the ground, in the way the Macaques, the Baboons, and Man can do. This is evidently caused by the shortness of the tendons of the muscles of the forearm and fingers, which do not permit stretching, even less overextension, of the fingers of the Orangutan so clearly demonstrated by the mentioned species (*cf.* Figs. 526, 527). Consequently, when the hand is placed with the palm down, the fingers are bent under, or the back surface of the hand is placed down.

An Orangutan hobbling on all fours, conse-

FIG. 534.—Orangutan or Orang-Utan (*Pongo pigmaeus*) observed in Lincoln Park Zoo, Chicago. *1* and *2*, front and side views in erect bipedal walk, demonstrating the inability to put toes and soles flat on the ground, which necessitates the maintenance of a precarious balance with the help of the upper extremities; *3*, first and second fingers of the left hand touching the toe end of the artist's shoe; *4*, index finger alone exploring artist's shoe; *5*, holding an apple between the thumb and index finger of the right hand, the arm extended and fruit generously offered to the observer; *6*, index finger of the left hand extended in an attempt to touch artist's hand; *7*, left hand holding lightly an apple between extended fingers opposed by the thumb; *8*, hand shaking of two friends in adjoining cages, the dark, shaggy hand being that of the Chimpanzee, the lower, lightly shaded hand that of the Orangutan.

quently, is a sorry sight. Its walk is remarkable for its clumsiness, and the way it differs from the human walk (Fig. 535, *10*). It consists of a hopping shuffle, in which the much longer arms are used as crutches to support the body, while the shriveled legs and feet are pushed forward between the arms to make the next step. This mode of progression markedly resembles the limping of a person with crippled legs walking on crutches. The short, deformed legs are never used alone as a support either in standing or in walking.

The hand of the Orangutan is noteworthy for its diminutive thumb (Fig. 540, sketch *9*). The thumb, however, is opposable, but the remaining long and solid fingers, especially the third and the fourth, are evidently more fit for grasping thick branches of the trees as a solid "hook" in brachiation than for performing delicate "epicritic" movements, as do the fingers of Man, Macaques, and Baboons when examining small objects under visual guidance.

The principal role of the Orangutan's fingers, then, is to function as strong, safe "hooks" for the powerful muscles of the arms and shoulders on which the heavy body of this large Ape swings much of the time during its brachiating progression in the tops of the trees. In this function, as in the Gibbon, the thumbs receded to an auxiliary instrument useful only for manipulation in feeding, as in the opening of the tough shells of the fruits grown on the trees (e.g., *Durian*). The use of the big toes of the feet, which are also relatively shorter and weaker than in the Gorilla and Chimpanzee, is not much different (Fig. 540, sketch *10*).

The preceding description and interpretation of the Orangutan's limbs is based on observation of two $2\frac{1}{2}$-year-old youngsters seen by the author in Lincoln Park Zoo, in Chicago, during 1953. In spite of their tender age and rather delicate build, they proved to be good, though rather deliberate, climbers on the bars of the cage and on the rope. Their walk, with the feet gathered into fistlike balls, however, was awkward, the outer edges alone being used for support. Both were alert, intelligent creatures, either playing together and occasionally teasing each other or intently observing the visitors and stretching their little hands to beg for food.

The characteristics described clearly indicate the organization of the limbs and, in fact, of the entire bodily machine of the Orangutan for exclusive existence in the tops of the trees, the Orangutan's natural home, where he finds food and shelter and from which he but rarely descends to the ground. The scanty observations by the travelers in the Orangutan's native countries Sumatra and Borneo agree with this interpretation. On this basis it is safe to conclude that the Orangutan is only remotely related to Man's ancestral line. The arboreal adaptation of his bodily equipment is so profound that it could not have permitted the readaptation necessary for a strictly terrestrial bipedal life. This must be said in spite of the many human-like traits this big Ape exhibits.

Not the least of these traits is the Orangutan's mental and emotional makeup, as the observation of another pair of somewhat older adolescents at present in the Brookfield Zoo showed (1953). Their age might be guessed as five or six years. They were lively and playful fellows. They were apparently quite happy with each other and had lots of fun. They played all day long with an old gunnysack, which they pulled over their heads again and again in an endless variety of ways. Or they rolled over in a pile of straw, scattering it over the floor of the cage. The climax of this performance appeared to be the piling of the straw over their heads so that it cascaded down their necks and bodies. Or they shoved the straw here and there or tried to heap it on the door frame of the cage. Then again they made themselves into balls, with arms and legs pulled to the body, and rolled over the floor, taking care to protect vital parts, especially the face and the eyes, with their hands. They resembled two happy human youngsters rolling about the floor as if their bodies were made of rubber and had no bones. Their behavior contrasted markedly with the dull, reserved, almost morose disposition of the adult Orangutans, who sometimes remained for hours in the same pose with hardly a motion noticeable. These four adolescent Orangutans illustrated well the highly developed, almost human, intellectual faculties of the advanced Primates. (*See* description of the Orangutan's behavior in captivity by W. H. Furness 1916 and by B. J. Benchley 1942, and in his native habitat by A. R. Wallace, in *Malay Archipelago*, 1869, and in A. Brehm's *Tierleben*.)

6. GORILLA.—The largest, rarest, and least known of the Anthropomorphous Apes, the Gorilla, lives in two, possibly more, species-scattered localities of Central Africa, from the lowlands of French Congo in the west to the dense forests on the slopes of Mounts Mikeno and Karisimbi around Lake Kivu, in the Belgian Congo. Because of his great scientific importance, the Gorilla is now protected in many regions. (*Cf.* sec. 4 [7, 8], this chapter.)

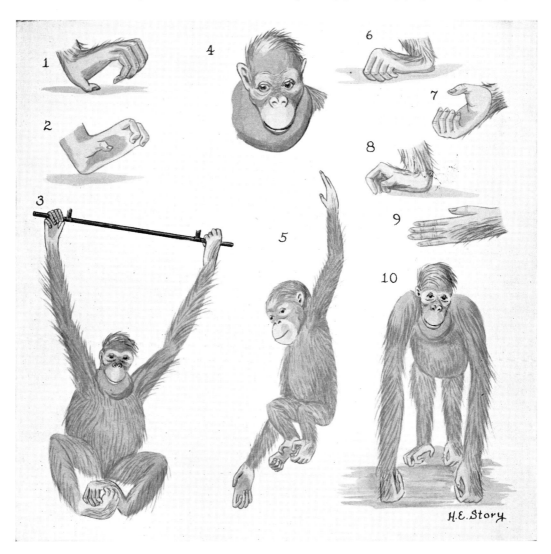

FIG. 535.—Orangutan or Orang-Utan observed at Lincoln Park Zoo, Chicago. *1*, medial, *2*, somewhat plantar, views of the left foot seen in walking, with heel and outer margin touching the ground, the remainder of the hollow sole off the ground, with long toes bent under, because of inability to extend the toes and foot straight and to place them squarely on the ground in the human manner; *3*, swinging on a trapeze, with shorter and weaker hind feet drawn up as useless appendages, illustrating the prevalent importance of the forelimbs in the arboreal, brachiating mode of locomotion; *4*, Orang's physiognomy expressing the placid disposition of this great frugivorous ape living in his secluded arboreal habitat; *5*, young specimen from the habitat group at the Chicago Natural History Museum, illustrating the intensive specialization of this Primate for arboreal life; *6*, lateral view of left foot in walking, with the long toes bent under, owing to the inability to stretch them in the way Man, Baboons, and Macaques can do; *7*, plantar view of right foot flexed in preparation for grasping a bar, showing remarkable similarity to human hand; *8*, inner view of right foot, with toes flexed, the outer margin of the sole and flexed toes alone resting on the ground, showing the inability of this arboreal Primate to extend the toes and the rest of the foot and to put them flat on the ground, as Man and Monkeys do; *9*, dorsal view of left hand with fingers fully extended, showing diminutive thumb not reaching to the metacarpo-phalangeal joint; *10*, front view in walking on all fours, with fully extended forelimbs but with all fingers and toes flexed.

As far as is known, this Ape is partial to a thick, primeval jungle. A few of them occasionally stray into transitional savanna, as mentioned in section 4, this chapter. The larger species native to the Mikeno-Karisimbi area is a pronounced mountain dweller, ranging above 8,500 and up to more than 12,000 feet.

Observed in a zoo, the Lowland Gorilla gives the impression of being a heavy-set and rather dull, but treacherous, animal (Figs. 536–39). When young, however, it is remarkably flexible in body, alert in senses, and surprisingly agile in bodily movements and behavior. It is almost as accomplished an acrobat on a trapeze and in climbing a rope as the Chimpanzee, being in this respect inferior only to the Gibbon. His climbing antics and acrobatics, which include frequent brachiations or climbing and swinging by the arms, are endless and are executed with great vigor and agility under continuous visual guidance. The shortness of the neck, characteristic of all large Apes, especially of the Gorilla, during his youth does not in the least interfere with the quick movements of his head in the assistance of the ocular movements indispensable for the visual control of the upper extremities.

The young and adolescent Gorilla is remarkably intelligent and resourceful, as exemplified by one about four to five years old, observed by the author in 1924 in the London Zoo, and again by five mostly adolescent Gorillas observed at Brookfield Zoo and Lincoln Park Zoo, in Chicago, during 1953. There was no end to the tricks these so human-like animals played on their keepers. Their inventive genius in devising various methods of use or games with simple objects such as an automobile tire was remarkable. Their intellect seemed to be continuously working, finding new tricks such as acrobatics on the trapeze or whirling on the floor, and the like. And all this busy activity was for the purpose of impressing the admiring audience whose reaction was attentively observed and appreciated. The behavior of the young Gorillas was true stage-acting, accompanied by all kinds of mannerism, although there was little change in facial expression, and the acting was mostly performed silently. (*See* for the behavior of John Daniel in F. Tilney, *The Brain from Ape to Man*, 1928; *see* for scientific observa-

tion and testing R. M. Yerkes 1927–28, and Bingham's experiments reported by Benchley 1942.)

The sensory and mental alertness, bodily agility, the flexibility of the limbs, and the generally amiable and humorous emotional disposition gradually change with advancing age, the large, powerful males becoming passive, immobile, morose, not to be lightly trusted. In the experience of Yerkes, in his psychophysical processes the Gorilla is slow, Man and Chimpanzee relatively quick, and the Orangutan perhaps intermediate—"Slow but sure, seems not to have carried her genus to preëminence in the grim struggle of organisms for survival and supremacy."

In walking, whether slow, running, hopping, or galloping, the Gorilla habitually uses all four extremities. It resorts to a bipedal walk only for a few steps (*cf.* Mrs. Benchley, and personal observation). The four longer fingers of the hands are held bent at the first phalangeal joints, and the second and third phalanges are placed with their backs more or less flat on the ground. In this way the hand is used as a "hoof." From the description of Malbrant & Maclatchy, summarized in the preceding section 4, it appears that sometimes the thumb, index, and middle fingers alone are used as a support in quadrupedal progression, the last two fingers being held bent at their joints in order to approximate them in length with the length of the outstretched thumb. This probably occurs in leisurely progression over soft ground. In captivity, according to our observation, the thumb hardly ever touches the ground.

The use of the Gorilla's foot, in both bipedal and quadrupedal standing and walking, is surprisingly similar to that of the human foot (due consideration being given to the essentially prehensile character of the Gorilla's foot, and the abduction of the big toe from the sagittal axis of the foot).

When the foot is put flat on the ground, it rests on it with its entire undersurface, from the heel to the tips of the toes. The toes likewise rest with their undersurfaces on the ground, with no indication of the bending-under of the toes at their joints, as is the rule in the Chimpanzee and even more so in the Orangutan. Nor is there the slightest indication of the emphasis

Fig. 536.—Young and adolescent Gorillas of the lowland variety (*Gorilla gorilla*), native of the French Cameroons of central West Africa, in a climbing, bipedal standing, sitting, and quadrupedal position, observed in Lincoln Park Zoo, Chicago. *1*, a young male, approximate age seven years, approximate weight 225 lbs., climbing side wall of his cage, left foot grasping hand-fashion a narrow shelf, with toes of right foot lightly resting on ground and supporting but little weight, left hand reaching behind, toward a trapeze just above, right hand securely grasping a narrow shelf, right arm pulling most of body weight, with all movements controlled by vision; *2*, same in upright posture, feet and toes placed flat on the ground, legs slightly flexed, with fists pounding his chest, a supposed expression of well-being, the bipedal gait being resorted to off and on for short periods of time; *3*, same sitting on the edge of a rubber tire and eating lettuce, which he holds in his right hand; *4*, a female, possibly from seven to eight years of age, her approximate weight 200 lbs., standing on all four limbs, ready to stroll about. Young Gorillas, as observed in zoölogical parks, are playful and full of tricks which they are ready to pull on their attendants. When grown, especially the huge and powerful males, attaining and exceeding 500 lbs. in weight, they become morose and unpredictable, making their management difficult. In nature their habits and behavior, of which little is as yet known, show them to be rather shy, retiring dwellers of deep jungles, living mostly on the ground and retiring to low limbs of trees for the night only. For other details *see* A. Brehm 1911–18, *Säugetiere;* C. E. Akeley 1923; Gregory & Raven 1937; and chap. XV, 4, 5, in this book.

on the outer edge of the sole regularly observed in the Orangutan.

The mechanics of the Gorilla's foot in walking is also practically identical with that of the human foot. When the foot is carried forward, as when taking a step, it and the extended toes are lifted clear off the ground, before being placed down again. In this, the toes are maximally extended, or rather overextended, the big toe abducted, and all toes held a little above the level of the sole. In this way the obstacles of the rough ground are easily cleared.

When the next step is initiated, the foot and the toes are set in motion in a nicely co-ordinated way. First the heel and the sole are lifted, the toes still remaining for a while on the ground. There is no dragging of the toes on the ground, and the extended toes and the foot are finally lifted and carried forward in making the next step. There is no indication whatsoever of

Fig. 537.—Attitudes, acts, and reactions of an adolescent Gorilla, observed at Lincoln Park Zoölogical Gardens, in Chicago. *1*, attentively listening to artist's voice humming a song, and trying to locate the source of the voice; *2*, eating an apple, holding it in his right hand, with the thumb opposed to other fingers, in human fashion; *3*, eating a banana, holding it with the fingers of his left hand, after having previously removed the skin; *4*, avidly inhaling cigarette smoke blown by the artist into his mouth, intentionally held open; *5*, cleverly directing the stream of water into his mouth by pressing a bubbling fountain with his left thumb. This plate shows the immensely complex performances in which the entire bodily machine co-operates with the cerebral integrator, co-ordinating its many parts, sensory and motor. The total impression is that of remarkable similarity to human behavior in comparable situations of sensory stimulation or volitional impulse.

Fig. 538.—Portrait and attitudes of "Bushman," an adult male Gorilla of the lowland variety (*Gorilla gorilla*), sketched from life at Lincoln Park Zoo in Chicago, 1947. *1*, sitting posture in right-side view, with left hand grasping a horizontal shelf and right hand reaching to the ground; *2*, walking on all fours, both hands resting on "knuckles," the toes of the right foot and the big toe extended, the sole resting flat on the ground, the toes of the left foot bent under; *3*, physiognomy characteristic of a fully grown male Gorilla, with a flat, furrowed forehead surmounted by a high crest decorated with erectile hair, with prominent brow ridges, relatively small eyes, broad and flat nose, large prognathous or projecting muzzle, with thick, prehensile lips, small chin, and diminutive, shriveled-up auricles, altogether not unlike a crude rendition of the human physiognomy; *4*, side view of the body slowly raised from a quadrupedal posture to an erect bipedal stature; *5*, front view in a sitting posture, the principal weight of the body resting on the haunches, supported both with flexed legs and with outstretched arms, with all fingers and toes flexed. The physical and sensory-mental resemblance of the Gorilla and of other great Apes to Man cannot be denied, except on preconception. The question of how this and other Primates could be fitted into the ancestral tree of Man has not been answered satisfactorily. The available evidence indicates that none of the Great Apes is directly ancestral to Man and that the human races may have originated from smaller Primates, more or less resembling modern Macaques and Baboons. (*See* text.)

walking on bent toes, as the Orangutan does, or of stepping on the outer edge of the foot, as is the Chimpanzee's habit. It all markedly resembles the walking mechanics of the human leg and foot, with all detailed movements executed nimbly (taking into account the Gorilla's much broader foot and the abducted big toe; *see* Fig. 540, *2*).

The resemblance of the use of the Gorilla's foot to that of the human foot is shown in the similarity of its tracks to human tracks, especially of the African natives, observed in nature. The enormous human-looking Gorilla tracks show the mark of a heel, which no other footprint, except the human, shows, according to Carl E. Akeley (1923).

The intermittent short attempts of the Gorilla at upright bipedal standing and walking are only passing intervals between the much longer periods of quadrupedal or rather quadrumanous standing or progression. Even in an upright bipedal stance, which is done well and firmly, the legs are rarely fully extended in human fashion, but habitually remain slightly bent at the knees. Hence the body weight never completely rests upon the skeleton and ligaments, as it does in Man, but must be partly assisted by muscular force.

The Gorilla's bipedalism and upright posture, according to this, in spite of his essentially terrestrial habit, must be considered as incipient. They may be compared with the early stages through which Man's Ancestors passed long ago. The Gorilla's bipedalism is probably far less advanced than was that of the *Australopithecus*, but it is of a somewhat higher degree than the bipedalism of the Chimpanzee and is definitely higher than that of the Orangutan. (*Cf.* D. J. Morton, *Evolution of the Human Foot*, 1924, and *Human Origin*, 1927.)

The hand of the Gorilla is broad and heavy, the fingers rather short and thick, the thumb relatively small (Fig. 540, *1*). The detailed proportions resemble those of the Macaque (*16*) rather than those of the Gibbon (*11*), Chimpanzee (*3*, *6*, *7*), and Orangutan (*9*, in same figure). More than in any of the Apes, the hands of the Gorilla resemble those of a heavy-set Man. This is especially true of the four fingers. The thumb, however, is relatively much smaller and weaker, in agreement with the reduced or absent thumb

in the rest of the higher Primates, except Man. In spite of this, the thumb is well opposed to other fingers, as is occasionally the big toe to other toes when the foot is used for grasping.

Rope climbing is done in human fashion, with great vigor and expertness. The bars of the cage are frequently held with the fingers, without the use of the thumb. Judging from the structure of his hands and their use, however, the Gorilla appears to be less capable of performing delicate manipulations than are the Macaques and Baboons but is probably more capable than the Orangutan, and possibly also than the Chimpanzee and the Gibbon. (*See* on this point, however, Benchley 1942, p. 253.)

The feet of the Gorilla conform in principle to the prehensile type of other Monkeys and Apes, closely resembling those of the Chimpanzee (Fig. 540, sketch *2*). In spite of their prehensile construction and broad, massive shape, they are well adapted for walking on flat ground, and especially on large limbs of the trees, where their broad soles, strong, abducted big toes, and the V-shaped position of both feet are very advantageous. Their adaptation for walking on flat ground, however, is less complete than that of the Baboons. They are definitely less fit for bipedal progression than the much narrower and relatively longer human feet, but more so than the feet of the Chimpanzee, and far more so than the feet of the Orangutan. The Gorilla's feet may be compared with the Gibbon's feet, which, in spite of the latter's narrow shape, are well adapted for walking on flat ground.

In appraising the bodily and functional equipment of the Gorilla, it appears that this largest and heaviest of the living Apes is more of a terrestrial dweller, even though he has not abandoned the arboreal habit to the extent that the Baboons have. His fingers cannot be straightened out, and even less overextended, as can those of the Macaques, Baboons, and Man; hence he is forced to walk on knuckles, resembling the Chimpanzee in this respect, but not to the degree found in the Orangutan. (Akeley found that when the Gorilla's arms are extended, his fingers are flexed, and can be straightened only when his wrist is bent.) Even so, the Gorilla has emancipated himself far more from the arboreal habit and has adapted himself better than the Chimpanzee, and far more so than the Orangutan, to a bipedal and semi-erect life on flat ground in a way and degree somewhat approaching Man.

In the Gorilla's "descent from the trees" several factors may have acted concurrently. One is the great bulk of the Gorilla, especially the physical strength of the males. (The famous "Bushman" of the Lincoln Park Zoo in Chicago, when in his prime, weighed 548 pounds on an empty stomach, and measured 6 feet and 2 inches in height; *cf. also* the accompanying figures.) The other is the formidable offensive and defensive weapons, such as the strong arms

Fig. 539.—Gorilla's hands and feet and their use in manipulation and locomotion. *1*, left hind foot in walking, heel placed first on the ground; *2*, right hand holding an apple between thumb, index, and middle fingers; *3*, left foot running on tiptoes, with the heel kept off the ground; *4*, left hand in locomotion: *4A*, first phase in a forward step, with fingers flexed; *4B*, second phase in a forward step, with fingers extended and touching the ground with their tips; *5*, breaking of a head of lettuce in halves with both hands, using pressure of thumbs to break the halves into smaller pieces; *6*, right foot in grasp of the left hand; *7A*, first act in walking, with the heel of left foot first placed on the ground; *7B*, second act in walking, with the outer margin of foot resting on the ground, with the remainder of the sole not quite on the ground; *8*, left hand holding a piece of lettuce; *9*, right hand holding a celery stalk between index and middle fingers; *10*, pressing with the left thumb a stream of water from a drinking fountain and directing it into his cupped right hand, which is raised to his lips The illustrated postures and manipulations of the Gorilla are comparable to those of human hands and feet, commensurate with the more delicate build of the latter.

and hands and powerful dentition, including long canine teeth, set in massive jaws, moved by proportionately strong masticating muscles, all carried by the powerful muscles of the head and neck, set upon a massive trunk.

It is likely that in the normal conditions of the Gorilla's habitat, this equipment would be more than sufficient to ward off potential enemies like the Lion, Leopard, and Hyena (*cf.* C. Akeley, and M. Jobe Akeley). Relative safety, then, permitted the Gorilla to spend most of his time on the ground, where in turn more food to nourish his bulky body was to be found than would be the case in the trees ("Bushman's" fare, consisting entirely of fruits and vegetables, with the addition of vitamins, according to Mr. L. S. Carpenter of the Lincoln Park Zoo in Chicago, often was more than 20 pounds at one meal). Thus, the quantity and quality of food appear to have been the prime "moving agents" which induced the Gorilla to come down from the treetops and which permitted him to lead a largely terrestrial existence. In the descent of the Gorilla to the semiterrestrial mode of life, the importance and usefulness of vision, the common heritage of all Primates, remained as essential for the maintenance and preservation of this species as it was in the life in the treetops.

7. Observation of the Monkeys and Apes, and the problem of Man's origin.— The Monkeys and Apes, like the members of other mammalian orders, are adapted to a great many ways of life, with the arboreal habit preponderating. A few may be exclusively terrestrial, as, for example, the Patas Monkey (*Erythrocebus patas*) of western Africa, who with his high legs, narrow feet, and digitigrade gait emulates the Cheetah, the fleet Hunting Leopard of Asia and Africa, equally adapted to desert conditions and to swift running.

Most of the Primates, however, are strictly or largely arboreal. This, especially in the larger species, has enforced a great deal of anatomical reorganization of the original conditions inherited from the insectivorous ancestors. Close arboreal adaptation is accentuated in all Anthropomorphous Apes, most in the Orangutan, and least in the Gorilla. This fact militates against a close phylogenetical relationship of the Apes to

Man, in spite of the numerous anatomical, biological, and psychic resemblances.

At one time, before they attained a state recognizable as human, the ancestors of Man may have resembled the smaller Monkeys like the Macaques and Baboons in many ways. It is probable that, like them, they were largely quadrupedal, or quadrumanous, with a strong tendency to sit on their buttocks in order to use their hands freely for manipulation under visual control. This tendency toward an upright sitting posture further developed into a frequent rising on the hind extremities, with occasional short bipedal runs.

The most powerful stimulus to increase this tendency to preponderantly and ultimately exclusively bipedal locomotion and upright attitude must have been the acquisition of food. Whether this was entirely carnivorous, as assumed by Professor Dart, or of a more diversified kind, with the products of plants representing a large or principal source, is further discussed in section 8. (*Cf.* observation of Macaques in their native habitat by Ridley 1895.)

Whatever the stimulus, the observation of the various Primates indicates that the ancestors of Man never could have become so completely adapted to arboreal life as are the present Apes, Gibbons, and all American and most Old World Monkeys. They probably never passed through a brachiating adaptation, with the enormous development of the upper extremities and shoulders and the reduction and deformation of lower extremities, but have continued the emphasis upon the lower limbs so clearly shown by the Macaques and Baboons.

The tendency to rise on the hind limbs may have begun very early in human evolution, probably long before the Anthropomorphous Apes became clearly outlined (*cf.* Ridley 1895). The great length of time required for this is indicated by the complete anatomical adjustment of prehistoric and modern humanity to an upright bipedal gait.

The transition from a quadrumanous to a bipedal posture must have been a long, slow process. There may have been many attempts in the past to accomplish this. Some have failed entirely. Other waves, arising in different parts of the world from different stock, possibly gave rise to different branches of the present human-

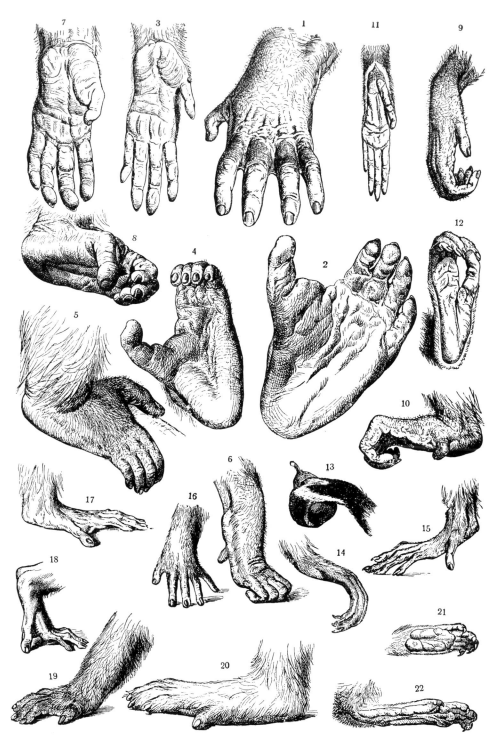

Fig. 540.—Hands and feet of the Monkeys and Apes, the parts of the body which, next to the organs of vision, are most intimately related to the habits of Primates and hence most responsible for their emergence from a general mammalian stock and for the origin of Man: *1*, back view of left hand of the Gorilla; *2*, plantar view of the left foot of the Gorilla; *3*, *7*, palmar views of left hands of Chimpanzee; *4*, plantar view of left foot of Chimpanzee; *5*, dorsal view of right foot of Chimpanzee resting on a tree limb; *6*, right hand of Chimpanzee supported on knuckles; *8*, left foot of Chimpanzee with toes bent, showing opposable big toe, an act not possible for the human foot; *9*, right hand of Orangutan; *10*, right foot of Orangutan in a grasping attitude as in clinching a branch, showing a diminutive big toe; *11*, volar aspect of left hand of the Gibbon Lar; *12*, plantar view of right foot of the Gibbon Lar, showing opposable big toe; *13*, left hand of the Gibbon Lar, holding fruit with all five fingers apposited; *14*, hand of the

ity summarized in *Homo sapiens* and to the prehistoric Hominidae.

The marked physical characteristics of the various human races, differing so completely from one another in some respects, even though practically all possessed the same or very similar intellectual potentialities, may be the common result of similar factors working from different angles for the same purpose. To determine the starting points of the various branches of modern humanity, to trace their particular evolutionary courses, and to identify the responsible factors should be the goal of modern anthropology.

SEC. 6. DARWIN'S VIEW ON THE ORIGIN OF MAN, AND ON THE CAUSES OF MAN'S PRE-EMINENT PLACE IN NATURE

In the second revised edition of his classical book *The Descent of Man* (1899, p. 47) in the section on "Natural Selection," Charles Darwin discussed in some detail the causes of Man's erect posture and its consequences:

We have now seen that man is variable in body and mind; and that the variations are induced, either directly or indirectly, by the same general causes, and obey the same general laws, as with the lower animals. Man has spread widely over the face of the earth, and must have been exposed, during his incessant migration, to the most diversified conditions. The inhabitants of Tierra del Fuego, the Cape of Good Hope, and Tasmania in the one hemisphere, and of the Arctic regions in the other, must have passed through many climates, and changed their habits many times, before they reached their present homes. The early progenitors of man must also have tended, like all other animals, to have increased beyond their means of subsistence; they must, therefore, occasionally have been exposed to a struggle for existence, and consequently to the rigid law of natural selection. Beneficial variations of all kinds will thus, either occasionally or habitually, have been preserved and injurious ones eliminated. I do not refer to strongly-marked deviations of structure, which occur only at long intervals of time, but to mere individual differences. We know, for instance, that the muscles of our hands and feet, which determine our powers of movement, are liable, like those of the lower animals, to incessant variability. If then the progenitors of man inhabiting any district, especially one undergoing some change in its conditions, were divided into two equal bodies, the one half which included all the individuals best adapted by their powers of movement for gaining subsistence, or for defending themselves, would on an average survive in greater numbers, and procreate more offspring than the other and less well endowed half.

Man in the rudest state in which he now exists is the most dominant animal that has ever appeared on this earth. He has spread more widely than any other highly organized form: and all others have yielded before him. He manifestly owes this immense superiority to his intellectual faculties, to his social habits, which lead him to aid and defend his fellows, and to his corporeal structure. The supreme importance of these characters has been proved by the final arbitrament of the battle for life. Through his powers of intellect, articulate language has been evolved; and on this his wonderful advancement has mainly depended. As Mr. Chancey Wright remarks: "a psychological analysis of the faculty of language shews, that even the smallest proficiency in it might require more brain power than the greatest proficiency in any other direction." He has invented and is able to use various weapons, tools, traps, etc., with which he defends himself, kills or catches prey, and otherwise obtains food. He has made rafts or canoes for fishing or crossing over to neighbouring fertile islands. He has discovered the art of making fire, by which hard and stringy roots can be rendered digestible, and poisonous roots or herbs innocuous.

Colobus Monkey or Guereza without a thumb; *15*, right foot of the same with toes almost stretched; *16*, left hand of *Macacus sinicus* or *M. radiatus* with fingers extended; *17*, left foot of same with toes resting flat; *18*, same with toes dorsoflexed as in progression; *19*, right hand of the dog-faced Baboon with fingers almost stretched flat; *20*, right foot of Baboon with toes resting flat on ground; *21* and *22*, hand and foot of the Marmoset Monkey, showing undifferentiated toes provided with claws instead of nails. Note disproportionately short, weak, and poorly opposable thumb in Apes and fingers which cannot be put flat on the ground (sketches *1, 3, 6, 7, 9, 11*), contrasting with long, strong, and easily opposable big toe in same (*2, 4, 5, 8, 10, 12*); shorter fingers and an opposable thumb, which, together with the palm of the hand, can be stretched and put flat on the ground in Monkeys (*16, 19*), and the ability of the foot and toes in the same to rest flat on the ground and support the weight of the body (*15, 17, 18, 20*). From A. Brehm's *Tierleben*, 4th ed., v. 13, p. 424, 1916, with special permission of the Bibliographisches Institut A.G. (Dr. E. List), Mannheim, Germany. (*Cf. also* W. L. Straus, Jr., in Am. J. Phys. Anthropol., vols. 27, 28, and in Quart. Rev. Biol., vols. 17 and 24.)

This discovery of fire, probably the greatest ever made by man, excepting language, dates from before the dawn of history. These several inventions, by which man in the rudest state has become so preeminent, are the direct results of the development of his powers of observation, memory, curiosity, imagination, and reason. I cannot, therefore, understand how it is that Mr. Wallace maintains, that "natural selection could only have endowed the savage with a brain a little superior to that of an ape."

Although the intellectual powers and social habits of man are of paramount importance to him, we must not underrate the importance of his bodily structure, to which subject the remainder of this chapter will be devoted; the development of the intellectual and social or moral faculties being discussed in a later chapter.

Even to hammer with precision is no easy matter, as every one who has tried to learn carpentry will admit. To throw a stone with as true an aim as a Fuegian in defending himself, or in killing birds, requires the most consummate perfection in the correlated action of the muscles of the hand, arm, and shoulder, and, further, a fine sense of touch. In throwing a stone or spear, and in many other actions, a man must stand firmly on his feet; and this again demands the perfect co-adaptation of numerous muscles. To chip a flint into the rudest tool, or to form a barbed spear or hook from a bone, demands the use of a perfect hand; for, as a most capable judge, Mr. Schoolcraft, remarks, the shaping fragments of stone into knives, lances, or arrow-heads, shews "extraordinary ability and long practice." This is to a great extent proved by the fact that primeval men practiced a division of labour; each man did not manufacture his own flint tools or rude pottery, but certain individuals appear to have devoted themselves to such work, no doubt receiving in exchange the produce of the chase. Archaeologists are convinced that an enormous interval of time elapsed before our ancestors thought of grinding chipped flints into smooth tools. One can hardly doubt, that a man-like animal who possessed a hand and arm sufficiently perfect to throw a stone with precision, or to form a flint into a rude tool, could, with sufficient practice, as far as mechanical skill alone is concerned, make almost anything which a civilized man can make. The structure of the hand in this respect may be compared with that of the vocal organs, which in the apes are used for uttering various signal-cries, or, as in one genus, musical cadences; but in man the closely similar vocal organs have become adapted through the inherited effects of use for the utterance of articulate language.

Turning now to the nearest allies of men, and therefore to the best representatives of our early progenitors, we find that the hands of the Quadrumana are constructed on the same general pattern as our own, but are far less perfectly adapted for diversified uses. Their hands do not serve for locomotion so well as the feet of a dog; as may be seen in such monkeys as the chimpanzee and orang, which walk on the outer margins of the palms, or on the knuckles. Their hands, however, are admirably adapted for climbing trees. Monkeys seize thin branches or ropes, with the thumb on one side and the fingers and palm on the other, in the same manner as we do. They can thus also lift rather large objects, such as the neck of a bottle, to their mouths. Baboons turn over stones, and scratch up roots with their hands. They seize nuts, insects, or other small objects with the thumb in opposition to the fingers, and no doubt they thus extract eggs and the young from the nests of birds. American monkeys beat the wild oranges on the branches until the rind is cracked, and then tear it off with the fingers of the two hands. In a wild state they break open hard fruits with stones. Other monkeys open mussel-shells with the two thumbs. With their fingers they pull out thorns and burs, and hunt for each other's parasites. They roll down stones, or throw them at their enemies: nevertheless, they are clumsy in these various actions, and, as I have myself seen, are quite unable to throw a stone with precision.

It seems to me far from true that because "objects are grasped clumsily" by monkeys, "a much less specialized organ of prehension" would have served them equally well with their present hands. On the contrary, I see no reason to doubt that more perfectly constructed hands would have been an advantage to them, provided that they were not thus rendered less fitted for climbing trees. We may suspect that a hand as perfect as that of man would have been disadvantageous for climbing; for the most arboreal monkeys in the world, namely, Ateles in America, Colobus in Africa, and Hylobates in Asia, are either thumbless, or their toes partially cohere, so that their limbs are converted into mere grasping hooks.

As soon as some ancient member in the great series of the Primates came to be less arboreal, owing to a change in its manner of procuring subsistence, or to some change in the surrounding conditions, its habitual manner of progression would have been modified: and thus it would have been rendered more strictly quadrupedal or bipedal. Baboons frequent hilly and rocky districts, and only from necessity climb high trees; and they have acquired almost the gait of a dog. Man alone has become a biped; and we can, I think, partly see how he has come to assume his erect attitude, which forms one of his most conspicuous characters. Man could not have attained his present dominant position in the world without the use of his hands, which are so admirably adapted to act in obedience to his will. Sir C. Bell insists that "the hand supplies all instruments, and by its correspondence with the intellect gives him universal dominion." But the hands and arms could hardly have become perfect enough to have manufactured weapons, or to have hurled stones and spears with a true aim, as long as they were habitually used for locomotion and for supporting the whole weight of the body, or, as before remarked, so long as they were especially fitted for climbing trees. Such rough treatment would also have blunted the sense of touch, on which their delicate use largely depends. From these causes alone it would have been an advantage to man to become a biped; but for many actions it is indispensable that the arms and whole upper part of the body should be free; and he must for this end stand firmly on his feet. To gain this great advantage, the feet have been rendered flat; and the great toe has been peculiarly modified, though this has entailed the almost complete loss of its power of prehension. It accords with the principle of the division of physiological labour, prevailing throughout the animal kingdom, that as the hands became perfected for prehension, the feet should have become perfected for support and locomotion. With some savages, however, the foot has not altogether lost its prehensile power, as shewn by their manner of climbing trees, and in using them in other ways.

If it be an advantage to man to stand firmly on his feet and to have his hands and arms free, of which, from his pre-eminent success in the battle of life, there can be no doubt, then I can see no reason why it should not have been advantageous to the progenitors of man to have become more and more erect or bipedal. They would thus have been better able to defend themselves with stones or clubs, to attack their prey, or otherwise to obtain food. The best built individuals would in the long run have succeeded best, and have survived in larger numbers. If the gorilla and a few allied forms had become extinct, it might have been argued, with great force and apparent truth, that an animal could not have been gradually converted from a quadruped into a biped, as all the individuals in an intermediate condition would have been miserably ill-fitted for progression. But we know (and this is well worthy of reflection) that the anthropomorphous apes are now actually in an intermediate condition; and no one doubts that they are on the whole well adapted for their conditions of life. Thus the gorilla runs with a sidelong shambling gait, but more commonly progresses by resting on its bent hands. The long-armed apes occasionally use their arms like crutches, swinging their bodies forward between them, and some kinds of Hylobates, without having been taught, can walk or run upright with tolerable quickness; yet they move awkwardly, and much less securely than man. We see, in short, in existing monkeys a manner of progression intermediate between that of a quadruped and a biped; but, as an unprejudiced judge [Broca in *Revue d'Anthropologie* 1872] insists, the anthropomorphous apes approach in structure more nearly to the bipedal than to the quadrupedal type.

As the progenitors of man became more and more erect, with their hands and arms more and more modified for prehension and other purposes, with their feet and legs at the same time transformed for firm support and progression, endless other changes of structure would have become necessary. The pelvis would have to be broadened, the spine peculiarly curved, and the head fixed in an altered position, all which changes have been attained by man. Prof. Schaaffhausen [transl. in Anthropolog. Rev., p. 428, year 1868, and in Owen's Anatomy of Vertebrates, v. 2, 1866, p. 551] maintains that "the powerful mastoid processes of the human skull are the result of his erect position;" and these processes are absent in the orang, chimpanzee, etc., and are smaller in the gorilla than in man. Various other structures, which appear connected with man's erect position, might here have been added. It is very difficult to decide how far these correlated modifications are the result of natural selection, and how far of the inherited effects of the increased use of certain parts, or of the action of one part on another. No doubt these means of change often co-operate: thus when certain muscles, and the crests of bone to which they are attached, become enlarged by habitual use, this shews that certain actions are habitually performed and must be serviceable. Hence the individuals which performed them best, would tend to survive in greater numbers.

The free use of the arms and hands, partly the cause and partly the result of man's erect position, appears to have led in an indirect manner to other modifications of structure. The early male forefathers of man were, as previously stated, probably furnished with great canine teeth; but as they gradually acquired the habit of using stones, clubs, or other weapons, for fighting with their enemies or rivals, they would use their jaws and teeth less and less. In this case, the jaws, together with the teeth, would become reduced in size, as we may feel almost sure from innumerable analogous cases. In a future chapter we shall meet with a closely parallel case, in the reduction or complete disappearance of the canine teeth in male ruminants, apparently in relation with the development of their horns; and in horses, in relation to their habit of fighting with their incisor teeth and hoofs.

In the quoted passage Darwin touched in an admirable way upon the principal factors responsible for the rise of Man and their interaction. In the following sections an attempt is made to analyze these factors further; their complex interplay and their respective value in molding, from one or from several higher Primates, the race or races of Mankind.

SEC. 7. ANALYSIS OF FACTORS RESPONSIBLE FOR THE ORIGIN OF MAN FROM AN INFRAHUMAN PRIMATE

1. Introductory remark.—The subject of the origin of Man from some earlier and less perfectly organized form, ever since, by virtue of Darwin's publications, it was recognized as a legitimate object of scientific inquiry, has been dealt with in numerous books, papers, and lectures. But as G. Elliot Smith pointed out in his essays on *The Evolution of Man*, most of these, while vastly enriching our detailed knowledge of Man's past and his status in nature, have "brought us so few indications of any serious attempt to probe into the really vital issues regarding the way in which the brain has acquired its highest powers" (G. E. Smith 1927). This situation has not materially changed during the subsequent thirty years (up to 1955). Since Elliot Smith, more deeply perhaps than most other writers, was absorbed by the problem of human origins, the following analysis and commentary on it is based principally upon his writings.

2. Prime factors which initiated human evolution.—Among the factors which have influenced the Lower Primates to assume human shape and character, time is essential. "Evolution needs vast periods of time for its operations." But time alone is not enough, other factors being absolutely necessary. Only when fortunate co-operation of all these various factors took place did there result the appearance of this most remarkable species of Mammals, Man.

What these other factors were has been a matter of much speculation. In the opinion of Elliot Smith, the prime factor was "the steady and uniform development of the brain along a well-defined course throughout the Primates right up to Man, which must give us the fundamental reason for 'Man's emergence and ascent', whatever other factors may contribute towards that consummation."

This raises an alternative question: Did the prehuman brain possess some autochthonous, innate property or impetus to increase in size and elaborateness and to follow a preordained course toward the human and impose itself upon the rest of the body and remodel it to make a Man, which would be quite incredible and contrary to all experience of observation? Or was the causal connection quite the reverse, and did the body of some particular Primate, because of its changed mode of living, become gradually reorganized into human shape, with the brain following and complementing this reorganization?

This latter contention is more likely, supported as it is by innumerable observations, including those described in the preceding chapter. In each of those instances it is obvious that the organisms as a whole and in all minute details are nicely adjusted to the particular tasks they fulfil.

The thesis to be tested here is whether the changed habits and other external circumstances of Human Ancestors have been the prime factor in bringing about an anatomical reorganization of the body, requiring also a more elaborate directing cerebral machine—or did the brain impose itself upon the rest of the body, which it shaped according to its liking, to make, from a lesser Primate, a Man?

The divergent human evolution, away from that of the Monkeys and Apes, with its emphasis on intellect, must have its particular causes. Even if reliable proof of a close anatomical kinship of Man is furnished, it still is possible that his line separated from the common ancestral stock at a time before the ancestors of the Apes became definitely specialized for arboreal life and Man's Ancestors, largely terrestrial, became entirely *epigeoi* or bipedal ground dwellers, with both corporeal and, secondarily, cerebral organization diverging very considerably from that of the Apes, with the cerebral change merely following.

3. ARBOREAL LIFE AND ITS CONSEQUENCES IN EARLY EVOLUTION.—The identical problem is presented by the increased learning capacity of the Tree Shrews and Monkeys: was it the result of the gradual perfection of the cerebral cortex, or was that perfection forced upon them because of the necessity imposed by the more demanding conditions of an arboreal habit?

The *neopallium* or "new cortex," so much increased in the Mammals, is, according to Elliot Smith, the instrument of "associative memory" most easily conforming to the *sensorium commune* of Aristotle. "In the forerunners of the Mammalia the cerebral hemisphere was predominantly olfactory in function." While this may be true, considering the hippocampal formation takes up much of the cortex, the entire cortex in the Lizards, for example, is small, and, whatever its role, it is of less weight in the total function of the brain, in comparison with the large and excellently organized optic lobes of the midbrain. Hence the Lizards and Birds must be considered predominantly "visual animals." The observations and tests, including those made on the Anole Lizard, Turtle, and Swallow, described in the preceding chapter, give ample support to this view.

On the basis of these facts it is easier to maintain the thesis that in the saurian ancestors of the Mammals the leading sense must have been sight, which, however, receded into the background as they had to squeeze through the "biological bottleneck." This greatly impaired their vision and in some species abolished it altogether. Hence in these the emphasis, largely or entirely, shifted to the senses of smell, touch, taste, and hearing. (*See* sections on Shrew, in the preceding chapter.)

In the readaptation to arboreal or aerial modes of life, olfactory dominance was again suppressed, and the sense of vision was restored to its former dominant role, as in the Tree Shrews, or audition became the leading sense, as in the Bats. In the first, visual dominance was accompanied by the expansion of the sensorimotor cortex, since, as Elliot Smith logically assumed, the agility of their movements required an efficient motor cortex and muscular sense. This, in turn, caused the sense of smell to recede, and the sense of vision, tactile sense, kinesthesis, and motility to increase, with a corresponding increase in the respective areae in the cerebral cortex. The actual anatomical findings in the brain of the Tree Shrew support this view, as our description and figures in the preceding chapter show.

But just how arboreal life has brought about these remarkable changes still remains a matter which merits further assiduous inquiry. It may be roughly granted that it is in Tupaia and the Primates "that these tendencies attain any really significant expression." But this statement needs to be qualified. Many other Mammals have a well-developed cerebral cortex. Such are the Carnivora, many Rodents, Elephants, Seals, and so on. Their behavior, their well-developed mentality, and their success in the "struggle for existence" are objective evidence of this.

The motivation of the early arboreal impetus, which in the long run resulted in the coming of the Primates, appears quite complex. It is difficult at this time to single out any particular factor which could be made responsible for their development. The agility of the arboreal Squirrels, for example, is at least as great as that of the Tree Shrews, as far as our own observations go (*see* preceding chapter).

"In the vast majority of living animals," according to Elliot Smith, "behaviour is dominated either by smell or vision." The olfactory dominance, with certain reserve, is true only in Lower Mammals. But even in the terrestrial Shrews audition and tactile senses must contribute a large share to their life's business. In many Fishes, Amphibians, Reptiles, Birds, and Mammals, while one or another sense more or less prevails, other senses nevertheless contribute an important share. In the Pike, for example, the sense of vision obviously is by far the most important; in the Bullhead the senses of smell and gustation. In the Sunfishes, in contrast, the senses of smell and taste are constantly used, even though vision predominates. In the Swallow the senses of vision and hearing lead, the first apparently being by far the most important. In the Tree Shrew vision is excellent, but olfaction is still important and is constantly resorted to. The Tarsier again has developed to an extraordinary degree both vision and audition, in this respect resembling its avian counterparts, the Owls.

Whether the sense of smell alone possesses "affective qualities," as Elliot Smith assumed, is more than questionable. Such qualities may also easily be found in the sense of hearing and in vision, and not only in the higher animals. When a hungry Pike sees a Sunfish, upon which it preys, the image on its retina evokes just as much of an "anticipatory" feeling of a good dinner as does the chemical stimulus from a decaying piece of meat in the olfactory and gustatory apparatus of the almost blind Bullhead. Each sense, therefore, is "affective" in Elliot Smith's sense, each having an "anticipatory memory" based upon phylogenetical and individual experience.

Also, to be useful, every sense, including smell and taste, must have more than "vaguest indications of spatial relations," else it would mislead. A Bullhead finds the bait very well and quickly by scent alone in the muddiest water.

Since vision must have begun practically simultaneously with the chemical senses, as discussed in chapter XIII, 2, it is not necessary to assume that animals which depend principally or entirely upon it get their sustenance in a roundabout way, via the transolfactory transmission of visual impulses, as Elliot Smith assumed, but more or less directly. This may be accepted as certain for such species as, for example, the Trout and the Northern Silverside, which catch insects flying above the water. Scent in this instance is entirely eliminated. Visual impulses in these species are directly transmitted to the co-ordinated motor nerve centers and other organs of execution, leaving the olfactory apparatus entirely or almost entirely aside.

If suppression or elimination of the olfactory receptors and centers is already found in the Fishes, visual organs must be provided on the higher levels of the animal scale, with an independent mechanism for spatial relations or attributes. There is, in fact, good reason to assume that in the Mammals, especially Primates, it is this apparatus upon which the sense of space is to a great extent based. But here we are touching upon an immensely complex problem which concerns the cerebral mechanism, largely still unknown, by which the various senses are capable of mutual influencing and integrating.

4. Erect posture, its origin and consequences for human evolution.—Ever since Charles Darwin published his book, *The Descent of Man* (1871), Man's erect posture has been one of the principal controversial topics in the discussions of Man's origin from some infrahuman form. In the passage quoted in section 6, Darwin discussed in some detail the probable causes, the manner of its development, and its consequences. "Man could not have attained his present dominant position in the world without the use of his hands, which are so admirably adapted to act in obedience to his will. . . . The free use of the arms and hands, partly the cause and partly the result of man's erect position, appears to have led in an indirect manner to other modifications of structure."

Elliot Smith, in the book mentioned, in support of his thesis of the leading role of the brain in the origin of Man, however, poses the following question: "If the erect attitude is to explain all [as according to Munro 1893], why did not the Gibbon become a man in Miocene times or earlier?"

The simple answer to this is the obvious advantage that life in the jungle had for the Gibbons. There was enough food there and plenty of shelter from powerful predators; hence, even now, in spite of the Tigers and Leopards, Gibbons remain plentiful in their present homeland, Siam, Burma, and Malaya. To abandon the jungle by entering the more or less treeless prairie would have meant starvation and death, unless the way of life was modified, principally by becoming swift bipeds, living in larger bands, with highly developed intelligence and the social habit of co-operation. And this is precisely what Man's Ancestors must have done. From this point of view, the Gibbon and the larger Apes (the Gorilla, Orangutan, and Chimpanzee) appear as the conservative remnants of a much more abundant population which remained in the shelter of the jungle, whereas the more venturesome strains, adaptable to more exacting conditions of prairie life, became humans. The Anthropomorphous Apes gave up the plains with their perils for the security of an arboreal asylum, but in giving up the struggle they also renounced progress.

The growth of the brain, in Elliot Smith's opinion, presumably driven by some innate urge, is the principal, possibly the only, factor responsible for the origin of Man. He says:

The whole of my argument has aimed at demonstrating that it is the steady growth and specialization of the brain that has been the fundamental factor in leading Man's ancestors step by step upward from the lowly Insectivore status, and through every earlier phase (Amphibian and Reptilian) in the evolution of Mammals—for Man's brain represents the consummation of precisely those factors that throughout the Vertebrata have brought their possessors to the crest of the wave of progress. But such advances as the assumption of the erect attitude are brought about because the brain has made a new posture and skilled movements of the hands possible and of definite use in the struggle for existence. Yet once such a stage has been attained, the very act of liberating the hands for the performance of more delicate movements opened the way for a farther advance in brain development to make the most of the more favourable conditions and the greater potentialities of the hands.

The growth and elaboration of the human brain, in Elliot Smith's opinion, briefly, is the primary factor; the erect posture and human character are its consequences. This reverses the logical argument which, to our way of thinking, should be, first, the functional requirement, then its consequent changes in bodily structures. (*See also* D. J. Morton 1927.)

What factors caused the growth and elaboration of the human brain, as interpreted by Smith, remains a mystery. It is much more logical and in accord with the ideas expressed and carefully documented in the preceding chapter to regard the growth and perfection of the human brain not as a cause, but as a consequence, of the changed mode of life, primarily of the terrestrial, upright gait and the emancipation of the arms and hands for exclusive use in manipulation, adopted by Man's Ancestors.

The brain, like any other bodily organ within the limits of its inherent capacities, had to increase in size and modify its internal structure in all its details under the influence of changed functional demands. The limits of the inherent capacities of the primate brain, fortunately, were wide (*see* for details L. Edinger 1911; Ariëns Kappers *et al.* 1936; N. Beccari 1943). If they had been as narrow as those of the brain of a Fish, a Lizard, or a Bird, no amount of functional stimulus would have availed. The ability

to fly developed by some Fishes was limited by the initial primitive organization of their limbs, while the Bats and Birds, beginning with more plastic limbs, could develop this mode of locomotion to perfection. The simian ancestors of Man, once they had embarked upon a roaming career in the open country and specialized in gathering fruits and in hunting animals for their sustenance, were forced gradually to increase their cerebral machine in size and elaboration, perfecting their senses of vision, audition, vocal intercommunication or speech, and their social instincts in that order. These functional and habitual factors, together with the manipulative ability of their hands, then, appear to be the principal pillars upon which the survival and progress of the human race or races were based.

The steady growth of the human brain and the elaboration of Man's mental faculties were not the cause, but the consequence, of the specialization of the legs and feet for locomotion and of the arms and hands for manipulation of objects, which received its principal stimulus from the erect posture and bipedal gait. The corresponding adaptation of the remainder of the body, including the senses and the brain, followed.

This view agrees well with the anatomical organization of the Promethean *Australopithecus*, discovered by Dart, with human legs and feet for walking erect and arms and hands for manipulation, but in possession of a brain only a little larger than in the present Anthropomorphous Apes. (*See* Le Gros Clark, *History of the Primates*, 1953, and his paper, 1954.)

5. Secondary factors impeding or facilitating the effect of the upright gait.—In the estimate of the phylogenetical role of the upright posture and the emancipation of the upper extremities from locomotion, other factors, some positive, some negative, must be considered.

The liberation of the arms and hands from locomotion may be only relative. In the Tarsier, for example, the usual posture is sitting on the haunches, with the arms and hands usually perfectly free, which can be used as auxiliaries in feeding, as described and illustrated in the preceding chapter. In spite of this freedom, however, the Tarsier's hands are poor prehensile instruments, of small use in performing delicate movements. They are used almost entirely as crude grabbing tools, in a wholesale manner. They are also used in assisting locomotion, in which the long and powerful legs are the principal propelling limbs. The manipulative ability of the Tarsier seems never to have been much developed, because of his leaping mode of progression and his nocturnal habit, which prevented his vision and his brain from progressive elaboration toward human status.

While the erect posture of the Tarsier was sufficient to prolong the existence of this ancient suborder in its tropical habitat, it did not eliminate the inhibitory effect of the negative factor, which was the nocturnal mode of life. In contrast, in the rise of Man powerful positive factors were at work, which fostered such progress. The diurnal habit, with full development of visual potentialities, upright gait, use of the hands under visual guidance, and social co-operation, with the development of speech, were the principal stimuli for a harmonious development of Man's senses and mentality.

The thesis of the primacy of the brain in human origin must be substantially qualified. The greatest concession one could make to Elliot Smith's viewpoint would be that erect posture and cerebral perfection were two reciprocally interconnected processes, tied by other factors, the most important being the emancipation of the upper extremities from locomotion and their exclusive use as instruments of the mind.

The interaction of the emancipated hands and the progressive perfection of the senses and mind, Elliot Smith formulates in these words: "The ability to perform skilled movements is conducive to a marked enrichment of the mind's structure and the high development of the neopallium, which is the material expression of that enrichment." This in turn stimulated the growth and elaboration of the rest of the cortex, and thus gave a powerful impulse to the growth of "the faculty of shaping its conduct in anticipation of results" or, briefly, of the reasoning power.

The ability to shape one's conduct in anticipation of the results, as a definition of the substance of reasoning, is, however, a widespread phenomenon. In its elemental form it is possessed even by the lowliest animals, for example, by a Paramecium, a Bacterium, or a Caterpillar. The lowliest Vertebrates, the Fishes, may develop a visual memory of long duration, as Darwin reported from observations of Möbius. And doesn't the Pike shape its conduct according to the anticipation of a fat Sunfish? In this light, the mentality of the higher animals, particularly the Primates, is but an immensely expanded and elaborately organized potentiality also possessed by the less advanced forms of animal life. They all have a common root—living matter. In Darwin's words, "there is no fundamental difference between man and the higher mammals in their mental faculties."

6. THE DEVELOPMENT OF HUMAN INTELLIGENCE, AND THE ORIGIN OF SPEECH.—The outstanding features of Man, in addition to his upright bipedal gait and the exclusive use of his arms and hands as manipulative instruments of mind guided by vision, are the great scope of his intelligence and the ability to speak and to understand speech. How his intelligence increased beyond that of all other animals and how speech developed were and remain problems awaiting a satisfactory answer.

"The increasing ability to perform actions demanding skill and delicacy received a great impetus," according to Elliot Smith, "when the hands were liberated for the exclusive cultivation of such skill; this perfection of cerebral control over muscular actions made it possible for the Ape-Man to learn to imitate the sounds around him, for the art of learning is a training not only of the motor centres and the muscles concerned, but also of all muscles, because posture involves the whole body and it is more or less concerned in every act. The benefits that accrued from educating the hands added to the power of controlling other muscles, such as those concerned with articulate speech."

The preceding thesis of a direct relationship between the increased manipulative proficiency of the hands and the origin of speech, however, is more than questionable. There is no causal connection between the two. One can readily see, on the other hand, such a connection between the increasing mental capacities of rising humanity and the more elaborate production and understanding of the sounds made by the organs of speech.

A sign language of gesticulation and physiognomic expressions may have developed simultaneously or at a slightly preceding phase, as predecessors and assistants to articulate vocal speech. In any case, they play a secondary role as a means of communication.

Articulate spoken language must have evolved from the early chaotic elements of gesticulation, grimacing, and inarticulate utterances. Its principal phylogenetical motivation, however, must have been the necessity for the invention of a means of communication, or transmission of thoughts, by organs not used either for locomotion or for manipulation—in other words, the vocal organs. Just as the legs and feet had to take over the entire burden of carrying the body in order to make the hands free for handling objects, so the vocal and associated organs had to take over practically the entire task of transmission of ideas, in order to free the hands. In this way the vocal organs, otherwise used only for physiological purposes, became employed for a very essential function. In vocal speech there is little or no need for gesticulating arms and hands or for the postural movements of other parts of the body, which all had to be kept free of such uses. This is especially true of the arms and hands, since they had to be employed as manipulative tools of the mind. The grimacing physiognomy, of no other use, was, on the other hand, useful in spoken language, employing, at least in part, the same apparatus.

Once articulate vocal language was sufficiently developed, it became a disseminator of thought and in turn a stimulator of the developing intellect, that is, of the intellectual mechanism of the brain.

Speech and the expanding intellectual powers were not the cause, however, but the consequence of an upright gait. Man's Ancestors did not begin to walk upright because they first developed a superior thinking machine, as Elliot Smith postulated, but were forced to grow a large and elaborate brain, with a complex structure, in order to provide centers for upright posture, manipulation of objects, and communication by spoken and auditory language. The de-velopment of the superior intelligence followed as a logical result.

The enormous expansion of the intellectual powers or of intellectual discrimination based upon acquired knowledge was rather secondary to the upright bipedal gait. It was the bipedal gait which made Man an enduring wanderer and a fast runner, and his hands efficient manipulators. And it was these two factors which immensely increased the scope of human experience, principally visual, in contrast to the modest mental scope of the largely sedentary jungle-dwelling Apes.

The evolution of speech necessarily followed the development of upright gait, roaming life, and the habit of hunting in packs and gathering fruits and tubers as a family team or group. In fact, as Elliot Smith thinks, "the acquisition of such fuller means of communication with his fellows by vocal symbols may have been one of the essential factors in converting Man's ultimate simian ancestor into a real man."

This view is in accord with Dart's discovery of *Australopithecus*, a Primate in possession of erect posture and human-like arms and hands, but a brain only half the size of the smallest modern human brain and but a little larger than that of a large Gorilla. It is likely, then, that a similar situation was present in Primates directly ancestral to Man, indicating the primacy of erect posture over that of the brain in human evolution.

The increase in intellectual powers and the gradual development of articulate speech must have been a very long and slow process. The initial condition may not have been radically different from the vocal utterances of the now living Monkeys and Apes. The duration of the formative phase of speech and its perfection, starting from this ill-defined moment, must have been quite long, extending over untold ages. How long this process of intellectual maturing lasted is only dimly indicated by modern languages, whose complexity becomes more apparent, the more ancient forms are studied (e.g., Sanskrit [Samskrta], Ancient Greek, Latin, etc.; on language *see* O. Jespersen 1922; Sapir 1939; *see also* C. Monakow 1914; H. Head 1920, 1923; and J. M. Nielsen 1946).

Such an extremely complex device of human intellectual intercourse presupposes that the duration of Man's mental evolution must be figured in hundreds of thousands of years, and probably a good deal more. This is in accord with other signs of prehistoric human activity, notably with prehistoric pictorial symbolism. Such is seen, for example, in the mural drawings in the caves of northern Spain (Altamira) and of southern France (Lascaux Cave), whose estimated age is from 15,000 to 30,000 years and perhaps much more. This evidence shows Man's visual functions, including color sense and aesthetic appreciation of forms, to have been at that early date practically as good as it is now.

7. The factors responsible for the rise of Man, and their interplay.—The various factors, whose interplay had brought about the coming of Man, Elliot Smith summarized as follows:

. . . the evolution of the Primates and the emergence of the distinctively human type of intelligence are to be explained primarily by a steady growth and specialization of certain parts of the brain; that such development could have occurred only in the Mammalia because they are the only plastic class of animals with a true organ of intelligence [i.e., the cerebral cortex]; that an arboreal mode of life started Man's ancestors on the way to pre-eminence, for it gave them the agility; and the specialization of the higher parts of the brain incidental to such a life gave them the seeing eye, and in course of time also the understanding ear; and that all the rest followed in the train of this high development of vision working on a brain which controlled ever-increasingly agile limbs.

This thesis of Elliot Smith may be accepted in a general way, with, however, certain qualifications: that all Vertebrates, certainly all Mammals, possess an organ of intelligence, even though in many it is small in size, of inferior structural complexity and functional efficiency; and that in the Lower Vertebrates it is not the cortex but other parts of the brain which phylogenetically preceded it and substitute for it; that the cortex proved to be the most successful in this sense; and that arboreal life by itself was not the cause, since the Birds are both arboreal and agile.

We may accept entirely the following words of Elliot Smith, that the solution of Man's origin "is not to be sought merely in comparisons of Man and the Anthropoid Apes. Man has emerged not by the sudden intrusion of some new element into the Ape's physical structure or the fabric of his mind, but by the culmination of those processes which have been operating in the same way in a long line of ancestors ever since the beginning of the Tertiary Period," and even much earlier.

8. Vision—the leading sense in the development of Man from an Infrahuman Primate.—The investigation of the eyes and visual centers of the brain in the various Vertebrates shows an advanced structure in those species of all classes largely or principally relying on sight. Among the Lizards, such are the Chameleon and Anole; among the Birds, the Eagle and the Swallow; among the Mammals, the Primates, as described in chapter XIV. The Primate Order depends so much upon the sense of sight as to deserve the designation "visual animals." Of all orders, in this order alone—from the lowest to the highest: the Monkeys, Apes, and Man, including the nocturnal Tarsier and Aotes—the central fovea and area of the retina, specialized for epicritic or refined vision, are universally found. This fact, together with the possession of hands and fingers fit to perform delicate manipulations under visual guidance, shows the overwhelming role that vision plays in the life of the Primates.

The specific question of what role vision played in the origin of Man has already been discussed on several occasions in this book. In his analysis of the possible causes, Elliot Smith found "a localized and precocious expansion of those areas of the brain which we associate with the power of articulate speech," and he thinks that "there are grounds for believing that the acquisition of true articulate speech was one of the essential factors in the emergence of Man's distinctive characters."

The examination of the endocranial casts of the primitive human races, for example, of Figure 33 in Elliot Smith's book, shows the occipital lobes of the Rhodesian Man, where visual centers are located, to be large and protruding far backward, whereas the temporal lobes, associated with hearing, are relatively small. This precocious phylogenetical development of the visual parts of the human brain, compared with other parts, especially with the poorly developed temporoparietal association area of Flechsig, indicates that vision was a step ahead of hearing and speech during human evolution. This, of course, has its parallel in all Higher Primates in which the refined epicritic vision is superior to the auditory sense. This interpretation is also in accord with the concept expounded previously in this chapter.

These and other facts and observations suggest that vision was the dominant sense in Man's Ancestors, whatever other factors have contributed to the emergence of human intelligence.

The identity and sequence of the factors which culminated in the formation of Man from an Infrahuman Primate may be imagined as follows. The arboreal habit had, from the beginning, enhanced the dominance of vision in the Primates. The terrestrial habit and the erect attitude of Man's Ancestors continued and increased the same emphasis upon vision. In the savanna-like habitat, away from the sheltering jungle, acute vision was even more important for survival. The upright gait and the emancipation of arms and hands from locomotion and their transformation into delicate grasping organs, capable of being used either together or singly, had further removed the senses of smell and taste from the source of food, making vision and, in a lesser degree, hearing the leading senses. An additional factor was the roaming habit, made possible by the swift bipedal locomotion. The impulse toward increased development of hearing, imposed by Man's social habits, made of it the most important auxiliary sense, indispensable in his struggle for life. The development of speech as the easiest means of intercommunication between the members of the family or tribe belongs in the same category.

These factors appear to be the principal pillars upon which the human mind was built. The brain, because of them, was forced to follow suit. Like any other bodily organ, it had to organize itself according to the increased functional demand. This again was possible because of the essential organization of the vertebrate, especially the primate, brain and because of the plastic potentialities of its tissue inherited from the Prevertebrate Ancestors.

The importance of stereoscopic vision in the origin of Man is not quite obvious, and even now its essence is not fully understood. Its role in human development, in contrast with the Infrahuman Primates and other Vertebrates, probably was overemphasized. Since binocular stereoscopic vision, in view of a practically identical anatomical arrangement, must be assumed to be the same or similar in all Higher Primates, certainly so in all Monkeys and Apes and even in the nocturnal Tarsier, and as a facultative arrangement in at least some Lizards and Birds, it could have been neither a primary nor a decisive factor. Hence binocular stereopsis could not have been the principal factor which prepared "the way for the further cultivation of those high powers of discrimination and understanding that are distinctive of the Human Family," as Elliot Smith believed. But, together with the upright gait, manipulative ability of the hands, and the development of speech, binocular stereopsis, further improved and elaborated, was an additional factor in human origin, just as were visual acuity and color perception. It was an expression of the general improvement and further refinement of the human visual apparatus, all required as a basis for harmonious human development.

SEC. 8. MAN'S EARLIEST ANCESTORS PRECEDING AND DURING THE ASSUMPTION OF ERECT POSTURE AND BIPEDAL GAIT

1. PROBLEM OF LINKING MAN WITH HIS INFRAHUMAN ANCESTORS.—The probable evolutionary process by which the ancestors of Man became transformed from the so-called "Quadrumans" into strict "Bipeds-Bimans," that is, Primates possessing "legs" and "feet" exclusively assigned to carry the body, while the "arms" and "hands" became entirely organs of manipulation directed by the "mind" and

largely guided by the sight, was described in detail in section 3, in this chapter. Also discussed were the probable factors which may have initiated and carried out this transformation.

In this picture of transformation, in the present state of our ignorance, much unfortunately remains hypothetical. The later successive stages toward the status of *Homo sapiens* may have resembled one or another or several of the so far known prehistoric human or human-like races, beginning with *Australopithecus, Pithecanthropus-Sinanthropus*, Neanderthal Man, and the Aurignacian or Cro-Magnon race, and finally culminating with the arrival of Modern Man. (Whether this was or was not the actual phylogenetical series which led to *Homo sapiens* or whether, perhaps, most or all mentioned types merely represented various side lines off the main stem remains a problem for future investigation.)

The earlier and more primitive stages which, on general grounds, must undoubtedly have preceded, the very "missing links" connecting the simian-like forms with the incipient humans, the stages which have "approximated very closely to a simian level," are now being discovered and their significance appraised (Le Gros Clark & Leakey 1950). Future investigation may perhaps determine whether any one of these was ancestral to Man or perhaps others linking more directly with the prosimian stock.

The difficulties of finding such "missing links" are not only technical, nor are they all caused by scarcity, in view of the abundant new paleontological material recently uncovered in East Africa. It is reasonable to think that the transformation from a simian to a prehuman form was a very gradual, slow process, spreading over a long stretch of time, and that the early Hominoids and possibly also Hominids had separated from the early Tarsioids or Cercopithecoids at least as far back as the Oligocene Epoch, or from 25 to 35 million years ago.

During this long space of time there must have been stages in the human ascent differing little from the usual simian organization. Such forms, even though in the direct ancestral line of Man, would hardly be distinguishable from some extinct collateral branch. Yet it was in precisely this critical stage that, under some specific stimulus, a germ began to grow which in the long run caused the human line to part from the lines of all other Primates. Figuratively speaking, it is probable that, if it were possible to recreate such simians, they could hardly be recognized as Man's direct ancestors and would be lost among the other extinct or living Primates. In fact, it is probable that such

identification could be made certain only if the entire chain of evidence were complete—a most unlikely event.

In spite of the probability that none of the now living Simians and most of those known to have lived in the past may have been the true "missing links," the gap between the Lower Primates, from which Man's line must have arisen, and the early prehistoric human races has been narrowed through recent discoveries. These may, at any rate, be used to plot in a general way the course of human evolution and to hypothesize about the appearance, habits, and environment of Man's simian-like and protohuman ancestors.

The first to be mentioned, but most recently made, are discoveries of the Miocene Hominoids or Apes, *Proconsul* and *Limnopithecus*. They flourished over wide parts of Africa, Asia, and Europe. Their geological age may be estimated at from 10 to 25 million years. The smallest of the *Proconsuls* were smaller than the Chimpanzee, the largest attaining the size of a large Gorilla. They were, however, more lightly built, embodying cercopithecoid features, indicating a terrestrial and not an arboreal habit. These Apes were definitely not arboreal brachiators but were terrestrial runners and leapers. Their bodily organization was generalized, allowing further specialization either along the pongid line or toward a "type of limb structure which might have permitted the gradual acquisition of an erect posture characteristic of the Hominidae" (Le Gros Clark 1950; Clark & Leakey 1950). Some of these Apes possibly served as the origin of the Hominidae (Le Gros Clark 1953), unless Man had an independent prosimian origin (Robinson 1952).

The other and even more spectacular discovery of *Australopithecus africanus*, formerly known as the "Taungs Ape" or "Taungs Ape-Man," made thirty years ago by R. A. Dart, in Johannesburg, South Africa, and amplified by further Australopithecines such as *Paranthropus* and *Plesianthropus* and others by R. Broom and his co-workers, definitely ties up the preceding and less advanced Primates with those which followed and were indisputably primitive Hominidae, as, for example, *Pithecanthropus* and *Sinanthropus*.

2. The African Australopithecinae or "Southern Apes."—This type, first discovered by Dart in 1924 at Taungs in Bechuanaland and subsequently amplified by additional specimens in the Transvaal, is remarkable in that it approached Man in the structure of the skull, limbs, pelvis, and dentition. The noteworthy exception was the brain. In its volume of 600 or 650 cc. it exceeded but little, according to Dart, the size of the brain of the Gorilla (500 gm., according to Obersteiner; 650 cc. in the largest Gorilla, according to Dart), and at the most it may have attained the volume of 700–800 or 850 cc., according to Broom. The australopithecine brain, then, was somewhat smaller than, or equal to, that of *Pithecanthropus* (775 gm.) and was considerably below the smallest modern human brain (1,000 gm. for man, 900 gm. for woman, according to Obersteiner).

The *Australopithecus* or "Southern Ape," as Dart called this primate type, was, accordingly, the earliest Primate to attain an erect posture and bipedal gait, even though his brain had advanced but little, if at all, beyond the best-developed brain of the large modern Apes.

The "Dartians," as the Australopithecines were named by Sir Arthur Keith, were the "ground-living anthropoids, human in posture, gait, and dentition, but still anthropoid in facial physiognomy and in size of brain" (Nature, 1947). (*See,* for illustrations, G. Elliot Smith, *The Evolution of Man*, 1927, Fig. 4; R. Broom & G. W. H. Schepers, *The South African Fossil Ape-Men, the Australopithecinae*, 1946, Pls. I and II; R. R. Gates, *Human Ancestry*, 1948, frontispiece and Pl. I; Le Gros Clark, Quart. J. Geol. Soc. London, v. 105, p. 13; Le Gros Clark, *History of the Primates*, 1953; and R. Moore, *Man, Time, and Fossils*, 1953, Pls. XXVI and XXVII.)

In his bodily organization, *Australopithecus* approached, or rather preceded, Man in several respects. In developing a real "forehead" and in his human dentition he "dared to emulate Man," as Dart expressed it. The brain of a juvenile was somewhat bigger than that of an adult Chimpanzee. His arms, hands, pelvis, feet, and legs were especially human-like. His head was also poised in a more nearly human fashion, pivoting closer to its center of gravity on the top of the spinal column than is the case in the modern Apes.

The Australopithecinae were, in the words of Le Gros Clark,

hominoids of small stature (probably similar in this respect to the pygmy races of present-day mankind), with brains not much larger relatively than those of the gorilla and chimpanzee, massive jaws showing many human features, a dentition fundamentally of human type . . . and limbs approximating in their structure and proportions to those of the Hominidae. They were evidently capable of standing and walking with an almost erect posture, and the hands and feet were relatively small and delicately built. . . .

So far as the *morphological* evidence at present available can be assessed, it seems a reasonable inference that they either represent a group which occupied a position quite close to the main line of later hominid evolution, or else they represent only slightly modified descendants of such a group.

The decision must depend partly on the geological age of the australopithecine deposits. (This age, according to the estimate of R. Broom 1950, would be from 1 to 5 million years or more, or approximately from the Middle Pliocene to the Early Pleistocene Epoch.)

The Australopithecinae, according to Dart, "are proto-human beings; and they are the most primitive hominids of whom we have knowledge."

The pertinent question, then, is how *Australopithecus* was able to develop human hands and bipedal gait without a human brain. Our logic demands that human hands could have evolved in no other way than as exclusive instruments of a mind which had attained at least the minimum characteristic human qualities. In Elliot Smith's thesis discussed in section 7, the primacy of the brain, secondarily followed by the reorganization of the rest of the body, was the principal argument.

This particular question was answered by Dart's further discoveries (1948, 1949). From the numerous remains of animals associated with those of *Australopithecus*, it is apparent that he was an intelligent, courageous, fleet-footed, terrestrial, meat-eating hunter. For his food supply he drew upon almost every kind of small and big game found in South Africa: Turtles, Birds, Insectivores, Rodents, small Bucks, Rock-Rabbits, Crabs, birds' eggs, two or three species of Baboons, fourteen Bovidae, three carnivores, such as the Lion, Hyena, and Jackal, two extinct species of Pigs, a Rhinoceros, Hippopotamus, two kinds of Giraffes, and the Elephant. The fauna indicates the Early Pleistocene Epoch, which may be roughly estimater at 1 million years ago.

Other considerations indicate that, in spite of his smallish brain, the *Australopithecus* must have been a clever hunter. Judging from the age of the remnants of his game, which include mostly juveniles and the aged, he caught it more by tricks and cunning stratagem than by power. The aged individuals, weakened by general decrepitude and disease, he could easily have overcome. But many juveniles, constantly under the surveillance of the powerful adults, he could have enticed away only by a trick. This assumption is justified when one considers the rather high intelligence and cunning of the Apes, such as Chimpanzee, Orang, and Gorilla, well attested by experiment and observation. (*Cf.* Köhler, Yerkes, Klüver, Bingham, Benchley, and my own observations; *see* secs. 4, 5, this chapter.)

"The profusion of the bone breccia," to quote Dart, "shows that they were capable and successful in their hunting of very big game." It also shows that *Australopithecus* subsisted largely, possibly entirely, on a meat diet. This in turn presupposes efficient techniques and methods of capturing game which made such extensive leaning upon hunting possible.

Since the weapons of these hunters were, at best, primitive, consisting of stones, large animal bones, or branches used as clubs, bludgeons, or bone breakers, or sharp bone splinters and stag and antelope antlers used as daggers, this further presupposes considerable mental ability to make such a technique successful. Their wits, however, were not sharp enough to devise a way of deliberately fashioning the edged tools and cutting weapons, a feat achieved during the next succeeding human evolutionary stage (*cf.* Oakley 1950).

The majority of skulls of Baboons, which in some regions represented the principal game, were found by Dart, Broom, and Schepers to have been fractured by heavy bludgeon blows or split open or smashed in a way indicating that they had been slain by some such weapon

as a piece of rock held in the hand or perhaps attached to a handle; or they showed round holes through which the brain had been extracted. Other skulls of Baboons showed double depressed fractures into which fit the hammer-shaped ends of long bones of large Ungulates which had been used as attacking bludgeons.

It is noteworthy that most australopithecine skulls also showed similar fractures, as Schepers found, indicating that these Protohuman Primates were not only assiduous hunters but also cruel cannibals. In attacking, the Australopithecinae favored a direct frontal approach to the quarry, which indicates that they were bold and courageous. Since the left side of the victim's skull was usually crushed, the right hand was used by preference to deliver the well-aimed *coup de grâce*. Dart writes:

> The deposits of Taungs, Sterkfontein, and Makapansgat tell us in this way a consistent, coherent story not of fruit-eating, forest-loving apes, but of the sanguinary pursuits and carnivorous habits of protomen. They were human not merely in being bipedal, in maintaining an upright posture, and in having the facial form and dental apparatus of humanity; they were also human in their cave life, in their love of flesh, in hunting wild game to secure meat, and in employing implements, whether wielded and propelled to kill during hunting, or systematically applied to the cracking of bones and the eating of food. There is only one physical feature—namely, brain quantity (not brain quality)—which separates these proto-men from early man. . . .
>
> Similarly, on the cultural side there is apparently no feature other than *the deliberate manufacture of stone tools* which separates these proto-men at the present time from early man.

Other findings of Dart indicate a systematic use of fire by *Australopithecus*, for example, the charred appearance of some bones accumulated in the "kitchen middens" which appear to have been deliberately fractured and split, in order to extract the marrow. This creature, then, is the first on record to master the making of fire, hence the epithet "Promethean" given to him by Dart as an allusion to Prometheus, the legendary hero of the ancient Greek saga.

The picture of this early protohuman creature, which subsisted principally, if perhaps not entirely, on big game, may be further sketched in from the information kindly furnished by Professor Dart (1952 and 1953):

One of the principal reasons for the early failure of European and American scientists to appreciate the significance of the Australopithecinae in the human evolutionary story was their quite natural lack of knowledge about South Africa.

Geographically and geologically South Africa is almost as much of a desert as North Africa. In one year five times as much water runs over the Niagara Falls as runs in all of the rivers in the whole of the Union of South Africa, taken together. An arid savannah country of this sort can maintain much game, but it has no forests or fruits to compare with the woodlands and the berries, apples, and nuts, etc., of Europe, Asia, and the Americas.

The earliest Primates arose from or are indistinguishable from the Insectivora, so their diet was doubtless insectivorous at the outset. The South African baboons are quadrupedal most of the time and turn over every stone for scorpions, raid birds' nests for their eggs and young, devour any small veld creature like grasshoppers, lizards, etc., with relish, and are reputed not only to attack lambs and ewes, but also to hunt buck. Their diet is essentially vegetarian tubers and bulbs, fresh shoots of plants and the raiding of the gardens and orchards of introduced plants, maize, melons, bananas etc., but as none of these is indigenous to South Africa, they would fare poorly if they were not omnivorous by nature.

The Australopithecinae, according to Professor Dart, leave no doubt that

there must have been an anthropoidal phase in human development and that the arboreal and terrestrial specialisations within the anthropoid group were fundamentally dietetic in origin, and expressions of herbivorous versus carnivorous specialisation respectively. . . .

Man's ancestors avoided extreme adaptation to the arboreal way of life because of their blood lust. The carnivorous propensities of the pronograde anthropoid stock, ancestral to mankind, weaned them away from the forest and its succulent leaves, roots, and fruits that attracted the living anthropoids and enticed man's ancestral stock into the savannah or prairie where there was enough wild game.

The terrestrialized baboons of Africa show us that savannah life is perfectly feasible for primitive anthropoidal creatures provided they have an omnivorous diet, *i.e.*, including insects, birds' eggs, and small game. There are those (like Straus of Johns Hopkins) who think that the human stock could have broken away from the primate stock at a cercopithecid stage and L. H. Wells showed that the foot of the baboon is in some ways closer to the foot of mankind than are the feet of living anthropoids. The Tarsier split-off would lie unnecessarily far back. There never would have been a theory of evolution if there were no monkeys and apes to fill in gaps between Tarsius and Man.

Whatever be the route of evolution we know both Tarsier and monkey have tails. Whatever the cause of the divergence between monkey and ape, it was fundamentally postural since it involved the loss of the tail. That means that in addition to a lot of sitting down and concurrent liberation of the hands (under the direction of the now reasonably stereoscopic eyes), the tail musculature instead of wagging a futile counterpoise behind could be concentrated on the cloacal evolution on the ventral aspect instead of being completely at the rear of the body.

One of the biggest factors in this increased sitting-down of anthropoids on their ischial tuberosities and thighs as compared with cercopithecids, to my mind, is the lengthening of the periods of gestation and especially of infancy, in creatures capable of manipulating their offspring and carrying them in or under their arms instead of their clinging instinctively to the maternal belly or back. What that entailed visually, manually, and posturally in the evolutionary story is more easily imaginable to you as a neurologist than it is to me to depict here.

When there was added to this anthropoidal squatting on their bottoms (not on their heels) which was essential for the improved manipulation of infants and other objects (that Reynolds recognised was implicit in their pelvic evolution), the further business of systematically hunting animals for food or robbing other carnivores of their prey, then the brandishing of clubs and flinging of rocks (which previously had been an occasional feat or temporary employment) became a vital necessity and, in consequence, the principal business of adolescent pre-human education.

With regard to fruits and cereals the South African flora is singularly lacking and there is no evidence of which I am aware, to indicate that our pre-human ancestors favoured either of these classes of vegetable food. Would not the varying colours of their potential enemies, both reptilian and mammalian, and the animals they hunted for food, be even more powerful stimuli for the evocation of colour-vision percepts in carnivorous creatures than are the colours of fruits to herbivorous creatures?

Since the Australopithecinae are the only pre-human creatures known to have had an erect posture and bipedal gait, and they lived in Early Pleistocene or Late Pliocene times, it can be said that man was erect before he became sufficiently manlike to be recognised by all scientists as human and that that was at least 1,000,000 years ago. It may have been twice as long.

According to G. B. Barbour (1949), the estimated time is that of Upper Pliocene or "distinctly more than a million years ago, and shortly before the onset of the colder climate which heralded the Great Ice Age in Europe and North America," and that Man lived in the caves of Makapansgat Valley in the Pliocene Epoch, at two stages in the Pleistocene, and again today. (*See* G. B. Barbour, *Makapansgat*, 1949, p. 146, for evidence of the use of fire; for further dating *see* Zeuner's *Dating the Past*, 1952.)

(The estimated time of the above-mentioned epochs is, according to Zeuner, for Holocene, or most recent, prehistory, 10,000 years; for Pleistocene, 1 million; for Pliocene, *ca.* 10 million; for Miocene, 15 million years in succession; the Holocene, or Postglacial, and the Pleistocene, or Ice Age, together make up the Quaternary Period, which followed the much longer Tertiary Period, consisting of Pliocene, Miocene, Oligocene, Eocene, and Paleocene Epochs, which together lasted approximately 58 million years.)

Professor Dart's conclusion is as follows:

So, disagreeable as it may be to contemplate, man appears to have become man by virtue of his ferocity. In this connection you may be interested to read Carveth Read's *The Origin of Man* in which he dealt with the hunting pack and its psychological inevitabilities. Despite what Elliot Smith had to say in *Human History* about the peace-loving characteristics of mankind as opposed to systematised war, we cannot avoid the philosophical implications of massacres, both those of historical record and those of prehistoric exposure, as at Krapina, Choukoutien, and Solo, to say naught of cannibalism both in fact and in ritual.

(For Krapina *see* Gorjanović-Kramberger; *cf. also* Weidenreich.)

Professor Dart's views may be further amplified by an excerpt from a letter from L. S. B. Leakey, curator of the Coryndon Museum, at Nairobi, Kenya, Africa. In his words:

I have no doubt at all that man originated in Africa, the presence of *Propliopithecus* in the Oligocene of Egypt; of the very numerous "apes" in the Lower Miocene of Kenya—*Proconsul* (3 species) and *Limnopithecus* (2 species) and *Sivapithecus;* and of the *Australopithecines* in South Africa, all point to this.

Equally, I have no doubt in my own mind that man never went through a highly arboreal stage or even a brachiating stage, but went direct from a quadrupedal animal living mainly on the ground and in open country (like Baboons do) to an upright gait.

I think the origin of man may be sought among the *Proconsul* and *Sivapithecus* group in the Lower Miocene of Kenya, and we have suggestions that their habitat was open country with *very numerous* fruits, nuts, and berries on bush rather than in forest.

(*Cf.* W. L Straus, Jr. 1949; Clark & Leakey 1950.)

There is evidence, according to Leakey, of some 158 different species of fruits and seeds not yet analyzed, found in the deposits of Kenya which yielded *Proconsul*, the associated fauna indicating a good deal of open grassland. The skeleton of this Ape suggests a quadrupedal gait, and its diet may also have included insects. The Australopithecinae, in the opinion of Leakey, are an offshoot from the human stock, and not direct ancestors.

The preceding quotations present a digest of the available information, and they illustrate the complexity of the problem of Man's rise to his present dominant place in nature. In the concluding sections of this chapter, we shall try to summarize our views on the subject and on the other problems related to it.

SEC. 9. REFLECTIONS ON *AUSTRALOPITHECUS* AND ON THE ORIGIN OF MANKIND

1. REORGANIZATION OF THE QUADRUMANOUS BODY FOR BIPEDAL GAIT, AND ITS CONSEQUENCES.—The discovery of *Australopithecus*, the earliest known human-like Primate, is of great interest in several respects. He was the first member of this order on record to develop an upright posture and the use of bipedal gait as the preponderant mode of locomotion (with the

exception of the leaping Tarsier). His arms and hands, in contrast with all other nontarsian Infrahuman Primates—irrespective of whether they were quadrumanous arboreal climbers, terrestrial walkers, or arboreal brachiators— became largely, perhaps entirely, emancipated from carrying the body weight. In consequence, his upper extremities became versatile tools and instruments of mind by which objects could be examined, principally by vision, and used for a variety of purposes, including the handling of the tools and weapons (stones, bludgeons).

The other consequence of bipedal gait and upright body posture and the reorganization of the rest of the bodily machine was the effect on the intellect. The continuous handling of objects, their close scrutiny by the sense of touch, deep sense, taste, and smell, and, above all, sight, brought information to the mind in an abundance never achieved by any of the Anthropoids, including the most advanced now living species.

Bipedal gait, upright posture, and flexible neck also made possible freedom and continuity of observation of near and far objects by the distance senses, especially vision. When these changes had been accomplished, the point was apparently reached where Man's line definitely began to climb toward the human state.

Australopithecus, however, could not have been the first departure of the human line from the primate stem or chain but was merely a link in that chain (if not part of a side line). The human line seems to have parted much earlier from a more generalized, essentially monkey-like, stock during the Early Miocene (20–25 million years) and Oligocene Epochs (25–35 million years in the past) and in this way had avoided completely the brachiating arboreal specialization. The absence of clear signs of a pronounced brachiating phase in human organization, which is so striking a feature of the Gibbons and of the large Anthropomorphous Apes, agrees with this. (*See* W. L. Straus, Jr., "The Riddle of Man's Ancestry," Quart. Rev. Biol., v. 24, p. 200, 1949; *see also* Klaatsch; Boule; Osborn 1928; Broom & Schepers 1946; Le Gros Clark 1950, 1953, 1954, in contrast to W. K. Gregory 1916, 1927, 1928, 1930; and D. J. Morton 1924, 1927.)

The phylogenetical line which eventually culminated in Man must have started very much earlier in the paleontological past. This line at the australopithecine stage may already have had a long history whose beginnings at the primate stem cannot as yet be precisely determined. (*Cf.* J. T. Robinson 1952, 1953.)

Another problem is whether or not these discovered Australopithecinae were an actual link in the phylogenetical line of the true Hominidae. It is possible that the human line had an origin independent from the primate stem and that at the period corresponding to the now known Australopithecs, roughly estimated as the late Pliocene and early Pleistocene, it had already outstripped that of the Australopithecs, leaving them as a phylogenetical remnant, as some evidence of Broom & Robinson (1950) seems to indicate. But even if this were the case, the Australopithecinae illustrate "a hypothetical picture of the ancestral forms which must presumably have immediately preceded the *Pithecanthropus* phase of human evolution" (according to Le Gros Clark 1950). Other considerations indicate that the australopithecine and similar types were not confined to South Africa but had wide distribution in other parts of that continent and very likely were also present in Asia (*see* J. T. Robinson 1953). From any one of these, or from several, the true human line or lines may have originated.

2. Positive and negative factors in the advancement of Man's early progenitors. —The question may be raised as to whether or not the circumstances of the habitat and habits of *Australopithecus*, or similar types, could have been conducive to further development toward true human status, and how they could have worked.

We are aware of two positive factors likely to foster the emergence of human intelligence. The first was the apparent ability of Man's progenitor at an early stage to use, or to fashion, mechanical tools and weapons from pieces of stone, wood, and bone, which greatly increased the effectiveness of his arms and hands as the executive limbs of the mind. The other factor was his use of fire, an invention which was a product of his intellect and mechanical skill. This in turn made it possible for him to prepare meat for food, a material repugnant in a raw state as sole fare to most other primate species, with the exception of the crab-eating Macaques and the Tarsier (*see* chap. XIV, 12). (Even Baboons, contrary to the belief of the natives, do not hunt larger game animals, according to Zuckerman 1932, although they certainly would eat smaller animals such as Rats, according to Klüver's experience.)

The adverse factor was the diet of *Australopithecus*, which, according to Dart, appears to have consisted entirely of meat. To catch animals in a grassland such as South Africa, the hunter must be in possession of sharp senses, sufficient intelligence, swift locomotion, aggressive weapons, and physical power. The carnivorous animals of the same region, the Lion, Leopard, and Hyena, are well provided with all. *Australopithecus* was also well equipped in all but one. His senses, especially vision, must have been acute, his mental powers of observation and integration were of a high order, he was an enduring walker and a fast runner, he possessed commensurately great physical strength. In one respect he was singularly deficient. He did not possess aggressive weapons comparable to the huge canines and sharp, shearing premolar and molar teeth and the large claws of the Carnivores. The only instruments that *Australopithecus* could use were his arms and hands, employed as grabbing, beating, strangling, and pulling tools directed by sharp senses, quick and resourceful intellect, performing skilful motor acts. To the Human Ancestors this mode of acquiring food would have sufficed, however, only as long as they subsisted on a plant diet and on animals that could be mastered with bare hands. To acquire a more abundant food supply by hunting larger game, it was necessary to use mechanical tools and weapons. In this respect *Australopithecus* may perhaps serve as an illustration of the very first use of bones and possibly sticks and stones as hunting weapons.

The bipedal gait and the emancipation of the upper extremities from locomotion alone, obviously, could never have launched Man's Ancestors upon the road of intellectual progress. The Birds, whose terrestrial locomotion is bipedal, show this. Another example is the larger species of Kangaroos, where the entire labor of locomotion is also performed by the powerful hind legs (in addition to the strong tail), the smaller forelegs being free. But here the comparison ends. The rather small and weak upper extremities of the strictly herbivorous Kangaroos are useful only for holding the branches of shrubs in browsing and other similar and little-diversified acts not requiring great skill or much intelligence.

A very different situation obtained with *Australopithecus*. To catch game, he had to use his higher senses, primarily vision, to the limit, to observe the animal's habits and to interpret them correctly. Finally, he had to overcome it by the skilful use of his arms and hands, directed by his superior intelligence. He had to compensate for the deficiency of aggressive bodily equipment by the clever use of his "grabbing extremities," his intellectual capabilities, his cunning, and his inventiveness.

In the life of *Australopithecus* every act of procuring food became a venture which began with a premeditated plan, continued as an exciting drama, and terminated with a resolving climax. Upon its success depended his survival.

The mind of *Australopithecus* was, therefore, largely dominated by concepts of "planned aggression," whose execution depended upon the powers of his intellect. In his struggle for existence the brain of *Australopithecus* became most important as a medium to contrive the use of primitive weapons—large ungulate bones, sticks, or stones as clubs—by which the power of his hands and arms was very much increased.

3. CARNIVOROUS HABIT PROBABLE DETERRENT TO ACHIEVEMENT OF HUMAN STATE. The bipedal locomotion of *Australopithecus* and the use of his upper extremities as instruments of the mind must have been a powerful stimulus toward human development. Doubt arises, however, in view of his exclusive meat diet. Such a habit may equally have been a deterrent. An example of this may be the Tarsier, whose purely carnivorous habit, in spite of an almost exclusive use of hind extremities for locomotion and the proportional emancipation of the arms and hands, did not help in the least to prevent it from becoming a living fossil, although the Tarsier's nocturnal adaptation was undoubtedly a potent factor which precluded any further advancement, as already discussed (*see* chap. XIV, 12).

Other primate experiments in the paleontological past which deviated from the preponderantly omnivorous trend by assuming rodent-like habits have all disappeared, with a single exception. Such were *Tetonius*, an Eocene Tarsioid, *Sinclairella* of the American Oligocene, *Carpolestes*, *Apatemys*, and *Plesiadapis* of the Paleocene and Eocene Epochs, which apparently were also all Tarsioids. The only still living example of this adaptation is the Aye-Aye (*Chiromys* or *Daubentonia madagascariensis*), which possesses a single remaining pair of enlarged incisors which it uses in the fashion of Rodents to gnaw through the bark of trees in search of insects. (*See* Parker & Haswell 1940, v. 2, Fig. 511; Romer, *Vertebrate Paleontology*, Figs. 268, 269; Brehm's *Tierleben;* Zuckerman 1933, Fig. 4.)

It is therefore possible that the Australopithecinae represented an aberrant branch of the advanced Primates which may have bogged down in an excessively carnivorous specialization, as their massive jaws and teeth would indicate (*see* jaws described by Dart 1948 and 1954; Broom & Robinson 1950; and Le Gros Clark 1953). The more versatile, omnivorous, and therefore more adaptable principal stream of bipedal Primates went on under better conditions and succeeded in developing their bodily character and sensory-mental abilities more harmoniously.

The infancy of Mankind may not have been so completely carnivorous as it would appear in the perspective of the Australopithecinae. But they are a dramatic demonstration of the ferocious, aggressive traits and the "blood lust" which must have been a potent factor also in Man's direct ancestors. Or else Man would have never risen, literally and figuratively, on his "legs" and would have never developed his "arms" and "hands" as the exclusive tools of his intellect.

Man's aggressive traits are well documented by prehistory, history, and everyday experience. Certainly Mankind behaved and behaves much of the time as if directly descended from the Australopithecs, whose dominant feature of character was aggressiveness (as their exclusively carnivorous habit, as in other Carnivora, demanded). But in Man's direct ancestors the carnivorous propensities and "blood lust" may have erupted only at times, periodically, incited either by hunger, opportunity, or emotion. Hence the ferocious instincts may have remained dormant for longer or shorter periods, during which Man's Ancestors pursued more peaceful occupations, gathering the fruits of the earth, in addition to hunting various animals, which may have been their chief source of sus-

tenance. Much of the time they may have been, therefore, peaceably inclined, but the "blood lust" was always there, ready to flare up at any opportune occasion.

As far as the newly discovered evidence shows, Man did not enter the world as an ascetic vegetarian and an angelic peace-lover, as the philosophers, moralists, and some overcharitable modern anthropologists would like us to believe, but as a clever competitor and a ruthless exploiter of the rest of nature.

4. OMNIVOROUS HABIT AN INCENTIVE TO THE RISE OF MAN.—The appraisal of the living habits of the Australopithecinae points toward a stage in human evolution not greatly different, but with more emphasis on omnivorous habits. Such omnivorous habits could have been cultivated only in the part or parts of the world where natural conditions were less extreme, neither the dry, grassy lands lacking fruits as South Africa, which made a carnivorous habit mandatory, nor swampy jungles of the type found in parts of South America, where arboreal life alone is possible. Such extensive regions are present in many parts of Eurasia and Africa, while Australia and the two Americas, for zoögeographical reasons, seem to have remained outside this phase of primate evolution.

In contrast with the severe uniformity of Bechuanaland and the Transvaal, the home of Mankind must have been varied in topography, with fair rainfall, a more gentle climate, and abundant and more diversified floral and faunal products. Here the more fortunate Protohumans had all the necessary opportunity to perfect their bipedal gait, upright posture, and especially their manipulative abilities: in gathering the fruits grown on the trees and bushes, in digging for edible roots and tubers from the soil, in collecting shells, eggs, and small animal life, and in supplementing this by intermittent hunting. The use of the hands for skilled acts guided by vision and regulated by senso-mobility was perfected in this way. And in the exercise of these activities, with the co-operation of other members of his family, group, or tribe, Man's intelligence further increased and finally culminated in the development of speech from inarticulate utterances.

The thesis of the omnivorous habit of Human

Ancestors, a diet of edible fruits, roots, stems, leaves, tubers, every kind of seeds or grain, and other products of plants, in addition to animal food, is supported by much evidence, albeit indirect.

In the prehistoric lake settlements of Europe, erected on piles, wheat, barley, linseed, and many varieties of seeds and fruits were found, together with the bones of the Stag, Ox, Pig, Sheep, Goat, Beaver, Fox, and Bison. This indicates that there was already at that time a well-advanced state of agriculture combined with hunting. The origins of this agriculture must, therefore, lie many thousands of years in the past (Anonymous 1932).

In primitive present-day societies, still entirely built upon the pattern of the Stone Age, both plant products and animal food play an important role. An instructive example is the Pitjendadjara tribe of Central Australia whose habits have been recently studied by C. P. Mountford (1946, 1951). In their efforts to wring a livelihood from their inhospitable homeland, they use only five implements: a spear and a spear thrower (by men) and wooden carrying dishes, grinding stones, and digging sticks (by women). The boomerang, an important weapon in other parts of Australia, is unknown to them; hence this tribe is probably less well equipped than any other in existence. The Pitjendadjara natives have no clothing whatever, and their only protection against inclement weather is fire and a wind shield, behind which they sleep, and the fire stick which they carry to keep warm (the temperature in the area which they inhabit may occasionally drop to 17° F.).

The diet of the Pitjendadjara is quite varied, "in fact, they ate," according to Mountford, "everything that was edible—grubs, lizards, ants, kangaroos, emus, grasses, and seeds of many kinds," besides hunting for Dingo, the native Australian dog, and for the marsupial "cat." Honey Ants, which are "as sweet as any honey," are a special delicacy. Grass seeds appear to be as important a food item to them as are grains and cereals in our own society. They often get "meat-hungry," hence are eager to hunt kangaroos and emus. (*See also* D. F. Thomson 1948; Mountford & Walker 1949; and H. Walker 1949.)

In another contemporary Stone Age tribe recently discovered in a secluded valley of New Guinea, fruits, both cultivated and wild, and other plant products, in addition to domesticated animals and game, are the source of food (R. Archbold 1941; E. T. Gilliard 1953; *cf. also* M. C. Burkitt *et al.* 1932).

The food of the Anthropomorphous Apes derives, with few exceptions, from plants, even though the Chimpanzee can be taught to eat meat in human fashion, according to Klüver's experience. Most of the Monkeys also seem to be chiefly plant-eaters. The only strictly carnivorous Primate in existence, excepting possibly some Macaques, is the Tarsier (*see* chap. XIV, 12). Most Monkeys, e.g., Rhesus Macaques, according to our own experience, shun meat in any form, whether raw or prepared. The South American Platyrrhines, however, also eat small animals, such as insects, snails, slugs, scorpions, birds and their eggs, and the like, as well as fruits. The only Primates, besides Man, which may have developed the habit of hunting larger game are the Baboons. But this, too, has been questioned by Zuckerman (1932; *see* sec. 4, this chapter). The Baboons, in Klüver's experience, however, are eager to catch live Rats and eat them with relish.

5. Living habits of Man's Ancestors the cause of their intellectual advancement. —The activity of Man during his early period, as far as it can be reconstructed, indicates hunting as the principal, and at times possibly the only, source of food. The Paleolithic and the succeeding Neolithic Periods reveal themselves as being entirely based on Man's intelligent production of stone and bone tools and weapons, such as clubs, axes, knives, scrapers, drills, and the like. (*See* Oakley 1950; *cf. also* Gilliard 1953.)

The astonishingly lifelike figures covering the walls and ceilings of the caves at Altamira, Lascaux, and many other caves, dating back from twelve to twenty or more thousands of years, vividly illustrate the kind of game the early hunters chased, and occasionally also show men in the act of hunting and their technique. This shows indubitably that game animals were an important source of food.

The question still remains as to whether or

not, during any period in the past, Man's Ancestors subsisted entirely on an animal diet. The prehistoric tools, weapons, and pictures may merely indicate the most difficult problem of Man's life, the acquisition of meat, hence the one which had impressed itself most vividly upon his imagination (*see* Movius 1953).

The habits of primitive races, such as those inhabiting New Guinea and Australia, indicate that plant food is at least an important source of subsistence. This view may be further supported by the observation of primitive societies of the recent past. The North American Indians, for example, whose level of civilization during pre-Columbian times was of the Stone Age, subsisted on both animal and plant food. Their tools and weapons were entirely made of stone, bone, stag antlers, leather, wood, and plant material, except for the occasional use of copper. With their primitive weapons, in spite of the abundance of game, especially in the prairie region of the Middle West, the procurement of meat was difficult, which made them rely much upon fruits gathered in the prairies and woods. Similar conditions were, or still are, present in other parts of the world. The Eskimos, living in a climate adverse to plant growth, seem to be the only primitive people subsisting entirely upon an animal diet, and in this way rather emphasize the exception. Whether the Massai tribe of Kenya live on a diet of milk and blood alone is not known.

By far the most important source of sustenance of the Infrahuman Primates is plants. This is entirely true of the tropics, hence the Infrahuman Primates are largely restricted to the tropics. Here the fruits grow mainly on the upper parts of the branches and can therefore be reached only by the Birds, the arboreal Primates, and the fruit-eating Bats, according to Gundersen & Hastings (Scient. Monthly, v. 59, p. 63, 1944). These animals are not only the principal consumers of tropical fruits but also the distributors of their seeds.

In their interdependence, these animals and the fruit-bearing trees resemble the relationship of the nut-bearing trees and the Squirrels of the temperate regions. It stands to reason that this dependence must have been mutually advantageous, or else it would have been discarded as a failure. Its success, however, is attested by its long duration and the advantages accruing to both the plants and the animals.

The plants benefited from the perfection of animal senses, as increased acuity, more delicate color vision, better stereopsis, more refined taste and smell, and more efficient locomotor and manipulative abilities made the animals more acute observers, detectors, and distributors of the seeds, by which the better fruit trees were more widely propagated.

The advantage to the animals was the selective improvement of plants, which resulted in the production of more abundant and more nourishing fruits.

The present situation may be defined as a neatly balanced natural economy between the fruit-producing plants and the fruit-consuming and seed-distributing animals, largely Primates, as discussed in section 2, this chapter.

The fruits which the American Monkeys, according to Gundersen & Hastings, consume are Annonas, Sapodilla, and Brazil Nuts. For the Old World the fruits of the Mango, Banana, Litchi, Citrus fruits, and many others, are mentioned. (*See also* especially H. N. Ridley 1930.)

The relationship between fruits and Monkeys, which resembles commensalism, is found only in the warm parts of the world suitable for the growth of fruit-producing trees. In the treeless or less forested areas the Primates have largely reverted to life on the ground. The Macaques and the Baboons have not disappeared but have adapted themselves in a greater or lesser degree to a terrestrial existence, subsisting largely on roots, tubers, the pith of the *Aloe*, insects, ostrich eggs, and other small life and consumable parts of plants. In regions under cultivation, orchards are a special target of their raids.

The hypothetical picture which one could draw of the life of Man's simian-like ancestors would not greatly differ from that of the more terrestrial Macaques and Baboons. They, too, must have subsisted largely on all kinds of food, such as fruits, edible stems, tubers, roots, and leaves, as well as on animal products like eggs, slugs, insects, shells, crabs, lizards, and young birds. When an occasion offered itself, they hunted for larger animals. Some strains, like the Australopithecinae, finally became entirely carnivorous, which may have sealed their doom. But in by far the greater area of the world populated by the primate material from which Mankind was gradually formed, the supply of meat was insufficient to permit, or to enforce, a strictly carnivorous habit. Hence the ancestors of Man had to draw on all available food supply, most of it grown on plants.

The gathering of fruits and other plant products, by and large, appears to have been the principal and older preoccupation of the Proto-humans, as it is still by far the principal source of sustenance of the now living Primates. While this limited the origin of Mankind to the tropical and subtropical parts of the globe, within which the transition of the strictly simian-like forms into more definitely human types must have taken place, it proved to be no insurmountable obstacle. A primate type invading a country beyond the heavy jungle, with variety of landscape and products, would, by necessity, as easily become a strict biped and manipulator of objects under visual guidance as did the savanna-inhabiting animal-hunting, carnivorous *Australopithecus*.

The gathering of fruits from low trees and bushes is just as easy and is carried out with as little bodily strain in an upright bipedal posture by a manipulating terrestrial biped, as by a more or less arboreal Primate from the branches of tall trees. But the great advantage of bipedalism was the emancipation from the heavy jungle and the acquisition of means of covering large territories of open landscape in swift marches—hence the ability to draw on a much more abundant food supply.

Through bipedalism, Man's Ancestors acquired the ability to move about quickly, to utilize all kinds of products of plant life, while they also did not neglect those animal products which were easily acquired. The varieties of fruits and other plant products required constant use of the senses, particularly visual acuity, pattern vision, and color sense, and a harmonious development of the other senses and manual skills, which in the long run were a potent stimulus for the development of the intellect.

The use of some tools and weapons must have begun very early in human evolution. Together with the discriminating judgment of their use and the habit of working in social teams, it compensated for the lack of formidable dentition and superior physical power, assuring Man's survival in competition with other animals and the rest of nature. The development of articulate speech as a superior means of intellectual communication and exchange of ideas, wholly outside the domain of locomotion and manipulation, finally cemented other faculties into a solid basis upon which Man's supremacy was established.

Many more factors than those discussed here have contributed to the transformation of one or of several Infrahuman Primates into human beings. What these factors were and how they have, in a complex interplay, influenced Human Ancestors was ably presented by Charles R. Darwin in his classical books *The Origin of Species* and *The Descent of Man* under various titles such as the "struggle for existence," "natural selection," "the survival of the fittest," and "sexual selection." Many other factors in this great drama of anthropogenesis, however, still remain unknown.

6. THE ADAPTABILITY OF MAN, THE PRIME CAUSE OF HIS WIDE DISTRIBUTION OVER THE GLOBE.—The changes in physical organization and mental makeup which transformed one or several Infrahuman Primates into Men had far-reaching consequences. They had enormously increased Man's ability to adapt himself to all climates, from the steaming tropical jungles and the dry, scorching deserts to the polar regions of eternal ice and snow. The advantage Man reaped from his adaptability in his "struggle for existence" over his primate rivals and other animals and over the many adversities of nature are demonstrated by his success.

The foremost advantage appears to be Man's adaptability to various climatic conditions and varieties of food. This advantage was primarily the consequence of Man's upright bipedal gait and of the emancipation of his arms and hands from locomotion and their exclusive use as the instruments of the mind. By this means civilization was created, that is, a better use of natural resources. This transformation made it possible for Man's Ancestors to spread beyond the tropical jungle, over the extensive hills and prairies of the temperate climates.

"Man," as Elliot Smith says, "has been a wanderer ever since he came into existence." Hence Man, more than all other Primates, long before the dawn of history was able to draw upon more abundant food supply and other natural resources, a tremendous advantage in comparison with other Primates, whose choice of foods and shelter was limited.

In this process of anthropogenesis, or the rise of Man, the brain, increasing in its powers, was more a consequence than a cause. It was a mighty assistant, enabling Man to exploit his surroundings to a far greater degree, but it does not seem to have been the primary agent. Marvelously organized as the human brain is, it is no more so than other bodily organs which perform specific functions.

7. THE BIRTHPLACE OF MAN.—Where the race or races of Mankind originated is a vast problem which can be reasonably solved only by long and diligent investigation. This is not the place to review, even sketchily, past efforts in this respect; therefore a few remarks may suffice.

Two of the Great Apes, the Gorilla and the Chimpanzee, Man's closest living relatives, inhabit Africa. Hence, with some reserve, Darwin's choice fell upon that continent. This view, because of the abundance of fossil australopithecine and Miocene pongid material, is also shared by Le Gros Clark, Dart, and Leakey (*see* preceding section). In this quite interesting and important problem, it will, however, be wise to postpone final judgment until more information is gathered about the past geological ages and more regions of the world are explored. Too little, unfortunately, is at present known to allow an apodictic statement.

The presence of the Orangutan and Gibbon in Malaya and on the neighboring islands, Dubois's discovery of *Pithecanthropus* in Java, the finds in Europe, India, and China, all indicate the spread of the Anthropomorphous Apes and early Hominidae over very extensive areas of the Old World. The discovery of the Taungs Ape-Man or *Australopithecus* again shows the great adaptability of the Primates to seemingly less favorable climatic conditions, such as South Africa, far away from abundant rainfall, great forests, and fruit-growing regions. The wide distribution of the Monkeys in Africa, Asia, and Europe, some in conditions little resembling the primeval jungles, as in North and South Africa, in the Himalayan Mountains, in China, and Japan, supports the same view.

"In the late Miocene of Europe and Africa and the Pliocene of Europe and southern Asia there are a considerable number of specimens seemingly representative of the higher anthropoids but for the most part of somewhat smaller size than the living chimpanzee and gorilla," according to A. S. Romer (1945). "These creatures were certainly anthropoid apes and not men . . . their characters, as far as known, would permit of their being ancestral to the chimpanzee and gorilla, and very probably they are close to the human line as well," according to the same author. The information available at present indicates a distribution of Primates over wide regions of the Old World, from whom Man's race or races had originated in a variety of places during the last 5 to 10 million years or earlier.

The immense territorial spread of the potential Human Ancestors and the actual early human remains, encompassing almost the entire Old World except Australia, ranging from North China and Borneo in the east, along the Himalaya Mountains to as far west as Spain, and to South Africa, is itself a demonstration of the great adaptability of the primate stock to diverse climatic and ecological conditions. But while the Great Apes and many Monkeys were more or less tied to the tropical zone, the ancestors of Man were very much more adaptable, which permitted them to spread, long before historic times, over vast parts of the globe.

This extensive territorial spread of the potential and actual Human Ancestors makes it more difficult to focus on any particular region as the true birthplace of Man. Moreover, it is highly probable that even those Primates directly in the line of human ancestry, during various succeeding phases of the evolution, did not remain at the same place but migrated over extensive territories, as their swift bipedal locomotion and omnivorous habits, in part at least, would demand and make possible.

This assumption, however, must be qualified by the fact of the presence of strongly differentiated races, such as the Caucasians, Negroes, Mongolians, Malayans, Australian aborigines, central African pygmies, and others. This strictly premodern localization, indicative of local racial formation, supports rather strongly the theory of polyphyletic or multiple human origins. The interbreeding of sharply differenti-ated races, in view of such strongly pronounced racial characters, would seem not to be decisive evidence against this view but rather indicates the common origin of all Mankind from the same basic primate stock sometime in the dis-tant past, the stock which still remains to be more precisely determined. (*Cf.* Gates 1948.)

EPILOGUE

Retrospect on the Role of Vision and Other Factors in the Origin of Man Together with a Speculation on the Future of Mankind

In the first part of this book we presented the investigations of the past by which the struc-ture of the vertebrate eye and of the visual pathways and centers of the brain, that is, the material basis of vision, was disclosed. In the second and third parts the gross and minute structures were described which make up the visual system, together with their blood supply, and the principal defects that vision suffers in variously localized lesions in pathological proc-esses. The fourth part of this book dealt with the problem of the origin of the vertebrate eye and the visual system, their varying organiza-tion depending on the mode of life of a particu-lar animal species and on the role vision played in the origin of Man. In this terminal section we will try to summarize the factors, especially vi-sion, whose complex interplay resulted in the rise of Man from an Infrahuman Primate, show how the same factors have molded the physical and mental character of Man, and tell what may reasonably be expected in the future.

Man, being a Primate, has naturally the same phylogenetical origin as other Primates, which is similar to that of other Vertebrates and, in a general way, to that of all other ani-mals. The vertebrate origin has its roots in the dim past of the early period of organic life on this planet.

What the animal forms were which even-tually became transformed into Vertebrates re-mains unknown. As far as it is possible to judge from the past record, illustrated by the early embryonic stages, the eye appears among the very first organs. It is the first and the largest part of the external cover, around which the young and as yet almost wholly undifferenti-ated neuroblastic cells gather and from which the nervous system, including the brain, devel-ops.

The precociousness of the ontogenetic devel-opment of the eye may in turn be interpreted as an indication that the photosensitive animal substance and the photoreceptors represented the matrix from which the eye and the Verte-brates phylogenetically originated and that the principal agent responsible for their emergence was physical solar light. Other indications again favor the concept of light as an initiator of life on earth. It is upon light that all animals and plants alike, in the final analysis, depend for their origin and existence.

The manner and degree of dependence upon light in the animal world seem to be as many as there are animal forms. Even in the higher plants the utilization of light is not indiscrimi-nate but is principally confined to the chloro-phyll-containing leaves, although there are no specific photoreceptors here. A similar whole-sale or undifferentiated utilization of light is found in numerous lowly organized animals. Here, however, various kinds of photoreceptor organs already appear where the light's action is concentrated or otherwise modified. This shows that the utilization of light by specific organs was and is the characteristic feature of all animal organization.

From the embryological evidence it may be assumed that at some time the Vertebrate An-cestors not only were sensitive to light but were able to concentrate and further to develop this photosensitiveness in special organs. These "optic primordia" in the very early period of vertebrate evolution became dominant organs, capable of acting as "organizers" of the cephalic end of the animal body. Possibly, they were principally responsible for, or were the initiators of, the bisymmetric organization of the vertebrate body along the vertical sagittal plane, with differentiation of the "right" and "left" halves, whereas the segmental arrangement of the body may have been the preceding, original phase initiated by other and even more basic factors. Also, the "optic primordia" must be charged, at least in part, with the responsibility all the consequences this implies for subsequent vertebrate evolution.

The Vertebrates, from as far back in the evolutionary past as it is possible to determine, were by choice the animals of light and sight. In virtue of this great affinity for light, they eventually developed true chamber eyes capable of producing images which permitted a more thorough utilization of light. Throughout

Fig. 541.—Classical marble sculpture, known as the "Aphrodite of Cnidos," the "foam-born" Goddess of Love and Beauty of Ancient Greece, identical with the Goddess Venus of the Romans. Representative of the feminine beauty and charm of the Caucasian Race. Undoubtedly, the Caucasian Race is a composite, consisting of numerous strains, as they became locally formed through relative isolation during past ages. But the type here represented is unquestionably a reproduction in marble of an actual living model, still found among the populations of southeastern Europe (Greeks, Serbs, Italians, perhaps French and Spaniards). It illustrates the final evolutionary product, in which the aesthetic visual sense, through the agency of sexual selection, has been the principal molding factor. Other branches of modern humanity, with different aesthetic concepts, have produced different types. By permission of the British Museum, London.

for differentiation of the "above" and "below," or "back" and "belly," an essential feature of all Vertebrates.

As the same embryological evidence shows, the orimental photoreceptor organs of the Vertebrate Ancestors must have given the impetus to the rise of a centralized nervous system, with their existence the Vertebrates remained faithful to their choice, the dependence on vision as their principal guide.

The highest forms of vertebrate life, the Birds and the Primates, are preponderantly guided by vision. A bird or a monkey with poor vision, not to speak of an absence of it, is unthinkable under natural conditions. The great dependence of Vertebrates upon vision is manifest, even though some and certainly many Mammals get along well with only a modicum of sight or none at all. How primate vision, under the influence of the arboreal habit, became perfected into a leading sense, was discussed in this and the preceding chapter. Many details of this absorbing story still remain obscure.

formance is reflected in the formidable increase of the human brain, in comparison with that of the Simians. This is most pronounced in the relative expansion of the "association regions," compared with the so-called "projection areae" of the cerebral cortex. These extensive regions, then, are the principal material substratum of Man's superior intellect. However, the increase and elaboration of the "projection areae" of the

Fig. 542.—Another classical marble statue, purporting to represent Heracles or Hercules, the mythological hero of Ancient Greece, who personified the manly strength and the adventurous spirit of youth. A realistic stone portrait of a living model, whose many representatives may still be found among the present population of Europe, especially in the territory of the ancient Roman Empire. It represents one of several types which incorporate the aesthetical concept of masculine beauty and strength of the Caucasian Race. It is the end-result of a long evolutionary process in which the aesthetic visual sense, besides the struggle for existence, has been the principal responsible factor. By permission of the British Museum, London.

Whatever the precise biological motivation of Man's emergence is, unbiased evidence points toward a common primate origin. Man's anatomical, physiological, mental, and emotional makeup springs from the same source as that of other Primates, even though it has immensely increased in scope and complexity. This development in psychomental and emotional per-

cortex and of other related parts of the brain also kept pace with the intellectualization of the human mind, as the very detailed cortical representation of parts of the extremities, such as the hands, fingers, tongue, and lips used in skilled acts and in speech shows.

Perhaps the greatest relative expansion and elaboration was achieved in parts of the brain serving auditory sensorimotor and visual speech—the principal tools and, in fact, largely the embodiments of the human intellect. A detailed phylogenetical appraisal of the degree and pattern of the human cerebral machine must, however, be deferred until the functions of large areas of the cortex, as yet undisclosed, are identified and their minute structure, especially synaptical relationships, become known and understood.

direction and under the immediate control of vision. This strict control of manipulations by sight, or "supervision," is even more apparent during the process of learning, where every minute manipulative act is guided and tested by sight, before it becomes semiautomatic or entirely automatic.

The functional influencing of the manipulative sensorimotor acts through vision, however, works also in the opposite direction, vision itself

Fig. 543.—Head of a Gaul, a classical marble portrait representing another variant in the manhood of the Caucasian Race. Same or similar type may frequently be found among the population of modern France and adjacent countries, in spite of the one hundred and more generations that have meanwhile come and gone since this realistic sculpture was made. By permission of the British Museum, London.

Man's superiority is principally based upon his upright gait and the emancipation of his arms and hands from locomotion. This made the upper extremities the exclusive mechanical instruments in the service of mind. The arms and hands became tools of the human "intellect" and "will," working closely under their

becoming more refined and the intellectual absorption and mental utilization more complete and lasting, as the skilled movements become more complex and more efficient. In what way, exactly, this manifest reciprocity was phylogenetically acquired and is individually achieved and what detailed anatomical, histological, an biochemical factors work together in this interplay may only be guessed, their disclosure remaining a future problem.

The human mind has the same phylogenetical roots and anatomical and physiological foundations as has the intellectual activity of the Infrahuman Primates. These roots and foundations are not greatly different from those of other Vertebrates and, in a more general than in other Primates and other animals, the human mind developed to a degree where it became overwhelming, all-embracing. In human life the mind has a far more dominant role than has the mental factor in the life of any other animal, not excluding the most advanced. Yet the component elements are similar in all. The difference seems to be not in the essentials but only in the relative proportions and arrange-

Fig. 544.—Asclepios, god of healing of the Ancient Greeks, equivalent of the Roman god Aesculapius. Another realistic portrait from the Classical Period, representing a fully mature masculine type of the Caucasian Race. Numerous representatives of this type may easily be seen among the present populations of central and northern Europe. By permission of the British Museum, London.

sense, are the same as of all other animals. Hence the human mind must be organized upon essentially the same pattern as the mind of other animals, especially the Primates.

The principal foundation of the human mind, like that of other Primates, is vision, the others being audition and senso-motility. But more ment of the components, in the subtleties and complexities which may be defined as "integration," or ability to combine various experiences into more complex ideational formulas and kinetic melodies, and to store these in greater volume in memory, to re-create them in the same form or in new combinations, and to use them either automatically or at will. Only in this restricted sense does the human species justify its scientific name *Homo sapiens* or "Wise" or "Prudent" Man.

What use Mankind has made in the past of its superior intellectual powers, how it behaved during history and behaves now, and what its past and present achievements, positive and negative, were and are, are recorded or stored in countless libraries, museums, and innumerable other places all over the face of the earth and can be seen everywhere.

What Man's conduct and accomplishments were during the much longer prehistoric times is but imperfectly disclosed through the study of less perishable products of his handiwork, such as stone implements and weapons, and from observations of primitive contemporary races. It would be futile to make even an attempt to summarize the contents of past human activity, because this has been done many times since Herodotus wrote his *History.*

Human achievements were possible, in the final analysis, because of the superb ability of Man's senses, especially vision, to observe objects and events and to store in mind the multitude of sensory impressions, to understand the meaning of these impressions, to integrate them in a logical way with one another, to communicate thoughts through articulate speech to other fellow-humans, to make intelligent plans for future conduct, and to put these plans into action through the use of the body and limbs, principally the hands and arms, largely under the control of vision.

Man's superior intelligence and logical thinking developed from modest beginnings during untold ages under the stimulus of upright posture and emancipation of arms and hands from locomotion, which, under visual guidance, became most versatile limbs devoted entirely to the service of the mind. This enabled Man to fashion every kind of tool and weapon, by means of which he became the master and exploiter of much of animate and inanimate nature. Man's intelligence thus became his most potent instrument in his struggle for existence.

In all his magnificence and with all his faults, Man is part and parcel of nature. Not a hair grows on his body, not a breath can he take, if all necessary conditions are not fulfilled. There

is nothing supranatural in the origin and life of Man, as he persistently wishes to imagine. Man is very far from standing "alone in the universe," as declared by G. G. Simpson (1953) but is as much an integral part of the nature which molded him as is a Sparrow on the fence, a Rabbit in the bush, or a Dandelion on the lawn. He is the result of the interplay of incalculably complex forces and factors which we have been able to uncover in only the smallest degree. Neither are these forces and factors, except in dimensions and complexity, very different from those which have created a Shark, a Lizard, or a Dog, all of whom Man resembles during his phylogenetical and ontogenetical development. Nor is Man's rise to the pinnacle of the animal realm in the least due to his own merit, earned and deserved because of his own effort, but the result of fortunate circumstances which created him and which eventually will dispose of him.

Whether Mankind, in spite of its immensely advanced intellectual powers and accumulated knowledge, is conscious of its true place in nature and is capable of adjusting its individual and collective behavior accordingly is doubtful. Hence it is logical to find it unable to solve its long-range problems as intelligently as it is capable of attending to its immediate affairs. It is therefore probable that Mankind will continue as heretofore to stumble along the unknown path of destiny, driven by a primeval urge of blind biological instincts until the termination of its natural cycle, in the same way as did the mighty Dinosaurs and the giant Sequoias.

What the immediate future of humanity will be is more of a subject for legitimate speculation. Man's character, molded in the severe struggle of the past, is physically, intellectually, and emotionally so firmly intrenched in its grooves that no radical change is to be expected in his conduct in the foreseeable future.

At times Mankind may, therefore, continue along the road of intellectual and material progress. Human ingenuity will continue to invent new machines, gadgets, weapons, and processes which will make life even more pleasant and certainly more complex and dangerous. But such basic features of human character, as the eternal striving for knowledge, truth, and justice, contrasting with ignorant reliance on irrational dogmas and mystic formulas; patient tolerance and passionate fanaticism; the lavish generosity and compassion and the greedy covetousness and envy; the tender love and the implacable hatred and violence, besides the primary physiobiologic urges of stilling the hunger and satisfying the instinct of procreation, will hardly be altered in any substantial way as the motives upon which human society is built.

astating destructiveness of Dart's "precocious *enfant terrible*" of the world merely increased their complexity and importance but did not essentially alter the relative influence of the two opposing motive forces. As in the past, what human hands create, other human hands destroy!

"Naked of body, delicate of skin, tender in both hand and foot, unfurnished with fangs or

Fig. 545.—Marble bust of Marcus Ulpius Trajanus or Trajan (A.D. 52 or 53–117), one of the most energetic and successful Roman Emperors, representative of a forceful, determined masculine type of the Caucasian Race. By permission of the British Museum, London.

Mankind, as far as known in the past and up to the present, has exhibited two faces, one godly, the other beastly. In one hand it carries the torch of enlightenment and benevolence, in the other the sword of death and destruction. The two principles, inherited from long before the times of Australopithecs, Neanderthalians, and Cro-Magnons, are seemingly inseparably united. The intellectual advancement and dev-

claws, man," in Dart's words, "subsists not by physical strength and muscular force, but by intellectual stealth and cunningly applied manual violence."

Mankind during an incalculably long and complex evolutionary process rose from the primeval ooze through an incessant struggle for survival, principally through the instrumentality of vision and light, to the life of self-consciousness and the realization of the world. Whether it will ever attain the status which would justify its name "Wise Man," given to it by Linné, is beyond our knowledge to foretell. To paraphrase Aristotle's words quoted in the Introduction—to foresee the fate of Mankind certainly is one of the most difficult things in the world!

Turning to the practical side of human af-

But vision has also higher, spiritual attributes capable of elevating human beings above the level of mere brutes struggling for existence. Vision makes us see and appreciate the smile on a friendly face, enjoy the endless beauties of nature, the multicolored flowers, birds, and fruits, the green meadows and somber deserts, the glorious sunrise and sunset, the majesty of the tall mountains and the sweeping horizon of

Fig. 546.—Gaius Julius Caesar (100–44 B.C.), famous general and statesman of Ancient Rome. Conqueror of Gaul and of Britain. First uncrowned ruler of the Roman Empire and prototype of the monarchical rulers during the succeeding twenty centuries. Author of the books *The Gallic War* and *The Civil War*. A realistic marble portrait representing the superior intellectual masculine type of the Caucasian Race, of which many representatives may be found among the modern nations of Europe and in America. By permission of the British Museum, London.

fairs, vision, just like life, is a heavenly gift bestowed upon Man for whatever use he is capable of putting it to. With it we are able to see and appreciate and understand countless objects necessary in our daily life and make use of them in many practical ways.

the ocean, the magnificence of an Alhambra and of a Taj Mahal, and all other things which make our visible world.

Through sight we judge our fellow-men and are principally guided in the choice of our friends and sexual mates. Through sight we appreciate the innumerable works of art and, in civilized societies, receive and preserve most of our knowledge.

The gateway of vision to the human mind is wide open, the avenue that leads to it is smooth and broad. Man's opportunity given to him by nature is great.

References: Abbie 1952, 1953; C. E. Akeley 1923 (*see also* M. L. Jobe Akeley); R. C. Andrews 1946; J. L. Angel 1950; Ariëns Kappers *et al.* 1936; E. A. Armstrong 1947; Ashton & Zuckerman 1951; G. B. Barbour 1949; Barnett, Eisenstadt & Zallinger 1954; F. Barth 1950; H. W. Bates 1863; L. F. de Beauford 1951; Beccari 1943; Beddard 1923; B. J. Benchley 1942; J. D. Bernal 1951; L. von Bertalanffy 1949; Bierens de Haan 1925, 1927, 1950; Bierens de Haan & Frima 1930; H. C. Bingham 1928, 1929, 1932; Blum, Chow & Pribram 1950; G. A. Brecher 1935, 1936; A. Brehm 1916; Breuil & Obermaier 1935; Brongersma 1942; Bronowski & Long 1952; R. Broom 1949, 1950; Broom & Schepers 1946; B. Burbridge 1948; C. R. Carpenter 1934, 1935, 1939, 1940, 1942; G. S. Carter 1948; Casteret 1924, 1948; Le Gros Clark 1924, 1927, 1934, 1935, 1937, 1945, 1946, 1947, 1948, 1949, 1950, 1951, 1952, 1953, 1954; Clark & Leakey 1950; F. E. Clements, E. V. Martin & F. L. Long 1950; E. T. Collins 1921; W. Comberg 1925; C. J. Connolly 1953; C. S. Coon 1950; J. Corbett 1953; E. W. Count 1950; Crandall 1945; D. J. Cunningham 1886; Darlington 1943; R. A. Dart 1925, 1948, 1949, 1954; C. G. Darwin 1952; C. R. Darwin 1859, 1871, 1873 (or later editions); D. D. Davis 1942; S. R. Detwiler 1924, 1938, 1939, 1940, 1941, 1943; L. R. Dice 1952; Th. Dobzhansky 1950; Dunn 1950; T. H. Eaton 1951; G. J. van Eck 1939; L. Edinger 1895, 1900, 1908–11; H. Ehrhardt 1924; C. H. Eigenmann 1903, 1909; Eiseley 1952; Elftman 1944; M. Ettlinger 1925; H. O. Forbes 1894; J. B. Frazer 1890 and subs.; J. W. French 1923; W. B. Furness 1916; Gagnebin 1947; W. E. Galt 1939; R. L. Garner 1900; R. R. Gates 1927, 1948; Gesell *et al.* 1949; Ghiselli 1937; Gilliard 1953; J. Goerttler 1950; Gorjanović-Kramberger 1906; Grassé 1950, v. 15; J. Gray 1944, 1953; W. K. Gregory 1916, 1923, 1927, 1928, 1929, 1930, 1934, 1935, 1938, 1940, 1941, 1944, 1951; Gregory & Hellman 1938, 1939; Gregory & McGregor 1926; Gregory & Raven 1937; W. F. Grether; K. Guenther 1931; Gundersen & Hastings 1944; M. Gusinde 1953; E. Haeckel 1866, 1870, 1891, 1894–96, 1899, 1904 (1905), 1908; J. B. S. Haldane 1949; E. R. Hall 1946; Hamilton & Coleman 1933; Hamilton & Goldstein 1933; Harlow 1950; Harlow *et al.* 1932; R. G. Harris *et al.* 1950; W. Harris 1904; Heberer 1952; L. Heck 1916; Hennig 1950; R. Hertwig 1907 (also later editions); Hesse & Doflein 1935–43; W. C. O. Hill 1950; F. Hochstetter 1952; Hooton 1940, 1942, 1943, 1947; Hooijer 1951; F. C. Howell 1951; Howells 1950; A. Hrdlička 1927; Hubrecht 1897; J. S. Huxley 1953; Igersheimer & Hahn-Haslinger 1926; E. Irmscher 1922–29; F. Wood Jones 1918, 1919, 1926, 1929, 1942, 1953; D. B. Judd 1952; G. Just 1925; S. Kasdon 1938; D. Katz 1935; A. Keith 1929, 1931, 1932, 1946, 1947, 1949; A. J. Kinnaman 1902; F. Kipp 1939; H. Klaatsch 1911, 1912, 1913; H. Klüver 1933; Klüver & Bucy 1937, 1938, 1939; F. Knoll 1921–22, 1924, 1925; O. Koehler 1923, 1924; Koenigswald 1937, 1940; Köppen & Wegener 1924; Kohl-Larsen 1943; Kolosváry 1934; Krogman 1950; Kühn & Ilse 1925; Langlands 1926–27, 1929; Lashley 1916, 1942, 1949, 1950; Leakey 1946, 1948; Löhner 1925; Lowther 1939; Lundman 1950; McCowen 1950; MacCurdy 1937; J. P. McMurrich 1927; Malbrandt & Maclatchy 1949; Th. R. Malthus 1798; E. N. Marais 1939; M. Maxwell 1928; Mayr 1950; R. A. Miller 1935, 1943, 1945; A. Montagu 1943, 1944, 1950, 1951, 1952; R. Moore 1953; R. C. Morris 1943; D. J. Morton 1924, 1927; Morton & Fuller 1954; F. W. Mott 1902, 1905, 1907, 1922; Ch. P. Mountford 1946, 1951; Mountford & Walker 1949; Movius 1953; Johannes Müller 1826; R. Munro 1893; H. W. Nissen 1931; K. P. Oakley 1950; A. F. Oparin 1953; H. F. Osborn 1916, 1928, 1930; Ostoya 1951; Ovio 1927; Parker & Haswell 1940; Parsons 1924; R. Pearl 1946; H. Petersen 1924; Pfungst 1912, 1924; Piveteau 1951 ff.; Plate 1922–24; Plath 1935; Pocock 1918, 1919, 1920, 1925; Porsch 1924, 1931; S. Ramón y Cajal 1898 (1899), 1909–11; C. Read 1925; Reagan 1930; Reichenow 1920, 1921; Révész 1925; H. N. Ridley 1930; J. T. Robinson 1952, 1953; Romer 1943, 1945, 1949; Rüschkamp 1944–47; T. C. Ruch 1941; H. J. Scherer 1944; H. Schmidt 1944–47; A. H. Schultz 1936, 1941,

1950; M. von Senden 1932; A. N. Sewertzoff 1929; Shapiro 1952; H. Shapley *et al.* 1953; Shelford 1944; Shepherd 1910; J. Sibree 1915; O. Sickenberg 1934; G. G. Simpson 1947, 1949, 1950, 1953; G. Elliot Smith 1919, 1921, 1925, 1926, 1927, 1930, 1932; J. Sowry 1895–1901; K. W. Spence 1934; R. Spruce 1908; T. D. Stewart 1950, 1952; W. L. Straus, Jr. 1940, 1941, 1942, 1949; Symposium on the "Origin and Evolution of Man," 1950; W. P. Taylor 1943; Teilhard de Chardin 1952; D. F. Thomson 1948; F. Tilney 1928; N. Tinbergen 1953; Trendelenburg & Schmidt 1930; E. L. Trouessart 1898–99; R. J. Trump 1923–24; Vandel 1949; H. Wagner 1932; W. Waldeyer 1909; E. P. Walker 1954; H. Walker 1949; A. R. Wallace 1853, 1860, 1869, 1871, 1881, 1891, 1905, 1916; Wallace & Dyer 1885; G. L. Walls 1942, 1953; Washburn 1950; D. M. S. Watson 1919, 1926, 1932, 1949; J. B. Watson 1909, 1914, 1915; M. Weber 1927–28; Weidenreich 1924, 1928, 1930, 1932, 1934, 1935, 1936, 1937, 1938, 1939, 1940, 1941, 1942, 1943, 1945, 1946; Weinert 1940, 1948, 1951; Weinstein 1945; Weinstein & Grether 1940; W. C. Wells 1792; E. N. Willmer 1949; F. Windar 1925; F. Windels 1948; Wojtusjak 1933; S. Wright 1939, 1949; W. M. Wundt 1900–1909, 1908–11, 1919; Yerkes 1915, 1916, 1925, 1927–29, 1943, 1951; Yerkes & Petrunkewitch 1925; Yerkes & Watson 1911–12; Yerkes & Yerkes 1929; Zeuner 1944, 1952; Zuckerman 1932, 1933, 1940, 1944, 1950; Zuckerman & Fulton; Zuckerman & Wallace 1932.

Bibliography

Bibliography

References marked with an asterisk (*) are those which the author was not able to examine personally.

A

ABBÉ, E.
1904–6. Gesammelte Abhandlungen. G. Fischer, Jena. 3 vols. For obituary *see* J. Rheinberg, J. Roy. Micr. Soc. London, p. 156, 1905.

ABBIE, A. A.
1933. The clinical significance of the anterior choroidal artery. Brain, v. 56, p. 233.
1933. The blood supply of the lateral geniculate body, with a note on the morphology of the choroidal arteries. J. Anat., v. 67, p. 491.
1934. The morphology of the fore-brain arteries, with especial reference to the evolution of the basal ganglia. *Ibid.*, v. 68, p. 433.
1934. The brain-stem and cerebellum of *Echidna aculeata*. Phil. Tr. Roy. Soc. London, ser. B, v. 224, p. 1.
1937. The anatomy of capsular vascular disease. M. J. Australia, v. 2, p. 564.
1938. The blood supply of the visual pathways. *Ibid.*, p. 199.
1939. The diencephalon: structural, functional and clinical considerations. *Ibid.*, p. 421.
1951. A new outlook on physical anthropology. Report of the Brisbane Meeting of Australian and New Zealand Association for the Advancement of Science, v. 28 (May).
1952. A new approach to the problem of human evolution. Tr. Roy. Soc. South Australia, p. 70.

ABBOTT, C. E.
1949. The behavior of *Anax junius*. Turtox News, v. 27, pp. 98, 138.

ABBOTT, W. L., & KLOSS, C. B.; *see* MILLER, G. S., 1902

ABDALLATIF
1810. Relation d'Égypte, par Abdallatif, médecine arabe de Bagdad. Traduite par M. S. DE SACY. Treutel & Würtz, Paris.

ABDERHALDEN, E.
1910–39. Handbuch der biologischen Arbeitsmethoden. Urban & Schwarzenberg, Berlin & Wien.

ABEL, O.
1919. Die Stämme der Wirbeltiere. W. de Gruyter & Co., Berlin & Leipzig.
1931. Die Stellung des Menschen im Rahmen der Wirbeltiere. G. Fischer, Jena.

ABELSDORFF, G.
1900. Zur Anatomie der Ganglienzellen der Retina. Arch. f. Augenh. (Graefe), v. 42, p. 188.
1907. Einige Bemerkungen über den Farbensinn der Tag- und Nachtvögel. *Ibid.*, v. 58, p. 64.
1916. Beiderseitiges zentrales Scotom bei im übrigen normalem Gesichtsfelde nach Hinterhauptschuss. Klin. Monatsbl. f. Augenh., v. 56, p. 172.
1919. Zur Frage der Existenz gesonderter Pupillarfasern im Sehnerven. *Ibid.*, v. 62, p. 170.

ABELSDORFF, G., & WESSELY, K.
1909. Vergleichend-physiologische Untersuchungen über den Flüssigkeitswechsel des Auges in der Wirbeltierreihe. Arch. f. Augenh., v. 64 (suppl. vol.), p. 65.

ABNEY, W. DE W.
1895. Colour vision. Longmans, Green & Co., London.

ABRAMSON, H. A., MOYER, L. C., & GORIN, M. H.
1942. Electrophoresis of proteins and the chemistry of cell surfaces. Reinhold Pub. Corp., New York.

ACHILINI, A. (ACHILLINUS)
1516. De humani corporis anatomia. Venetiis. Another ed. 1521. J. A. et fratres de Sabio, Venetiis.
1520. Annotationes anatomiae. H. de Benedictis, Bologna.
*1545. Alexandri Achillini Bononiensis opera omnia. H. Scotus, Venetiis.

ACHUCARRO, N.
1915. De l'évolution de la névroglie, et spécialement de ses relations avec l'appareil vasculaire. Trab. (Trav.) del lab. de invest. biol. Madrid, v. 13, p. 169.

ACKERMANN, J. F.
1813. De nervei systematis primordiis commentatio. Schwan & Goetz, Manhemii & Heidelbergae.

ACKERMANN, J.-T.
*1791. De nervorum opticorum inter se nexu. M. Bibliothek (Blumenbach), v. 3, p. 2. *See also* D. Weber, in Arch. f. Physiol. (Reil), v. 6, p. 282.

ADAMKIEWICZ, A.
1900. Das Regenbogensehen. Neurol. Centralbl.,
v. 19, pp. 642, 1050.

ADAMS, A.
1848–50. The zoology of the voyage of H.M.S.
Samarang during the years 1845, 1846; 4
parts in 1 vol., Vertebrata, by J. E. GRAY.

ADAMS, C.
1910. Vie & œuvres de Descartes. L. Cerf, Paris.

ADAMS, C., & TANNERY, P.
1902–9. Œuvres de Descartes: v. 6, p. 79, "La dioptrique" (1637); v. 11, p. 217, "Description du corps humaine" (1648). L. Cerf,
Paris.

ADAMS, E. Q.
1923. A theory of color vision. Psychol. Rev., v.
30, p. 56.

ADAMS, G.
1746. Micrographia illustrata, or, the knowledge
of the microscope explain'd: etc. London.
1792. An Essay on Vision, briefly explaining the
Fabric of the Eye, and the Nature of Vision:
intended for the service of those whose
Eyes are Weak or Impaired: enabling them
to form an accurate idea of the true state of
their sight, the means of preserving it, together with proper rules for ascertaining
when spectacles are necessary, and how to
choose them without injuring sight. By
G. A., Mathematical Instrument Maker to
His Majesty, and Optician to His Royal
Highness the Prince of Wales. The Second
Edition. London: Printed for the Author,
by R. Hindmarsh, etc.

ADAMS, L. A., & EDDY, S.
1949. Comparative anatomy. John Wiley & Sons,
New York.

ADAMÜK, E.
1880. Zur Frage über die Kreuzung der Nervenfasern im Chiasma nervorum opticorum des
Menschen. Arch. f. Ophth. (Graefe), v. 26
(2), p. 187.

ADDISON, W. H. F., & DONALDSON, H. H.
1933. On the area of the sunken cerebral cortex as
determined from the length and depth of
selected sulci in three classes of human
brains: scholars, hospital whites, hospital
negroes. J. Comp. Neurol., v. 57, p. 429.

ADELMANN, H. B.
1929–37. Experimental studies on the development of the eye. J. Exper. Zoöl., v. 54, pp.
249, 291; v. 57, p. 223; v. 75, p. 199.
1934. A study of cyclopia in Amblystoma punctatum with special reference to the mesoderm.
Ibid., v. 67, p. 217.

1936. The problem of cyclopia. Quart. Rev. Biol.,
v. 11, pp. 161, 284.

ADES, H. W.
1941. Connections of the medial geniculate body
in the cat. Arch. Neurol. & Psychiat., v. 45,
p. 138.

ADES, H. W., & FELDER, R.
1942. The acoustic area of the monkey. J. Neurophysiol., v. 5, p. 49.

ADES, H. W., & RAAB, D.
1948. Destruction and restitution of a visual discrimination habit after cortical lesions.
Anat. Rec., v. 100, p. 633. (Abstr.)

ADIE, W. J.
1930. Permanent hemianopia in migraine and
subarachnoid haemorrhage. Lancet, v. 219,
p. 237.

ADLER, A.
1933. Zur Lokalisation des Konvergenzzentrums
und der Kerne der glatten Augenmuskeln.
Ztschr. f. d. ges. Neurol. u. Psychiat., v.
145, p. 185.
1935. Zur Topik der corticalen Geschmacks-
sphäre. Ibid., v. 152, p. 25.
1944. Disintegration and restoration of optic recognition in visual agnosia: analysis of a case.
Arch. Neurol. & Psychiat., v. 51, p. 243.

ADLER, A., & PÖTZL, O.
1936. Ueber eine eigenartige Reaktion auf Meska-
lin bei einer Kranken mit doppelseitigen
Herden in der Sehsphäre. Jahrb. f. Psychiat., v. 53, p. 13.

ADLER, F. H.
1953. Physiology of the eye. Clinical application.
2d ed. C. V. Mosby Co., St. Louis, Mo.

ADLER, F. H., AUSTIN, G., & GRANT, F. C.
1948. Localizing value of visual fields in patients
with early chiasmal lesions. Arch. Ophth.,
ser. 2, v. 40, p. 579.

ADLER, F. H., & FLIEGELMAN, M.
1934. Influence of fixation on the visual acuity.
Arch. Ophth., v. 12, p. 475.

ADLER, F. H., & MEYER, G. P.
1935. The mechanism of the fovea. Tr. Am.
Ophth. Soc., v. 33, p. 266.

ADRIAN, E. D.
1928. The basis of sensation: the action of the
sense organs. Christopher, London; Norton
& Co., New York.
1930. The mechanism of the sense organs. Physiol.
Rev., v. 10, p. 336.
1932. The messages in sensory nerve fibres. Harvey Lect., ser. 27, p. 57.
1933. The all-or-nothing reaction. Ergebn. d.
Physiol., v. 35, p. 744.

1935. The mechanism of nervous action: electrical studies of the neurone. University of Pennsylvania Press, Philadelphia.

1941. Afferent discharges to the cerebral cortex from peripheral sense organs. J. Physiol., v. 100, p. 159.

1943. The dominance of vision. Tr. Ophth. Soc. United Kingdom, v. 63, p. 194.

1945. The electric response of the human eye. J. Physiol., v. 104, p. 84.

1946. Rod and cone components in the electric response of the eye. *Ibid.*, v. 105, p. 24.

1947. The physical background of perception. Clarendon Press, Oxford.

ADRIAN, E. D., & MATTHEWS, R.

1927. The action of light on the eye. Part I. The discharge of impulses in the optic nerve and its relation to the electric changes in the retina. J. Physiol., v. 63, p. 378.

1927-28. Part II. The processes involved in retinal excitation. *Ibid.*, v. 64, p. 279.

1928. Part III. The interaction of retinal neurones. *Ibid.*, v. 65, p. 273.

1934. The Berger rhythm: potential changes from the occipital lobes in man. Brain, v. 57, p. 355.

ÄRENBÄCK-CHRISTIE-LINDE, A.

1900. Zur Anatomie des Gehirnes niederer Säugetiere. Anat. Anz., v. 18, p. 8.

1907. Der Bau der Soriciden und ihre Beziehungen zu anderen Säugetieren. Morphol. Jahrb., v. 36, p. 465.

AGADSCHANIANZ

1906. Ueber das kortikale Sehzentrum. Neurol. Centralbl., v. 25, p. 1017. (Paper read Feb. 26, 1904.)

AGAR, W. E.

1943. A contribution to the theory of the living organism. Melbourne University Press & Oxford University Press.

AGUILLON (AGUILONIUS), F.

1613. Optica Agvilonii. Francisci Agvilonii e Societate Iesu Opticorum Libri Sex Philosophis iuxtà ac Mathematicis utiles. Antwerpiae, ex Officina Plantiniana, Apud Viduam et Filios Io. Moreti. M.DC.XIII.

1613. ROHR, M. (trans.), Auswahl aus der Behandlung des Horopters bei Fr. Aguilonius um 1613. Ztschr. f. ophth. Optik, v. 11, p. 41, 1923.

AHLENSTIEL, H.

1948. Farbsinn-Störungen in anschaulicher Darstellung. Natur. u. Volk (Ber. d. Senckenberg. naturforsch. Gesellsch.), v. 78, p. 50.

AIRY, G. B.

1865. The astronomer royal on hemiopsy. Phil. Mag. & J. Sc., 4th ser., v. 30, p. 19.

AIRY, H.

1870. On a distinct form of transient hemiopsia. Phil. Tr. Roy. Soc. London, v. 160 (1), p. 247; Proc. Roy. Soc. London, v. 18, p. 212.

AITKEN, H. F.

1909. A report on the circulation of the lobar ganglia; made to J. B. Ayer. Boston M. & Surg. J., v. 160, suppl.

AKELAITIS, A. J.

1941-42. Studies on the corpus callosum. Arch. Neurol. & Psychiat., v. 45, p. 788; v. 48, pp. 108, 914.

1944. A study of gnosis, praxis and language following section of corpus callosum and anterior commissure. J. Neurosurg., v. 1, p. 94.

AKELEY, C. E.; for obituary see FISHER 1927

1923. In brightest Africa. Garden City Pub. Co., Garden City, N.Y.

AKELEY, M. L. JOBE

1929. Carl Akeley's Africa. Dodd, Mead & Co., New York.

1950. Congo Eden. Dodd, Mead & Co., New York.

AKKERINGA, L. J.

1934. Ueber das Grundnetz in der Retina. Ztschr. f. mikr.-anat. Forsch., v. 36, p. 607.

ALAERTS

1935. Nouvelle théorie sur la vision du relief. La priorité de points périphériques de la rétine. Arch. d'opht., v. 52, p. 320.

ALAJOUANINE, T.

1948. Aphasia and artistic realization. Brain, v. 71, p. 229.

ALAJOUANINE, T., & THUREL, R.

1931. Révision des paralysies des mouvements associés des globes oculaires. Rev. neurol., v. 1, p. 125.

ALBERTOTTI, G.

1914. Note critiche e bibliografiche riguardanti la storia degli occhiali. Ann. di ottal., v. 43, p. 328.

1922. Lettera intorno alla invenzione degli occhiali. *Ibid.*, v. 50, p. 85.

1923. Lenti ed'occhiali. Cecchini, Roma.

*1924. Altri dati riguardanti la storia degli occhiali. Tipogr. Seminario, Padova. (*See also* Ztschr. f. ophth. Optik, v. 12, p. 160.)

ALBERTUS MAGNUS

13th cent. De sensu et sensato.

13th cent. Opus philosophiae naturalis etc. Brixiae 1490; Venetiis 1496. (*See* W. Sudhoff, Arch. f. Gesch. d. Med., v. 7, p. 149, 1913.)

ALBINUS, B. S.
1756. Academicarum annotationum liber tertius. Leidae. Ap. J. & H. Verbeek. Chap. 14, "De membrana, quam vocant retinam," p. 59. Lib. 5, cap. 1 (on retina); lib. 7, cap. 4, "De tunica Ruyschiana & choroidea oculi," p. 39.

ALBRÄCHT & BIELSCHOWSKY, A.
1908. Demonstration und Besprechung eines Falles von Seelenblindheit. Berlin. klin. Wchnschr., v. 45, p. 1076; also Fortschr. d. Med., v. 26, p. 234.

ALCOATIN (ALCOATI)
1159. Congregatio sive liber de oculis quem compilavit Alcoatin, christianus toletanus Anno dominicae Incarnationis MCLIX. Publié d'après les manuscrits des bibliothèques de Metz et d'Erfurt, avec introduction sur l'histoire des oculistes arabes par P. Pansier. J.-B. Baillière et Fils, Paris, 1903. *In:* P. PANSIER, "Collectio ophthalmologica veterum auctorum," Fasc. 2.

*1159. Le "Tractatus de aegritudinibus oculorum" d'Alcoatin (1159) d'après les manuscrits des bibliothèques de Strasbourg et d'Erfurt. By P. PANSIER. A. Maloine, Paris, probably 1901 or 1902.

ALCOCK, N. M.
1898. On the vascular system of the Chiroptera. Proc. Zoöl. Soc. London, p. 58.

ALDAMA, J.
1930. Cytoarchitektonik der Grosshirnrinde eines 5-jährigen und eines 1-jährigen Kindes. Ztschr. f. d. ges. Neurol. u. Psychiat., v. 130, p. 532.

ALEXANDER
1867. Ein Fall von hemiopischer Gesichtsfeldbeschränkung. Klin. Monatsbl. f. Augenh., v. 5, p. 88.

ALEXANDER, G.
1905. Zur Frage der phylogenetischen, vikariierenden Ausbildung der Sinnesorgane. Ztschr. f. Psychol. u. Physiol. d. Sinnesorg., v. 38, p. 24.

ALEXANDER, G. F.
1934. Ocular dioptrics and lenses. W. Wood & Co., Baltimore.

ALEXANDER, J.
1948. Life, its nature and origin. Reinhold Pub. Corp., New York.

ALEXANDER, L.
1942. The vascular supply of the strio-pallidum. Research Pub. A. Research Nerv. & Ment. Dis., v. 21, p. 77.

ALEXANDER, L., & PUTNAM, T. J.
1938. Pathological alterations of cerebral vascular patterns. Research Pub. A. Research Nerv. & Ment. Dis., v. 18, p. 438. Williams & Wilkins Co., Baltimore.

ALEXANDER-SCHÄFER, G.
1907. Vergleichend-physiologische Untersuchungen über die Sehschärfe. Arch. f. d. ges. Physiol. (Pflüger), v. 119, p. 571.

ALEXANDER OF TRALLES
*6th cent. A.D. Περὶ τῶν ἐν ὀφθαλμοῖς παθῶν, or On the diseases of the eyes (from PUSCHMANN 1886).

ALEZAIS, H., & D'ASTROS, L.
1892. La circulation artérielle du pédoncule cérébral. J. d. anat. et physiol. v. 28, p. 519.

AL-FĀRĀBĪ
*10th cent. *See* VINCENTIUS BELLOVACENSIS or VINCENT OF BEAUVAIS, Speculum naturale, lib. 25, cap. 43.

ALFORD, L. B.
1948. Cerebral localization. Outline of a revision. Nerv. & Ment. Dis. Monog., No. 77. New York.

ALHAZEN & VITELLO (*see also* IBN AL-HAITHAM)
1572. Opticae thesaurus Alhazeni Arabis libri septem, nunc primum editi. Eiusdem liber De Crepusculis & Nubium ascensionibus. Item Vitellonis Thuringopoloni Libri X. Omnes instaurati, figuris illustrati & aucti, adiectis etiam in Alhazenum commentarijs, A Federico Risnero. Cum privilegio Caesareo & Regis Galliae ad sexennium. Basileae, per Episcopios. MDLXXII.

ᶜALĪ IBN AL-ᶜABBĀS (IBN AL-RŪMĪ)
1523. Liber totius medicinae, etc., a Stephano ex Arabica lingua in Latinam . . . reductus. Lugduni.

1903. Le livre royal (Al-Malakī). *In:* P. DE KONING, Trois traités d'anatomie arabes, p. 90. E. J. Brill, Leide.

ᶜALĪ IBN ᶜĪSĀ (ᶜALĪ BEN ᶜISSĀ)
10th cent. Epistola Jhesu filii Haly de cognitione infirmitatum oculorum sive Memoriale oculariorum quod compilavit Ali ben Issa. In P. PANSIER, "Collectio ophthalmologica veterum auctorum," v. 1, p. 185. J.-B. Baillière & Fils, Paris, 1903.

10th cent. Tadhkirat al-Kaḥḥālīn, or The oculist's memorandum book. Latin ed. *In:* P. PANSIER, "Collectio ophthalmologica veterum auctorum," v. 3, p. 185. J.-B. Baillière & Fils, Paris, 1903. English ed. by WOOD, 1936.

10th cent. Memorandum book of a tenth-century oculist, for the use of modern ophthalmologists. A translation of the Tadhkirat of Ali ibn Isa of Baghdad (*ca*. A.D. 940 1010), the most complete, practical and original of all the early textbooks on the eye and its diseases. Northwestern University Press, Chicago.

ALISON, W. P.
1836. On single and correct vision, by means of double and inverted images on the retinae. Tr. Roy. Soc. Edinburgh, v. 13, p. 472.

ALLBUTT, T. C.
1921. Greek medicine in Rome. Macmillan Co., Ltd., London.

ALLEE, W. C.
1949. Principles of animal ecology. W. B. Saunders Co., Philadelphia.

ALLEN, A. A.
1948. Sea bird cities off Audubon's Labrador. Nat. Geog. Mag., v. 93, p. 755.
1950. Voices of the night. *Ibid*., v. 97, p. 507.
1951. The bird's year. *Ibid*., v. 99, p. 791.
1951. Duck hunting with a color camera. *Ibid*., v. 100, p. 514.
1951. Stalking birds with color camera. Nat. Geog. Soc., Washington, D.C.

ALLEN, F.
1945. The delineation of retinal zones with dark tube vision. Canad. J. Research, A, v. 23, p. 21.
1950. The neural oscillatory effect in colour vision. Acta ophth., v. 27, p. 599.

ALLEN, G. M.
1939. Bats. Harvard University Press, Cambridge, Mass.

ALLEN, I. M.
1928. Unusual sensory phenomena following removal of a tumor of the sensory cortex. J. Neurol. & Psychopath., v. 9, p. 133.
1930. A clinical study of tumours involving the occipital lobe. Brain, v. 53, p. 194.

ALLEN, P.
1943. Problems connected with the development of the telescope (1609–1687). Isis, v. 34, p. 302.

ALLEN, R. M.
1947. The microscope. D. Van Nostrand Co., New York.

ALLEN, T. D., & CARMAN, H. F.
1938. Homonymous hemianopic paracentral scotoma: report of a case. Arch. Ophth., v. 20 (77), p. 846.

ALLEN, W. F.
1945. Effect of destroying three localized cerebral cortical areas for sound on correct conditioned differential responses of the dog's foreleg. Am. J. Physiol., v. 144, p. 415.

ALLERS, R.
1916. Ueber Schädelschüsse. J. Springer, Berlin.

ALMEIDA LIMA, P.
1950. Cerebral angiography. Oxford University Press, New York.

ALOUF, I.
1929. Die vergleichende Cytoarchitektonik der Area striata. J. f. Psychol. u. Neurol., v. 38, p. 5.

ALPERS, B. J., FORSTER, F. M., & HERBUT, P. A.
1948. Retinal, cerebral and systemic arteriosclerosis; a histopathologic study. Arch. Neurol. & Psychiat., v. 60, p. 440.

AL-RĀZĪ (RHAZES, MUHAMMAD IBN ZAKARĪYA ABU BAKR AL RHĀZĪ)
10th cent. Continens. Translated by P. PANSIER, intended to be v. 3 of his "Collectio ophthalmalogica veterum auctorum," but because of lack of funds never published. *See* v. 2, p. clx.

Early 10th cent. A.D. Le livre intitulé al-Manṣūrī sur la médecine par Muḥammed ibn Zakariyyā al-Rāzī. *In:* P. DE KONING, Trois traités d'anatomie arabes. E. J. Brill, Leide, 1903.

1511. Liber ad Almansorem. *In:* Opera parva Abubetri filii Zachariae, etc. Lugduni. (*Cf.* W. BRONNER 1900.)

ALTMANN, H. W.
1952. Morphologische Bemerkungen zur Funktion des Ganglienzellkernes. Naturwiss., v. 39, p. 348.

ALTMANN, R.
1880. Zur Theorie der Bilderzeugung. Arch. f. Anat. u. Entw., p. 111.
1880. Ueber die Vorbemerkungen des Hrn. Prof. Abbe zu seinen "Grenzen der geometrischen Optik." *Ibid*., p. 354; *also* 1882, p. 52.

ALTSCHUL, R.
1954. Endothelium, its development, morphology, function, and pathology. Macmillan Co., New York.

ALVERDES, F.
1927. Social life in the animal world. Harcourt, Brace & Co., New York.

ALZHEIMER, A.
1910. Beiträge zur Kenntnis der pathologischen Neuroglia, p. 401. Histol. u. histopath. Arb., ed. NISSL & ALZHEIMER, v. 3 [3].

AMERICAN WILD LIFE ILLUSTRATED. W. H. WISE &
    Co., New York, 1946

AMES, A., GLIDDON, G. H., & OGLE, K. N.
    1932. Size and shape of ocular images. I. Methods
        of determination and physiologic signifi-
        cance. Arch. Ophth., v. 7, p. 576.

AMES, A., & OGLE, K. N.
    1932. Size and shape of ocular images. III. Visual
        sensitivity to differences in the relative size
        of the ocular images of the two eyes. Arch.
        Ophth., v. 7, p. 904.

AMMON, F. A.
    1830. De genesi et usu maculae luteae in retina
        oculi humani obviae. Vinariae (Weimar).
    1830. V. Sömmerring's Centralloch der Netzhaut.
        Ztschr. f. d. Ophth. (Ammon), v. 1, p. 114.
    1832. Skizze einer Entwickelungsgeschichte des
        menschlichen Auges nach eigenen Unter-
        suchungen entworfen. *Ibid.*, v. 2, p. 503.
    1858. Die Entwicklungsgeschichte des mensch-
        lichen Auges. Arch. f. Ophth. (Graefe), v. 4
        (1), p. 1.

ANDERS, H. E., & EICKE, W. J.
    1939. Ueber Veränderungen an Gehirngefässen
        bei Hypertonie. Zentralbl. f. d. ges. Neurol.
        u. Psychiat., v. 94, p. 357.

ANDERSEN, E. E., & WEYMOUTH, F. W.; *see also*
    WEYMOUTH; AVERILL & WEYMOUTH
    1923. Visual perception and the retinal mosaic.
        I. Retinal mean local signs—an explanation
        of the fineness of binocular perception of dis-
        tance. Am. J. Physiol., v. 64, p. 561.

ANDERSON, J.
    1878. Anatomical and zoölogical researches: com-
        prising an account of the zoölogical results
        of the two expeditions to western Yunnan
        in 1868 and 1875. 2 vols. B. Quaritch, Lon-
        don.

ANDERSON, R. S.
    1948. Chemiluminescence in aqueous solutions.
        Ann. New York Acad. Sc., v. 49, p. 337.

ANDRAL, G.
    1840. Clinique médicale, ou choix d'observations
        recueillies à l'hôpital de la Charité. Vol. 5:
        Maladies de l'encéphale. Fortin, Masson &
        Cie, Paris.

ANDREW, W.
    1943. The reticular nature of glia fibers in the
        cerebrum of the frog and in the higher ver-
        tebrates. J. Comp. Neurol., v. 79, p. 57.

ANDREW, W., & ASHWORTH, C. T.
    1915. The adendroglia: a new concept of the mor-
        phology and reactions of the smaller neurog-
        lial cells. J. Comp. Neurol., v. 82, p. 101.

ANDREWS, E. A.
    1893. An undescribed acraniate: *Asymmetron lu-
        cayannum.* Studies Biol. Lab. Johns Hop-
        kins Univ., v. 5, p. 213.
    1893. The Bahama *Amphioxus.* Johns Hopkins
        Univ. Circ., v. 12, p. 104.

ANDREWS, R. C.
    1946. Meet your ancestors: a biography of primi-
        tive man. Viking Press, New York.
    1951. Nature's ways; how nature takes care of its
        own. Crown Publishers, New York.

ANDREWS, R. C., GRANGER, W., *et al.*
    1932. The new conquest of Central Asia. Natural
        history of Central Asia, v. 1. American Mu-
        seum of Natural History, New York.

ANGEL, F.
    1931. Un lézard remarcable: le caméléon. Terre et
        vie, v. 1, p. 464.

ANGEL, J. L.
    1950. Population size and microevolution in
        Greece. Cold Spring Harbor Symp. Quant.
        Biol., v. 15, p. 343.

ANGÉLIS, P.
    1909. Hémianopsie homonyme droite avec cécité
        verbal pure. Rev. gén. de clin. et de thérap.,
        v. 23, p. 103.

ANGELUCCI, A.
    1890. Untersuchungen über die Sehthätigkeit der
        Netzhaut und des Gehirns. Roth, Giessen.

ANONYMUS I
    ca. 1150 A.D. Demonstratio anatomica. Also Ana-
        tomia porci (*originally* Anatomia parva; *for
        a long time also erroneously known as* Ana-
        tomia porci Cophonis, since it was printed
        as an appendix to Coplio's Tractatus de
        arte medendi). This and Demonstratio ana-
        tomica, and Anatomia of Magister Richar-
        dus (*ca.* 1130–80 A.D.) were the first short
        guides on anatomy in medieval Europe. *See*
        de Renzi, Collectio Salernitana and Magister
        Richardus, Anatomia (*ca.* 1130–80).
    13th or 14th cent. Anatomia oculi. Brit. Mus.,
        Sloane Coll. MSS No. 420. *See* Sudhoff,
        Arch. f. Gesch. d. Med., v. 8, p. 1, 1915.

ANONYMUS II
    1937. Willebrord Snell—he transformed ancient
        guess into definite law. *In:* Ed. focus, v. 8,
        No. 2. Bausch & Lomb, New York.

ANONYMUS-WINTHROP
    1944. Monte Cassino and Salerno: two early Itali-
        an medical centers. Clin. excerpts, v. 18, p.
        131. Winthrop Chemical Co., New York.

ANONYMOUS I
    1932. Article: Lake dwellings, Encyclopaedia Bri-
        tannica, 14th ed., v. 13, p. 602.

ANONYMOUS II
  1943. Dwellers in darkness. Texas Game & Fish, Austin, v. 1, pp. 7, 14.
  1946. Mighty miners (moles). Ohio Conserv. Bull., v. 10, p. 2.
  1946. Bats on the wing. Iowa Conservation, v. 5, p. 47.

ANTHONY, A., & VALLOIS, H.
  1913. Considérations anatomiques sur le type adaptif primitif des microchéiroptères. Internat. Monatsschr. f. Anat. u. Physiol., v. 30, p. 169.

ANTHONY, H. E.
  1928. Field book of North American Mammals. G. P. Putnam's Sons, New York.

ANTHONY, J.
  1943. Évolution du complex calcarin des primates. Mammalia, v. 7, p. 91.
  1943. L'évolution des plis de passage pariéto-occipitaux de Gratiolet chez les singes platyrhiniens. Bull. mus. nat. hist. nat. Paris, 2d ser., v. 15, p. 267.
  1945. La genèse du crochet de l'hippocampe. *Ibid.*, v. 17, p. 286.

ANTHONY, R.
  1912. Contribution à l'étude morphologique générale des charactères d'adaptation à la vie arboricale chez les vertébrés. Ann. sc. nat. zool., v. 15, p. 101.
  1913. L'encéphale de l'homme fossile de La Quina. Bull. & mém. Soc. anthropol. Paris, ser. 6, v. 4, p. 117.
  1928. Leçons sur le cerveau. Cours d'anatomie comparée du muséum. Encéphale envisagé dans son ensemble. Télencéphale. G. Doin et Cie, Paris.
  1935. Étude du cerveau d'un savant biologiste et médecin (examination of brain of C. v. Monakow). Schweiz. Arch. f. Neurol. u. Psychiat., v. 36, p. 1. *See also* Monakow.

ANTON, G.
  1895. Ueber Störungen des Orientierungsvermögens. Neurol. Centralbl., v. 14, p. 955. *Also* Wien. klin. Rundschau, v. 9, p. 698.
  1896. Blindheit nach beiderseitiger Gehirnerkrankung mit Verlust der Orientierung im Raume. Mitt. d. Ver. d. Aerzte in Steiermark, v. 33, p. 41.
  1898. Ueber Herderkrankungen des Gehirns, welche vom Patienten selbst nicht wahrgenommen werden. Wien. klin. Wchnschr., v. 11, p. 227. *Also* Mitt. d. Ver. d. Aerzte in Steiermark, v. 35, p. 10.
  1899. Ueber die Selbstwahrnehmung der Herderkrankungen des Gehirns durch den Kranken bei Rindenblindheit und Rindentaubheit. Arch. f. Psychiat., v. 32, p. 86.
  1906. Ueber den Wiederersatz der Funktion bei Erkrankungen des Gehirns. Monatsschr. f. Psychiat. u. Neurol., v. 19, p. 1.
  1930. Theodor Meynert; seine Person, sein Wirken und sein Werk: eine fachgeschichtliche Studie. J. Psychol. u. Neurol., v. 40, p. 256.

ANTONI, N. R. E.
  1914. Ausbreitung und Flächenbeziehung der Area striata im menschlichen Gehirn. Folia neurobiol., v. 8, p. 265.

APÁTHY, S.
  1894. Das leitende Element in den Muskelfasern von *Ascaris*. Arch. f. mikr. Anat., v. 43, p. 886.
  1897. Das leitende Element des Nervensystems und seine topographischen Beziehungen zu den Zellen. Mitth. a.d. zool. stat. zu Neapel, v. 12, p. 495.
  1907. Bemerkungen zu den Ergebnissen Ramón y Cajals, etc. Anat. Anz., v. 31, pp. 481, 523.
  1908. Der Vergleich der Neurofibrillen mit Protoplasmaströmen oder Protoplasmafäden. Folia neuro-biol., v. 1, p. 289.
  1912. Neuere Beiträge zur Schneidetechnik. Ztschr. f. wissensch. Mikr., v. 29, p. 449.

APOLANT, H.
  1896. Ueber die Beziehung des Nervus oculomotorius zum Ganglion ciliare. Arch. f. mikr. Anat. u. Entw., v. 47, p. 655.

APPLETON, A. B.
  1911. Descriptions of two brains of natives of India. J. Anat., v. 45, p. 85.

AQUAPENDENS, HIERONYMUS FABRICIUS AB AQUAPENDENTE (*see also* CAPPARONI 1926; FAVARO 1919)
  1600. Hieronymi Fabricii ab Aquapendente de visione, voce, auditu. On p. 1: H——i F——i ab A. De Oculo Visus Organo Liber, etc. Per Franciscum Bolzettam, Venetiis. Also later editions under different title. *See also* Opera omnia.
  1603. De venarum ostiolis. Facsimile ed. by K. J. FRANKLIN. Charles C Thomas, Springfield, Ill.; Baltimore, Md., 1933.
  1737. De oculo. Lugduni Batavorum.
  1738. Opera omnia anatomica et physiologica, hactenus variis locis ac formis edita . . . in unum volumen redacta, etc. Cum praefatione Bernardi Siegfrid Albini. Johann van Kerckhem, Leyden.

ARAGO, D. F. J.
  1824. Note du rédacteur (on transient hemianopia). Ann. de chimie & phys., v. 27, p. 109.

ARAGO, D. F. J.—*Continued*
1839. Le daguerréotype. Compt. rend. Acad. d. sc., v. 9, p. 250.
1859. Biographies of distinguished scientific men. Ticknor & Fields, Boston.

ARANZI, J. C. (ARANTIUS)
1595. De humano foetu; anatomicarum observationum liber; etc. Ap. Barth. Carampellum, Venetiis. *See* Anat. Observ., pp. 64, 66, 69, 70.

ARCHAMBAULT; *see* LA SALLE D'A.

ARCHBOLD, R.
1941. Unknown New Guinea. Nat. Geog. Mag., v. 79, p. 315.

AREY, L. B.
1915. The occurrence and the significance of photomechanical changes in the vertebrate retina—an historical survey. J. Comp. Neurol., v. 25, p. 535.
1916. The movements in the visual cells and retinal pigment of the lower vertebrates. *Ibid.*, v. 26, p. 121.
1916. The function of the efferent fibers in the optic nerve of fishes. *Ibid.*, p. 213.
1916. Changes in the rod-visual cells of the frog due to the action of light. *Ibid.*, p. 429.
1919. A retinal mechanism of efficient vision. *Ibid.*, v. 30, p. 343.
1928. Visual cells and retinal pigment. *In:* E. V. COWDRY, Special cytology, v. 2, p. 889. P. B. Hoeber, New York.
1932. Retina, chorioid and sclera. *In:* PENFIELD, Cytology & cellular pathology of the nervous system, v. 2, p. 743. *See also* E. V. COWDRY, Special cytology, v. 2.
1937. The numerical relation of retinal ganglion cells to optic nerve fibers in vertebrates. Anat. Rec., v. 70, suppl. 1, p. 85. (Abstr.)
1946. Developmental anatomy. 5th ed. W. B. Saunders Co., Philadelphia.

AREY, L. B., & BICKEL, W. H.
1935. The number of nerve fibers in the human optic nerve. Anat. Rec., v. 58 (suppl.), p. 3.

AREY, L. B., BRUESCH, S. R., & CASTANARES, S.
1942. The relation between eyeball size and the number of optic nerve fibers in the dog. J. Comp. Neurol., v. 76, p. 417.

AREY, L. B., & GORE, M.
1942. The numerical relation between the ganglion cells of the retina and the fibers in the optic nerve of the dog. J. Comp. Neurol., v. 77, p. 609.

AREY, L. B., & JENNINGS, W. K.
1944. The effect of darkness and temperature on the retinal pigment and visual cells of the frog's eye when transferred into the belly cavity. J. Comp. Neurol., v. 79, p. 487.

AREY, L. B., & MUNDT, G. H.
1941. A persistent diurnal rhythm in visual cones. Anat. Rec., v. 79, suppl. 1, p. 5.

AREY, L. B., & SCHAIBLE, A. J.
1934. The nerve-fiber composition of the optic nerve. Anat. Rec. v. 58 (suppl.), p. 3.

ARGENTIER, J.
*1565. Joh. Argenterii Opera (1592), 3 vols. Ciottus, Venet.

ARGYLL ROBERTSON, D. (*see also* G. Mackay in Klin. Monatsbl. f. Augenh., 1909, v. 1, p. 308)
1863. Calabar bean as a new agent in ophthalmic medicine. Edinburgh M. J., v. 8 (2), p. 815.
1863. Note on the Calabar bean. *Ibid.*, p. 1115.
1869. On an interesting series of eye-symptoms in a case of spinal disease, with remarks on the action of belladonna on the iris, etc. *Ibid.*, v. 14 (2), p. 696.
1869. Four cases of spinal myosis; with remarks on the action of light on the pupil. *Ibid.*, v. 15 (1), p. 487.

ARIËNS KAPPERS, C. U.
1908. Weitere Mitteilungen über Neurobiotaxis. Folia neuro-biol., v. 1, p. 507.
1909. The phylogenesis of the palaeo-cortex and archi-cortex compared with the evolution of the visual neo-cortex. Arch. Neurol. (Mott), v. 4, p. 161.
1911. Brodmanns vergleichende Lokalisations-Lehre der Grosshirnrinde in ihren Principien dargestellt auf Grund des Zellenbaus. Ztschr. f. Psychol., v. 58, p. 277.
1913. Cerebral localization and the significance of sulci. Proc. XVIIth Internat. M. Cong. London, 1913 (*see* Folia neuro-biol., v. 8, p. 52, 1914).
1914. Ueber das Rindenproblem und die Tendenz innerer Hirnteile sich durch Oberflächenvermehrung, statt Volumzunahme zu vergrössern. Folia neuro-biol., v. 8, p. 507.
1916–17. Further contributions on neurobiotaxis. IX. An attempt to compare the phenomena of neurobiotaxis with other phenomena of taxis and tropism. The dynamic polarization of the neurone. J. Comp. Neurol., v. 27, p. 261.
1917. Versuch einer Erklärung des Verhaltens an der Synapse. Psychiat. en neurol. bl., v. 21, p. 440.
1919. The logetic character of growth. J. Comp. Neurol., v. 31, p. 51.
1922. Phenomena of neurobiotaxis in the optic

system. *In:* Libro en honor de D. S. Ramón y Cajal, v. 1, p. 267.

1927. On neurobiotaxis: a psychical law in the structure of the nervous system. Acta psychiat. et neurol., v. 2, p. 118.

1928. The development of the cortex and the functions of its different layers. *Ibid.,* v. 3, p. 115.

1929. The evolution of the nervous system in invertebrates, vertebrates and man. De Erven F. Bohn, Haarlem.

1933. The forebrain arteries in plagiostomes, reptiles, birds and monotremes. Proc. Kon. Akad. Wetensch. Amsterdam, v. 36, p. 52.

1933. The fissuration on the frontal lobe of *Sinanthropus pekinensis* Black, compared with the fissuration in Neanderthalmen. *Ibid.,* p. 802.

1934. Feinerer Bau und Bahnverbindungen des Zentralnervensystems. *In:* BOLK, GÖPPERT, KALLIUS, & LUBOSCH, Handb. d. vergl. Anat. d. Wirbeltiere, v. 2 (1), p. 319.

1934. In memoriam Santiago Ramón y Cajal. Psychiat. en neurol. bl., v. 38, p. 783.

1935. Development of the different layers of the cerebral cortex with reference to some pathological cases: the forebrain of prehistoric races. Tr. Coll. Physicians, Philadelphia, v. 3, p. 20.

1937. The endocranial casts of the Ehringsdorf and *Homo soloensis* skulls. J. Anat., v. 71, p. 61.

1939. Anatomie comparée des connexions centrales du huitième nerf dans la série des vertébrés. Oto-rhino-laryng. internat., v. 27, p. 337.

1939. Comparison of the endocranial casts of the *Pithecanthropus erectus* skull found by Dubois and von Koenigswald's *Pithecanthropus* skull. Proc. Kon. nederl. Akad. Wetensch. Amsterdam, v. 42, p. 30.

1941. Neurobiotactic influences in the arrangement of midbrain and 'tween-brain centres. *Ibid.,* v. 44, p. 130.

1941. The oculomotor nucleus of the electric stargazers: *Astroscopus guttatus* and *Astroscopus y-graecum. Ibid.,* p. 369.

1941. Introductory note on the phylogenetic and ontogenetic development of the cortex cerebri. *Ibid.,* p. 521.

1941. Clarence Luther Herrick en Charles Judson Herrick, naar aanleiding van het vijftigharig bestaan van het Journal of Comparative Neurology. Nederl. tijdschr. v. geneesk., v. 85, p. 1362.

ARIËNS KAPPERS, C. U., HUBER, G. C., & CROSBY, E. C.

1936. The comparative anatomy of the nervous system of vertebrates, including man. 2 vols. Macmillan Co., New York.

ARISTARCHOS OF SAMOS; *see* T. HEATH 1913

ARISTOTLE (ARISTOTÉLES)

4th cent. B.C. The works of Aristotle. Clarendon Press, Oxford, 1913–31; vol. 3: De anima, Parva naturalia (De sensu); v. 4: Historia animalium (book 1, chaps. 9, 10; book 3, chap. 18); v. 5: De partibus animalium (book 2, chaps. 13–15); v. 6: De coloribus; v. 7: Problemata.

ARLDT, T.

1917–22. Handbuch der Palaeogeographie. Gebrüder Borntraeger, Leipzig.

ARMAIGNAC, H.

1881. De la cécité des mots. J. de méd. de Bordeaux, p. 190.

ARMSTRONG, E. A.

1947. Bird display and behaviour. L. Drummond, Ltd., London.

ARMSTRONG, J. A.

1950. An experimental study of optic pathways in *Lacerta vivipara.* J. Anat., v. 84, p. 70. (Abstr.)

1950. An experimental study of the visual pathways in a reptile (*Lacerta vivipara*). *Ibid.,* p. 146.

ARNALDUS DE VILLANOVA (*see also* LALANDE 1896)

ca. 1308. Libellus regiminis de confortatine visus. *In:* P. PANSIER, "Collectio ophthalmologica veterum auctorum," Fasc. 1, 1903. J.-B. Ballière & Fils, Paris.

ARNDT, R.

1867–69. Studien über die Architektonik der Grosshirnrinde des Menschen. Arch. f. mikr. Anat., v. 3, p. 441; v. 4, p. 407; v. 5, p. 317.

ARNOLD, F.

1832. Anatomische und physiologische Untersuchungen ueber das Auge des Menschen. K. Groos, Heidelberg & Leipzig.

1838. Bemerkungen über den Bau des Hirns und Rückenmarks, nebst Beiträgen zur Physiologie des zehnten und eilften Hirnnerven, etc. Höhr, Zürich.

1838–42. Tabulae anatomicae. 4 vols. Orell, Fuessli et Soc., Turici (Zürich); P. Balz, Stuttgart.

1845–51. Handbuch der Anatomie des Menschen etc. Herder'sche Buchhandlung, Freiburg i.Br.

ARONSON, L. R., & PAPEZ, J. W.
1934. Thalamic nuclei of *Pithecus* (*Macacus*) *rhesus*. II. Arch. Neurol. & Psychiat., v. 32, p. 27.

ARROL, W. J., JACOBI, R. B., & PANETH, F. A.
1942. Meteorites and the age of the solar system. Nature, v. 149, p. 235.

ARTOM, G.
1925. Untersuchungen über die Myelogenese des Nervensystems der Affen. Arch. f. Psychiat. u. Nervenkr., v. 75, p. 169.

ASCHAFFENBURG, G.
1928. Handbuch der Psychiatrie. F. Deuticke, Wien.
1939. Ueber Arteriosklerose. Zentralbl. f. d. ges. Neurol. u. Psychiat., v. 94, p. 344.

ASCHER, K. W.
1942. Aqueous veins; preliminary note. Am. J. Ophth., v. 25, p. 31.
1946. Further observations on aqueous veins. *Ibid.*, v. 29, p. 1373.

ASCHOFF, L., KÜSTER, E., & SCHMIDT, W. J.
1938. Hundert Jahre Zellforschung. Gebrüder Borntraeger, Berlin.

ASHIKAGA, RIKURO
1934. Ueber die Beziehung zwischen dem Sehzentrum und dem Gesichtsfeld. Acta Soc. ophth. japon., v. 38, p. 1.

ASHTON, E. H., & ZUCKERMAN, S.
1951. Some cranial indices of *Plesianthropus* and other primates. Am. J. Phys. Anthropol., N.S., v. 9, p. 283.

ASK-UPMARK, E.
1932. On the cortical projection of the temporal half-moon of the visual field (Swed.). Acta ophth., v. 10, p. 271. Abstr. in Zentralbl. f. d. ges. Ophth., v. 28, p. 624, 1933.

ATKINSON, D. T.
1937. The ocular fundus in diagnosis and treatment. Lea & Febiger, Philadelphia.

ATKINSON, T. G.
1944. Oculo-refractive encyclopedia and dictionary. 3d ed. Professional Press, Inc., Chicago, Ill.

ATLAS, D., & INGRAM, W. R.
1937. A note on the topography of the pretectal region in monkey. J. Comp. Neurol., v. 66, p. 291.

AUBARET, J. B. M. E.
1903. Recherches sur les origines réelles des fibres optiques. Thèse Bordeaux.

AUBERT, H.
1857. Beiträge zur Kenntniss des indirecten Sehens. (2) Ueber die Grenzen der Farbenwahrnehmung auf den seitlichen Theilen der Retina. Arch. f. Ophth. (Graefe), v. 3 (2), p. 38.
1865. Physiologie der Netzhaut. E. Morgenstern, Breslau.
1876. Physiologische Optik. *In:* GRAEFE & SAEMISCH, Handb. d. ges. Augenh., 1st ed., v. 2, p. 393.

AUBERT, H., & FÖRSTER, R.
1857. Beiträge zur Kenntniss des indirecten Sehens. (1) Untersuchungen über den Raumsinn der Retina. Arch. f. Ophth. (Graefe), v. 3 (2), p. 1.

AUDUBON, J. J.
1941. The birds of America. Macmillan Co., New York. (*See also* earlier editions.)

AUERBACH, L.
1898. Nervenendigung in den Centralorganen. Neurol. Centralbl., v. 17, p. 445.

AUERSPERG, A.
1939. Blickbewegung und optischer Erfassungsakt. Ztschr. f. d. ges. Neurol. u. Psychiat., v. 165, p. 209.

AUSTIN, G. M., LEWEY, F. H., & GRANT, F. C.
1949. Studies on the occipital lobe. 1. Significance of small areas of preserved central vision. Arch. Neurol. & Psychiat., v. 62, p. 204.

AUTRUM, H.
1950. Die Belichtungspotentiale und das Sehen der Insekten (Untersuchungen an *Calliphora* und *Dixippus*). Ztschr. f. vergl. Physiol., v. 32, p. 176.
1950. Tiere orientieren sich am blauen Himmel. Umschau, v. 50, p. 621.
1952. Ueber zeitliches Auflösungsvermögen und Primärvorgänge im Insektenauge. Naturwiss., v. 39, p. 290.

AUTRUM, H., & STUMPF, H.
1950. Das Bienenauge als Analysator für polarisiertes Licht. Ztschr. f. Naturforsch., v. 56, p. 116.
1953. Elektrophysiologische Untersuchungen über das Farbensehen von *Calliphora*. Ztschr. f. vergl. Physiol., v. 35, p. 71.

AVERILL, H. L., & WEYMOUTH (*see also* WEYMOUTH; ANDERSEN & WEYMOUTH)
1925. Visual perception and the retinal mosaic. II. The influence of eye-movements on the displacement threshold. J. Comp. Psychol., v. 5, p. 147.

AVICENNA; *see* IBN SĪNĀ

AXENFELD, T.
1915. Hemianopische Gesichtsfeldstörungen nach Schädelschüssen. Klin. Monatsbl. f. Augenh., v. 55, p. 126.

1923. Lehrbuch und Atlas der Augenheilkunde. G. Fischer, Jena. (Also later eds.)

AYER, A. A.
1948. The anatomy of *Semnopithecus entellus.* Indian Pub. House, Ltd., Madras.

AYER, J. B., & AITKEN, H. F.
1907. Brief on the arteries of the corpus striatum. Boston M. & Surg. J., v. 156, p. 768.

AYRES, W. C.
1884. Der Blutlauf in der Gegend des gelben Flecks. Arch. f. Augenh., v. 13, p. 29.

AYSCOUGH, J.
*1750. A short account of the nature and use of spectacles; in which is recommended a kind of glass for spectacles, preferable to any hitherto made use of for that purpose. London.

B

BAARMANN, J.
*1882. Ibn al-Haitams Abhandlung über das Licht. Inaug.-Diss., Halle a.S.; *also* Ztschr. f. d. deutsch. morgenländ. Gesellsch., v. 36, p. 195; *see also* Wiedemann, v. 38, p. 145.

BAB, W.
1921. Die Ursachen der Kriegsblindheit. Berlin. klin. Wchnschr., v. 58, p. 512.
1923. Die Zahl der Kriegsblinden in Deutschland nebst Bemerkungen über das Kriegsblindenwesen anderer Länder. Klin. Monatsschr. f. Augenh., v. 70, p. 187.

BABCOCK, H. L.
1914. The food habits of the short-tailed shrew. Science, v. 40, p. 526.

BABUCHIN, A.
1863-64. Beiträge zur Entwickelungsgeschichte des Auges, besonders der Retina. Würzburg. naturwiss. Ztschr., v. 4, p. 71. (*See* supplement to same in v. 5, pp. 127, 141.)

BACH, L.
1895. Die Nervenzellenstructur der Netzhaut in normalen und pathologischen Zuständen. Die menschliche Netzhaut nach Untersuchungen mit der Golgi-Cajal'schen Methode. Arch. f. Ophth. (Graefe), v. 41 (3), p. 62.
1899. Wo haben wir bei Tabes und Paralyse den Sitz der zur reflectorischen Pupillenstarre führenden Störung zu suchen? Centralbl. f. Nervenh., v. 22, p. 631.
1899. Experimentelle Untersuchungen über den Verlauf der Pupillarfasern und das Reflexcentrum der Pupille. Ber. d. Deutsch. ophth. Gesellsch. Heidelberg, v. 27, p. 98.

1901. Bemerkungen zur Methodik der Pupillenuntersuchung, zu den Ursachen der Anisokorie und Störungen der Pupillenbewegung. *Ibid.*, v. 29, p. 20.
1904. Was wissen wir über Pupillenreflexzentren und Pupillenreflexbahnen? Ztschr. f. Augenh., v. 11, p. 105.
1904. Das Verhalten der Pupillen bei der Konvergenz und Akkommodation. *Ibid.*, v. 12, p. 725.
1905. Ueber Pupillenreflexzentren und Pupillenreflexbahnen. *Ibid.*, v. 13, p. 260.
1909. Der Sphinkterkern und die Uebertragung des Lichtreflexes der Pupille im Vierhügel. *Ibid.*, v. 22, pp. 110, 352.

BACH, L., & SEEFELDER, R.
1914. Atlas zur Entwicklungsgeschichte des menschlichen Auges. W. Engelmann, Leipzig & Berlin.

BACON, ROGER (*see also:* LITTLE, R. BACON, Essays; and BOUYGES)
13th cent. Perspectiva (various manuscripts).
1859. Opera quaedam hactenus inedita. Vol. 1, containing: I. Opus tertium; II. Opus minus; III. Compendium philosophiae. Edited by J. S. BREWER. Longman, Green, Longman & Roberts, London.
1897-1900. The "Opus majus" . . . edited, with introduction and analytical table, by J. H. BRIDGES. 3 vols. Clarendon Press, Oxford.
1928. The *Opus major.* A translation of R. B. BURKE. 2 vols. University of Pennsylvania Press, Philadelphia.

BACQ, Z. M.
1935. La transmission chimique des influx dans le système nerveux autonome. Ergebn. d. Physiol. (Asher & Spiro), v. 37, p. 82.

BADAL
1888. Contribution à l'étude des cécités psychiques; alexie, agraphie, hemianopsie inférieure, trouble du sens de l'espace. Arch. d'opht., v. 8, p. 97; Gaz. hebd. sc. méd. de Bordeaux, v. 9, pp. 294, 307, 320.

BADER, A.
1933. Entwicklung der Augenheilkunde im 18. und 19. Jahrhundert, mit besonderer Berücksichtigung der Schweiz. B. Schwalbe & Co., Basel.

BADERMANN
1920. Ueber die Optik der Griechen. Central-Zeitung f. Optik u. Mechanik, v. 41, pp. 451, 464, 479.

BAER, K. E. VON
1827. De ovi mammalium et hominis genesi; epistolam ad Academiam Imperialem Scienti-

arum Petropolitanam dedit Carolus Ernestus a Baer zoologiae prof. publ. ord. regiomontanus. Cum tabula aenea. Lipsiae, sumptibus Leopoldi Vossii. MDCCCXXVII.

1828-37-88. Ueber Entwickelungsgeschichte der Thiere. Beobachtung und Reflexion von Dr. Karl Ernst v. Baer. Königsberg 1828 (1st part), 1837 (2d part). Bei den Gebrüdern Bornträger; 1888 (Schlussheft), Wilh. Koch.

BAEUMKER, C.
1908. Witelo, ein Philosoph und Naturforscher des XIII. Jahrhunderts. Beitr. z. Gesch. d. Phil. d. Mittelalt., v. 3, Fasc. 2.
1928. Studien und Charakteristiken zur Geschichte der Philosophie, insbesondere des Mittelalters. Aschendorff, Verlag, Münster i.W.

BAGLEY, C., JR., & LANGWORTHY, O. R.
1926. The forebrain and midbrain of the alligator with experimental transection of the brain stem. Arch. Neurol. & Psychiat., v. 16, p. 154.

BAILEY, F. W., & RILEY, C. F. C.
1931. Colour vision and the formation of associations with reference to light of various wavelengths in the parakeet, *Melopsittacus undulatus* (Shaw). Tr. Roy. Canad. Inst., v. 18, p. 47.

BAILEY, P.
1924. Contribution to the study of aphasia and apraxia. Arch. Neurol. & Psychiat., v. 11, p. 501.
1933. Intracranial tumors. Charles C Thomas, Springfield, Ill.

BAILEY, P., & BONIN, G. VON
1945. The cytoarchitecture of the cerebral cortex in the chimpanzee. Anat. Rec., v. 91, p. 265. (Abstr.)
1946. Concerning cytoarchitectonics. Tr. Am. Neurol. A., 71st ann. meet., p. 89.
1951. The isocortex of man. University of Illinois Press, Urbana, Ill.

BAILEY, P., BONIN, G., GAROL, H. W., & McCULLOCH, W. S.
1943. Functional organization of temporal lobe of monkey (*Macaca mulatta*) and chimpanzee (*Pan satyrus*). J. Neurophysiol., v. 6, p. 121.
1943. Long association fibers in cerebral hemispheres of monkey and chimpanzee. *Ibid.*, p. 129.

BAILEY, P., BONIN, G. VON, & McCULLOCH, W. S.
1948. Association fibers of the cerebral cortex. Anat. Rec., v. 100, p. 637.
1950. The isocortex of the chimpanzee. University of Illinois Press, Urbana, Ill.

BAILEY, P., & DAVIS, E. W.
1942. Effects of lesions of the periaqueductal gray matter in the cat. Proc. Soc. Exper. Biol. & Med., v. 51, p. 305.

BAILEY, P., DUSSER DE BARENNE, J. G., GAROL, H. W., & McCULLOCH, W. S.
1940. Sensory cortex of chimpanzee. J. Neurophysiol., v. 3, p. 469.

BAILEY, P., GAROL, H. W., & McCULLOCH, W. S.
1941. Functional organization and interrelation of cerebral hemispheres in chimpanzee. Am. J. Physiol., v. 133, p. 200.
1941. Functional organization and interrelation of cerebral hemispheres in cat. *Ibid.*, p. 287.
1941. Functional organization and interrelation of cerebral hemispheres in monkey. *Ibid.*, p. 383.
1941. Cortical origin and distribution of corpus callosum and anterior commissure in chimpanzee (*Pan satyrus*). J. Neurophysiol., v. 4, p. 564.

BAILEY, V.
1888. Report on some of the results of a trip through parts of Minnesota and Dakota. Ann. Rep. Dept. Agr. Washington, p. 426, 1887.
1925. Bats of the Carlsbad Cavern. Nat. Geog. Mag., v. 48, p. 321.
1926. A biological survey of North Dakota. ("North American Fauna," No. 49.) Government Printing Office, Washington, D.C.

BAILLARGER, J.-P. (J. G. F.)
1840. Recherches sur la structure de la *couche corticale* des circonvolutions du cerveau; etc. Mém. Acad. de méd. de Paris, v. 8, p. 148; also separate reprint by J.-B. Baillière, Paris; (for biography *see* Y. Magnan, in France méd., v. 49, p. 473, 1902, and v. 50, p. 17, 1903; *see also* J. F. Fulton, in Gesnerus, v. 8, p. 85, 1951).

BAILLIART, P., COUTELA, C., REDSLOB, E., VELTER, E., & ONFRAY, R.
1939. Traité d'ophtalmologie. Masson & Cie, Paris.

BAIR, H. L.
1940. Some fundamental physiologic principles in study of the visual field. Arch. Ophth., v. 24, p. 10.

BAIR, H. L., & HARLEY, R. D.
1940. Midline notching in the normal field of vision. Am. J. Ophth., v. 23, p. 183.

BAIRD, J. W.
1905. The color sensitivity of the peripheral retina. Carnegie Institution of Washington, Washington, D.C.

BAJANDUROW, B. I., & PEGEL, W. A.
1932. Der bedingte Reflex bei Fröschen. Ztschr. f. vergl. Physiol., v. 18, p. 284.

BAKER, H.
1743. The microscope made easy: or, 1. The nature, uses, and magnifying powers of the best kinds of microscopes, etc. 2d ed. R. Dodsley, London.
1753. Employment for the microscope. R. Dodsley, London.

BAKER, R. H.
1946. Astronomy. D. Van Nostrand Co., New York.

BAKKER, S. P.
1920. Ein Abzess in der rechten Seite des Chiasma nervorum opticorum. Psychiat. en neurol. bl., v. 24, p. 297.

BALADO, M.
1930. Sobre el artículo del Dr. E. P. Fortin "Falsedad de las concepciones actuales de la retina. etc." Arch. de oftal. de Buenos Aires, v. 5, p. 443.

BALADO, M., ADROGUE, E., & FRANKE, E.
1928. Contribución al estudio anatómico de las hemianopsias en cuadrante. Bol. Inst. clín. quir., v. 4, p. 520.

BALADO, M., & FRANKE, E.
1929. Sobre el modo de penetración de las fibras de la bandeleta óptica en el cuerpo geniculado externo. Rev. Soc. argent. de biol., v. 5, p. 707.
1930. Degeneración alternada de las capas del cuerpo geniculado externo, del hombre, después de la extirpación del globo ocular derecho. Arch. argent. de neurol., v. 6, p. 77.
1931. Estudios sobre las vías ópticas. I. El cuerpo geniculado externo del hombre. II. Estructura histológica de las capas del C. G. E. del hombre. III. El pregeniculado (gris pregeniculado, griseum praegeniculatum), del hombre. Bol. Inst. clín. quir., v. 7, pp. 5, 21, 32.
1931. Geniculado externo del Maimon—*Pithecus nemestrinus nemestrinus*, Linneo. Día méd., v. 3, p. 890.
1933. Trayecto de la radiación óptica en el hombre. Arch. argent. de neurol., v. 8, p. 117.
1937. Das Corpus geniculatum externum. Eine anatomisch-klinische Studie. ("Monog. a. d. Gesamtgeb. d. Neurol. u. Psychiat.," ed. O. FOERSTER *et al.*, Fasc. 62.)

BALADO, M., & MALBRÁN, J.
1932. Sobre la localización de la mácula en el hombre. Acción méd., v. 2, p. 107; Arch. de oftal. de Buenos Aires, v. 7, p. 259.

BALADO, M., MALBRÁN, J., & FRANKE, E.
1934. Doble incongruencia hemianópsica de origen cortical (estudio anatómo-clínico). Arch. argent. de neurol., v. 10, p. 201.

BALASSA, L.
1923. Zur Psychologie der Seelentaubheit. Deutsche Ztschr. f. Nervenh., v. 77, p. 143.

BALBUENA, F. F.
1922. Una fórmula para la aplicación del método de Cajal a los cortes de retina. Trab. del lab. de invest. biol. Madrid, v. 20, p. 31.
1923. A new technique for the application of the reduced silver nitrate method of Cajal to sections of the retina. Arch. Ophth., v. 52, p. 358. *See also:* Bull. et mém. Soc. franç., d'opht., v. 38, p. 552, 1925, and v. 5 (2), p. 286, 1930; Zentralbl. f. d. ges. Ophth., v. 22, p. 766, 1929; Compt. rend. XIII. Conc. Ophth. Amsterdam-Haag, v. 1, p. 243, 1929; Gac. méd. español, 1930; Arch. de oftal. Hispano-Am., p. 338, 1936; Ann. d'ocul., v. 176, p. 782.

BALDUS, K.
1924. Untersuchungen über Bau und Funktion des Gehirns der Larve und Imago von Libellen. Ztschr. f. wissensch. Zool., v. 121, p. 557.
1926. Experimentelle Untersuchungen über die Entfernungslokalisation der Libellen. Ztschr. f. vergl. Physiol., v. 3, p. 475.

BALFOUR, F. M.
1885. The works of F. M. Balfour. Memorial ed. 4 vols. Macmillan & Co., Ltd., London.

BÁLINT, R.
1909. Seelenlähmung des "Schauens," optische Ataxie, räumliche Störung der Aufmerksamkeit. Monatsschr. f. Psychiat. u. Neurol., v. 25, p. 51.

BALL, J. M.
1910. Andreas Vesalius, the reformer of anatomy. Medical Science Press, St. Louis, Mo.
1927. Modern ophthalmology. 6th ed. 2 vols. F. A. Davis Co., Philadelphia.

BALL, S., COLLINS, F. D., MORTON, R. A., & STUBBS, A. L.
1948. Chemistry of visual process. Nature, v. 161, p. 424.

BALLANTYNE, A. J.
1941. The histological interpretation of appearances in the fundus oculi. A scheme for methodical investigation. Brit. J. Ophth., v. 25, p. 480.
1943. The ocular manifestations of spontaneous subarachnoid haemorrhage. *Ibid.*, v. 27, p. 383.

BALLANTYNE, A. J.—*Continued*
1946. The nerve fibre pattern of the human retina. Tr. Ophth. Soc. United Kingdom, v. 66, p. 179.

BALLET, G.
1888. Le langage intérieur et les diverses formes de l'aphasie. F. Alcan, Paris.

BALLOU, G.
1953. Shrews—but untamed. Nature Mag., v. 46, p. 241.

BANKS, E.
1931. A popular account of the mammals of Borneo. J. Roy. Asiat. Soc. (Malay. Br., Singapore), v. 9, Part 2, p. 1.

BAQUIS, E.
1890. La retina della faina. Anat. Anz., v. 5, p. 366.

BARACZ, S.
1916. Ueber Hirn- und Schädelschussverletzungen. Inaug.-Diss., Heidelberg.

BÁRÁNY, E. H.
1947. The influence of intra-ocular pressure on the rate of drainage of aqueous humour. Stabilization of intra-ocular pressure or of aqueous flow. Brit. J. Ophth., v. 31, p. 160.

BÁRÁNY, E., GRANIT, R., & ZOTTERMAN, Y.
1941. The special senses. Part I. Hearing (Bárány). Part II. Visual receptors (Granit). Part III. Vibratory sensations and pain (Zotterman). Ann. Rev. Physiol., v. 3, p. 449.

BÁRÁNY, R.
1924. La bipartition de la couche interne des grains est-elle l'expression anatomique de la représentation isolée des champs visuels monoculaires dans l'écorce cérébrale? Trav. du lab. de recherches biol. Madrid, v. 22, p. 359.
1925. Ist die Zweiteilung der inneren Körnerschicht (Brodmann) der anatomische Ausdruck der gesonderten Repräsentation der monokulären Gesichtsfelder in der Hirnrinde? J. f. Psychol. u. Neurol., v. 31, p. 289.
1925. Réponse aux remarques critiques du professeur S. E. Henschen. Trav. du lab. de recherches biol. Madrid. v, 23, p. 425. (*See* Henschen's article in same vol., p. 217.)
1927. La bipartition de la couche moléculaire des grains de l'écorce visuelle et son importance pour la vue binoculaire. Riv. oto-neuro-oftal., v. 4, p. 141.
1927. Die Localisierung der Nachbilder in der Netzhaut mit Hilfe der Purkinje'schen Aderfigur (Nachbild-Aderfigurmethode). Ein Mittel zur directen Bestimmung des Fixierpunktes und der korrespondierenden Netzhautstellen nebst Bemerkungen zum Rindenmechanismus der Korrespondenz der Netzhäute. Nova acta reg. Soc. sc. Upsaliensis.
1928. Ueber Störungen des Tonunterscheidungsvermögens und Verwandlung von Tönen in Geräusche, nebst Bemerkungen zur Theorie des Gehörs. Acta oto-laryng., v. 12, p. 11.
1930. Kortikaler Mechanismus der Sprache. Ein Konstruktionsversuch. J. f. Psychol. u. Neurol., v. 40, p. 282.
1931. Theorie des kortikalen Mechanismus der Association (des bedingten Reflexes) und des Sukzessivvergleichs. Proc. First Internat. Neurol. Cong. Bern, p. 235; Deutsche Ztschr. f. Nervenh., v. 124, p. 140, 1932.

BÁRÁNYI, B., VOGT, C., & VOGT, O.
1923. Zur reizphysiologischen Analyse der kortikalen Augenbewegungen. J. f. Psychol. u. Neurol., v. 30, p. 87.

BARBAZAN, M.
1914. Les hémianopsies dans les traumatismes du crâne par armes à feu. Thèse de Paris.

BARBENSI, G.
1947. Regimen sanitatis salernitanum cura di G. Barbensi. Editore Leo S. Olschki, Firenze.

BARBOUR, G. B.
1949. Ape or man? An incomplete chapter of human ancestry from South Africa. Ohio J. Sc., v. 49, p. 129.
1949. Makapansgat. Scient. Monthly, v. 69, p. 141.

BARBOUR, T.
1944. The solenodons of Cuba. Proc. New England Zoöl. Club, v. 23, p. 1.

BARD, L.
1905. De la persistance des sensations lumineuses dans le champ aveugle des hémianopsiques. Semaine méd., v. 25, p. 253.
1922. De quelques points particuliers de la physiologie de la vision. Hémianopsie et réflexes hémianopsiques, indice local des images et tache aveugle, perception des distances, rôle des pigments rétiniens et des batonnets. Arch. d'opht., v. 39, p. 449.

BARD, P.
1938. Studies on the cortical representation of somatic sensibility. Harvey Lect., v. 33, p. 143.

BARD, P., & BROOKS, C. M.
1934. Localized cortical control of some postural reactions in cat and rat together with evidence that small cortical remnants may function normally. Research Pub. A. Research Nerv. & Ment. Dis., v. 13, p. 107.

BARD, P., & RIOCH, D. McK.
1937. A study of four cats deprived of neocortex and additional portions of forebrain. Johns Hopkins Hosp. Bull., v. 60, p. 73.

BARDELEBEN, K.
1899–1934. Handbuch der Anatomie des Menschen, v. 4 (1, 2), Nervensystem, by Th. ZIEHEN. G. Fischer, Jena.

BARKAN, O.
1936. The structure and functions of the angle of the anterior chamber and Schlemm's canal. Arch. Ophth., v. 15, p. 101.

BARKAN, O., & BARKAN, H.
1930. Central and paracentral homonymous hemianopic scotomas. Am. J. Ophth. (ser. 3), v. 13, p. 853.

BARKER, L. F.
1901. The nervous system and its constituent neurones. D. Appleton & Co., New York.

BARKHUUS, A.
1945. Medical surveys from Hippocrates to the world travellers.—Medical geographies.—Geomedicine and geopolitics. Ciba Symp., v. 6, pp. 1986, 1997, 2017.

BARKOW, H. C. L.
1865. Vergleichung des Negerhirns mit dem Gehirn des Europäers. *In:* Erläuterung zur Skelet- und Gehirnlehre oder comparative Morphologie, v. 3, p. 75. F. Hirt, Breslau.

BARLETTA, V.
1930. Sopra due casi di emianopsia omonima e di anopsia omonima in quadranti di origine corticali. Ann. ottal., v. 58, p. 353.

BARLOW, N.; *see* DARWIN, C. R.

BARNES, T. C., & BEUTNER, R.
1941. The nature of the nerve impulse. Anat. Rec., v. 81 (suppl.), p. 42. (Abstr.)
1946. The production of electricity by nerve. Science, v. 104, p. 569.
1947. Electrogenic properties of acetylcholine. Nature, v. 159, p. 307.

BARNETT, L., EISENSTAEDT, A., & ZALLINGER, R. F.
1954. The world we live in. Part XI. The rain forest. Life, September 20, p. 76.

BARR, M. L.
1940. Axon reaction in motor neurons and its effect upon the end-bulbs of Held-Auerbach. Anat. Rec., v. 77, p. 367.
1940. Some observations on the morphology of the synapse in the cat's spinal cord. J. Anat., v. 74, p. 1.

BARRATT, J. O. W.
1900. Observations on the structure of the 3d, 4th and 6th cranial nerves. J. Physiol., v. 25, p. xxiii.

BARRELL, J.
1915. Influence of Silurian-Devonian climates on the rise of air-breathing vertebrates. Bull. Geol. Soc. Amer., v. 27, p. 387.

BARRETT, J.
1921. A case of voluntary control of fusion faculty. M. J. Australia, v. 1, p. 131; *also* M. Press, N.S., v. 111, p. 278.

BARRIS, R. W.
1935. Disposition of fibers of retinal origin in the lateral geniculate body. Course and termination of fibers of the optic system in the brain of the cat. Arch. Ophth., v. 14, p. 61.
1936. A pupillo-constrictor area in the cerebral cortex of the cat and its relationship to the pretectal area. J. Comp. Neurol., v. 63, p. 353.

BARRIS, R. W., & INGRAM, W. R.
1934. Optic connections of the mid-brain and thalamus. Anat. Rec. (suppl.), v. 58, p. 3.

BARRIS, R. W., INGRAM, W. R., & RANSON, S. W.
1935. Optic connections of the diencephalon and midbrain of the cat. J. Comp. Neurol., v. 62, p. 117.

BARRON, D. H.
1948. Observations on the forces concerned in the formation of fissures of the cerebrum. Anat. Rec., v. 100, p. 639. (Abstr.)

BARTELMEZ, G. W.
1915. Mauthner's cells and the nucleus motorius tegmenti. J. Comp. Neurol., v. 25, p. 87.
1915. The morphology of the synapse in vertebrates. Arch. Neurol. & Psychiat., v. 4, p. 122.
1922. The origin of the otic and optic primordia in man. J. Comp. Neurol., v. 34, p. 201.
1923. The subdivisions of the neural folds in man. *Ibid.*, v. 35, p. 231.

BARTELMEZ, G. W., & BLOUNT, M. P.
1954. The formation of neural crest from the primary optic vesicle in man. "Contr. Embryol.," No. 233. Carnegie Inst. Washington.

BARTELMEZ, G. W., & EVANS, H. M.
1926. Development of the human embryo during the period of somite formation, including embryos with 2 to 16 pairs of somites. "Contr. Embryol.," No. 85. Carnegie Inst. Washington.

BARTELMEZ, G. W., & HOERR, N. L.
1933. The vestibular club endings in *Ameiurus.* Further evidence on the morphology of the synapse. J. Comp. Neurol., v. 57, p. 401.

BARTELS, M.
1904. Die fibrilläre Struktur der Ganglienzellen-schicht der Netzhaut. Ztschr. f. Augenh., v. 11, p. 288.
1907. Ueber Fibrillen und Fibrillensäure in den Nervenfasern des Opticus. Ber. d. Deutsch. ophth. Gesellsch. Heidelberg, v. 34, p. 56.
1908. Ueber Primitivfibrillen in den Achsencylin-dern des Nervus opticus und über die Wer-tung varicöser Achsencylinder. Arch. f. Augenh., v. 59, p. 168.
1920. Aufgaben der vergleichenden Physiologie der Augenbewegungen. Arch. f. Ophth. (Graefe), v. 101, p. 299.
1925. Binokularsehen und Sehnervenkreuzung. Ztschr. f. Augenh., v. 56, p. 346.
1931. Vergleichendes über Augenbewegungen. *In:* BETHE *et al.*, Handb. d. norm. u. path. Physiol., v. 12 (2), p. 1113.

BARTH, F.
1950. On the relationships of early primates. Am. J. Phys. Anthropol., v. 8, N.S., p. 139.

BARTHOLIN, CASPAR
1645. Institutiones anatomicae. Lugd. Batav., ap. F. Hackium. (1st ed. 1611.)

BARTHOLIN, THOMAS
1651. Anatomia reformata. Lugd. Batav. Ex Off. F. Hackii. Several subsequent editions (4th, Lugd. 1677).

BARTHOLOW, R.
1874. Experimental investigations into the func-tions of the human brain. Am. J. M. Sc., v. 67, N.S., p. 305.

BARTISCH, G.
1583. ΟΦΘΑΛΜΟΔΟΥΛΕΙΑ (Ophthalmodouleia) Das ist, Augendienst. Etc. Gedruckt zu Dressden durch Mathes Stöckel. Yale Uni-versity, New Haven, Conn. Another ed. Nürnberg, 1686.

BARTKY, W.
1935. Highlights of astronomy. University of Chi-cago Press, Chicago.

BARTLETT, N. R., & GAGNÉ, R. M.
1939. On binocular summation at threshold. J. Exper. Psychol., v. 25, p. 91.

BARTLEY, S. H.
1932. Action potentials of the optic cortex under the influence of strychnine. Am. J. Physiol., v. 103, p. 203.
1938. A central mechanism in brightness discrimi-nation. Proc. Soc. Exper. Biol. & Med., v. 38, p. 535.
1940. The relation between cortical response to visual stimulation and changes in the alpha rhythm. J. Exper. Psychol., v. 27, p. 624.
1941. Vision: a study of its basis. D. Van No-strand Co., New York.
1942. A factor in visual fatigue. Psychosom. Med., v. 4, p. 369.
1942. The features of the optic-nerve discharge underlying recurrent vision. J. Exper. Psy-chol., v. 30, p. 125.
1942. Visual sensation and its dependence on the neurophysiology of the optic pathway. *In:* Biol. Symp., v. 7, p. 87. J. Cattell Press, Lancaster, Pa.
1943. Some parallels between pupillary "reflexes" and brightness discrimination. J. Exper. Psychol., v. 32, p. 110.

BARTLEY, S. H., & BISHOP, G. H.
1933. The cortical response to stimulation of the optic nerve in the rabbit. Am. J. Physiol., v. 103, p. 159.
1933. Factors determining the form of the electri-cal response from the optic cortex of the rabbit. *Ibid.*, p. 173.
1940. Optic nerve response to retinal stimulation in the rabbit. Proc. Soc. Exper. Biol. & Med., v. 44, p. 39.
1942. Some features of the optic-nerve discharge in the rabbit and cat. J. Cell. & Comp. Physiol., v. 19, p. 79.

BARTLEY, S. H., & FRY, G. A.
1934. An indirect method for measuring stray light within the human eye. J. Opt. Soc. America, v. 24, p. 342.

BARTLEY, S. H., & HEINBECKER, P.
1940. Effect of insulin on nerve activity. Am. J. Physiol., v. 131, p. 509.

BARTLEY, S. H., O'LEARY, J., & BISHOP, G. H.
1937. Differentiation by strychnine of the visual from the integrating mechanisms of optic cortex in the rabbit. Am. J. Physiol., v. 120, p. 604.

BASILE, G.
1938. Ricerche anatomiche sulla topografia delle vene vorticose. Ann. di ottal., v. 66, p. 100.

BASLER, A.
1937. Netzhautfunktionen. *In:* E. ABDERHALDEN, Handb. d. biol. Arbeitsmeth., Abt 5, Teil 6(1).

BASTIAN, H. C.
1875. On paralysis from brain disease in its com-mon forms. Macmillan & Co., Ltd., London.
1880. The brain as an organ of mind. D. Appleton & Co., New York.
1898. A treatise on aphasia and other speech de-fects. H. K. Lewis, London. Also German trans., 1902.

BATEMAN, F.
1890. On aphasia, or loss of speech, and the localization of the faculty of articulate language. 2d ed. J. & A. Churchill, London.

BATES, H. W.
1863. The naturalist on the river Amazon. A record of adventures, habits of animals, sketches of Brazilian and Indian life, and aspects of nature under the equator, during eleven years of travel. J. Murray, London. Also subsequent eds.

BATES, W. H.
1943. The Bates method for better eyesight without glasses. Henry Holt & Co., New York.

BATSON, O. V.
1944. Anatomical problems concerned in the study of cerebral blood flow. Fed. Proc., v. 3, p. 139.

BAUDOUIN, A., LHERMITTE, J., & LEREBOULLET, J.
1930. Une observation anatomo-clinique d'hémorragie du thalamus. Rev. neurol., v. 37 (2), p. 102.

BAUER, H.
1911. Die Psychologie Alhazens, auf Grund von Alhazens Optik dargestellt. Beitr. z. Gesch. d. Phil. d. Mittelalt., v. 10, fasc. 5.

BAUER, K. F.
1948. Ueber die zwischenzellige Organisation des Nervengewebes. Ztschr. f. Anat. u. Entw., v. 114, p. 53.
1948. Die histogenetischen Grundgesetze der cerebralen Grisea. Klin. Wchnschr., v. 26, p. 321.

BAUER, V.
1909. Ueber sukzessiven Helligkeitskontrast bei Fischen. Zentralbl. f. Physiol., v. 23, p. 593.
1910. Ueber das Farbenunterscheidungsvermögen der Fische. Arch. f. d. ges. Physiol. (Pflüger), v. 133, p. 7.
1911. Zu meinen Versuchen über das Farbenunterscheidungsvermögen der Fische. *Ibid.*, v. 137, p. 622.

BAUHIN, CASPAR
1621. Theatrum Anatomicum Caspari Bauhini Basileen. Archiatri Infinitis locis auctum, ad morbos accommodatum & ab erroribus ab Authore repurgatum, observationibus & figuris aliquot novis aeneis illustratum. Opera sumptibusque Iohan. Theodori De Bry. M.DC.XXI.

BAUMGARDT, E.
1944–45. Sur le mécanisme de l'excitation visuelle liminaire; minimum d'énergie et constante de temps τ. Année psychol., v. 45–46, p. 57.

1947. Sur la loi spatiale de la brillance liminaire en vision extrafovéale. Compt. rend. Acad. d. sc., v. 225, p. 259.
1947. Les lois empiriques de l'excitation visuelle établies quantitativement à l'aide du calcul des probabilités (l'excitation liminaire). Compt. rend. Soc. de biol., v. 141, p. 7.
1947. L'excitation visuelle liminaire traitée par le calcul des probabilités. L'interrelation de la surface et de la durée. *Ibid.*, p. 94.
1947. Sur les mécanismes de l'excitation visuelle. 1. La théorie photochimique et la nature quantique et statistique de l'excitation liminaire. Arch. d. sc. physiol., v. 1, p. 257.
1952. Sehmechanismus und Quantumstruktur des Lichtes. Naturwiss., v. 39, p. 388.

BAUMGARDT, E., & BUJAS, Z.
1952. L'influence de la fréquence de stimulation électrique intermittente sur le phosphène liminaire. Compt. rend. Soc. de biol., v. 146, p. 424.

BAUMGARDT, E., & MAGIS, C.
1954. Sur un cas exceptionnel d'achromatopsie. J. de physiol., v. 46, p. 237.

BAUMGARDT, E., & SEGAL, J.
1946. La fonction inhibitrice dans le processus visuel. Compt. rend. Soc. de biol., v. 140, p. 231.
1946. Un dispositif permettant de réaliser des stimuli lumineux de durée ultra-courte et de forme quelconque mais constante. *Ibid.*, p. 255.
1946. L'inhibition rétroactive dans la vision, démontrée par la méthode des temps de réaction. *Ibid.*, p. 267.
1946. Le mécanisme neuronique de la fonction inhibitrice. *Ibid.*, p. 325.
1946. Instabilité de la sensation naissante et sensibilité différentielle. *Ibid.*, p. 327.
1946. La localisation du mécanisme inhibiteur dans la perception visuelle. *Ibid.*, p. 431.

BAUMGARTEN, P.
1878. Hemiopie nach Erkrankung der occipitalen Hirnrinde. Centralbl. f. d. med. Wissensch., v. 16, p. 369.
1878. Zur sog. Semidecussation der Opticusfasern. *Ibid.*, p. 561.
1881. Zur Semidecussation der Opticusfasern. Arch. f. Ophth. (Graefe), v. 27 (1), p. 342. (*Cf. also* sec. 2, p. 301, and sec. 3, p. 247, same volume.)

BAUMHAUER, E. H.
*1843. De sententia philosophorum Graecorum de visu luminibus et coloribus. Inaug. diss. Trajecti ad Rhenum (Utrecht).

BAURMANN, M.
　1933. Die Anatomie und Physiologie des Glaskörpers. Ergebn. d. Path., v. 26 (suppl. vol.), p. 121.
　1934. Studien über die Glaskörper-Fadensubstanz. Arch. f. Ophth. (Graefe), v. 132, p. 302.

BAUSCH & LOMB OPTICAL CO.
　1935. Ophthalmic lenses, their history, theory and application. Rochester, N.Y.
　1940. Milestones in optical history. Rochester, N.Y.

BAXANDALL, D.
　1922–23. Early telescopes in the Science Museum, from an historical standpoint. Tr. Opt. Soc., v. 24, p. 304.

BAYLISS, L. E., LYTHGOE, R. J., & TANSLEY, K.
　1936. Some new forms of visual purple found in sea fishes, with a note on the visual cells of origin. Proc. Roy. Soc. London, ser. B, v. 120, p. 95.

BEAL, F. E. L., McATEE, W. L., & KALMBACH, E. R.
　1941. Common birds of southeastern United States in relation to agriculture. U.S. Dept. Interior, Fish & Wildlife Serv., Conserv. Bull. 15.

BEAN, R. B.
　1905–6. Some racial peculiarities of the Negro brain. Am. J. Anat., v. 5, p. 353.

BEAR, R. S., & SCHMITT, F. O.
　1939. Electrolytes in the axoplasm of the giant nerve fibers of the squid. J. Cell. & Comp. Physiol., v. 14, p. 205.

BEATTIE, J.
　1927. The anatomy of the common marmoset (*Hapale jacchus* Kuhl). Proc. Zoöl Soc. London, p. 593.

BEAUFORT, L. F. DE
　1951. Zoögeography of the land and inland waters. Sidgwick & Jackson, Ltd., London.

BEAUREGARD, H.
　1875. Recherches sur le mode d'entrecroisement des nerfs optiques chez les oiseaux. Compt. rend. Soc. de biol., ser. 6, v. 2, p. 344.

BEAUVIEUX, J.
　1916–17. Les troubles visuels dans les blessures par coup de feu de la sphère visuelle corticale ou des radiations optiques. Arch. d'opht., v. 35, pp. 410, 458, 560, 617.
　1930. Les hémianopsies transitoires par angiospasme. Rev. d'oto-neuro-opht., v. 8, p. 94.

BEAUVIEUX, J., PIECHAUD, F., & RUDEAU
　1929. Céphalées et spasmes vasculaires en ophtalmologie. Rev. d'oto-neuro-opht., v. 7, p. 619.

BEAUVIEUX, J., & RISTICH-GOELMINO
　1926. De la vascularisation du centre cortical de la macula. Arch. d'opht., v. 43, p. 5.

BEAUVIEUX, J., & RISTITCH, K.
　1924. Les vaisseaux centraux du nerf optique. Arch. d'opht., v. 41, p. 352.

BEAVER, W. C.
　1946. General biology. 3d ed. C. V. Mosby Co., St. Louis, Mo.

BECCARI, N.
　1943. Neurologia comparata anatomo-funzionale dei vertebrati compreso l'uomo. Sansoni Edizioni Scientifiche, Firenze.

BECHER, E.
　1911. Gehirn und Seele. Carl Winter Verlag, Heidelberg.

BECHTEREV, W. (BECHTEREV, BECKTEREW, BECKHTEREV)
　1883. Experimentelle Untersuchungen über die Kreuzung der Sehnerven-Fasern im Chiasma nn. opticorum. Neurol. Centralbl., v. 2, p. 53.
　1883. Die Function der Sehhügel (Thalami optici). Experimentelle Untersuchungen. *Ibid.*, p. 78.
　1883. Experimentelle Ergebnisse über den Verlauf der Sehnervenfasern auf ihrer Bahn von den Kniehöckern zu den Vierhügeln. *Ibid.*, p. 265.
　1883. Ueber den Verlauf der die Pupille verengernden Nervenfasern im Gehirn und über die Localisation eines Centrums für die Iris und Contraction der Augenmuskeln. Arch. f. d. ges. Physiol. (Pflüger), v. 31, p. 60.
　1884. Ueber die nach Durchschneidung der Sehnervenfasern im Inneren der Grosshirnhemisphären (in der Nachbarschaft des hinteren Abschnittes der inneren Kapsel) auftretenden Erscheinungen. Neurol. Centralbl., v. 3, p. 1.
　1891. Zur Frage über die äusseren Associationsfasern der Hirnrinde. *Ibid.*, v. 10, p. 682.
　1894. Ueber pupillenverengernde Fasern. *Ibid.*, v. 13, p. 802.
　1898. Ueber kortikale Centra beim Affen. *Ibid.*, v. 17, p. 139.
　1898. Die partielle Kreuzung der Sehnerven in dem Chiasma höherer Säugethiere. *Ibid.*, p. 199.
　1898. Die Resultate der Untersuchungen mit Reizung von hinteren Partien der Hemisphären und des Frontallappens beim Affen. *Ibid.*, p. 720.
　1898. Bewusstsein und Hirnlokalisation. An ad-

dress. German translation from the Russian by R. Weinberg. A. Georgi, Leipzig.

1899. Ueber pupillenverengernde und pupillenerweiternde Centra in den hinteren Theilen der Hemisphärenrinde bei den Affen. Arch. f. Anat. u. Physiol. (Physiol. Abth.), p. 25.

1900. Ueber pupillenverengernde und Accommodationscentra der Gehirnrinde. Neurol. Centralbl., v. 19, p. 386.

1901. Ueber das corticale Sehcentrum. Monatsschr. f. Psychiat. u. Neurol., v. 10, p. 432.

1906. Sehcentrum der Hirnrinde. Neurol. Centralbl., v. 25, p. 1018.

1908–11. Die Funktionen der Nervencentra. 3 vols. G. Fischer, Jena.

1909. Ueber die Lokalisation der motorischen Apraxie. Monatsschr. f. Psychiat. u. Neurol., v. 25, p. 42.

1926. Sbornik posvyashchónnyĭ Vladímiru Miháylovichu Béhterevu k sorok-lyétiyu professórskoĭ dyeyátelnosti (1885–1925). (Anniversary vol. for Bechterew. Izdan: Gosud. Psihonevrol. Akad. etc., Leningrad.

BECK, E.

1925. Zur Exaktheit der myeloarchitektonischen Felderung des Cortex cerebri. J. f. Psychol. u. Neurol., v. 31, p. 281.

1928. Die myeloarchitektonische Felderung des in der Sylvischen Furche gelegenen Teiles des menschlichen Schläfenlappens. *Ibid.*, v. 36, p. 1.

1928. Das Hörzentrum des Schimpansen in seinem myeloarchitektonischen Aufbau. *Ibid.*, p. 325.

1929. Der myeloarchitektonische Bau des in der Sylvischen Furche gelegenen Teiles des Schläfenlappens beim Schimpansen (*Troglodytes niger*). *Ibid.*, v. 38, p. 309.

1930. Ist die Area striata ein einheitlich gebautes Rindenfeld? Arch. f. Psychiat. u. Nervenkr., v. 90, p. 879; Zentralbl. f. d. ges. Neurol. u. Psychiat., v. 56, p. 471.

1930. Die Myeloarchitektonik der dorsalen Schläfenlappenrinde beim Menschen. J. f. Psychol. u. Neurol., v. 41, p. 129.

1940. Morphogenie der Hirnrinde. Monog. a. d. Gesamtgeb. d. Neurol. u. Psychiat., v. 69.

BECK, E., & KLEIST, K.

1931. Neuere Ergebnisse in der Erforschung von Bau, Leistungen und Störungen der Sehsphäre. Forsch. u. Fortschr., v. 7, pp. 412, 425.

BECK, T.

1909. Die galenischen Hirnnerven in moderner Beleuchtung. Arch. f. Gesch. d. Med., v. 3, p. 110.

BECKÉ, A.

1904. Die bei Erkrankungen des Hinterhauptlappens beobachteten Erscheinungen mit spezieller Berücksichtigung der okularen Symptome. Ztschr. f. Augenh., v. 11, pp. 227, 318.

BECKER, H.

1939. Experimentelle Verschlüsse von Arterien und Venen des Gehirns und ihre Einwirkung auf das Gewebe. Zentralbl. f. d. ges. Neurol. u. Psychiat., v. 94, p. 356.

BECKER, O.

1879. Ein Fall von angeborener einseitiger totaler Farbenblindheit. Arch. f. Ophth. (Graefe), v. 25 (2), p. 205.

1881. Die Gefässe der menschlichen Macula lutea, abgebildet nach einem Injectionspräparate von Heinrich Müller. *Ibid.*, v. 27 (1), p. 1.

BECKMANN, J. W., & KUBIE, L. S.

1929. A clinical study of twenty-one cases of tumor of the hypophyseal stalk. Brain, v. 52, p. 127.

BEDDARD, F. E.

1895. Contributions to the anatomy of the anthropoid apes. Tr. Zoöl. Soc. London, v. 13, pp. 177, 218.

1901. Some notes upon the brain and other structures of centetes. Novitates zool., v. 8, p. 89.

1923. Mammalia. *In:* Cambridge natural history, v. 10. Macmillan & Co., Ltd., London.

BEDELL, A. J.

1929. Photographs of the fundus oculi. F. A. Davis Co., Philadelphia.

1950. The macula in the elderly. Am. J. Ophth., v. 33, p. 1681.

BEDNARSKI, A.

1929. Das anatomische Augenbild von Johann Peckham, etc. Arch. f. Gesch. d. Med. (Sudhoff), v. 22, p. 352.

1930. On the "Perspective" of J. Peckham, with an anatomical sketch of the brain and of the eyes in the Cracow manuscript of Sędziwoj Czechel from the year 1430 (Polish). Nowiny Lekarskie (Poznań).

1931. Die anatomischen Augenbilder in den Handschriften des Roger Bacon, Johann Peckham und Witelo. Arch. f. Gesch. d. Med. (Sudhoff), v. 24, p. 60.

1933. On the Cracow manuscripts of the "Perspective" of the Archbishop John Peckham (Polish). Arch. hist. i fil. med., v. 12.

1935. Obout Witelo (Polish). Klin. Oczna, v. 3.

BEEBE, W.

1930. The Bermuda oceanographic expedition. Bull. New York Zoöl. Soc., v. 33, p. 35.

BEEBE, W.—*Continued*
  1930. A quarter mile down in the open sea. *Ibid.*, p. 201.
  1931. A round trip to Davy Jones's locker: peering into mysteries a quarter mile down in the open sea, by means of the bathysphere. Nat. Geog. Mag., v. 59, p. 653.
  1932. Depths of the sea. *Ibid.*, v. 61, p. 64.
  1932. Wanderer under sea. *Ibid.*, v. 62, p. 740.
  1934. A half mile down. *Ibid.*, v. 66, p. 661.
  1934. Half mile down. Harcourt, Brace & Co., New York.
  1934. Deep-sea fishes of the Bermuda oceanographic expeditions. Family Idiacanthidae. Zoologica, v. 16, p. 149.
  1947. Book of bays. Harcourt, Brace & Co., New York; B. Head, London.
  1949. High jungle. Duell, Sloan & Pearce, New York.

BEEBE, W., & HOLLISTER, G.
  1930. Log of the bathysphere. Bull. New York Zoöl. Soc., v. 33, p. 249.

BEER, G. J.
  1813–17. Lehre von den Augenkrankheiten. 2 vols. Camesina, Wien.

BEER, T.
  1892. Studien über die Accommodation des Vogelauges. Arch. f. d. ges. Physiol. (Pflüger), v. 53, p. 175.
  1894. Die Accommodation des Fischauges. *Ibid.*, v. 58, p. 523.
  1898. Die Accommodation des Auges bei den Reptilien. *Ibid.*, v. 69, p. 507.
  1898. Die Accommodation des Auges bei den Amphibien. *Ibid.*, v. 73, p. 501.
  1901. Ueber primitive Sehorgane. Wien. klin. Wchnschr., v. 14, pp. 225, 285, 314.

BEEVOR, C. E.
  1907. The cerebral arterial supply. Brain, v. 30, p. 403.
  1909. On the distribution of the different arteries supplying the human brain. Phil. Tr. Roy. Soc. London, ser. B, v. 200, p. 1.

BEEVOR, C. E., & COLLIER, J.
  1904. A contribution to the study of the cortical localisation of vision. A case of quadrantic hemianopia with pathological examination. Brain, v. 27, p. 153.

BEEVOR, C., & HORSLEY, V.
  1886. A minute analysis (experimental) of the various movements produced by stimulating in the monkey different regions of the cortical centre for the upper limb, as defined by Prof. Ferrier. Phil. Tr. Roy. Soc. London, ser. B, v. 178, p. 153.

  1888. A further minute analysis by electric stimulation of the so-called motor region of the cortex cerebri in the monkey. *Ibid.*, v. 179, p. 205.
  1891. A record of the results obtained by electrical excitation of the so-called motor cortex and internal capsule in an orang-outang (*Simia satyrus*). *Ibid.*, v. 181, p. 129.
  1891. Traumatic abscess of the region of the left angular gyrus with right hemianopsia (limited fields) and word blindness treated by operation. Brit. M. J., v. 2, p. 1099.
  1894. A further minute analysis by electric stimulation of the so-called motor region (facial area) of the cortex cerebri in the monkey (*Macacus sinicus*). Phil. Tr. Roy. Soc. London, ser. B, v. 185, p. 39.
  1902. On the pallio-tectal or cortico-mesencephalic system of fibres. Brain, v. 25, p. 436.

BEHR, C.
  1909. Zur topischen Diagnose der Hemianopsie. Arch. f. Ophth. (Graefe), v. 70, p. 340.
  1916. Die homonymen Hemianopsien mit einseitigem Gesichtsfelddefekt im "rein temporalen halbmondförmigen Bezirk des binokularen Gesichtsfeldes." Klin. Monatsbl. f. Augenh., v. 56, p. 161.
  1921. Die Weite der Pupille bei den typischen Pupillenstörungen. Klin. Monatsschr. f. Augenh., v. 66, p. 363.
  1924. Die Lehre von den Pupillenbewegungen. J. Springer, Berlin. *Also in:* GRAEFE & SAEMISCH, Handb. d. ges. Augenh., 3d ed., v. 2 (Untersuchungsmethoden).
  1925. Ergebnisse der Pupillenforschung. Zentralbl. f. d. ges. Ophth., v. 14, p. 465.
  1931. Die Erkrankungen der Sehbahn vom Chiasma aufwärts. *In:* SCHIECK & BRÜCKNER, Kurzes Handbuch der Ophthalmologie, v. 6, p. 245. J. Springer, Berlin.
  1935. Beitrag zur Anatomie und Klinik des septalen Gewebes und des Arterieneinbaus im Sehnervenstamm. Arch. f. Ophth. (Graefe), v. 134, p. 227.

BEHRENS, D. S. G.
  *1733. Dissertatio de vulnere cerebri non semper et absolute letali. Francfort a.M.

BEHRMAN, S.
  1951. Amaurosis fugax et amaurosis fulminans. Arch. Ophth., ser. 2, v. 45, p. 458.

BEIDELMAN, R. G.
  1950. The cinereous shrew below 6,000 feet, north central Colorado. J. Mammal., v. 31, p. 459.

BELANGER, C.
  1834. Voyage aux Indes-Orientales, etc. A. Bertrand, Paris.

BELL, A. E.
1947. Christian Huygens and the development of science in the seventeenth century. E. Arnold & Co., London. (Review in Nature, v. 162, p. 472.)

BELL, C.
1811. Idea of a new anatomy of the brain. *In:* Medical classics, v. 1, p. 105, 1936–37. Williams & Wilkins Co., Baltimore.
1823. On the motions of the eye in illustration of the uses of the muscles and nerves of the orbit. *Ibid.*, p. 173.

BELL, J. & C.
1829. The anatomy and physiology of the human body, v. 3, p. 10, "Of the eye." 7th ed. Longmans *et al.*, London.

BELL, L.
1908. The physiological basis of illumination. Proc. Am. Acad. Arts & Sc., v. 43, p. 75.

BELLONCI, J.
1888. Ueber die centrale Endigung des Nervus opticus bei den Vertebraten. Ztschr. f. wissensch. Zool., v. 47, p. 1.

BELLOUARD, V.
1880. De l'hémianopsie, précédée d'une étude d'anatomie sur l'origine et l'entre-croisement des nerfs optiques. Thèse de Paris. V.-A. Delahaye, Paris.

BELLOWS, J. G.
1935. The biochemistry of the lens. IV. The origin of pigment in the lens. Arch. Ophth., v. 14, p. 99.

BELLOWS, S. E.
1921. Gunshot wounds of brain with visual field defects. Am. J. Ophth., ser. 3, v. 4, p. 884.

BENARY, W.
1922. Studien zur Untersuchung der Intelligenz bei einem Fall von Seelenblindheit. Psychol. Forsch., v. 2, p. 209.

BENCHLEY, B. J.
1942. My friends, the apes. Little, Brown & Co., Boston.

BENDER, M. B.
1945. Synkinetic pupillary phenomena and the Argyll Robertson pupil. Arch. Neurol. & Psychiat., v. 53, p. 418.
1945. Polyopia and monocular diplopia of cerebral origin. *Ibid.*, v. 54, p. 323.

BENDER, M. B., & FULTON, J. F.
1938. Functional recovery in ocular muscles of a chimpanzee after section of oculomotor nerve. J. Neurophysiol., v. 1, p. 144.

BENDER, M. B., & FURLOW, L. T.
1945. Phenomenon of visual extinction in homonymous fields and psychologic principles involved. Arch. Neurol. & Psychiat., v. 53, p. 29.
1945. Visual disturbances produced by bilateral lesions of the occipital lobes with central scotomas. *Ibid.*, p. 165.

BENDER, M. B., & KRIEGER, H. P.
1951. Visual function in perimetrically blind fields. Arch. Neurol. & Psychiat., v. 65, p. 72.

BENDER, M. B., & NATHANSON, M.
1950. Patterns in allesthesia and their relation to disorder of body scheme and other sensory phenomena. Arch. Neurol. & Psychiat., v. 64, p. 501.

BENDER, M. B., & TEUBER, H. L.
1946. Disturbances in the visual perception of space after brain injury. Tr. Am. Neurol. A., 71st ann. meet., p. 159.
1946. Nystagmoid movements and visual perception; their interrelation in monocular diplopia. Arch. Neurol. & Psychiat., v. 55, p. 511.
1946. Phenomena of fluctuation, extinction and completion in visual perception. *Ibid.*, p. 627.
1946. Ring scotoma and tubular fields; their significance in cases of head injury. *Ibid.*, v. 56, p. 300.
1947–48. Spatial organization of visual perception following injury to the brain. *Ibid.*, v. 58, p. 721; v. 59, p. 39.
1948. Disorders in the visual perception of motion. Tr. Am. Neurol. A., 73d ann. meet., p. 191.

BENDER, M. B., TEUBER, H. L., & BATTERSBY, W. S.
1951. Visual field defects after gunshot wounds of higher visual pathways. Tr. Am. Neurol. A., 76th ann. meet., p. 192.

BENDER, M. B., & WECHSLER, I. S.
1942. Irregular and multiple homonymous visual field defects. Arch. Ophth., v. 28, p. 904.

BENDER, M. B., & WEINSTEIN, E. A.
1943. Functional representation in the oculomotor and trochlear nuclei. Arch. Neurol. & Psychiat., v. 49, p. 98.
1944. The effects of stimulation and lesion of the median longitudinal fasciculus in the monkey. *Ibid.*, v. 52, p. 106; and Tr. Am. Neurol. A., 70th ann. meet., p. 184.

BENDICK, A. J., & BALSER, B. H.
1936. Cerebral roentgenoscopy as an aid in pneumoventriculography and encephalography. Am. J. Roentgenol., v. 35, p. 790.

BENEDETTI, E.
1921. Intorno alla morfologia del cervello di *Proteus anguineus* e sull'esistenza del suo nervo

ottico. Atti Acad. naz. dei Lincei. rend. (2 sem.), v. 30, p. 429.

1922. Intorno all'esistenza del nervo ottico e del cerveletto nel *Proteus anguineus Laur.* Atti Cong. Soc. prog. sc. Roma, I.F., p. 598; and Mon. zool. ital., v. 32, p. 32 (Rend. unione zool. ital.).

1933. Il cervello e i nervi cranii del *Proteus anguineus Laur.* Mem. Ist. ital. di speleol., ser. biol., Mem. III, p. 1.

BENEDICT, W. L.
1942. Multiple sclerosis as an etiologic factor in retrobulbar neuritis. Arch. Ophth., v. 28, p. 988.

BENEKE, F. W.(?)
1862. (A note on the use of anilin dyes in histology.) Correspbl. d. Ver. f. gemeinsch. Arb., No. 59, p. 980.

BENIUC, M.
1933. Bewegungssehen, Verschmelzung und Moment bei Kampffischen. Ztschr. f. vergl. Physiol., v. 19, p. 724.

BENNER, J.
1938. Untersuchungen über die Raumwahrnehmung der Hühner. Ztschr. f. wissensch. Zool., v. 151, p. 382.

BENÖHR, R.
1905. Ein Fall von centraler Blindheit (Erweichungsherde in beiden Occipitallappen). Inaug. diss., F. Fiencke, Kiel.

BENOIT, F.
1926. L'angle cornéo-iridien, organe d'élimination de l'humeur aqueuse. Arch. d'opht., v. 43, p. 352.

BÉRANECK, E.
1890. L'œil primitif des vertébrés. Arch. d. sc. phys. et nat., v. 24, p. 361.

BERENGARIO DA CARPI (BERENGARIUS CARPENSIS, CARPUS, GIACOMO BERENGARIO DA CARPI, BARIGAZZI)
1514. Anothomia Mundini noviter impressa ac per Carpum castigata. Bologna.

1521. Carpi Commentaria cum amplissimis additionibus super Anatomia Mundini cum textu eiusdem in pristinum et verum nitorem redacto. Bologna. (*See also* Mondino de' Luzzi, and Putti 1937.)

BERENS, C.
1936. Eye and its diseases. W. B. Saunders Co., Philadelphia.

BERENS, C., & SELLS, S. B.
1944-50. Experimental studies of fatigue of accommodation. Arch. Ophth., v. 31, p. 148; Am. J. Ophth., v. 33, p. 47.

BERGER, C.
1942. A comparison, under different degrees of brightness, of minimum visual distances of two luminous points and of a broken circle. Am. J. Psychol., v. 55, p. 354.

1950. Experiments on the legibility of symbols of different width and height. Acta Ophth., v. 28, p. 423.

BERGER, C., McFARLAND, R. A., HALPERIN, M. H., & NIVEN, J. I.
1943. The effect of anoxia on visual resolving power. Am. J. Psychol., v. 56, p. 395.

BERGER, H.
1899. Ein Beitrag zur Localisation in der Capsula interna. Monatsschr. f. Psychiat. u. Neurol., v. 6, p. 114.

1899. Beiträge zur feineren Anatomie der Grosshirnrinde. *Ibid.*, p. 405.

1900. Experimentell-anatomische Studien über die durch den Mangel optischer Reize veranlassten Entwicklungshemmungen im Occipitallappen des Hundes und der Katze. Arch. f. Psychiat. u. Nervenkr., v. 33, p. 521.

1901. Experimentelle Untersuchungen über die von der Sehsphäre aus ausgelösten Augenbewegungen. Monatsschr. f. Psychiat. u. Neurol., v. 9, p. 185.

1911. Ein Beitrag zur Lokalisation der kortikalen Hörzentren des Menschen. *Ibid.*, v. 29, p. 439.

1921. Ueber Gehirnbefunde bei schweren Schädelverletzungen und nach Granateinschlag in nächster Nähe. Arch. f. Psychiat. u. Nervenkr., v. 63, p. 311.

1926. Zur Physiologie der motorischen Region des Menschen und über die Messung der Fortpflanzungsgeschwindigkeit der Nervenerregung in den zentralen Abschnitten des menschlichen Nervensystems. *Ibid.*, v. 77, p. 321.

1926. Ueber Rechenstörungen bei Herderkrankungen des Grosshirns. *Ibid.*, v. 78, p. 238.

1929-30. Ueber das Elektrenkephalogramm des Menschen. I. *Ibid.*, v. 87, p. 527; also J. f. Psychol. u. Neurol., v. 40, p. 60.

BERGER, O.
1885. Zur Lokalisation der corticalen Sehsphäre beim Menschen. Breslau. aerztl. Ztschr., v. 7, pp. 1, 28, 38, 51.

BERGER, P.
1951. Le mode d'activité des cellules rétiniennes et la richesse de leurs noyaux en caroténoïdes. Compt. rend. Soc. de biol., v. 145, p. 360.

BERGER, P., & SEGAL, J.
1951. La sensibilité du pourpre rétinien régénéré à partir de l'orangé transitoire. Compt. rend. Acad. d. sc., v. 232, p. 1136.
1951. La présence de maxima périodiques dans la courbe de sensibilité scotopique. *Ibid.*, p. 1241.

BERGMANN, C.
1854. Zur Kenntniss des gelben Flecks der Netzhaut. Ztschr. f. ration. Med., N.F., v. 5, p. 245.
1858. Anatomisches und Physiologisches über die Netzhaut des Auges. *Ibid.*, 3d ser., v. 2, p. 83.

BERGSON, H. L.
1896. Matière et mémoire: essai sur la relation du corps à l'esprit. F. Alcan, Paris.
1944. Creative evolution. Modern Library, New York.

BERGSTRÄSSER, G.
1913. Ḥunain ibn Isḥāḳ und seine Schule. E. J. Brill, Leiden.

BERILL, N. J.
1951. The living tide. Gollancz, London.

BERINGER, K., & STEIN, J.
1930. Analyse eines Falles reiner Alexie. Zentralbl. f. d. ges. Neurol. & Psychiat., v. 56, p. 475; also Ztschr. f. d. ges. Neurol. & Psychiat., v. 123, p. 472.

BERITOV (BERITOFF, BERITASHVILI), I. S.
1937. General physiology of the muscular and nervous systems (in Russian). State Pub. Biol. & Med., Moscow & Leningrad.
1937. Excitation and inhibition in the central nervous system, regarded from the point of view of its neuron-neuropil structure. Tr. Physiol. Inst. Tbilisi (Tiflis), No. 3, p. 75.

BERITOV, I., & CHICHINADZE, N.
1936. Localisation of visual perception in the pigeon. Bull. Biol. & Med. Exper. U.S.S.R., v. 2, p. 106.
1937. On the localization of cortex processes evoked by visual stimulation. Tr. J. Beritashvili Physiol. Inst., No. 3, p. 361.

BERKELEY, G.
1709. An essay towards a new theory of vision. *In:* The Works of George Berkeley, D.D.; Formerly Bishop of Cloyne, Including his Posthumous Works, by A. C. Fraser, in four volumes. Clarendon Press, Oxford, 1901. *See* v. 1, pp. 95, 127. (*See also* B. Chancey 1942; M. Murray 1944.)

BERKLEY, W. L., & BUSSEY, F. R.
1950. Altitudinal hemianopia: report of two cases. Am. J. Ophth., ser. 3, v. 33, p. 593.

BERL, V.
1902. Einiges über die Beziehungen der Sehbahnen zu dem vorderen Zweihügel der Kaninchen. Arb. a. d. Neurol. Inst. Wien (Obersteiner), v. 8, p. 308.

BERLIN, R.
1858. Beitrag zur Strukturlehre der Grosshirnwindungen. Diss., Erlangen. A. E. Junge, Erlangen.
1893. Ueber die Schätzung der Entfernung bei Thieren. Ztschr. f. vergl. Augenh., v. 7, p. 1.

BERLINER, M. L.
1943–49. Biomicroscopy of the eye: slit lamp microscopy of the living eye. 2 vols. P. B. Hoeber–Harper & Bros., New York.

BERMAN, A. J., ROBINSON, F., & PRIBRAM, K. H.
1951. Problems concerning functions of frontal agranular cortex. Fed. Proc., v. 10, No. 1, p. 1.

BERNAL, J. D.
1951. The physical basis of life. Routledge & Kegan Paul, London. (2d impression 1952.)

BERNARD, CLAUDE
1858. Leçons sur la physiologie et la pathologie du système nerveux. J. B. Baillière & Fils, Paris.

BERNARD, F.
1937. Recherches sur la morphogénèse des yeux composés des arthropodes. Bull. biol. franç. & belg., suppl. v. 23.

BERNAYS, A.
1933. Die Farbenfibel von Wilhelm Ostwald. Naturwiss., v. 21, p. 864.

BERNHARD, C. G.
1940. Contributions to the neurophysiology of the optic pathway. Acta physiol. Scandinav., v. 1, suppl. 1, p. 1.
1942. The negative component *PIII* in the retinogram of the tortoise. *Ibid.*, v. 3, p. 132.
1942. Temporal sequence of component potentials in the frog's retina and the electrotonic potential in the optic nerve. *Ibid.*, p. 301.
1942. Isolation of retinal and optic ganglion response in the eye of *Dytiscus*. J. Neurophysiol., v. 5, p. 32.

BERNHARD, C. G., & GRANIT, R.
1946. Nerve as model temperature end organ. J. Gen. Physiol., v. 29, p. 257.

BERNHARD, C. G., & SKOGLUND, C. R.
1941. Selective suppression with ethylalcohol of inhibition in the optic nerve and of the negative component *PIII* of the electroretinogram. Acta physiol. Scandinav., v. 2, p. 10.

BERNHAUT, M., GELLHORN, E., & RASMUSSEN, A. T.
1953. Experimental contributions to problem of consciousness. J. Neurophysiol., v. 16, p. 21.

BERNHEIMER, S.
1889. Ueber die Entwickelung und den Verlauf der Markfasern im Chiasma nervorum opticorum des Menschen. Arch. f. Augenh., v. 20, p. 133; also Arch. Ophth., v. 20, p. 163, 1891. Separately published by J. F. Bergmann, Wiesbaden.

1891. Ueber die Sehnervenwurzeln des Menschen. J. F. Bergmann, Wiesbaden.

1896. Die Sehnervenkreuzung beim Menschen. Wien. klin. Wchnschr., v. 9, p. 767.

1898. Experimentelle Untersuchungen über die Bahnen der Pupillenreaktion. Sitzungsb. d. Kaiserl. Akad. d. Wissensch. Wien, math.-nat. Cl., v. 107, Part 3, p. 98.

1899. Experimentelle Studien zur Kenntniss der Bahnen der synergischen Augenbewegungen beim Affen und der Beziehungen der Vierhügel zu denselben. *Ibid.*, v. 108, p. 299.

1899. Die Wurzelgebiete der Augennerven, ihre Verbindungen und ihr Anschluss an die Gehirnrinde. *In:* GRAEFE & SAEMISCH, Handb. d. ges. Augenh., v. 1, chap. 6.

1899. Die Beziehungen der vorderen Vierhügel zu den Augenbewegungen. Wien. klin. Wchnschr., v. 12, p. 1310.

1900. Anatomische und experimentelle Untersuchungen über die corticalen Sehcentren. Klin. Monatsbl. f. Augenh., v. 38, p. 541.

1900. Die corticalen Sehcentren. Wien. klin. Wchnschr., v. 13, p. 955.

1900. Der rein anatomische Nachweis der ungekreuzten Sehnervenfasern beim Menschen. Arch. f. Augenh., v. 40, p. 155.

1901. Die Lage des Sphinkterzentrums. Arch. f. Ophth. (Graefe), v. 52, p. 302.

1904. Die Gehirnbahnen der Augenbewegungen. *Ibid.*, v. 57, p. 363.

1904. "Ueber Ursprung und Verlauf des Nervus oculomotorius im Mittelhirn." Monatsschr. f. Psychiat. u. Neurol., v. 15, p. 151.

1906. Anophthalmus congenitus und die Sehbahn. Arch. f. Ophth. (Graefe), v. 65, p. 99.

1907. Zur Kenntnis der Guddenschen Commissur. *Ibid.*, v. 67, p. 78.

1909. Weitere experimentelle Studien zur Kenntnis der Lage des Sphinkter- und Levatorkerns. *Ibid.*, v. 70, p. 539.

1910. Die Wurzelgebiete der Augennerven, ihre Verbindungen und ihr Anschluss an die Hirnrinde. *In:* GRAEFE & SAEMISCH, Handb. d. ges. Augenh., v. 1, chap. 6. 2d ed. W. Engelmann, Leipzig.

BERNOULLI, J. J.
1901. Griechische Ikonographie mit Ausschluss Alexanders und der Diadochen. F. Bruckmann, München.

BERRES, J.(?)
1833. Zur Genesis, Physiologie und Pathologie des Foramen centrale retinae humanae. Ztschr. f. d. Ophth. (Ammon), v. 3, p. 265.

BERRY, G. A.
1918. Remarks suggested by Dr. Gordon Holmes's paper, "Disturbances of visual orientation." Brit. J. Ophth., v. 2, p. 597.

BERRY, R. J. A.
1938. A cerebral atlas, illustrating the differences between the brains of mentally defective and normal individuals with a social, mental, and neurological record of 120 defectives during life. Oxford University Press, London.

BERTALANFFY, L. VON
1928. Kritische Theorie der Formbildung. ("Abh. z. theoret. Biol.," ed. J. SCHAXEL, Fasc. 27.) Gebrüder Borntraeger, Berlin.

1932–42. Theoretische Biologie. 2 vols. Gebrüder Borntraeger, Berlin. 2d ed., 1951. A. Francke, Bern.

1933. Modern theories of development: an introduction to theoretical biology. Oxford University Press, London.

1937. Das Gefüge des Lebens. B. G. Teubner, Leipzig & Berlin.

1949. Vom Molekül zur Organismenwelt. Grundfragen der modernen Biologie. Akademische Verlagsgesellschaft Athenaion, Potsdam.

1952——. Handbuch der Biologie. Akademische Verlagsgesellschaft Athenaion, Konstanz.

BERTEAU, B., & JONES, D. S.
1950. The dilator mechanism of the pupil. Anat. Rec., v. 106, p. 264. (Abstr.)

BERTEIN, P.
1926. Les lésions des nerfs optiques dans les traumatismes occipitaux. Arch. d'opht., v. 43, p. 287.

BERTKAU, P.
1886. Die Augen der Spinnen. Arch. f. mikr. Anat., v. 27, p. 589.

BERTRANDI, G.
*1745. Ophthalmographia.

BERTWISTLE, A. P.
1946. A descriptive atlas of radiographs. C. V. Mosby Co., St. Louis, Mo.

BERZE, J.
1910. Bemerkungen zur Theorie der Halluzinationen. Arch. f. Psychiat. u. Nervenkr., v. 46, p. 1009.

1919. Zur Frage der Localisation der Vorstellungen. Ztschr. f. d. ges. Neurol. u. Psychiat. (Orig.), v. 44, p. 213.

BESSE, J.
1701–2. Recherche analytique de la structure des parties du corps humain. 2 vols. J. D. Camus, Toulouse.

BEST, F.
1901. Ueber die Grenzen der Sehscharfe. Ber. d. Deutsch. ophth. Gesellsch. Heidelberg, v. 28, p. 129.
1908. Die Ausdehnung des pupillomotorisch wirksamen Bezirks der Netzhaut. Arch. f. Augenh., v. 61, p. 319.
1917. Hemianopsie und Seelenblindheit bei Hirnverletzungen. Arch. f. Ophth. (Graefe), v. 93, p. 49.
1919. Ueber Störungen der optischen Lokalisation bei Verletzungen und Herderkrankungen im Hinterhauptlappen. Neurol. Centralbl., v. 38, p. 427.
1919. Zur Theorie der Hemianopsie und der höheren Sehzentren. Arch. f. Ophth. (Graefe), v. 100, p. 1.
1920. Zur Untersuchung zentraler Sehstörungen. Neurol. Centralbl., v. 39, p. 290.
1920. Ergebnisse der Kriegsjahre für die Kenntnis der Sehbahnen und Sehzentren. Zentralbl. f. d. ges. Ophth., v. 3, pp. 193, 241.
1923. Ueber electrische Theorien des Sehens. Klin. Monatsbl. f. Augenh., v. 71, p. 220.
1930. Die Kreuzung der sensorischen und motorischen Bahnen und Cajals Theorie. Ber. d. Deutsch. ophth. Gesellsch. Heidelberg, v. 48, p. 14.

BETHE, A.
1900. Ueber die Neurofibrillen in den Ganglionzellen von Wirbelthieren und ihre Beziehungen zu den Golginetzen. Arch. f. mikr. Anat., v. 55, p. 513.
1903. Allgemeine Anatomie und Physiologie des Nervensystems. G. Thieme, Leipzig.
1910. Die Beweise für die leitende Funktion der Neurofibrillen. Anat. Anz., v. 37, p. 129.
1931. Plastizität und Zentrenlehre. *In:* BETHE *et al.*, Handb. d. norm. u. path. Physiol., v. 15 (2) [Correlationen, v. 1 (2)], p. 1175.
1933. Die Plastizität (Anpassungsfähigkeit) des Nervensystems. Naturwiss., v. 21, p. 214.
1937–38. Rhythmik und Periodik, besonders im Hinblick auf die Bewegungen des Herzens und der Meduse. Arch. f. d. ges. Physiol. (Pflüger), v. 239, p. 41.

BETHE, A., BERGMANN, G., EMBDEN, G., & ELLINGER, A.
1926–32. Handbuch der normalen und pathologischen Physiologie, etc. V. 9 (1929): Allgemeine Physiologie der Nerven und des Zentralnervensystems; v. 10 (1927): Spezielle Physiologie des Zentralnervensystems der Wirbeltiere; v. 11 (1926): Receptionsorgane I (Tangoreceptoren, Thermoreceptoren, Chemoreceptoren, Phonoreceptoren, Statoreceptoren); v. 12 (1929–31): Receptionsorgane II (Photoreceptoren 1 & 2); v. 15 (2) (1931): Correlationen 1 (2); v. 18 (1932): Supplement. J. Springer, Berlin.

BETHE, A., & FISCHER, A.
1931. Die Anpassungsfähigkeit (Plastizität) des Nervensystems. *In:* BETHE *et al.*, Handb. d. norm. u. path. Physiol., v. 15 (2) [Correlationen 1 (2)], p. 1045.

BETZ, W.
1874. Anatomischer Nachweis zweier Gehirnzentra. Centralbl. f. d. m. Wissensch., v. 12, pp. 578, 595.
1881. Ueber die feinere Structur der Gehirnrinde des Menschen. *Ibid.*, v. 19, pp. 193, 209.

BEUTNER, R., & BARNES, T. C.
1941. Electrical activity of acetylcholine. Science, v. 94, p. 211.
1946. Phase boundary potentials as the origin of electrical phenomena in nerve. Anat. Rec., v. 94, p. 369. (Abstr.)

BHĀVAPRAKĀŚA; *see* ESSER 1930

BHISAGRATNA, KAVIRAJ K. L.
ca. 1st cent. A.D. Suśruta Samhitā. English translation, Calcutta 1907–16.

BIANCHI, L.
1900. Die Psychotopographie des Hirnmantels und die Flechsig'sche Theorie. Centralbl. f. Nervenh., v. 23, p. 644.
1911. Le syndrome pariétal. Arch. ital. de biol., v. 55, p. 188.
1922. La fonction musicale du cerveau et sa localisation. Scientia, year 32, v. 16 (July–Dec.), p. 25.

BICHAT, X.
1801–3. Traité d'anatomie descriptive. 5 vols. Gabon & Cie, Paris. (*See* v. 2, Sense organs.)
1812. Anatomie général, appliquée à la physiologie et à la médecine. Brosson, Paris.
1822. Recherches physiologiques sur la vie et la mort. 4th ed. Gabon, Paris.

BIDDER, F.
1839. Zur Anatomie der Retina, insbesondere zur Würdigung der stabförmigen Körper in derselben. Arch. f. Anat., Physiol. u. wissensch. Med., ed. J. MÜLLER, p. 371. (*See also* remark by Henle.)

BIDDER, F.—*Continued*

1841. Zweiter Beitrag zur Anatomie der Retina. *Ibid.*, p. 248.

BIDLOO, G.

1685. Anatomia humani corporis. Amstelodami, sumpt. vid. I. à Someren, etc. Another ed., Lugduni Batavorum, 1739.

*1715. De oculis et visu variorum animalium. Lugduni Batavorum.

BIDYĀDHAR, NABIN KISHORE

1939. Suśruta and his ophthalmic operations. Arch. Ophth., v. 22, p. 550.

BIEHL, C.

1907. Beitrag zur Lehre von der Beziehung zwischen Labyrinth und Auge. Arb. a. d. Neurol. Inst. Wien (Obersteiner), v. 15, p. 71.

BIELSCHOWSKY

1915. Sehstörungen infolge intrakranieller Schussverletzungen. München. med. Wchnschr., v. 52, p. 551.

BIELSCHOWSKY, A.

1908. Diskussion über die Vorträge der Herren Schwarz, Albracht und Bielschowsky (über einen Fall Seelenblindheit). München. med. Wchnschr., v. 55 (1), p. 939.

1909. Zur Frage der Lokalisierung assoziierter Blicklähmungen. Monatsschr. f. Psychol. u. Neurol., v. 25, p. 267.

1937. Methoden zur Untersuchung des binokularen Sehens und des Augenbewegungsapparates. *In:* E. ABDERHALDEN, Handb. d. biol. Arbeitsmeth., Abt. V, Teil 6 (1).

BIELSCHOWSKY, M.

1904. Die Silberimprägnation der Neurofibrillen. J. Psychol. u. Neurol., v. 3, p. 169.

1905. Die histologische Seite der Neuronenlehre. *Ibid.*, v. 5, p. 128.

1921. Schichtungsplan der menschlichen Grosshirnrinde. Festschr. Kaiser Wilhelm Gesellsch. z. Förder. d. Wissensch.; also Zentralbl. f. d. ges. Neurol. u. Psychiat., v. 26, p. 146.

1928. Nervengewebe. *In:* MÖLLENDORFF, Handb. d. mikr. Anat., v. 4 (1), pp. 1, 9, 97, 119.

1935. Allgemeine Histologie und Histopathologie des Nervensystems. *In:* BUMKE & FOERSTER, Handb. d. Neurol., v. 1, p. 35.

BIELSCHOWSKY, M., & POLLACK, B.

1904. Zur Kenntnis der Innervation des Säugethierauges. Neurol. Centralbl., v. 23, p. 387.

BIEMOND, A.

1929. Experimenteel-anatomisch onderzoek omtrent de corticofugale optische verbindingen bij aap en konijn. Doctor's thesis. P. H. Vermeulen, Amsterdam. Also Ztschr. f. d.

ges. Neurol. u. Psychiat., v. 129, p. 65. Abstr. in Deutsche Ztschr. f. Nervenh., v. 113, p. 304.

BIERENS DE HAAN, J. A.

1925. Experiments on vision in monkeys. I. The colour-sense of the pig-tailed macaque (*Nemestrinus nemestrinus* L.). J. Comp. Psychol., v. 5, p. 417.

1925. Ueber Wahrnehmungskomplexe und Wahrnehmungselemente bei einem niederen Affen (*Nemestrinus nemestrinus*). Zool. Jahrb., v. 42, p. 272.

1925. Der relative Wert von Form- und Farbenmerkmalen in der Wahrnehmung der Affen. Biol. Zentralbl., v. 45, p. 727.

1927. Versuche über das Sehen der Affen. IV. Das Erkennen gleichförmiger und ungleichförmiger Gegenstände bei niederen Affen. V. Erkennen Affen in zweidimensionalen Abbildungen ihnen bekannte Gegenstände wieder? Ztschr. f. vergl. Physiol., v. 5, p. 699.

1950. Animal psychology: its nature and its problems. Hutchinson's University Library, London.

BIERENS DE HAAN, J. A., & FRIMA, M. J.

1930. Versuche über den Farbensinn der Lemuren. Ztschr. f. vergl. Physiol., v. 12, p. 603.

BIESIADECKI, A.

1861. Ueber das Chiasma nervorum opticorum des Menschen und der Thiere. Sitzungsb. d. math.-naturwiss. Cl. d. Kaiserl. Akad. d. Wissensch., Wien, v. 42, p. 86.

BIGELOW, H. B., & WELSH, W. W.

1924. Fishes of the Gulf of Maine. Bull. U.S. Bur. Fisheries, v. 40, No. 965.

BILCHICK, E. B.

1940. Diseases of the sphenoid sinus. Arch. Otolaryng., v. 32, p. 1031.

BILLS, M. A.

1920. The lag of visual sensation in its relation to wave-lengths and intensity of light. Psychol. Monog., v. 28, p. 1.

BINET, A.

1888. Sur les rapports entre l'hémianopie et la mémoire visuelle. Rev. phil., v. 26, p. 481.

BINET, A., & SIMON, T.

1908. Langage et pensée. Ann. psychol., p. 284.

BING, R.

1923. Gehirn und AUGE. Kurzgefasste Darstellung der physiopathologischen Zusammenhänge zwischen beiden Organen, sowie der Augensymptome bei Gehirnkrankheiten. J. F. Bergmann, München.

1924. Topische Gehirndiagnostik. *In:* KRAUS &

Brugsch, Spezielle Pathologie und Therapie innerer Krankheiten, v. 10 (Part 1).

1925. Allgemeine Symptomatologie der Gehirnkrankheiten. *In:* Mohr & Staehelin, Handbuch d. inn. Krankheiten, v. 5 (Part 1).

1940. Compendium of regional diagnosis in lesions of the brain and spinal cord. C. V. Mosby Co., St. Louis, Mo.

Bing, R., & Schwarz, L.
1918. Contribution à la localisation de la stéréognosie. Schweiz. Arch. f. Neurol. u. Psychiat., v. 4, p. 187.

Bingham, H. C.
1922. Visual perception of the chick. ("Behavior Monog.," v. 4, No. 4.) Williams & Wilkins Co., Baltimore.

1928. Sex development in apes. ("Comparative Psychology Monog.," v. 5, ser. No. 23.) Johns Hopkins Press, Baltimore.

1929. Chimpanzee translocation by means of boxes. ("Comparative Psychology Monog.," v. 5, ser. No. 25.) Johns Hopkins Press, Baltimore.

1929. Selective transportation by chimpanzees. ("Comparative Psychology Monog.," v. 5, ser. No. 26.) Johns Hopkins Press, Baltimore.

1932. Gorillas in a native habitat. ("Carnegie Inst. Washington Pub.," No. 426.)

Binswanger, L.
1936. Vom Sinn der Sinne. Schweiz. Arch. f. Neurol. u. Psychiat., v. 38, p. 1.

Birch-Hirschfeld, A.
1900. Beitrag zur Kenntnis der Netzhautganglienzellen unter physiologischen und pathologischen Verhältnissen. Arch. f. Ophth. (Graefe), v. 50, p. 166.

Bird, C. H. G., & Schäfer, E. A.
1895. Observations on the structure of the central fovea of the human eye. Internat. Monatsschr. f. Anat. u. Physiol., v. 12, pp. 1, 247.

Birdsell, J. B.
1950. Some implications of the genetical concept of race in terms of spatial analysis. Cold Spring Harbor Symp. Quant. Biol., v. 15, p. 259.

Birge, E. A., & Juday, C.
1931–32. Solar radiation and inland lakes. Tr. Wisconsin Acad. Sc., Arts & Letters, v. 26, p. 383; v. 27, p. 523.

Birge, H. L.
1945. Ocular war neuroses. Arch. Ophth., ser. 2, v. 33, p. 440.

Birren, F.
1949. Color psychology and color therapy. McGraw-Hill Book Co., New York.

Birukow, G.
1937. Untersuchungen über den optischen Drehnystagmus und über die Sehschärfe des Grasfrosches (*Rana temporaria*). Ztschr. f. vergl. Physiol., v. 25, p. 92.

1939. Purkinjesches Phänomen und Farbensehen beim Grasfrosch (*Rana temporaria*). *Ibid.*, v. 27, p. 41.

1939. Beobachtungen über Reizverteilung der Farben in reinen Zapfennetzhäuten. *Ibid.*, p. 322.

Birukow, G., & Knoll, M.
1952. Tages- und Dämmerungssehen von Froschlarven nach Aufzucht in verschiedenen Lichtbedingungen. Naturwiss., v. 39, p. 494.

Bischoff, E.
1900. Beitrag zur Anatomie des Igelgehirnes. Anat. Anz., v. 18, p. 348.

Bischoff, T. L. W.
1842. Entwickelungsgeschichte der Säugethiere und des Menschen. L. Voss, Leipzig.

1870. Die Grosshirnwindungen des Menschen mit Berücksichtigung ihrer Entwicklung bei dem Fötus und ihrer Anordnung bei den Affen. Abh. d. Kon. Bairisch. Akad. d. Wissensch., math.-phys. Cl., v. 10 (I, II), p. 389.

Bishop, G. H.
1933. Cyclic changes in excitability of the optic pathway of the rabbit. Am. J. Physiol., v. 103, p. 213.

1933. Fiber groups in the optic nerve. *Ibid.*, v. 106, p. 460.

1935. Electrical responses accompanying activity of the optic pathway. Arch. Ophth., v. 14, p. 992.

1936. The interpretation of cortical potentials. Cold Spring Harbor Symp. Quant. Biol., v. 4, p. 305.

1941. The relation of bioelectric potentials to cell functioning. Ann. Rev. Physiol., v. 3, p. 1.

Bishop, G. H., & O'Leary, J. S.
1940. Electrical activity of the lateral geniculate of cats following optic nerve stimuli. J. Neurophysiol., v. 3, p. 308.

1942. The polarity of potentials recorded from the superior colliculus. J. Cell. & Comp. Physiol., v. 19, p. 289.

1942. Factors determining the form of the potential record in the vicinity of the synapses of of the dorsal nucleus of the lateral geniculate body. *Ibid.*, p. 315.

BISHOP, S. C.
1943. Handbook of salamanders: the salamanders of the United States, of Canada, and of Lower California. Comstock Pub. Co., Ithaca, N.Y.

BJERRUM, J.
1883. Undersögelser over lyssans og formsans i forskellige öjensygdomme. Nord med. ark., v. 15, No. 1, p. 1, and No. 8, p. 1.
1883. Bemaerkninger om amblyopia centralis og om undersøgelsen af naethindefunktionerne. Hospitalstid., 3d ser., v. 1, pp. 937, 961.
1884. Untersuchungen über den Lichtsinn und den Raumsinn bei verschiedenen Augenkrankheiten. Arch. f. Ophth. (Graefe), v. 30 (2), p. 201.
1886. Ueber den Helligkeitssinn. Cong. périod. Internat. sc. méd. (Internat. m. cong.), Compt.-rend., v. 3, sec. d'opht., p. 11.
1886. Ueber die Refraktion bei Neugeborenen. *Ibid.*, p. 207.
1890. Ueber eine Zufügung zur gewöhnlichen Gesichtsfeldmessung und über das Gesichtsfeld beim Glaukom. Internat. m. Cong. Verhandl., v. 4, Part 10, p. 66.
1891. Eine Bemerkung über den Helligkeitssinn, etc. Arch. f. Ophth. (Graefe), v. 37 (3), p. 261.

BLACK, D.
1915. Brain in primitive man. Cleveland M. J., v. 14, p. 177.
1915. A note on the sulcus lunatus in man. J. Comp. Neurol., v. 25, p. 129.
1932. On the endocranial cast of the adolescent *Sinanthropus* skull. Phil. Tr. Roy. Soc. London, ser. B, v. 112, p. 263.
1933. The brain cast of *Sinanthropus:* a review. J. Comp. Neurol., v. 57, p. 361.

BLAIR, E., & ERLANGER, J.
1932–33. Comparison of properties of individual axons in the frog. Proc. Soc. Exper. Biol. & Med., v. 30, p. 728.

BLAKE, R.
1953. Birds of Mexico: a guide for field identification. University of Chicago Press, Chicago.

BLANCHAN, N.
1903. How to attract the birds and other talks about bird neighbours. Doubleday, Page & Co., New York.

BLANFORD, W. T.
1881–91. The fauna of British India, including Ceylon and Burma. Taylor & Francis, London.

BLASIUS, G.
1673. Gerardi Blasii Med. Doct. & Prof. Miscellanea anatomica, hominis, brutorumque variorum, fabricam diversam magnâ parte exhibentia. Amstolodami, Apud Casparum Commelinum. MDCLXXIII.

BLEULER, E.
1893. Ein Fall von aphasischen Symptomen, Hemianopie, amnestische Farbenblindheit und Seelenlähmung. Arch. f. Psychiat., v. 25, p. 32.
1923. Biologische Psychologie. Ztschr. f. d. ges. Neurol. u. Psychiat., v. 83, p. 554.
1925. Lokalisation der Psyche. Allg. Ztschr. f. Psychiat., v. 80, p. 305.
1932. Naturgeschichte der Seele und ihres Bewusstwerdens: mnestische Biopsychologie. J. Springer, Berlin.
1933. Die Mneme als Grundlage des Lebens und der Psyche. Naturwiss., v. 21, p. 100.

BLISS, A. F.
1943. Derived photosensitive pigments from invertebrate eyes. J. Gen. Physiol., v. 26, p. 361.
1946. The chemistry of daylight vision. *Ibid.*, v. 29, p. 277.
1948. The mechanism of retinal vitamin A formation. J. Biol. Chem., v. 172, p. 165.
1948. The absorption spectra of visual purple of the squid and its bleaching products. *Ibid.*, v. 176, p. 563.

BLOCH, H.
1906. Ueber abnormen Verlauf der Papillengefässe. Klin. Monatsbl. f. Augenh., v. 44, p. 413.

BLOOM, S. M., MERZ, E. H., & TAYLOR, W. W.
1946. Nutritional amblyopia in American prisoners of war liberated from the Japanese. Am. J. Ophth., ser. 3, v. 29, p. 1248.

BLOSSOM, P. M.
1932. A pair of long-tailed shrews (*Sorex cinereus c.*) in captivity. J. Mammal., v. 13, p. 136.

BLUM, F.
1893. Der Formaldehyd als Härtungsmittel. Ztschr. f. wissensch. Mikr., v. 10, p. 314.
1926. Formaldehyd (Formol, Formalin). *In:* R. KRAUSE, Enzyklopädie der mikr. Technik, v. 2, p. 791. Urban & Schwarzenberg, Berlin & Wien.

BLUM, J. S., CHOW, K. L., & PRIBRAM, K. H.
1950. A behavioral analysis of the organization of the parieto-temporo-preoccipital cortex. J. Comp. Neurol., v. 93, p. 53.

BLUM, M., WALKER, A. E., & RUCH, T. C.
1943. Localization of taste in the thalamus of *Macaca mulatta.* Yale J. Biol. & Med., v. 16, p. 175.

BLUMENBACH, J. F.
1815. Handbuch d. vergl. Anatomie. 2d ed., Dieterich, Göttingen; 3d ed. 1824. English translation from 1st ed.: Short system of comparative anatomy, 1807.

BLUNTSCHLI, H.
1910. Beobachtungen über das Relief der Hirnwindungen und Hirnvenen am Schaedel, über die Venae cerebri und die Pacchionischen Granulationen bei den Primaten. Morphol. Jahrb., v. 41, p. 110.

BLYTH, E.
1875. Catalogue of mammals and birds of Burma. J. Roy. Asiat. Soc. Bengal, Part 2, extra No., August, p. 31.

BÓBRINSKOY, N. A., KUZNETSÓV, B. A., & KUZYÁKIN, A. P.
1944. Opredyétely mlyekopitáyushchih SSSR. ("Classifier of mammals of Soviet Republics.") Gossud. Izdát-vo Sovyétskaya Naúka, Moskvá.

BOCHENEK, A.
1908. Ueber die zentrale Endigung des Nervus opticus. Bull. internat. Acad. sc. Cracovie, Cl. sc.-math. & nat., p. 91, 1909.

BOCK, E.
1903. Die Brille und ihre Geschichte. J. Šafář, Wien.

BODENHEIMER, E., & KORBSCH, H.
1929. Klinisch-anatomischer Beitrag zur Pupillarfasertheorie. Arch. f. Ophth. (Graefe), v. 121, p. 46.

BODIAN, D.
1935. The projection of the lateral geniculate body on the cerebral cortex of the opossum, *Didelphis virginiana*. J. Comp. Neurol., v. 62, p. 469.
1937. An experimental study of the optic tracts and retinal projection of the Virginia opossum. *Ibid.*, v. 66, p. 113.
1937. The structure of the vertebrate synapse: a study of the axon endings on Mauthner's cell and neighboring centers in the goldfish. *Ibid.*, v. 68, p. 117.
1939-40. Studies on the diencephalon of the Virginia opossum. *Ibid.*, v. 71, p. 259; v. 72, p. 207.
1940. Further notes on the vertebrate synapse. *Ibid.*, v. 73, p. 323.
1942. Cytological aspects of synaptic function. Physiol. Rev. v. 22, p. 146.
1942. Studies on the diencephalon of the Virginia opossum. Part III. The thalamo-cortical projection. J. Comp. Neurol., v. 77, p. 525.

BODIAN, D., & MELLORS, R. C.
1945. The regenerative cycle of motoneurons, with special reference to phosphatase activity. J. Exper. Med., v. 81, p. 469.

BOEGEHOLD, H., & ROHR, M.
1928-40. Forschungen zur Geschichte der Optik. J. Springer, Berlin. (*See also* Ztschr. f. Instrumentenkunde; Rohr & Boegehold 1934; and Ztschr. f. ophth. Optik, v. 24, pp. 101, 145.)

BOEHM, E. F.
1916. Notes on some South Australian bats. South Australian Nat., v. 23, p. 10.

BÖHMER, F.
1865. Zur pathologischen Anatomie der Meningitis cerebromedullaris epidemica. Aerztl. Intelligenzbl. (München), v. 12, p. 539.

BOEKE, J.
1902. On the structure of the light-percepting cells in the spinal cord, on the neurofibrillae in the ganglion cells and on the innervation of the striped muscles in *Amphioxus lanceolatus*. Proc. Kon. Akad. Wetensch. Amsterdam, sec. sc., v. 5, p. 350.
1914. André Vésal comme réformateur de l'anatomie. Janus, v. 19, p. 508.
1926. Die Beziehungen der Nervenfasern zu den Bindegewebselementen und Tastzellen. Das periterminale Netzwerk der motorischen und sensiblen Nervenendigungen, seine morphologische und physiologische Bedeutung, Entwicklung und Regeneration. Ztschr. f. mikr.-anat. Forsch., v. 4, p. 448.
1934. Sinnesorgane. I. Allgemeines über Beziehungen zu Wirbellosen und zur Ontogenie und über die Einteilung der Sinnesorgane. *In:* BOLK, GÖPPERT, KALLIUS, & LUBOSCH, Handb. d. vergl. Anat. d. Wirbeltiere, v. 2 (2), p. 841.
1934. Organe mit Endknospen und Endhügeln nebst eingesenkten Organen. *Ibid.*, p. 949.
1936. Synaptology. *In:* The problems of nervous physiology and of behavior: jubilee symposium dedicated to the 25th anniversary of Prof. T. Beritashvili (J. S. Beritoff), p. 63. Georgian Branch of the Academy of Sciences of U.S.S.R., Tiflis-Tbilisi.
1938. Ueber die Verbindungen der Nervenzellen untereinander und mit den Erfolgsorganen. Anat. Anz., suppl. (Verhandl. Anat. Gesellsch.), v. 85, p. 111.
1938. Sympathetic groundplexus and reticuline fibers. An answer etc. to Nonidez. *Ibid.*, v. 86, pp. 129, 150.
1940. Problems of nervous anatomy. Oxford University Press, London.
1941-42. Zur Frage der Synapse (und des periter-

minalen Netzwerkes; glomeruli cerebellosi; synapses "à distance"). Acta néerl. morphol., v. 4, p. 31.

1943–45. Das Problem der interstitiellen Zellen in der nervösen Endformation. *Ibid.*, v. 5, p. 131.

1943–45. Die Entwicklung der motorischen Endplatten bei den Säugetieren, mit besonderer Berücksichtigung der Kernverhältnisse und der interstitiellen Elemente in der nervösen Endformation. *Ibid.*, p. 189.

1949. The sympathetic endformation, its synaptology, the interstitial cells, the periterminal network, and its bearing on the neurone theory. Discussion and critique. Acta anat., v. 8, p. 18.

BOELL, E. J., COSTELLO, D. P., DETWILER, S. R., FRANKHAUSER, G., HOLTFRETER, J., NICHOLAS, F. S., ROSE, S. M., RUDNICK, D., & STONE, L. S.

1948. Recent studies in the mechanisms of embryonic development. Ann. New York Acad. Sc., v. 49, p. 661.

BÖLSCHE, W.

1906. Haeckel, his life and work. T. Fisher Unwin, London.

1908–11. Tierbuch, eine volkstümliche Naturgeschichte. 3 vols. G. Bondi, Berlin.

BOERHAAVE, HERMANN

1734. *Institutiones Medicae.* In cuis annuae Exercitationis Domesticos Digestae ab Hermanno Boerhaave. Editio Leydenensis quinta prioribus longe auctior. Lugduni Batavorum, Apud Theodorum Haak, Samuel Luchtmans, Joh. & Herm. Verbeek, 1734, et Rotterodami Apud Joan. Dan. Beman. (*Cf.* p. 508, "De visu.")

1745. Hermanni Boerhaave, Phil. & Med. D. Inst. Collegii Pract. Bot. & Chem. Prof. in Acad. Lugd. Bat. Praes. Coll. Chir. Soc. Reg. Scient. Lond. & Acad. Reg. Scient. Paris. Sod. *Praelectiones Academicae.* In proprias Institutiones Rei Medicae edidit, et notas addidit Albertus Haller, Phil. & Med. D. Med. Anat. Bot. Chir. P.P.O. Archiater & Consil. Aul. Regius & Elector. Socc. Regg. Angl. & Suec. Sod. In 5 vols. Editio Gottingensis Altera Emendata. Gottingae, Apud Abram Vandenhoek, Acad. Typogr. MDCCXLV. Cum privilegio Regis Poloniae & Electoris Saxoniae. (6 vols., 1739–50.)

BÖRNSTEIN, W. S.

1940. Cortical representation of taste in man and monkey. Yale J. Biol. & Med., v. 12, p. 719; v. 13, p. 133.

BÖTTCHER, A.

1869. Ueber Entwickelung und Bau des Gehörlabyrinths nach Untersuchungen an Säugethieren. 1. Theil. Verhandl. Kaiserl. Leop.-Carol. Deutsch. Akad. Naturforsch. Dresden, v. 35, No. 5.

BOHM, E., & GERNANDT, B.

1950. Comparison of off-on ratios in retina and geniculate body. Acta physiol. Scandinav., v. 21, p. 187.

BOHR, N.

1933. Licht und Leben. Naturwiss., v. 21, p. 245.

BOK, B. J., & WATSON, F. G.

1940. Astronomical aspects of the age of the earth. Report of the Commission on Measurement of Geologic Time. National Research Council, Washington.

1940. Astronomic considerations. *Ibid.*, p. 91.

BOK, S. T.

1929. Der Einfluss der in den Furchen und Windungen auftretenden Krümmungen der Grosshirnrinde auf die Rindenarchitektur. Ztschr. f. d. ges. Neurol. u. Psychiat., v. 121, p. 682; Psychiat. en neurol. bl., v. 33, p. 220.

BOLDREY, E. B., & PENFIELD, W.

1937. Somatic motor and sensory representation in the cerebral cortex of man as studied by electrical stimulation. Brain, v. 60, p. 389.

BOLK, L.

1910. Beiträge zur Affenanatomie. VII. Das Gehirn von Gorilla. Ztschr. f. Morphol. u. Anthropol., v. 12, p. 141.

BOLL, F.

1877. Zur Anatomie und Physiologie der Retina. Arch. f. Physiol., p. 4.

1881. Thesen und Hypothesen zur Licht- und Farbenempfindung. *Ibid.*, p. 1; also Klin. Monatsbl. f. Augenh., v. 19, p. 287.

BOLLACK, J.

1920. Hémianopsie bitemporale par traumatisme de guerre. Ann. d'ocul., v. 157, p. 27.

BOLTON, J. S.

1900. The exact histological localisation of the visual area of the human cerebral cortex. Phil. Tr. Roy. Soc. London, ser. B, v. 193, p. 165; *also* Proc. Roy. Soc. London, v. 67, p. 216, 1901.

1903. The functions of the frontal lobes. Brain, v. 26, p. 215.

1903. The histological basis of amentia. Arch. Neurol. (Mott), v. 2, p. 424.

1911. A contribution to the localisation of cerebral function, based on the clinico-pathological study of mental diseases. Brain, v. 33, p. 26.

1933. The cortical localisation of cerebral function. (Henderson Trust Lecture, No. 12.) Oliver & Boyd, Edinburgh & London.

BOLTON, J. S., BRAMWELL, B., & ROBINSON, W.
1915. Bilateral lesion of the occipital lobes with retention of macular as distinct from panoramic vision. Brain, v. 38, p. 447.

BONCOMPAGNI, B.
1851. Della vita e delle opere di Gherardo Cremonese, etc. Atti Accad. pontif. de' nuovi Lincei, an. IV, sess. VII. Tipogr. d. Belle Arti, Roma.
1871. Intorno ad un manoscr. dell'ottica di Vitellione, etc. Bull. bibl. e di storia d. sci. mat. e fis. (Boncompagni), v. 4, p. 78.
1871. Intorno ad una traduzione latina dell'ottica di Tolomeo. *Ibid.*, p. 470; v. 6, p. 159.

BONHOEFFER, K.
1915. Doppelseitige symmetrische Schläfen- und Parietallappenherde als Ursache vollständiger dauernder Worttaubheit bei erhaltener Tonskala, verbunden mit taktiler und optischer Agnosie. Monatsschr. f. Psychiat. u. Neurol., v. 37, p. 17.
1918. Partielle reine Tastlähmung. *Ibid.*, v. 43, p. 141; *also* Berl. klin. Wchnschr., v. 54, p. 1250.
1924. Die Entwickelung der Anschauungen von der Grosshirnfunktion in den letzten 50 Jahren. Deutsche med. Wchnschr., v. 50, p. 1708.
1928. Klinisch-anatomische Beiträge zur Pathologie des Sehhügels und der Regio subthalamica. Monatsschr. f. Psychiat. u. Neurol., v. 67, p. 253.

BONHOMME, JEAN
1748. Traité de la céphalotomie ou description anatomique des parties que la tête renferme. F. Girard, Avignon.

BONIN, G. VON
1934. Why is the cerebral cortex folded? Anat. Rec., v. 48 (suppl. to March, 1934) (No. 4), p. 5.
1934. On the size of man's brain as indicated by skull capacity. J. Comp. Neurol., v. 59, p. 1.
1938. The cerebral cortex of the cebus monkey. *Ibid.*, v. 69, p. 181.
1939. Studies of the size of the cells in the cerebral cortex. III. The striate area of man, orang and cebus. *Ibid.*, v. 70, p. 395.
1942. The striate area of primates. *Ibid.*, v. 77, p. 405.
1944. The cerebral cortex of the galago. Anat. Rec., v. 88, p. 422. (Abstr.)
1945. The cortex of galago. "Illinois Monog. Med.

Sc.," v. 5, No. 3. University of Illinois Press, Urbana, Ill.
1950. Essay on the cerebral cortex. Charles C Thomas, Springfield, Ill.

BONIN, G. VON, & BAILEY, P.
1947. The neocortex of *Macaca mulatta*. University of Illinois Press, Urbana, Ill.

BONIN, G. VON, GAROL, H. W., & McCULLOCH, W. S.
1942. The functional organization of the occipital lobe. Biol. Symp., v. 7, p. 165. J. Cattell Press, Lancaster, Pa.; *also* Anat. Rec., v. 79, suppl. 1, p. 10. (Abstr.)

BONNER, W. E.
1926. Monocular color blindness. Am. J. Ophth., 3d ser., v. 9, p. 603.

BONNET, CHARLES
*1755. Essai de psychologie. Londres.
1764. Contemplation de la nature. 2 vols. M.-M. Rey, Amsterdam. 3d ed., 1767 pub. at Yverdon. English trans., 1766: The contemplation of nature. T. Longmans, T. Becket & P. A. Hondt, London.
1768. Considérations sur les corps organisés, où l'on traite de leur origine, de leur développement, de leur réproduction, &c. & où l'on a rassemblé en abrégé tout ce que l'histoire naturelle offre de plus certain & de plus intéressant sur ce sujet. Par C. B., des Académies d'Angleterre, de Suède, de l'Institut de Bologne, Correspondant de l'Acad. Royal des Sciences, &c. 2d ed. 2 vols. A Amsterdam, chez Marc Michel Rey, MDCCLXVIII. (1st ed., 1762.)
1770. La palingénésie philosophique, ou idées sur l'état passé et sur l'état futur des êtres vivans. 2 vols. A Munster, chez Philippe Henry Perrenon.
1775. Essai analytique sur les facultés de l'âme, par Ch. B., etc. 3d ed. A Copenhague et à Genève, chez Cl. Philibert, MDCCLXXV. (1st ed., 1759.)

BONNET, P.
1932. Les sinus périorbitaires (étude topographique). Ann. d'anat. path., v. 9, p. 23.

BONVICINI, G., & PÖTZL, O.
1907. Einiges über die "reine Wortblindheit." Arb. a. d. Neurol. Inst. Wien (Obersteiner), v. 16, p. 522.

BOQUET, F. J. C. J.
1925. Histoire de l'astronomie. Payot, Paris.

BOREL, G.
1907. Fall von Seelenblindheit. Deutsche med. Wchnschr., v. 33, p. 1072.

BOREL, P.
*1655. De vero telescopii inventore, cum brevi omnium conspicillorum historia, ubi de eorum confectione ac usu, seu de effectibus agitur. Haag.

BORING, E. G.
1950. A history of experimental psychology. 2d ed. Appleton-Century-Crofts, New York.

BORK-FELTKAMP, A. J. VAN
1939. Some results of an investigation on six brains of Kenya natives. Acta néerl. morphol. norm. et path., v. 3, p. 23.

BORNSCHEIN, H., & GERNANDT, B.
1950. Selective removal of the nerve discharge component from the cochlear potential during anoxia. Acta physiol. Scandinav., v. 21, p. 81.

BORNSTEIN, M.
1911. Remarques sur l'apraxie, à propos d'un cas d'apraxie idéatrice avec autopsie. Anthropologie, v. 1, p. 233.

BOROWSKI, M. L.
1929. Blinzelabwehrreflex. Sein biologisches Wesen und seine Veränderungen als neues Symptom bei Hemiplegie. Deutsche Ztschr. f. Nervenh., v. 110, p. 134.

BORYSIEKIEWICZ, M.
1887. Untersuchungen über den feineren Bau der Netzhaut. Toeplitz & Deuticke, Leipzig & Wien.
1887. Demonstration of preparations of human fovea. Anat. Anz. (Verh.), suppl., v. 7, p. 270.
1894. Weitere Untersuchungen über feineren Bau der Netzhaut. F. Deuticke, Leipzig & Wien.

BOSTROEM, A.
1925. Ueber optische Trugwahrnehmungen bei Hinterhauptsherden. Monatsschr. f. Psychiat. u. Neurol., v. 57, p. 210.
1929. Die Verwertbarkeit psychischer Symptome bei Erkennung und Lokaldiagnose von Hirntumoren. Deutsche Ztschr. f. Nervenh., v. 109, p. 162.
1936. Allgemeine und psychische Symptome bei Erkrankungen des Grosshirns. In: O. BUMKE & O. FOERSTER, Handb. d. Neurol., v. 6, p. 961.
1939. Die Klinik der Kreislaufstörungen des Gehirns vom Standpunkt der Neurologie und Psychiatrie. Zentralbl. f. d. ges. Neurol. u. Psychiat., v. 94, p. 348; also Ztschr. f. d. ges. Neurol. u. Psychiat., v. 167, p. 375.

BOUCHAUD
1905. Un cas de surdité verbal avec cécité complète, hemiplégie et convulsions épileptiformes. Arch. gén. de méd., v. 82 (1), p. 217.

BOUDET, G.
1909. Hémianopsie latéral homonyme droite. Perte du sens d'orientation. Ramollissement du lobe occipital. Rev. neurol., v. 18, p. 1318.

BOUILLAUD, J.
1825. Recherches cliniques propres à démontrer que la perte de la parole correspond à la lésion des lobules antérieurs du cerveau, et à confirmer l'opinion de M. Gall, sur la siège de l'organe du langage articulé. Arch. gén. de méd., v. 8, p. 25.
1825. Traité clinique et physiologique de l'encéphalite, ou inflammation du cerveau, et de ses suites, telles que le ramollissement, la suppuration, les abscès, les tubercules, le squirrhe, le cancer, etc. J.-B. Baillière, Paris.
1827. Recherches expérimentales sur les fonctions du cerveau. J. de physiol. (Magendie), v. 10, p. 36, 1830.
1830. Recherches expérimentales sur les fonctions du cerveau et sur celles de sa portion antérieure en particulière. Ibid., p. 91.
1839. Exposition de nouveaux faits à l'appui de l'opinion qui localise dans les lobules antérieurs, du cerveau le principe législateur de la parole; examen préliminaire des objections dont cette opinion a été le sujet: mémoire lu à l'Académie de médecine (séance du 29 octobre 1836). Expérience, J. de méd. et de chir., v. 4, pp. 289, 305. (See also response by Gerdy, ibid., No. 126.)
1865. Sur l'aphasie. Mém. Acad. de méd. Paris; also Gaz. hebd. de méd., Paris, 2d ser., v. 2, p. 417.

BOUIN, P.
*1894. Sur les connexions des dendrites des cellules ganglionaires dans la rétine. Bibliog. Anat., v. 2, p. 110.
1895. Contribution à l'étude du ganglion moyen de la rétine chez les oiseaux. J. anat. et physiol., v. 31, p. 313.

BOULE, M.
1913. L'homme fossile de la Chapelle-aux-Saints. Masson & Cie, Paris.
1937. Le Sinanthrope. Anthropologie, v. 47, p. 1.
1946. Les hommes fossiles: éléments de paléontologie humaine. 3d ed. Masson & Cie, Paris. (Review by Le Gros Clark in Nature, v. 159, p. 553.)

BOULE, M., & ANTHONY, R.
1911. L'encéphale de l'homme fossile de la Chapelle-aux-Saints. Anthropologie, v. 22, p. 129.

BOULE, M., & VALLOIS, H.-V.
1952. Les hommes fossiles. Masson & Cie, Paris.

BOUMA, P. J.
1947. Physical aspects of colour: an introduction to the scientific study of colour stimuli and colour sensations. N. V. Philips Gloeilampenfabricken (Philips Industries), Eindhoven, Netherlands.

BOUMAN, K. H.
1905. Experimenteele onderzoekingen over het cerebrale optische stelsel. Academische proefschrift etc., Amsterdam. Te Groningen bij J. B. Wolters.
1909. Ueber die klinisch-diagnostische Bedeutung der binasalen Hemianopsie und über den Bau des Chiasma nervorum opticorum beim Menschen. Monatsschr. f. Psychiat. u. Neurol., v. 25, p. 387.
1910. Over secundaire degeneratie na verwoesting van het corpus geniculatum externum. Psychiat. en neurol. bl., v. 14, p. 339.
1934. "Le miracle grec." *Ibid.*, v. 38, p. 335.

BOUMAN, L.
1928. Cécité verbale pure. Psychiat. en neurol. bl., v. 32, p. 328.

BOUMAN, M. A., & VELDEN, H. A. VAN DER
1947. The two-quanta explanation of the dependence of the threshold values and visual acuity on the visual angle and the time of observation. J. Opt. Soc. Amer., v. 37, p. 908.

BOUNOURE, L.
1949. L'autonomie de l'être vivant. Presses Universitaires de France, Paris.

BOURNE, M. C., CAMPBELL, D. A., & TANSLEY, K.
1938. Hereditary degeneration of the rat retina. Brit. J. Ophth., v. 22, p. 613.

BOUVERET, L.
1887. Observation de cécité totale par lésion cortical; ramollissement de la face interne de deux lobes occipitaux. Lyon méd., v. 56, p. 337; also Rev. gén. d'opht., v. 6, p. 481.

BOUYGES, M.
1930. Roger Bacon, a-t-il lu des livres arabes? Arch. d'hist. doct. et litt. du moyen-âge, v. 5, p. 311.

BOVERI, T.
1904. Ueber die phylogenetische Bedeutung der Sehorgane des *Amphioxus*. Zool. Jahrb., suppl., v. 7, p. 409.

BOVERI, V.
1924. Untersuchungen über das Parietalauge der Reptilien. Inaug.-Diss., Univ. Zürich. A. Bonniers Boktrykeri, Stockholm.

BOWMAN, WILLIAM; for biography *see* J. HIRSCH-

BERG *in:* GRAEFE & SAEMISCH, Handb. d. ges. Augenh., 2d ed., v. 14 (4), p. 197
1847. Lectures on the parts concerned in the operations on the eye, and on the structure of the retina delivered at the Royal London Ophthalmic Hospital, Moorfields, June, 1847. (Pub. in London M. Gaz., 1848.) To which are added, a paper on the vitreous humor; and also a few cases of ophthalmic disease. Longman, Brown, Green, & Longmans, London 1849. (In part reprinted in "Medical Classics," v. 5, p. 292.) (*See also* Todd, R. B., & Bowman, W., The physiological anatomy and physiology of man. 2 vols. J. W. Parker & Son, London, 1859.)
1892. The collected papers. 2 vols. Edited by J. BURDON-SANDERSON & J. W. HULKE. Harrison & Sons, London.
1940. Selections from the writings of Sir William Bowman. Williams & Wilkins Co., Baltimore.

BOZLER, E.
1927. Untersuchungen über das Nervensystem der Coelenteraten. Part 1. Ztschr. f. Zellforsch. u. mikr. Anat., v. 5, p. 244; Part 2. Ztschr. f. vergl. Physiol., v. 6, p. 255.

BRACH, J.
1949. Le comportement animal et la genèse de l'intelligence. Mont-Blanc, Paris.

BRACHET, DALCQ, & GÉRARD
1935. Traité d'embryologie des vertébrés. Masson & Cie, Paris.

BRADFORD, G.
1926. Darwin. Houghton Mifflin Co., Boston.

BRADLEY, O. C.
1934. M. retractor bulbi (oculi) in Carnivora and Ungulata. J. Anat., v. 68, p. 65.

BRÄNDSTEDT, G.
1935. Untersuchungen über Minimum perceptibile und Distinktionsvermögen des Auges, besonders hinsichtlich ihres Verhaltens bei Myopie. Acta ophth., suppl., v. 5.

BRAIN, W. R.
1941. Visual object-agnosia with special reference to the Gestalt theory. Brain, v. 64, p. 43.
1941. Visual disorientation with special reference to lesions of the right cerebral hemisphere. *Ibid.*, p. 244.
1947. Diseases of the nervous system. ("Oxford Medical Publications.") 3d ed. Oxford University Press, New York & London.

BRAMWELL, B.
1915. Bilateral lesion in the occipital lobes correctly diagnosed twenty-four years before death, with histo-pathological report by Dr. J. Shaw Bolton, showing the position of

the cortical area for macular as distinct from non-macular or panoramic vision. Edinburgh M. J., ser. 3, v. 15, p. 4.

1915. Lesions of the occipital lobe and affection of vision. *Ibid.*, p. 165.

1915. A long shot. [Diagnosis of bilateral lesion of the occipital lobes by B. Bramwell; confirmed by autopsy twenty-four years later.] Brit. M. J., v. 2, p. 412.

BRAMWELL, B., BOLTON, J. S., & ROBINSON, W.

1915. Bilateral lesion of the occipital lobes with retention of macular as distinct from panoramic vision. Brain, v. 38, p. 447.

BRAMWELL, E.

1927. A case of cortical deafness. Brain, v. 50, p. 579.

1928. The upward movement of the eyes. *Ibid.*, v. 51, p. 1.

BRANDENBURG, G.

1887. Ein Fall von homonymer rechtsseitiger Hemianopsie mit Alexie und Trochlearislähmung. Arch. f. Ophth. (Graefe), v. 33 (3), p. 93.

BRAUER, A.

1902. Ueber den Bau der Augen einiger Tiefseefische. Verhandl. d. deutsch. zool. Gesellsch., v. 12, p. 42.

1908. Die Tiefseefische. *In:* Wissenschaftliche Ergebnisse der deutschen Tiefsee-Expedition auf dem Dampfer Valdivia, Part 2 (anatomy), v. 15, p. 1 (ed. by CHUN). G. Fischer, Jena.

BRAUN, G.

1861. Eine Notiz zur Anatomie und Bedeutung der Stäbchenschicht der Netzhaut. Sitzungsb. d. math.-nat. Cl. Akad. Wissensch. Wien, v. 42, p. 15.

BRAUS, H., & ELZE, C.

1932–40. Anatomie des Menschen, vols. 3 & 4. J. Springer, Berlin.

BRAZIER

1892. Du trouble des facultés musicales dans l'aphasie. Étude sur les représentations mentales des sons et des symboles musicaux. Rev. phil. de la France et de l'étrang., v. 34, p. 337.

BRAZIER, M. A. B.

1952. The electrical activity of the nervous system. Macmillan Co., New York.

BREASTED, J. H.

1922. The Edwin Smith papyrus. New York Hist. Soc. Quart. Bull., v. 6, p. 5.

1924. Historical tradition and oriental research. Proc. Nat. Acad. Sc., v. 10; Ann. Rep. Smithsonian Inst. for 1924, p. 409.

1930. The Edwin Smith surgical papyrus. Published in facsimile and hieroglyphic transliteration with translation and commentary by J. H. Breasted. ("University of Chicago Oriental Institute Publications," Vols. III, IV.) University of Chicago Press, Chicago.

BRECHER, G. A.

1935. Die Verschmelzungsgrenze von Lichtreizen beim Affen. Ztschr. f. vergl. Physiol., v. 22, p. 539.

1936. Die subjectiven Helligkeitswerte des Spektrums beim Affen. *Ibid.*, v. 23, p. 771.

1942. Form und Ausdehnung der Panumschen Areale bei fovealem Sehen. Arch. f. d. ges. Physiol. (Pflüger), v. 246, p. 315.

BRECKENRIDGE, W. J.

1946. Minnesota's birds of prey (1. Hawks; 2. Broadwinged & soaring hawks; 3. Bird hawks, eagles & vultures; 4. Larger owls; 5. Smaller owls). Conserv. Bull. No. 10. Minnesota Dept. Conservation, St. Paul, Minn.

1946. Notes on natural history: shorebirds. Conserv. Volunteer, v. 9 (July–Aug.), p. 36. St. Paul, Minn.

1947. Minnesota's birds of the waterways (1. Loons & grebes; 2. Cormorants & pelicans; 3. Herons; 4. Rails; 5. Gulls & terns). Conserv. Bull. No. 11. Minnesota Dept. Conservation, St. Paul, Minn.

BREDER, C. M., JR.

1932. On the habits and development of certain Atlantic *Synentognathi*. Pap. Tortugas Lab. Carnegie Inst. Washington, v. 28, p. 1, 1934.

BREDER, C. M., JR., & GRESSER, E. B.

1939. The eye structure of the four-eyed blenny, *Dialommus fuscus* Gilbert. Zoologica, v. 24, p. 239.

BREGMAN, E.

1892. Ueber experimentelle aufsteigende Degeneration motorischer und sensibler Hirnnerven. Arb. Inst. Anat. u. Phys. d. C.N.S. Wien, v. 1, p. 73.

BREHM, ALFRED EDMUND

1911–18. Brehms Tierleben. Allgemeine Kunde des Tierreichs. 4th ed., 13 vols. V. 1: Niedere Tiere; v. 2: Die Vielfüssler, Insekten und Spinnenkerfe; v. 3: Fische; vols. 4 & 5: Lurche und Kriechtiere; vols. 6, 7, 8, & 9: Vögel; vols. 10, 11, 12, & 13: Säugetiere. Bibliographisches Institut, Leipzig & Wien. (*See also* earlier editions.)

BREHM, V.

1936. Ueber die tiergeographischen Verhältnisse der circumantarktischen Süsswasserfauna.

Biol. Rev. Cambridge Phil. Soc., v. 11, p. 477.

BREMER, J. L.
1920–21. Recurrent branches of the abducent nerve in human embryos. Am. J. Anat., v. 28, p. 371; Anat. Rec., v. 18, p. 223.

BREUIL, H., & OBERMAIER, H.
1935. The cave of Altamira at Santillana del Mar, Spain. Tipografia de Archivos, Madrid.

BREWSTER, SIR DAVID
1835. A treatise on optics. 2d American ed. Carey, Lea & Blanchard, Philadelphia.
1862. Letters on natural magic. Harper & Bros., New York.
1865. On hemiopsy, or half-vision. Tr. Roy. Soc. Edinburgh, v. 24, p. 15, 1867; also Phil. Mag., 4th ser., v. 29, p. 503.
1866. On a new property of retina. Tr. Roy. Soc. Edinburgh, v. 24, p. 327, 1867.

BRICKNER, R. M.
1934. An interpretation of frontal lobe function based upon the study of a case of partial bilateral frontal lobectomy. *In:* Localization of function in the cerebral cortex. Research Pub. A. Research Nerv. & Ment. Dis., v. 13, p. 259. Williams & Wilkins Co., Baltimore.
1936. The intellectual functions of the frontal lobes. Macmillan Co., New York.

BRIDGES, W.
1940. The blind fish of La Cueva Chica. Bull. New York Zoöl. Soc., v. 43, p. 74.

BRIDGMAN, C. S., & SMITH, K. U.
1945. Bilateral neural integration in visual perception after section of the corpus callosum. J. Comp. Neurol., v. 83, p. 57.

BRIGGS, W.
1685. Ophthalmo-graphia, sive oculi ejusque partium descriptio anatomica, etc. 2d ed. London. 1st ed. 1676.

BRISSAUD, E.
1902. Cécité verbale pure. Ramollissement de la région calcarine gauche. Dégénérescence du splénium et du tapétum du coté droit. Nouv. iconogr. Salpêtr., v. 15, p. 281.

BROBEIL, A.
1950. Hirndurchblutungsstörungen. G. Thieme, Stuttgart.

BROCA, P.
1861. Perte de la parole. Ramollissement chronique et destruction du lobe antérieur gauche du cerveau. Bull. Soc. anthropol., v. 2, p. 235.
1861. Remarques sur le siège de la faculté du langage articulé, suivies d'une observation d'aphémie (perte de la parole). Bull. Soc. anat. Paris, year 36, 2d ser., v. 6, p. 330.
1861. Nouvelle observation d'aphémie produite par un lésion de la moitié postérieure des deuxième et troisième circonvolutions frontales. *Ibid.*, p. 398.
1863. Localisation des fonctions cérébrales. Siège du langage articulé. Bull. Soc. anthropol., v. 4, p. 200.
1863. Discussion on aphasia. Bull. Soc. anat. Paris, year 38, 2d ser., v. 8, pp. 372–401.
1864. Sur l'aphémie. *Ibid.*, v. 9, pp. 293, 296.
1864. Sur le siège de la faculté du langage articulé. Aphémie traumatique; lésions de la troisième circonvolution frontale gauche. Bull. Soc. anthropol., v. 5, p. 362.
1864. Deux cas d'aphémie traumatique produite par les lésions de la troisième circonvolution frontale gauche. Bull. Soc. chir., 2d ser., v. 5, p. 51.
1864. Sur les mots aphémie, aphasie, aphrasie. Gaz. des hôp., v. 37, p. 35.
1865. Éloge funèbre de Pierre Gratiolet prononcé sur sa tombe le 16 février 1865. Mém. Soc. anthropol., v. 2, p. cxii.
1865. Sur le siège de la faculté du langage articulé. Bull. Soc. anthropol., v. 6, p. 377 (also pp. 412, 417).
1865. Sur la faculté du langage articulé. *Ibid.*, p. 493.
1866. Aphasie traumatique. *Ibid.*, v. 1, 2d ser., p. 396.
1866. Discussion sur la faculté du langage. *Ibid.*, 2d ser., v. 1, p. 377 (following paper by Voisin: Sur le siège et la nature de la faculté du langage, p. 369).
1877. Report of the commission by Baillarger, Gavarret & Broca on the paper by A. de Fleury entitled: De l'inégalité dynamique des deux hémisphères cérébraux. Bull. Acad. de méd de Paris, 2d ser., v. 6, p. 508.
1880. Paul Broca: life and bibliography of publications. Rev. anthropol., 2d ser., v. 2 (or v. 9 of complete ser.), p. 577 (p. 600).
1888. Siège de la faculté du langage articulé. Mém. d'anthropol. *In:* S. POZZI, Œuvres complètes de Paul Broca, v. 5. Reinwald, Paris.

BROCK, S.
1949. Injuries of the brain and spinal cord and their coverings. 3d ed. Williams & Wilkins Co., Baltimore.

BROCKELMANN, C.
1898–1902. Geschichte der arabischen Literatur. 2 vols. E. Felber, Weimar. Other eds. at Leiden, 1937, 1943.

BRODA, E. E., GOODEVE, C. F., & LYTHGOE, R. J.
1940. The weight of the chromophore carrier in the visual purple molecule. J. Physiol., v. 98, p. 397.

BRODAL, A.
1948. Neurological anatomy in relation to clinical medicine. Oxford University Press, New York.

BRODMANN, K.
1903–8. Beiträge zur histologischen Lokalisation der Grosshirnrinde. J. f. Psychol. u. Neurol. I. Mitt. Die Regio Rolandica, v. 2, p. 79, 1903. II. Der Calcarinatypus, v. 2, p. 133, 1904. III. Die Rindenfelder der niederen Affen, v. 4, p. 177, 1905. IV. Der Riesenpyramidentypus und sein Verhalten zu den Furchen bei den Karnivoren, v. 6, p. 108, 1906. V. Ueber den allgemeinen Bauplan des Cortex palii bei den Mammaliern und zwei homologe Rindenfelder im besonderen. Zugleich ein Beitrag zur Furchenlehre, v. 6, p. 275. VI. Die Cortexgliederung des Menschen, v. 10, p. 231, 1908. VII. Die cytoarchitektonische Cortexgliederung der Halbaffen (Lemuriden), v. 12 (suppl.), p. 287, 1908.

1904. Demonstration zur Cytoarchitektonik der Grosshirnrinde mit besonderer Berücksichtigung der histologischen Lokalisation bei einigen Säugetieren. Allg. Ztschr. f. Psychiat., v. 61, p. 765; also Neurol. Centralbl., v. 23, p. 489.

1907. Bemerkungen über die Fibrillogenie und ihre Beziehungen zur Myelogenie mit besonderer Berücksichtigung des Cortex Cerebri. Neurol. Centralbl. v. 26, p. 338.

1907. Zur histologischen Lokalisation des menschlichen Scheitellappens. *Ibid.*, p. 1130.

1908. Ueber Rindenmessungen. Zentralbl. f. Nervenh. u. Psychiat., v. 31 (19), p. 781.

1909. Vergleichende Lokalisationslehre der Grosshirnrinde in ihren Prinzipien dargestellt auf Grund des Zellenbaues. J. A. Barth, Leipzig. 2d printing, 1925.

1910. Feinere Anatomie des Grosshirns. *In:* LEWANDOWSKY, Handb. d. Neurol., v. 1 (1), p. 206.

1911. Neue Probleme der Rindenlokalisation. Neurol. Centralbl., v. 30, p. 696.

1912. Neue Ergebnisse über die vergleichende Lokalisation der Grosshirnrinde mit besonderer Berücksichtigung des Stirnhirns. Anat. Anz., v. 41 (suppl.), p. 157.

1913. Neue Forschungsergebnisse der Grosshirnrindenanatomie mit besonderer Berücksich-

tigung anthropologischer Fragen. Verhandl. 85. Versamml. d. deutsch. Naturforsch., p. 200.

1914. Physiologie des Gehirns. *In:* F. KRAUSE, Allgemeine Chirurgie der Gehirnkrankheiten (part of Neue deutsche Chir., ed. BRUN). F. Enke, Stuttgart.

1918. Individuelle Variationen der Sehsphäre und ihre Bedeutung für die Klinik der Hinterhauptschüsse. Allg. Ztschr. f. Psychiat., v. 74, p. 564; Neurol. Centralbl., v. 37, p. 419.

1918–20. Obituaries by W. Spielmeyer (München. med. Wchnschr., v. 65, p. 1138, 1918), O. Vogt (J. f. Psychol. u. Neurol., v. 24, p. i, 1919), F. Nissl (Ztschr. f. d. ges. Neurol. u. Psychiat. [Origin.], v. 45, p. 329, 1919), L. Schwarz (Schweiz. Arch. f. Neurol. u. Psychiat., v. 4, p. 184, 1919–20), and Haymaker & Baer (The founders of neurology, 1953).

BRODY, S.
1934. Preliminary investigation concerning the representation of the fovea in the external geniculate body of the monkey. Proc. Kon. Akad. Wetensch. Amsterdam, v. 37, Part 2, p. 724.

BROEK, A. J. P. VAN DER
1908. Ueber einige anatomische Merkmale von *Ateles*, in Zusammenhang mit der Anatomie der Platyrrhinen. Anat. Anz., v. 33, p. 111.

BRONGERSMA, L. D.
1942. De hoogere apen en hun verspreiding in het geologisch verleden. Mensch en Maatschapij, Tweemaandelijksch Tijdschr., Amsterdam, v. 18, p. 130.

BRONK, D. W.
1936. The activity of nerve cells. Cold Spring Harbor Symp. Quant. Biol., v. 4, p. 170.

1938. The influence of circulation on the activity of nerve cells. Research Pub. A. Research Nerv. & Ment. Dis., v. 18, p. 298. Williams & Wilkins Co., Baltimore.

1939. Synaptic mechanisms in sympathetic ganglia. J. Neurophysiol., v. 2, p. 380.

BRONK, D. W., LARRABEE, M. G., & DAVIS, P. W.
1946. The rate of oxygen consumption in localized regions of the nervous system; in presynaptic endings and in cell bodies. Fed. Proc., v. 5, p. 11.

BRONN, H. G.
1924. Die Klassen und Ordnungen des Tier-Reichs, v. 6, Part 1, Book 1: Pisces (Fische). Einleitendes, Leptocardii und Cyclostomi. C. F. Winter, Leipzig.

BRONNER, W.
1900. Die Augenheilkunde des Rhazes etc. G. Schade, Berlin.

BRONOWSKI, J., & LONG, W. M.
1952. Statistics of discrimination in anthropology. Am. J. Phys. Anthropol., v. 10, N.S., p. 385.

BROOKS, C. McC., & ECCLES, J. C.
1947. An electrical hypothesis of central inhibition. Nature, v. 159, p. 760.

BROOM, R.
1932. The mammal-like reptiles of South Africa and the origin of mammals. H. F. & G. Witherby, London.
1934. Les origines de l'homme. Payot, Paris.
1942. Some points in the anatomy of the australopithecines, p. 59. ("South African Biol. Soc. Pamphlets [Pretoria]," No. 11.)
1946. The illustrations of the Australopithecinae. Nature, v. 158, p. 714.
1948. Robert Broom commemorative volume, ed. A. L. DU TOIT. Royal Society of South Africa, 1948. Abstr. in Nature, v. 162, p. 795, by D. M. S. WATSON.
1949. Discoveries of ape-men in South Africa. Man, v. 49, p. 128.
1950. The South-African ape-men, and the age of the deposits in which they occur. Quart. J. Geol. Soc. London, v. 105 (Proc.), p. xlii.
1950. The genera and species of the South African fossil ape-men. Am. J. Phys. Anthropol., v. 8, N.S., p. 1.

BROOM, R., & ROBINSON, J. T.
1950. Man contemporaneous with the Swartkrans ape-man. Am. J. Phys. Anthropol., v. 8, N.S., p. 151.
1950. Note on the skull of the Swartkrans ape-man *Paranthropus crassidens. Ibid.*, p. 295.
1950. Notes on the pelves of the fossil ape-men. *Ibid.*, p. 489.
1952. Swartkrans ape-man—*Paranthropus crassidens.* Transvaal Museum, Pretoria.

BROOM, R., ROBINSON, J. T., & SCHEPERS, G. W. H.
1950. The Sterkfontein ape-man, *Plesianthropus.* ("Transvaal Museum Memoirs," No. 4.) Pretoria.

BROOM, R., & SCHEPERS, G. W. H.
1946. The South African fossil ape-men, the Australopithecinae. ("Transvaal Museum Memoirs," No. 2.) Pretoria.

BROUGH, J.
1936. On the evolution of bony fishes during the Triassic period. Biol. Rev. Cambridge Phil. Soc., v. 11, p. 385.

BROUWER, B.
1917. Ueber die Sehstrahlung des Menschen. Monatsschr. f. Psychiat. u. Neurol., v. 41, pp. 129, 203.
1918. Klinisch-anatomische Untersuchungen über den Oculomotoriuskern. Ztschr. f. d. ges. Neurol. u. Psychiat., v. 40, p. 152.
1919–20. Examen anatomique du système nerveux central des deux chats décrits par J. G. Dusser de Barenne. Arch. néerl. de physiol., v. 4, p. 124.
1926. Untersuchungen über die Projektion der Retina im Zentralnervensystem. Deutsche Ztschr. f. Nervenh., v. 89, p. 9.
1927. Anatomical, phylogenetical and clinical studies on the central nervous system. Williams & Wilkins Co., Baltimore.
1928. Ueber die zentrifugale Beeinflussung von zentripetalen Systemen im Zentralnervensystem. Deutsch. Ztschr. f. Nervenh., v. 105, p. 9. (Dutch translation in Psychiat. en neurol. bl., v. 32, p. 320.)
1930. Ueber die Projektion der Makula auf die Area striata des Menschen. J. f. Psychol. u. Neurol., v. 40, p. 147.
1931. Over chiasma-aandoeningen. Nederl. tijdschr. v. geneesk., v. 75, p. 2683.
1932. Certain aspects of the anatomical basis of the phylogeny of encephalization. *In:* Localization of function in the cerebral cortex, Research Pub. A. Research Nerv. & Ment. Dis., v. 13, p. 3. Williams & Wilkins Co., Baltimore.
1932. Projection of the retina on the cortex in man. *Ibid.*, p. 529.
1936. Chiasma, Tractus opticus, Sehstrahlung und Sehrinde. *In:* O. BUMKE & O. FOERSTER, Handb. d. Neurol., v. 6, p. 449.

BROUWER, B., VAN HEUVEN, G. J., & BIEMOND, A.
1929. Experimentell-anatomische Untersuchungen über die optischen Systeme im Gehirn. Proc. Kon. Akad. Wetensch. Amsterdam, v. 31, p. 603.

BROUWER, B., & ZEEMAN, W. P. C.
1925. Experimental anatomical investigations concerning the projection of the retina on the primary optic centres in apes. J. Neurol. & Psychopath., v. 6, p. 1.
1926. The projection of the retina in the primary optic neuron in monkeys. Brain, v. 49, p. 1.

BROUWER, B., ZEEMAN, W. P. C., & HOUWER, A. W. M.
1923. Experimentell-anatomische Untersuchungen über die Projektion der Retina auf die primären Opticuszentren. Schweiz. Arch. f. Neurol. u. Psychiat., v. 13, p. 118.

BROWMAN, L. G.
1942. The effect of bilateral optic enucleation on the voluntary muscular activity of the albino rat. J. Exper. Zoöl., v. 91, p. 331; also J. Comp. Psychol., v. 36, p. 33.

BROWMAN, L. G., & RAMSEY, F.
1943. Embryology of microphthalmos in *Rattus norvegicus*. Arch. Ophth., v. 30, p. 338.

BROWN, E. V. L., & KRONFELD, P. C.
1930. The acuity of binocular depth perception in hemianopia. Arch. Ophth., v. 4, p. 626.

BROWN, E. W.
1931. The age of the earth from astronomical data. Bull. Nat. Research Council, No. 80, p. 460.

BROWN, G. L.
1951. The sympathetic innervation of the extrinsic ocular muscles. J. Physiol., v. 112, p. 211.

BROWN, R. H.
1936. Color vision in the rabbit. J. Gen. Psychol., v. 14, p. 83.

BROWN, SANGER
1888. Experiments on special sense localisation in the cortex cerebri of the monkey. M. Rec., v. 34, p. 113.

BROWN, S., & SCHÄFER, E. A. (*see also* SCHÄFER)
1888. An investigation into the functions of the occipital and temporal lobes of the monkey's brain. Phil. Tr. Roy. Soc. London, ser. B, v. 179, p. 303.

BROWN, T. GRAHAM
1922. Reflex orientation of the optical axes and the influence upon it of the cerebral cortex. Arch. néerl. physiol., v. 7, p. 571.
1927. Die Grosshirnhemisphären. *In:* BETHE *et al.*, Handb. d. Physiol., v. 10, p. 418.

BROWN, T. G., & SHERRINGTON, C. S.
1911. Observations on the localization in the motor cortex of the baboon (*Papio anubis*). J. Physiol., v. 43, p. 209.

BROWN-SÉQUARD, C. E.
1860. Course of lectures on the physiology and pathology of the central nervous system. Collins, Philadelphia.
1872. Recherches sur la communication de la rétine avec l'encéphale. Arch. de physiol., v. 4, p. 261.
1877. Introduction à une série de mémoires sur la physiologie et la pathologie des diverses parties de l'encéphale. Arch. de physiol., v. 4, pp. 409, 655.
1877. Dual character of the brain. ("Smithsonian Miscellaneous Collection," v. 15, art. 3.) Smithsonian Institution, Washington.
1879. Doctrines relatives aux principales actions des centres nerveux. G. Masson, Paris. (Extrait de Gaz. hebd. de méd. et chir.)
1889. Recherches sur la localisation des conducteurs des impressions sensitives dans les diverses parties de l'encéphale, et sur la pathogénie des anesthésies du centre encéphalique. Arch. de physiol., v. 1, p. 484.
1890. Preuves de l'insignifiance d'une expérience célèbre de M. M. V. Horsley et Beevor sur les centres appelés moteurs. *Ibid.*, v. 2 (22), p. 199.
1890. Nombreux cas de vivisection pratiquée sur le cerveau de l'homme, leur verdict contre la doctrine des centres psycho-moteur. *Ibid.*, p. 762.
1892. Localisation prétendue de fonctions diverses dans les centres nerveux et surtout dans certaines parties des organes auditifs. *Ibid.*, v. 4, p. 366.

BROWNE, E. G.
1921. Arabian medicine. Cambridge University Press, Cambridge.

BRUCE, J., & WALMSLEY, R.
1939. Beesley and Johnston's manual of surgical anatomy. 5th ed. Oxford University Press, New York.

BRÜCKE, E.
1844. Ueber de physiologische Bedeutung der stabförmigen Körper etc. Arch. f. Anat., Physiol. u. wissensch. Med. (J. Müller), p. 444.
1845. Anatomische Untersuchungen über die sogenannten leuchtenden Augen bei den Wirbelthieren. *Ibid.*, p. 387.
1846. Ueber den Musculus Cramptonianus und den Spannmuskel der Chorioidea. *Ibid.*, p. 370.
1847. Ueber das Leuchten der menschlichen Augen. *Ibid.*, p. 225.
1847. Anatomische Beschreibung des menschlichen Augenapfels. G. Reimer, Berlin.

BRÜCKE, E. T.
1929. Beziehungen zwischen Ganglienzellen, Grau und langen Bahnen. Theorien der Zentrenfunktion. *In:* BETHE *et al.*, Handb. d. norm. u. path. Physiol., v. 9, p. 771.
1929. Diffuses und zentralisiertes Nervensystem. *Ibid.*, p. 791.

BRÜCKE, E. W.
1873-74. Vorlesungen über Physiologie. 2 vols. W. Braumüller, Wien.

BRÜCKNER, A.
1917. Zur Frage der Lokalisation des Contrastes und verwandter Erscheinungen in der Sehsinnsubstanz. Ztschr. f. Augenh., v. 38, p. 1.

1927. Experimentelles und Kritisches zur Theorie des Farbensehens. Ber. d. Deutsch. ophth. Gesellsch. Heidelberg, v. 46, p. 159.

BRUESCH, S. R.
1942. Staining myelin sheaths of optic nerve fibers with osmium tetroxide vapor. Stain Technol., v. 17, p. 149.

BRUESCH, S. R., & AREY, L. B.
1940. An enumeration of myelinated and unmyelinated fibers in the optic nerve of vertebrates. Anat. Rec., suppl. (Am. A. Anat.), v. 76, p. 10.
1942. The number of myelinated and unmyelinated fibers in the optic nerve of vertebrates. J. Comp. Neurol., v. 77, p. 631.

BRUETSCH, W. L.
1948. Etiology of optochiasmatic arachnoiditis. Arch. Neurol. & Psychiat., v. 59, p. 215.

BRUGI, G.
1937. Particolarità strutturali del *Nucleus corporis geniculati lateralis* del neonato. Anat. Anz., v. 84, p. 113.
1939. Ulteriori ricerche sopra alcune nuove particolarità strutturali del metatalamo dell'uomo. Arch. ital. di anat. e di embriol. v. 42, p. 439.

BRUGIA, R.
1929. Révision de la doctrine des localisations cérébrales. Unité segmentaire des réflexes. Masson, Paris.

BRUMMELKAMP, R.
1940. On the cephalization stage of *Pitchecanthropus erectus* and *Sinanthropus pekinensis*. Proc. Kon. nederl. Akad. Wetensch., v. 43, p. 741.
1943–45. Fissuration de l'écorce. Acta néerl. morphol., v. 5, p. 52.
1946. The model of Lillie in connection with the growth of the nerve-fibre. Proc. Kon. nederl. Akad. Wetensch., v. 48, p. 360, 1945.

BRUN, R.
1914. Die Raumorientierung der Ameisen und das Orientierungsproblem im allgemeinen. Eine kritisch-experimentelle Studie; zugleich ein Beitrag zur Theorie der Mneme. G. Fischer, Jena.

BRUNELLE
1890. Cécité verbale et hémianopsie homonyme latérale droite. Bull. méd. nord. Lille, v. 29, p. 633.

BRUNET, P., & MIELI, A.
1935. Histoire des sciences: antiquité. Payot, Paris.
1953. Histoire des sciences: moyen âge. Payot, Paris (in project).

BRUNNER, G.
1934. Ueber die Sehschärfe der Elritze (*Phloxinus laevis*) bei verschiedenen Helligkeiten. Ztschr. f. vergl. Physiol., v. 21, p. 296.

BRUNNER, H., & SPIEGEL, E. A.
1919. Vergleichend-anatomische Studien am Hapalidengehirn. Folia neuro-biol., v. 11, p. 171.

BRUNO, G.
1936. Sulla inserzione ciliare e sul probabile significato istologico delle fibre della zonula dello Zinn. Ann. di ottal., v. 64, p. 400.

BRUNS, L.
1888. Fall von Dyslexie mit Störung der Schrift. Neurol. Centralbl., v. 7, pp. 38, 68.
1894. Neuer Fall von Alexie mit rechtseitiger homonymer Hemianopsie. *Ibid.*, v. 13, pp. 8, 50.
1896. Ueber Seelenlähmung. Festschrift anlässl. 50-jähr. Bestehens d. Prov.-Irren Anst. Nietleben bei Halle a/S. etc. F. C. Vogel, Leipzig.
1900. Ueber zwei Fälle von Tumor im linken Hinterhauptslappen. Allg. Ztschr. f. Psychiat., v. 57, p. 866.

BRYANT, M. D.
1945. Phylogeny of nearctic Sciuridae. Am. Midland Naturalist, v. 33, p. 257.

BUCCIANTE, L.
1933. Le variazioni dei vasi centrali della retina studiate con metodo statistico seriale. Boll. Soc. ital. biol. sper., v. 8, p. 1770.
1933. Modalità della inserzione dei muscoli sul bulbo oculare nell'uomo. Monit. Zool. ital., v. 44 (suppl.), p. 246.

BUCHER, V. M., & BÜRGI, S. M.
1950. Some observations on the fiber connections of the di- and mesencephalon in the cat. I. Fiber connections of the tectum opticum. J. Comp. Neurol., v. 93, p. 139.

BUCHSBAUM, R. M.
1948. Animals without backbones: an introduction to the invertebrates. University of Chicago Press, Chicago.

BUCK, A. H.
1917. The growth of medicine from the earliest times to about 1800. Yale University Press, New Haven, Conn.

BUCK, J. B.
1948. The anatomy and physiology of the light organ in fireflies. Ann. New York Acad. Sc., v. 49, p. 397.

BUCY, P. C.
1941. The relationship of the temporal lobes to primate behavior. Tr. Kansas City Acad. Med., p. 223, 1939–41.

Bucy, P. C., & Klüver, H.
1940. Anatomic changes secondary to temporal lobectomy. Arch. Neurol. & Psychiat., v. 44, p. 1142.

Bucy, P. C., et al.
1944. The precentral motor cortex. University of Illinois Press, Urbana, Ill.

Buddenbrock, W. von
1921. Handlungstypen der niederen Tiere und ihre tierpsychologische Bewertung. Berlin. klin. Wchnschr., v. 58, p. 923.
1932. Article: Sight, sense of, Encyclopaedia Britannica, 14th ed., v. 20, p. 628.
1935. Eine neue Methode zur Erforschung des Formensehens der Insekten. Naturwiss., v. 23, p. 98.
1935. Versuche über die Wahrnehmungsgrenzen des Insektenauges. Ibid., p. 154.
1937–39. Grundriss der vergleichenden Physiologie. 2d ed. 2 vols. Gebrüder Borntraeger, Berlin.
1952. Vergleichende Physiologie. Vol. 1: Sinnesphysiologie. Birkhäuser, Basel.

Buddenbrock, W., & Friedrich, H.
1933. Neue Beobachtungen über die kompensatorischen Augenbewegungen und den Farbensinn der Taschenkrabben (Carcinus maenas). Ztschr. f. vergl. Physiol., v. 19, p. 747.

Budge, E. A. W.
1913. Syrian anatomy, pathology and therapeutics or "The book of medicines." 2 vols. Humphrey Milford, Oxford University Press, London & New York.

Bürger, M.
1939. Die chemischen Altersveränderungen an den Gefässen. Zentralbl. f. d. ges. Neurol. u. Psychiat., v. 94, p. 346.

Bütschli, J. A. O.
1910–34. Vorlesungen über vergleichende Anatomie. 6 vols. Lieferung 3 (Sinnesorgane und Leuchtorgane), 1925. W. Engelmann, Leipzig; J. Springer, Berlin.

Büttner, K.
1927. Untersuchungen an Hirnstamm und Kleinhirn mittels der Faserungsmethode. Ztschr. f. Anat., v. 84, p. 534.
1932. Akkommodation und spektrale Dispersion des menschlichen Auges. Ztschr. f. ophth. Optik, v. 20, p. 35.

Buffon, G. L. L.
1769. Histoire naturelle générale et particulière. 13 vols. Panckoucke, Paris; C. Plonteux, Liège.

Bugnion, E., & Popoff, N.
1914–15. Les yeux des insectes nocturnes. Arch. d'anat. micr., v. 16, p. 261.

Bulač, C. O.
1931. Zur Morphologie der Neuroglia im Nervus opticus und in der Retina nach Methoden der spanischen Schule (Ramón y Cajal). Ztschr. f. Augenh., v. 74, p. 248.

Bull, C. S.
1885. Two cases of unilateral temporal hemianopsia. Tr. Am. Ophth. Soc., 21st meet., p. 115.

Bull, H. O.
1935. Studies on conditioned responses in fishes. III. Wave-length discrimination in Blennius pholis L. J. Marine Biol. A. United Kingdom, v. 20, p. 347.

Bull, O.
1883. Bemerkungen über den Farbensinn unter verschiedenen physiologischen und pathologischen Verhältnissen. Arch. f. Ophth. (Graefe), v. 29 (3), p. 71.

Bullo, J.
1945. Contribuciones de la escuela de Cajal sobre histopatologia de la neuroglia y microglia. Arch. histol. norm. y pat., v. 2, p. 425.

Bumke, O.
1924–28. Ueber die gegenwärtigen Strömungen in der klinischen Psychiatrie. Zentralbl. f. d. ges. Neurol. u. Psychiat., v. 40, p. 108; and Wien. klin. Wchnschr., v. 41, p. 981.
1928–32. Handbuch der Geisteskrankheiten. 11 vols. J. Springer, Berlin.

Bumke, O., & Foerster, O.
1935–37. Handbuch der Neurologie. J. Springer, Berlin. Also Ergänzungsserie, Hefte 69 and 70, in Monog. a. d. Gesamtgeb. d. Neurol. u. Psychiat., 1940.

Bumke, O., & Trendelenburg, W.
1911. Beiträge zur Kenntnis der Pupillarreflexbahnen. Klin. Monatsbl. f. Augenh., v. 49 (2), p. 145.

Bumm, A.
1899. Experimentelle Untersuchungen über das Ganglion ciliare der Katze. Verhandl. d. Gesellsch. deutsch. Naturforsch. u. Aerz, v. 71, p. 304.

Bunge, E.
1928. Ueber homonyme Hemianopsie. S. Karger, Berlin.

Bunge, P.
1884. Ueber Gesichtsfeld und Faserverlauf im optischen Leitungsapparat. M. Niemeyer, Halle.

BUNTING, W. H.
1898. Notes on the localisation of a centre in the brain cortex for raising the upper eyelid. Lancet, v. 2, p. 479.

BUNTS, A. T., & CHAFFEE, J. S.
1944 Agenesis of the corpus callosum with possible porencephaly. Arch. Neurol. & Psychiat., v. 51, p. 35.

BUONANNI, F.
1691. Observationes circa viventia, etc. Romae, Typis D. A. Herculis.

BURCKHARDT, J.
1941. Die Kultur der Renaissance in Italien. Safari-Verlag, Berlin. Other editions and translations. *See also* following books by the same author: Griechische Kulturgeschichte, Weltgeschichtliche Betrachtungen, and Geschichte der Renaissance in Italien.

BURCKHARDT, R.
1902. Die Einheit des Sinnesorgansystems bei den Vertebraten. Verhandl. internat. Zoologencong. (1901), p. 621.

BURDACH, F.
1883. Zur Faserkreuzung im Chiasma und in den Tractus nervorum opticorum. Arch. f. Ophth. (Graefe), v. 29 (3), p. 135.

BURDACH, K. F.
1819–22–26. Vom Baue und Leben des Gehirns. 3 vols. Leipzig, In der Dyk'schen Buchhandlung.
1826–40. Die Physiologie als Erfahrungswissenschaft. L. Voss, Leipzig.
1848. Rueckblick auf mein Leben: Selbstbiographie. L. Voss, Leipzig.

BURGGRAEVE, A.
1841. Études sur André Vésale, précédées d'une notice historique sur sa vie et ses écrits. C. Annoot-Braeckman, Gand.

BURIAN, H. M.
1951. Anomalous retinal correspondence; its essence and its significance in diagnosis and treatment. Am. J. Ophth., ser. 3, v. 34, p. 237.

BURKAMP, W.
1923. Versuche über das Farbenwiedererkennen der Fische. Ztschr. f. Sinnesphysiol., v. 55, p. 133.

BURKHARDT, L.
1931. Ueber Bau und Leistung des Auges einiger amerikanischer Urodelen. Ztschr. f. vergl. Physiol., v. 15, p. 637.

BURKITT, M. C., CRAWFORD, O. G. S., HALL, H. R. H., PEAKE, H. J. E., & SMITH, R. A.
1932. Article: Archeology, Encyclopaedia Britannica, 14th ed., v. 2, p. 232. (*See also* articles: Africa, America, Asia, Australia, and Europe.)

BURMEISTER, H.
1846. Beiträge zur näheren Kenntniss der Gattung *Tarsius*. G. Reimer, Berlin.

BURNET, J.
1892. Early Greek philosophy. A. Black, London.

BURNETT, S. B.
1884. Die Farbenempfindung und Farbenblindheit. Arch. f. Augenh., v. 13, p. 241.

BURNETT, S. M.
1887. Clinical contributions to the study of ringscotoma. Tr. Am. Ophth. Soc., 23d meet., p. 435.

BURNS, D.
1951. Some properties of isolated cortex in the unanaesthetized cat. J. Physiol., v. 112, p. 156.

BUROW, A.
1863. Notiz betreffend die Beobachtung des eigenen Augenhintergrundes. Arch. f. Ophth. (Graefe), v. 9 (1), p. 155.

BURR, H. S.
1928. The central nervous system of *Orthagoriscus mola*. J. Comp. Neurol., v. 45, p. 33.
1932. An electro-dynamic theory of development suggested by studies of proliferation rates in the brain of *Amblystoma*. *Ibid.*, v. 56, p. 347.
1932. Determinants of organization in the cerebral hemispheres. *In:* Localization of function in the cerebral cortex. Research Pub. A. Research Nerv. & Ment. Dis., v. 13, p. 39. Williams & Wilkins Co., Baltimore.
1943. Neuroid transmission in Mimosa. Anat. Rec., v. 85, p. 300. (Abstr.)

BURRELL, H.
1927. The platypus. Its discovery, zoölogical position, form and characteristics, habits, life history, etc. Angus & Robertson, Sydney.

BURRI, C.
1942. Process of learning simultaneous binocular vision. Arch. Ophth., v. 28, p. 235.

BURROUGHS, J.
1900. Squirrels and other fur-bearers. Houghton Mifflin Co., Boston. (Also other eds.)
1926. Sharp eyes and other papers. Houghton Mifflin Co., Boston.

BURSTEIN, J., & LÖNNBERG, F.
1937. Distribution of fibre size in the frog's optic nerve. Skandinav. Arch. f. Physiol., v. 76, p. 22.

BURTON, M.
1949. The story of animal life. 2 vols. Cleaver-Hume Press, London.

Burton-Opitz, R.
1899. Johannes Evangeliste Purkinje. J. Am. Med. Assoc., v. 22, p. 813.

Buscaino, V. M.
1946. Neurobiologia delle percezioni. Edizioni Scientifiche Italiane, Napoli.

Busch, A.
1918. Untersuchungen an Sehhirnverletzten. München. med. Wchnschr., v. 65, p. 920.
1921. Ueber die Ausfallserscheinungen nach Sehhirnverletzungen und einige Vorrichtungen zur Prüfung der optischen Orientierung und der Arbeitsanpassung. Ztschr. f. angew. Psychol., v. 19, p. 156.

Bushmakin, N. D.
1928. Contribution to the problem of the study of brain in human races (in Russian). Cong. Russ. Zool., Anat. & Histol. Leningrad. German trans.: Zur Frage über das Rassenstudium des Gehirns. Anat. Ber., v. 19, p. 249, 1928.
1928. Characteristics of the brain of the Mongol race. Am. J. Phys. Anthropol., v. 12, p. 221.
1936. The brain of the Jakuts. *Ibid.*, v. 21, p. 29.

Butcher, E. O.
1938. The structure of the retina of *Fundulus heteroclitus* and the regions of the retina associated with the different chromatophoric responses. J. Exper. Zoöl., v. 79, p. 275.

Butler, A. J.
1902. The Arab conquest of Egypt. Clarendon Press, Oxford.

Butler, C. J.
1949. The honeybee: an introduction to her sense physiology and behavior. Clarendon Press, Oxford.

Butler, T. H.
1933. Scotomata in migrainous subjects. Brit. J. Ophth., v. 17, p. 83.

Buttler, P.
1933. A check list of fifteenth century books in the Newberry Library and in other libraries of Chicago. Newberry Library, Chicago.

Buxton, B. H.
1912. The origin of the vertebrate eye. Arch. f. vergl. Ophth., v. 2, p. 405; v. 3, pp. 85, 227.

Buys, M., & Bogaert, L. van
1927. Gliome épendymaire du cervelet. Étude neurologique. État des fonctions vestibulaires. Intervention et évolution chirurgicales. Rev. neurol., v. 1, p. 421.

Buytendijk, F. J. J.
1928. Psychologie des animaux. Payot, Paris.

Buzzi, F.
1782. Nuove sperienze fatte sull'occhio umano. Opuscoli scelti sulle scienze e sulle arti,
Milano, v. 5, p. 85; *also* J. d. Erfindungen, Theorien u. Wiedersprüche etc., 14. St., Intelligenzbl., No. X, p. 117.

Bychowski, G.
1937. Frontalsyndrome und Parietookzipitalsyndrome. Jahrb. f. Psychiat., v. 54, p. 283.

Bychowski, Z.
1909. Beiträge zur Nosographie der Apraxie. Monatsschr. f. Psychiat. u. Neurol., v. 25 (suppl.), p. 1.
1920. Ueber das Fehlen der Wahrnehmung der eigenen Blindheit bei zwei Kriegsverletzten. Neurol. Centralbl., v. 39, p. 354.

Byrne, J. G.
1937. Effect of stimulation of cortex cerebri on effector mechanisms which mediate movements of iris and membrana tympani. J. Nerv. & Ment. Dis., v. 85, p. 528.
1942. Studies on the physiology of the eye. H. K. Lewis & Co., London.

C

Cable, L. E.
1928. Food of bullheads. Rep. U.S. Com. Fish., Appendix 2, p. 27.

Cade, T.
1951. Carnivorous ground squirrels on St. Lawrence Island, Alaska. J. Mammal., v. 32, p. 358.
1952. Notes on the activity of shrews along Yukon River. *Ibid.*, v. 34, p. 120.

Caesemaker
*1845. Notice historique sur les lunettes et les verres optiques. Gand.

Cahalane, V. H.
1947. Mammals of North America. Macmillan Co., New York.

Cahn, A. R.
1924. An ecological study of certain southern Wisconsin fishes (esp. Brook Silverside, *Labidesthes siculus*, and Cisco, *Leucichthys artedi*), p. 3, 1927. ("Illinois Biol. Monog.," v. 11, No. 1.)

Cain, A. J.
1954. Animal species and their evolution. Hutchinson's University Library, London.

Cairney, J.
1926. A general survey of the forebrain of *Sphenodon punctatum*. J. Comp. Neurol., v. 42, p. 255.

Cajal; *see* Ramón y Cajal

Caldanius, L. M. A.
1791. Institutiones anatomicae auctore L.M.A. Caldanio. Venetiis, MDCCXCI. [2 vols.] Sumptibus Jo: Antonii Pezzana. Superiorum Permissu, ac Privilegio.

CALESTANI, V.
1947. Natura in maschera; mimetismo e appariscenza negli animali e nelle piante. ("Piccola scientifica," 2d ser.) Garzanti, Milano.

CALLAHAN, A.
1941. Annular scotoma. Am. J. Ophth., ser. 3, v. 24, p. 196.

CALORI, L.
1865. Cervello di un negro di Guinea illustrato con otto tavole lithographice. Mem. Accad. Bologna, ser. II, v. 5, p. 177.

CALVERT, A. F., & GALLICHAN, W. M.
1907. Cordova, a city of the Moors. J. Lane, London & New York.

CAMPBELL, A. C. P.
1938. The vascular architecture of the cat's brain. Research Pub. A. Research Nerv. & Ment. Dis., v. 18. Williams & Wilkins Co., Baltimore.

CAMPBELL, A. W.
1904. Histological studies in cerebral localisation. Brain, v. 27, p. 143.
1905. Histological studies on the localisation of cerebral function. Cambridge University Press, Cambridge.
1938. Obituary, by L. R. Parker, W. S. Dawson & J. A. L. Wallace. M. J. Australia, v. 1, p. 181.

CAMPBELL, B.
1951. Re-interpretation of the structure of the cerebral cortex. Anat. Rec., v. 109, p. 277. (Abstr.)

CAMPBELL, DONALD
1926. Arabian medicine and its influence on the Middle Ages. 2 vols. Kegan Paul, Trench, Trubner & Co., London.

CAMPBELL, DOROTHY
1947. Binocular vision. Brit. J. Ophth., v. 31, p. 321.

CAMPBELL, J.
1818. Ueber das Sehen. Deutsches Arch. f. Physiol. (Meckel), v. 4, p. 110. Originally in Ann. Phil., v. 10, p. 17, 1817.

CAMPENHOUT; *see* VAN CAMPENHOUT

CAMPER, P.
1746. Dissertatio de visu. In Disput. select., ed. A. HALLER, v. 4, p. 225.
1746. Dissertatio de quibusdam oculi partibus. *Ibid.*, p. 261.
1792. Discours prononcés par feû Mr. Pierre Camper, en l'Acadêmie de dessein d'Amsterdam, sur le moyen de représenter d'une manière sûre les diverses passions qui se manifestent sur le visage; sur l'étonnante conformité qui existe entre les quadrupèdes, les oiseaux, les poissons et l'homme; et enfin sur le beau physique: publiés par son fils Adrien Gilles Camper, Traduits du Hollandoîs par Denis Bernard Quatremere d'Isjonval. A Utrecht, chez B. Wild et J. Altheer.

CAMPION, G. G., & SMITH, G. ELLIOT
1934. The neural basis of thought. Harcourt, Brace & Co., New York.

CANELLA, M.-F.
1936. Les problèmes du chiasma et de la vision binoculaire; quelques recherches sur la vision monoculaire. J. de psychol. norm. et path., v. 33, p. 696.
1937. Quelques observations sur le comportement visuel des poissons à fovea. Compt. rend. Soc. de biol., v. 124, p. 405.

CANFIELD, W. B.
1886. Vergleichend anatomische Studien über den Accommodations-Apparat des Vogelauges. Arch. f. mikr. Anat., v. 28, p. 121.

CANNON, D.
1949. Explorer of the human brain: the life of Santiago Ramón y Cajal (1852–1934). H. Schuman, New York.

CANNON, W. B.
1934. The story of the development of our ideas of chemical mediation of nerve impulses. Am. J. M. Sc., v. 188, p. 145.

CANTILO, H.
1929. La céphalée dans la migraine ophtalmique. Rev. d'oto-neuro-opht., v. 7, p. 639.

CANTONNET, A.
1915. Blessures de guerre. Arch. d'opht., v. 34, pp. 582, 651.

CANTOR, M.
1872. Euclide e il suo secolo. Saggio storico matematico. Bull. bibl. e di storia d. sc. mat. e fis. (Boncompagni), v. 5, p. 1; German trans. in Ztschr. f. Math. u. Phys., v. 12, p. 1, 1867.

CANTOR, T.
1846. Catalogue of mammalia inhabiting the Malayan peninsula and islands. J. Roy. Asiatic Soc. Bengal, v. 15, p. 188.

CAPPARONI, P.
1923. "Magistri Salernitani nondum cogniti." A contribution to the history of the Medical School of Salerno, etc. J. Bale, Sons & Danielsson, London.
1928–32. Profili bio-bibliografici di medici e naturalisti celebri italiani dal sec. XV° al sec. XVIII°. 2 vols. Ist. naz. med. farm. "Serono," Roma.

CARDANUS, H.
1580. Hieronymi Cardani Mediolanensis, medici, *De subtilitate* Libri XXI. Ab ipsa authoris recognitione, nunc demum emaculatiores & longè perfectiores redditi. Lugduni, Apud Bartholomaeum Honoratum. M.D.L.XXX. (Biol. Libr., University of Chicago.)

CARLANDER, K. D.
1950. Handbook of freshwater fishery biology. William C. Brown, Dubuque, Iowa.

CARLEVARO, G.
1943. Sulla teoria delle aberazzioni monochromatiche nell'ochio umano. Rosenberg & Seller, Torino.

CARLSON, H. B., GELLHORN, E., & DARROW, C. W.
1941. Representation of the sympathetic and parasympathetic nervous systems in the forebrain of the cat. Arch. Neurol. & Psychiat., v. 45, p. 105.

CARLSSON, A.
1910. Die Macroscelididae und ihre Beziehungen zu den übrigen Insektivoren. Zool. Jahrb., v. 28, p. 349.
1922. Ueber die Tupaiidae und ihre Beziehungen zu den Insectivora und den Prosimiae. Acta zool., v. 3, p. 227.

CARMALT, W. H.
1879. A description of a modification of Förster's perimeter. Tr. Am. Ophth. Soc., 15th meet., p. 584.

CARPENTER, C. R.
1934. A field study of the behavior and social relations of howling monkeys (*Alouatta palliata*). ("Comp. Psychol. Monog.," v. 10, No. 48.)
1935. Behavior of red spider monkeys in Panama. J. Mammal., v. 16, p. 171.
1938. A survey of wild life conditions in Atjeh, North Sumatra. Netherl. Comm. Internat. Nat. Protect., Commun. No. 12. Amsterdam.
1939. Behavior and social relations of free-ranging primates. Scient. Monthly, v. 48, p. 319.
1940. A field study in Siam of the behavior and social relations of the gibbon (*Hylobates lar*). ("Comp. Psychol. Monog.," v. 16, No. 5, ser. No. 84.)
1942. Sexual behavior of free ranging rhesus monkeys (*Macaca mulatta*). J. Comp. Psychol., v. 33, pp. 113, 143.
1942. Societies of monkeys and apes. Biol. Symp., v. 8, p. 177.

CARPENTER, W. B.
1901. The microscope and its revelations. 8th ed. J. & A. Churchill, London.

CARPENTIER, L., & THIEULIN, G.
1927. Mesure directe de la grandeur des images rétiniennes chez le chien et le chat. Compt. rend. Acad. d. sc., v. 184, p. 1085.

CARPUS (JACOBUS CARPENSIS); *see* BERENGARIO DA CARPI

CARR, A. F.
1952. Handbook of turtles; turtles of the United States, Canada, and Baja California. Comstock Pub. Assoc., Ithaca, N.Y.

CARR, H. A.
1935. An introduction to space perception. Longmans, Green & Co., New York, London & Toronto.

CARRA DE VAUX, B.
1900. Les grands philosophes: Avicenne. F. Alcan, Paris.
1921–26. Les penseurs de l'Islam. 5 vols. P. Genthner, Paris.

CARRIÈRE, J.
1885. Die Sehorgane der Thiere vergleichend-anatomisch dargestellt. R. Ohtenbourg, München & Leipzig.

CARTER, G. S.
1948. Colour and colour vision in animals. Nature, v. 162, p. 600.

CARTESIUS; *see* DES CARTES

CARUS, C. G.
1814. Versuch einer Darstellung des Nervensystems und insbesondre des Gehirns nach ihrer Bedeutung, Entwickelung und Vollendung im thierischen Organismus. Von C. G. C., Med. Doct. und Privatdocent zu Leipzig. Mit sechs Kupfertafeln. Bey Breitkopf und Härtel, Leipzig.
1865–66. Lebenserinnerungen und Denkwürdigkeiten. F. A. Brockhaus, Leipzig.

CASAMAJOR, L.
1913. A case of tumor of the right temporal lobe. M. Rec., v. 83, p. 866.

CASANOVA, P.
1923. L'incendie de la bibliothèque d'Alexandrie par les Arabes. Rev. d. biblioth., v. 33, p. 253.

CASCIO; *see* LO CASCIO

CASE, T. J.
1942. Alpha waves in relation to structures involved in vision. Biol. Symp., v. 7, p. 107. J. Cattell Press, Lancaster, Pa.

CASON, H.
1922. The conditioned pupillary reaction. J. Exper. Psychol., v. 5, p. 108.

CASTALDI, L.
1923–26. Studii sulla struttura & sullo sviluppo del mesencefalo. Ricerche in cavia cobaya I,

II, III. Arch. ital. di anat. e di embriol., v. 20, p. 23; v. 21, p. 172; v. 23, p. 481.

CASTEEL, D. B.
1911. The discriminative ability of the painted turtle. J. Anim. Behavior, v. 1, p. 1.

CASTERET, N.
1924. Discovering the oldest statues in the world. Nat. Geog. Mag., v. 46, p. 123.
1948. Lascaux Cave, cradle of world art. *Ibid.*, v. 94, p. 771.

CASTIGLIONI, A.
1932. Italian medicine. Paul B. Hoeber, New York.
1947. A history of medicine. A. A. Knopf, New York.

CASTILLO Y QUARTIELLERS, R. DEL
1907. Die Augenheilkunde in der Römerzeit. Translated from the Spanish by M. NEUBURGER. F. Deuticke, Leipzig & Wien.

CASTRO, F. DE
1950. Die normale Histologie des peripheren vegetativen Nervensystems. Das Synapsen-Problem: anatomisch-experimentelle Untersuchungen. Verhandl. d. deutsch. Gesellsch. f. Path., v. 34, p. 1.
1951. Sur la structure de la synapse dans les chemocepteurs: leur mécanisme d'excitation et rôle dans la circulation sanguine locale. Acta physiol., v. 22, p. 14.

CATCHPOLE, H. R., & FULTON, J. F.
1939. Tarsiers in captivity. Nature, v. 144, p. 514.
1943. The oestrous cycle in *Tarsius:* observations on a captive pair. J. Mammal., v. 24, p. 90.

CATTANEO, D.
1922. La struttura della retina nei vertebrati. Ann. di ottal. e clin. ocul., v. 50, p. 349.
1923. I fenomeni degenerativi e rigenerativi nelle vie visive in seguito a lesioni del nervo ottico. Riv. di pat. nerv. e ment., v. 28, p. 61.

CAULIACUS; *see* CHAULIAC, GUY DE

CAZAUVIEILH, J. B.
*1827. Recherches anatomico-physiologiques sur l'encéphale considéré chez l'adolescent, l'adult et le vieillard. (Probably a dissertation.) Paris.

CELSUS, A. C. (AULUS CORNELIUS)
ca. 20 A.D. On medicine. Translated by G. F. COLLIER. 3d ed. Longman & Co., London, 1840. Various Latin editions entitled Medicinae libri octo; De medicina; De re medica. An English translation by A. LEE, 1831–36. (Celsus lived during the period of Augustus and Tiberius.)
1st cent. A.D. A. C. Celsi De medicina, libri octo, ad fidem optimorum librorum denuo recen-

suit, adnotatione critica indicibusque instruxit Ch. Daremberg. Teubner, Leipzig; Haar & Steinert, Paris, 1859.
1st cent. A.D. Aulus Cornelius Celsus über die Arzneiwissenschaft in acht Büchern. 2d ed. by W. FRIEBOES. F. Vieweg & Sohn, Braunschweig, 1906.

CENI, C.
1939. Die Quantität und die Qualität des Gedankens und die interhemisphärischen Beziehungen. Arch. f. Psychiat., v. 109, p. 379.

CERISE, L.
1916–17. Deux cas d'hémianopsie double avec conservation de la vision maculaire. Arch. d'opht., v. 35, p. 297.

CHABRUN, H.
1926. Du phénomène d'accommodation rétinienne. Mécanisme de la vision. Arch. d'opht., v. 43, p. 551.

CHACKO, L. W.
1948. The laminar pattern of the lateral geniculate body in the primates. J. Neurol., Neurosurg. & Psychiat., v. 11, p. 211.
1948. An analysis of fibre-size in the human optic nerve. Brit. J. Ophth., v. 32, p. 457.
1949. Relation of color sensitivity in the visual field to the laminar pattern in the lateral geniculate body. Arch. Ophth., v. 42, p. 402.
1949. A preliminary study of the distribution of cell size in the lateral geniculate body. J. Anat., v. 83, p. 254.
1952. The blood supply of the lateral geniculate body in relation to its functional areas in man. J. Anat. Soc. India, v. 1, p. 11.
1954. A comparative study of the distribution of the fibre size in the optic nerve of mammals. *Ibid.* v. 3, p. 11.
1954. The lateral geniculate body in Lemuroidea. *Ibid.*, p. 24.
1954. The percentage volume of the lateral geniculate body in relation to the total brain volume in the primates. *Ibid.*, p. 36.

CHAILLOU, F. H.
1863. Observations sur ramollissement multiple du cerveau et du cervelet. Bull. Soc. anat. Paris, 2d ser., v. 8, p. 70.

CHAMBERLAIN, T. C.
1900. On the habitat of the early vertebrates. J. Geol., v. 8, p. 400.

CHAMBERS, B. M.
1951. Meningioma of the tuberculum sellae: report of a case. Arch. Ophth., v. 45, p. 228.

CHAMBERS, R., *et al.*
1950. Structure in relation to cellular function. Ann. New York Acad. Sc., v. 50, art. 8.

CHAMLIN, M.
1948. Recording of visual fields. Am. J. Ophth., v. 31, p. 565.
1949. Minimal defects in visual field studies. Arch. Ophth., v. 42, p. 126.

CHAMPION, F. W.
1934. The jungle in sunlight and shadow. Charles Scribner's Sons, New York.

CHANCE, B.
1942. George Berkeley and "An essay towards a new theory of vision." Tr. Am. Ophth. Soc., v. 40, p. 43.
1944. Johannes Müller—a sketch of his life and ophthalmologic works. *Ibid.*, v. 42, p. 230.

CHANET, PIERRE
1649. Traité de l'esprit de l'homme, et de ses fonctions. Par le sieur Chanet. A Paris, chez Augustin Courbé, dans la Galerie du Palais, à la Palme. M.DC.XLIX. Avec privilège du Roy.

CHANG, H. C., HSIEH, W. M., LI, T. H., & LIM, R. K. S.
1938. Humoral transmission of nerve impulses at central synapses. IV. Liberation of acetylcholine into the cerebrospinal fluid by the afferent vagus. Chinese J. Physiol., v. 13, p. 153.

CHANG, H.-T., & RUCH, T. C.
1946. The spinal origin of the ventral supraoptic decussation (Gudden's commissure) in the spider monkey. Anat. Rec., v. 94 (Am. A. Anat.), p. 71.
1949. Spinal origin of the ventral supraoptic decussation (Gudden's commissure) in the spider monkey. J. Anat., v. 83, p. 1.

CHANG, M.
1936. Neural mechanism of monocular vision. I. Disturbances of monocular pattern discrimination in the albino rat after destruction of the cerebral visual area. II. Pattern discrimination in the monocular rat before and after destruction of the visual area and in the rat deprived of the visual area on one side before and after severance of the contralateral optic nerve. Chinese J. Psychol., v. 1, pp. 10, 91.

CHAPMAN, F. M.
1912. Color key to North American birds. D. Appleton & Co., New York.
1929. My tropical air castle; nature studies in Panama. D. Appleton & Co., New York & London.
1932. Handbook of birds of eastern North America. D. Appleton & Co., New York & London.

1938. Life in an air castle; nature studies in the tropics. D. Appleton–Century Co., New York & London.

CHAPMAN, H. C.
1904. Observations on *Tupaia*, with reflections on the origin of primates. Proc. Acad. Nat. Sc. Philadelphia, v. 16, p. 148.

CHAPOT, V.
1928. The Roman world. K. Paul, Trench, Trubner & Co., London; A. A. Knopf, New York.

CHARAKA
2d cent. A.D. Charaka-Samhita. Translated into English and published by AVINASH CHANDRA KAVIRATNA. Calcutta.

CHARCOT, J.-M.
1876–80. Leçon sur les localisations dans les maladies du cerveau et de la moelle épinière faites à la faculté de médecine de Paris. Recueillies et publiées par Bourneville et E. Brissaud. Prog. med., V. Andrien Delahaye, Paris; Cerf & Fils, Versailles.

CHARD, R. D.
1939. Visual acuity in the pigeon. J. Exper. Psychol., v. 24, p. 588.

CHARD, R. D., & GUNDLACH, R. H.
1938. The structure of the eye of the homing pigeon. J. Comp. Psychol., v. 25, p. 249.

CHARLTON, H. H.
1933. The optic tectum and its related fiber tracts in blind fishes. A. *Troglichthys rosae* and *Typhlichthys eigenmanni*. J. Comp. Neurol., v. 57, p. 285.

CHARPENTIER, A.
1888. La lumière et couleurs au point de vue physiologique. J. B. Baillière & Fils, Paris.

CHASAN, B.
1927. Zur Frage der Cytoarchitektonik der *Area striata* (Rinde vom Calcarinatypus) in ihren Beziehungen zur zentralen optischen Leitung. Schweiz. Arch. f. Neurol. u. Psychiat., v. 21, p. 283.

CHASE, A. M.
1938. Photosensitive pigments from the retina of the frog. Science, v. 87, p. 238.
1948. The chemistry of cypridine luciferin. Ann. New York Acad. Sc., v. 49, p. 353.

CHASE, W. H.
1938. Cerebral thrombosis, hemorrhage and embolism, pathological principles. Research Pub. A. Research Nerv. & Ment. Dis., v. 18, p. 365. Williams & Wilkins Co., Baltimore.

CHATELIN, C.
1918. Les blessures du cerveau; formes cliniques. 2d ed. Masson & Cie, Paris.

CHATELIN & PATRIKIOS
1917. Phénomènes d'irritation de la sphère visuelle et mal comitial consécutifs à une blessure de la pointe du lobe occipitale gauche. Rev. neurol., v. 24 (1), p. 259.

CHAUCHARD, A., & CHAUCHARD, B.
1928. Rôle des collatérales des artères vertébrales et carotides dans l'irrigation de l'écorce cérébrale. Compt. rend. Soc. de biol., v. 99, p. 1628.

CHAUFFARD, A.
1888. De la cécité subite par lésions combinées des deux lobes occipitaux (anopsie corticale). Rev. de méd., v. 8, p. 131.

CHAULIAC, GUY DE
1363. La grande chirurgie de Guy de Chauliac ... composée en l'an 1363, revue et collationnée sur les manuscrits et imprimés latins et français ... par E. Nicaise. F. Alcan, Paris, 1890. (*See*, for description of eye structures, pp. 44 ff.)
1546. Ars chirurgica Gvidonis Cauliaci Medici celeberrimi lucubrationes chirurgicae ab infinitis prope mendis emendatae; ac instrumentorum chirurgicorum formis, quae in alijs impressionibus desiderabatur, exornatae. Bruni preterea Theodorici, Rolandi, Lanfranci et Bertapaliae. Venetiis, Apud Iuntas, MDXLVI.

CHAUVIN, R.
1949. Physiologie de l'insecte. Les grandes fonctions, le comportement, écophysiologie. Inst. nat. rech. agron., Paris.

CHAVASSE, F. B.
1939. Worth's squint or the binocular reflexes and the treatment of strabismus, 7th ed. P. Blakiston's Son & Co., Philadelphia.

CHERUBIN D'ORLÉANS (FRANÇOIS LASSÈRE)
1671. La dioptrique oculaire, ou la théorique, la positive, et la méchanique, de l'oculaire dioptrique en toutes ses espèces. Par le Père Cherubin d'Orléans, Capucin. A Paris, chez Thomas Jolly & Simon Benard. M.DC.-LXXI. Avec privilège du Roy.
1678. De visione perfecta sive de amborum visionis axium concursu in eodem objecti puncto. Authore P. Cherubino Aurelianensi, Capucino. Parisiis, Apud Sebastianum Mabre-Cramoisy, etc. M.DC.LXXVIII.

CHESELDEN, W.
1728. An account of some observations made by a young gentleman who was born blind, or lost his sight so early, that he had no remembrance of ever having seen, and was couch'd between 13 and 14 years of age. Phil. Tr. Roy. Soc. London, v. 35, p. 447.

1728. An application of the instruments used, in a new operation on the eyes. *Ibid.*, p. 451.

CHEVALIER, A. G.
1940. The origin of the medieval universities.— The founding of the medical faculty of Montpellier.—Medical teaching at Montpellier.—Famous medical teachers of Montpellier.—The "antimony-war," a dispute between Montpellier and Paris.—Rabelais at Montpellier. Ciba Symp., v. 2, No. 1.
1944. The beginnings of the School of Salerno. Constantinus Africanus and the influence of the Arabs on Salerno. The "Regimen sanitatis Salernitanum." The Salernitan physician. Historical notes. *Ibid.*, v. 5, No. 12.

CHEVALLEREAU, A.
1879. Recherches sur les paralysies oculaires consécutives à des traumatismes cérébraux. V.-A. Delahaye, Paris.

CHEVALLEREAU, A., & POLACK, A.
1907. De la coloration jaune de la macula. Ann. d'ocul., v. 138, p. 241.

CHI, T. K., & CHUN CHANG
1941. The sulcal pattern of the Chinese brain. Am. J. Phys. Anthropol., v. 28, p. 167.

CHIARINI, P.
1904–6. Changements morphologiques que l'on observe dans la rétine des vertébrés par l'action de la lumière et de l'obscurité. Arch. ital. de biol., v. 42, p. 303; v. 45, p. 337.

CHIEVITZ, J. H.
1887. Die Area und Fovea centralis retinae beim menschlichen Foetus. Internat. Monatsschr. f. Anat. u. Physiol., v. 4, p. 201.
1888. Entwickelung der Fovea centralis retinae. Anat. Anz., v. 3, p. 579; and (Verhandl.), v. 3, p. 89.
1889. Die Area centralis retinae. Anat. Anz. (Verhandl.), v. 4, p. 77.
1889. Untersuchungen über die Area centralis retinae. Arch. f. Anat. u. Entw., suppl., p. 139.
1890. Untersuchungen über die Entwickelung der Area und Fovea centralis retinae. Arch. f. Anat. u. Entw., p. 332.
1891. Ueber das Vorkommen der Area centralis retinae in den vier höheren Wirbelthierklassen. *Ibid.*, p. 311.
1904. Anatomiens historie. En raekke foredrag samlede og udgivne af E. Hauch. Gyldendalske Boghandel, Nordisk Forlag, Kjøbenhavn & Kristiania.

CHILD, C. M.
1921. Origin and development of the nervous system. University of Chicago Press, Chicago.

CHILD, C. M.—*Continued*
  1924. Physiological foundations of behavior. Henry Holt & Co., New York.
  1941. Patterns and problems of development. University of Chicago Press, Chicago.

CHITTY, H., & CHITTY, D.
  1945. Canadian arctic life enquiry, 1942–43. J. Anim. Ecol., v. 14, p. 37.

CHODIN, A.
  1877. Ueber die Empfindlichkeit fur Farben in der Peripherie der Netzhaut. Arch. f. Ophth. (Graefe), v. 23 (3), p. 177.

CHOPARD, L.
  1932. Un cas de microphtalmie lié à l'atrophie des ailes chez une blatte cavernicole. Livre du centenaire de la Société entomologique de France, p. 485.
  1949. Le mimétisme. Les colorations animales, dissimulation des formes et déguisements, ressemblances mimétiques. Payot, Paris.

CHOROSCHKO, W. K.
  1923. Die Stirnlappen des Gehirns in funktioneller Beziehung. Ztschr. f. d. ges. Neurol. u. Psychiat., v. 83, p. 291.

CHOULANT, J. L.
  1841. Handbuch der Bücherkunde für die ältere Medicin. 2 vols. L. Voss, Leipzig. Facsimile ed. by Verlag d. Münchner Drucke, München, 1926.
  1852. History and bibliography of anatomic illustration, etc. Translated by M. FRANK. University of Chicago Press, Chicago, 1920.

CHOW, K. L.
  1950. A retrograde cell degeneration study of the cortical projection field of the pulvinar in the monkey. J. Comp. Neurol., v. 93, p. 313.

CHRISTENSEN, E.
  1946. The bats of Carlsbad Caverns. *In:* Animal kingdom (bulletin published by New York Zoöl. Soc.), v. 49, p. 98.

CHRISTIAN, J. J.
  1950. Behavior of the mole (*Scalopus*) and the shrew (*Blarina*). J. Mammal., v. 31, p. 281.

CHRISTIANSEN, V.
  1902. Ein Fall von Schussläsion durch die centralen optischen Bahnen. Nord. med. ark., v. 35, Sec. 2, Part 2, No. 7, p. 1. Also in Friedreich's Blätter f. gerichtl. Med., v. 25, No. 43. Abstr. in Jahresber. Ophth., v. 33, p. 437, 1903.
  1930. Difficultés de diagnostic différentiel des tumeurs suprasellaires. Concil. Ophth. XIII, 1929, v. 3 (Part 3), p. 81.

CHRISTIE, W.
  1943. Moles. Gardener's Chron., Pangbourne, ser. 3, v. 113, p. 164.

CHRISTISON, J. S.
  1899. The brain and its functions. J. Am. Med. Assoc., v. 32, p. 751.

CHU, H.-N.
  1932. The cell masses of the diencephalon of the opossum, *Didelphis virginiana*. ("Monog. Nat. Research Inst. Psychol.," No. 2.) Peiping.
  1932. The fiber connections of the diencephalon of the opossum, *Didelphis virginiana* ("Monog. Nat. Research Inst. Psychol.," v. 3.) Peiping.

CHUN, C.
  1903. Ueber Leuchtorgane und Augen von Tiefsee-Cephalopoden. Verhandl. deutsch. zool. Gesellsch., v. 13, p. 67.

CHUTE, W. H.
  1944. Guide to the John G. Shedd Aquarium. Published by the Aquarium, Chicago.

CHVOSTEK, F.
  1892. Beiträge zur Theorie der Hallucinationen. Jahrb. f. Psychiat., v. 11, p. 267.

CITTERT, P. H. VAN
  1933. The "van Leewenhoek microscope" in possession of the University of Utrecht. Proc. Kon. Akad. Wetensch. Amsterdam, v. 36, p. 194.

CLAES, E.
  1939. Contribution à l'étude physiologique de la fonction visuelle. I. Analyse oscillographique de l'activité spontanée et sensorielle de l'aire visuelle corticale chez le chat non anesthésié. Arch. internat. de physiol., v. 48, p. 181; *also* Zentralbl. f. d. ges. Neurol. u. Psychiat., v. 94, p. 466.
  1939. II. Étude des centres oculomoteurs corticaux chez le chat non anesthésié. Arch. internat. de physiol., v. 48, p. 238. III. Activités pupillo-motrices du diencéphale et du mésencéphale chez le chat non anesthésié. *Ibid.*, p. 261.

CLAESSENS, F. J.
  *1783. De decussatione fibrarum cerebri unius lateris ad aliud, atque decussatione nervorum, praecipue opticorum. *In:* Louvain Diss., v. 3, p. 26.

CLAPARÈDE, E.
  1906. Agnosie et asymbolie à propos d'un soidisant cas d'aphasie tactile. Rev. neurol., v. 14, p. 803.

CLARK, B., JOHNSON, M. L., & DREHER, R. E.
  1946. The effect of sunlight on dark adaptation. Am. J. Ophth., v. 29, p. 828.

CLARK, D. A., HUGHES, J., & GASSER, H. S.
1935. Afferent functions in the group of nerve fibers of slowest conduction velocity. Am. J. Physiol., v. 114, p. 69.

CLARK, E.
1913. Anatomy in the Far East. Anat. Rec., v. 7, p. 237.

CLARK, E. R., & WENTSLER, N. E.
1938. Pial circulation studied by long-continued direct inspection. Research Pub. A. Research Nerv. & Ment. Dis., v. 18, p. 218. Williams & Wilkins Co., Baltimore.

CLARK, G.
1948. The lateral geniculate nucleus of the spider monkey. Anat. Rec., v. 100, p. 650. (Abstr.)

CLARK, J. H.
1922. A photo-electric theory of color vision. J. Opt. Soc. Amer., v. 6, p. 813.

CLARK, S. L.
1937. Innervation of the intrinsic muscles of the eye of the cat. J. Comp. Neurol., v. 66, p. 307.

CLARK, W. E. LE GROS
1924. Notes on the living tarsier (*Tarsius spectrum*). Proc. Zoöl. Soc. London, p. 217.
1924. On the brain of the tree-shrew (*Tupaia minor*). *Ibid.*, p. 1053.
1925. On the skull of *Tupaia*. *Ibid.*, p. 559.
1925. The visual cortex of primates. J. Anat., v. 59, p. 350.
1926. On the anatomy of the pen-tailed tree-shrew. Proc. Zoöl. Soc. London, p. 1179.
1926. The mammalian oculomotor nucleus. J. Anat., v. 60, p. 426.
1927. Exhibition of photographs of the tree-shrew (*Tupaia minor*). Remarks on the tree-shrew, *Tupaia minor*, with photographs. Proc. Zoöl. Soc. London, p. 254.
1927. Description of the cerebral hemispheres of the brain of a gorilla (John Daniels II). J. Anat., v. 61, p. 467.
1928. On the brain of the Macroscelididae (*Macroscelides* and *Elephantulus*). *Ibid.*, v. 62, p. 245.
1929. The thalamus of *Tupaia minor*. *Ibid.*, v. 63, p. 117.
1930. The thalamus of *Tarsius*. *Ibid.*, v. 64, p. 371.
1931. The brain of *Microcebus murinus*. Proc. Zoöl. Soc. London, p. 463.
1931. Degeneration of optic tract fibers in the rat. J. Anat., v. 66, p. 138. (Abstr.)
1932. The brain of the Insectivora. Proc. Zoöl. Soc. London, p. 975.
1932. The structure and connections of the thalamus. Brain, v. 55, p. 406.

1932. A morphological study of the lateral geniculate body. Brit. J. Ophth., v. 16, p. 264.
1932. An experimental study of thalamic connections in the rat. Phil. Tr. Roy. Soc. London, ser. B, v. 222, p. 1.
1933. The medial geniculate body and the nucleus isthmi. J. Anat., v. 67, p. 536.
1934. The spectral tarsier. Illust. London News, Feb. 10, p. 196.
1934. The asymmetry of the occipital region of the brain and skull. Man, v. 34, p. 35.
1934. Early forerunners of man: a morphological study of the evolutionary origin of the primates. W. Wood & Co., Baltimore.
1935. Man's place among primates. Man, v. 35, p. 1.
1936. The topography and homologies of the hypothalamic nuclei in man. J. Anat., v. 70, p. 203.
1936. The thalamic connections of the temporal lobe of the brain in the monkey. *Ibid.*, p. 447.
1936. Functional localization in the thalamus and hypothalamus. J. Ment. Sc., v. 82, p. 99.
1937. The status of *Pithecanthropus*. Man, v. 37, p. 60.
1937. The cortical projection of the pulvinar in the macaque monkey. Brain, v. 60, p. 126.
1940. Anatomical basis of colour vision. Nature, v. 146, p. 558.
1941. Observations on the association fibre system of the visual cortex and the central representation of the retina. J. Anat., v. 75, p. 225.
1941. The laminar organization and cell content of the lateral geniculate body in the monkey. *Ibid.*, p. 419.
1941. The lateral geniculate body in the platyrrhine monkeys. *Ibid.*, v. 76, p. 131.
1942. The cells of Meynert in the visual cortex of the monkey. *Ibid.*, v. 76, p. 369.
1942. The Doyne memorial lecture: the anatomy of cortical vision. Tr. Ophth. Soc. London, v. 62, p. 229, 1943.
1942. The visual centres of the brain and their connexions. Physiol. Rev., v. 22, p. 205.
1944. The anatomy of the nervous system. J. Ment. Sc., v. 90, p. 36.
1945. Note on the palaeontology of the lemuroid brain. J. Anat., v. 79, p. 123.
1945. The oldest human fossils. Discovery (London), v. 6, p. 102.
1946. Significance of the Australopithecinae. Nature, v. 157, p. 863; v. 158, p. 714.
1947. Anatomical pattern as the essential basis of

sensory discrimination. (Boyle lecture.) Blackwell Scientific Publications, Oxford.

1947. Observations on the anatomy of the fossil Australopithecinae. J. Anat., v. 81, p. 300. (Abstr., p. 381.)

1947. A new light on man's early history. Picture Post, July 5.

1947. The Pan-African Congress on Prehistory: Human Palaeontol. Sec. Man, v. 47, No. 100, p. 101.

1947. The Pan-African Congress on Prehistory—Anthropology. Nature, v. 159, p. 216.

1947. The importance of the fossil Australopithecinae in the study of human evolution. Sc. Prog., v. 35, p. 377.

1948. The connexions of the frontal lobes of the brain. Lancet, v. 1, p. 353.

1948. Anatomical studies of fossil Hominoidea from Africa. Proc. Pan-African Cong. on Prehistory.

1948. Observations on certain differential rates of somatic evolution in the primates. R. Broom Commemor., v. 171. Roy. Soc. South Africa, Cape Town.

1949. The laminar pattern of the lateral geniculate nucleus considered in relation to colour vision. Doc. Ophth., v. 3, p. 57.

1950. Certain considerations of the Australopithecinae. Abstract of communication to the International Anatomical Congress, Oxford. (Typewritten communication.)

1950. South African fossil hominoids. Nature, v. 165, p. 893; v. 166, p. 791.

1950. Fossil apes and man. Spectator, v. 184, p. 38.

1950. New palaeontological evidence bearing on the evolution of the Hominoidea. Quart. J. Geol. Soc. London, v. 105, p. 225.

1950. On fossil Miocene apes. *Ibid.* (Proc.), p. ii.

1950. "Ape-men" of South Africa. Antiquity, v. 24, p. 179.

1952. A note on certain cranial indices of the Sterkfontein skull No. 5. Am. J. Phys. Anthropol., v. 10, p. 1.

1952. Hominid characters of the australopithecine dentition. J. Roy. Anthrop. Inst., v. 80, Parts I and II.

1953. History of the primates: an introduction to the study of fossil man. 3d ed. British Museum (Natural History), London.

1954. The antiquity of *Homo sapiens* in particular and of the Hominidae in general. Sc. Prog., No. 167 (July), p. 377.

1954. Reason and fallacy in the study of fossil man. Adv. Sc., No. 43 (December).

1955. The fossil evidence for human evolution. University of Chicago Press, Chicago.

CLARK, W. E. LE GROS, & BOGGON, R. H.

1935. The thalamic connections of the parietal and frontal lobes of the brain in the monkey. Phil. Tr. Roy. Soc. London, ser. B, v. 224, p. 313.

1947. A possible central mechanism for colour vision. Nature, v. 100, p. 123.

CLARK, W. E. LE GROS, COOPER, D. M., & ZUCKERMAN, S.

1936. The endocranial cast of the chimpanzee. J. Roy. Anthrop. Inst., v. 66, p. 249.

CLARK, W. E. LE GROS, & LEAKEY, L. S. B.

1950. Diagnoses of East African Miocene Hominoidea. Quart. J. Geol. Soc. London, v. 105, p. 260.

1951. Fossil mammals of Africa: the Miocene Hominoidea of East Africa, No. 1. British Museum (Natural History), London.

CLARK, W. E. LE GROS, McKEOWN, T., & ZUCKERMAN, S.

1939. Visual pathways concerned in gonadal stimulation in ferrets. Proc. Roy. Soc. London, ser. B, v. 126, p. 449.

CLARK, W. E. LE GROS, & MEDAWAR, P. B.

1945. Essays on growth and form, presented to D'Arcy W. Thompson. Clarendon Press, Oxford.

CLARK, W. E. LE GROS, & PENMAN, G. G.

1934. The projection of the retina in the lateral geniculate body. Proc. Roy. Soc. London, ser. B, v. 114, p. 291.

CLARK, W. E. LE GROS, & RUSSELL, W. R.

1938. Cortical deafness without aphasia. Brain, v. 61, p. 375.

CLARK, W. E. LE GROS, & SUNDERLAND, S.

1939. Structural changes in the isolated visual cortex. J. Anat., v. 73, p. 563.

CLARKE, G. L.

1936. On the depth at which fish can see. Ecology, v. 17, p. 452.

CLARKE, R. H., & HENDERSON, E. E.

1920. Investigation of the central nervous system. Johns Hopkins Hosp. Rep., special vol.

CLARKE, R. W.

1943. The respiratory exchange of *Tarsius spectrum.* J. Mammal., v. 24, p. 94.

CLASING, T.

1923. Beitrag zur Kenntnis des Nervensystems und der Sinnesorgane der Mytiliden. Jena. Ztschr. f. Naturwiss., v. 59, p. 261.

CLASSEN, A.

1876. Physiologie des Gesichtssinnes zum ersten Mal begründet auf Kant's Theorie der

Erfahrung. Fr. Vieweg & Sohn, Braunschweig.

CLAUDE, H.
1909. Un cas d'hémiplégie droite avec apraxie du côté gauche, cécité verbale, agraphie, et topoanesthésie d'origine psychique. Bull. et mém. Soc. méd. d. hôp. de Paris, ser. 3, v. 28, p. 89.

CLAUSEN, H. J., & MOFSHIN, B.
1939. The pineal eye of the lizard (*Anolis carolinensis*), a photoreceptor as revealed by oxygen consumption studies. J. Cell. & Comp. Physiol., v. 14, p. 29.

CLAY, R. S.
1938. A review of the mechanical improvements of microscopes in the last forty years. J. Roy. Micros. Soc., v. 58, p. 1.

CLAY, R. S., & COURT, T. H.
1932. The history of the microscope compiled from original instruments and documents, up to the introduction of the achromatic microscope. C. Griffin & Co., London.

CLEMEN, C. C.
1927. Die Religionen der Erde. F. Bruckmann, München. 1931. English trans.: Religions of the world. Harcourt, Brace & Co., New York & Chicago. French ed., Payot, Paris.

CLEMENTS, F. E., MARTIN, E. V., & LONG, F. L.
1950. Adaptation and origin in the plant world: the role of environment in evolution. Chronica Botanica Co., Waltham, Mass.

CLEMMESEN, V.
1944. Central and indirect vision of the light-adapted eye. Acta physiol. Scandinav., v. 9, suppl. 27. Copenhagen.

CLENDENING, L.
1942. Source book of medical history. P. B. Hoeber, New York & London.

CLERICI, A.
1943. Retinografia: studio fotografico del fondo oculare. Istituto Editoriale Cisalpino, Milano, Varese.

CLOUD, P. E.
1949. Some problems and patterns of evolution exemplified by fossil invertebrates. Evolution, v. 2, p. 322.

COATS, G. W.
1945. Some observations on wild-life in the Black Hills during the past sixty-five years. South Dakota Conserv. Digest, Pierre, v. 12.

COBB, S.
1925. On the application of micrometry to the study of the area striata. J. f. Psychol. u. Neurol., v. 31, p. 261.
1938. Cerebral circulation. A critical discussion of the symposium. Research Pub. A. Research Nerv. & Ment. Dis., v. 18, p. 719. Williams & Wilkins Co., Baltimore.

COBB, S., & LENNOX, W. G.
1944. Cerebral circulation—intrinsic control and clinical phenomena. Fed. Proc., v. 3, p. 151.

COBLENTZ, W. W.
1920. A comparison of photo-electric cells and the eye. Am. J. Physiol. Opt., v. 1, p. 41.

COBLENTZ, W. W., & EMERSON, W. B.
1917. Glasses for protecting the eyes from injurious radiations. ("Tech. Papers Bureau of Standards," No. 93.) Government Printing Office, Washington.

COCCIUS, E. A.
1868. Der Mechanismus der Accommodation des menschlichen Auges. B. G. Teubner, Leipzig.

COCHRAN, D. M.
1952. Nature's tank, the turtle. Nat. Geog. Mag., v. 101, p. 665.

COENEN, L.
1943. Clinisch-anatomisch onderzoek over een gezwel in de linker praemotorische zone der groote hersenen. Proc. Kon. nederl. Akad. Wetensch. (natuurk.), Amsterdam, v. 52, p. 429.

COGAN, D. G.
1948. Neurology of the ocular muscles. Charles C Thomas, Springfield, Ill.

COGHILL, G. E.
1914–36. Correlated anatomical and physiological studies of the growth of the nervous system of amphibia. J. Comp. Neurol., v. 24, p. 161; v. 26, p. 247; v. 37, pp. 37, 71; v. 40, p. 47; v. 41, p. 95; v. 42, p. 1; v. 45, p. 227; v. 51, p. 311; v. 53, p. 147; v. 57, p. 327; v. 64, p. 135.
1929. Anatomy and the problem of behavior. Cambridge University Press, Cambridge.
1930. The structural basis of the integration of behavior. Proc. Nat. Acad. Sc., v. 16, p. 637.
1933. The neuro-embryologic study of behavior: principles, perspective and aim. Science, v. 78, p. 131.
1933. Growth of a localized functional center in a relatively equipotential nervous organ. Arch. Neurol. & Psychiat., v. 30, p. 1086.
1936. Integration and motivation of behavior as problems of growth. J. Genet. Psychol., v. 48, p. 3; also, Soviet. psychonevrol. (in Russian), v. 9, p. 4.
1938. Space-time as a pattern of psycho-organismal mentation. Am. J. Psychol., v. 51, p. 759.
1940. Early embryonic somatic movements in birds and in mammals other than man.

"Monog. Soc. Research Child Development," v. 5, No. 2. National Research Council, Washington, D.C.

1943. Flexion spasms and mass reflexes in relation to the ontogenic development of behavior. J. Comp. Neurol., v. 79, p. 463.

COHEN, I. J., & WEISBERG, H. K.

1950. Vertical heterotopia of the macula. Arch. Ophth., v. 44, p. 419.

COHEN, M. R., & DRABKIN, I. E.

1948. A source book in Greek science. McGraw-Hill Book Co., New York.

COHN, H.

1874. Ueber Hemiopie bei Hirnleiden. Klin. Monatsbl. f. Augenh., v. 12, p. 203.

1879. Sehschärfe und Farbensinn der Nubier. Centralbl. f. prakt. Augenh., v. 3, p. 197.

COHN, H. A., & PAPEZ, J. W.

1930. A comparative study of the visuosensory or striate area in the two hemispheres of the human brain. Am. J. Phys. Anthropol., v. 14, p. 405.

COHNHEIM, J. F.

1872. Untersuchungen ueber die embolischen Processe. A. Hirschwald, Berlin.

1882. Vorlesungen über allgemeine Pathologie: ein Handbuch für Aerzte und Studierende. 2d ed. 2 vols. A. Hirschwald, Berlin.

1885. Gesammelte Abhandlungen. A. Hirschwald, Berlin.

1889. Lectures on general pathology: a handbook for practitioners and students, 2 vols. New Sydenham Society, London.

COITER, VOLCHER

1573. Externarum et internarum principalium *Humani Corporis partium tabulae*, atque anatomicae exercitationes observationesque variae, novis, diversis, ac artificiosissimis figuris illustratae, Philosophis, Medicis, in primis autem Anatomico studio addictis summè utiles. Autore Volchero Coiter Frisio Groeningensi, Inclytae Reipublicae Noribergensis Medico Physico et Chirurgo. Ad Amplissimum et Prudentissimum inclytae urbis noribergensis senatum. Tabularum, Figurarum, et Opusculorum, quae in huius libri compaginem inclusa sunt, elenchum et ordinem post praefationem invenies. Cum gratia et privilegio Caesareae Maiestatis, ad annos sex. Noribergae, In Officina Theodorici Gerlatzeni. M.D.LXXIII.

COLAS-PELLETIER, M.

1940. Histo-physiologie comparée de l'œil des vertébrés et les théories de la vision. Bull. biol., v. 74, p. 101.

COLBERT, E. H.

1949. Progressive adaptations as seen in the fossil record. *In:* JEPSEN *et al.*, Genetics, paleontology, and evolution, p. 390.

COLD SPRING HARBOR SYMP. QUANT. BIOL., v. 4,

1936. Cold Spring Harbor, Long Island, N.Y.

COLE, F. J.

1944. A history of comparative anatomy from Aristotle to the eighteenth century. Macmillan & Co., London.

COLE, L. W., & LONG, F. M.

1909. Visual discrimination in raccoons. J. Comp. Neurol., v. 19, p. 657.

COLE, W. H.

1939. The effect of temperature on the color change of *Fundulus* in response to black and to white backgrounds in fresh and in sea water. J. Exper. Zoöl., v. 80, p. 167.

COLEMAN, T. B., & HAMILTON, W. F.

1933. Colorblindness in the rat. J. Comp. Psychol., v. 15, p. 177.

COLLENS, W. S., & WILENSKY, N. D.

1953. Peripheral vascular diseases. Charles C Thomas, Springfield, Ill.

COLLET & GRUBER

1905. Cécité corticale. Lyon méd., v. 105, p. 1005.

COLLIER, J.

1927. Nuclear ophthalmoplegia, with especial reference to retraction of the lids and ptosis and to lesions of the posterior commissure. Brain, v. 50, p. 488.

1930. Localization of function in the nervous system. Brit. M. J., v. 1, pp. 55, 77.

COLLIER, J., & BUZZARD, F.

1901. Descending mesencephalic tracts in cat, monkey, and man. Brain, v. 24, p. 177.

COLLINS, E. T.

1921. Changes in the visual organs correlated with the adoption of arboreal life and with the assumption of the erect posture. Tr. Ophth. Soc. United Kingdom, v. 41, p. 10.

COLLINS, SAMUEL

1685. A system of anatomy, treating of the body of man, beasts, birds, fish, insects, and plants. 2 vols. In the Savoy, Printed by Thomas Newcomb, MDCLXXXV.

COLMAN, J. S.

1950. The sea and its mysteries. G. Bell & Sons, London.

COLMAN, W. S.

1901. Case of (?) "mind blindness." Brain, v. 24, p. 172.

COLOMBO, R.; *see* COLUMBUS

COLSON, Z. W.
1951. Verhoeff's theory of normal binocular vision; an elementary introduction. Am. J. Ophth., v. 34, p. 200.

COLUCCI, C.
1894. Conccquenze della recisione del nervo ottico nella retina di alcuni vertebrati. Atti R. Accad. med.-chir. di Napoli, v. 48, p. 14; also Ann. di nevrol. (Torino), N.S., v. 11, p. 191, 1893. Abstr.: Neurol. Centralbl., v. 13, p. 536.

COLUMBUS (COLOMBO), R.
1559. Realdi Columbi, Cremonensis, De re anatomica, libri XV. Venetiis.

COLVIN, S. S., & BURFORD, C. C.
1909. The color perception of three dogs, a cat and a squirrel. Psychol. Monog., v. 11, p. 1.

COMBERG, W.
1920. Zur Untersuchung des peripheren Gesichtsfeldes. Ber. d. Deutsch. ophth. Gesellsch. Heidelberg, v. 42, p. 268.
1925. Die Dysmorphopsie der Hirnverletzten: ein Erklärungsversuch. Arch. f. Ophth. (Graefe), v. 115, p. 349.

COMMITTEE ON COLORIMETRY, OPTICAL SOCIETY OF AMERICA
1953. The science of color. Thomas Y. Crowell Co., New York.

COMRIE, J. D.
1909. Medicine among the Assyrians and Egyptians in 1500 B.C. Edinburgh M. J., v. 2, p. 119.

CONCILIUM OPHTHALMOLOGICUM XIII
1930. International ophthalmological congress held in 1929. *See* v. 3 (3): Symposium on suprasellar tumors, pp. 1 (Van Bogaert), 65 (Holmes), 81 (Christiansen), and 97 (Cushing).

CONE, W., & BARRERA, S. E.
1931. The brain and the cerebrospinal fluid in acute aseptic cerebral embolism. Arch. Neurol. & Psychiat., v. 25, p. 523.

CONE, W., & MCMILLAN, J. A.
1932. The optic nerve and papilla. *In:* W. PENFIELD, Cytology & cellular pathology of the nervous system, v. 2, p. 1267.

CONEL, J. LEROY
1939–55. The postnatal development of the human cerebral cortex. 5 vols. Harvard University Press, Cambridge, Mass.

CONGRÈS INTERNATIONAL DE PSYCHIATRIE, DE NEUROL., DE PSYCHOL. ETC., Amsterdam, 1907; Compt. rend., 1908

CONN, H. J.
1948. The evolution of histological staining.—The staining of fixed tissue.—Vital staining. Ciba Symp., v. 7, pp. 271, 280, 294.
1948. The history of staining. Biotech Publications, Geneva, N.Y.
1953. Biological stains. Biotech Publications, Geneva, N.Y.

CONN, H. J., & DARROW, M. A.
1946. Staining procedures used by the Biological Stain Commission. Biotech Publications, Geneva, N.Y.

CONNOLLY, C. J.
1925. Adaptive changes in shade and color of *Fundulus*. Biol. Bull., v. 48, p. 56.
1933. The brain of a mountain gorilla, "Okero" (G. Beringei). Am. J. Phys. Anthropol., v. 17, p. 291.
1936. The fissural pattern of the primate brain. *Ibid.*, v. 21, p. 301.
1940. Development of the cerebral sulci. *Ibid.*, v. 26, p. 113.
1941–43. The fissural pattern in the brain of Negroes and whites. *Ibid.*, v. 28, p. 133 (the frontal lobes); v. 29, p. 225 (the parietal and temporal lobes); N.S., v. 1, p. 363 (the occipital lobe).
1950. External morphology of the primate brain. Charles C Thomas, Springfield, Ill.
1953. Brain morphology and taxonomy. Anthropol. Quart. (primitive man), v. 26 (N.S., v. 1), p. 35.

CONSTANTIN AFRICANUS (*see also* CORNER 1927 and SUDHOFF 1932)
11th cent. Constantini monachi Montiscassini Liber de oculis. *In:* P. PANSIER, "Collectio ophthalmologica veterum auctorum," v. 2, p. 157. J.-B. Baillière & Fils, Paris, 1903–33.
1536–39. Opera, conquisita undique magno studio, jam primum typis evulgata. Basiliae.

CONTENAU, G.
1936. Assyriens et babyloniens. Histoire générale de la médecine publiée sous la direction du Prof. Laignel-Lavastine, pp. 49–88. Michel, Paris.
1938. La médecine en Assyrie et en Babylonie. Libraire Maloine, Paris.

CONTINO, F.
1939. Das Auge des *Argyropelecus hemigymnus:* Morphologie, Bau, Entwicklung und Refraktion. Arch. f. Ophth. (Graefe), v. 140, p. 390.

COOK, F. A.
1946. Squirrels. Mississippi Game & Fish, v. 10. Jackson.

Cook, N.
  1939. Notes on captive *Tarsius carbonarius*. J. Mammal., v. 20, p. 173.
  1939. My road to India. L. Furman, New York.

Cook, W. H., Walker, J. H., & Barr, M. L.
  1951. A cytological study of transneuronal atrophy in the cat and rabbit. J. Comp. Neurol., v. 94, p. 267.

Coolidge, H. J., Jr.
  1933. *Pan paniscus:* pigmy chimpanzee from south of the Congo River. Am. J. Phys. Anthropol., v. 18, p. 1.

Coon, C. S.
  1939. The races of Europe. Macmillan Co., New York.
  1950. Race concept and human races. Cold Spring Harbor Symp. Quant. Biol., v. 15, p. 247.

Cooper, E. R. A.
  1945. The development of the human lateral geniculate body. Brain, v. 68, p. 222.

Cooper, S., & Daniel, P. M.
  1949. Muscle spindles in human extrinsic eye muscles. Brain, v. 72, p. 1.

Cooper, S., Daniel, P. M., & Whitteridge, D.
  1949. Afferent discharges from extraocular muscles. J. Physiol., v. 108, p. 41 (Proc.).
  1950. Cells of origin of proprioceptive fibers from eye-muscles. *Ibid.*, v. 111, p. 25 (Proc.).

Cope, E. D.
  1873. On a habit of a species of *Blarina*. Am. Naturalist, v. 7, p. 490.
  1885. The Lemuroidea and the Insectivora of the Eocene period of North America. *Ibid.*, v. 19, p. 457.

Coppez, H.
  1911. Un cas d'hémianopsie double et simultanée. J. de méd. de Bruxelles, v. 16, p. 474. (Summarized in Klin. Monatsbl. f. Augenh., v. 50, p. 342.)

Coppez, H., & Fritz, A.
  1930. Présentation d'un schéma des voies optiques. J. de neurol. et psychiat., v. 30, p. 75.

Coppez, H., & Martin, P.
  1927. Tumeurs de la base du crâne. Rev. neurol., v. 1, p. 684.

Cords, R.
  1925. Zur Physiologie und Pathologie der Sehstrahlung. München. med. Wchnschr., v. 72, p. 2003.
  1926. Optisch-motorisches Feld und optisch-motorische Bahn. Ein Beitrag zur Physiologie und Pathologie der Rindeninnervation der Augenmuskeln. Arch. f. Ophth. (Graefe), v. 117, p. 58.
  1927. Quantitatives zum optomotorischen Nystagmus. Ber. d. Deutsch. ophth. Gesellsch. Heidelberg, v. 46, p. 172.

Cords, R., & Nolzen, L.
  1928. Weitere Untersuchungen über den optokinetischen (optomotorischen) Nystagmus. Arch. f. Ophth. (Graefe), v. 120, p. 506.

Corner, G. W.
  1919. Anatomists in search of the soul. Ann. M. Hist., v. 2, p. 1.
  1927. Anatomical texts of the earlier Middle Ages: a study in the transmission of culture. Carnegie Inst. Washington, Washington, D.C.
  1930. Clio medica—anatomy. Paul B. Hoeber, New York.
  1931. The rise of medicine at Salerno. Paul B. Hoeber, New York.
  1944. Ourselves unborn. Yale University Press, New Haven, Conn.

Corning, H. K.
  1909. Lehrbuch der topographischen Anatomie für Studierende und Aerzte. J. F. Bergmann, Wiesbaden. (*Cf.* A. Hafferl 1953.)

Corti, A.
  1850. Beitrag zur Anatomie der Retina. Arch. f. Anat., Physiol. u. wissensch. Med. (J. Müller), p. 273.
  1854. Histologische Untersuchungen angestellt an einem Elephanten. Ztschr. f. wissensch. Zool., v. 5, p. 87.

Cosmettatos, G. F.
  1931. De la structure du centre visuel cérébral chez les anophtalmes congénitaux. Arch. d'opht., v. 48, p. 282.

Cosse & Délord
  1917. Hémianopsie latérale homonyme droite, compliquée d'hémianopsie en quadrant inférieur gauche. Ann. d'ocul., v. 154, p. 118.

Costa; *see* Da Costa

Cott, H. B.
  1940. Adaptive coloration in animals. Oxford University Press, New York; Methuen & Co., London.

Couery, F.
  1944. Golden eagle vs. bighorn sheep. Montana Wildlife Bull., v. 1, p. 2.

Count, E. W.
  1944. Brain- and body-weight in man: its antecedents in growth and evolution. Anat. Rec., v. 88, p. 427. (Abstr.)
  1950. This is race: an anthology selected from the international literature on the races of man. H. Schuman, New York.

COURVILLE, C. B.
1928. Auditory hallucinations provoked by intra-cranial tumors. J. Nerv. & Ment. Dis., v. 67, p. 265.
1950. Pathology of the central nervous system: a study based upon a survey of lesions found in a series of forty thousand autopsies. Pacific Press Publishing Association, Mountain View, Calif.

COUSIN, V.
1824. Œuvres de Descartes. "L'homme," in v. 4, p. 335; "La dioptrique," in v. 5, p. 1. F. G. Levrault, Paris.

COWAN, A.
1932. Concerning a membrane between the vitreous and the anterior chamber, seen after removal of the crystalline lens and its capsule. Am. J. Ophth., v. 15, p. 125.
1932. The hyaloid membrane of the vitreous. Ibid., p. 428.
1946. Ocular imagery. Arch. Ophth., v. 35, p. 42.

COWDRY, E. V.
1928. Special cytology, the form and functions of the cell in health and disease; a textbook for students of biology and medicine, ed. E. V. COWDRY. 2 vols. Paul B. Hoeber, New York.
1932. The neurone. General character. In: W. PENFIELD, Cytology & cellular pathology of the nervous system, v. 1, p. 1.
1950. A textbook of histology; functional significance of cells and intercellular substances. 4th ed. Lea & Febiger, Philadelphia.

COXE, A. C.
1885. Latin Christianity: its founder, Tertullian. In: The ante-Nicene fathers, edited by A. ROBERTS and J. DONALDSON; revised by A. C. COXE, v. 3. Christian Literature Publishing Co., Buffalo, N.Y.

CRAIGHEAD, F. & J.
1940. In quest of the golden eagle. Nat. Geog. Mag., v. 77, p. 693.

CRAIGHEAD, J. & F.
1937. Adventures with birds of prey. Nat. Geog. Mag., v. 72, p. 109.

CRAIGIE, E. H.
1920. On the relative vascularity of various parts of the central nervous system of the albino rat. J. Comp. Neurol., v. 31, p. 429.
1928. Observations on the brain of the humming bird (Chrysolampis mosquitus, Linn. and Chlorostilbon caribaeus Lawr.). Ibid., v. 45, p. 377.
1931. The cell masses in the diencephalon of the humming bird. Proc. Kon. nederl. Akad. Wetensch. Amsterdam, v. 34, p. 1038.
1932. The cell structure of the cerebral hemisphere of the humming bird. J. Comp. Neurol., v. 56, p. 135.
1938. The comparative anatomy and embryology of the capillary bed of the central nervous system. Research Pub. A. Research Nerv. & Ment. Dis., v. 18. Williams & Wilkins Co., Baltimore.
1938. Vascularity in the brain of the frog (Rana pipiens). J. Comp. Neurol., v. 69, p. 453.
1940. Measurements of vascularity in some hypothalamic nuclei of the albino rat. Research Pub. A. Research Nerv. & Ment. Dis., v. 20, p. 310.
1940. The cerebral cortex in palaeognathine and neognathine birds. J. Comp. Neurol., v. 73, p. 179.
1942. The capillary bed of the central nervous system in a member of a second genus of Gymnophiona-Siphonops. J. Anat., v. 76, p. 56.
1942. Vascularization in the brain of reptiles. IV. Quantitative studies in the American alligator. Ibid., p. 347.
1942. Vascularity in the brain of the American alligator. Anat. Rec., v. 82, p. 460. (Abstr.)
1943. The capillary bed in the cerebral hemispheres of certain lungfishes. Ibid., v. 85, p. 305. (Abstr.)
1945. The architecture of the cerebral capillary bed. Biol. Rev., v. 20, p. 113.

CRAIGIE, E. H., & BRICKNER, R. M.
1927. Structural parallelism in the midbrain and 'tweenbrain of teleosts and birds. Proc. Kon. nederl. Akad. Wetensch. Amsterdam, v. 30, p. 695.

CRAIK, K. J. W.
1940. Origin of visual after-images. Nature, v. 145, p. 512.

CRAMER, A.
1855. Physiologische Abhandlung über das Accommodations-Vermögen der Augen. Prätorius & Seyde, Leer.
1898. Beitrag zur Kenntnis der Optikuskreuzung im Chiasma und des Verhaltens der optischen Centren bei einseitiger Bulbusatrophie. Anat. Hefte (Merkel & Bonnet), v. 10, p. 415.
1899. Neuere Arbeiten über die Lokalisation geistiger Vorgänge. Centralbl. f. allg. Path., v. 10, p. 441.

CRAMPTON, P.
1813. The description of an organ by which the eyes of birds are accommodated to the different distance of objects. Thomson's Ann. Phil., v. 1, p. 170; also Gilbert's Ann. d. Physik, v. 59, p. 278.

CRANDALL, L. S.
 1945. Family affairs on Gibbon Island. Animal
 kingdom, v. 48, p. 165.
 1946. Five ways of obtaining animals. *Ibid.*, v. 49,
 pp. 165, 170.
CREED, R. S.
 1930. Crossed connexions of the cerebral hemispheres with the muscles and sense organs.
 Nature, v. 125, p. 307.
CREED, R. S., DENNY-BROWN, D., ECCLES, J. C.,
 LIDDELL, E. G. T., & SHERRINGTON, C. S.
 1932. The reflex activity of the spinal cord.
 Clarendon Press, Oxford.
CREW, H.
 1940. The Photismi de lumine of Maurolycus.
 Macmillan Co., New York.
CRINIS; *see* DE CRINIS, M.
CRITCHLEY, M.
 1930. The anterior cerebral artery and its syndromes. Brain, v. 53, p. 120.
 1953. The parietal lobes. E. Arnold & Co., London.
CRITCHLEY, M., & IRONSIDE, R. N.
 1926. The pituitary adamantinomata. Brain, v.
 49, p. 437.
CROISET, M.
 1932. La civilisation de la Grèce antique. Payot,
 Paris.
CROSBY, E. C.
 1917. The forebrain of *Alligator mississippiensis.*
 J. Comp. Neurol., v. 27, p. 325.
CROSBY, E. C., & HENDERSON, J. W.
 1948. The mammalian midbrain and isthmus regions. Part II. Fiber connections of the superior colliculus. B. Pathways concerned in
 automatic eye movements. J. Comp. Neurol., v. 88, p. 53.
CROSBY, E. C., & WOODBURNE, R. T.
 1940. The comparative anatomy of the preoptic
 area and the hypothalamus. Research Pub.
 A. Research Nerv. & Ment. Dis., v. 20,
 p. 52.
CROSS, F. R.
 1909. The brain structures concerned in vision and
 the visual field. (Bradshaw Lecture.) J. W.
 Arrowsmith, Bristol.
 1914. Homonymous hemianopia without other
 evidence of organic disease. Tr. Ophth. Soc.
 United Kingdom, v. 34, p. 200.
CROUCH, R. L.
 1933. Nuclear configuration of thalamus of *Macacus rhesus.* Proc. Soc. Exper. Biol. & Med.,
 v. 30, p. 1319.
 1933. Nuclear configuration of subthalamus and
 hypothalamus of *Macacus rhesus. Ibid.*, p.
 1321.

1934. The nuclear configuration of the hypothalamus and the subthalamus of *Macacus rhesus.* J. Comp. Neurol., v. 59, p. 431.
1934. Nuclear configuration of thalamus of *Macacus rhesus. Ibid.*, p. 451.
1936. The efferent fibers of Edinger-Westphal nucleus. *Ibid.*, v. 64, p. 365.
1940. The efferent fibers of the thalamus of
 Macacus rhesus. II. The anterior nuclei,
 medial nuclei, pulvinar, and additional
 studies of the ventral nuclei. *Ibid.*, v. 72,
 p. 177.
CROUCH, R. L., & THOMPSON, J. K.
 1938. The efferent fibers of the thalamus of
 Macacus rhesus. I. Lateral and ventral nuclei. J. Comp. Neurol., v. 69, p. 255.
 1939. Autonomic functions of the cerebral cortex.
 J. Nerv. & Ment. Dis., v. 89, p. 328.
CROUIGNEAU, G.
 1884. Étude clinique et expérimentale sur la vision
 mentale. Delalain Frères, Paris.
CROUZON & VALENCE
 1923. Un cas d'alexie pure. Bull. et mém. Soc.
 méd. d. hôp. de Paris, ser. 3, v. 47, p. 1145.
CROWCROFT, P.
 1951. Keeping British shrews in captivity. J.
 Mammal., v. 32, p. 354.
 1951. Live-trapping British shrews. *Ibid.*, p. 355.
CROZIER, W. J.
 1917. The photoreceptors of *Amphioxus.* Anat.
 Rec., v. 11, p. 520.
CROZIER, W. J., & WOLF, E.
 1938. On the duplexity theory of visual response
 in vertebrates. II. Proc. Nat. Acad. Sc., v.
 24, p. 538. (For additional references *see*
 Polyak, The retina.)
 1939. The flicker response contour for the gecko
 (rod retina). J. Gen. Physiol., v. 22, p. 555.
 1941. The simplex flicker threshold contour for the
 zebra finch. *Ibid.*, v. 24, p. 625.
CROZIER, W. J., WOLF, E., & ZERRAHN-WOLF, G.
 1938. On the duplexity theory of visual response
 in vertebrates. Proc. Nat. Acad. Sc., v. 24,
 p. 125.
CRUICKSHANK, A. D.
 1947. Wings in the wilderness. Oxford University
 Press, New York & London.
CRUVEILHIER, J.
 1830–42. Anatomie pathologique du corps humain. 2 vols. J.-B. Baillière, Paris.
 1834–36. Anatomie descriptive. 4 vols. Béchet
 Jeune, Paris.
 1838. Anatomie du système nerveux de l'homme.
 Béchet Jeune, Paris.

1839–40. La faculté du langage a-t-elle un siège dans le cerveau, et ce siège est-il dans les lobes antérieurs de cet organe? Bull. Acad. roy. de méd., p. 334. (Here discussion by Rochoux *et al.*)

1849–64. Traité d'anatomie pathologique générale. 5 vols. J.-B. Baillière, Paris.

1852. Traité d'anatomie descriptive. 3d ed. (*see* v. 4, p. 609, on optic nerve and chiasma). Labé, Paris. (1st ed. 1845; *also* later eds.)

Cruze, W. W.
1935. Maturation and learning in chicks. J. Comp. Psychol., v. 19, p. 371.

Csermély, H. M.
1939. Changes in visual center in hemianopia (in Hungarian). Szemeszet, v. 75, p. 18; summary in Zentralbl. f. d. ges. Ophth., v. 44, p. 638.

Cuénot, L.
1952. Phylogénèse du règne animal. *In:* P.-P. Grassé, Traité de zoologie, v. 1, p. 1.

Cullen, G. M.
1914. The passing of Vesalius. Edinburgh M. J., v. 13, pp. 324, 388.

Culler, E. A., & Mettler, F. A.
1934. Conditioned behavior in a decorticate dog. J. Comp. Psychol., v. 18, p. 291.

1934. Observations upon conduct of a thalamic dog: hearing and vision in decorticated animals. Proc. Soc. Exper. Biol. & Med., v. 31, p. 607.

Cuming, H.
1838. A letter on *Tarsius spectrum*. Proc. Zoöl. Soc. London, Part VI, p. 67.

Cuming, H. S.
1855. On spectacles. J. Brit. Archaeol. A., v. 11, p. 144.

Cumston, C. G.
1926. An introduction to the history of medicine from the time of the pharaohs to the end of the 18th century. K. Paul, Trench, Trubner & Co., London; A. A. Knopf, New York.

Cunningham, D. J.
1886. The lumbar curve in man and the apes with an account of the topographical anatomy of chimpanzee, orang-utan, and gibbon. ("Cunningham Memoirs," No. 2.) Royal Irish Academy, Dublin.

1890. On cerebral anatomy. Brit. M. J., v. 2, p. 277.

1890. The intraparietal sulcus of the brain. J. Anat., v. 24, p. 135.

1890. The complete fissures of the human cerebrum, and their significance in connection with the growth of the hemisphere and the appearance of the occipital lobe. *Ibid.*, p. 309.

1891. The rolandic and calcarine fissures—a study of the growing cortex of the cerebrum. *Ibid.*, v. 31, p. 586.

Cunningham, D. J. (& V. Horsley)
1892. Contribution to the surface anatomy of the cerebral hemispheres. With a chapter upon cranio-cerebral topography by V. Horsley. ("Cunningham Memoirs," No. 7.) Royal Irish Academy, Dublin.

Cunningham, D. J. (G. E. Smith & W. E. Le Gros Clark)
1943. Cunningham's text-book of anatomy, ed. J. C. Brash & E. B. Jamieson. Oxford University Press, New York.

Cunningham, J. T.
1919–20. Development of *Tarsius*. Proc. Zoöl. Soc. London, p. 495.

Curran, E. J.
1909. A new association fiber tract in the cerebrum, with remarks on the fiber tract dissection method of studying the brain. J. Comp. Neurol., v. 19, p. 645.

Curschmann, H.
1879. On hemianopia and on the visual brain centers (in German). Centralbl. f. Augenh., v. 3, p. 181; also Verhandl. Cong. inn. Med., v. 6, p. 163, 1887.

1881. Case of hemianopia with autopsy. Arch. f. Psychiat., v. 11, p. 822; Berlin. klin. Wchnschr., v. 17, p. 317, 1880.

Curtis, B.
1938. The life story of the fish. Appleton-Century Co., New York.

Curtis, H. J.
1940. Intercortical connections of corpus callosum as indicated by evoked potentials. J. Neurophysiol., v. 3, p. 407.

1940. An analysis of cortical potentials mediated by the corpus callosum. *Ibid.*, p. 414.

Curtis, W. C.
1947. Textbook of general zoölogy. 4th ed. John Wiley & Sons, New York.

Curtze, M.
1871. Sur l'orthographe du nom et sur la patrie de Witelo (Vitellion). Bull. bibl. e di storia d. sc. mat. e fis. (Boncompagni), v. 4, p. 49.

*1901. Die Dunkelkammer. Himmel u. Erde, v. 3, p. 225.

Cusanus, Nicolaus
1741. De berillo. In v. 2 of Opuscula varia Nicolai de Cusa, Norimbergae. 2 vols. in one. (For contents *see* catalogue of Bibliothèque Nationale, v. 34, col. 908, under "Cusa.")

CUSHING, H.
1909. A note upon the faradic stimulation of the postcentral gyrus in conscious patients. Brain, v. 32, p. 44.
1921. Distortions of the visual fields in cases of brain tumors: the field defects produced by temporal lobe lesions. Tr. Am. Neurol. A., 47th meet., p. 374.
1922. The field defects produced by temporal lobe lesions. Brain, v. 44, p. 341
1930. The chiasmal syndrome of primary optic atrophy and bitemporal field defects in adult patients with a normal sella turcica. Concil. Ophth. XIII, 1929, v. 3 (Part 3), p. 97.
1943. The Harvey Cushing collection of books and manuscripts. Henry Schuman, New York.
1943. A bio-bibliography of Andreas Vesalius. Henry Schuman, New York.

CUSHING, H., & EISENHARDT, S.
1929. Meningiomas arising from the tuberculum sellae. Arch. Ophth., N.S., v. 1, p. 1.

CUSHING, H., & HEUER, G. J.
1911. Distortions of the visual fields in cases of brain tumor: statistical studies. Bull. Johns Hopkins Hosp., v. 22, p. 190.
1911. Distortions of the visual fields in cases of brain tumor. Dyschromatopsia in relation to stages of choked disc. J. Am. Med. Assoc., v. 57, p. 200.

CUSHING, H., & WALKER, C. B.
1912. Distortions of the visual fields in cases of brain tumor. Binasal hemianopia. Arch. Ophth., v. 41, p. 559.
1915. Chiasmal lesions with especial reference to bitemporal hemianopsia. Brain, v. 37, p. 341.
1916. Studies of optic nerve atrophy in association with chiasmal lesions. Arch. Ophth., v. 45, p. 407.
1918. Chiasmal lesions with especial reference to homonymous hemianopsia with hypophyseal tumor. Ibid., v. 47, p. 119.

CUVIER, GEORGE
1845. Leçons d'anatomie comparée. 3 vols. Fortin, Masson & Cie, Paris.

CYON, E. VON
1908. Das Ohrlabyrinth als Organ der mathematischen Sinne für Raum und Zeit. J. Springer, Berlin.
1912. Gott und Wissenschaft. 2 vols. Veit & Co., Leipzig.

CZAPSKI, S.
1904. Image formation in optical instruments from the standpoint of geometrical optics. J. Springer, Berlin.
1906. Geometrische Optik. In: A. WINKELMANN, Handb. d. Phys. 2d ed., v. VI. J. A. Barth, Leipzig. See also other articles by Czapski and other authors on related subjects in the same volume.

CZAPSKI, S., & EPPENSTEIN, O.
1924. Grundzüge der Theorie der optischen Instrumente nach Abbe. J. A. Barth, Leipzig.

D

DABELOW, A.
1931. Ueber Korrelationen in der phylogenetischen Entwickelung der Schädelform. II. Beziehungen zwischen Gehirn und Schädelbasisform bei den Mammaliern. Morphol. Jahrb., v. 67, p. 84.

DA COSTA, A. C.
1947. Sur quelques faits cytologiques de l'histogénèse de la rétine. Acta anat., v. 4, p. 79.

DA COSTA ANDRADE, E. N.
1932. Article: Radiation, Encyclopaedia Britannica, 14th ed., v. 18, p. 875.

DA CRUZ LIMA, E.
1945. Mammals of Amazonia. Contr. Mus. Pará. Belém & Rio de Janeiro.

DAKIN, W. J.
1910. The eye of pecten. Quart. J. Micr. Sc., v. 55, p. 49.
1928. The eyes of *Pecten, Spondylus, Amussium*, and allied lamellibranchs, with a short discussion on their evolution. Proc. Roy. Soc. London, ser. B, v. 103, p. 355.

DALCQ, A.
1941. L'œuf et son dynamisme organisateur. A. Michel, Paris.

DALE, H.
1937. Transmission of nervous effects by acetylcholine. Harvey Lect., v. 32, p. 229.

DALÉN, A.
1906. Ueber die anatomische Grundlage der Alkohol-Tabaksamblyopie. Mitt. a. d. Augenklin. d. Carol. med.-chir. Inst. Stockholm, v. 1, Fasc. 8, p. 1.

DALQUEST, W. W.
1947. Notes on the natural history of the bat *Corynorhinus rafinesquii* in California. J. Mammal., v. 28, p. 17.

DALRYMPLE, JOHN
1834. The anatomy of the human eye. Longman, Rees, Orme, Brown, & Green, London.

DALTON, J. C.
1881. Centres of vision in the cerebral hemispheres. M. Rec., v. 19, p. 337.

DALTON, JOHN
1794. Extraordinary facts relating to vision of

colours. Mem. Manchester Lit. & Phil. Soc., v. 5 (1), p. 28, 1798.

DAMEL, C. S.
1936. Anatomia de la arteria y vena central de la retina en su porción orbitaria y neural. Arch. de oftal. Buenos Aires, v. 11, pp. 57, 153, 345.

DAMIANOS, SON OF HELIODOROS OF LARISSA (*see also* HELIODÓROS)
*Early part of 4th cent. Δαμιανοῦ τοῦ Ἡλιοδώρου Λαρισσαίου κεφαλεία τῶν ὀπτικῶν ὑποθέυεων. German trans. by R. SCHÖNE. Berlin, 1897.
*Early part of 4th cent. Κεφάλαια τῶν ὀπτικῶν ὑποθέσεων.

DAMPIER DAMPIER-WHETHAM, W. C.
1929. A history of science and its relation with philosophy and religion. Cambridge University Press, Cambridge.

DANA, C. L.
1907. The cerebral localisation of aphasia and its classification on an anatomical basis. New York M. J., v. 86, p. 240.

D'ANCONA, U.
1939. Der Kampf ums Dasein. *In:* Abhandl. z. exakt. Biol., ed. L. VON BERTALANFFY, v. 1. Gebrüder Borntraeger, Berlin.

DANDY, W. E.
1922. Prechiasmal tumors of the optic nerves. Am. J. Ophth., v. 5, p. 169.
1930. Changes in our conceptions of localization of certain functions in the brain. Am. J. Physiol., v. 93, p. 2.
1933. Physiological studies following extirpation of the right cerebral hemisphere. Bull. Johns Hopkins Hosp., v. 53, p. 31.
1946. The location of the conscious center in the brain—the corpus striatum. *Ibid.*, v. 79, p. 34.
1948. The brain. *In:* DEAN LEWIS, Practice of Surgery, v. 12, chap. I.

DANDY, W. E., & GOETSCH, E.
1910–11. The blood supply of the pituitary body. Am. J. Anat., v. 11, p. 137.

DANIEL, P.
1946. Spiral nerve endings in the extrinsic eye muscles of man. J. Anat., v. 80, p. 189.

DANIELS, B.
1932. Ueber die homonyme Hemianopsie bei Migräne. Ztschr. f. Augenh., v. 77, p. 67.

DANIS, P. C.
1948. The functional organization of the third-nerve nucleus in the cat. Am. J. Ophth., v. 31, p. 1122.

DANTE ALIGHIERI
13th & 14th centuries. Vision and optics in Dante's writings. (*See* Passera.)

DAREMBERG, C.
1854–56. Galien. Œuvres anatomiques, physiologiques et médicales, traduites pour la première fois en français. 2 vols. J.-B. Baillière & Fils, Paris.
1865. La médecine dans Homère. Didier & Cie, Paris.
1865. La médecine: histoire et doctrines. Didier & Cie; J.-B. Baillière & Fils, Paris.
1869. État de la médecine entre Homère et Hippocrate: anatomie, physiologie, pathologie, médecine militaire, histoire des écoles médicales. Didier & Cie, Paris.
1870. Histoire des sciences médicales comprenant l'anatomie, la physiologie, la médecine, la chirurgie et les doctrines de pathologie générale. 2 vols. J.-B. Baillière & Fils, Paris.

DAREMBERG, C., & SAGLIO, E.
1877–1912. Dictionnaire des antiquités grecques et romaines. 5 vols. Hachette & Cie, Paris.

DARKSCHEWITSCH (DARKŠEVIČ), L. O.
1886. Ueber die sogenannten primären Opticus-centren und ihre Beziehung zur Grosshirnrinde. Arch. f. Anat. u. Physiol. (Anat. Abt.), p. 249.
1891. Ueber die Kreuzung der Sehnervenfasern. Arch. f. Ophth. (Graefe), v. 37 (1), p. 1.

DARLINGTON, D. C.
1943. Race, class, and mating in the evolution of man. Nature, v. 152, p. 315.

DART, R. A.
1925. *Australopithecus africanus*—the ape-man of South Africa. Nature, v. 115, p. 195.
ca. 1948. Adventures with *Australopithecus*. (A separate reprint without source.)
ca. 1948. The first human mandible from the Cave of Hearths, Makapansgat. South African Archaeol. Bull., Cape Town, v. 3 (12).
1948. A promethean *Australopithecus* from Makapansgat Valley. Nature, v. 162, p. 375.
1948. The infancy of *Australopithecus*. *In:* R. BROOM, Commemorative volume, p. 143.
1948. The Makapansgat proto-human *Australopithecus prometheus*. Am. J. Phys. Anthropol., N.S., v. 6, p. 259.
1948. The adolescent mandible of *Australopithecus prometheus*. *Ibid.*, p. 391.
1949. The predatory implemental technique of *Australopithecus*. *Ibid.*, N.S., v. 7, p. 1.
1949. The cranio-facial fragment of *Australopithecus prometheus*. *Ibid.*, p. 187.
1949. Innominate fragments of *Australopithecus prometheus*. *Ibid.*, p. 301.
1954. The adult female lower jaw from Makapansgat. Nature, v. 173, p. 286.

DARTNALL, H. J. A.
 1948. Visual purple and the photopic luminosity curve. Brit. J. Ophth., v. 32, p. 793.
 1948. Indicator yellow and retinene₁. Nature, v. 162, p. 222.
 1950. Colour photography of visual purple solutions. Brit. J. Ophth., v. 34, p. 447.
 1950. New photosensitive pigments from the tench retina. Nature, v. 166, p. 207.

DARTNALL, H. J. A., & GOODEVE, C. F.
 1937. Scotopic luminosity curve and the absorption spectrum of visual purple. Nature, v. 139, p. 409.

DARTNALL, H. J. A., GOODEVE, C. F., & LYTHGOE, R. J.
 1936. The quantitative analysis of the photochemical bleaching of visual purple solutions in monochromatic light. Proc. Roy. Soc. London, ser. A, v. 156, p. 158.
 1938. The effect of temperature on the photochemical bleaching of visual purple solutions. *Ibid.*, v. 164, p. 216.

DARTNALL, H. J. A., & THOMSON, L. C.
 1949–50. Retinal oxygen supply and macular pigmentation. Nature, v. 164, p. 876; v. 165, p. 524.

DARWIN, C. G.
 1932. Article: Light, Encyclopaedia Britannica, 14th ed., v. 14, p. 57.
 1952. The next million years. Rupert Hart-Davis, London.

DARWIN, CHARLES ROBERT; for biography *see* F. DARWIN; MOLESCHOTT, O. HERTWIG, WALDEYER, LLOYD, MOORE; *see also* A. R. WALLACE
 1839. Journal of researches into the natural history and geology of the countries visited during the voyage of H.M.S. "Beagle," round the world under the command of Captain Fitz Roy, R.N. H. Colburn, London. (2d ed., 1845.)
 1859. The origin of species by means of natural selection or the preservation of favoured races in the struggle for life. D. Appleton & Co., London.
 1871. The descent of man, and selection in relation to sex. 2d ed. (1874), revised and augmented. J. Murray, London, 1899.
 1873. The expressions of the emotions in man and animals. D. Appleton & Co., New York, 1929.
 1903. More letters of Charles Darwin: a record of his work in a series of hitherto unpublished letters. Edited by FRANCIS DARWIN and A. C. SEWARD. J. Murray, London; D. Appleton & Co., New York.

 1925. The life and letters of Charles Darwin, including an autobiographical chapter. D. Appleton & Co., New York & London.
 1928. Darwin's house at Downe. Scient. Monthly, v. 26, p. 90.
 1930. A naturalist's voyage round the world in H.M.S. "Beagle." H. Milford, Oxford University Press, London.
 1945. Charles Darwin and the voyage of the Beagle, ed. N. BARLOW, Pilot Press, London.
 1950. Charles Darwin's autobiography, with his notes and letters depicting the growth of the "Origin of species," edited by SIR FRANCIS DARWIN, and an introductory essay, "The meaning of Darwin," by G. G. SIMPSON. H. Schuman, New York.

DARWIN, FRANCIS
 1888. The life and letters of Charles Darwin, including an autobiographical chapter, edited by his son, FRANCIS DARWIN. 3 vols. J. Murray, London.

DAVENPORT, H. A., & BARNES, J. R.
 1935. The strip method for counting nerve fibers or other microscopic units. Stain Technol., v. 10, p. 139.

DAVIDOFF, L. M., & DYKE, C. G.
 1934–35. The demonstration of normal cerebral structures by means of encephalography. Bull. Neurol. Inst. New York, v. 3, pp. 138, 418; v. 4, p. 91.
 1951. The normal encephalogram. 3d ed. Lea & Febiger, Philadelphia.

DAVIES, A. M.
 1937. Evolution and its modern critics. T. Murby & Co., London.

DA VINCI; *see* LEONARDO DA VINCI

DAVIS, D. D.
 1942. Review of G. L. WALLS's The vertebrate eye and its adaptive radiation. J. Mammal., v. 23, p. 453.
 1949. Comparative anatomy and the evolution of vertebrates. *In:* JEPSEN *et al.*, Genetics, paleontology, and evolution, p. 64.

DAVIS, D. E.
 1945. The annual cycle of plants, mosquitoes, birds, and mammals in two Brazilian forests. Ecol. Monog. (Durham), v. 15, p. 243.

DAVIS, H.
 1936. Some aspects of the electrical activity of the cerebral cortex. Cold Spring Harbor Symp. Quant. Biol., v. 4, p. 285.

DAVIS, H. S.
 1937. Care and diseases of trout. U.S. Bur. Fish. Invest. Rep. No. 35, p. 1.

Davis, L. E.
  1921. An anatomical study of the inferior longitudinal fasciculus. Arch. Neurol. & Psychiat., v. 5, p. 370.
Davis, W. B., & Joeris, L.
  1945. Notes on the life-history of the little short-tailed shrew. J. Mammal., v. 26, p. 136.
Davison, C., & Goodhart, S. P,
  1931. Spasmodic lateral conjugate deviation of the eyes. Arch. Neurol. & Psychiat., v. 25, p. 87.
Davison, C., Goodhart, S. P., & Needles, W.
  1934. Cerebral localization in cerebrovascular disease. *In:* Localization of function in the cerebral cortex. Research Pub. A. Research Nerv. & Ment. Dis., v. 13, p. 435. Williams & Wilkins Co., Baltimore.
Davson, H.
  1949. The physiology of the eye. Blakiston Co., Philadelphia & Toronto.
Dawson, B. H.
  1950. The blood supply of the human hypothalamus. J. Anat., v. 84, p. 80. (Abstr.)
Dawson, W. L., *et al.*
  1923. The birds of California. 4 vols. South Moulton Co., San Diego, Los Angeles, & San Francisco.
Day, W.
  1923. The birth of kinematography, and its antecedents. Tr. Opt. Soc. London, v. 24, p. 69.
Daza de Valdés, Benito (*see also* M. Márquez)
  1623. Uso de los antoios para todo genero de vistas: en que se enseña a conocer los grados que a cada uno le faltan de su vista, y los que tienen qualesquier antojos. Y assi mismo a que tiempo se an de usar, y como se pediran en ausencia, con otros avisos importantes, a la utilidad y conservacion de la vista. Por el L. Benito Daça de Valdes, Notario de el Santo Oficio de la Ciudad de Sevilla. Dedicado a Nuestra Señora de la Fuensanta de la Ciudad de Cordova. Con Privilegio. Impresso en Sevilla, por Diego Perez Año de 1623. Facsimile edition by Impr. de Cosano, Madrid, 1923.
Dean, B.
  1901. Notes on living *Nautilus.* Am. Naturalist, v. 35, p. 819.
  1916-23. A bibliography of fishes. 3 vols. American Museum of Natural History, New York.
Deaver, J. B.
  1904. Surgical anatomy. P. Blakiston's Son & Co., Philadelphia.
De Beer, G. R.
  1940. Embryos and ancestors. Clarendon Press, Oxford.

Debierre, C. M.
  1907. Le cerveau et la moelle épinière avec application physiologique et médico-chirurgicale. F. Alcan, Paris.
De Bono, F. P.
  1893. Sulla localizzazione del centro corticale per la elevazione della palpebra superiore. Arch. di ottal., v. 1, pp. 36, 101.
Dechâles, C.-F. M.
  1674. Cursus seu mundus mathematicus. 3 vols. Ex officina Anissoniana, Lugduni.
Dechambre, A.
  1864-82. Dictionnaire encyclopédique des sciences médicales. P. Asselin, G. Masson, Paris.
De Crinis, M.
  1938. Anatomie der Sehrinde. ("Monog. a. d. Gesamtgeb. d. Neurol. u. Psychiat.," Fasc. 64.) J. Springer, Berlin.
  1939. Meynert und seine Lehren in ihrer Bedeutung für die heutige Psychiatrie. Ztschr. f. d. ges. Neurol. u. Psychiat., v. 165, p. 17.
Dedekind, F.
  1909. Beiträge zur Entwicklungsgeschichte der Augengefässe des Menschen. Anat. Hefte, v. 38, p. 1.
Deevey, E. S., Jr.
  1951. Life in the depths of a pond. Scient. American, v. 185, p. 68.
De Feyfer, F. M. G.
  1914. Die Schriften des Andreas Vesalius. Janus, v. 19, p. 435.
De Grazia, F.; *see* Grazia, F. de
Deiters, O.
  1863. Untersuchungen über Gehirn und Rückenmark des Menschen und der Säugethiere. Nach dem Tode des Verfassers herausgegeben und bevorwortet von M. Schultze. F. Vieweg & Sohn, Braunschweig, 1865.
Dejean, C.
  1926. Étude anatomique et embryologique sur la membrane hyaloïde de l'œil des mammifères. Son rôle dans la formation des milieux de l'œil. Ses limites, sa structure. Arch. d'opht., v. 43, p. 257.
Dejerine, J.
  1892. Contribution à l'étude anatomopathologique et clinique des différentes variétés de cécité verbale. Mém. Soc. de biol. Paris, v. 44, p. 61.
  1895-1901. Anatomie des centres nerveux. 2 vols. Rueff & Cie, Paris.
  1906. L'aphasie sensorielle. Presse méd., v. 14 (2), p. 437.
  1926. Sémiologie des affections du système nerveux. Masson & Cie, Paris.

DEJERINE, J., & PÉLISSIER, A.
　1914. Contribution à l'étude de la cécité verbale pure. Encéphale, v. 2, p. 1.

DEJERINE, J., & ROUSSY, G.
　1906. Le syndrome thalamique. Rev. neurol., v. 14, p. 521.

DEJERINE, J., & THOMAS, A.
　1904. Contribution à l'étude de l'aphasie sensorielle, Rev. Neurol., v. 12, p. 805.

DE JONG, H.
　1927. Totale Agnosie als Aeusserung von Paläo-Intellekt. Deutsche Ztschr. f. Nervenh., v. 96, p. 208.

DE KLEIJN, A.
　1912. Ueber die ophthalmologischen Erscheinungen bei Hypophysistumoren und ihre Variabilität. Arch. f. Ophth. (Graefe), v. 80, p. 307.

DELAGE, Y.
　1920. Suggestion sur la raison d'être de la double fovéa des rapaces diurnes. Compt. rend. Acad. d. sc., Paris, v. 170, p. 425.

DE LA HIRE, PHILIPPE
　1689. Dissertation sur les différens accidens de la vue. Paris. Other eds. 1694, 1730, last mentioned in his Œuvres diverses de M. de La Hire. La Compagnie des Libraires, Paris.
　*1694. Dissertatio de visu & variis ejus casibus. Lutetiae Parisiorum (Paris).
　1709. De quelques faits d'optique, et de la manière dont se fait la vision. Mém. hist. Acad. roy. d. sc., Paris, p. 95, 1733.
　1730. Dissertation sur les différens accidens de la vuë. Mém. Acad. roy. d. sc., Paris, v. 9, p. 530.
　1730. Dissertation sur la conformation de l'œil. Ibid., v. 10, p. 680, 1666–99 (paper dated 1685).

DELAMBRE, J.-B. J.
　1812. Die Optik des Ptolemäus, verglichen mit der Euclid's, Alhazen's und Vitellio's (frei bearbeitet von L. W. GILBERT). Ann. d. Phys., v. 40 (N.F., v. 10), p. 371.
　1817. Histoire de l'astronomie ancienne. 2 vols. V. Courcier, Paris.
　1821. Histoire de l'astronomie moderne. 2 vols. V. Courcier, Paris.

DE LANGE, S. J.
　1910. The descending tracts of the corpora quadrigemina. Folia. neuro-biol., v. 3, p. 633.
　1911. Das Vorderhirn der Reptilien. Ibid., v. 5, p. 548.
　1913. Das Zwischenhirn und das Mittelhirn der Reptilien. Ibid., v. 7, p. 67.

DE LA PEYRONIE; see PEYRONIE, F. G. DE LA

DELBRÜCK, A.
　1890. Zur Lehre von der Kreuzung der Nervenfasern im Chiasma nervorum opticorum. Arch. f. Psychiat., v. 21, p. 746.

DELBUE, A.
　1918. Necrologio for P. Panizza. Fracastoro, v. 14, p. 35.

DEL DUCA, M.
　1930. Ricerche anatomiche sull'occhio del cameleonte, Zentralbl. f. d. ges. Ophth., v. 26, p. 639.

DE LINT, J. G.
　1914. Les portraits de Vésale. Janus, v. 19, p. 410.
　1926. Atlas of the history of medicine: anatomy. P. B. Hoeber, New York.

DELORME
　1918–19. Les scotomes dans le glaucome chronique. Arch. d'opht., v. 36, p. 577.

DELSMANN, H. C.
　1912–13. Der Ursprung der Vertebraten: eine neue Theorie. Zool. Anz., v. 41, p. 175; Mitt. a. d. Zool. Stat. zu Neapel, v. 20, p. 647.

DE METS
　1925. La traité d'optique de François d'Aguilon. Bull. & mém. Soc. franç. d'opht., v. 38, p. 233.

DEMOCRITOS OF ABDERA
　4th–5th cent. B.C. Sammlung der Fragmente Democritos. Edited by E. MULLACH. Berlin, 1843, Phragmenta philosophorum Graecorum, v. 1, p. 359, 1860, edited by E. MULLACH, Paris; see also Wissowa, Enzyklopädie der classischen Altertumswissenschaften, 1903.

DEMOLL, R.
　1914. Die Augen von Limulus. Zool. Jahrb., v. 38, p. 443.
　1917. Die Sinnesorgane der Arthropoden. F. Vieweg & Sohn, Braunschweig.

DEMOOR, J.
　1921. La question des localisations cérébrales. Soc. roy. de sc. méd. et nat. Bruxelles, Ann. et Bull. des séances, v. 75, p. 71.

DEMPSEY, E. W., & MORISON, R. S.
　1943. The electrical activity of a thalamocortical relay system. Am. J. Physiol., v. 138, p. 283.

DENDY, A.
　1909. The intracranial vascular system of Sphenodon. Phil. Tr. Roy. Soc. London, ser. B, v. 200, p. 403.
　1910. On the structure, development, and morphological interpretation of the pineal organs and adjacent parts of the brain in the tuatara (Sphenodon punctatus). Proc. Roy. Soc. London, ser. B, v. 82, p. 629.

DENEFFE, V.

1893. Étude sur la trousse d'un chirurgien gallo-romain du 3ᵉ siècle. H. Caals, Anvers.

1896. Les oculistes gallo-romains au IIIᵉ siècle. H. Caals, Anvers.

DENHARDT, R. M.

1947. The horse of the Americas. University of Oklahoma Press, Norman.

DENISSENKO, G.

1880. Einige Beobachtungen über die Gefässe in der Fovea centralis der Netzhaut des Menschen. Centralbl. f. d. med. Wissensch., v. 18, p. 866.

DENNY-BROWN, D.

1932. Theoretical deductions from the physiology of the cerebral cortex. J. Neurol. & Psychopath., v. 13, p. 52.

DERCUM, F. X.

1907. A case of aphasia, both "motor" and "sensory," with integrity of the left third frontal convolution: lesion in the lenticular zone and inferior longitudinal fasciculus. J. Nerv. & Ment. Dis., v. 34, p. 681.

DE RENZI; *see* RENZI, DE

DES CARTES, DU PERRON (DES-CARTES, DESCARTES, CARTESIUS), RENÉ or RENATUS; *see also* C. ADAMS; ADAMS & TANNERY; V. COUSIN; E. S. HALDANE

*1636 or 1638. La dioptrique. *In:* his Discourse de la méthode. J. Maire, Leyde.

1656. Passiones animae. *In his:* Opera philosophica, v. 1. 2 vols. Apud J. Jansonium Juniorem, Amstelodami.

1662. De homine figuris et latinitate donatus. Moyard & Leffen, Leyden.

(1662) 1677. Tractatus de homine, et de formatione foetus. Quorum prior notis perpetuis Ludovici de la Forge, M.D. illustratur. Amstelodami, apud Elsevirum. (First pub. in French; first Latin ed. 1662, 2d 1677; *cf. also* Œuvres de Descartes, pub. par V. Cousin, 1824.)

1677. L'homme de René Descartes, et la formation du fœtus, avec les remarques de Louis de la Forge, a quoy l'on a ajouté Le monde ou traité de la lumière du mesme autheur. 2d ed. C. Angot, Paris. First ed. either 1662 or 1664.

1677. L'homme, et la formation du fœtus, avec les remarques de Louis de la Forge, à quoy l'on a ajouté Le monde ou traité de la lumière du mesme autheur. 2d ed., reveuë & corrigée.

1685. Dioptrice. *In:* Opera philosophica. Amstelodami, Ex Typogr. Blaviani. (First pub. in French, 1637.)

1686. Renati Des-Cartes Tractatus de homine, et de formatione fœtus. Quorum prior notis perpetuis Ludovicus De La Forge, M.D. illustratur. Amstelodami, Ex Typogr. Blaviana, MDCLXXXVI. Sumptibus Societatis.

1824–26. Œuvres de Descartes, publiées par VICTOR COUSIN. 5 vols. F. G. Levrault, Paris.

1835. Œuvres philosophiques de Descartes, publiées d'après les textes originaux, avec notices, sommaires et éclaircissements par ADOLPHE GARNIER. 4 vols. L. Hachette, Paris.

DE SCHWEINITZ, G. E.

1923. The Bowman Lecture: concerning certain ocular aspects of pituitary body disorders mainly exclusive of the usual central and peripheral hemianopic field defects. Tr. Ophth. Soc. United Kingdom, v. 43, p. 12.

DE SCHWEINITZ, G. E., & HOLLOWAY, T. B.

1912. A clinical communication on certain visual field defects in hypophysis disease with special reference to scotomas. J. Am. Med. Assoc., v. 59, p. 1041.

DESMOULINS, A.

1840. On the "transverse fold" of the retina and the visual acuity. *See* Baillarger, J., Recherches sur la structure de la couche corticale des circonvolutions du cerveau. Mém. Acad. roy. de méd. de Paris, v. 8, p. 149; also, as a separate reprint, p. 38. J.-B. Baillière, Paris.

DESMOULINS, A., & MAGENDIE, F.

1825. Anatomie du système nerveux des animaux à vertèbres, appliquée à la physiologique et à la zoologie. Méguignon-Marvis, Paris. (Two parts and atlas.)

DETWILER, S. R.

1916. The effect of light on the retina of the tortoise and of the lizard. J. Exper. Zoöl., v. 20, p. 165.

1923. The identity of the developing visual cells in *Amblystoma* larvae as revealed by their responses to light. J. Comp. Neurol., v. 36, p. 113.

1923. An experimental study of the gecko retina. *Ibid.*, p. 125.

1923. Photomechanical responses in the retina of *Eremias argus*. J. Exper. Zoöl., v. 37, p. 89.

1923. Some experimental observations on the retina of the gecko. Proc. Soc. Exper. Biol. & Med., v. 20, p. 214.

1924. Studies on the retina (rods of nocturnal mammals). J. Comp. Neurol., v. 37, p. 481.

1929. Some observations upon grafted eyes of frog larvae. Arch. f. Entw.-Mech. (Roux), v. 116, p. 555.

DETWILER, S. R.—*Continued*

1936. Neuroembryology. Macmillan Co., New York.

1939. Comparative studies upon the eyes of nocturnal lemuroids, monkeys and man. Anat. Rec., v. 74, p. 129.

1940. The eye of *Nycticebus tardigrada*. *Ibid.*, v. 76, p. 295.

1940. Comparative anatomical studies of the eye, with especial reference to the photoreceptors. J. Opt. Soc. Amer., v. 30, p. 42.

1941. The eye of the owl monkey (*Nyctipithecus*). Anat. Rec., v. 80, p. 233.

1943. Vertebrate photoreceptors. Macmillan Co., New York.

1944. Excitation and retinal pigment migration in the frog. J. Comp. Neurol., v. 81, p. 137.

1945. On the role of chemical factors in retinal photomechanical responses. Am. J. Anat., v. 77, p. 117.

DETWILER, S. R., & LAURENS, H.

1921. The structure of the retina of *Phrynosoma cornutum*. J. Comp. Neurol., v. 32, p. 347.

1921. Histogenesis of the visual cells in *Amblystoma*. *Ibid.*, v. 33, p. 493.

DETWILER, S. R., & LEWIS, R.

1926. Temperature and retinal pigment migration in the eyes of the frog. J. Comp. Neurol., v. 41, p. 153.

DEUTSCH, H.

1929. Die Veränderungen des Corpus geniculatum externum bei tabischer Opticusatrophie und ihre Bedeutung für die Kenntnis der Normalstruktur dieses Ganglion. Arb. a. d. Neurol. Inst. Wien, v. 31, p. 129.

DEUTSCHMANN, R.

1883. Zur Semidecussation im Chiasma nerv. opt. des Menschen. Arch. f. Ophth. (Graefe), v. 29 (1), p. 323.

DE VECCHI, P.

1921. Modern Italian surgery, and old universities of Italy. P. B. Hoeber, New York.

DE VOSS, J. C., & GANSON, R.

1915. Color blindness of cats. J. Anim. Behavior, v. 5, p. 115.

DE VRIES, E.

1910. Experimentelle Untersuchungen über die Rolle der Neuroglia bei secundärer Degeneration grauer Substanz. Arb. a. d. hirnanat. Inst. Zürich (Monakow), v. 4, p. 1.

1913. Zircumscripter Zellausfall im äusseren Kniehöcker bei Tumor der Fissura calcarina. Folia neuro-biol., suppl., v. 7, p. 48.

DE VRIES, H. E.

1943. The quantum character of light and its bearing upon threshold of vision, the differential sensitivity and visual acuity of the eye. Physica, v. 10, p. 553.

1946. Concentration of visual purple in the human eye. Nature, v. 158, p. 303.

1946. On the basic sensation curves of the three-color theory. J. Opt. Soc. Amer., v. 36, p. 121.

1947. Kleurenzien. Natuurk., v. 13, p. 179.

1948. The luminosity curve of the eye as determined by measurements with the flicker photometer. Physica, v. 14, p. 319.

1948. The fundamental response curves of normal and abnormal dichromatic and trichromatic eyes. *Ibid.*, p. 367.

1948. Minimum perceptible energy and Brownian motion in sensory processes. Nature, v. 161, p. 63.

1948. Die Reizschwelle der Sinnesorgane als physikalisches Problem. Experientia, v. 4, p. 205.

1948. Der Einfluss der Temperatur des Auges auf die spektrale Empfindlichkeitskurve. *Ibid.*, p. 357.

1948. The heredity of the relative numbers of red and green receptors in the human eye. Genetica, v. 24, p. 199.

1949. Light quanta and vision. J. Opt. Soc. Amer., v. 39, p. 201; and Rev. d'opt., v. 28, p. 101.

1949. Comments at Colour Vision Conference, Cambridge, 1947. Doc. Ophth., v. 3, p. 92.

DE VRIES, H., JIELOF, R., & SPOOR, A.

1950. Properties of the human eye with respect to linearly and circularly polarized light. Nature, v. 166, p. 958.

DEXLER, H.

1897. Untersuchungen über den Faserverlauf im Chiasma des Pferdes und über den binoculären Sehact dieses Thieres. Arb. a. d. Neurol. Inst. Wien, v. 5, p. 179.

1921. Tierpsychologie als Naturwissenschaft. Neurol. Centralbl., v. 40, suppl., p. 113.

DEXLER, H., & FREUND, L.

1906. Contributions to the physiology and biology of the dugong. Am. Naturalist, v. 40, p. 49.

DEYL, J.

1895. Ueber den Sehnerven bei Siluroiden und Acanthopsiden. Anat. Anz., v. 11, p. 8.

1896. Ueber den Eintritt der Arteria centralis retinae in den Sehnerv beim Menschen. *Ibid.*, p. 687.

1896. Contribution à l'étude de l'anatomie comparée du nerf optique. Bibliog. anat., v. 4, p. 61. Also Akad. d. Wissensch., Prag.

DE ZERBIS (GABRIELE GERBI)

1502. Liber anatomine corporis humani et singulorum membrorum illius. Venice.

D'Hollander, F.; *see* Hollander, F.

Diard

　1820. Report of a meeting of the Asiatic Society of Bengal for March 10, 1820. Asiatic J. Month. Reg., v. 10, p. 477.

Dice, L. R.

　1952. Natural communities. University of Michigan Press, Ann Arbor.

Dickerson, M. C.

　1907. The frog book: North American toads and frogs, with a study of the habits and life histories of those of the northeastern states. Doubleday, Page & Co., New York.

Dickson, W. E. C., Pritchard, G. C., Savin, L. H., & Sorsby, A.

　1944. Two cases of visible emboli in retinal arteries. Brit. J. Ophth., v. 28, p. 1.

Dide, M.

　1938. Les désorientations temporo-spatiales et la prépondérance de l'hémisphère droit dans les agnoso-akinésies proprioceptives. Encéphale, v. 33 (2), p. 276.

Dieckmann-Vogt, O.; *see* Vogt, O.

Diehl, C.

　1925. History of the Byzantine Empire. Princeton University Press, Princeton.

Diemerbroeck, I.

　1683. Anatome corporis humani. Lugduni, sumpt. M. & J. H. Huguetan.

Diercks, G.

　1882. Die Araber im Mittelalter und ihr Einfluss auf die Cultur Europas. O. Wiegand, Leipzig.

　1887. Die arabische Kultur im mittelalterlichen Spanien. ("Samml. gemeinverst. wissensch. Vortr.," ed. R. Virchow & F. von Holtzendorff, N.F., 2d ser., Fasc. 8.) J. F. Richter, Hamburg.

Dietel, H.

　1931. Beobachtungen über die individuelle Anatomie der Oberfläche des Okzipitallappens von 25 unterfränkischen Gehirnen. Ztschr. f. Anat. u. Entw., v. 95, p. 171.

Dieter, W.

　1927. Ueber die subjectiven Farbenempfindungen bei angeborenen Störungen. Ztschr. f. Sinnesphysiol., v. 58, p. 73.

Dill, S.

　1899. Roman society in the last century of the Western Empire. Macmillan & Co., Ltd., London.

Di Marzio, Q.

　1937. Fundus oculi: diagnostica oftalmoscopica. Stab. L. Salomone, Roma.

Di Marzio, Q., & Fumarola, C.

　1930. Les troubles des mouvements associés des yeux. Rev. d'oto-neuro-opht., v. 8, p. 299.

Dimitrijević, D. T.

　1940. Zur Frage der Sprachrestitution bei der Aphasie der Polyglotten. Ztschr. f. d. ges. Neurol. u. Psychiat., v. 168, p. 277.

Dimmer, F.

　1894. Beiträge zur Anatomie und Physiologie der Macula lutea des Menschen. F. Deuticke, Leipzig & Wien.

　1899. Zur Lehre von den Sehnervenbahnen. Arch. f. Ophth. (Graefe), v. 48, p. 473.

　1899. Ueber die Sehnervenbahnen. Ber. d. Deutsch. ophth. Gesellsch. Heidelberg, v. 27, p. 237.

　1902. Demonstration von Photogrammen nach Schnittpräparaten durch die Fovea. *Ibid.*, v. 30, p. 362.

　1907. Die Photographie des Augenhintergrundes. Klin. Monatsbl. f. Augenh. (suppl.), v. 45, p. 256.

　1907. Die Macula lutea der menschlichen Netzhaut und die durch sie bedingten entoptischen Erscheinungen. Arch. f. Ophth. (Graefe), v. 65, p. 486.

　1915. Zwei Fälle von Schussverletzungen der zentralen Sehbahnen. Wien. klin. Wchnschr., v. 28, p. 519.

　1921. Der Augenspiegel und die ophthalmoskopische Diagnostik. F. Deuticke, Leipzig & Wien.

Dingler, H.

　1937–38. Die "Physik des 20. Jahrhunderts." Ztschr. f. d. ges. Naturwiss., v. 3, p. 321.

Disney, A. N., Hill, C. F., & Baker, W. E.

　1928. Origin and development of the microscope as illustrated by catalogues of the instruments and accessories, in the collections of the Royal Microscopical Society. Preceded by an historical survey of optical science. London.

Ditmars, R. L.

　1935. The reptile book: a comprehensive, popularized work on the structure and habits of the turtles, tortoises, crocodilians, lizards and snakes which inhabit the United States and northern Mexico. Doubleday, Doran & Co., Garden City, N.Y.

　1946. The reptiles of North America: a review of the crocodilians, lizards, snakes, turtles and tortoises inhabiting the United States and northern Mexico. Doubleday & Co., Garden City, N.Y.

Dmitri, Ivan

　1940. Kodachrome and how to use it. Simon & Schuster, New York.

DOBELL, C.
1932. Antony van Leeuwenhoek. Harcourt, Brace & Co., New York & London.

DOBRIN, M. B.
1947. Measurements of underwater noise produced by marine life. Science, v. 105, p. 19.

DOBROWOLSKY, W.
1886. Ueber die Empfindlichkeit des normalen Auges gegen Farbentöne auf der Peripherie der Netzhaut. Arch. f. Ophth. (Graefe), v. 32 (1), p. 9.
1887. Ueber die Ursachen der Erythropsie. *Ibid.*, v. 33 (2), p. 213.

DOBSON, G. A.
1882–83. A monograph of the insectivora, systematic and anatomical. In 2 parts. J. Van Voorst, London.

DOBZHANSKY, T.
1945. Genetics and macro-evolution. A review of G. G. SIMPSON, Tempo and mode in evolution. J. Heredity, v. 36, p. 112.
1950. Human diversity and adaptation. Cold Spring Harbor Symp. Quant. Biol., v. 15, p. 385.
1951. Genetics and the origin of species. Columbia University Press, New York.

DODGSON, M. C. H.
1948. Physical nature of mouse brain. Nature, v. 162, p. 253.

DÖLLINGER, I.
1814. Beitrag zur Entwicklungsgeschichte des menschlichen Gehirns. Brönner, Frankfurt.
1818. Ueber das Strahlenblaettchen im menschlichen Auge. Verhandl. Leop.-Carol. Acad. d. Naturforsch. (Nova acta phys.-med. Acad. Caes. Leop.-Carol. Nat. Curios.), v. 9, p. 265.

DÖLLKEN, A.
1898. Die Reifung der Leitungsbahnen im Thiergehirn. Neurol. Centralbl., v. 17, p. 996.
1937. Mechanismen im Gehirn einseitig begabter Menschen. Ztschr. f. d. ges. Neurol. u. Psychiat., v. 157, p. 323.

DOESSCHATE; *see* TEN DOESSCHATE

DOGIEL, A. S.
1883. Die Retina der Ganoiden. Arch. f. mikr. Anat., v. 22, p. 419.
1884. Ueber die Retina des Menschen. Internat. Monatsschr. f. Anat., v. 1, p. 143.
1885. Zur Frage über den Bau der Retina bei *Triton cristatus*. Arch. f. mikr. Anat., v. 24, p. 451.
1888. Ueber das Verhalten der nervösen Elemente in der Retina der Ganoiden, Reptilien, Vögel und Säugethiere. Anat. Anz., v. 3, p. 133.

1888. Ueber die nervösen Elemente in der Netzhaut der Amphibien und Vögel. *Ibid.*, p. 342.
1891–92. Ueber die nervösen Elemente der Retina des Menschen. Arch. f. mikr. Anat., v. 38, p. 317; v. 40, p. 29.
1893. Zur Frage über den Bau der Nervenzellen und über das Verhältniss ihres Axencylinder-(Nerven-)Fortsatzes zu den Protoplasmafortsätzen (Dendriten). *Ibid.*, v. 41, p. 62.
1893. Neuroglia der Retina des Menschen. *Ibid.*, v. 41, p. 612.
1893. Zur Frage über das Verhalten der Nervenzellen zu einander. Arch. f. Anat. u. Entw., p. 429.
1895. Die Retina der Vögel. Arch. f. mikr. Anat., v. 44, p. 622.
1895. Die Struktur der Nervenzellen der Retina. *Ibid.*, v. 46, p. 394.
1895. Ein besonderer Typus von Nervenzellen in der mittleren gangliösen Schicht der Vogel-Retina. Anat. Anz., v. 10, p. 750.

DOHRN, C. A.
1875. Der Ursprung der Wirbelthiere und das Princip des Functionswechsels. W. Engelmann, Leipzig.
1885. Studien zur Urgeschichte des Wirbelthierkörpers. X. Zur Phylogenese des Wirbelthierauges. Mitt. a. d. zool. Stat. zu Neapel, v. 6, p. 432.

DOLECEK, R. L., & LAUNAY, J. DE
1945. Entoptic mapping of the Purkinje blue arcs. J. Opt. Soc. Amer., v. 35, p. 676.

DOLLMAN, J. G.
1932. Article: Insectivora, Encyclopaedia Britannica, 14th ed., v. 12, p. 401.

DONAHUE, H. C.
1950. Migraine and its ocular manifestations. Arch. Ophth., v. 43, p. 96.

DONALDSON, H. H.
1892. The extent of the visual area of the cortex in man, as deduced from the study of Laura Bridgman's brain. Am. J. Psychol., v. 4, p. 503.

DONDERS, F. C.; for biography *see* H. W. WILLIAMS
1852–89. Onderzoekingen gedaan in het physiologische laboratorium der Utrechtsche Hoogeschool. Utrecht.
1864. On the anomalies of accommodation and refraction of the eye. With a preliminary essay on physiological dioptrics. ("Publications of the New Sydenham Society," v. 22.) London.
1867. Das binoculare Sehen und die Vorstellung

von der dritten Dimension. Arch. f. Ophth. (Graefe), v. 13 (1), p. 1.

1877. Die Grenzen des Gesichtsfeldes in Beziehung zu denen der Netzhaut. *Ibid.*, v. 23 (2), p. 254.

1877. Die quantitative Bestimmung des Farbenunterscheidungsvermögens. *Ibid.*, (4), p. 282.

1879. Ueber Farbenblindheit. Klin. Monatsbl. f. Augenh., v. 17, p. 66.

1881. Sur les systèmes chromatiques. Ann. d'ocul., v. 86, pp. 109, 197.

1881. Ueber Farbensysteme. Arch. f. Ophth. (Graefe), v. 27 (1), p. 155.

DONNER, K. O.
1950. The spike frequencies of mammalian retinal elements as a function of wave-length of light. Acta physiol. Scandinav., v. 21, suppl. 72.

DONNER, K. O., & WILLMER, E. N.
1950. An analysis of the response from single visual-purple-dependent elements, in the retina of the cat. J. Physiol., v. 111, p. 160.

DOR, H.
1899. Centre cortical de la vision. Mém. Lyon Soc. d. sc. méd., v. 38, p. 18.

DOUGHERTY, T. F.
1944. Studies on the cytogenesis of microglia and their relation to cells of the reticulo-endothelial system. Am. J. Anat., v. 74, p. 61.

DOVE, H. W.
1837–49. Repertorium der Physik, 8 vols. Veit & Co., Berlin. (*See* v. 2: Litteratur der Optik, for early references on optics.)

DOZY, R.
1932. Histoire des Musulmans d'Espagne, 3 vols. E. J. Brill, Leyde.

DOZY, R., & STOKES, F. G.
1913. Spanish Islam. Chatto & Windus, London.

DRÄSECKE, J.
1903. Das Gehirn der Chiropteren. Monatsschr. f. Psychiat. u. Neurol., v. 13 (Ergh.), p. 448.

1906. Gehirngewicht und Intelligenz. Arch. f. Rassen- u. Gesellschafts-Biol., v. 3, p. 499.

DRESEL, K.
1924. Die Funktionen eines grosshirn- und striatumlosen Hundes. Klin. Wchnschr., v. 3, p. 2231.

DRESEL, K., & ROTHMANN, H.
1924–25. Völliger Ausfall der Substantia nigra nach Exstirpation von Grosshirn und Striatum. Ztschr. f. d. ges. Neurol. u. Psychiat., v. 94, p. 781.

DREWS, L. C.
[1]1941. Autofundoscopy (autoretinovasoentoscopy; auto-ophthalmoscopy of Eber; Purkinje fig-

ure of Walker). Am. J. Ophth., v. 24, p[1] 1403.

1943. Further observations on autofundoscopy (auto-ophthalmoscopy of Eber; Purkinje figure of Walker). *Ibid.*, v. 26, p. 1143.

DREYER, J. L. E.
1906. History of the planetary system from Thales to Kepler. Cambridge University Press, Cambridge.

DROHOCKI, Z.
1937–38. Die spontane elektrische Spannungsproduktion der Grosshirnrinde im Wach- und Ruhezustand. Arch. f. d. ges. Physiol. (Pflüger), v. 239, p. 658.

1939. Ueber den feineren Bau der Hirnrinde auf Grund der Elektroencephalographie. Ztchr. f. d. ges. Neurol. u. Psychiat., v. 164, p. 657.

DROOGLEEVER FORTUYN, A. B.
1911. De cytoarchitectonie der groote-hersenschors van eenige knaagdieren. Acad. proefschr. Amsterdam. Holkema's Boekhandel, Amsterdam.

1914. Cortical cell-lamination of some rodents. Arch. Neurol. (Mott), v. 6, p. 220.

1920. Vergleichende Anatomie des Nervensystems. I. Die Leitungsbahnen im Nervensystem der wirbellosen Tiere. Part of C. U. ARIËNS KAPPERS, Vergleichende Anatomie des Nervensystems. De Erven F. Bohn, Haarlem.

DRUAULT, A.
1904. Description of the retina. *In:* POIRIER and CHARPY, Traité d'anatomie humain, v. 5, p. 1073 (Les organes des sens).

DRUDE, P.
1929. The theory of optics. Longmans, Green & Co., London, New York, Toronto.

DRYANDER (EICHMANN), JOHANNES
1537. Anatomia, hoc est, corporis humani dissectionis pars prior, in qua singula quae ad caput spectant recensantur membra . . . deliniantur. Item: Anatomia porci, ex tradicione Cophonis; infantis, ex Gabriele de Zerbis. Marpurgi.

DUANE, A.
1931. Binocular vision and projection. Arch. Opth., v. 5, p. 734.

DUBOIS, E.
1894. *Pithecanthropus erectus*, eine menschliche Uebergangsform aus Java. Landesdruckerei, Batavia.

1896. On *Pithecanthropus erectus:* a transitional form between man and the apes. Scient. Tr. Roy. Dublin Soc., v. 6 (ser. II), Part 1.

DuBois, E.—*Continued*

1898. The braincast of *Pithecanthropus erectus.* Proc. Internat. Cong. Zoöl., Cambridge, p. 78.

1899. *Pithecanthropus erectus*—a form from the ancestral stock of mankind. Smithsonian Inst. Ann. Rep., p. 445; *also* Anat. Anz., v. 12, p. 1.

1924. On the principal characters of the cranium and the brain, the mandible and the teeth of *Pithecanthropus erectus.* Proc. Kon. Akad. nederl. Wetensch. Amsterdam, v. 27, p. 265.

1933. The shape and the size of the brain in *Sinanthropus* and in *Pithecanthropus. Ibid.,* v. 36, p. 415.

1940. The fossil human remains discovered in Java by Dr. G. H. R. von Koenigswald and attributed by him to *Pithecanthropus erectus,* in reality remains of *Homo sapiens soloensis. Ibid.,* v. 43, pp. 494, 842, 1268.

DuBois-Poulsen, A.

1952. Le champ visuel: topographie normale et pathologique de ses sensibilités. Masson & Cie, Paris.

Du Bois-Reymond, Claude

1881. Ueber die Zahl der Empfindungskreise in der Netzhautgrube. Diss. G. Schade, Berlin.

1886. Seheinheit und kleinster Sehwinkel. Arch. f. Ophth. (Graefe), v. 32 (3), p. 1.

Du Bois-Reymond, E.

*1870. Leibnitz'sche Gedanken in der neueren Wissenschaft. *See* J. Hirschberg, Notiz zur Theorie des Sehens. Arch. f. Ophth. (Graefe), v. 22 (4), p. 118.

Du Bois-Reymond, R., & Silex, P.

1899. Ueber kortikale Reizung der Augenmuskeln. Arch. f. Anat. u. Physiol. (physiol. Abt.), p. 174.

1899. Ueber die centrale Innervation der Augenmuskeln. Neurol. Centralbl., v. 18, p. 1093.

Duckworth, W. L. H.

1908. The brains of aboriginal natives of Australia in the Anatomy School, Cambridge University. J. Anat., v. 42, pp. 69, 176, 271.

1915. Morphology and anthropology. 2d ed. Cambridge University Press, Cambridge.

Duggan, W. F.

1943. Clinical vascular physiology of the eye. Am. J. Ophth., v. 26, p. 354.

Duhem, P.

1913–17. Le système du monde: histoire des doctrines cosmologiques de Platon à Copernic. 5 vols. A. Hermann & Fils, Paris.

Duke-Elder, S., & Davson, H.

1943. The significance of the distribution ratios of nonelectrolytes between plasma and the intra-ocular fluid. Brit. J. Ophth., v. 27, p. 431.

1948. The present position of the problem of the intra-ocular fluid and pressure. *Ibid.,* v. 32, p. 555.

Duke-Elder, S., *et al.*

1949. Studies on the intra-ocular fluids. 1. The reducing substances in the aqueous humour and vitreous body. 2. The penetration of certain ions into the aqueous humour and vitreous body. 3. The penetration of some nitrogenous substances into the intra-ocular fluids. 4. The dialysation of aqueous humour against plasma. Brit. J. Ophth., v. 33, pp. 21, 329, 452, 593.

Duke-Elder, S., Quilliam, J. C., & Davson, H.

1940. Some observations on the present position of our knowledge of the intra-ocular fluid. Brit. J. Ophth., v. 24, p. 421.

Duke-Elder, W. S.

1932–52. Text-book of ophthalmology. 4 vols. C. V. Mosby Co., St. Louis, Mo.; H. Kimpton, London.

1947. Ophthalmology during the war and in the future. Am. J. Ophth., v. 30, p. 1073.

Du Laurens (Laurentius), André

1597. Discourse de la conservation de la veue, des maladies mélancholiques, des catarrhes, et de la vieillesse. Reveuz de nouveau et augmontez de plusieurs chapitres J Mettayer, Paris. Other French eds.; also Latin ed.: Discursus de visus nobilitate ejusdem per diaetam conservandi vera methodo, etc. Monachi, 1618.

1599. A discourse of the preservation of the sight, etc. Translated by R. Surphlet. R. Jackson, London. (H. Milford, Oxford University Press, London, 1938.)

1599. Historia anatomica humani corporis. 2d ed. Francoforti ap. M. Beckerum, imp. Th. de Brij.

1603. De visu, eiusque causis et affectibus. Francoforti. French trans., 1646.

Dumesnil, R., & Bonnet-Roy, F.

1947. Les médecins célèbres. L. Mazenod, Genève.

Dunbar-Brander, A. A.

1923. Wild animals in central India. E. Arnold & Co., London.

Dungern, E.

1920. Die Schichtungstheorie des Farbensehens. Arch. f. Ophth. (Graefe), v. 102, p. 346.

Dunlap, J. W.

1934. The organization of learning and other traits in chickens ("Comp. Psychol. Monog.," v. 9, No. 44.) Johns Hopkins Press, Baltimore.

DUNLAP, K., & LOKEN, R. D.
1942. Vitamin A for color-blindness. Science, v. 95, p. 554.

DUNN, L. C.
1950. Race concept and human races. Cold Spring Harbor Symp. Quant. Biol., v. 15, p. 353.

DUNN, L. C., & DOBZHANSKY, T. G.
1946. Heredity, race, and society. Penguin Books, New York.

DUNSCOMBE, M. W.
1912–13. On the evolution of eye-glasses and spectacles. Optician, v. 45, p. 25.

DUPUY-DUTEMPS
1904. Sur les fibres commissurales périphériques inter-rétiniennes chez le chien. Bull. & mém. Soc. franç. d'opht., v. 21, p. 188.
1911. Trajet des faisceaux direct et croisé dans le nerf optique. *Ibid.*, v. 28, p. 526.

DUPUY-DUTEMPS, LAGRANGE, H., & FAVORY, A.
1925. De l'atrophie optique par compression tumorale du chiasma. Ann. d'ocul., v. 162, p. 241.

DURANT, W.
1953. The Renaissance: a history of civilization in Italy from 1304 to 1576 A.D. Simon & Schuster, New York.

DURET, H.
1873. Note sur la distribution des vaisseaux capillaires dans le bulbe rachidien. Progrès méd., v. 1, p. 270.
1873. Note sur les artères nourricières et sur les vaisseaux capillaires de la moëlle épinière. *Ibid.*, p. 284.
1873. Sur la distribution des artères nourricières du bulbe rachidien. Arch. de physiol., v. 5, p. 97.
1874. Recherches anatomiques sur la circulation de l'encéphale. *Ibid.*, 2d ser., v. 1, pp. 60, 316, 664, 919.
1910. Revue critique de quelques recherches récentes sur la circulation cérébrale. Encéphale, v. 5, p. 7.

DURSY, E.
1855. Beiträge zur Naturgeschichte der deutschen Schlangen. Arch. f. Naturgesch. (Wiegmann), v. 21 (1), p. 282.

DURWARD, A.
1930. The cell masses in the brain of *Sphenodon punctatum.* J. Anat., v. 65, p. 8.

DUSI, J. L.
1951. The nest of a short-tailed shrew. J. Mammal., v. 32, p. 115.

DUSSER DE BARENNE, J. G.
1919. Recherches expérimentales sur les fonctions du système nerveux central, faites en particulier sur deux chats dont néopallium avait été enlevé. Arch. néerl. physiol., v. 4, p. 31.
1934. Central levels of sensory integration. Research Pub. A. Research Nerv. & Ment. Dis., v. 15, p. 274.
1934. Some aspects of the problem of "corticalization" of function and of functional localization in the cerebral cortex. *In:* Localization of function in the cerebral cortex. Research Pub. A. Research Nerv. & Ment. Dis., v. 13, p. 85. Williams & Wilkins Co., Baltimore.

DUSSER DE BARENNE, J. G., GAROL, H. W., & McCULLOCH, W. S.
1941. Physiological neuronography of the corticostriatal connections. Research Pub. A. Research Nerv. & Ment. Dis., v. 21, p. 246.

DUSSER DE BARENNE, J. G., & KLEINKNECHT, F.
1924. Ueber den Einfluss der Reizung der Grosshirnrinde auf den allgemeinen Blutdruck. Ztschr. f. Biol., v. 82, p. 13.

DUSSER DE BARENNE, J. G., & McCULLOCH, W. S.
1936. Functional boundaries in the sensory-motor cortex of the monkey. Proc. Soc. Exper. Biol. & Med., v. 35, p. 329.
1937. Local stimulatory inactivation within the cerebral cortex, the factor for extinction. Am. J. Physiol., v. 118, p. 510.
1938. Functional organization in the sensory cortex of the monkey (*Macaca mulatta*). J. Neurophysiol., v. 1, p. 69.
1939. Factors for facilitation and extinction in the central nervous system. *Ibid.*, v. 2, p. 319.
1939. Physiological delimitation of neurones in the central nervous system. Am. J. Physiol., v. 127, p. 620.
1941. Functional interdependence of sensory cortex and thalamus. J. Neurophysiol., v. 3, p. 304.
1941. Suppression of motor response obtained from area 4 by stimulation of area 4s. *Ibid.*, p. 311.

DUSSER DE BARENNE, J. G., & SAGER, O.
1937. Sensory functions of the optic thalamus of the monkey (*Macacus rhesus*): symptomatology and functional localization investigated with the method of local strychninization. Arch. Neurol. & Psychiat., v. 38, p. 913.

DUSSER DE BARENNE, J. G., & ZIMMERMAN, H. M.
1935. Changes in the cerebral cortex produced by thermocoagulation: a suggestion to neurosurgery. Arch. Neurol. & Psychiat., v. 33, p. 123.

DUTT, K. C.
1938. Cataract operations in the prehistoric age. Arch. Ophth., v. 20 (77), p. 1.

Duus, P.
1939. Ueber psychische Störungen bei Tumoren des Orbitalhirns. Arch. f. Psychiat., v. 109, p. 596.

Duval, M.
1887. L'aphasie depuis Broca. Bull. Soc. anthropol., Paris, 3d ser., v. 10, p. 743; *also* Rev. scient., Paris, v. 40, p. 769; published separately by A. Hennuyer, Paris, 1888.
1889. Atlas d'embryologie. G. Masson, Paris.
1895. Hypothèse sur la physiologie des centres nerveux: théorie histologique du sommeil. Compt. rend. Soc. de biol., ser. 10, v. 2, p. 74. (*See* here remarks by J.-P. Morat on p. 114.)
1900. Les neurones, l'amiboïdisme nerveux et la théorie histologique du sommeil. Rev. d. l'École d'anthropol. Paris, v. 10, p. 37.

Duval, R.
1899. La littérature syriaque. ("Bibliothèque de l'enseignement de l'histoire ecclésiastique; anciennes littératures chrétiennes," v. 2.) V. Lecoffre, Paris.

Dvořák-Theobald, G.
1934. Schlemm's canal: its anastomoses and anatomic relations. Tr. Am. Ophth. Soc., v. 32, p. 574.

Dvorine, I.
1944. Dvorine color perception testing charts. Charles C Thomas, Springfield, Ill.; Waverly Press, Baltimore.

Dymond, J. R., & Vladykov, V. D.
1934. The distribution and relationship of the salmonoid fishes of North America and North Asia. Proc. Fifth Pacific Sc. Cong., p. 3741.

Dyson, F.
1923. Large telescopes. Tr. Opt. Soc. London, v. 24, p. 61.

E

Eadie, W. R.
1944. The short-tailed shrew and field mouse predation. J. Mammal., v. 25, p. 359.
1952. Shrew predation and vole population on a localized area. *Ibid.*, v. 33, p. 185.

Earle, C.
1897. On the affinities of *Tarsius:* a contribution to the phylogeny of the primates. Am. Naturalist, v. 31, pp. 569, 680.

Easson, L. H., & Stedman, E.
1937. The specificity of choline esterase. Biochem. J., v. 31, p. 1723.

Eaton, T. H.
1951. Comparative anatomy of the vertebrates. Harper & Bros., New York.

Ebers, G. M.
1875. Papyrus Ebers. Das hermetische Buch über die Arzneimittel der alten Aegypter in hieratischer Schrift. 2 vols. W. Engelmann, Leipzig.
1889. Papyrus Ebers. Die Maasse und das Kapitel über die Augenkrankheiten. 2 vols. S. Hirzel, Leipzig.

Eberstaller
1884. Zur Oberflächen-Anatomie der Grosshirn-Hemisphären. Wien. med. Blätter, v. 7, pp. 479, 543, 610, 644.

Ebner, V.
1902. Vom Sehorgane. *In:* Kölliker, Handb. d. Gewebelehre, 6th ed., v. 3, pp. 771, 809.
1920. Gustaf Magnus Retzius. Almanach d. Akad. d. Wissensch. Wien.

Eccles, J. C.
1936. Synaptic and neuro-muscular transmission. Ergebn. d. Physiol. (Asher & Spiro), v. 38, p. 339; and Physiol. Rev., v. 17, p. 538.
1937. The discharge of impulses from ganglion cells. J. Physiol., v. 91, p. 1.
1942–43. Synaptic potentials and transmission in sympathetic ganglion. *Ibid.*, v. 101, p. 465.
1944–45. The nature of synaptic transmission in a sympathetic ganglion. *Ibid.*, v. 103, p. 27.
1953. The neurophysiological basis of mind. Clarendon Press, Oxford.

Eccles, J. C., & Sherrington, C. S.
1930. Numbers and contraction-values of individual motor-units examined in some muscles of the limbs. Proc. Roy. Soc. London, ser. B, v. 106, p. 326.

Echlin, F. A.
1942. Vasospasm and focal cerebral ischemia. Arch. Neurol. & Psychiat., v. 47, p. 77.

Eck, G. J. van
1939. Farbensehen und Zapfenfunction bei der Singdrossel. Arch. néerl. de zool., v. 3, p. 450.

Ecker, A.
1868. Zur Entwicklungsgeschichte der Furchen und Windungen der Grosshirnhemisphären im Foetus des Menschen. Arch. f. Anthropol., v. 3, p. 203.
1869. Die Hirnwindungen des Menschen nach eigenen Untersuchungen. F. Vieweg & Sohn, Braunschweig.
1873. The cerebral convolutions of man, represented according to original observations, especially upon their development in the foetus. Intended for the use of physicians. By A. E., Professor of Anatomy and Comparative Anatomy in the University of

Freiburg, Baden. Translated by Robert T. Edes, M.D. D. Appleton & Co., New York.

Eckstein, A.
1935. Untersuchungen über die Angioarchitektonik im frühen Kindesalter. Ztschr. f. d. ges. Neurol. u. Psychiat., v. 154, p. 298.

Economo, C.
1926. Die Bedeutung der Hirnwindungen. Allg. Ztschr. f. Psychiat., v. 84, p. 123.
1927. Zellaufbau der Grosshirnrinde des Menschen. Zehn Vorlesungen. J. Springer, Berlin.
1928. Bemerkungen zu dem Aufsatz von Marthe Vogt "Ueber omnilaminäre Strukturdifferenzen und lineare Grenzen der architektonischen Felder der hinteren Zentralwindung des Menschen." J. f. Psychol. u. Neurol., v. 36, p. 320.
1928. La cytoarchitectonie et la cérébration progressive. Rev. neurol., v. 35 (2), p. 643.
1929. Der Zellaufbau der Grosshirnrinde und die progressive Cerebration. Ergebn. d. Physiol., v. 29, p. 83.
1929. The cytoarchitectonics of the human cerebral cortex. Oxford University Press, London.
1930. Nochmals zur Frage der arealen Grenzen in der Hirnrinde. Ztschr. f. d. ges. Neurol. u. Psychiat., v. 124, p. 309.
1930. Zur Frage des Vorkommens der Affenspalte beim Menschen im Lichte der Cytoarchitektonik. *Ibid.*, v. 130, p. 419.
1931. Ueber progressive Cerebration und über die Erforschung der anatomischen Grundlagen der Begabung. Wien. klin. Wchnschr., v. 44 (1), p. 597.

Economo, C., Fuchs, A., & Pötzl, O.
1918. Die Nachbehandlung der Kopfverletzungen. Ztschr. f. d. ges. Neurol. u. Psychiat. (Orig.), v. 43, p. 276.

Economo, C., & Horn, L.
1930. Ueber Windungsrelief, Masse und Rindenarchitektonik der Supratemporalfläche, ihre individuellen und ihre Seitenunterschiede. Ztschr. f. d. ges. Neurol. u. Psychiat., v. 130, p. 678.

Economo, C., & Koskinas, G. N.
1925. Die Cytoarchitektonik der Hirnrinde des erwachsenen Menschen. J. Springer, Wien & Berlin.

Ectors, L., Brookens, N. L., & Gerard, R. W.
1938. Autonomic and motor localization in the hypothalamus. Arch. Neurol. & Psychiat., v. 39, p. 789.

Eddington, A. S.
1930. Speech at the Kepler monument in Weilder-Stadt. Naturwiss., v. 18, p. 941.
1933. The expanding universe. Macmillan Co., New York; Cambridge University Press, Cambridge.

Eddy, S.
1945. Little-known fishes of Minnesota. (*See* on catfish, p. 11, and on small fishes, p. 28.) Minnesota Dept. Conserv. Bull. No. 9. St. Paul, Minn.

Eddy, S., & Surber, T.
1947. Northern fishes, with special reference to the upper Mississippi Valley. University of Minnesota Press, Minneapolis.

Edgerton, H. E., Niedrach, R. J., & Van Riper, W.
1951. Freezing the flight of hummingbirds. Nat. Geog. Mag., v. 100, p. 245.

Edgren, J. G.
1895. Amusie (musikalische Aphasie). Deutsche Ztschr. f. Nervenh., v. 6, p. 1.

Edinger, L.
1888–1903. Untersuchungen über die vergleichende Anatomie des Gehirns. Abh. d. Senckenberg. naturforsch. Gesellsch. Frankfurt, v. 15, p. 89; v. 18, p. 3; v. 19, p. 313; v. 20, pp. 161, 343.
1892. Ueber die Entwickelung unserer Kenntnisse von der Netzhaut des Auges. Ber. d. Senckenberg. naturforsch. Gesellsch., p. 165.
1893. Ueber die Bedeutung der Hirnrinde etc. Verhandl. d. Cong. f. inn. Med., Wiesbaden, v. 12, p. 350; *also* English trans. in J. Comp. Neurol., v. 3, p. 69.
1893. Ueber den phylogenetischen Ursprung der Rindencentren und über den Riechapparat. Arch. f. Psychiat., v. 25, p. 584.
1895. Ueber die Entwicklung des Rindensehens. *Ibid.*, v. 27, p. 950.
1895. Untersuchungen über die vergleichende Anatomie des Gehirns. II. Das Zwischenhirn, etc. Abh. d. Senckenberg. naturforsch. Gesellsch., v. 18, p. 1.
1896. Neue Studien über das Vorderhirn der Reptilien. *Ibid.*, v. 19, p. 313.
1896. Die Entwickelung der Gehirnbahnen in der Thierreihe. Allg. med. Central-Zeitung, v. 65, pp. 949, 961; Verhandl. Ges. deutsch. Naturforsch. u. Ärzte, Theil 2 (2), p. 285; Deutsche med. Wchnschr., v. 22, p. 621.
1899. Das Gedächtnis der niederen Vertebraten. Neurol. Centralbl., v. 18, p. 956.
1900. Hirnanatomie und Psychologie. 25. Wanderversamml. d. Neurol. Baden-Baden. Arch. f. Psychiat., v. 33, p. 663; *also* Brain

anatomy and psychology. Monist, v. 11, p. 339, 1900–1901.

1902. Geschichte eines Patienten, dem operativ der ganze Schläfenlappen entfernt war, ein Beitrag zur Kenntniss der Verbindungen des Schläfenlappens mit dem übrigen Gehirne. Deutsches Arch. f. klin. Med., v. 73, p. 304.

1906. Einiges vom "Gehirn" des Amphioxus. Anat. Anz., v. 28, p. 417.

1906. On the sense of hearing in frogs (correspondence with Yerkes). J. Comp. Neurol., v. 16, p. 166.

1908–11. Vorlesungen über den Bau der nervösen Zentralorgane des Menschen und der Tiere. Vol. 1: Das Zentralnervensystem des Menschen und der Säugetiere, 8th ed., 1911. Vol. 2: Vergleichende Anatomie des Gehirns, 7th ed., 1908. F. C. W. Vogel, Leipzig.

EDINGER, L., & FISCHER, B.
1913. Ein Kind mit fehlendem Grosshirn (Verhandl. d. südwestdeutsch. Neurol. u. Irr.). Ztschr. f. d. ges. Neurol. u. Psychiat. (Ref.), v. 7, p. 499.

1913. Ein Mensch ohne Grosshirn. Arch. f. d. ges. Physiol. (Pflüger), v. 152, p. 535.

EDINGER, L., & WALLENBERG, A.
1899. Untersuchungen über das Gehirn der Tauben. Anat. Anz., v. 15, p. 245.

EDINGER, T.
1929. Die fossilen Gehirne. J. Springer, Berlin.

1937. Paläoneurologie. Fortschr. d. Paläontol., v. 1, p. 235.

1949. Evolution of the horse brain. ("Geol. Soc. Amer. Mem.," No. 25.) New York.

EDRIDGE-GREEN, F. W.
1916. Binocular vision. Ophthalmoscope, v. 14, p. 315.

1916. Some subjective phenomena of vision and their explanation on the theory of vision. Ibid., p. 370.

1920. The theory of vision. Brit. J. Ophth., v. 4, p. 409.

1945. Persistence of vision. Nature, v. 155, p. 178.

EHRENBERG, C. G.
1833. Nothwendigkeit einer feineren mechanischen Zerlegung des Gehirns und der Nerven von der chemischen. . . . Ann. d. Phys. u. Chem. (Poggendorff), v. 28 (104), p. 449.

1834. Bemerkung zu vorherigem Aufsatz. Ibid., v. 31, p. 119. (See also article by C. Krause in the same volume.)

1836. Beobachtungen einer unbekannten auffallenden Structur des Seelenorgans bei Menschen und Thieren. Abh. d. kön. Akad. d. Wissensch. Berlin, p. 665, 1834.

1838. Die Infusionsthierchen als vollkommene Organismen. L. Voss, Leipzig.

EHRENHARDT, H.
1937. Formensehen und Sehschärfebestimmungen bei Eidechsen. Ztschr. f. vergl. Physiol., v. 24, p. 248.

EHRENWALD, H.
1930. Ueber das "Lesen" mit Umgehung des optischen Wahrnehmungsapparates. (Befunde bei einem Fall von reiner Wortblindheit.) Ztschr. f. d. ges. Neurol. u. Psychiat., v. 123, p. 204.

EHRHARD, H.
1924. Messende Untersuchungen über den Farbensinn der Vögel. Zugleich ein Beitrag zur Lehre von den Schmuckfarben. Zool. Jahrb. (Allg. Zool. u. Physiol.), v. 41, p. 489.

EHRLICH, P.
1885. Zur biologischen Verwertung des Methylenblau. Centralbl. f. d. med. Wissensch., v. 23, p. 113.

1886. Ueber die Methylenblaureaction der lebenden Nervensubstanz. Deutsche med. Wchnschr., 12th year, p. 49; and Biol. Centralbl., v. 6, p. 214.

EICHMANN; see DRYANDER

EIGENMANN, C. H.
1903. The eyes of the blind vertebrates of North America. V. The history of the eye of the blind fish Amblyopsis from its appearance to its disintegration in old age. In: E. L. Mark's Anniversary vol., p. 167.

1909. Cave vertebrates of America: a study in degenerative evolution, p. 241. ("Carnegie Inst. Washington Pub.," No. 104.)

EIGENMANN, C. H., & SCHAFER, G. D.
1900. The mosaic of single and twin cones in the retina of fishes. Am. Naturalist, v. 34, p. 109.

EINSTEIN, A.
1940. Considerations concerning the fundaments of theoretical physics. Nature, v. 145, p. 920; Science, v. 91, p. 487.

EISELEY, L. C.
1952. Fossil man: a personal credo. Am. J. Phys. Anthropol., N.S., v. 10, p. 1.

EISENTRAUT, M.
1943. Zehn Jahre Fledermausberingung. Zool. Anz., v. 144, p. 20.

EISLER, P.
1930. Die Anatomie des menschlichen Auges. In: SCHIECK & BRÜCKNER, Kurz. Handb. d. Ophth., v. 1, p. 1.

ELFTMAN, H.
1944. The bipedal walking of the chimpanzee. J. Mammal., v. 25, p. 67.

ELGOOD, C. L.
1951. A medical history of Persia and the eastern caliphate, from the earliest times until the year A.D. 1932. Cambridge University Press, Cambridge.

ELIAS, H.
1950. Similarity of the vascular pattern in the liver to that in the retina. Anat. Rec., v. 106, p. 191. (Abstr.)

ELLERMAN, J. R.
1940–49. Families and genera of living rodents. British Museum, London.

ELLIOT, D. G.
1910. On the genus *Presbytis*, Eschr., and "Le Tarsier," Buffon, with descriptions of two new species of tarsier. Bull. Am. Mus. Nat. Hist., v. 28, p. 151.
1912. A review of the primates. ("Monog. Am. Mus. Nat. Hist.," vols. 1, 2, & 3.) New York.

ELLIOT, R. H.
1918. The Indian operation of couching for cataract. Brit. J. Ophth., v. 2, p. 64. Also a special volume at H. K. Lewis & Co., London, 1917.

ELLIOT, W. (*see* G. R. WATERHOUSE in Proc. Zool. Soc. London, 1849, p. 106, and Mammals, Pl. XIII.)

ELLIOTT, J. S.
1914. Outlines of Greek and Roman medicine. W. Wood & Co., New York.

ELLIS, W.
1782. An authentic narrative of a voyage of Capt. Cook and Capt. Clerke in Ships *Resolution* and *Discovery*, 1776, 1777, 1778, 1779, and 1780. 2 vols. G. Robinson, London.

ELSBERG, C. A.
1932. The meningeal fibroblastomas on the under surface of the temporal lobe, and the surgical treatment. Bull. Neurol. Inst. New York, v. 2, p. 95.

ELSBERG, C. A., & SPOTNITZ, H.
1937. Some neural components of the visual response. Am. J. Physiol., v. 118, p. 792.
1937. Factors which influence dark adaptation. J. Physiol., v. 120, p. 689.
1937. The sense of vision. Bull. Neurol. Inst. New York, v. 6, pp. 233, 234, 243, 253.
1938. A theory of retino-cerebral function with formulas for threshold vision and light and dark adaptation at the fovea. Am. J. Physiol., v. 121, p. 454.

ELSCHNIG, A.
1888. Opticociliares Gefäss. Arch. f. Augenh., v. 18, p. 295.
1897. Cilioretinale Gefässe. Arch. f. Ophth. (Graefe), v. 44, p. 144; *also* Compt. rend. Cong. internat. méd., v. 6, sec. 11, p. 273.
1898. Ueber optico-ciliare Gefässe. Klin. Monatsbl. f. Augenh., v. 36, p. 93.
1900. Der normale Sehnerveneintritt des menschlichen Auges. Denkschr. d. math. naturw. Kl. d. K. Akad. d. Wissensch. Wien, v. 70, p. 219.

ELTON, C. S.
1932. Article: Ecology, animal, Encyclopaedia Britannica, 14th ed., v. 7, p. 915.
1950. The ecology of animals. 3d ed. John Wiley & Sons, New York.

ELVIDGE, A. R.
1938. The cerebral vessels studied by angiography. Research Pub. A. Research Nerv. & Ment. Dis., v. 18, p. 110. Williams & Wilkins Co., Baltimore.

ELWYN, H.
1946. Diseases of the retina. Blakiston Co., Philadelphia & Toronto.

ELZE, C.
1929. Einige Fasersysteme des menschlichen Grosshirns mit der Abfaserungsmethode untersucht. (1. Sehstrahlung, 2. Cingulum, 3. Fornix, 4. Commissura anterior.) Ztschr. f. Anat. u. Entw., v. 88, p. 166.
1940. Sehorgan, *Organon visus. In:* H. BRAUS, Anatomie des Menschen, v. 4 (2), p. 392.

EMBDEN, G.
1901. Primitivfibrillenverlauf in der Netzhaut. Arch. f. mikr. Anat., v. 57, p. 570.

EMERSON, A. E.
1938. Termite nests—a study of the phylogeny of behavior. Ecol. Monog., v. 8, p. 247.

EMERSON, S. A., & MARTIN, L. C.
1925. The effect of peripheral stimulation of the retina on the contrast sensibility of the fovea. Proc. Roy. Soc. London, ser. B, v. 98, p. 353.

EMERY, C.
*1875. La terminazione del nervo ottico nella retina dei batraci urodeli. Atti d. Soc. ital. di sc. nat., v. 18, p. 391.

EMSLEY, H. H.
1952. Visual optics. Hatton Press, London.

ENCYCLOPAEDIA BRITANNICA
1929–32. A new survey of universal knowledge, 14th ed., 24 vols. *See* articles: Distribution of animals, Camera obscura, Light, Plank-

ton, Sight, Vision, Zoölogical regions, etc. (*See also* later eds.)

ENGEL, S.
1931. Störungen des Gesichtsfeldes. Fortschr. d. Neurol., Psychiat. u. Grenzgeb., v. 3, p. 388.

ENGELHARDT, F.
1924. Tentakelapparat und Auge von *Ichthyophis*. Jena. Ztschr. f. Naturwiss., v. 60, p. 241.

ENGELKING, E.
1921. Ueber die Pupillenreaktion bei angeborener totaler Farbenblindheit. Ein Beitrag zum Problem der pupillomotorischen Aufnahmeorgane. Klin. Monatsbl. f. Augenh., v. 66, p. 707.
1925. Ueber die anomal-trichromatischen Farbensysteme. Ber. d. Deutsch. ophth. Gesellsch. Heidelberg, v. 45, p. 83.
1927. Was wissen wir von Uebergangsformen zwischen anomaler Trichromasie und normalem Farbensinn? *Ibid.*, v. 46, p. 154.
1927. Netzhautort und Stellungsfaktor. (Eine interessante klinische Demonstration in ihrer lokalisatorischen Bedeutung.) Klin. Monatsbl. f. Augenh., v. 78, p. 546.
1934. Ueber die physiologische Bedeutung der Farbenschärfe. *Ibid.*, v. 93, p. 243.

ENGELMANN, T. W.
1885. Ueber Bewegungen der Zapfen und Pigmentzellen der Netzhaut unter dem Einfluss des Lichtes und des Nervensystems. Arch. f. d. ges. Physiol. (Pflüger), v. 35, p. 498.

ENGERTH, G., & HOFF, H.
1930. Ein Fall von Halluzinationen im hemianopischen Gesichtsfeld. Beitr. z. Genese d. opt. Halluzinationen. Monatsschr. f. Psychiat. u. Neurol., v. 74, p. 246.
1931. Ein weiterer Beitrag zur Lehre von der Stirnhirnfunktion. Ztschr. f. d. ges. Neurol. u. Psychiat., v. 129, p. 332.

ENGERTH, G., HOFF, H., & PÖTZL, O.
1935. Zur Patho-Physiologie der hemianopischen Halluzinationen. Ztschr. f. d. ges. Neurol. u. Psychiat., v. 152, p. 399.

ENRÍQUEZ, M. LÓPEZ
1926. Oligodendroglía de las vías ópticas. Bol. r. Soc. españ. de hist. nat., v. 26, p. 301.

ERBSLÖH, W.
1902. Ueber einen Fall von Occipitaltumor, ein Beitrag zur Frage der Desorientiertheit sowie zur Frage der Lokalisation psychischer Störungen. Monatsschr. f. Psychiat. u. Neurol., v. 12, p. 161.

ERGGELET, H.
1916. Geschichtliches zur Kenntnis des Akkommodationsvorganges. Ztschr. f. ophth. Optik, v. 3, p. 18.
1921. Versuch zur beidäugigen Tiefenwahrnehmung bei hoher Ungleichsichtigkeit. Klin. Monatsbl. f. Augenh., v. 66, p. 685.
1929. Lichtbilder des Augenhintergrundes. Arch. f. Augenh., vols. 100–101, p. 402.

ERGGELET, H., & WIMMER, M.
1928. Ueber das ultrarote Absorptionsspektrum der Augenmedien und des Wassers. Ztschr. f. ophth. Optik, v. 16, p. 97.

ERICKSON, H. A.
1933. Light intensity at different depths in lake water. J. Opt. Soc. Amer., v. 23, p. 170.

ERLANGER, J.
1939. The initiation of impulses in axons. J. Neurophysiol., v. 2, p. 370.

ERLANGER, J., & BLAIR, E. A.
1940. Facilitation and difficilitation effected by nerve impulses in peripheral fibers. J. Neurophysiol., v. 3, p. 107.

ERLANGER, J., & GASSER, H. S.
1930. The action potential in fibers of slow conduction in spinal roots and somatic nerves. Am. J. Physiol., v. 92, p. 43.
1937. Electrical signs of nervous activity. (Eldridge Reeves Johnson Foundation Lect.) University of Pennsylvania Press, Philadelphia.

ESCHER-DESRIVIÈRES, J.
1937. La perception des objets en mouvement à la périphérie du champ visuel. Déterminations quantitatives. Bull. Soc. d'opht. Paris, v. 49, p. 587.

'ESPINASSE, P. G.
1934. The development of the hypophysio-portal system in man. J. Anat., v. 68, p. 11.

ESSEN, J. VAN
1938. Zur Funktion des Tapetum lucidum; zugleich ein Beitrag zur Sinnesphysiologie selbstleuchtender Tiere. Ztschr. f. Sinnesphysiol., v. 67, p. 245.

ESSER, A. A. M.
1930. Die Ophthalmologie des Bhāvaprakāśa. Stud. z. Gesch. d. Med. (Sudhoff & Sigerist), Fasc. 19.
1934. Die Ophthalmologie des Suśruta. *Ibid.*, Fasc. 22.

ESTABLE, C.
1928. Apuntes sobre la retina. An. Inst. neurol. Montevideo, v. 1, p. 328.
1928. Bemerkungen über die Retina. Zentralbl. f. d. ges. Ophth., v. 21, p. 210, 1929.
1947. Nonvisual functions of the retina. Paper read at the second Pan-American Congress

of Ophtholmology in Montevideo, 1945. Arch. Ophth., v. 38, p. 405.

ESTIENNE; *see* STEPHANUS

ETTLINGER, M.
1925. Beiträge zur Lehre von der Tierseele und ihrer Entwicklung. Aschendorffsche Verlagsbuchh. Veröff. d. kath. Inst. f. Phil. Albertus-Magnus-Akad zu Köln, v. 1 (6).

EUCLID (EUCLEIDES)
Ca. 300 B.C. Opera omnia, ed. I. L. HEIBERG & H. MENGE. 9 vols. (v. 7: Optica). B. G. Teubner, Lipsiae (Leipzig), 1883–1916. (*See also* T. L. Heath.)

EULER, L.
1745. Sur la lumière et les couleurs. Hist. Acad. roy. sc. & belles-lettres Berlin, p. 17 (wissenschaftliche Mittheilungen).
1752. Essai d'une explication physique des couleurs engendrées sur des surfaces extrêmement minces. *Ibid.*, p. 262.
1753. Examen d'une controverse sur la loi de réfraction des rayons de différentes couleurs par rapport à la diversité des milieux transparents par lesquels ils sont transmis. *Ibid.*, p. 294.
1754. De la réfraction de la lumière en passant par l'atmosphère selon les divers degrés tant de la chaleur que de l'élasticité de l'air. *Ibid.*, p. 131.
1754. Recherches physiques sur la diverse réfrangibilité des rayons de lumière. *Ibid.*, p. 200.
1757. Règles générales pour la construction des télescopes et des microscopes de quelque nombre de verres qu'ils soient composés. *Ibid.*, p. 283. (*See also* 1761, p. 201.)
1765. Sur la théorie générale de la dioptrique. Hist. Acad. roy. sc. Paris, p. 180, 1773.
1769–71. Dioptricae pars prima (-tertia) continens librum primum (-tertium) de explicatione principiorum, ex quibus constructio tum telescopiorum quam microscopiorum est petenda. Impensis Academiae Imperialis Scientiarum, Petropolis.

EUSTACHIO, BARTOLOMMEO
1552 (1714). Tabulae anatomicae clarissimi viri Bartholomaei Eustachii quas è tenebris tandem vindicatas et Sanctissimi Domini Clementis XI. Pont. Max. munificentiâ dono acceptas praefatione, notisque illustravit, ac ipso suae bibliothecae dedicationis die publici juris fecit Jo. Maria Lancisius, intimus cubicularius, & archiater pontificius. Romae MDCCXIV. Ex Officina Typographica Francisci Gonzagae in Via lata. Praesidium permissu. Other editions Amsterdam, 1722, and Leyden, 1761.

EVANS, F. G.
1944. The morphological status of the modern Amphibia among the Tetrapoda. J. Morphol., v. 74, p. 43.
1951. Notes on a population of the ground squirrel (*Citellus tridecemlineatus*) in an abandoned field in southeastern Michigan. J. Mammal., v. 32, p. 437.

EVANS, J. N.
1939. Classic characteristics of defects of the visual field. Arch. Ophth., v. 22 (O.S., v. 79), p. 410.
1941. A scotoma associated with menstruation. Am. J. Ophth., v. 24, p. 507.

EVANS, J. N., & BROWDER, J.
1943. A problem of split macula—visual field study. Tr. Am. Ophth. Soc., v. 41, p. 167.

EVANS, J. P., & McEACHERN, D.
1938. The circulatory changes in cerebral vascular occlusion and in cerebral cicatrization. Research Pub. A. Research Nerv. & Ment. Dis., v. 18, p. 379. Williams & Wilkins Co., Baltimore.

EVANS, M. S.
1946. Monocular vision training. Williams & Wilkins Co., Baltimore.

EVERSBUSCH, O.
1882. Vergleichende Studien über den feineren Bau der Iris. I. Der anatomische Grund der spaltförmigen Pupille. Ztschr. f. vergl. Augenh., v. 1, p. 49.
1885. Vergleichende Studien über den feineren Bau der Iris der Säugethiere. *Ibid.*, v. 3, p. 33.

EWALD, A.
1878. Ueber die entoptische Wahrnehmung der Macula lutea und des Sehpurpurs. Untersuch. physiol. Inst. Univ. Heidelberg, v. 2, p. 241.

EWALD, A., & KÜHNE, W.
1877. Untersuchungen über den Sehpurpur. Untersuch. physiol. Inst. Univ. Heidelberg, v. 1, pp. 139, 248, 370.

EWALD, C. A.
1898. Ein Fall von centraler Augenmuskellähmung. Berlin. klin. Wchnschr., v. 53, p. 175.

EWALD, G.
1931. Ueber die Notwendigkeit einer pathophysiologischen Unterlegung der psychiatrischen Krankheitseinteilung. Ztschr. f. d. ges. Neurol. u. Psychiat., v. 131, p. 18.

EWALD, J. R.
1922. Schallbildertheorie und Erkenntnistheorie. Ztschr. f. Sinnesphysiol., v. 53, p. 213.

EWART, J. C., & THIN, G.
  1877. On the structure of the retina. J. Anat. & Physiol., v. 11, p. 96.
EWENS, G. F. W.
  1893. A theory of cortical visual representation. Brain, v. 16, p. 475.
EXNER, S.
  1876. Ueber das Sehen von Bewegungen und die Theorie des zusammengesetzten Auges. Sitzungsb. d. Akad. Wissensch. Wien, math.-naturw. Cl., Abt. 3, v. 72, p. 156.
  1881. Untersuchungen über die Localisation der Functionen in der Grosshirnrinde des Menschen. W. Braumüller, Wien.
  1886. Ueber die Functionsweise der Netzhautperipherie und den Sitz der Nachbilder. Arch. f. Ophth. (Graefe), v. 32 (1), p. 233.
  1891. Die Physiologie der facettierten Augen von Krebsen und Insecten. F. Deuticke, Leipzig & Wien.
  1894. Entwurf zu einer physiologischen Erklärung der psychischen Erscheinungen. F. Deuticke, Wien.
  1898. Studien auf dem Grenzgebiete des localisierten Sehens. Arch. f. d. ges. Physiol. (Pflüger), v. 73, p. 117.
  1904. Ueber den centralen Sehact. Neurol. Centralbl., v. 24, p. 851.
  1904. Zur Kenntnis des zentralen Sehaktes. Ztschr. f. Psychol. u. Physiol. d. Sinnesorg., v. 36, p. 194.
EYCLESHYMER, A. C.
  1893. The development of the optic vesicles in Amphibia. J. Morphol., v. 8, p. 189.
  1895. The early development of *Amblystoma*, with observations on some other vertebrates. *Ibid.*, v. 10, p. 343.

F

FABRI, H.
  1667. Synopsis optica. Lugduni, sumpt. H. Boissat & G. Remeus.
FABRICIUS, FABRIZIO, FABRICI; *see* AQUAPENDENS
FABRITIUS, H.
  1924. Ueber Störungen des Bewusstseins bei lokalisierten Gehirnaffektionen und ihre Abhängigkeit von der Lage des Herdes. Monatsschr. f. Psychiat. u. Neurol., v. 55, p. 1.
  1928. Ein Fall von sensorischer Aphasie mit Störungen der Zungensensibilität (Tastkreise). *Ibid.*, v. 68, p. 192.
FAHIE, J. J.
  1921. The scientific works of Galileo (1564–1642). *In:* C. SINGER, Studies in the history and method of science, v. 2, p. 205.

FALCAO, P.
  1944. Localization of cerebral lesion. Arg. brasil. de oftal., v. 7, p. 1. Abstr. in Arch. Ophth., v. 34, p. 252, 1945.
FALLER, A.
  1948. Die Entwicklung der makroskopisch-anatomischen Präparierkunst von Galen bis zur Neuzeit. Acta anat., suppl. 7. S. Karger, Basel.
FALLOPPIO, GABRIELLO
  1561. Gabrielis Falloppii medicis Mutinensis Observationes anatomicae. Ad Petrum Mannam medicum Cremonensem. Cum Privilegio Summi Pontificis, Regis Philippi, Senatusque Veneti. Venetiis. Apud Marcum Antonium Ulmum MDLXI.
FAURE-BEAULIEU & JACQUET, E.
  1924. Alexie pure, reliquat d'agnosie visuelle. Rev. neurol., v. 2, p. 495.
FAVARO, A.
  1886. L'ottica di C. Tolomeo, etc. Bull. bibl. e. di storia d. sc. mat. e fis. (Boncompagni), v. 19, p. 115.
FAVARO, G.
  1919. Il terzo centenario della morte di Girolamo Fabrici d'Aquapendente. Tipografia G. B. Randi, Padova.
FAVORY, A.
  1926. Les syndromes chiasmatiques d'origine syphilitique. Arch. d'opht., v. 43, p. 204.
  1926. Le syndrome chiasmatique. Étude clinique, pathogénique, thérapeutique. G. Doin, Paris.
FAWCETT, E.
  1896. The origin and the intracranial course of the ophthalmic artery, and the relationship they bear to the optic nerve. J. Anat., v. 30, p. 49.
FAWCETT, E., & BLACHFORD, J. V.
  1905. The circle of Willis: an examination of 700 specimens. J. Anat., v. 40, p. 63.
FAY, T., & GRANT, F. C.
  1923. Lesions of the optic chiasm and tracts with relation to the adjacent vascular structures. Arch. Neurol. & Psychiat., v. 9, p. 739.
FAZAKAS, A.
  1928. Ueber die zentrale und periphere Farbensehschärfe. Arch. f. Ophth. (Graefe), v. 120, p. 555.
FAZAKAS, S.
  1931. Beiträge zum Mechanismus und zur Anatomie des Tränensackes. Klin. Monatsbl. f. Augenh., v. 87, p. 731.
  1932. Die Topographie der Nebenhöhlen mit besonderer Berücksichtigung der Augenner-

ven. Zentralbl. f. d. ges. Ophth., v. 28, p. 494.

FEARING, F.

1930. Reflex action. A study in the history of physiological psychology. Williams & Wilkins Co., Baltimore.

FECHNER, G. T.

1907. Elemente der Psychophysik. 3d ed., 2 vols. Breitkopf & Härtel, Leipzig. First ed. 1860.

FEDOROV (FIÓDOROV), B. G.

1935. Untersuchungen des Regenerationsmechanismus der interneuronalen Synapse. Russ. Ark. Anat., v. 14, p. 77.

1935. Essai de l'étude intravitale des cellules nerveuses et des connexions dans le système nerveux autonome. Trav. du lab. de recherches biol. Madrid, v. 30, p. 403. English abstract in Anat. Anz. (Verh. Anat. Ges.), v. 83 suppl., p. 179.

FEDOROW, B. G., & MATWEJEWA, S. J.

1935. La structure des connexions interneuronales dans le système nerveux autonome da la grenouille. Trav. du lab. de recherches biol. Madrid, v. 30, p. 379.

FEDOROWA (FYÓDOROVA), VERA

1930. Zur Frage über die Empfindlichkeit des Auges gegen die Farbtonänderung. J. f. Psychol. u. Neurol., v. 40, p. 65.

FEENSTRA, T. P.

1922. Sur les mouvements de l'iris. Arch. néerl. physiol., v. 7, p. 251.

FEIGENBAUM, A., & KORNBLUETH, W.

1946. Paralysis of convergence with bilateral ring scotoma following injury to occipital region. Arch. Ophth., v. 35, p. 218.

FEINSTEIN, W.

1928. Die Erweiterungsreflexe der Pupillen und ihr Fehlen bei der Dementia praecox. Arch. f. Psychiat., v. 85, p. 329.

FELDBERG, W.

1942–43. Synthesis of acetylcholine in sympathetic ganglia and cholinergic nerves. J. Physiol., v. 101, p. 432.

FELDBERG, W., FESSARD, A., & NACHMANSOHN, D.

1940. The cholinergic nature of the nervous supply to the electrical organ of the torpedo (*Torpedo marmorata*). J. Physiol., v. 97, p. 3P.

FELDBERG, W., & GADDUM, J. H.

1934. Chemical transmitter at synapses in sympathetic ganglion. J. Physiol., v. 81, p. 305.

FELIX, C. H.

1926. Crossed quadrantic hemianopsia. Brit. J. Ophth., v. 10, p. 191.

FÉRÉ, C.

1882. Contribution à l'étude des troubles fonctionnels de la vision par lésions cérébrales (amblyopie croisée et hémianopsie). A. Delahaye & E. Crossnier, Paris.

1885. Trois autopsies pour servir à la localisation cérébrale des troubles de la vision. Arch. de neurol., v. 9, p. 222.

FERNEL, J. (FERNELIUS AMBIANATES; *see also* C. S. SHERRINGTON)

1542. Joannis Fernelij Ambianatis, De naturali parte medicinae libri septem, ad Henricum Francisci Galliae Regis filium. Apud Simonem Colinaeum. Parisijs. Anno M.D. XLII. Cum privilegio.

FERRARO, A.

1924. Étude anatomique du système nerveux central d'un chien dont le pallium a été enlevé. Zuidam, Utrecht.

1926. Su di una via poco conosciuta del corpus geniculatum laterale. (Fasciculus arcuatus corporis geniculati lateralis.) Nota prev. Atti Soc. ital. oto-neuro-oftal.; *also* Zentralbl. f. d. ges. Neurol. u. Psychiat., v. 46, p. 514, 1927.

FERREE, C. E., & RAND, G.

1918. Lighting in its relation to the eye. Proc. Am. Phil. Soc., v. 57, p. 440.

1920. The extent and shape of the zones of color sensitivity in relation to the intensity of the stimulus light. Am. J. Physiol. Opt., v. 1, p. 185; Am. J. Ophth., ser. 3, v. 3, p. 772.

FERRIER, D.

1874. Experimental researches in cerebral physiology and pathology. West Riding Lunatic Asylum Med. Rep., v. 3, 1873; J. Anat. & Physiol., v. 8, p. 152.

1875. Experiments on the brains of monkeys (2d ser.). (Croonian Lect.). Phil. Tr. Roy. Soc. London, v. 165, p. 433.

1878. The localisation of cerebral disease, being the Gulstonian Lectures of the Royal College of Physicians for 1878. Smith, Elder & Co., London.

1881. Cerebral amblyopia and hemiopia. Brain, v. 3, p. 456.

1886. The functions of the brain. G. P. Putnam's Sons, London. First ed. 1876.

1889. Schäfer on the temporal and occipital lobes. Brain, v. 11, p. 7. (*See also* Schäfer's reply, p. 145.)

FERRIER, D., & TURNER, W. A.

1898. An experimental research upon cerebrocortical afferent and efferent tracts. Proc. Roy. Soc. London, v. 62, p. 1.

FERRIER, D., & TURNER, W. A.—*Continued*

1898. On cerebro-cortical afferent and efferent tracts. Phil. Tr. Roy. Soc. London, ser. B, v. 190, p. 1.

1901. Experimental lesions of the corpora quadrigemina in monkeys. Brain, v. 24, p. 27.

FERRIER, D., & YEO, G. F.

1884. A record of the experiments on the effects of lesions of different regions of the cerebral hemispheres. Phil. Tr. Roy Soc London, v. 175, p. 479.

FERRIS, E. B.

1941. Objective measurement of relative intracranial blood flow in man, with observations concerning hydrodynamics of the craniovertebral system. Arch. Neurol. & Psychiat., v. 46, p. 377.

FESSLER, F.

1920. Zur Entwicklungsmechanik des Auges. Arch. f. Entw., v. 46, p. 169.

FEUCHTWANGER, E.

1923. Periodische Störungen des Sehens nach Hirnschädigung. München. med. Wchnschr., v. 70, p. 983.

1923. Die Funktionen des Stirnhirns. ("Monog. a. d. Gesamtgeb. d. Neurol. u. Psychiat.," Fasc. 38.) J. Springer, Berlin.

1926. Zur pathologischen Psychologie des optischen Raum- und Gestalterfassens. Ber. ü. d. 9. Kong. f. exper. Psychol.; *also* Zentralbl. f. d. ges. Neurol. u. Psychiat., v. 49, p. 262.

1930. Amusie. Studien zur pathologischen Psychologie der akustischen Wahrnehmung und Vorstellung und ihrer Strukturgebiete besonders in Musik und Sprache. ("Monog. a. d. Gesamtgeb. d. Neurol. u. Psychiat.," Fasc. 57.) J. Springer, Berlin.

FICARRA, B. J.

1948. Essays on historical medicine. Froben Press, New York.

FICK, A.

1864. Lehrbuch der Anatomie und Physiologie der Sinnesorgane. M. Schauenburg, Lahr.

FICK, A. E.

1898. Ueber Stäbchensehschärfe und Zapfensehschärfe. Arch. f. Ophth. (Graefe), v. 45 (2), p. 336.

FICK, A. E., & GÜRBER, A.

1890. Ueber Erholung der Netzhaut. Arch. f. Ophth. (Graefe), v. 36 (2), p. 245.

FIELD, E. J., GRAYSON, J., & ROGERS, A. F.

1951. Observations on the blood flow in the spinal cord of the rabbit. J. Physiol., v. 114, p. 56.

FIELD, E. J., & HARRISON, R. J.

1947. Anatomical terms: their origin and derivation. W. Heffer, Cambridge, England.

FILEHNE, W.

1922. Ueber foveale Wahrnehmung scheinbarer Ruhe an bewegten Körpern und deren Lokalisation, sowie über die Aberration der Sterne. Ztschr. f. Sinnesphysiol., v. 53, p. 234.

FILIMÓNOFF, I. N.

1929. Zur embryonalen und postembryonalen Entwicklung der Grosshirnrinde des Menschen. J, f, Psychol. u. Neurol., v. 39, p. 323.

1931–33. Ueber die Variabilität der Grosshirnrindenstruktur. I. Allgemeine Betrachtungen. II. Regio occipitalis beim erwachsenen Menschen. III. Regio occipitalis bei den höheren und niederen Affen. *Ibid.*, v. 42, p. 210; v. 44, p. 1; v. 45, p. 69.

1947. A rational subdivision of the cerebral cortex. Arch. Neurol. & Psychiat., v. 58, p. 296.

FILIMÓNOFF, I. N., & SARKISOFF, S. A.

1935. Les travaux de l'Institut du Cerveau, Moscou, v. 1 (papers by G. I. Polyakóff; E. P. Kónonova, I. A. Stankévitsch & J. G. Schéwtschenko, A. S. Tschérnycheff & S. M. Blinków).

FINCHAM, E. F.

1924–25. Photomicrographs of sections of the human eye. Tr. Opt. Soc. London, v. 26, p. 198.

1926. The changes in the form of the crystalline lens in accommodation. Am. J. Physiol. Optics, v. 7, p. 469; *also* Tr. Opt. Soc. London, v. 26, p. 239.

1928–29. The function of the lens capsule in the accommodation of the eye. Tr. Opt. Soc. London, v. 30, p. 101.

1937. The mechanism of accommodation. Brit. J. Ophth., monog. suppl. 8, pp. 1–80.

FINGERMAN, M., & BROWN, F. A.

1952. A "Purkinje shift" in insect vision. Science, v. 116, p. 171.

FINKELSTEIN, F. E.

1935. Ueber zwei Fälle von *Anophthalmus congenitus* mit besonderer Berücksichtigung der zentralen optischen Bahnen. Schweiz. Arch. f. Neurol. u. Psychiat., v. 37, p. 3.

FINLEY, K. H.

1938. The capillary bed of the paraventricular and supra-optic nuclei of the hypothalamus. Research Pub. A. Research Nerv. & Ment. Dis., v. 18, p. 94. Williams & Wilkins Co., Baltimore; *also* J. Comp. Neurol., v. 71, p. 1, 1939.

1940. Angio-architecture of the hypothalamus and its peculiarities. Research Pub. A. Research Nerv. & Ment. Dis., v. 20, p. 286.

FISCHEL, A.
  1914. Ueber gestaltende Ursachen bei der Entwicklung des Auges. Prager med. Wchnschr., v. 39, p. 313.
  1918. Zur Frage der Bildungsursachen des Auges. Arch. f. Entw.-Mech. d. Org., v. 44, p. 647.
  1921. Ueber normale und abnorme Entwicklung des Auges. I. Ueber Art und Ort der ersten Augenanlage sowie über die formale und kausale Genese der Cyclopie. II. Zur Entwicklungsmechanik der Linse. *Ibid.*, v. 49, p. 383.
FISCHEL, W.
  1930. Weitere Untersuchung der Ziele der tierischen Handlung. Ztschr. f. vergl. Physiol., v. 11, p. 523.
  1938. Psyche und Leistung der Tiere. W. de Gruyter & Co., Berlin.
FISCHER, F. P.
  1925. Ueber die Beeinflussung des Blutumlaufes der Netzhaut. Arch. f. Augenh., v. 96, p. 97.
  1928. Ueber die Darstellung der Hornhautoberfläche und ihrer Veränderungen im Reflexbild. *Ibid.*, v. 98, p. 1.
  1929. Vitalfärbung am Auge. Kolloidchem. Beihefte, v. 28, p. 333.
  1929. Über die Permeabilität der Hornhaut und über Vitalfärbungen des vorderen Bulbusabschnittes mit Bemerkungen über die Vitalfärbung des Plexus chorioideus. Arch. f. Augenh., v. 100, p. 480.
  1931. Die klinische Bedeutung der Hornhautdurchlässigkeit. Klin. Monatsbl. f. Augenh., v. 86, p. 298.
  1931. Ueber die Diffusion des Hämoglobins in kolloide und molekulardisperse Lösungen. Kolloid-Ztschr., v. 57, p. 166.
  1932. Ueber Spinnbarkeit des Glaskörpers tierischer und menschlicher Augen. *Ibid.*, v. 61, p. 265.
  1932. Elektrostatische Messungen am lebenden Auge. Arch. f. Augenh., v. 106, p. 428.
  1934. Die Quellung der Augenlinse. Kolloid-Ztschr., v. 67, p. 317.
  1938. Der Wasserhaushalt des Auges und seiner Teile. Doc. Ophth., v. 1, p. 79.
  1940. The biochemistry and metabolism of the eye. Mod. Trends in Ophth., p. 348.
FISCHER, I.
  1932–33. Biographisches Lexikon der hervorragenden Aerzte der letzten fünfzig Jahre, 2 vols. Urban & Schwarzenberg, Berlin & Wien.
FISCHER, M. H.
  1931. Die Orientierung im Raume bei Wirbeltieren und beim Menschen. *In:* BETHE *et al.*, Handb. d. norm. u. path. Physiol., v. 15 (2), p. 909.
  1932. Körperstellung und Körperhaltung bei Fischen, Amphibien, Reptilien und Vögeln. *In:* BETHE *et al.*, Handb. d. norm. u. path. Physiol., v. 18, p. 390.
  1932. Elektrobiologische Erscheinungen an der Hirnrinde. I. Arch. f. d. ges. Physiol. (Pflüger), v. 230, p. 161.
  1933. Elektrobiologische Erscheinungen an der Hirnrinde bei Belichtung eines Auges. II. *Ibid.*, v. 233, p. 738.
FISCHER, M. H., & LÖWENBACH, H.
  1935. Messende Untersuchungen über Sehferne und Sehtiefe. Arch. f. d. ges. Physiol. (Pflüger), v. 235, p. 609.
FISCHER-VON BÜNAU, H., & FISCHER, F. P.
  1932. Hat der Glaskörper einen Stoffwechsel? Arch. f. Augenh., v. 106, p. 463.
FISHER, C.
  1927. Carl Akeley and his work. Scient. Monthly, v. 24, p. 97.
FISHER, C. M.
  1951. Transient monocular blindness associated with hemiplegia. Trans. Am. Neurol. A. (76th ann. meet.), p. 154.
FISHER, J. H.
  1918. Migraine. Proc. Roy. Soc. Med., v. 12, p. 49.
FISHER, T. W.
  1896. The neuron theory and cerebral localization. Proc. Am. Med.-Psychol. A., 52d meet., p. 101.
FITZGERALD, A.
  1935. Rearing marmosets in captivity. J. Mammal., v. 16, p. 181.
FLASHMAN, J. F.
  1908. The morphology of the brain of the Australian aboriginal. Rep. Path. Lab. Lun. Dpt., New South Wales Government, v. 1 (3), p. 1; abstr. in Zentralbl. f. Anthropol., v. 14, p. 279.
FLATAU, E., & JACOBSOHN, L.
  1899. Handbuch der Anatomie und vergleichenden Anatomie des Centralnervensystems der Säugethiere, v. 1. S. Karger, Berlin.
FLECHSIG, P.
  1873–1927; for the bibliography of his writings *see* F. Quensel 1917, and R. A. Pfeifer 1930.
  1873. Ueber einige Beziehungen zwischen sekundären Degenerationen und Entwicklungsvorgängen im menschlichen Rückenmark. Arch. d. Heilk., v. 14, p. 464; *also* Centralbl. f. med. Wissensch., p. 280.

FLECHSIG, P.—*Continued*

1874. Ueber Entwicklung der Markweisse im centralen Nervensystem des Menschen. Allg. Ztschr. f. Psychiat., v. 30, p. 112.

1876. Die Leitungsbahnen im Gehirn und Rückenmark des Menschen auf Grund entwickelungsgeschichtlicher Untersuchungen. W. Engelmann, Leipzig.

1877–78 Ueber "Systemerkrankungen" im Rükkenmark. Arch. d. Heilk., v. 18, pp. 101, 289; v. 19, pp. 53, 441.

1878. Systemerkrankungen des Rückenmarks. W. Wigand, Leipzig.

1878. Capsula interna des Gehirns. Centralbl. f. d. med. Wissensch., v. 16, p. 321.

1881. Zur Anatomie und Entwicklungsgeschichte der Leitungsbahnen im Grosshirn des Menschen. Arch. f. Anat. u. Entw., p. 12.

1883. Plan des menschlichen Gehirns. Veit & Co., Leipzig.

1885. Untersuchungen über die Schleifenschicht. By W. Bechterew. Communicated by Flechsig. Ber. d. kgl. sächs. Gesellsch. d. Wissensch. Leipzig, math.-phys. Kl., v. 37, p. 241.

1889. Ueber eine neue Färbungsmethode des centralen Nervensystems und deren Ergebnisse bezüglich des Zusammenhanges von Ganglienzellen und Nervenfasern. *Ibid.*, v. 41, p. 328.

1894. Zur Entwickelungsgeschichte der Associationssysteme im menschlichen Gehirn. Neurol. Centralbl., v. 13, p. 606.

1894. Ueber ein neues Eintheilungsprincip der Grosshirn-Oberfläche. *Ibid.*, pp. 674, 809.

1895. Weitere Mittheilungen über die Sinnes- und Associationscentren des menschlichen Gehirns. *Ibid.*, v. 14, pp. 1118, 1177.

*1896. Ueber die Localisation der geistigen Vorgänge, insbesondere der Sinnesempfindungen des Menschen. Veit & Co., Leipzig.

1896. Weitere Mittheilungen über den Stabkranz des menschlichen Grosshirns. Neurol. Centralbl., v. 15, p. 2.

1896. Notiz, die "Schleife" betreffend. *Ibid.*, p. 449.

1896. Demonstration of brain sections (by Jacobsohn). *Ibid.*, p. 623.

1896. Gehirn und Seele. Rede, gehalten am 31. October 1894 in der Universitätskirche zu Leipzig. Veit & Co., Leipzig. 2d ed. *Also* Neurol. Centralbl., v. 15, p. 661.

1896. Die Localisation der geistigen Vorgänge. Neurol. Centralbl., v. 15, pp. 999, 1003.

1898. Neue Untersuchungen über die Mark-
bildung in den menschlichen Grosshirnlappen. *Ibid.*, v. 17, p. 977.

1899. Demonstration of sections of the brain showing successive development of fiber systems. *Ibid.*, v. 18, p. 1060.

1900. Ueber die Projections- und Associationscentren des menschlichen Grosshirns. *Ibid.*, v. 19, p. 828. (*See here also* critique by Hitzig and Monakow.)

1901. Ueber die entwickelungsgeschichtliche (myelogenetische) Flächengliederung der Grosshirnrinde des Menschen. Arch. ital. de biol., v. 36, p. 30.

1903. Weitere Mittheilungen über die entwickelungsgeschichtlichen (myelogenetischen) Felder in der menschlichen Grosshirnrinde. Neurol. Centralbl., v. 22, p. 202.

1904. Einige Bemerkungen über die Untersuchungsmethoden der Grosshirnrinde, insbesondere des Menschen. Ber. d. kgl. sächs. Gesellsch. Wissensch., Leipzig, math.-phys. Kl., v. 56, p. 177; Arch. f. Anat. u. Entw., p. 337, 1905.

1905. Hirnphysiologie und Willenstheorie. Ostwalds Ann. d. Naturphil., v. 4, p. 475; Atti Cong. internat. di psicol., Roma, v. 5, p. 73, 1906.

1907. Zur Anatomie der Hörsphäre des menschlichen Gehirns. Ber. d. kgl. sächs. Gesellsch. d. Wissensch., Leipzig, math.-phys. Kl., v. 59, p. 397.

1908. Bemerkungen über die Hörsphäre des menschlichen Gehirns. Neurol. Centralbl., v. 27, pp. 2, 50.

1920. Anatomie des menschlichen Gehirns und Rückenmarks auf myelogenetischer Grundlage. G. Thieme, Leipzig.

1921. Die myelogenetische Gliederung der Leitungsbahnen des Linsenkerns beim Menschen. Ber. ü. d. Verhandl. d. sächs. Akad. d. Wissensch., Leipzig, math.-phys. Kl., v. 73, p. 295.

1927. Meine myelogenetische Hirnlehre. Mit biographischer Einleitung. J. Springer, Berlin.

FLEDELIUS, M.

1934. A propos de l'hémianopsie d'origine traumatique. Arch. d'opht., v. 51, p. 561.

FLEISCHER, B.

1914. Zur Pathologie und Therapie der Hypophysistumoren. Klin. Monatsbl. f. Augenh., v. 52 (N.F., v. 17), p. 625.

1916. Ueber den Ausfall bzw. die Erhaltung des nur von einem Auge bestrittenen sichelförmigen Aussenteils des binokularen Gesichtsfeldes (des "temporalen Halbmondes") durch Schussverletzung. Ber. d. Deutsch. ophth. Gesellsch. Heidelberg, v. 40, p. 63; Klin. Monatsbl. f. Augenh. v. 57, p. 140.

FLEISCHER, B., & ENSINGER, T.

1920. Homonym-hemianopische Gesichtsfeldstörungen nach Schädel- spez. Hinterhauptschüssen. Klin. Monatsbl. f. Augenh., v. 65, p. 181.

FLEISCHER, E.

1942. Farbensehen. Arch. f. d. ges. Physiol. (Pflüger), v. 246, p. 803.

FLEISCHL, E.

1883. Die Vertheilung der Sehnervenfasern über die Zapfen der menschlichen Retina. Sitzungsb. d. kaiserl. Akad. d. Wissensch. Wien, math.-naturwiss. Cl., Abt. 3, v. 87, p. 246.

FLEMMING, W.

1895. Ueber den Bau der Spinalganglienzellen bei Säugethieren, und Bemerkungen über den der centralen Zellen. Arch. f. mikr. Anat., v. 46, p. 379.

FLESCH, J.

1908. Verbale Alexie mit Hemiachromatopsie. Wien. med. Wchnschr., v. 58, p. 2367.

FLORES, A.

1911. Die Myeloarchitektonik und die Myelogenie des Cortex cerebri beim Igel (*Erinaceus europaeus*). J. Psychol. u. Neurol., v. 17, p. 215.

FLOREY, H.

1925. Microscopical observation on the circulation of the blood in the cerebral cortex. Brain, v. 48, p. 43.

FLOURENS, P.-J.-M. (*see also* VULPIAN 1887)

1824. Recherches expérimentales sur les propriétés et les fonctions du système nerveux dans les animaux vertébrés, par P. F. A Paris, chez Crevot, Libraire-éditeur. Another ed., J.-B. Baillière, Paris, 1842.

1824. Versuche und Untersuchungen über die Eigenschaften und Verrichtungen des Nervensystems bei Thieren mit Rückenwirbeln. Reinsche Buchhandlung, Leipzig.

1842. Examen de la phrénologie. Paulin, Paris.

1846. Phrenology examined. Translated from the 2d ed., 1845. Hogan & Thompson, Philadelphia.

FLOWER, S. S.

1900. On the mammalia of Siam and the Malay Peninsula. Proc. Zoöl. Soc. London, p. 306.

1925–31. Contributions to our knowledge of the duration of life in vertebrate animals. *Ibid.*, I. Fishes (1925, p. 247); II. Batrachians (p. 269); III. Reptiles (p. 911); IV. Birds (p. 1365); V. Mammals (1931, p. 145).

1935. Further notes on the duration of life in animals. I. Fishes: as determined by otolith and scale-readings on living individuals. *Ibid.*, p. 265.

FLOWER, W. H.

1862. On the anatomy of *Pithecia monachus*. Proc. Zoöl. Soc. London, p. 326.

1863. On the posterior lobes of the cerebrum of the quadrumana. Phil. Tr. Roy. Soc. London, v. 152, p. 185.

FOERSTER, O.

1923. Die Topik der Hirnrinde in ihrer Bedeutung für die Motilität. Deutsche Ztschr. f. Nervenh., v. 77, p. 124.

1924. Encephalographische Erfahrungen. Ztschr. f. d. ges. Neurol. u. Psychiat., v. 94, p. 512.

1926. Zur operativen Behandlung der Epilepsie. Deutsche Ztschr. f. Nervenh., v. 89, p. 137.

1926. Die Pathogenese des epileptischen Krampfanfalles. Einleitender Ueberblick, Klinik und Therapie. *Ibid.*, v. 94, p. 15.

1927. Die Leitungsbahnen des Schmerzgefühls. Sonderbände zu Bruns Beitr. z. klin. Chirurgie. Urban & Schwarzenberg, Berlin & Wien.

1929. Beiträge zur Pathophysiologie der Sehbahn und der Sehsphäre. J. Psychol. u. Neurol., v. 39, p. 463; *also* Arch. Neurol. & Psychiat., v. 24, p. 172.

1931. Cerebral cortex in man. Lancet, v. 2, p. 309.

1934. Ueber die Bedeutung und Reichweite des Lokalisationsprinzips im Nervensystem. Verhandl. d. Deutsch. Gesellsch. f. inn. Med. Wiesbaden, v. 46, p. 117.

1936. The motor cortex in man in the light of Hughlings Jackson's doctrines. Brain, v. 59, p. 135.

1936. Symptomatologie der Erkrankungen des Grosshirns. Motorische Felder und Bahnen. *In:* BUMKE & FOERSTER, Handb. d. Neurol., v. 6, p. 1.

1939. Ein Fall von Agenesie des Corpus callosum verbunden mit einem Diverticulum paraphysarium des Ventriculus tertius. Ztschr. f. d. ges. Neurol. u. Psychiat., v. 164, p. 380.

1939. Operativ-experimentelle Erfahrungen beim Menschen über den Einfluss des Nervensystems auf den Kreislauf. Zentralbl. f. d. ges. Neurol. u. Psychiat., v. 94, p. 352.

FOERSTER, O., GAGEL, O., & MAHONEY, W.

1936. Ueber die Anatomie, Physiologie und Pathologie der Pupillarinnervation. Verhandl. d. Deutsch. Gesellsch. f. inn. Med. Wiesbaden, v. 48, p. 386.

FOERSTER, O., & LOEWI, M.
1932. Ueber die Beziehung von Vorstellung und Wahrnehmung bei Schädigung afferenter Leitungsbahnen. Ztschr. f. d. ges. Neurol. u. Psychiat., v. 139, p. 658.

FOERSTER, O., & PENFIELD, W.
1930. The structural basis of traumatic epilepsy and results of radical operation. Brain, v. 53, p. 99. (*See also* Penfield 1933, 1935, 1937.)
1930. Der Narbenzug am und im Gehirn bei traumatischer Epilepsie in seiner Bedeutung für das Zustandekommen der Anfälle und für die therapeutische Bekämpfung derselben. Ztschr. f. d. ges. Neurol. u. Psychiat., v. 125, p. 475.

FÖRSTER, RICHARD; for biography *see* J. HIRSCHBERG, in GRAEFE & SAEMISCH, Handb. d. ges. Augenh., 2d ed., v. 15 [1], p. 159
1867. Mensurations du champ visuel monoculaire, dans diverses maladies de la rétine et du nerf optique. Ann. d'ocul., v. 59, p. 5, 1868; *also* Klin. Monatsbl. f. Augenh., v. 5, p. 293, and v. 7, p. 411.
1867. Ueber Gesichtsfeldmessungen. Klin. Monatsbl. f. Augenh., v. 5, p. 293.
1869. Vorzeigung des Perimeter. *Ibid.*, v. 7, p. 411.
1877. Beziehungen der Allgemein-Leiden und Organ-Erkrankungen zu Veränderungen und Krankheiten des Sehorgans. *In:* GRAEFE & SAEMISCH, Handb. d. Augenh., 1st ed., v. 7, p. 59.
1890. Ueber Rindenblindheit. Arch. f. Ophth. (Graefe), v. 36 (1), p. 94.

FOIX, C., & HILLEMAND, P.
1925. Les syndromes de la région thalamique. Presse méd., v. 33, p. 113.

FOIX, C., & MASSON, A.
1923. Le syndrome de l'artère cérébrale postérieure. Presse méd., v. 31, p. 361.

FOIX, C., & NICOLESCO, J.
1925. Les noyaux gris centraux et la région mésencéphalo-sous-optique. Masson & Cie, Paris.

FOIX, C., & SCHIFF-WERTHEIMER, S.
1925. Double hémianopsie avec intégrité du champ maculaire. Cerveau droit: syndrome de la cérébrale postérieure. Cerveau gauche: troubles aphasiques et apraxie idéomotrice. Rev. neurol., v. 1, p. 361.

FOLEY, J. O.
1943. Composition of the cervical sympathetic trunk. Proc. Soc. Exper. Biol. & Med., v. 52, p. 212.

FOLEY, J. P.
1940. The "baboon boy" of South Africa. Science, v. 91, p. 618.

FONTANA, FELIX
1795. Treatise on the venom of the viper; etc. To which are annexed, observations on the primitive structure of the animal body, etc. 2 vols. J. Cuthell, London; 1st ed. 1782. Italian original: Ricerche fisiche sopra'l veneno della vipera, Lucca; also French, 1781; an earlier English ed., 1787; and a German ed., 1787.

FONTANA, FRANCISCUS
1646. Novae coelestium terrestriumque rerum observationes. Ap. Gaffarum, Neapoli.

FORBES, A.
1936. Conduction in axon and synapse. Cold Spring Harbor Symp. Quant. Biol., v. 4, p. 163.
1939. Problems of synaptic function. J. Neurophysiol., v. 2, p. 465.

FORBES, A., RENSHAW, B., & REMPEL, B.
1937. Units of electrical activity in the cerebral cortex. Am. J. Physiol., v. 119, p. 309.

FORBES, H. O.
1894. A hand-book to the primates. 2 vols. W. H. Allen & Co., London.

FORBES, H. S.
1928. Cerebral circulation. I. Observation and measurement of pial vessels. Arch. Neurol. & Psychiat., v. 19, p. 751.

FORBES, H. S., & COBB, S.
1938. Vasomotor control of cerebral vessels. Research Pub. A. Research Nerv. & Ment. Dis., v. 18, p. 201. Williams & Wilkins Co., Baltimore.

FORBES, S. A., & RICHARDSON, R. E.
1908 (1920). The fishes of Illinois. 1st and 2d eds. Nat. Hist. Surv. Illinois.

FORBUSH, E. H., & MAY, J. B.
1939. Natural history of the birds of eastern and central North America. Houghton Mifflin Co., Boston.

FOREEST, PIETER VAN
1591. Observationum et curationum medicinalium libri quinque: nempe XI. De morbis oculorum & palpebrarum. Etc. Lugduni Batavorum, ex officina Plantiniana, apud F. Raphelengium.

FOREL, A. H.
1872. Beiträge zur Kenntniss des Thalamus opticus und der ihn umgebenden Gebilde bei den Säugethieren. Sitzungsb. d. Akad. Wissensch. Wien, math.-naturwiss. Cl., v. 66, Part 3, p. 25.

1887. Einige hirnanatomische Betrachtungen und Ergebnisse. Arch. f. Psychiat., v. 18, p. 162.

1904. Ants and some other insects; an inquiry into the psychic powers of these animals, with an appendix on the peculiarities of their olfactory sense. Open Court Pub. Co., Chicago.

1907. Gesammelte hirnanatomische Abhandlungen. Reinhard, München.

1908. The senses of insects. Methuen & Co., London.

1921. Le monde social des fourmis du globe comparé à celui de l'homme. Librarie Kundig, Genève.

1929. The social world of the ants compared with that of man. A. & C. Boni, New York.

FOREL, O. L.

1919. Contribution à l'étude des traumatismes cérébraux. Schweiz. Arch. f. Neurol. u. Psychiat., v. 4, p. 170.

FORREST, J. W.

1949. Refractive index and its measurement. Ed. Focus, v. 20, No. 1, p. 19. Bausch & Lomb Optical Co., Rochester, N.Y.

FORSTER, E., & SCHLESINGER, E.

1915. Ueber die physiologische Pupillenunruhe und die Psychoreflexe der Pupille. Monatsschr. f. Psychiat. u. Neurol., v. 37, p. 197.

FORTIN, E.-P.

1925. Essai sur la localisation histologique de quelques phénomènes entoptiques. Investigation sur de petits appareils dioptriques. Ann. d'ocul., v. 162, p. 809.

1925. Investigations sur la fovéa de l'œil. Semana méd., Buenos Aires, v. 32 (2), p. 605.

1926. On Henle's fiber layer (in Spanish). Arch. de oftal. Buenos Aires, v. 1, p. 414.

1926. Investigations histologiques sur certains éléments de la rétine. Compt. rend. Acad. d. sc., v. 183, p. 452.

1926. Structure de la couche neuro-épithéliale de la rétine. Compt. rend. Soc. de biol., v. 95, p. 1158.

1927. Significado de la ausencia de sangre en la mitad externa de la retina. Red capilar de los granos internos y acción del músculo ciliar sobre la circulación ocular. Rev. Soc. argent. de biol., v. 3, p. 353.

1930. Descripción de una capa notable de capilares retinianos. Estud. clín. de la capa de granos internos. Arch. de oftal. Buenos Aires, v. 5, p. 166.

1930. Falsedad de las concepciones actuales de la retina. *Ibid.*, p. 301; *also* Rev. de especial., v. 5, p. 387. (*See* Balado in Arch. de oftal. Buenos Aires, v. 5, p. 443.)

FORTUYN; *see* DROOGLEEVER FORTUYN

FOSTER, M.

1901. Lectures on the history of physiology during the sixteenth, seventeenth and eighteenth centuries. Cambridge University Press, Cambridge.

FOUCAULT, M.

1922. Les sensations visuelles élémentaires en dehors de la région centrale de la rétine. Ann. psychol., v. 22, p. 1.

FOVILLE, A. L.

1844. Traité complet de l'anatomie, de la physiologie et de la pathologie du système nerveux cérébro-spinal. Première partie. Anatomie. Atlas. Fortin, Masson & Cie, Paris.

FOVILLE, A. L., & PINEL-GRANDCHAMP, F.

1825. Recherches sur le siège spécial de différentes fonctions du système nerveux. Mém. étab. therm. du Mont-d'Or, Paris.

FOWLER, M. J.

1942. Value of orthoptic fusion training exercises in strabismus and related conditions. Arch. Ophth., v. 28, p. 507.

FOX, C. A., FISHER, R. R., & DESALVA, S. J.

1948. The distribution of the anterior commissure in the monkey (*Macaca mulatta*). J. Comp. Neurol., v. 89, p. 245.

FOX, D. L.

1953. Animal biochromes and structural colours. Cambridge University Press, Cambridge.

FOX, J. C., JR., & GERMAN, W. J.

1935. Observations following left (dominant) temporal lobectomy. Arch. Neurol. & Psychiat., v. 33, p. 791.

1936. Macular vision following cerebral resection. *Ibid.*, v. 35, p. 808.

FOX, J. C., & HOLMES, G.

1926. Optic nystagmus and its value in the localisation of cerebral lesions. Brain, v. 49, p. 333.

FRACASSATUS, CAROLUS

1687. Caroli Fracassati Phil. & Med. Bonon. ac Pisis Anatomici Dissertatio Epistolica Responsoria *De Cerebro*, ad Clarissimum, ac Experientissimum Virum, Messanae Primarium Medicinae Professorem, D. Marcellum Malpighium Bononiensem. In Marcelli Malpighii etc. Operum tomus secundus, p. 125. (Prob. written late 1664 or early 1665.)

FRAGONARD

*1797. *In:* MOREAUX, Exposé des résultats des plusieurs recherches sur la tâche jaune, etc. Mém. de la Soc. méd. d'émulation, Paris, 1 année. Pour l'an V. An VI.

FRAISSE, P.

1881. Ueber Molluskenaugen mit embryonalem Typus. Ztschr. f. wissensch. Zool., v. 35, p. 461.

FRALICK, F. B.

1941–42. Surgical anatomy of the eye and orbit. Tr. Am. Acad. Ophth. & Laryng., v. 46, p. 85. (*See also* Surg., Gynec. & Obst., v. 74, p. 509.)

FRALICK, F. B., & CROSBY, E.

1943–44. Anatomy of the orbit. Tr. Am. Acad. Ophth. & Otolaryng., v. 48, p. 467.

FRANCIS, E. T. B.

1934. The anatomy of the salamander. Oxford University Press, London.

FRANCK, J., & LOOMIS, W. E.

1949. Photosynthesis in plants. Iowa State College Press, Ames.

FRANKL-HOCHWART, L.

1902. Zur Kenntnis der Anatomie des Gehirns der Blindmaus (*Spalax typhlus*). Arb. a. d. neurol. Inst. Wien (Obersteiner), v. 8, p. 190.

FRANKLIN, I.

1942. Fusion, projection, and stereopsis. Am. J. Ophth., v. 25, p. 1316.

FRANKLIN, K. J.

1937. A monograph on veins. Charles C Thomas, Springfield, Ill.

FRANZ, J. C. A.

1841. Memoir of the case of a gentleman born blind, and successfully operated upon in the eighteenth year of his age. Proc. Roy. Soc. London, v. 131, p. 303.

FRANZ, S. I.

1902. On the functions of the cerebrum. I. The frontal lobes in relation to the production and retention of simple sensory-motor habits. Am. J. Physiol., v. 8, p. 1.

1906. Observations on the function of the association areas (cerebrum) in monkeys. J. Am. Med. Assoc., v. 47, p. 1464.

1907. On the functions of the cerebrum: the frontal lobes. Arch. Psychol., v. 1, p. 1.

1910. On the association functions of the cerebrum. J. Phil., v. 7, p. 673.

1911. On the functions of the cerebrum: concerning the lateral portions of the occipital lobes. Am. J. Physiol., v. 28, p. 308.

1911–16. The functions of the cerebrum. Psychol. Bull., v. 8, p. 111; v. 10, p. 125; v. 11, p. 131; v. 13, p. 149.

1912. New phrenology. Science, v. 35, p. 321.

1923. Conception of cerebral functions. Psychol. Rev., v. 30, p. 438.

FRANZ, S. I., & LAFORA, G. R.

1910–11. On the functions of the cerebrum: the occipital lobes. Psychol. Monog., v. 13, No. 4, p. 1.

FRANZ, V.

1904. Das Vogelauge. Zool. Jahrb., v. 28, p. 73.

1905. Zur Anatomie, Histologie und funktionellen Gestaltung des Selachierauges. Jena. Ztschr. f. Naturwiss., v. 40, p. 697.

1906. Beobachtungen am lebenden Selachierauge. *Ibid.*, v. 41, p. 429.

1907. Bau des Eulenauges und Theorie des Teleskopauges. Biol. Centralbl., v. 27, pp. 271, 341.

1909. Das Vogelauge. Zool. Jahrb. (Anat. u. Ontogenie), v. 28, p. 73.

1911. Studien zur vergleichenden Anatomie des Auges der Säugetiere. Arch. f. vergl. Ophth., v. 2, pp. 180, 269.

1912. Beiträge zur Kenntnis des Mittelhirns und Zwischenhirns der Knochenfische. Folia neuro-biol., v. 6, p. 402.

1912. Studien zur vergleichenden Anatomie der Augen der Säugetiere. Arch. f. vergl. Ophth., v. 2, pp. 180, 269.

1913. Sehorgan. *In:* OPPEL, Lehrb. d. vergl. mikr. Anat. d. Wirbeltiere, v. 7. G. Fischer, Jena.

1923. Morphologie des Augenbechers und der Augenlinse. Ergebn. d. Anat. u. Entw., v. 24, p. 293.

1923. Haut, Sinnesorgane und Nervensystem der Akranier. Jena. Ztschr. f. Naturwiss., v. 59, p. 401. ("Fauna et anatomia ceylanica," No. 13, v. 2 [5].)

1924. Die Sinnesfunktion des Gehirnbläschens des Lanzettfisches (*Branchiostoma lanceolatum*, Pall.). Biol. Zentralbl., v. 44, p. 9; and Verhandl. d. Deutsch. zool. Gesellsch., p. 42.

1924. Lichtsinnversuche am Lanzettfisch zur Ermittlung der Sinnesfunktion des Stirn- oder Gehirnbläschens. Wissensch. Meeresuntersuch., Abt. Helgol., v. 15, No. 14.

1924. Geschichte der Organismen. G. Fischer, Jena.

1927. Morphologie der Akranier. Ergebn. d. Anat. u. Entw., v. 27, p. 464.

1931. Die Akkommodation des Selachierauges und seine Abblendungsapparate, nebst Befunden an der Retina. Zool. Jahrb. (Allg. Zool. u. Physiol.), v. 49, p. 323.

1934. Die Spirale in den Stäbchen der Wirbeltiernetzhaut und der vermeintliche Plättchenzerfall nach verschiedenen Untersuchungsmethoden. Biol. Zentralbl., v. 54, p. 76.

1934. Vergleichende Anatomie des Wirbeltierauges. *In:* Bolk *et al.*, Handb. d. vergl. Anat. der Wirbeltiere, v. 2 (2), p. 989.

1935. Der biologische Vervollkommnungsbegriff. Naturwiss., v. 23, p. 695.

Franz, V., & Steche, O.

1914. Die Fische. *In:* A. Brehm, Tierleben, v. 3, p. 20 (*cf.* chap. on lancelet).

Franz, W.

1942. Zur Theorie des Farbensehens. Arch. f. d. ges. Physiol. (Pflüger), v. 246, p. 112.

Fraunhofer, Joseph

1905. Bestimmung des Brechungs- und Farbenzerstreuungsvermögens verschiedener Glasarten in Bezug auf die Vervollkommnung achromatischer Fernröhre. (Ostwalds "Klassiker der exakten Wissenschaften," No. 150.) W. Engelmann, Leipzig.

Frazer, J. G.

1890. The golden bough. 2 vols. Macmillan & Co., London. *Also* later revised and expanded editions. An abridged ed. 1922, and Aftermath 1936. *See also:* Questions on the customs, beliefs and languages of savages, 1907; Totemism and exogamy, 1910 and 1935; Totemica, 1937; The belief in immortality and the worship of the dead, 1913–24; Folklore in the Old Testament, 1918, abridged, 1923; Man, God, and immortality, 1927; Myths of the origin of fire, 1930; The fear of the dead in primitive religions, 1933–36; Creation and evolution in primitive cosmogonies, 1935; Anthologia anthropologica, 1938–39.

Frazier, C. H.

1936. Tumor involving the frontal lobe alone: a symptomatic survey of one hundred and five verified cases. Arch. Neurol. & Psychiat., v. 35, p. 525.

Frazier, C. H., & Ingham, S. D.

1920. A review of the effect of gunshot wounds of the head. Arch. Neurol. & Psychiat., v. 3, p. 17.

Frazier, C. H., & Rowe, S. N.

1934. Certain observations upon the localization in fifty-one verified tumors of the temporal lobe. Research Pub. A. Research Nerv. & Ment. Dis., v. 13, p. 251. Williams & Wilkins, Baltimore.

Frederikse, A.

1931. The lizard's brain: an investigation on the histological structure of the brain of *Lacerta vivipara*. C. C. Callenbach, Baarn (Holland).

Freeman, G. L., & Papez, J. W.

1930. The effect of subcortical lesions on the visual discrimination of rats. J. Comp. Psychol., v. 11, p. 185.

Freeman, W., & Watts, J. W.

1939. Interpretation of function of frontal lobe based upon observations in 48 cases of prefrontal lobotomy. Yale J. Biol. & Med., v. 11, p. 527.

1941. The frontal lobes and consciousness of the self. Psychosom. Med., v. 3, p. 111.

1942. Psychosurgery. Intelligence, emotion and social behavior following prefrontal lobotomy for mental disorders. Charles C Thomas, Springfield, Ill.

1946. Retrograde degeneration in the thalamus following prefrontal lobotomy. Tr. Am. Neurol. A., 71st ann. meet., p. 150.

French, J. W.

1923. Stereoscopy re-stated. Tr. Opt. Soc. London, v. 24, p. 226; Am. J. Physiol. Optics, v. 7, p. 250, 1926.

Frenkel, H.

1916–17. Sur un cas de scotome paramaculaire avec abaissement de l'acuité visuelle par blessure de la région occipitale. Arch. d'opht., v. 35, p. 218.

Fresnel, Augustin Jean

1866–70. Œuvres complètes. 3 vols. Vols. 1 and 2: Théorie de la lumière; v. 3: Phares et appareils d'éclairage. Imprimerie impérial, Paris.

Freund, C. S.

1889. Ueber optische Aphasie und Seelenblindheit. Arch. f. Psychiat., v. 20, p. 276.

1916. Subdural gelegenes Aneurysma der Carotis interna als Ursache der Kompression eines Tractus opticus. Klin. Monatsbl. f. Augenh., v. 56, p. 468.

Frey, E.

1933. Ueber die basale Opticuswurzel und die caudalen Verbindungen der Commissura transversa Gudden der Vögel. Proc. Kon. nederl. Akad. Wetensch. Amsterdam, v. 36, p. 351.

1935. Experimentelle Untersuchungen über die basale optische Wurzel beim Meerschweinchen. *Ibid.*, v. 38, p. 767.

1935. Die basale optische Wurzel des Meerschweinchens. *Ibid.*, p. 775.

1937. Vergleichend-anatomische Untersuchungen über die basale optische Wurzel, die Commissura transversa Gudden und über eine Verbindung der Netzhaut mit dem vegetativen Gebiet im Hypothalamus durch eine "dorsale hypothalamische Wurzel" des Nervus opticus bei Amnioten. Schweiz. Arch. f. Neurol. u. Psychiat., v. 39, p. 255.

1938. Studien über die hypothalamische Optikuswurzel der Amphibien. I. *Rana mugiens, Rana esculenta, Bombinator pachypus* und *Pipa pipa.* Proc. Kon. nederl. Akad. Wetensch. Amsterdam, v. 41, p. 1004.

1938. Studien über die hypothalamische Optikuswurzel der Amphibien. II. *Proteus anguineus* und die phylogenetische Bedeutung der hypothalamischen Optikuswurzel. *Ibid.,* p. 1015.

1947–48. Degenerationsstudien über das optische Gebiet im Hypothalamus des Meerschweinchens. Acta anat., v. 4, p. 123.

FREY, M. VON

1927–28. Die Gliederung des Tastsinns. Zentralbl. f. d. ges. Neurol. u. Psychiat., v. 47, p. 772; Deutsche Ztschr. f. Nervenh., v. 101, p. 155.

FREY, W.

1939. Arteriosklerose. Zentralbl. f. d. ges. Neurol. u. Psychiat., v. 94, p. 345.

FREY-WYSSLING, A.

1938. Submikroskopische Morphologie des Protoplasmas und seiner Derivate. ("Protoplasma-Monog.," v. 15.) Gebrüder Borntraeger, Berlin.

FRIANT, M.

1940. Nouvelle interprétation de la morphologie de l'insula humaine. Conclusion d'un ensemble de recherches sur le territoire néopalléal operculisé des mammifères et, en particulier, des primates. Bull. Mus. nat. hist. nat. Paris, 2d ser., v. 12, p. 195.

FRIEDE, R.

1933. Zur Variabilität der Form der menschlichen Erwachsenenhornhaut. Arch. f. Augenh., v. 108, p. 249.

FRIEDEMANN, M.

1911–12. Die Cytoarchitektonik des Zwischenhirns der Cercopitheken mit besonderer Berücksichtigung des Thalamus opticus. J. f. Psychol. u. Neurol., v. 18, p. 309.

FRIEDENWALD, H.

1944. The Jews and medicine. Johns Hopkins Press, Baltimore.

FRIEDENWALD, J. S.

1929. Pathology of the eye. Macmillan Co., New York.

1936. Mechanism of Schlemm's canal. Arch. Ophth., v. 16, p. 65.

1944. Dynamic factors in the formation and re-

absorption of aqueous humour. Brit. J. Ophth., v. 28, p. 503.

FRIEDENWALD, J. S., & STIEHLER, R. D.

1935. Structure of the vitreous. Arch. Ophth., v. 14, p. 789.

1938. Circulation of the aqueous. VII. A mechanism of secretion of the intraocular fluid. *Ibid.,* v. 20 (77), p. 761.

FRIEDMAN, A. P., & NIELSEN, J. M.

1942. A case of bilateral lesions of area 19 of Brodmann. Bull. Los Angeles Neurol. Soc., v. 7, p. 209.

FRIEDMAN, B.

1931. The blue arcs of the retina. Arch. Ophth., v. 6, p. 663.

1942. Observations on entoptic phenomena. *Ibid.,* v. 28, p. 285.

1942. Unusual disciform retinal lesion with heterotopia maculae. *Ibid.,* p. 444.

FRIEDMAN, E.

1934. Neurological aspects of hoarseness. New York State J. Med., v. 34, p. 1.

FRIEDMAN, H., & SMITH, F. D., JR.

1950. A contribution to the ornithology of northeastern Venezuela. Proc. U.S. Nat. Mus., v. 100, p. 411. Smithsonian Inst. Washington, Washington, D.C.

FRIEDMANN, H.

1946. The birds of north and middle America. Government Printing Office, Washington, D.C.

FRIEDRICH, P. L.

1909. Ueber kompensatorische Vorgänge an der Hirnrinde. Monatsschr. f. Psychiat., v. 26 (suppl.), p. 129.

FRIEDRICH, W., & SCHREIBER, H.

1942. Das Sehen des menschlichen Auges im Ultraviolett. Die extrafovealen Schwellenwerte für 365 mμ und 546 mμ. 1. Mitt. Arch. f. d. ges. Physiol. (Pflüger), v. 246, p. 621. 2. Mitt. *Ibid.,* p. 790.

FRISCH, K. VON

1912. Ueber die Farbenanpassung des *Crenilabrus.* Zool. Jahrb. (Allg. Zool. u. Physiol.), v. 33, p. 151.

1912. Färbung und Farbensinn der Tiere. Sitzungsb. d. Gesellsch. f. Morphol. u. Physiol. München, v. 28, p. 30.

1912. Ueber farbige Anpassung bei Fischen. Zool. Jahrb. (Allg. Zool. u. Physiol.), v. 32, p. 171.

1912. Sind die Fische farbenblind? *Ibid.,* v. 33, p. 107.

1913. Weitere Untersuchungen über den Farbensinn der Fische. *Ibid.,* v. 34, p. 43.

1914. Der Farbensinn und Formensinn der Biene. *Ibid.*, v. 35, p. 1.

1923. Das Problem des tierischen Farbensinnes. Naturwiss., v. 11, p. 470.

1924. Sinnesphysiologie der Wassertiere. Verhandl. d. Deutsch. zool. Gesellsch., v. 29, p. 34.

1924. Sinnesphysiologie und "Sprache" der Bienen. Naturwiss., v. 12, p. 981.

1925. Farbensinn der Fische und Duplizitätstheorie. Ztschr. f. vergl. Physiol., v. 2, p. 393.

1947. Duftgelenkte Bienen im Dienste der Landwirtschaft und Imkerei. J. Springer, Wien.

1948. Aus dem Leben der Bienen. 4th ed. J. Springer, Wien.

1950. Bees, their vision, chemical senses, and language. Cornell University Press, Ithaca, N.Y.

1951. Orientierungsvermögen und Sprache der Bienen. Naturwiss., v. 38, p. 105.

FRITSCH, G.

1900. Vergleichende Untersuchungen menschlicher Augen. Sitzungsb. d. kgl. preuss. Akad. d. Wissensch., p. 636.

1907. Vergleichende Untersuchungen der Fovea centralis des Menschen. Anat. Anz., v. 30, p. 462.

1908. Ueber Bau und Bedeutung der Area centralis des Menschen. Reiner, Berlin.

1908. Ueber den Bau und die Bedeutung der histologischen Elemente in der Netzhaut des Auges besonders am Ort des deutlichsten Sehens, bei verschiedenen Menschenrassen. Anat. Anz. (Verhandl.), v. 32 (suppl.), p. 141.

1911. Beiträge zur Histologie des Auges von *Pteropus*. Ztschr. f. wissensch. Zool., v. 98, p. 388.

1911–12. Der Ort des deutlichsten Sehens in der Netzhaut der Vögel. *Ibid.*, v. 110, p. 76; Arch. f. mikr. Anat., v. 78, p. 245.

1912. Hermann Munk† (obituary). Deutsch. med. Wchnschr., v. 38, p. 2085.

1912. Ueber das Parietalorgan der Fische als funktionierendes Organ. Sitzungsb. d. Gesellsch. f. Morphol. u. Physiol., München, v. 27, p. 16.

FRITSCH, G., & HITZIG, E.

1870. Ueber die elektrische Erregbarkeit des Grosshirns. Arch. f. Anat., Physiol. & wissensch. Med. (Reichert & Du Bois-Reymond), p. 300; *also in:* HITZIG, Untersuchungen über das Gehirn, p. 1, 1874.

FRITSCH, J.

1892. Nachruf an Th. Meynert. Jahrb. f. Psychiat., v. 11, p. 1.

FRÖBES, J.

1920. Aus der Vorgeschichte der psychologischen Optik. Ztschr. f. Psychol., v. 85, p. 1.

FRÖHLICH, F. W.

1913. Vergleichende Untersuchungen über den Licht- und Farbensinn. Deutsch. med. Wchnschr., v. 39, p. 1453.

1921. Grundzüge einer Lehre vom Licht- und Farbensinn. Ein Beitrag zur allgemeinen Physiologie der Sinne. G. Fischer, Jena.

1921. Untersuchungen über Flimmererscheinungen im Sehfeld. Deutsch. med. Wchnschr., v. 47, p. 314.

1921. Ueber oszillierende Erregungsvorgänge im Sehfelde. Ztschr. f. Sinnesphysiol., v. 52, p. 52.

FROLOV, Y. (I. P.)

1937. Fish who answer the telephone, and other studies in experimental biology. K. Paul, Trench, Trubner & Co., London.

FRORIEP, A.

1906. Die Entwickelung des Auges der Wirbeltiere. *In:* O. HERTWIG, Handb. d. vergl. u. exper. Entwickelungslehre d. Wirbeltiere, v. 2 (2), p. 139. G. Fischer, Jena.

1906. Ueber den Ursprung des Wirbeltierauges. München. med. Wchnschr., v. 53 (2), p. 1739.

1906. Ueber die Herleitung des Wirbeltierauges vom Auge der Ascidienlarve. Anat. Anz., suppl., v. 29, p. 145.

1911. Die Lehren Franz Joseph Galls beurteilt nach dem Stand der heutigen Kenntnisse. Rede am Geburtstag des Kaisers im Festsaal der Universität Tübingen gehalten. J. A. Barth, Leipzig. Summary in J. f. Psychol. u. Neurol., v. 19, p. 59, 1912.

1911. Ist F. J. Gall an der Entdeckung des Brocaschen Sprachzentrums beteiligt? Ztschr. f. d. ges. Neurol. u. Psychiat. (Orig.), v. 5, p. 293.

FRY, G. A., & BARTLEY, S. H.

1934. Electrical responses of the retinal ganglion cell axons. J. Cell. & Comp. Physiol., v. 5, p. 291.

FUCHS, A.

1925. Zur Anatomie des Glioma retinae. Ber. d. Deutsch. ophth. Gesellsch. Heidelberg, v. 45, p. 8.

FUCHS, A., & PÖTZL, O.

1917. Beitrag zur Klinik und Anatomie der Schussverletzungen im Bereich der engeren Sehsphäre. (Unvollständiges parazentrales Skotom bei intaktem peripheren Sehen.) Jahrb. f. Psychiat., v. 38, p. 115.

FUCHS, E.
1907. Oculomotoriuslähmung ohne Beteiligung der Binnenmuskeln bei peripheren Läsionen. Arb. a. d. neurol. Inst. Wien (Obersteiner), v. 15, p. 1.

FUCHS, E., & FUCHS, A.
1945. Lehrbuch der Augenheilkunde, 18th ed. F. Deuticke, Wien.

FUCHS, LEONHARD
1539. Alle Krankheyt der Augen. Cited in biography of H. Vogtherr of Strassburg. (*Cf.* Allgemeine deutsche Biographie.)

FUCHS, S.
1893. Ueber einige neuere Fortschritte in der Anatomie und Physiologie der Arthropodenaugen. Ztschr. f. Psychol. u. Physiol. d. Sinnesorg., v. 4, p. 351.

FUCHS, W.
1920. Untersuchungen über das Sehen der Hemianopiker und Hemiamblyopiker. I. Verlagerungserscheinungen. Ztschr. f. Psychol., v. 84, p. 67.
1920. Untersuchungen über das Sehen der Hemianopiker und Hemiamblyopiker. II. Die totalisierende Gestaltauffassung. *In:* A. GELB and K. GOLDSTEIN, Psychologische Analysen hirnpathologischer Fälle. J. A. Barth, Leipzig.
1922. Eine Pseudofovea bei Hemianopikern. Psychol. Forsch., v. 1, p. 157.

FÜRBRINGER, M.
1904. Zur Frage der Abstammung der Säugetiere. Festschrift E. Haeckel.

FÜRST, C. M.
1904. Zur Kenntnis der Histogenese und des Wachstums der Retina. Acta Univ. Lunden. —Lunds Univ. Årsskr., Part 2, v. 40, p. 1.

FÜRSTNER, C.
1878. Ueber eine eigenthümliche Sehstörung bei Paralytikern. Arch. f. Psychiat., v. 8, p. 162.
1879. Weitere Mittheilungen über eine eigenthümliche Sehstörung bei Paralytikern. *Ibid.*, v. 9, p. 90.

FUERTES, L. A., & OSGOOD, W. H.
1936. Artist and naturalist in Ethiopia. Doubleday, Doran & Co., Garden City, N.Y.

FUJIMORI, A.
1935. Studien über den Tenonschen Raum und die Tenonsche Kapsel. Acta Soc. ophth. Japon., v. 39, suppl. 25.

FUJITA, T.
1934. Ueber die periphere Ausbreitung des N. facialis beim Menschen. Morphol. Jahrb., v. 73, p. 578.

FUKALA, V.
1901. Historischer Beitrag zur Augenheilkunde. Arch. f. Augenh., v. 22, p. 203.

FULTON, J. F.
1928. Observations upon the vascularity of the human occipital lobe during visual activity. Brain, v. 51, p. 310.
1929. Horner and the syndrome of paralysis of the cervical sympathetic. Arch. Surg., v. 18, p. 2023.
1934. Paralyses of cortical origin. Proc. California Acad. Med., 1933–34, p. 1.
1936. Cerebral regulation of autonomic function. Proc. Interstate Post-grad. M. Assembly of North America, p. 149.
1937. Spasticity and the frontal lobes: a review. New England J. Med., v. 217, p. 1017.
1937. A note on Francesco Gennari and the early history of cytoarchitectural studies of the cerebral cortex. Bull. Inst. Hist. Med., v. 5, p. 895.
1939. A trip to Bohol in quest of *Tarsius.* Yale J. Biol. & Med., v. 11, p. 561.
1943. Functional interrelation of cerebral cortex with basal ganglia and cerebellum. *In:* Essays in biology, in honor of Herbert M. Evans, p. 203. University of California Press, Berkeley & Los Angeles.
1949. Physiology of the nervous system. Oxford University Press, New York. 3d. ed.
1950. Jules Baillarger and his discovery of the six layers of the cerebral cortex. Gesnerus, v. 8, p. 85.

FULTON, J. F., & BAILEY, P.
1929–30. Tumors in the region of the third ventricle: their diagnosis and relation to pathological sleep. J. Nerv. & Ment. Dis., v. 69, pp. 1, 145, 261; *also* Arch. argent. de neurol., v. 5, p. 3.
1930. Nueva contribución sobre los tumores del tercer ventrículo. Su asociación con el sindrome de Recklinghausen y con el edema de Quincke. Arch. argent. de neurol., v. 5, p. 3.

FULTON, J F., & DUSSER DE BARENNE, J. G.
1933. The representation of the tail in the motor cortex of primates, with special reference to spider monkeys. J. Cell. & Comp. Physiol., v. 2, p. 399.

FULTON, J. F., HOFF, P. M., & PERKINS, H. T.
1945. A bibliography of visual literature, 1939–1944. Prepared by the Committee on Aviation Medicine, Division of Medical Sciences, National Research Council, Acting for the Committee on Medical Research,

Office of Scientific Research and Development, Washington, D.C.

FULTON, J. F., & INGRAHAM, F. D.
1929. Emotional disturbances following experimental lesions of the base of the brain (prechiasmal). J. Physiol., v. 67, p. xxvii.

FULTON, J. F., JACOBSEN, C. F., & KENNARD, M. A.
1932. A note concerning the relation of the frontal lobes to posture and forced grasping in monkeys. Brain, v. 55, p. 524.

FULTON, J. F., & NACHMANSOHN, D.
1943. Acetylcholine and the physiology of the nervous system. Science, v. 97, p. 569.

FUNKE, O.
1865. Zur Lehre von den Empfindungskreisen der Netzhaut. Ber. ü. d. naturforsch. Gesellsch. zu Freiburg i.Br., v. 3 (2), p. 89.

FURLANI, G.
1925. Giovani il Filopono e l'incendio della biblioteca di Alessandria. Bull. Soc. roy. archéol. d'Alexandria, No. 21, N.S., v. 6, p. 58.

FURNARI, S.
1845. Voyage médical dans l'Afrique septentrionale ou de l'ophthalmologie considérée dans ses rapports avec les différentes races. J.-B. Baillière, Paris.

FURNESS, W. H.
1916. Observations on the mentality of chimpanzees and orangutans. Proc. Am. Phil. Soc., v. 55, p. 281.

FUSE, G.
1912. Ueber den Abduzenskern der Säuger. Arb. hirnanat. Inst. Zürich (Monakow), v. 6, p. 401.
1914. Beiträge zur Anatomie des Bodens des IV. Ventrikels. *Ibid.*, v. 8, p. 213.
1916. Ueber das gewundene Grau im vorderen Zweihügel, den Nucleus olivaris Corp. quadrigemini anterioris beim Menschen. *Ibid.*, v. 10, p. 95.
1936. Das gewundene Grau oder der Olivenkern des vorderen Zweihuegels—Nuc. olivaris corp. quadr. ant. bei Mensch und Tier. Arb. anat. Inst. Sendai, v. 19, p. 49.

G

GABRIELI, G.
1923. Avicenna. Archeion, v. 4, p. 258.

GADOW, H.
1902. The origin of the mammalia. Ztschr. f. Morphol. & Anthropol., v. 4, p. 345.

GAFFRON, M.
1934. Untersuchungen über das Bewegungssehen bei Libellenlarven, Fliegen und Fischen. Ztschr. f. vergl. Physiol., v. 20, p. 299.

GAGE, S. H.
1941. The microscope. 17th ed. Comstock Pub. Co., Ithaca, N.Y.

GAGEL, O.
1928. Zur Topik und feineren Histologie der vegetativen Kerne des Zwischenhirns. Ztschr. f. Anat. u. Entw., v. 87, p. 558.

GAGNEBIN, E.
1947. Le transformisme et l'origine de l'homme. Masson & Cie, Paris.

GALAMBOS, R.
1942. The avoidance of obstacles by flying bats: Spallanzani's ideas (1794) and later theories. Isis, v. 34, p. 132.
1942. Cochlear potentials elicited from bats by supersonic sounds. J. Acoust. Soc. Amer., v. 14, p. 41.
1943. Flight in the dark: a study of bats. Scient. Monthly, v. 56, p. 155.

GALAMBOS, R., & DAVIS, H.
1943. The response of single auditory-nerve fibers to acoustic stimulation. J. Neurophysiol., v. 6, p. 39.
1944. Inhibition of activity in single auditory nerve fibers by acoustic stimulation. *Ibid.*, v. 7, p. 287.

GALAMBOS, R., & GRIFFIN, D. R.
1942. Obstacle avoidance by flying bats: the cries of bats. J. Exper. Zoöl., v. 89, p. 475; *also* Isis, v. 34, p. 132.

GALAMBOS, R., & LOWY, K.
1945. The electrical activity of single optic nerve fibers in cats. Fed. Proc., v. 4, p. 22.

GALEMAERTS
1903. Les centres optiques primaires après l'énucléation ou l'atrophie du globe oculaire. Policlin. Bruxelles, v. 12, p. 361.
1924. Anophtalmie congénitale et familiale. Bull. & mém. Soc. franç. d'opht., v. 37, p. 272; Ann. d'ocul., v. 161, p. 490.

GALEN (GALENOS)
2d cent. *See* for bibliography Beck 1909; Deneffe 1893, 1896; Heinrichs 1914; Ilberg 1889–97, 1905; Kassel 1911; Katz 1890; Meyer-Steineg 1911, 1912, 1913; Milne 1907; Neuburger 1906; Nöldecke 1805; Pagel 1915; Puschmann 1889; Puschmann, Neuburger & Pagel 1902–3; M. Simon; Sudhoff 1912; Töply 1898; J. Walsh.
2d cent. On the utility of the parts of the human body (De usu partium, etc.). *See* various Latin eds.; *also* Œuvres anatomiques etc. de Galien, ed. C. DAREMBERG, 2 vols., J.-B. Baillière, Paris, 1854; *also* De Hippocratis et

Platonis decretis, book 7, chaps. 3 ff., and De nervorum dissectione, chap. 2.

2d cent. On the natural faculties. W. Heinemann, London; G. P. Putnam's Sons, New York, 1916.

1533. Claudii Galeni Pergameni, Secundum Hippocratem medicorum facile principis, De usu partium corporis humani libri XVII, etc. Basileae (Basel), per Andr. Cratandrum, et Joan. Bebelium, Anno M.D.-XXXIII.

1541–42. Opera omnia, etc. 5 vols. Apud heredes Juntae, Venetiis. (According to Sudhoff 1921, this Giunta's edition was prepared by Vesalius; this edition is present in the Surgeon-General's Library, Washington; the University of Illinois has Giunta's 3d edition, 1556; the University of Chicago has the editions of 1597 and 1609; *see also* H. Cushing, A bio-bibliography of Andreas Vesalius, pp. 63–72.)

1597. *Galeni opera* ex septima Iuntarum editione, etc. Venetiis, Apud Iuntas, MDXCVII.

1597. Galeni De nervorum dissectione ad tyrones, liber integer. Augustino Gadaldino Mutinensi interprete. *In:* Galeni opera ex septima Iuntarum editione, p. 53.

1597. Galeni De anatomicis administrationibus libri novem. A Joanne Andernaco latinitate donati. Et post diligentissimas Andreae Vesallij Bruxellensis, & aliorum quoque castigationes, pluribus in locis emendati. *In.* Galeni opera ex septima Iuntarum editione, p. 63.

1597. Galeni De usu partium corporis humani libri XVII. Nicolao Rhegino Calabro interprete, denuo ab Augustino Gadaldino plerisque in locis emendati. *In:* Galeni opera ex septima Iuntarum editione, p. 113.

1597. Galeni De Hippocratis, et Platonis decretis libri novem. In quorum primo quaedam in principio desiderantur. Ioanne Bernardo Feliciano interprete. Ab Alexandro Iustiniano Chio medico ad vetustorum exemplarium graecorum fidem accuratissime castigati. *In:* Galeni opera ex septima Iuntarum editione, p. 231.

1805. Galen, vom Nutzen der Theile des menschlichen Körpers, aus dem Griechischen übersetzt und mit Anmerkungen begleitet von G. J.-Fr. Nöldeke, erstes Buch. Schultze, Oldenburg.

1821–33. Galeni opera omnia, ed. C. G. Kühn, Lipsiae.

1854. Œuvres anatomiques, physiologiques, et médicales de Galien, traduites sur les textes imprimés et manuscrits accompagnées des sommaires, de notes, de planches et d'une table des matières, précédées d'une introduction ou étude biographique, littéraire et scientifique sur Galien, par le Dr. Ch. Daremberg, bibliothécaire de la bibliothèque Mazarine, bibliothécaire honoraire de l'Académie de médecine, etc. 2 vols. J.-B. Baillière, Paris.

1906. Sieben Bücher Anatomie des Galen, ed. M. Simon, Leipzig. (With Latin and German text.)

1939–48. Werke. (German translation.) Hippokrates Verlag, Stuttgart. (So far published, Books 1–6 of Gesundheitslehre, and Books 1 & 2 of Die Kräfte der Nahrungsmittel.)

Galezowski, X.

1868. Physiologie des sensations lumineuses et colorées de la rétine. Ann. d'ocul., v. 59, p. 14.

Galilei, Galileo

1610. Sidereus nuncius, etc. Venetiis, apud T. Bagglionum. (Another edition 1610 in Francofurti, and 1653 typis J. Flesher, Londini.)

1718. Opere di Galileo Galilei Nobile Fiorentino Accademico Linceo Già Lettore delle Mattematiche nelle Università di Pisa, e di Padova, dipoi Sopraordinario nello Studio di Pisa, Primario Filosofo, e Mattematico Del Serenissimo Gran Duca Di Toscana. Nuova Edizione. Coll'aggiunto di varij Trattati dell'istesso Autore non più dati alle stampe. In Firenze MDCCXVIII. Nella Stamp. di S.A.R. Per Gio: Gaetano Tartini, & Santi Franchi Con licenza de'Superiori. 3 vols.

1880. The sidereal messenger of Galileo Galilei and a part of the Preface to Kepler's Dioptrics containing the original account of Galileo's astronomical discoveries. A translation with introduction and notes by Edward Stafford Carlos. Rivingtons, London; University Press, Edinburgh.

Gall, Franz Joseph (*see* H. Liepmann 1909)

1825. Sur les fonctions du cerveau et sur celles de chacune de ses parties. 6 vols. J.-B. Baillière, Paris.

Gall, F. J., & Spurzheim, G.

1809. Recherches sur le système nerveux en général, et sur celui du cerveau en particulier; mémoire présenté à l'Institut de France, le 14 Mars 1808; suivi d'observations sur le rapport qui en été fait à cette compagnie par ses commissaires. Paris, F. Schoell; H. Nicolle.

1810–19. Anatomie et physiologie du système nerveux en général, et du cerveau en particulier. Avec des observations sur la possibilité de reconnoître plusieurs dispositions intellectuelles et morales de l'homme et des animaux, par la configuration de leurs têtes. 4 vols. and atlas. F. Schoell, Paris.

GALLENGA, R.

1932. Contributo allo studio embriologico, descrittivo e topografico del muscolo lacrimale di Duverney-Horner. Rassegna ital. di ottal., v. 1, p. 96.

GALLUS

1902. Zur Frage der Ringscotome. Ztschr. f. Augenh., v. 7, p. 361.

GALT, W. E.

1939. The capacity of the rhesus and cebus monkey and the gibbon to acquire differential response to complex visual stimuli. Genet. Psychol. Monog., v. 21, p. 387.

GAMPER, E.

1918. Zur Klinik der Sensibilitätsstörungen bei Rindenläsionen. Monatsschr. f. Psychiat. u. Neurol., v. 43, p. 21.

GANS, A.

1916. Ueber Tastblindheit und über Störungen der räumlichen Wahrnehmung der Sensibilität. Ztschr. f. d. ges. Neurol. u. Psychiat. (Orig.), v. 31, p. 303.

1922. Das Handcentrum in der linken hinteren Zentralwindung. *Ibid.*, v. 75, p. 689.

GANSER, S.

1878. Ueber die vordere Hirncommissur der Säugethiere. Arch. f. Psychiat. u. Neurol., v. 9, p. 286.

1880. Untersuchungen über das Gehirn des Maulwurfs. Habilitationsschrift, München.

1882. Vergleichend-anatomische Studien über das Gehirn des Maulwurfs. Morphol. Jahrb. (Gegenbaur), v. 7, p. 591.

1882. Ueber die periphere und centrale Anordnung der Sehnervenfasern und über das Corpus bigeminum anterius. Arch. f. Psychiat. u. Nervenkr., v. 13, p. 341.

GARBOWSKI, T.

1898. Amphioxus als Grundlage der Mesodermtheorie. Anat. Anz., v. 14, p. 473.

GARCIA MIRANDA, A.

1944. The central scotomas as an early symptom in the diagnosis of intracranial conditions. Arch. Soc. oftal. Hispano-Am., v. 4, p. 30. (Abstr. in Arch. Ophth., v. 36, p. 508, 1946.)

GARDNER, W. J.

1933. The removal of the right cerebral hemisphere for infiltrating glioma; report of a case. J. Am. Med. Assoc., v. 101, p. 823.

GARLAND, J.

1949. The story of medicine. Houghton Mifflin Co., Boston.

GARNER, R. L.

1900. Apes and monkeys: their life and language. Ginn & Co., Boston & London.

GARRISON, F. H.

1929. An introduction to the history of medicine. W. B. Saunders Co., Philadelphia & London.

GARRISON, F. H., & MORTON, L. T.

1943. A medical bibliography: a check-list of texts illustrating the history of the medical sciences. Grafton & Co., London.

GARROD, A. H.

1879. Notes on the visceral anatomy of the tupaia of Burmah (*Tupaia belangeri*). Proc. Zoöl. Soc. London, p. 301.

GARTEN, S.

1907. Die Veränderungen der Netzhaut durch Licht. *In:* GRAEFE & SAEMISCH, Handb. d. ges. Augenh., v. 3, chap. 12, appendix.

GARTNER, S.

1951. Ocular pathology in the chiasmal syndrome. Am. J. Ophth., v. 33, p. 593.

GASKELL, W. H.

1898–1900. On the origin of vertebrates deduced from the study of ammocoetes. J. Anat. & Physiol., v. 32, p. 513; v. 33, p. 154; v. 34, p. 465.

1908. The origin of vertebrates. Longmans, Green & Co., New York.

GASNE, G.

1898. Sens stéréognostique et centres d'association. Nouv. Iconog. Salpêtr., v. 11, p. 46.

GASSENDUS, P.

1653. Institutio astronomica. Londini, Typ. J. Flesher. Prost. ap. C. Bee.

1657. The Mirrour of true Nobility & Gentility. Being the Life of The Renowned Nicolaus Claudius Fabricius Lord of Peiresk, Senator of the Parliament at Aix. Written by the Learned Petrus Gassendus, Professor of the Mathematicks to the King of France. Englished by W. Rand, Doctor of Physick. Vivit post Funera Virtus. London, Printed by J. Streater for Humphrey Moseley, and are to be sold at his Shop at the Princes Arms in St. Pauls Church-yard. 1657.

GASSER, H. S.
1934. Electrical phenomena in nerve. Suppl. to Science, v. 79.
1935. Conduction in nerves in relation to fiber types. Research Pub. A. Research Nerv. & Ment. Dis., v. 15, p. 35.
1937. The control of excitation in the nervous system. Harvey Lect., ser. 32, p. 169.
1939. Axons as samples of nervous tissue. J. Neurophysiol., v. 2, p. 361.

GASSER, H. S., ERLANGER, J., BRONK, D. W., LORENTE DE NÓ, R., & FORBES, A.
1939. Symposium on the synapse. Charles C Thomas, Springfield, Ill., & Baltimore.

GASSER, O.
1935. Ueber die Existenz des Canalis hyaloideus bei Mensch und Tier. Arch. f. Ophth. (Graefe), v. 134, p. 297.

GASTEIGER, H.
1934. Klinische Beobachtungen über die Ausdehnung des pupillomotorisch wirksamen Bezirkes der Netzhaut. Arch. f. Augenh., v. 108, p. 553.

GATES, R. R.
1927. A botanist in the Amazon Valley; an account of the flora and fauna in the land of floods. H. F. & G. Witherby, London.
1948. Human ancestry from a genetical point of view. Harvard University Press, Cambridge, Mass.

GATES, W. H.
1936. Keeping bats in captivity. J. Mammal., v. 17, p. 268.

GAUCKLER, E.
1922. Le professeur J. Dejerine, 1849–1917. Masson & Cie, Paris.

GAUPP, E.
1896–1904. A. Ecker's und R. Wiedersheim's Anatomie des Frosches. Auf Grund eigener Untersuchungen durchaus neu bearbeitet von Dr. Ernst Gaupp. 2d ed. F. Vieweg & Sohn, Braunschweig.
1911. Ueber den N. trochlearis der Urodelen und über die Austrittstellen der Gehirnnerven aus dem Schädelraum im allgemeinen. Anat. Anz., v. 38, p. 401.

GAUPP, R.
1899. Ueber corticale Blindheit. Monatsschr. f. Psychiat. u. Neurol., v. 5, p. 28.
1939. Die Lehren Kraepelins in ihrer Bedeutung für die heutige Psychiatrie. Ztschr. f. d. ges. Neurol. u. Psychiat., v. 165, p. 47.

GAUSS, H.
1930. Ueber den Gefässverlauf in der Netzhaut. Arch. f. Ophth. (Graefe), v. 123, p. 427.

GAUSS, K. F.
1841. Dioptrische Untersuchungen. Dieteriche Buchhandlung, Göttingen.

GEHLER, J. S. T.
1828. Physikalisches Wörterbuch. E. B. Schwikkert, Leipzig. *See* article "Gesicht" by MUNCKE, v. 4 (2), p. 1364.

GEHUCHTEN; *see* VAN GEHUCHTEN

GEIGER, L.
1882. Renaissance und Humanismus in Italien und Deutschland. G. Grote, Berlin.

GEIRINGER, M.
1938. Die Beziehung der basalen Optikuswurzel zur Hypophyse und ihre Bedeutung für den Farbwechsel der Amphibien. Anat. Anz., v. 86, p. 202.

GEIST, F. D.
1930. The brain of the rhesus monkey. J. Comp. Neurol., v. 50, p. 333.

GELB, A.
1923. Ueber eine eigenartige Sehstörung ("Dysmorphopsie") infolge von Gesichtsfeldeinschränkung. Ein Beitrag zur Lehre von den Beziehungen zwischen "Gesichtsfeld" und "Sehen." Psychol. Forsch., v. 4, p. 38.
1926. Die psychologische Bedeutung pathologischer Störungen der Raumwahrnehmung. Ber. ü. d. 9. Kong. f. exper. Psychol., p. 23.

GELB, A., & GOLDSTEIN, K.
1918. Zur Psychologie des optischen Wahrnehmungs- und Erkennungsvorganges. Ztschr. f. d. ges. Neurol. u. Psychiat. (Orig.), v. 41, p. 1.
1918. Das "röhrenförmige Gesichtsfeld" nebst einer Vorrichtung für perimetrische Gesichtsfelduntersuchungen in verschiedenen Entfernungen. Neurol. Centralbl., v. 37, p. 738.
1920. Psychologische Analysen hirnpathologischer Fälle auf Grund von Untersuchungen Hirnverletzter. J. A. Barth, Leipzig.
1920. Ueber den Einfluss des vollständigen Verlustes des optischen Vorstellungsvermögens auf das taktile Erkennen. Ztschr. f. Psychol., v. 83, p. 1.
1920. Ueber den Wegfall von "Oberflächenfarben." *Ibid.*, v. 84, p. 193.
1922. Psychologische Analysen hirnpathologischer Fälle auf Grund von Untersuchungen Hirnverletzter. VII. Ueber Gesichtsfeldbefunde bei abnormer "Ermüdbarkeit" des Auges (sog. "Ringskotome"). Arch. f. Ophth. (Graefe), v. 109, p. 387.
1925. Ueber Farbennamenamnesie. Nebst Be-

merkungen über das Wesen der amnestischen Aphasie überhaupt und die Beziehung zwischen Sprache und dem Verhalten zur Umwelt. Psychol. Forsch., v. 6, p. 127.

1925. Zur Frage der gegenseitigen funktionellen Beziehung der geschädigten Sehsphäre bei Hemianopsie (Mikropsie infolge der Vorherrschaft der Vorgänge in der geschädigten Sehsphäre). *Ibid.*, p. 187.

GELLHORN, E.

1925. Beiträge zur Kenntnis der Stoffwechselvorgänge in der Retina und der Sehsphäre auf Grund experimenteller Untersuchungen über den Verlauf von Gesichtsempfindungen und -wahrnehmungen. Ber. d. Deutsch. ophth. Gesellsch. Heidelberg, v. 45, p. 77.

1942. Anoxia in relation to the visual system. *In:* Biol. Symp., v. 7, p. 73. J. Cattell Press, Lancaster, Pa.

1943. Autonomic regulations, their significance for physiology, psychology and neuropsychiatry. Interscience Publishers, New York.

GENDEREN STORT, A. G. H. VAN

1886. Ueber Form- und Ortsveränderungen der Elemente in der Sehzellenschicht nach Beleuchtung. Ber. ü. d. ophth. Gesellsch. Stuttgart, v. 18 (2), p. 43.

1887. Ueber Form- und Ortsveränderungen der Netzhautelemente unter Einfluss von Licht und Dunkel. Arch. f. Ophth. (Graefe), v. 33 (3), p. 229.

GENNARI, F.

1782. Francisci Gennari Parmensis medicinae doctoris collegiati De peculiari structura cerebri nonnullisque eius morbis.—Paucae aliae anatom. observat. accedunt. Parmae, ex regio typographeo M.DCC.LXXXII. Cum approbatione.

GERARD OF CREMONA (GERARDUS OR GHERALDUS CREMONENSIS; G. LOMBARDUS; GHERARDO CREMONESE or G. DA CREMONA); *see* BONCOMPAGNI 1851; SUDHOFF 1914, 1930; NALLINO

GÉRARD, G.

1904. Les voies optiques extra-cérébrales. J. Anat. & Physiol., v. 40, p. 22.

1911. Le nerf optique et les voies optiques. Écho méd. du Nord, v. 15, p. 37.

GÉRARD, P., & ROCHON-DUVIGNEAUD, A.

1930. L'œil et la vision des mégachéiroptères. Arch. de biol., v. 11, p. 151.

GERARD, R. W.

1931. Nerve conduction in relation to nerve structure. Quart. Rev. Biol., v. 6, p. 59.

1934. The chemical activity of nerve. Suppl. to Science, v. 79.

1936. Factors controlling brain potentials. Cold Spring Harbor Symp. Quant. Biol., v. 4, p. 292.

1937. Brain metabolism and circulation. Research Pub. A. Research Nerv. & Ment. Dis., v. 18, p. 316. Williams & Wilkins Co., Baltimore.

1938. Anoxia and neural metabolism. Arch. Neurol. & Psychiat., v. 40, p. 985.

1941. The interaction of neurones. Ohio J. Sc., v. 41, p. 160.

GERARD, R. W., MARSHALL, W. H., & SAUL, L. J.

1933. Cerebral action potentials. Proc. Soc. Exper. Biol. & Med., v. 30, p. 1123; *also* Am. J. Physiol., v. 109, p. 38.

1936. Electrical activity of the cat's brain. Arch. Neurol. & Psychiat., v. 36, p. 675.

GERBI, GABRIELE; *see* DE ZERBIS

GERDY, P. N.

1839. Réponse à la lecture du mémoire de M. Bouillaud, sur la localisation de la faculté intellectuelle qui préside au langage articulé. L'expérience, J. de méd. et de chir., v. 4, p. 344.

GERHARDT, E., & KREHT, H.

1933. Zur Volumen- und Oberflächengrösse der Area striata. J. f. Psychol. u. Neurol., v. 45, p. 220.

GERLACH, H.

1937. Die Kenntnisse der alten Kulturvölker von den gesunden und kranken Sinnesorganen auf Grund ihrer Anschauungen von der Heilkunde. Arch. f. Gesch. d. Med. (Sudhoff), v. 27, p. 271.

GERLACH, J.

1858. Mikroskopische Studien aus dem Gebiete der menschlichen Morphologie. F. Enke, Erlangen.

1872. Von dem Rückenmark. *In:* STRICKER, Handb. d. Lehre v. d. Geweben, v. 2, p. 665. *Also:* The spinal cord. *In:* STRICKER, Manual of human and comp. histol., v. 2, p. 327. London.

GERLACH, L.

1881. Ueber die Gefässe der Macula lutea. Sitzungsb. d phys.-med. Gesellsch. Erlangen, v. 13, p. 63.

GERLING, C. L.

1839. Ueber die Beobachtung von Netzhautbildern. Ann. d. Phys. u. Chem. (Poggendorff), 2d ser., v. 16, p. 243.

GERMAN, W. J., & BRODY, B. S.

1940. The external geniculate bodies. Degeneration studies following occipital lobectomy. Arch. Neurol. & Psychiat., v. 43, p. 997.

GERMAN, W. J., & FOX, J. C.

1934. Observations following unilateral lobectomies. Research Pub. A. Research Nerv. & Ment. Dis., v. 13, p. 378. Williams & Wilkins Co., Baltimore.

GERNANDT, B.

1947. Colour sensitivity, contrast and polarity of the retinal elements. J. Neurophysiol., v. 10, p 303,

GERNANDT, B., & GRANIT, R.

1947. Single fibre analysis of inhibition and the polarity of the retinal elements. J. Neurophysiol., v. 10, p. 295.

GERSTMANN, J.

1915. Ueber Sensibilitätsstörungen von spino-segmentalem Typus bei Hirnrindenläsionen nach Schädelschussverletzungen. Wien. med. Wchnschr., v. 65, pp. 991, 1748.

1916. Weiterer Beitrag zur Frage der kortikalen Sensibilitätsstörungen von spino-segmentalem Typus. Monatsschr. f. Psychiat. u. Neurol., v. 39, p. 198; *also* Wien. med. Wchnschr., v. 65, p. 1748, 1915.

1918. Reine taktile Agnosie. Monatsschr. f. Psychiat. u. Neurol., v. 46, p. 329.

1918. Ein Beitrag zur Lehre von der Lokalisation der Sensibilität in der Grosshirnrinde. Neurol. Centralbl., v. 37, p. 434.

1924. Fingeragnosie. Eine umschriebene Störung der Orientierung am eigenen Körper. Wien. klin. Wchnschr., v. 37, p. 1010.

1927. Fingeragnosie und isolierte Agraphie—ein neues Syndrom. Ztschr. f. d. ges. Neurol. u. Psychiat., v. 108, p. 152.

1927. Studien zur Symptomatologie der Stirnhirnerkrankungen. I. Ueber die frontale Astasie und Abasie. Wien. klin. Wchnschr., v. 40, p. 1133.

1930. Zur Symptomatologie der Herderkrankungen in der Uebergangsregion der unteren Parietal- und mittleren Okzipitalwindungen. Deutsch. Ztschr. f. Nervenh., v. 116, p. 46.

1942. Problem of imperception of disease and of impaired body territories with organic lesions. Relation to body schemes and its disorders. Arch. Neurol. & Psychiat., v. 48, p. 890.

GERSTMANN, J., & KESTENBAUM, A.

1930. Monokuläres Doppeltsehen bei cerebralen Erkrankungen. I. Mitt. Ztschr. f. d. ges. Neurol. u. Psychiat., v. 128, p. 42.

GERWER, A. W.

1898. Ueber die Gehirncentra der associierten Augenbewegungen. Neurol. Centralbl., v. 17, p. 716.

GESCHER, J.

1925. Selbstbeobachtungen eines relativ Grünsichtigen mit Unterwertigkeit für Rot. Untersuchungen über locale Adaptation und Purkinjesches Nachbild. Arch. f. Augenh., v. 96, p. 72.

1925. Zur Physiologie der entoptischen Sichtbarkeit der Blutbewegung im Auge. *Ibid.*, p. 419.

GESELL, A., ILG, F. L., & BULLIS, G. E.

1949. Vision, its development in infant and child. Paul B. Hoeber–Harper & Bros., New York.

GHEURY DE BRAY, M. E. J.

1939. Interpretation of the red-shift of the light from extra-galactic nebulae. Nature, v. 144, p. 285.

GHISELLI, E. E.

1937. The superior colliculus in vision. J. Comp. Neurol., v. 67, p. 451.

1937. Encephalization of brightness discrimination in mammals. Science, v. 86, p. 618.

GHOSH, A. K.

1945. The Indian fauna during 1943–44. Current Sc. (Bangalore), v. 14, p. 240.

GIACOSA, P.

1901. Magistri salernitani nondum editi: catalogo ragionato delle esposizioni di storia della medicina aperta in Torino nel 1898. Frat. Broca, Torino.

GIBBON, E.

1776–88. The history of the decline and fall of the Roman Empire. 2 vols. G. Virtue, London & New York (prob. 1848 or 1849; also modern eds.).

GIBBS, F. A., MAXWELL, H., & GIBBS, E. L.

1947. Volume flow of blood through the human brain. Arch. Neurol. & Psychiat., v. 57, p. 137.

GIBSON, G. A.

1903. Case of right homonymous hemianopia. Brain, v. 26, p. 302.

GIBSON, THOMAS

1694. The anatomy of humane bodies epitomized. Awnsham & J. Churchill, London.

GIERKE, H.

1884–85. Färberei zu mikroskopischen Zwecken. Ztschr. f. wissensch. Mikr., v. 1, pp. 62, 372, 497; v. 2, pp. 13, 164.

GIFFORD, S. R.

1937. Handbook of ocular therapeutics. 2d ed. Lea & Febiger, Philadelphia.

1947. Textbook of ophthalmology. 4th ed. W. B. Saunders Co., Philadelphia.

GILBERT, L. W.
*1812. Die Optik des Ptolemaeus, verglichen mit der Euklids, Alhazens und Vitellos von Delambre. Gilberts Ann., v. 40. (*See* Delambre 1812.)

GILBERT, M. S.
1935. The early development of the human diencephalon. J. Comp. Neurol., v. 62, p. 81.

GILDEA, E. F., & COBB, S.
1930. The effects of anemia on the cerebral cortex of the cat. Arch. Neurol. & Psychiat., v. 23, p. 876.

GILL, D., & EDDINGTON, A. S.
1932. Article: Telescope, Encyclopaedia Britannica, 14th ed., v. 21, p. 904.

GILL, W.
1892. The South Pacific and New Guinea past and present. C. Potter, Sydney.

GILLETT, W. G.
1925. The histologic structure of the eye of the soft-shelled turtle. Am. J. Physiol. Opt., v. 6, p. 592.

GILLETTE, J. M.
1943. Ancestorless man: the anthropological dilemma. Scient. Monthly, v. 57, p. 533.

GILLIARD, E. T.
1953. New Guinea's rare birds and Stone Age men. Nat. Geog. Mag., v. 103, p. 421.

GILLILAN, L. A.
1939. The connections of the nucleus of the basal optic root in various mammals. Anat. Rec., v. 73 (suppl.), p. 21.
1941. The connections of the basal optic root (posterior accessory optic tract) and its nucleus in various mammals. J. Comp. Neurol., v. 74, p. 367.

GIOVANARDI, E.
1881. Intorno ad un caso di anoftalmia doppia congenita (mancanza dei nervi ottici, atrofia dei lobi occipitali). Riv. sper. di freniat., v. 7, p. 244.

GIRARDI, M.
*1724. *In:* J. D. SANTORINI, De oculo observationes anatomicae. Recurti, Venetiis.

GIRNDT, O., & LEMPKE, H.
1937–38. Ueber optomotorische Reaktionen von Katzen ohne Neocortex. Arch. f. d. ges. Physiol. (Pflüger), v. 239, p. 544 (*see also* Scharrer, p. 566).

GISI, J.
1907. Das Gehirn von *Hatteria punctata*. Lippert & Co., Naumburg; *also* Zool. Jahrb. (Abt f. Anat.), v. 25, p. 71.

GLADSTONE, R. J., & WAKELEY, C. P. G.
1940. The pineal organ. Baillière, Tindall & Cox, London.

GLASSER, O.
1944. Medical physics. Year Book Publishers, Inc., Chicago. 2d vol., 1950.

GLEES, P.
1939. Ueber Zellzusammenhänge im Zentralnervensystem der Selachier. Acta neerl. morphol., v. 2, p. 170.
1941. The termination of optic fibres in the lateral geniculate body of the cat. J. Anat., v. 75, p. 434.
1942. The termination of optic fibres in the lateral geniculate body of the rabbit. *Ibid.*, v. 76, p. 313.
1944. The contribution of the median fillet and strio-hypothalamic fibres to the dorsal supra-optic decussation, with a note on the termination of the lateral fillet. *Ibid.*, v. 78, p. 113.

GLEES, P., & LE GROS CLARK, W. E.
1941. The termination of optic fibres in the lateral geniculate body of the monkey. J. Anat., v. 75, p. 295.

GLEICHEN, A.
1917. Beitrag zur Theorie der Sehschärfe. Arch. f. Ophth. (Graefe), v. 93, p. 303.

GLICK, D.
1938. Studies on the specificity of choline esterase. J. Biol. Chem., v. 125, p. 729.
1939. Further studies on the specificity of choline esterase. *Ibid.*, v. 130, p. 527.

GLOBUS, J. H.
1936. Intracranial hemorrhage: its anatomical forms and some of their clinical features. New York State J. Med., v. 36, p. 681.
1938. Massive cerebral hemorrhage. Research Pub. A. Research Nerv. & Ment. Dis., v. 18, p. 438. Williams & Wilkins Co., Baltimore.

GLOBUS, J. H., & SILVERSTONE, S. M.
1935. Diagnostic value of defects in visual fields and other ocular disturbances associated with supratentorial tumors of the brain. Arch. Ophth., v. 14, p. 325.

GLORIEUX, P.
1929. Anatomie et connexions thalamiques chez le chien. J. de neurol. et de psychiat., v. 29, p. 525.

GNAUCK, R.
1883. Ein Fall von Hemianopsia heteronyma lateralis. Neurol. Centralbl., v. 2, p. 193.

GNEISSE, K.
1922. Die Entstehung der Gestaltvorstellungen, unter besonderer Berücksichtigung neuerer Untersuchungen von kriegsgeschädigten Seelenblinden. Arch. f. d. ges. Psychol., v. 42, p. 295.

GOBRECHT, H., & OERTEL, H.
1953. Der Sehvorgang beim Dämmerungssehen unter Berücksichtigung der Quantennatur des Lichtes. Ztschr. f. Phys., v. 135, p. 541.

GODDING, E. W.
1945. The testing of night vision. Some basic requirements, with introduction and causes of abnormality. Tr. Illumin. Engineer. Soc. London, v. 10, p. 27. Abstr. in Bull. War Med., v. 5, p. 730.

GODINOV, V. M.
1930. The arterial system of the brain. Am. J. Phys. Anthropol., v. 14, p. 359.

GODLOWSKI, W.
1936. Les centres sous-corticaux du regard et des mouvements associés des globes oculaires. Étude expérimentale. Krakow.
1938. Experimentelle Untersuchungen über die durch Reizung des Zwischen- und Mittelhirns hervorgerufenen assoziierten Augenbewegungen. Ztschr. f. d. ges. Neurol. u. Psychiat., v. 162, p. 160.

GOEBEL, O.
1938. Empfindung und Vorstellung im Seh- und Hörbereich. Ztschr. f. d. ges. Neurol. u. Psychiat., v. 162, p. 443.

GOEDBLOED, J.
1934. Studien am Glaskörper. Arch. f. Ophth. (Graefe), v. 132, p. 323; v 133, p. 1.

GÖPFERT, H.
1922. Beiträge zur Frage der Restitution nach Hirnverletzungen. Ztschr. f. d. ges. Neurol. u. Psychiat., v. 75, p. 411.

GÖPPERT, H. R., & COHN, F.
1849. Ueber die Rotation des Zellinhaltes von *Nitella flexilis*. Bot. Zeitung, v. 7, pp. 665, 681, 697, 713.

GOERTTLER, K.
1950. Entwicklungsgeschichte des Menschen. J. Springer Verlag, Berlin.

GÖTHLIN, G. F.
1943. The fundamental colour sensations in man's colour sense. Kgl. svensk. vetenskaps. handl. (3), v. 20, No. 7, pp. 1–76. (Review by ROAF, Nature, v. 153, p. 235; *also* Arch. Ophth., v. 36, p. 529.)

GOLDBY, F.
1934. The cerebral hemispheres of *Lacerta viridis*. J. Anat., v. 68, p. 157.
1941. The normal histology of the thalamus in the phalanger, *Trichosurus vulpecula. Ibid.*, v. 75, p. 197.
1942. An experimental study of the thalamus in the phalanger, *Trichosurus vulpecula. Ibid.*, v. 77, p. 195.

GOLDMAN, E. A.
1925. The predatory animal problem and the balance of nature. J. Mammal., v. 6, p. 28.

GOLDMANN, H.
1949. Slit-lamp examination of the vitreous and the fundus. Brit. J. Ophth., v. 33, p. 242.

GOLDSCHMIDT, M.
1950. A new test for function of the macula lutea. Arch. Ophth., v. 44, p. 129.

GOLDSCHMIDT, R.
1908–09. Das Nervensystem von *Ascaris lumbricoides*. Ein Versuch, in den Aufbau eines einfachen Nervensystems einzudringen. Ztschr. f. wissensch. Zool., v. 90, p. 73; v. 92, p. 306.
1910. Das Nervensystem von *Ascaris lumbricoides* and *megalocephala*, etc. Festschrift z. 60. Geburtstag R. Hertwigs, v. 2, p. 253. G. Fischer, Jena.

GOLDSCHMIDT, R. B.
1940. The material basis of evolution. (Silliman Memorial Lect.) Yale University Press, New Haven; Oxford University Press, London.

GOLDSMITH, J.
1939. Slit-lamp observations during experimental intracapsular extraction of cataract. Arch. Ophth., v. 22, p. 792.

GOLDSTEIN, K.
1908. Zur Theorie der Halluzinationen. Studien über normale und pathologische Wahrnehmung. Arch. f. Psychiat. u. Nervenkr., v. 44, pp. 584, 1036.
1910. Einige prinzipielle Bemerkungen zur Frage der Lokalisation psychischer Vorgänge im Gehirn. Med. Klin., v. 6, p. 1363.
1916. Ueber corticale Sensibilitätsstörungen. Ztschr. f. d. ges. Neurol. u. Psychiat. (Orig.), v. 33, p. 494.
1917. Die transkortikalen Aphasien. Ergebn. d. Neurol. u. Psychiat., v. 2, p. 349.
1919. Ludwig Edinger. Ber. d. Senckenberg. naturforsch. Gesellsch., v. 49, p. 143.
1923. Die Topik der Grosshirnrinde in ihrer klinischen Bedeutung. Deutsch. Ztschr. f. Nervenh., v. 77, p. 7.
1923. Ueber die Abhängigkeit der Bewegungen von optischen Vorgängen. Bewegungsstörungen bei Seelenblinden. Monatsschr. f. Psychiat. u. Neurol., v. 54, p. 141.
1923. Zur Frage der Restitution nach umschriebenem Hirndefekt. Schweiz. Arch. f. Neurol. u. Psychiat., v. 13, p. 283.
1925. Zur Theorie der Funktion des Nervensystems. Arch. f. Psychiat., v. 74, p. 370.

1927. Die Lokalisation in der Grosshirnrinde nach den Erfahrungen am kranken Menschen. *In:* BETHE *et al.,* Handb. d. norm. u. path. Physiol., v. 10, p. 600.

1931. Ueber die Plastizität des Organismus auf Grund von Erfahrungen am nervenkranken Menschen. *In:* BETHE *et al.,* Handb. d. norm. u. path. Physiol., v. 15 (2), Correlationen, v. 1 (2), p. 1131.

1934. Ueber monokuläre Doppelbilder. Ihre Entstehung und Bedeutung für die Theorie von der Function des Nervensystems. Jahrb. f. Psychiat., v. 51, p. 16.

1936. The significance of the frontal lobes for mental performances. J. Neurol. & Psychopath., v. 17, p. 27.

1942. Aftereffects of brain injuries in war. Their evaluation and treatment. The application of psychologic methods in the clinic. Grune & Stratton, New York.

GOLDSTEIN, K., & GELB, A.
1918. Das "röhrenförmige Geschichtsfeld" nebst einer Vorrichtung für perimetrische Gesichtsfelduntersuchungen in verschiedenen Entfernungen. Neurol. Centralbl., v. 37, p. 738.

1918–19. Psychologische Analysen hirnpathologischer Fälle auf Grund von Untersuchungen Hirnverletzter. Ztschr. f. d. ges. Neurol. u. Psychiat., v. 41 (Orig.), p. 1; *also* Ztschr. f. Sinnesphysiol., v. 83, p. 1.

GOLDSTEIN, K., & REICHMANN, F.
1920. Ueber corticale Sensibilitätsstörungen, besonders am Kopfe. Ztschr. f. d. ges. Neurol. u. Psychiat. (Orig.), v. 53, p. 49.

1920. Ueber praktische und theoretische Ergebnisse aus den Erfahrungen an Hirnschussverletzten. Ergebn. d. inn. Med. u. Kinderh., v. 18, p. 405.

GOLDSTEIN, K., & ROSENTHAL, O.
1930. Zum Problem der Wirkung der Farben auf den Organismus. Schweiz. Arch. f. Neurol. u. Psychiat., v. 26, p. 3.

GOLDSTERN, H. N.
1915. Die Sehrinde. Eine rassen-anatomische Studie an Judenhirnen. Inaug.-Diss. zur Erlangung der Doktorwürde der hohen medizinischen Fakultät der Universität Bern. Buchdruckerei H. Stolz, Bern.

GOLGI, C.
1873. Sulla struttura della sostanza grigia del cervello. Gazz. med. ital. Lombardo, ser. 6, v. 6. (*See* abstr. in Centralbl. f. d. med. Wissensch., v. 11, p. 806.)

1878. Un nuovo processo di tecnica microscopica. Rend. d. r. Ist. Lomb. di sc. e let., 2d ser., v. 12, Fasc. 5.

1878. Di una nuova reazione apparentemente nera delle cellule nervose cerebrali etc. Archivio per le sc. med., v. 3, No. 11.

1891. La rete nervosa diffusa degli organi centrali del sistema nervoso. Rend. d. r. Ist. Lomb. di sc. e let., 2d ser., v. 24; *also* Arch. ital. de biol., v. 15, p. 434. (In French.)

1903. Opera omnia. 3 vols. U. Hoepli, Milano. *See* v. 1, p. 143; and v. 2, pp. 579, 607, 721.

GOLTZ, F.
1881. Ueber die Verrichtungen des Grosshirns. Gesammelte Abh. E. Strauss, Bonn.

1892. Der Hund ohne Grosshirn. Arch. f. d. ges. Physiol. (Pflüger), v. 51, p. 570.

1899. Beobachtungen an einem Affen mit verstümmeltem Grosshirn. *Ibid.,* v. 76, p. 411.

GÓMEZ OCAÑA, J.
1894. Memoria sobre demostración experimental de los centros visuales del cerebro. Ann. r. Acad. de med. Madrid, v. 14, pp. 298, 365.

1897. Bosquejo de una nueva teoría de la vision. Rev. trimestr. microg., v. 2, p. 163.

GOMPERZ, T.
1929–39. Greek thinkers: a history of ancient philosophy. Translated by L. MAGNUS & G. G. BERRY. 4 vols. J. Murray, London.

GONIN, J.
1911. Du champ visuel aveugle dans l'hémianopsie. Ann. d'ocul., v. 145, p. 1.

GOODDY, W.
1949. Sensation and volition. Brain, v. 72, p. 312.

GOODMAN, L.
1949. Recurrent hypertensive cerebral thrombosis. Clinicopathologic analysis of six cases with discussion of pathogenesis. Arch. Neurol. & Psychiat., v. 62, p. 445.

GOODRICH, E. S.
1930. Studies on the structure and development of vertebrates. Macmillan & Co., London.

GORDON, A.
1907. The localization of the motor area based on exact faradization. J. Am. Med. Assoc., v. 48, p. 2107.

GORDON, B. L.
1942. Ancient medical jurisprudence with special reference to the eye. Arch. Ophth., v. 28, p. 860.

1949. Medicine throughout antiquity. F. A. Davis Co., Philadelphia.

1949. The romance of medicine: the story of the evolution of medicine from occult practices and primitive times. 2d ed. F. A. Davis Co., Philadelphia.

GORDON, J.
1815. A system of human anatomy. W. Blackwood & J. Anderson & Co., Edinburgh.

GORJANOVIĆ-KRAMBERGER, K.
1906. Der diluviale Mensch von Krapina in Kroatien. Ein Beitrag zur Paläoanthropologie. C. W. Kreidel, Wiesbaden.

GOSSEN, H.
1939. The legacy of Greece and medical thought in ancient Rome. The physician in ancient Rome. The therapeutic methods of the Roman physician. Superstitition in Roman medicine. Hygiene in ancient Rome. Series of articles published in Ciba Symp., v. 1, No. 2.

GOTTSCHE, C. M.
1834. Ueber die Retina im Auge der Grätenfische. Arch. f. Anat., Physiol. u. wissensch. Med. (J. Müller), p. 457.
1836. Ueber den Bau der Retina des Menschen und der Säugethiere. Pract. u. krit. Mitt. a. d. Geb. d. Med. (Pfaff), N.F., v. 2, p. 40; *also in* Jahresb. in J. Müller's Arch. f. Anat., Physiol. u. wissensch. Med., p. viii, 1837.

GOURFEIN-WELT & REDAILLÉ
1921. Obere rechtsseitige Quadrantenhemianopsie. Klin. Monatsbl. f. Augenh., v. 67, p. 332; Schweiz. med. Wchnschr., v. 2, p. 1124.
1921. Hémianopsie en quadrant supérieur; étude anatomique et clinique. Rev. gén. d' opht., v. 35, p. 340.

GOVI, G. (*see also* FAVARO)
1885. L'ottica di Claudio Tolomeo da Eugenio, ammiraglio di Sicilia, scrittore del secolo XII, ridotta in latino sovra la traduzione araba di un testo greco imperfetto ora per la prima volta conforme a un codice della Biblioteca Ambrosiana, etc. G. B. Paravia e I. Vigliardi, Torino.

GOWERS, W. R.
1876. The state of the arteries in Bright's disease. Brit. M. J., v. 2, p. 743.
1878. Pathologischer Beweis einer unvollständigen Kreuzung der Sehnerven beim Menschen. Centralbl. f. d. med. Wissensch., v. 16, p. 562.
1895. Subjective visual sensations. Tr. Ophth. Soc. United Kingdom, v. 15, p. 1.

GRADLE, H. S.
1923. The intraneural course of the optic nerve fibers. Tr. Am. Acad. Ophth. & Otolaryng., v. 28, p. 234.

GRAEFE, ALBRECHT VON
1854. Ueber Doppelsehen nach Schieloperationen und Incongruenz der Netzhäute. Arch. f. Ophth. (Graefe), v. 1 (1), p. 82.
1856. Ueber die Untersuchung des Gesichtsfeldes bei amblyopischen Affectionen. *Ibid.*, v. 2 (2), p. 258.

GRAEFE, A., & SAEMISCH, E. T.
1874–1932. Handbuch der gesamten Augenheilkunde. 1st ed., 1874–80; 2d ed., 1899–1930; 3d ed., 1912–32. W. Engelmann, Leipzig; J. Springer, Berlin.

GRAGE, H.
1930. Hirnlokalisatorische Bemerkungen eines seltenen Falles von Kopfsteckschuss mit Demonstration von Röntgenbildern. Arch. f. Psychiat. u. Nervenkr., v. 90, p. 174.
1930. Ein seltener Fall von Kopfsteckschuss im rechten Schläfenlappen mit schwerer Stirnhirnverletzung. J. f. Psychol. u. Neurol., v. 40, p. 356.

GRAHAM, C. H.
1933. The relation of nerve response and retinal potential to number of sense cells illuminated in an eye lacking lateral connections. J. Cell. & Comp. Physiol., v. 2, p. 295.

GRAHAM, C. H., & HARTLINE, H. K.
1935. The response of single visual sense cells to lights of different wave lengths. J. Gen. Physiol., v. 18, p. 917.

GRAHAM, E. H.
1947. The land and wildlife. Oxford University Press, New York.

GRAHAM, H. T., & O'LEARY, J. L.
1941. Fast central fibers in fish. Properties of Mauthner and Müller fibers of medullospinal system. J. Neurophysiol., v. 4, p. 224.

GRAHAM, J. R., & WOLFF, H. G.
1938. Mechanism of migraine headache and action of ergotamine tartrate. Research Pub. A. Research Nerv. & Ment. Dis., v. 18, p. 638. Williams & Wilkins Co., Baltimore.

GRANDIDIER, A.
1875–1901. Histoire physique, naturelle et politique de Madagascar. Imprimerie nationale, Paris.

GRANICH, L.
1947. Aphasia: a guide to retraining. Grune & Stratton, New York.

GRANIT, R.
1930. Comparative studies on the peripheral and central retina. I. On interaction between distant areas in the human eye. Am. J. Physiol., v. 94, p. 41.
1931. The retina as a nervous center. Arch. Ophth., 2d ser., v. 6, p. 104.
1932. The physiological significance of the retinal

synapses. Phys. & Opt. Soc. Rep. etc., Great Britain, p. 263.

1933. The components of the retinal action potential in mammals and their relation to the discharge in the optic nerve. J. Physiol., v. 77, p. 207.

1935. Two types of retinae and their electrical responses to intermittent stimuli in light and dark adaptation. *Ibid.*, v. 85, p. 421.

1936. Die Elektrophysiologie der Netzhaut und des Sehnerven. Mit besonderer Berücksichtigung der theoretischen Begründung der Flimmermethode. Levin & Munksgaard, Copenhagen. *Also* Acta Ophth., v. 14, suppl. 8.

1937. The retinal centre as an amplifier of potential differences. Nature, v. 139, p. 719.

1937. Absorption curve for visual purple and the electrical response of the frog's eye. *Ibid.*, v. 140, p. 972.

1938. On the possibilities of analyzing the processes in the central nervous system. (Swedish with an English summary.) Nord. med. tidskr., v. 15, p. 121.

1938. Processes of adaptation in the vertebrate retina in the light of recent photochemical and electrophysiological research. Doc. Ophth., v. 1, p. 7.

1941. The retinal mechanism of color reception. J. Opt. Soc. Amer., v. 31, p. 570.

1941. Rotation of activity and spontaneous rhythms in the retina. Acta physiol. Scandinav., v. 1, p. 370.

1941. The "red" receptor of *Testudo*. *Ibid.*, p. 386.

1941. Isolation of colour-sensitive elements in a mammalian retina. *Ibid.*, v. 2, p. 93.

1941. A relation between rod and cone substances, based on scotopic and photopic spectra of *Cyprinus*, *Tinca*, *Anguilla*, and *Testudo*. *Ibid.*, p. 334.

1942. Colour receptors of the frog's retina. *Ibid.*, v. 3, p. 137.

1942. Spectral properties of the visual receptor elements of the guinea pig. *Ibid.*, p. 318.

1942. The photopic spectrum of the pigeon. *Ibid.*, v. 4, p. 118.

1943. A physiological theory of colour perception. Nature, v. 151, p. 11.

1943. "Red" and "green" receptors in the retina of *Tropidonotus*. Acta physiol. Scandinav., v. 5, p. 108.

1943. The spectral properties of the visual receptors. *Ibid.*, p. 219.

1944. The dark-adaptation of mammalian visual receptors. *Ibid.*, v. 7, p. 216.

1944. Stimulus intensity in relation to excitation and pre- and post-excitatory inhibition in isolated elements of mammalian retinae. J. Physiol., v. 103, p. 103.

1945. Isolation of the mammalian colour receptors with micro-electrodes. Nature, v. 155, p. 711.

1945. The colour receptors of the mammalian retina. J. Neurophysiol., v. 8, p. 195.

1945. The electrophysiological analysis of the fundamental problem of colour reception. Proc. Phys. Soc. (London), v. 57, p. 447.

1945. Some properties of post-excitatory inhibition, studied in the optic nerve with micro-electrodes. Ark. f. Zool. (Stockholm), v. 36, A, p. 1.

1945. Frithiof Holmgren och upptäckten av näthinnans elektriska belysnings-reaktion. Lychnos, p. 132.

1946. The distribution of excitation and inhibition in single-fibre responses from a polarized retina. J. Physiol., v. 105, p. 45.

1946. The 1944 Nobel prize for physiology and medicine was awarded, on October the 26th, jointly to Joseph Erlanger and Herbert Spencer Gasser. Les Prix Nobel en 1940–1944. Stockholm, Kungl. Boktryckeriet. P. A. Norstedt & Söner.

1947. Mechanism of colour vision. Nature, v. 159, p. 417. (Review of E. N. WILLMER, Retinal structure and colour vision: a restatement and an hypothesis.)

1947. Sensory mechanisms of the retina, with an appendix on electroretinography. Geoffrey Cumberlege, Oxford University Press, London, New York, & Toronto.

1950. Physiology of vision. Ann. Rev. Physiol., v. 12, p. 485.

1950. The organization of the vertebrate retinal elements. Ergebn. d. Physiol., v. 46, p. 31.

1950. Autogenetic inhibition. EEG Clin. Neurophysiol., v. 2, p. 417.

1950. Reflex self-regulation of muscle contraction and autogenetic inhibition. J. Neurophysiol., v. 13, p. 351.

1951. The antagonism between the on- and off-systems in the cat's retina. Année psychol., v. 50, p. 129.

GRANIT, R., & HARPER, P.

1930. Synaptic reactions in the eye. Am. J. Physiol., v. 95, p. 211.

GRANIT, R., & HELME, T.

1939. Changes in retinal excitability due to polarization and some observations on the relation between the processes in retina and nerve. J. Neurophysiol., v. 2, p. 556.

GRANIT, R., & MUNSTERHJELM, A.
1937. The electrical responses of dark-adapted frogs' eyes to monochromatic stimuli. J. Physiol., v. 88, p. 436.

GRANIT, R., MUNSTERHJELM, A., & ZEWI, M.
1939. The relation between concentration of visual purple and retinal sensitivity to light during dark adaptation. J. Physiol., v. 96, p. 31.

GRANIT, R., RUBINSTEIN, B., & THERMAN, P. O.
1935. A new type of interaction experiment with the retinal action potential. J. Physiol. (Proc.), v. 85, p. 421.

GRANIT, R., & STRÖM, G.
1951. Autogenetic modulation of excitability of single ventral horn cells. J. Neurophysiol., v. 14, p. 113.

GRANIT, R., & SVAETICHIN, G.
1939. Principles and technique of the electrophysiological analysis of colour reception with the aid of microelectrodes. Upsala läk. förhandl., v. 45, p. 161.

GRANIT, R., & THERMAN, P. O.
1935. Excitation and inhibition in the retina and in the optic nerve. J. Physiol., v. 83, p. 359.
1937. Excitation and inhibition in the off-effect of the retina. *Ibid.*, v. 91, p. 127.
1938. The "slow potentials" associated with excitation and inhibition in the excised eye. *Ibid.* (Proc.), v. 93, p. 9.

GRANIT, R., THERMAN, P. O., & WREDE, C. M.
1938. Selective effects of different adapting wavelengths on the dark-adapted frog's retina. Skandinav. Arch. f. Physiol., v. 80, p. 142.

GRANIT, R., & WREDE, C. M.
1937. The electrical responses of light-adapted frogs' eyes to monochromatic stimuli. J. Physiol., v. 89, p. 239.

GRANT, D.
1903. Case of hemianaesthesia affecting the skin and special senses with crossed amblyopia and achromatopia. Brain, v. 26, p. 469.

GRASSÉ, P.-P.
1952. Traité de zoologie. 17 vols. Masson & Cie, Paris.

GRASSET, J.
1907. La fonction du langage et la localisation des centres psychiques dans le cerveau. Rev. de phil., v. 10, p. 5.

GRASSUS, BENEVENUTUS, OF JERUSALEM
1929. De oculis, etc. Written probably during 11th cent.; first published in print at Ferrara, 1474; translated by C. A. WOOD, 1929. Stanford University Press, Stanford, Calif. (*See* N. Scalinci 1935.)

GRATIOLET, L.-P. (*see also* LEURET & GRATIOLET)
1854. Note sur les expansions des racines cérébrales du nerf optique et sur leur terminaison dans une région determinée de l'écorce des hémisphères. Compt. rend. Acad. d. sc., v. 39, p. 274.
1854. Mémoire sur les plis cérébraux de l'homme et des primates. A Bertrand, Paris.
1855. Mémoire sur la structure des hémisphères du cerveau dans l'homme et les primates. Compt. rend. Acad. d. sc., v. 41, p. 16.

GRAY, H.
1850. On the development of the retina and optic nerve, and of the membranous labyrinth and auditory nerve. Phil. Tr. Roy. Soc. London, v. 140, p. 189.

GRAY, H., & GOSS, C. M.
1948. Anatomy of the human body. Lea & Febiger, Philadelphia.

GRAY, J.
1944. Chimpanzees: a psycho-biological review. Discovery, v. 5, p. 121.
1953. How animals move. Cambridge University Press, Cambridge.

GRAY, J. E.
1848. Description of a new genus of insectivorous mammalia, or Talpidae, from Borneo. Proc. Zoöl. Soc. London, p. 23; *also* Ann. Mag. Nat. Hist., ser. 2, v. 2, p. 212.
1850. Vertebrata. *In:* A. ADAMS, Zoölogy of the voyage of H. M. S. Samarang, p. 18. Reeve & Benham, London.
1865. Notice of a species of *Tupaia* from Borneo, in the collection of the British Museum. Proc. Zoöl. Soc. London, p. 322.

GRAY, P. A.
1924. The cortical lamination pattern of the opossum, *Didelphis virg.* J. Comp. Neurol., v. 37, p. 221.

GRAY, P. A., & TURNER, E. L.
1924. The motor cortex of the opossum. J. Comp. Neurol., v. 36, p. 375.

GREEAR, J. N.
1942. Pits, or crater-like holes, in the optic disk. Arch. Ophth., v. 28, p. 467.

GREEAR, J. N., & McGAVIC, J. S.
1946. Visual disturbances associated with head injuries. Arch. Ophth., v. 36, p. 33.

GREEFF, R.
1894. Die Spinnenzellen (Neurogliazellen) im Sehnerven und in der Retina. Arch. f. Augenh., v. 29, p. 324.
1898. S. Ramón y Cajals neuere Beiträge zur Histologie der Retina. Ztschr. f. Psychol. u. Physiol. d. Sinnesorg., v. 16, p. 161.

1899. Discussion on "amacrine cells." Ber. d. Deutsch. ophth. Gesellsch. Heidelberg, v. 27, p. 107.

1899 (1900). Die mikroskopische Anatomie des Sehnerven und der Netzhaut. *In:* GRAEFE & SAEMISCH, Handb. d. ges. Augenh., 2d ed., v. 1, chap. 5.

1913–14. Die Anfänge der eigentlichen Brillen. Ztschr. f. ophth. Optik, v. 1, p. 11.

1913–14. Eine Brille von vor 1500. *Ibid.*, p. 46.

1913–14. Ein interessanter Anachronismus, das Jesuskind mit der Brille. *Ibid.*, p. 73.

1917. Nikolaus von Cusas Buch "De beryllo." *Ibid.*, v. 5, p. 42.

1917. Die Veglia des Carlo Dati über die Erfindung der Brillen. *Ibid.*, p. 65.

1918. Die Briefe des Francesco Redi über die Erfindung der Brillen. *Ibid.*, v. 6, p. 1.

1918. C. A. Manzinis: L'occhiale all'occhio. *Ibid.*, p. 36.

1918. Daza de Valdes': Uso de los Antojos. *Ibid.*, p. 97.

1919. D. M. Manni: Degli occhiali da naso. Ueber die Nasenbrillen. *Ibid.*, v. 7, p. 1.

1919. Cornelius Meyer: De gli occhiali (Ueber die Brillen), Anno 1689. *Ibid.*, p. 49.

1921. Eine Fälschung aus der Geschichte der Brille. *Ibid.*, v. 9, p. 9.

1922. Ovale Scheiben. *Ibid.*, v. 10, p. 66.

1923. Der Beril des mittelhochdeutschen Dichters Albrecht. 1270. *Ibid.*, v. 11, p. 66.

1923. Der vergrössernde Krystall des Konrad von Würzburg. *Ibid.*, p. 98.

1924. Frühe Sehhilfen (bril, glasz, ɼarillen). *Ibid.*, v. 12, p. 1.

1924. Zwei frühe niederländische Brillennachweise. *Ibid.*, p. 33.

1924. Ueber Spiegel und Augenspiegel zum Lesen. Ein Beitrag zur ältesten Brillengeschichte. Ztschr. f. Augenh., v. 52, p. 311.

1925. Die älteste Brillendarstellung auf einem Tafelbild (anno 1404). Arch. f. Augenh., v. 96, p. 65. (*See also* Ztschr. f. ophth. Optik, v. 13, p. 174.)

1927. Zur Vereinheitlichung der Gesichtsfeldaufnahmen. Ber. d. Deutsch. ophth. Gesellsch. Heidelberg, v. 46, p. 167.

GREENE, C. W.
1935. The distribution of Wisconsin fishes. Wisconsin Conserv. Comm., Madison, Wis.

GREENIDGE, A. H. J.
1901. Roman public life. Macmillan & Co., London & New York.

GREGG, D. A., & SHIPLEY, R. E.
1944. Experimental approaches to the study of the cerebral circulation. Fed. Proc., v. 3, p. 144.

GREGG, F. M., JAMISON, E., WILKIE, R., & RADINSKY, T.
1929. Are dogs, cats, and racoons color blind? J. Comp. Psychol., v. 9, p. 379.

GREGORY, D.
1715. Elements of catoptrics and dioptrics. E. Curll, London.

GREGORY, W. K.
1910. The orders of mammals. Bull. Am. Mus. Nat. Hist., v. 27, p. 321.

1916. Studies on the evolution of primates. Part I. The Cope-Osborn theory of trituberculy and the ancestral molar patterns of the primates. Part II. Phylogeny of recent and extinct anthropoids with special reference to the origin of man. *Ibid.*, v. 35, p. 239.

1920. On the structure and relations of *Notharctus*. Mem. Am. Mus. Nat. Hist., N.S., v. 3, Part 2.

1922. The origin and evolution of the human dentition. Williams & Wilkins Co., Baltimore.

1923. The gorilla's foot. Nature, v. 112, pp. 758, 933.

1924. Australia, the land of living fossils. Nat. Hist., v. 24, p. 1.

1927. The origin of man from the anthropoid stem —when and where? Proc. Am. Phil. Soc., v. 66, p. 439.

1927. Mongolian mammals of the "Age of Reptiles." Scient. Monthly, v. 24, p. 225.

1927. The Mongolian age of mammals. *Ibid.*, p. 337.

1927. How near is the relationship of man to the chimpanzee-gorilla stock? Quart. Rev. Biol., v. 2, p. 549.

1927. *Hesperopithecus* apparently not an ape nor man. Science, v. 66, p. 579.

1927–29. The palaeomorphology of the human head: ten structural stages from fish to man. I. The skull in norma lateralis. II. The skull in norma basalis. Quart. Rev. Biol., v. 2, p. 267; v. 4, p. 233.

1928. Were the ancestors of man primitive brachiators? Proc. Am. Phil. Soc., v. 67, p. 129.

1928. The upright posture of man: a review of its origin and evolution. *Ibid.*, p. 339.

1928. Reply to Professor Wood-Jones's note: "Man and the anthropoids." Am. J. Phys. Anthropol., v. 12, p. 253.

1928. The lineage of man. *In:* F. MASON (ed.), Creation by evolution, p. 270. Macmillan Co., New York.

1929. Is the pro-dawn man a myth? Human Biol., v. 1, p. 153. (An answer to H. F. Osborn: Is the ape-man a myth? p. 4.)

GREGORY, W. K.—*Continued*

1929. The palaeomorphology of the human head: ten structural stages from fish to man. Quart. Rev. Biol., v. 2, p. 267; v. 4, p. 233.

1930. The origin of man from a brachiating anthropoid stock. Science, v. 71, p. 645.

1930. A critique of Professor F. Wood-Jones's paper: Some landmarks in the phylogeny of the primates. Human Biol., v. 2, p. 99.

1930. "Irreversibility of evolution" and the origin of man. Am. J. Phys. Anthropol., v. 14, p. 84.

1930. A critique of Professor Osborn's theory of human origin. *Ibid.*, p. 133.

1930. Some stages in the adaptive radiation of the teleostome skull. Copeia, p. 56.

1930. The animal ancestry of man. *In:* E. V. COWDRY (ed.), Human biology and racial welfare, p. 53. P. B. Hoeber, New York.

1932. Article: Mammalia, Encyclopaedia Britannica, 14th ed., v. 14, p. 748.

1933. The new anthropogeny: twenty-five stages of vertebrate evolution, from Silurian chordate to man. Science, v. 77, p. 29.

1933. Basic patents in nature. *Ibid.*, v. 78, p. 561.

1934. The origin, rise and decline of *Homo sapiens*. Scient. Monthly, v. 39, p. 481.

1934. Man's place among the anthropoids. Three lectures on the evolution of man from the lower vertebrates. Clarendon Press, Oxford; Oxford University Press, New York.

1935. The pelvis from fish to man: a study in paleomorphology. Am. Naturalist, v. 69, p. 193.

1935. The roles of undeviating evolution and transformation in the origin of man. *Ibid.*, p. 385.

1936. On the meaning and limits of irreversibility of evolution. *Ibid.*, v. 70, p. 517.

1936. The transformation of organic designs: a review of the origin and development of the earlier vertebrates. Biol. Rev., Cambridge Phil. Soc., v. 11, p. 311.

1938. Man's place among the primates. Palaeobiology, v. 6, p. 208.

1940. An evolutionist looks at the Maoris. Nat. Hist., v. 45, p. 132.

1940. Fashion designs in the world of shells. *Ibid.*, v. 46, p. 160.

1941. Grandfather fish and his descendants. *Ibid.*, v. 48, p. 148.

1943. Environment and locomotion in mammals. *Ibid.*, v. 51, p. 222.

1944. Australia—the story of a continent. *Ibid.*, v. 53, p. 360.

1944. The age of man. Am. Mus. Nat. Hist., New York.

1946. "Cat's-eye" explained. Nat. Hist., v. 55, p. 310.

1947. The monotremes and the palimpsest theory. Bull. Am. Mus. Nat. Hist., v. 88, p. 1.

1951. Evolution emerging: a survey of changing patterns from primeval life to man. 2 vols. Macmillan Co., New York.

GREGORY, W. K., & HELLMAN, M.

1923. Further notes on the molars of *Hesperopithecus* and of *Pithecanthropus*. Bull. Am. Mus. Nat. Hist., v. 48, p. 509.

1926. The dentition of *Dryopithecus* and the origin of man. Anthrop. Papers Am. Mus. Nat. Hist., v. 28 (1), p. 1.

1926. The crown pattern of fossils and recent human molar teeth and their meaning. Nat. Hist., v. 26, p. 300.

1926. Palaeontology of the human dentition. Internat. J. Orthodont., v. 12, p. 1027.

1938. Evidence of the Australopithecine man-apes on the origin of man. Science, v. 88, p. 615.

1939. The dentition of the extinct South-African man-ape, *Australopithecus* (*Plesianthropus*) *transvaalensis* Broom. A comparative and phylogenetic study. Ann. Transvaal Mus., v. 10, p. 339.

GREGORY, W. K., HELLMAN, M., & LEWIS, G. E.

1938. Fossil anthropoids of the Yale-Cambridge India expedition of 1935. ("Pub. Carnegie Inst. Washington," No. 495.)

GREGORY, W. K., & McGREGOR, J. H.

1926. A dissenting opinion as to dawn men and ape men. Nat. Hist., v. 26, p. 270. (Reply to Osborn's paper.)

GREGORY, W. K., & RAVEN, H. C.

1937. In quest of gorillas. Darwin Press, New Bedford, Mass.

GREGORY, W. K., & SIMPSON, G. G.

1926. Cretaceous mammal skulls from Mongolia. Am. Mus. Novitates, No. 225.

GRENACHER, H.

1874. Zur Entwickelungsgeschichte der Cephalopoden. Zugleich ein Beitrag zur Morphologie der höheren Mollusken. Ztschr. f. wissensch. Zool., v. 24, p. 419.

1879. Untersuchungen über das Sehorgan der Arthropoden, insbesondere der Spinnen, Insecten und Crustaceen. Vandenhoeck & Ruprecht, Göttingen.

1880. Ueber die Augen einiger Myriapoden. Arch. f. mikr. Anat., v. 18, p. 415.

1886. Abhandlungen zur vergleichenden Anatomie des Auges. Abh. naturforsch. Gesellsch. zu Halle, v. 16, p. 207.

GRETHER, W. F.
1939. Color vision and color blindness in monkeys. ("Comp. Psychol. Monog.," v. 15, No. 4, ser. No. 76.)
1940. Chimpanzee color vision. I. Hue discrimination at three spectral points. II. Color mixture proportions. III. Spectral limits. J. Comp. Psychol., v. 29, p. 167.
1940. A comparison of human and chimpanzee spectral hue discrimination curves. J. Exper. Psychol., v. 26, p. 394.
1941. Comparative visual acuity thresholds in terms of retinal image widths. J. Comp. Psychol., v. 31, p. 23.
1941. Spectral saturation curves for chimpanzee and man. J. Exper. Psychol., v. 28, p. 419.
1942. The magnitude of simultaneous color contrast and simultaneous brightness contrast for chimpanzee and man. *Ibid.*, v. 30, p. 69.

GREVING, R.
1925. Beiträge zur Anatomie des Zwischenhirns und seiner Funktion. II. Der anatomische Verlauf eines Faserbündels des Nervus opticus beim Menschen (Tr. supraopticothalamicus), zugleich ein Beitrag zur Anatomie des unteren Thalamusstieles. Arch. f. Ophth. (Graefe), v. 115, p. 523.
1926. Beiträge zur Anatomie der Hypophyse und deren Funktion. II. Das nervöse Regulationssystem des Hypophysenhinterlappens (der Nucleus supraopticus und seine Fasersysteme). Ztschr. f. d. ges. Neurol. u. Psychiat., v. 104, p. 466.
1928. Die zentralen Anteile des vegetativen Nervensystems. *In:* W. VON MÖLLENDORFF, Handb. der mikr. Anat. d. Mensch., v. 4 (1), p. 917.

GRIFFIN, D. R.
1944. How bats guide their flight by supersonic echos. Am. J. Physics, v. 12, p. 342.
1944. Echolocation by blind men, bats and radar. Science, v. 100, p. 589.
1946. The mechanism by which bats produce supersonic sounds. Anat. Rec., v. 96, p. 519. (Abstr.)
1946. Mystery mammals of the twilight (bats). Nat. Geog. Mag., v. 90, p. 117.
1946. Supersonic cries of bats. Nature, v. 158, p. 46.
1950. The navigation of bats. Scient. Amer., v. 183 (2), p. 52.
1950. Measurements of the ultrasonic cries of bats. J. Acoust. Soc. Amer., v. 22, p. 247.

GRIFFIN, D. R., HUBBARD, R., & WALD, G.
1947. The sensitivity of the human eye to infrared radiation. J. Opt. Soc. Amer., v. 37, p. 546.

GRIGNOLO, F.
1919. Le lesioni dell'apparato visivo nelle ferite di guerra del cranio. Gior. r. Accad. med. Torino, v. 82, p. 58.

GRIMALDI, F. M.
1665. Physicomathesis de lumine, coloribus et iride. V. Benatii, Bononiae.

GRINNELL, J.
1921. The principle of rapid peering in birds. Univ. California Chron., p. 392.

GRIÑO, A.
1948. Morphological details of the oligodendroglia and description of a method for its staining in celloidine or paraffin embedded material. J. Neuropath., v. 7, p. 113.

GRMEK, D.
1955. In memoriam.† Prof. Dr. Stjepan Poljak. Liječnički Vjesnik (Zagreb), v. 77, Nos. 3–4, p. 235.

GROEBBELS, F.
1922. Untersuchungen über den Thalamus und das Mittelhirn der Vögel. Anat. Anz., v. 57, p. 385.
1925. Die Vogelstimme und ihre Probleme. Biol. Zentralbl., v. 45, p. 231.
1932–37. Der Vogel. Bau, Funktion, Lebenserscheinung, Einpassung. 2 vols. Gebrüder Borntraeger, Berlin.

GROENOUW, A.
1892. Ueber doppelseitige Hemianopsie centralen Ursprunges. Arch. f. Psychiat., v. 23, p. 339.
1893. Ueber die Sehschärfe der Netzhautperipherie und eine neue Untersuchungsmethode derselben. Arch. f. Augenh., v. 26, p. 85.

GRÖNVALL, H.
1938. On changes in the fundus oculi and persisting injuries to the eye in migraine. Acta Ophth., v. 16, p. 602.

GRÖPPEL, F., HAASS, F., & KOHLRAUSCH, A.
1938. Aktionsströme und Gesichtsempfindungen des menschlichen Auges. Ztschr. f. Sinnesphysiol., v. 67, p. 207.

GROETHUYSEN, G.
1921. Ueber das Verhalten der motorischen und optischen Unterschiedsempfindlichkeit bei Erkrankungen des Sehorgans. Ber. d. Deutsch. ophth. Gesellsch., 1920, v. 42, p. 255.
1921. Ueber die Beziehungen zwischen motorischer und optischer Unterschiedsempfindlichkeit bei normalen und krankhaften Zuständen

des Sehorgans. Arch. f. Augenh., v. 87, p. 152.

1929. Dioptrik des Auges. Refraktionsanomalien. Augenleuchten und Augenspiegel. *In:* BETHE et al., Handb. d. norm. u. path. Physiol., v. 12 (1), Receptionsorgane 2 (Photoreceptoren 1), p. 70.

GROSS, J.
1903. Ueber die Sehnervenkreuzung bei den Reptilion. Zool. Jahrb. (Abt. f. Anat.), v. 17, p. 763; *also* Biol. Centralbl., v. 10, p. 869.

GROSSMANN & MAYERHAUSEN
1877. Beitrag zur Lehre vom Gesichtsfeld bei Säugethieren. Arch. f. Ophth. (Graefe), v. 23 (3), p. 217.

GROTE, L. R.
1923–29. Die Medizin der Gegenwart in Selbstdarstellungen. 8 vols. F. Meiner, Leipzig.

GRÜNBAUM, A. A.
1915. Ueber die psychophysiologische Natur des primitiven optischen Bewegungseindrucks. Folia neuro-biol., v. 9, p. 699.

1917. On the nature and progress of visual fatigue. Proc. Kon. Akad. Wetensch. Amsterdam, v. 19, p. 167.

1917. Psychophysische und psychophysiologische Untersuchungen über Erscheinungen des Flimmerns und optische Ermüdung. Arch. f. d. ges. Physiol. (Pflüger), v. 166, p. 473.

GRÜNBAUM, A. S. F., & SHERRINGTON, C. S. (*see also* LEYTON & SHERRINGTON)
1901. Observations on the physiology of the cerebral cortex of some of the higher apes. Proc. Roy. Soc. London, v. 69, p. 206.

1902. Note on the arterial supply of the brain in anthropoid apes. Brain, v. 25, p. 270.

1903. Observations on the physiology of the cerebral cortex of the anthropoid apes. Proc. Roy. Soc. London, v. 72, p. 152.

GRUENING, E.
1886. A case of tumor of the left occipital lobe with right homonymous hemianopsia (with autopsy). Tr. Am. Ophth. Soc., 22d meet., p. 349.

GRÜNTHAL, E.
1930. Vergleichend anatomische und entwicklungsgeschichtliche Untersuchungen über die Zentren des Hypothalamus der Säuger und des Menschen. Arch. f. Psychiat. u. Nervenkr., v. 90, p. 216.

GRUNDFEST, H.
1931. The sensibility of the sun-fish, *Lepomis*, to monochromatic radiation of low intensities. J. Gen. Physiol., v. 15, p. 307.

1932. The spectral sensibility of the sun-fish as

evidence for a double visual system. *Ibid.*, p. 507.

1940. Bioelectric potentials. Ann. Rev. Physiol., v. 2, p. 213.

GRUNDFEST, H., & GASSER, H. S.
1938. Properties of mammalian nerve fibers of slowest conduction. Am. J. Physiol., v. 123, p. 307.

GRUNER, O. C.
1930. A treatise on the Canon of medicine of Avicenna, incorporating a translation of the first book. Luzac & Co., London.

GUDDEN, B. VON
1870. Ueber einen bisher nicht beschriebenen Nervenfasernstrang im Gehirne der Säugethiere und des Menschen. Arch. f. Psychiat., v. 2, p. 364. *Also* Gesammelte u. hinterl. Abh., p. 117.

1870. Experimentaluntersuchungen über das periphersche und centrale Nervensystem. Arch. f. Psychiat. u. Nervenkr., v. 2, p. 693.

1874–79. Ueber die Kreuzung der Fasern im Chiasma Nervorum opticorum. Arch. f. Ophth. (Graefe), v. 20 (2), p. 249; v. 21 (3), p. 199; v. 25 (1), p. 1; v. 25 (4), p. 237.

1881. Ueber den Tractus peduncularis transversus. Arch. f. Psychiat., v. 11, p. 415.

1881. Mittheilung über das Ganglion interpedunculare. *Ibid.*, v. 11, p. 424.

1881. Ueber die Kerne der Augenbewegungsnerven. *In:* Bernhard von Gudden's Gesammelte u. hinterl. Abh., p. 183.

1881. Experimente, durch die man die verschiedenen Bestandtheile des Tractus opticus zu isoliren im Stande ist. *Ibid.*, p. 184.

1882. Ueber die verschiedenen Nervenfasernsysteme in der Retina und im Nervus opticus. *Ibid.*, p. 187.

1885. Ueber die Sehnerven, die Sehtractus, das Verhältniss ihrer gekreuzten und ungekreuzten Bündel, ihre Seh- und Pupillarfasern und die Centren der letzteren. *Ibid.*, p. 198.

1886. Demonstration der Sehfasern und Pupillarfasern des Nervus opticus. Sitzungsb. d. Gesellsch. f. Morphol. u. Physiol., v. 1, p. 169.

1889. Gesammelte und hinterlassene Abhandlungen. Ed. H. GRASHEY. J. F. Bergmann, Wiesbaden. *See also* Nissl, Allg. Ztschr. f. Psychiat., v. 51, p. 527, 1895.

1889. Ueber die Frage der Localisation der Funktionen der Grosshirnrinde. *In:* Gesammelte u. hinterl. Abh., p. 200; *also* Allg. Ztschr. f. Psychiat., v. 42, p. 478, 1886.

1889. Augenbewegungs-Nerven. *In:* Gesammelte u. hinterl. Abh., p. 211.

GUDDEN, H.
1900. Ueber einen eigenartigen Fall von transitorischer amnestischer Aphasie. Neurol. Centralbl., v. 19, p. 56.

GUDGER, E. W.
1944. The earliest winged fish-catchers. Scient. Monthly, v. 59, p. 120.

GÜDEMANN, M.
1873. Das jüdische Unterrichtswesen während der spanisch-arabischen Periode. C. Gerold's Sohn, Wien.

GUENELLON, PETRUS
1686. Extrait d'une lettre écrite à M. G. Charleton ... le 15 mars 1686, touchant l'anatomie de l'œil. Extrait des Nouvelles de la républiques des lettres, Mars 1686, v. 6, p. 319.

GÜNTHER, A.
1876. Remarks on some Indian and, more especially, Bornean mammals. Proc. Zoöl. Soc. London, p. 424, Pl. 36.

GUENTHER, K.
1931. A naturalist in Brazil: the record of a year's observation of her flora, her fauna, and her people. Houghton Mifflin Co., Boston & New York.

GÜNTHER, N.
1952–53. Studien zur physiologischen Optik. Optik, v. 9, pp. 441, 523; v. 10, pp. 241, 243, 303, 304.

GUIBÉ, J.
1939. Contribution à l'étude d'une espèce, *Apterina pedestris* Meigen. Bull. biol., suppl., v. 26.

GUIBÉ, J., & VERRIER, M.-L.
1940. Les relations entre le développement de l'œil et de l'aile chez les insectes. À propos du diptère *Apterina pedestris* Meigen. Bull. biol., v. 74, p. 177.

GUIDI, G. (VIDIUS)
1611. Vidi Vidii, Florentini, De anatome corporis humani libri VII; LXXVIII tabulis illustrata. Venetiis. Another ed., Francofurti.

GUILLERY, H.
1894. Einiges über den Formensinn. Arch. f. Augenh., v. 28, p. 263.
1895. Ueber die räumlichen Beziehungen des Licht- und Farbensinnes. *Ibid.*, v. 31, p. 204.
1896. Vergleichende Untersuchungen über Raum-, Licht- und Farbensinn in Zentrum und Peripherie der Netzhaut. Ztschr. f. Psychol. u. Physiol. d. Sinnesorg., v. 12, p. 243.
1897. Zur Physiologie des Netzhautcentrums. Arch. f. d. ges. Physiol. (Pflüger), v. 66, p. 401.
1897. Ueber die Empfindungskreise der Netzhaut. *Ibid.*, v. 68, p. 120.
1897. Begriff und Messung der centralen Sehschärfe, etc. Arch. f. Augenh. v. 35, p. 35.
1897. Weitere Untersuchungen über den Lichtsinn. Ztschr. f. Psychol. u. Physiol. d. Sinnesorg., v. 13, p. 187.
1898. Bemerkung über Raum- und Lichtsinn. *Ibid.*, v. 16, p. 264.
1905. Weitere Untersuchungen zur Physiologie des Formensinnes. Arch. f. Augenh., v. 51, p. 209.
1931. Sehschärfe. *In:* BETHE *et al.*, Handb. d. norm. u. path. Physiol., v. 12 (2), p. 745.

GULLIVER, G.
1868. On fovea centralis in the eye of the fish. J. Anat. & Physiol., v. 2, p. 12.

GULLSTRAND, A.
1902. Die Constitution des im Auge gebrochenen Strahlenbündels. Arch. f. Ophth. (Graefe), v. 53, p. 185.
1902. Bemerkungen über die Farbe der Macula. Ber. d. Deutsch. ophth. Gesellsch. Heidelberg, v. 30, p. 153.
1906. Die Farbe der Macula centralis retinae. Arch. f. Ophth. (Graefe), v. 62, pp. 1, 378.
1907. Zur Maculafrage. *Ibid.*, v. 66, p. 141.
1918. Die Macula centralis im rotfreien Lichte. Klin. Monatsbl. f. Augenh., v. 60, p. 289.

GUNDERSEN, A., & HASTINGS, G. T.
1944. Interdependence in plant and animal evolution. Scient. Monthly, v. 59, p. 63.

GUNDLACH, R. H.
1933. The visual acuity of homing pigeons. J. Comp. Psychol., v. 16, p. 327.

GUNDLACH, R. H., CHARD, R. D., & SKAHEN, J. R.
1945. The mechanism of accommodation in pigeons. J. Comp. Psychol., v. 38, p. 27.

GUNN, M.
1877. A contribution to the minute anatomy of the human retina. J. Anat. & Physiol., v. 11, p. 357; *see also* p. 516.
1884. On the eye of *Ornithorhynchus paradoxus*. *Ibid.*, v. 18, p. 400.

GUNTER, R.
1951. The absolute threshold for vision in the cat. J. Physiol., v. 114, p. 8.

GUNTHER, R. T.
1923–45. Early science in Oxford. 14 vols. Printed for the subscribers, Oxford.

GURDJIAN, E. S.
1926. The hypothalamus in the rat. Anat. Rec., v. 32, p. 208.
1927. The diencephalon of the albino rat. J. Comp. Neurol., v. 43, p. 1.

GURDJIAN, E. S., & BAILEY, L. J.
1936. Paralysis of the third cranial nerve due to spontaneous hemorrhage within the nerve in latter's intracranial course. J. Nerv. & Ment. Dis., v. 84, p. 61.

GUREWITSCH, M., & BYCHOWSKY, G.
1928. Zur Architektonik der Hirnrinde (Isocortex) des Hundes. J. f. Psychol. u. Neurol., v. 35, p. 283.

GUSINDE, M.
1953. Anthropological investigations of the Bushmen of South Africa. Anthropol. Quart. (Prim. Man), v. 26 (N.S., v. 1), p. 21.

GUTTMANN, E.
1942. Aphasia in children. Brain, v. 65, p. 205.

GUTTMANN, E., & SPATZ, H.
1929. Die Meningiome des vorderen Chiasmawinkels, eine gut charakterisierte Gruppe der Meningiome. Nervenarzt, v. 2, p. 581.

GUY, L. P.
1946. A ruler for measurement of visual fields on the tangent screen. Arch. Ophth., v. 36, p. 617.

H

HAAB, O.
1879. Die Farbe der Macula lutea und die entoptische Wahrnehmung des Sehpurpurs. Klin. Monatsbl. f. Augenh., v. 17, p. 387.
1891. Der Hirnrindenreflex der Pupille. Festschr. z. Feier K. W. v. Nägeli u. A. v. Kölliker, etc. A. Müller, Zürich.

HAAB, O. (& HUGUENIN)
1882. Ueber Cortex-Hemianopie. Klin. Monatsbl. f. Augenh., v. 20, p. 141.

HAAS, A. E.
1907. Antike Lichttheorien. Arch. f. Gesch. d. Phil., v. 20, p. 345.
1920. Die ältesten Beobachtungen auf dem Gebiete der Dioptrik. Arch. f. d. Gesch. d. Naturwiss. u. d. Technol., v. 9, p. 108.

HACK, R.
1909. Eine seltene Missbildung am Sehnerveneintritt. Arch. f. Augenh. (Graefe), v. 63, p. 312.

HADDAEUS, E.
1889. Ueber Prüfung und Deutung der Pupillensymptome. Arch. f. Augenh., v. 20, p. 46.

HADEN, H. C.
1947. The development of the ectodermal framework of the optic nerve, with especial reference to the glial lamina cribrosa. Am. J. Ophth., v. 30, p. 1205.

HAECKEL, E. H.; for biography see BÖLSCHE 1906
1866. Allgemeine Anatomie (generelle Morphologie) der Organismen. Kritische Grundzüge der mechanischen Wissenschaft von den entwickelten Formen der Organismen, begründet durch die Descendenz-Theorie. 2 vols. G. Reimer, Berlin.
1870. Natürliche Schöpfungsgeschichte. 2d ed. G. Reimer, Berlin. English trans.: The history of creation. 1876 and later; most recent: 2 vols. D. Appleton & Co., New York.
1874. Anthropogenie, oder Entwickelungsgeschichte des Menschen. W. Engelmann. English trans.: The evolution of man. G. P. Putnam's Sons, New York, 1910. Also other eds.
1875. Ziele und Wege der heutigen Entwickelungsgeschichte. H. Dufft, Jena. Suppl. to Jena. Ztschr. f. Naturwiss., v. 10.
1878. Ueber die Individualität des Thierkörpers. Jena. Ztschr. f. Naturwiss., v. 12 (N.F., v. 5), p. 1.
1884. Indische Reisebriefe. 2d ed. Gebrüder Paetel, Berlin.
1891. Bildungsgeschichte unserer Sinnesorgane. See also: Anthropogenie. 4th ed., v. 2, p. 657; or English trans., v. 2, p. 583 (on the evolution of sense organs).
1894–96. Systematische Phylogenie. Entwurf eines natürlichen Systems der Organismen auf Grund ihrer Stammesgeschichte. 3 vols. G. Reimer, Berlin. (See v. 3, Systematische Phylogenie der Wirbelthiere, 1895.)
1899. Die Welträthsel. E. Strauss, Bonn. Also later eds. English trans.: The riddle of the universe. Harper & Bros., New York & London, 1901.
1901. Aus Insulinde. Malayische Reisebriefe. E. Strauss, Bonn. English trans.: Letters from East Indies and Malaysia.
1904. Die Lebenswunder. Ergänzungsband zu dem Buche über die Welträthsel. A. Kröner, Stuttgart. English trans.: The wonders of life. Harper & Bros., New York & London.
1905–7. Ernst Haeckel's Wanderbilder. W. Koehler'sche Verlagsbuchhandlung, Gera-Untermhaus.
1906. Haeckel, his life and work. By W. BÖLSCHE. T. Fisher Unwin, London.
1908. Unsere Ahnenreihe (Progonotaxis hominis). Festschr. 350 jähr. Jubelfeier der Thüringer Universität Jena. G. Fischer, Jena.
1914. Die Natur als Künstlerin. Vita Verlag, Berlin-Ch.

HAECKER, V.
1900. Der Gesang der Vögel. Seine anatomischen und biologischen Grundlagen. G. Fischer, Jena.

HAESER, H.
1875–82. Lehrbuch der Geschichte der Medicin

und der epidemischen Krankheiten. 3 vols. H. Dufft, Jena.

HAFFERL, A.
1953. Lehrbuch der topographischen Anatomie. Springer-Verlag, Berlin, Göttingen, Heidelberg.

HAGEDOORN, A.
1930. Beitrag zur Entwicklungsgeschichte des Auges. Arch. f. Augenh., v. 102, pp. 33, 393.
1936. Comparative anatomy of the eye. Arch. Ophth., v. 16, p. 783.

HAGEN, S.
1921. Weitere Untersuchungen über die Regeneration des Kammerwassers im menschlichen Auge. Klin. Monatsbl. f. Augenh., v. 66, p. 493.

HAGEN, V. W. VON
1945. South America called them. Explorations of the great naturalists La Condamine, Humboldt, Darwin, Spruce. A. A. Knopf, New York.

HAGGAR, R. A., & BARR, M. L.
1950. Quantitative data on the size of synaptic end-bulbs in the cat's spinal cord. J. Comp. Neurol., v. 93, p. 17.

HAHN, ERNA
1916. Ueber den Farbensinn der Tagvögel und die Zapfenölkugeln. Ztschr. f. wissensch. Zool., v. 116, p. 1.

HAHN, ERNST
1895. Pathologisch-anatomische Untersuchung des Lissauer'schen Falles von Seelenblindheit. Arb. a. d. psychiat. Klin. Breslau, Heft 2, p. 105. *See also* H. Lissauer, Ein Fall von Seelenblindheit nebst einem Beitrage zur Theorie desselben. Arch. f. Psychiat., v. 21, p. 222, 1890.

HAHN, W. L.
1908. Some habits and sensory adaptations of cave-inhabiting bats. Biol. Bull., v. 15, p. 135.

HAIG, C.
1948. The relation of cone surface area to total light flux at the intensity limin. Anat. Rec., v. 101, p. 664. (Abstr.)
1949. Light flux constancy at the intensity limin of the eye for total receptor cross-sectional areas. Fed. Proc., v. 8, p. 65.

HAIN, L. F. T.
1826–31. Repertorium bibliographicum. 2 vols. J. G. Cotta, Stuttgartiae.

HALBEN, R.
1903. Fall geheilter Wortblindheit mit Persistenz rechtsseitiger Hemianopsie. Ztschr. f. Augenh., v. 10, p. 487.

HALDANE, E. S.
1905. Descartes. His life and times. J. Murray, London.

HALDANE, J. B. S.
1949. Human evolution: past and present. *In:* JEPSEN *et al.*, Genetics, paleontology, and evolution, p. 405.
1949. Is evolution a myth? Watts & Paternoster Press, London.

HALE, E. B.
1949. Part I. Social facilitation of maze performance in normal and forebrainless green sunfish, *Lepomis cyanellus*. Part II. Effect of forebrain lesions on the aggressive behavior of green sunfish, *Lepomis cyanellus*. Thesis, University of Chicago.

HALL, A.
1945. The origin and purposes of blinking. Brit. J. Ophth., v. 29, p. 445.

HALL, E. RAYMOND
1946. Zoölogical subspecies of man at the peace table. J. Mammal., v. 27, p. 358.

HALLAUER, O.
1915. Die Brille 100 Jahre vor und 100 Jahre nach der Erfindung der Buchdruckerkunst. Festschr. zum 50-jähr. Bestehen der Baseler Universitäts-Augenheilklinik. Helbing-Lichtenbahn, Basel.

HALLER, ALBRECHT; *see* for biography MICHAUD, Biographie universelle, v. 18, p. 368, and Allgemeine Deutsche Biographie, v. 10, p. 420
1752. De partibus corporis humani sensilibus et irritabilibus. Comm. Soc. reg. scient. Gotting., v. 2, p. 114. (Gesellschaft der Wissenschaften zu Goettingen.)
1769. Elementa Physiologiae Corporis Humani. Auctore Alberto v. Haller, Praeside Societatis Reg. Scient. Götting. Sodali Acadd. Reg. Scient. Paris. Reg. Chir. Gall. Imper. Berolin. Suecic. Bononiens. Arcad. Bavar. Societ. Scient. Britann. Upsal. Bot. Flor. Helvet. In Senatu Supremo Bernensi Ducentumviro. Tomus quartus: Cerebrum. Nervi. Musculi. Tomus quintus: Sensus Externi-Interni. (*Cf. here* Liber xvi, Visus; Sec. I, Oculi tutamina, p. 306; sec. II, Oculus, p. 345; sec. III, Lux et colores, p. 443; sec. IV, Visio, p. 464.) Lausannae, Sumptibus Francisci Grasset & Sociorum. MDCCLXIX.
1773. De partibus corporis humani sentientibus et irritabilibus. Sermo tertius. Novi Comm. Soc. reg. scient. Gotting., v. 3, p. 1.
1774–76. Bibliotheca anatomica. Qua scripta ad anatomen et physiologiam facientia a rerum

initiis recensentur, etc. 2 vols. Tiguri, apud Orell, Gessner, Fuessli, et Soc.

1936. A dissertation on the sensible and irritable parts of animals. Johns Hopkins Press, Baltimore. Reprinted from Bull. Inst. Hist. Med., v. 4, No. 8, 1936.

HALLER, A., & ZINN, J. G.

1756. Mémoires sur la nature sensible et irritable du corps animal. 4 vols. M. M. Bousquet, Lausanne.

HALLER, B.

1895. Beiträge zur Kenntnis der Morphologie von *Nautilus pompilius*. *In:* R. SEMON, Zool. Forschungsreisen in Australien, etc., v. 5, p. 187.

1900. Vom Bau des Wirbeltiergehirnes. III. *Mus*, nebst Bemerkungen über das Hirn von *Echidna*. Morphol. Jahrb., v. 28, p. 347.

1907. Mitteilungen über das Grosshirn von *Pteropus edulis*. Anat. Anz., v. 30, p. 69.

1908. Die phyletische Entfaltung der Grosshirnrinde. Arch. f. mikr. Anat., v. 71, p. 350.

1910. Die Mantelgebiete des Grosshirns von den Nagern aufsteigend bis zum Menschen. *Ibid.*, v. 76, p. 305.

1910. Zur Ontogenie der Grosshirnrinde der Säugetiere. Anat. Anz., v. 37, p. 282.

HALLER VON HALLERSTEIN, V.

1934. Aeussere Gliederung des Zentralnervensystems. *In:* BOLK, GÖPPERT, KALLIUS & LUBOSCH, Handb. d. vergl. Anat. d. Wirbeltiere, v. 2 (1), p. 1.

1934. Kranialnerven. *In:* BOLK, GÖPPERT, KALLIUS & LUBOSCH, Handb. d. vergl. Anat. d. Wirbeltiere, v. 2 (1), p. 541.

HALPERN, F.

1930. Kasuistischer Beitrag zur Funktion des Stirnhirns. Arch. f. Psychiat. u. Nervenkr., v. 90, p. 446.

HALSTEAD, W. C.

1947. Brain and intelligence: a quantitative study of the frontal lobes. University of Chicago Press, Chicago.

HALSTEAD, W. C., KNOX, G. W., WOOLF, J. I., & WALKER, A. E.

1942. Effects of intensity and wave length on driving cortical activity in monkeys. J. Neurophysiol., v. 5, p. 483.

HALSTEAD, W. C., WALKER, A. E., & BUCY, P. C.

1940. Sparing and nonsparing of "macular" vision associated with occipital lobectomy in man. Arch. Ophth., v. 24, p. 948.

HAMBERGER, G. A.

1696. Disputatio de opticis oculorum vitiis. *In:* A. HALLER, Bibliotheca anatomica, v. 1, p. 754.

HAMBURGER, V.

1926. Versuche über Komplementär-Farben bei Ellritzen (*Phoxinus laevis*). Ztschr. f. vergl. Physiol., v. 4, p. 286.

HAMILTON, E.

1942. The great age of Greek literature. W. W. Norton & Co., New York.

1944. The Greek way. Nat. Geog. Mag., v. 85, p. 257.

HAMILTON, W. F., & COLEMAN, T. B.

1933. Trichromatic vision in the pigeon as illustrated by the spectral hue discrimination curve. J. Comp. Psychol., v. 15, p. 183.

HAMILTON, W. F., & GOLDSTEIN, J. L.

1933. Visual acuity and accommodation in the pigeon. J. Comp. Psychol., v. 15, p. 193.

HAMILTON, W. J., JR.

1930. The food of the *Soricidae*. J. Mammal., v. 11, p. 26.

1937. The biology of microtine cycles. J. Agr. Research, v. 54, p. 779.

1939. American mammals. Their lives, habits, and economic relations. McGraw-Hill Book Co., New York & London.

1940. The biology of the smoky shrew (*Sorex fumens fumens* Miller). Zoologica, v. 25, p. 473.

1941. The food of small forest mammals in eastern United States. J. Mammal., v. 22, p. 250.

1944. The biology of the little short-tailed shrew, *Cryptotis parva*. *Ibid.*, v. 25, p. 1.

HAMMARBERG, K.

1893. Studien über Klinik und Pathologie der Idiotie, nebst Untersuchungen über die normale Anatomie der Hirnrinde. E. Berling, Upsala.

HANCOCK, W. I.

1906. Ring scotoma. Roy. London Ophth. Hosp. Rep., v. 16, p. 496.

HANKE, V.

1900. Ueber das rudimentäre Auge der europäischen Blindmaus. Ber. d. Deutsch. ophth. Gesellsch. Heidelberg, v. 28, p. 206.

1900. Das rudimentäre Auge der europäischen Blindmaus (*Spalax typhlus*). Arch. f. Ophth. (Graefe), v. 51, p. 321.

1903. Das Gehirn eines congenitalen, bilateralen Anophthalmus. Arb. a. d. neurol. Inst. Wien (Obersteiner), v. 10, p. 58.

1904. Anophthalmus congenitus bilateralis. Arch. f. Ophth. (Graefe), v. 57, p. 28.

HANKINSON, T. L.

1924. The habitat of the brook trout in Michigan. Papers Michigan Acad. Sc., v. 2, p. 197, 1922.

HANNOVER, A.

1840. Ueber die Netzhaut und ihre Gehirnsubstanz bei Wirbelthieren, mit Ausnahme des Menschen. Arch. f. Anat., Physiol. u. wissensch. Med. (J. Müller), p. 320.

1840. Die Chromsäure, ein vorzügliches Mittel bei mikroskopischen Untersuchungen. *Ibid.*, p. 549.

1843. Ueber die Structur der Netzhaut der Schildkröte. *Ibid.*, p. 314.

1844. Recherches microscopiques sur le système nerveux. P. G. Philipsen, Copenhagen.

1852. Das Auge. Beiträge zur Anatomie, Physiologie und Pathologie dieses Organs. L. Voss, Leipzig.

1852. Ueber die sogenannte Plica retinae. *In:* his Das Auge.

1852. Ueber den Bau des Chiasma opticum mit daran geknüpften Bemerkungen über das Sehen. *In:* his Das Auge.

1854. Zur Anatomie und Physiologie der Retina. Ztschr. f. wissensch. Zool., v. 5, p. 17.

1876. La rétine de l'homme et des vertébrés. A. F. Höst & Fils, Copenhagen.

HANSEMANN, D.

1899. Ueber das Gehirn von Hermann von Helmholtz. Ztschr. f. Psychol. u. Physiol. d. Sinnesorg., v. 20, p. 1.

1907. Ueber die Gehirne von Th. Mommsen (Historiker), R. W. Bunsen (Chemiker) und Ad. v. Menzel (Maler). E. Schweizerbart'sche Verlagsbuchhandlung (E. Nägele), Stuttgart.

HANSTRÖM, B.

1928. Some points on the phylogeny of nerve cells and of the central nervous system of invertebrates. J. Comp. Neurol., v. 46, p. 475.

1928. Vergleichende Anatomie des Nervensystems der wirbellosen Tiere unter Berücksichtigung seiner Funktion. J. Springer, Berlin.

HARDESTY, I.

1904. On the development and nature of the neuroglia. Am. J. Anat., v. 3, p. 229.

HARDY, A. C., & PERRIN, F. H.

1932. The principles of optics. McGraw-Hill Book Co., New York.

HARDY, L. H.

1949. Investigation of visual space. Arch. Ophth., v. 42, p. 551.

HARDY, L. H., RAND, G., & RITTLER, M. C.

1951. Investigation of visual space: the Blumenfeld alleys. Arch. Ophth., v. 45, p. 53.

HARE, K., & HINSEY, J. C.

1942. The autonomic nervous system. Ann. Rev. Physiol., v. 4, p. 407.

HARE, W. K., MAGOUN, H. W., & RANSON, S. W.

1935. Pathways for pupillary constriction. Location of synapses in the path for the pupillary light reflex and of constrictor fibers of cortical origin. Arch. Neurol. & Psychiat., v. 34, p. 1188.

HARGITT, C.

1912. Behavior and color changes of tree frogs. J. Anim. Behavior, v. 2, p. 51.

HARLESS, J. C. F.

*1801. Versuch einer vollständigen Geschichte der Hirn- und Nervenlehre im Alterthume. J. C. Schubert, Erlangen.

HARLOW, H. F.

1950. The effect of large cortical lesions on learned behavior in monkeys. Science, v. 112, p. 428.

HARLOW, H. F., UEHLING, H., & MASLOW, A. H.

1932. Comparative behavior of primates. I. Delayed reaction tests on primates from the lemur to the orang-outan. J. Comp. Psychol., v. 13, p. 313.

HARMAN, P. J.

1946. Brain volume and volume of neo-cortex in mammals. Anat. Rec., v. 94, p. 468. (Abstr.)

1947. On the significance of fissuration of the isocortex. J. Comp. Neurol., v. 87, p. 161.

1949. Cytoarchitecture of infant and adult human lateral geniculate nucleus. Anat. Rec., v. 103, p. 541. (Abstr.)

HARMAN, P. J., & SOLNITZKY, O.

1943. The comparative anatomy of the lateral geniculate complex of *Cebus fatuellus* and *Ateles ater.* Anat. Rec., v. 85, p. 315. (Abstr.)

1944. The lateral geniculate complex of the platyrrhine monkey, *Cebus fatuellus.* J. Comp. Neurol., v. 81, p. 227.

HARMS, H.

1926. Ueber das Vorkommen der Stauungspapille bei Hypophysentumoren. Arch. f. Augenh., v. 97, p. 46.

HARMS, W.

1914. Ueber die Augen der am Grunde der Gewässer lebenden Fische. Zool. Anz., v. 44, p. 35.

HARPER, F.

1945. Extinct and vanishing mammals of the old world. Am. Committee for International Wild Life Protection, spec. pub. No. 12. New York.

HARRINGTON, D. O.

1939. Localizing value of incongruity in defects in the visual fields. Arch. Ophth., v. 21, p. 453.

HARRIS, A. J., HODES, M. C. R., & MAGOUN, H. W.

1944. The afferent path of the pupillodilator reflex in the cat. J. Neurophysiol., v. 7, p. 231.

HARRIS, J.
1775. Treatise of optics. B. White, London.

HARRIS, S. T.
1928. A case of aneurysm of the anterior cerebral artery causing compression of the optic nerves and chiasma. Brit. J. Ophth., v. 12, p. 15.

HARRIS, W.
1897. Hemiopia, with especial reference to its transient varieties. Brain, v. 20, p. 308.
1904. Binocular and stereoscopic vision in man and other vertebrates, with its relation to the decussation of the optic nerves, the ocular movements, and the pupil light-reflex. *Ibid.*, v. 27, p. 107.
1935. The fibers of the pupillary reflex and the Argyll Robertson pupil. Arch. Neurol. & Psychiat., v. 34, p. 1194.

HARRISON, H. H.
1948. American birds in color. William H. Wise & Co., New York.

HARRISON, J. L., & TRAUB, R.
1950. Rodents and insectivores from Selangor, Malaya. J. Mammal., v. 31, p. 337.

HARRISON, P. W.
1909. An effort to determine the sensory path from the ocular muscles. Bull. Johns Hopkins Hosp., v. 20, p. 113.

HARRISON, R. G.
1908. Observations on the living developing nerve fiber. Anat. Rec., v. 1, p. 116.
1908. Embryonic transplantation and development of the nervous system. *Ibid.*, v. 2, p. 385.
1910. The outgrowth of the nerve fiber as a mode of protoplasmic movement. J. Exper. Zoöl., v. 9, p. 787.
1912. The cultivation of tissues in extraneous media, etc. Anat. Rec., v. 6, p. 181.
1924. Neuroblast versus sheath cell in the development of peripheral nerves. J. Comp. Neurol., v. 37, p. 123.

HARROW, B.
1950. Textbook of biochemistry. W. B. Saunders Co., Philadelphia.

HARTING, PIETER
1866. Das Mikroscop. Theorie, Gebrauch, Geschichte und gegenwärtiger Zustand desselben. 2d ed. F. Vieweg & Sohn, Braunschweig. First German ed., 1859; original ed. in Dutch: Het mikroskoop, deszelfs gebruik, geschiedenis en tegenwoordige toestand. 3 vols. Utrecht, 1848–50.

HARTINGER, H.
1927. Alfred Vogts Arbeiten über die Strah-
lungswirkungen auf das Auge und seine Teile. Ztschr. f. ophth. Optik., v. 14, p. 148.
1934. Ueber den optischen Augendrehpunkt. *Ibid.*, v. 22, p. 65.
1936. Das Zeiss-Projektionsperimeter nach L. Maggiore. *Ibid.*, v. 24, p. 39.
1938. Die Netzhautphotographie mit Glühlampenlicht. *Ibid.*, v. 26, p. 1.

HARTLINE, H. K.
1928. A quantitative and descriptive study of the electrical response to illumination of the arthropode eye. Am. J. Physiol., v. 83, p. 466.
1930. The dark adaptation of the eye of *Limulus*, as manifested by its electric response to illumination. J. Gen. Physiol., v. 13, p. 379.
1934. Intensity and duration in the excitation of single photo-receptor units. J. Cell. & Comp. Physiol., v. 5, p. 229.
1935. Impulses in single optic nerve fibers of the vertebrate retina. Am. J. Physiol., v. 113, p. 59.
1938. The discharge of impulses in the optic nerve of *Pecten* in response to illumination of the eye. J. Cell. & Comp. Physiol., v. 11, p. 465.
1938. The response of single optic nerve fibers of the vertebrate eye to illumination of the retina. Am. J. Physiol., v. 121, p. 400.
1940. The receptive field of the optic nerve fibers. *Ibid.*, v. 130, p. 690
1940. The effects of spatial summation in the retina on the excitation of the fibers in the optic nerve. *Ibid.*, p. 700.
1940. The nerve messages in the fibers of the visual pathway. J. Opt. Soc. Amer., v. 30, p. 239.
1942. Sense organs. Ann. Rev. Physiol., v. 4, p. 445.
1942. The neural mechanisms of vision. Harvey Lect., ser. 37, p. 39.

HARTLINE, H. K., & GRAHAM, C. H.
1932. Nerve impulses from single receptors in the eye. J. Cell. & Comp. Physiol., v. 1, p. 277.
1932. Nerve impulses from single receptors in the eye of *Limulus*. Proc. Soc. Exper. Biol. & Med., v. 29, p. 613.

HARTLINE, H. K., & McDONALD, R.
1941. Dark adaptation of single visual cells. Am. J. Physiol., v. 133, p. 321.

HARTMAN, C. G., & STRAUS, W. L. (eds.)
1933. The anatomy of the rhesus monkey (*Macaca mulatta*). Williams & Wilkins Co., Baltimore.

HARTMANN, F.
1927. Die strukturellen Voraussetzungen für

"Wahrnehmung und Gefühl." J. f. Psychol. u. Neurol., v. 37, p. 458.

HARTMANN, M.

1937. Philosophie der Naturwissenschaften. J. Springer, Berlin.

1948. Allgemeine Biologie. Eine Einführung in die Lehre vom Leben. G. Fischer, Jena.

HARTMANN, R.

1883. Die menschlichen Affen und ihre Organisation im Vergleich zur menschlichen. F. A. Brockhaus, Leipzig. English trans.: Anthropoid apes. K. Paul, Trench & Co., London, 1885. French trans.: Les singes anthropoïdes et leur organisation comparée à celle de l'homme. F. Alcan, Paris. Also an American ed. by D. Appleton & Co., New York, 1886.

HARTRIDGE, H.

1918. Chromatic aberration and resolving power of the eye. J. Physiol., v. 52, p. 175.

1920. The inversion of the retinal image. *Ibid.*, v. 54, p. vi.

1922. Visual acuity and the resolving power of the eye. *Ibid.*, v. 57, p. 52.

1944. Visibility of yellow. Nature, v. 153, p. 775.

1945. Colour vision of the fovea centralis. *Ibid.*, v. 155, p. 391.

1945. The colour of small objects. J. Physiol. (Proc.), v. 104, p. 2P.

1945. The change from trichromatic to dichromatic vision in the human retina. Nature, v. 155, p. 657.

1945. Acoustic control in the flight of bats. *Ibid.*, v. 156, p. 490.

1946. Supersonic cries of bats. *Ibid.*, v. 158, p. 135.

1947. The visual perception of fine detail. Phil. Tr. Roy. Soc. London, ser. B, v. 232, p. 519.

1947. The diameters and intercentre distances of the foveal cones. Proc. Physiol. Soc. London (J. Physiol.), v. 106, p. 28.

1949. Comments on Dr. Rand's letter on Hartridge's article on physiology of vision. Arch. Ophth., v. 42, p. 193.

HARTSOEKER, NIKOLAS

1694. Essai de dioptrique, par Nicolas Hartsoeker. A. Paris, chez Jean Anisson, Directeur de l'Imprimerie Royale, etc. MDCXCIV.

HARVEY, E. N.

1940. Living light. Princeton University Press, Princeton.

1948. Introductory remarks: a general survey of bioluminescence. *In:* Bioluminescence, pub. in Ann. New York Acad. Sc., v. 49, p. 327.

HARVEY, H. W.

1928. Biological chemistry and physics of sea water. Cambridge University Press, Cambridge.

1945. Recent advances in the chemistry and biology of sea water. Cambridge University Press, Cambridge.

HARVEY, J. E.

1950. The effects of permanent and temporary occlusion of the middle cerebral artery in the monkey. Thesis, University of Chicago.

HASKINS, C. H.

1927. Studies in the history of medieval science. Harvard University, Cambridge.

1927. The renaissance of the twelfth century. Harvard University, Cambridge.

HASSE, C.

1867. Vorläufige Mittheilung über den Bau der Retina. Nachr. v. d. kgl. Gesellsch. d. Wissensch. Göttingen, p. 130.

1867. Beiträge zur Anatomie der menschlichen Retina. Ztschr. f. rat. Med., 3d ser., v. 29, p. 238.

1876. Zur Anatomie des *Amphioxus lanceolatus*. Morphol. Jahrb. (Gegenbauer), v. 1, p. 282.

HATSCHEK, R.

1903. Sehnervenatrophie bei einem Delphin. Arb. a. d. neurol. Inst. Wien (Obersteiner), v. 10, p. 223.

1908. Beitrag zur Frage der Menschenähnlichkeit des Ateles-Gehirns. Anat. Anz., v. 32, p. 389.

HATT, R. T.

1929. The red squirrel: its life history and habits. Roosevelt Wild Life Ann., v. 2, p. 11.

HATZFELD, J.

1926. Histoire de la Grèce ancienne. Payot, Paris.

HAUPTMANN, A.

1931. Zur Frage der Halluzinationen im hemianopischen Gesichtsfeld. Ztschr. f. d. ges. Neurol. u. Psychiat., v. 131, p. 90.

1931. Zur Symptomatologie der Erkrankungen des rechten Schläfenlappens. Deutsch. Ztschr. f. Nervenh., vols. 117–19, p. 170.

HAUSMAN, L. A.

1946. Field book of eastern birds. G. P. Putnam's Sons, New York.

HAUSMANN, W.

1923. Ueber die Lichtwirkung auf den Menschen und die Tiere. Naturwiss., v. 11, p. 915.

HAVET, J.

1899. La structure du chiasma optique et des masses ganglionnaires cérébroidales de l'*Astacus fluviatilis*. Rev. trimestr. microg., v. 4, p. 109.

1922. La structure du système nerveux des actinies. Leur mécanisme neuro-musculaire.

In: Libro en honor de D. S. Ramón y Cajal,
v. 1, p. 477.

HAWTHORNE, C. O.
1914. Cases in which homonymous hemianopia is
the principal or only evidence of organic disease. Tr. Ophth. Soc. United Kingdom, v.
34, p. 195; Policlinico, v. 18, p. 78.

HAYASHI, M., & NAKAMURA, R.
1913–14. Ueber die Hinterhauptlappen des Japa-
ner-Gehirns. Mitt. a. d. med. Fak. d. Kaiserl.
Univ. Tokyo, v. 11, p. 239.

HAYMAKER, W.
1948. Guide to the exhibit on the history of neuropathology. Army Medical Library. Army
Institute of Pathology, Washington, D.C.

HAYMAKER, W., & BAER, K. A.
1953. The founders of neurology. Charles C
Thomas, Springfield, Ill.

HEAD, H.
1915. Hughlings Jackson on aphasia and kindred
affections of speech. Brain, v. 38, p. 1.
1920. Aphasia and kindred disorders of speech.
(Linacre lect.) *Ibid.*, v. 43, p. 87. *Also:*
Aphasia, an historical review. (Hughlings
Jackson Lect.) *Ibid.*, v. 43, p. 390.
1923. Speech and cerebral localization. *Ibid.*, v.
46, p. 355.
1926. Aphasia and kindred disorders of speech. 2
vols. Macmillan Co., New York & London.

HEAD, H., & RIDDOCH, G.
1920. Sensory disturbances in the hand following
injuries of the cerebral cortex. Brit. M. J.,
v. 2, p. 782.

HEAPE, W.
1887. The development of the mole (*Talpa euro-
pea*). Quart. J. Micr. Sc., v. 27, p. 123.

HEATH, T. L.
1913. Aristarchus of Samos, the ancient Copernicus: a history of Greek astronomy to
Aristarchus. Clarendon Press, Oxford.
1921. A history of Greek mathematics. 2 vols.
Clarendon Press, Oxford.
1926. The thirteen books of Euclid's Elements,
translated from the text of Heiberg, with introduction and commentary. 2d ed., 3 vols.
Cambridge University Press, Cambridge.
(*See also* Euclid.)
1932. Greek astronomy. J. M. Dent & Sons, London & Toronto; E. P. Dutton & Co., New
York.

HEBB, D. O.
1938. The innate organization of visual activity.
III. Discrimination of brightness after removal of the striate cortex in the rat. J.
Comp. Psychol., v. 25, p. 427.

HEBERER, G.
1943. Die Evolution der Organismen. Ergebnisse
und Probleme der Abstammungslehre.
G. Fischer, Jena.
1952. Fortschritte in der Erforschung der Phylogenie der Hominoidea. Springer-Verlag,
Berlin.

HEBOLD, O.
1891. Der Faserverlauf im Sehnerven. Neurol.
Centralbl., v. 10, p. 167.
1892. Die Sehnervenkreuzung beim Menschen.
Arch. f. Ophth. (Graefe), v. 38 (1), p. 221.

HECHST, B.
1933. Ueber das Verhalten der äusseren Kniehöcker und der Sehrinde bei einseitiger
peripherer Blindheit. Arch. f. Psychiat. u.
Nervenkr., v. 100, p. 19.

HECHT, S. (*see also* SHLAER); for biography *see*
WALD 1948
1919. The photic sensitivity of *Ciona intestinalis.*
J. Gen. Physiol., v. 1, p. 147.
1919. Sensory equilibrium and dark adaptation in
Mya arenaria. Ibid., p. 545.
1919. The nature of the latent period in the photic
response of *Mya arenaria. Ibid.*, p. 657.
1919. The effect of temperature on the latent period in the photic response of *Mya arenaria.
Ibid.*, p. 667.
1920. The photochemical nature of the photosensory process. *Ibid.*, v. 2, p. 229.
1920. Intensity and the process of photoreception.
Ibid., p. 337.
1920. The dark adaptation of the human eye.
Ibid., p. 499.
1921. The photochemistry of the sensitivity of
animals to light. Science, v. 53, p. 347; J.
Opt. Soc. Amer., v. 5, p. 227.
1921. Photochemistry of visual purple. I. The
kinetics of the decomposition of visual
purple by light. J. Gen. Physiol., v. 3, p. 1.
1921. Photochemistry of visual purple. II. The
effect of temperature on the bleaching of
visual purple by light. *Ibid.*, p. 285.
1921. Time and intensity in photosensory stimulation. *Ibid.*, p. 367.
1921. The relation between the wave-length of
light and its effect on the photosensory process. *Ibid.*, p. 375.
1922. The nature of foveal dark adaptation.
Ibid., v. 4, p. 113.
1923. Sensory adaptation and the stationary
state. *Ibid.*, v. 5, p. 555.
1924. Intensity discrimination and the stationary
state. *Ibid.*, v. 6, p. 355.
1924. Photochemistry of visual purple. III. The

relation between the intensity of light and the rate of bleaching of visual purple. *Ibid.*, p. 731.

1924. The visual discrimination of intensity and the Weber-Fechner law. *Ibid.*, v. 7, p. 235.

1925. The general physiology of vision. Am. J. Physiol. Opt., v. 6, p. 303.

1926. The effect of exposure period and temperature on the photosensory process in *Ciona*. J. Gen. Physiol., v. 8, p. 291.

1927. The kinetics of dark adaptation. *Ibid.*, v. 10, p. 781.

1928. The relation between visual acuity and illumination. J. Gen. Physiol., v. 11, p. 255.

1928. The influence of temperature on the photosensory latent period. *Ibid.*, p. 649.

1928. The relation of time, intensity and wavelength in the photosensory system of *Pholas*. *Ibid.*, p. 657.

1928. On the binocular fusion of colors and its relation to theories of color vision. Proc. Nat. Acad. Sc., v. 14, p. 237.

1929. The nature of the sensitivity of animals to light. J. Opt. Soc. Amer. & Rev. Scient. Instr., v. 18, p. 264.

1930. The development of Thomas Young's theory of color vision. J. Opt. Soc. Amer., v. 20, p. 231.

1931. The interrelation of various aspects of color vision. *Ibid.*, v. 21, p. 615.

1931. Die physikalische Chemie und die Physiologie des Sehaktes. Ergebn. d. Physiol. (Asher & Spiro), v. 32, p. 243.

1932. A quantitative formulation of colour-vision. *In:* The physical and optical societies report of a joint discussion on vision, p. 126. Cambridge University Press, Cambridge.

1934. The nature of the photoreceptor process. *In:* C. Murchison (ed.), A handbook of gen. exper. psychol., p. 704.

1935. Intensity discrimination. Cold Spring Harbor Symp. Quant. Biol., v. 3, p. 230.

1935. A theory of visual intensity discrimination. J. Gen. Physiol., v. 18, p. 767.

1937. The instantaneous visual threshold after light adaptation. Proc. Nat. Acad. Sc., v. 23, p. 227.

1937. Rods, cones, and the chemical basis of vision. Physiol. Rev., v. 17, p. 239.

1938. The nature of the visual process. Harvey Lect., ser. 33, p. 35; Bull. New York Acad. Med., v. 14, p. 21.

1940. The minimum energy required for vision. Anat. Rec., v. 78, suppl. 1, p. 93. (Abstr.)

1940. The chemistry of vision. *In:* Ridley & Sorsby, Modern trends in ophth., p. 328.

1942. The chemistry of visual substances. Ann. Rev. Biochem., v. 11, p. 465.

1942. Papers relating to vision by Selig Hecht. J. Opt. Soc. Amer., v. 32, p. 40.

1942. Energy relations in vision. *In:* Biol. Symp., v. 7 (Visual mechanisms), p. 1. J. Cattell Press, Lancaster, Pa.

1942. The quantum relations of vision. J. Opt. Soc. Amer., v. 32, p. 42.

1944. Energy and vision. Am. Scientist, v. 32, p. 159.

1947. Explaining the atom. Viking Press, New York.

Hecht, S., Haig, C., & Chase, A. M.
1937. The influence of light adaptation on subsequent dark adaptation of the eye. J. Gen. Physiol., v. 20, p. 831.

Hecht, S., Haig, C., & Wald, G.
1936. The dark adaptation of retinal fields of different size and location. J. Gen. Physiol., v. 19, p. 321.

Hecht, S., Hendley, C. D., Frank, S. R., & Haig, C.
1946. Anoxia and brightness discrimination. J. Gen. Physiol., v. 29, p. 335.

Hecht, S., Hendley, C. D., Ross, S., & Richmond, P. N.
1948. The effect of exposure to sunlight on night vision. Am. J. Ophth., v. 31, p. 1573.

Hecht, S., & Hsia, Yun
1945. Dark adaptation following light adaptation to red and white lights. J. Opt. Soc. Amer., v. 35, p. 261.

1948. Colorblind vision. I. Luminosity losses in the spectrum for dichromats. J. Gen. Physiol., v. 31, p. 141.

Hecht, S., & Mandelbaum, J.
1939. The relation between vitamin A and dark adaptation. J. Am. Med. Assoc., v. 112, p. 1910.

Hecht, S., & Mintz, E. U.
1939. The visibility of single lines at various illuminations and the retinal basis of visual resolution. J. Gen. Physiol., v. 22, p. 593.

Hecht, S., Peskin, J. C., & Patt, M.
1938. Intensity discrimination in the human eye. II. The relation between $\Delta I/I$ and intensity for different parts of the spectrum. J. Gen. Physiol., v. 22, p. 7.

Hecht, S., & Pirenne, M. H.
1940. The sensibility of the nocturnal long-eared owl in the spectrum. J. Gen. Physiol., v. 23, p. 709.

Hecht, S., & Shlaer, S.
1936. Intermittent stimulation by light. V. The relation between intensity and critical fre-

quency for different parts of the spectrum. J. Gen. Physiol., v. 19, p. 965.

1936. The color vision of dichromats. I. Wavelength discrimination, brightness distribution, and color mixture. *Ibid.*, v. 20, p. 57.

1936. The color vision of dichromats. II. Saturation as the basis for wavelength discrimination and color mixture. *Ibid.*, p. 83.

1938. An adaptometer for measuring human dark adaptation. J. Opt. Soc. Amer., v. 28, p. 209.

HECHT, S., SHLAER, S., & PIRENNE, M. H.
1942. Energy, quanta, and vision. J. Gen. Physiol., v. 25, p. 819.

HECHT, S., SHLAER, S., SMITH, E. L., HAIG, C., & PESKIN, J. C.
1948. The visual functions of the complete colorblind. J. Gen. Physiol., v. 31, p. 459.

HECHT, S., SHLAER, S., & VERRIJP, C. D.
1934. Intermittent stimulation by light. II. The measurement of critical fusion frequency for the human eye. J. Gen. Physiol., v. 17, p. 237.

HECHT, S., & SMITH, E. L.
1936. Intermittent stimulation by light. VI. Area and the relation between critical frequency and intensity. J. Gen. Physiol., v. 19, p. 979.

HECHT, S., & VERRIJP, C. D.
1934. Intermittent stimulation by light. III. The relation between intensity and critical fusion frequency for different retinal locations. J. Gen. Physiol., v. 17, p. 251.

1934. Intermittent stimulation by light. IV. A theoretical interpretation of the quantitative data of flicker. *Ibid.*, p. 269.

HECHT, S., & WALD, G.
1934. The visual acuity and intensity discrimination of *Drosophila*. J. Gen. Physiol., v. 17, p. 517.

HECHT, S., & WILLIAMS, R. E.
1922. The visibility of monochromatic radiation and the absorption spectrum of visual purple. J. Gen. Physiol., v. 5, p. 1.

HECHT, S., & WOLF, E.
1929. The visual acuity of the honey bee. J. Gen. Physiol., v. 12, p. 727.

1929. The visual acuity of the bee and its relation to illumination. Proc. Nat. Acad. Sc., v. 15, p. 178.

1932. Intermittent stimulation by light. I. The validity of Talbot's law for *Mya*. J. Gen. Physiol., v. 15, p. 369.

HECHT, S., WOLF, E., & WALD, G. D.
1929. The visual acuity of insects. Am. J. Physiol., v. 90, p. 381.

HECK, L.
1916. Herren- oder Hochtiere (Primates). *In:*

A. BREHM, Tierleben, v. 13, Die Säugetiere, v. 4, p. 380.

HEGNER, C. A.
1915. Ueber seltene Formen von hemianopischen Gesichtsfeldstörungen nach Schussverletzungen. Klin. Monatsbl. f. Augenh., v. 55, p. 642.

1937. Refraktion, Sehschärfe, Akkommodation und Refraktionsanomalien des Auges. *In:* E. ABDERHALDEN, Handb. d. biol. Arbeitsmeth. Abt. V, Teil 6 (1), p. 463.

HEGNER, C. A., & NAEF, M. E.
1923. Intermittierende Erblindung nach Schädeltrauma. München. med. Wchnschr., v. 70, p. 502.

HEIBERG, J. L.
1925. Geschichte der Mathematik und der Naturwissenschaften im Altertum. C. H. Beck, München.

HEIDENHAIN, A.
1927. Beitrag zur Kenntnis der Seelenblindheit. Monatsschr. f. Psychiat. u. Neurol., v. 66, p. 61.

HEIDENHAIN, M.
1911. Plasma und Zelle. *In:* BARDELEBEN, Handb. d. Anat., sec. 6, p. 687 (Die nervöse Substanz). G. Fischer, Jena.

HEIDENHAIN, R.
1888. Johannes Evangelista Purkinje. Allg. Deutsch. Biographie, v. 26, p. 717.

HEIDERMANN, C.
1928. Messende Untersuchungen über das Formensehen der Cephalopoden und ihre optische Orientierung im Raume. Zool. Jahrb. (Allg. Zool. u. Physiol.), v. 45, p. 409.

1933. Grundzüge der Tierpsychologie. G. Fischer, Jena.

HEIER, P.
1948. Fundamental principles in the structure of the brain. A study of the brain of *Petromyzon fluviatilis*. Acta anat., suppl. VIII. Ohlsson, Lund.

HEILBRONNER, K.
1908. Zur Symptomatologie der Aphasie mit besonderer Berücksichtigung der Beziehung zwischen Sprachverständniss, Nachsprechen und Wortfindung. Arch. f. Psychiat. u. Nervenkr., v. 43, pp. 234, 698.

HEILIG, G.
1916. Kriegsverletzungen des Gehirns in ihrer Bedeutung für unsere Kenntnis von den Hirnfunktionen. Ztschr. f. d. ges. Neurol. u. Psychiat. (Orig.), v. 33, p. 408.

HEILIGTAG, F.
1910. Ein Fall von traumatischer Alexie. Deutsch. med. Wchnschr., v. 36, p. 2147.

HEIM DE BALSAC, H.
1936. Biogéographie des mammifères et des oiseaux de l'Afrique du Nord. Laboratoire d'Évolution des Êtres organisés, Paris.

HEIMAN, M.
1942. Riboflavin: significance of its photodynamic action and importance of its properties for the visual act. Arch. Ophth., v. 28, p. 493.

HEIN, S. A. A.
1913. Over oogleden en fornices conjunctivae bij teleostomi. Tijdschr. d. nederl. dierk. vereen., ser. 2, v. 12, p. 238.

HEINBECKER, P., & BARTLEY, S. H.
1940. Action of ether and nembutal on the nervous system. J. Neurophysiol., v. 3, p. 219.

HEINE, L.
1898. Physiologisch-anatomische Untersuchungen über die Accommodation des Vogelauges. Arch. f. Ophth. (Graefe), v. 45 (3), p. 469.
1900. Sehschärfe und Tiefenwahrnehmung. *Ibid.*, v. 51, p. 146.
1901. Ueber bimaculares Sehen. Ber. d. Deutsch. ophth. Gesellsch. Heidelberg, v. 28, p. 125.
1902. Demonstration des Zapfenmosaiks der menschlichen Fovea. *Ibid.*, v. 29, p. 265.
1906. Das Auge des Gorilla. Jena. Ztschr. f. Naturwiss., v. 41, p. 612.
1918. Ueber Ophthalmoskopie im weissen und farbigen Lichte. Arch. f. Ophth. (Graefe), v. 97, p. 271.
1926. Beiträge zur Anatomie der Macula lutea. Arch. f. Augenh., v. 97, pp. 144, 278, 502.
1935. Anatomisch - physiologisch - pathologische Grundlagen der Stereoskopie. Naturwiss., v. 23, p. 855.

HEINEMANN, C.
1864. Bemerkungen über den bindegewebigen Stützapparat in der Netzhaut des Vogelauges. Arch. f. path. Anat. u. Physiol. (Virchow), v. 30, p. 256.
1877. Beiträge zur Anatomie der Retina. Arch. f. mikr. Anat., v. 14, p. 409.

HEINERSDORFF, H.
1897. Centrale beiderseitige Amaurose infolge von metastatischen Abscessen in beiden Occipitallappen ohne sonstige Herdsymptome. Deutsch. med. Wchnschr., v. 23, p. 230.

HEINRICHS, H.
1913. Die Ueberwindung der Autorität Galens durch Denker der Renaissancezeit. Diss. Hanstein, Bonn.

HEISTER, D. L.
1721. D. Laurentii Heisters Anatom. Chirurg. ac Theor. Med. Prof. Publ. Helmstadiensi, wie auch vornehmen Mitgliedes der Käyser-

und Königl. Berlinischen Academie, *Compendium Anatomicum*, Welches die gantze Anatomie aufs allerkürtzeste in sich begreifft, aus dem Lateinischen in das Teutsche übersetzet von Maximilian Lentnern, Studioso Chirurgiae. Mit Kupfferstichen. Breslau, In Verlag Michael Huberts, 1721.

HEKLER, A.
1912. Die Bildniskunst der Griechen und Römer. J. Hoffmann, Stuttgart.

HELD, H.
1890. Der Ursprung des tiefen Markes der Vierhügelgegend. Neurol. Centralbl., v. 9, p. 481.
1904. Ueber den Bau der Neuroglia und über die Wand der Lymphgefässe in Haut und Schleimhaut. Abh. d. kgl. sächs. Gesellsch. d. Wissensch., math.-phys. Kl., Leipzig, v. 28, p. 199.
1905. Zur Kenntnis einer neuro-fibrillären Continuität im Centralnervensystem der Wirbelthiere. Arch. f. Anat. u. Entw., p. 55.
1906. Zur weiteren Kenntnis der Nervenendfüsse und zur Struktur der Sehzellen. Abh. d. kgl. sächs. Gesellsch. d. Wissensch., math.-phys. Kl., v. 29, p. 143.
1907. Kritische Bemerkungen zu der Verteidigung der Neuroblasten- und der Neuronentheorie durch R. Cajal. Anat. Anz., v. 30, p. 369.
1909. Ueber die Neuroglia marginalis der menschlichen Grosshirnrinde. Monatsschr. f. Psychiat. u. Neurol., v. 26 (Ergh.), p. 360.
1927. Das Grundnetz der grauen Hirnsubstanz. *Ibid.*, v. 65, p. 68.
1929. Die Lehre von den Neuronen und vom Neurencytium und ihr heutiger Stand. *In:* ABDERHALDEN, Fortschr. d. naturwiss. Forsch., N.F., Fasc. 8. Urban & Schwarzenberg, Berlin.

HELIODOROS OF LARISSA (*see also* DAMIANOS)
Early part of 4th cent. A.D. Ἡλιοδώρου Λαρισσαίου Κεφάλαια τῶν ὀπτικῶν. Heliodori Larissaei Capita opticorum. Ad Hetrusci codicis fidem Graece & Latine edita; & recensita. Ex bibliotheca Fr. Lindenbrogi. In librario Heringiano. An. CIꝹ.IꝹ.CX.

HELL, J.
1926. The Arab civilization. W. Heffer & Sons, Cambridge.

HELLENDALL, H.
1897. Ein Beitrag zu der Frage der Kreuzung der Sehnerven. Arch. f. Physiol. (His), p. 497.

HELLER, E.
1910. New species of insectivores from British East Africa, Uganda, and Sudan. Smithsonian Misc. Coll., v. 56, p. 1.

HELLER, E.—*Continued*
1912. New races of insectivores, bats and lemurs from British East Africa. *Ibid.*, v. 60, p. 1.

HELMHOLTZ, H.
1843. De fabrica systematis nervosi evertebratorum. Inaug. diss. Berolini.
1851. Beschreibung eines Augen-Spiegels zur Untersuchung der Netzhaut im lebenden Auge. A. Förstner'sche Verlagsbuchhandlung, Berlin. *In:* K. Sudhoff, Klassiker der Medizin. J. A. Barth, Leipzig, 1910. English: The description of an ophthalmoscope. Trans. T. H. SHASTID. Cleveland Press, Chicago, 1916. (*See also* E. Landolt, Arch. d'opht., v. 14, p. 721, 1894.)
1855. Ueber die Accommodation des Auges. Arch. f. Ophth. (Graefe), v. 1 (2), p. 1.
1863. Die Lehre von den Tonempfindungen als physiologische Grundlage für die Theorie der Musik. F. Vieweg & Sohn, Braunschweig. English trans. by A. J. ELLIS: On the sensation of tone as a physiological basis for the theory of music. Longmans, Green & Co., London, 1885 and 1930.
1882–95. Wissenschaftliche Abhandlungen. 3 vols. J. A. Barth, Leipzig.
1884. Vorträge und Reden. 2 vols. F. Vieweg & Sohn, Braunschweig.
1894. Ueber den Ursprung der richtigen Deutung unserer Sinneseindrücke. Ztschr. f. Psychol. u. Physiol. d. Sinnesorg., v. 7, p. 81.
1921. Schriften zur Erkenntnistheorie. J. Springer, Berlin.
1924–25. Treatise on physiological optics. 3 vols. G. Banta Publ. Co., Menasha, Wis. Translated from 3d ed. of the Handb. d. physiol. Optik. L. Voss, Hamburg & Leipzig, 1909.

HELMREICH, G.
*1909. Γαληνου, περὶ χρείας μορίων. Leipzig.

HEMNETER, E.
1940. Embalming in ancient Egypt. Ciba Symp., v. 1, No. 10.

HEMPELMANN, F.
1926. Tierpsychologie vom Standpunkte des Biologen. Akad. Verlagsgesellsch. M.B.H., Leipzig.

HENCKEL, F.
1898. Beiträge zur Entwickelungsgeschichte des menschlichen Auges. Anat. Hefte (Merkel & Bonnet), v. 10, p. 485.

HENCKEL, K. O.
1928. Studien über Primordialcranium und die Stammesgeschichte der Primaten. Morphol. Jahrb., v. 59, p. 105.
1928. Das Primordialkranium von *Tupaia* und der Ursprung der Primaten. Zeitschr. f. Anat. u. Entw., v. 86, p. 204.

HENDERSON, C. G.
1917. Blindness in India and the possibility of its diminution. King Bros. & Pott's, St. Leonards-on-Sea, England. *Also* Brit. J. Ophth., v. 2, p. 539, 1918.

HENDERSON, T.
1941. The mechanism of aqueous secretion in mammalia. Brit. J. Ophth., v. 25, p. 30.
1941. The mechanism of the intra-ocular pressure in mammalia. *Ibid.*, p. 349.

HENLE, J. (*see also* F. MERKEL 1891 and 1909)
1838. Kritik der in- und ausländischen medicinischen Literatur. Jahrb. d. Med. (Schmidt), v. 19, p. 337.
1839. Anmerkung zu Remak. Arch. f. Anat., Physiol. u. wissensch. Med. (J. Müller), p. 170.
1839. Anmerkung zu Bidder. *Ibid.*, p. 385.
1841. Allgemeine Anatomie. *In:* S. T. SOEMMERRING, Vom Baue des menschlichen Körpers, v. 6, pp. 657, 772, 783, 787. Voss, Leipzig.
1852. Versuche und Beobachtungen an einem Enthaupteten. Ztschr. f. rat. Med., N.F., v. 2, p. 299.
1855–73. Handbuch der systematischen Anatomie des Menschen. 3 vols. F. Vieweg & Sohn, Braunschweig. (*See* v. 2, p. 601, Sinnesapparate, and v. 3, Part 2, Nervenlehre.) Also later eds.
1861. Ueber den Bau der Retina-Stäbchen beim Menschen. Nachr. Univ. u. Kgl. Gesellsch. d. Wissensch. Göttingen, p. 17.
1864. Ueber die äussere Körnerschichte der Retina. Nachr. Kgl. Gesellsch. d. Wissensch. u. Univ. Göttingen, p. 119.
1864. Weitere Beiträge zur Anatomie der Retina. *Ibid.*, p. 305.
1871. Handbuch der Nervenlehre des Menschen. *In:* his Handb. d. system. Anat. d. Mensch., v. 3 (2). F. Vieweg & Sohn, Braunschweig. 2d ed., 1879.

HENNEBERG
1918. Reine Worttaubheit. Neurol. Centralbl., v. 37, pp. 426, 539.

HENNIG, E.
1944–47. Etappen der Menschwerdung. Natur u. Volk (Ber. d. Senckenberg. Gesellsch.), v. 74, p. 21.
1950. Der Werdegang des Menschengeschlechts. Dr. M. Matthiesen & Co. Kg. Tübingen.

HENRY DE MONDEVILLE; *see* MONDEVILLE, H. DE
HENSCHEN, S. E. (*see also* O. PÖTZL 1926)
1890–1930. Klinische und anatomische Beiträge zur Pathologie des Gehirns. Part 1, Alm-

quist & Wiksell, Upsala, 1890; Part 2, 1892; Part 3, 1896; Part 4, 1911; Parts 5 & 6, Nordiska Bokhandeln, Stockholm, 1920; Part 7, Selbstverlag by author, Stockholm, 1922; Part 8, 1930. (*See also* J. f. Psychol. & Neurol., v. 40, p. 382.)

1893. On the visual path and centre. Brain, v. 16, p. 170.

1894. Sur les centres optiques cérébraux. Rev. gén. d'opht., v. 13, p. 337.

1895. Sur le centre optique cérébral. Atti dell'XI Cong. med. internaz., Roma, 1894, v. 4 (Psichiat.), p. 93.

1897–98. Ueber Lokalisation innerhalb des äusseren Kniehöckers. Neurol. Centralbl., v. 16, p. 923; v. 17, p. 194.

1900. Sur le centre cortical de la vision. Compt. rend. 13th internat. Cong. med., Paris, v. 12, sec. on ophthalmology, p. 232.

1903. La projection de la rétine sur la corticalité calcarine. Semaine méd., 23, p. 125.

1909. Ueber inselförmige Vertretung der Makula in der Sehrinde des Gehirns. Med. Klin., v. 5 (2), p. 1321.

1910. Zentrale Sehstörungen. *In:* M. LEWANDOWSKY, Handb. d. Neurol., v. 1, p. 891.

1911. Ueber circumscripte Nutritionsgebiete im Occipitallappen und ihre Bedeutung für die Lehre vom Sehzentrum. Arch. f. Ophth. (Graefe), v. 78, p. 195.

1911. Ueber circumscripte arteriosklerotische Nekrosen (Erweichungen) in den Sehnerven, im Chiasma und in den Tractus. *Ibid.*, p. 212.

1912. Spezielle Symptomatologie und Diagnostik der intrakraniellen Sehbahnaffektionen. *In:* M. LEWANDOWSKY, Handb. d. Neurol., v. 3 (Spez. Neurol., v. 2), p. 751.

1917. Ueber das Sehzentrum. Neurol. Centralbl., v. 36, p. 946.

1918. Ueber die Hörsphäre. J. f. Psychol. u. Neurol., v. 22, Ergh. 3. (*See also* Klose, in Monatsschr. f. Psychiat. u. Neurol., v. 48, p. 63, 1920.)

1918–19. On the hearing sphere. Acta oto-laryng., v. 1, p. 423.

1919. Ueber die Geruchs- und Geschmackszentren. Monatsschr. f. Psychiat. u. Neurol., v. 45, p. 121.

1919. Ueber Sinnes- und Vorstellungszentren in der Rinde des Grosshirns. Zugleich ein Beitrag zur Frage des Mechanismus des Denkens. Ztschr. f. d. ges. Neurol. u. Psychiat., v. 47 (Orig.), p. 55.

1919. Ueber Sprach-, Musik- und Rechenmecha-

nismen und ihre Lokalisation im Grosshirn. *Ibid.*, v. 52 (Orig.), p. 273.

1920. Klinische und anatomische Beiträge zur Pathologie des Gehirns. V. Ueber Aphasie, Amusie und Akalkulie. Nordiska Bokhandeln, Stockholm.

1920. Les altérations de la faculté du langage, de la musique, et du calcul. Rev. neurol., v. 36, p. 1089.

1922–23. Ueber Sinnesempfindungen und Vorstellungen aus anatomisch-klinischem Gesichtspunkte. Acta med. Scandinav., v. 57, p. 458.

1923. 40-jähriger Kampf um das Sehzentrum und seine Bedeutung für die Hirnforschung. Ztschr. f. d. ges. Neurol. u. Psychiat., v. 87, p. 505.

1923. On sensations, perceptions and conceptions from an anatomico-clinical point of view. Proc. Internat. Cong. Psychol., Oxford, p. 359.

1925. On the main problem of the investigation of the brain, especially the localisation (in Spanish). Med. germ.-hispano.-am., v. 2, p. 561. (*See* abstr. in Zentralbl. f. d. ges. Neurol. u. Psychiat., v. 42, p. 7, 1926.)

1925. Autobiography. *In:* L. R. GROTE, Die Medizin der Gegenwart in Selbstdarstellungen, v. 5, p. 35. F. Meiner, Leipzig.

1925. Ueber die Lokalisation einseitiger Gesichtshalluzinationen. Kritische Bemerkungen anlässlich Professor P. Schröders diesbezüglicher Abhandlung. Arch. f. Psychiat. u. Nervenkr., v. 75, p. 630.

1925. Bemerkung zu A. Picks "Lokalisatorische Tendenzen in der Aphasielehre." Ztschr. f. d. ges. Neurol. u. Psychiat., v. 99, p. 518.

1925. Ueber die Funktion der rechten Hirnhemisphäre im Verhältnis zu der linken, in bezug auf Sprache, Musik und Rechnen. *Ibid.*, v. 100, p. 1.

1925. On the anatomical substratum of the mono- and binocular vision (in Swedish). Hygiea, v. 87, p. 555.

1925. Mémoire sur la base anatomique de la vision mono- et binoculaire. Remarques critiques à propos de la nouvelle hypothèse de R. Bárány. Trav. du lab. de recherches biol. Madrid, v. 23, p. 217; Hygiea, v. 87, p. 555. (*See* Bárány's reply in same vol. of Travaux, p. 425.)

1926. On the localisation of certain psychic processes, in particular of the one-sided hemianopic hallucinations (in Swedish). Hygiea, v. 88, p. 321. (Possibly also in Part 6 or 8 of his Beitr. z. Pathol. d. Gehirns.)

1926. Zur Anatomie der Sehbahn und des Sehzentrums. Arch. f. Ophth. (Graefe), v. 117, p. 403.

1926. Die Vertretung der beiden Augen in der Sehbahn und in der Sehrinde. I. Die Vertretung der beiden Augen im Corpus geniculatum externum. Arch. f. Ophth. (Graefe), v. 117, p. 419.

1926. On the function of the right hemisphere of the brain in relation to the left in speech, music and calculation. Brain, v. 10, p. 110.

1926. Zu der Entdeckung des Sehzentrums. Bemerkung zu der Erwiderung von Prof. Lenz auf die Arbeit Henschens: "40-jähriger Kampf, etc." Ztschr. f. d. ges. Neurol. u. Psychiat., v. 102, p. 368.

1926. Om agrafi. Finsk. läk. handl., v. 68, p. 977.

1927. Aphasiesysteme. Monatschr. f. Psychiat., v. 65, p. 87.

1927. Zur Lokalisation der Rechenfunktionen. Anlässlich Hans Bergers Schrift: Ueber Rechenstörungen bei Herderkrankungen des Grosshirns. Arch. f. Psychiat. u. Nervenkr., v. 79, p. 375.

1928. Zur Entwicklung der Aphasielehre. Monatsschr. f. Ohrenh., v. 62, p. 823.

1929. The structure and the function of the cerebral cortex (in Swedish). Hygiea, v. 91, p. 417.

1929. Ljussinnesceller och färgsinnesceller i hjärnen. *Ibid.*, p. 705.

1929. Ueber die Bewusstheit unserer Empfindungen und Vorstellungen. J. f. Psychol. u. Neurol., v. 37, p. 101.

1930. Lichtsinn- und Farbensinnzellen im Gehirn. Deutsch. Ztschr. f. Nervenh., v. 113, pp. 146, 305; *also in:* his Klin. u. anat. Beitr. z. Path. d. Gehirns, Part 8. Stockholm.

1931. Ueber spezifische Lichtsinn- und Farbensinnzellen im Gehirn. Acta psychiat. & neurol., v. 6, p. 347; *also* Zentralbl. f. d. ges. Neurol. u. Psychiat., v. 24, p. 551 (*see also* Hygiea, v. 92, in Swedish).

HENSEN, V.

1865. Ueber das Auge einiger Cephalopoden. Ztschr. f. wissensch. Zool., v. 15, p. 155.

1865. Ueber eine Einrichtung der Fovea centralis retinae, welche bewirkt, das feinere Distanzen als solche, die dem Durchmesser eines Zapfens entsprechen, noch unterschieden werden können. Arch. f. path. Anat. u. Physiol. (Virchow), v. 34, p. 401.

1866. Ueber den Bau des Schneckenauges und über die Entwickelung der Augentheile in der Thierreihe. Arch. f. mikr. Anat., v. 2, p. 399.

1867. Ueber das Sehen in der Fovea centralis. Arch. f. path. Anat. u. Physiol. (Virchow), v. 39, p. 475.

1868. Bemerkung zu W. Krause: Die Membrana fenestrata der Retina. Arch. f. mikr. Anat., v. 4, p. 347.

HENSHALL, J. A.

1919. Bass, pike and perch and other game fishes of America. Stewart & Kidd Co., Cincinnati.

HEPPENSTALL, C. A.

1946. Moles. Pennsylvania Game News, v. 16, pp. 10, 25.

1946. Bats. *Ibid.*, pp. 13, 27.

1946. Shrews. *Ibid.*, v. 17, pp. 12, 29.

HERDER, J. G.

1784–91. Ideen zur Philosophie der Geschichte. 4 vols. J. F. Hartknoch, Riga & Leipzig.

HERGET, H. M.

1944. "The glory that was Greece." Nat. Geog. Mag., v. 85, p. 290.

HERING, E.

1868. Die Lehre vom binocularen Sehen. W. Engelmann, Leipzig.

1868. Bemerkungen zu der Abhandlung von Donders über das binoculare Sehen. Arch. f. Ophth. (Graefe), v. 14 (1), p. 1.

1870. Ueber das Gedächtnis als eine allgemeine Funktion der organisirten Materie. Vortrag gehalten in der feierl. Sitzung der Kaiserl. Akad. d. Wissenschaften am 30. Mai 1870. *In:* Almanach d. Kaiserl. Akad. d. Wissensch. Wien, v. 21, p. 253.

1870. Memory as a general function of organized matter. *In:* Memory: lectures on the specific energies of the nervous system, p. 1. Open Court Pub. Co., Chicago & London, 1913.

1879. Der Raumsinn und die Bewegungen der Augen. *In:* L. HERMANN, Handb. d. Physiol., v. 3 (1), p. 343.

1889. Ueber die Hypothesen zur Erklärung der peripheren Farbenblindheit. Arch. f. Ophth. (Graefe), v. 35 (4), p. 63.

1890. Die Untersuchung einseitiger Störungen des Farbensinnes mittels binocularer Farbengleichungen. *Ibid.*, v. 36 (3), p. 1.

1890. Zur Diagnostik der Farbenblindheit. *Ibid.*, v. 36 (1), p. 217.

1895. Ueber angebliche Blaublindheit der Zapfensehzellen. Arch. f. d. ges. Physiol. (Pflüger), v. 61, p. 106.

1898. On the theory of nerve-activity. Academic discourse delivered before the University of Leipzig, May 21, 1898. *In:* Memory: lectures on the specific energies of the nervous system. Open Court Pub. Co., Chicago & London, 1913.

1905–20. Grundzüge der Lehre vom Lichtsinn. *In:* GRAEFE & SAEMISCH, Handb. d. ges. Augenh., v. 3, chap. 13. 2d ed. W. Engelmann, Leipzig (J. Springer, Berlin).

1913. Memory: lectures on the specific energics of the nervous system: (1) Memory as a general function; (2) The specific energies of the nervous system; (3) The theory of the nerve-activity. Open Court Pub. Co., Chicago & London.

1915. Das Purkinjesche Phänomen im zentralen Bezirke des Sehfeldes. Arch. f. Ophth. (Graefe), v. 90, p. 1.

1931. Wissenschaftliche Abhandlungen. 2 vols. G. Thieme, Leipzig.

HERINGA, C. G.
1923. The anatomical basis of nerve conduction. Psychiat. en neurol. bl., v. 27, p. 13.

HERMANIDES, S. R., & KÖPPEN, M.
1903. Ueber die Furchen und über den Bau der Grosshirnrinde bei den Lissencephalen insbesondere über die Localisation des motorischen Centrums und der Sehregion. Arch. f. Psychiat., v. 37, p. 616.

HERMANN, F.
1908. Gehirn und Schädel. Eine topographisch-anatomische Studie in photographischer Darstellung. G. Fischer, Jena.

HERMANN, L.
1879–83. Handbuch der Physiologie. F. C. W. Vogel, Leipzig.

HERMANS, T. G.
1940. The perception of size in binocular, monocular, and pin-hole vision. J. Exper. Psychol., v. 27, p. 203.

HERO OR HERON OF ALEXANDRIA
Ca. 3d cent. A.D. Rationes dimetiendi et commentatio dioptrica. Recensuit Herm. Schoene.—Herons v. Alexandria Vermessungslehre und Dioptra. Griechisch und deutsch von Herm. Schöne. *In:* Heronis Alexandrini Opera quae supersunt omnia, vol. 3. B. G. Teubner, Leipzig.

HERODOTOS OF HALICARNASSOS
5th cent. B.C. The history of Herodotos, trans. G. RAWLINSON, ed. M. KOMROFF. Tudor Pub. Co., New York, 1936.

HERRICK, C. J.
1899. The cranial and first spinal nerves of *Menidia;* a contribution upon the nerve components of the bony fishes. Arch. Neurol. & Psychopath., v. 2, p. 21.

1904. Organ and sense of taste in fishes. Bull. U.S. Fish. Comm. for 1902. Washington, D.C.

1910. The morphology of the forebrain in amphibia and reptilia. J. Comp. Neurol., v. 20, p. 413.

1914. The medulla oblongata of larval *Amblystoma. Ibid.*, v. 24, p. 343.

1917. The internal structure of the midbrain and thalamus of *Necturus. Ibid.*, v. 28, p. 215.

1921. A sketch of the origin of the cerebral hemispheres. *Ibid.*, v. 32, p. 429.

1922. Some factors in the development of the amphibian nervous system. Anat. Rec., v. 23, p. 291.

1922. Functional factors in the morphology of the forebrain of fishes. *In:* Libro en honor de D. S. Ramón y Cajal, v. 1, p. 143.

1924. Neurological foundations of animal behavior. Henry Holt & Co., New York.

1925. The amphibian forebrain. III. The optic tracts and centers of *Amblystoma* and the frog. J. Comp. Neurol., v. 39, p. 433.

1925. Morphogenetic factors in the differentiation of the nervous system. Physiol. Rev., v. 5, p. 112.

1927. Brains of rats and men. A survey of the origin and biological significance of the cerebral cortex. University of Chicago Press, Chicago.

1927. The amphibian forebrain. IV. The cerebral hemispheres of *Amblystoma*. J. Comp. Neurol., v. 43, p. 231.

1929. Anatomical patterns and behavior patterns. Physiol. Zoöl., v. 2, p. 439.

1929. The thinking machine. University of Chicago Press, Chicago. 2d ed., 1932.

1930. Localization of function in the nervous system. Proc. Nat. Acad. Sc., v. 16, p. 643.

1930. The order of nature. Monist, v. 40, p. 182.

1933. The evolution of cerebral localization patterns. Science, v. 78, p. 439.

1933. Morphogenesis of the brain. J. Morphol., v. 54, p. 233.

1933. The amphibian forebrain. VI. *Necturus.* J. Comp. Neurol., v. 58, p. 1.

1933. The amphibian forebrain. VII. The architectural plan of the brain. *Ibid.*, p. 481.

1933. The amphibian forebrain. VIII. Cerebral hemispheres and pallial primordia. *Ibid.*, p. 737.

1934. The amphibian forebrain. IX. Neuropil and other interstitial nervous tissue. *Ibid.*, v. 59, p. 93.

1934. The amphibian forebrain. X. Localized functions and integrating functions. *Ibid.*, p. 239.

1934. The hypothalamus of *Necturus. Ibid.*, p. 375.

1934. Factors of neural integration and neural disorder. *In:* M. BENTLEY & E. V. COWDRY, The problem of mental disorder, p. 197. New York, 1934.

1934. The interpeduncular nucleus of the brain of *Necturus.* J. Comp. Neurol., v. 60, p. 111.

1935. The membranous parts of the brain, meninges and their blood vessels in *Amblystoma. Ibid.,* v. 61, p. 297.

1935. A topographic analysis of the thalamus and midbrain of *Amblystoma. Ibid.,* v. 62, p. 239.

1936. Conduction pathways in the cerebral peduncle of *Amblystoma. Ibid.,* v. 63, p. 293.

1936. Neurobiological foundations of modern humanism. Proc. Inst. Med. Chicago, v. 11, p. 86.

1936. Mechanisms of nervous adjustment. *In:* Problems of nervous physiology and of behavior. Symp. dedicated to Prof. Beritashvili, Acad. Sc. U.S.S.R., Georg. Br., p. 51, Tbilisi.

1938. The brains of *Amblystoma punctatum* and *A. tigrinum* in early feeding stages. J. Comp. Neurol., v. 69, p. 391.

1939. Internal structure of the thalamus and midbrain of early feeding larvae of *Amblystoma. Ibid.,* v. 70, p. 89.

1939. Cerebral fiber tracts of *Amblystoma tigrinum* in midlarval stages. *Ibid.,* v. 71, p. 511.

1940. The hypothalamus. A review of the monograph by Fulton, Ranson & Frantz. Science, v. 91, p. 619.

1941. Development of the optic nerves of *Amblystoma.* J. Comp. Neurol., v. 74, p. 473.

1941. The eyes and optic paths of the catfish, *Ameiurus. Ibid.,* v. 75, p. 255.

1941. The optic system of fibers in brain of urodele amphibians. Anat. Rec., v. 79, suppl. 1, p. 31. (Abstr.)

1941. Optic and postoptic systems of fibers in the brain of *Necturus.* J. Comp. Neurol., v. 75, p. 487.

1942. Optic and postoptic systems in the brain of *Amblystoma tigrinum. Ibid.,* v. 77, p. 191.

1943. The cranial nerves. A review of fifty years. Denison Univ. Bull., J. Scient. Lab., v. 38, p. 41.

1944. Apparatus of optic and visceral correlation in the brain of *Amblystoma.* J. Comp. Psychol., v. 37, p. 97.

1944. The fasciculus solitarius and its connections in amphibians and fishes. J. Comp. Neurol., v. 81, p. 307.

1945. The natural history of experience. Phil. Sc., v. 12, p. 57.

1948. The brain of the tiger salamander, *Ambystoma tigrinum.* University of Chicago Press, Chicago.

1949. A biological survey of integrative levels. *In:* Philosophy for the future, p. 222. Macmillan Co., New York.

1949. George Ellett Coghill, naturalist and philosopher. University of Chicago Press, Chicago.

1950. Article: Evolution and mind. Encyclopaedia Britannica, v. 8, p. 929.

HERRICK, C. J., & COGHILL, G. E.

1915. The development of reflex mechanisms in *Amblystoma.* J. Comp. Neurol., v. 25, p. 65.

HERRICK, C. J., & CROSBY, E. C.

1918. A laboratory outline of neurology. W. B. Saunders Co., Philadelphia & London.

HERRICK, C. L.

1891. Studies on the brains of some American fresh-water fishes. J. Comp. Neurol., v. 1, p. 228.

1892. Mammals of Minnesota. (Minn. Geol. & Nat. Hist. Surv. Bull. 7.) Harrison & Smith, State Printers, Minneapolis.

1894. The seat of consciousness. J. Comp. Neurol., v. 4, p. 221.

HERRICK, F. H.

1905. Home life of wild birds. G. P. Putnam's Sons, New York & London.

1924. An eagle observatory. Daily life of the American eagle: late phase. Auk, v. 41, pp. 89, 389, 517.

1924. Nests and nesting habits of the American eagle. *Ibid.,* p. 213; Ann. Rep. Smithsonian Inst., p. 263.

1934. The American eagle. D. Appleton–Century Co., New York & London. *Also* Western Reserve Univ. Biol. Lab. Contr., Cleveland, 1933.

1935. Wild birds at home. D. Appleton–Century Co., New York & London.

1938. Audubon the naturalist. D. Appleton–Century Co., New York & London.

HERRMANN, G.

1924. Lokaldiagnostische Betrachtungen über eine akustische Aura. Med. Klin., v. 20 (1), p. 378.

1928. Zur Frage der morphologischen Beziehungen des Argyll-Robertson. Allg. Ztschr. f. Psychiat., v. 88, p. 353.

1928. Scheinbare hysterische Blindheit bei einer Hypophysengangscyste. Monatschr. f. Psychiat., v. 67, p. 51.

1929. Herde im Corpus geniculatum laterale bei multipler Sklerose. Ztschr. f. d. ges. Neurol. u. Psychiat., v. 118, p. 405.

1929. Die mechanischen Druckrichtungen bei

Hirntumoren und ihre lokalisatorische Verwertbarkeit. *Ibid.*, v. 122, p. 323.

HERRMANN, G., & PÖTZL, O.

1926. Ueber die Agraphie und ihre lokaldiagnostische Beziehungen. Abh. a. d. Neurol. etc. (Beihefte z. Monatsschr. f. Psychiat. u. Neurol.), Fasc. 35. S. Karger, Berlin.

1928. Die optische Allaesthesie. Studien zur Psychopathologie der Raumbildung. Abh. a. d. Neurol. etc. (Beihefte z. Monatsschr. f. Psychiat. u. Neurol.), Fasc. 47. S. Karger, Berlin.

1928. Die Projektion des zentralen Sehens im Zwischenhirn. Med. Klin., v. 24, p. 880.

HERTEL, E.

1899. Die Folgen der Sehnervendurchschneidung bei jungen Thieren. Ber. d. Deutsch. ophth. Gesellsch. Heidelberg, v. 27, p. 108.

HERTER, K., & SGONINA, K.

1933. Dressurversuche mit Igeln. Ztschr. f. vergl. Physiol., v. 18, p. 481; v. 21, p. 450.

HERTWIG, O.

1893–98. Die Zelle und die Gewebe. G. Fischer, Jena. Same republished under the title: Allgemeine Biologie, in several editions. English trans.: The cell; outlines of general anatomy and physiology. Swan, Sonnenschein & Co., London, 1909.

1900. Die Entwicklung der Biologie im 19. Jahrhundert. Verhandl. d. Gesellsch. d. deutsch. Naturforsch. u. Aerzte, v. 72, p. 41.

1906. Handbuch der vergleichenden und experimentellen Entwickelungslehre der Wirbeltiere. 3 vols. G. Fischer, Jena.

1909. Zur Erinnerung an Charles Darwin. Deutsch. med. Wchnschr., v. 35, p. 233.

HERTWIG, R.

1907. Lehrbuch der Zoologie. G. Fischer, Jena.

HERTZ, H.

1945. Relation between fibre diameter and action potential of single nerve fibres. J. Physiol., v. 104, p. 1P. (Proc.)

HERTZ, H. R.

1894–95. Gesammelte Werke. 3 vols. J. A. Barth, Leipzig.

HERTZ, M.

1935. Die Untersuchungen über den Formensinn der Honigbiene. Naturwiss., v. 23, p. 618.

HERZOG, E., & GÜNTHER, B.

1938. Das Synapsenproblem im Sympathicus. Ztschr. f. d. ges. Neurol. u. Psychiat., v. 160, p. 550.

HERZOG, F.

1906. Ueber die Sehbahn, das Ganglion opticum basale und die Fasersysteme am Boden des dritten Hirnventrikels in einem Falle von Bulbusatrophie beider Augen. Deutsch. Ztschr. f. Nervenh., v. 30, p. 223.

HERZOG, H.

1905. Experimentelle Untersuchung zur Physiologie der Bewegungsvorgänge in der Netzhaut. Arch. f. Anat. u. Physiol., Physiol. Abt., p. 413.

HESCHELER, K., & BOVERI, V.

1923. Zur Beurteilung des Parietalauges der Wirbeltiere. Vierteljahrschr. d. naturforsch. Gesellsch. Zürich, v. 68, p. 398.

HESCHL

1880. Zur Geschichte des zusammengesetzten Mikroskops. Arch. f. mikr. Anat., v. 18, p. 391.

HESCHL, R. L.

1878. Ueber die vordere quere Schläfenwindung des menschlichen Grosshirns. Aus Anlass der 25-jährigen Jubiläums-Feier der Wiener Landes-Irrenanstalt veröffentlicht von Dr. R. L. H., K. K. Professor der path. Anat. in Wien. Wilhelm Braumüller, K. K. Hof- und Universitätsbuchhändler, Wien, 1878.

HESS, C.

1889. Beschreibung des Auges von *Talpa europaea* und von *Proteus anguineus*. Arch. f. Ophth. (Graefe), v. 35 (1), p. 1.

1890. Untersuchung eines Falles von halbseitiger Farbensinnstörung am linken Auge. *Ibid.*, v. 36 (3), p. 24.

1905. Zur Pathologie des papillo-macularen Faserbündels. Arch. f. Augenh., v. 53, p. 201.

1907. Untersuchungen über die Ausdehnung des pupillomotorisch wirksamen Bezirkes der Netzhaut und über die pupillomotorischen Aufnahmeorgane. *Ibid.*, v. 58, p. 182.

1908. Untersuchungen zur Physiologie und Pathologie des Pupillenspieles. *Ibid.*, v. 60, p. 327.

1909. Untersuchungen über den Lichtsinn der Fische. *Ibid.*, v. 64 (Ergh.), p. 1.

1910. Untersuchungen über den Lichtsinn bei Reptilien und Amphibien. Arch. f. d. ges. Physiol., v. 132, p. 255.

1910. Die Accommodation bei Tauchervögeln. Arch. f. vergl. Ophth., v. 1, p. 153.

1912. Vergleichende Physiologie des Gesichtssinnes. *In:* H. WINTERSTEIN, Handb. d. vergl. Physiol., v. 4, p. 1.

1913. Ueber die Entwicklung von Lichtsinn und Farbensinn in der Tierreihe. Verhandl. d. Gesellsch. deutsch. Naturforsch. u. Aerzte, Part I, p. 127.

1914. Die Entwicklung von Lichtsinn und Farbensinn in der Tierreihe. Vortrag. J. F. Bergmann, Wiesbaden.

1914. Untersuchungen zur Physiologie des Gesichtssinnes der Fische. Ztschr. f. Biol., v. 63, p. 245.

1916. Das Differential-Pupilloskop. Eine Methode zur messenden Bestimmung von Störungen des Pupillenspieles. Arch. f. Augenh., v. 80, p. 213.

1919. Ueber Gesichtsfeld, Silberglanz und Sehqualitäten der Fische und über die Lichtverteilung im Wasser. Ztschr. f. Biol., v. 70, p. 9.

1919. Untersuchungen über die Methoden der klinischen Perimetrie. 1. Ueber Punktperimetrie. 2. Ueber Farbenperimetrie. Arch. f. Augenh., v. 84, p. 1; v. 85, p. 1.

1922. Farbenlehre. Ergebn. d. Physiol. (Asher & Spiro), v. 20, p. 1.

1922. Zwischenstufen zwischen partieller und totaler Farbenblindheit. Arch. néerl. physiol., v. 7, p. 179.

1922. Ueber "Sehfasern" und "Pupillenfasern" im Sehnerven. Med. Klin., v. 18, p. 1214.

1929. Pupille. *In:* Bethe *et al.*, Handb. d. norm. u. path. Physiol., v. 12 (1), Receptionsorgane 2 (1), p. 176.

1937. Methoden zur Untersuchung des Licht- und Farbensinnes sowie des Pupillenspieles. *In:* Abderhalden, Handb. d. biol. Arbeitsmeth., Abt. 5, Teil 6 (1), p. 159.

Hess, W. N.

1924. Reactions to light in the earthworm, *Lumbricus terrestris* L. J. Morphol. & Physiol., v. 39, p. 515.

1925. Nervous system of the earthworm, *Lumbricus terrestris* L. *Ibid.*, v. 40, p. 235.

1925. Photoreceptors of *Lumbricus terrestris*, with special reference to their distribution, structure, and function. *Ibid.*, v. 41, p. 63.

1937. The nervous system of *Dolichoglossus kowalevskyi*. J. Comp. Neurol., v. 68, p. 161.

1938. Reactions to light and photoreceptors of *Dolichoglossus kowalevskyi*. J. Exper. Zoöl., v. 79, p. 1.

1943. Visual organs of invertebrate animals. Scient. Monthly, v. 57, p. 489.

Hess, W. R.

1934. Plastizitätslehre und Lokalisationsfrage. Verhandl. d. Deutsch. Gesellsch. f. inn. Med. (Wiesbaden), v. 46, p. 212.

1939. Das Zwischenhirn und die Regulation von Kreislauf und Atmung. Schweiz. Arch. f. Neurol. u. Psychiat., v. 43, p. 413.

Hessberg

1915. Hirnverletzungen mit Augenstörungen. Berlin. klin. Wchnschr., v. 52, p. 141.

Hesse, F.

1880. Ueber die Vertheilung der Blutgefässe in der Netzhaut. Arch. f. Anat. u. Entw., p. 219.

Hesse, R.

1896–1902. Untersuchungen über die Organe der Lichtempfindung bei niederen Thieren. I. Die Organe der Lichtempfindung bei den Lumbriciden. Ztschr. f. wissensch. Zool., v. 61, p. 393. II. Die Augen der Plathelminthen, insonderheit der tricladen Turbellarien. *Ibid.*, v. 62, p. 527. III. Die Sehorgane der Hirudineen. *Ibid.*, p. 671. IV. Die Sehorgane des Amphioxus. *Ibid.*, v. 63, p. 456. V. Die Augen der polychäten Anneliden. *Ibid.*, v. 65, p. 446. VI. Die Augen einiger Mollusken. *Ibid.*, v. 68, p. 379. VII. Von den Arthropoden-Augen. *Ibid.*, v. 70, p. 347. VIII. Weitere Thatsachen. Allgemeines. *Ibid.*, v. 72, p. 565.

1898. Die Lichtempfindung des *Amphioxus*. Anat. Anz., v. 14, p. 556.

1902. Ueber die Retina des Gastropodenauges. Verhandl. d. Deutsch. zool. Gesellsch., p. 121.

1903. Ueber den Bau der Stäbchen und Zapfen der Wirbeltiere. *Ibid.*, p. 33.

1904. Ueber den feineren Bau der Stäbchen und Zapfen einiger Wirbelthiere. Zool. Jahrb., suppl., v. 7, p. 471.

1908. Das Sehen der niederen Tiere. G. Fischer, Jena.

1910. Der Tierkörper als selbständiger Organismus. Teubner, Leipzig & Berlin.

1929. Einfachste Photoreceptoren ohne Bilderzeugung und verschiedene Arten der Bilderzeugung. Bedeutung der Bilderzeugung, der Auflösung der lichterregbaren Schicht und der optischen Isolierung. *In:* Bethe *et al.*, Handb. d. norm. u. path. Physiol., v. 12 (1), Receptionsorgane 2 (1), p. 3. Lochcamera-Auge. *Ibid.*, p. 60. Das musivische Auge und seine Funktion. *Ibid.*, p. 61. Dämmerungstiere. *Ibid.*, p. 714.

1932. Article: Distribution of animals. Encyclopaedia Britannica, 14th ed., v. 7, p. 432.

1935. Die Ueberlegenheit der Wirbeltiere. Naturwiss., v. 23, p. 105.

1935. Der Haushalt der Insecten. *Ibid.*, p. 615.

1951. Ecological animal geography. John Wiley & Sons, New York.

Hesse, R., & Doflein, F.

1935–43. Tierbau und Tierleben in ihrem Zusammenhang betrachtet. 2d ed., 2 vols. G. Fischer, Jena.

HEUBNER, O.
1872. Zur Topographie der Ernährungsgebiete der einzelnen Hirnarterien. Centralbl. f. d. med. Wissensch., v. 10, p. 817.
1874. Die luetische Erkrankung der Hirnarterien. F. C. W. Vogel, Leipzig.

HEUSE
1880. Eine Beobachtung über das Eigenlicht der Macula lutea. Arch. f. Ophth. (Graefe), v. 26 (3), p. 147.

HEUVEN; *see* VAN HEUVEN

HEYL, P. R.
1929. The history and the present status of the physicist's concept of light. J. Opt. Soc. Amer., v. 18, p. 183.

HIBBEN, S. G.
1950. Effects of new light sources on human vision. Arch. Ophth., v. 43, p. 1128.

HICKEY, J. J.
1943. A guide to bird watching. Oxford University Press, London & New York.

HICKS, S. P., & WARREN, S.
1950. Introduction to neuropathology. McGraw-Hill Book Co., New York.

HIDANO, K.
1926. Ueber das Netzhautbild. Arch. f. d. ges. Physiol. (Pflüger), v. 212, p. 163.
1926. Eine Methode zur objektiven Demonstration des Netzhautbildes und seiner Aenderungen durch verschiedene Faktoren. Arch. f. Ophth. (Graefe), v. 117, p. 286.

HIERONYMUS FABRICIUS AB AQUAPENDENTE; *see* AQUAPENDENS

HILBERT, R.
1898. Das atypische Flimmerscotom. Centralbl. f. Augenh., v. 22, p. 105.

HILDRETH, H. P.
1940. The insertion of the levator palpebrae muscle. Tr. Am. Ophth. Soc., v. 38, p. 470.

HILGARD, E. R., & MARQUIS, D. G.
1935. Acquisition, extinction, and retention of conditioned lid responses to light in dogs. J. Comp. Psychol., v. 19, p. 29.
1936. Conditioned eyelid responses in monkeys, with a comparison of dog, monkey, and man. Psychol. Monog., No. 212 (v. 47, p. 186).

HILGARD, E. R., & WENDT, G. R.
1933. The problem of reflex sensitivity to light studied in a case of hemianopsia. Yale J. Biol. & Med., v. 5, p. 373.

HILGENBERG, L., & KIRFEL, W.
1941. Vāgbhaṭa's Aṣṭāngahṛdayasaṃhitā, ein altindisches Lehrbuch der Heilkunde, etc. E. J. Brill, Leiden.

HILL, J.
1770. The construction of timber, from its early growth; explained by the microscope, and proved from experiments. Printed for the author, and sold by R. Baldwin, London.

HILL, J. E.
1945. Bat radar. Current Sc. (Bangalore), v. 14, p. 296.

HILL, J. P.
1919. The affinities of *Tarsius* from the embryological aspect. Proc. Zoöl. Soc. London, p. 476.
1932. The developmental history of the primates. Phil. Tr. Roy. Soc. London, ser. B, v. 221, p. 45.

HILL, R. T.
1946. Anatomy of the head and neck. Lea & Febiger, Philadelphia.

HILL, W. C. O.
1939. Observation on a giant Sumatran orang. Am. J. Phys. Anthropol., v. 24, p. 449.
1950. Man's relation to the apes. Man, v. 50, p. 161.
1953. Primates: comparative anatomy and taxonomy. I. Strepsirhini. Edinburgh University Press, Edinburgh.

HILLARP, N. A.
1946. Structure of the synapse and the peripheral innervation apparatus of the autonomic nervous system. Acta anat., v. 2, p. 9; *ibid.*, suppl., v. 4.

HILLEBRAND, F.
1893. Die Stabilität der Raumwerte auf der Netzhaut. Ztschr. f. Psychol. u. Physiol. d. Sinnesorg., v. 5, p. 1.
1920. Die Ruhe der Objekte bei Blickbewegungen. Jahrb. f. Psychiat., v. 40, p. 213.
1929. Lehre von den Gesichtsempfindungen auf Grund hinterlassener Aufzeichnungen. J. Springer, Berlin.

HILPERT, P.
1930. Ueber parietale Aphasie. Arch. f. Psychiat. u. Nervenkr., v. 90, p. 167.
1930. Die Bedeutung des linken Parietallappens für das Sprechen. Ein Beitrag zur Lokalisation der Leitungsaphasie. J. f. Psychol. u. Neurol., v. 40, p. 225.
1931. Aphatische Störungen bei Prozessen im Bereich des linken Gyrus supramarginalis. Zentralbl. f. d. ges. Neurol. u. Psychiat., v. 61, p. 273.

HILZHEIMER, M., & HECK, L. (*see also* BREHM)
1916. Die Säugetiere. *In:* A. BREHM, Tierleben, 4th ed., v. 13, Säugetiere, v. 4.

HIMWICH, H. E.
  1951. Brain metabolism and cerebral disorders. Williams & Wilkins Co., Baltimore.

HINDE, A.
  1894. A contribution to the study of the location and physiology of the visual cerebral center. M. Rec., v. 46, p. 679.

HINDZÉ, B.
  1930. Die Hirnarterien des Schimpansen. Ztschr. f. Morphol. u. Anthropol., v. 27, p. 468.
  1933. Quelques notes supplémentaires sur la méthode de préparation de tout le système des artères de l'encéphale. Arch. d'anat., v. 17, p. 397.

HINE, M. L.
  1918. The recovery of fields of vision in concussion injuries of the occipital cortex. Brit. J. Ophth., v. 2, p. 12.

HINELINE, G. M. W.
  1927. Color vision in the mudminnow. J. Exper. Zoöl., v. 47, p. 85.

HINES, MARION
  1921. The embryonic cerebral hemisphere in man. J. Anat., v. 55, p. 292.
  1925. The midbrain and thalamus of *Ornithorhynchus paradoxus*. Anat. Rec. (Proc.), v. 29, p. 361.
  1929. On cerebral localization. Physiol. Rev., v. 9, p. 462.
  1929. The brain of *Ornithorhynchus anatinus*. Phil. Tr. Roy. Soc. London, ser. B, v. 217, p. 155.
  1934. Cyto-architecture of the cerebral cortex in man. Research Pub. A. Research Nerv. & Ment. Dis., v. 13, p. 26. Williams & Wilkins Co., Baltimore.
  1940. Movements elicited from precentral gyrus of adult chimpanzees by stimulation with sine wave currents. J. Neurophysiol., v. 3, p. 442.
  1942. Recent contributions to localization of vision in the central nervous system. Arch. Ophth., v. 28, p. 913.

HINES, M., & BOYNTON, E. P.
  1940. The maturation of "excitability" in the precentral gyrus of the young monkey (*Macaca mulatta*). Pub. Carnegie Inst. Washington, No. 518, p. 309.

HINGSTON, R. W. G.
  1928. Problems of instinct and intelligence. Macmillan Co., New York; also French trans., Payot, Paris.

HINSEY, J. C., RANSON, S. W., & DIXON, H. H.
  1930. Responses elicited by stimulation of the mesencephalic tegmentum in the cat. Arch. Neurol. & Psychiat., v. 24, p. 966.

HINSEY, J. C., RANSON, S. W., & McNATTIN, R. F.
  1930. The role of the hypothalamus and mesencephalon in locomotion. Arch. Neurol. & Psychiat., v. 23, p. 1.

HINSHELWOOD, J., MACPHAIL, A., & FERGUSON, A. R.
  1904. A case of wordblindness, with right homonymous hemianopia. Brit. M. J., v. 2, p. 1304.

HIPPEL, A
  1875. Beobachtungen an einem mit doppelseitiger Cataract geborenen, erfolgreich operirten Kinde. Arch. f. Ophth. (Graefe), v. 21 (2), p. 101.
  1880. Ein Fall von einseitiger, congenitaler Roth-Grün-Blindheit bei normalem Farbensinn des anderen Auges. *Ibid.*, v. 26 (2), p. 176.
  1881. Ueber einseitige Farbenblindheit. *Ibid.*, v. 27 (3), p. 47.
  1899. Ueber einen neuen Fall von totaler Farbenblindheit. Ber. d. Deutsch. ophth. Gesellsch. Heidelberg, v. 27, p. 150.

HIPPEL, E.
  1898. Ueber das normale Auge des Neugeborenen. Arch. f. Ophth. (Graefe), v. 45, p. 286.
  1921. Allgemeines über Lokalisation in der optischen Leitungsbahn. *In:* GRAEFE & SAEMISCH, Handb. d. ges. Augenh., v. 7 (B), p. 223.
  1921. Die Erkrankungen des Chiasma. *Ibid.*, p. 504.
  1922–23. Die Krankheiten des Sehnerven. *In:* GRAEFE & SAEMISCH, Handb. d. ges. Augenh., 2d ed., v. 7, Part 2. J. Springer, Berlin.

HIPPOCRATES
  1839–61. Œuvres complètes. Traduction nouvelle etc. par É. Littré. 10 vols. J.-B. Baillière, Paris.
  1849. Genuine works. Translated by F. ADAMS. 2 vols. Sydenham Society, London.
  1950. The medical works of Hippocrates. A new translation from the original Greek made especially for English readers by the collaboration of John Chadwick and W. N. Mann. Blackwell Scient. Pub., Oxford.

HIRAKO, GOICHI
  1923. Ueber Myelinisation und myelogenetische Lokalisation des Grosshirns beim Kaninchen. Schweiz. Arch. f. Neurol. u. Psychiat., v. 13, p. 325.

HIRASAWA, K., & KARIYA, K.
  1936. Ueber die korticalen extrapyramidalen Fasern aus dem motorischen Rindenfeld (Area *4 a, b, c*) beim Affen (*Macacus rhesus*). Folia anat. japon., v. 14, p. 603.

HIRASAWA, K., & KATO, K.
1935. Ueber die Fasern, insbesondere die corticalen extrapyramidalen aus den Areae 8 (α, β, γ, δ) und 9 (*c*, *d*) der Grosshirnrinde beim Affen. Folia anat. japon., v. 13, p. 189.

HIRE; *see* DE LA HIRE

HIRSCH, A.
1869. Ein Wort zur Geschichte der Cataract-Extraction im Alterthume. Klin. Monatsbl. f. Augenh., v. 7, p. 282.
1877. Geschichte der Augenheilkunde. *In:* GRAEFE & SAEMISCH, Handb. d. ges. Augenh., 1st ed., v. 7 (5), p. 235.

HIRSCH, F. E.
1943. Copernicus after 400 years. The man who set the earth in motion. Saturday Rev., v. 26, No. 22, p. 11.

HIRSCH, O.
1921. Ueber Augensymptome bei Hypophysentumoren und ähnlichen Krankheitsbildern. Ztschr. f. Augenh., v. 45, p. 294.

HIRSCHBERG, J.
1875. Zur Semidecussation der Sehnervenfasern im Chiasma des Menschen. Arch. f. path. Anat. u. Physiol. (Virchow), v. 65, p. 116.
1876. Notiz zur Theorie des Sehens. Arch. f. Ophth. (Graefe), v. 22 (4), p. 118.
1876. Zur Frage der Sehnervenkreuzung. Arch. f. Augen- u. Ohrenh., v. 5, p. 137. *Also:* On the question of the decussation of the optic nerves. Arch. Ophth. & Otol., v. 5, p. 188.
1876. Historical notice concerning the doctrine of the smallest visual angle. Ophth. Hosp. Rep., v. 9, p. 16.
1882. Zur vergleichenden Ophthalmoskopie. Arch. f. Physiol. (Du Bois-Reymond), p. 81.
1887. Die Augenheilkunde bei den Griechen. Arch. f. Ophth. (Graefe), v. 33 (1), p. 47.
1890. Ueber die Augenheilkunde der alten Aegypter. *In:* Aegypten: geschichtliche Studien eines Augenarztes. G. Thieme, Leipzig.
1891. Ueber Sehstörungen durch Gehirngeschwulst. Neurol. Centralbl., v. 10, p. 449.
1898. Die Optik der alten Griechen. Ztschr. f. Psychol. u. Physiol. d. Sinnesorg., v. 16, p. 321.
1899–1918. Geschichte der Augenheilkunde. *In:* GRAEFE & SAEMISCH, Handb. d. ges. Augenh. 2d ed., W. Engelmann, Leipzig; J. Springer, Berlin. 1899, v. 12 (Egypt, India, Greece, Rome). 1908, v. 13 (Middle Ages, including Arabs, Renaissance, early modern time). 1911, v. 14 [1] (18th & first half of 19th cent.); v. 14 [2] (Germany, 1800–1850). 1912, v. 14 [3] (France, 1800–

1850). 1914, v. 14 [4] (England, 1800–1850). 1915–18, v. 14 [5–7] (Italy, 1800–1850, America, etc.). 1918, v. 15 [1, 2] (reform of ophthalmology).
1904. Die anatomischen Abbildungen bei den Arabern. Centralbl. f. prakt. Augenh., v. 28, p. 292.
1905. Die arabischen Lehrbücher der Augenheilkunde. Abh. d. Kgl. preuss. Akad. d. Wissensch. Berlin. Phil. u. hist. Abh., p. 1.
1905 (1908). Geschichte der Augenheilkunde bei den Arabern. *In:* GRAEFE & SAEMISCH, Handb. d. ges. Augenh., v. 13 (2).
1908. Zum Leipziger Augendurchschnittsbilde aus dem Ende des 15. Jahrhunderts. Arch. f. Gesch. d. Med., v. 1, p. 316.
1908. Geschichte der Augenheilkunde im Mittelalter und in der Neuzeit. *In:* GRAEFE & SAEMISCH, Handb. d. ges. Augenh., v. 13.
1911. Die Augenheilkunde in der Neuzeit. *In:* GRAEFE & SAEMISCH, Handb. d. ges. Augenh., v. 14.
1918. Der griechische Kanon der Augenheilkunde und sein Fortwirken bis auf unsre Tage. Arch. f. Ophth. (Graefe), v. 97, p. 301.

HIRSCHBERG, J., & LIPPERT, J.
1902. Die Augenheilkunde des Ibn Sina. Aus dem Arabischen übersetzt und erläuteret. Veit & Co., Leipzig.

HIRSCHBERG, J., LIPPERT, J., & MITTWOCH, E.
1904–5. Die arabischen Augenärzte nach den Quellen bearbeitet. 2 vols. Veit & Co., Leipzig.

HIRSCHLER, P.
1942. Anthropoid and human endocranial casts. Diss. Amsterdam. N.V. Noord-Holland. Uitgevers Maatschappij.

HIS, W.
1880. Abbildungen über das Gefässsystem der menschlichen Netzhaut und derjenigen des Kaninchens. Arch. f. Anat. u. Entw., p. 224.
1887. Zur Geschichte des menschlichen Rückenmarkes und der Nervenwurzeln. Abh. d. math.-phys. Cl. d. Kgl. sächs. Gesellsch. d. Wissensch. Leipzig, v. 13, p. 477.
1888. Zur Geschichte des Gehirns sowie der centralen und peripherischen Nervenbahnen. *Ibid.*, v, 14, p. 339.
1890. Die Neuroblasten und deren Entstehung im embryonalen Marke. *Ibid.*, v. 15, p. 311.
1890. Histogenese und Zusammenhang der Nervenelemente. Arch. f. Anat. u. Physiol. (Anat. Abt.) (suppl.), p. 95.
1893. Ueber den Aufbau unseres Nervensystems. Berlin. klin. Wchnschr., v. 30, pp. 957, 996.

His, W.—*Continued*

1904. Die Entwickelung des menschlichen Gehirns während der ersten Monate. S. Hirzel, Leipzig.

Hitti, P. K.

1951. History of Syria, including Lebanon and Palestine. Macmillan & Co., Ltd., London.

1951. History of the Arabs from the earliest times to the present. 5th ed. Macmillan & Co., Ltd., London.

Hitzig, E. (*see also* Fritsch & Hitzig 1870)

1872. Ueber einen interessanten Abscess der Hirnrinde. Arch. f. Psychiat., v. 3, p. 231.

1873. Ueber äquivalente Regionen am Gehirn des Hundes, des Affen und des Menschen. *In:* Untersuch. ü. d. Gehirn, p. 126, 1874.

1874. Untersuchungen über das Gehirn: Abhandlungen physiologischen und pathologischen Inhalts. A. Hirschwald, Berlin. *Also* Centralbl. f. d. med. Wissensch., v. 12, pp. 184, 375, 548, 821.

1887. A case of sensory aphasia with autopsy (in German). Verhandl. Cong. inn. Med., v. 6, p. 165.

1900. Ueber das corticale Sehen des Hundes. Arch. f. Psychiat., v. 33, p. 707.

1901. Ueber das corticale Sehen beim Hunde. Neurol. Centralbl., v. 20, p. 286 (*also* v. 19, p. 1129). *See also* Centralbl. f. Nervenh., v. 23, p. 665.

1901. Hughlings Jackson und die motorischen Rindencentren im Lichte physiologischer Forschung. Neurol. Centralbl., v. 20, p. 164.

1901–03. Alte und neue Untersuchungen über das Gehirn. Arch. f. Psychiat. u. Nervenkr., v. 34, p. 1; v. 35, pp. 275, 585; v. 36, p. 1; v. 37, pp. 277, 849.

1902. Demonstration zur Physiologie des corticalen Sehens. Neurol. Centralbl., v. 21, pp. 422, 434.

1903. Einige Bemerkungen zu der Arbeit C. v. Monakow's "Ueber den gegenwärtigen Stand der Frage nach der Localisation im Grosshirn." Arch. f. Psychiat. u. Nervenkr., v. 36, p. 907.

1904. Physiologische und klinische Untersuchungen über das Gehirn. A. Hirschwald, Berlin.

1905. Welt und Gehirn. Ein Essay. A. Hirschwald, Berlin.

Hjort, J.

1867. Ein Fall von hemiopischer Gesichtsfeldbeschränkung. Nekropsie. Klin. Monatsbl. f. Augenh., v. 5, p. 166.

Hoadley, L.

1926. Developmental potencies of parts of the early blastoderm of the chick. I. The first appearance of the eye. J. Exper. Zoöl., v. 43, p. 151.

Hoche, A.

1892. Doppelseitige Hemianopsia inferior und andere sensorisch-sensible Störungen bei einer funktionellen Psychose. Arch. f. Psychiat., v. 23, p. 70.

1896. Ueber die centralen Bahnen zu den Kernen der motorischen Hirnnerven. Neurol. Centralbl., v. 15, p. 607.

Hochecker, T.

1873. Ueber angeborene Farbenblindheit. Arch. f Ophth. (Graefe), v. 19 (3), p. 1.

Hochstetter, F.

1919–29. Beiträge zur Entwicklungsgeschichte des menschlichen Gehirns. 2 parts. F. Deuticke, Wien & Leipzig.

1937. Ueber einige Fälle einer bisher anscheinend noch nicht beobachteten Varietät der A. cerebralis posterior des Menschen. Ztschr. f. Anat. u. Entw., v. 107, p. 633.

1939. Ueber die Entwicklung und Differenzierung der Hüllen des menschlichen Gehirnes. Morphol. Jahrb., v. 83, p. 359.

1942. Ueber die harte Hirnhaut und ihre Fortsätze bei den Säugetieren, nebst Angaben über die Lagebeziehung der einzelnen Hirnteile dieser Tiere zueinander, zu den Fortsätzen der harten Hirnhaut und zur Schädelkapsel. Denkschr. d. Akad. d. Wissensch. Wien, math.-naturwiss. Kl., v. 106.

1943. Beiträge zur Entwicklungsgeschichte der kraniozerebralen Topographie des Menschen. *Ibid.*, v. 106.

1952. Ueber die Entwicklung der Form der menschlichen Gliedmassen. Denkschr. Oest. Akad. d. Wissensch., math.-naturwiss. Kl., v. 109 (4).

Hodes, R.

1940. The efferent pathway for reflex pupillomotor activity. Am. J. Physiol., v. 131, p. 144.

Hodes, R., & Magoun, H. W.

1942. Pupillary and other responses from stimulation of the frontal cortex and basal telencephalon of the cat. J. Comp. Neurol., v. 76, p. 461.

Hodgkin, A. L.

1937. Evidence for electrical transmission in nerve. I. and II. J. Physiol., v. 90, pp. 183, 211.

Hodgkin, A. L., & Huxley, A. F.

1945. Resting and action potentials in single nerve fibres. J. Physiol., v. 104, p. 176.

HODGKIN, T.
1885–99. Italy and her invaders. 8 vols. Clarendon Press, Oxford. 2d ed., 1892–1916.

HOERR, N. L.
1936. Cytological studies by the Altmann-Gersh freezing-drying method. III. The pre-existence of neurofibrillae and their disposition in the nerve fiber. Anat. Rec., v. 66, p. 81.

HÖSEL, O.
1905. Ueber die Markreifung der sogenannten Körperfühlssphäre und der Riech- und Sehstrahlung des Menschen. Arch. f. Psychiat. u. Nervenkr., v. 39, p. 195.

HOESSLY, G. F.
1947. Untersuchungen am Zentralnervensystem mit dem Phasenkontrast-Mikroskopierverfahren. Acta anat., v. 3, p. 371.

HOEVE, H. J. H.
1909. A modern method of teaching the anatomy of the brain. Anat. Rec., v. 3, p. 247.

HOEVE, J. VAN DER
1912. Die Farbe der Macula lutea. Arch. f. Ophth. (Graefe), v. 80, p. 132.
1922. L'action des muscles de l'œil. Arch. néerl. physiol., v. 7, p. 268.

HOFE, K. VOM
1925. Ueber die absolute Lokalisation bei unwillkürlichen Augenbewegungen. Arch. f. Augenh., v. 96, p. 85.
1927. Untersuchungen über den Ablauf der Dunkeladaptation. Ber. d. Deutsch. ophth. Gesellsch. Heidelberg, v. 46, p. 305.

HOFF, E. C.
1937. The structure of the intraneuronal junctions (synapses) of the brain and cord and peripheral ganglia. London Hosp. Gaz., v. 40, p. 129.

HOFF, H.
1929. Beiträge zur Relation der Sehsphäre und des Vestibularapparates. Ztschr. f. d. ges. Neurol. u. Psychiat., v. 121, p. 751.
1930. Die zentrale Abstimmung der Sehsphäre. Abh. a. d. Neurol. etc., suppl. to Monatschr. f. Psychiat. u. Neurol., Fasc. 54. S. Karger, Berlin.

HOFF, H., & HOFFMANN, T.
1930. Ein Beitrag zur Stirnhirnfunktion und ihre Beziehung zur Sprache und Gang. Ztschr. f. d. ges. Neurol. u. Psychiat., v. 126, p. 253.

HOFF, H., & KAMIN, M.
1930. Reizversuche im linken Sulcus interparietalis beim Menschen. Ztschr. f. d. ges. Neurol. u. Psychiat., v. 125, p. 693.

HOFF, H., & PÖTZL, O.
1933. Ueber cerebral bedingte Polyopie und verwandte Erscheinungen. Jahrb. f. Psychiat., v. 50, p. 35.
1935. Ueber ein diagonal orientiertes hemianopisches Skotom bei vasculärer Läsion der cerebralen Sehsphäre. Ztschr. f. d. ges. Neurol. u. Psychiat., v. 152, p. 422.
1935. Zur diagnostischen Bedeutung der Polyopie bei Tumoren des Occipitalhirnes. *Ibid.*, p. 433.
1935. Ueber die Grosshirnprojektion der Mitte und der Aussengrenzen des Gesichtsfelds. Jahrb. f. Psychiat., v. 52, p. 121.
1935. Ueber ein neues parieto-occipitales Syndrom. *Ibid.*, p. 173.
1937. Ueber die labyrinthären Beziehungen von Flugsensationen und Flugträumen. Monatsschr. f. Psychiat. u. Neurol., v. 97, p. 193.
1937. Ueber Transformationen zwischen Körperbild und Aussenwelt. Wien. klin. Wchnschr., v. 50, p. 347.
1937. Ueber ein eigenartiges Syndrom bei einem Tumor im Mittelhirn. Jahrb. f. Psychiat., v. 54, p. 13.
1937. Ueber Polyopie und gerichtete hemianopische Halluzinationen. *Ibid.*, p. 55.
1937. Anatomische Untersuchung eines Falles von instrumentaler Amusie. *Ibid.*, p. 89.
1938. Anatomischer Befund eines Falles mit Zeitrafferphänomen. Deutsch. Ztschr. f. Nervenh., v. 145, p. 150.
1938. Anisotropie des Sehraums bei occipitaler Herderkrankung. *Ibid.*, p. 179.

HOFF, J. H. VAN'T
1900. Ueber die Entwicklung der exacten Naturwissenschaften im 19. Jahrhundert. Verhandl. d. Gesellsch. deutsch. Naturforsch. u. Aerzte, v. 72, p. 28.

HOFFMAN, B. L.
1951. An experimental study of the effects of electrical stimulation of the insular cortex on blood pressure, respiration, and gastric motility in *Macaca mulatta*. Thesis, University of Chicago.

HOFFMANN, C. K.
1876–77. Zur Anatomie der Retina. Niederl. Arch. f. Zool., v. 3, pp. 1, 195, 217.

HOFFMANN, H.
1925. Moderne Probleme der Tiergeographie. Naturwiss., v. 13, p. 77.

HOFMANN, F. B.
1916. Die Lehre vom Raumsinn des Doppelauges. Ergebn. d. Physiol., v. 15, p. 238.
1920. Physiologische Optik (Raumsinn). *In:*

GRAEFE & SAEMISCH., Handb. d. ges. Augenh., 2d ed., v. 3, chap. 13.

1920–25. Die Lehre vom Raumsinn des Auges. 2 vols. J. Springer, Berlin.

HOHMAN, L. B.

1929. The efferent connections of the cerebellar cortex; investigations based upon experimental extirpations in the cat. Research Pub. A. Research Nerv. & Ment. Dis., v. 6, p. 445.

HOLBOURN, A. H. S.

1948. The fundamental colour sensations. Nature, v. 162, p. 26.

HOLDEN, W. A.

1895. Observations on cases of hemiachromatopsia, indicating the non-existence of a separate cortical color center. Arch. Ophth., v. 24, p. 447; Arch. f. Augenh., v. 32, p. 139, 1896.

1904 (1905). A case of mind blindness, unique in that the entire mesial surface of both occipital lobes and both optic radiations were preserved. Tr. Am. Ophth. Soc., v. 10, p. 286; Am. J. M. Sc., v. 129, p. 782.

HOLL, M.

1905. Leonardo da Vinci und Vesal. Arch. f. Anat. u. Entw., p. 111. (*See* K. Sudhoff, Arch. f. Gesch. d. Med., v. 1, p. 67, 1908.)

1905. Ein Biologe aus der Wende des XV. Jahrhunderts, Leonardo da Vinci. Leuschner & Lubensky, Graz.

1907. Zur vergleichenden Anatomie des Hinterhauptlappens. Sitzungsb. d. Kaiserl. Akad. Wissensch. Wien, math.-naturwiss. Kl., Abt. 3, v. 116, p. 89.

1908. Ueber Furchen und Windungen der Scheitel-Hinterhauptgegend an den Gehirnen der Affen der neuen Welt. *Ibid.*, v. 117, p. 9.

1908. Zur vergleichenden Morphologie der "vorderen Insel" des menschlichen Gehirns. *Ibid.*, p. 325.

1908. Die Insel des Menschen- und Affenhirns in ihrer Beziehung zum Schläfenlappen. *Ibid.*, p. 365.

1909. Ueber bisher unbekannte Bildungen im hintersten Inselgebiet des Menschen- und Affenhirns. *Ibid.*, v. 118, p. 129.

1909. Die Entwicklung der Bogenwindung an der hinteren Insel des Menschen- und Affenhirns. *Ibid.*, p. 265.

1909. Die erste äussere Uebergangswindung der Ateles-Gehirne. *Ibid.*, p. 507.

1910. Untersuchung uber den Inhalt der Abhandlung Roths: "Die Anatomie des Leonardo da Vinci." Arch. f. Anat. u. Physiol., Anat. Abt. (Waldeyer), pp. 115, 319.

1915. Vesals Anatomie des Gehirns. *Ibid.*, p. 115.

HOLLÄNDER, B.

1899. Historisches über die Lokalisation der psychischen Tätigkeiten im Gehirn mit besonderer Berücksichtigung der Lehren Gall's. L. Schumacher, Berlin.

1928. The centenary of Francis Joseph Gall. M. Life, v. 35, p. 373.

HOLLANDER, F.

1922. Recherches anatomiques sur les couches optiques. Les voies cortico-thalamiques et les voies cortico-tectales. Arch. de biol. (Paris), v. 32, p. 249.

1928. Sur les fonctions des couches optiques. Bruxelles-méd., v. 8, p. 1563.

HOLLANDER, F., & DE GREEF, M. E.

1925. Nouvelles recherches sur les couches optiques. La systématisation des voies cortico-thalamiques. Compt. rend. Cong. d. méd. alién. & neurol. Bruxelles, 1924, p. 255.

HOLLANDER, F., & STOFFELS, J.

1937. Nouveau procédé de localisation pour les recherches sur le cortex cérébral: le palliogramme. J. belge de Neurol. et de Psychiat., v. 37, p. 1.

HOLLINSHEAD, W. H.

1954. Anatomy for surgeons. V. 1. Head and neck. P. B. Hoeber, New York.

HOLM, E.

1922. Das gelbe Maculapigment und seine optische Bedeutung. Arch. f. Ophth. (Graefe), v. 108, p. 1.

HOLMES, A.

1931. Radioactivity and geological time. Bull. Nat. Research Council, No. 80, p. 124.

1937. The age of the earth. Thomas Nelson & Sons, London & New York.

HOLMES, E. G.

1932. The metabolism of brain and nerve. Ann. Rev. Biochem., v. 1, p. 487.

HOLMES, G. M.

1901. The nervous system of the dog without a forebrain. J. Physiol., v. 27, p. 1.

1917. Visual localization and orientation. Brit. M. J., v. 2, p. 826.

1918. Disturbances of vision by cerebral lesions. Brit. J. Ophth., v. 2, p. 353.

1918. Disturbances of visual orientation. Brit. J. Ophth., v. 2, pp. 449, 506. (*See also* paper by Berry, p. 597.)

1919. The cortical localization of vision. Brit. M. J., v. 2, p. 193.

1919. Disturbances of visual space perception. *Ibid.*, p. 230.

1920. Tumours involving the optic nerves and tracts. Tr. Ophth. Soc. United Kingdom, v. 40, p. 207.

1921. Palsies of the conjugate ocular movements. Brit. J. Ophth., v. 5, p. 241.

1927. Disorders of sensation produced by cortical lesions. Brain, v. 50, p. 413.

1930. Suprasellar tumours. Concil. Ophth. XIII, 1929, v. 3 (Part 3), p. 65.

1931. A contribution to the cortical representation of vision. Brain, v. 54, p. 470.

1934. The representation of the mesial sectors of the retinae in the calcarine cortex. Jahrb. f. Psychiat. u. Neurol., v. 51, p. 39.

1938. The cerebral integration of the ocular movements. Brit. M. J., v. 2, p. 107.

1945. The organization of the visual cortex in man. Proc. Roy. Soc. London, v. 132, p. 348.

1946. Introduction to clinical neurology. E. & S. Livingstone, Edinburgh.

HOLMES, G., & HEAD, H.
1911. A case of lesion of the optic thalamus with autopsy. Brain, v. 34, p 255.

HOLMES, G., & HORRAX, G.
1919. Disturbances of spatial orientation and visual attention, with loss of stereoscopic vision. Arch. Neurol. & Psychiat., v. 1, p. 385.

HOLMES, G., & LISTER, W. T.
1916. Disturbances of vision from cerebral lesions, with special reference to the cortical representation of the macula. Brain, v. 39, p. 34; Proc. Roy. Soc. Med., p. 57.

HOLMES, S. J.
1944. The problem of organic form. Scient. Monthly, v. 59, pp. 226, 253, 379.

HOLMGREN, N.
1918. Zur Kenntnis der Parietalorgane von *Rana temporaria*. Ark. f. zool., v. 11, p. 1.

1922. Points of view concerning forebrain morphology in lower vertebrates. J. Comp. Neurol., v. 34, p. 391.

HOLMYARD, E. J.
1940. Islam's contributions to science. Nature, v. 145, p. 4.

HOLWAY, A. H.
1937. On the precision of photometric observations. J. Opt. Soc. Amer., v. 27, p. 120.

1938. On color changes without variation of wavelength. Am. J. Psychol., v. 51, p. 429.

HOLWAY, A. H., & HURVICH, L. M.
1938. Visual differential sensitivity and retinal area. Am. J. Psychol., v. 51, p. 687.

HOLZER, W.
1923. Ueber die Bestandteile des Heldschen Gliasyncytiums. Ztschr. f. d. ges. Neurol. u. Psychiat., v. 87, p. 167.

HOMANN H.
1924. Zum Problem der Ocellenfunktion bei den Insekten. Ztschr. f. vergl. Physiol., v. 1, p. 541.

HOME, E.
1798. An account of the orifice in the retina of the human eye, etc. Phil. Tr. Roy. Soc. London, Part 2, p. 332.

1800. Untersuchungen über die Oeffnung in der Netzhaut verschiedener Thiere. Arch. f. Physiol. (Reil), v. 4, p. 440.

1822. On the anatomical structure of the eye. (Croonian Lect.) Phil. Tr. Roy. Soc. London, v. 112, p. 76; *also* Deutsch. Arch. f. d. Physiol. (Meckel), v. 8, p. 410, 1823.

HOMO, LÉON P.
1930. La civilisation romaine. Payot, Paris.

HONIGMANN, H.
1921. Untersuchungen über Lichtempfindlichkeit und Adaptierung des Vogelauges. Arch. f. Physiol. (Pflüger), v. 189, p. 1.

HONJO, I.
1935. Die Wirkung monochromatischen Lichtes auf die motorischen Elemente der Knochenfischnetzhaut. Ztschr. f. vergl. Physiol., v. 22, p. 293.

1939. Farbensinn der Feuersalamanderlarven. Mem. Coll. Sc., Kyoto Imp. Univ., ser. B, v. 15, p. 207.

HOOGSTRAAL, H.
1947. The "inside story" of the tarsier. Chicago Nat. Hist. Mus., v. 18, Nos. 11, 12.

HOOIJER, D. A.
1951. Questions relating to a new large anthropoid ape from the Mio-Pliocene of the Siwaliks. Am. J. Phys. Anthropol., N.S., v. 9, p. 79.

1951. The geological age of *Pithecanthropus*, *Meganthropus*, and *Gigantopithecus*. *Ibid.*, p. 265.

HOOKE, R.
1705. The posthumous works. S. Smith & B. Walford, London.

HOOTON, E. A.
1940. Why men behave like apes, and vice versa, or body and behavior. Princeton University Press, Princeton.

1942. Man's poor relations. Doubleday, Doran & Co., New York.

1943. Why we study apes and monkeys? Fauna, v. 5, p. 2.

1947. Up from the ape. Macmillan Co., New York.

HOPE, C. E.
1944. Studying owl pellets. Canad. Nature, v. 6, p. 22.

HOPF, L.
1904. Die Anfänger der Anatomie bei den alten Kulturvölkern. Ein Beitrag zur Geschichte der Anatomie. J. U. Kern's Verlag (Max Müller), Breslau.

HOPKINS, A. E.
1927. Experiments on color vision in mice in relation to the duplicity theory. Ztschr. f. vergl. Physiol., v. 6, p. 299.

HOPPE, E.
1926. Geschichte der Physik. F. Vieweg & Sohn, Braunschweig. French trans.: Histoire de la physique. Payot, Paris, 1928.

HOPPE, H. H.
1921. A syndrome of the visuopsychic cortical area—based on stable hallucinations and defective visual association in a sane person. Arch. Neurol. & Psychiat., v. 6, p. 674.

HOPSTOCK, H.
1921. Leonardo as anatomist. Stud. Hist. & Meth. Sc. (Singer), v. 2, p. 151. Clarendon Press, Oxford.

HORA, S. L.
1938. Notes on the biology of the freshwater grey-mullet, *Mugil corsula* Hamilton, with observations on the probable mode of origin of aerial vision in fishes. J. Bombay Nat. Hist. Soc., v. 40, p. 62.

HORÁNSZKY, N.
1936. Kniehöcker und Sehrinde bei einseitiger Opticusatrophie (Einäugigkeit). Klin. Monatsbl. f. Augenh., v. 97, p. 438.

HORIO, G.
1938. Die Farb- und Formdressur an Karpfen. Jap. J. M. Sc., Part III (Biophysics), v. 4, p. 395.

HORN, A.
*1813. The seat of vision determined. London.

HORN, L.
1930. Die Supratemporalflächen eines Taubstummengehirnes. Ztschr. f. d. ges. Neurol. u. Psychiat., v. 130, p. 758.

HORN, L., & HELFAND, M.
1932. Korrelative Rindenveränderungen im Gehirn einer einseitig Blinden. Wien. klin. Wchnschr., v. 45, p. 1309.

HORN, L., & PÖTZL, O.
1934. Ueber Hyperpathie und Verschiebung von Lokalzeichen bei Herderkrankungen des Grosshirns. Jahrb. f. Psychiat., v. 51, p. 49.

HORNSEY, W. M.
1944. Moles. Gardener's Chron., Pangbourne, ser. 3, v. 113, p. 239.

HOROWITZ, N. H.
1945. On the evolution of biochemical synthesis. Proc. Nat. Acad. Sc., v. 31, p. 153.

HORRAX, G.
1923. Visual hallucinations as a localizing phenomenon. With especial reference to their occurrence in tumors of the temporal lobes. Arch. Neurol. & Psychiat., v. 10, p. 532.

HORRAX, G., & PUTNAM, T. J.
1932. The field defects and hallucinations produced by tumours of the occipital lobe. Brain, v. 55, p. 499.

HORSFIELD, T.
1851. Catalogue of mammalia in the museum of the Hon. East India Company. London.

HORSLEY, V.
1909. The function of the so-called motor area of the brain. (Linacre Lect.) Brit. M. J., v. 2, p. 125.

HORSLEY, V., & CLARKE, R. H.
1908. The structure and function of the cerebellum examined by a new method. Brain, v. 31, p. 45.

HORSLEY., V., & SCHÄFER, E. A. (*see also* SCHÄFER)
1887. A record of experiments upon the functions of the cerebral cortex. Phil. Tr. Roy. Soc. London, ser. B, v. 179, p. 1.

HORST, C. J.; *see* VAN DER HORST

HOSCH, F.
1878. Hemianopsie und Sehnervenkreuzung. Corresp.-Bl. f. schweiz. Aerzte, v. 8, p. 555.
1878. Zur Lehre von der Sehnervenkreuzung. Klin. Monatsbl. f. Augenh., v. 16, p. 281.
1891. Ehrlich's Methylenblaumethode und ihre Anwendung auf das Auge. Arch. f. Ophth. (Graefe), v. 37 (3), p. 37.
1895. Bau der Säugethiernetzhaut nach Silberpräparaten. *Ibid.*, v. 41 (3), p. 84.
1901. Fall von sogenannter kortikaler Hemianopie und Alexie. Ztschr. f. Augenh., v. 5, p. 5.

HOSE, C.
1893. A descriptive account of the mammals of Borneo. E. Abbott, diss. (Norfolk, England).
1927. Fifty years of romance and research. Hutchinson & Co., London.

HOSOYA, Y., OKITA, T., & AKUNE, T.
1938. Ueber die lichtempfindliche Substanz in der Zapfennetzhaut. Tohoku J. Exper. Med., v. 34, p. 532.

HOTTA, G.
1906. Das Auge der anthropoiden Affen. Beiträge

zur vergleichenden Anatomie, mit besonderer Berücksichtigung der Irismuskulatur. Arch. f. Ophth. (Graefe), v. 62, p. 250.

HOUSSAY, B. A., *et al.*
1950. Human physiology. McGraw-Hill Book Co., New York.

HOVELACQUE, A.
1927. Anatomie des nerfs craniens et rachidiens et du système grand sympathique chez l'homme. Gaston Doin & Cie, Paris.

HOVELACQUE, A., & REINHOLD, P.
1917. Note sur la constitution du sinus caverneux. Rev. anthropol., v. 27, p. 277.

HOVIUS, J.
1740. Tractatus de circulari humorum motu in oculis. Lugduni Bat., ap. G. Potvliet.

HOWARD, A. D.
1908. The visual cells in vertebrates, chiefly in *Necturus maculosus*. J. Morphol., v. 19, p. 561.

HOWE, H. S., & McKINLEY, E.
1927. Cerebral circulation. Arch. Neurol. & Psychiat., v. 18, p. 81.

HOWELL, A. B.
1930. Aquatic mammals. Their adaptations to life in the water. Charles C Thomas, Springfield, Ill., and Baltimore.
1944. Speed in animals—their specialization for running and leaping. University of Chicago Press, Chicago.

HOWELL, A. H.
1929. Revision of the American chipmunks (genera *Tamias* and *Eutamias*). North American Fauna, No. 52.

HOWELL, C. D.
1939. The responses to light in the earthworm, *Pheretima agrestis Goto and Hatai*, with special reference to the function of the nervous system. J. Exper. Zoöl., v. 81, p. 231.

HOWELL, F. C.
1951. The place of Neanderthal man in human evolution. Am. J. Phys. Anthropol., N.S., v. 9, p. 379.

HOWELL, W. H.
1925. Inhibition. Physiol. Rev., v. 5, p. 161.

HOWELLS, W. W.
1950. Origin of the human stock. Concluding remarks of the chairman. Cold Spring Harbor Symp. Quant. Biol., v. 15, p. 79.

HOWORTH, H. H.
1876–1927. History of the Mongols. 4 vols. Longmans, Green & Co., London.

HRDLIČKA, A.
1901. An Eskimo brain. Am. Anthropologist, N.S., v. 3, p. 454.

1927. Quadrupedal progression in the human child. Am. J. Phys. Anthropol., v. 10, p. 347.
1939. Practical anthropometry. Wistar Institute, Philadelphia.

HSIANG-TUNG CHANG & RUCH, T. C.
1949. Spinal origin of the ventral supraoptic decussation (Gudden's commissure) in the spider monkey. J. Anat., v. 83, p. 1.

HSU, S.-H., HWANG, K., & CHU, H.-N.
1942. A study of the cardiovascular changes induced by stimulation of the motor cortex in dogs. Am. J. Physiol., v. 137, p. 468.

HUANG-TI NEI-CHING SU-WÊN
1949. The Yellow Emperor's classic of internal medicine. Williams & Wilkins Co., Baltimore.

HUBBS, C. L.
1921. An ecological study of the life-history of the fresh-water atherine fish *Labidesthes sicculus*. Ecology, v. 2, p. 262.
1938. Fishes from the caves of Yucatan. Pub. Carnegie Inst. Washington, No. 491, p. 261.

HUBBS, C. L., & COOPER, G. P.
1936. Minnows of Michigan. Bull. Cranbrook Inst. Sc., No. 8. Bloomfield Hills, Mich.

HUBBS, C. L., & LAGLER, K. F.
1949. Fishes of the Great Lakes region. Bull. Cranbrook Inst. Sc., No. 26. Bloomfield Hills, Mich.

HUBER, G. C., & CROSBY, E. C.
1926. On thalamic and tectal nuclei and fiber paths in the brain of the American alligator. J. Comp. Neurol., v. 40, p. 97.
1929. The nuclei and fiber paths of the avian diencephalon, with consideration of telencephalic and certain mesencephalic centers and connections. *Ibid.*, v. 48, p. 1.
1929. Somatic and visceral connections of the diencephalon. Arch. Neurol. & Psychiat., v. 22, p. 187.
1933. The reptilian optic tectum. J. Comp. Neurol., v. 57, p. 57.
1933. A phylogenetic consideration of the optic tectum. Proc. Nat. Acad. Sc., v. 19, p. 15.
1934. The influences of afferent paths on the cytoarchitectonic structure of the submammalian optic tectum. Psychiat. en neurol. bl., v. 38, pp. 459, 723.

HUBER, G. C., CROSBY, E. C., WOODBURNE, R. T., GILLILAN, L. A., BROWN, J. O., & TAMTHAI, B.
1943. The mammalian midbrain and isthmus regions. I. The nuclear pattern. J. Comp. Neurol., v. 78, p. 129.

HUBRECHT, A. A. W.
1897. The descent of the primates. (Princeton lect.) Charles Scribner's Sons, New York.

HUBRECHT, A. A. W., & KEIBEL, F.

1907. Normentafeln zur Entwicklungsgeschichte des Koboldmaki (*Tarsius spectrum*) und des Plumplori (*Nycticebus tartigradus*). G. Fischer, Jena.

HUDGINS, C. V.

1933. Conditioning and the voluntary control of the pupillary light reflex. J. Genet. Psychol., v. 8, p. 3.

HÜBOTTER, F.

1920. 3000 Jahre Medizin. O. Rothacker, Berlin.

1929–35. Biographisches Lexikon der hervorragenden Aerzte aller Zeiten und Völker. 2d ed., 6 vols. Urban & Schwarzenberg, Berlin & Wien.

HÜFLER, E.

1895. Ueber den Faserverlauf im Sehnerven des Menschen. Deutsch. Ztschr. f. Nervenh., v. 7, p. 96.

HÜFNER, G.

1867. Versuch einer Erklärung der im Santonrausche beobachteten Erscheinung von partieller Farbenblindheit im Sinne der Young'schen Theorie. Arch. f. Ophth. (Graefe), v. 13 (2), p. 309.

HUETTNER A. F.

1949. Fundamentals of comparative embryology of the vertebrates Macmillan Co., New York.

HUGHES, A. L., & DuBRIDGE, L. A.

1932. Photoelectric phenomena. McGraw-Hill Book Co., New York.

HUGHES, B., & SCHLOSBERG, H.

1938. Conditioning in the white rat. IV. The conditioned lid reflex. J. Exper. Psychol., v. 23, p. 641.

HUGHES, E. B. C.

1943. Selected cases illustrating the value of quantitative perimetry in neurosurgical diagnosis. Tr. Ophth. Soc. United Kingdom, v. 63, p. 143.

1943. Injury to the optico-chiasmal junction—a case report. Brit. J. Ophth., v. 27, p. 367.

1945. Indirect injury of the optic chiasma—a case report. *Ibid.*, v. 29, p. 629.

HUGUENIN, G. (*see also* HAAB & HUGUENIN)

1875. Ueber einige Punkte der Hirn-Anatomie. Arch. f. Psychiat., v. 5, p. 189.

1875. Beiträge zur Anatomie des Hirns. *Ibid.*, p. 341.

1878. Ein Beitrag zur Physiologie der Grosshirnrinde. Corresp.-Bl. f. schweiz. Aerzte, v. 8, p. 665.

HULKE, J. W.

1864. A contribution to the anatomy of the amphibian and reptilian retina. Ophth. Hosp. Rep. London, v. 4, p. 243.

1866. On the chameleon's retina. Phil. Tr. Roy. Soc. London, v. 156, p. 223.

1867. On the retina of amphibia and reptiles. J. Anat. & Physiol., v. 1, p. 94.

1868. On the anatomy of the fovea centralis of the human retina. Phil. Tr. Roy. Soc. London, v. 157, p. 109.

1868. Notes on the anatomy of the retina of the common porpoise (*Phocaena communis*). J. Anat. & Physiol., v. 2, p. 19.

1869. Note on the blood-vessel-system of the retina of the hedgehog. Monthly Micr. J., v. 1, p. 360.

1869. The histology of the eye. *Ibid.*, v. 2, p. 227.

HULSHOFF, D. J.

1917. The relation of the plis de passage of Gratiolet to the ape fissure. Proc. Kon. Akad. Wetensch. Amsterdam, v. 19, p. 104.

1917. The ape fissure—sulcus lunatus—in man. *Ibid.*, p. 219.

HULTKRANTZ, J. W.

1929. Gehirnpraeparation mittels Zerfaserung. Anleitung zum makroskopischen Studium des Gehirns. J. Springer, Berlin

1935. Brain preparations by means of defibrillation or blunt dissection; a guide to the macroscopic study of the brain. W. Heinemann, London.

HUMBOLDT, A. VON

*1805–23. Voyages aux régions equinoctiales du Nouveau-Continent, fait en 1799–1804. 4 vols. Paris.

1814–29. Personal narrative of travels to the equinoctial regions of the New Continent during the years 1799–1804. 7 vols. Longman, Hurst, Rees, Orme & Brown, London; ed. in 3 vols. by H. G. Bohn, London, 1852–53.

1815–32. Reise in die Aequinoctialgegenden des neuen Continents in den Jahren 1799, 1800, 1802, 1803 und 1804. 6 vols. J. G. Cotta, Stuttgart & Tübingen; another ed., 4 vols. in 2, Stuttgart, 1874.

1826. Ansichten der Natur. 2d ed., 2 vols. J. G. Cotta, Stuttgart & Tübingen; 3d ed., 1849. English trans.: Aspects of nature. Lea & Blanchard, Philadelphia, 1849.

1869. Kosmos. Entwurf einer physikalischen Weltbeschreibung. Amerikanische Jubiläums-Ausgabe. F. W. Thomas & Söhne, Philadelphia.

HUMPHREY, O. D.
1894. On the brain of the snapping turtle, *Chelydra serpentina*. J. Comp. Neurol., v. 4, p. 73.

HUN, H. (*see also* LaSalle Archambault 1924)
1887. A clinical study of cerebral localisation illustrated by seven cases. Am. J. M. Sc., v. 93, p. 140.

ḤUNAIN IBN ISḤĀḲ
9th cent. The book of the ten treatises on the eye, ed. M. Meyerhof. Government Press, Cairo, Egypt, 1928.

HUNDT, M.
*1501. Anthropologium, de hominis dignitate natura et proprietatibus. Leipzig.

HUNSICKER, W. C., Jr., & Spiegel, E. A.
1933. Conduction of cortical impulses to the autonomic nervous system. Proc. Soc. Exper. Biol. & Med., v. 31, p. 974.

HUNT, E. E.
1952. Human constitution: an appraisal. Am. J. Phys. Anthropol., N.S., v. 10, p. 55.

HUNT, R.
1924. A theory of the mechanism underlying inhibition in the central nervous system. Arch. Neurol. & Psychiat., v. 11, p. 418.

HUNT, T.
1951. Breeding of *Cryptotis parva* in Texas. J. Mammal., v. 32, p. 115.

HUNTER, J. I.
1923. Oculomotor nucleus of *Tarsius* and *Nycticebus*. Brain, v. 46, p. 38.

HUNTER, R. H.
1931. A short history of anatomy. J. Bale, Sons & Danielson, London.

HURD-MEAD, K. C.
1938. Women in medicine. Haddam Press, Haddam, Conn.

HURVICH, L. M., & Jameson, D.
1951. A psychological study of white. III. Adaptation as variant. J. Opt. Soc. Amer., v. 41, p. 787.
1953. Spectral sensitivity of the fovea. I. Neutral adaptation. *Ibid.*, v. 43, p. 485. (*See also* Jameson & Hurvich.)
1954. Spectral sensitivity of the fovea. III. Heterochromatic adaptation. *Ibid.*, v. 44, p. 213.

HUSCHKE, E.
1832. Ueber die erste Entwicklung des Auges und die zusammenhängende Cyclopie. Deutsch. Arch. f. d. Anat. u. Physiol. (Meckel), v. 6, p. 1; Ztschr. f. Ophth. (Ammon), v. 3, p. 341.
1833–35. Untersuchungen über einige Streit-

punkte in der Anatomie des menschlichen Auges. *Ibid.*, v. 3, p. 1; v. 4, p. 272.
1844. Lehre von den Eingeweiden und Sinnesorganen des menschlichen Körpers. *In:* S. T. Sömmerring, Vom Baue des menschl. Körpers, v. 5, p. 710.
1854. Schädel, Hirn und Seele des Menschen und der Thiere, etc. F. Mauke, Jena.

HUSSON, G.
1937. Alhazen, the desert scientist. Ed. Focus, v. 8, No. 1.

HUTTON, E. L.
1943. Results of prefrontal leucotomy. Lancet, v. 1, p. 362.

HUXLEY, J. S.
1923. Essays of a biologist. A. A. Knopf, New York.
1931. Africa view. Harper & Bros., New York & London.
1942. Evolution. The modern synthesis. G. Allen & Unwin, London; Harper & Bros., New York, 1943.
1946. Species and evolution. Endeavor, v. 5, p. 3.
1955. Evolution in action. Harper & Bros., New York.

HUXLEY, T. H.
1861. On the brain of *Ateles paniscus*. Proc. Zoöl. Soc. London, p. 247.
1871. A manual of the anatomy of vertebrated animals. J. & A. Churchill, London.
1894. Bishop Berkeley on the metaphysics of sensation. *In:* T. H. Huxley, Collected essays, v. 6, p. 243. Appleton & Co., New York.
1894. On sensation and the unity of structure of sensiferous organs. *Ibid.*, p. 288.
1898–1902. The scientific memoirs of T. H. Huxley. 4 vols. Macmillan & Co., London.

HUYGENS, CHRISTIAAN
1653–66–85–92. Dioptrique. *In:* Œuvres complètes de Christiaan Huygens publiées par la Société hollandaise des Sciences, v. 13 (1, 2). Martinus Nijhoff, La Haye, 1916.
1678. Traité de la lumière. Où sont expliquées les causes de ce qui luy arrive dans la reflexion, & dans la refraction. Et particulièrement dans l'étrange refraction du cristal d'Islande. Etc. A Leide, chez Pierre van der Aa, marchand libraire. MDCXC. (*See also* Straub.)
1690. Treatise on light. Macmillan & Co., Ltd., London 1912. *Also:* Hist. Acad. Sc. Paris, ser. 1, v. 1, p. 283, 1733 (orig. pub. 1679).
1888–1950. OEuvres complètes de Christiaan Huygens, publiées par la Société hollandaise

des Sciences. 22 vols. Martinus Nijhoff, La Haye.

1945. Treatise on light, etc. Translated by S. THOMPSON. University of Chicago Press, Chicago.

HUYSMANS, J. H. B. M., & FISCHER, F. P.

1941. Ueber den Gasstoffwechsel der Linse und des Glaskörpers. Ophthalmologica, v. 102, p. 275.

HUZELLA, T.

1941. Die zwischenzellige Organisation auf der Grundlage der Interzellulartheorie und der Interzellularpathologie. G. Fischer, Jena.

HYDE, I. H.

1903. The nerve distribution in the eye of *Pecten irradians*. E. L. Mark anniversary vol., p. 471. Henry Holt & Co., New York.

HYKEŠ, O. V.

1928. Přírodovědecké práce J. E. Purkyně v zrcadle kritiky jiných badatelů. Ce qui a été écrit sur les travaux scientifiques de Jan Evangelista Purkyně (Purkinje) par les biologistes. Knihotisk. Jedn. českoslov. mat. a. fys., Praha (Prague).

HYLAND, H. H.

1950. Prognosis in spontaneous subarachnoid hemorrhage. Arch. Neurol. & Psychiat., v. 63, p. 61.

HYMAN, L. H.

1942. Comparative vertebrate anatomy. University of Chicago Press, Chicago.

HYNDMAN, O. R.

1939. The central visual system. Evidence against bilateral representation through the splenium of the corpus callosum. Arch. Neurol. & Psychiat., v. 42, p. 735.

1952. The origin of life and the evolution of living things. Philosophical Library, New York.

HYNDMAN, O. R., & DULIN, W. J.

1939. The superior colliculi. Their function as estimated from a case of tumor. Arch. Surg., v. 38, p. 471.

HYRTL, J.

1839. Berichtigungen über das Ciliarsystem des menschlichen Auges. Oest. med. Jahrb., v. 19, p. 1.

I

IBN AL-HAITHAM (*see also* ALHAZEN and NAZIF BEY)

11th cent. Kitāb al-manāẓir (Book of optics). Arab MSS in Fatih Sultan Library, No. 3212–16; Ayasofya Library, No. 2448; Köprülü Library, No. 952; Ahmet Salis Library (Topkapu Saray), No. 1899, all at Istanbul, Turkey. Early Latin MSS at the Royal Observatory, Edinburgh; British Museum Library, London; Bodleian Library, Oxford; Trinity College, Cambridge. *See also:* Alhazen, Baarmann, M. Krause, Narducci, Polyak 1941, Rescher, Sarton, Wiedemann.

IBN RUSHD (AVERROËS)

End of 12th cent. Kitab al-kullīyāt fī al-ṭibb, or Book of medical generalities, or *Colliget* of Latin writers, trans. into Latin, A.D. 1255. Several Latin eds. but no modern ed. or trans. *See* Fukala in Arch. f. Augenh. (Graefe), v. 22, 1901.

1474. Aristotelis Meteorum libri IV, latine, cum commentariis Averrois. Opera L. Canozii, Patavii. (Commentary to Aristotle's Meteorology.)

*1553. Averrois Cordubensis colliget libri VII. Venetiis.

IBN SĪNĀ (AVICENNA) (*see also* G. GABRIELI, HIRSCHBERG & LIPPERT, and P. KRAUS)

11th cent. Kitāb al-kānūn fī al-ṭibb, or The canon of medicine. Various Latin and a modern Arabic ed. *See* Sarton 1927–31 and Polyak 1941, p. 508. An English trans.: A treatise on the Canon of medicine of Avicenna, incorporating a translation of the first book, by O. C. Gruner. Luzac & Co., London, 1930.

*Early 11th cent. Al-Shafaā, a philosophical treatise in part against emanation hypothesis of light (its publication announced by Wiedemann's school, 1890).

*1658. Abualj ibn Tsina, Canon medicinae, etc. Ed. V. P. PLEMPIUS. Louvain.

IGERSHEIMER, J.

1918–20. Zur Pathologie der Sehbahn. I. Klinische und anatomische Studien zur Lehre vom Gesichtsfelde. II. Ueber Hemianopsie. III. Das Verhalten der Dunkeladaptation bei Erkrankungen der optischen Leitungsbahn. IV. Gesichtsfeldverbesserung bei Hemianopikern. V. Klinische Beiträge zur Sehnervenpathologie. Arch. f. Ophth. (Graefe), v. 96, p. 1; v. 97, p. 105; v. 98, p. 67; v. 100, p. 357; v. 101, p. 79.

1920. Die Bedeutung des Gesichtsfeldes für die Kenntnis des Verlaufs und der Endigung der Sehnervenfasern in der Netzhaut. *Ibid.*, v. 101, p. 105. (For answer by Van der Hoeve, *see* v. 102, p. 184.)

1940. General hypertension and peripheral optic pathways. Am. J. Ophth., ser. 3, v. 23, p. 1243.

1947. Binasal hemianopsia. Arch. f. Ophth., ser. 2, v. 38, p. 248.

IGERSHEIMER, J., & HAHN-HASLINGER, E.
1926. Physiologische und experimentell-pathologische Untersuchungen über das Farbensehen der Hühner. Arch. f. Augenh., v. 97, p. 163.

ILBERG, I.
1889–97. Ueber die Schriftstellerei des Klaudios Galenos. Rhein. Mus. f. Philol., v. 44, p. 207; v. 47, p. 489; v. 51, p. 165; v. 52, p. 591.

ILBERG, J.
1905. Aus Galens Praxis. Ein Kulturbild aus der römischen Kaiserzeit. Neue Jahrb. f. d. klass. Altertum, v. 15, p. 276.

IMAMURA, S.
1903. Ueber die kortikalen Störungen des Sehaktes und die Bedeutung des Balkens. Arch. f. d. ges. Physiol. (Pflüger), v. 100, p. 495.

IMOGAWA, M., & SAKUMA, S.
1935. Experimentelle Untersuchung über die cortikalen extrapyramidalen Bahnen aus dem hinteren Teile der lateralen Fläche der Grosshirnhemisphäre beim Kaninchen. Kaibôgaku Zasshi (Anat. Soc. Japan), v. 8, p. 631. Citation and abstract in Jap. J. M. Sc., Anatomy, v. 6, p. 231.

INGALLS, N. W.
1914. The parietal region in the primate brain. J. Comp. Neurol., v. 24, p. 291.
1922–23. The dilatator pupillae and the sympathetic. *Ibid.*, v. 35, p. 163.

INGHAM, S. D.
1940. The functional relations of the primary, secondary, and tertiary visual cortical areas. Bull. Los Angeles Neurol. Soc., v. 5, p. 12.

INGLES, L. G.
1947. Mammals of California. Stanford University Press, Stanford, Calif.

INGRAM, W. M.
1942. Snail associates of *Blarina brevicauda talpoides* (Say). J. Mammal., v. 23, p. 255.

INGRAM, W. R.
1940. Nuclear organization and chief connections of the primate hypothalamus. Research Pub. A. Research Nerv. & Ment. Dis., v. 20, p. 195.

INGRAM, W. R., RANSON, S. W., & BARRIS, R. W.
1934. The red nucleus. Its relation to postural tonus and righting reactions. Arch. Neurol. & Psychiat., v. 31, p. 768.

INGRAM, W. R., RANSON, S. W., & HANNETT, F. L.
1931. Pupillary dilatation produced by direct stimulation of the tegmentum of the brain stem. Am. J. Physiol., v. 98, p. 687.

INGRAM, W. R., RANSON, S. W., HANNETT, F. I., ZEISS, R. F., & TERWILLIGER, E. H.
1932. Result of stimulation of the tegmentum with the Horsley-Clarke stereotaxic apparatus. Arch. Neurol. & Psychiat., v. 28, p. 513.

INGVAR, S.
1923. On thalamic evolution. Acta med. Scandinav., v. 59, p. 696.
1925. Zur Phylogenese des Zwischenhirns, besonders des Sehhügels. Deutsch. Ztschr. f. Nervenh., v. 83, p. 302.
1928. On the pathogenesis of the Argyll-Robertson phenomenon. Bull. Johns Hopkins Hosp., v. 43, p. 363.

INOUYE, T.
1909. Die Sehstörungen bei Schussverletzungen der kortikalen Sehsphäre, nach Beobachtungen an Verwundeten der letzten japanischen Kriege. W. Engelmann, Leipzig.

IRMSCHER, E.
1922–29. Pflanzenverbreitung und Entwicklung der Kontinente. Mitt. d. Inst. allg. Bot. Hamburg, v. 5, p. 17; v. 8, p. 170.

IRVINE, S. R.
1950. Amblyopia ex anopsia: observations on retinal inhibition, scotoma, projection, discrimination of light differences and visual acuity. Arch. Ophth., ser. 2, v. 43, p. 960.

ISSA BEY, AHMED
1928. Histoire des Bimaristans (hôpitaux) dans le monde islamique. Cairo.

ISSERLIN, M.
1929–36. Die pathologische Physiologie der Sprache. Ergebn. d. Physiol. (Asher & Spiro), v. 29, p. 129; v. 33, p. 1; v. 34, p. 1065; v. 38, p. 674.
1936. Aphasie. *In:* O. BUMKE & O. FOERSTER, Handb. d. Neurol., v. 6, p. 626.

IVES, H. E.
1940. The measurement of velocity with atomic clocks. Science, v. 91, p. 79.

J

JABOULAY, M.
1886. Relations des nerfs optiques avec le système nerveux central. Thèse. A. Davy, Paris.

JACKSON, E.
1941. Function and structure of the eye. Am. J. Ophth., v. 24, p. 277.

JACKSON, H. H. T.
1926. An unrecognized water shrew from Wisconsin. J. Mammal., v. 7, p. 57.
1928. A taxonomic review of the American longtailed shrews. North-Am. Fauna, No. 51.

JACKSON, J. HUGHLINGS

1861. Cases of reflex (?) amaurosis with coloured vision. Roy. London Ophth. Hosp. Rep., v. 3, p. 286.

1863. Unilateral epileptiform seizures attended by temporary defect of sight. M. Times & Gaz., v. 1, p. 588.

1863. Epileptiform seizures—aura from the thumb —attacks of coloured vision. *Ibid.*, p. 589.

1863. Observations on defects of sight in brain disease. Roy. London Ophth. Hosp. Rep., v. 4, p. 10; *also* M. Class., v. 3, p. 918, 1938–39. Williams & Wilkins Co., Baltimore.

1864. Loss of speech. Its association with valvular disease of the heart and hemiplegia on the right side. London Hosp. Rep., v. 1, p. 388; M. Times & Gaz., v. 2, p. 166; Brit. M. J., v. 1, p. 572.

1864. Clinical remarks on defects of sight in diseases of the nervous system. M. Times & Gaz., v. 1, p. 480.

1864. Note on amaurosis in hemiplegia. *Ibid.*, v. 2, p. 87.

1865. Hemiplegia on the right side with defect of speech—autopsy. *Ibid.*, p. 283.

1866. Note on the functions of the optic thalamus. London Hosp. Rep., v. 3, p. 373.

1866. Notes on the physiology and pathology of language, etc. M. Times & Gaz., v. 1, p. 659.

1866. Hemiplegia of left side with defect of speech. *Ibid.*, v. 2, p. 210; Lancet, v. 1, pp. 316, 457.

1868. Observations on the physiology of language. Brit. M. J., v. 2, p. 259; M. Times & Gaz., v. 2, p. 275.

1869. On localisation. M. Times & Gaz., v. 1, p. 600.

1869. Unit of constitution of the nervous system. *Ibid.*, v. 2, p. 481.

1873. On the anatomical and physiological localisation of movements in the brain. Lancet, v. 1, pp. 84, 162, 232.

1875. Partial convulsion from brain disease bearing on experiments of Hitzig and Ferrier. M. Times & Gaz., v. 1, pp. 578, 606, 661; v. 2, pp. 94, 264.

1875. Autopsy on a case of hemiopia with hemiplegia and hemianaesthesia. Lancet, v. 1, p. 722.

1875. Clinical and physiological researches on the nervous system. I. On the anatomical and physiological localisation of movements in the brain. Low, Churchill. *Also in* his: Selected writings, v. 1, p. 37.

1875. Clinical observations on cases of disease of the nervous system (*see here:* colour-sight in some cases of amaurosis). Lancet, v. 1, p. 85.

1876. Coloured vision as an "aura" in epilepsy. Roy. London Ophth. Hosp. Rep., v. 8, p. 91; *also* Brit. M. J., 1874, v. 1, p. 174

1878–80. On affections of speech from disease of the brain. Brain, v. 1, p. 304; v. 2, pp. 203, 323.

1879. On psychology and the nervous system. M. Press & Circ., v. 2, pp. 199, 239, 283, 409, 429.

1880. Aphasia with left hemiplegia. Lancet, v. 1, p. 637.

1884. Evolution and dissolution of the nervous system. Brit. M. J., v. 1, pp. 591, 660, 703.

1888. Remarks on evolution and dissolution of the nervous system. J. M. Sc., v. 33, p. 25.

1925. Neurological fragments. ("Oxford medical publications.") H. Milford, Oxford University Press, London.

1931–32. Selected writings. 2 vols. Hodder & Stoughton, London.

JACOB, A.

1819. An account of a membrane in the eye, now first described. Phil. Tr. Roy. Soc. London, Part 1, p. 300; *also* Arch. f. Physiol. (Meckel), v. 6, p. 302.

1823. Inquiries respecting the anatomy of the eye. M.-Clin. Tr. London, v. 12, p. 487.

JACOBSEN, C. F.

1931. A study of cerebral function in learning. The frontal lobes. J. Comp. Neurol., v. 52, p. 271.

1932. The influence of motor and premotor area lesions upon the retention of skilled movements in monkeys and chimpanzees. *In:* Localization of function in the cerebral cortex. Research Pub. A. Research Nerv. & Ment. Dis., v. 13, p. 225. Williams & Wilkins Co., Baltimore.

1935. Functions of frontal association areas in primates. Arch. Neurol. & Psychiat., v. 33, p. 558.

1936. Studies of cerebral function in primates. I. The functions of the frontal association areas in monkeys. ("Comp. Psychol. Monog.," v. 13, No. 63.)

JACOBSEN, C. F., & ELDER, J. H.

1936. Studies of cerebral function in primates. II. The effect of temporal lobe lesions on delayed response in monkeys. ("Comp. Psychol. Monog.," v. 13, No. 63.)

JACOBSEN, C. F., WOLFE, J. B., & JACKSON, T. A.

1935. An experimental analysis of the functions of

the frontal association areas in primates. J. Nerv. & Ment. Dis., v. 82, p. 1.

JACOBSOHN, L.

1896. Zur Frage der Sehnervenkreuzung. Neurol. Centralbl., v. 15, p. 838.

JACOBSOHN-LASK, L.

1924. Die Kreuzung der Nervenbahnen und die bilaterale Symmetrie des tierischen Körpers. Abh. a. d. Neurol., Psychiat., Psychol., etc., Fasc. 26. S. Karger, Berlin.

1928. Warum kreuzen sich die Leitungsbahnen im Zentralnervensystem? (Eine Ergänzung.) Ztschr. f. d. ges. Neurol. u. Psychiat., v. 112, p. 317.

JACQUEAU

1900. La double hémianopsie homonyme. 13th Internat. Cong. Med., Paris, Compt. rend., v. 12, sec. opht., p. 250.

JAENSCH, E. R.

1909. Zur Analyse der Gesichtswahrnehmungen. Ztschr. f. Psychol. u. Physiol. d. Sinnesorg. (Ergbd.), v. 4, p. 1.

JAFFE, N. S.

1950. Localization of lesions causing Horner's syndrome. Arch. Ophth., ser. 2, v. 44, p. 710.

JAGOR, F.

1866. Singapore, Malacca, Java. J. Springer, Berlin.

1873. Reisen in den Philippinen. Weidmann, Berlin. *Also* English trans.: Travels in the Philippines. Chapman & Hall, London.

JAHN, T. L.

1946. The kinetics of visual processes. III. Dark adaptation. Anat. Rec., v. 94, p. 377. (Abstr.)

1946. The kinetics of visual processes. I. Critical flicker frequency as a function of intensity. *Ibid.*, p. 422. (Abstr.)

1946. The kinetics of visual processes. II. Brightness discrimination and visual acuity as functions of intensity. *Ibid.*, p. 422. (Abstr.)

JAHN, T. L., & WULFF, V. J.

1943. Spectral sensitivity of the compound eye of *Dytiscus*. Anat. Rec., v. 87, p. 452. (Abstr.)

JAKOB, A.

1927–29. Normale und pathologische Anatomie und Histologie des Grosshirns. V. 1: Normale Anatomie und Histologie, und allgemeine Histopathologie des Grosshirns. V. 2 (1): Spezielle Histopathologie des Grosshirns. *In:* G. ASCHAFFENBURG, Handb. d. Psychiat. F. Deuticke, Leipzig.

JAKOB, C.

1911. Das Menschenhirn. J. G. Lehmann, München.

1912. Ueber die Ubiquität der sensomotorischen Doppelfunktion der Hirnrinde als Grundlage einer neuen, biologischen Auffassung des corticalen Seelenorgans. J. f. Psychol. u. Neurol., v. 19, p. 379; *also* München. med. Wchnschr., v. 59, p. 466.

JAKOB, C., & ONELLI, C.

1911. Vom Tierhirn zum Menschenhirn. Vergleichend morphologische, histologische und biologische Studien zur Entwicklung der Grosshirnhemisphären und ihrer Rinde. Part I. J. F. Lehmann's Verlag, München.

JAKOBY, E.

1905. Ueber die Neuroglia des Sehnerven. Klin. Monatsbl. f. Augenh., v. 41 (1), p. 129.

JAMESON, D., & HURVICH, L. M.

1951. Use of spectral hue–invariant loci for the specification of white stimuli. J. Exper. Psychol., v. 41, p. 455.

1953. Spectral sensitivity of the fovea. II. Dependence on chromatic adaptation. J. Opt. Soc. Amer., v. 43, p. 552. (*See also* Hurvich & Jameson.)

JAMIESON, E. B.

1909. The means of displaying, by ordinary dissection, the larger tracts of white matter of the brain in their continuity. J. Anat. & Physiol., v. 43, p. 225.

JANBON, M., & VIALLEFONT, H.

1931. Hallucinose dans un hémichamp visuel par spasme de la sylvienne. Rev. d'oto-neuro-opht., v. 9, pp. 52, 94.

JANIN, J.

1772. Mémoires et observations anatomiques, physiologiques et physiques sur l'œil, et sur les maladies qui affectent cet organe; avec un précis des opérations & des remedes qu'on doit pratiquer pour les guérir. Frères Perisse, Lyon; P. F. Didot, Paris; T. Barrois, Paris.

JANOTA, O.

1938. Sur l'apraxie constructive et sur les troubles apparentés de l'apperception et de l'expression des rapports spatiaux. Encéphale, v. 33, p. 173.

JANSEN, J.

1929. A note on the optic tract in teleosts. Proc. Kon. Akad. Wetensch. Amsterdam, v. 32, p. 1105.

1930. The brain of Myxine glutinosa. J. Comp. Neurol., v. 49, p. 359.

JANY, L.

1879. Zur Hemianopsia temporalis. Centralbl. f. prakt. Augenh., v. 3, p. 101.

1882. Ein Fall von rechtsseitiger Hemianopie und

Neuroretinitis in Folge eines Gliosarcoms im linken Occipitallappen. Arch. f. Augenh., v. 11, p. 190.

JARMER, K.
1928. Das Seelenleben der Fische. R. Oldenbourg, München & Berlin.

JATZOW, R.
1885. Beitrag zur Kenntniss der retrobulbären Propagation des Chorioidealsarcoms und zur Frage des Faserverlaufs im Sehnervengebiete. Arch. f. Ophth. (Graefe), v. 31 (2), p. 205.

JAYLE, G. E.
1941. Mouvements conjugués des globes oculaires et nystagmus. Masson & Cie, Paris.

JEANS, J. H.
1930. The mysterious universe. Macmillan Co., New York; Cambridge University Press, Cambridge. Also later eds.

JEFFERSON, G.
1919. Gunshot wounds of the scalp with special reference to the neurological signs. Brain, v. 42, p. 93.
1937. Removal of right or left frontal lobes in man. Brit. M. J., v. 2, p. 199.
1937. Compression of the chiasma, optic nerves, and optic tracts by intracranial aneurysms. Brain, v. 60, p. 444.

JEFFERSON, J. M.
1941. A study of the subcortical connections of the optic tract system of the ferret, with special reference to gonadal activation by retinal stimulation. J. Anat., v. 75, p. 107.

JELEŃSKA-MACIESZYNA, S.
1911. Auf- und absteigende Bahnen des hinteren Vierhügels beim Kaninchen. Neurol. Centralbl., v. 30, p. 473.
1913. Ueber die in den vorderen Vierhügeln des Kaninchens entspringenden Bahnen. Folia neuro-biol., v. 7 (Sommer-Ergh.), p. 23.

JELGERSMA, G.
1906. Der Ursprung des Wirbeltierauges. Morphol. Jahrb., v. 35, p. 377.

JELLIFFE, S. E.
1898. Bibliographical contribution to the cytology of the nerve cell. Arch. Neurol. & Psychopath., v. 1, p. 441.
1929. Diencephalic vegetative mechanisms; anatomy and physiology. Arch. Neurol. & Psychiat., v. 21, p. 838.
1932. Psychopathology of forced movements and oculogyric crises of lethargic encephalitis. ("Monog. ser.," No. 55.) Nerv. & Ment. Dis. Pub. Co., New York.

JELLINEK, A.
1933. Zur Phänomenologie der Amusie (expressive Amusie und Aphasie eines Lautensängers). Jahrb. f. Psychiat. u. Neurol., v. 50, p. 115.

JENDRÁSSIK, E.
1907. Ueber den Mechanismus und die Lokalisation der psychischen Vorgänge. Neurol. Centralbl., v. 26, p. 194.

JENNINGS, H. S.
1906. Behavior of the lower organisms. Columbia University Press, New York.
1935. Genetic variations in relation to evolution; a critical inquiry into the observed types of inherited variation, in relation to evolutionary change. Princeton University Press, Princeton.

JENSEN, V. A.
1936. Studies on the branching of the retinal blood vessels. Acta ophth., v. 14, p.100.

JENTZSCH, F.
1925. Die neuere Entwicklung der geometrischen Optik. Naturwiss., v. 13, p. 861.

JEPSEN, G. L.
1944. Phylogenetic trees. Tr. New York Acad. Sc., ser. 2, v. 6, p. 81.

JEPSEN, G. L., MAYR, E., & SIMPSON, G. G.
1949. Genetics, paleontology, and evolution. Princeton University Press, Princeton, N.J.

JERDON, T. C.
1867. The mammals of India; a natural history of all the animals known to inhabit continental India. Thomason College Press, Roorkee.

JOHANNIDES, D. P.
1880. Die gefässlose Stelle der menschlichen Retina und deren Verwerthung zur Bestimmung der Ausdehnung der Macula lutea. Arch. f. Ophth. (Graefe), v. 26 (2), p. 111.

JOHNSON, G. L.
1892. Bemerkungen über die Macula lutea. Arch. f. Augenh., v. 25, p. 157.
1893. Observations on the refraction and vision of the seal's eye. Proc. Zoöl. Soc. London, p. 719.
1894. Observations on the ophthalmoscopic appearance of the eyes of the order primates. *Ibid.*, p. 183.
1896–97. Beobachtungen an der Macula lutea. Arch. f. Augenh., v. 32, p. 65; v. 33, p. 337; v. 35, p. 171.
1901. Contributions to the comparative anatomy of the mammalian eye, chiefly based on ophthalmoscopic examination. Phil. Tr. Roy. Soc. London, ser. B, v. 194, p. 1.
1927. Contribution to the comparative anatomy of the reptilian and the amphibian eye (ophthalmoscopic). *Ibid.*, v. 215, p. 315.

JOHNSON, G. T.
  1921–22. A survey of the physiology of cerebration. J. Abnorm. & Social Psychol., v. 16, p. 115.
JOHNSON, H. M.
  1914. Visual pattern-discrimination in the vertebrates. I. Problems and methods. J. Anim. Behavior, v. 4, p. 319.
  1914. Comparative visual acuity in the dog, the monkey and the chick. *Ibid.*, p. 340.
  1916. Effective differences in width of visible striae for the monkey and the chick. *Ibid.*, v. 6, p. 169.
JOHNSON, M.
  1924. Camera trails in Africa. Grosset & Dunlap; Century Co., New York & London.
JOHNSON, R. E.
  1946. Pickerel in Minnesota? Conserv. Volunteer, v. 9, No. 53, July–August, p. 6.
JOHNSON, T. H.
  1935. Homonymous hemianopia: some practical points in its interpretation, with a report of forty-nine cases in which the lesion in the brain was verified. Tr. Am. Ophth. Soc., v. 33, p. 90.
JOHNSTON, J. B.
  1905. The morphology of the vertebrate head. J. Comp. Neurol., v. 15, p. 175.
  1908. A new method of brain dissection. Anat. Rec., v. 2, p. 344.
  1909. The morphology of the forebrain vesicle in vertebrates. J. Comp. Neurol., v. 19, p. 457.
  1910. The evolution of the cerebral cortex. Anat. Rec., v. 4, p. 143.
JOHNSTONE, J. A.
  1932. Article: Plankton, Encyclopaedia Britannica, 14th ed., v. 17, p. 1001.
JOKL, A.
  1918–19. Zur Entwickelungsgeschichte des Wirbeltierauges. Anat. Anz., v. 51, p. 209.
  1923. Ueber den Verschluss der fötalen Augenbecherspalte, die Entwicklung der Sehnerveninsertion und die Bildung ektodermaler und mesodermaler Zapfen im embryonalen Reptilienauge. Ztschr. f. Anat. u. Entw., v. 68, p. 523.
JOLLY, J.
  1901. Medicin. *In:* G. BÜHLER, Grundriss der Indo-Arischen Philologie und Altertumskunde, v. 3 (10). K. J. Trübner, Strassburg.
JOLLY, P.
  1892. Nekrolog Theodor Meynert. Arch. f. Psychiat., v. 24, p. iii.

JOLY, C. J., & WATERHOUSE, J.
  1932. Article: Camera obscura, Encyclopaedia Britannica, 14th ed., v. 4, p. 658.
JONES, F. WOOD
  1918. The problem of man's ancestry. Society for the Promotion of Christian Knowledge, London.
  1919. The general anatomy of *Tarsius*. Proc. Zoöl. Soc. London, p. 491.
  1926. Arboreal man. E. Arnold & Co., London.
  1929. Man's place among the mammals. E. Arnold & Co., London.
  1942. The principles of anatomy as seen in the hand. Williams & Wilkins Co., Baltimore.
  1953. Trends of life. E. Arnold & Co., London.
JONES, H. S.
  1908. The Roman Empire, B.C. 29—A.D. 476. G. P. Putnam's Sons, New York.
JONES, L. A., & HIGGINS, G. C.
  1947. Photographic granularity and graininess. III. Some characteristics of the visual system of importance in the evaluation of graininess and granularity. J. Opt. Soc. Amer., v. 37, p. 217.
JONES, T. W.
  1833. Notice relative to the pigmentum nigrum of the eye. Edinburgh M. & Surg. J., v. 40, p. 77.
JOOS, G.
  1931. Wiederholungen des Michelson-Versuchs. Naturwiss., v. 19, p. 784.
JORDAN, D. S., EVERMANN, B. W., & CLARK, H. W.
  1930. Check list of the fishes and fishlike vertebrates of North and Middle America north of the northern boundary of Venezuela and Colombia. Rep. U.S. Comm. Fish., 1928.
JORDAN, H.
  1934. Gehirn und Seele. Sudhoff's Arch. f. Gesch. d. Med. u. Nat., v. 27, p. 250.
JOSEFSON, A.
  1915. Gesichtsfeldstörungen bei den Hypophysistumoren, mit besonderer Rücksicht auf die bitemporale Hemianopsie. Klin. Monatsbl. f. Augenh., v. 55, p. 636.
JOSEPH, H.
  1904. Ueber eigentümliche Zellstrukturen im Zentralnervensystem von Amphioxus. Anat. Anz., suppl., v. 25, p. 16.
  1928. Morphologisch-physiologische Anmerkungen über Amphioxus. Biol. gen., v. 4, p. 237.
JOSEPHSON, G. S.
  1911. The John Crerar Library. A list of books on the history of science. With supplements 1917 and 1942. Chicago.

JOSSERAND
1902. Cécité corticale. Absence de réaction pupillaire. Recueil d'opht., ser. 3, v. 24, pp. 385, 457.

JOUKOWSKY
1901. Contribution à l'étude de l'anatomie pathologique de l'hémianopsie d'origine intracérébrale. Nouv. Iconog. Salpêtr., v. 14, p. 1.

JOURDAIN, A.
1843. Recherches critiques sur l'âge et l'origine des traductions latins d'Aristote et sur des commentaires grecs ou arabes employés par les docteurs scholastiques. New ed. Joubert, Paris. Earlier ed., 1819.

JOY, H. H.
1947. Agnostic alexia without agraphia, following trauma; report of a case. Tr. Am. Ophth. Soc., v. 45, p. 292.
1948. Agnostic alexia without agraphia following trauma. Am. J. Ophth., ser. 3, v. 31, p. 811.
1949. Agnostic alexia without agraphia following trauma; report of a case. Arch. Ophth., ser. 2, v. 41, p. 514.

JUBA, A.
1933. Ueber das Projektionsfeld des zentralen Sehens im äusseren Kniehöcker und in der Sehrinde des Menschen. Ztschr. f. d. ges. Neurol. u. Psychiat., v. 147, p. 121; *also in* Hirnpath. Beitr., ed. SCHAFFER & MISKOLCZY, v. 13.
1934. Die korticale Doppelvertretung der Makula und die Projektion der Sehrinde auf den äusseren Kniehöcker des Menschen. Klin. Monatsbl. f. Augenh., v. 93, p. 595.
1935. Zur Lokalisation der Maculafaserung innerhalb der Sehstrahlung. Ztschr. f. d. ges. Neurol. u. Psychiat., v. 154, p. 123.
1936. Ueber vollständigen Balkenmangel bei einem 39-jährigen geistig normalen Menschen. *Ibid.*, v. 156, p. 45.
1939. Die optischen Verbindungen der oberen Vierhügelgegend. *Ibid.*, v. 164, p. 273.
1944. Der Makula-Anteil der Sehstrahlung. (Ueber die Lagerung der Makulafasern in der Sehstrahlung und über die kortikale Doppelvertretung des centralen Sehens.) Schweiz. Arch. f. Neurol. u. Psychiat., v. 54, p. 142.

JUBA, A., & SZATMÁRI, A.
1937. Ueber seltene hirnanatomische Befunde in Fällen von einseitiger peripherer Blindheit. Klin. Monatsbl. f. Augenh., v. 99, p. 173.

JUDD, D. B.
1929. Least retinal illumination by spectral light required to evoke the "blue arcs of the retina." J. Opt. Soc. Amer., v. 18, p. 172.
1945. Standard response functions for protanopic and deuteranopic vision. *Ibid.*, v. 35, p. 199.
1952. Color in business, science, and industry. John Wiley & Sons, New York.

JUNG, J.
1928. Zur Diagnose der Erkrankungen des Chiasma. Klin. Monatsbl. f. Augenh., v. 81, p. 577.

JUNG, R.
1939. Epilepsie und vasomotorische Reaktionen. Zentralbl. f. d. ges. Neurol. u. Psychiat., v. 94, p. 360.

JURINE, LOUIS
1798. Experiments on bats deprived of sight. Phil. Mag., v. 1, p. 136; originally in J. de phys.

JUST, E. E.
1931. Die Rolle des kortikalen Cytoplasmas bei vitalen Erscheinungen. Naturwiss., v. 19, pp. 953, 980, 998.

JUST, G.
1925. Zur Vererbung der Farbensinnstufen beim Menschen. Arch. f. Augenh., v. 96, p. 406.

K

KABAT, H., & SCHADEWALD, M.
1941. The relative susceptibility of the synaptic terminals and of the perikaryon to arrest of the circulation of the brain. Am. J. Path., v. 17, p. 833.

KAES, T.
1893. Beiträge zur Kenntniss des Reichtums der Grosshirnrinde des Menschen an markhaltigen Nervenfasern. Arch. f. Psychiat., v. 25, p. 695.
1907. Die Grosshirnrinde des Menschen in ihren Massen und in ihrem Fasergehalt. G. Fischer, Jena.

KAFKA, G.
1914. Einführung in die Tierpsychologie auf experimenteller und ethologischer Grundlage. J. A. Barth, Leipzig.

KAHLER, H.
1922. Ueber vasomotorische Störungen bei zerebralen Hemiplegien. Zugleich ein Beitrag zur Lokalisation des Vasomotorenzentrums beim Menschen. Wien. klin. Wchnschr., v. 35, p. 219.

KAHLMETER, G.
1916. Drei Fälle von Tabes bzw. progressive Paralyse vortäuschendem Hypophysentumor. Deutsch. Ztschr. f. Nervenh., v. 54, p. 173.

KAHMANN, H.

1930. Untersuchungen über die Linse, die Zonula ciliaris, Refraktion und Akommodation von Säugetieren. Zool. Jahrb. (Allg. Zool. u. Physiol.), v. 48, p. 509.

1931. Notizen zur Sinnesbiologie der Säugetiere. Zool. Garten, N.F., v. 4, p. 27.

1933. Zur Kenntnis der Netzhaut der Reptilien. Zool. Anz., v. 102, p. 117.

1934. Ueber das Vorkommen einer Fovea centralis im Knochenfischauge. *Ibid.*, v. 106, p. 40.

1934. Zur Biologie des Gesichtssinns der Reptilien. *Ibid.*, v. 108, p. 311.

1935. Zum fovealen Sehen der Wirbeltiere. Sitzungsb. d. Gesellsch. naturforsch. Freunde, Berlin, Nos. 8–10, p. 290.

1935. Ueber das foveale Sehen der Wirbeltiere. II. Gesichtsfeld und Fovea centralis. *Ibid.*, p. 361.

1936. Über das foveale Sehen der Wirbeltiere. I. Über die Fovea centralis und die Fovea lateralis bei einigen Wirbeltieren. Arch. f. Ophth. (Graefe), v. 135, p. 265.

KAHN, F.

1926–31. Das Leben des Menschen. 5 vols. Franckh., Stuttgart.

KAJIKAWA, J.

1923. Beiträge zur Anatomie des Vogelauges. Arch. f. Ophth. (Graefe), v. 112, p. 260.

KAKESHITA, T.

1925. Zur Anatomie der operkularen Temporalregion. (Vergleichende Untersuchungen der rechten und linken Seite.) Arb. a. d. Neurol. Inst. Wien, v. 27, p. 292.

KALBERLAH

1903. Ueber die Augenregion und die vordere Grenze der Sehsphäre Munk's. Arch. f. Psychiat., v. 37, p. 1014.

KALISCHER, O.

1909. Weitere Mitteilungen über die Ergebnisse der Dressur als physiologischer Untersuchungsmethode auf dem Gebiete des Gehör-, Geruchs- und Farbensinnes. Arch. f. Anat. u. Physiol. (Physiol. Abt.), p. 303. Abstr. in Neurol. Centralbl., v. 29, p. 129.

KALLAY, J.

1951. Healed tooth fractures in a Krapina Neanderthal. Am. J. Phys. Anthropol., N.S., v. 9, p. 369.

KALLIUS, E.

1894. Untersuchungen über die Netzhaut der Säugetiere. Anat. Hefte (Merkel & Bonnet), v. 3, p. 526.

1897. Bemerkung zu einer Arbeit über die Retina von Ramón y Cajal. Anat. Anz., v. 13, p. 151.

1898. Ueber die Fovea centralis von *Hatteria punctata*. *Ibid.*, v. 14, p. 623.

1898–1905. Sehorgan. Anat. Hefte (Merkel & Bonnet), Ergebn., v. 7, p. 286; v. 8, p. 272; v. 10, p. 367; v. 12, p. 419; v. 13, p. 253; v. 14, p. 234.

KAMĀL AL-DĪN ABŪ AL-ḤASSAN AL-FĀRISĪ

1316. Tanqīḥ al-Manāẓir li-Ḍawī al-Abṣār wa al-Baṣā'ir, or Making optics understandable for those who possess perspicacity and insight. Manuscripts in Ayasofya Library, Istanbul, Turkey; at Rampur and Bankipore, India; University Library, Leyden, Holland; British Museum, London. Modern ed. in 2 vols. Haidarabad, India, 1928–30.

KAMMERER, P.

1925. The inheritance of acquired characteristics. Boni & Liveright, New York.

KANDINSKY, V.

1881. Zur Lehre von den Hallucinationen. Arch. f. Psychiat. u. Nervenkr., v. 11, p. 453.

KANT, IMMANUEL

1796. Letter to S. T. Soemmerring. *In:* T. SOEMMERING, Ueber das Organ der Seele, p. 81. F. Nicolovius, Königsberg.

1878. Kritik der reinen Vernunft. Text der Ausgabe 1781 mit Beifügung sämmtlicher Abweichungen der Ausgabe 1787. Herausgeben von Dr. KARL KEHRBACH. Zweite verbesserte Auflage. Ph. Reclam jun., Leipzig. (*See also* J. von Kries, Naturwiss., v. 12, p. 318, 1924.)

KANZER, M., & BENDER, M. B.

1939. Spatial disorientation with homonymous defects of the visual field. Arch. Ophth., v. 21, p. 439.

KAPLAN, H. A., RABINER, A. M., & BROWDER, J.

1953–54. Anatomical study of the arteries of the midbrain, pons, and medulla. The perforating arteries of the base of the forebrain. Tr. Am. Neurol. A., 78th meet., p. 54, and 79th meet., p. 38.

KAPUŚCIŃSKI, W.

1948. On symptoms of the pulse in the central retinal artery. Brit. J. Ophth., v. 32, p. 881.

KARNOSH, L. J., & GARDNER, W. J.

1941. An evaluation of the physical and mental capabilities following removal of the right cerebral hemisphere. Cleveland Clin. Quart., v. 8, p. 94.

KARPE, G.

1945. The basis of clinical electroretinography. Acta ophth., suppl. 24.

KARPLUS, J. P.

1902. Ueber ein Australiergehirn, nebst Bemerkungen über einige Negergehirne. Arb. a. d. neurol. Inst. Wien, v. 9, p. 118.

1937. Die Physiologie der vegetativen Zentren. (Auf Grund experimenteller Erfahrungen.) *In:* BUMKE & FOERSTER, Handb. d. Neurol., v. 2, p. 402.

KARPLUS, J. P., & KREIDL, A.

1909-11. Gehirn und Sympathicus I. Zwischenhirnbasis und Halssympathicus. Arch. f. d. ges. Physiol. (Pflüger), v. 129, p. 138. II. Ein Sympathicuszentrum im Zwischenhirn. *Ibid.*, v. 135, p. 401. III. Sympathicusleitung im Gehirn und Halsmark. *Ibid.*, v. 143, p. 109. *See also* v. 171, p. 192, and v. 203, p. 533.

1912. Ueber die Pupillarreflexbahn. Klin. Monatsbl. f. Augenh., v. 50 (1), p. 586.

1912. Affen ohne Grosshirn. Wien. klin. Wchnschr., v. 25, p. 107.

1913. Ueber die Bahn des Pupillarreflexes (die reflektorische Pupillenstarre). Arch. f. d. ges. Physiol. (Pflüger), v. 149, p. 115.

1913. Ueber experimentelle reflektorische Pupillenstarre. Neurol. Centralbl., v. 32, p. 82.

1914. Ueber Totalexstirpation einer und beider Grosshirnhemisphären an Affen. Arch. f. Physiol., p. 155.

KARSTEN, H.

1923. Das Auge von *Periophthalmus koelreuteri*. Jena. Ztschr. f. Naturwiss., v. 59, p. 115.

KASDON, S.

1938. Localization of function in the posterior parietal lobe of the chimpanzee: an experimental study by the discrimination method. M.D. thesis, Yale University (unpub.).

KASSEL, K.

1911. Galens Lehre von der Stimme. Ztschr. f. Laryng., Rhin. u. ihre Grenzgeb., v. 4, p. 243.

KATO, K.

1934. Zur biologischen Bedeutung der Kreuzung der Leitungsbahnen im Zentralnervensystem. Folia anat. japon., v. 12, p. 319.

KATZ, D.

1935. The world of colour. Paul, Trench, Trubner & Co., London.

KATZ, D., & RÉVÉSZ, G.

1921. Experimentelle Studien zur vergleichenden Psychologie. Versuche mit Hühnern. Ztschr. f. angew. Psychol., v. 18, p. 307.

KATZ, O.

1890. Die Augenheilkunde des Galenus. Erster (theoretischer) Theil. Ueber Anatomie und Physiologie des Sehorgans. Inaug.-Diss. Berlin. Buchdruckerei von Gustav Schade (Otto Francke), Berlin.

KATZENSTEIN, E.

1931. Veränderungen der Pupillenform bei Commotio et Contusio cerebri. Schweiz. Arch. f. Neurol. u. Psychiat., v. 27, p. 286.

1932. Kasuistischer Beitrag zur Frage der juvenilen Gefässerkrankungen im Gehirn unter besonderer Berücksichtigung der Verhältnisse in den Plexus chorioidei; nebst einigen Bemerkungen zur Anatomie der zentralen optischen Bahnen. *Ibid.*, v. 28, p. 237.

1953. Zentenarfeier für Constantin von Monakow. Neue Zürcher Zeitung, Dezember, No. 2996, Blatt 3.

KAUDERS, O.

1929. Ueber polyglotte Reaktionen bei einer sensorischen Aphasie. Ztschr. f. d. ges. Neurol. u. Psychiat., v. 122, p. 651.

1937. Ein Fall von isolierter sensorischer Amusie und partieller Geräuschagnosie. Jahrb. f. Psychiat., v. 54, p. 119.

KAVIRATNA, AVINASH CHANDRA, & KAVIBHUSHANA, PARESHNATH SARMA

1890-1911. Charaka-Saṁhitā. Calcutta.

KAWATA, A.

1927. Zur Myeloarchitektonik der menschlichen Hirnrinde. Arb. a. d. Neurol. Inst. Wien, v. 29, p. 191.

KEDROVSKIY, B. V.

1935. O reálynosti fibrilyárnych struktúr v zhivóy nyérvnoy klyétke (On the reality of fibrillar structures in the living nerve cell). Biol. Zhur., v. 4, p. 825 (in Russian).

KEEGAN, J. J.

1916. A study of a plains Indian brain. J. Comp. Neurol., v. 26, p. 403.

KEELER, C. E.

1930. A histological basis to explain constant differences in action-current response from certain points on the retina of the horned toad, *Phrynosoma cornutum*. J. Morphol. & Physiol., v. 50, p. 193.

KEEN, W. W.

1874. A sketch of the early history of practical anatomy. J. B. Lippincott & Co., Philadelphia.

KEEN, W. W., & THOMSON, W.

1871. Gunshot-wound of the brain, followed by fungus cerebri, and recovery with hemiopsia. Tr. Am. Ophth. Soc., 8th meet., p. 122.

KEHRER, F.

1913. Beiträge zur Aphasielehre mit besonderer

Berücksichtigung der amnestischen Aphasie. Arch. f. Psychiat., v. 52, p. 103.

KEIBEL, F.
1906. Die Entwicklungsgeschichte des Wirbeltierauges. Klin. Monatsbl. f. Augenh., v. 44, p. 112.
1928. Beiträge zur Anatomie, zur Entwicklungsgeschichte und zur Stammesgeschichte der Sehorgane der Cyclostomen. Jahrb. f. Morphol. u. mikr. Anat., Abt. 2, v. 12, p. 391.

KEIL, F. L.
1950. The origin of flightless birds. Thesis, University of Chicago.

KEILLER, W.
1927. Nerve tracts of the brain and cord. Macmillan Co., New York.

KEITH, A.
1929. The antiquity of man. 2 vols. Williams & Norgate, London.
1931. New discoveries relating to the antiquity of man. Williams & Norgate, London.
1932. Article: Man, evolution of, Encyclopaedia Britannica, 14th ed., v. 14, p. 758.
1939. A resurvey of the anatomical features of the Piltdown skull with some observations on the recently discovered Swanscombe skull. J. Anat., v. 73, pp. 155, 234.
1946. Essays on human evolution. Watts & Co., London.
1947. Australopithecinae or Dartians. Nature, v. 159, p. 377.
1949. A new theory of human evolution. Philosophical Library, New York.

KEKCHEYEV, K.
1944. Problem of night vision. Am. Rev. Soviet Med., v. 1, p. 300. (Cited and abstr. in Arch. Ophth., ser. 2, v. 38, p. 282, 1947.)

KELLER, A. D., & STEWART, L.
1932. The superior colliculus and the pupillary light reflex in the cat. Am. J. Physiol., v. 101, p. 64.

KELLER, C. J.
1939. Die Regelung der Blutversorgung des Gehirnes. Zentralbl. f. d. ges. Neurol. u. Psychiat., v. 94, p. 346.

KELLER, H. A.
1908. The world I live in. Century Co., New York. Another ed., 1920.

KELLERMANN, M.
1879. Anatomische Untersuchungen atrophischer Sehnerven, mit einem Beitrag zur Frage der Sehnervenkreuzung im Chiasma. F. Enke, Stuttgart. Also in Klin. Monatsbl. f. Augenh., v. 17.

KELLOGG, W. N., & KOHLER, R.
1952. Reactions of the porpoise to ultrasonic frequencies. Science, v. 116, p. 250.

KEMPNER, W.
1949. Treatment of heart and kidney disease and of hypertensive and arteriosclerotic vascular disease with the rice diet. Ann. Int. Med., v. 31, p. 821.
1951. Hypertension—wound stripe of our civilization (an unsigned article). Ed. Focus, v. 22, No. 2.

KEMPNER, W., PESCHEL, E., & STARKE, H.
1949. Rice diet in malignant hypertension. Am. Pract., v. 3, p. 556.

KENDALL, D.
1948. Thrombosis of intracranial veins. Brain, v. 71, p. 386.

KENDALL, W. C.
1917. The pikes; their geographical distribution, habits, culture, and commercial importance. (U.S. Bureau of Fisheries, Doc. 853.) Government Printing Office, Washington, D.C.

KENNEDY, F.
1911. The symptomatology of temporosphenoidal tumors. Arch. Int. Med., v. 8, p. 317.

KENNEDY, F., WORTIS, S. B., & WORTIS, H.
1938. The clinical evidence for cerebral vasomotor changes. Research Pub. A. Research Nerv. & Ment. Dis., v. 18, p. 670. Williams & Wilkins Co., Baltimore.

KENNEL, J. VON
1891. Die Ableitung der Vertebratenaugen von den Augen der Anneliden. Dorpat. Schnakenburgs Buchdruckerei.

KENNICOTT, R.
1857–59. The quadrupeds of Illinois, injurious and beneficial to the farmer. Rep. Comm. Pat., Agriculture for 1856–58. Washington.

KENYON, F. C.
1896. The brain of the bee. J. Comp. Neurol., v. 6, p. 133.

KEPLER, J. (*see also* PLEHN 1921; EDDINGTON, JASCHNOFF, KOPFF, and ROHR in Naturwiss., v. 18, pp. 941, 946, 949, 1930)
1604. Ad Vitellionem Paralipomena, quibus Astronomiae pars optica traditur, etc. Francofurti, ap. Cl. Marnium & Haer. J. Aubrii. New ed. by F. HAMMER, in Gesammelte Werke, ed. W. DYCK and M. CASPAR; C. H. Beck'sche Verlagsbuchhandlung, München, 1939. Part trans. by F. PLEHN, ed. M. VON ROHR: Grundlagen d. geom. Optik etc. (Ostwalds "Klassiker d. exakt. Wissensch.,"

No. 198.) Akad. Verlagsgesellschaft, Leipzig, 1922.

1609. Neue Astronomie (*Astronomia nova*), übersetzt und eingeleitet von Max Caspar, etc. R. Oldenbourg, München-Berlin 1929.

1611. Dioptrice seu demonstratio eorum quae visui & visibilibus propter conspicilla non ita pridem inventa accidunt. Etc. Augustae Vindelicorum (Augsburg), typ. D. Franci. Trans. by F. Plehn. Dioptrik oder Schilderung der Folgen, die sich aus der unlängst gemachten Erfindung der Fernrohre für das Sehen und die sichtbaren Gegenstände ergeben. (Ostwalds "Klassiker d. exakt. Wissensch.," No. 144.) W. Engelmann, Leipzig, 1904. (*See also* Rohr, Naturwiss., v. 18, p. 941.)

*1858–71. Joannis Kepleri astronomi Opera omnia. Ed. Dr. C. Frisch. 8 vols. Heyder & Zimmer, Francofurti a.M. & Erlangae.

1920–21. J. Keplers Behandlung des Sehens, by F. Plehn. Ztschr. f. ophth. Optik, v. 8, p. 154; v. 9, pp. 13, 14, 73, 103, 143, 177.

*1937—— Gesammelte Werke, ed. W. v. Dyck and M. Caspar. C. H. Beck'sche Verlagsbuchhandlung, München. (So far, 3 vols.)

Kepner, W. A., & Foshee, A. M.
1917. The effect of light and dark upon the eye of *Prorhynchus applanatus* Kennel. Anat. Rec., v. 11, p. 523.

Kern, H. M., & Straus, W. L.
1949. The femur of *Plesianthropus*. Am. J. Phys. Anthropol., v. 7, p. 53.

Kerr, J. G.
1924. An experiment in binocular vision. Tr. Ophth. Soc. United Kingdom, v. 44, p. 183.

1932. Archaic fishes—*Lepidosiren*, *Protopterus*, *Polypterus*—and their bearing upon problems of vertebrate morphology. Jena. Ztschr. f. Naturwiss., v. 67, p. 419.

Kerschner, C. M.
1943. Blood supply of the visual pathway. Meador Pub. Co., Boston.

Keschner, M., Bender, M. B., & Strauss, I.
1936. Mental symptoms in cases of tumor of the temporal lobe. Arch. Neurol. & Psychiat., v. 35, p. 572.

Kessler, L.
1871. Untersuchungen über die Entwickelung des Auges, angestellt am Hühnchen und Triton. H. Laakman, Dorpat.

1877. Zur Entwickelung des Auges der Wirbelthiere. F. C. W. Vogel, Leipzig.

Kessler, M., & Kennard, M. A.
1940. Studies of motor performance after parietal

ablation in monkeys. J. Neurophysiol., v. 3, p. 248.

Kestenbaum, A.
1927. Monokuläre und binokuläre Sehschärfe. Ztschr. f. Augenh., v. 63, p. 159.

1932. Zur topischen Diagnostik der Hemianopsie. *Ibid.*, v. 76, p. 241.

1946. Clinical methods of neuro-ophthalmologic examination. Grune & Stratton, New York.

Ketham, Joannes de
1925. The Fasciculo di medicina, Venice 1493, with an introduction by C. Singer. 2 parts. ("Monumenta medica," v. 2.) R. Lier & Co., Florence.

Key, A., & Retzius, G.
1875. Studien in der Anatomie des Nervensystems und des Bindegewebes, v. 1, p. 188 (Die Scheiden und die Scheidenräume des Opticus, etc.); p. 194 (Der innere Bau und die Saftbahnen des Opticus). Stockholm.

Khairallah, A. A.
1946. Outline of Arabic contributions to medicine and the allied sciences. Beirut.

Kiesow, F.
1922. Ueber bilaterale Mischung von Licht- und Geruchsempfindungen. Arch. néerl. de physiol., v. 7, p. 281.

Kikai, K.
1930. Ueber die Vitalfärbung des hinteren Bulbusabschnittes. Arch. f. Augenh., v. 103, p. 541.

Kilham, L.
1951. Mother and young of *Sorex cinereus fontenalis* in captivity. J. Mammal., v. 32, p. 115.

Kilian, H. F.
1828. Die Universitäten Deutschlands in medicinisch-naturwissenschaftlicher Hinsicht betrachtet von Dr. H. F. Kilian. Mit dem Bildnisse des Herrn Geheimraths, Ritter von Sömmerring. Neue akademische Buchhandlung von Karl Groos, Heidelberg & Leipzig.

Kindahl, M.
1944. On the development of the hand and the foot of *Tarsius tarsius* and *Microcebus myoxinus*. Acta zool., v. 25, p. 49.

King, A. B., & Walsh, F. B.
1949. Trauma to the head with particular reference to the ocular signs. I. Injuries involving the cranial nerves. II. Continuation. Am. J. Ophth., ser. 3, v. 32, pp. 191, 379.

Kinnaman, A. J.
1902. Mental life of two *Macacus rhesus* monkeys in captivity. Am. J. Psychol., v. 13, pp. 98, 173.

KINOSITA, S.
1942–44. Zur Oberflächenanatomie der Grosshirnhcmisphäre des Macacus rhesus. Fol. anat. japon., v. 22, p. 699.

KINSEY, V. E.
1948. Spectral transmission of the eye to ultraviolet radiations. Arch. Ophth., v. 39, p. 508.

KINSEY, V. E., & GRANT, W. M.
1944. The secretion diffusion theory of intraocular fluid dynamics. Brit. J. Ophth., v. 28, p. 355.

KIPP, F.
1939. Das Auftreten der Gegenfarben in der Natur in seiner Bedeutung für das Verständnis des Wahrnehmungsvorganges. Ztschr. f. d. ges. Naturwiss., v. 5, p. 227.

KIRBY, D. B.
1932. The anterior vitreous in health and in disease. Arch. Ophth., v. 7, p. 241.
1941. Procedures in intracapsular cataract extraction: a new method. Tr. Am. Ophth. Soc., v. 39, p. 115.

KIRCHER, A.
1646. Ars Magna Lucis et Umbrae, etc. Romae, sumpt. H. Scheus. Ex typogr. L. Grignani.

KISS, F.
1947. The blood-vascular system of the eyeball. J. Anat., v. 81, p. 378. (Abstr.)

KITTO, H. D. F.
1951. The Greeks. A study of the character and history of an ancient civilization, and of the people who created it. Penguin Books, Hardmondsworth, Middlesex.

KLAATSCH, H. A. L.
1910. Menschenrassen und Menschenaffen. Korrespondenzbl. Deutsch. Gesellsch. f. Anthropol., v. 41, p. 91.
1911. Die Stellung des Menschen im Naturganzen. *In:* O. ABEL *et al.*, Die Abstammungslehre; zwölf gemeinverständliche Vorträge über die Deszendenztheorie, etc. G. Fischer, Jena.
1912. Die Entstehung und Erwerbung der Menschenmerkmale. 2. Der Menschenfuss und der aufrechte Gang. Fortschr. d. naturwiss. Forsch. (Abderhalden), p. 210.
1913. Die Einwirkung der aufrechten Körperhaltung und ihre Folgen für den menschlichen Organismus. Jahres-Ber. Schlesisch. Gesellsch. f. vaterländ. Cult., v. 91 (2), Abt. I, p. 6.
1913. Die Erwerbung der aufrechten Haltung und ihre Folgen. Anat. Anz. (Verhandl. d. anat. Gesellsch.), v. 44, p. 161.

KLAAUW (*see* VAN DER KLAAUW)

KLARFELD, B.
1925. Der heutige Stand der Neuronlehre. Klin. Wchnschr., v. 4 (2), p. 2481.

KLEESATTEL, C.
1952. Zur Ultraschall-Orientierung der Fledermäuse. Naturwiss., v. 39, p. 574.

KLEIJN, A. DE
1912. Ueber die ophthalmologischen Erscheinungen bei Hypophysistumoren und ihre Variabilität. Arch. f. Ophth. (Graefe), v. 80, p. 307.

KLEIN, E.
1914. Brillenmacher im Mittelalter und ihre Erzeugnisse. Central-Zeitung f. Optik u. Mechanik, v. 35, pp. 363, 372.

KLEIN, R.
1926. Ueber einen Fall von gerichteter optischer Halluzination mit Fusionsstörungen des halluzinierten Raumes. Ztschr. f. d. ges. Neurol. u. Psychiat., v. 104, p. 449.
1928. Ueber frontale Störungen des Gehens und des Gesanges. Monatsschr. f. Psychiat. u. Neurol., v. 69, p. 12.
1929. Denkinhalt und Aphasie. Ztschr. f. d. ges. Neurol. u. Psychiat., v. 121, p. 36.
1930. Ueber die Empfindung der Körperlichkeit. *Ibid.*, v. 126, p. 453.

KLEINT, H.
1937. Versuche über die Wahrnehmung. Ztschr. f. Psychol., v. 141, p. 9.

KLEISS, E.
1944–45. Die Arteria cerebralis anterior. Anat. Anz., v. 95, p. 353.

KLEIST, K.
1906. Ueber Apraxie. Monatsschr. f. Psychiat. u. Neurol., v. 19, p. 269.
1906. Fragestellungen in der allgemeinen Psychopathologie. Arch. f. Psychiat., v. 41, p. 770.
1912. Der Gang und der gegenwärtige Stand der Apraxieforschung. Ergebn. d. Neurol. u. Psychiat., v. 1, p. 343.
1918–19. Die Hirnverletzungen in ihrer Bedeutung für die Lokalisation der Hirnfunktionen. Allg. Ztschr. f. Psychiat., v. 74, p. 542; Neurol. Centralbl., v. 37, p. 414.
1924. Ueber die gegenwärtigen Strömungen in der klinischen Psychiatrie. Ztschr. f. d. ges. Neurol. u. Psychiat., v. 40, p. 114.
1926. Die einzeläugigen Gesichtsfelder und ihre Vertretung in den beiden Lagen der verdoppelten inneren Körnerschicht der Sehrinde. Klin. Wchnschr., v. 5 (1), p. 3.
1926. Gehirnpathologische und gehirnlokalisatorische Ergebnisse, vornehmlich auf Grund

von Kriegshirnverletzungen. Sbornik posvyas. V. M. Bechterevu, p. 201. Izdan. Gossud. Psichonevrol. Akad. etc., Leningrad. (Anniversary vol. for Bechterev.)

1927. Gegenhalten (motorischer Negativismus), Zwangsgreifen und Thalamus opticus. Monatsschr. f. Psychiat. u. Neurol., v. 65, p. 317.

1928. Gehirnpathologische und lokalisatorische Ergebnisse über Hörstörungen, Geräuschtaubheiten und Amusien. *Ibid.*, v. 68, p. 853.

1928. Ueber sensorische Aphasien. J. f. Psychol. u. Neurol., v. 37, p. 146.

1929. Schlafstörungen bei Herderkrankungen des Gehirns. Zentralbl. f. d. ges. Neurol. u. Psychiat., v. 51, p. 235.

1929. Gehirnpathologische und lokalisatorische Ergebnisse. 3. Mitt. Ueber sensorische Aphasien. J. f. Psychol. u. Neurol., v. 37, p. 146.

1930. Zur hirnpathologischen Auffassung der schizophrenen Grundstörungen: die alogische Denkstörung. Arch. f. Psychiat. u. Nervenkr., v. 90, p. 850; Zentralbl. f. d. ges. Neurol. u. Psychiat., v. 56, p. 457.

1930. Gehirnpathologische und lokalisatorische Ergebnisse. 4. Mitt. Ueber motorische Aphasien. J. f. Psychol. u. Neurol., v. 40, p. 338.

1931. Gehirnpathologische und lokalisatorische Ergebnisse. V. Mitt. Das Stirnhirn im engeren Sinne und seine Störungen. Ztschr. f. d. ges. Neurol. u. Psychiat., v. 131, p. 442.

1934. Kriegsverletzungen des Gehirns in ihrer Bedeutung für die Hirnlokalisation und Hirnpathologie. *In:* O. von SCHJERNING, Handb. d. aerztl. Erfahrungen im Weltkriege 1914–18 (vol. 4, Part 2, p. 343 *in:* Geistes- und Nervenkrankheiten, ed. K. BONHOEFFER), J. A. Barth, Leipzig, 1922–34.

1934. Gehirnpathologie vornehmlich auf Grund der Kriegserfahrungen. *In:* O. von SCHJERNING, Handb. d. aerztl. Erfahrungen im Weltkriege 1914–18, v. 4 (2), p. 343. J. A. Barth, Leipzig.

KLEMPIN, I.

1921. Ueber die Architektonik der Grosshirnrinde des Hundes. J. f. Psychol. u. Neurol., v. 26, p. 229.

KLEYN (*see* KLEIJN)

KLIENEBERGER, O.

1916. Ueber Schädelschüsse. Deutsch. med. Wchnschr., v. 42, p. 309.

KLINCKOWSTRÖM, A.

1894. Beiträge zur Kenntniss des Parietalauges. Zool. Jahrb. (Anat. & Ontog.), v. 7, p. 249.

1895. Beiträge zur Kenntniss der Augen von *Anableps tetrophthalmus*. Skandinav. Arch. f. Physiol., v. 5, p. 67.

KLOSE, R.

1920. Das Gehirn eines Wunderkindes (des Pianisten Gosevin Sökeland). Ein Beitrag zur Lokalisation des musikalischen Talentes im Gehirn. Monatsschr. f. Psychiat. u. Neurol., v. 48, p. 63. (*See also* Henschen, J. f. Psychol. u. Neurol., v. 22, Ergh. 3, 1918.)

KLOSS, C. B.

1903. In the Andamans and Nicobars. The narrative of a cruise in the schooner "Terrapin," with notices of the islands, their fauna, ethnology, etc. J. Murray, London.

1911. On a collection of mammals and other vertebrates from the Trenggann Archipelago. J. Fed. Malay States Mus., v. 4, p. 175.

KLOSSOWSKI, B.

1930. Ueber die intertraktalen Fasern und die Leitungssysteme des Bodens des 3. Ventrikels. Arch. f. Psychiat. u. Nervenkr., v. 91, p. 37.

KLÜVER, H.

1926. An experimental study of the eidetic type. Genet. Psychol. Monog., v. 1, p. 71.

1926. Mescal visions and eidetic vision. Am. J. Psychol., v. 37, p. 502.

1927. Visual disturbances after cerebral lesions. Psychol. Bull., v. 24, p. 316.

1928. Mescal. Kegan Paul, Trench, Trubner & Co., London.

1930. Fragmentary eidetic imagery. Psychol. Rev., v. 37, p. 441.

1931. The equivalence of stimuli in the behavior of monkeys. J. Genet. Psychol., v. 39, p. 3.

1931. Zur Psychologie der Veränderungsauffassung bei niederen Affen. Ztschr. f. angew. Psychol., Beiheft 59, p. 132.

1931–33. The eidetic child. *In:* CARL MURCHISON, Handbook of child psychology, p. 643. Clark University Press, Worcester, Mass.; entitled: Eidetic imagery, in 2d ed., p. 699.

1933. Behavior mechanisms in monkeys. University of Chicago Press, Chicago.

1933. The eidetic type. Research Pub. A. Research Nerv. & Ment. Dis., v. 14, p. 150.

1935. A tachistoscopic device for work with subhuman primates. J. Psychol., v. 1, p. 1.

1935. Use of vacuum tube amplification in establishing differential motor reactions. *Ibid.*, p. 45.

1935. An auto-multi-stimulation reaction board for use with sub-human primates. *Ibid.*, p. 123.

1936. An analysis of the effects of the removal of the occipital lobes in monkeys. *Ibid.*, v. 2, p. 49.

1937. Re-examination of implement-using behavior in a cebus monkey after an interval of three years. Acta psychol., v. 2, p. 347.

1937. Certain effects of lesions of the occipital lobes in macaques. J. Psychol., v. 4, p. 383.

1941. Visual functions after removal of the occipital lobes. *Ibid.*, v. 11, p. 23.

1942. Functional significance of the geniculo-striate system. Biol. Symp., v. 7, p. 253.

1942. Mechanisms of hallucinations. *In:* Studies in personality, p. 175. McGraw-Hill Book Co., New York.

1951. Functional differences between the occipital and temporal lobes with special reference to the interrelations of behavior and extra-cerebral mechanisms. *In:* L. A. JEFFRESS (ed.), Cerebral mechanisms in behavior. John Wiley & Sons, New York.

1952. Brain mechanisms and behavior with special reference to the rhinencephalon. Journal-Lancet, v. 72, p. 567.

1955. Porphyrins in relation to the development of the nervous system. *In:* H. WAELSCH (ed.), Biochemistry of the developing nervous system. Academic Press, New York.

1955. Stephen Polyak, M.D. 1889–1955. Arch. Ophth., v. 54, p. 314. (*See also* Am. J. Psychol., v. 68, p. 675; Bull. Alumni A. School M. Univ. Chicago, v. 11, No. 3, p. 3.)

1955. Stephen Polyak (1889–1955). J. Comp. Neurol., v. 103, p. 1. (For bibliography *see* pp. 6–9.)

KLÜVER, H., & BARRERA, E.

1953. A method for the combined staining of cells and fibers in the nervous system. J. Neuropath. & Exper. Neurol., v. 12, p. 400.

1954. On the use of azaporphin derivatives (phthalocyanines) in staining nervous tissue. J. Psychol., v. 37, p. 199.

KLÜVER, H., & BRUNSCHWIG, A.

1947. Oral carcinoma in a monkey colony. Cancer Research, v. 7, p. 627.

KLÜVER, H., & BUCY, P. C.

1937. "Psychic blindness" and other symptoms following bilateral temporal lobectomy in rhesus monkeys. Am. J. Physiol., v. 119, p. 352.

1938. An analysis of certain effects of bilateral temporal lobectomy in the rhesus monkey, with special reference to "psychic blindness." J. Psychol., v. 5, p. 33.

1939. A preliminary analysis of the functions of the temporal lobes in monkeys. Tr. Am. Neurol. A., p. 170.

1939. Preliminary analysis of functions of the temporal lobes in monkeys. Arch. Neurol. & Psychiat., v. 42, p. 979.

KLÜVER, H., & WEIL, A.

1948. Carcinomas of the tongue in monkeys and pathologic changes in the central nervous system. J. Neuropath. & Exper. Neurol., v. 7, p. 144.

KLUGH, A. B.

1927. Ecology of the red squirrel. J. Mammal., v. 8, p. 1.

KNAPP, J. H.

1861. Ueber die Asymmetrie des Auges in seinen verschiedenen Meridianebenen. Arch. f. Ophth. (Graefe), v. 8 (2), p. 185.

KNAPPERT, L.

1914. L'église et la science au temps de Vésale. Janus, v. 19, p. 420.

KNISELY, M. H.

1951. An annotated bibliography on sludged blood. Postgrad. Med., v. 10, No. 1.

KNISELY, M. H., & BLOCH, E. H.

1948. Demonstration of the method and apparatus currently used in making microscopic studies of the circulating blood and local vessels of the bulbar conjunctiva of living unanesthetized human beings. Anat. Rec., v. 100, p. 768 (Am. A. Anat., demonstration No. 42).

KNISELY, M. H., BLOCH, E. H., & WARNER, L.

1946. Microscopic observations of living blood and vessel walls are a necessary part of the preselection of normal animals for biological experiments. Anat. Rec., v. 94, p. 550 (Am. A. Anat., demonstration No. 54).

KNOLL, F.

1921–22. Insekten und Blumen. Experimentelle Arbeiten zur Vertiefung unserer Kenntnisse über die Wechselbeziehungen zwischen Pflanzen und Tieren. Abh. d. zool.-bot. Gesellsch. Wien, v. 12. Summary in Biol. Zentralbl., v. 44, p. 399.

1924. Blütenökologie und Sinnesphysiologie der Insekten. Naturwiss., v. 12, p. 988.

1925. Lichtsinn und Blütenbesuch des Falters von *Deilephila livornica*. Ztschr. f. vergl. Physiol., v. 2, p. 329.

KNOLL, P.
1869. Beiträge zur Physiologie der Vierhügel. Beitr. z. Anat. u. Physiol., v. 4, p. 109.

KNOPF, A.
1931. The age of the earth. Bull. Nat. Research Council, No. 80, p. 3. National Academy of Sciences, Washington, D.C.

1931. Age of the ocean. *Ibid.*, p. 65. National Academy of Sciences, Washington, D.C.

1949. Time in earth history. *In:* JEPSEN, MAYR & SIMPSON, Genetics, paleontology, and evolution. Princeton University Press, Princeton, N.J.

KNOPF, A., BROWN, E. W., HOLMES, A., KOVARIK, A. F., LANE, A. C., & SCHUCHERT, C.
1931. Physics of the earth. IV. The age of the earth. Bull. Nat. Research Council, No. 80. National Academy of Sciences, Washington, D.C.

KNOX, R.
1823. On the discovery of the foramen centrale of the retina in the eyes of the reptiles. Edinburgh Phil. J., v. 9, p. 358; and Tr. Werner. Soc. Edinburgh, v. 5, p. 1.

KOBY, F. E.
1921. Hémianopsie inférieure monoculaire avec altérations rétiniennes visibles surtout à la lumière anérythre. Arch. d'opht., v. 38, p. 365.

1930. A propos de l'épaisseur de la cornée vivante. Rev. gén. d'opht., v. 44, p. 222.

KOCH, J. L. A.
1880. Ueber das Gedächtnis. Mit Bemerkungen zu dessen Pathologie. Ztschr. f. Phil., v. 78, p. 218.

KOCH, S. L.
1916. The structure of the third, fourth, fifth, sixth, ninth, eleventh, and twelfth cranial nerves. J. Comp. Neurol., v. 26, p. 541.

KODAMA, S.
1926–29. Ueber die sogenannten Basalganglien. Schweiz. Arch. f. Neurol. u. Psychiat., v. 18, p. 179; v. 19, p. 152; v. 20, p. 209; v. 23, pp. 38, 179.

KÖBCKE, H.
1936. Die Angiographie der Hirngefässe. Deutsch. med. Wchnschr., v. 62, p. 1874.

KOEHLER, O.
1923. Lichtsinn und Blumenbesuch des Taubenschwanzes (*Macroglossus stellatarum*). Naturwiss., v. 11, p. 742.

1924. Ueber das Farbensehen von *Daphnia magna* Straus. Ztschr. f. vergl. Physiol., v. 1, p. 84.

KÖHLER, W.
1917. Die Farbe der Sehdinge beim Schimpansen und beim Haushuhn. Ztschr. f. Psychol., v. 77, p. 248.

1918. Aus der Anthropoidenstation auf Teneriffa. IV. Nachweis einfacher Strukturfunktionen beim Schimpansen und beim Haushuhn. Ueber eine neue Methode zur Untersuchung des bunten Farbensystems. Abh. d. preuss. Akad. d. Wissensch., phys.-math. Kl., No. 2.

1922. Gestaltprobleme und Anfänge einer Gestalttheorie. Jahresb. ü. d. ges. Physiol. u. exper. Pharmakol., v. 3, p. 512.

1924. Bemerkungen zum Leib-Seele-Problem. Deutsch. med. Wchnschr., v. 50, p. 1269.

1924. The mentality of apes. Harcourt, Brace & Co., New York; Kegan Paul, Trench, Trubner & Co., London. Also later eds.

1947. Gestalt Psychology. H. Liveright, New York. 1st ed., 1929.

KOEHRING, V.
1950. Lecture notes on vertebrate origins. Turtox News, v. 28, p. 190.

KOELLIKER (KÖLLIKER), A.; for obituary *see* WALDEYER 1906
1851. Ueber einige an der Leiche eines Hingerichteten angestellte Versuche und Beobachtungen. Ztschr. f. wissensch. Zool., v. 3, p. 37.

1854. Mikroskopische Anatomie oder Gewebelehre des Menschen, v. 2, Part 2, pp. 605, 648. Engelmann, Leipzig. English ed.: Manual of human microscopic anatomy, pp. 725, 739. Lippincott, Philadelphia.

1861. Entwicklungsgeschichte des Menschen und der höheren Thiere. Akad. Vortr. W. Engelmann, Leipzig.

1866–67. Zur Erinnerung an Heinrich Müller. Würzburg. naturwiss. Ztschr., v. 6, p. 29.

1887. Die Untersuchungen von Golgi über den feineren Bau des zentralen Nervensystems. Anat. Anz., v. 2, p. 480.

1889–1902. Handbuch der Gewebelehre des Menschen. 3 vols. *See* v. 2, Nervensystem des Menschen und der Thiere, 1896. W. Engelmann, Leipzig.

1896. Nachweis der vollständigen Kreuzung des Opticus beim Menschen, Hund, Katze, Fuchs und Kaninchen. Anat. Anz. (Verhandl.), v. 12, p. 13. (*See also* Merkel, Mihalkovics, Retzius, Held.)

1899. Demonstration des Chiasmas von Säugern und vom Menschen. Verhandl. d. Gesellsch. deutsch. Naturforsch. u. Aerzte, v. 71, Part 2, p. 450.

1899. Ueber das Chiasma. Anat. Anz. (Verhandl.), v. 16, p. 30.

1899. Erinnerungen aus meinem Leben. W. Engelmann, Leipzig.

1899. Neue Beobachtungen zur Anatomie des Chiasma opticum. Festschr. z. Feier d. 50-jähr. Bestehens der phys.-med. Gesellsch. in Würzburg, p. 113.

1900. Gegen die Entstehung der Nerven aus Zellensträngen. Anat. Anz., v. 18, p. 511.

1902. Die Golgi-Feier in Pavia. *Ibid.*, v. 22, p. 325.

KÖLLIKER, A., & MÜLLER, H.

1852. Zur Anatomie und Physiologie der Retina. Verhandl. d. phys.-med. Gesellsch. Würzburg, v. 3, pp. 316, 336.

1853. Note sur la structure de la rétine humaine. Compt. rend. Acad. d. sc., v. 37, p. 488.

KÖLLNER, H.

1920. Der Augenhintergrund bei Allgemeinerkrankungen. J. Springer, Berlin.

1929. Die Abweichungen des Farbensinnes. *In:* BETHE *et al.*, Handb. d. norm. u. path. Physiol., v. 12 (1), p. 502.

KÖNIG, A.

1851–1901. Gesammelte Abhandlungen zur physiologischen Optik. J. A. Barth, Leipzig, 1903.

1899. Bemerkungen über angeborene totale Farbenblindheit. Ztschr. f. Psychol. u. Physiol. d. Sinnesorg., v. 20, p. 425. (*Cf.* Uhthoff 1899.)

1929. Physiologische Optik. *In:* W. WIEN, F. HARMS, & H. LENZ, Handb. d. Experimentalphysik, v. 20 (1). Akademische Verlagsgesellschaft M.B.H., Leipzig.

1937. Die Fernrohre und Entfernungsmesser. J. Springer, Berlin.

KÖNIG, D.

1934. Der vordere Augenabschnitt der Schildkröten und die Funktion seiner Muskulatur. Jena. Ztschr. f. Naturwiss., v. 69, p. 223.

KOENIGSBERGER, L.

1902–3. Hermann von Helmholtz. 3 vols. F. Vieweg & Sohn, Braunschweig. An abridged English ed., Oxford, 1908.

KOENIGSWALD, G. H. R. VON

1937. New "missing link" found (*Homo soloensis*); man aged 1,000,000 years. Chicago Daily News, Friday, December 10.

1940. Neue *Pithecanthropus*-Funde 1936–1938; ein Beitrag zur Kenntnis der Praehominiden. Dienst Mijnbouw Nederl.-Indie, Wetensch. Mededeel., Batavia, No. 28, pp. 1–232.

KOEPPE, L.

1918. Die Lösung der Streitfrage, ob das lebende Netzhautzentrum eine gelbe Farbe besitzt oder nicht. München. med. Wchnschr., v. 65, p. 1175.

1920. Die Mikroskopie des lebenden Auges. J. Springer, Berlin.

1921. Lässt sich das retinale Sehen rein physikalisch erklären? München. med. Wchnschr., v. 68, p. 475.

1921. Die normale Histologie des lebenden Auges. Ergebn. d. Anat. u. Entw., v. 23, p. 340.

1937. Die biophysikalischen Untersuchungsmethoden der normalen und pathologischen Histologie des lebenden Auges. *In:* E. ABDERHALDEN, Handb. d. biol. Arbeitsmeth., Abt. 5, Part 6, p. 1.

KÖPPEN, M., & LÖWENSTEIN, S.

1905. Studien über den Zellenbau der Grosshirnrinde bei den Ungulaten und Karnivoren und über die Bedeutung einiger Furchen. Monatsschr. f. Psychiat. u. Neurol., v. 18, p. 481.

KÖPPEN, W., & WEGENER, A.

1924. Die Klimate der geologischen Vorzeit. Gebrüder Borntraeger, Berlin.

KÖRNYEY, S.

1926. Zur Faseranatomie des Striatum, des Zwischen- und Mittelhirns auf Grund der Markreifung in den ersten drei Lebensmonaten. Ztschr. f. Anat. u. Entw., v. 81, p. 620.

1928. Zur vergleichenden Morphologie des lateralen Kniehöckers der Säugetiere. Arb. a. d. neurol. Inst. Wien (Obersteiner), v. 30, p. 93.

1939. Klinische Syndrome bei funktionellen Kreislaufstörungen. Zentralbl. f. d. ges. Neurol. u. Psychiat., v. 94, p. 355.

KOFFKA, K.

1931. Die Wahrnehmung von Bewegung. *In:* BETHE *et al.*, Handb. d. norm. u. path. Physiol., v. 12 (2), p. 1166.

1931. Psychologie der optischen Wahrnehmung. *Ibid.*, p. 1215.

KOHL, C.

1890. Einige Bemerkungen über Sinnesorgane des *Amphioxus lanceolatus*. Zool. Anz., v. 13, p. 182.

1892. Rudimentäre Wirbeltieraugen. Teil I. Biblioth. zool., Heft 13, p. 1.

KOHL, K.

1926. "Ueber das Licht des Mondes." Eine Untersuchung von Ibn al Haitham. Sitzungsb. d. phys.-med. Soc. zu Erlangen, vols. 56–57, p. 305.

KOHL-LARSEN, L.

1943. Auf den Spuren des Vormenschen. Forschungen, Fahrten und Erlebnisse in Deutsch-

Ostafrika (Deutsche Afrika-Expedition 1934–36 und 1937–39). 2 vols. Strecker & Schröder, Stuttgart. A review in Natur u. Volk (Ber. d. Senckenberg. naturforsch. Gesellsch.), v. 74, p. 52.

KOHLBRUGGE, J. H. F.

1903. Die Variationen an den Grosshirnfurchen der Affen mit besonderer Berücksichtigung der Affenspalte. Ztschr. f. Morphol. u. Anthropol., v. 6, p. 191.

1906. Die Gehirnfurchen der Javanen. Verhandl. d. Kon. Akad. Wetensch. Amsterdam, Sec. 2, Part 12, No. 4.

1908. Untersuchungen über Grosshirnfurchen der Menschenrassen. Ztschr. f. Morphol. u. Anthropol., v. 11, p. 596.

1909. Die Gehirnfurchen malayischer Völker verglichen mit denen der Australier und Europäer. Ein Beitrag zur Evolutionslehre. Verhandl. d. Kon. Akad. Wetensch. Amsterdam, Sec. 2, Part 15, No. 1.

1935. Le cerveau suivant les races. Bull. & mém. Soc. d'anthropol. Paris, v. 6, p. 61.

KOHLHANS (KOLHANSIUS), M. J. C.

1663. Tractatus opticus, etc. Lipsiae, sumpt. F. Lankisch, lit. J. E. Hahnii.

KOHLRAUSCH, A.

1930. Lösung des Problems der Qualitätenleitung in der einzelnen Opticusfaser. Zentralbl. f. d. ges. Ophth., v. 24, p. 187.

1931. Elektrische Erscheinungen am Auge. *In:* BETHE *et al.*, Handb. d. norm. u. path. Physiol., v. 12 (2), p. 1393. Tagessehen, Dämmersehen, Adaptation. *Ibid.*, p. 1499.

1932. Die elektrischen Vorgänge im Sehorgan. *In:* F. SCHIECK & A. BRÜCKNER, Kurzes Handb. d. Ophth., v. 2, p. 118.

KOHNSTAMM, O., & QUENSEL, F.

1908. Ueber den Kern des hinteren Längsbündels, etc. Neurol. Centralbl., v. 27, p. 242.

KOHTS, N.

1928. Recherches sur l'intelligence du chimpanzé par la méthode de "choix d'après modèle." J. de psychol. norm. et path., v. 25, p. 255. (*See also* pub. from Zool. Psychol. Lab. Museum Darwinianum, Moscow 1921; in Russian.)

1930. Les aptitudes motrices adaptives du singe inférieur. J. de psychol. norm. et path., v. 27, p. 412.

KOIKEGAMI, H., & IMOGAWA, M.

1937. Ueber die Fasern, insbesondere die kortikalen extrapyramidalen aus der Area 19a der Grosshirnrinde beim Affen. Morphol. Jahrb., v. 77, p. 587.

KOLISKO, A.

1891. Ueber die Beziehung der Arteria chorioidea anterior zum hinteren Schenkel der inneren Kapsel des Gehirns. A. Hölder, Wien.

KOLLARITS, J.

1918. Ueber mehrfach geschichtete und kombinierte visuelle Vorstellungen und ihre Analogie mit Kunstversuchen, Traumbildern und Halluzinationen. J. f. Psychol. u. Neurol., v. 22, p. 171.

KOLLROS, J. J.

1942. Experimental studies on the development of the corneal reflex in amphibia. J. Exper. Zoöl., v. 89, p. 37.

1947. The dependence of optic lobe development upon the eye in Anurans. Anat. Rec., v. 99, p. 654. (Abstr.)

1948. Control of cell number in the optic lobes of Anurans. *Ibid.*, v. 101, p. 660. (Abstr.)

KOLMER, W.

1911. Zur Kenntnis des Auges der Macrochiropteren. Ztschr. f. wissensch. Zool., v. 97, p. 91.

1912. Zur Frage nach der Anatomie des Makrochiropterenauges. Anat. Anz., v. 40, p. 626.

1924. Ueber die Augen der Fledermäuse. Verhandl. d. zool.-bot. Gesellsch. Wien, v. 74–75, p. 29, Nov. 1926; Ztschr. f. Anat. u. Entw., v. 73, p. 645.

1925. Bemerkungen über Adaptationsvorgänge in den Sehelementen. Arch. f. Ophth. (Graefe), v. 115, p. 310.

1927. Das Fehlen einer Choriocapillaris im Auge des Siebenschläfers *Myoxus myoxus* und die Capillarversorgung von dessen Netzhaut. Ztschr. f. Anat. u. Entw., v. 84, p. 171.

1928. Ueber die Struktur der Sehzellen von *Branchiostoma lanceolatum.* Biol. gen., v. 4, p. 256.

1930. Das Auge des Amazonenpapageis, *Amazona aestiva.* Arch. f. Ophth. (Graefe), v. 124, p. 625.

1930. Ueber das Vorkommen von Gefässen in den äusseren Netzhautschichten einiger Säugetiere. *Ibid.*, p. 668.

1930. Zur Kenntnis des Auges der Primaten. Ztschr. f. Anat. u. Entw., v. 93, p. 679.

1931. Ueber das Auge des Murmeltieres (*Marmotta marmotta*). *Ibid.*, v. 96, p. 806.

KOLMER, W., & LAUBER, H.

1936. Auge. *In:* W. VON MÖLLENDORFF, Handb. d. mikr. Anat. d. Mensch., v. 3 (2). J. Springer, Berlin.

KOLODNY, A.

1928. The symptomatology of tumours of the temporal lobe. Brain, v. 51, p. 385.

KOLOSVÁRY, G.
1934. A study of color vision in the mouse (*Mus musculus* L.) and the souslik (*Citellus citellus* L.). J. Genet. Psychol., v. 44, p. 473.

KONING, P. DE
1903. Trois traités d'anatomie arabes par Muḥammed Ibn Zakariyyā al-Rāzī, ʿAli Ibn al-ʿAbbās et ʿAli Ibn Sīnā. E. J. Brill, Leiden.

KONONOFF, E.
1921. Anatomie und Physiologie des Hinterhauptslappens auf Grund klinischer, pathologisch-anatomischer und experimenteller Untersuchungen. Diss., Moscow. Abstr. in Zentralbl. f. d. ges. Neurol. u. Psychiat., v. 30, p. 226.

KONORSKI, J.
1948. Conditioned reflexes and neuron organization. Cambridge University Press, Cambridge.

KOOY, F. A.
1921. Over den sulcus lunatus bij indonesiërs. Acad. proefschr. F. van Rossen, Amsterdam. *Also* Psychiat. en neurol. bl., v. 25, p. 145.

KOOY, J. M., & KLEIJN, A. DE
1910. Ueber einige Fälle von Optiscusleiden und die inselförmige Gestaltung des Gesichtsfeldes. Arch. f. Ophth. (Graefe), v. 77, p. 476.

KOPFF, A.
1930. Johannes Kepler in seinen Briefen. Naturwiss., v. 18, p. 949.

KOPSCH, F.
1896. Das Augenganglion der Cephalopoden. Anat. Anz., v. 11, p. 361.
1899. Mitteilungen über das Ganglion opticum der Cephalopoden. Internat. Monatsschr. f. Anat. u. Physiol., v. 16, p. 33.

KORNMÜLLER, A. E.
1932. Architektonische Lokalisation bioelektrischer Erscheinungen auf der Grosshirnrinde. I. Mitt. Untersuchungen am Kaninchen bei Augenbelichtung. J. f. Psychol. u. Neurol., v. 44, p. 447.
1933. Bioelektrische Erscheinungen architektonischer Felder. Eine Methode der Lokalisation auf der Grosshirnrinde. Deutsche Ztschr. f. Nervenh., v. 130, p. 44.
1934. Zum Problem der Lokalisation auf der Grosshirnrinde auf Grund bioelektrischer Studien. Naturwiss., v. 22, p. 414.
1937. Die bioelektrischen Erscheinungen der Hirnrindenfelder. G. Thieme, Leipzig.

KORNMÜLLER, A. E., & JANZEN, R.
1939. Ueber lokalisierte hirnbioelektrische Erscheinungen bei Kranken, insbesondere Epi-

leptikern. Ztschr. f. d. ges. Neurol. u. Psychiat., v. 165, p. 372.

KORSCHELT, E.
1936. Vergleichende Entwicklungsgeschichte der Tiere (Korschelt & Heider). 2 vols. G. Fischer, Jena.

KOSAKA, K., & HIRAIWA, K.
1915. Zur Anatomie der Sehnervenbahnen und ihrer Zentren. Folia neuro-biol., v. 9, p. 367.

KOVARIK, A. F.
1931. Calculating the age of minerals from radioactivity data and principles. Bull. Nat. Research Council, No. 80, p. 73.

KOWALEWSKY, A.
1871. Weitere Studien über die Entwicklung der einfachen Ascidien. Arch. f. mikr. Anat., v. 7, p. 101.

KRAATZ, W. C.
1950. Comments on vertebrate origins. Turtox News, v. 28, p. 226.

KRABBE, K. H.
1931. Salomon Eberhard Henschen (obituary). Acta psychiat. & neurol., v. 6, p. 1.
1939–47. Morphogenesis of the vertebrate brain. 4 vols. E. Munksgaard, Copenhagen.
1942. Studies on the morphogenesis of the brain in lower mammals. E. Munksgaard, Copenhagen.

KRAEPELIN, E. (*see also* R. GAUPP 1939; WEYGANDT 1927)
1918. Ziele und Wege der psychiatrischen Forschung. Ztschr. f. d. ges. Neurol. u. Psychiat., v. 42 (Orig.), p. 169.
1927. Verzeichnis der wissenschaftlichen Veröffentlichungen E. Kraepelins (gesammelt von der Deutsch. Forsch. f. Psychiat. in München), Arch. f. d. ges. Psychol., v. 58, p. xxiv.

KRAFFT, C. F.
1945. Ether and matter. Dietz Printing Co., Richmond, Va.

KRAINER, L.
1936. Zur Anatomie und Pathologie der Sehbahn und der Sehrinde. Deutsch. Ztschr. f. Nervenh., v. 141, p. 177.

KRAINER, L., & SUWA, K.
1936. Zur anatomischen Projektion und zur Lehre von der Doppelversorgung der Macula. Jahrb. f. Psychiat., v. 53, p. 35.

KRAUPA, E.
1914. Ueber "zirkumskripte grubenförmige Ektasie" am Augenhintergrunde. Ztschr. f. Augenh., v. 31, p. 149.

KRAUS, P.

1932. Eine arabische Biographie Avicennas (German translation of Avicenna's biography by ABŪ ᶜUBAYAD AL ǦURǦÂNÎ). Klin. Wchnschr., v. 11, p. 1880.

KRAUSE, A. C.

1933. Ancient Egyptian ophthalmology. Bull. Inst. Hist. Med., v. 1, p. 258. (Suppl. to Bull. Johns Hopkins Hosp., v. 53.)

1934. Assyro-Babylonian ophthalmology. Ann. M. Hist., N.S., v. 6, p. 42.

1934. The biochemistry of the eye. Johns Hopkins Press, Baltimore.

1942. The photochemistry of visual purple. *In:* Biol. Symp., v. 7, p. 23. Jacques Cattell Press, Lancaster, Pa.

KRAUSE, A. C., & SIBLEY, J. A.

1946. Metabolism of the retina. Arch. Ophth., v. 36, p. 328.

KRAUSE, C.

1832. Einige Bemerkungen über den Bau und die Dimensionen des menschlichen Auges. Arch. f. Anat. u. Physiol. (Meckel), p. 86.

1834. Ueber die gekrümmten Flächen der durchsichtigen Theile des Auges. Ann. d. Physik u. Chem. (Poggendorff), v. 31, p. 93.

1834. Einige Bemerkungen über die feinsten Nervenfasern. *Ibid.*, p. 113.

1836. Fortsetzung der Untersuchungen über die Gestalt und die Dimensionen des Auges. *Ibid.*, v. 39, p. 529.

KRAUSE, C. F. T.

1841–42. Handbuch der menschlichen Anatomie. 2 vols. (On retina, yellow spot, etc., *see* v. 1, Part 2, p. 535.) Hahn, Hannover.

KRAUSE, F.

1911. Chirurgie des Gehirns und Rückenmarkes. 2 vols. Urban & Schwarzenberg, Berlin. American ed.: Surgery of the brain and spinal cord. 3 vols. Rebman & Co., New York, 1909–12.

1914. Die allgemeine Chirurgie der Gehirnkrankheiten. *In:* BRUN, Neue Deutsche Chirurgie, vols. 11–12. F. Enke, Stuttgart.

1924. Die Sehbahn in chirurgischer Beziehung und die faradische Reizung des Sehzentrums. Klin. Wchnschr., v. 3, p. 1261.

KRAUSE, K.

1898. Experimentelle Untersuchungen über die Sehbahnen des Goldkarpfen (*Cyprinus auratus*). Arch. f. mikr. Anat., v. 51, p. 820.

KRAUSE, M.

1936. Stambuler Handschriften islamischer Mathematiker. Quellen u. Stud. z. Gesch. d. Math., Astr. u. Phys., Abt. B, v. 3, p. 437.

KRAUSE, R.

1926–27. Enzyklopädie der mikroskopischen Technik. 3 vols. Urban & Schwarzenberg, Berlin & Wien.

KRAUSE, W.

*1855. Die Brechungsindices der durchsichtigen Medien des menschlichen Auges. Hahn'sche Hofbuchhandlung, Hannover.

1861. Ueber den Bau der Retina-Stäbchen beim Menschen. Ztschr. f. rat. Med., dritte Reihe, v. 11, p. 175.

*1861. Anatomische Untersuchungen. Hahn'sche Hofbuchhandlung, Hannover.

1867. Zapfen-Ellipsoide und Stäbchen-Ellipsoide der Retina. Nachr. v. d. Kgl. Gesellsch. d. Wissensch. Göttingen, p. 419.

1867–68. Ueber die Endigung des N. opticus. Arch. f. Anat., Physiol. u. wissensch. Med. (Reichert & Du Bois-Reymond), pp. 243, 643, 1867; p. 256, 1868.

1868. Ueber Stäbchen und Zapfen der Retina. Nachr. v. d. Kgl. Gesellsch. d. Wissensch. Göttingen, p. 484.

1873. Histologische Notizen. Centralbl. f. d. med. Wissensch., v. 11, p. 817.

1875. Die Nerven der Arteria centralis retinae, sowie über eine Fovea centralis beim Frosch. Arch. f. Ophth. (Graefe), v. 21 (1), p. 296.

1876. Die Nerven-Endigung in der Retina. Arch. f. mikr. Anat., v. 12, p. 742.

1880. Ueber die Fasern des Sehnerven. Arch. f. Ophth. (Graefe), v. 26 (2), p. 102.

1881. Ueber die Retinazapfen der nächtlichen Thiere. Arch. f. mikr. Anat., v. 19, p. 309.

1884–95. Die Retina. Internat. Monatsschr. f. Anat. u. Histol., v. 1, p. 225; v. 3, pp. 8, 41; v. 5, p. 132; v. 6, pp. 206, 250; v. 8, p. 414; v. 9, pp. 150, 157, 197; v. 10, pp. 12, 33, 68; v. 11, pp. 1, 69; v. 12, pp. 49, 105.

1894. Die Retina der Vögel. *Ibid.*, v. 11, pp. 1, 69.

1897. Die Farbenempfindung des Amphioxus. Zool. Anz., v. 20, p. 513.

1898. Die Lichtempfindung des Amphioxus. Anat. Anz., v. 14, p. 470. (*See also* R. Hesse, p. 556.)

KRAUSS, W. M., DAVISON, C., & WEIL, A.

1928. The measurement of cerebral and cerebellar surfaces. Arch. Neurol. & Psychiat., v. 19, p. 454.

KRAVITZ, D.

1931. The value of quadrant field defects in the localization of temporal lobe tumors. Am. J. Ophth., v. 14, p. 781.

1938. Studies on the visual fields in cases of verified tumor of the brain. Arch. Ophth., v. 20 (77), p. 437.

KRAVKOV, S. V.

1938. The influence of the dark adaptation on the critical frequency of flicker for monochromatic lights. Acta ophth., v. 16, p. 375.

1941. Color vision and the autonomic nervous system. J. Opt. Soc. Amer., v. 31, p. 335.

1944. Yan Purkinye i naúka o zryéniyi (J. Purkinje and the knowledge of vision; in Russian). Vyestnik oftal., v. 23 (5), p. 3.

KRAWANY, J.

1905. Untersuchungen über das Zentralnervensystem des Regenwurms. Arb. a. d. zool. Inst. Wien, v. 15, p. 281.

KRAYENBÜHL, H.

1939. Die Bedeutung der Gesichtsfeldbestimmung in der Diagnostik der Schläfen- und Hinterhauptlappen. Schweiz. med. Wchnschr., v. 20, p. 1028.

KRECHEVSKY, I.

1936. Brain mechanisms and brightness discrimination learning. J. Comp. Psychol., v. 21, p. 405.

KREHL, L.

1910. Pathologische Physiologie. F. C. W. Vogel, Leipzig.

KREIKER, A.

1930. Ueber die Lichtreflexion der normalen Netzhautoberfläche. Arch. f. Ophth. (Graefe), v. 123, p. 446.

KREMBS, B.

*1900. Bacons Optik. Natur u. Offenbarung, v. 46, p. 545.

KREMER, A.

1920. The Orient under the caliphs. University of Calcutta, India.

KRETSCHMER, E.

1939. Medizinische Psychologie. 5th ed. G. Thieme, Leipzig.

KREUZFUCHS, S.

1903. Ueber den Dilatationsreflex der Pupille auf Verdunklung. Arb. a. d. Neurol. Inst. Wien (Obersteiner), v. 10, p. 275.

KRIEG, W. J. S.

1946. Connections of the cerebral cortex. I. The albino rat. A. Topography of the cortical areas. J. Comp. Neurol., v. 84, p. 221.

1946. Connections of the cerebral cortex. I. The albino rat. B. Structure of the cortical areas. *Ibid.*, v. 84, p. 277.

1947. Connections of the cerebral cortex. I. The albino rat. C. Extrinsic connections. *Ibid.*, v. 86, p. 267.

KRIES, J. VON

1896. Ueber das Purkinje'sche Phänomen und sein Fehlen auf der Fovea centralis. Centralbl. f. Physiol., v. 10, p. 1.

1896. Ueber die Funktion der Netzhautstäbchen. Ztschr. f. Psychol. u. Physiol. d. Sinnesorg., v. 9, p. 81.

1896. Ueber die functionellen Verschiedenheiten des Netzhaut-Centrums und der Nachbartheile. Arch. f. Ophth. (Graefe), v. 42 (3), p. 95.

1897-1925. Abhandlungen zur Physiologie der Gesichtsempfindungen. 5 vols. J. A. Barth, Leipzig.

1898. Ueber die materiellen Grundlagen der Bewusstseinserscheinungen. Universität-Programm Freiburg i.B. C. Lehmann's Nachf., Freiburg i.B. *Also* J. C. B. Mohr, Tübingen & Leipzig.

1905. Zur Psychologie der Sinne. *In:* W. NAGEL, Handb. d. Physiol. d. Mensch., v. 3, p. 16. F. Vieweg & Sohn, Braunschweig.

1905. Die Gesichtsempfindungen. *Ibid.*, p. 109 and esp. pp. 184, 266.

1920. Ueber die zwingende und eindeutige Bestimmtheit des physikalischen Weltbildes. Naturwiss., v. 8, p. 237.

*1923. Allgemeine Sinnesphysiologie. F. C. W. Vogel, Leipzig.

1923. Zur physiologischen Farbenlehre. Klin. Monatsbl. f. Augenh., v. 70, p. 577.

1924. Kants Lehre von Zeit und Raum in ihrer Beziehung zur modernen Physik. Naturwiss., v. 12, p. 318. (*See also* Helmholtz, Treatise on physiol. optics, v. 3, 1924-25.)

1929. Zur Lehre von den dichromatischen Farbensystemen. *In:* BETHE *et al.*, Handb. d. norm. u. path. Physiol., v. 12 (1), p. 585.

1929. Zur Theorie des Tages- und Dämmerungssehens. *Ibid.*, p. 679.

KRISCH, H.

1926. Die cerebralen Reaktionsweisen. Ztschr. f. d. ges. Neurol. u. Psychiat., v. 102, p. 425.

KRISCH, W.

1933. Eine neue Theorie der Sinnesorgane. Naturwiss., v. 21, p. 876.

KRISZAT, G.

1940. Untersuchungen zur Sinnesphysiologie, Biologie und Umwelt des Maulwurfs (*Talpa europaea* L.). Ztschr. f. Morphol. u. Ökol. d. Tiere, v. 36, p. 446.

KROGH, A.

1924. The anatomy and physiology of capillaries. Yale University Press, New Haven.

KROGMAN, W. M.

1943. The anthropology of the eye. Ciba Symp., v. 5, p. 1607.

1946. Review of F. WEIDENREICH, Apes, giants, and man. Science, v. 104, p. 516.

1950. Classification of fossil men. Cold Spring Harbor Symp. Quant. Biol., v. 15, p. 119.

KROHN, A.

1839–42. Nachträgliche Beobachtungen über den Bau des Auges der Cephalopoden. Verhandl. d. K. Leopold.-Karol. Akad. d. Naturforsch. (*Nova acta nat. curios.*), v. 19, Abt. 2, p. 41.

KRONFELD, A.

1922. Ueber neuere pathopsychisch-phänomenologische Arbeiten. Zentralbl. f. d. ges. Neurol. u. Psychiat., v. 28, p. 441.

KRONFELD, P. C.

1927. Pupillenlehre. Ztschr. f. Augenh., v. 63, pp. 288, 377.

1929. The central visual pathway. Arch. Ophth., v. 2, p. 709.

1931. Sehbahn (1926–1929). Ztschr. f. Augenh., v. 74, p. 267.

1932. The temporal half-moon. Tr. Am. Ophth. Soc., v. 30, p. 431.

1938. Introduction to ophthalmology. Charles C Thomas, Springfield, Ill.

KRONFELD, P. C., McHUGH, G., & POLYAK, S. L.

1943. The human eye in anatomical transparencies. Bausch & Lomb Press, Rochester, N.Y. 2d ed., 1944.

KRONTHAL, P.

1916. Gehirn und Seele. Monatsschr. f. Psychiat. u. Neurol., v. 39, p. 294.

KROVITZ, D.

1948. Visual-field interpretations in chiasmal lesions. Am. J. Ophth., ser. 3, v. 31, p. 415.

KRÜCKMANN, E.

1906. Ueber die Entwicklung und Ausbildung der Stützsubstanz im Sehnerven und der Netzhaut. Klin. Monatsbl. f. Augenh., v. 44, p. 162.

KRZYWANEK, F. W., & GLAUB, M.

1935. Ist die verschiedene Sehschärfe unserer Haustiere durch die dioptrische Einrichtung ihrer Augen bestimmt? Arch. f. d. ges. Physiol. (Pflüger), v. 236, p. 348.

KUBIE, L. S., & HETLER, D. M.

1928. Cerebral circulation. Action of hypertonic solution; study of circulation in cortex by means of color photography. Arch. Neurol. & Psychiat., v. 20, p. 749.

KUBITSCHEK, P. E.

1928. The symptomatology of tumors of the frontal lobe. Arch. Neurol. & Psychiat., v. 20, p. 559.

KUDLEK, F.

1908. Zur Physiologie des Gyrus supramarginalis. Deutsch. med. Wchnschr., v. 34, p. 722.

KÜHL, A.

1920. Physiologisch - optische Bildbegrenzung. Ztschr. f. ophth. Optik, v. 8, p. 129.

1927. Sehschärfe, Beleuchtungsstärke und Riccòscher Satz. *Ibid.*, v. 14, p. 129.

KÜHN, A.

1919. Die Orientierung der Tiere im Raume. G. Fischer, Jena.

1925. Versuche über das Unterscheidungsvermögen der Bienen und Fische für Spektrallichter. Nachr. d. Gesellsch. d. Wissensch. Göttingen, math.-phys. Kl., 1924, p. 66.

1929. Phototropismus und Phototaxis der Tiere. *In:* BETHE *et al.*, Handb. d. norm. u. path. Physiol., v. 12 (1), p. 17.

KÜHN, A., & ILSE, D.

1925. Die Anlockung von Tagfaltern durch Pigmentfarben. Biol. Zentralbl., v. 45, p. 144.

KÜHNE, W.

1877. Zur Photochemie der Netzhaut. Untersuch. Physiol. Inst. Univ. Heidelberg, v. 1, p. 1. Ueber den Sehpurpur. *Ibid.*, p. 15. Ueber die Verbreitung des Sehpurpurs im menschlichen Auge. *Ibid.*, p. 105. Das Sehen ohne Sehpurpur. *Ibid.*, p. 119.

1877. Ueber das Vorkommen des Sehpurpurs. Centralbl. f. d. med. Wissensch., v. 15, p. 257.

1878. Ueber die Darstellung von Optogrammen im Froschauge. Untersuch. Physiol. Inst. Univ. Heidelberg, v. 1, p. 225. Beobachtungen über Druckblindheit. *Ibid.*, v. 2, p. 46. Beobachtungen an der frischen Netzhaut des Menschen. *Ibid.*, p. 69. Fortgesetzte Untersuchungen über die Retina und die Pigmente des Auges. *Ibid.*, p. 89. Notizen zur Anatomie und Physiologie der Netzhaut. Macula lutea und Fovea centralis. Netzhautpigment der Raubvögel. Vorkommen der Sehleiste. *Ibid.*, pp. 378, 380, 383.

1882. Beobachtungen zur Anatomie und Physiologie der Retina. 1. Netzhaut des Menschen. 2. Notiz über die Augen einiger Nachtthiere. *Ibid.*, v. 4, pp. 280, 282.

KÜHNE, W., & SEWALL, H.

1879. Zur Physiologie des Sehepithels, insbesondere der Fische. Untersuch. Physiol. Inst. Univ. Heidelberg, v. 3, p. 221.

KÜHNE, W., & STEINER, J.

1880. Ueber das electromotorische Verhalten der

Netzhaut. Untersuch. Physiol. Inst. Univ. Heidelberg, v. 3, p. 327.

1881. Ueber electrische Vorgänge im Sehorgan. *Ibid.*, v. 4, p. 64.

KÜKENTHAL, W., & KRUMBACH, T.

1925–40. Handbuch der Zoologie. Eine Naturgeschichte der Stämme des Tierreiches. W. De Gruyter & Co., Berlin & Leipzig.

KÜKENTHAL, W., & ZIEHEN, T.

1889. Das Centralnervensystem der Cetaceen. *In:* W. KÜKENTHAL, Vergl.-anat. u. entwicklungsgesch. Untersuch. an Walthieren, v. 1, chap. 3, p. 77. G. Fischer, Jena. (Denkschr. d. med.-nat. Gesellsch. zu Jena, v. 3.)

1895. Untersuchungen über die Grosshirnfurchen der Primaten. Jena. Ztschr. f. Naturwiss., v. 29, p. 1.

KÜMMELL, R.

1925. Doppelte Gefässversorgung der Netzhaut. Ber. d. Deutsch. ophth. Gesellsch. Heidelberg, v. 45, p. 275.

KÜPFER, MAX

1916. Die Sehorgane am Mantelrande der Pecten-Arten. Entwicklungsgeschichtliche und neuro-histologische Beiträge, mit anschliessenden vergleichend-anatomischen Betrachtungen. G. Fischer, Jena.

KÜPPERS, E.

1922. Der Grundplan des Nervensystems und die Lokalisation des Psychischen. Ztschr. f. d. ges. Neurol. u. Psychiat., v. 75, p. 1.

1923. Weiteres zur Lokalisation des Psychischen. (Versuch einer Analyse der Vorderhirnfunktionen.) *Ibid.*, v. 83, p. 247.

1923. Ueber den Ursprung und die Bahnen der Willensimpulse. *Ibid.*, v. 86, p. 274.

1925. Die Auflösung des Leib-Seele-Problems. Arch. f. Psychiat. u. Nervenkr., v. 74, p. 565.

KÜSTERMANN, K.

1897. Ueber doppelseitige homonyme Hemianopsie und ihre begleitenden Symptome. Monatsschr. f. Psychiat. u. Neurol., v. 2, p. 335.

KUFFLER, S. W.

1953. Discharge patterns and functional organization of mammalian retina. J. Neurophysiol., v. 16, p. 37.

KUGEL, L.

1890. Ueber Extinction der Netzhautbilder des schielenden Auges beim doppeläugigen Sehen. Arch. f. Ophth. (Graefe), v. 36 (1), p. 66.

KUGELBERG, I.

1932. Photographische Abbildung der Farben des

Augenhintergrundes. Acta ophth., v. 10, p. 312.

1934. Der Augenhintergrund in infrarotem Licht. *Ibid.*, v. 12, p. 179.

1937. Ophthalmoskopische Studien in monochromatischem sukzessiv veränderlichem Licht. I. Der normale Augenhintergrund. Almquist & Wiksells Boktryckeri-A.-B., Uppsala.

1937. Zur Technik der Augenhintergrundphotographie. Ztschr. f. ophth. Optik, v. 25, p. 130.

KUHLENBECK, H.

1920–21. Zur Morphologie des Urodelenvorderhirns. Jena. Ztschr. f. Naturwiss., v. 57, p. 463.

1921. Zur Histologie des Anurenpalliums. Anat. Anz., v. 54, p. 280.

1921. Die Regionen des Anurenvorderhirns. *Ibid.*, p. 304.

1922. Zur Morphologie des Gymnophionenhirns. Jena. Ztschr. f. Naturwiss., v. 58, p. 453.

1922. Ueber den Ursprung der Grosshirnrinde. Eine phylogenetische und neurobiotaktische Studie. Anat. Anz., v. 55, p. 337.

1924. Ueber den Ursprung der Basalganglien des Grosshirns. *Ibid.*, v. 58, p. 49.

1924. Ueber die Homologien der Zellmassen im Hemisphärenhirn der Wirbeltiere. Folia anat. japon., v. 2, p. 325.

1925. Weitere Mitteilungen zur Genese der Basalganglien: ueber die sogenannten Ganglienhügel. Anat. Anz., v. 60, p. 33.

1925. Ueber die morphologische Bedeutung der *Arteriae laterales corporis striati* bei Reptilien. Weitere Mitteilungen zur Genese der Basalganglien. Folia anat. japon., v. 3, p. 157.

1926. Betrachtungen über den funktionellen Bauplan des Zentralnervensystems. *Ibid.*, v. 4, p. 111.

1927. Vorlesungen über das Zentralnervensystem der Wirbeltiere. Eine Einführung in die Gehirnanatomie auf vergleichender Grundlage. G. Fischer, Jena.

1928. Bemerkungen zur Morphologie des Occipitallappens des menschlichen Grosshirns. Anat. Anz., v. 65, p. 273.

1928. Ueber die sogenannte Affenspalte des Occipitalhirns. Med. Klin., v. 24, p. 937.

1929. Ueber die Grundbestandteile des Zwischenhirnbauplans der Anamnier. Morphol. Jahrb., v. 63, p. 50.

1929. Die Grundbestandteile des Endhirns im

Lichte der Bauplanlehre. Anat. Anz., v. 67, p. 1.

1934. Ueber die beiden Hauptprinzipien in der vergleichenden Hirnforschung. Psychiat. en neurol. bl., v. 38, p. 214.

1935–36. Ueber die morphologische Stellung des Corpus geniculatum mediale. Anat. Anz., v. 81, p. 28.

1937. The ontogenetic development of the diencephalic centers in a bird's brain (chick) and comparison with the reptilian and mammalian diencephalon. J. Comp. Neurol., v. 66, p. 23.

KUHLENBECK, H., & MILLER, R. N.

1942. The pretectal region of the human brain. Anat. Rec., v. 82, p. 472. (Abstr.)

KUHNT, H.

1877. Zur Architektonik der Retina. Ber. d. Deutsch. ophth. Gesellsch. Heidelberg, v. 10, p. 72 (Klin. Monatsbl. f. Augenh., v. 15, Beilageheft, p. 72).

1877. Zur Kenntniss des Pigmentepithels. Centralbl. f. med. Wissensch., v. 15, p. 337.

1879. Zur Kenntniss des Sehnerven und der Netzhaut. Arch. f. Ophth. (Graefe), v. 25 (3), p. 179.

1881. Ueber den Bau der Fovea centralis des Menschen. Ber. d. Deutsch. ophth. Gesellsch. Heidelberg, v. 10, p. 141.

1881. Ueber farbige Lichtinduction. Arch. f. Ophth. (Graefe), v. 27 (3), p. 1.

1890. Histologische Studien an der menschlichen Netzhaut. Jena. Ztschr. f. Naturwiss., v. 24 (17), p. 177.

KUNTZ, A.

1953. The autonomic nervous system. Lea & Febiger, Philadelphia.

KUPFFER, C.

1872. Zur Entwickelung der einfachen Ascidien. Arch. f. mikr. Anat., v. 8, p. 358.

1890. Die Entwicklung von *Petromyzon planeri*. *Ibid.*, v. 35, p. 469.

1894. Studien zur vergleichenden Entwicklungsgeschichte des Kopfes der Kranioten. II. Die Entwicklung des Kopfes von *Ammocoetes planeri*. J. F. Lehmann, München.

KURODA, R.

1923. Studies of audition in reptiles. J. Comp. Psychol., v. 3, p. 27.

KURZ, E.

1924. Das Chinesengehirn, ein Beitrag zur Morphologie und Stammesgeschichte der gelben Rasse. Ztschr. f. Anat. u. Entw., v. 72, p. 199.

KURZVEIL, F.

1909. Beitrag zur Lokalisation der Sehsphäre des Hundes. Arch. f. d. ges. Physiol. (Pflüger), v. 129, p. 607.

KUSCHEL, J.

1924. Ein Fall von Halbringskotom nach Bluterguss in die Papille zur genaueren Bestimmung der Sehnervenstrahlung. Ztschr. f. Augenh., v. 52, p. 79.

KUSSMAUL, A.

1877. Die Stoerungen der Sprache. F. C. W. Vogel, Leipzig. 3d ed., 1885; 4th ed., 1910. Also published as suppl. to v. 12 of Handb. d. spec. Path. u. Therapie.

L

LACK, D.

1949. The significance of ecological isolation. *In:* JEPSEN *et al.*, Genetics, paleontology, and evolution, p. 299.

LADAME, P.

1900. Reine motorische Aphasie ohne Agraphie (Aphemie). Neurol. Centralbl., v. 19, p. 826.

1919. Les localisations cérébrales d'après von Monakow. Rev. neurol., v. 26, p. 32.

LADD-FRANKLIN, C.

1926. The blue arcs of the retina: "seeing your own nerve currents." J. Opt. Soc. Amer., v. 12, p. 494.

1928. Alternative theories to account for the reddish blue arcs and the reddish blue glow of the retina. *Ibid.*, v. 16, p. 333.

LADEKARL, P. M.

1934. Ueber Farbendistinktion bei Normalen und Farbenblinden. Acta ophth., suppl., v. 3.

LAGLER, K. F.

1949. Studies in freshwater fishery biology. J. W. Edwards, Ann Arbor, Mich.

LA GORCE, J. O.

1952. The book of fishes. National Geographic Society, Washington, D.C.

LAGRANGE, H., BERTRAND, I., & GARCIN, R.

1929. Sur un cas de cécité corticale par ramollissement des deux cunei; étude anatomo-clinique. Rev. neurol., v. 1, p. 417.

LAGUNA, G. A. DE

1930. Dualism and gestalt psychology. Psychol. Rev., v. 37, p. 187.

LAIGNEL-LAVASTINE, M.

1936–49. Histoire générale de la médecine, de la pharmacie, de l'art dentaire, et de l'art vétérinaire. 3 vols. A. Michel, Paris.

LALANDE, E.

1896. Arnaud de Villeneuve, sa vie et ses œuvres. Thèse pour le doctorat en médecine, etc. Chamuel, Paris.

LAMACQ, L.
1897. Les centres moteurs corticaux du cerveau humain déterminés d'après les effets de l'excitation faradique des hémisphères cérébraux de l'homme. Arch. clin. Bordeaux, v. 6, p. 491.

LAMARCK, J.-B.-P.-A.
1809. Philosophie zoologique ou exposition des considérations relatives à l'histoire naturelle des animaux. 2 vols. Dentu, Paris. New ed., F. Savy, Paris, 1873.
1914. Zoölogical philosophy. Macmillan & Co., Ltd., London.

LAMBERT, R. K.
1934. A method for the study of the retinal circulation. Arch. Ophth., v. 12, p. 868.

LA MONTE, F.
1945. North American game fishes. Doubleday & Doran, Garden City, N.Y.

LAMPMAN, B. H.
1946. The coming of the pond fishes. Binfords & Mort, Portland, Ore.
1947. A note on the predaceous habit of the water shrew. J. Mammal., v. 28, p. 181.

LAMY, H.
1895. Hémianopsie avec hallucinations dans la partie abolie du champ de la vision. Rev. neurol., v. 3, p. 129; Cong. d. méd. alién. et neurol. de France, Proc.-verb., v. 5, p. 291, 1894.

LANCASTER, W. B.
1938. Aniseikonia. Arch. Ophth., v. 20, p. 907.
1942. Nature, scope, and significance of aniseikonia. *Ibid.*, v. 28, p. 767.

LANCHESTER, F. W.
1934. Discontinuities in the normal field of vision. J. Anat., v. 68, p. 224.

LANCISI, J. M.
1739. Dissertatio de sede cogitandis animae ad D. Joan. Fantonum, in Opera varia, v. 2, p. 104. Venetiis.

LANDAU, E.
1914 (1915). Die Sehrinde. Eine anthropologische Studie an Schweizerhirnen. Mitt. d. naturforsch. Gesellsch. Bern, p. 112.
1915. Zur vergleichenden Anatomie des Hinterhauptlappens. Folia neuro-biol., v. 9, p. 727. (*Also* French ed., 1916.)
1915. Zur Frage der Hirnrindenschichtung. *Ibid.*, p. 757.
1916. Les limites du cortex visuel chez l'homme. Rev. neurol., v. 23, p. 932.
1923. Anatomie des Grosshirns. Formanalytische Untersuchungen. E. Bircher, Bern.
1933. Symptomatologie des opercules de l'écorce

visuelle. Arch. d'anat., d'histol. et d'embryol., v. 17, p. 99 (101).
1938. La stratification de l'écorce cérébrale. Compt. rend. A. Anat., v. 33, p. 261.

LANDESBERG
1869. Casuistische Mittheilungen, etc. (Earliest description of arcuate scotomas.) Arch. f. Ophth. (Graefe), v. 15, p. 194.
1869. Ausbruch von Glaukom in Folge eines Streifschusses. Eigentümliche Gesichtsfeldbeschränkung. *Ibid.*, p. 204.

LANDI, B.
1542. Bassiani Landi . . . de humana historia vel singularum hominis partium cognitione libri duo. J. Oporinum, Basileae.
1605. Anatomiae corporis humani . . . libri duo. Typis ac sumptibus J. Spiessii et J. J. Porsii, Francofurti.

LANDI, O.
1541. Forcianae quaestiones, in quibus varia Italorum ingenia explicatur, multaque alia scitu non indigna. Apud B. Westhemerum, Basileae.
1543. Paradossi, cioè sententie fuori del comun parere, novellamente venute in luce. G. Pullon da Trino, Lione.

LANDOLT, E.
1871. Die directe Entfernung zwischen Macula lutea und N. opticus. Centralbl. f. d. med. Wissensch., v. 9, p. 705.
1871. Beitrag zur Anatomie der Retina vom Frosch, Salamander und Triton. Arch. f. mikr. Anat., v. 7, p. 81.
1875. Des localisations dans les maladies cérébrales. Prog. méd., v. 3, p. 768.
1894. H. de Helmholtz. Esquisse biographique. Arch. d'opht., v. 14, p. 721. (Helmholtz' letter concerning his discovery of the ophthalmoscope.)

LANDOLT, F.
1901. Les recherches ophtalmoscopiques de Lindsay Johnson et leur signification au point de vue de l'anatomie comparée. Arch. d'opht., v. 21, p. 716.

LANDOLT, M.
1926. L'émeraude de Néron. Arch. d'opht., v. 43, p. 102.

LANE, H. H.
1917. The correlation between structure and function in the development of the special senses of the white rat. University of Oklahoma Press, Norman.

LANG, A.
1901. Lehrbuch der vergleichenden Anatomie der wirbellosen Thiere. G. Fischer, Jena.

LANGE, C.
1925. On brains with total and partial lack of the corpus callosum and on the nature of the longitudinal callosal bundle. J. Nerv. & Ment. Dis., v. 62, p. 449.

LANGE, F. A.
1908. Geschichte des Materialismus und Kritik seiner Bedeutung in der Gegenwart. 8th ed. 2 vols. J. Baedeker, Leipzig.

LANGE, J.
1930. Fingeragnosie und Agraphie (eine psycho-pathologische Studie). Monatsschr. f. Psychiat. u. Neurol., v. 76, p. 129.
1936. Agnosien und Apraxien. *In:* O. BUMKE & O. FOERSTER, Handb. d. Neurol., v. 6, p. 807.

LANGE, J., & WAGNER, W.
1938. Kompensationsschritte bei Zerstörung des linken Occipitallappens durch einen Tumor. Ztschr. f. d. ges. Neurol. u. Psychiat., v. 161, p. 199.

LANGE, O.
1893. Vorzeigen infantiler Netzhautpräparate. Ber. d. Deutsch. ophth. Gesellsch. Heidelberg, v. 23, p. 236.
1901. Zur Anatomie des Auges des Neugeborenen. Klin. Monatsbl. f. Augenh., v. 39, pp. 1, 202.
1908. Eine Erklärung der verschiedenen Anordnung der Netzhautschichten im Wirbeltiere und dem Auge der Wirbellosen. Centralbl. f. prakt. Augenh., v. 32, p. 131.

LANGE, S. J.; *see* DE LANGE, S. J.

LANGE, V.
1943. Ueber das Vorkommen von Acetylcholin im hell- und dunkeladaptierten Auge. Ztschr. f. physiol. Chem., v. 279, p. 73.

LANGENBECK, B. C. R.
1836. De retina observationes anatomico-pathologicae. Gottingae, typ. Dieterich. *Also* Arch. f. Anat., Physiol. u. wissensch. Med. (J. Müller), 1837, Jahresb. p. vii, and Repertorium (Valentin), v. 1, p. 162, 1837.

LANGENDORFF
1899. Ueber die Associationscentren der Hirnrinde. München. med. Wchnschr., v. 46, p. 428.

LANGERHANS, P.
1876. Zur Anatomie des *Amphioxus lanceolatus.* Arch. f. mikr. Anat., v. 12, p. 290.

LANGLANDS, N. M. S.
1926–27. Contributions to the theory of stereoscopic vision. Tr. Opt. Soc. London, v. 28, p. 83.
1929. Experiments on binocular vision. Reports of the committee upon the physiology of vision. ("Spec. Rep. Ser.," No. 133.) London, H. M. Stationery Office.

LANGLEY, J. N.
1921. The autonomic nervous system. I. W. Heffer & Sons, Cambridge, England.

LANGWORTHY, O. R.
1928. The area frontalis of the cerebral cortex of the cat, its minute structure and physiological evidence of its control of the postural reflex. Bull. Johns Hopkins Hosp., v. 42, p. 20.
1929. A correlated study of the development of reflex activity in fetal and young kittens and the myelinization of tracts in the nervous system. "Contr. Embryol.," v. 20, No. 114. Carnegie Inst. Washington.

LANGWORTHY, O. R., & RICHTER, C. P.
1930. The influence of efferent cerebral pathways upon the sympathetic nervous system. Brain, v. 53, p. 178.

LANGWORTHY, O. R., & TAUBER, E. S.
1937. The control of the pupillary reaction by the central nervous system: a review. J. Nerv. & Ment. Dis., v. 86, p. 462.

LANKESTER, E. R.
1875. Observations on the development of the cephalopoda. Quart. J. Micr. Sc., v. 15, p. 37.
1880. Degeneration. A chapter in Darwinism. Macmillan & Co., Ltd., London.

LANNEGRACE
1889. Influence des lésions corticales sur la vue. Arch. de méd. expér., v. 1, pp. 87, 289.

LANNOIS, M., & JABOULAY, N.
1896. L'hémianopsie dans les abscès cérébraux d'origine otique. Rev. de méd., v. 16, p. 659; Rev. hebd. de laryng., v. 16, p. 673; Arch. internat. laryng., v. 9, p. 210.

LA PEYRONIE; *see* PEYRONIE

LAPICQUE, C.
1936. Étude sur la formation des images rétiniennes. Rev. d'opht., v. 15, p. 121.

LAPINSKY, M. N.
1897. Zur Frage über das Lumen der Gehirncapillaren. Deutsch. Ztschr. f. Nervenh., v. 9, p. 169.

LAQUEUR, L.
1899. Ueber einen Fall von doppelseitiger homonymer Hemianopsie mit Erhaltung eines minimalen centralen Gesichtsfeldes mit Sectionsbefund. Ber. d. Deutsch. ophth. Gesellsch. Heidelberg (1898), v. 27, p. 218.
1904. Noch einmal die Lage des Centrums der Macula lutea im menschlichen Gehirn.

Arch. f. path. Anat. u. Physiol. (Virchow),
v. 175, p. 407.

1908. Beitrag zur Lehre vom Verhalten der Pupille unter pathologischen Verhältnissen.
Arch. f. Augenh., v. 59, p. 327.

LAQUEUR, L., & SCHMIDT, M. B.

1899. Ueber die Lage des Centrums der Macula
lutea im menschlichen Gehirn. Arch. f.
path. Anat. u. Physiol. (Virchow), v. 158,
p. 466.

LARSELL, O.

1929. The effect of experimental excision of one
eye on the development of the optic lobe and
opticus layer in larvae of the tree-frog
(*Hyla regilla*). J. Comp. Neurol., v. 48, p.
331.

1948. The development and subdivisions of the
cerebellum of birds. *Ibid.*, v. 89, p. 123.

1951. Anatomy of the nervous system. D. Appleton–Century Co., New York.

LARSEN, H.

1922. Demonstration mikroskopischer Präparate
vom monochromatischen Auge. Verhandl.
d. ophth. Gesellsch. Wien, v. 8, p. 101.

LaSALLE ARCHAMBAULT

1905. Le faisceau longitudinal inférieur et le
faisceau optique central. Rev. neurol., v. 13,
p. 1053.

1906. Le faisceau longitudinal inférieur et le
faisceau optique central. Quelques considérations sur les fibres d'association du cerveau. Nouv. iconog. Salpêtr., v. 19, pp. 103,
178, 561; Rev. neurol., v. 4, p. 1206.

1909. The inferior longitudinal bundle and the
geniculo-calcarine fasciculus; a contribution
to the anatomy of the tract-systems of the
cerebral hemisphere. Albany M. Ann., v. 30,
p. 118.

1924. Henry Hun, 1854–1924. Arch. Neurol. &
Psychiat., v. 11, p. 711.

LASAREFF, P.

1924. Die Anwendung der Ionentheorie der Reizung auf die Erscheinungen des Dunkelse-
hens. J. f. Psychol. u. Neurol., v. 30, p. 296.

LASHLEY, K. S.

1916. The color vision of birds. I. The spectrum of
the domestic fowl. J. Anim. Behavior, v. 6,
p. 1.

1922. Studies of cerebral function in learning. IV.
Vicarious function after destruction of the
visual areas. Am. J. Physiol., v. 59, p. 44.

1926. Studies of cerebral function in learning. VII.
The relation between cerebral mass, learning, and retention. J. Comp. Neurol., v. 41,
p. 1.

1929. Brain mechanisms and intelligence. A quantitative study of injuries to the brain. University of Chicago Press, Chicago.

1930. The mechanism of vision. III. The comparative visual acuity of pigmented and albino
rats. J. Genet. Psychol., v. 37, p. 481.

1930. Basic neural mechanisms in behavior. Psychol. Rev., v. 37, p. 1.

1931. Mass action in cerebral function. Harvey
lect., ser. 26, p. 46.

1931. The cerebral areas necessary for pattern vision in the rat. J. Comp. Neurol., v. 53, p.
419.

1932. The mechanism of vision. V. The structure
and image-forming power of the rat's eye.
J. Comp. Psychol., v. 13, p. 173.

1932. A reanalysis of data on mass action in the
visual cortex. J. Comp. Neurol., v. 54, p. 77.

1933. Integrative functions of the cerebral cortex.
Physiol. Rev., v. 13, p. 1.

1934. The projection of the retina upon the primary optic centers of the rat. J. Comp. Neurol., v. 59, p. 341.

1934. The projection of the retina upon the cerebral cortex of the rat. *Ibid.*, v. 60, p. 57.

1935. The mechanism of vision. XII. Nervous
structures concerned in the acquisition and
retention of habits based on reactions to
light. ("Comp. Psychol. Monog.," v. 11,
serial No. 52, p. 43.)

1938. The thalamus and emotion. Psychol. Rev.,
v. 45, p. 42.

1938. The mechanism of vision. XV. Preliminary
studies of the rat's capacity for detail vision.
J. Gen. Psychol., v. 18, p. 123.

1939. The mechanism of vision. XVI. The functioning of small remnants of the visual cortex. J. Comp. Neurol., v. 70, p. 45.

1941. Thalamo-cortical connections of the rat's
brain. *Ibid.*, v. 75, p. 67.

1941. Patterns of cerebral integration indicated by
the scotomas of migraine. Arch. Neurol. &
Psychiat., v. 46, p. 331.

1941. Coalescence of neurology and psychology.
Proc. Am. Phil. Soc., v. 84, p. 461.

1942. The problem of cerebral organization in vision. Biol. Symp., v. 7, p. 301. Jacques Cattell Press, Lancaster, Pa.

1942. The mechanism of vision. XVII. Autonomy
of the visual cortex. J. Genet. Psychol., v.
60, p. 197.

1943. Studies of cerebral function in learning. XII.
Loss of the maze habit after occipital lesions
in blind rats. J. Comp. Neurol., v. 79, p. 431.

1944. Studies of cerebral function in learning.

XIII. Apparent absence of transcortical association in maze learning. *Ibid.*, v. 80, p. 257.

1947. Structural variation in the nervous system in relation to behavior. Psychol. Rev., v. 54, p. 325.

1948. The mechanism of vision. XVIII. Effects of destroying the visual "associative areas" of the monkey. Genet. Psychol. Monog., v. 37, p. 107.

1949. Persistent problems in the evolution of mind. Quart. Rev. Biol., v. 24, p. 28.

1950. In search of the engram. Symp. Soc. Exper. Biol. (No. IV, Physiological mechanisms in animal behaviour).

LASHLEY, K. S., CHOW, K. L., & SEMMES, J.
1951. An examination of the electrical field theory of cerebral integration. Psychol. Rev., v. 58, p. 123.

LASHLEY, K. S., & CLARK, G.
1946. The cytoarchitecture of the cerebral cortex of Ateles: a critical examination of architectonic studies. J. Comp. Neurol., v. 85, p. 223.

LASHLEY, K. S., & FRANK, M.
1932. The mechanism of vision. VI. The lateral portion of the area striata in the rat: a correction. J. Comp. Neurol., v. 55, p. 525.

1934. The mechanism of vision. X. Postoperative disturbances of habits based on detail vision in the rat after lesions in the cerebral visual areas. J. Comp. Psychol., v. 17, p. 355.

LASHLEY, K. S., & FRANZ, S. I.
1917. The effects of cerebral destruction upon habit-formation and retention in the albino rat. Psychobiology, v. 1, p. 71.

LASHLEY, K. S., & McCARTHY, D. A.
1926. The survival of the maze habit after cerebellar injuries. J. Comp. Psychol., v. 6, p. 423.

LASHLEY, K. S., & WILEY, L. E.
1933. Mass action in relation to the number of elements in the problem to be learned. J. Comp. Neurol., v. 57, p. 3.

LASSÈRE, FRANÇOIS; *see* CHERUBIN D'ORLÉANS

LASSIGNARDIE & MANINE
1923. Balle de shrapnell logée dans le lobe occipital gauche au voisinage du pli courbe. Hémianopsie latérale homonyme droite et cécité verbale. Ann. d'ocul., v. 160, p. 719.

LATUMETEN, J. A.
1924. Over de Kernen van den nervus oculomotorius. Doctoral thesis. P. den Boer, Utrecht.

LAUBENTHAL, F.
1938. Zur Pathologie des Raumerlebens, unter besonderer Berücksichtigung des Sehraumes.

Ztschr. f. d. ges. Neurol. u. Psychiat., v. 162, p. 202.

LAUBER, H.
1902. Anatomische Untersuchungen des Auges von *Cryptobranchus japonicus*. Anat. Hefte (Merkel & Bonnet), v. 20, p. 1.

1925. Ein Normalperimeter und die Grundlagen zur Vereinheitlichung der Gesichtsfeldaufnahmen. Ber. d. Deutsch. ophth. Gesellsch Heidelberg, v. 45, p. 80.

1927. Die ophthalmoskopische Differentialdiagnose der infra- und supranukleären Hemianopsie, zugleich ein Beitrag zur Topographie der Faserverteilung in der Netzhaut. *Ibid.*, v. 46, p. 89; Klin. Monatsbl. f. Augenh., v. 78, p. 863.

1931. Die Anatomie des Ciliarkörpers, der Aderhaut und des Glaskörpers. *In:* GRAEFE & SAEMISCH, Handb. d. ges. Augenh., 2d ed., v. 1, Part 2, chap. iii (2). J. Springer, Berlin.

1944. Das Gesichtsfeld. J. F. Bergmann, München; J. Springer Verlag, Berlin & Vienna. (Cited & reviewed in Arch. Ophth., ser. 2, v. 35, p. 587.)

LAUBER, H. (& KOLMER, W.)
1936. Auge. *In:* W. VON MÖLLENDORFF, Handb. d. mikr. Anat. d. Mensch., v. 3 (2). J. Springer, Berlin.

LAURENS, H.
1923. Studies on the relative physiological value of spectral lights. III. The pupillomotor effects of wave-lengths of equal energy content. Am. J. Physiol., v. 64, p. 97.

1924. Studies on the relative physiological value of spectral lights. IV. The visibility of radiant energy. *Ibid.*, v. 67, p. 348.

LAURENS, H., & DETWILER, S. R.
1921. The structure of the retina of *Alligator mississippiensis* and its photomechanical changes. J. Exper. Zoöl., v. 32, p. 207.

LAURENS, H., & WILLIAMS, J. W.
1917. Photomechanical changes in the retina of normal and transplanted eyes of *Amblystoma* larvae. J. Exper. Zoöl., v. 23, p. 71.

LAURENT, P.
1941. Observations sur les cheiroptères du Midi de la France appartenant à la collection Siepi. Bull. Mus. hist. nat. Marseille, v. 1, p. 290.

LAURENTIUS; *see* DU LAURENS

LAWLESS, J. J.
1941. Changes in the central nervous system produced by anoxia. Anat. Rec., v. 79, suppl. 1, p. 41. (Abstr.)

LAWRENCE, B.
1945. Brief comparison of short-tailed shrew and reptile poisons. J. Mammal., v. 26, p. 393.

LAWRENTJEW, B. J.

1934. Experimentell-morphologische Studien über den feineren Bau des autonomen Nerven-systems. IV. Weitere Untersuchungen über die Degeneration und Regeneration der Synapsen. Ztschr. f. mikr.-anat. Forsch., v. 35, p. 71.

LAWSON, A., PARSONS, J., WRIGHT, W. D., PICKARD, R., & POLLAK, H.

1943. General discussion on scientific and clinical aspects of night vision. Tr. Ophth. Soc. United Kingdom, v. 63, p. 61. (*See also* Riddell; Livingston.)

LAYMAN, J. D.

1936. The avian visual system. I. Cerebral functions of the domestic fowl in pattern vision. ("Comp. Psychol. Monog.," No. 58, v. 12.) Johns Hopkins Press, Baltimore.

LAZORTHES, G.

1949. Le système neurovasculaire; étude anatomique, physiologique, pathologique et chirurgicale. Masson & Cie, Paris.

LEA, D. E.

1946. Actions of radiations on living cells. Cambridge University Press, Cambridge.

LEAKE, C. D.

1940. Ancient Egyptian therapeutics. Ciba Symp., v. 1, No. 10.

LEAKEY, L. S. B.

1946. Man's ancestry in Africa. Nature, v. 158, p. 479.

1948. Miocene fossil of ape's skull. London Times, October 30, p. 3.

LEBEDINSKAIA, S. I., & ROSENTHAL, J. S.

1935. Reactions of a dog after removal of the cerebral hemispheres. Brain, v. 58, p. 412.

LEBENSOHN, J. E.

1941. Wollaston and hemianopsia. Am. J. Ophth., ser. 3, v. 24, p. 1053.

LEBER, T.

1865. Untersuchungen über den Verlauf und Zusammenhang der Gefässe im menschlichen Auge. Arch. f. Ophth. (Graefe), v. 11 (1), p. 1.

1865. Anatomische Untersuchungen über die Blutgefässe des menschlichen Auges. Denkschr. d. Akad. d. Wissensch. Wien, math.-naturw. Kl., v. 24, p. 297.

1869. Ueber das Vorkommen von Anomalien des Farbensinnes bei Krankheiten des Auges, etc. Arch. f. Ophth. (Graefe), v. 15 (3), p. 26.

1872. Bemerkungen über die Circulations-Verhältnisse des Opticus und der Retina. *Ibid.*, v. 18 (2), p. 25.

1872. Die Blutgefässe des Auges. *In:* S. STRICKER, Handb. d. Lehre v. d. Geweben d. Mensch. u. d. Thiere. 2 vols. W. Engelmann, Leipzig, 1871–72.

1877. Die Sehstörungen durch Erkrankung der Opticuscentren, der Tractus optici und des Chiasma. *In:* GRAEFE & SAEMISCH, Handb. d. ges. Augenh., v. 5, p. 929.

1880. Bemerkungen über das Gefässsystem der Netzhaut in der Gegend der Macula lutea. Arch. f. Ophth. (Graefe), v. 26 (2), pp. 127, 271.

1903. Die Circulations- und Ernährungsverhältnisse des Auges. *In:* GRAEFE & SAEMISCH, Handb. d. ges. Augenh., 2d ed., v. 2 (2), p. 1. W. Engelmann, Leipzig.

LEBLANC, E.

1925. Les muscles orbitaires des reptiles. Étude des muscles chez *Chameleo vulgaris*. Bull. Soc. hist. nat. Alger, v. 16, p. 49.

1926. Les artères de la région infundibulo-tubérienne. Trav. du lab. anat. Alger, p. 14.

1928. Les artères de la fosse interpédonculaire et l'espace perforé postérieur. Rapports des artères et des groupes cellulaires. *Ibid.*, p. 16.

LEBLANC, L.

1928. Recherches sur la systématisation des voies cortico-thalamiques. Cellule, v. 38, p. 351.

LE BON, G.

1884. La civilisation des Arabes. Firmin-Didot & Cie, Paris.

LEBOUCQ, G.

1908-9. Contribution à l'étude de l'histogenèse de la rétine chez les mammifères. Arch. d'anat. micr., v. 10, p. 555.

LE CAT, C. N.

1744. Traité des sens. 2d ed. J. Wetstein, Amsterdam. (First ed., Rouen, 1740.) Another ed.: G. Cavelier, Paris, 1742. Also an English trans.: A physical essay on the senses. R. Griffiths, London, 1750.

1767. Traité des sensations et des passions en général, et des sens en particulier, etc. 2 vols. Vallat-La-Chapelle, Paris.

LECHE, G. F.

1905. Ein eigenartiges Säugethierhirn, nebst Bemerkungen über den Hirnbau der Insektivoren. Anat. Anz., v. 26, p. 577.

LE CLERC, DANIEL

1729. Histoire de la médecine. I. van der Kloot, La Haye. First ed., J. A. Chouet & D. Ritter, Geneva, 1696.

LECLERC, L.
1876. Histoire de la médecine arabe. Exposé complet des traductions du grec. Les sciences en orient, leur transmission à l'occident par les traductions latines. 2 vols. E. Leroux, Paris. (*See also* Deutsch. Arch. f. Gesch. d. Med., v. 1, pp. 356, 437.)

LE DANOIS, E.
1949. Vie et mœurs des poissons, des plus hauts lacs de montagne aux grandes profondeurs de l'océan. Payot, Paris.

LEDERER, R.
1908. Veränderungen an den Stäbchen der Froschnetzhaut unter Einwirkung von Licht und Dunkelheit. Centralbl. f. Physiol., v. 22, p. 762.

LE DOUBLE
1902. Sur quelques variations des trous optiques. Compt. rend. A. Anat., 4ᵉ sess., Montpellier, p. 209.

LEE, R. J.
1870. On the organs of vision in the common mole. Proc. Roy. Soc. London, ser. B, v. 18, p. 322.

LEERSUM; *see* VAN LEERSUM

LEEUWENHOEK, A. VAN
1674–84. More observations from Mr. Leewenhook. Phil. Tr. Roy. Soc. London, v. 9, p. 178.
1684–(1722). De formatione tumoris Cristallini, etc. *In:* ANTONII A LEEUWENHOEK, Regiae Societatis Anglicanae Socii, ARCANA NATURAE DETECTA. Editio Novissima, Auctior et Correctior. Lugduni Batavorum, apud Arnold: Langerak, p. 66.
1718. Send-Brieven, etc. Adriaan Beman, te Delft.
1719. Epistolae physiologicae super compluribus naturae arcanis; etc. Apud Adrianum Beman, Delphis.
1719. Epistolae ad Societatem regiam Anglicam, etc. Apud Joh. Arnold. Langerak, Lugduni Batavorum.
1939–48. Alle de brieven. 3 vols. N. V. Swets & Zeitlinger, Amsterdam. (*See* v. 3.)

LEGALLOIS, J. J. C.
1812. Expériences sur le principe de la vie notamment sur celui des mouvements du cœur, et sur le siège de ce principe. D'Hautel, Paris. English trans.: Experiments on the principle of life. M. Thomas, Philadelphia, 1813.
1824. Œuvres de Cᵃʳ. Legallois. 2 vols. Le Rouge, Paris.

LE GRAND, Y.
1937. Recherches sur la diffusion de la lumière dans l'œil humain. Rev. d'opht., v. 16, pp. 201, 241.
1952. Optique physiologique, V. 1 (2d ed.). La dioptrique de l'œil et sa correction. Ed. "Revue d'optique," Paris.

LE GROS CLARK; *see* CLARK, W. E. LE GROS

LEHMANN, F. E.
1945. Einführung in die physiologische Embryologie. Birkhäuser, Basel.

LEHMANN, H.
1926. Ein Fall von ungewöhnlicher einseitiger Hemianopsia inferior. Ztschr. f. Augenh., v. 59, p. 145.

LEHOT, C. J.
*1823–28. Nouvelle théorie de la vision. *See:* his Mémoires, v. 4, 1828. Hugard-Courcier, Paris.

LEIKIND, M. C.
1941. The discovery of pathogenic germs. Ancient ideas of infection. The invention of the microscope and the discovery of bacteria. Spontaneous generation and fermentation. The final victory. Chronology of the discovery of pathogenic germs. Ciba Symp., v. 2, No. 11.

LEINFELDER, P. J.
1938. Retrograde degeneration in the optic nerves and retinal ganglion cells. Tr. Am. Ophth. Soc., v. 36, p. 307.
1940. Retrograde degeneration in the optic nerves and tracts. Am. J. Ophth., v. 23, p. 795.

LEINFELDER, P. J., & BLACK, N. M., JR.
1941. Experimental transposition of the extraocular muscles in monkeys. Am. J. Ophth., v. 24, p. 1115.

LEIX, A.
1940. Medicine and the intellectual life of Babylonia. The medical knowledge of Babylonia. Assyro-Babylonian medical magic. Some recent literature on Babylonian medicine. Ciba Symp., v. 2, No. 9.

LEKSELL, LARS
1945. The action potential and excitatory effects of the small ventral root fibres to skeletal muscle. Acta physiol. Scandinav., v. 10, suppl. 31.

LEMKE, G.
1935. Beiträge zur Lichtorientierung und zur Frage des Farbensehens der Planarien. Ztschr. f. vergl. Physiol., v. 22, p. 298.

LEMMON, R. S.
1947. How to attract the birds. American Garden Guild and Doubleday & Co., Garden City, N.Y.

LEMOINE, A. N.
1938. Lesion of the optic tract probably the result of infected sphenoid sinus. Arch. Ophth., v. 20 (77), p. 966.

LEMON, H. B.
1934. From Galileo to cosmic rays. University of Chicago Press, Chicago.

LEMOS, M.
1906. Note sur un cas de perte de la vision mentale des objets (formes et couleurs) dans la mélancholie anxieuse. Rev. neurol., v. 14, pp. 389, 870.

LENARD, P.
1933. Great men of science. Macmillan Co., New York.

LENHOSSÉK, M.
1887. Beobachtungen am Gehirn des Menschen. Anat. Anz., v. 2, p. 451.
1892. Der feinere Bau des Nervensystems. Fortschr. d. Med., v. 10, pp. 571, 613, 665, 713, 801, 845, 889, 937, 981.
1894. Zur Kenntniss der Netzhaut der Cephalopoden. Ztschr. f. wissensch. Zool., v. 58, p. 636.
1895. Der feinere Bau des Nervensystems im Lichte neuester Forschungen. Eine allgemeine Betrachtung der Strukturprinzipien des Nervensystems nebst einer Darstellung des feineren Baues des Rückenmarkes. 2d ed. Fischer's Medicin. Buchhandlung H. Kornfeld, Berlin.
1896. Histologische Untersuchungen am Sehlappen der Cephalopoden. Arch. f. mikr. Anat., v. 47, p. 45.
1899. Kritisches Referat über die Arbeit A. Bethe's, etc. Neurol. Centralbl., v. 18, pp. 242, 301.
1910. Ueber die physiologische Bedeutung der Neurofibrillen. Anat. Anz., v. 36, pp. 257, 321.
1922. Ueber den Sehnerv der Schlangen. *In:* Libro en honor de D. S. Ramón y Cajal, v. 1, p. 1.
1935. Santiago Ramón y Cajal (1852–1934). Naturwiss., v. 23, p. 503.

LENNOX, W. G.
1941. Science and seizures; new light on epilepsy and migraine. Harper & Bros., New York.

LENNOX, W. G., GIBBS, F. A., & GIBBS, E. L.
1938. The relationship in man of cerebral activity to blood flow and to blood constituents. *In:* The circulation, Research Pub. A. Research Nerv. & Ment. Dis., v. 18, p. 277. Williams & Wilkins Co., Baltimore.

LENY, R.
*1795. Remarkable case of a boy, who lost a considerable portion of brain, and who recovered, without detriment to any faculty mental or corporeal. M. Comment., v. 9, p. 519.

LENZ, G.
1905. Beiträge zur Hemianopsie. Klin. Monatsbl. f. Augenh., v. 43 (suppl.), p. 263.
1909. Zur Pathologie der cerebralen Sehbahn unter besonderer Berücksichtigung ihrer Ergebnisse für die Anatomie und Physiologie. Arch. f. Ophth. (Graefe), v. 72, pp. 1, 197.
1910. Organisation und Lokalisation des Sehzentrums. Berlin. klin. Wchnschr., v. 47, p. 603.
1912. Zur Lehre vom Farbensinnzentrum. Ber. ü. d. 38. Versamml. Deutsch. ophth. Gesellsch., Heidelberg, p. 9.
1913. Zur Entwicklung der Sehsphäre. Ber. ü. d. 39. Versamml. Deutsch. ophth. Gesellsch. Heidelberg, p. 42.
1914. Die hirnlokalisatorische Bedeutung der Makulaaussparung im hemianopischen Gesichtsfelde. Klin. Monatsbl. f. Augenh., v. 53, p. 30.
1916. Die histologische Lokalisation des Sehzentrums. Arch. f. Ophth. (Graefe), v. 91, p. 264.
1921. Zwei Sektionsfälle doppelseitiger zentraler Farbenhemianopsie. Ztschr. f. d. ges. Neurol. u. Psychiat., v. 71, p. 135.
1922. Die Sehsphäre bei Missbildungen des Auges. Arch. f. Ophth. (Graefe), v. 108. p. 101.
1924. Erwiderung auf die Arbeit Henschens: 40 jähriger Kampf um das Sehzentrum und seine Bedeutung für die Hirnforschung. Ztschr. f. d. ges. Psychiat. u. Neurol., v. 90, p. 628.
1924. Untersuchungen über das Kerngebiet des Okulomotorius. Klin. Monatsbl. f. Augenh., v. 72, p. 769.
1924. Die Kriegsverletzungen der zerebralen Sehbahn. *In:* M. LEWANDOWSKY, Handb. d. Neurol., suppl. Part 1, p. 668. J. Springer, Berlin.
1925. Ueber akut auftretende bzw. transitorische Pupillenstörungen. Ber. ü. d. 45. Zusamkft. Deutsch. ophth. Gesellsch. Heidelberg, v. 45, p. 119.
1926. Der jetzige Stand der Lehre von der Sehbahn und dem Sehzentrum. Karger, Berlin.
1927. Ergebnisse der Sehsphärenforschung. Zentralbl. f. d. ges. Ophth., v. 17, p. 1.
1927. Untersuchungen über die intrazerebrale Bahn des Pupillarreflexes. Klin. Monatsbl. f. Augenh., v. 78, p. 875; Ber. ü. d 46.

Zusamkft. Deutsch. ophth. Gesellsch. Heidelberg, pp. 140, 153; Zentralbl. f. d. ges. Neurol. u. Psychiat., v. 49, p. 523.

1929. Untersuchungen über die anatomische Grundlage von Pupillenstörungen, insbesondere der reflektorischen Pupillenstarre. Ber. ü. d. 47. Zusamkft. Deutsch. ophth. Gesellsch. Heidelberg, p. 234.

1930. Das Verhalten des Corpus geniculatum externum und der Area striata bei doppelseitiger und einseitiger Blindheit. Verhandl. d. 13. internat. Kong. f. Ophth., v. 1, p. 328; Zentralbl. f. d. ges. Neurol. u. Psychiat., v. 59, p. 577.

LEONARDI, E.
1930. Fondo oculare del cane. Ann. di ottal., v. 58, p. 18.

LEONARDO DA VINCI
1452–1519. Il codice atlantico. 6 vols. U. Hoepli, Milano, 1894.

1909–16. Quaderni d'anatomia. 6 vols. J. Dybwad Christiania (Oslo).

1938. The notebooks. 2 vols. Reynal & Hitchcock, New York.

1952. Leonardo da Vinci on the human body. The anatomical, physiological, and embryological drawings of Leonardo da Vinci. With translations, emendations and a biographical introduction by C. D. O'MALLEY and J. B. DE C. M. SAUNDERS. Henry Schuman, New York.

LEONHARD, K.
1939. Die Bedeutung optisch-räumlicher Vorstellungen für das elementare Rechnen. Ztschr. f. d. ges. Neurol. u. Psychiat., v. 164, p. 321.

LEONOWA (LEONOWA-LANGE), O.
1893. Ueber das Verhalten der Neuroblasten des Occipitallappens bei Anophthalmie und Bulbusatrophie, und seine Beziehungen zum Sehakt. Arch. f. Anat. u. Entw., p. 308.

1896. Beiträge zur Kenntniss der secundären Veränderungen der primären optischen Centren und Bahnen in Fällen von congenitaler Anophthalmie und Bulbusatrophie bei neugeborenen Kindern. Arch. f. Psychiat. u. Nervenkr., v. 28, p. 53.

1909. Zur pathologischen Entwickelung des Centralnervensystems. Das Verhalten der Rinde der Sulci calcarini in einem Falle von Microphthalmia bilateralis congenita. *Ibid.*, v. 45, p. 77.

LEPLAT, G.
1912. Développement et structure de la membrane vasculaire de l'œil des oiseaux. Arch. de biol., v. 27, p. 403.

1913. Les plastosomes des cellules visuelles et leur rôle dans la différentiation des cônes et des bâtonnets. Anat. Anz., v. 45, p. 215.

1932. De la structure du corps vitré. Bull. A. Anat., v. 27, p. 388.

LEREBOULLET, P., & MOUZON, J.
1917. Hallucinations de la vue et crises Jacksoniennes dans un cas de lésion du cortex visuel. Paris méd., v. 7, p. 19.

LESCHENAULT DE LA TOUR (1807); see GEOFFROY *in:* BELANGER, Voyage aux Indes-Orientales, Zoologie, p. 104, 1835

LEUBE, W.
1900. Ueber die Entwicklung der Naturwissenschaften und Medicin im 16., 17. und 18. Jahrhundert. Verhandl. d. Gesellsch. deutsch. Naturforsch. u. Aerzte, v. 72, p. 21.

LEUCKART, R.
1876. Organologie des Auges. *In* GRAEFE & SAEMISCH, Handb. d. ges. Augenh., 1st ed., v. 2 (2), p. 145. W. Engelmann, Leipzig.

LEURET, F., & GRATIOLET, P.
1839–57. Anatomie comparée du système nerveux considérée dans ses rapports avec l'intelligence. 2 vols. and atlas. J.-B. Baillière & Fils, Paris.

LEVI, G., & MEYER, H.
1937. Die Struktur der lebenden Neuronen. Die Frage der Präexistenz der Neurofibrillen. Anat. Anz., v. 83, p. 401.

1938. Présentation de cultures d'un nombre restreint d'éléments nerveux avec quelques considérations sur les rapports d'interdépendance entre les neurones. Compt. rend. A. Anat., v. 33, p. 312.

LEVI, H.
1907. Ein Fall von Alexie mit Hemianopsie. Württemberg. med. Korrespondenzbl., v. 77, p. 437.

LÉVI-PROVENÇAL, É.
*1932. L'Espagne musulmane au Xème siècle. Institutions et vie sociale. Larose, Paris.

LEVICK
1866. Abscess of brain. Am. J. M. Sc., v. 52, p. 413.

LEVIN, G.
1936. Racial and "inferiority" characters in the human brain. Am. J. Phys. Anthropol., v. 22, p. 345.

LEVIN, P. M.
1936. The efferent fibers of the frontal lobe of the monkey, *Macaca mulatta*. J. Comp. Neurol., v. 63, p. 369.

LEVIN, P. M., & BRADFORD, F. K.
1938. The exact origin of the cortico-spinal tract

in the monkey. J. Comp. Neurol., v. 68, p. 411.

LEVINE, J.
1945–52. Studies in the interrelations of central nervous structures in binocular vision. I. The lack of bilateral transfer of visual discriminative habits acquired monocularly by the pigeon. II. The conditions under which interocular transfer of discriminative habits takes place in the pigeon. J. Genet. Psychol., v. 67, pp. 105, 131. III. Localization of the memory trace as evidenced by the lack of inter- and intraocular habit transfer in the pigeon. *Ibid.*, v. 82, p. 19.

LEVINSOHN, G.
1902. Ueber die Beziehungen zwischen Grosshirnrinde und Pupille. Ztschr. f. Augenh., v. 8, p. 518.
1904. Beiträge zur Physiologie des Pupillarreflexes. Arch. f. Ophth. (Graefe), v. 59, pp. 191, 436.
1909. Ueber die Beziehungen der Grosshirnrinde beim Affen zu den Bewegungen des Auges. *Ibid.*, v. 71, p. 313.
1909. Experimental-Untersuchungen über die Beziehungen des vorderen Vierhügels zum Pupillarreflex. *Ibid.*, v. 72, p. 367.
1913. Der optische Blinzelreflex. Ztschr. f. d. ges. Neurol. u. Psychiat., v. 20, p. 377.
1920. Auge und Nervensystem. Die Beziehungen des Auges zum normalen und kranken Cerebrospinalnervensystem. J. F. Bergmann, München & Wiesbaden.

LEWANDOWSKY, M.
1907. Ueber Abspaltung des Farbensinnes durch Herderkrankung des Gehirns. Berlin. klin. Wchnschr., v. 44, p. 1444 (Cong. Amsterdam), and Monatsschr. f. Psychiat., v. 23, p. 488.
1910–14. Handbuch der Neurologie. 5 vols. J. Springer, Berlin.

LEWIS, B.
1878. On the comparative structure of the cortex cerebri. Brain, v. 1, p. 79.

LEWIS, DEAN, *et al.*
1948. Lewis' practice of surgery, v. 12 (brain, etc.). W. F. Prior Co., Hagerstown, Md.

LEWIS, E.; *see* VESEY, E. B.

LEWIS, F. T.
1942. The introduction of biological stains: employment of saffron by Vieussens and Leeuwenhoek. Anat. Rec., v. 83, p. 229.

LEWIS, G. C.
1939. Notes on a pair of tarsiers from Mindanao. J. Mammal., v. 20, p. 57.

LEWIS, W. B., & CLARKE, H.
1878. The cortical lamination of the motor area of the brain. Proc. Roy. Soc. London, v. 27, p. 38.

LEY, J.
1932. Contribution à l'étude du ramollissement cérébral envisagée au point de vue de la pathogénie de l'ictus apoplectique. J. de neurol. & de psychiat., v. 32, pp. 785, 895.

LEYDIG, F.
1853. Anatomisch-histologische Untersuchungen über Fische und Reptilien. G. Reimer, Berlin.
1861. Die Augen und neue Sinnesorgane der Egel. Arch. f. Anat., Physiol. u. wissensch. Med., p. 588.
1891. Das Parietalorgan der Amphibien und Reptilien. Abh. d. Senckenberg. naturforsch. Gesellsch., v. 16, p. 441.
1894. Einiges zum Bau der Netzhaut des Auges. Zool. Jahrb. (Anat. u. Ontog.), v. 7, p. 309.
1896. Zur Kenntnis der Zirbel und Parietalorgane. Abh. d. Senckenberg. naturforsch. Gesellsch., v. 19, p. 217.

LEYTON A. S. F., & SHERRINGTON, C. S. (*see also* GRÜNBAUM & SHERRINGTON)
1917. Observations on the excitable cortex of the chimpanzee, orang-outang, and gorilla. Quart. J. Exper. Physiol., v. 11, p. 135.

LHERMITTE, J.
1929. Le lobe frontal. Données expérimentales anatomo-cliniques et psychopathologiques. Encéphale, v. 24, p. 87.

LHERMITTE, J. J., & AJURIAGUERRA, J. DE
1942. Psychopathologie de la vision. Masson & Cie, Paris.

LIBBY, G. F.
1925. Medullated nerve fibers involving the macula. Am. J. Ophth., ser. 3, v. 8, p. 713.

LIBET, B.
1939. Control of the potential rhythm of the isolated frog brain. J. Neurophysiol., v. 2, p. 153.

LIBET, B., & GERARD, R. W.
1941. Steady potential fields and neurone activity. J. Neurophysiol., v. 4, p. 438.

LIBRI-CARUCCI DALLA SOMMAJA, G. B. I. T.
1838–41. Histoire des sciences mathématiques en Italie, depuis la Renaissance des lettres jusqu'à la fin du dix-septième siècle. 4 vols. J. Renouard & Cie, Paris.

LICHTIG, I.
1938. Die Entstehung des Lebens durch stetige Schöpfung. Noord-Holland. Uitgevers Maatschappij, Amsterdam.

LIDDELL, E. G. T.
1938. Observations on nervous release. Brain, v. 61, p. 410.

LIDDELL, E. G. T., & PHILLIPS, C. G.
1951. Overlapping areas in the motor cortex of the baboon. J. Physiol., v. 112, p. 392.

LIDDELL, H. S.
1941. Physiological psychology. Ann. Rev. Physiol., v. 3, p. 487.

LIDZ, T.
1942. The amnestic syndrome. Arch. Neurol. & Psychiat., v. 47, p. 588.

LIEBERMAN, A. A.
1951. Visual hallucinations due to irritation of the occipital lobe: report of a case. Arch. Neurol. & Psychiat., v. 65, p. 242.

LIEPMANN, H.
1897. Fall von rechter Hemianopsie mit Farbensinnstörung der linken Gesichtsfeldhälfte. Allg. Ztschr. f. Psychiat., v. 53, p. 399.

1900. Das Krankheitsbild der Apraxie (motorischen Asymbolie) auf Grund eines Falles von einseitiger Apraxie. Monatsschr. f. Psychiat. u. Neurol., v. 8, pp. 15, 102, 182.

1905. Die linke Hemisphäre und das Handeln. München. med. Wchnschr., v. 52, pp. 2322, 2375.

1905. Ueber Störungen des Handelns bei Gehirnkranken. S. Karger, Berlin.

1905–6. Der weitere Krankheitsverlauf bei dem einseitig Apraktischen und der Gehirnbefund auf Grund von Serienschnitten. Monatsschr. f. Psychiat. u. Neurol., v. 17, p. 289; v. 19, p. 217.

1906. Linksseitige Dyspraxie Rechtsgelähmter. Neurol. Centralbl., v. 25, p. 284.

1906. Vier Fälle von Dyspraxie bei linkshirnigen Herden. Berlin. klin. Wchnschr., v. 43, p. 1231.

1907. Ueber die Funktion des Balkens beim Handeln und die Beziehungen von Aphasie und Apraxie zur Intelligenz. Med. Klin., v. 3, pp. 725, 765.

1907. Ueber die Rolle des Balkens beim Handeln und das Verhältnis der aphasischen und apraktischen Störungen zur Intelligenz. Berlin. klin. Wchnschr., v. 44, p. 901.

1909. Die Krankheiten des Gehirns. *In:* H. CURSCHMANN, Lehrbuch der Nervenkrankheiten. J. Springer, Berlin.

1909. Franz Joseph Gall. Deutsch. med. Wchnschr., v. 35, p. 979.

1912. Zur Lokalisation der Hirnfunktion mit besonderer Berücksichtigung der Beteiligung der beiden Hemisphären an den Gedächtnisleistungen. Ztschr. f. Psychol., v. 63, p. 1.

1920. Apraxie. Ergebn. d. ges. Med., v. 1, p. 516.

LIEPMANN, H., & MAAS, O.
1907. Klinisch-anatomischer Beitrag zur Lehre von der Bedeutung der linken Hemisphäre und des Balkens für das Handeln. Deutsch. med. Wchnschr., v. 33, p. 1114.

1907. Fall von linksseitiger Agraphie und Apraxie bei rechtsseitiger Lähmung. J. f. Psychol. u. Neurol., v. 10, p. 214.

LIEPMANN, H., & MULLER, F.
1910. Die Ausdehnung des Herdes im Falle W. J. f. Psychol. u. Neurol., v. 17, p. 58.

LIEPMANN, H., & QUENSEL, F.
1909. Ein neuer Fall von motorischer Aphasie mit anatomischem Befund. Monatsschr. f. Psychiat. u. Neurol., v. 26, p. 188.

LIEPMANN, H., & STORCH, E.
1902. Der mikroskopische Gehirnbefund bei dem Falle Gorstelle. Monatsschr. f. Psychiat. u. Neurol., v. 11, p. 115.

LIEUTAUD, J.
1742. Essais anatomiques, contenant l'histoire exacte de toutes les parties qui composent le corps de l'homme, avec la maniere de dissequer. P.-M. Huart, Paris.

LILLIE, H. I., & LILLIE, W. I.
1928. The effect of sinusitis on certain syndromes of chiasmal tumors. Laryngoscope, v. 38, p. 761.

LILLIE, R. S.
1928. Analogies between physiological rhythms and the rhythmical reactions in inorganic systems. Science, v. 67, p. 593.

1929. Circuit transmission and interference of activation waves in living tissues and in passive iron. *Ibid.,* v. 69, p. 305.

1929. The physical nature of nervous action. Am. J. Psychiat., v. 9, p. 461.

1931. The conditions of recovery of transmissivity of newly repassivated iron wires in nitric acid. J. Gen. Physiol., v. 14, p. 349.

1932. Protoplasmic action and nervous action. University of Chicago Press, Chicago.

1935. The electrical activation of passive iron wires in nitric acid. J. Gen. Physiol., v. 19, p. 109.

1936. The passive iron wire model of protoplasmic and nervous transmission and its physiological analogues. Biol. Rev. Cambridge Phil. Soc., v. 11, p. 181.

1945. General biology and philosophy of organism. University of Chicago Press, Chicago.

LILLIE, W. I.
1925. Ocular phenomena produced by temporal lobe tumors. Tr. Sec. Ophth. of Am. Med. Assoc., p. 198; J. Am. Med. Assoc., v. 85, p. 1465.
1927. Ocular syndrome of pituitary tumor complicated by extraneous factors. Am. J. Ophth., v. 10, p. 885.
1930. Homonymous hemianopia primary sign of tumors involving lateral part of the transverse fissure. *Ibid.*, v. 13, p. 13.

LIMA; *see* DA CRUZ LIMA, E.

LIMBOURG, R. DE
*1777. Observation sur une plaie considerable du cerveau faite par un coup de fusil. J. de méd., Paris, v. 48, p. 224.

LINDE, M.
1900. Hemianopsie auf einem Auge mit Geruchshallucinationen. Ein Beitrag zur Kenntnis der Sehbahn. Monatsschr. f. Psychiat. u. Neurol., v. 7, p. 44.

LINDEMANN, V. F.
1940. The respiratory mechanism of the frog retina. Physiol. Zoöl., v. 13, p. 411.
1947. The metabolism of the developing chick retina. Anat. Rec., v. 99, p. 635. (Abstr.)

LINDENBERG, R.
1939. Ueber die Anatomie der cerebralen Form der Thromboendangiitis obliterans (v. Winiwarter-Buerger). Zentralbl. f. d. ges. Neurol. u. Psychiat., v. 94, p. 356.

LINDNER, K.
1934. Zum Aufbau des Glaskörpers. Ber. d. Deutsch. ophth. Gesellsch. Heidelberg, v. 50, p. 86.

LINEBACK, P.
1927. Observations on the fovea centralis of two human and seven monkey pairs of eyes. Anat. Rec., v. 35, p. 19. (Abstr. of Am. A. Anat.)

LINKSZ, A.
1950. Physiology of the eye. V. 1, Optics. Grune & Stratton, New York.

LINT; *see* DE LINT

LISSÁK, K.
1939. Liberation of chemical mediators by stimulating isolated nerves. Am. J. Physiol., v. 126, p. P564.

LISSAUER, H.
1890. Ein Fall von Seelenblindheit nebst einem Beitrage zur Theorie derselben. Arch. f. Psychiat., v. 21, p. 222. (*See also* E. Hahn, Pathologisch-anatomische Untersuchung des Lissauer'schen Falles von Seelenblindheit. Arb. a. d. psychiat. Klin. Breslau, No. 2, p. 105, 1895.)

LISSÍTSA, F. M.
1936. Efferent fibers of the parietal cortex (in Russian). Soviet psychonevrol., v. 12, p. 77.

LISTING, J. B.
1845. Beitrag zur physiologischen Optik. Bandenhoeck & Ruprecht, Göttingen. *Also in:* OSTWALD's "Klassiker der exakten Wissenschaften," No. 147, 1905 (*see* biography); *also* W. Engelmann, Leipzig, 1905.
1853. Mathematische Discussion des Ganges der Lichtstrahlen im Auge. *In:* R. WAGNER, Handwörterbuch der Physiologie, v. 4, p. 451. F. Vieweg & Sohn, Braunschweig.

LITTLE, A. G.
1914. Roger Bacon. Essays, etc. Clarendon Press, Oxford. *See* Little, On Roger Bacon's life and works, p. 1; Wiedemann, Roger Bacon und seine Verdienste um die Optik, p. 185; Vogl, Roger Bacons Lehre von der sinnlichen Spezies und vom Sehvorgang, p. 205; Würschmidt, Roger Bacons Art des wissenschaftlichen Arbeitens, dargestellt nach seiner Schrift *De speculis*, p. 229.

LITTLE, W. S.
1886. Absence of the optic chiasm and other cerebral commissures; temporal hemianopia. Tr. Am. Ophth. Soc., 22d meet., p. 367.

LIVINGSTON, P. C.
1943. The scientific and clinical aspects of night vision. Tr. Ophth. Soc. United Kingdom, v. 63, p. 51. (*See also* Riddell; Lawson *et al.*)

LIVINGSTON, W. K.
1933. Thrombosis of arteries of extremities, brain, heart and kidney, with a general discussion of vascular disease. West. J. Surg., v. 41, p. 21.

LLORCA, F. O.
1932. The lymphatics of the adnexa of the globe. Rev. de cir. Buenos Aires, v. 11, p. 162.

LLOYD, M. C.
1928. Darwin the scientist could also play. A picture of his life at Down House, which has been presented to Britain as his memorial. New York Times Mag., December 2, p. 8.

LLOYD, R. I.
1926. Visual field studies. Technical Press, New York.

LOBÉ, J. P.
1742. Dissertatio medica inauguralis de oculo humano. *In:* A. HALLER, Disput. select., v. 7 (2), p. 65, 1751.

Lo Cascio, G.
1924. Sulle cause del colorito rosso del fondo oculare. Ann. di ottal., v. 52, p. 333.
1924. Il senso luminoso nelle parti periferiche della retina nell'occhio umano. *Ibid.*, p. 386.
1930. Moderne vedute sul meccanismo sensoriale della visione. *Ibid.*, v. 58, p. 353.

Locher, C. J. S.
1933. Untersuchungen über den Farbensinn von Eichhörnchen. E. J. Brill, Leiden.

Lockard, I.
1948. Certain developmental relations and fiber connections of the triangular gyrus in primates. J. Comp. Neurol., v. 89, p. 349.

Locy, W. A.
1894. The derivation of the pineal eye. Anat. Anz., v. 9, p. 169.
1901. Malpighi, Swammerdam and Leeuwenhoek. Pop. Science Monthly, v. 8, p. 561.
1910. Biology and its makers. Henry Holt & Co., New York. *Also* later printings and editions.
1925. The growth of biology. Henry Holt & Co., New York.

Loddoni, G.
1930. Sul decorso delle fibre nervose nel nervo ottico e nella retina. Ann. di ottal., v. 58, p. 468.

Lodge, O.
1925. Ether and reality. Hodder & Stoughton, London; George H. Doran Co., New York.
1926. Evolution and creation. George H. Doran Co., New York.
1929. Energy. E. Benn, London; Jonathan Cape & H. Smith, New York.
1932. Article: Ether, Encyclopaedia Britannica, 14th ed., v. 8, p. 751.

Lodge, W. O.
1946. Bitemporal hemianopia. Brit. J. Ophth., v. 30, p. 276.

Loeb, J.
1884. Die Sehstörungen nach Verletzung der Grosshirnrinde. Arch. f. d. ges. Physiol. (Pflüger), v. 34, p. 67.
1885. Die elementaren Störungen einfacher Funktionen nach oberflächlicher Verletzung des Grosshirns. *Ibid.*, v. 37, p. 51.
1886. Beiträge zur Physiologie des Grosshirns. *Ibid.*, v. 39, p. 265.
1891. Ueber Geotropismus bei Thieren. *Ibid.*, v. 49, p. 175.
1899. Einleitung in die vergleichende Gehirn-Physiologie und vergleichende Psychologie, mit besonderer Berücksichtigung der wirbellosen Thiere. J. A. Barth, Leipzig.
1900. Comparative physiology of the brain and comparative psychology. J. Murray, London. *Also* German ed.
1915. The blindness of the cave fauna and the artificial production of blind fish embryos by heterogeneous hybridization and by low temperatures. Biol. Bull. Marine Biol. Lab. Wood's Hole, v. 29, p. 50.

Löhner, L.
1925. Ueber Entstehungsgeschichte und Funktionen des menschlichen Haarkleides. Biol. Zentralbl., v. 44, p. 384.

Löhr, W.
1939. Ueber Kreislaufstörungen im Gehirn, bedingt durch Gefässkrankheiten und raumbeengende Prozesse in arteriographischer Darstellung. Zentralbl. f. d. ges. Neurol. u. Psychiat., v. 94, p. 351.

Lönnberg, E.
1941. Notes on members of the genera *Alouatta* and *Aotus*. Ark. f. Zool. (Stockh.), v. 33A, p. 4.

Lönnberg, E., Favaro, G., Mozejko, B., & Rauther, M.
1924. *Pisces* (Fische). *In:* H. G. Bronn, Klassen und Ordnungen des Tier-Reichs, v. 6, Part 1, Book 1, Einleitendes, *Leptocardii* und *Cyclostomi*.

Loepp, W. H.
1912. Ueber die zentrale Opticusendigung beim Kaninchen. Anat. Anz., v. 40, p. 309.

Loeser, J. A.
1931. Die psychologische Autonomie des organischen Handelns. Gebrüder Borntraeger, Berlin.
1940. Animal behaviour. Impulse, intelligence, instinct. Macmillan & Co., Ltd., London.

Loeser, L.
1909. Das Verhalten der Sehschärfe in farbigem Licht. Arch. f. Ophth. (Graefe), v. 69, p. 479.

Löwe, L.
1878. Die Histogenese der Retina nebst vergleichenden Bemerkungen über die Histogenese des Central-Nervensystems. Arch. f. mikr. Anat., v. 15, p. 596.

Loewenstein, A.
1942. Studies of the retina in bulk. Some observations on the unstained human retina. Arch. Ophth., v. 27, p. 73.

Löwenstein, K.
1911. Zur Kenntnis der Faserung des Hinterhaupts- und Schläfenlappens (Sehstrahlung, unteres Längsbündel, Türcksches Bündel), nebst klinischen Bemerkungen über Tu-

moren des rechten Schläfenlappens. Arb. a.
d. hirnanat. Inst. Zürich, v. 5, p. 241.

Löwenstein, K., & Borchardt, M.
1918. Symptomatologie und elektrische Reizung
bei einer Schussverletzung des Hinterhauptlappens. Deutsch. Ztschr. f. Nervenh., v. 58,
p. 246.

Loewi, O.
1931. The humoral transmission of nervous impulse. Harvey Lect., ser. 28, p. 218; Arch.
f. d. ges. Physiol. (Pflüger), v. 189, p. 239,
1921.

Lohmann, W.
1912. Zur Sehstörung der Hemianopiker. Arch. f.
Ophth. (Graefe), v. 80, p. 270.

Loken, R. D.
1942. The Nela test of color vision. ("Comp. Psychol. Monog.," v. 17, No. 6, ser. No. 90.)

Lo Monaco & Canobbio
*1902. Sui disturbi visivi e sulle degenerazioni che
sussegnono al taglio di una bandelletta ottica. Clin. ocul., pp. 849, 881.

Long, E.
1913. Aphasie par lésion de l'hémisphère gauche
chez un gaucher. Rev. neurol., v. 25, p. 339;
Encéphale, p. 520, 1913.

Longet, F. A.
1842. Anatomie et physiologie du système nerveux
de l'homme et des animaux vertébrés. 2 vols.
Fortin, Masson & Cie, Paris.

Longhi, L.
1939. La deviazione della marcia negli emianopsi-
ci. Contributo allo studio delle reazioni ot-
tico-motorie. Riv. sper. di freniat., v. 63, p.
5.

Longley, W. H., & Hildebrand, S. F.
1941. Systematic catalogue of the fishes of Tortugas, Florida. With observations on color,
habits, and local distribution. Papers Tortugas Lab. Carnegie Inst. Washington, v. 34,
p. 1.

Loo, Y. T.
1930-31. The forebrain of the opossum, *Didelphis
virginiana*. I. Gross anatomy. II. Histology.
J. Comp. Neurol., v. 51, p. 13; v. 52, p. 1.

López Enríquez, M.
1926. Las células de Río-Hortega en los procesos
patológicos de la retina y nervio óptico. Bol.
Soc. españ. de biol., v. 12, p. 79.
1926. Existencia de células de Hortega "microglia"
en la retina y vías ópticas. Bol. Soc. españ.
hist. nat., v. 26, p. 294.
1926. Oligodendroglia de las vías ópticas. *Ibid.*,
p. 301.

1927. Las células del Hortega de la retina y vías
ópticas en estado normal y patológico.
Arch. de oftal. hispano-am., v. 27, p. 322.
1930. Neuer Beitrag zur Kenntnis der Oligodendroglia der Sehbahnen. Ueber die Morphologie und Verteilung der Hortega-Zellen
in der Netzhaut und im Sehnerven. Zentralbl. f. d. ges. Ophth., v. 22, p. 765.

Lorente de Nó, R.
1922. La corteza cerebral del ratón. Prim. con-
trib. La cort. acúst. Trab. (Trav.) del lab. de
invest. biol. Madrid, v. 20, p. 41.
1923. Las conexiones cerebelobulbares. Bol. Soc.
españ. de biol., v. 10, p. 100.
1923. Algo acerca de la fisiología de la corteza
cerebelosa y de sus sistemas eferentes. *Ibid.*,
p. 103.
1927. Ein Beitrag zur Kenntnis der Gefässver-
teilung in der Hirnrinde. J. f. Psychol. u.
Neurol., v. 35, p. 19.
1933. Studies on the structure of the cerebral cortex. I. The area entorhinalis. *Ibid.*, v. 45,
p. 381.
1934. Studies on the structure of the cerebral cortex. II. Continuation of the study of the
ammonic system. *Ibid.*, v. 46, p. 113.
1935. The plan of stratification of the cerebral cortex. Anat. Rec., v. 61, suppl. 1, p. 33.
1936. Inhibition of motoneurons. *In:* Problems of
nerv. physiol. & behavior. Jubilee Symp. for
J. Beritashvili (J. S. Beritoff), Tiflis, published by the Georgian Branch of the Academy of Sciences of U.S.S.R., p. 231.
1938. Analysis of the activity of the chains of in-
ternuncial neurons. J. Neurophysiol., v. 1,
p. 207.
1938. Cerebral cortex (chap. XV, first 3 secs.). *In:*
J. F. Fulton, Physiology of the nervous system, pp. 291–325.
1939. Transmission of impulses through cranial
motor nuclei. *Ibid.*, v. 2, p. 402.
1940. Release of acetylcholine by sympathetic
ganglia and synaptic transmission. Science,
v. 91, p. 501.
1946-47. Correlation of nerve activity with polarization phenomena. Harvey lect., ser. 42, p.
43.
1947. A study of nerve physiology. ("Studies from
the Rockefeller Institute for medical research," vols. 131 and 132.) Rockefeller Institute for Medical Research, New York.

Lorenz, G. F.
1927. Ueber Ontogenese und Phylogenese der
Tupaiahand. Morphol. Jahrb., v. 58, p. 431.

LORENZ, K.
1951. Ausdrucksbewegungen höherer Tiere. Naturwiss., v. 38, p. 113.

LORENZ, K. Z.
1952. King Solomon's ring. New light on animal ways. Thomas Y. Crowell Co., New York.

LOTMAR, R.
1933. Neue Untersuchungen über den Farbensinn der Bienen, mit besonderer Berücksichtigung des Ultravioletts. Ztschr. f. vergl. Physiol., v. 19, p. 673.

LOW, F. N.
1943. The peripheral visual acuity of 100 subjects. Am. J. Physiol., v. 140, p. 83.
1951. Peripheral visual acuity. Arch. Ophth., v. 45, p. 80.

LOWENSTEIN, O., & LOEWENFELD, I. E.
1950. Role of sympathetic and parasympathetic systems in reflex dilatation of the pupil; pupillographic studies. Arch. Neurol. & Psychiat., v. 64, p. 313.
1950. Mutual role of sympathetic and parasympathetic in shaping of the pupillary reflex to light; pupillographic studies. *Ibid.*, p. 341.

LOWTHER, F. DE L.
1939. The feeding and grooming habits of the galago. Zoologica, v. 24, p. 477.
1940. A study of the activities of a pair of *Galago senegalensis moholi* in captivity. *Ibid.*, v. 25, p. 433.

LUBBOCK, J.
1888. On the senses, instincts, and intelligence of animals, with special reference to insects. Kegan Paul, Trench & Co., London. Also later eds., and a German trans.

LUBOSCH, W.
1909. Besprechung einer neuen Theorie der Licht- und Farbenempfindung nebst einem Excurs über die stammesgeschichtliche Entstehung des Wirbeltierauges. Morphol. Jahrb., v. 39, p. 146.
1929. Ein merkwürdiger Fall von Affenspaltenrest. Anat. Anz., v. 67, p. 493.

LUBSEN, J.
1921. Over de projectie van het netvlies op het tectum opticum bij een beenvisch. Nederl. tijdschr. v. geneesk. (Amsterdam Neurol.-Vereen., Sept. 3), p. 1258. (*Cf. also* Ariëns Kappers *et al.*, 1936, p. 908.)

LUCAS, K., & ADRIAN, E. D.
1917. The conduction of the nervous impulse. Longmans, Green & Co., London.

LUCAS, N. S., HUME, E. M., & SMITH, H. H.
1927. On the breeding of the common marmoset in captivity when irradiated with ultra-violet rays. Proc. Zoöl. Soc. London, p. 447.

LUCIANI, L.
1881. I centri psicho-motori della corteccia cerebrale nella scimmia. Arch. ital. mal. nerv., v. 18, p. 15.
1885. On the sensorial localisations in the cortex cerebri. Brain, v. 7, p. 145.
1911 21. Human physiology. Trans. F. A. WELBY. 5 vols. Macmillan & Co., Ltd., London.

LUCIANI, L., & SEPPILLI, G.
1886. Die Functions-Localisation auf der Grosshirnrinde an Thierexperimenten und klinischen Fällen nachgewiesen. Denickes Verlag, Leipzig.

LUCIANI, L., & TAMBURINI, A.
1879. Ricerche sperimentali sulle funzioni del cervello. II. Com. Centri psico-sensori corticali. Riv. sper. di freniat., v. 5, p. 1.
1879. Studi clinici sui centri sensori corticali. Ann. Univ. di med. e chir., v. 247, p. 293.

LUDVIGH, E.
1938. Determination and significance of the scotopic retinal visibility curve. Arch. Ophth., v. 20 (77), p. 713.
1941. Extrafoveal visual acuity as measured with Snellen test-letters. Am. J. Ophth., v. 24, p. 303.
1949. Visual acuity while one is viewing a moving object. Arch. Ophth., v. 42, p. 14.

LUDVIGH, E., & McCARTHY, E. F.
1938. Absorption of visible light by the refractive media of the human eye. Arch. Ophth., v. 20 (77), p. 37.

LUDWIG, M.-E.
1939. Beitrag zur Frage der Bedeutung der unterwertigen Hemisphäre. Ztschr. f. d. ges. Neurol. u. Psychiat., v. 164, p. 735.

LUDWIG, W.
1932. Das Rechts-Links-Problem im Tierreich und beim Menschen. ("Monog. a. d. Gesgeb. d. Physiol. d. Pfl. u. d. Tiere," v. 27.) J. Springer, Berlin. (Abstr. in Naturwiss., v. 21, p. 253.)

LÜHE, M.
1913. Protozoa. *In:* A. LANG, Handb. d. Morphol., v. 1, p. 1. G. Fischer, Jena.

LUGARO, E.
1899. Considerazioni critiche intorno alla ipotesi di S. R. Cajal sul significato degli incrociamenti sensoriali, sensitivi e motori. Riv. di patol. nerv. e ment., v. 4, p. 241.

LUKIN, E. I.
1936. The factors of the evolution of fresh-water

fauna (in Russian). Prátsi Naúk.-Dosl. zool.-biol. Inst. Charkov, v. 1, p. 130.

Lull, R. S.

1946. Review of F. Weidenreich, Apes, giants, and man. Am. J. Sc. (New Haven), v. 244, p. 740.

Lullies, H.

1937. Ueber die Vorgänge bei der Nervenleitung. Biol. Zentralbl., v. 57, p. 249.

Lundman, B.

1950. Anthropological maps of the Nordic countries. Cold Spring Harbor Symp. Quant. Biol., v. 15, p. 337.

Lungwitz, W.

1937. Zur myeloarchitektonischen Untergliederung der menschlichen Area praeoccipitalis (Area *19* Brodmann). J. f. Psychol. u. Neurol., v. 47, p. 607.

Luntz, A.

1937. The reactions to light and their regulation in the green unicellular organisms (in Russian). Biol. Zhur. Moscow, v. 5, p. 1091.

Lunz, M. A.

1897. Zwei Fälle von kortikaler Seelenblindheit. Neurol. Centralbl., v. 16, p. 751.

Luppino, G. B.

1930. L'azione della luce sul pigmento retinico della scimmia. Zentralbl. f. d. ges. Ophth., v. 26, p. 654.

Lussana, F., & Lemoigne, A.

1871. Fisiologia dei centri nervosi encefalici. P. Prosperini, Padova.

Lutz, A.

1921. Ueber eine seltene Form von Gesichtsfeldstörungen: Beginn als gekreuzte binasale Tetrantanopsie und Uebergang in eine Art von heteronyme horizontale Hemianopsie. Klin. Monatsbl. f. Augenh., v. 66, p. 654.

1921. Ueber einen Fall von gekreuzter Hemiplegie (Millard-Gubler) nebst einigen Bemerkungen über den Verlauf der pupillenerweiternden und der vestibulo-okularen Fasern im Hirnstamme. *Ibid.*, p. 669.

1923. Ueber die Bahnen der Blickwendung und deren Dissoziierung. *Ibid.*, v. 70, p. 213.

1923. L'hémianopsie unioculaire d'origine centrale. Ann. d'ocul., v. 160, p. 265.

1925. Ueber einseitige Ophthalmoplegia internuclearis anterior. (Beschreibung eines neuen Falles in Verbindung mit heterolateraler Herabsetzung des automatischen Blinzelreflexes und Verlust der Reaktionsfähigkeit der homolateralen vertikalen Bogengänge.) Arch. f. Ophth. (Graefe), v. 115, p. 695.

1925. Ueber asymmetrische homonyme Hemianopsie und Hemiakinesis pupillaris. *Ibid.*, v. 116, p. 184.

1928. Ueber binasale Hemianopie. *Ibid.*, v. 119, p. 423.

1930. Ueber einige weitere Fälle von binasaler Hemianopsie. *Ibid.*, v. 125, p. 103.

1931. Ueber die nervösen Bahnen der Tränenabsonderung und deren Störungen. *Ibid.*, v. 126, p. 304.

1937. Berichtigung zur Arbeit N. v. Horánszky über "Kniehöcker und Sehrinde bei einseitiger Optikusatrophie." Klin. Monatsbl. f. Augenh., v. 98, p. 79.

Luyet, B. J.

1940. The case against the cell theory. Science, v. 91, p. 252.

Luzzi; *see* Mondino de' Luzzi

Lydekker, R.

1916. Wild life of the world. A descriptive survey of the geographical distribution of animals. 3 vols. F. Warne & Co., London & New York.

Lyle, D. J.

1947. Neuro-ophthalmology. Charles C Thomas, Springfield, Ill.

1949. Changes in the visual fields confirmed by pathologic diagnosis. Arch. Ophth., ser. 2, v. 41, p. 387; J. Am. Med. Assoc., v. 133, p. 517, 1947.

Lyle, H. M.

1926. The biology of fishes. Macmillan Co., New York.

Lyon, E. P.

1926. Talks on physiological optics. Am. J. Physiol. Opt., v. 7, pp. 323, 615.

Lyon, M. W.

1913. Treeshrews: an account of the mammalian family Tupaiidae. Proc. U.S. Nat. Mus., No. 1976, v. 45, p. 1. Government Printing Office, Washington, D.C.

Lyssenkow, N. K., & Filatow, W. P.

1926. Ein Fall von Zyklopie beim Pferd. Arch. f. Augenh., v. 97, p. 314.

Lythgoe, R. J.

1926. Reports of the Committee upon the Physiology of Vision. I. Illumination and visual capacities. A review of recent literature. ("Spec. Rep. Ser.," No. 104, Privy Council, M. Research Council.) H.M. Stationery Office, London.

1936. Visual perceptions under modern conditions. Tr. Illumin. Engin. Soc., London, v. 1, p. 3.

LYTHGOE, R. J.—*Continued*

1937. The absorption spectra of visual purple and of indicator yellow. J. Physiol., v. 89, p. 331.

1938. Some observations on the rotating pendulum. Nature, v. 141, p. 474.

1938. The structure of the retina and the role of its visual purple. Proc. Phys. Soc., v. 50, p. 321; Cambridge University Press, Cambridge.

LYTHGOE, R. J., & GOODEVE, C. F.

1937. Visual purple. Tr. Ophth. Soc. United Kingdom, v. 57, p. 88.

LYTHGOE, R. J., & PHILLIPS, L. R.

1938. Binocular summation during dark adaptation. J. Physiol., v. 91, p. 427.

LYTHGOE, R. J., & QUILLIAM, J. P.

1938. The thermal decomposition of visual purple. J. Physiol., v. 93, p. 24.

M

MACALISTER, A., & X.

1932. Article: Phrenology, Encyclopaedia Britannica, 14th ed., v. 17, p. 849.

MACAN, T. T., & WORTHINGTON, E. B.

1951. Life in lakes and rivers. Collins, London.

MACASKILL, J.

1945. A case of occipital lobe injury. Brit. J. Ophth., v. 29, p. 626.

McATEE, W. L.

1935. Food habits of common hawks. U.S. Dept. Agriculture Circ. No. 370.

MacBRIDE, E. W.

1919. Summing up the discussion on *Tarsius*. Proc. Zoöl. Soc. London, p. 497.

MacCALLAN, A. F.

1927. The birth of ophthalmology and its development in early Arabic literature. Brit. J. Ophth., v. 11, p. 63.

1930. Mediaeval ophthalmology in Mesopotamia. *Ibid.*, v. 14, p. 506.

McCONNELL, A. A.

1933. Fields of vision in connection with intracranial lesions. Brit. M. J., v. 2, p. 226.

McCOTTER, R. E., & FRALICK, F. B.

1942. A comprehensive description of the orbit, orbital content, and associated structures, with clinical applications. Section of Instruction, Am. Acad. Ophth. & Otolaryng.

McCOUCH, G. P.

1945. Conduction and synaptic transmission in the nervous system. Ann. Rev. Physiol., v. 7, p. 455.

McCOWAN, P. K., & COOK, L. C.

1928. Oculogyric crises in chronic epidemic encephalitis. Brain, v. 51, p. 285.

McCOWN, T. D.

1950. Classification of fossil men. Cold Spring Harbor Symp. Quant. Biol., v. 15, p. 87.

McCRADY, E.

1934. The motor nerves of the eye in albino and gray Norway rats. J. Comp. Neurol., v. 59, p. 285.

McCULLOCH, W. S.

1938. Irreversibility of conduction in the reflex arc. Science, v. 87, p. 65.

1944. Cortico-cortical connections. *In:* P. C. BUCY, The precentral motor cortex, p. 211. Univ. of Illinois Press, Urbana, Ill. Also 2d ed., 1949.

McCULLOCH, W. S., & GAROL, H. W.

1941. Cortical origin and distribution of corpus callosum and anterior commissure in the monkey (*Macaca mulatta*). J. Neurophysiol., v. 4, p. 555.

McCULLOCH, W. S., GAROL, H. W., BAILEY, P., & BONIN, G. VON

1942. The functional organization of the temporal lobe. Anat. Rec., v. 82, p. 430. (Abstr.)

MacCURDY, G. G. (ed.)

1937. Early man, as depicted by leading authorities at the International Symposium, Acad. of Natural Sciences, Philadelphia, March, 1937. J. B. Lippincott Co., Philadelphia & New York.

McDONALD, D. A., & POTTER, J. M.

1951. The distribution of blood to the brain. J. Physiol., v. 114, p. 356.

MACDONALD, H. M.

1934. Theories of light. Brit. A. Adv. Sc., London, Rep. 104th meet., p. 19.

McDOUGALL, R. S.

1942. The mole. Its life history, habits, and economic importance. Highland and Agr. Soc. Scotland, Edinburgh, 5th ser., v. 54, p. 80.

McDOUGALL, W.

1901. On the seat of the psycho-physical processes. Brain, v. 24, p. 577.

1903. The nature of inhibitory processes within the nervous system. *Ibid.*, v. 26, p. 153.

McEWAN, M. R.

1938. A comparison of the retina of the mormyrids with that of various teleosts. Acta zool., v. 19, p. 427.

MACEWEN, W.

1893. Atlas of head sections. Macmillan Co., New York.

McFARLAND, R. A., HALPERIN, M. H., & NIVEN, J. I.

1944. Visual thresholds as an index of physiological imbalance during anoxia. Am. J. Physiol., v. 142, p. 328.

1945. Visual thresholds as an index of the modification of the effects of anoxia by glucose. *Ibid.*, v. 144, p. 378.

1946. Visual thresholds as an index of physiological imbalance during insulin hypoglycemia. *Ibid.*, v. 145, p. 299.

McFARLAND, R. A., HURVICH, L. M., & HALPERIN, M. H.

1943. The effect of oxygen deprivation on the relation between stimulus intensity and the latency of visual after-images. Am. J. Physiol., v. 140, p. 354.

McFARLAND, R. A., KNEHR, C. A., & BERENS, C.

1939. Metabolism and pulse rate as related to reading under high and low levels of illumination. J. Exper. Psychol., v. 25, p. 65.

McFIE, J., PIERCY, M. F., & ZANGWILL, O. L.

1950. Visual spatial agnosia associated with lesions of the right cerebral hemisphere. Brain, v. 73, p. 167.

McGOVERN, W. M.

1927. Jungle paths and Inca ruins. Century Co., New York & London.

MACH, E.

1868. Ueber die Abhängigkeit der Netzhautstellen voneinander. Vierteljahrsschr. f. Psychiat., v. 2, p. 38; *also* Böhm. Gesellsch. d. Wissensch. (Sitzungsb., p. 10).

1886. Beiträge zur Analyse der Empfindungen. G. Fischer, Jena.

1906. Ueber den Einfluss räumlich und zeitlich variierender Lichtreize auf die Gesichtswahrnehmung. Sitzungsb. d. Wien. Akad. d. Wissensch., v. 115, Part 2a, p. 633.

1922. Die Analyse der Empfindungen und das Verhältnis des Physischen zum Psychischen. G. Fischer, Jena.

1925. The principles of physical optics. An historical and philosophical treatment. E. P. Dutton & Co., New York; Methuen & Co., London.

McINTOSH, F. C.

1938. Liberation of acetylcholine by the perfused superior cervical ganglion. J. Physiol., v. 94, p. 155.

McKENDRICK, J. G.

1899. Hermann Ludwig Ferdinand von Helmholtz. Longmans, Green & Co., New York.

MACKENZIE, I.

1934. Degeneration of lateral geniculate bodies. A contribution to the pathology of the visual pathways. J. Path. & Bact., v. 39, p. 113.

MACKENZIE, I., MEIGHAN, S., & POLLOCK, E. N.

1933. On the projection of the retinal quadrants on the lateral geniculate bodies, and the relationship of the quadrants to the optic radiations. Tr. Ophth. Soc. United Kingdom, v. 53, p. 142.

MACKENZIE, W.

1841. The physiology of vision. Longman, Orme, Brown, Green & Longmans, London.

McKIBBEN, P. S.

1913. The eye-muscle nerves in *Necturus*. J. Comp. Neurol., v. 23, p. 153.

1937. Surgical anatomy of the head and neck. William Wood & Co., Baltimore.

MacKINNEY, L. C.

1937. Early mediaeval medicine, with special reference to France and Chartres. Johns Hopkins Press, Baltimore.

McMULLEN, W. H.

1926. Migraine from the ophthalmic standpoint. Brit. M. J., v. 2, p. 769.

McMURRICK, J. P.

1927. The evolution of the human foot. Am. J. Phys. Anthropol., v. 10, p. 165.

1930. Leonardo da Vinci the anatomist (1452–1519). Williams & Wilkins Co., Baltimore.

McNAUGHTON, F. L.

1938. The innervation of the intracranial blood vessels and dural sinuses. *In:* The circulation, Research Pub. A. Research Nerv. & Ment. Dis., v. 18, p. 178. Williams & Wilkins Co., Baltimore.

McREYNOLDS, J. O.

1929. The crystalline lens system in man and in the lower animals. J. Am. Med. Assoc., v. 93, p. 1132.

MADDOX, E. E.

*1902. Die Motilitätsstörungen des Auges. Leipzig.

MÄRK, W.

1944–45. Zur Frage der Verschlussfähigkeit normaler Arterien. Anat. Anz., v. 95, p. 235.

MAGENDIE, F.

1816–17. Précis élémentaire de physiologie. 2 vols. Méquignon-Marvis, Paris.

1822. Expériences sur les fonctions des racines des nerfs rachidiens. J. de physiol. expér., v. 2, p. 276.

1822. Expériences sur les fonctions des racines des nerfs qui naissent de la moelle épinière. *Ibid.*, p. 366.

1823. Mémoire sur quelques découvertes récentes relatives aux fonctions du système nerveux. Lu à la séance publique de l'Académie des Sciences, le 2 juin 1823. Méquignon-Marvis, Paris.

MAGENDIE, F.—*Continued*

1828. A memoir on some recent discoveries relative to the functions of the nervous system. J. Nimmo, London.

1839. Leçons sur les fonctions et les maladies du système nerveux, professées au Collège de France par M. Magendie, recueillies et rédigées par C. James, revue par le professeur. 2 vols. Ebrard, Paris

MAGGIORE, L.

1924. L'ora serrata nell'occhio umano. Ann. ottal., v. 52, p. 625.

1929. Sul valore funzionale dei singoli segmenti che compono i coni ed i bastoncelli nell'atto visivo. *Ibid.*, v. 57, p. 289.

1930. Sulla differenziazione funzionale delle singole parti costituenti i coni e i bastoncelli nell'atto visivo. Zentralbl. f. d. ges. Ophth., v. 22, p. 658.

MAGISTER RICARDUS

Ca. 1130–80 A.D. Anatomia.

MAGITOT, A.

1908. Contribution à l'étude de la circulation artérielle et lymphatique du nerf optique et du chiasma. Thèse, Paris.

1910. Étude sur le développement de la rétine humaine. Ann. d'ocul., v. 143, p. 241.

1921. L'iris, étude physiologique sur la pupille et ses centres moteurs. O. Doin, Paris.

1946. Physiologie oculaire clinique. Masson & Cie, Paris.

MAGITOT, A., & HARTMANN, E.

1927. Définition et limites de la cécité corticale. Rev. d'oto-neuro-ocul., v. 5, p. 81.

MAGNAN, V.

1902. La vie de Baillarger. France méd., v. 49, p. 473; v. 50, p. 17.

MAGNESS, J. R.

1951. How fruit came to America. Nat. Geog. Mag., v. 100, p. 325.

MAGNUS, A., & DE KLEYN, A.

1932. Körpergewicht, Gleichgewicht und Bewegung bei Säugern. *In:* BETHE *et al.*, Handb. d. norm. u. path. Physiol., v. 18, p. 300.

MAGNUS, H.

1873. Die makroskopischen Gefässe der menschlichen Netzhaut. Versuch einer Schematisirung und Nomenclatur des Netzhautgefässsystems. Eine augenärztliche Abhandlung. Verlag von Wilhelm Engelmann, Leipzig.

1876. Die Staarauszichung bei den Griechen und Römern. Arch. f. Ophth. (Graefe), v. 22 (2), p. 141.

1877. Die Kenntniss der Sehstörungen bei den Griechen und Römern. *Ibid.*, v. 23 (3), p. 24.

1878. Der augenärztliche Stand in seiner geschichtlichen und culturhistorischen Entwickelung. Deutsch. Arch. f. Gesch. d. Med., v. 1, p. 43.

*1878. Die Anatomie des Auges bei den Griechen und Römern. Veit & Co., Leipzig. (*See* Deutsch. Arch. f. Gesch. d. Med., v. 1, p 253.)

1879. Beiträge zur Kenntniss der physiologischen Optik und der Ophthalmotherapie der Alten. Klin. Monatsbl. f. Augenh., v. 17, p. 223.

1880. Ein Fall von angeborener totaler Farbenblindheit. Centralbl. f. prakt. Augenh., v. 4, p. 373.

1894. Ein Fall von Rindenblindheit. Deutsch. med. Wchnschr., v. 20, p. 73.

1900. Die Anatomie des Auges in ihrer geschichtlichen Entwickelung. Augenärztliche Unterrichtstafeln. Für den akademischen und Selbst-Unterricht. Herausgegeben von Prof. Dr. H. Magnus. Heft XX. 13 farbige Tafeln mit Text. J. U. Kern's Verlag (Max Müller), Breslau.

*1901. Die Augenheilkunde der Alten. J. U. Kern's Verlag (M. Müller), Breslau.

MAGNUE, R.

1899. Beiträge zur Pupillenreaktion des Aales und Froschauges. Ztschr. f. Biol., v. 38, p. 403.

1902. Die Pupillarreaktion der Octopoden. Arch. f. d. ges. Physiol. (Pflüger), v. 92, p. 623.

1922. Körperstellung und Labyrinthreflexe beim Affen. *Ibid.*, v. 193, p. 396.

1924. Körperstellung. J. Springer, Berlin.

1925. Animal posture. (Croonian Lect.) Proc. Roy. Soc. London, ser. B, v. 98, p. 339.

1926. Some results of studies in the physiology of posture. Lancet, v. 2, pp. 531, 585.

MAGOUN, H. W.

1935. Maintenance of the light reflex after destruction of the superior colliculus in the cat. Am. J. Physiol., v. 111, p. 91.

1940. Descending connections from the hypothalamus. Research Pub. A. Research Nerv. & Ment. Dis., v. 20, p. 270.

MAGOUN, H. W., ATLAS, D., HARE, W. K., & RANSON, S. W.

1936. The afferent path of the pupillary light reflex in the monkey. Brain, v. 59, p. 234.

MAGOUN, H. W., BARRIS, R. W., & RANSON, S. W.

1932. Stimulation of the hypothalamus with the Horsley-Clarke stereotaxic instrument. Anat. Rec., v. 52 (suppl.), p. 24.

MAGOUN, H. W., & RANSON, S. W.
1935. The central path of the light reflex: a study of the effect of lesions. Arch. Ophth., v. 13, p. 791.
1935. The afferent path of the light reflex. A review of literature. *Ibid.*, p. 862.
1939. Retrograde degeneration of the supraoptic nuclei after section of the infundibular stalk in the monkey. Anat. Rec., v. 75, p. 107.
1942. The supraoptic decussations in the cat and monkey. J. Comp. Neurol., v. 76, p. 435.

MAGOUN, H. W., RANSON, S. W., & MAYER, L. L.
1935. The pupillary light reflex after destruction of the posterior commissure in the cat. Am. J. Ophth., v. 18, p. 624.

MAHONEY, V. P., & LINHART, W. O.
1943. Amblyopia in hysteria. War Med., v. 3, p. 503; abstr. and cited in Arch. Neurol. & Psychiat., v. 53, p. 77, 1945.

MAIER, N. R. F.
1932. The effect of cerebral destruction on reasoning and learning in rats. J. Comp. Neurol., v. 54, p. 45.

MAIER, N. R. F., & SCHNEIRLA, T. C.
1935. Principles of animal psychology. McGraw-Hill Book Co., New York.

MAISON, G. L., GRETHER, W. F., & SETTLAGE, P. H.
1937. Monocular color discrimination after unilateral occipital lobectomy in rhesus monkeys. J. Comp. Psychol., v. 25, p. 451.

MAISON, G. L., SETTLAGE, P., & GRETHER, W. F.
1938. Experimental study of macular representation in the monkey. Arch. Neurol. & Psychiat., v. 40, p. 981.

MAÎTRE-JAN, A.
1707. Traité des maladies de l'œil et des remedes propres pour leur guerison enrichi d'experiences de physique. A Troyes, chez Jaques le Febure, etc. Another ed. Paris, 1741. German trans.: Tractat von den Kranckheiten des Auges. Nürnberg, 1725.

MAJANO, N.
1903. Ueber Ursprung und Verlauf des Nervus oculomotorius im Mittelhirn. Monatsschr. f. Psychiat., v. 13, pp. 1, 139, 229, 291.

MALACARNE, M. V. G.
1776. Nuova esposizione della vera struttura del cerveletto umano. G. M. Briolo, Torino.
1780. Encefalotomia nuova universale. 3 parts in one. G. Briolo, Torino. (Also 1791.)

MALAMUD, W.
1927. The role played by the cutaneous senses in spatial perceptions. J. Nerv. & Ment. Dis., v. 66, p. 585.

MALÁYEV, A.
1934. On the extent, shape, and size of the cortical visual center, the striate area (in Russian). German abstr. in J. f. Psychol. u. Neurol., v. 16, p. 38.

MALBRÁN, J.
1939. Die binasale Hemianopsie (abstr. of Spanish paper). Zentralbl. f. d. ges. Neurol. u. Psychiat., v. 94, p. 105.
1940. Consideraciones anatomoclínicas sobre la vía óptica retroquiasmatica. El Ateneo, Buenos Aires.

MALBRANT, R., & MACLATCHY, A.
1949. Faune de l'Équateur Africain Français, v. 1 (birds), v. 2 (mammals), part of Encyclopédie biologique, vols. 35, 36. P. Lechevalier, Paris.

MALGAIGNE, J. F.
1830. Théorie nouvelle de la vision. J. de physiol. (Magendie), v. 10, p. 255; *also* Mém. Acad. d. sc. Paris.

MALL, F. P.
1905. On the development of the blood-vessels of the brain in the human embryo. Am. J. Anat., v. 4, p. 1.
1905. Wilhelm His. His relation to institutions of learning. *Ibid.*, p. 139.
1914. On stages in the development of human embryos from 2 to 25 mm. long. Anat. Anz., v. 46, p. 78.

MALLORY, F. B.
1941. Obituary. Science, v. 94, p. 430.

MALMO, R. B.
1942. Interference factors in delayed response in monkeys after removal of frontal lobes. J. Neurophysiol., v. 5, p. 295.

MALONE, E. F.
1910. Ueber die Kerne des menschlichen Diencephalon. Neurol. Centralbl., v. 29, p. 290; *also* Anh. z. d. Abh. d. Kgl. preuss. Akad. d. Wissensch., phys.-math. Cl.
1916. The nuclei tuberis laterales and the so-called ganglion opticum basale. ("Johns Hopkins Hosp. Rep.," v. 17, p. 441.)

MALPIGHI, M.
1664. Marcelli Malpighii exercitatio epistolica de Cerebro. Clarissimo & Amicissimo Viro Carolo Fracassato, Pisis Medicinae Professori Ordinario, Marcellus Malpighius S.P.D. *In:* M. MALPIGHII, Opera omnia. Operum tomus secundus, p. 113. Lugduni Batavorum, 1687.
1687. De cerebri cortice. *In:* M. MALPIGHII, Opera omnia. Operum tomus secundus, p. 269. Lugduni Batavorum.

Malpighi, M.—*Continued*

1687. Opera omnia, seu Thesaurus locupletissimus botanico-medico-anatomicus. 2 vols. Lugduni Batavorum, ap. Petrum Vander Aa.

1687. Marcelli Malpighii Philosophi & Medici Bononiensis, è Societate Regia, Operum tomus secundus, etc. Lugduni Batavorum, apud Petrum vander Aa.

Malthus, T. R.

1798. An essay on the principle of population, etc. Reeves & Turner, London, 1888.

Manchot, E.

1929. Abgrenzung des Augenmaterials und anderer Teilbezirke in der Medullarplatte; die Teilbewegungen während der Auffaltung (Farbmarkierungsversuche an Keimen von Urodelen). Arch. f. Entw. d. Org., v. 116, p. 689.

Mandelbaum, J., & Mintz, E. U.

1941. The sensitivities of the color receptors as measured by dark adaptation. Am. J. Ophth., v. 24, p. 1241.

Mandelbaum, J., & Sloan, L. L.

1947. Peripheral visual acuity with special reference to scotopic illumination. Am. J. Ophth., v. 30, p. 581.

Mandelstamm, E.

1867. Beitrag zur Physiologie der Farben. Arch. f. Ophth (Graefe), v. 13 (2), p. 399.

1873. Ueber Sehnervenkreuzung und Hemiopie. *Ibid.*, v. 19 (2), p. 39; Centralbl. f. d. med. Wissensch., v. 11, p. 339.

1875. Zur Frage über Hemiopie. Klin. Monatsbl. f. Augenh., v. 13, p. 94.

Manfredi, Hieronymo

1490. Anothomia. *In:* C. Singer, A study in early Renaissance anatomy, with a new text: the *Anothomia* of Hieronymo Manfredi, transcribed and translated by A. Mildred Westland. (C. Singer's "Studies in the History and Method of Science," v. 1, p. 79, 1917.)

Mangold, E.

1909. Unsere Sinnesorgane und ihre Funktion. Quelle & Meyer, Leipzig. 2d ed., 1919.

Mangold, O.

1928–31. Das Determinationsproblem. Ergebn. d. Biol., v. 3, p. 152; v. 5, p. 290; v. 7, p. 193.

1928. Probleme der Entwicklungsmechanik. Naturwiss., v. 16, p. 661.

1931. Das Determinationsproblem. III. Das Wirbeltierauge in der Entwicklung und Regeneration. Ergebn. d. Biol., v. 7, p. 193.

Mankowski, B. N.

1929. Zur Frage der Lokalisation der Sensibilität in der Hirnrinde des Menschen. Arch. f. Psychiat. u. Nervenkr., v. 88, p. 179.

Mann, I.

1927. The developing third nerve nucleus in human embryos. J. Anat., v. 61, p. 424.

1928. The regional differentiation of the vertebrate retina. Am. J. Ophth., v. 11, p. 515.

1928. The process of differentiation of the retinal layers in vertebrates. Brit. J. Ophth., v. 12, p. 449.

1931. Iris pattern in the vertebrates. Tr. Zool. Soc. London, v. 21, p. 355.

1937. Developmental abnormalities of the eye. Cambridge University Press, Cambridge.

1950. The development of the human eye. Grune & Stratton, New York.

Mann, L.

1919. Ueber Störungen des Raumsinnes der Netzhaut oder der optischen Lokalisation bei Herderkrankungen im Gebiete der Sehstrahlung ("Paropsie"). Neurol. Centralbl., v. 38, p. 212.

Mann, W. A.

1944. Direct utilization of the eye as a camera. Tr. Am. Ophth. Soc., v. 42, p. 495; Am. J. Ophth., v. 28, p. 451.

Mann-Fischer, G.

1944. El cerebro de *Marmosa elegans*. Imp. "El Esfuerzo," Santiago de Chile.

1946. Ojo y visión de las ballenas. Biológica, Fasc. 4, p. 23.

Manni, D. M.

*1738. Degli occhiali da naso inventati da Salvino Armati gentiluomo fiorentino. Trattato istorico di Domenico Maria Manni Accademico Fiorentino. In Firenze MDCCXXXVIII, nella stamperia D'Anton-Maria Albizzini. Con licenza de' Superiori. 2d ed., 1741.

Manolesco, M.

1928. Hémianopsie double avec conservation de la vision maculaire à la suite d'une tumeur du lobe occipital gauche. Ann. d'ocul., v. 165, p. 215.

Manouelian, J.

1905. Étude sur l'origine du nerf optique. J. Anat. & Physiol., v. 41, p. 458.

Manten, A.

1948. Phototaxis, phototropism, and photosynthesis in purple bacteria and blue-green algae. Drukkerij Schotanus & Jens, Utrecht

Manzini, C. A.

1660. L'occhiale all'occhio, etc. Benacci, Bologna.

Marais, E. N.

1939. My friends the baboons. Methuen & Co., London.

MARBURG, O.

1903. Basale Opticuswurzel und Tractus peduncularis transversus. Arb. a. d. Neurol. Inst. Wien (Obersteiner), v. 10, p. 66; *also* Centralbl. f. Physiol., v. 17, p. 30.

1907. Beiträge zur Kenntnis der Grosshirnrinde der Affen. *Ibid.*, v. 16, p. 581.

1910. Mikroskopisch-topographischer Atlas des menschlichen Zentralnervensystems mit begleitendem Texte. 2d ed. F. Deuticke, Wien.

1917. Vergleichend anatomische Studien über den Nucleus hypothalamicus und die hypothalamische Striatumfaserung. Jahrb. f. Psychiat. u. Neurol., v. 38, p. 184.

1926. Zur Frage der Bedeutung der Schichtbildung im Grau der Hirnrinde. Sbornik posvyas. V. M. Bechterevu, p. 195. Gossud. Psichonevrol. Akad., etc., Leningrad. Anniversary vol. for Bechterev.

1939. Modern views regarding the anatomy and physiology of the vestibular tracts. Laryngoscope, v. 49, p. 631.

1942. Primary endings of the optic nerve in man and in animals. Arch. Ophth., v. 28, p. 61.

MARBURG, O., & WARNER, F. J.

1947. The pathways of the tectum (anterior colliculus) of the midbrain in cats. J. Nerv. & Ment. Dis., v. 106, p. 415.

MARCHAND, F.

1882. Beitrag zur Kenntniss der homonymen bilateralen Hemianopsie und der Faserkreuzung im Chiasma opticum. Arch. f. Ophth. (Graefe), v. 28 (2), p. 63.

1893. Die Morphologie des Stirnlappens und der Insel der Anthropomorphen. G. Fischer, Jena.

1909. Ueber die normale Entwicklung und den Mangel des Balkens im menschlichen Gehirn. Abh. math.-phys. Kl. kgl. sächs. Gesellsch. d. Wissensch. Leipzig, v. 31, p. 369.

MARCHANT, J.

1916. Alfred Russel Wallace. Letters and reminiscences. 2 vols. Cassel & Co., London.

MARCHESANI, O.

1926. Die Morphologie der Glia im Nervus opticus und in der Retina, etc. Arch. f. Ophth. (Graefe), v. 117, p. 575.

1927. Die drei Gliaarten in der Retina und im Sehnerven. Zentralbl. f. d. ges. Ophth., v. 17, p. 428.

1930. Untersuchungen über die Glia. II. Mitt. Das Glioma retinae. Arch. f. Augenh., v. 103, p. 484.

1939. Ueber die Bedeutung der Kreislaufstörungen des Auges im allgemeinen Krankheitsgeschehen. Zentralbl. f. d. ges. Neurol. u. Psychiat., v. 94, p. 350.

MARCHESINI, E.

1933. Sulla morfologia del seno sfenoidale e dei canali ottici studiati mediante la transilluminazione. Rassegna ital. di ottal., v. 2, p. 575.

MARCHI, V.

1886–87. Sulle degenerazioni consecutive alla estirpazione totale e parziale del cervelletto. Riv. sper. di freniat., v. 12, p. 50; v. 13, p. 446.

1891. Sull'origine e decorso dei peduncoli cerebellari e sui loro rapporti cogli altri centri nervosi. *Ibid.*, v. 17, p. 357.

MARCHI, V., & ALGERI, G.

1885. Sulle degenerazioni discendenti consecutive a lesioni della corteccia cerebrale. Nota prev. Riv. sper. di freniat., v. 11, p. 492.

1886. Sulle degenerazioni discendenti consecutive a lesioni sperimentali in diverse zone della corteccia cerebrale. *Ibid.*, v. 12, p. 208.

MARCY, D.

1943. Night life of the bush baby. Animal Kingdom, v. 46, p. 99.

MARENGHI, G.

1900–1901. Contributo alla fina organizzazione della retina. Anat. Anz. (Verh.), suppl., v. 18, p. 12; Atti r. Accad. d. Lincei, Mem. cl. Sc. fis., mat. e nat., ser. 5, v. 4, p. 4 (1901).

MARIE, P.

1906. Ramollissement cérébral; lésions des fibres du faisceau longitudinal inférieur (here also addition by Dejerine). Rev. Neurol., v. 14, p. 291.

1922. Existe-t-il dans le cerveau humain des centres innés ou préformés de langage? Presse méd., v. 30, p. 177.

1926–28. Travaux et mémoires. 2 vols. Masson & Cie, Paris.

MARIE, P., BOUTTIER, H., & VAN BOGAERT, L.

1924. Sur un cas de tumeur préfrontale droite. Troubles de l'orientation dans l'espace. Rev. neurol., v. 31 (2), p. 209.

MARIE, P., & CHATELIN, C.

1914–15. Les troubles visuels dus aux lésions des voies optiques intracérébrales et de la sphère visuelle corticale dans les blessures du crâne par coup de feu. Rev. neurol., v. 28 (2), p. 882.

1915. Les troubles visuels dus aux lésions des voies optiques intracérébrales dans les blessures de l'encéphale par coup de feu. Bull. & mém. Acad. méd. de Paris, v. 74, p. 535.

1916. Les troubles visuels consécutifs aux blessures des voies optiques centrales et de la sphère visuelle corticale: hémianopsies en quadrant supérieur; hémiachromatopsies. Rev. neurol., v. 29 (1), p. 138.

1916. Scotomes paramaculaires hémianopsiques par lésion occipitale et scotome maculaire par lésion rétinienne unilatérale chez le même blessé. *Ibid.*, v. 30 (2), p. 112.

1916. Troubles visuels. *Ibid.*, p. 619.

MARIE, P., & LÉRI, A.

1905. Persistance d'un faisceau intact dans les bandelettes optiques après atrophie complète des nerfs: le "faisceau résiduaire de la bandelette." Le ganglion optique basal et ses connexions. Rev. neurol., v. 13, p. 493.

1911. Considérations cliniques et anatomiques sur la cécité corticale. Ann. d'ocul., v. 146, p. 277.

MARINESCO, G.

1911. Quelques recherches de paliométrie. Rev. neurol., v. 21, p. 281.

MARIOTTE, E.

1668. A new discovery touching vision. Tr. Roy. Soc. London, v. 3, p. 668. *Also* Acta erudit., an. 1683, Lipsiae (Leizick), p. 67; and Hist. Acad. sc. Paris, ser. 1, v. 1, p. 102, 1733; and in collected works, 2 vols., Leiden, 1717.

1668. Nouvelle découverte touchant la veüe. [Extrait d'une lettre de M. l'abbé Mariotte à M. Pecquet. Réponse de M. Pecquet à la lettre de M. l'abbé Mariotte.] Impr. de F. Léonard, Paris.

1669. Sur l'organe de la vision. Hist. Acad. sc. Paris, ser. 1, v. 1, p. 102, 1733.

*1679. Traité de couleurs. *See also* Hist. Acad. sc. Paris, ser. 1, v. 1, p. 291, 1733.

1740. De la nature des couleurs. *In:* Œuvres de M. Mariotte, de l'Académie royale des sciences; comprenant tous les traitez de cet auteur, tant ceux qui avoient déja paru séparément, que ceux qui n'avoient pas encore été publiés, p. 195. Imprimées sur les exemplaires les plus exactes & les plus complets; revûe & corrigées de nouveau. Nouvelle Édition. A La Haye, Chez Jean Neaulme, MDCCXL.

MARKUS, H. C.

1934. Life history of the blackhead minnow (*Pimephales promelas*). Copeia, No. 3, p. 116.

MARLOW, S. B.

1947. Field of vision in chronic glaucoma. Arch. Ophth., ser. 2, v. 38, p. 43.

MARPLE, C. D., & WRIGHT, I. S.

1950. Thromboembolic conditions and their treatment with anticoagulants. Charles C Thomas, Springfield, Ill.

MARQUARDT, J.

1886. Das Privatleben der Römer. 2 parts. *In:* J. MARQUARDT & T. MOMMSEN, Handb. d. römischen Alterthümer, v. 7. Hirzel, Leipzig.

MÁRQUEZ, M.

1900. Nuevas consideraciones acerca de los entrecruzamientos motores del aparato de la visión. Rev. trimestr. micr., v. 5, p. 73.

1923. El libro del Lic. Benito Daza de Valdés *Uso de los antojos* y comentarios a propósito del mismo. Madrid, Imprenta y Encuadernación de Julio Cosano. ("Biblioteca clásica de la medicina española," v. 4.) Real Academia nacional de medicina, Madrid.

1924. Einseitiges Argyll-Robertson-Phänomen im Verlaufe eines pulsierenden Exophthalmus traumatischen Ursprungs. Einige Betrachtungen über Lichtreflexe und andere pupilläre Mitbewegungen. Klin. Monatsbl. f. Augenh., v. 73, p. 588.

1930. Sur la double innervation du muscle droit interne de l'œil. Rev. d'oto-neuro-opht., v. 8, p. 343.

MARQUIS, D. G.

1932. Effects of removal of the visual cortex in mammals, with observations on the retention of light discrimination in dogs. *In:* Localization of function in the cerebral cortex, Research Pub. A. Research Nerv. & Ment. Dis., v. 13, p. 558. Williams & Wilkins Co., Baltimore.

1935. Phylogenetic interpretation of the functions of the visual cortex. Arch. Neurol. & Psychiat., v. 33, p. 807.

MARQUIS, D. G., & HILGARD, E. R.

1936. Conditioned lid responses to light in dogs after removal of the visual cortex. J. Comp. Psychol., v. 22, p. 157.

1937. Conditioned responses to light in monkeys after removal of the occipital lobes. Brain, v. 60, p. 1.

MARSHALL, W. H.

1951. Predation on shrews by frogs. J. Mammal., v. 32, p. 219.

MARSHALL, W. H., & TALBOT, S. A.

1942. Recent evidence for neural mechanisms in vision leading to a general theory of sensory acuity. *In:* Biol. symp., v. 7, p. 117. Jacques Cattell Press, Lancaster, Pa.

MARSHALL, W. H., WOOLSEY, C. N., & BARD, P.
1941. Observations on cortical somatic sensory mechanisms of cat and monkey. J. Neurophysiol., v. 4, p. 1.

MARTIN, E. V.
1950. Adaptation and origin in the plant world; the role of environment in evolution. Chronica Botanica Co., Waltham, Mass.

MARTIN, J. P.
1937. A dissection of the lower half of the optic radiation. Tr. Ophth. Soc. United Kingdom, v. 57 (1), p. 141.

MARTIN, L. C.
1923. Surveying and navigational instruments from the historical standpoint. Tr. Opt. Soc. London, v. 24, p. 289.
1926. The distribution of light in elementary optical images. *Ibid.*, v. 27, p. 249.

MARTIN, L. C., & KANIOWSKI, W.
1947. Flash visual acuity. Nature, v. 159, p. 25.

MARTIN, L. C., & PEARSE, R. W. B.
1947. The comparative visual acuity and ease of reading in white and coloured light. Brit. J. Ophth., v. 31, p. 129.

MARTIN, P.
1925. Hémianopsies quadrantales par lésion des radiations optiques. J. de neurol. et psychiat., v. 25, pp. 785, 810.

MARTIN, P., & CUSHING, H.
1923. Primary gliomas of the chiasm and optic nerves in their intracranial portion. Arch. Ophth., v. 52, p. 209.

MARTIN, T. H.
1868. Textes anciens sur les verres comburants par réfraction. Bull. di bibl. e di storia d. sc. mat. e fis. (Boncompagni), v. 1, p. 157.
1871. Sur des instruments d'optique faussement attribués aux anciens par quelques savants modernes. *Ibid.*, v. 4, p. 165.
1871. Ptolémée, auteur de l'optique traduite en latin par Ammiratus Eugenius Siculus sur une traduction arabe incomplète, est-il le même que Claude Ptolémée, auteur de l'Almageste? *Ibid.*, p. 466.

MARTINOTTI, C.
1887. Sulla struttura del nastro di Vicq-d-'Azyr. Contribuzione allo studio della corteccia cerebrale. Gior. sc. nat., v. 18, p. 269.
1890. Contributo allo studio della corteccia cerebrale e all'origine dei nervi. German trans.: Beitrag zum Studium der Hirnrinde und dem Centralursprung der Nerven. Internat. Monatsschr. f. Anat. u. Physiol., v. 7, p. 69.

MARUI, K.
1918. On the finer structure of the synapse of the Mauthner cell, etc. J. Comp. Neurol., v. 30, p. 127.

MARX, E.
1909. Die Ursache der roten Farbe des normalen ophthalmoskopisch beobachteten Augenhintergrundes. Arch. f. Ophth. (Graefe), v. 71, p. 141.

MARX, E., & TRENDELENBURG, W.
1911. Ueber die Genauigkeit der Einstellung des Auges beim Fixieren. Ztschr. f. Sinnesphysiol., v. 45, p. 87.

MASON, P. F.
1850. The natural productions of Burmah. American Mission Press, T. S. Ranney, Maulmain.

MASSA, NICCOLÒ
1536. Liber introductorius anatomiae sive dissectionis corporis humani. Inaedibus Francisci Bindoni ac Maphei Pasini socii . . . impressum, Venetiae.

MASSAUT, H.
1896. Experimentaluntersuchungen über den Verlauf der den Pupillarreflex vermittelnden Fasern. Arch. f. Psychiat. u. Nervenkr., v. 28, p. 432.

MASSON, A.
1923. Contribution à l'étude des syndromes du territoire de la artère cérébrale postérieure. Thèse, Paris.

MASSONNAT, E.
1909. Contribution à l'étude des pupipares. Ann. Univ. Lyon, N.S., I. Sciences méd., v. 28. A. Rey, Lyon; J.-B. Baillière & Fils, Paris.

MAST, S. O.
1910. Reactions in *Amoeba* to light. J. Exper. Zoöl., v. 9, p. 265.
1911. Light and the behavior of organisms. J. Wiley & Sons, New York.
1916. Changes in shade, color, and pattern in fishes, and their bearing on the problems of adaptation and behavior, with especial reference to the flounders, *Paralichthys* and *Ancyclopsetta*. Bull. Bur. Fish. U.S., v. 34 (for 1914), p. 173.
1917. The relation between spectral color and stimulation in the lower organisms. J. Exper. Zoöl., v. 22, p. 471.
1922. Eyes in *Volvox* and their function. Anat. Rec., v. 24, p. 397.
1926. Reactions to light in Volvox, with special reference to the process of orientation. Ztschr. f. vergl. Physiol., v. 4, p. 637.
1927. Reversal in photic orientation in Volvox and the nature of photic stimulation. *Ibid.*, v. 5, p. 730.

Mast, S. O.—*Continued*

1927. Response to electricity in Volvox and the nature of galvanic stimulation. *Ibid.*, p. 739.

1927. Structure and function of the eye-spot in unicellular and colonial organisms. Arch. f. Protistenk., v. 60, p. 197.

Mathews, F. S.

1921. Field book of wild birds and their music. G. P. Putnam's Sons, New York.

Mathewson, W. R.

1946. Meningioma of the tuberculum sellae with bi-temporal hemianopia. Brit. J. Ophth., v. 30, p. 92.

Matisse, G.

1947–49. Le rameau vivant du monde. 3 vols. Presses universitaires de France, Paris.

Matthes, E.

1934. Geruchsorgan. *In:* Bolk, Göppert, Kallius & Lubosch, Handb. d. vergl. Anat. d. Wirbeltiere, v. 2 (2), p. 879.

Matthew, W. D.

1939. Climate and evolution. 2d ed. New York Academy of Sciences, New York.

1943. Relations of the orders of mammals. J. Mammal., v. 43, p. 304.

Matthew, W. D., & Granger, W. A.

1915. A revision of the Lower Eocene Wasatch and Wind River faunas. Part 4. Entelonychia, primates, insectivora. Bull. Am. Mus. Nat. Hist., v. 34, pp. 1, 311, 329, 429.

Matthews, B. H. C.

1931. The response of a single end organ. J. Physiol., v. 71, p. 64.

1931. The response of a muscle spindle during active contraction of a muscle. *Ibid.*, v. 72, p. 153.

1933. Nerve endings in mammalian muscle. *Ibid.*, v. 78, p. 1.

Matthews, L. H., & Matthews, B. H. C.

1939. Owls and infra-red radiation. Nature, v. 143, p. 983.

Matthews, S. A.

1933. Changes in the retina of *Fundulus* after cutting the optic nerve and the blood vessels running to the eye. J. Exper. Zoöl., v. 66, p. 175.

Matthiessen, L.

1879. Ueber die geometrische Gestalt der theoretischen Retina des periskopischen schematischen Auges. Arch. f. Ophth. (Graefe), v. 25 (4), p. 257.

Mauss, T.

1908. Die faserarchitektonische Gliederung der Grosshirnrinde bei den niederen Affen. J. f. Psychol. u. Neurol., v. 13, p. 263.

1911. Die faserarchitektonische Gliederung des Cortex cerebri der anthropomorphen Affen. *Ibid.*, v. 18, p. 410.

Mawas, J.

1910. Notes cytologiques sur les cellules visuelles de l'homme et de quelques mammifères. Compt. rend. A. d'anat., v. 12, p. 113.

1937. Note sur la capsule de Tenon et sa signification histologique. Bull. Soc. opht. Paris, v. 2, p. 110.

Maxwell, J. C.

1854–55. Experiments on colour, as perceived by the eye, with remarks on colour-blindness. Tr. Roy. Soc. Edinburgh, v. 21, p. 275, 1857; *also* Scient. Papers, Cambridge, v. 1, p. 410, 1890.

1855. On the theory of colours in relation to colour-blindness, letter of Jan. 4, 1885, to G. Wilson, supplements to Research on colour-blindness, by G. Wilson. Southerland-Knox, Edinburgh.

1856. On the theory of compound colours with reference to mixture of blue and yellow lights. Brit. A. Adv. Sc., rep. 26th meet., Tr. Sec., p. 12.

1861. On the theory of compound colours, and the relations of the colours of the spectrum. Phil. Tr. Roy. Soc. London, v. 150, p. 57.

1873. Treatise on electricity and magnetism. 2 vols. Clarendon Press, Oxford. 2d ed., 1881; 3d ed., 1892.

1890. Scientific papers. 2 vols. Cambridge University Press, Cambridge. Photographic reprint, 1927.

Maxwell, M.

1928. The home of the eastern gorilla. J. Bombay Nat. Hist. Soc., v. 32, p. 436.

May, B.

1908. Ein Fall totaler Farbenblindheit. Ztschr. f. Sinnesphysiol., v. 42, p. 69.

May, C. H.

1949. Manual of the diseases of the eye. 20th ed. Williams & Wilkins Co., Baltimore.

May, R. M., & Detwiler, S. R.

1925. The relation of transplanted eyes to developing nerve-centers. J. Exper. Zoöl., v. 43, p. 83.

Mayendorf; *see* Niessl von Mayendorf

Mayer

1820. Das Auge, ein Hohlspiegel. Deutsch. Arch. f. d. Physiol. (Meckel), v. 6, p. 54.

Mayer, J. C. A.

1779. Anatomisch-physiologische Abhandlung vom Gehirn, Rueckmark, und Ursprung der Nerven. G. J. Decker, Berlin & Leipzig.

MAYER, L. L.
1940. The optic pathway. Arch. Ophth., v. 23, p. 382; *also* J. Am. Med. Assoc., v. 112, p. 1494.

MAYER-GROSS, W., & STEIN, J.
1928. Pathologie der Wahrnehmung. *In:* BUMKE (ed.), Handb. d. Geisteskrankheiten, v. 1 (1), p. 351.

MAYERHAUSEN, G.
1883. Noch einmal der gefässlose Bezirk der menschlichen Retina. Arch. f. Ophth. (Graefe), v. 29 (1), p. 150.

1883. Beitrag zur Kenntniss der Photopsien in der Umgebung des Fixirpunktes. *Ibid.*, v. 29 (4), p. 199.

MAYNARD, C. J.
1889. Singular effects produced by the bite of a short-tailed shrew, *Blarina brevicauda*. Contr. Sc., Newtonville, v. 1, p. 57.

MAYO, H.
1842. The nervous system and its functions. J. W. Parker, London.

MAYR, E.
1942. Systematics and the origin of species from the viewpoint of a zoölogist. Columbia University Press, New York.

1949. Speciation and systematics. *In:* JEPSEN *et al.*, Genetics, paleontology, and evolution, p. 281.

1950. Taxonomic categories in fossil hominids. Cold Spring Harbor Symp. Quant. Biol., v. 15, p. 109.

MAZZA, A.
1891. Metodo sperimentale per lo studio dei centri corticali della visione nella scimmia. Ann. di ottal., v. 20, p. 44.

MAZZATINTI, G.
1890–1950. Inventari dei manoscritti delle biblioteche d'Italia. L. S. Olschki, Firenze.

MEADER, R. G.
1934. The optic system of the teleost, *Holocentrus*. J. Comp. Neurol., v. 60, p. 361.

1936. Accommodation and its reflex pathways in the teleosts. Yale J. Biol. & Med., v. 8, p. 511.

1938. Physiological and anatomical consequences of forebrain ablation in the teleost, *Holocentrus*. Anat. Rec., suppl. 3, p. 55.

1939. On the time and place of experimental myelin degeneration in the optic pathways. Proc. Kon. nederl. Akad. Wetensch., Amsterdam, v. 42, p. 526.

MEADER, R. G., & HAGEDOORN, A.
1940. Finer localization of retinal projection on the primary optic centers in mammals. Anat. Rec., v. 76, suppl. 2, p. 41. (Abstr.)

MEARNS, E. A.
1905. Description of new genera and species of mammals from the Philippine Islands. Proc. U.S. Nat. Mus., v. 28, p. 425.

MECKEL, J. F.
1815. Versuch einer Entwicklungsgeschichte der Centraltheile des Nervensystems in den Säugethieren. Deutsch. Arch. f. d. Physiol. (Meckel), v. 1, p. 1.

1815–20. Handbuch der menschlichen Anatomie. 4 vols. Buchhandlung des Hallischen Waisenhauses, Halle & Berlin.

1821–31. System der vergleichenden Anatomie. 5 vols. Rengersche Buchhandlung, Halle.

MEES, C. E. K.
1932. Article: Photography, Encyclopaedia Britannica, 14th ed., v. 17, p. 799.

MEESMANN, A.
1927. Die Mikroskopie des lebenden Auges an der Gullstrandschen Spaltlampe mit Atlas typischer Befunde. Urban & Schwarzenberg, Berlin & Wien.

MEGGENDORFER, F.
1916. Ueber Vortäuschung verschiedener Nervenkrankheiten durch Hypophysentumoren. Deutsch. Ztschr. f. Nervenh., v. 55, p. 1.

MEIGE, H.
1904. Migraine ophtalmique, hémianopsie et aphasie transitoires, etc. Rev. neurol., v. 12, p. 961.

MELLER, J.
1953. Ophthalmic surgery. Blakiston Co., New York.

MELLUS, E. L.
1901. Bilateral relations of the cerebral cortex. Proc. A. Am. Anat., 14th sess., p. 159; Bull. Johns Hopkins Hosp., v. 12, p. 108.

MELSON, E. W.
1938. Hermann von Helmholtz. Ed. Focus, v. 9, No. 1.

MENABONI, A. & S.
1950. Birds. Rinehart & Co., New York.

MENDEL, E.
1883. Ueber die Affenspalte. Neurol. Centralbl., v. 2, p. 217.

MENDEL, K.
1914. Ueber Rechtshirnigkeit bei Rechtshändern. Neurol. Centralbl., v. 33, p. 291.

MENDELSOHN, S.
1944. The mortuary craft of ancient Egypt. Ciba Symp., v. 6, p. 1795.

MENNER, E.
1929. Untersuchungen über die Retina mit besonderer Berücksichtigung der äusseren

Körnerschicht. Ein Beitrag zur Duplizitätstheorie. Ztschr. f. vergl. Physiol., v. 8,
p. 761.

1930. Zapfen in der Retina der Maus. Ztschr. f.
Zellforsch., v. 11, p. 53.

1930. Ueber die Stützelemente in der Retina der
Wirbeltiere. *Ibid.*, p. 414.

1931. Ueber die Retina einiger Kleinaffen aus den
Familien Callitrichidae und Cebidae. Zool.
Anz., v. 95, p. 1.

1938. Die Bedeutung des Pecten im Auge des Vo-
gels für die Wahrnehmung von Bewegungen,
nebst Bemerkungen über seine Ontogenie
und Histologie. Zool. Jahrb. (Allg. Zool. &
Physiol.), v. 58, p. 481.

MERKEL, F.

1869. Ueber die Macula lutea des Menschen und
die Ora serrata einiger Wirbelthiere. W.
Engelmann, Leipzig.

1870. Zur Kenntnis der Stäbchenschichte der
Retina. Arch. f. Anat., Physiol. & wissensch.
Med., p. 642.

1874. Makroskopische Anatomie [orbit, optic
nerve, eye, etc.]. *In:* GRAEFE & SAEMISCH,
Handb. d. ges. Augenh., 1st ed., v. 1 (1),
p. 1.

1876. Ueber die menschliche Retina. Arch. f.
Ophth. (Graefe), v. 22 (4), p. 1; Klin.
Monatsbl. f. Augenh., v. 15, p. 205.

1885–90. Handbuch der topographischen Anatomie, v. 1. F. Vieweg & Sohn, Braunschweig.

1891. Jacob Henle, ein deutsches Gelehrtenleben.
Nach Aufzeichnungen und Erinnerungen
erzählt von Fr. Merkel. F. Vieweg & Sohn,
Braunschweig.

1892–94. Sehorgan. Anat. Hefte (Merkel & Bonnet), Ergebn., v. 1, p. 233; v. 2, p. 236; v. 3,
p. 281.

1893. Ueber die Entwickelung der Anatomie.
Festrede im Namen der Georg-Augusts-
Universität zur akademischen Preisver-
theilung am III. Juni MDCCCXCIII.
Dieterichsche Univ.-Buchdruckerei, Göt-
tingen.

1909. Jakob Henle. Gedächtnisrede gehalten im
Anatomischen Institut zu Göttingen am 19.
Juli 1909 dem hundertsten Geburtstag des
Gelehrten von Fr. Merkel. F. Vieweg &
Sohn, Braunschweig.

MERKEL, F., & KALLIUS, E.

1901. Makroskopische Anatomie des Auges. *In:*
GRAEFE & SAEMISCH, Handb. d. ges. Augenh., 2d ed., v. 1 (1), p. 1, 1910.

MERKEL, F., & ORR, W.

1892. Das Auge des Neugeborenen, etc. Anat.
Hefte (Ref. u. Beitr.), v. 1, p. 271.

MERKER, E.

1926. Die Empfindlichkeit feuchthäutiger Tiere
im Lichte. Zool. Jahrb. (Allg. Zool. u.
Physiol.), v. 42, p. 487.

1934. Die Sichtbarkeit ultravioletten Lichtes.
Biol. Rev., v. 9, p. 49.

1937. Der Lichttod feuchthäutiger, wechselwar-
mer Tiere. Naturwiss., v. 25, p. 70.

1937–39. Die physikalische Leistung des Fischauges in kurzwelligem Licht. Zool. Jahrb.
(Allg. Zool. u. Physiol.), v. 58, p. 330; v. 59,
p. 391.

1938. Der Einfluss kurzwelligen Lichtes auf die
Tierwelt. Bioklim. Beibl., v. 5, p. 167.

1939. Drei Fälle verschiedener Lichtdurchlässig-
keit der Augenlinsen von Wirbeltieren.
Biol. Zentralbl., v. 59, p. 87.

MERRIAM, C. H.

1884 (1886). The mammals of the Adirondack region (northeastern New York). L. S. Foster,
New York.

MERRITT, H. H., & ARING, C. D.

1938. The differential diagnosis of cerebral vascu-
lar lesions. Research Pub. A. Research Nerv.
& Ment. Dis., v. 18, p. 682. Williams &
Wilkins Co., Baltimore.

MERRITT, H. H., METTLER, F. A., & PUTNAM, T. J.

1947. Fundamentals of clinical neurology. Blakiston Co., Philadelphia.

MERRITT, H. H., & MOORE, M.

1933. The Argyll Robertson pupil. An anatomic-
physiologic explanation of the phenomenon,
with a survey of its occurrence in neurosyphilis. Arch. Neurol. & Psychiat., v. 30,
p. 357.

MERTON, H.

1905. Ueber die Retina von Nautilus und einigen
dibranchiaten Cephalopoden. Ztschr. f. wissensch. Zool., v. 79, p. 325.

MERY, JEAN

1704. Des mouvements de l'iris et par occasion de
la partie principale de l'organe de la vûë.
Hist. Acad. roy. d. sc., Paris, p. 261.

1704. Von den Bewegungen der Iridis; und von
dem vornehmsten Werckzeuge des Gesichts.
In: A. MAÎTRE-JAN, Tractat von den
Kranckheiten des Auges, p. 55, 1725. Orig.
in Hist. Acad. roy. d. sc., Paris, 1704.

MERZBACHER, L.

1903. Untersuchungen über die Function des Centralnervensystems der Fledermaus. Arch. f.
d. ges. Physiol. (Pflüger), v. 96, p. 572.

1903. Untersuchungen an winterschlafenden Fledermäusen. *Ibid.*, v. 97, p. 569.

1903. Einige Beobachtungen an winterschlafenden Fledermäusen. Centralbl. f. Physiol., v. 16, p. 709.

MERZBACHER, L., & SPIELMEYER, W.

1903. Beiträge zur Kenntnis des Fledermausgehirns, besonders der corticomotorischen Bahnen. Neurol. Centralbl., v. 22, p. 1050.

MESSIMY, R., & FINAN, J. L.

1937. Les effets, chez le singe, de l'ablation des lobes préfrontaux. Modifications de l'activité et du mode réactionnel. Compt. rend. Soc. de biol., v. 126, p. 201.

1937. Les effets, chez le singe, de l'ablation des lobes préfrontaux. Modifications des réflexes notamment des réflexes de posture. Modification du système autonome. *Ibid.*, p. 203.

METCALF, M. M.

1906. Salpa and the phylogeny of the eyes of vertebrates. Anat. Anz., v. 29, p. 526.

METTLER, F. A.

1932. Connections of the auditory cortex of the cat. J. Comp. Neurol., v. 55, p. 139.

1933. Brain of *Pithecus rhesus* (*M. rhesus*). Am. J. Phys. Anthropol., v. 17, p. 309.

1935. Corticifugal fiber connections of the cortex of *Macaca mulatta*. The occipital region. J. Comp. Neurol., v. 61, p. 221. The parietal region. *Ibid.*, v. 62, p. 263; The temporal region. *Ibid.*, v. 63, p. 25.

1942. Neuroanatomy. C. V. Mosby Co., St. Louis.

1943. Extensive unilateral cerebral removals in the primate: physiologic effects and resultant degeneration. J. Comp. Neurol., v. 79, p. 185.

1945. Effects of bilateral simultaneous subcortical lesions in the primate. J. Neuropath. & Exper. Neurol., v. 4, p. 99.

1945. Fiber connections of the corpus striatum of the monkey and baboon. J. Comp. Neurol., v. 82, p. 169.

METZ, A.

1868. The anatomy and histology of the human eye. Office of the M. and Surg. Reporter, Philadelphia.

METZ, A., & SPATZ, H.

1924. Die Hortegaschen Zellen (das sogenannte "dritte Element") und über ihre funktionelle Bedeutung. Ztschr. f. d. ges. Neurol. u. Psychiat., v. 89, p. 138.

METZGER, E.

1925. Ueber das physiologische Substrat der optisch-motorischen Erlebniseinheit. Ber. d. Deutsch. ophth. Gesellsch. Heidelberg, v. 45, p. 97.

METZGER, W.

1936. Gesetze des Sehens. W. Kramer, Frankfurt a.M.

MEYER, A.

1892. Ueber das Vorderhirn einiger Reptilien. Ztschr. f. wissensch. Zool., v. 55, p. 63.

1907. The connections of the occipital lobes and the present status of the cerebral visual affections. Tr. A. Am. Physicians, v. 22, p. 7.

1912. The temporal lobe detour of the optic radiations and its importance for the diagnosis of temporal lobe lesions. Tr. Am. Neurol. A., 37th meet., p. 201, 1911.

MEYER, A., & MEYER, M.

1945. *Boutons terminaux* in the cerebral cortex. J. Anat., v. 79, p. 180.

MEYER, A. B.

1895. Eine neue Tarsius-Art. Abh. u. Ber. d. Kgl. zool. u. anthrop.-ethnog. Mus. Dresden, v. 5, No. 1.

1897–99. Säugethiere vom Celebes- und Philippinen-Archipel. Abh. u. Ber. d. Kgl. zool. u. anthrop.-ethnog. Mus. Dresden, v. 6, No. 6, pp. 8, 9; v. 7, No. 7, p. 4.

MEYER, A. W.

1930. Malpighi as anatomist. Science, v. 72, p. 234.

1931–32. Essays on the history of embryology. California & West. Med., v. 35, p. 447; v. 36, pp. 40, 105, 176, 241, 341, 394; v. 37, pp. 41, 111, 184, 243.

1938. Leeuwenhoek as experimental biologist. Osiris, v. 3, p. 103.

1939. The rise of embryology. Stanford University Press, Stanford, Calif.; Oxford University Press, London.

MEYER, F.

1887. Zur Anatomie der Orbitalarterien. Morphol. Jahrb. (Gegenbaur), v. 12, p. 414.

MEYER, H. H.

1934. Kausalitätsfragen in der Biologie. Naturwiss., v. 22, p. 598.

MEYER, K. H.

1937. The origin of bioelectric phenomena. Tr. Faraday Soc., v. 33, p. 1049.

MEYER, O.

1900. Ein- und doppelseitige homonyme Hemianopsie mit Orientirungsstörungen. Monatsschr. f. Psychiat. u. Neurol., v. 8, p. 440.

MEYERHOF, M.

1914. Histoire du chichm, remède ophtalmique des Égyptiens. Janus, v. 19, p. 261.

1915. Beitrag zur unteren Hemianopsie nach

Schädelschuss. Klin. Monatsbl. f. Augenh., v. 56, p. 62.

1920. Die Optik der Araber. Ztschr. f. ophth. Optik, v. 8, pp. 16, 42, 86; *also* Deutsch. opt. Wchnschr., 1917.

1926. New light on Ḥunain ibn Isḥâq and his period. Isis, v. 8, p. 685.

1930. Von Alexandrien nach Bagdad. Ein Beitrag zur Geschichte des philosophischen und medizinischen Unterrichts bei den Arabern. Sitzungsb. d. preuss. Akad. d. Wissensch., phil.-hist. Kl., Berlin, p. 389.

1933. La fin de l'école d'Alexandrie d'après quelques auteurs arabes. Archéion, v. 15, p. 1.

1940. Eye diseases in ancient Egypt. Ciba Symp., v. 1, No. 10.

1944. The background and origins of Arabian pharmacology. Pharmacology during the golden age of Arabian medicine. Arabian pharmacology in North Africa, Sicily, and the Iberian Peninsula. The sources of the history of Arabian medicine. *Ibid.*, v. 6, pp. 1847, 1857, 1868, 1873.

1945. Sultan Saladin's physician on the transmission of Greek medicine to the Arabs. Bull. Hist. Med., v. 18, p. 169.

MEYERHOF, M., & PRÜFER, C.

1911. Die Augenanatomie des Ḥunain b. Isḥâq. Arch. f. Gesch. d. Med. (Sudhoff), v. 4, p. 163.

1913. Die Lehre vom Sehen bei Ḥunain b. Isḥâq. *Ibid.*, v. 6, p. 21.

MEYER-STEINEG, T.

1912. Chirurgische Instrumente des Altertums. Jena. med.-hist. Beiträge, v. 1. G. Fischer, Jena.

1912–13. Studien zur Physiologie des Galenos. I–IV. Arch. f. Gesch. d. Med., v. 5, p. 172; v. 6, p. 417.

1913. Ein Tag im Leben des Galen. E. Diederichs, Jena.

MEYER-STEINEG, T., & SUDHOFF, K.

1922. Geschichte der Medizin im Ueberblick. 2d ed. G. Fischer, Jena.

MEYNERT, T.; for biography *see* ANTON 1930; DE CRINIS 1939

1865. Anatomie der Hirnrinde und ihrer Verbindungsbahnen mit den empfindenden Oberflächen und den bewegenden Massen. *In:* M. LEIDESDORF, Lehrb. d. psychiat. Krankheiten. Erlangen.

1867. Studien über die Bestandtheile der Vierhügel, soweit sie in den nächst unterhalb gelegenen Querschnitten der Brücke gege-

ben sind. Ztschr. f. wissensch. Zool., v. 17, p. 655.

1867–68. Der Bau der Gross-Hirnrinde und seine örtlichen Verschiedenheiten, nebst einem pathologisch-anatomischen Corollarium. Vierteljahrsschr. f. Psychiat. (Leidesdorf & Meynert), v. 1, p. 77; v. 2, p. 88.

1868. Ueber die Nothwendigkeit und Tragweite einer anatomischen Richtung in der Psychiatrie. Wien. med. Wchnschr., v. 18, pp. 573, 589.

1868–69. Neuere Untersuchungen über den Bau der Grosshirnrinde und ihre örtlichen Verschiedenheiten. Wien. med. Presse, v. 9, p. 1166; Wochenbl. d. k. k. Gesellsch. d. Aerzte in Wien, v. 8, p. 450; Med. Jahrb., v. 17, p. 13.

1869. Beiträge zur Kenntniss der centralen Projection der Sinnesoberflächen. Sitzungsb. d. Akad. Wissensch., Wien, math.-nat. Cl., v. 60 (2), p. 547, 1870.

1869. Ueber die Bedeutung der Erkrankungen der Grosshirnrinde, begründet auf deren äusserer Gestaltung und inneren Bau. Allg. Wien. med. Zeitung, v. 14, pp. 107, 115; *also* Oesterr. Ztschr. f. prakt. Heilk., v. 15, p. 229.

1872. Vom Gehirne der Säugethiere. *In:* S. STRICKER, Handb. d. Lehre v. d. Geweben d. Mensch. u. d. Thiere, v. 2, p. 694. *See also* (in English trans.: Manual of human and comparative histology, ed. STRICKER, v. 2, p. 367) The brain of mammals.

1877. Die Windungen der convexen Oberfläche des Vorder-Hirnes bei Menschen, Affen und Raubthieren. Arch. f. Psychiat., v. 7, p. 257.

1886. Demonstration sagittaler Hirnschnitte von Menschen nebst kurzem Vortrage. Neurol. Centralbl., v. 5, p. 456.

1887. Die anthropologische Bedeutung der frontalen Gehirnentwicklung. Jahrb. f. Psychiat., v. 7, p. 1.

1892. Psychiatry: a clinical treatise on diseases of the fore-brain based upon a study of its structure, functions, and nutrition. G. P. Putnam's Sons, New York & London.

MICHAELIS, E.

1877. Albrecht von Graefe. Sein Leben und Wirken. G. Reimer, Berlin.

MICHAELIS, G. A.

1838. Ueber die Retina, besonders über die Macula lutea und das Foramen centrale. Verhandl. d. Leopold.-Carol. Akad. d. Naturforsch. (Nova acta, etc.), v. 19 (2), p. 1, 1842.

See also Arch. f. Anat., Physiol. u. wissensch. Med. (J. Müller), 1837, Jahresb., p. xii.

MICHAELIS, P.
1796. Ueber einen gelben Fleck und ein Loch in der Nervenhaut des menschlichen Auges. J. d. Erfind., Theorien u. Widersprüche, 15. Stück, p. 3. Kurze Bemerkungen (on the discovery of the yellow spot). *Ibid.*, 17. Stück, pp. 121, 127.

MICHAELS, D. D.
1952. Nature and distribution of retinal receptor mechanisms. Optomet. World, April, p. 24; June, p. 40.
1952. The chemistry of the visual process. J. Am. Optomet. A., January, p. 329.

MICHAELS, J. J.
1931. Fanning as a structural pattern in the nervous system. J. Nerv. & Ment. Dis., v. 74, p. 46.

MICHAELS, J. J., & KRAUS, W. M.
1930. Measurements of cerebral and cerebellar surfaces. IX. Measurement of cortical areas in cat, dog and monkey. Arch. Neurol. & Psychiat., v. 24, p. 94.

MICHAELSON, I. C.
1948. The mode of development of the vascular system of the retina, with some observations on its significance for certain retinal diseases. Tr. Ophth. Soc. United Kingdom, v. 68, p. 137.
1948. Vascular morphogenesis in the retina of the cat. J. Anat., v. 82, p. 167.

MICHAELSON, I. C., & CAMPBELL, A. C. P.
1940. Anatomy of finer retinal vessels, and some observations on their significance in certain retinal diseases. Tr. Ophth. Soc. United Kingdom, v. 60, p. 71.

MICHEL, J.
1873. Ueber den Bau des Chiasma nervorum opticorum. Arch. f. Ophth. (Graefe), v. 19 (2), p. 59; (3), p. 375.
1874. Ueber die Ausstrahlungsweise der Opticusfasern in der menschlichen Retina. *In:* Beitr. z. Anat. u. Phys. als Festgabe C. Ludwig, p. lvi. F. C. W. Vogel, Leipzig.
1877. Zur Frage der Sehnerven-Kreuzung im Chiasma. Arch. f. Ophth. (Graefe), v. 23 (2), p. 227.
1887. Ueber Sehnervendegeneration und Sehnervenkreuzung. *In:* Festschr. d. med. Fac. d. Univ. Würzburg zur Feier des LXX Geburtstages des Dr. Albert von Kölliker. Wiesbaden, J. Bergmann.

MICHEL, K.
1933. Die Akkommodation des Schlangenauges. Jena. Ztschr. f. Naturwiss., v. 66, p. 577.

MICHELSON, A. A.
1927. Studies in optics. University of Chicago Press, Chicago.
1931. Die Relativbewegung der Erde gegen den Lichtäther. Naturwiss., v. 19, p. 779.

MIDLO, C.
1935. Dermatoglyphics in *Tupaia lacernata lacernata.* J. Mammal., v. 16, p. 35.

MILES, P. W.
1951. Testing visual fields by flicker fusion. Arch. Neurol. & Psychiat., v. 65, p. 39.

MILES, W. R.
1940. Modification of the human-eye potential by dark and light adaptation. Science, v. 91, p. 456.
1949. A functional analysis of regional differences in the human fovea. J. Opt. Soc. Amer., v. 39, p. 630.

MILLER, G. S.
1902. The mammals of the Andaman and Nicobar Islands. Proc. U.S. Nat. Mus., v. 24, p. 751.
1911. Descriptions of two new genera and sixteen new species of mammals from the Philippine Islands. *Ibid.*, v. 38, p. 391.

MILLER, H. R.
1942. Central autonomic regulations in health and disease with special reference to the hypothalamus. Grune & Stratton, New York.

MILLER, R.
1942. Newton's rings—the optical yardstick. Ed. Focus (Bausch & Lomb), v. 13, No. 2, p. 23.

MILLER, R. A.
1935. Functional adaptation in the forelimb of the sloths. J. Mammal., v. 16, p. 38.
1943. Functional and morphological adaptations in the forelimbs of the slow lemurs. Am. J. Anat., v. 73, p. 153.
1945. The ischial callosities of primates. Am. J. Anat., v. 76, p. 67.

MILLER, R. G.
1945. Food habits of Yosemite mammals as indicated by their teeth. Part 3. Moles and shrews (Insectivora), bats (Chiroptera). Yosemite Nature Notes, v. 24, p. 54.

MILLER, R. N.
1940. The diencephalic cell mass of the teleost, *Corydora paliatus.* J. Comp. Neurol., v. 73, p. 345.

MILLS, C. K.
1891. On the localisation of the auditory centre. Brain, v. 14, p. 465.
1895. The anatomy of the cerebral cortex and the localisation of functions. *In:* F. X. DERCUM (ed.), A text-book on nervous diseases by

American authors, p. 381. Lea Bros. & Co., Philadelphia.

1896. Cerebral localisation in the light of recent histological researches. J. Am. Med. Assoc., v. 26, p. 23.

1899. Anomia and paranomia, with some considerations regarding a naming center in the temporal lobe. J. Nerv. & Ment. Dis., v. 26, p. 757.

1927. Discussion on cortical localization, Brain, v. 50, p. 467.

1929. Cerebral localization and failures in written language. Arch. Neurol. & Psychiat., v. 22, p. 1127.

MILLS, C. K., & McCONNELL, J. W.

1895. The naming centre, with the report of a case indicating its location in the temporal lobe. J. Nerv. & Ment. Dis., v. 22 (N.S., v. 20), p. 1.

MILLS, C. K., & SCHWEINITZ, G. E.

1896. The association of hemianopsia with certain symptom-groups, chiefly with reference to the diagnosis of the site of the lesion. Philadelphia Hosp. Rep., v. 3, p. 91.

MILLS, C. K., & WEISENBURG, T. H.

1906. The subdivision of the representation of cutaneous and muscular sensibility and of stereognosis in the cerebral cortex. J. Nerv. & Ment. Dis., v. 33, p. 617.

MILLS, L.

1938. Ocular dominance. Arch. Ophth., v. 20, p. 105.

MILNE, J. S.

1907. Surgical instruments in Greek and Roman times. Clarendon Press, Oxford.

MILNE, L. J., & MILNE, M. J.

1943. Selection of colored lights by night-flying insects. Anat. Rec., v. 87, p. 457. (Abstr.)

1948. Arizona is the horned toad state. Arizona Highways, v. 24, No. 10, October, p. 24.

MINCKLER, J.

1940. The morphology of the nerve terminals of the human spinal cord as seen in black silver preparations, with estimates of the total number per cell. Anat. Rec., v. 77, p. 9.

1941. Distribution of nerve terminals (boutons) in the human spinal cord. Arch. Neurol. & Psychiat., v. 45, p. 44.

1942. Pathologic alterations in surface relationships and morphology at the human synapse. Am. J. Path., v. 18, p. 1061.

MINER, N.

1951. Integumental specification of sensory neurons in the genesis of cutaneous local sign. University of Chicago thesis—summary.

MINGAZZINI, G.

1893. Intorno alla morfologia dell' "Affenspalte." Anat. Anz., v. 8, p. 191.

1908. Lesioni di anatomia clinica dei centri nervosi. Unione tipografica, Torino.

1913. Ueber die Beteiligung beider Hirnhemisphären an der Funktion der Sprache (gleichzeitig ein pathologisch-anatomischer Beitrag zum Studium einiger Hirnformationen). Folia neuro-biol., v. 7, p. 1.

1915. Ueber den gegenwärtigen Stand unserer Kenntnis der Aphasielehre. Monatsschr. f. Psychiat. u. Neurol., v. 37, p. 150.

1922. Der Balken. Eine anatomische, physiopathologische und klinische Studie. Monog. a. d. Gesgeb. d. Neurol. u. Psychiat., v. 28. J. Springer, Berlin.

1925. Ueber den heutigen Stand der Aphasielehre. Klin. Wchnschr., v. 4 (2), p. 1289.

1928. Beitrag zur Morphologie der äusseren Grosshirnhemisphärenoberfläche bei den Anthropoiden (Schimpanse und Orang). Arch. f. Psychiat., v. 85, p. 1.

1928. Das Mittelhirn. *In:* MÖLLENDORFF, Handb. d. mikr. Anat., v. 4 (1), p. 644.

MINKOWSKI, M.

1910. Zur Physiologie der kortikalen Sehsphäre. Neurol. Centralbl., v. 29, p. 1362.

1911. Zur Physiologie der cortikalen Sehsphäre. Deutsch. Ztschr. f. Nervenh., v. 41, p. 109; Arch. f. d. ges. Physiol. (Pflüger), v. 141, p. 171.

1912. Experimentelle Untersuchungen über die Beziehungen des Grosshirns zum Corpus geniculatum externum. Neurol. Centralbl., v. 22, p. 1470.

1913. Experimentelle Untersuchungen über die Beziehungen der Grosshirnrinde und der Netzhaut zu den primären optischen Zentren, besonders zum Corpus geniculatum externum. Arb. a. d. hirnanat. Inst. Zürich, v. 7, p. 255.

1914. Ueber die Sehrinde und ihre Beziehungen zu den primären optischen Zentren. Monatsschr. f. Psychiat. u. Neurol., v. 35, p. 420.

1917. Étude sur la physiologie des circonvolutions rolandiques et pariétales. Schweiz. Arch. f. Neurol. u. Psychiat., v. 1, p. 389.

1920. Ueber die anatomischen Bedingungen des binocularen Sehens im Bereich der zentralen optischen Bahnen. Verhandl. d. Schweiz. Naturforsch. Gesellsch., 101th sess., p. 231; Schweiz. med. Wchnschr., v. 51, p. 307, 1921.

1920. Ueber den Verlauf, die Endigung und die

zentrale Repräsentation von gekreuzten und ungekreuzten Sehnervenfasern bei einigen Säugetieren und beim Menschen. Schweiz. Arch. f. Neurol. u. Psychiat., v. 6, p. 201; v. 7, p. 268.

1922. Sur les conditions anatomiques de la vision binoculaire dans les voies optiques centrales. Encéphale, v. 17, p. 65.

1923–24. Étude sur les connexions anatomiques des circonvolutions rolandiques, pariétales et frontales. Schweiz. Arch. f. Neurol. u. Psychiat., v. 12, pp. 71, 227; v. 14, p. 255; v. 15, p. 97.

1928. Sur un cas d'aphasie chez un polyglotte. Rev. neurol., v. 1, p. 361.

1930. Auge und Gehirn. Liječnički Vjesnik, v. 52, p. 491; Zentralbl. f. d. ges. Ophth., v. 24, p. 632.

1931. Constantin von Monakow. Schweiz. Arch. f. Neurol. u. Psychiat., v. 27, p. 1.

1932. Salomon Eberhard Henschen (obituary). *Ibid.*, v. 29, p. 179.

1932. Zur Frage der zentralen Repräsentation von gekreuzten und ungekreuzten Sehnervenfasern in den zentralen optischen Bahnen, besonders im Corpus geniculatum externum. Deutsch. Ztschr. f. Nervenh., v. 124, p. 154.

1934. Zur Frage der Endigung und der Repräsentation von gekreuzten und ungekreuzten Sehnervenfasern im Corpus geniculatum externum. Psychiat. en neurol. bl., v. 38, p. 514; Deutsch. Ztschr. f. Nervenh., v. 124, p. 154, 1932.

1936. Aperçu d'histoire de la neurologie à Zurich. Arch. internat. de neurol., v. 55 (28 ser.), p. 531; *also* Guide offic. Cong. méd. alién. & neurol., etc., à Zurich.

1939. Zur Kenntnis der cerebralen Sehbahnen. Schweiz. med. Wchnschr., v. 20, p. 990.

1953. Zentenarfeier für Constantin von Monakow. Neue Zürcher Zeitung, 9. Dezember, Bl. 3, No. 2996.

MINNICH, D. E.
1939. The light response of the marine tubificid worm, *Clitellio arenarius* (O. F. Müller). J. Exper. Zoöl., v. 82, p. 397; Bull. Mt. Desert Island Biol. Lab., p. 25, 1938.

MINSKY, H.
1942. Concept of a zonular chamber. Arch. Ophth., v. 28, p. 214.

MIRTO, D.
1895. Sulla fina anatomia del tetto ottico dei pesci teleostei e sull'origine reale del nervo ottico. Riv. sper. di freniat., v. 21, p. 136.

MISCH, W.
1928. Ueber corticale Taubheit. Ztschr. f. d. ges. Neurol. u. Psychiat., v. 115, p. 567.

MISKOLCZY, D.
1926. Warum kreuzen sich die zentralen Bahnen des Nervensystems? Ztschr. f. Anat. u. Entw., v. 81, p. 641.

MITCHELL, P. C.
1919. Character of *Tarsius*. Proc. Zoöl. Soc. London, p. 196.

MÖBIUS, P. J.
1903. Ueber Farbe und Raum. Centralbl. f. Nervenh., v. 26, p. 451.

1905. Franz Joseph Gall. *In:* MÖBIUS, Ausgewählte Werke, v. 7. J. A. Barth, Leipzig.

MÖHRES, F. P.
1952. Die Ultraschall-Orientierung der Fledermäuse. Naturwiss., v. 39, p. 273. (*See also* Hollmann, p. 384; Kleesattel, p. 574, in same vol.)

MOEHRING, P. H. G.
1739. Historiae medicinales junctus fere ubique corollariis proxin medicam illustrantibus. Amstelodami. Later ed. Apud Arksteum et Merkum, Amstelodami, 1761.

MOELI, C.
1889. Ueber Befunde bei Erkrankungen des Hinterhauptslappens. Neurol. Centralbl., v. 8, p. 439.

1891. Veränderungen des Tractus und Nervus opticus bei Erkrankungen des Occipitalhirns. Arch. f. Psychiat. u. Nervenkr., v. 22, p. 73.

1898. Ueber atrophische Folgezustände in Chiasma und Sehnerven. *Ibid.*, v. 30, p. 907.

1905. Ueber das centrale Höhlengrau bei vollständiger Atrophie des Sehnerven. *Ibid.*, v. 39, p. 437.

MÖLLENDORFF, W. VON
1928–36. Handbuch der mikroskopischen Anatomie des Menschen, v. 3 (2) Auge; v. 4 (1) Nervensystem. J. Springer, Berlin.

MOELLER, J. H.
1749. Observationes circa tunicam retinam et nervum opticum. *In:* Disput. select. (A. Haller), v. 7 (2), p. 187.

MOENCH, L. G.
1951. Headache. 2d ed. Year Book Publishers, Chicago, Ill.

MOGEY, J. M.
1949. Review of A. KEITH, A new theory of human evolution. Man, v. 49, p. 22.

MOHR, A.
1879. Ein Beitrag zur Frage der Semidecussation im Chiasma nervorum opticorum. Arch. f. Ophth. (Graefe), v. 25 (1), p. 57.

MOHR, C. E.
  1942. Results of ten years' bat marking in Pennsylvania. Proc. Pennsylvania Acad. Sc., v. 16, p. 32.
MOHR, T., & BÖHM, L.
  1921. Doppelseitiger Verschluss der Arteria centralis retinae durch Embolie bei Endocarditis verrucosa mit Sektionsbefund und mikroskopischer Untersuchung der Bulbi. Klin. Monatsbl. f. Augenh., v. 66, p. 812.
MOLINELLI, P. P.
  *1731. De Bononiensi scientiarum instituto atque academia commentarii.
MOLINETTI, A.
  1669. Antonii Molinetti Phil. et Medici Veneti Prima Sede in Celeberimo Patavino Lyceo Theoricae Medicinae & Anatomes Professoris *Dissertationes Anatomicae et Pathologicae de Sensibus* & eorum organis. Patavii MDCLXIX. In Typographia Matthaei Bolzetta de Cadorinis. Superiorum Permissu, et Privilegio. *Also* Apud P. Balleonium, Venetiis 1675.
MOLLIER, G.
  1938. Der Bau des menschlichen Ciliarmuskels. Anat. Anz., v. 85 (suppl.), p. 240.
MOLLWEIDE, K.
  1925. Einheitscharakter des seelischen Geschehens und Lokalisationsprinzip. Ztschr. f. d. ges. Neurol. u. Psychiat., v. 98, p. 615.
MOLYNEAUX, W.
  1692. *Dioptrica Nova. A Treatise of Dioptricks*, in Two Parts Wherein the Various Effects and Appearances of *Spherick Glasses*, both Convex and Concave, Single and Combined, in Telescopes and Microscopes, Together with their Usefulness in many Concerns of Humane Life, are explained. By William Molyneaux of Dublin Esq; Fellow of the Royal Society. Ex Visibilibus Invisibila. London: Printed for Benj. Tooke, MDCXCII.
MOMMSEN, T.
  1856–85. Römische Geschichte. 4 vols. Weidmann'sche Buchhandlung, Berlin.
MONAKOW, C. (*see also* MINKOWSKI 1931, 1936, 1953)
  1881. Beitrag zur Localisation von Hirnrindentumoren. Arch. f. Psychiat. u. Nervenkr., v. 11, p. 613.
  1882. Ueber einige durch Exstirpation circumscripter Hirnrindenregionen bedingte Entwickelungshemmungen des Kaninchengehirns. *Ibid.*, v. 12, p. 141.
  1882. Weitere Mittheilungen über durch Exstirpation circumscripter Hirnrindenregionen be-

dingte Entwickelungshemmungen des Kaninchengehirns. *Ibid.*, p. 535.
  1883. Sobre los centros de origen del nervio óptico y sus relaciones con la corteza cerebral. Trab. (Trav.) del lab. de invest. biol. Madrid, v. 18, p. 261, 1920. (Manuscript of this paper was handed over to the editor in 1883, as a footnote on title-page indicates, but for some unexplained reason it was not published until almost thirty years later.)
  1883–92. Experimentelle und pathologisch-anatomische Untersuchungen über die Beziehungen der sogenannten Sehsphäre zu den infracorticalen Opticuscentren und zum N. opticus. Arch. f. Psychiat. u. Nervenkr., v. 14, p. 699; v. 16, pp. 151, 317; v. 20, p. 714; v. 23, p. 609; v. 24, p. 229.
  1890. Makroskopische pathologisch-anatomische Hirnpräparate. Arch. f. Psychiat. u. Nervenkr., v. 21, p. 651.
  1895. Experimentelle und pathologisch-anatomische Untersuchungen über die Haubenregion, den Sehhügel und die Regio subthalamica, nebst Beiträgen zur Kenntnis früh erworbener Gross- und Kleinhirndefecte. *Ibid.*, v. 27, p. 1.
  1899. Zur Anatomie und Pathologie des unteren Scheitelläppchens. *Ibid.*, v. 31, p. 1.
  1900. Pathologische und anatomische Mittheilungen über die optischen Centren des Menschen. Arch. f. Psychiat., v. 33, p. 696: Neurol. Centralbl., v. 19, p. 680.
  1902. Die Varietäten in der Anlage der Fissura calcarina und die Fissura retrocalcarina. Arch. f. Psychiat., v. 36, p. 330.
  1902–4. Ueber den gegenwärtigen Stand der Frage nach der Lokalisation im Grosshirn. Ergebn. d. Physiol. (Asher & Spiro), v. 1 (2), p. 534; v. 3 (2), p. 100.
  1905. Gehirnpathologie. *In:* H. NOTHNAGEL, Spez. Path. u. Therap., v. 9 (1). A. Hölder, Wien.
  1910. Die Lokalisation der Hirnfunktionen. J. f. Psychol. u. Neurol., v. 17, p. 185.
  1914. Die Lokalisation im Grosshirn und der Abbau der Funktion durch kortikale Herde. J. F. Bergmann, Wiesbaden.
  1924. Fünfzig Jahre Neurologie. O. Füssli, Zürich.
  1925. Grundlagen der biologischen Psychiatrie. Schweiz. Arch. f. Neurol. u. Psychiat., v. 16, p. 100.
MONAKOW, C., & MOURGUE, R.
  1928. Introduction biologique à l'étude de la neurologie et de la psychopathologie. Intégra-

tion et désintégration de la fonction. F. Alcan, Paris.

MONBRUN, A. A.

1914. L'hémianopsie en quadrant. Thèse, Paris.

1917. Les hémianopsies en quadrant et le centre cortical de la vision. Presse méd., v. 25, p. 607.

1919. Le centre cortical de la vision et les radiations optiques. Les hémianopsies de guerre et la projection rétinienne cérébrale. Arch. d'opht., v. 36, p. 641.

1924. Note sur la vascularisation artérielle des voies optiques au point de vue clinique. Médecine, v. 5, p. 266.

MONBRUN, A. A., & GAUTRAND, G.

1920. Quatre observations d'hémianopsie double. Arch. d'opht., v. 37, p. 232.

MONDEVILLE, H. DE

1304. Die Anatomie des Heinrich von Mondeville. Pub. by Pagel. G. Reimer, Berlin, 1889. (Chaps. 37–42 on eye.)

1889. Die Anatomie des Heinrich von Mondeville. Nach einer Handschrift der Königlichen Bibliothek zu Berlin vom Jahre 1304, zum ersten Male herausgegeben von Dr. Pagel. G. Reimer, Berlin.

MONDINO DE' LUZZI (MUNDINUS)

1316. Anothomia Mundini a capite usque ad pedes. First printed 1478 at Pavia. Anatomia Mundini cum annotationibus Arnaldi di Villanova in margine positis, 1528. MS Codex Urbinas 246, dated 1316 A.D. in Bibl. Apost. Vat. in Rome. (*See* Sudhoff, Arch. f. Gesch. d. Med., v. 8, p. 7, 1915; Singer, Monumenta med. Florence, 1925; Carpi or Carpus.)

1493. Anathomia. *In:* Fasciculo di medicina, Venice, 1493, with an introduction, etc., by C. SINGER. 2 parts. R. Lier & Co., Florence, 1925. Monumenta med., v. 2. The original in 2 parts, the English translation in part 1 (*see also* Ketham & Singer).

MONK, G. S.

1937. Light. Principles and experiments. Mc-Graw-Hill Book Co., New York & London.

MONNIER, A. M.

1936. Physical and chemical aspects of neuro-muscular transmission. Cold Spring Harbor Symp. Quant. Biol., v. 4, p. 111.

MONNIER, M.

1949. L'électrorétinogramme de l'homme. Electro-encephalog. & Clin. Neurophysiol., v. 1, p. 87.

MONNIER, M., & STREIFF, E. B.

1940. Die Messung des Netzhautarteriendruckes

im Tierversuch. Arch. f. d. ges. Physiol. (Pflüger), v. 243, p. 479.

MONRO, A.

1783. Observations on the structure and functions of the nervous system. Edinburgh: printed for, and sold by, William Creech; and by T. Cadell, P. Emsley, J. Murray, and T. Longman, London. Another copy: Edinburgh: printed for, and sold by, William Creech; and Joseph Johnson, in St. Paul's Church-yard, London.

1797. Three treatises. On the brain, the eye, and the ear. Printed for Bell & Bradfute, Edinburgh; and for G. G. & J. Robinson, and J. Johnson, London.

MONTAGU, M. F. ASHLEY

1943. Relations between body-size, waking activity, size of eyeballs, and the origin of social life in the primates. Nature, v. 152, p. 573.

1944. Meet Tarsius. Man's most distant ancestor, distinguished genealogically, is interesting personally. Technol. Rev., v. 46, p. 139.

1944. Review of F. WEIDENREICH, The skull of *Sinanthropus pekinensis*, etc. Am. Anthropologist, v. 46, p. 402.

1950. A consideration of the concept of race. Cold Spring Harbor Symp. Quant. Biol., v. 15, p. 315.

1950. Review of E. A. HOEBEL, Man in the primitive world: an introduction to anthropology. (McGraw-Hill Book Co., New York, 1949), Am. J. Phys. Anthropol., v. 8, N.S., p. 499.

1951. Statement on race. Review by R. W. EHRICH. Am. J. Phys. Anthropol., N.S., v. 9, p. 375.

1952. Neanderthal and the modern type of man. *Ibid.*, v. 10, p. 368.

MONTALTI, MARIO

1928. Le eminenze bigemine anteriori dell'uomo. Ann. di ottal., v. 56, p. 1.

MONTALTO, PHILIPP

1606. Philippi Montalto Lusitani Medicinae Doctoris Optica Intra Philosophiae, & Medicinae aream, De visu, de visus organo, & obiecto theoriam accuratè complectens. Ad Sereniss. Hetruriae Principem D. Cosmum Medicem. Florentiae Apud Cosmum Iuntam. Cum Licentia Superiorum. 1606.

MONTUCLA, J. F.

1758. Histoire des mathématiques, etc. C. A. Jombert, Paris. New ed. by H. AGASSE, and by JÉROME DE LELANDE. Paris, 1799–1802.

MOODY, P. A.

1953. Introduction to evolution. Harper & Bros., New York.

MOONEY, A. J.

1947. Right temporal lobe abscess. Tr. Ophth. Soc. United Kingdom, v. 67, p. 505.

1948. Traumatic lesion of the optic chiasm. *Ibid.*, v. 68, p. 565.

1948. Traumatic lesion of the left occipital lobe. *Ibid.*, p. 567.

MOORE, G. A.

1944. The retinae of two North American teleosts, with special reference to their tapeta lucida. J. Comp. Neurol., v. 80, p. 309.

MOORE, G. A., POLLOCK, H. R., & LIMA, D.

1950. The visual cells of *Ericymba buccata* (Cope). J. Comp. Neurol., v. 93, p. 289.

MOORE, MATHEW T., & STERN, K.

1938. Vascular lesions in the brain stem and occipital lobe occurring in association with brain tumours. Brain, v. 61, p. 70.

MOORE, R.

1953. Man, time, and fossils. The story of evolution. A. A. Knopf, New York.

MOORE, R. F.

1925. Medical ophthalmology. 2d ed. J. & J. Churchill, London; P. Blakiston's Son & Co., Philadelphia.

MOOREN

1888. Gesichtsstörungen in ihrem Abhängigkeitsverhältniss von Occipitallappenerkrankung. Neurol. Centralbl., v. 7, p. 218.

MORANO, F.

1872. Die Pigmentschicht der Retina. Arch. f. mikr. Anat., v. 8, p. 81.

MORAT, J.-P.

1895. Remarques sur le mode d'action des poisons nerveux, à propos d'une communication antérieure de M. Mathias Duval. Compt. rend. Soc. de biol., v. 47 (ser. 10, v. 2), p. 114. (*See also* p. 74.)

MORAX, V.

1916. L'hémianopsie par contusion du crâne. Ann. d'ocul., v. 153, p. 112.

1917. Projectiles intra-crâniens multiples ayant donné lieu à plusieurs syndromes oculaires; hémianopsie homonyme, kératite neuroparalytique, paralysie des dextro-gyres. *Ibid.*, v. 154, p. 300.

1919. Discussion des hypothèses faites sur les connexions corticales des faisceaux maculaires. *Ibid.*, v. 156, p. 25.

MORAX, V., MOREAU, F., & CASTELAIN

1919. Les différents types d'altérations de la vision maculaire dans les lésions traumatiques occipitales. Ann. d'ocul., v. 156, p. 1.

MORDEN, J.

1884. On the mole. Canadian Sportsman & Naturalist, v. 3, p. 283.

MOREAU, F.

1918. Sur les troubles de la vision maculaire produits par les lésions traumatiques de la région occipitale. Ann. d'ocul., v. 155, p. 357.

MOREAU, R. E.

1930. On the age of some races of birds. Ibis, ser. 12, v. 6, p. 229.

MORGAGNI, G. B.

1719. Adversaria anatomica omnia. Patavii (Padua). (*See also* Valsalva 1740, v. 2, p. 239, Epist. anat. 17.)

1761. De sedibus, et causis morborum per anatomen indagatis libri quinque. Ex typographia Remondiniana, Venetiis.

1763. Opuscula miscellanea quorum non pauca nunc primum prodeunt, tres in partes divisa. Ex typographia Remondiniana, Venetiis.

1769. The seats and causes of disease investigated by anatomy. Trans. B. ALEXANDER. 3 vols. A. Millar, and T. Cadell, London. Also published by Wells & Lilly, Boston; H. C. Carey & I. Lea, Philadelphia, 1824.

1940. Selections from De sedibus et causis morborum. ("Medical Classics," comp. E. C. KELLY, v. 4, No. 7.) Williams & Wilkins Co., Baltimore.

MORGAN, A. H.

1930. Field book of ponds and streams. G. P. Putnam's Sons, New York.

MORGAN, T. H.

1932. The scientific basis of evolution. W. W. Norton & Co., New York.

MORIN, F.

1948. Sulla cosidetta radice ipotalamica del nervo ottico. Boll. Soc. ital. di biol. sper., v. 24, p. 153.

MORIN, P.

1929. Tumeur frontale gauche antéro-rolandique. Prédominance des troubles psychiques, etc. Encéphale, v. 24, p. 81.

MORISON, R. S., & DEMPSEY, E. W.

1943. Mechanism of thalamocortical augmentation and repetition. Am. J. Physiol., v. 138, p. 297.

MORLEY, H.

1915. Anatomy in long clothes: an essay on Andreas Vesalius. Privately printed, Chicago.

MOROFF, T.

1922. Cyto-histogenese und Bau der Stäbchen und Zapfen der Retina bei Anuren. Anat. Anz., v. 55, p. 316.

Morris, C. W.
1926. An investigation of oculomotor reflexes in visual perception. Am. J. Physiol. Opt., v. 7, p. 339.

Morris, H.
1942. Morris' human anatomy, ed. J. P. Schaeffer. Blakiston Co., Philadelphia.

Morris, R. C.
1943. Rivers as barriers to the distribution of gibbons. J. Bombay Nat. Hist. Soc., v. 43, p. 656.

Morris, R. F.
1943. The small forest mammals of New Brunswick and the Gaspé. Acad. Naturalist (Bull. Nat. Hist. Soc. New Brunswick), v. 1, p. 27.

Morrison, L. R.
1929. Anatomical studies of the central nervous system of dogs without forebrain or cerebellum. E. F. Bohn, Haarlem.

Morrison, P. R., & Pearson, O. P.
1946. The metabolism of a very small mammal. Science, v. 104, p. 287.

Morrison, P. R., Ryser, F. A., & Dawe, A. R.
1953. Physiological observations on a small shrew. Fed. Proc., v. 12, p. 100.

Morsier, G.
1929. Le syndrome préfrontal, l'amnésie de fixation. Encéphale, v. 24, p. 19.

Morton, D. J.
1924. Evolution of the human foot. I & II. Am. J. Phys. Anthropol., v. 5, p. 305; v. 7, p. 1.
1927. Human origin. Correlation of previous studies of primate feet and posture with other morphologic evidence. *Ibid.*, v. 10, p. 173.
1954. Human locomotion and body form. Williams & Wilkins Co., Baltimore.

Morton, R. A.
1944. Chemical aspects of the visual process. Nature, v. 153, p. 69.

Morton, R. A., & Godwin, T. W.
1944. Preparation of retinene *in vitro*. Nature, v. 153, p. 405.

Moruzzi, G.
1939. Contribution à l'électrophysiologie du cortex moteur: facilitation, afterdischarge et épilepsie corticales. Arch. internat. de physiol., v. 49, p. 33.

Motokawa, K.
1942. Das Elektroretinogramm des Menschen und seine Beziehung zur Unterschiedsschwelle der Lichtempfindlichkeit und zur Sehschärfe. Jap. J. M. Sc., Biophysics, v. 8, p. 135.
1942. Die Abhängigkeit des Aktionsstroms der menschlichen Netzhaut von Reizintensität und Gesichtsfeldgrösse. Tohoku J. Exper. Med., v. 43, p. 371.
1945. Die Helligkeitsverteilung im Dispersionsspektrum und die Aktionsströme der menschlichen Netzhaut. *Ibid.*, v. 48, p. 267.
1949. Retinal processes and their role in color vision. J. Neurophysiol., v. 12, p. 291.
1949. Physiological studies on mechanism of color reception in normal and color-blind subjects. *Ibid.*, p. 465.
1949. Physiological induction in human retina as basis of color and brightness contrast. *Ibid.*, p. 475.

Motokawa, K., & Ebe, M.
1952. Selective stimulation of color receptors with alternating currents. Science, v. 116, p. 92.

Mott, F. W.
1902. Structure of the brain in relation to its function. Proc. Roy. Inst. Great Britain, v. 16, p. 125.
1905-7. The progressive evolution of the structure and functions of the visual cortex in *Mammalia*. Tr. Ophth. Soc. United Kingdom, v. 25, p. liii (Bowman Lect.); Arch. Neurol. (Mott), v. 3, p. 1.
1907. Bilateral lesion of the auditory cortical area: complete deafness and aphasia. Arch. Neurol. (Mott), v. 3, p. 401; Brit. M. J., v. 2, p. 310.
1922. Body and mind: the origin of dualism. Arch. Neurol. (Mott), v. 8 (reprinted from Lancet, 1922, v. 1, p. 1).

Mott, F. W., & Halliburton, W. D.
1908. Localisation of function in the lemur's brain. Proc. Roy. Soc. London, ser. B, v. 80, p. 136.

Mott, F. W., & Kelley, A. M.
1908. Complete survey of the cell lamination of the cerebral cortex of the lemur. Proc. Roy. Soc. London, ser. B, v. 80, p. 488.

Mott, F. W., & Schaefer, E. A.
1890. On associated eye-movements produced by cortical faradization of the monkey's brain. Brain, v. 13, p. 165.
1890. On movements resulting from faradic excitation of the corpus callosum in monkeys. *Ibid.*, p. 174.

Mott, F. W., Schuster, E., & Halliburton, W. D.
1910. Cortical lamination and localisation in the brain of the marmoset. Proc. Roy. Soc. London, ser. B, v. 82, p. 124.

Mott, F. W., Schuster, E., & Sherrington, C. S.
1911. Motor localisation in the brain of the gibbon, correlated with a histological examination. Folia neuro-biol., v. 5, p. 699.

Moulton, H. F.
1948. Velocity of photons. Nature, v. 162, p. 303.

MOUNTFORD, C. P.
1946. Earth's most primitive people. Nat. Geog. Mag., v. 89, p. 89.
1948. Brown men and red sand. Wanderings in wild Australia. Robertson & Mullens, Melbourne. 3d ed., F. A. Praeger, Inc., New York, 1951.

MOUNTFORD, C. P., & WALKER, H.
1949. Exploring stone age Arnhem Land. Nat. Geog. Mag., v. 96, p. 745.

MOUTIER, F.
1908. L'aphasie de Broca. G. Steinheil, Paris.

MOVIUS, H. L.
1953. Archaeology and the earliest art. Scient. American, v. 189, p. 30.

MÜHLBACH, N. T.
*1816. Inquisitio optico-physiologica de visus sensu. In bibliopolio Camesinano, Vindobonae.

MÜLLER, D.
1930. Sinnesphysiologische und psychologische Untersuchungen an Musteliden. Ztschr. f. vergl. Physiol., v. 12, p. 293.

MÜLLER, D. E.
1861. Visus dimidiatus bedingt durch eine Geschwulst auf der Sella turcica. Arch. f. Ophth. (Graefe), v. 8 (1), p. 160.

MÜLLER, F.
1930. Injektionstechnik. *In:* E. ABDERHALDEN, Handb. d. biol. Arbeitsmeth., Abt. V, Teil 1, p. 167. Urban & Schwarzenberg, Berlin & Wien.

MÜLLER, F. W.
1908. Ueber cranio-cerebrale Topographie. Ergebn. Anat. & Entw. (Merkel & Bonnet), v. 18, p. 216.

MÜLLER, F. W. P.
1921. Die Zellgruppen im Corpus geniculatum mediale des Menschen. Monatsschr. f. Psychiat. u. Neurol., v. 49, p. 251.

MÜLLER, G. E.
1923. Zur Theorie des Stäbchenapparates und der Zapfenblindheit. Ztschr. f. Sinnesphysiol., v. 54, pp. 9, 102.
1930. Ueber die Farbenempfindungen. Psychophysische Untersuchungen. 2 vols. Suppl. 18 to Ztschr. f. Psychol. J. A. Barth, Leipzig.
1932. Kleine Beiträge zur Psychophysik der Farbenempfindungen. I. Die nutritive Minderstellung der *Pm*-Substanz. II. Zur Frage des fovealen Purkinjeschen Phänomens. III. Das Dämmerungsblau. Ztschr. f. Sinnesphysiol., v. 62, pp. 53, 67, 89.
1934. Ueber die Entstehung der elektrischen Gesichtsempfindungen. *Ibid.*, v. 65, p. 274.

MÜLLER, HANS
1952. Bau und Wachstum der Netzhaut des Guppy (*Lebistes reticulatus*). Zool. Jahrb. (Allg. Zool.), v. 63, p. 275.

MÜLLER, HEINRICH
1851. Ueber sternförmige Zellen der Retina. Verhandl. d. phys.-med. Gesellsch. Würzburg, v. 2, p. 216.
1851. Zur Histologie der Netzhaut. Ztschr. f. wissensch. Zool., v. 3, p. 234.
1852. Bemerkungen über den Bau und die Funktion der Retina. Verhandl. d. phys.-med. Gesellsch. Würzburg, v. 3, p. 336.
1853. Ueber einige Verhältnisse der Netzhaut bei Menschen und Thieren. *Ibid.*, v. 4, p. 96.
1854. Ueber die entoptische Wahrnehmung der Netzhautgefässe, insbesondere als Beweismittel für die Lichtperception durch die nach hinten gelegenen Netzhautelemente. *Ibid.*, v. 5, p. 411.
1856. Observations sur la structure de la rétine de certains animaux. Compt. rend. Acad. d. sc., v. 43, p. 743.
1856–57. Anatomisch-physiologische Untersuchungen über die Retina des Menschen und der Wirbelthiere. Ztschr. f. wissensch. Zool., v. 8, p. 1.
1858. Einige Bemerkungen über die Binnenmuskeln des Auges. Arch. f. Ophth. (Graefe), v. 4 (2), p. 277.
1858–62. Ueber das Auge des Chamäleon. Verhandl. d. phys.-med. Gesellsch. Würzburg, v. 8, p. xxi; Würzburg. naturwiss. Ztschr., v. 3, p. 10.
1859. Ueber die elliptischen Lichtstreifen Purkinje's. Verhandl. d. phys.-med. Gesellsch. Würzburg, v. 9, p. xxx.
1861. Ueber das ausgedehnte Vorkommen einer dem gelben Fleck der Retina entsprechenden Stelle bei Thieren. Würzburg. naturwiss. Ztschr., v. 2, p. 139.
1861. Bemerkung über die Zapfen am gelben Fleck des Menschen. *Ibid.*, p. 218.
1863. Ueber das Vorhandensein zweier Foveae in der Netzhaut vieler Vogelaugen. Klin. Monatsbl. f. Augenh., v. 1, p. 438.
1872. Gesammelte und hinterlassene Schriften zur Anatomie und Physiologie des Auges. W. Engelmann, Leipzig.
1881. *See* O. BECKER, Die Gefässe der menschlichen Macula, etc. Arch. f. Ophth. (Graefe), v. 27 (1), p. 1.

MÜLLER, HERMANN
1873. Die Befruchtung der Blumen durch Insekten. W. Engelmann, Leipzig.

MÜLLER, H. F.

1892. Zeittafeln zur Geschichte der Mathematik, Physik und Astronomie bis zum Jahre 1500. B. G. Teubner, Leipzig.

MÜLLER, JOHANNES

1826. Zur vergleichenden Physiologie des Gesichtssinnes des Menschen und der Thiere, nebst einem Versuch über die Bewegungen der Augen und über den menschlichen Blick. C. Cnobloch, Leipzig.

1826. Ueber die phantastischen Gesichtserscheinungen. Eine physiologische Untersuchung mit einer physiologischen Urkunde des Aristoteles über den Traum, den Philosophen und Aerzten gewidmet. J. Hölscher, Coblenz. New ed., 1927.

1835–40. Handbuch der Physiologie des Menschen für Vorlesungen. 2 vols. J. Hölscher, Coblenz.

1837. Jahresbericht über die Fortschritte der anatomisch-physiologischen Wissenschaften im Jahre 1836. Arch. f. Anat., Physiol. u. wissensch. Med. (J. Müller), pp. i, vii.

1840. Von den Sinnen. *In:* J. MÜLLER, Handb. d. Physiol. d. Mensch. f. Vorlesungen, v. 2, p. 247.

1840. Vom Gesichtssinn. *Ibid.*, p. 276.

1840. Vom Seelenleben. *Ibid.*, p. 503.

1842. Ueber den Bau und die Lebenserscheinungen des *Branchiostoma lubricum* Costa, *Amphioxus lanceolatus* Yarrell. Abh. d. Kgl. Akad. Wissensch. Berlin, phys. Abh., p. 79, 1844.

MÜLLER, L. R.

1931. Lebensnerven und Lebenstriebe. J. Springer, Berlin.

MÜLLER, L. R., & DAHL, W.

1910. Die Beteiligung des sympathischen Nervensystems an der Kopfinnervation. Deutsch. Arch. f. klin. Med., v. 99, p. 48.

MÜLLER, S.

1855. Reizen en onderzoekingen en Sumatra, gedaan op last der Nederlandsche Indische regering, tusschen de jaren 1833 en 1838. K. Fuhri, 's Gravenhage.

1857. Reizen en onderzoekingen in den Indischen archipel, gedaan op last der Nederlandsche Indische regering, tusschen de jaren 1828 en 1836. Nieuwe uitgave. 2 vols. F. Müller, Amsterdam.

MÜLLER, W.

1874. Ueber die Stammesentwicklung des Sehorgans der Wirbelthiere. *In:* Beitr. z. Anat. u. Physiol. als Festgabe C. Ludwig, p. 76. F. C. W. Vogel, Leipzig.

MÜNZER, E., & WIENER, H.

1898. Beiträge zur Anatomie und Physiologie des Centralnervensystems der Taube. Monatsschr. f. Psychiat. u. Neurol., v. 3, p. 379.

1902. Das Zwischen- und Mittelhirn des Kaninchens und die Beziehungen dieser Teile zum übrigen Centralnervensystem, mit besonderer Berücksichtigung der Pyramidenbahn und Schleife. *Ibid.*, v. 12, p. 241.

MÜNZER, F. T.

1928. Schussverletzung des rechten Hinterhauptlappens, des X. und XII. Hirnnerven. (Ein Beitrag zur Frage der Lokalisation des temporalen Halbmondes des Gesichtsfeldes.) Ztschr. f. d. ges. Neurol. u. Psychiat., v. 117, p. 562.

MUENZINGER, K. F., & REYNOLDS, H. E.

1936. Color vision in white rats. I. Sensitivity to red. J. Genet. Psychol., v. 48, p. 58.

MULLER, H. J.

1949. Redintegration of the symposium on genetics, paleontology, and evolution. *In:* JEPSEN *et al.*, Genetics, paleontology, and evolution, p. 421.

MUNCIE, W.

1935. Fingeragnosia (Gerstmann). Bull. Johns Hopkins Hosp., v. 57, p. 330.

MUNDINUS; *see* MONDINO DE' LUZZI

MUNK, H.; for biography *see* FRITSCH 1912; ROTHMANN 1909

1878. Professor H. Munk's Untersuchungen zur Physiologie der Grosshirnrinde. Deutsch. med. Wchnschr., v. 4, p. 533. (*See also* Verhandl. d. physiol. Gesellsch., Nos. 16, 17, 1877; Nos. 9, 10, 1878; *also* Berlin. klin. Wchnschr., No. 35, 1877; and p. 581, footnote, 1879.)

1878–79. Weiteres zur Physiologie der Sehsphäre der Grosshirnrinde. Arch. f. Physiol. (Du Bois-Reymond), pp. 162, 547, 599, 1878; p. 581, 1879.

1879. Physiologie der Sehsphäre der Grosshirnrinde. Centralbl. f. prakt. Augenh., v. 3, p. 255.

1880. Ueber die Sehsphäre und die Riechsphäre der Grosshirnrinde. Arch. f. Physiol. (Du Bois-Reymond), p. 449.

1880. Die Functionen des Grosshirns. Arch. f. wissensch. u. pract. Thierh., v. 6, p. 72.

1881. Ueber die Functionen der Grosshirnrinde. Gesammelte Mitt. a. d. J. 1877–80. A. Hirschwald, Berlin. 2d ed. up to 1889, pub. 1890. 3d ed. entitled: Ueber die Functionen von Hirn und Rückenmark, pub. 1909, contains papers published 1891–1908.

MUNK, H.—*Continued*

1881. Zur Physiologie der Grosshirnrinde. Arch. f. Physiol. (Du Bois-Reymond), p. 455.

1883. Lecture on cerebral functions. Nature, v. 28, p. 431.

1889. Ueber die centralen Organe für das Sehen und das Hören bei den Wirbelthieren. Sitzungsb. d. Kgl. Preuss. Akad. d. Wissensch. Berlin, 2. Halbband, p. 615.

1890. Of the visual area of the cerebral cortex, and its relation to eye movements. Brain, v. 13, p. 45.

1891. Sehsphäre und Raumvorstellungen. Internat. Beitr. z. wissensch. Med. (Festschr. f. R. Virchow), v. 1, p. 355. A. Hirschwald, Berlin.

1892–96. Ueber die Fühlsphaeren der Grosshirnrinde. Sitzungsb. d. Kgl. Preuss. Akad. d. Wissensch. Berlin. *Also in:* MUNK, Ueber die Functionen von Hirn und Rückenmark. A. Hirschwald, Berlin.

1894. Ueber den Hund ohne Grosshirn. Arch. f. Physiol. (Du Bois-Reymond), p. 355.

1899–1901. Ueber die Ausdehnung der Sinnessphären in der Grosshirnrinde. Sitzungsb. d. Kgl. Preuss. Akad. Wissensch. Berlin, v. 2, p. 936, 1899; p. 770, 1900; p. 1149, 1901. *Also in:* MUNK, Ueber die Functionen von Hirn und Rückenmark, pp. 163, 178, 201, 1909. A. Hirschwald, Berlin.

1902. Zur Physiologie der Grosshirnrinde. Deutsch. med. Wchnschr. (Vereins-Beilage), v. 28, p. 166.

1910. Zur Anatomie und Physiologie der Sehsphäre der Grosshirnrinde. Sitzungsb. d. Kgl. Preuss. Akad. Wissensch. Berlin, p. 996.

MUNK, H., & OBREGIA

1890. Sehsphaere und Augenbewegungen. Sitzungsb. d. Kgl. Preuss. Akad. Wissensch. Berlin, v. 1, p. 53.

MUNN, N. L.

1934. Further evidence concerning color blindness in rats. J. Genet. Psychol., v. 45, p. 285.

1950. Handbook of psychological research on the rat. An introduction to animal psychology. Houghton Mifflin Co., Boston.

MUNN, N. L., & COLLINS, M.

1936. Discrimination of red by white rats. J. Genet. Psychol., v. 48, p. 72.

MUNOZ URRA

1921. Les variations de trajet dans les neuroblastes de la rétine embryonnaire. Ann. d'ocul., v. 158, p. 43.

MUNRO, D.

1938. Cranio-cerebral injuries, their diagnosis and treatment. Oxford University Press, London.

MUNRO, J. A.

1945. Preliminary report on the birds and mammals of Glacier National Park, British Columbia. Canadian Field-Naturalist, v. 59, p. 175.

MUNRO, R.

1893. Presidential address on the erect posture of man. Report of the British Association for the Advancement of Science, sec. H (Anthropology), p. 885.

MURALT, A. L. VON

1946. Die Signalübermittlung im Nerven. Verlag Birkhäuser, Basel.

MURATORI, L. A.

1723–51. Rerum Italicarum scriptores ab anno aerae christianae quingentesimo ad millesimum quingentesimum quorum potissima pars nunc primum in lucem prodit. . . . Ex typographia Societatis Palatinae. Mediolani. (25 vols. in 28.)

1738–42. Antiquitates Italicae medii aevi. 6 vols. Milan. German trans: Geschichte von Italien. J. Schuster, Leipzig, 1745–49.

1748–70. Rerum Italicarum scriptores ab anno aerae christianae millesimo ad millesimum sexcentesimum quorum potissima pars nunc primum in luce prodit ex florentinarum bibliothecarum codicibus. 2 vols. Ex typographia P. C. Viviani, Florentiae.

MURCHISON, C. (ed.)

1934. Handbook of general experimental psychology. Clark University Press, Worcester, Mass.; Oxford University Press, London.

MUREDDU, G.

1930. Sul rapporto numerico fra le cellule visive e le cellule ganglionari della retina humana. Ann. ottal., v. 58, pp. 142, 247.

MURIE, A.

1944. The wolves of Mount McKinley. Government Printing Office, Washington, D.C. *Also:* Living wilderness, v. 10, p. 9, 1945.

MURIE, O. J.

1927. The Alaska red squirrel providing for winter. J. Mammal., v. 8, p. 37.

MURR, E.

1927. Ueber die Entwicklung und den feineren Bau des Tapetum lucidum der Feliden. Ztschr. f. Zellforsch. u. mikr. Anat., v. 6, p. 315.

1929. Zur Entwicklungsphysiologie des Auges. I. Experimentelle Untersuchungen über den Einfluss des Lichtes auf das Wachstum der Sehzellen. II. Vergleichend chronometrische und ökologische Studien an der Retina der Carnivoren und Ungulaten. Biol. Zentralbl., v. 49, pp. 156, 346.

1930. Zur besseren Unterscheidung von Stäbchen und Zapfen in der Retina der Wirbeltiere. Ztschr. f. Zellforsch. u. mikr. Anat., v. 10, p. 386.

MURRAY, E.
1939. Binocular fusion and the locus of "yellow." Am. J. Psychol., v. 52, p. 117.

MURRAY, M.
1944. An introduction to Bishop Berkeley's theory of vision. Brit. J. Ophth., v. 28, p. 600.

MURRAY, W. J. C.
1944. Grey squirrels. Canadian Nature, v. 5, p. 104.

MUSKENS, L. J. J.
1914. An anatomico-physiological study of the posterior longitudinal bundle in its relation to forced movements. Brain, v. 36, p. 352.

1927. An anatomo-physiological study of the supra-vestibular tractus in *Columba domestica*. Proc. Akad. v. Wetensch. Amsterdam, sec. sc., v. 30, p. 455.

1929. The tracts and centers in the pigeon dominating the associated movements of the eyes (and other movable parts) in the sense of lateral deviation in the horizontal and of rotation in the frontal plane. J. Comp. Neurol., v. 48, p. 267.

1930. Zum Studium der Blicklähmungen, Blickkrämpfe und gewisser Nystagmusformen, insbesondere derjenigen in der vertikalen Richtung. Deutsch. Ztschr. f. Nervenh., v. 115, p. 81.

1930. On tracts and centers involved in the upward and downward associated movements of the eyes after experiments in birds. J. Comp. Neurol., v. 50, p. 289.

1934. Das supra-vestibuläre System bei den Tieren und beim Menschen, mit besonderer Berücksichtigung der Klinik der Blicklähmungen, der sogen. Stirnhirnataxie, der Zwangsstellungen und der Zwangsbewegungen. N. V. Noord-Hollandsche Uitgeversmattschapij, Amsterdam.

1936. Die loco-(und oculo-)motorische Funktion der Kerne der hinteren Commissur und Kerne des zentralen Höhlengraus des Mesencephalons. Ergebnisse der anatomophysiologischen und vergleichend anatomischen Forschung. Jahrb. f. Psychiat., v. 53, p. 117.

MUSSEN, A. T.
1923. A cytoarchitectural atlas of the brain stem of the Macaccus rhesus. J. f. Psychol. u. Neurol., v. 29, p. 451.

MYERS, B. D.
1901. The chiasma of the toad (*Bufo lentiginosus*) and some other vertebrates. Ztschr. f. Morphol., v. 3, p. 183.

1902. Beitrag zur Kenntniss des Chiasmas und der Commissuren am Boden des dritten Ventrikels. Arch. f. Anat. u. Entw., p. 347.

MYERS, R. E.
1955. Interocular transfer of pattern discrimination in cats following section of crossed optic fibers. J. Comp. & Physiol. Psychol., v. 48, p. 470.

N

NACHMANSOHN, D.
1939. Cholinestérase dans le système nerveux central. Bull. Soc. chim. biol., v. 21, p. 761.

1939. Sur l'inhibition de la cholinestérase. Compt. rend. Soc. de biol., v. 130, p. 1065.

1940. On the physiological significance of choline esterase. Yale J. Biol. & Med., v. 12, p. 565.

NACHMANSOHN, D., COX, R. T., COATES, C. W., & MACHADO, A. L.
1942. Action potential and enzyme activity in the electrical organ of *Electrophorus electricus* (Linnaeus). J. Neurophysiol., v. 5, p. 499.

1943. Phosphocreatine as energy source of the action potential. Proc. Soc. Exper. Biol. & Med., v. 52, p. 97.

NACHMANSOHN, D., & MEYERHOF, B.
1941. Relation between electrical changes during nerve activity and concentration of choline esterase. J. Neurophysiol., v. 4, p. 348.

NACHMANSOHN, D., & STEINBACH, H. B.
1942. Localization of enzymes in nerves. I. Succinic dehydrogenase and vitamin B_1. J. Neurophysiol., v. 5, p. 109.

NACHMANSOHN, D., STEINBACH, H. B., MACHADO, A. L., & SPIEGELMAN, S.
1943. Localization of enzymes in nerves. II. Respiratory enzymes. J. Neurophysiol., v. 6, p. 203.

NACHMANSOHN, D., *et al.*
1946. The physico-chemical mechanism of nerve activity. Ann. New York Acad. Sc., v. 47, p. 375.

NÄCKE, P.
1910. Beiträge zur Morphologie der Hirnoberfläche. Arch. f. Psychiat. u. Nervenkr., v. 46, p. 610.

NAGEL, A.
1861. Das Sehen mit zwei Augen und die Lehre von den identischen Netzhautstellen. C. F. Winter, Leipzig & Heidelberg.

NAGEL, W. A.
1894. Ein Beitrag zur Kenntnis des Lichtsinnes augenloser Thiere. Biol. Centralbl., v. 14, p. 810.
1894. Vergleichend physiologische und anatomische Untersuchungen über den Geruchs- und Geschmackssinn und ihre Organe mit einleitenden Betrachtungen aus der allgemeinen vergleichenden Sinnesphysiologie. F. Nägele, Stuttgart
1896. Der Lichtsinn augenloser Thiere: eine biologische Studie. G. Fischer, Jena.
1905–10. Handbuch der Physiologie des Menschen. 5 vols. F. Vieweg & Sohn, Braunschweig.
1907. Der Farbensinn des Hundes. Zentralbl. f. Physiol., v. 21, p. 205.

NAGEL, W. O.
1944. Squirrels and squirrel hunting. Missouri Conservationist, v. 5, pp. 1, 10.

NALLINO, C. A.
1932. Il Gherardo Cremonese, etc. Rend. R. Accad. naz. d. Lincei, cl. d. sc. morali, storiche e filolog., ser. ses., v. 8, p. 386.

NANSEN, F.
1887. The structure and combination of the histological elements of the central nervous system. Bergens Mus. Aarsberetning for 1886, p. 27.
1888. Die Nervenelemente, ihre Struktur und Verbindung im Centralnervensystem. Anat. Anz., v. 3, p. 157.

NAPOLI, F.
1876. Alla vita ed ai lavori di Francesco Maurolico. Bull. di bibl. e di storia d. sc. mat. e fis. (Boncompagni), v. 9, pp. 1, 23 ff.

NARDUCCI, E.
1871. Intorno ad una traduzione italiana, fatta nel secolo decimoquarto, del trattato d'ottica d'Alhazen, etc. Bull. di bibl. e di storia d. sc. mat. e fis. (Boncompagni), v. 4, pp. 1, 137.

NATHAN, P. W., & ALDREN, J. W.
1942. The efferent pathway for pupillary contraction. Brain, v. 65, p. 343.

NAUTA, W. J. H., & BUCHER, V. M.
1954. Efferent connections of the striate cortex in the albino rat. J. Comp. Neurol., v. 100, p. 257.

NAUTA, W. J. H., & VAN STRAATEN, J. J.
1947. The primary optic centres of the rat. An experimental study by the "bouton" method. J. Anat., v. 81, p. 127.

NAVILLE, F.
1918. Mémoires d'un médecin aphasique. Arch. de psychol., v. 17, p. 1.

NAYRAC, P.
1930. Technique pour la mesure de la surface cérébrale. Compt. rend. Soc. de biol., v. 105, p. 657.

NAZIF BEY, MUSTAFA
1942. Al-Ḥasan ibn al-Haitham. Part 1 (Arabic). Nuri Press, Cairo.

NEAL, H. V.
1914. The morphology of the eye-muscle nerves. J. Morphol., v. 25, p. 1.
1921. Nervus and plexus lesions. J. Comp. Neurol., v. 33, p. 65.

NEAL, H. V., & RAND, H. W.
1936. Comparative anatomy. P. Blakiston's Son & Co., Philadelphia.
1939. Chordate anatomy. P. Blakiston's Son & Co., Philadelphia.

NEEDHAM, J.
1936. Order and life. Yale University Press, New Haven.
1944. Biochemistry and morphogenesis. Cambridge University Press, Cambridge.

NEEDHAM, J. G.
1951. Dragonflies—rainbows on the wing. Nat. Geog. Mag., v. 100, p. 215.

NEEDHAM, J. G., & HEYWOOD, H. B.
1929. A handbook of the dragonflies of North America. Charles C Thomas, Springfield, Ill.

NEEDHAM, J. G., & LLOYD, J. T.
1937. The life of inland waters. Comstock Publishing Co., Ithaca, N.Y.

NEEDHAM, J. G., & NEEDHAM, P. R.
1941. A guide to the study of fresh-water biology. Comstock Publishing Co., Ithaca, N.Y.

NEEDHAM, J. G., et al.
1941. A symposium on hydrobiology. University of Wisconsin Press, Madison.

NEEDHAM, P. R.
1938. Trout streams. Comstock Publishing Co., Ithaca, N.Y.

NEIMER, W. T.
1946. Oculomotor nuclear complex in chimpanzee. Anat. Rec., v. 94, p. 544. (Proc. Am. A. Anat., demonstration 37.)

NEMESIOS (NEMESIUS)
4th cent. A.D. Περὶ φύσεως ἀνθρώπου (or On the nature of man). Other editions: De natura hominis, ex officina C. Plantini, Antwerpiae, 1565. The nature of man, printed by M. F. for H. Taunton, London, 1636. De natura hominis denuo edidit Christian Frideric, Matthaei, Halae Magdeburgiae, 1802.

NERINCX, É.
1943. Contribution à l'étude des senses chez les cheiroptères. Mammalia, v. 7, p. 110.

1944. Notes sur l'éthologie et l'écologie des cheiroptères de Belgique. Bull. Mus. roy. hist. nat. belg. Bruxelles, v. 20, p. 24.

NESSLER, A.
1891. Ueber die nach Verletzungen der Hinterhauptlappen auftretenden Störungen (Inaug. Diss.). C. Goeller, Strassburg.

NETTER, F. H.
1948. The Ciba collection of medical illustrations, Ciba Pharmaceutical Products, Summit, N.J.

NETTLESHIP, E.
1874–76. Some cases of variations of the retinal blood-vessels. Ophth. Hosp. Rep., v. 8, p. 512.
1874–76. Unusually tortuous retinal arteries; no diseases of eyes, but a high degree of hypermetropia. *Ibid.*, p. 514.
1875. Note on the retinal blood-vessels of the yellow-spot-region. *Ibid.*, v. 8 (2), p. 260.
1876. Unusual distribution of retinal blood-vessels. Brit. M. J., v. 1, p. 161.
1879–80. Observations of visual purple in the human eye. J. Physiol., v. 2, p. 38.
1904–5. Notes on the blood vessels of the optic disc in some of the lower animals. Tr. Ophth. Soc. United Kingdom, v. 25, p. 338.

NETTLESHIP, E., & EDMUNDS, W.
1881. Two cases of symmetrical amblyopia of slow progress, with central scotoma, in patients suffering from diabetes. Microscopical examination of the optic nerve in one case. Tr. Ophth. Soc. United Kingdom, v. 1, p. 124.

NEUBURGER, M.
1897. Die historische Entwicklung der experimentellen Gehirn- und Rückenmarksphysiologie vor Flourens. F. Enke, Stuttgart.
1906–11. Geschichte der Medizin. 2 vols. F. Enke, Stuttgart. English trans.: History of medicine. H. Frowde, London; Oxford University Press, London, 1910–25.
1910. Ludwig Türck als Neurologe. Jahrb. f. Psychiat., v. 31, p. 1.

NEUGEBAUER, O., *et al.*
1930–38. Quellen und Studien zur Geschichte der Mathematik, Astronomie und Physik, begründet von O. Neugebauer, J. Stenzel, O. Toeplitz; herausgegeben von O. Neugebauer und O. Toeplitz.

NEUKIRCHEN, F. A.
1900. Ein Fall von doppelseitiger kortikaler Hemianopsie verbunden mit taktiler Aphasie und Orientierungsstörungen. Diss., Marburg.

NEUMANN, J.
1921. Ueber die Fovea centralis bei Affen (Macacus rhesus und Macacus nemestrinus) und beim Menschen. Inaug. Diss., Leipzig. O. Richter, Zeulenroda i.Th.

NEUMAYER, L.
1895. Histologische Untersuchungen über den feineren Bau des Centralnervensystems von *Esox lucius* mit Berücksichtigung vergleichend-anatomischer und physiologischer Verhältnisse. Arch. f. mikr. Anat., v. 44, p. 345.
1897. Der feinere Bau der Selachier-Retina. *Ibid.*, v. 48, p. 83.

NEURATH, R.
1908. Degenerationspathologische Befunde einiger Projektionsleitungen bei einem Falle von cerebraler Kinderlähmung. (Symmetrische Herde in der Opercularregion mit konsekutiver Degeneration der Hörstrahlung, des sagittalen Occipitalmarkes und eines Teiles der Stirnhirnstrahlung nebst klinischen Bemerkungen über das Hörzentrum.) Arb. a. d. neurol. Inst. Wien, v. 17, p. 72.

NEWHALL, S. M.
1937. The constancy of the blue arc phenomenon. J. Opt. Soc. Amer., v. 27, p. 165.

NEWMAN, H. H.
1939. The phylum chordata. Biology of vertebrates and their kin. Macmillan Co., New York.

NEWTON, ISAAC
1704. Opticks: or, a Treatise of the Reflexions, Refractions, Inflexions and Colours of Light; etc. S. Smith & B. Walford, London. Modern reprints of the 1730 edition, the last corrected by the author, published by McGraw-Hill Book Co., New York, 1931, and by Dover Publications, New York, 1952. *Also:* I. Newtoni Opera quae extant omnia, ed. S. HORSLEY. 5 vols. J. Nichols, London, 1779–85.

NGOWYANG, G.
1934. The cytoarchitectural subdivisions of the area striata of human brain. Coshu, v. 18, p. 947. (In Chinese and English.)
1935. Die cytoarchitektonischen Unterfelder der Area striata beim Menschen. Nat. Centr. Univ. Sc. Rep., Nanking, ser. B, v. 2, p. 1.
1936. Ueber Rassengehirne. Ztschr. f. Rassenkunde, v. 3, p. 26.
1937. Structural variations of the visual cortex in primates. J. Comp. Neurol., v. 67, p. 89.

NICAISE, V.
1902. Notes pour servir à l'histoire de l'anatomie

au XVIᵉ siècle et de la période prévésalienne. Bull. Soc. franç. d'hist. de la méd., v. 1, p. 133.

NICATI, W.
1878. Experimenteller Beweis einer unvollständigen Kreuzung im Chiasma der Sehnerven. Centralbl. f. d. med. Wissensch., v. 16, p. 449.
1878. Preuve expérimentale du croisement incomplète des fibres nerveuses dans le chiasma des nerfs optiques. Section longitudinale et médiane du chiasma non suivie de cécité. Compt. rend. Acad. d. sc., v. 86, p. 1472.
1878. De la distribution des fibres nerveuses dans le chiasma des nerfs optiques. Arch. de physiol., 2d ser., v. 5, p. 658.
1895. Théorie de la couleur. Arch. d'opht., v. 15, p. 1.

NICHOLLS, J. V. V.
1938. The effect of section on the posterior ciliary arteries in the rabbit. Brit. J. Ophth., v. 22, p. 672.

NICHOLS, L. N.
1936. Cliff swallow. *In:* PEARSON & BURROUGHS, Birds of America, Part 3, p. 84.

NICHTERLEIN, O. E., & GOLDBY, F.
1944. An experimental study of optic connexions in the sheep. J. Anat., v. 78, p. 59.

NICOLAS, E.
1930. Veterinary and comparative ophthalmology. H. & W. Brown, London.

NIDA, M.
1924. Contribution à l'étude des phénomènes visuels d'excitation du cortex occipital. Diss., Paris.

NIEDEN, A.
1879. Ein Fall von Atrophie des einen Sehnervenstammes mit nahezu gleichmässigem und normalem Dickendurchmesser der beiden Tractus optici. Centralbl. f. prakt. Augenh., v. 3, p. 136.
1883. Ein Fall von einseitiger temporaler Hemianopsie des rechten Auges nach Trepanation des linken Hinterhauptbeines. Arch. f. Ophth. (Graefe), v. 29 (3), p. 143; (4), p. 271.

NIELSEN, J. M.
1946. Agnosia, apraxia, aphasia—their value in cerebral localization. 2d ed. P. B. Hoeber, New York.
1946. A textbook of clinical neurology. P. B. Hoeber, New York.
1950. Cerebral localization in aphasia and agnosia. Arch. Neurol. & Psychiat., v. 64, p. 748.

NIESSL VON MAYENDORF, E.
1903. Vom Fasciculus longitudinalis inferior. Arch. f. Psychiat., v. 37, p. 537.
1904. Seelenblindheit und Alexie, zwei subcorticale Störungen des centralen Sehens. Verhandl. d. 21. Kong. f. Inn. Med., p. 510.
1904. Zur Theorie des kortikalen Sehens. Arch. f. Psychiat u. Nervenkr., v. 30, p. 686.
1905. Ein Abszess im linken Schläfenlappen. (Als Beitrag zur Lehre von der Lokalisation der Seelenblindheit und Alexie.) Deutsch. Ztschr. f. Nervenh., v. 29, p. 385.
1906. Ueber eine direkte Leitung vom optischen zum kinästhetischen Rindenzentrum der Wort- und Buchstabenbilder. Wien. klin. Wchnschr., v. 19, p. 1335; Neurol. Centralbl., v. 26, p. 722.
1907. Die Diagnose auf Erkrankung des linken Gyrus angularis. Monatsschr. f. Psychiat. u. Neurol., v. 22, pp. 145, 225.
1907. Ueber den Eintritt der Sehbahn in die Hirnrinde des Menschen. Neurol. Centralbl., v. 26, p. 786.
1908. Ueber die Lokalisation der motorischen Aphasie. Berlin. klin. Wchnschr., v. 45, p. 1481.
1908. Das Rindencentrum der optischen Wortbilder. Arch. f. Psychiat. u. Nervenkr., v. 43, p. 633.
1908. Casuistische Mittheilungen zur Pathologie des Stirnhirns. *Ibid.*, p. 1175.
1908. Zur Kenntnis der gestörten Tiefenwahrnehmung. Deutsch. Ztschr. f. Nervenh., v. 34, p. 322.
1909. Ueber die physiologische Bedeutung der Hörwindung. Monatsschr. f. Psychiat. u. Neurol., v. 25, p. 97.
1911. Die aphasischen Symptome und ihre kortikale Lokalisation. W. Engelmann, Leipzig.
1913. Ueber die Grenzen und Bedeutung der menschlichen Hörsphäre. Arch. f. Psychiat. u. Nervenkr., v. 53, pp. 764, 1202.
1914. Ueber den Fasciculus corporis callosi cruciatus (das gekreuzte Balken-Stabkranzbündel). Monatsschr. f. Psychiat. u. Neurol., v. 36, p. 415.
1919. Ueber die klinischen Formen der Tastblindheit. Ztschr. f. d. ges. Neurol. u. Psychiat. (Orig.), v. 50, p. 82.
1920. Die Assoziationssysteme des menschlichen Vorderhirns. Arch. f. Physiol. (Rubner), p. 283.
1920. Ueber den Ursprung und Verlauf der basalen Züge des unteren Längsbündels. Arch. f. Psychiat. u. Nervenkr., v. 61, p. 273.

1921. Die sogenannte Radiatio optica (das Stratum sagittale internum des Scheitel- und Hinterhauptlappens). Arch. f. Ophth. (Graefe), v. 104, p. 293.

1921. Projektionsfaserung und Stammstrahlung. Arch. f. Psychiat. u. Nervenkr., v. 63, p. 551.

1922. Der Sehhügelstiel des inneren Kniehöckers und seine physiologische Bedeutung. Arch. f. d. ges. Psychol., v. 42, p. 235.

1922–23. Das corticale Lokalisationsproblem im Lichte der jüngsten Forschungen. Zentralbl. f. d. ges. Neurol. u. Psychiat., v. 30, p. 375; Deutsch. Ztschr. f. Nervenh., v. 77, p. 177.

1923. Die Psychopathologie als Naturwissenschaft. Zentralbl. f. d. ges. Neurol. u. Psychiat., v. 31, p. 59.

1925. Ein Fall von umschriebener Halluzinose und vom Gehirnmechanismus der Halluzination. Ztschr. f. d. ges. Neurol. u. Psychiat., v. 99, p. 313.

1925. Dysarthrie und ihre zerebralen Lokalisationen. Deutsch. Ztschr. f. Nervenh., v. 84, p. 170.

1925. Seelenblindheit. Klin. Wchnschr., v. 4 (1), p. 451.

1925. Kritische Studien zur Methodik der Aphasielehre. (Abh. a. d. Neurol., etc., Heft 27, pub. by Monatsschr. f. Psychiat. u. Neurol.) S. Karger, Berlin.

1925. Zur Lokalisationsfrage der kutanen Sensibilität in der Hirnrinde. Deutsch. Ztschr. f. Nervenh., v. 86, p. 220.

1926. On "Tractus corporis callosi cruciatus." *Ibid.*, v. 94, p. 173.

1926. Vom Sehhügelstiel des inneren Kniehöckers. Monatsschr. f. Psychiat. u. Neurol., v. 61, p. 365.

1926. Ueber die anatomische und psychische Assoziation. Arch. f. d. ges. Psychol., v. 55, p. 251; Zentralbl. f. d. ges. Neurol. u. Psychiat., v. 43, p. 252.

1926. Die Schweifkernbahnen. Deutsch. Ztschr. f. Nervenh., v. 95, p. 122; Zentralbl. f. d. ges. Neurol. u. Psychiat., v. 44, p. 802.

1926. Ueber die sog. Brocasche Windung und ihre angebliche Bedeutung für den Sprachakt. Monatsschr. f. Psychiat. u. Neurol., v. 61, p. 129.

1926. Henschens Prioritätsstreit um die Entdeckung der Sehsphäre. *Ibid.*, p. 312.

1927. Ueber Seelenblindheit. Zentralbl. f. d. ges. Neurol. u. Psychiat., v. 47, p. 828.

1930. Vom Lokalisationsproblem der artikulierten Sprache. J. A. Barth, Leipzig.

1930. Ueber die Projektion des äusseren Kniehöckers auf die Hirnrinde. Klin. Monatsbl. f. Augenh., v. 85, p. 586.

1930. Das Restitutionsprinzip im Hirnleben. Deutsch. Ztschr. f. Nervenh., v. 116, p. 55.

1931. Ueber Gesichtshalluzinationen. Klin. Monatsbl. f. Augenh., v. 86, p. 395.

1932. Ueber die Lokalisation und Pathologie der corticalen Macula. Zentralbl. f. d. ges. Ophth., v. 27, p. 180.

1933–37. Beiträge zur Lehre von der Seelenblindheit. I–VIII. Mitt. Ztschr. f. d. ges. Neurol. u. Psychiat., v. 149, p. 68; v. 150, p. 643; v. 152, p. 345; v. 159, pp. 226, 251, 284, 306, 326.

1934. Sur un cas de démence infantile et juvénile avec amaurose. Encéphale, v. 29, p. 561.

1936. Ueber die Existenz angeblicher Erweichungsherde im Sehnerv, Chiasma und Traktus opticus. Ztschr. f. Augenh., v. 90, p. 241.

1936. Ueber die hirnpathologischen Grundlagen der optischen Halluzinationen. Arch. f. d. ges. Psychol., v. 97, p. 132.

NIPPERT, O.

1931. Zur Morphologie und Genese der Fossa temporalis mit besonderer Berücksichtigung der lateralen Orbitalwand. Ztschr. f. Morphol. u. Anthropol., v. 29, p. 1.

NISSEN, H. W.

1931. A field study of the chimpanzee. Observations of chimpanzee behavior and environment in western French Guinea. ("Comp. Psychol. Monog.," v. 8, ser. No. 36.)

NISSL, F.

1885. Ueber die Untersuchungsmethoden der Grosshirnrinde. Tagebl. d. 58. Versamml. Deutsch. Naturforsch. u. Aerzte, p. 506.

1889. Die Kerne des Thalamus beim Kaninchen. Tagebl. d. 62. Versamml. Deutsch. Naturforsch. u. Aerzte, p. 509.

1894. Ueber eine neue Untersuchungsmethode des Centralorgans speciell zur Feststellung der Localisation der Nervenzellen. Centralbl. f. Nervenh. u. Psychiat., v. 17, p. 337.

1894. Ueber die sogenannte Granula der Nervenzellen. Neurol. Centralbl., v. 13, pp. 676, 781, 810.

1895. Bernhard von Gudden's hirnanatomische Experimentaluntersuchungen. Allg. Ztschr. f. Psychiat., v. 51, p. 527.

1895. Ueber die Nomenklatur in der Nervenzellenanatomie und ihre nächsten Ziele. Neurol. Centralbl., v. 14, pp. 66, 104.

1897. Ueber die örtlichen Bauverschiedenheiten

der Hirnrinde. Arch. f. Psychiat. u. Nervenkr., v. 29, p. 1025.

1898. Die Hypothese der specifischen Nervenzellenfunction. Allg. Ztschr. f. Psychiat., v. 54, p. 1.

1900. Die Neuronenlehre vom pathologisch-anatomischen und klinischen Standpunkte. Verhandl. d. Gesellsch. deutsch. Naturforsch. u. Aerzte, v. 72, p. 211; Neurol. Centralbl., v. 19, p. 1078.

1903. Die Neuronenlehre und ihre Anhänger. G. Fischer, Jena.

1907. Experimentalergebnisse zur Frage der Hirnrindenschichtung. Neurol. Centralbl., v. 26, p. 1142; Monatsschr. f. Psychiat. u. Neurol., v. 23, p. 186.

1911. Zur Lehre der Lokalisation in der Grosshirnrinde des Kaninchens. I. Völlige Isolierung der Hirnrinde beim neugeborenen Tier. Sitzungsb. d. Heidelberg. Akad. d. Wissensch., naturwiss. Kl., 38. Abh.

1913. Grosshirnanteile des Kaninchens. Arch. f. Psychiat., v. 52, p. 867. (Festschr. f. Sioli.)

1927. Nervensystem. *In:* R. KRAUSE, Enzyklopädie der mikroskopischen Technik, v. 3, p. 1636. 3d ed. Urban & Schwarzenberg, Berlin & Wien.

NOBACK, C. R., & PAFF, G. H.
1948. Gross anatomy of the visual pathways in man. Anat. Rec., v. 100, p. 782. (Demonstration 59.)

NOBLE, D.
1846. The brain and its physiology. J. Churchill, London.

NOBLE, G. K.
1931. The biology of the *Amphibia*. McGraw-Hill Book Co., New York.

NOBLE, G. K., & CURTIS, B.
1939. The social behavior of the jewel fish, *Hemichromis bimaculatus*. Bull. Am. Mus. Nat. Hist., v. 76 (1), p. 1.

NÖLDEKE, G. J. F.
1805. Galen, vom Nutzen der Theile des menschlichen Körpers, etc. Erstes Buch (von der Hand). Schultz'esche Buchhandlung, Oldenburg.

NOLL, A.
1915. Ueber das Sehvermögen und das Pupillenspiel grosshirnloser Tauben. Arch. f. Physiol. (Rubner), p. 350.

1922. Zur Kenntnis des Verlaufs der Pupillenfasern beim Vogel. Pflüger's Arch. f. Physiol., v. 196, p. 629.

1935. Zur Phylogenie des Lidschlages. Anat. Anz., v. 79, p. 396.

NOLTE, W.
1932. Experimentelle Untersuchungen zum Problem der Lokalisation des Assoziationsvermögens im Fischgehirn. Ztschr. f. vergl. Physiol., v. 18, p. 255.

NONIDEZ, J. F.
1936–37. The nervous "terminal reticulum." A critique. Anat. Anz., v. 82, p. 348; v. 84, pp. 1, 315.

NONIDEZ, J. F., & HARE, K.
1942. Experimental verification of the differences in the argyrophilia of sympathetic postganglionics and of other nerve fibers. J. Comp. Neurol., v. 76, p. 91.

NORDENSKIÖLD, E.
1932. The history of biology. A survey. A. A. Knopf, New York & London. German trans.: Die Geschichte der Biologie. G. Fischer, Jena, 1926.

NORDENSON, J. W., & NORDMARK, T.
1928. Bemerkungen zur Frage über die Farbe der Macula centralis retinae. Upsala läkaref. förh., N.F., v. 33, p. 499.

NORMAN, J. R.
1936. A history of fishes. E. Benn, London.

NORRIS, W. F., & SHAKESPEARE, E. O.
1877. A contribution to the anatomy of the human retina. Am. J. M. Sc., N.S., v. 74, p. 402.

NOTHNAGEL, H.
1879. Topische Diagnostik der Gehirnkrankheiten. A. Hirschwald, Berlin.

NOTHNAGEL & NAUNYN
1887. Ueber die Localisation der Gehirnkrankheiten. Verhandl. d. Cong. f. inn. Med., v. 6, pp. 109, 132; Neurol. Centralbl., v. 6, p. 213.

NOVIKOV, M. (NOVIKOFF or NOWIKOFF)
1907. Ueber das Parietalauge von *Lacerta agilis* und *Anguis fragilis*. Biol. Centralbl., v. 27, pp. 364, 405.

1910. Untersuchungen über den Bau, die Entwicklung und die Bedeutung des Parietalauges von Sauriern. Ztschr. f. wissensch. Zool., v. 96, p. 118.

1928. Purkyně a Baer. Paralela z dějin přirodovědy. Sbornik Přirodovecky, v. 5, p. 1.

1929. J. E. Pourkygné et sa conception organique de la nature. Trav. scient. Univ. pop. russe de Prague, v. 2, p. 24.

1932. Ueber den Bau der Komplexaugen von *Periplaneta* (*Stylopyga*) *orientalis* L. Jena. Ztschr. f. Naturwiss., v. 67, p. 58.

1932. Ueber die morphologische Bedeutung der Sehorgane von Chordaten. Biol. Zentralbl., v. 52, p. 548.

1932. Les analogies dans la structure des œux

chez les animaux cordés et acordés. Acad.
tschèque d. sc., Bull. internat., cl. sc.
math., nat. & méd., v. 33, p. 131.

1934. Zur Frage der morphologischen Beziehungen zwischen Sehorganen und Drüsen.
Ztschr. f. Morphol. u. Oek. d. Tiere, v. 29,
p. 374.

1944–45. Zur Frage über den Parallelismus im
Bau der tierischen Organe, insbesondere der
Augen. Anat. Anz., v. 95, p. 118.

NOYES, H. D.
1884. Zwei Fälle von Hemiachromatopsie. Arch. f.
Augenh., v. 13, p. 123.

NUËL, J. P.
1887. Du développement phylogénétique de l'organe visuel des vertébrés. Arch. de biol.,
v. 7, p. 389.

1892. De la vascularisation de la choroïde et de la
nutrition de la rétine principalement au
niveau de la fovea centralis. Arch. d'opht.,
v. 12, p. 70.

NUNNELEY, T.
1858. On the structure of the retina. Quart. J.
Micr. Sc., v. 6, p. 217.

NUSSBAUM, M.
1908. Entwicklungsgeschichte des menschlichen
Auges. *In:* GRAEFE & SAEMISCH, Handb. d.
ges. Augenh., 2d ed., v. 2, Part 1.

O

OAKLEY, K. P.
1950. Man the tool-maker. British Museum (Natural History), London.

OBERSTEINER, H.
1892. Die Bedeutung einiger neuerer Untersuchungsmethoden für die Klärung unserer
Kenntnisse vom Aufbau des Nervensystems.
Arb. a. d. Neurol. Inst. Wien, v. 1, p. 130.

1912. Anleitung beim Studium des Baues der
nervösen Zentralorgane im gesunden und
kranken Zustande. 5th ed. F. Deuticke,
Leipzig & Wien.

OBERSTEINER, H., & REDLICH, E.
1902. Zur Kenntnis des Stratum (Fasciculus) subcallosum (Fasciculus nuclei caudati) und
des Fasciculus fronto-occipitalis (reticulirtes
cortico-caudales Bündel). Arb. a. d. Neurol.
Inst. Wien (Obersteiner), v. 8, p. 286.

OBRADOR, S.
1943. Effect of hypothalamic lesions on electrical
activity of cerebral cortex. J. Neurophysiol.,
v. 6, p. 81.

OBREGIA, A.
1890. Ueber Augenbewegungen bei Sehsphären-

reizung. Arch. f. Anat. u. Physiol. (physiol.
Abt.), p. 260.

OCAÑA; *see* GOMEZ OCAÑA
O'CONNELL, J. E. A.
1934. Some observations on the cerebral veins.
Brain, v. 57, p. 484.

O'DAY, K. J.
1936. A preliminary note on the presence of
double cones and oil droplets in the retina of
marsupials. J. Anat., v. 70, p. 465.

1938. The retina of the Australian mammal. M. J.
Australia, v. 1, p. 326.

1938. The visual cells of the platypus (*Ornithorhynchus*). Brit. J. Ophth., v. 22, p. 321.

1939. The visual cells of Australian reptiles and
mammals. Tr. Ophth. Soc. Australia, v. 1,
p. 12.

1940. The fundus and fovea centralis of the
albatross (*Diomedea cauta cauta* Gould).
Brit. J. Ophth., v. 24, p. 201.

OEHMIG
1915. Ein Fall von rechtsseitiger homonymer
Hemianopsie nach Granatsplitterverletzung
am Hinterkopfe. Deutsch. med. Wchnschr.,
v. 41, p. 239.

ØSTERBERG, G. A.
1935. Topography of the layer of rods and cones
in the human retina. Acta Ophth., suppl. 6.

OGATA, S.
1912. Ueber eine Fortsatzbildung am vorderen
Rande des Chiasma nervorum opticorum.
Virchow's Arch. f. path. Anat., v. 210, p. 50.

OGLE, K. N.
1937–38. Die mathematische Analyse des Längshoropters. Arch. f. d. ges. Physiol. (Pflüger),
v. 239, p. 748.

1939. Relative sizes of ocular images of the two
eyes in asymmetric convergence. Arch.
Ophth., v. 22 (O.S., v. 79), p. 1046.

OGLE, K. N., MUSSEY, F., & PRANGEN, A. D.
1949. Fixation disparity and the fusional processes
in binocular single vision. Am. J. Ophth., v.
32, p. 1069.

OGLE, W.
1882. Aristotle on the parts of animals. K. Paul,
Trench & Co., London.

OGNEV, S. I.
1947–48. Zvéri SSSR i prilezháshchih stran (The
mammals of USSR and adjacent countries).
Izdat. Akad. Nauk SSSR, vols. 5, 6. Moskvá & Leningrád.

OHATA, YUTAKA
1929. Ueber die Verbindung zwischen dem Tectum
opticum und dem roten Kern beim Vogel.
Okayama-Igakkai-Zasshi, v. 41, p. 1453.

OHM, J.
1921. Analyse des Doppeltsehens. Klin. Monatsbl. f. Augenh., v. 66, p. 20.
1932. Optokinetischer Nystagmus und Nystagmographie im Dienste der Hirndiagnostik. Arch. f. Augenh., v. 106, pp. 185, 531.
1943. Die Mikroneurologie des Auges und seiner Bewegung. F. Enke, Stuttgart

OKLAHOMA UNIVERSITY BIOLOGICAL SURVEY
1950. Researches on the amphibia of Oklahoma, by ARTHUR N. BRAGG [and others]. University of Oklahoma Press, Norman.

OLDBERG; *see* URY & OLDBERG

OLDENBERG, O.
1949. Introduction to atomic physics. McGraw-Hill Book Co., New York.

O'LEARY, J. L.
1937. Structure of the primary olfactory cortex of the mouse. J. Comp. Neurol., v. 67, p. 1.
1940. A structural analysis of the lateral geniculate nucleus of the cat. *Ibid.*, v. 73, p. 405.
1941. Structure of the area striata of the cat. *Ibid.*, v. 75, p. 131.

O'LEARY, J. L., & BISHOP, G. H.
1938. The optically excitable cortex of the rabbit. J. Comp. Neurol., v. 68, p. 423.
1938. Margins of the optically excitable cortex in the rabbit. Arch. Neurol. & Psychiat., v. 40, p. 482.
1943. Analysis of potential sources in the optic lobe of duck and goose. J. Cell. & Comp. Physiol., v. 22, p. 73.

O'LEARY, J. L., & GRAHAM, H. T.
1941. Fast central fibers in fish. Properties of Mauthner and Müller fibers of medullospinal system. J. Neurophysiol., v. 4, p. 224.

OLMSTED, E. W., & OLMSTED, E. P.
1951. The physiologic limits of vision in physiographic observation. Science, v. 113, p. 176.

OLMSTED, J. M. D.
1944. François Magendie; pioneer in experimental physiology and scientific medicine in XIX century France. Henry Schuman, New York.

OLOFF
1916. Ueber psychogene Kriegsschädigungen des Auges. Ber. ü. d. 40. Versamml. Deutsch. ophth. Gesellsch. Heidelberg, p. 304.

OLSON, T. A.
1932. Some observations on the interrelationships of sunlight to aquatic plant life and fishes. Tr. Am. Fish. Soc., v. 62, p. 278.

OLSZEWSKI, J.
1950. Cécile and Oskar Vogt. Arch. Neurol. & Psychiat., v. 64, p. 812.

O'MALLEY, C. D., & SAUNDERS, J. B. DE C. M.
1952. Leonardo da Vinci on the human body. Henry Schuman, New York.

OOSTEN, J. V.; *see* VAN OOSTEN

OPARIN, A. I.
1953. The origin of life. Macmillan Co., New York.

OPIN, L.
1939. Vision binoculaire et vision spatiale. *In:* P. BAILLIART *et al.*, Traité d'opht., v. 2, p. 769. Masson & Cie, Paris.

OPPENHEIM, H.
1913. Lehrbuch der Nervenkrankheiten für Aerzte und Studierende. 2 vols. 6th ed. S. Karger, Berlin.

OPPENHEIM, S.
1913. Das Gehirn des Homo neandertalensis sive primigenius. Naturwiss., v. 1, p. 955.
1940. Metrische und deskriptive Merkmale des menschlichen und tierischen Auges. Tab. biol., v. 22, Part 1, p. 54.

OPPENHEIMER, J. M.
1942. Postulated factors controlling decussation of Mauthner's fibers in *Fundulus* embryos. Anat. Rec., v. 82, p. 435. (Abstr.)
1950. The development of *Fundulus heteroclitus* embryos in solutions of metrazol. J. Exper. Zoöl., v. 113, p. 65.
1950. Functional regulation in *Fundulus heteroclitus* with abnormal central system. *Ibid.*, v. 115, p. 461.
1950. Anomalous optic chiasma in *Fundulus* embryos. Anat. Rec., v. 108, p. 477.

OPPENOORTH, W. F. F.
1937. The place of *Homo soloensis* among fossil men. *In:* G. G. McCURDY (ed.), Early man, p. 349. J. B. Lippincott Co., Philadelphia & New York.

ORIONE, J.
1950. Teoria visual espacial. El factor visual espacial como causa determinante en la evolución y la culminación humana. N. Zielony en Pasteur 356, Buenos Aires.

ORLANDO, R.
1933. Sobre atrofia alternada de las capas del cuerpo geniculado externo en el hombre. Arch. argent. de neurol., v. 9, p. 122.

ORLEY, A.
1949. Neuroradiology. Charles C Thomas, Springfield, Ill.

ORTON, G. L.
1951. Direct development in frogs. Turtox News, v. 29, p. 2.

OSAWA, G.
1898. Beiträge zur Lehre von den Sinnesorganen

der *Hatteria punctata*. Arch. f. mikr. Anat., v. 52 p. 268.

1899. Ueber die Fovea centralis von *Hatteria punctata*. Anat. Anz., v. 15, p. 226.

Osborn, C. M.

1935. The physiology of color change in flatfishes. J. Exper. Zoöl., v. 81, p. 479.

Osborn, H. F.

1896. Dentition of lemurs and the systematic position of Tarsius. Science, N.S., v. 4, p. 745.

1910. The age of mammals in Europe, Asia, and North America. (Harris Lect., Northwestern University, 1908.) Macmillan Co., New York.

1916. Men of the old Stone Age. Their environment, life and art. Charles Scribner's Sons, New York.

1917. The origin and evolution of life, on the theory of action, reaction and interaction of energy. Charles Scribner's Sons, New York.

1928. The influence of bodily locomotion in separating man from the monkeys and apes. Scient. Monthly, v. 26, p. 385.

1929. Ancient migration routes of central Asia. Science, v. 70, p. 638.

1930. The discovery of tertiary man. *Ibid.*, v. 71, p. 1.

Oshinomi, T.

1929. Ein Beitrag zur Kenntnis des Corpus geniculatum externum. Okayama-Igakkai Zasshi, v. 41, p. 2274.

1930. Ueber die Sehbahnen, welche die primären Sehzentren mit der Sehrinde verbinden, besonders mit Rücksicht auf die Verbindung zwischen dem Corpus geniculatum externum und dem Hinterhauptpol. *Ibid.*, v. 42, p. 253.

1930. On the degeneration of the ganglion cells of the retina after the lesion of the primary visual centers, especially of the lateral geniculate body, and of the optic tract. With a supplement on the histology of normal ganglion cells in some mammals, birds and teleosts (in Japanese). Acta Soc. ophth. jap., v. 34, p. 881.

Osler, W.

1929. Bibliotheca Osleriana. A catalogue of books illustrating the history of medicine and science. Clarendon Press, Oxford.

Ossenkopp, G. J.

1925. Uebersicht unserer derzeitigen Kenntnis von den fossilen niederen Primaten. Ergebn. d. Anat. u. Entw., v. 26, p. 463.

Osterhout, W. J. V.

1931. Electrical phenomena in the living cell. Harvey Lect., ser. 25, p. 169.

Ostertag, B.

1944. Die Sektionstechnik des Gehirns und des Rückenmarks nebst Anleitung zur Befunderhebung. J. Springer, Berlin.

Ostoya, P.

1951. Les théories de l'évolution. Origines et histoire du transformisme et des idées qui s'y rattachent. Payot, Paris.

Ostwald, W.

1902–38. Ostwald's Klassiker der exakten Wissenschaften. W. Engelmann, Leipzig.

1923. Physikalische Farbenlehre. 2d ed. (Die Farbenlehre, Book 2.) First ed., 1919. Verlag Unesma, Leipzig.

Otero, J. M., & Plaza, L.

1946. Contribución al estudio de la agudeza visual con lamparas espectrales. An. de fís. y quím., v. 42, p. 408.

Otero de Navascués, J. M.

1945. Discurso leído en el acto de su recepción, etc. R. Acad. de cienc. exact., fís. y nat., Madrid.

Oulmont, P.

1889. Cécité subite par ramollissement des deux lobes occipitaux. Gaz. hebd. méd. et chir., v. 26, p. 607.

Overbosch, J. F. A.

1927. Experimenteel-anatomische onderzoekingen over de projectie der retina in het centrale zenuwstelsel. Academisch proefschrift, etc. H. J. Paris, Amsterdam.

Ovio, J. (G.)

1927. Anatomie et physiologie de l'œil dans la série animale. Félix Alcan, Paris. (Also in Italian.)

1928. Uno dei fattori della inferiorità visiva della retina fuori del punto di fissazione e teoria ottica della retina. Ann. di ottal., v. 56, p. 1057.

Owen, R.

1832. Memoir on the pearly nautilus. Printed by R. Taylor, London.

Ozorio de Almeida, M.

1944. L'inhibition et la facilitation dans le système nerveux central et périphérique. Atlantica Editora, Rio de Janeiro.

P

Pacini, F.

1845. Nuove ricerche microscopiche sulla tessitura intima della retina nell'uomo, nei vertebrati, nei cefalopodi e negli insetti. Nuovi. ann. d. sc. nat. e rend. d. sess. d. Soc. agr. e d. accad. d. sc. d. Ist. di Bologna, 2d ser., v. 4, pp. 59, 71, 97, 161. German ed., Freiburg, 1847.

PACKER, A. D.
1941. An experimental investigation of the visual system in the phalanger, *Trichosurus vulpecula.* J. Anat., v. 75, p. 309.
1949. A comparison of endocranial cast and brain of an Australian aborigine. *Ibid.,* v. 83, p. 195.

PAGANO, G.
1897. Sulle vie associative periferiche del nervo ottico. Riv. di pat. nerv. e ment., v. 2, p. 70.

PAGEL, J. L.
1915. Einführung in die Geschichte der Medizin. S. Karger, Berlin.

PAGENSTECHER, A. H.
1916. Ueber Sehstörungen nach Schussverletzung am Hinterhaupt. Arch. f. Augenh., v. 80, p. 229.

PALLARÈS, J.
1931. Un cas d'hémianopsie double avec conservation de la vision maculaire, après la naissance. Ann. d'ocul., v. 168, p. 45.

PALMAR, C. E.
1954. Scotland's golden eagles at home. Nat. Geog. Mag., v. 105, p. 273.

PALMER, E. L.
1949. Fieldbook of natural history. Whittlesey House–McGraw-Hill Book Co., New York.

PALMER, R. S.
1947. Notes on some Maine shrews. J. Mammal., v. 28, p. 13.

PALMER, S. C.
1912. The numerical relations of the histological elements in the retina of *Necturus maculosus* (Raf.). J. Comp. Neurol., v. 22, p. 405.

PALMGREN, A.
1921. Embryological and morphological studies on the midbrain and cerebellum of vertebrates. Acta zool., v. 2, p. 1.

PALUMBI, G.
1932. Il comportamento della capsula del Tenon in corrispondenza dei vasi e nervi ciliari posteriori. Ric. morfol., v. 12, p. 391.

PANAS, P.
1894. Traité des maladies des yeux. 2 vols. G. Masson, Paris.

PANIZZA, BARTOLOMEO (*see also* A. DELBUE)
1855–56. Osservazioni sul nervo ottico. Mem. d. I. R. Ist. Lombardo d. sc., lett. e arti, v. 5, p. 375; Gior. dell'I. R. Ist. Lombardo d. sc., lett. e arti, e bibl. ital., v. 7, p. 237.

PANSCH, A.
1868. Ueber die typische Anordnung der Furchen und Windungen auf den Grosshirn-He-misphären des Menschen und der Affen. Arch. f. Anthropol., v. 3, p. 227.

PANSIER, P.
1901. Histoire des lunettes. A. Maloine, Paris.
1903–33. Collectio ophtalmologica veterum auctorum. 7 fasc. in 2 vols. Contents: Arnaldi de Villanova, J. de Casso, Alcoatin, Ali ben Issa, David Armenicus, Mag. Zacharia, Anonymus, Constantin Africanus, Galen's letter to Corisius. History of Arabian ophthalmology in v. 1, p. 41. History of ophthalmology in western Europe during the Middle Ages, v. 2, p. 99. J.-B. Baillière, Paris.

PANTIN, C. F. A.
1941. The origin of life. Nature, v. 148, p. 40.

PANUM, P. L.
1858. Physiologische Untersuchungen über das Sehen mit zwei Augen. Schwerssche Buchhandlung, Kiel.
1859. Die scheinbare Grösse der gesehenen Objecte. Arch. f. Ophth. (Graefe), v. 5 (1), p. 1.

PAPARCONE, M. E.
1925. Historical note on trachoma. Bull. & mém. Soc. franç. d'opht., v. 38, p. 367.

PAPEZ, J. W.
1927. The brain of Helen H. Gardener (Alice Chenoweth Day). Am. J. Phys. Anthropol., v. 11, p. 29.
1929. The brain of Burt Green Wilder, 1841–1925. J. Comp. Neurol., v. 47, p. 285.
1929. Comparative neurology. Thomas Y. Crowell Co., New York.
1930. The brain of Sutherland Simpson, 1863–1926. J. Comp. Neurol., v. 51, p. 165.
1932. The thalamic nuclei of the nine-banded armadillo (*Tatusia novemcincta*). *Ibid.,* v. 56, p. 49.
1935. Thalamus of turtles and thalamic evolution. *Ibid.,* v. 61, p. 433.
1938. Thalamic connections in a hemidecorticate dog. *Ibid.,* v. 69, p. 103.
1939. Connections of the pulvinar. Arch. Neurol. & Psychiat., v. 41, p. 277.
1942. Ventral branch of the optic radiations in man. A microscopic study. Anat. Rec., v. 82, p. 475.
1942. A summary of fiber connections of the basal ganglia with each other and with other portions of the brain. Research Pub. A. Research Nerv. & Ment. Dis., v. 21, p. 21.
1944. Structures and mechanisms underlying the cerebral functions. Am. J. Psychol., v. 57, p. 291.

PAPEZ, J. W., & FREEMAN, G. L.
1930. Superior colliculi and their fiber connections in the rat. J. Comp. Neurol., v. 51, p. 409.

PAPEZ, J. W., & RUNDLES, R. W.
1938. Thalamus of a dog without a hemisphere due to a unilateral congenital hydrocephalus. J. Comp. Neurol., v. 69, p. 89.

PAPEZ, J. W., & STATLER, W. A.
1940. Connections of the red nucleus. Arch. Neurol. & Psychiat., v. 44, p. 776.

PAPPENHEIM, S. M.
*1842. Die specielle Gewebelehre des Auges mit Rücksicht auf Entwicklungsgeschichte und Augenpraxis. G. P. Aderholz, Breslau.

PARACELSUS
16th cent. Four treatises, trans. by C. L. TEMKIN, G. ROSEN, G. ZILBOORG & H. E. SIGERIST. ("Publications of the Institute of the History of Medicine.") Johns Hopkins Press, Baltimore, 1941.

PARINAUD, H.
1881. Des modifications pathologiques de la perception de la lumière, des couleurs, et des formes, et des différentes espèces de sensibilité oculaire. Compt. rend. Soc. de biol., v. 33, p. 222.

1884. Sur la sensibilité visuelle. Compt. rend. Acad. d. sc., v. 99, p. 241.

1884. De l'intensité lumineuse des couleurs spectrales; influence de l'adaptation rétinienne. *Ibid.*, p. 987.

1885. Sur l'existence de deux espèces de sensibilité à la lumière. *Ibid.*, v. 101, p. 821.

1894. La sensibilité de l'œil aux couleurs spectrales; fonctions des éléments rétiniens et du pourpre visuel. Ann. d'ocul., v. 112, p. 228.

1896. Les nouvelles idées sur les fonctions de la rétine. Arch. d'opht., v. 16, p. 87.

1898. La vision. Doin, Paris.

PARKER, A. J.
1910. Morphology of the cerebral convolutions with special reference to the order of primates. J. Acad. Nat. Sc., ser. 2, v. 10, p. 247.

PARKER, G. H.
1903. The optic chiasma in teleosts and its bearing on the asymmetry of the heterostomata (flat fishes). Bull. Mus. Comp. Zoöl., v. 40, p. 221.

1908. The origin of the lateral of vertebrate eyes. Am. Naturalist, v. 42, p. 601.

1908. The sensory reactions of *Amphioxus*. Proc. Am. Acad. Arts & Sc., v. 43, p. 413.

1909. The integumentary nerves of fishes as photoreceptors and their significance for the origin of the vertebrate eyes. Am. J. Physiol., v. 25, p. 77.

1919. The elementary nervous system. J. B. Lippincott Co., Philadelphia & London.

1922. Smell, taste, and allied senses in the vertebrates. J. B. Lippincott Co., Philadelphia.

1923. The origin and development of the nervous system. Scientia, v. 34, p. 23.

1929. What are neurofibrils? Am. Naturalist, v. 43, p. 97.

1929. The neurofibril hypothesis. Quart. Rev. Biol., v. 4, p. 155.

1930. Chromatophores. Biol. Rev., v. 5, p. 59.

1932. The movements of the retinal pigment. Ergebn. d. Biol., v. 9, p. 239.

1934. Introduction to physical and chemical changes in nerve during activity. Science, v. 79 (suppl.).

1940. A modern conception of the action of the nervous system. *Ibid.*, v. 92, p. 319.

PARKER, G. H., BROWN, F. A., JR., & ODIORNE, J. M.
1935. The relation of the eyes to chromatophoral activities. Proc. Am. Acad. Arts & Sc., v. 69, p. 439.

PARKER, G. H., & VAN HENSEN, A. P.
1917. The reception of mechanical stimuli by the skin, lateral-line organs, and ears in fishes, especially in *Ameiurus*. Am. J. Physiol., v. 44, p. 463.

PARKER, L. R., DAWSON, W. S., & WALLACE, J. A. L.
1938. Alfred Walter Campbell (obituary). M. J. Australia, v. 1, p. 181.

PARKER, T. J., & HASWELL, W. A.
1940. A text-book of zoölogy. Revised by O. LOWENSTEIN & C. FORSTER-COOPER. 6th ed. 2 vols. Macmillan & Co., Ltd., London.

PARRY, D. A.
1947. The function of the insect ocellus. J. Exper. Biol., v. 24, p. 211.

PARSONS, H.
1902. Degenerations following lesions of the retina in monkeys. Brain, v. 25, p. 257.

PARSONS, J. H.
1901. On dilatation of the pupil from stimulation of the cortex cerebri. J. Physiol., v. 26, p. 366.

1921. The evolution of visual perception. Tr. Ophth. Soc. United Kingdom, v. 41, p. 97.

1924. An introduction to the study of colour vision. 2d ed. Cambridge University Press, Cambridge.

1925. The Bowman Lecture on the foundations of vision. Lancet, v. 2, p. 123.

1927. An introduction to the theory of perception. Cambridge University Press, Cambridge.

PARSONS, J. H.—*Continued*

1929. Dyscritic vision: the role of the rods. Compt. rend. XIII. Concil. Ophth. Amsterdam-Haag, p. 321.

1930. Colour vision and its anomalies. Brit. J. Ophth., v. 14, p. 97.

1930–31. The Thomas Young oration. Young's theory of colour vision (1801–1931). Tr. Opt. Soc. London, v. 32, p. 165.

1936. The electrical response of the eye to light. Brit. J. Ophth., v. 20, p. 1.

1943. Light and vision. *Ibid.*, v. 27, p. 321.

PARSONS, J. H., & DUKE-ELDER, S.

1948. Diseases of the eye. 11th ed. Macmillan Co., New York.

PARTRIDGE, M.

1950. Pre-frontal leucotomy: a survey of 300 cases personally followed over $1\frac{1}{2}$–3 years. Charles C Thomas, Springfield, Ill.

PASCAL, J. I.

1942. Parallactic angle in binocular depth perception. Arch. Ophth., v. 28, p. 258.

1945. Cardinal points in the static and in the dynamic eye. *Ibid.*, v. 34, p. 319.

1952. Studies in visual optics. C. V. Mosby Co., St. Louis.

PASCHEFF, C.

1922. Die zerebralen Ringskotome und seltenere nervöse Augenstörungen nach Kriegsverletzungen am Kopf. Arch. f. Augenh., v. 91, p. 233.

PASS, K. E.

1939. Ueber die subarachnoidale Blutung. Zentralbl. f. d. ges. Neurol. u. Psychiat., v. 94, p. 349.

PASSERA, E.

1921. Le cognizioni oftalmologiche di Dante. Arch. di storia d. sc. (Mieli ed.), v. 3, p. 1.

PATERSON, A.

1944. Concentric restriction of vision from unilateral cerebral lesions. Tr. Ophth. Soc. United Kingdom, v. 64, p. 115.

PATERSON, A., & ZANGWILL, O. L.

1944. Recovery of spatial orientation in the post-traumatic confusional state. Brain, v. 67, p. 54.

1944. Disorders of visual space perception associated with lesions of the right cerebral hemisphere. *Ibid.*, p. 331.

PATRIKIOS, J. S.

1950. Ophthalmoplegic migraine. Arch. Neurol. & Psychiat., v. 63, p. 902.

PATRY, A.

1939. Hallucination visuelle consciente chez le vieillard. Schweiz. med. Wchnschr., v. 20, p. 1090.

PATTEN, B. M.

1917. Reactions of the whip-tail scorpion to light. Anat. Rec., v. 11, p. 522.

PATTEN, W.

1886. Eyes of molluscs and arthropods. Mitt. a. d. zool. Stat. zu Neapel, v. 6, p. 542.

PATTON, H. D., & RUCH, T. C.

1944. Preference thresholds for quinine hydrochloride in chimpanzee, monkey, and rat. J. Comp. Psychol., v. 37, p. 35.

PAULY, A. F., & WISSOWA, G.

1894–1937. Paulys Real-Encyclopädie der classischen Altertumswissenschaft. New ed. by G. WISSOWA and W. KROLL. 56 vols. J. B. Metzlersche Verlagsbuchhandlung, Stuttgart.

PAUSCHMANN, G.

1920. Zur Geschichte der linsenlosen Abbildung. Arch. f. d. Gesch. d. Naturwiss. u. d. Technik, v. 9, p. 86.

PAVÍA, J. L.

1936. Oftalmoscopía y retinografía infrarojas. Rev. oto-neuro-oftal., v. 11, p. 298; Cong. argent. de oftal., v. 2, p. 230.

PAVILLARD, J.

1952. Classe des phytomonadines ou volvocales Francé, 1894. *In:* P.-P. GRASSÉ, Traité de zoologie, v. 1, p. 153.

PAVLOV (PAWLOW), I. P.

1908. Ueber die bedingten Reflexe bei Zerstörung verschiedener Regionen der Gehirnhemisphären beim Hunde. Berlin. klin. Wchnschr., v. 45, p. 1299.

1926. Die höchste Nerventätigkeit (das Verhalten) von Tieren. 3d ed. Trans. G. VOLBROTH. J. F. Bergmann, Wiesbaden.

1927. Conditioned reflexes. Trans. G. V. ANREP. Oxford University Press, London.

1928. Lectures on conditioned reflexes. Twenty-five years of objective study of the higher nervous activity (behavior) of animals. International Publishing Co., New York; M. Lawrence, London.

1930. A brief outline of the higher nervous activity. *In:* Psychologies of 1930, chap. 11, p. 207. Clark University Press, Worcester, Mass.

1941. Conditioned reflexes and psychiatry. International Publishing Co., New York.

PAVLOW, M.

1900. Les voies descendantes des tubercules quadrijumeaux supérieurs. Névraxe, v. 1, pp. 57, 129.

1900. Les connexions centrales du nerf optique chez le lapin. *Ibid.*, p. 235; *see also* pp. 57, 129, 151, 271, 331.

1900. Un faisceau descendant de la substance réticulaire du mésencéphale. *Ibid.*, p. 271.

1900. Quelques points concernant le rôle physiologique du tubercule quadrijumeau supérieur du noyau rouge et de la substance réticulaire de la calotte. *Ibid.*, p. 331.

PAWLOWSKI
*1860. Chiasma nervorum opticorum. Inaug. Diss., Moscow. (In Russian.)

PAZ SOLDAN, C. E.
1944. El cuatricentenario de la "Fábrica" de Andreas Vesalius, y las bases anatómicas de la Escuela médica de Lima. Lima, Peru.

PEACOCK, G.
1855. Life of Thomas Young, M.D., F.R.S., &c., and one of the eight foreign associates of the National Institute of France. By GEORGE PEACOCK, D.D., F.R.S., F.G.S., F.R.A.S., F.C.P.S., etc., Dean of Ely, Lowndean Professor of Astronomy in the University of Cambridge, and formerly Fellow and Tutor of Trinity College. London, John Murray, Albemarle Street, 1855.

PEARCE, J., & GERARD, R. W.
1942. The respiration of neurones. Am. J. Physiol., v. 136, p. 49.

PEARL, R.
1946. Man the animal. Principia Press, Bloomington, Ind.

PEARSE, A. S.
1936. Zoölogical names. A list of phyla, classes, and orders. Duke University Press, Durham, N.C.

PEARSON, A. A.
1943. The trochlear nerve in human fetuses. J. Comp. Neurol., v. 78, p. 29.

1944. The oculomotor nucleus in the human fetus. *Ibid.*, v. 80, p. 47.

1951. A modification of the Golgi technique. Anat. Rec., v. 109, p. 405. (Abstr.)

PEARSON, O. P.
1942. On the cause and nature of a poisonous action produced by the bite of a shrew (*Blarina brevicauda*). J. Mammal., v. 23, p. 159.

1946. Scent glands of the short-tailed shrew. Anat. Rec., v. 94, p. 615.

1950. Keeping shrews in captivity. J. Mammal., v. 31, p. 351.

PEARSON, O. P., & PEARSON, A. K.
1947. Owl predations in Pennsylvania, with notes on the small mammals of Delaware county. J. Mammal., v. 28, p. 137.

PEARSON, T. G.
1936. Thrushes, thrashers, and swallows. Nat. Geog. Mag., v. 69, p. 523.

PEARSON, T. G., BURROUGHS, J., *et al.*
1936. Birds of America. Garden City Publishing Co., Garden City, N.Y.

PECHUEL-LOESCHE, E.
1879–1907. Die Loango-Expedition ausgesandt von der Deutschen Gesellschaft zur Erforschung Aequatorial-Africas, 1873–76. 3 vols.; v. 3 by P.-L. P. FROHBERG, Leipzig.

PECKHAM, JOHN
1482. Prospectiva communis domini Johannis archiepiscopi Cantuariensis fratris ordinis minorum etc. P. Cornenus, Milan. (Original written during 13th cent. A.D.; other editions: Leipzig, 1504; Venice, 1504, 1505?; Nuremberg, 1542; Cologne, 1508, 1542, 1627; Italian trans., Venice, 1593.)

PECKHAM, R. H.
1947. Protection and maintenance of night vision for military personnel. Arch. Ophth., ser. 2, v. 38, p. 569.

PECQUET, J.
1668. Nouvelle découverte touchant la veüe. (Extrait d'une lettre de M. l'abbé Mariotte à M. Pecquet. Réponse de M. Pecquet à la lettre de M. l'abbé Mariotte.) F. Leonard, Paris.

1676. Lettres écrites par MM. Mariotte, Pecquet et Perrault sur le sujet d'une nouvelle découverte touchant la veüe faite par M. Mariotte. Recueil de plusieurs traitez de mathématique de l'Académie royal des Sciences, Paris. (*Cf.* Catalogue of the Bibliothèque Nationale, art. "Mariotte," v. 107, col. 6.)

PEDEN, J. K., & BONIN, G. VON
1947. The neocortex of *Hapale*. J. Comp. Neurol., v. 86, p. 37.

PEELE, T. L.
1942. Cytoarchitecture of individual parietal areas in the monkey (*Macaca mulatta*) and the distribution of the efferent fibers. J. Comp. Neurol., v. 77, p. 693.

1944. Acute and chronic parietal lobe ablations in monkeys. J. Neurophysiol., v. 7, p. 269.

PEET, M. M.
1948. The cranial nerves. *In:* DEAN LEWIS, Practice of surgery, v. 12, chap. ii. W. F. Prior Co., Hagerstown, Md.

PEMBERTON, H.
1719 (1751). Dissertatio physico-medica de facultate oculi, qua ad diversas rerum conspectarum distantias se accommodat, etc. *In:* A. HALLER, Disput. select., v. 7 (2), p. 137.

PENARD, S.

1935. Zur Frage der Beziehungen zwischen Sehrinde und primären optischen Zentren auf Grund von experimentellen Studien am Affen. Schweiz. Arch. f. Neurol. u. Psychiat., v. 36, p. 131.

PENFIELD, W.

1928. A method of staining oligodendroglia and microglia. Am. J. Path., v. 4, p. 153.

1929. Diencephalic autonomic epilepsy. Arch. Neurol. & Psychiat., v. 22, p. 358.

1932. Cytology & cellular pathology of the nervous system. P. B. Hoeber, New York.

1933 The evidence for a cerebral vascular mechanism in epilepsy. Ann. Int. Med., v. 7, p. 303. (*See also* Foerster & Penfield 1930.)

1935. Focal epileptic discharge in a case of tumour of the posterior temporal region. Canad. M. A. J., v. 33, p. 32.

1937. The circulation of the epileptic brain. Research Pub. A. Research Nerv. & Ment. Dis., v. 18, p. 605.

1937–38. The cerebral cortex and consciousness. Harvey Lect., ser. 32, p. 35; Arch. Neurol. & Psychiat., v. 40, p. 417.

PENFIELD, W., & BOLDREY, E.

1937. Somatic motor and sensory representation in the cerebral cortex of man as studied by electrical stimulation. Brain, v. 60, p. 389

PENFIELD, W., & ERICKSON, T. C.

1941. Epilepsy and cerebral localization. Charles C Thomas, Springfield, Ill.

PENFIELD, W., & EVANS, J.

1934. Functional defects produced by cerebral lobectomies. *In:* Localization of function in the cerebral cortex. Research Pub. A. Research Nerv. & Ment. Dis., v. 13, p. 352. Williams & Wilkins Co., Baltimore.

1935. The frontal lobe in man: a clinical study of maximum removals. Brain, v. 58, p. 115.

PENFIELD, W., EVANS, J. P., & MacMILLAN, J. A.

1935. Visual pathways in man with particular reference to macular representation. Arch. Neurol. & Psychiat., v. 33, p. 816.

PENFIELD, W., & GAGE, L.

1934. Cerebral localization of epileptic manifestations. *In:* Localization of function in the cerebral cortex. Research Pub. A. Research Nerv. & Ment. Dis., v. 13, p. 593. Williams & Wilkins Co., Baltimore. *Also* Arch. Neurol. & Psychiat., v. 30, p. 709.

PENFIELD, W., JASPERS, H., & McNAUGHTON, F.

1954. Epilepsy and the functional anatomy of the human brain. Little, Brown & Co., Boston.

PENFIELD, W., & RASMUSSEN, T.

1950. The cerebral cortex of man. A clinical study of localization of function. Macmillan Co., New York.

PENMAN, G. G.

1934. The representation of the areas of the retina in the lateral geniculate body. Tr. Ophth. Soc. United Kingdom, v. 54, p. 232.

PENNYBACKER, J.

1943. Papilloedema due to intracranial venous obstruction. Tr. Ophth. Soc. United Kingdom, v. 63, p. 333.

PERGENS, E.

1904. Geschichtliches über das Netzhautbildchen und den Optikuseintritt. Klin. Monatsbl. f. Augenh., v. 42 (1), p. 137.

PERITZ, G.

1915. Zwei Fälle von Gehirnschüssen mit Lagegefühlsstörungen, Astereognosis, trophischen Veränderungen und halbseitiger Blutdrucksteigerung. Neurol. Centralbl., v. 34, p. 140.

PERKINS, F. T., & WHEELER, R. H.

1931. Configurational learning in the goldfish. ("Comp. Psychol. Monog.," v. 7, No. 31.)

PERLIA

1889. Ueber ein neues Opticuscentrum beim Huhne. Arch. f. Ophth. (Graefe), v. 35 (1), pp. 20, 282.

PERLMAN, H. B., & CASE, T. J.

1944. Mechanism of ocular movement in man. Arch. Otolaryng., v. 40, p. 457.

PERROT, G., & CHIPIEZ, C.

1882–1914. Histoire de l'art dans l'antiquité. 10 vols. Hachette & Cie, Paris.

PESKIN, J. C.

1942. The regeneration of visual purple in the living animal. J. Gen. Physiol., v. 26, p. 27.

PESME, P.

1931. Scotome hémianopsique maculaire avec hémiachromatopsie. Rev. d'oto-neuro-opht., v. 9, p. 13.

PETELLA, G.

1902–3. Emianopsia bilaterale omonima destra e cecità verbale. Contributo clinico alla dottrina dell'afasia visiva e considerazioni. Arch. di ottal., v. 10, p. 45.

PETER, K.

1920. Die Zweckmässigkeit in der Entwicklungsgeschichte. Eine finale Erklärung embryonaler und verwandter Gebilde und Vorgänge. J. Springer, Berlin.

PETER, L. C.

1941. Extra-ocular muscles. 3d ed. Lea & Febiger, Philadelphia.

PÉTERFI, T.

1929. Das leitende Element. *In:* BETHE *et al.*, Handb. d. norm. u. path. Physiol., v. 9, p. 79.

PETERS, A.

1896. Ueber die Beziehung zwischen Orientirungsstörungen nach ein- und doppelseitiger Hemianopsie. Arch. f. Augenh., v. 32, p. 175.

1924. Aeltere Urkunden zur Brillengeschichte. Ztschr. f. ophth. Optik, v. 12, pp. 47, 107.

PETERSEN, H.

1923–24. Berichte über Entwicklungsmechanik. I. Entwicklungsmechanik des Auges. Ergebn. d. Anat. u. Entw., v. 24, p. 327; v. 25, p. 623.

1924. Ueber die Bedeutung der aufrechten Körperhaltung für die Eigenart des menschlichen Umweltbildes. Naturwiss., v. 12, p. 186.

PETERSON, E. W., & HENNEMAN, E.

1948. Cortico-collicular connections in the macaque. Tr. Am. Neurol. A., 73d meet., p. 119.

PETERSON, F.

1891. A second note upon homonymous hemiopic hallucinations. New York M. J., v. 53, p. 121.

1895. The new phrenology. Am. M. & Surg. Bull., v. 8, p. 1415.

PETERSON, R. T.

1947. A field guide to the birds. Houghton Mifflin Co., Boston.

PETIT, F. POURFOUR DU; *see* POURFOUR DU PETIT

PETIT, G., & ROCHON-DUVIGNEAUD, A.

1929. L'œil et la vision de l'*Halicorne dugong* Erxl. Bull. Soc. zool. de France, v. 54, p. 129.

PETTIGREW, T. J.

1838–40. Medical portrait gallery. Biographical memoirs of the most celebrated physicians, surgeons, etc., who have contributed to the advancement of medical science. 4 vols. Fisher, Son & Co., London.

PEYERIMHOFF, P. DE

1915. Les variations de l'œil et de l'antenne chez *Bythinus diversicornis* Raffr. Bull. Soc. ent. de France, p. 149.

PEYRONIE, F. G. DE LA

1709. Observations sur les maladies du cerveau, par lesquelles on tâche de découvrir le véritable lieu du cerveau dans lequel l'âme exerce ses fonctions. Read in 1708 at the Soc. roy. d. Sc. Montpellier. Published, 1709, in J. de Trévoux 1709, and again in Mém. Acad. d. sc., Paris, for 1741 (1744), and in Mém. Soc. roy. d. sc., Montpellier, 1766.

1741. Observations par lesquelles on tâche de découvrir la partie du cerveau où l'âme exerce ses fonctions. Mém. Acad. roy. d. sc., Paris, p. 199, 1744. (*See also* Sur le siège de l'âme dans le cerveau, *in* Hist. Acad. roy. d. sc., Paris, p. 39, 1744.)

PFEFFER, G.

1932. Ueber die Zeit der Abtrennung Madagaskars vom äthiopischen Festlande. Jena. Ztschr. f. Naturwiss., v. 67, p. 80.

PFEIFER, B.

1912. Ueber experimentelle Untersuchungen am Zwischenhirn und Mittelhirn. Neurol. Centralbl., v. 31, p. 1458.

1913. Beitrag zur funktionellen Bedeutung des Sehhügels auf Grund experimenteller Untersuchungen. *Ibid.*, v. 32, p. 1547.

1914. Experimentelle Untersuchungen über die Funktion des Thalamus opticus. Deutsch. Ztschr. f. Nervenh., v. 51, p. 206.

1918. Zur Lokalisation der Motilität und Sensibilität in der Hirnrinde. *Ibid.*, v. 58, p. 216.

1920. Die Störungen der Sensibilität im Gebiete der Genito-Analhaut bei Hirnverletzten. Ztschr. f. d. ges. Neurol. u. Psychiat. (Orig.), v. 53, p. 5.

1923. Die Bedeutung psychologischer Leistungs- und Arbeitsprüfungen für die Topik der Grosshirnrinde. Deutsch. Ztschr. f. Nervenh., v. 77, p. 139.

1924. Die psychischen Störungen nach Kriegsverletzungen des Gehirns. *In:* LEWANDOWSKY, Handb. d. Neurol., suppl., p. 493.

PFEIFER, R. A.

1919. Die Störungen des optischen Sucheaktes bei Hirnverletzten. Deutsch. Ztschr. f. Nervenh., v. 64, p. 140.

1920. Myelogenetisch-anatomische Untersuchungen über das kortikale Ende der Hörleitung. Abh. d. math.-phys. Kl. Sächs. Akad. Wissensch., v. 37 (2).

1921. Neueste Ergebnisse auf dem Gebiete der Gehirnforschung. Naturwiss., v. 9, p. 938.

1921. Die Lokalisation der Tonskala innerhalb der korticalen Hörsphäre des Menschen. Monatsschr. f. Psychiat., v. 50, p. 7.

1924. Die anatomische Darstellung des zentralen Abschnittes der Sehleitung. Ber. d. Deutsch. ophth. Gesellsch. Heidelberg, v. 44, p. 95.

1925. Myelogenetisch-anatomische Untersuchungen über den zentralen Abschnitt der Sehleitung. Monog. a. d. Gesamtgeb. d.

Neurol. u. Psychiat., Fasc. 43. J. Springer, Berlin.

1928. Die Angioarchitektonik der Grosshirnrinde. J. Springer, Berlin.

1930. Paul Flechsig†. Sein Leben und sein Wirken. Schweiz. Arch. f. Neurol. u. Psychiat., v. 26, p. 258. (*See* bibliography.)

1930. Hirnpathologischer Befund in einem Fall von doppelseitiger Hemianopsie mit Makulaaausspaⅼung. J. f. Psychol. u. Neurol., v. 40, p. 319.

1930. Die nervösen Verbindungen des Auges mit dem Zentralorgan. *In:* F. SCHIECK & A. BRÜCKNER, Kurzes Handb. d. Ophth., v. 1, p. 387. J. Springer, Berlin.

1930. Grundlegende Untersuchungen für die Angioarchitektonik des menschlichen Gehirns. J. Springer, Berlin.

1931. Anastomosen der Hirngefässe, dargestellt am asphyktisch hyperämischen Kindergehirn. J. f. Psychol. u. Neurol., v. 42, p. 1.

1932. Der Aufbau der Funktionen in der Hörsphäre. Monatsschr. f. Psychiat. u. Neurol., v. 81, p. 327.

1936. Pathologie der Hörstrahlung und der corticalen Hörsphäre. *In:* BUMKE & FOERSTER, Handb. d. Neurol., v. 6, p. 533.

1940. Die angioarchitektonische areale Gliederung der Grosshirnrinde. G. Thieme, Leipzig.

PFEIFFER, J. B., & KUNKLE, E. C.

1951. Fluctuations in cranial arterial tone as measured by histamine "responsiveness." Tr. Am. Neurol. A. (76th ann. meet.), p. 244.

PFISTER, J.

1890. Ueber Form und Grösse des Intervaginalraums des Sehnerven im Bereich des Canalis opticus. Arch. f. Ophth., v. 36 (1), p. 83.

PFLÜGER, E.

1899. Beobachtungen an total Farbenblinden. Ber. d. Deutsch. ophth. Gesellsch. Heidelberg, v. 27, p. 166.

PFLUGK, A.

1906. Ueber die Akkommodation des Auges der Taube nebst Bemerkungen über die Akkommodation des Affen (*Macacus cynomolgus*) und des Menschen. J. F. Bergmann, Wiesbaden.

1919. Bemerkungen zu Greeffs Aufsatz über Manni. Ztschr. f. ophth. Optik, v. 7, p. 73.

1922. Die Meisterzeichen der Nürnberger Brillenmacher. Arch. f. Augenh., v. 91, p. 341.

1927. Beiträge zur Geschichte der Brille aus alten Abbildungen. Ztschr. f. ophth. Optik, v. 14, p. 138.

1929. Ein Beitrag zur Geschichte der Brillenerzeugung Venedigs im 18. Jahrhundert. *Ibid.*, v. 17, p. 65.

1932. Neue Wege zur Erforschung der Lehre von der Akkommodation. Arch. f. Ophth. (Graefe), v. 128, p. 179.

PFLUGK, A., & ROHR, M.

1918. Beiträge zur Entwicklung der Kenntnis von der Brille. Ztschr. f. Augenh., v. 40, p. 50.

PFUNGST, O.

1912. Zur Psychologie der Affen. Ber. ü. d. 5. Kong. f. exper. Psychol., p. 200.

1924. Biologie und Psychologie der Affen in ihrer Bedeutung für den Menschen. Schriften d. naturforsch. Gesellsch. Danzig, N.F., v. 17, Fasc. 2, p. 13.

1924. Die Bedeutung der Affenbiologie für den Menschen. Deutsch. med. Wchnschr., v. 50, p. 1005.

PHILIPSON, W. R.

1952. The immaculate forest: an account of an expedition to unexplored territories between the Andes and the Amazon. Philosophical Library, New York.

PHILLIPS, G.

1933. Perception of flicker in lesions of the visual pathways. Brain, v. 56, p. 464.

PICARD, E.

1924. Les théories de l'optique et l'œuvre d'Hippolyte Fizeau. Gauthier-Villars & Cie, Paris.

PICARD, F.

1923. Recherches biologiques et anatomiques sur *Melittobia acasta* Walk. Bull. Biol., v. 57, p. 469.

PICHLER, A.

1900. Zur Lehre von der Sehnervenkreuzung im Chiasma des Menschen. Ztschr. f. Heilk., v. 21, p. 12.

1900. Der Faserverlauf im menschlichen Chiasma. Nach Marchipräparaten dargestellt. *In:* H. MAGNUS, Augenärztliche Unterrichtstafeln, Heft XXII. J. U. Kern's Verlag (Max Müller), Breslau.

PICK, A.

1881. Beitrag zur Lehre von den Hallucinationen. Jahrb. f. Psychiat., v. 2, p. 44.

1892. Beiträge zur Lehre von den Störungen der Sprache. Arch. f. Psychiat. u. Nervenkr., v. 23, p. 896.

1893. Ueber allgemeine Gedächtnissschwäche als Folge cerebraler Herderkrankung. Prager med. Wchnschr., v. 18, pp. 451, 465.

1894. Ueber die topographischen Beziehungen zwischen Retina, Opticus und gekreuztem

Tractus beim Kaninchen. Neurol. Centralbl., v. 13, p. 729.

1895. Ueber die topisch-diagnostische Bedeutung der Sehstörung bei Gehirnerkrankung. Prager med. Wchnschr., v. 20, pp. 1, 16.

1898. Beiträge zur Pathologie und pathologischen Anatomie des Centralnervensystems mit Bemerkungen zur normalen Anatomie desselben. S. Karger, Berlin.

1901. Neue Mitteilungen über Störungen der Tiefenlokalisation. Neurol. Centralbl., v. 20, p. 338.

1907. Ueber Störungen der motorischen Funktionen durch die auf sie gerichtete Aufmerksamkeit. Wien. klin. Rundschau, v. 21, p. 1.

1908. Ueber eine besondere Form von Orientierungsstörung und deren Vorkommen bei Geisteskranken. Deutsch. med. Wchnschr., v. 34, p. 2014.

1908. Ueber Störungen der Orientierung am eigenen Körper. Arb. a. d. psychiat. Klin. Prag, v. 1, p. 1.

1909. On the localisation of agrammatism. Rev. Neurol. & Psychiat., v. 7, p. 757.

1913. Die agrammatischen Sprachstörungen. Studien zur psychologischen Grundlegung der Aphasielehre. Monog. a. d. Gesamtgeb. d. Neurol. u. Psychiat., v. 7. J. Springer, Berlin.

1915. Zur Lehre vom Verhältnis zwischen pathologischer Vorstellung und Halluzination. Monatsschr. f. Psychiat. u. Neurol., v. 37, p. 269.

1918. Historisches zur Lehre von der topographischen Anordnung in den Sehbahnen und -zentren. Neurol. Centralbl., v. 37, p. 70.

1920. Das halbhundertjährige Jubiläum der Entdeckung der Rindenzentren. Deutsch. med. Wchnschr., v. 46, p. 18.

1920. Zur Frage der fehlenden Selbstwahrnehmung cerebral bedingter Sinnesdefekte, insbesondere der Blindheit. Arch. f. Augenh., v. 86, p. 98.

1921. Die neurologische Forschungsrichtung in der Psychopathologie. Abh. a. d. Neurol., Psychiat., Psychol., Fasc. 13.

1922. Störung der Orientierung am eigenen Körper. Beitrag zur Lehre vom Bewusstsein des eigenen Körpers. Psychol. Forsch., v. 1, p. 303.

PICK, A., & HERRENHEISER, J.
1895. Untersuchungen über die topographischen Beziehungen zwischen Retina, Opticus und gekreuztem Tractus opticus beim Kaninchen. Nova Acta Kaiserl. Leop.-Carol. d. Akad. d. Naturforsch., v. 66, No. 1. (Abstr. in Centralbl. f. Nervenh., v. 19, p. 151.)

PICKERING, G. W.
1951. Headache. Proc. Inst. Med. Chicago, v. 18, p. 226.

PICKFORD, R. W.
1944. The Ishihara test for colour blindness. Nature, v. 153, p. 656.

1945. Darkened violet in colour vision. Ibid., v. 156, p. 506.

1946. Factorial analysis of colour vision. Ibid., v. 157, p. 700.

1947. Binocular colour combinations. Ibid., v. 159, p. 268.

1947. Sex differences in colour vision. Ibid., p. 606.

1947. Frequencies of sex-linked red-green colour vision defects. Ibid., v. 160, p. 335.

1948. Darkening of red in protanopes. Ibid., v. 161, p. 27.

1948. Race, pigmentation and colour vision. Ibid., p. 687.

1948. Human colour vision and Granit's theory. Ibid., v. 162, p. 414.

1948. Multiple allelomorphs in colour vision. Ibid., p. 684.

1948. Colour blindness in the left eye following an accident. Brit. J. Psychol., v. 39 (2), p. 73.

1949. Individual differences in colour vision and their measurement. J. Psychol., v. 27, p. 153.

1949. Colour vision of heterozygotes for sex-linked red-green defects. Nature, v. 163, p. 804.

1949. A study of the Ishihara test for colour blindness. Brit. J. Psychol., v. 40 (2), p. 71.

1949. Brightness and saturation of colours in red-green defectives. Nature, v. 164, p. 236.

1950. Three pedigrees for colour blindness. Ibid., v. 165, p. 82.

1951. Individual differences in colour vision. Routledge & Kegan Paul, London.

1951. Colour vision of an albino. Nature, v. 168, p. 954.

1952. A pedigree for green anomaly. Ibid., v. 169, p. 503.

1953. Inheritance of minor colour vision variations. Ibid., v. 171, p. 1167.

1953. A pedigree for three types of colour-vision defect. Ibid., v. 172, p. 1010.

1954. Some problems of anomalous colour vision. Brit. J. Psychol. (Gen.), v. 45 (2), p. 115.

PIÉRON, H.
1916. Des degrés de l'hémianopsie corticale: l'hémiastéréopsie. Compt. rend. Soc. de biol., v. 79, p. 1055.

1923. Le cerveau et la pensée. F. Alcan, Paris.

English trans.: C. K. Ogden, Thought and the brain. Harcourt, Brace & Co., New York, 1927.

1930. Le problème de la vision des couleurs. Bull. Soc. opht. Paris, v. 42, p. 473.

1932. Les bases sensorielles de la connaissance. Année psychol., v. 33, p. 1.

1936. La connaissance sensorielle et les problèmes de la vision. Hermann & Cie, Paris.

1937. L'évolution de la sensation lumineuse. Am. J. Psychol., v. 50, p. 23.

1943. Le mécanisme de la vision des couleurs. Sciences, v. 43, p. 265.

1945. Aux sources de la connaissance. La sensation guide de vie. Librairie Gallimard, Paris.

Piersol, G. A.
1930. Piersol's human anatomy, etc. 9th rev. ed. J. B. Lippincott Co., Philadelphia.

Pietschmann, V.
1929. Acrania. *In:* Kükenthal, Handb. d. Zool., v. 6 (1), p. 1.

Pike, F. H.
1918. Remarks on von Monakow's Die Lokalisation im Grosshirn. J. Comp. Neurol., v. 29, p. 485.

1943. Entropy and the degeneration of photoreceptors in perpetual darkness. Anat. Rec., v. 87, p. 466. (Abstr.)

1944. On the origin of the nervous system of vertebrates. *Ibid.*, v. 89, p. 573. (Abstr.)

1946. The biogenic law and the phylogeny of the nervous system. *Ibid.*, v. 96, p. 581. (Abstr.)

1916. Degeneration of the primitive embryonic nervous system and the ancestry of vertebrates. *Ibid.*, p. 582. (Abstr.)

Piltz, J.
1899. Ueber ein Hirnrindencentrum für einseitige, contralaterale Pupillenverengerung (beim Kaninchen). Neurol. Centralbl., v. 18, p. 875.

1900. Weitere Mittheilungen über die beim energischen Augenschluss stattfindende Pupillenverengerung. *Ibid.*, v. 19, p. 837.

Pincus
1916. Klinische Beobachtungen an Hinterhauptschüssen. Ber. d. Deutsch. ophth. Gesellsch. Heidelberg, v. 40, p. 56.

Pincussen, L.
1921. Biologische Lichtwirkungen, ihre physikalischen und chemischen Grundlagen. Ergebn. d. Biol. (Asher & Spiro), v. 19, p. 79.

1930. Photobiologie. Grundlagen—Ergebnisse—Ausblicke. G. Thieme, Leipzig.

Pinéas, H.
1926. Der Mangel an Krankheitsbewusstsein und seine Variationen als Symptom organischer Erkrankungen. Deutsch. Ztschr. f. Nervenh., v. 94, p. 238.

Pineles, F.
1896. Zur pathologischen Anatomie der reflectorischen Pupillenstarre. Arb. a. d. Neurol. Inst. Wien (Obersteiner), v. 4, p. 101.

Pines, J. L.
1927. Zur Architektonik des Thalamus opticus beim Halbaffen (*Lemur catta*). J. f. Psychol. & Neurol., v. 33, p. 31.

Pines, L.
1899. Untersuchungen über den Bau der Retina mit Weigerts Neurogliamethode. Ztschr. f Augenh., v. 2, p. 252.

Pines, L. J., & Maiman, R. M.
1939. Cells of origin of fibers of corpus callosum. Arch. Neurol. & Psychiat., v. 42, p. 1076.

Pinkston, J. O., & Rioch, D. McK.
1938. The influence of the cerebral cortex on peripheral circulation. Am. J. Physiol., v. 121, p. 49.

Pirenne, M. H.
1948. Vision and the eye. Chapman & Hall, London.

1953. The absolute sensitivity of the eye and the variation of visual acuity with intensity. Brit. M. Bull., v. 9, p. 61.

Pirenne, M. H., & Denton, E. J.
1952. Accuracy and sensitivity of the human eye. Nature, v. 170, p. 1039.

Piša, A.
1939. Ueber den binokularen Gesichtsraum bei Haustieren. Arch. f. Ophth. (Graefe), v. 140, p. 1.

Pisani, D.
1926. I tumori del lobo frontale. Contributo clinico ed anatomo-patologico. Riv. oto-neurooftal., v. 3, p. 289.

Pischinger, A.
1938. Ueber den Feinbau des Glaskörpers. Wien. klin. Wchnschr., v. 2, p. 1028.

Pisko, F. J.
1876. Licht und Farbe. Eine gemeinfassliche Darstellung der Optik. 2d ed. R. Oldenbourg, München.

Pitt, F.
1927. Animal mind. G. Allen & Unwin, Ltd., London.

1931. The intelligence of animals. Studies in comparative psychology. G. Allen & Unwin, London.

PITTARD, E.
  1943. A propos de la position phylétique du *Pithecanthropus erectus*. Peut-il être considéré comme un gibbon géant? Compt. rend. Soc. phys. & hist. nat. Genève, v. 60, p. 32.

PITTS, R. F., LARRABEE, M. G., & BRONK, D. W.
  1939. An analysis of hypothalamic cardio-vascular control. Am. J. Physiol., v. 134, p. 359.

PIVETEAU, J.
  1951. Images des mondes disparus. Masson & Cie, Paris.
  1953. Traité de paléontologie. V. 4: L'origine des vertébrés. Leur expansion dans les eaux douces et le milieu marin. V. 5: La sortie des eaux. Naissance de la tétrapodie. L'exubérance de la vie végétative. La conquête de l'air. V. 6: L'origine des mammifères et les aspects fondamentaux de leur évolution. Mammifères. V. 7: Vers la forme humaine. Le problème biologique de l'homme. Les époques de l'intelligence. Masson & Cie, Paris. (In press.)

PLAGGE, M. W.
  1819. Neue physikalische Ansichten des Sehens. Deutsch. Arch. f. d. Physiol. (Meckel), v. 5, p. 97. Neuer Beitrag zur Lehre vom Sehen. *Ibid.*, v. 7, p. 213.

PLATE, L.
  1922–24. Allgemeine Zoologie und Abstammungslehre. 4 vols. G. Fischer, Jena. (*See* Zweiter Teil: Die Sinnesorgane der Tiere.)
  1924. Ueber den Ursprung der Wirbeltiere. Anat. Anz., v. 58, p. 39.
  1926. Lamarckismus und Erbstockhypothese. Ztschr. f. indukt. Abstammungs- u. Vererbungslehre, v. 43, p. 88. (*See also* p. 114.)
  1928. Ueber Vervollkommnung, Anpassung und die Unterscheidung von niederen und höheren Tieren. Zool. Jahrb. (Allg. Zool.), v. 45, p. 745.
  1929. Vitalismus und Mechanismus in einer neuen biologischen Auffassung. Scientia, v. 46, p. 13.
  1932. Vererbungslehre. Mit besonderer Berücksichtigung der Abstammungslehre und des Menschen. V. 1: Mendelismus. G. Fischer, Jena.

PLATEAU, J. A. F.
  1878. Bibliographie analytique des principaux phénomènes subjectifs de la vision, depuis les temps anciens jusqu'à la fin du XVIIIᵉ siècle, suivie d'une bibliographie simple pour la partie écoulée du siècle actuel. Mém. Acad. roy. sc., lett., etc. de Belgique, Bruxelles, v. 42. (*Cf. also* v. 43.)

PLATH, M.
  1935. Ueber das Farbenunterscheidungsvermögen des Wellensittichs. Ztschr. f. vergl. Physiol., v. 22, p. 691.

PLATO
  5th–4th cent. B.C. Article: Plato, Encyclopaedia Britannica, 14th ed., v. 18, p. 48. For additional references *see* appended bibliography, p. 64.

PLATTER, FELIX
  1603. Felicis Plateri Archiatri et Profess. Basil. De Corporis Humani Structura et Usu Libri III. Etc. Basileae, apud Ludovicum König. (1st ed., 1583.)
  1614. Felicis Plateri Archiatri et Profes. Basil. Observationum, in Hominis Affectibus plerisque, corpori et animo, functionum laesione, dolore, aliaque molestiâ et vitio incommodantibus, Libri Tres. Etc. Basileae, Impensis Ludovici König, Typis Conradi Waldkirchii. MDCXIIII.

PLEHN, F.
  1904. Dioptrik oder Schilderung der Folgen, die sich aus der unlängst gemachten Erfindung der Fernrohre für das Sehen und die sichtbaren Gegenstände ergeben, by J. Kepler, 1611. *In:* OSTWALD, Klassiker d. exakt. Wissensch., No. 144. W. Engelmann, Leipzig.
  1920–21. J. Keplers Behandlung des Sehens. Ztschr. f. ophth. Optik, v. 8, p. 154; v. 9, pp. 13, 40, 73, 103, 143, 177.
  1922. Grundlagen der geometrischen Optik (im Anschluss an die Optik des Witelo), by J. Kepler, 1604. Trans. F. PLEHN; ed. M. VON ROHR. *In:* OSTWALD, Klassiker d. exakt. Wissensch., No. 198. Akad. Verlagsgesellschaft, Leipzig.

PLEMP (PLEMPIUS), V. F.
  *1632. Ophthalmographia sive tractatio de oculi fabrica. H. Laurentii, Amstelodami. Other editions, Louvain, 1648, 1659.
  1648. Vopisci Fortunati Plempii Amsteledamensis, Artium & Medicinae Doctoris, atque in Academia Lovaniensi Practicen Primo loco Profitentis, *Ophthalmographia* Sive Tractatio de Oculo. Editio Altera. Cui praeter alia accessere affectionum ocularium curationes. Ad Illustrissimum & Excellentissimum Dominum D. Gasparem de Bracamonte y Gusman, Comitem de Pennaranda. Lovanii Typis ac sumptibus Hieronymi Nempaei Anno M.DC.XLVIII.

PLENK, F.
  1876. Ueber Hemiopie und Sehnervenkreuzung. Arch. f. Augen- u. Ohrenh., v. 5, p. 140.

POCOCK, R. I.

1918. On the external characters of the lemurs and *Tarsius*. Proc. Zoöl. Soc. London, p. 19.

1919. Structure of *Tarsius*. *Ibid.*, p. 494.

1920. On the external characters of the South American monkeys. *Ibid.*, p. 91.

1925. Additional notes on the external characters of some platyrrhine monkeys. *Ibid.*, p. 27.

1925. The external characters of the catarrhine monkeys and apes. *Ibid.*, p. 1479.

1939–41. The fauna of British India, including Ceylon and Burma. Mammalia, v. 1 (Primates & Carnivora), v. 2 (Carnivora). Taylor & Francis, London.

PÖTZL, O.

1914–15. Tachystoskopisch provozierte optische Halluzinationen bei einem Falle von Alkoholhalluzinose mit rückgebildeter zerebraler Hemianopsie. Jahrb. f. Psychiat. u. Neurol., v. 35, p. 141.

1916. Ueber optische Hemmungserscheinungen in der Rückbildungsphase von traumatischer Läsion des Hinterhauptslappens. Wien. med. Wchnschr., v. 66, p. 1389.

1918. Ueber die räumliche Anordnung der Zentren in der Sehsphäre des menschlichen Grosshirns. Wien. klin. Wchnschr., v. 31, p. 745.

1918. Bemerkungen über den Augenmassfehler der Hemianopiker. *Ibid.*, pp. 1149, 1183.

1919. Vergleichende Betrachtung mehrerer Herderkrankungen in der Sehsphäre. Jahrb. f. Psychiat., v. 39, p. 402.

1924. Ueber ein neuartiges Syndrom bei Herderkrankungen des Stirnhirnpoles. Ztschr. f. d. ges. Neurol. u. Psychiat., v. 91, p. 147.

1926. S. E. Henschen. Ueber das Lebenswerk eines grossen Hirnforschers. Med. Klin., v. 22, p. 512.

1928. Ueber die Grosshirnprojektion des horizontalen Gesichtsfeldmeridians. Wien. klin. Wchnschr., v. 41, p. 1009.

1928. Die optisch-agnostischen Störungen. Die Aphasielehre. *In:* G. ASCHAFFENBURG, Handb. d. Psychiat., spez. T. 3, Abt. 2 (1). F. Deuticke, Wien.

1930. Lokalisationsproblem der artikulierten Sprache. J. A. Barth, Leipzig.

1932. Zum gegenwärtigen Stand der Aphasielehre. Wien. med. Wchnschr., v. 82, p. 783.

1933. Polyopie und gnostische Störungen. Ein Beitrag zur Pathophysiologie der zerebralen Sehstörungen. Jahrb. f. Psychiat., v. 50, p. 57.

1933. Ueber zwei Fälle mit temporaler Aura. *Ibid.*, p. 78.

1937. Zum Apraxieproblem. *Ibid.*, v. 51, p. 133.

1937. Zur Pathologie der optischen Agnosien mit verhältnismässig geringer Lesestörung. Ztschr. f. d. ges. Neurol. & Psychiat., v. 160, p. 255.

1938. Ueber die Beteiligung des Thalamus am Sehakt. Wien. klin. Wchnschr., v. 51, p. 1001.

1939. Zur Pathologie der Amusie. Ztschr. f. d. ges. Neurol. u. Psychiat., v. 165, p. 187.

1940. Ueber Interferenzen zwischen linkshirniger und rechtshirniger Tätigkeit. (Alternierende Halbseitentaubheit. Induzierte taktile Agnosie.) Wien. med. Wchnschr., v. 90, p. 6.

1941. Labyrinth und Occipitalrinde. Ztschr. f. d. ges. Neurol. u. Psychiat., v. 174, p. 592.

1942. Hirnpathologie der Schwebesensationen. Wien. klin. Wchnschr., v. 55, p. 921.

1943. Bemerkungen zum Problem der kortikalen Vorgänge bei der akustischen Wahrnehmung. Monatsschr. f. Ohrenh. u. Laryngo-Rhin., v. 77, p. 422.

1943. Ueber Verkehrtsehen. Ztschr. f. d. ges. Neurol. u. Psychiat., v. 176, p. 780.

1943. Ueber Anfälle von Thalamustypus. *Ibid.*, p. 793.

1944. Zur Frage der Eigenleistung der Kleinhirnrinde. Deutsch. Ztschr. f. Nervenh., v. 156, p. 171.

1946. Die Pathophysiologie der thalamisch bedingten Hörstörung. Monatsschr. f. Ohrenh. u. Laryngo-Rhin., vols. 79–80, p. 28.

1949. Ueber einige zentrale Probleme des Farbensehens. Wien. klin. Wchnschr., v. 61, p. 706.

PÖTZL, O., & BEICHL, L.

1943. Anatomischer Befund bei nuclearer Lähmung des Vertikalblicks. Ztschr. f. d. ges. Neurol. u. Psychiat., v. 176, p. 801.

PÖTZL, O., & HOFF, H.

Ca. 1943. Ueber einige beachtenswerte Sensationen bei Herderkrankungen des Thalamus. Festschr. Dr. Reinhold, p. 168.

PÖTZL, O., & UIBERALL, H.

1937. Zur Pathologie der Amusie. Wien. klin. Wchnschr., v. 50, p. 770.

PÖTZL, O., & URBAN, H.

1935. Ueber die isoliert erhaltene temporale Sichel bei zerebraler Hemianopsie. Monatsschr. f. Psychiat. u. Neurol., v. 92, p. 67.

POGGENDORF, D.

1952. Die absoluten Hörschwellen des Zwergwelses (*Amiurus nebulosus*) und Beiträge zur Physik des Weberschen Apparates der

Ostariophysen. Ztschr. f. vergl. Physiol., v. 34, p. 222.

POGGENDORFF, J. C.

1863–1939. Biographisch-literarisches Handwörterbuch für Mathematik, Astronomie, Physik mit Geophysik, Chemie, Kristallographie und verwandte Wissensgebiete. J. A. Barth, Leipzig (1863–1904), and Verlag Chemie, Berlin (1926——).

POHL, R. W.

1940. Einführung in die Optik. J. Springer, Berlin.

POIRIER, P., & CHARPY, A.

1901–4. Traité d'anatomic humaine, vols. 3 & 5. Masson & Cie, Paris.

POLACK, A.

1923. Le chromatisme de l'œil. Ann. d'ocul., v. 160, p. 977.

POLIAK, POLJAK; *see* POLYAK, S.

POLICE, G.

1928. Gli elementi visivi e le fibre radiali della retina di Axolotl di *Amblistoma mexicanum*. Arch. di ottal., v. 35, p. 120.

1932. Sull'interpretazione morfologica delle fibre radiali nella retina dei vertebrati. Arch. zool. ital., v. 17, p. 449.

POLIMANTI, O.

1910. Beiträge zur Physiologie des Nervensystems und der Bewegung bei den niederen Tieren. I. *Branchiostoma lanceolatum* Yarr (*Amphioxus*). Arch. f. Physiol. (Rubner), p. 129.

1911. Nouvelles expériences pour démontrer que l'augmentation de la sensibilité dans le centre rétinique est moindre que dans les portions plus ou moins excentriques. Compt. rend. Soc. de biol., v. 71, p. 585.

POLLIOT, H.

1921. Les images de projection dans la vision binoculaire, etc. Arch. d'opht., v. 38, p. 547.

1926. Variations du diamètre apparent des objets dans la vision binoculaire. *Ibid.*, v. 43, p. 415.

POLLOCK, L. J.

1930. Cerebral localization. Ann. Int. Med., v. 4, p. 21.

POLLOCK, W. B. I.

1945. The antiquity of ophthalmology. Brit. J. Ophth., v. 29, p. 252.

1946. Arabian ophthalmology. *Ibid.*, v. 30, p. 445.

POLYAK, S. (*see also* POLIAK and POLJAK); for biography *see* P. BAILEY, Anat. Rec., v. 122, p. 648; R. GRANIT, Science, v. 122, p. 64; GRMEK 1955; KLÜVER 1955

1923. Structural peculiarities of the spinal cord in *Pterygistes noctula*. (In Croatian with a German summary.) Liječn. Vjesnik, Karlovac (Croatia, Yugoslavia).

1924. Die Struktureigentümlichkeiten des Rückenmarkes bei den Chiropteren. (Zugleich ein Beitrag zu der Frage über die spinalen Zentren des Sympathicus.) Ztschr. f. Anat. u. Entw., v. 74, p. 509.

1924. Ueber die Intermediärzone im Rückenmark der Säuger und ihr Verhältnis zu dem vegetativen Nervensystem. Liječn. Vjesnik anniv. vol., p. 468.

1926. The connections of the acoustic nerve. J. Anat., v. 60, p. 465.

1926. Die Verbindungen der Area striata (intrahemisphaerale, kommissurale, palliodienzephalische, palliotektale Fasern) bei der Katze und deren funktionelle Bedeutung. Ztschr. f. d. ges. Neurol. u. Psychiat. v. 100, p. 545.

1926. Untersuchungen am Oktavussystem der Säugetiere und an den mit diesem koordinierten motorischen Apparaten des Hirnstammes. J. f. Psychol. u. Neurol., v. 32, p. 170.

1926. On the most recent investigations of the auditory system of mammals. Bechterew's anniv. vol. (Leningrad), p. 27. (Russian text with German summary.)

1927. An experimental study of the association, callosal, and projection fibers of the cerebral cortex of the cat. J. Comp. Neurol., v. 44, p. 197.

1930. Die zuführenden Bahnen des Vorderhirns und ihre Rindenbeziehungen auf Grund experimenteller Untersuchungen an Affen. Ztschr. f. d. ges. Neurol. u. Psychiat., v. 125, p. 138.

1932. The main afferent fiber systems of the cerebral cortex in primates. University of California Pub. in Anatomy, v. 2. University of California Press, Berkeley; *cf. also* Research Pub. A. Research Nerv. & Ment. Dis., v. 13, p. 535.

1933. A contribution to the cerebral representation of the retina. J. Comp. Neurol., v. 57, p. 541.

1935. Structure of the retina in primates. Acta ophth., v. 13, p. 52.

1936. Minute structure of the retina in monkeys and apes. Arch. Ophth., v. 15, p. 477.

1938. Chapters: The nervous tissue and The eye. *In:* A. A. MAXIMOW & W. BLOOM, A textbook of histology, 2d and 3d eds. W. B. Saunders Co., Philadelphia & London.

1941. The retina. University of Chicago Press, Chicago. (Corrected reprint 1948.)

1942. Anatomy of the retina. Biol. Symp., v. 7,

p. 193. Jacques Cattell Press, Lancaster, Pa.

1942. The representation of the central foveae and of the horizontal meridians in the visual radiation (radiatio optica) of the human brain. J. Mt. Sinai Hosp., v. 9, No. 4, p. 698.

1949. Retinal structure and colour vision. Doc. ophth., v. 3, p. 24.

1953. Santiago Ramón y Cajal and his investigation of the nervous system. J. Comp. Neurol., v. 98, p. 1.

1955. Article: Eye, human; anatomy of the eye. Encyclopaedia Britannica, v. 9, p. 5.

POLYAK, S., & HAYASHI, R.

1936. The cerebral representation of the retina in the chimpanzee. Brain, v. 59, p. 51.

POLYAK, S., JUDD, D. K., & McHUGH, G.

1946. The human ear in anatomical transparencies. Sonotone Corporation, Elmsford, N.Y.

POLYAK, S. (with P. C. KRONFELD & G. McHUGH)

1944. The human eye in anatomical transparencies. Bausch & Lomb Press, Rochester, N.Y.

POOLEY, T. R.

1877. Rechtseitige binoculare Hemiopie bedingt durch eine Gummigeschwulst im linken hinteren Gehirnlappen. Arch. f. Augen- u. Ohrenh., v. 6, p. 27.

POPA, G. T., & FIELDING, U.

1930. A portal circulation from the pituitary to the hypothalamic region. J. Anat., v. 65, p. 88.

1933. Hypophysio-portal vessels and their colloid accompaniment. *Ibid.*, v. 67, p. 227.

POPE, C. H.

1944. Amphibians and reptiles of the Chicago area. Chicago Natural History Museum, Chicago.

1946. Turtles of the United States and Canada. A. A. Knopf, New York.

POPOFF, N.

1886. Zur Frage vom Ursprungsgebiete der Fasern der vorderen Commissur in der Hirnrinde des Menschen. Neurol. Centralbl., v. 5, p. 521.

1927. Zur Kenntnis der Grösse der Area striata und die Methodik ihrer Ausmessung. J. f. Psychol. u. Neurol., v. 34, p. 238.

POPPELREUTER, W.

1917–18. Die psychischen Schädigungen durch Kopfschuss im Kriege 1914/16 mit besonderer Berücksichtigung der pathopsychologischen, pädagogischen, gewerblichen und sozialen Beziehungen. 2 vols. L. Voss, Leipzig.

1922. Ueber Hirnverletztenpsychologie. Ber. ü. d.

VII. Kong. f. exper. Psychol. G. Fischer, Jena.

1923. Zur Psychologie und Pathologie der optischen Wahrnehmung. (*a*) Ueber die perimakuläre Amblyopie und vorgetäuschte apperzeptive Seelenblindheit. (*b*) Ueber das motorisch nachfahrende pseudo-optische Erkennen. (*c*) Ueber die amorphen Gestalten. (*d*) Stufenabbau und Stufenaufbau des Sehoyotems. Ztschr. f. d. ges. Neurol. u. Psychiat., v. 83, p. 26.

POPPER, E.

1918. Beitrag zur kortikalen Lokalisation der Sensibilität. Neurol. Centralbl., v. 37, p. 447.

1919. Zur Organisation der sensiblen Rindenzentren. Ztschr. f. d. ges. Neurol. u. Psychiat. (Orig.), v. 51, p. 310.

POPPI, U.

1928. Sindrome talamo-capsulare per rammollimento nel territorio dell'arteria coroidea anteriore. Riv. pat. nerv. & ment., v. 33, p. 505.

1928. La sindrome anatomo-clinica conseguente a lesione dell'arteria coroidea anteriore. Riv. neurol., v. 1, p. 468.

PORSCH, O.

1924. Zukunftsaufgaben der Vogelblumenforschung auf Grund neuesten Tatbestandes. Naturwiss., v. 12, p. 993.

1931. Grellrot als Vogelblumenfarbe. Biol. gen., v. 7, p. 647.

PORTA, J.-B.

1558. Magiae Naturalis, Sive *De Miraculis* rerum naturalium libri IIII. Io. Baptista Porta Neapolitano Auctore. Neapoli Apud Matthiam Cancer. M.D.LVIII. Cum Gratia et Privilegio Per Decennium. Also numerous subsequent enlarged editions. English trans.: Natural Magick by John Baptista P., a Neapolitane: in twenty books, etc. London, printed for T. Young, and Sam. Speed, etc., 1658.

1593. Joan. Baptistae Portae Neap. *De Refractione* Optices Parte: Libri Novem. Ex Officina Horatij Salviani. Neapoli, Apud Io. Iacobum Carlinum, & Antonium Pacem, 1593.

PORTAL, A.

*1770–73. Histoire de l'anatomie et de la chirurgie. 6 vols. P. F. Didot, Paris.

PORTERFIELD, W.

1759. A treatise on the eye, the manner and phaenomena of vision. In 2 vols. By W. P., M.D., Fellow of the Royal College of Physicians in Edinburgh, 1759. A. Miller, London; G. Hamilton & J. Balfour, Edinburgh.

PORTIER, P.
1923. La vision chez le fou de Bassan. Rev. franç. d'ornithol., v. 15, p. 99.
1923. Interprétation physiologique de la double fovéa des rapaces diurnes. Compt. rend. Soc. de biol., v. 88, p. 330.

PORTMANN, A.
1948. Die Tiergestalt. Studien über die Bedeutung der tierischen Erscheinung. F. Reinhardt, Basel.

POSNER, A.
1945. A contribution to the theory of binocular vision supported by three cases of latent nystagmus. Am. J. Ophth., v. 28, p. 392.

POSSEK, R.
1905. Ein Fall von kortikaler Hemianopsie nach einem Trauma. Ztschr. f. Augenh. (suppl.), v. 13, p. 794.

POUGH, R. H.
1949. Audubon bird guide. Small land birds of eastern & central North America from southern Texas to central Greenland. Doubleday, Garden City, N.Y.

POULARD, A., & SAINTON, P.
1910. Double hémianopsie avec persistance du faisceau maculaire. Bull. & mém. Soc. méd. de Paris, ser. 3, v. 29, p. 311.

POURFOUR DU PETIT, F. (FRANÇOIS)
1710. Lettres d'un médecin des hôpitaux à un autre médecin de ses amis. C. G. Albert, Namur.
1727. Mémoire dans lequel il est démontré que les nerfs intercostaux fournissent des rameaux qui portent des esprits dans les yeux. Mém. Acad. d. sc. Paris, p. 1.
1736. Description anatomique de l'œil de l'espèce de hibou appelé Ulula. *Ibid.*, p. 121.

POUSSEPP, L.
1923. Contribution aux recherches sur la localisation de l'aphasie visuelle. Presse méd., v. 31 (2), p. 564.

POWELL, T. P. S.
1952. Residual neurons in the human thalamus following decortication. Brain, v. 75, p. 571.

POYNTER, C. W. M., & KEEGAN, J. J.
1915. A study of the American Negro brain. J. Comp. Neurol., v. 25, p. 183.

PRESTON, T.
1928. The theory of light. Macmillan & Co., Ltd., London.

PREUSSE, M.
1882. Ueber das Tapetum der Haussäugethiere. Arch. f. wissensch. u. pract. Thierh., v. 8, p. 264.

PREYER, W.
1881. Zur Theorie der Farbenblindheit. Centralbl. f. d. med. Wissensch., v. 19, p. 1.

PRIESTLEY, J.
1772. The history and present state of discoveries relating to vision, light, and colours. London, J. Johnson.

PRINCE, J. H.
1949. Visual development. E. & S. Livingstone, Edinburgh.

PRINCE OF WIED; *see* WIED-NEUWIED

PROBST, M.
1899. Ueber vom Vierhügel, von der Brücke und vom Kleinhirn absteigende Bahnen. Deutsch. Ztschr. f. Nervenh., v. 15, p. 192.
1899. Ueber die Lokalisation des Tonvermögens. Arch. f. Psychiat., v. 32, p. 387.
1900. Ueber den Verlauf der Sehnervenfasern und deren Endigung im Zwischen- und Mittelhirn. Monatsschr. f. Psychiat., v. 8, p. 165.
1900. Physiologische, anatomische und pathologisch-anatomische Untersuchungen des Sehhügels. Arch. f. Psychiat., v. 33, p. 721.
1901. Zur Kenntnis des Bindearmes, der Haubenstrahlung und der Regio subthalamica. Monatsschr. f. Psychiat., v. 10, p. 288.
1901. Ueber den Bau des vollständig balkenlosen Grosshirnes sowie über Mikrogyrie und Heterotopie der grauen Substanz. Arch. f. Psychiat., v. 34, p. 709.
1901. Ueber den Verlauf der centralen Sehfasern (Rinden-Sehhügelfasern) und deren Endigung im Zwischen- und Mittelhirne und über die Associations- und Commissurenfasern der Sehsphäre. *Ibid.*, v. 35, p. 22.
1901. Zur Kenntniss des Faserverlaufes des Temporallappens, des Bulbus olfactorius, der vorderen Commissur und des Fornix nach entsprechenden Exstirpations- und Durchschneidungsversuchen. Arch. f. Anat. u. Entw., p. 338.
1901. Ueber den Verlauf und die Endigung der Rindensehhügelfasern des Parietallappens. *Ibid.*, p. 357.
1901. Zur Kenntniss des Sagittalmarkes und der Balkenfasern des Hinterhauptlappens. Jahrb. f. Psychiat., v. 20, p. 320.
1902. Experimentelle Untersuchungen über die Anatomie und Physiologie der Leitungsbahnen des Gehirnstammes. Arch. f. Anat. u. Entw. (suppl. v.), p. 147.
1902. Ueber den Verlauf der centralen Sehfasern (Rinden-Sehhügelfasern) und deren Endigung im Zwischen- und Mittelhirne und über die Associations- und Commissuren-

fasern der Sehsphäre. Arch. f. Psychiat., v. 35, p. 22.

1903. Ueber die Rinden-Sehhügelfasern des Riechfeldes, über das Gewölbe, die Zwinge, die Randbogenfasern, über die Schweifkernfaserung und über die Vertheilung der Pyramidenfasern im Pyramidenareal. Arch. f. Anat. u. Entw., p. 138.

1903. Zur Kenntniss der Grosshirnfaserung und der cerebralen Hemiplegie. Sitzungsb. math.-nat. Kl. Akad. Wissensch. Wien, v. 112, Part III, p. 581.

1903. Ueber die Leitungsbahnen des Grosshirns mit besonderer Berücksichtigung der Anatomie und Physiologie des Sehhügels. Jahrb. f. Psychiat. u. Neurol., v. 23, p. 18.

1903. Ueber die anatomischen und physiologischen Folgen der Halbseitendurchschneidung des Mittelhirns. *Ibid.*, v. 24, p. 219.

1905. Ueber die Kommissur von Gudden, Meynert und Ganser und über die Folgen der Bulbusatrophie auf die zentrale Sehbahn. Monatsschr. f. Psychiat. u. Neurol., v. 17, p. 1.

1906. Ueber die zentralen Sinnesbahnen und die Sinneszentren des menschlichen Gehirnes. Sitzungs. math.-nat. Kl. Akad. Wissensch. Wien, v. 115, Part III, p. 103.

PROCHASKA (PROCHASCA), G.

1779. De structura nervorum, tractatus anatomicus. R. Graeffer, Vindobonae.

1780–84. Adnotationum accademicarum fasciculi tres. 3 vols. W. Gerle, Prague.

1797. Lehrsätze aus der Physiologie des Menschen. 2 vols. C. F. Wappler, Wien.

1800. Opera minorum anatomici, physiologici et pathologici argumenti, pars I. 2 vols. Wappler & Beck, Viennae.

1812. Disquisitiones anatomico-physiologicae organismi corporis humani. A. de Haykul, Viennae.

PROSSER, C. L.

1934. Effect of the central nervous system on responses to light in *Eisenia foetida*, Sav. J. Comp. Neurol., v. 59, p. 61.

PRUS, J.

1899. Untersuchungen über elektrische Reizung der Vierhügel. Wien. klin. Wchnschr., v. 12, p. 1124.

1899. Bemerkungen zu dem Aufsatze des Herrn Docenten Dr. Bernheimer: Die Beziehungen der vorderen Vierhügel zu den Augenbewegungen. *Ibid.*, p. 1311.

PTOLEMY (PTOLEMÁÏOS, PTOLEMAEUS)

2d cent. A.D. Optics ('Οπτική πραγματέια or Practice of optics). Book was translated from Greek into Arabic, and subsequently into Latin by Eugenius, a Sicilian admiral (*see* Govi). (*Cf. also* Haskins, Delambre, Favaro, Halma, Heiberg, Hanitius.)

PÜTTER, A.

1902. Die Augen der Wassersäugetiere. Zool. Jahrb. (Anat. & Ontog.), v. 17, p. 99.

1908–12. Organologie des Auges. *In:* GRAEFE & SAEMISCH, Handb. d. ges. Augenh., 2d ed., v. 2, Part 1; 3d ed., Part 1, chap. 10.

1911. Vergleichende Physiologie. G. Fischer, Jena.

PURKINJE (PURKYNĚ), J. E.; for biography, *see* BURTON-OPITZ, HYKEŠ, NOVIKOV, HEIDENHAIN, & STUDNIČKA

1819. Beobachtungen und Versuche zur Physiologie der Sinne. 1. Beiträge zur Kenntniss des Sehens in subjektiver Hinsicht. J. G. Calve, Prag. Also 1823.

1823. Commentatio de examine physiologico organi visus et systematis cutanei, quam pro loco in gratioso medicorum ordine rite obtinendo die XXII Decembris MDCCXIII, H.X., L.C., publice defendet J.E.P., med. Doctor, Physiologiae et Pathologiae Prof. publ. ord. des. Etc. Vratisl. (Breslau-Wroclaw), Typis Universitatis.

1825. Neuere Beiträge zur Kenntniss des Sehens in subjectiver Hinsicht. Reimer, Berlin.

1918–37. Sebrané spisy—Opera omnia. 2 vols. (In German and Latin.) Spol. Česk. Lék. Praha (Prague).

1948. Opera selecta. Cura societatis Spolek Českých Lékařů, Pragae, MCMXLVIII.

PURTSCHER, O.

1880. Ueber Kreuzung und Atrophie der *Nervi* und *Tractus optici*. Arch. f. Ophth. (Graefe), v. 26 (2), p. 191.

PURVES-STEWART, J.

1945. Diagnosis of nervous diseases. 9th ed. Williams & Wilkins, Baltimore.

PUSCHMANN, T.

1889. Geschichte des medizinischen Unterrichts von den ältesten Zeiten bis zur Gegenwart. Veit & Co., Leipzig.

PUSCHMANN, T., NEUBURGER, M., & PAGEL, J.

1902–5. Handbuch der Geschichte der Medizin. 3 vols. G. Fischer, Jena.

PUTNAM, T. J.

1926. Studies on the central visual system. II. A comparative study of the form of the geniculo-striate visual system of mammals. Studies on the central visual connections. III. The general relationships between the external geniculate body, optic radiation and visual cortex in man: report of two cases. Studies on the central visual system. IV. The details of the organization of the geniculo-striate system in man. Arch. Neurol. & Psychiat., v. 16, pp. 285, 566, 683.

1934. Discussion of paper by Penfield, Evans, and MacMillan. Tr. Am. Neurol. A., 60th meet., p. 45.

1937. The cerebral circulation: some new points in its anatomy, physiology and pathology. J. Neurol. & Psychopath., v. 17, p. 193.

PUTNAM, T. J., & ALEXANDER, L.

1938. Tissue damage resulting from disease of cerebral blood vessels. *In:* The circulation. Research Pub. A. Research Nerv. & Ment. Dis., v. 18, p. 544. Williams & Wilkins Co., Baltimore.

PUTNAM, T. J., & LIEBMAN, S.

1942. Cortical representation of the macula lutea, with special reference to the theory of bilateral representation. Arch. Ophth., v. 28, p. 415.

PUTNAM, T. J., & PUTNAM, I. K.

1926. Studies on the central visual system. I. The anatomic projection of the retinal quadrants on the striate cortex of the rabbit. Arch. Neurol. & Psychiat., v. 16, p. 1.

PUTTI, V.

1937. Berengario da Carpi. Saggio biografico e bibliografico seguito dalla traduzione del "De fractura calvae sive cranei." ("Classici italiani della medicina," Vol. III.) L. Cappelli, Bologna.

PYCRAFT, W. P.

1913. Courtship of animals. Hutchinson & Co., London; Henry Holt & Co., New York, 1914.

Q

QUAIN (E. A. SCHÄFER & J. SYMINGTON)

1909–12. Elements of anatomy, vols. 2 (part 1) and 3 (parts 1 & 2). Longmans, Green & Co., London & New York.

QUARANTA, J. V., & EVANS, L. T.

1949. The visual learning of *Testudo vicina*. Anat. Rec., v. 105, p. 580. (Abstr.)

QUATREMÈRE, M.; *see* RASHĪD AL-DĪN

QUENSEL, F.

1906. Beiträge zur Kenntnis der Grosshirnfaserung. Monatsschr. f. Psychiat. u. Neurol., v. 20, pp. 36, 166, 266, 353.

1908. Ueber Erscheinungen und Grundlagen der Worttaubheit. Deutsch. Ztschr. f. Nervenh., v. 35, p. 25.

1909. Der Symptomenkomplex der sogenannten transkortikalen motorischen Aphasie. Mo-

natsschr. f. Psychiat. u. Neurol. (Erg.-B.), v. 26, p. 259.

1917. Paul Flechsig zum 70. Geburtstag. Deutsch. med. Wchnschr., v. 43, p. 818.

1927. Ein Fall von rechtsseitiger Hemianopsie mit Alexie und zentral bedingtem monokulärem Doppeltsehen. Monatsschr. f. Psychiat. u. Neurol., v. 65, p. 173.

1931. Erkrankungen der höheren optischen Zentren. *In:* SCHIECK & BRÜCKNER, Kurz. Handb. d. Ophth., v. 6, p. 324. J. Springer, Berlin.

QUENSEL, F., & PFEIFER, R. A.

1922 23. Ein Fall von reiner sensorischer Amusie. Deutsch. Ztschr. f. Nervenh., v. 77, p. 156; Ueber reine sensorische Amusie. Ztschr. f. d. ges. Neurol. u. Psychiat., v. 81, p. 311. (*Cf. also* Zentralbl. f. d. ges. Neurol. u. Psychiat., v. 30, p. 363.)

QUIDOR, A., & HÉRUBEL, M.

1930. Les perceptions visuelles. Ann. d'ocul., v. 167, p. 185.

1930. Enregistrement et projection de la couleur et du relief. *Ibid.*, p. 191.

R

RAAB, W.

1953. Hormonal and neurogenic cardio-vascular disorders. Williams & Wilkins Co., Baltimore.

RABINOWITCH, E. I.

1945–51. Photosynthesis and related processes. I. Chemistry of photosynthesis, chemosynthesis and related processes in vitro and in vivo. II (1). Spectroscopy and fluorescence of photosynthetic pigments; kinetics of photosynthesis. Interscience Publishers, Inc., New York.

RABL, C.

1917. Ueber die bilaterale oder nasotemporale Symmetrie des Wirbeltierauges. Arch. f. mikr. Anat., v. 90, p. 261.

RABL-RÜCKHARDT, H.

1890. Sind die Ganglienzellen amöboid? Neurol. Centralbl., v. 9, p. 199.

1894. Einiges über das Gehirn der Riesenschlange. Ztschr. f. wissensch. Zool., v. 58, p. 694.

RAD, C. VON

1931. Kasuistischer Beitrag zur Symptomatologie der Herderkrankungen in der Uebergangsregion des Parietal- und Occipitallappens. Ztschr. f. d. ges. Neurol. u. Psychiat., v. 131, p. 273.

RADEMAKER, G. G. J.

1926. Die Bedeutung der roten Kerne und des übrigen Mittelhirns für Muskeltonus, Kör-

perstellung und Labyrinthreflexe. J. Springer, Berlin.

1931. Das Stehen. J. Springer, Berlin.

1937. Experimentelle Physiologie des Hirnstammes. (Mit Ausnahme der vegetativen Funktionen.) *In:* BUMKE & FOERSTER, Handb. d.
Neurol., v. 2, p. 187.

RADEMAKER, G. G. J., & TER BRAAK, J. W. G.

1948. On the central mechanism of some optic
reactions. Brain, v. 71, p. 48.

RÁDL, E.

1910. Ueber spezifisch differenzierte Leitungsbahnen. Anat. Anz., v. 36, p. 385.

1915. Zur Morphologie der Sehzentren der
Knochenfische. Morphol. Jahrb., v. 49, p.
509.

RADOS, A., & CANDIAN, F. L.

1921. Arterielle Anastomosen verschiedener reti-
naler Gefäss-Systeme im Verlaufe einer
Embolie des Hauptstammes. Klin. Monatsbl. f. Augenh., v. 66, p. 797.

RAEHLMANN, E.

1873. Beiträge zur Lehre vom Daltonismus und
seiner Bedeutung für die Young'sche Farbentheorie. Arch. f. Ophth. (Graefe), v. 19
(3), p. 88.

1876. Ueber den Daltonismus und die Young'sche
Farbentheorie. *Ibid.*, v. 22 (1), p. 29.

1907. Zur Anatomie und Physiologie des Pigmentepithels der Netzhaut. Ztschr. f.
Augenh., v. 17, p. 1.

1907. Zur vergleichenden Physiologie des Gesichtssinnes. Beitrag zur Theorie der Licht-
und Farbenempfindung auf anatomisch-
physikalischer Grundlage. G. Fischer, Jena.

RAFFLES, T. S.

1822. Descriptive catalogue of a zoölogical collection, etc., in the Island of Sumatra, etc.
(read 1820). Tr. Linnean Soc. London, v. 13,
p. 239.

RAIFORD, M. B.

1949. Binasal hemianopsia; report of two cases.
Am. J. Ophth., ser. 3, v. 32, p. 99.

RAILTON

1892. Intracranial tumor with definite loss of the
left upper quadrant of the field of vision
Brit. M. J., v. 1, p. 442.

RAMAGE, M. C.

1947. Notes on keeping bats in captivity. J. Mammal., v. 28, p. 60.

RAMÓN Y CAJAL, PEDRO

1890. Investigaciones sobre los centros ópticos de
los vertebrados. Tesis del doctorado. Gac.
sanit. Barcelona, v. 3, p. 10.

*1890. Investigaciones de histología comparada en

los centros de la visión de diferentes vertebrados. Zaragoza.

1891. El encéfalo de los reptiles. Trab. del lab.
histol. Zaragoza. Tipografía de la Casa
provincial de Caridad, Barcelona.

1894. Investigaciones micrográficas en el encéfalo
de los batracios y reptiles. Cuerpos genicula-
dos y tuberculos cuadrigéminos de los mamí-
feros. La Dereche, Zaragoza.

1896. Estructura del encéfalo del cameleón, Rev.
trimestr. microg., v. 1, p. 46.

1896. L'encéphale des amphibiens. Bibliog. anat.,
v. 4, p. 232.

1897. El fascículo longitudinal posterior en los
reptiles. Rev. trimestr. microg., v. 2, p. 153.

1898. Centros ópticos de las aves. *Ibid.*, v. 3, p.
141.

1899. El lóbulo óptico de los peces (teleosteos).
Ibid., v. 4, p. 87.

1917. Nuevo estudio del encéfalo de los reptiles.
Trab. (Trav.) del lab. de invest. biol.
Madrid, v. 15, p. 83; v. 16, p. 309.

1922. El cerebro de los batracios. *In:* Libro en
honor de D. S. Ramón y Cajal, v. 1, p. 13.

1943. Lóbulos ópticos de las aves. Trab. Inst.
Cajal de invest. biol. Madrid, v. 35, p. 3.

RAMÓN Y CAJAL, SANTIAGO

1889. Sur la morphologie et les connexions des éléments de la rétine des oiseaux. Anat. Anz.,
v. 4, p. 111,

1891. Sur la fine structure du lobe optique des
oiseaux et sur l'origine réelle des nerfs
optiques. J. internat. d'anat. et physiol., v.
8, p. 337.

1892–93. La rétine des vertébrés. Cellule, v. 9, p.
119; Trav. du lab. de recherches biol. Madrid, v. 28, Appendix, 1933. German trans.
by GREEFF, 1894.

1893. Neue Darstellung vom histologischen Bau
des Centralnervensystems. Arch. f. Anat. u.
Entw., pp. 319, 399.

1893. Ueber den Bau der Rinde des unteren Hinterhauptlappens der kleinen Säugethiere.
Ztschr. f. wissensch. Zool., v. 56, p. 664.

1894. Die Retina der Wirbelthiere. Untersuchungen mit der Golgi-Cajal'schen Chromsilber-
methode und der Ehrlich'schen Methylenblaufärbung. J. F. Bergmann, Wiesbaden.

1895. Apuntes para el studio del bulbo raquídeo,
cerebelo y origen de los nervios encefálicos.
An. Soc. españ. de hist. nat., v. 24, p. 5.

1895. Algunas conjeturas sobre el mecanismo
anatómico de la ideación, asociación y aten-
ción. Rev. de med. y cir. práct. Madrid, v.
36, p. 497.

1895. Einige Hypothesen über den anatomischen Mechanismus der Ideenbildung, der Association und der Aufmerksamkeit. Arch. f. Anat. u. Entw., p. 367.

1896. Nouvelles contributions à l'étude histologique de la rétine et à la question des anastomoses des prolongements protoplasmiques. J. anat. et physiol., v. 32, p. 481.

1896. Sobre las relaciones de las células nerviosas con las neuróglicas. Rev. trimestr. microg., v. 1, p. 38.

1896. Las espinas colaterales de las células del cerebro teñidas por el azul de metileno. *Ibid.*, p. 123.

1896. El azul de metileno en los centros nerviosos. *Ibid.*, p. 151.

1896. Allgemeine Betrachtungen über die Morphologie der Nervenzellen. Arch. f. Anat. u. Physiol., Anat. Abt., p. 187.

1896. Beitrag zum Studium der Medulla oblongata, des Kleinhirns und des Ursprungs der Gehirnnerven. J. A. Barth, Leipzig.

1897. Leyes de la morfología y dinamismo de las células nerviosas. Rev. trimestr. microg., v. 2, p. 1.

1897. Algo sobre la significación fisiológica de la neuroglia. *Ibid.*, p. 33.

1897. Ueber die Beziehungen der Nervenzellen zu den Neurogliazellen, anlässlich des Auffindens einer besonderen Zellform des Kleinhirns. Monatsschr. f. Psychiat., v. 1, p. 62.

1898. Estructura del kiasma óptico y teoría general de los entrecruzamientos de las vías nerviosas. Rev. trimestr. microg., v. 3, p. 15.

1899. Die Structur des Chiasma opticum nebst einer allgemeinen Theorie der Kreuzung der Nervenbahnen. J. A. Barth, Leipzig.

1899–1904. Textura del sistema nervioso del hombre y de los vertebrados. Estudios sobre el plan estructural y composición histológica de los centros nerviosos adicionados de consideraciones fisiológicas fundadas en los nuevos descubrimientos. 2 vols. Librería de Nicolás Moya, Madrid.

1900–6. Studien über die Hirnrinde des Menschen. J. A. Barth, Leipzig.

1902. Die Endigung des äusseren Lemniscus oder die sekundäre akustische Nervenbahn. Deutsch. med. Wchnschr., v. 28, p. 275.

1903. Sobre un foco gris especial relacionado con la cinta óptica. Trab. (Trav.) del lab. de invest. biol. Madrid, v. 2, p. 1.

1903. Las fibras nerviosas de origen cerebral del tubérculo cuadrigémino anterior y tálamo óptico. *Ibid.*, p. 5.

1903. Estudios talámicos. *Ibid.*, p. 31.

1903. Consideraciones críticas sobre la teoría de A. Bethe, acerca de la estructura y conexiones de las células nerviosas. *Ibid.*, p. 101.

1904. El retículo neurofibrilar en la retina. *Ibid.*, v. 3, p. 185. Das Neurofibrillennetz der Retina. Internat. Monatsschr. f. Anat. u. Physiol., v. 21, p. 369.

1906. Génesis de las fibras nerviosas del embrión y observaciones contrarias á la teoría catenaria. Trab. (Trav.) del lab. de invest. biol. Madrid, v. 4, p. 227.

1906. Notas preventivas sobre la degeneración y regeneración de las vías nerviosas centrales. *Ibid.*, p. 295.

1907. Die histogenetischen Beweise der Neuronentheorie von His und Forel. Anat. Anz., v. 30, p. 113.

1908. Nouvelles observations sur l'évolution des neuroblastes, avec quelques remarques sur l'hypothèse neurogénétique de Hensen-Held. *Ibid.*, v. 32, pp. 1, 65.

1908. L'hypothèse de la continuité d'Apathy. Réponse aux objections de cet auteur contre la doctrine neuronale. Trab. (Trav.) del lab. de invest. biol. Madrid, v. 6, p. 21.

1908. L'hypothèse de Mr. Apáthy sur la continuité des cellules nerveuses entre elles. Réponse aux objections de cet auteur contre la doctrine neuronale. Anat. Anz., v. 33, pp. 418, 468.

1909. Nota sobre la estructura de la retina de la mosca (*M. vomitoria L.*). Trab. (Trav.) del lab de invest. biol. Madrid, v. 7, p. 217.

1909–11. Histologie du système nerveux de l'homme et des vertébrés. 2 vols. A. Maloine, Paris.

1913. Sobre un nuevo proceder de impregnación de la neuroglia y sus resultados en los centros nerviosos del hombre y animales. Trab. (Trav.) del lab. de invest. biol. Madrid, v. 11, p. 219.

1913. Contribución al conocimiento de la neuroglia del cerebro humano. *Ibid.*, p. 255.

1915. Plan fundamental de la retina de los insectos. Bol. Soc. españ. de biol. (ses. del M. de noviembre).

1917. Contribución al conocimiento de la retina y centros ópticos de los cefalópodos. Trab. (Trav.) del lab. de invest. biol. Madrid, v. 15, p. 1.

1918. Observaciones sobre la estructura de los ocelos y vías nerviosas ocelares de algunos insectos. *Ibid.*, v. 16, p. 109.

1919. La desorientación inicial de las neuronas

retinianas de axon corto. (Algunos hechos favorables a la concepción neurotrópica.) *Ibid.*, v. 17, p. 65.

1920. Algunas observaciones contrarias a la hipótesis *syncytial* de la regeneración nerviosa y neurogénesis normal. *Ibid.*, v. 18, p. 275.

1921. Textura de la corteza visual del gato. *Ibid.*, v. 19, p. 113.

1922. Estudios sobre la fina estructura de la corteza regional de los roedores. *Ibid.*, v. 20, p. 1.

1922. Publicaciones de la junta para el homenaje a Cajal. Libro en honor de D. S. Ramón y Cajal. Trabajos originales de sus admiradores y discípulos, extranjeros y nacionales. 2 vols. Jimenez & Molena, Impresores, Madrid.

1923. Studien über die Sehrinde der Katze. J. f. Psychol. u. Neurol., v. 29, p. 161.

1923. Recuerdos de mi vida. 3d ed. Imprenta de Juan Pueyo, Madrid. (*See also* Lenhossék 1935; Sprong 1935; Tello 1935.)

1924. Studien über den feineren Bau der regionalen Rinde bei den Nagetieren. J. f. Psychol. u. Neurol., v. 30, p. 1.

1925. Contribution à la connaissance de la névroglie cérébrale et cérébelleuse dans la paralysie générale progressive. Trav. du lab. de recherches biol. Madrid, v. 23, p. 157.

1925. Autobiography. *In:* L. R. Grote, Die Medizin der Gegenwart in Selbstdarstellungen, v. 5, p. 131. F. Meiner, Leipzig.

1926. Sur les fibres mousseuses et quelques points douteux de la texture de l'écorce cérébelleuse. *In:* Studi neurologici ded. a E. Tanzi. Tipogr. Sociale Torinese, Torino.

1928. Degeneration and regeneration of the nervous system. Oxford University Press, London.

1929. Études sur la neurogenèse de quelques vertébrés. Recueil de mes principales recherches concernant la genèse des nerfs, la morphologie et la structure neuronale, l'origine de la névroglie, les terminaisons nerveuses sensorielles, etc. Tipografía artística, Madrid.

1929–30. Considérations critiques sur le rôle trophique des dendrites et leurs prétendues relations vasculaires. Trav. du lab. de recherches biol. Madrid, v. 26, p. 107.

1929–30. Signification probable de la morphologie des neurones des invertébrés. *Ibid.*, p. 131.

1932. Études sur la névroglie (macroglie). *Ibid.* v. 27, p. 377.

1933. Neuronismo o reticularismo? Las pruebas

objetivas de la unidad anatómica de las células nerviosas. Arch. neurobiol., psicol., etc., Madrid, v. 13, pp. 217, 579.

1934. Die Neuronenlehre und die periterminalen Netze Boeke's. Arch. f. Psychiat. u. Nervenkr., v. 102, p. 322.

1934. Les preuves objectives de l'unité anatomique des cellules nerveuses. Trav. du lab. de recherches biol. Madrid, v. 29, p. 1.

1935. Die Neuronenlehre. *In:* Bumke & Foerster, Handb. d. Neurol., v. 1, p. 887.

1935. Santiago Ramón y Cajal, 1852–1934. Sa formation et son œuvre. Résumé de son autobiographie. Trav. du lab. de recherches biol. Madrid, v. 30, p. 1.

1937. Recollections of my life. Mem. Am. Phil. Soc., v. 8, Part 1. (For other biographies *see* Lenhossék 1935; Sprong 1935; Tello 1935; Cannon 1949; Trueta 1952; Polyak 1953.)

Ramón y Cajal, S., & Castro, F. de
1933. Elementos de técnica micrográfica del sistema nervioso. Tipografía artística, Madrid.

Ramón y Cajal, S., & Sánchez, D.
1915. Contribución al conocimiento de los centros nerviosos de los insectos. I. Retina y centros ópticos. Trab. (Trav.) del lab. de invest. biol. Madrid, v. 13, p. 1.

Ramsay, B. P., Cleveland, E. L., & Koppius. O. T.
1941. Proton theory of optical resolving power. J. Opt. Soc. Amer., v. 31, p. 296.

Ramsay, B. P., Koppius, O. T., & Cleveland, E. L.
1941. Physical interpretations of resolving power. J. Opt. Soc. Amer., v. 31, p. 202.

Ramsay, F. E.
1901. The optic lobes and optic tracts of *Amblyopsis spelaeus* De Kay. J. Comp. Neurol., v. 11, p. 40.

Ramström, O. M.
1930. Swedenborg on the cerebral cortex as the seat of psychical activity. Tr. Internat. Swedenborg Cong., p. 56.

Rand, A. L.
1935. On the habits of some Madagascar mammals. J. Mammal., v. 16, p. 89.

1943. How bats in flight avoid obstacles. Canad. Field-Naturalist, v. 57, p. 94.

Rand, G.
1946. Relation between illumination and visual efficiency. Arch. Ophth., v. 35, p. 509.

Rand, H. W.
1950. The chordates. Blakiston Co., Philadelphia.

Ranke, H.
1933. Medicine and surgery in ancient Egypt. Bull. Hist. Med. Johns Hopkins Univ., v. 1, p. 237.

RANSON, S. W.
1921. A description of some dissections of the internal capsule, the corona radiata and the thalamic radiation to the temporal lobe. Arch. Neurol. & Psychiat., v. 5, p. 361.
1937. Some functions of the hypothalamus. Harvey Lect., ser. 32, p. 92.
1947. The anatomy of the nervous system. Its development and function. Revised by S. L. Clark. W. B. Saunders Co., Philadelphia & London.

RANSON, S. W., & INGRAM, W. R.
1931. A method for accurately locating points in the interior of the brain. Proc. Soc. Exper. Biol. & Med., v. 28, p. 577.

RANSON, S. W., & MAGOUN, H. W.
1933. Respiratory and pupillary reactions induced by electrical stimulation of the hypothalamus. Arch. Neurol. & Psychiat., v. 29, p. 1179.
1933. The central path of the pupilloconstrictor reflex in response to light. *Ibid.*, v. 30, p. 1193.
1939. The hypothalamus. Ergebn. d. Physiol., v. 41, p. 56.

RANSON, S. W., RANSON, S. W., JR., & RANSON, M.
1941. Corpus striatum and thalamus of a partially decorticate monkey. Arch. Neurol. & Psychiat., v. 46, p. 402.

RANVIER, L.
1889. Traité technique d'histologie. F. Savy, Paris.

RASDOLSKY, I.
1925. Beiträge zur Architektur der grauen Substanz des Rückenmarks. (Unter Benutzung einer neuen Methode der Färbung der Nervenfasernkollateralen.) Virchows Arch. f. path. Anat. u. Physiol., v. 257, p. 356.

RASHEVSKY, N.
1948. Mathematical biophysics. University of Chicago Press, Chicago.

RASHĪD AL-DĪN, FAZL ALLĀH
Early 14th cent. Histoire des Mongols de la Perse, etc., ed. M. QUATREMÈRE. Imprimerie Royal, Paris, 1836.

RASMUSSEN, A. T.
1936. Tractus tecto-spinalis in the cat. J. Comp. Neurol., v. 63, p. 501.
1940. Effects of hypophysectomy and hypophysial stalk resection on the hypothalamic nuclei of animals and man. Research Pub. A. Research Nerv. & Ment. Dis., v. 20, p. 245. (*See also* Endocrinology, v. 23, p. 263; v. 27, p. 219; Cyclopedia of Med., Surg. & Spec., 1939.)

1940. Studies of the VIIIth cranial nerve of man. Laryngoscope, v. 50, p. 67.
1943. The extent of recurrent geniculo-calcarine fibers (loop of Archambault and Meyer) as demonstrated by gross brain dissection. Anat. Rec., v. 85, p. 277.
1945. The principal nervous pathways. Neurological charts and schemas with explanatory notes. Macmillan Co., New York.
1947. Some trends in neuroanatomy. W. C. Brown Co., Dubuque, Iowa.

RAUBER, A. A.
1914. Lehrbuch der Anatomie des Menschen. Ed. F. KOPSCH. 6 vols. G. Thieme, Leipzig. Also later eds.

RAVAISSON-MOLLIEN, C. L.
1881. Les écrits de Léonard de Vinci, à propos de la publication intégrale des douze manuscrits inédits de la Bibliothèque de l'Institut. A. Quantin, Paris.

RAVEN, H. C., and COLLABORATORS
1950. The anatomy of the gorilla, arranged and edited by W. K. GREGORY. Columbia University Press, New York.

RAWDON-SMITH, A. F.
1938. Theories of sensation. Cambridge University Press, Cambridge.

RAYLEIGH (J. W. STRUTT)
1899–1920. Scientific papers. 6 vols. Cambridge University Press, Cambridge.

RAYMOND, F., LEJONNE, P., & GALEZOWSKI, J.
1906. Cécité corticale par double hémianopsie. Rev. neurol., v. 14, p. 680.

REA, R. L.
1941. Neuro-ophthalmology. 2d ed. C. V. Mosby, St. Louis, Mo.

READ, C.
1925. Man and his superstitions. Cambridge University Press, Cambridge.

READE, J.
1820. Experiments for a new theory of vision. Ann. Phil., London, v. 15, p. 260.

REAL-ENCYCLOPÄDIE DER CLASSISCHEN ALTERTUMSWISSENSCHAFT
1893–1937. New ed. by G. WISSOWA *et al.*, pub. by W. KROLL. J. B. Metzlersche Verlagsbuchhandlung, Stuttgart (so far, 56 vols.). (*See also* Pauly & Wissowa.)

RECKLINGHAUSEN, F.
1859. Netzhautfunctionen. Arch. f. Ophth. (Graefe), v. 5 (2), p. 127.

REDDINGIUS, R. A.
1898. Das sensumotorische Sehwerkzeug. W. Engelmann, Leipzig.

REDIKORZEW, W.
1900. Untersuchungen über den Bau der Ocellen der Insekten. Ztschr. f. wissensch. Zool., v. 68, p. 581.
1905. Ueber das Sehorgan der Salpen. Morphol. Jahrb., v. 34, p. 204.

REDLICH, E.
1895. Ueber die sogenannte subcorticale Alexie. Arb. a. d. Neurol. Inst. Wien (Obersteiner), v. 3, p. 1.
1903–5. Zur vergleichenden Anatomie der Associationssysteme des Gehirns der Säugetiere. I. Das Cingulum. II. Der Fasciculus longitudinalis inferior. *Ibid.*, v. 10, p. 104; v. 12, p. 109.
1907. Ueber den Mangel der Selbstwahrnehmung des Defektes bei cerebral bedingter Blindheit. Neurol. Centralbl., v. 26, p. 919.
1915–28. Zur Topographie der Sensibilitätsstörungen am Rumpfe bei der zerebralen Hemianaesthesie. *Ibid.*, v. 34, p. 850; Monatsschr. f. Psychiat. u. Neurol., v. 68, p. 453.

REDLICH, E., & BONVICINI, G.
1907. Ueber mangelnde Wahrnehmung (Autoanästhesie) der Blindheit bei cerebralen Erkrankungen. Neurol. Centralbl., v. 26 p. 945. (*Cf. also* p. 919.)
1908. Ueber das Fehlen der Wahrnehmung der eigenen Blindheit bei Hirnkrankheiten. F. Deuticke, Leipzig & Wien.
1910. Anatomischer Befund in einem Falle zerebraler Blindheit. Wien. klin. Wchnschr., v. 23, p. 79.
1911. Weitere klinische und anatomische Mitteilungen über das Fehlen der Wahrnehmung der eigenen Blindheit bei Hirnkrankheiten. Neurol. Centralbl., v. 30, pp. 227, 301.

REDLICH, F. C., & DORSEY, J. F.
1945. Denial of blindness by patients with cerebral disease. Arch. Neurol. & Psychiat., v. 53, p. 407.

REEKEN, C. G. VAN
1856. Ontleedkundig onderzoek van den toestel voor accommodatie van het oog. Onderzoekingen gedan in het Laboratorium der Utrechtsche Hoogeschool, v. 7, p. 249, 1854–55; *also* Nederl. Lancet, 3d ser., v. 5, p. 1, 1855–56.

REESE, A. B.
1935. The occurrence of ciliary processes on the iris. Am. J. Ophth., v. 18, p. 6.

REESE, A. M.
1917. The reactions of the crimson-spotted newt, *Diemyctylus viridescens*, to light. Anat. Rec., v. 11, p. 521.

REEVES, C. D.
1919. Discrimination of light of different wavelengths by fish. Behavior Monog., v. 4, No. 3.

REEVES, P.
1917. The minimum radiation visually perceptible. Astrophys. J., p. 167; J. Opt. Soc. Amer., v. 1, p. 176.
1920. The reaction of the eye to light. Tr. Opt. Soc. London, v. 22, p. 1.

REGAN, C. T.
1930. The classification of the primates. Nature, v. 125, p. 125.

REICH, M.
1874. Zur Histologie der Hechtretina. Arch. f. Ophth. (Graefe), v. 20 (1), p. 1.
1879. Ueber die Sehschärfe bei den Georgien. Centralbl. f. prakt. Augenh., v. 3, p. 301.

REICHARD, M.
1918. Zur Frage der pathologisch-anatomischen Grundlage der reflektorischen Pupillenstarre. Neurol. Centralbl., v. 37, p. 7.

REICHARDT, M.
1919. Theoretisches über die Psyche. J. f. Psychol. u. Neurol., v. 24, p. 168.

REICHENBACH, H.
1933. Kant und die Naturwissenschaft. Naturwiss., v. 21, pp. 601, 624.

REICHENOW, E.
1920. Biologische Beobachtungen an Gorilla und Schimpanse. Sitzungsb. d. Gesellsch. d. Naturforsch. Freunde zu Berlin, p. 1.
1921. Ueber die Lebensweise des Gorilla und des Schimpansen. Naturwiss., v. 9, p. 73.

REICHERT, C. (or K.) B.
1841. Bericht über die Fortschritte der mikroskopischen Anatomie in den Jahren 1839 und 1840. Arch. f. Anat., Physiol. u. wissensch. Med., pp. clxii, cxcvii.
1859–61. Der Bau des menschlichen Gehirns durch Abbildungen mit erläuterndem Texte dargestellt von C. B. Reichert, Professor der Anatomie und vergleichenden Anatomie an der Universität zu Berlin. 2 parts. Verlag von Wilhelm Engelmann, Leipzig.

REIGHARD, J.
1920. The breeding behavior of the suckers and minnows. Biol. Bull., v. 38, p. 1.

REIL, D. J. C.
1797. Die Falte, der gelbe Fleck und die durchsichtige Stelle in der Netzhaut des Auges. Arch. f. d. Physiol. (Reil & Autenrieth), v. 2, p. 468.

1809. Untersuchungen über den Bau des grossen Gehirns im Menschen. *Ibid.*, v. 9, p. 136.

1809. Das Hirnschenkel-System oder die Hirnschenkel-Organisation im grossen Gehirn. *Ibid.*, p. 147.

1809. Das Balken-System oder die Balken-Organisation im grossen Gehirn. *Ibid.*, p. 172.

1809. Die Sylvische Grube oder das Thal, das gestreifte grosse Hirnganglium, dessen Kapsel und die Seitentheile des grossen Gehirns. *Ibid.*, p. 195.

1809. Das verlängerte Rückenmark, die hinteren, seitlichen und vörderen Schenkel des kleinen Gehirns, etc. *Ibid.*, p. 485.

1812. Die vördere Commissur im grossen Gehirn. *Ibid.*, v. 11, p. 89.

1812. Nachträge zur Anatomie des grossen und kleinen Gehirns. *Ibid.*, p. 345.

REILLY, C.
1948. Colored animated moving picture of the gross anatomy of the visual pathways in man. Anat. Rec., v. 100, p. 783. (Abstr., no information.)

REINHARD, C.
1886–87. Zur Frage der Hirnlocalisation mit besonderer Berücksichtigung der cerebralen Sehstörungen. Arch. f. Psychiat., v. 17, p. 717; v. 18, pp. 240, 449.

REINÖHL, F.
1940. Abstammungslehre. Hohenlohe'sche Buchhandlung, Oehringen.

REISCH, GREGOR
1508. Margarita Philosophica cum additionibus novis: ab auctore suo studiosissima revisione tertio supadditis. Jo. Schottus Argeñ. lectore. S. Hanc eme / non praessam mendaci stigmate / Lector; Pluribus ast auctam perlege: doctus eris. Basileae. 1508. Earlier ed. 1504; also 1525.

REISEK, J.
1895. L'entrée du nerf optique chez quelques rongeurs. Bibliog. anat., v. 3, p. 74.

REITMANN
1904. Ueber einen Fortsatz des Chiasma nervi optici. Arch. f. path. Anat. & Physiol. (Virchow), v. 177, p. 171.

REMAK, R.
1839. Zur mikroskopischen Anatomie der Retina. Arch. f. Anat., Physiol. u. wissensch. Med. (J. Müller), p. 165. (*See also* Henle's remark on p. 170.)

1843. Ueber den Inhalt der Nervenprimitivröhren. *Ibid.*, p. 197.

1853. Sur les fibres nerveuses ganglieuses chez l'homme et chez les animaux vertébrés. Compt. rend. Acad. d. sc., v. 36, p. 914.

1853. Ueber gangliöse Nervenfasern beim Menschen und bei den Wirbelthieren. Berlin. Monatsber., Verhandl. d. Preuss. Akad. d. Wissensch., p. 293.

1853. Sur la structure de la rétine. Compt. rend. Acad. d. sc., v. 37, p. 663. (*See also* Allg. med. Centralzeitung, 1854.)

1854. Ueber den Bau der Retina und der Ganglien. Deutsch. Klinik, v. 6, p. 177.

1855. Ueber den Bau der grauen Säulen im Rückenmarke der Säugethiere. *Ibid.*, v. 7, p. 295.

RENAUT, J. L.
1893–99. Traité d'histologie pratique. *See* v. 2, Part 2, p. 1114, Organe de la vision-rétine. Rueff & Cie, Paris.

1895. Sur les cellules nerveuses multipolaires et la théorie du "Neurone" de Waldeyer. Bull. Acad. méd. de Paris, 3d ser., v. 33, p. 207.

1899. Le neurone et la mémoire cellulaire. Rev. scient., ser. 4, v. 12, p. 321.

RENDAHL, H.
1924. Embryologische und morphologische Studien über das Zwischenhirn beim Huhn. Acta zool., v. 5, p. 241.

RENOUARD, P. V.
1846. Histoire de la médecine depuis son origine jusqu'au XIXe siècle. J.-B. Baillière, Paris. Also English ed., 1867.

RENSCH, B.
1947. Neuere Probleme der Abstammungslehre. Die transspezifische Evolution. F. Enke, Stuttgart.

RENZI, S. DE
1845–48. Storia della medicina italiana. 5 vols. Filiatre-Sebezio, Napoli.

1854. Collectio Salernitana, ossia documenti inediti, e trattati di medicina appartenenti alla scuola medica salernitana, raccolti ed illustrati da G. E. T. Henschel, C. Daremberg, E. S. de Renzi; premessa la storia della scuola, etc. Tipografia del Filiatre-Sebezio, Napoli.

*1857. Storia documentata della scuola medica di Salerno. 2d ed. Napoli.

RESCHER, O.
1913. Ueber arabische Manuskripte der Lālelī-Moschee. *In:* Le monde oriental, v. 7, p. 96. A. B. Akademiska Bokhandeln, Uppsala. (Here, p. 110, first mention made of an Arabic MS of Ibn al-Haitham's Optics; *cf.* also M. Krause 1936.)

RESNIKOV, C. M.
*1897. Zur Lehre von dem Bau der Netzhaut. Untersuchungen nach der Methode Golgi-

Cajal. Inaug. Diss. St. Petersburg (prob. in Russian).

RETZIUS, G.; for biography *see* V. EBNER 1920

1881. Beiträge zur Kenntniss der inneren Schichten der Netzhaut des Auges. Biol. Untersuch., v. 1, p. 89.

1891. Zur Kenntniss des centralen Nervensystems der Würmer. *Ibid.*, N.F., v. 2, p. 1.

1891. Zur Kenntniss des centralen Nervensystems von *Amphioxus lanceolatus. Ibid.*, p. 29.

1892. Das Nervensystem der Lumbricinen. *Ibid.*, v. 3, p. 1.

1895. Ueber den Bau des sog. Parietalauges von Ammocoetes. *Ibid.*, v. 7, p. 22.

1896. Das Menschenhirn. Studien in der makroskopischen Morphologie. 2 vols. P. A. Norstedt & Söner, Stockholm.

1898. Das Gehirn des Astronomen Hugo Gyldéns. Biol. Untersuch., N.F., v. 8, p. 1.

1898. Ueber das Auftreten des Sulcus centralis und der Fissura calcarina im Menschenhirn. *Ibid.*, p. 59.

1898. Zur Kenntnis der lateralen Fläche des Mesencephalons und ihrer Umgebung. *Ibid.*, p. 65.

1898. Die Methylenblaufärbung bei dem lebenden Amphioxus. *Ibid.*, p. 118.

1900. Das Gehirn des Mathematikers Sonja Kovalevski. *Ibid.*, v. 9, p. 1.

1901. Zur Frage von den sogenannten transitorischen Furchen des Menschenhirnes. Verhandl. d. anat. Gesellsch., v. 15, p. 91.

1902. Zur Kenntniss der Gehirnbasis und ihrer Ganglien beim Menschen. Biol. Untersuch., N.F., v. 10, p. 67.

1904. Die Membrana limitans interna der Netzhaut des Auges. *Ibid.*, v. 11, p. 82.

1905. Punktsubstanz, "nervöses Grau" und Neuronenlehre. *Ibid.*, v. 12, p. 1.

1905. Zur Kenntnis vom Bau der Selachier-Retina. *Ibid.*, p. 55.

1906. Das Affenhirn in bildlicher Darstellung. (Cerebra simiarum illustrata.) G. Fischer, Jena.

1908. The principles of the minute structure of the nervous system, etc. Proc. Roy. Soc. London, ser. B., v. 80, p. 414.

1920. Biography of Gustav Magnus Retzius, by V. EBNER. Almanach d. Akad. d. Wissensch., Wien, p. 127.

REUSS, A. VON

1876. Casuistische Beiträge zur Kenntniss des Flimmerscotoms. Wien. med. Presse, v. 17, pp. 7, 52, 126, 188, 231, 297, 366, 392.

REVAULT-D'ALLONNES

1920. Le mécanisme de la pensée. Les schèmes mentaux. Rev. phil. France & étrang., v. 90, p. 161.

RÉVÉSZ, B.

1917. Geschichte des Seelenbegriffes und der Seelenlokalisation. F. Enke, Stuttgart.

RÉVÉSZ, G.

1921. Tierpsychologische Untersuchungen. (Versuche an Hühnern). Ztschr. f. Psychol., v. 88, p. 130.

1922. Zur Analyse der tierischen Handlung. Theoretische und experimentelle Beiträge zur vergleichenden Psychologie. Arch. néerl. physiol., v. 7, p. 469.

1925. Experimental study in abstraction in monkeys. J. Comp. Psychol., v. 5, p. 293.

1937. The problem of space with particular emphasis on specific sensory spaces. Am. J. Psychol., v. 50, p. 429.

RHAZES; *see* AL RĀZĪ

RHEITA; *see* SCHYRLEUS DE RHEITA

RICARDUS ANGLICUS (MAGISTER RICHARDUS, RICHARD OF WENDOVER)

*1242–52. Anatomia Richardi Anglici. Ad fidem codicis ms. a. 1634 in bibliotheca Palatina Vindobonensi conservati primum ed. Ritter Rob. v. Töply. I. Šafář, Wien, 1902.

RICCÒ, H.

1876. Ueber die Farbenwahrnehmung. Arch. f. Ophth. (Graefe), v. 22 (1), p. 282.

RICHET, C.

1892. Des lésions cérébrales dans la cécité psychique expérimentale chez le chien. Compt. rend. Soc. de biol., v. 4, N.S., p. 237.

RICHTER, A.

1885. Ueber die optischen Leitungsbahnen des menschlichen Gehirns. Allg. Ztschr. f. Psychiat., v. 41, p. 636.

1885. Zur Frage der optischen Leitungsbahnen des menschlichen Gehirns. Arch. f. Psychiat., v. 16, p. 639.

1886–88. Ueber die Windungen des menschlichen Gehirns. Arch. f. path. Anat. u. Physiol. (Virchow), v. 106, p. 390; v. 108, p. 398; v. 113, p. 118.

1889. Pathologisch-Anatomisches und Klinisches über die optischen Leitungsbahnen des menschlichen Gehirns. Arch. f. Psychiat., v. 20, p. 504.

RICHTER, C. P.

1931. The grasping reflex in the new-born monkey. Arch. Neurol. & Psychiat., v. 26, p. 784.

RICHTER, C. P., & HINES, M.
1932. Experimental production of the grasp reflex in adult monkeys by lesions of the frontal lobes. Am. J. Physiol., v. 101, p. 87.
1937. Increased general activity produced by prefrontal and striatal lesions in monkeys. Tr. Am. Neurol. A., 63d ann. meet., p. 107; Brain, v. 61, p. 1.

RICHTER, H.
1918. Kortikal bedingte isolierte Lähmung der rechten Hand. Neurol. Centralbl., v. 37, p. 450.

RIDDELL, W. J. B.
1943. The scientific and clinical aspects of night vision. Tr. Ophth. Soc. United Kingdom, v. 63, p. 43. (*See also* Livingston; Lawson *et al.*)

RIDDOCH, G.
1917. Dissociation of visual perceptions due to occipital injuries, with especial reference to appreciation of movement. Brain, v. 40, p. 15.
1935. Visual disorientation in homonymous half-fields. *Ibid.*, v. 58, p. 376.
1941. Phantom limbs and body shape. *Ibid.*, v. 64, p. 197.

RIDGWAY, R., & FRIEDMANN, H.
1901–50. The birds of North and Middle America. Government Printing Office, Washington, D.C.

RIDLEY, F., & SORSBY, A.
1940. Modern trends in ophthalmology. Butterworth & Co., London.

RIDLEY, H. N.
1894. On the dispersal of seeds by mammals. J. Straits Branch, Roy. Asiatic Soc., v. 25, p. 11.
1895. The mammals of the Malay Peninsula. Nat. Sc., v. 6, pp. 23, 89, 161.
1930. The dispersal of plants throughout the world. L. Reeve & Co., Ashford, Kent, England.

RIEDINGER, F.
1932. Die Schärfe der Wahrnehmung von Linienversetzungen. Ztschr. f. ophth. Optik, v. 20, p. 33.

RIESE, W.
1924. Formprobleme des Gehirns (Körperform und Hirnform). J. f. Psychol. u. Neurol., v. 31, p. 233.
1926. Ueber anatomische und funktionelle Differenzen im optischen System. *Ibid.*, v. 32, p. 281.
1930. Apraxie der Lidöffnung (Analyse einer Bewegungsstörung). *Ibid.*, v. 40, p. 347.

1940. Structure et fonction du cerveau du macaque nouveau-né (*Macaca cynomolgus* L.). Bull. Mus. nat. d'hist. nat., Paris, 2d ser., v. 12, p. 92.
1942. The principle of integration. Its history and its nature. J. Nerv. & Ment. Dis., v. 96, p. 296.
1943. The principle of evolution of nervous function. *Ibid.*, v. 98, p. 255.
1943. The cellular structure of the marsupialian cortex. Naturaliste canad., v. 70, p. 139.
1946. Structure and function of the cerebral cortex in the new-born cat. Confin. Neurol. (Basel), v. 7, p. 55.

RIESE, W., & SMYTH, G. E.
1940. The cytology of the cortex in the opossum (*Didelphys virginiana*) considered in relation to some general problems of cortical evolution. Proc. Kon. nederl. Akad. v. Wetensch., v. 43, p. 403.

RIESEN, A. H.
1947. The development of visual perception in man and chimpanzee. Science, v. 106, p. 107.

RIESMAN, D.
1935. The story of medicine in the Middle Ages. P. B. Hoeber, New York.

RIGHETTI, R.
1897. Sulla mielinizzazione delle fibre della corteccia cerebrale umana nei primi mesi di vita. Riv. pat. nerv. & ment., v. 2, p. 347.
1903. Contributo clinico e anatomo-patologico allo studio dei gliomi cerebrali e all'anatomia delle vie ottiche centrali. *Ibid.*, v. 8, pp. 241, 289.

RIGNANO, E.
1928. Zur Gestalttheorie. Scientia (Riv. di sc.), v. 43, p. 323.

RILEY, H. A.
1930. The central nervous system control of the ocular movements and the disturbances of this mechanism. Arch. Ophth., v. 4, pp. 640, 885.
1932. Migraine. Bull. Neurol. Inst. New York, v. 2, p. 429.

RIOCH, D. McK.
1929–31. Studies on the diencephalon of Carnivora. J. Comp. Neurol., v. 49, pp. 1, 121; v. 53, p. 319.
1940. Neurophysiology of the corpus striatum and globus pallidus. Psychiatry, v. 3, p. 119.

RIOCH, D. McK., WISLOCKI, G. B., & O'LEARY, J. L.
1940. A précis of preoptic, hypothalamic and hypophysial terminology with atlas. Research Pub. A. Research Nerv. & Ment. Dis., v. 20, p. 3.

Río-Hortega, P. del
1916. Estructura fibrilar del protoplasma neuróglico y origen de las gliofibrillas. Trab. (Trav.) del lab. de invest. biol. Madrid, v. 14, p. 269.
1928. Tercera aportación al conocimiento morfológico e interpretación funcional de la oligodendroglía. Mem. r. Soc. españ. hist. nat., v. 14, p. 7.
1932. Microglia. *In:* Penfield, Cytology & cellular pathology of the nervous system, v. 2, p. 481.

Riolan, J.
1618. Ioannis Riolani Filii, Doctoris Medici, Ordine et Origine Parisiensis, Anatomes & Pharmaciae Professoris Regij, *Anthropographia*. Ex proprijs, & novis Observationibus collecta, concinata. In qua facilis, ac fidelis, & accurate Manuductio. Ad Anatomem traditur, prout ab ipso quotannis publice, & privatim, docetur, administratur, & demonstratur. In Celeberrima Parisiensi Academia. Parisiis, Ex Officina Plantiniana. Apud Hadrianum Perier, viâ Iacobaeâ. M.DC.XVIII. Cum Privilegio Regis.
1620. Ioannis Riolani Praelectiones in Libros Physiologicos, & de Abditis rerum caussis: etc. Parisiis. Ex Officina Plantiniana, Apud Hadrianum Perier, etc. M.DC.XX.

Ripley, D., & Weber, W. A.
1950. Strange courtship of birds of paradise. Nat. Geog. Mag., v. 97, p. 247.

Ris, F.
1899. Ueber den Bau des Lobus opticus der Vögel. Arch. f. mikr. Anat., v. 53, p. 106.

Risner, F.
1606. Opticae libri quatuor ex voto Petri Rami novissimo per Fridericum Risnerum ejusdem in mathematicis adjutorem olim conscripti. W. Wesselio, Cassellis.

Ritter, C.
1859. Ueber den Bau der Stäbchen und äusseren Endigungen der Radialfasern an der Netzhaut des Frosches. Arch. f. Ophth. (Graefe), v. 5 (2), p. 101.
1862. Ueber die Elemente der äusseren Körnerschicht. *Ibid.*, v. 8 (2), p. 115.
1864. Die Structur der Retina dargestellt nach Untersuchungen über das Walfischauge. W. Engelmann, Leipzig.
1864. Ueber die Bedeutung des gelben Fleckes. Ztschr. f. rat. Med., v. 21, p. 290.
1891. Zur Histologie der Zapfen der Fischretina. Internat. Monatsschr. f. Anat. u. Physiol., v. 8, p. 128.

1891. Studien über die Stäbchenschicht der Vögel. *Ibid.*, p. 241.

Ritter, H., & Walzer, R.
1934. Arabische Uebersetzungen griechischer Aerzte in Stambuler Bibliotheken. Sitzungsb. d. Preuss. Akad. d. Wissensch., Berlin, phil.-hist. Kl., p. 801.

Roaf, H. E.
1926. The influence of one coloured light on the sensitivity of the eye to the same and other colours. J. Physiol. (Proc.), v. 62, p. xxi.
1929. The absorption of light by the coloured globules in the retina of the domestic hen. Proc. Roy. Soc. London, ser. B., v. 105, p. 371.
1930. Visual acuity in light of different colours. *Ibid.*, v. 106, p. 276.
1930. Crossed connection of the cerebral hemispheres with the muscles and sense organs. Nature, v. 125, p. 203.
1930–33. Colour vision. *Ibid.*, v. 126, p. 825; Physiol. Rev., v. 13, p. 43.
1938. Methods of testing for colour vision and theoretical deductions from observations on colour vision. Brit. M. J., v. 2, p. 440.
1939. The relation of the retinae to the cerebral cortex. Tr. Ophth. Soc. London, v. 59, p. 383.
1939. The recognition of colour. *Ibid.*, p. 395.

Roberts, L.
1951. Localization of speech in the cerebral cortex. Tr. Am. Neurol. A. (76th ann. meet.), p. 43.

Robertson, D. Argyll; *see* Argyll Robertson

Robertson, W. T., & Edwards, E.
1868. Photographs of eminent medical men of all countries. 2 vols. J. Churchill, London.

Robinson, H. C., & Kloss, C. B.; *see* Thomas & Wroughton 1909

Robinson, J. T.
1952. Note on the skull of *Proconsul africanus*. Am. J. Phys. Anthropol., N.S., v. 10, p. 7.
1953. Meganthropus, Australopithecines and hominids. *Ibid.*, v. 11, p. 1.

Roch, M.
1941. L'écorce visuelle, variations de ses limites anatomiques et de sa structure cytoarchitectonique. Thèse. Lausanne.

Rochat, G. F.
1922. Étude quantitative du fusionnement binoculaire des couleurs complémentaires. Arch. néerl. de physiol., v. 7, p. 263.

Roche, W. L.
1925. The distal retina and interstitial cells of the eye of Pecten. J. Roy. Micr. Soc. London, p. 145.

Rochon-Duvigneaud, A.
1903. Anatomie de l'appareil nerveux sensoriel de

la vision: rétine, nerf optique, centres optiques. Encyc. franç. d'opht., v. 1, p. 551. O. Doin, Paris.

1907. Recherches sur la fovéa de la rétine humaine, etc. Arch. d'anat. micr., v. 9, p. 315.

1917. Les fonctions des cônes et des bâtonnets. Ann. d'ocul., v. 154, p. 633.

1919. L'œil de l'aigle. *Ibid.*, v. 156, p. 376.

1919. Quelques données sur la fovéa des oiseaux. *Ibid.*, p. 717.

1919. La double fovéa rétinienne des rapaces diurnes. Compt. rend. Acad. d. sc., v. 169, p. 43.

1920. La vision et l'œil de l'homme à point de vue de l'anatomie et de physiologie comparée. Bull. et mém. Soc. d'anthropol. Paris, 7th ser., p. 1.

1920. La situation des fovéae simples et doubles dans la rétine des oiseaux et le problème de leurs relations fonctionnelles. Ann. d'ocul., v. 157, p. 673.

1921. Contribution à la physiologie de la vision de la chouette chevêche. *Ibid.*, v. 158, p. 561.

1921. La vision et l'œil des oiseaux. Bull. biol. franç. et Belg., v. 54, p. 109.

1922. Une méthode de détermination du champ visuel chez les vertébrés. Ann. d'ocul., v. 159, p. 561; Bull. et mém. Soc. franç. d'opht., v. 35, p. 296.

1923. Topographie et fonctions des fovéae centrales et des fovéae latérales chez les oiseaux pourvus de deux fovéae rétiniennes. Ann. d'ocul., v. 160, p. 769.

1923. La vision des oiseaux. La Nature, v. 51 (1), pp. 267, 284, 300, 316, 329, 348.

1924. Lignes visuelles des foveae centrales (à vision indépendante) et des foveae latérales (à vision associée) chez le faucon crécerelle. Compt. rend. Acad. d. sc., v. 178, p. 2272.

1925. La réfraction des petits yeux chez les animaux et l'utilisation des images rétiniennes défectueuses. Bull. et mém. Soc. franç. d'opht., v. 38, p. 209.

1925. La vision des animaux appréciée par la comparaison de leur rétine avec la rétine humaine. Bull. Mus. nat. d'hist. nat. Paris, v. 31, p. 224.

1926. Comment un appareil d'optique précis, l'œil, a pu être réalisé avec des tissus mous. Bull. et mém. Soc. franç. d'opht., v. 39, p. 73.

1926. Enquête sur l'orientation du pigeon voyageur et son mécanisme. La Nature, v. 54 (2), p. 24.

1928. Sur l'œil de l'aigle fauve du Maroc. Bull. Soc. sc. nat. du Maroc, v. 8, p. 160.

1928. L'œil de la taupe et les problèmes qu'il soulève. Ann. d'ocul., v. 165, p. 801.

1929. La vision des oiseaux. Alauda, v. 1, p. 336.

1929. L'œil et la vision de la marmotte. Compt. rend. XIII. Concil. Ophth., Amsterdam & Haag, p. 319.

1931. Les yeux des reptiles. Bull. Mus. nat. d'hist. nat. Paris, 2d ser., v. 3, p. 399.

1933. Esquisse d'une ophtalmologie comparée des vertébrés. Ann. d'ocul., v. 170, p. 1.

1933. Notes sur quelques points du développement de l'œil chez *Scyllium canicula* et *Acanthias vulgaris*. Arch. de zool. expér. et gén., v. 75, p. 221.

1933. Le caméléon et son œil. Ann. d'ocul., v. 170, p. 177.

1933. Un chapitre de la vision des oiseaux: comment leurs yeux sont-ils associés? Alauda, v. 2, p. 178.

1933. Recherches sur l'œil et la vision chez les vertébrés. Imprimerie Barnéoud, Laval.

1933. Les divers modes d'association des yeux dans la série des vertébrés. Vision indépendante, vision associée, vision conjuguée. Imprimerie Alençonnaise, Alençon.

1934. L'indépendance des mouvements oculaires chez les amammaliens. J. de Psychol., v. 31, p. 462.

1934. Notes d'ophtalmologie comparée. I. Les yeux des musaraignes. II. Les yeux de la chouette chevêche. Bull. Soc. zool. de France, v. 59, p. 218.

1934. La défense des rapaces. Oiseau & rev. franç. d'ornithol., v. 4, N.S., p. 168.

*1934. La fovéa et ses fonctions dans la série des vertébrés. Soc. franç. d'opht.

1939. Anatomie et physiologie comparée. *In:* BAILLIART, COUTELA, REDSLOB, & VELTER, Traité d'ophtalmologie, v. 1, p. 745. Masson & Cie, Paris.

1943. Les yeux et la vision des vertébrés. Masson & Cie, Paris.

ROCHON-DUVIGNEAUD, A., BOURDELLE, E., & DUBAR, J.

1925. Appareils pour la détermination du champ visuel anatomique par la méthode de l'image transsclérale. Compt. rend. Acad. d. sc., v. 180, p. 542.

1925. Détermination du champ visuel anatomique monoculaire du cheval par la méthode de l'image transsclérale. Compt. rend. Acad. d. sc., v. 180, p. 765.

1925. Essai de détermination du champ visuel anatomique binoculaire du cheval. *Ibid.*, v. 181, p. 145.

ROCHON-DUVIGNEAUD, A., & QUENTIN
*1917. Variation et valeur fonctionelle de la grandeur de la cornée chez les vertébrés diurnes et nocturnes. Bull. Soc. opht. Paris.

ROCHON-DUVIGNEAUD, A., & RODE, P.
1943. Valeur systématique de la vascularisation rétinienne des mammifères. Mammalia (Paris), v. 7, p. 56.

ROCHON-DUVIGNEAUD, A., & ROULE, L.
1927. Observations sur le comportement visuel et la structure de l'œil chez *Blennius basiliscus*, CV. Bull. Mus. nat. d'hist. nat. Paris, v. 33, p. 139.

ROCHON-DUVIGNEAUD, A., & VEIL, C.
1936. Dégradation des fonctions motrices et des réactions électriques des muscles de l'œil des oiseaux. Compt. rend. Soc. de biol., v. 121, p. 825.

ROELOFS, C. O.
1924. Ueber die Lokalisation mittels des Gesichtssinnes. Arch. f. Ophth. (Graefe), v. 113, p. 239.
1926. Die Fusionsbewegungen der Augen. Arch. f. Augenh., v. 97, p. 229.

ROELOFS, C. O., & BEND, J. H.
1930. Betrachtungen und Untersuchungen über den optokinetischen Nystagmus. Arch. f. Augenh., v. 102, p. 551.

ROELOFS, C. O., & ZEEMANN, W. P. C.
1919. Ueber den Wettstreit der Konturen. Arch. f. Ophth. (Graefe), v. 99, p. 79.
1919. Die Sehschärfe im Halbdunkel, zugleich ein Beitrag zur Kenntnis der Nachtblindheit. *Ibid.*, p. 174.

RØNNE (ROENNE, RÖNNE), H.
1906. Fälle von angeborener totaler Farbenblindheit. Klin. Monatsbl. f. Augenh., v. 44 (suppl.), p. 193.
1909. Rührt die Optikusatrophie durch Tabes von einem Leiden der Ganglienzellen oder der Nervenfasern her? Arch. f. Ophth. (Graefe), v. 72, p. 481.
1910. Pathologisch-anatomische Untersuchungen über alkoholische Intoxikationsamblyopie. *Ibid.*, v. 77, p. 1. (Here older references.)
1910. Ueber den Faserverlauf im Chiasma, beleuchtet durch einige Gesichtsfelduntersuchungen. Klin. Monatsbl. f. Augenh., v. 48 (2), p. 455.
1911. Gesichtsfeldsstudien über das Verhältnis zwischen der peripheren Sehschärfe und dem Farbensinn, speziell die Bedeutung derselben für die Prognose der Sehnervenatrophie. *Ibid.*, v. 49 (1), p. 154.
1911. Ueber die Bedeutung der makularen Aus-

sparung im hemianopischen Gesichtsfelde. *Ibid.* (2), p. 289.
1912. Ein Fall von Sehnervenatrophie bei Tabes mit einseitiger nasaler Hemianopsie. *Ibid.*, v. 50 (1), p. 452.
1912. Ueber das Vorkommen eines hemianopischen zentralen Skotoms bei disseminierter Sklerose und retrobulbärer Neuritis (*Neuritis chiasmatis et tractus optici*). *Ibid.* (2), p. 440.
1913. Zur pathologischen Anatomie der diabetischen Intoxikationsamblyopie. (Beitrag zur Pathogenese der neurogenen Zentralskotome.) Arch. f. Ophth. (Graefe), v. 85, p. 489.
1913. Ueber das Vorkommen von Nervenfaserndefekten im Gesichtsfelde und besonders über den nasalen Gesichtsfeldsprung. Arch. f. Augenh., v. 74, p. 180.
1914. Einige Fälle von hysterischem Gesichtsfelddefekt. Klin. Monatsbl. f. Augenh., v. 52, p. 372.
1914. Ueber doppelseitige Hemianopsie mit erhaltener Makula. *Ibid.*, v. 53, p. 470.
1914. Die anatomische Projektion der Macula im Corpus geniculatum ext. Ztschr. f. d. ges. Neurol. u. Psychiat. (Orig.), v. 22, p. 469.
1915. Ueber die Inkongruenz und Asymmetrie im homonym hemianopischen Gesichtsfeld. Klin. Monatsbl. f. Augenh., v. 54, p. 399.
1915. Ueber akute Retrobulbärneuritis, im Chiasma lokalisiert. *Ibid.*, v. 55, p. 68.
1916. Bemerkungen anlässlich C. Behrs Arbeit über einseitige Hemianopsie. *Ibid.*, v. 56, p. 501.
1917. Die Organisation des corticalen Sehcentrums und sein Verhältnis zum Gesichtsfelde. Ztschr. f. d. ges. Neurol. u. Psychiat. (Refer. & Erg.), v. 14, p. 497.
1919. Ueber Quadranthemianopsie und die Lage der Makulafasern in der okzipitalen Sehbahn. Klin. Monatsbl. f. Augenh., v. 63, p. 358.
1921. Ueber klinische Perimetrie. Arch. f. Augenh., v. 87, p. 137.
1924. On visual field charts. Acta ophth., v. 2, p. 154.
1927. The different types of defects of the field of vision. J. Am. Med. Assoc., v. 89, p. 1860.
1928. On non-hypophyseal affections of the chiasma. Acta ophth. Scandinav., v. 6, p. 332.
1936. Die Architektur des corticalen Sehzentrums durch Selbstbeobachtung bei Flimmerscotom beleuchtet. Acta ophth., v. 14, p. 341.
1938. The focal diagnostic of the visual path. *Ibid.*, v. 16, p. 446.

1942. The ontogenesis of the course of the macular fibers. *Ibid.*, v. 19, p. 199.

1944. Die Architektur der menschlichen Sehbahn. Acta path. et microbiol. Scandinav., suppl., v. 51; Acta ophth., v. 21, p. 137; Acta psychiat. & neurol., suppl., v. 28, p. 1.

RÖSSLER, F.

1936. Hieronymus Sirturus. Ztschr. f. ophth. Optik, v. 24, p. 1.

RÖTHIG, P.

1923. Ueber das Zwischenhirn der Amphibien. Arch. f. mikr. Anat. & Entw., v. 98, p. 616.

1924. Ueber die Faserzüge im Zwischenhirn der Urodelen. Ztschr. f. mikr.-anat. Forsch., v. 1, p. 5.

1926. Ueber die Faserzüge im Vorder- und Zwischenhirn der Anuren. *Ibid.*, v. 5, p. 23.

1927. Ueber die Faserzüge im Mittelhirn, Kleinhirn und der Medulla oblongata der Urodelen und Anuren. *Ibid.*, v. 10, p. 381.

ROGALSKI, T.

1946. The visual paths in a case of unilateral anophthalmia with special reference to the problem of crossed and uncrossed visual fibres. J. Anat., v. 80, p. 153.

1946. Crossed and uncrossed optic fibres in microphthalmia. *Ibid.*, p. 215. (Abstr. of paper read at May, 1943, meeting.)

ROGALSKI, T., & RYMASZEWSKI, O.

1946. Crossed and uncrossed optic fibres of the dog. J. Anat., v. 80, p. 228.

ROGER, H., & REBOUL-LACHAUX, J.

1921. Le syndrome excito-visuel du champ aveugle des hémianopsiques. Encéphale, v. 16, p. 573.

ROGER, ROLAND, BRUNO, THEODORIC, SALICETO, LANFRANC, GUY DE CHAULIAC

*1546. Ars chirurgica. Venetiis. (*See also* Chauliac, Guy de.)

ROGER BACON; *see* BACON, ROGER

ROHAULT, J.

1671. Traité de physique. 2 vols. D. Thierry, Paris.

ROHR, M. VON

1905. Ueber perspektivische Darstellungen und die Hülfsmittel zu ihrem Verständnis. Ztschr. f. Instrumentenkunde, v. 25, pp. 293, 329, 361 (Okt., Nov. & Dez.).

1916. Zur Kenntnis älterer Ansichten über das beidäugige Sehen. *Ibid.*, v. 36, pp. 200, 224; Naturwiss., v. 5, p. 42, 1917.

1917. Zur Brillenherstellung vor 300 Jahren. Deutsch. opt. Wchnschr., v. 2, p. 1.

1917. Die Entwicklung des Monokels. Naturwiss., v. 5, p. 5.

1917. Die Entwicklung der Brille. *Ibid.*, p. 202.

1918. Das Auge und die Brille. 2d ed. B. G. Teubner, Leipzig.

1919. Besprechungen. Die Entwicklung der Brille. VI. Naturwiss., v. 7, p. 209.

1919. Ausgewählte Stücke aus Christoph Scheiners Augenbuch. Ztschr. f. ophth. Optik, v. 7, pp. 35, 53, 76, 101, 121.

1920. Die Grundpunkte und die Bildfindung durch ein Zeichenverfahren. Central-Zeitung f. Optik u. Mechanik, v. 41, pp. 1, 17, 29, 41, 53.

1920. Acht Vorlesungen zur Geschichte der Brille. *Ibid.*, pp. 383, 393, 405, 415, 429, 443, 456, 472.

1920. Optische Bemerkungen zur Regensburger Brillenmacherordnung um 1600. Ztschr. f. ophth. Optik., v. 8, p. 97.

1920. Zur Würdigung von Scheiners Augenstudien. Arch. f. Augenh., v. 86, p. 247.

1921. Die Brille als optisches Instrument. 1st ed., W. Engelmann, Leipzig, 1911; 2d ed., J. Springer, Berlin.

1922. Bausteine zur Brillengeschichte. Arch. f. Augenh., v. 91, p. 333.

1922. Ein Versuch zur Ermittelung der optischen Kenntnisse der Brillenhersteller um das Jahr 1600. Ztschr. f. ophth. Optik, v. 10, pp. 1, 33.

1922. Zwei Aufsätze von W. Ch. Wells (*1757, †1817). *Ibid.*, pp. 12, 38, 68, 97.

1923. Auswahl aus der Behandlung des Horopters bei Fr. Aguilonius um 1613. *Ibid.*, v. 11, p. 41.

1923. Zwei Abhandlungen von Thomas Young. *Ibid.*, p. 102.

1923. Die Entwicklung der Brille. Naturwiss., v. 11, p. 249.

1923–24. Contributions to the history of spectacle trade from the earliest times to Th. Young's appearance. Tr. Opt. Soc. London, v. 25, p. 41; v. 26, p. 175.

1924. Die Entwicklungsjahre der Kunst, optisches Glas zu schmelzen. Naturwiss., v. 12, p. 781; Central-Zeitung f. Optik u. Mechanik, v. 46, p. 48, 1925.

1924. Der Sehvorgang und seine Unterstützung durch Brillengläser nach Maurolycus im Jahre 1554. Ztschr. f. ophth. Optik, v. 12, p. 14.

1925. Additions to our knowledge of old spectacles. Tr. Opt. Soc. London, v. 26, p. 175.

1925. Zur Entwicklung der dunklen Kammer (camera obscura). Central-Zeitung f. Optik u. Mechanik, v. 46, pp. 233, 255, 272, 286, 303.

1927–28. Aus der Geschichte der Brille. Mit besonderer Berücksichtigung der auf der Greeffschen beruhenden Jenaischen Sammlung. *In:* Jahrbuch des Vereins Deutsch. Ingenieure, v. 17, Berlin; abstr. in Deutsch. opt. Wchnschr., v. 14, p. 178.

1928. Zur Förderung optischer Erkenntnis durch englische Aerzte um den Ausgang des 18. Jahrhunderts. Ztschr. f. ophth. Optik, v. 16, pp. 10, 70, 111; v. 17, pp. 19, 48.

1928. Moritz von Rohr zum 60. Geburtstag, by H. Hartinger. Deutsch. opt. Wchnschr., v. 14, p. 175.

1928. Glas als Rohstoff. Ztschr. f. ophth. Optik, v. 16, p. 90.

1930. Kepler und seine Erklärung des Sehvorganges. Naturwiss., v. 18, p. 941.

1932. Die Erkenntnis von dem wahren Wesen des Lichtbildes und ihr Einfluss auf das Verständnis für die optischen Geräte im allgemeinen. *Ibid.*, v. 20, pp. 496, 514.

1933. Die Abbildung im Auge vom Standpunkt des Ophthalmologen. *Ibid.*, v. 21, p. 845.

1937. Der Strahlengang im Auge und in medizinisch-optischen Instrumenten. *In:* E. Abderhalden, Handb. d. biol. Arbeitsmeth., Abt. V, Teil 6 (1), p. 595.

1940. Ueber die Entwicklung der heutigen optischen Geräte. Ztschr. f. ophth. Optik, v. 28, pp. 101, 146.

Rohr, M. von, & Boegehold, H.
1934. Das Brillenglas als optisches Instrument. J. Springer, Berlin.

Rohr, M. von, *et al.*
1904. Die Theorie der optischen Instrumente. V. 1: Die Bilderzeugung in optischen Instrumenten vom Standpunkte der geometrischen Optik. J. Springer, Berlin. (Also English trans.)

Rolando, L.
1809. Saggio sopra la vera struttura del cervello dell'uomo, degl'animali e sopra le funzioni del sistema nervoso. Sassari 1809. Nella stamperia da S.S.R.M. Privilegiata (con approvazione).

1828. Saggio sopra la vera struttura del cervello e sopra le funzioni del sistema nervoso di L. R., Professore d'Anatomia nella R. Università, etc. 2d ed., 3 vols. Torino, 1828, presso l'editore Pietro Marietti, librajo in via di Po. Con permissione.

Rollet & Jacqueau
1898. Anatomie topographique de la macula. Ann. d'ocul., v. 119, p. 431.

Romanes, G. J.
1947. The prenatal medullation of the sheep's nervous system. J. Anat., v. 81, p. 64.

Romeis, B.
1932. Taschenbuch der mikroskopischen Technik. 13th ed. R. Oldenbourg, München & Berlin. 15th ed., Mikroskopische Technik. Leibniz Verlag, München, 1948.

Romer, A. S.
1941. Man and the vertebrates. 3d ed. University of Chicago Press, Chicago.

1945. Vertebrate paleontology. University of Chicago Press, Chicago.

1946. The early evolution of fishes. Quart. Rev. Biol., v. 21, p. 33.

1949. Time series and trends in animal evolution. *In:* Jepsen *et al.*, Genetics, paleontology, and evolution, p. 103.

1949. The vertebrate body. W. B. Saunders Co., Philadelphia & London.

Romer, A. S., & Grove, B. H.
1935. Environment of the early vertebrates. Am. Mid. Naturalist, v. 16, p. 805.

Roncoroni, L.
1911. Ricerche sulla citoarchitettura corticale. Riv. pat. nerv. & ment., v. 16, p. 1.

1911. Le funzioni dei lobi prefrontali in rapporto ai dati architettonici. *Ibid.*, p. 521.

1920. La dottrina di Luciani, Tamburini e Seppilli sulla funzionalità della corteccia cerebrale e i dati architettonici. Riv. sper. di freniat., v. 44, p. 209.

1927. Caratteri differenziali delle aree citoarchitettoniche pre e postrolandiche. *Ibid.*, v. 51, p. 223.

Rose, J. E., & Woolsey, C. N.
1943. A study of thalamo-cortical relations in the rabbit. Bull. Johns Hopkins Hosp., v. 73, p. 65.

Rose, M.
1912. Histologische Lokalisation der Grosshirnrinde bei kleinen Säugern (Rodentia, Insectivora, Chiroptera). J. f. Psychol. u. Neurol., v. 19 (suppl.).

1929. Die Inselrinde des Menschen und der Tiere. *Ibid.*, v. 37, p. 467.

1930. Cytoarchitektonischer Atlas der Grosshirnrinde der Maus. *Ibid.*, v. 40, p. 1.

1930. Vergleichende Zytoarchitektonik der Grosshirnrinde. Fortschr. d. Neurol. u. Psychiat., v. 2, p. 263.

1935. Cytoarchitektonik und Myeloarchitektonik der Grosshirnrinde. *In:* Bumke & Foerster, Handb. d. Neurol., v. 1, p. 588.

Roseboom, M.
1939. Concerning the optical qualities of some microscopes made by Leeuwenhoek. J. Roy. Micr. Soc., 3d ser., v. 59, p. 177.

Rosenberg, H.
  1878. Der Malayische Archipel. Land und Leute in Schilderungen, gesammelt während eines dreissigjährigen Aufenthaltes in den Kolonien. G. Weigel, Leipzig.

Rosenblueth, A.
  1937. The transmission of sympathetic nerve impulses. Physiol. Rev., v. 17, p. 514.
  1950. The transmission of nerve impulses at neuroeffector junctions and peripheral synapses. Technology Press, M.I.T., Cambridge, Mass.; John Wiley & Sons, New York.

Rosenfeld, M.
  1923. Die Lokalisation der Grosshirnfunktionen. Klin. Wchnschr., v. 2 (1), p. 1101.
  1924. Ueber Bewusstseinszentren. Deutsch. med. Wchnschr., v. 50, p. 1271.
  1928. Ueber Stirnhirnpsychosen. *Ibid.*, v. 54, p. 85.

Rosenmeyer
  1915. Fall von transitorischer Rindenblindheit durch Verletzung am Hinterhaupt. München. med. Wchnschr., v. 62, p. 18.

Rosett, J.
  1933. Myth of the occipitofrontal association tracts. Arch. Neurol. & Psychiat., v. 30, p. 1248.
  1933. Intercortical systems of the human cerebrum, mapped by means of new anatomic methods. Columbia University Press, New York.
  1936. The lines of cleavage of the fibrous tissue of the human cerebrum. Bull. Neurol. Inst. New York, v. 5, p. 316.
  1939. The mechanism of thought, imagery, and hallucination. Columbia University Press, New York.

Ross, E. J.
  1949. The formation of the intra-ocular fluids. Studies of the urea component of the aqueous humour. Brit. J. Ophth., v. 33, p. 310.

Ross, W. D.
  1923. Aristotle. 5th ed., 1949. Methuen & Co., London. French trans.: Aristote: la vie et les œuvres. Payot, Paris, 1930.

Rossi
  1925. La vision et la physique moderne. Essai d'une théorie nouvelle. Bull. et mém. Soc. franç. d'opht., v. 38, p. 239.

Rossi, I., & Roussy, G.
  1907. Étude anatomique d'un cas de syndrome de Weber avec hémianopsie; foyer de ramollissement dans le pédoncule, dans les corps genouillés externe et interne et la bandelette optique. Rev. neurol., v. 15, p. 529.

  1907. Syndrome de Weber avec hémianopsie datant de 28 ans. Nouv. iconog. Salpêtr., v. 20, p. 185.

Rossolimo, G.
  1896. Ueber Hemianopsie und einseitige Ophthalmoplegie vasculären Ursprungs. Neurol. Centralbl., v. 15, p. 626.

Rostand, J.
  1947. Charles Darwin. 2d ed. Gallimard, Paris.

Rostovtzeff, M.
  1926. The social & economic history of the Roman Empire. Clarendon Press, Oxford. (2d ed. announced.)
  1926–27. A history of the ancient world. V. 1: The Orient and Greece; v. 2: Rome. Clarendon Press, Oxford.
  1933. Storia economica e sociale dell'Impero Romano. "La nuova Italia," Firenze.
  1941. The social & economic history of the Hellenistic world. 3 vols. Clarendon Press, Oxford.

Roth, H.
  1925. Psychologische Untersuchungen an nichtdomestizierten Nagern, namentlich der Hausmaus. Ztschr. f. Psychol., v. 97, p. 62.

Roth, M.
  1892. Andreas Vesalius Bruxellensis. G. Reimer, Berlin.
  1905. Vesal, Estienne, Tizian, Leonardo da Vinci. Arch. f. Anat. u. Entw., p. 79.
  1907. Die Anatomie des Leonardo da Vinci. *Ibid.* (suppl.).

Roth, Martin
  1949. Disorders of the body image caused by lesions of the right parietal lobe. Brain, v. 72, p. 89.

Roth, W.
  1911. Ein paar interessante Aquarienfische. Deutsche Fischerei-Korresp., v. 15, p. 107.

Rothfuchs
  1915. Komplette homonyme Hemianopsie. Deutsch. med. Wchnschr., v. 41, p. 514.

Rothmann, H.
  1923. Zusammenfassender Bericht über den Rothmannschen grosshirnlosen Hund nach klinischer und anatomischer Untersuchung. Ztschr. f. d. ges. Neurol. u. Psychiat., v. 87, p. 247.

Rothmann, M.
  1909. Hermann Munk zum 70. Geburtstag. Deutsch. med. Wchnschr., v. 35, p. 258.
  1909. Demonstration zur Physiologie der Grosshirnrinde. (Hund 60 Tage nach totaler Grosshirnexstirpation.) Neurol. Centralbl., v. 28, pp. 614, 840, 1045.

ROTHMANN, M.—*Continued*

1910. Ueber neuere Ergebnisse der Hirnphysiologie. Klin. Wchnschr., v. 47, p. 757.

1912. Demonstration des Sektionsbefundes des grosshirnlosen Hundes. Neurol. Centralbl., v. 31, pp. 867, 1050.

1912. Hermann Munk (obituary). *Ibid.*, p. 1343.

ROUSSILLE DE CHAMSERU, J. F. J.

*1770. An retina primarium visionis instrumentum? Quillau, Paris.

ROUSSY, G.

1907. La couche optique (étude anatomique, physiologique et clinique). Le syndrome thalamique. Thèse, Paris.

1909. Deux nouveaux cas de lésions de la couche optique suivis d'autopsie. Syndrome thalamique pur et syndrome thalamique mixte. Rev. neurol., Part 1, p. 301.

ROUSSY, G., & MOSINGER, M.

1934. Étude anatomique et physiologique de l'hypothalamus. Rev. neurol. Part 1, p. 848.

1934. Sur le noyau tangentiel de l'hypothalamus et ses connexions. *Ibid.*, Part 2, p. 651.

1936. La systématisation du système nerveux et les correlations entre le système neuro-somatique et le système neuro-végétatif. J. de physiol. et path. gén., v. 34, p. 486.

ROUX, G. H.

1947. The cranial development of certain Ethiopian "insectivores" and its bearing on the mutual affinities of the group. Acta zool., v. 28, p. 165.

ROUX, J.

1898. Réflexes rétino-rétiniens. Arch. d'opht., v. 18, p. 395.

ROWBOTHAM, G. F.

1949. Acute injuries of the head. Their diagnosis, treatment, complications and sequels. E. & S. Livingstone, Edinburgh.

ROZEMEYER, H. C., & STOLTE, J. B.

1931. Die Netzhaut des Frosches in Golgi-Cox Präparaten. Ztschr. f. mikr.-anat. Forsch., v. 23, p. 98.

RUBINO, A.

1933. The arterial supply of the cerebral cortex in a Chinese brain. Proc. Kon. Akad. Wetensch. Amsterdam, v. 36, p. 694.

RUBINSTEIN, H. S., & DAVIS, C. L.

1947. Stereoscopic atlas of neuroanatomy. Grune & Stratton, New York.

RUCH, T. C.

1941. Bibliographia primatologica. A classified bibliography of primates other than man. Part I: Anatomy, embryology & quantitative morphology; physiology, pharmacology & psychobiology; primate phylogeny & miscellanea. Charles C Thomas, Springfield, Ill., & Baltimore.

RUCH, T. C., BLUM, M., & BROBECK, J.

1941. Taste disturbances from thalamic lesions in monkeys. Am. J. Physiol., v. 133, p. P433.

RUCH, T. C., & FULTON, J. F.

1935. Cortical localization of somatic sensibility. The effect of precentral, postcentral and posterior parietal lesions upon the performance of monkeys trained to discriminate weights. *In:* Sensation, its mechanisms and disturbances. Research Pub. A. Research Nerv. & Ment. Dis., v. 15, p. 289. Williams & Wilkins Co., Baltimore.

RUCH, T. C., FULTON, J. F., & GERMAN, W. J.

1938. Sensory discrimination in monkey, chimpanzee and man after lesions of the parietal lobe. Arch. Neurol. & Psychiat., v. 39, p. 919.

RUCH, T. C., & PATTON, H. D.

1946. The relation of the deep opercular cortex to taste. Fed. Proc., v. 5, No. 1 (2), p. 89.

RUCH, T. C., & SHENKIN, H. A.

1943. The relation of area *13* of the orbital surface of the frontal lobes to hyperactivity and hyperphagia in monkeys. J. Neurophysiol., v. 6, p. 349.

RUCKER, C. W.

1946. The interpretation of visual fields. A manual prepared for the use of graduates in medicine. Am. Acad. Ophth. & Otolaryng.

1950. Neuro-ophthalmology. Arch. Ophth., ser. 2, v. 44, p. 733.

RUCKER, C. W., & KEYS, T. E.

1950. The atlases of ophthalmoscopy, 1850–1950. Mayo Clinic, Rochester, Minn.

RUDD, R. L.

1953. Notes on maintenance and behavior of shrews in captivity. J. Mammal., v. 34, p. 118.

RUDOLPHI, D. K. A.

*1802. Anatomisch-physiologische Abhandlungen, Berlin; Abh. d. Akad. Wissensch. Berlin, 1816–17.

1823. Grundriss der Physiologie, v. 2 (1), pp. 172 ff. Dümmler, Berlin.

RÜBEL, E.

1913. Hemianopisches Ringskotom. (Unvollständige doppelseitige Hemianopsie). Klin. Monatsbl. f. Augenh., v. 51 (2), p. 705.

RÜCHARDT, E.

1952. Sichtbares und unsichtbares Licht. Springer, Berlin.

RÜDINGER, N.
1882. Ein Beitrag zur Anatomie der Affenspalte und der Interparietalfurche beim Menschen nach Race, Geschlecht und Individualität. *In:* Beitr. z. Anat. u. Embryol. als Festgabe J. Henle, p. 186. Bonn.

RÜSCHKAMP, F.
1944–47. Wo liegen die Wurzeln der Sapiens-Menschheit? Natur u. Volk (Ber. d. Senckenberg. Naturforsch. Gesellsch., v. 77, p. 30).

RUETE, C. G. T.
1853–54. Lehrbuch der Ophthalmologie für Aerzte und Studierende. 2d ed. 2 vols. F. Vieweg & Sohn, Braunschweig.

RUFFIN, H., & STEIN, J.
1930. Ueber den cerebralen Abbau von Sinnesleistungen. Deutsch. Ztschr. f. Nervenh., v. 116, p. 56.

RÛFOS (from Ephesos, RÛFUS)
1st & 2d cent. On naming the parts of the human body. Œuvres de Rufus d'Ephèse, ed. C. E. RUELLE. Anepigraphon, or The anonymous treatise on the anatomy of the parts of the human body. *Ibid.*, ed. C. DAREMBERG and C. E. RUELLE. Imprimerie Nationale, Paris, 1879.

RUNDLES, R. W., & PAPEZ, J. W.
1938. Fiber and cellular degeneration following temporal lobectomy in the monkey. J. Comp. Neurol., v. 68, p. 267.

RUSBY, H. H.
1933. Jungle memories. Whittlesey House, McGraw-Hill Book Co., New York & London.

RUSHTON, W. A. H.
1949. The structure responsible for action potential spikes in the cat's retina. Nature, v. 164, p. 743.
1950. Giant ganglion cells in the cat's retina. J. Physiol., v. 111 (Proc. Physiol. Soc., p. 26P).

RUSKA, J. F.
1935. Uebersetzung und Bearbeitungen von Al-Rāzī's Buch Geheimnis der Geheimnisse. Quellen u. Stud. z. Gesch. d. Naturwiss. u. Med., v. 4 (3), p. 1.

RUSSELL, E. S., & BULL, H. O.
1932. A selected bibliography of fish behavior. J. Conserv. Perm. Internat. Explor. Mer., v. 7, p. 255.

RUSSELL, H. N.
1917. The minimum radiation visually perceptible. Astrophys. J., v. 45, p. 60.

RUSSELL, J. S. R.
1894. An experimental investigation of eye movements. J. Physiol., v. 17, p. 1.

1895. The influence of the cerebrum and cerebellum on eye movements. Brit. M. J., v. 2, p. 951.

RUTHERFORD, E.
1924. The electrical structure of matter. Ann. Rep. Smithsonian Inst., p. 161, 1925.

RUYSCH, F.
1737. Opera omnia anatomico-medico-chirurgica. 4 vols. Amstelodami. Ap. Janssonio-Waesbergios. *See* v. 2, Epist. Anat., Probl. 13, De oculorum tunicis, by C. WEDEL, approx. 1700.

RYAN, R. E.
1954. Headache. Diagnosis and treatment. C. V. Mosby Co., St. Louis, Mo.

RYBERG, O.
1947. Studies on bats and bat parasites, especially with regard to Sweden and other neighbouring countries of the north. Svensk Natur, Stockholm.

RYDER, H. W., ESPEY, F. F., KIMBELL, F. D., PODOLSKY, B., KRISTOFF, F. V., EVANS, J. P., LAMB, D., BARNES, E., & BROSENE, W.
1951. A general theory of the control of intracranial pressure. Tr. Am. Neurol. A. (76th ann. meet.), p. 173.

RYFF, W. H.
1541. Des aller fürtrefflichsten geschöpfes . . . wahrhaftige Beschreibung der Anatomie. Balthasar Beck, Strassburg. (*See* K. Sudhoff, Augenanatomiebilder im 15. und 16. Jahrhundert, in Stud. z. Gesch. d. Med., Heft 1, p. 19, 1907.)

RYLANDER, G.
1939. Personality changes after operations on the frontal lobes. A clinical study of 32 cases. E. Munksgaard, Copenhagen.

RYSER, F. A.; *see* MORRISON, RYSER, & DAWE

S

SABATIER, R. B.
1798. Traité complet d'anatomie, ou description de toutes les parties du corps humain. 4 vols. T. Barrois, le jeune, Paris. Earlier eds., P. F. Didot, 1775; T. Barrois, 1791, both in Paris.

SABBADINI, D.
1923–24. Sulla patogenesi delle emianopsie omonime transitorie. Riv. oto-neuro-oftal., v. 1, p. 385.

SABIN, F. R.
1905. On Flechsig's investigations of the brain. Bull. Johns Hopkins Hosp., v. 16, p. 45.
1910–11. Description of a model showing the tracts of fibers medullated in a new-born baby's brain. Am. J. Anat., v. 11, p. 113.

Sachs, B.

1907. Discussion of aphasia with presentation of cases. J. Nerv. & Ment. Dis., v. 34, p. 602.

1908. Two cases of aphasia relieved by operation and their bearing on modern theories of aphasia. *Ibid.*, v. 35, p. 561.

Sachs, E.

1946. Abnormal delay of visual perception. Arch. Neurol. & Psychiat., v. 56, p. 198.

Sachs, H.

1892. Das Hemisphärenmark des menschlichen Grosshirns. I. Der Hinterhauptslappen. Arb. a. d. psychiat. Klin. Breslau (Wernicke), v. 1. G. Thieme, Leipzig.

1893. Vorträge über Bau und Thätigkeit des Grosshirns und die Lehre von der Aphasie und Seelenblindheit. Preuss & Jünger, Breslau.

1895. Das Gehirn des Förster'schen Rindenblinden. Arb. a. d. psychiat. Klin. Breslau, v. 2, pp. 53, 121.

1896. Ein Beitrag zur Frage des "fronto-occipitalen" Associationsbündels. Allg. Ztschr. f. Psychiat., v. 53, p. 181.

1897. Ueber Flechsig's Verstandescentren. Monatsschr. f. Psychiat., v. 1, pp. 199, 288.

Sachs, M.

1891. Ueber die specifische Lichtabsorption des gelben Fleckes der Netzhaut. Arch. f. d. ges. Physiol. (Pflüger), v. 50, p. 574.

1907. Ueber absolute und relative Lokalisation. Arb. a. d. Neurol. Inst. Wien (Obersteiner), v. 15, p. 463.

Sachs, T.

1888. Ungewöhnliche Formen hemianopischer Gesichtsstörung. Wien. klin. Wchnschr., v. 1, pp. 453, 477.

Sacken

1879. Neuere Erwerbungen der Antikensammlung des A. h. Kaiserhauses. Ein römisches Vergrösserungsglass. Archaeol.-Epigr. Mitt. aus Oesterreich, v. 3, p. 151.

Sälzle, K.

1933. Untersuchungen an Libellenlarven über das Sehen bewegter Objekte. Ztschr. f. vergl. Physiol., v. 18, p. 347.

1936. Untersuchungen über das Farbsehvermögen von Opossum, Waldmäusen, Rötelmäusen und Eichhörnchen. Ztschr. f. Säugetierk., v. 11, p. 106.

Saemisch, E. T.

1865. Laterale Hemiopie, durch einen Tumor bedingt. Klin. Monatsbl. f. Augenh., v. 3, p. 51.

Saenger, A.

1903. Ueber zirkumskripte tuberkulöse Meningitis. München. med. Wchnschr., v. 50, p. 991.

1918. Ueber die durch die Kriegsverletzungen bedingten Veränderungen im optischen Zentralapparat. Deutsch. Ztschr. f. Nervenh., v. 59, p. 192; Neurol. Centralbl., v. 36, p. 855, 1917.

1919. Ein Fall von dauernder zerebraler Erblindung nach Hinterhauptsverletzung. Neurol. Centralbl., v. 38, p. 210.

Sager, O.

1933. Recherches sur la somatotopie sensitive dans le thalamus des singes, étudiées par la méthode de la dégénérescence rétrograde. E. F. Bohn, Haarlem.

1935. Étude anatomique du système nerveux d'un chien auquel on a extirpé deux hémisphères cérébraux et le cervelet. Quelques considérations physiologiques. E. T. Bohn, Haarlem.

Sahmen, H.

*1854. Disquisitiones microscopicae de chiasmatis optici textura. Diss. Dorpat. Typ. viduae J. C. Schumanni et C. Mattieseni, Dorpati Livonorum.

Sahs, A. L.

1942. Vascular supply of the monkey's spinal cord. J. Comp. Neurol., v. 76, p. 403.

St. Augustin

5th cent. A.D. Aurelii Augustini Hipponensis episcopi Opera omnia. Migne, Parisiis 1844.

5th cent. A.D. Aurelii Augustini *De Genesi* ad litteram libri duodecim, recensuit Josephus Zycha. Pragae, Vindobonae, Lipsiae 1894.

St.-Martin

1931. Sur l'efficacité et l'importance diagnostique des vaso-dilatateurs, de l'acétylcholine en particulier, dans les angiospasmes rétiniens. Ann. d'ocul., v. 168, p. 102.

Saint-Yves, C. de

1730. Tractat von denen Krankheiten der Augen. J. A. Rüdiger, Berlin. In French, probably originally pub. in 1722, Paris.

Sakuma, S.

1937. Ueber die Faserbeziehungen der Areae 7a und 7b. Unter besonderer Berücksichtigung der corticalen extrapyramidalen Bahnen beim Affen. Ztschr. f. mikr.-anat. Forsch., v. 42, p. 70.

Ṣalāḥ al-Dīn

*1296. Kitāb nūr al-ᶜujūn (Book of the eye light). In part translated in J. Hirschberg, J. Lippert, & E. Mittwoch, Die arabischen Augenärzte nach den Quellen bearbeitet, v.

2, p. 195. Veit & Co., Leipzig, 1905. *See also* Graefe-Saemisch, v. 3, pp. 32, 77.

SALERNO
1947. Aforismi della scuola Salernitana. Organizzazione Tipografica, Roma.

SALICETO, GULIELMUS DE
1275. Cyrurgia. Another ed., probably first in print: La Ciroscia di Guglielmo di Saliceto. Filippo di Pietro, Venetiis 1474. Other eds., Piacenza, 1476; Lyon, 1492; Milan, 1504; Paris, 1507.

SALOMONSON, J. K. A. W.
1921. A new photographic and a new demonstration ophthalmoscope. Brit. J. Ophth., v. 5, p. 163.

SALZER, F.
1880. Ueber die Anzahl der Sehnervenfasern und der Retinazapfen im Auge des Menschen. Sitzungsb. d. Kaiserl. Akad. d. Wissensch. Wien, Abt. 3, math.-naturw. Cl., v. 81, Fasc. 1, p. 7.

SALZMANN, M.
1912. The anatomy and physiology of the human eyeball in the normal state. University of Chicago Press, Chicago.

SAMELSOHN, J.
1880. Zur Topographie des Faserverlaufes im menschlichen Sehnerven. Centralbl. f. d. med. Wissensch., v. 18, p. 418.
1882. Zur Anatomie und Nosologie der retrobulbären Neuritis (Amblyopia centralis). Arch. f. Ophth. (Graefe), v. 28 (1), p. 1.
1882. Seelenblindheit. Berlin. klin. Wchnschr., v. 19, p. 326; also Sitzungsb. d. niederrh. Gesellsch. f. Natur- u. Heilk. Bonn, p. 126 (Verhandl. d. naturhist. Ver. d. preuss. Rheinl. u. Westph., v. 38).

SAMUEL, VISCOUNT
1951. Essay in physics. With a letter from Dr. Albert Einstein. B. Blackwell, Oxford.

SAMUELS, B.
1935. Recessus hyaloideo-capsularis. Tr. Ophth. Soc. United Kingdom, v. 55, p. 507.

SAMUELS, S. S.
1950. Management of peripheral arterial diseases. Oxford University Press, New York.

SÁNCHEZ, D.
1909–12. El sistema nervioso de los hirudíneos. Trab. (Trav.) del lab. de invest. biol. Madrid, v. 7, p. 31; v. 10, p. 1.
1916. Datos para el conocimiento histogénico de los centros ópticos de los insectos. Evolución de algunos elementos retinianos del *Pieris brassicae*, L. *Ibid.*, v. 14, p. 189.

1918. Sobre ciertos elementos aisladores de la retina periférica del *Pieris brassicae*, L. *Ibid.*, v. 16, p. 1.
1918–19. Sobre el desarrollo de los elementos nerviosos en la retina del *Pieris brassicae*, L. *Ibid.*, p. 213; v. 17, pp. 1, 117.
1920. Sobre la existencia de un aparato tactil en los ojos compuestos de las abejas. *Ibid.*, v. 18, p. 207.
1923. Action spécifique des bâtonnets rétiniens des insectes. Trav. du lab. de recherches biol. Madrid, v. 21, p. 143.
1940. Contribution à la connaissance des centres nerveux des insectes. Trab. del Inst. Cajal de invest. biol., v. 32, p. 123.

SAND, A.
1935. The comparative physiology of colour response in reptiles and fishes. Biol. Rev., v. 10, p. 361.

SANDER, W.
1875. Ueber eine affenartige Bildung am Hinterhauptslappen eines menschlichen Gehirns. Arch. f. Psychiat., v. 5, p. 842.

SANFORD, H. C., & BAIR, H. L.
1939. Visual disturbances associated with tumors of the temporal lobe. Arch. Neurol. & Psychiat., v. 42, p. 21.

SANNA, G.
1930. Sul comportamento della guaina durale del nervo ottico a livello dell'inserzione sclerale, nell'occhio umano. Ann. di ottal., v. 58, p. 238.

SÁNTHA, K.
1932. Ueber das Verhalten der primären optischen Zentren bei einseitiger peripherer Blindheit. Arch. f. Ophth. (Graefe), v. 129, p. 224.
1938. Temporo-occipitale Jackson-Epilepsie. Ztschr. f. d. ges. Neurol. u. Psychiat., v. 163, p. 432.

SÁNTHA, K., & CIPRIANI, A.
1938. Focal alterations in subcortical circulation resulting from stimulation of the cerebral cortex. *In:* The circulation of the brain and spinal cord. Research Pub. A. Research Nerv. & Ment. Dis., v. 18, p. 346.

SANTORINI, G. D.
1724. Observationes Anatomicae Jo: Dominici Santorini. Supremi Magistratus salutis Venet: Protomedici, & in Veneto Lyceo Anatomes Professoris. Petro I. Magno Imperatori, Totiusque Magnae, Parvae, & Albae Russiae Autocratori, Magno Duci Moschoviae, Chioviae, Vladimiriae, Novogradiae, Czaro Casani, &c. D.D.D. Venetiis, Apud Jo: Baptistam Recurti,

MDCCXXIV. Superiorum Permissu. (Another ed. 1775?)

*1724. De oculo. Observationes anatomicae. Venetiis.

1775. Jo: Dominici Santorini Anatomici Summi Septemdecim Tabulae Quas Nunc Primum Edit Atque Explicat Iisque Alias Addit De Structura Mammarum Et De Tunica Testis Vaginali Michael Girardi In Regia Parmensi Universitate Anatomes Professor Primarius Et Caesar. Leopold. Carol. Acad. Natur. Curios. Socius. Parmae Ex Regia Typographia. CIƆ.IƆCC.LXXV.

SANTORIO (SANCTORIUS), SANTORIO

*1660. Opera omnia. 4 vols. Apud F. Brogiollum, Venetiis.

SAPIR, E.

1939. Language. An introduction to the study of speech. Harcourt, Brace & Co., New York.

SARALACERA, or SICILACERA

*Middle Ages. In Arabic: prob. Sirr al-asrār; in Latin: Secreta secretorum. Modern ed. by J. Ruska, 1935 or 1937.

SARKISOFF, S. A., & FILIMONOFF, I. N.

1938. Les travaux de l'Institut du cerveau, vols. 3–4, Moscou. (Papers by I. N. Filimonoff, I. N. Stankevitsch, G. I. Polyakoff, E. Kononova, M. O. Gourevitsch & A. A. Chatschatourian, S. M. Blinkow, J. G. Schewtschenko, A. S. Tchernycheff, S. A. Sarkisoff, M. N. Livanoff.)

SARTON, G. (*see also* NAZIF BEY)

1927–31. Introduction to the history of science. 2 vols. Williams & Wilkins Co., Baltimore.

1931. The history of science and the new humanism. Henry Holt & Co., New York.

1936. The unity and diversity of the Mediterranean world. Osiris, v. 2, p. 406.

SATTLER, H.

1876. Ueber den feineren Bau der Chorioidea des Menschen, nebst Beiträgen zur pathologischen und vergleichenden Anatomie der Aderhaut. Arch. f. Ophth. (Graefe), v. 22 (2), p. 1.

1887. Anatomische und physiologische Beiträge zur Akkommodation. Ber. d. Deutsch. ophth. Gesellsch. Heidelberg, v. 19, p. 3; Arch. f. Augenh., v. 18, p. 194, 1888.

SAUCEROTTE, N. S. (or L. S.)

*1769. Mémoire sur les contre-coups dans les lésions de la tête. Acad. Roy. de chir., mém. sur les sujets proposés pour les prix, nouv. éd., v. 4, p. 290, 1819.

SAUNDERS, J. B. deC. M.

1943. Vesalius and Don Carlos. *In:* Essays in biology in honor of H. M. Evans, p. 529. University of California Press, Berkeley.

SAUNDERS, J. B. deC. M., & O'MALLEY, C. D.

1950. The illustrations from the works of Andreas Vesalius of Brussels. World Publishing Co., Cleveland & New York.

SAWYER, F. E.

1944. Notes on the water shrew. Jour. Soc. Preserv. Fauna Empire, Hertford, Part I, p. 47.

SAXÉN, L.

1954. The development of the visual cells. Ann. Acad. sc. Fennicae, ser. A, IV. Biology, No. 23, pp. 1–93.

SCALINCI, N.

1931. Benvenuto Grasso (o Grasseo) e l'oftalmiatria della scuola Salernitana. Riv. storia d. sc. med., v. 22, p. 399.

*1935. Questioni biografiche su Benvenuto Grassi Ierosolimitano.... Rassegna di clin. e terap., v. 34 (suppl.), p. 190 (probably also in Atti Accad. di storia dell'arte sanitaria).

1936. La nosologia e la terapia nell'ars probatissima oculorum di Benvenuto Grasso, medico-oculista salernitano del sec. XIII. Ann. di ottal., v. 64, pp. 116, 188. (*Cf.* Zentralbl. f. d. ges. Ophth., v. 37, p. 644, 1937.)

1936. Le caratteristiche culturali dell'opera di Benvenuto Grasso, medico-oculista salernitano. Riv. storia di sc. med., v. 27, p. 424.

SCAMMON, R. E., & WILMER, H. A.

1950. Growth of the components of the human eyeball. II. Comparison of the calculated volumes of the eyes of the newborn and of adults and their components. Arch. Ophth., v. 43, p. 620. (For Part I, Wilmer & Scammon, *see* p. 599.)

SCARFF, J. E.

1940. Primary cortical centers for movements of upper and lower limbs in man. Arch. Neurol. & Psychiat., v. 44, p. 243.

SCARLETT, H. W., & INGHAM, S. D.

1922. Visual defects caused by occipital lobe lesions. Arch. Neurol. & Psychiat., v. 8, p. 225.

SCARPA, A.

1806. Practical observations on the principal diseases of the eyes. Translated from the Italian by J. BRIGGS. T. Cadell & W. Davis, London.

SCHADEWALD, M.

1941. Effects of cutting the trochlear and abducens nerves on the end-bulbs about the cells of the corresponding nuclei. J. Comp. Neurol., v. 74, p. 239.

1942. Transynaptic effect of neonatal axon section on bouton appearance about somatic motor cells. *Ibid.*, v. 77, p. 739.

SCHÄFER (SCHAEFER), E. A.
1887. Ueber die motorischen Rindencentren des Affen-Gehirns. Beitr. z. Physiol., Anniv. vol. C. Ludwig. F. C. W. Vogel, Leipzig.
1888. Experiments on special sense localisations in the cortex cerebri of the monkey. Brain, v. 10, p. 362. (*See also* Ferrier's critique, v. 11, p. 7, and Schäfer's reply, p. 145.)
1889. Experiments on the electrical excitation of the visual area of the cerebral cortex in the monkey. *Ibid.*, v. 11, p. 1, 1889. (*See also* Brown & Schäfer; Horsley & Schäfer.)
1889. On the functions of the temporal and occipital lobes: a reply to Dr. Ferrier. *Ibid.*, p. 145.
1900. The cerebral cortex. *In:* E. A. SCHÄFER, Text-book of physiology, v. 2, p. 697.

SCHÄFER, E. A., & MOTT, J. W.
1891. On movements resulting from electrical stimulation of the corpus callosum in the monkey. Verhandl. d. 10. internat. med. Cong. Berlin, v. 2, 2. Abt., p. 51.

SCHAEFER, H.
1936. Ueber die mathematischen Grundlagen einer Spannungstheorie der elektrischen Nervenreizung. Arch. f. d. ges. Physiol. (Pflüger), v. 237, p. 722.

SCHAEFER, H., GÖPFERT, Y. C. M., & SALAMANCA Y YANVILA, R. E.
1936. Experimentelle Grundlagen einer Spannungstheorie der elektrischen Nervenreizung. Arch. f. d. ges. Physiol. (Pflüger), v. 237, p. 737.

SCHAEFFER, J. P.
1924. Some points in the regional anatomy of the optic pathway, with especial reference to tumors of the hypophysis cerebri and resulting ocular changes. Anat. Rec., v. 28, p. 243.

SCHAFFER, J.
1890. Die Färbung der menschlichen Retina mit Essigsäurehämatoxylin. Sitzungsb. d. Kaiserl. Akad. d. Wissensch. Wien, Abt. 3, math.-naturw. Cl., v. 99, Fasc. 2, p. 110.

SCHAFFER, K.
1910. Ueber doppelseitige Erweichung des Gyrus supramarginalis. Monatsschr. f. Psychiat., v. 27, p. 53.
1912. Hirnpathologische Beiträge. II. (Hemiplegie, Hemianaesthesie und Hemianopsie, verursacht durch subinsuläre Blutung und temporo-parietale Erweichung. Beitrag zur Anatomie der zentralen Sehbahn.) Ztschr.

f. d. ges. Neurol. u. Psychiat. (Orig.), v. 10, p. 234.
1930. Beitrag zur Insel-Linsenkernaphasie. J. f. Psychol. u. Neurol., v. 40, p. 180.

SCHALL, E.
1926. Klinischer und anatomischer Befund eines Falles von Embolie einer Macula-Arterie ohne Gefässveränderung. Ztschr. f. Augenh., v. 59, p. 339.

SCHALTENBRAND, G., & COBB, S.
1930. Clinical and anatomical studies on two cats without neocortex. Brain, v. 53, p. 449.

SCHANZ, F.
1918. Licht und Leben. Arch. f. Ophth. (Graefe), v. 96, p. 172.
1922. Zur Theorie des Sehens. Ztschr. f. Augenh., v. 47, p. 351.

SCHAPER, A.
1893. Zur Histologie der menschlichen Retina, spec. der Macula lutea und der Henle'schen Faserschicht. Arch. f. mikr. Anat., v. 41, p. 147.
1899. Die nervösen Elemente der Selachier-Retina in Methylenblaupräparaten. Nebst einigen Bemerkungen über das "Pigmentepithel" und die konzentrischen Stützzellen. *In:* Festschrift C. Kupffer, p. 1. G. Fischer, Jena.

SCHARRER, E.
1929. Ueber Hell- und Dunkelstellung im Fischauge bei einseitiger Belichtung. Ztschr. f. vergl. Physiol., v. 11, p. 104.
1937. Gefäss und Nervenzelle. Ztschr. f. d. ges. Neurol. u. Psychiat., v. 158, p. 93.
1937. Ueber ein vegetatives optisches System. Klin. Wchnschr., v. 16, p. 1521.
1937. Mikroskopische Untersuchung der von Girndt und Lempke benutzten Katzen ohne Neocortex. Arch. f. d. ges. Physiol. (Pflüger), v. 239, p. 566.
1938. Ueber cerebrale Endarterien. Ztschr. f. d. ges. Neurol. u. Psychiat., v. 162, p. 401.
1940. Further experiments on the regeneration of end-arteries in the brain of the opossum. J. Exper. Zoöl., v. 85, p. 365.
1940. Arteries and veins in the mammalian brain. Anat. Rec., v. 78, p. 173.
1941. Neurosecretion. I. The nucleus preopticus of *Fundulus heteroclitus* L. J. Comp. Neurol., v. 74, p. 81. II. Neurosecretory cells in the central nervous system of cockroaches. *Ibid.*, p. 93.
1944. A comparison of cerebral vascular patterns in vertebrates and invertebrates. Anat. Rec., v. 88, p. 456. (Abstr.)

SCHARRER, E., & SCHARRER, B.
1940. Secretory cells within the hypothalamus. Research Pub. A. Research Nerv. & Ment. Dis., v. 20, p. 170.

SCHEEL, L.
*1874. Ueber das Chiasma nervor. optic. bei den Wirbelthieren und beim Menschen. Diss. Rostock. Suppl. to Klin. Monatsbl. f. Augenh., v. 12. *See* Jahresb. Ophth. (Nagel), v. 5, p. 68.

SCHEERER, R.
1923. Beitrag zur Frage der sog. abirrenden Sehnervenfasern. Klin. Monatsbl. f. Augenh., v. 71, p. 674.
1925. Theorie des Blutumlaufs in der Netzhaut. Ber. d. Deutsch. ophth. Gesellsch. Heidelberg, v. 45, p. 59.

SCHEIDT, WALTER
1934. Biologische Psychologie. R. Hermes, Hamburg.
1935. Eine neue Erklärung des Farbensehens. Forsch. u. Fortschr., v. 11, p. 228.
1937. Grundlagen einer neurologischen Psychologie. G. Fischer, Jena.
1938. Neue Forschungen zur physiologischen Optik und zur Psychologie des Sehens. Arch. f. Ophth. (Graefe), v. 139, p. 85.
1948. Lehrbuch der Anthropologie. R. Hermes Verlag, Hamburg.

SCHEINER, CHRISTOPH
1617. Refractiones Coelestes, sive Solis Elliptici Phaenomenon illustratum, in quo Variae atque Antiquae astronomorum circa hanc materiam difficultates enodantur, dubia multiplicia dissolvuntur, via ad multa recondita eruenda sternitur: Opusculum tam Astronomis quam Physicis perquam utile, perque necessarium. Auctore Christophoro Scheiner Societ. Jesu Presbytero. 1617. Ingolstadii, Ex Officina Typographica, Ederiana, apud Elis. Angermariam.
1619. Oculus Hoc Est: Fundamentum Opticum, etc. Oenoponti (Innsbruck), ap. D. Agricolam. Another ed., London 1652, and elsewhere. (*See also* Rohr, Ztschr. f. ophth. Optik, v. 7; Arch. f. Augenh., v. 86, p. 263.)
1626–30. Rosa Ursina, etc. Bracciani, Apud Andream Phaeum.

SCHEINKER, I. M.
1945. Changes in cerebral veins in hypertensive brain disease and their relation to cerebral hemorrhage; clinical pathologic study. Arch. Neurol. & Psychiat., v. 54, p. 395.

SCHELSKE, R.
1863. Zur Farbenempfindung. Arch. f. Ophth. (Graefe), v. 9 (3), p. 39.

SCHEPERS, G. W. H.
1948. Evolution of the forebrain—the fundamental anatomy of the telencephalon. Maskew Miller Ltd., Cape Town, South Africa.

SCHERER, H. J.
1944. Vergleichende Pathologie des Nervensystems der Säugetiere, unter besonderer Berücksichtigung der Primaten. G. Thieme, Leipzig.

SCHERZER, K. VON
1861–63. Narrative of the circumnavigation of the globe by the Austrian frigate Novara, etc. Saunders, Otley & Co., London.

SCHEURING, L.
1921. Beobachtungen und Betrachtungen über die Beziehungen der Augen zum Nahrungserwerb bei Fischen. Zool. Jahrb. (Allg. Zool. u. Physiol.), v. 38, p. 113.

SCHIECK, F., & BRÜCKNER, A.
1930–32. Kurzes Handbuch der Ophthalmologie. 7 vols. J. Springer, Berlin.

SCHIEFFERDECKER, P.
1886. Studien zur vergleichenden Histologie der Retina. Arch. f. mikr. Anat., v. 28, p. 305.
1887. Ueber das Fischauge. Anat. Anz. (Verh.), v. 2, p. 389.
1906. Neurone und Neuronenbahnen. J. A. Barth, Jena.

SCHIEMENZ, F.
1924. Ueber den Farbensinn der Fische. Ztschr. f. vergl. Physiol., v. 1, p. 175.

SCHIEMENZ, P.
1924. Die Nahrung unserer Süsswasserfische. Naturwiss., v. 12, p. 522.

SCHIESS
1863. Beitrag zur Anatomie der Retinastäbchen. Ztschr. f. rat. Med., 3d ser., v. 18, p. 129.

SCHIFF, J. M.
1858–59. Lehrbuch der Physiologie des Menschen. M. Schauenburg & Co., Lahr.
1894–98. Moritz Schiff's gesammelte Beiträge zur Physiologie. Recueil des mémoires physiologiques de Maurice Schiff. 4 vols. B. Benda, Lausanne.

SCHIFF-WERTHEIMER, S.
1926. Les syndromes hémianopsiques dans le ramollissement cérébral. Thèse. O. Doin, Paris.

SCHIFF-WERTHEIMER, S., & FOIX, C.; *see* FOIX & SCHIFF-WERTHEIMER

SCHIFF-WERTHEIMER, FOIX, CHAVANY, & HILLEMAND
1925. Oblitération de l'artère choroïdienne antérieur: ramollissement de son territoire cérébral; hémiplégie; hémianesthésie; hé-

mianopsie. Bull. Soc. opht. Paris, v. 37, p. 221.

SCHILDER, P.

1922. Ueber elementare Halluzinationen des Bewegungssehens. Ztschr. f. d. ges. Neurol. u. Psychiat., v. 80, p. 424.

1934. Localization of the body image (postural model of the body). *In:* Localization of function in the cerebral cortex. Research Pub. A. Research Nerv. & Ment. Dis., v. 13, p. 466.

SCHILLER, P.

1934. Kinematoskopisches Sehen der Fische. Ztschr. f. vergl. Physiol., v. 20, p. 454.

SCHIMKEWITSCH, W.

1921. Lehrbuch der vergleichenden Anatomie der Wirbeltiere. E. Schweizerbart, Stuttgart.

SCHIÖTZ, H.

1889. Ein Beitrag zu der Lehre von den Verhältnissen der Augenmuskeln. Arch. f. Augenh., v. 20, p. 1.

SCHIRMER, P.

1895. Subjektive Lichtempfindung bei totalem Verluste des Sehvermögens durch Zerstörung der Rinde beider Hinterhauptslappen. Diss. Marburg. Druck von L. Döll, Kassel. *Also* Klin. Monatsbl. f. Augenh., v. 34, p. 321.

SCHIRMER, R.

1864. Ueber das ophthalmoscopische Bild der Macula lutea. Arch. f. Ophth. (Graefe), v. 10 (1), p. 148.

SCHLAGENHAUFER, F.

1897. Anatomische Beiträge zum Faserverlauf in den Sehnervenbahnen und Beitrag zur tabischen Sehnervenatrophie. Arb. a. d. Neurol. Inst. Wien (Obersteiner), v. 5, p. 1.

SCHLAMP, K. W.

1892. Das Auge des Grottenolms (*Proteus anguineus*). Ztschr. f. wissensch. Zool., v. 53, p. 537.

SCHLAPP, M.

1898. Der Zellenbau der Grosshirnrinde des Affen *Macacus cynomolgus*. Arch. f. Psychiat., v. 30, p. 583.

1902-3. The microscopic structure of cortical areas in man and some mammals. Am. J. Anat., v. 2, p. 259.

SCHLEGEL, H., & MÜLLER, S.

*1843. Over de op de oostindische eilanden levende soorten van het geslacht *Hylogalea. In:* TEMMINCK's Vehandel. over de Natuurl. Geschied. d. Nederland. overzee. Bezitt. (Zool., Part 1), p. 153 (Mamm.), 1839-44. (*See* Pls. 26, 27.)

SCHLEICH, G.

1922. Vergleichende Augenheilkunde. *In:* GRAEFE & SAEMISCH, Handb. d. ges. Augenh. 2d ed., v. 10 (*B*, chap. 21), p. 1.

SCHLEIDEN, M. J.

1838. Beiträge zur Phytogenesis. Arch. f. Anat., Physiol. u. wissensch. Med., p. 137. English trans.: Sydenham Society, 1847.

SCHLESINGER, B.

1928. Zur Auffassung der optischen und konstruktiven Apraxie. Ztschr. f. d. ges. Neurol. u. Psychiat., v. 117, p. 649.

1939. The venous drainage of the brain, with special reference to the Galenic system. Brain, v. 62, p. 274.

1940-41. The angioarchitecture of the thalamus in the rabbit. J. Anat., v. 75, p. 176.

SCHLEZINGER, N. S., ALPERS, B. J., & WEISS, B. P.

1945. Suprasellar meningiomas associated with scotomatous field defects. Arch. Ophth., ser. 2, v. 33, p. 415.

SCHLIEPER, C.

1927. Farbensinn der Tiere und optomotorische Reaktionen. Ztschr. f. vergl. Physiol., v. 6, p. 453.

SCHMID, B.

1936. Zur Psychologie der Caniden (Wolf-Hund-Fuchs). Zentralbl. f. Kleintierk. u. Pelztierk., v. 12, p. 1.

SCHMIDT, C. F.

1950. The cerebral circulation in health and disease. Charles C Thomas, Springfield, Ill.

SCHMIDT, C. F., & HENDRIX, J. P.

1938. The action of chemical substances on cerebral blood-vessels. *In:* The circulation of the brain and spinal cord. Research Pub. A. Research Nerv. & Ment. Dis., v. 18, p. 229.

SCHMIDT, H.

1944-47. Die neuesten Frühmenschen-Funde im Fernen Osten. Natur u. Volk (Ber. d. Senckenberg. Naturforsch. Gesellsch.), v. 77, p. 38.

SCHMIDT, K. P.

1938. Turtles of the Chicago area. Field Museum of Natural History, Chicago.

1945. Evolution, succession, and dispersal. Am. Midl. Naturalist, v. 33, p. 788.

1947. "First-timers" from the Philippines. Animal Kingdom, v. 50, pp. 139, 165.

SCHMIDT, K. P., & DAVIS, D. D.

1941. Field book of snakes of the United States and Canada. G. P. Putnam's Sons, New York.

SCHMIDT, W. J.

1951. Polarisationsoptische Analyse der Verknüpfung von Protein- und Lipoidmolekeln, erläutert am Aussenglied der Sehzellen der

Wirbeltiere. Pubbl. stat. zool. Napoli, v. 23 (suppl.), p. 158.

1952. Wie entstehen die Schillerfarben der Federn? Naturwiss., v. 39, p. 313.

SCHMIDT-RIMPLER, H.

1874. Die Farbe der Macula lutea im Auge des Menschen. Centralbl. f. d. med. Wissensch., v. 12, p. 900; *also* Sitzungsb. d. Gesellsch. z. Beförd. d. ges. Naturwiss. i. Marburg, 1875.

1875. Die Macula lutea, anatomisch und ophthalmoscopisch. Arch. f. Ophth. (Graefe), v. 21 (3), p. 17.

1889. Corticale Hemianopsie mit secundärer Opticus-Degeneration. Arch. f. Augenh., v. 19, p. 296.

1893. Doppelseitige Hemianopsie mit Sectionsbefund. *Ibid.*, v. 26, p. 181.

1904. Die Farbe der Macula lutea. Arch. f. Ophth. (Graefe), v. 57, p. 24.

SCHNAASE, L.

1890. Alhazen. Ein Beitrag zur Geschichte der Physik. Schriften d. naturforsch. Gesellsch. in Danzig, v. 7, Fasc. 3, p. 140. Also separate reprint, Stargard.

SCHNAUDIGEL

1906. Demonstration von Neurofibrillen in den Retinaganglienzellen der Selachier. Ber. d. Deutsch. ophth. Gesellsch. Heidelberg, v. 32, p. 329.

SCHNEIDER, A.

1903. Die Psychologie Alberts des Grossen. Beitr. z. Gesch. d. Phil. d. Mittelalters, v. 4 (5, 6). Aschendorffsche Buchhandlung, Münster.

SCHNEIDER, E. E.

1945. Colour phenomena in ultra-violet vision. Nature, v. 155, p. 176.

SCHNEIDER, E. E., GOODEVE, C. F., & LYTHGOE, R. J.

1939. The spectral variation of the photosensitivity of visual purple. Proc. Roy. Soc. London, ser. A, v. 170, p. 102.

SCHNEIDER, G.

1905. Ergebnisse zoologischer Forschungsreisen in Sumatra. Säugetiere. Zool. Jahrb., v. 23, p. 1.

SCHNEIDER, K. V.

*1660–62. De catarrhis, etc. 5 vols. D. T. Mavii & E. Schumacheri, Wittenbergae.

SCHNEIDER-ORELLI, M.

1907. Untersuchungen über das Auge von *Anableps tetrophthalmus*. Mitt. d. naturforsch. Gesellsch. Bern, p. 87, 1908.

SCHNURMANN, F.

1920. Untersuchungen an Ellritzen über Farbenwechsel und Lichtsinn der Fische. Ztschr. f. Biol., v. 71, p. 69.

SCHOB, F.

1930. Totale Erweichung beider Grosshirnhemisphären bei einem zwei Monate alten Säugling. J. f. Psychol. u. Neurol., v. 40, p. 365.

SCHÖBL, J.

1878. Ueber die Blutgefässe des Auges der Cephalopoden. Arch. f. mikr. Anat., v. 15, p. 215.

SCHÖN, W.

1876. Zur Lehre vom binocularen indirecten Sehen. Arch. f. Ophth. (Graefe), v. 22 (4), p. 31.

SCHOEPFLE, G., & YOUNG, J. Z.

1936. The structure of the eye of Pecten. Biol. Bull., v. 71, p. 403.

SCHOLZ, W.

1939. Histologische Untersuchungen über Form, Dynamik und pathologisch-anatomische Auswirkung funktioneller Durchblutungsstörungen des Hirngewebes. Zentralbl. f. d. ges. Neurol. u. Psychiat., v. 94, p. 352.

SCHOMBURGK, R. H.

1841. Robert Hermann Schomburgk's Reisen in Guiana und am Orinoko während der Jahre 1835–1839. Nach seinen Berichten und Mittheilungen an die Geographische Gesellschaft in London. Herausgegeben von O. A. Schomburgk. Mit einem Vorwort von Alexander von Humboldt, und dessen Abhandlung über einige wichtige astronomische Positionen Guiana's. Verlag von Georg Wigand, Leipzig.

1847–48. Reisen in British-Guiana in den Jahren 1840–44. 3 vols. J. J. Weber, Leipzig.

SCHORGER, A. W.

1947. The sense of smell in the short-tailed shrew. J. Mammal., v. 28, p. 180.

SCHOTT, G.

1671. Magia Optica, Das ist, Geheime doch naturmässige Gesichts- und Augenlehr, etc. J. A. Cholins, Bamberg. Later ed., 1674.

SCHOTT, GASPAR

1657. Magia Universalis Naturae et Artis, etc., in four parts: I. Optica, II. Acoustica, III. Mathematica, IV. Physica. Sumptibus Haeredum Joannis Godefridi Schönwetteri Bibliop. Francofurtens. Herbipoli Excudebat Henricus Pigrin Typographus Herbipolensis. Anno M.DC.LVII.

SCHOUTE, G. J.

1902. Der Netzhautzapfen in seiner Funktion als Endorgan. Ztschr. f. Augenh., v. 8, p. 419.

SCHREITMÜLLER, W., & RELINGHAUS, H.

1925. Untersuchungen am lebenden Auge sowie Bemerkungen über die Lebensweise des indischen Kletterfisches (*Anabas scandens* Dald.). Arch. f. Naturgesch., v. 91, Abt. A, 7. Heft, p. 109.

SCHRENKEISEN, R.
1938. Field book of fresh-water fishes of North America north of Mexico. G. P. Putnam's Sons, New York.

SCHRIEVER, H.
1936. Die Summation nervöser Erregungen. Ergebn. d. Physiol. (Asher & Spiro), v. 38, p. 877.

SCHROEDER, A. H.
1927–29. Ueber das Prinzip der Endigung der Sehnervenfasern in der Calcarinarinde und ihre funktionelle Gliederung. Zentralbl. f. d. ges. Neurol. u. Psychiat., v. 45, p. 675; Ztschr. f. d. ges. Neurol. u. Psychiat., v. 121, p. 508.

SCHRÖDER, P.
1901. Das fronto-occipitale Associationsbündel. Monatsschr. f. Psychiat. u. Neurol., v. 9, p. 81.
1915. Von den Halluzinationen. *Ibid.*, v. 37, p. 1.
1925. Ueber Gesichtshalluzinationen bei organischen Hirnleiden. Arch. f. Psychiat., v. 73, p. 277.
1926. Zur Frage der Neuronenlehre. Klin. Wchnschr., v. 5 (1), p. 366.
1927. Grosshirnlokalisation und Psychiatrie. Monatsschr. f. Psychiat. u. Neurol., v. 65, p. 298.
1939. Die Lehren Wernickes in ihrer Bedeutung für die heutige Psychiatrie. Ztschr. f. d. ges. Neurol. u. Psychiat., v. 165, p. 38.

SCHRÖDINGER, E.
1925. Ueber die subjektiven Sternfarben und die Qualität der Dämmerungsempfindung. Naturwiss., v. 13, p. 373.

SCHRUTZ, A.
1902. Die Medizin der Araber. *In:* T. PUSCHMANN *et al.*, Handb. d. Gesch. d. Med., v. 1, p. 589. G. Fischer, Jena.

SCHUBERT, G.
1938–39. Die binokulare Koordination der Sehfunktion. Arch. f. d. ges. Physiol. (Pflüger), v. 241, p. 470.
1943–44. Grundlagen der beidäugigen Koordination. *Ibid.*, v. 247, p. 279.

SCHUBERT, G., & BURIAN, H.
1936–37. Die Fusionsreaktion, eine bisher unbekannte Reaktion der Pupille. Arch. f. d. ges. Physiol. (Pflüger), v. 238, p. 184.

SCHUCHERT, C.
1931. Geochronology or the age of the earth on the basis of sediments and life. Bull. Nat. Research Council, No. 80, p. 10.

SCHÜTZ, H.
1902. Ueber die Beziehungen des unteren Längsbündels zur Schleife und über ein neues motorisches Stabkranzsystem. Neurol. Centralbl., v. 21, p. 885.

SCHULTZ, A. E.
1949. Altitudinal hemianopia during streptomycin therapy. Am. J. Ophth., ser. 3, v. 32, p. 211.

SCHULTZ, A. H.
1936. Characters common to higher primates and characters specific for man. Quart. Rev. Biol., v. 11, pp. 259, 425.
1940. The size of the orbit and of the eye in primates. Am. J. Phys. Anthropol., v. 26, p. 389.
1941. The relative size of the cranial capacity in primates. *Ibid.*, v. 28, p. 273.
1950. Origin of the human stock. The specializations of man and his place among the catarrhine primates. Cold Spring Harbor Symp. Quant. Biol., v. 15, p. 37.

SCHULTZ, J. H.
1939. Psyche und Kreislauf. Zentralbl. f. d. ges. Neurol. u. Psychiat., v. 94, p. 349.

SCHULTZ, L. P., & MURAYAMA, H.
1939. Fishing in Pacific Coast Streams. Nat. Geog. Mag., v. 75, p. 185.

SCHULTZ, P.
1897. Gehirn und Seele. Deutsch. med. Wchnschr., v. 23, p. 88

SCHULTZE, MAX J. S. (*see* G. SCHWALBE 1874)
1859. Observationes de retinae structura penitiori. Apud A. Marcum, Bonnae.
1861. Ueber Muskelkörperchen und das, was man eine Zelle zu nennen habe. Arch. f. Anat., Physiol. u. wissensch. Med. (Reichert & Du Bois-Reymond), p. 1.
1861. Zur Kenntniss des gelben Fleckes und der Fovea centralis des Menschen- und Affen-Auges. *Ibid.*, p. 784.
1866. Ueber den gelben Fleck der Retina, seinen Einfluss auf normales Sehen und auf Farbenblindheit. M. Cohen & Sohn, Bonn.
1866. Zur Anatomie und Physiologie der Retina. Arch. f. mikr. Anat., v. 2, pp. 165, 175; *also* Verhandl. d. naturhist. Ver. d. preuss. Rheinl. u. Westph. (Bonn), Sitzungsb., v 23, pp. 33, 49.
1867. Ueber Stäbchen und Zapfen der Retina. Arch. f. mikr. Anat., v. 3, p. 215.
1867. Bemerkungen über Bau und Entwickelung der Retina. *Ibid.*, p. 371.
1867. Ueber die Endorgane des Sehnerven im Auge der Gliederthiere. *Ibid.*, p. 404.
1868. Bemerkungen zu dem Aufsatze des Dr. W.

Steinlin (über Zapfen und Stäbchen der Retina). *Ibid.*, v. 4, p. 22.

1868. Untersuchungen über die zusammengesetzten Augen der Krebse und Insecten. M. Cohen & Sohn, Bonn.

1869. Die Stäbchen in der Retina der Cephalopoden und Heteropoden. Arch. f. mikr. Anat., v. 5, p. 1.

1869. Ueber die Nervenendigung in der Netzhaut des Auges bei Menschen und bei Thieren. *Ibid.*, p. 379.

1871. Ueber den Bau der Netzhaut im Auge der Neunaugen (*Petromyzon fluviatilis*). Verhandl. d. naturhist. Ver. d. preuss. Rheinl. u. Westph. (Bonn), Sitzungsb., v. 28, p. 133.

1871. Neue Beiträge zur Anatomie und Physiologie der Retina des Menschen. Arch. f. mikr. Anat., v. 7, p. 244.

1871. Ueber das Tapetum in der Chorioides des Auges der Raubthiere. Sitzungsb. d. Niederrh. Gesellsch. f. Natur- und Heilk., p. 210; *also* Verhandl. d. naturhist. Ver. d. preuss. Rheinl. u. Westph. (Bonn), v. 29, 1872.

1871. Allgemeines über die Structurelemente des Nervensystems. *In:* S. STRICKER, Handb. d. Lehre v. d. Geweben, v. 1, p. 108. W. Engelmann, Leipzig.

1872. Ueber den Bau der Netzhaut von *Nyctipithecus felinus.* Sitzungsb. d. Niederrh. Gesellsch. f. Natur- u. Heilk., p. 158; *also* Verhandl. d. naturhist. Ver. d. preuss. Rheinl. u. Westph. (Bonn), v. 29.

1872. Ueber die Netzhaut des Störs. Sitzungsb. d. Niederrh. Gesellsch. f. Natur- u. Heilk., p. 193; *also* Verhandl. d. naturhist. Ver. d. preuss. Rheinl. u. Westph. (Bonn), v. 29.

1872. Sehorgan. I. Die Retina. *In:* STRICKER, Handb. d. Lehre von d. Geweben, v. 2, p. 977; English trans: STRICKER, Manual of human and comparative histology, v. 3, p. 213, 1873.

SCHUMACHER, G.

1937. Ueber das Verhalten der monokularen und binokularen Reizwelle während der Dunkeladaptation des Tages- und Dämmerungsapparates. Acta ophth., v. 15, p. 1.

SCHUMANN, F.

1921. Untersuchungen über die psychologischen Grundprobleme. II. Die Dimensionen des Sehraumes. Ztschr. f. Psychol., v. 86, p. 253.

SCHUSTER, E. H. J.

1911. Cortical cell lamination of the hemispheres of *Papio hamadryas.* Quart. J. Micr. Sc., v. 56, p. 613.

SCHUSTER, P.

1909. Beitrag zur Kenntnis der Alexie und verwandter Störungen. Monatsschr. f. Psychiat. u. Neurol., v. 25 (suppl.), p. 349.

1917. Beitrag zur Lehre von den sensiblen Zentren der Grosshirnrinde. Neurol. Centralbl., v. 36, p. 331.

1921. Zur Pathologie der vertikalen Blicklähmung. Deutsch. Ztschr. f. Nervenh., v. 70, p. 97.

1936. Beiträge zur Pathologie des Thalamus opticus. I. Mitt. Kasuistik. Gefässgebiet der A. thalamo-geniculata, der A. thalamo-perforata, der A. tubero-thalamica und der A. lenticulo-optica. Arch. f. Psychiat. u. Nervenkr., v. 105, p. 358.

1937. Beiträge zur Pathologie des Thalamus opticus. IV. Mitt. Motorische Störungen, Thalamushand, mimische und Affektbewegungen, dysarthrische Störungen, vegetative Funktionen, Blicklähmung, Beziehungen zu den psychischen Funktionen. *Ibid.*, v. 106, p. 201.

SCHUSTER, P., & CASPER, J.

1930. Anatomische Untersuchungen über die Bedeutung des Stirnhirns für das Zwangsgreifen und ähnliche Erscheinungen. Deutsch. Ztschr. f. Nervenh., v. 116, p. 87.

SCHUSTER, P., TATERKA, H. T., & NIESSL VON MAYENDORF, E.

1927. Zur Klinik der Seelenblindheit. Zentralbl. f. d. ges. Neurol. u. Psychiat., v. 47, p. 825.

SCHWAB, O.

1925. Zur Diagnose der Schläfenlappentumoren. Deutsch. Ztschr. f. Nervenh., v. 84, p. 38.

1928. Die Topik der Sensibilitätsstörungen bei Läsionen der sensiblen Leitungsbahnen und Zentren. Zentralbl. f. d. ges. Neurol. u. Psychiat., v. 47, p. 776; Deutsch. Ztschr. f. Nervenh., v. 101, p. 211.

SCHWAB, S. I.

1927. Changes in personality in tumours of the frontal lobe. Brain, v. 50, p. 480.

SCHWAGMEYER, W.

1952. Die Entwicklung des Augenspiegels. Naturwiss., v. 39, p. 269.

SCHWALBE, G. A.

1874. Mikroskopische Anatomie des Sehnerven, der Netzhaut und des Glaskörpers. *In:* GRAEFE & SAEMISCH, Handb. d. ges. Augenh., 1st ed., v. 1, p. 321.

1874. Max Schultze (obituary). Arch. f. mikr. Anat., v. 10, p. i; *also* Allg. Deutsch. Biographie, v. 10.

1887. Lehrbuch der Anatomie der Sinnesorgane. E. Besold, Erlangen.

1904. Ueber das Gehirnrelief bei Säugetieren. Ztschr. f. Morphol. u. Anthropol., v. 7, p. 203.

SCHWANN, T.
1838. Mikroskopische Untersuchungen über die Uebereinstimmung in der Structur und dem Wachstum der Thiere und Pflanzen. G. E. Reimer, Berlin. English trans.; Microscopical researches into the accordance in the structure and growth of animals and plants. Sydenham Society, London, 1847.

SCHWARTZ, H. G., & ROSENBLUETH, A.
1935. Reflex responses of the nictitating membrane. Am. J. Physiol., v. 112, p. 422.

SCHWARZ, E.
1929. Das Vorkommen des Schimpansen auf dem linken Kongo-Ufer. Rev. Zool. Bot. Afr., v. 16, p. 423.

SCHWARZ, S.
1935. Ueber das Mausauge, seine Akkommodation, und über das Spitzmausauge. Jena. Ztschr. f. Naturwiss., v. 70, p. 113.

SCHWEGLER, A.
1848. Geschichte der Philosophie im Umriss. Neue erweiterte Ausgabe von J. Stern. Ergänzt von R. v. Delius. Ph. Reclam jun., Leipzig, 1855. Also other editions.

SCHWEIGGER, C. (*see also* HORSTMANN, Arch. f. Augenh., v. 53, p. i, 1905)
1876. Hemiopie und Sehnervenleiden. Arch. f. Ophth. (Graefe), v. 22 (3), p. 276.
1879. Notiz über die mediane Gesichtsfeldgrenze. *Ibid.*, v. 25 (1), p. 254.
1891. Ein Fall von beiderseitiger Hemiopie. Arch. f. Augenh., v. 22, p. 336.

SCHWEINFURTH, G.
1874. The heart of Africa. Three years' travels and adventures in the unexplored regions of Central Africa from 1868 to 1871. 2 vols. Harper & Bros., New York.

SCHWEINITZ; *see* DE SCHWEINITZ

SCHWEITZER, A.
1950. The animal world of Albert Schweitzer; jungle insights into reverence of life. Beacon Press, Boston.

SCHWEITZER, A., & WRIGHT, S.
1937. The action of eserine and related compounds and of acetylcholine on the central nervous system. J. Physiol., v. 89, p. 165.
1937. The anti-strychnine action of acetylcholine, prostigmine and related substances and of central vagus stimulation. *Ibid.*, v. 90, p. 310.
1938. Action of hordenine compounds on the central nervous system. *Ibid.*, v. 92, p. 422.

SCHYRLEUS DE RHEITA, ANTONIUS MARIA
1645. Oculus Enoch et Eliae sive Radius Sidereomysticus Planetarum Veros Motus Solo Excentrico Tradens Nova et Incunda Continens Conditorem Siderum Eiusque per Facta Visibilia Magnalia Praedicans. Antwerpiae, Apud Hieronymum Verdussium. Anno Domini M.DC.XLIIIII.

SCIAMANNA, E.
1882. Gli avversari delle localizzazioni cerebrali. Arch. di psichiat., sc. pen. ed. antropol. crim., etc., v. 3, p. 209.
1905. Funzioni psichiche e corteccia cerebrale. Ann. d. Ist. psich. Roma, v. 4, p. 22.

SCLATER, W. L.
1924–30. Systema avium aethiopicarum. A systematic list of the birds of the Ethiopian region. 2 parts. British Ornithologists' Union, London.

SCLATER, W. L., & SCLATER, P. L.
1899. The geography of mammals. Kegan Paul, Trench, Trübner & Co., London.

SCOBEE, R. G., & GREEN, E. L.
1946. A center for ocular divergence: does it exist? Am. J. Ophth., ser. 3, v. 29, p. 422.

SCOTT, J. G.
1945. The eye of the West African Negro. Brit. J. Ophth., v. 29, p. 12.

SCOTT, J. M. D., & ROBERTS, F.
1923. Localisation of the vaso-motor centre. J. Physiol., v. 58, p. 168.

SCOTT, J. P., *et al.*
1951. Methodology and techniques for the study of animal societies. New York Academy of Science, New York.

SCOTT, W. B.
1937. A history of the land mammals in the Western Hemisphere. Macmillan Co., New York.

SCULLICA, F.
1928. La visione maculare in condizioni normali e patologiche. Ann. di ottal., v. 56, p. 779.

SECRETA SECRETORUM; *see* SARALACERA

SÉDILLOT, L.-A.
1868. De l'école de Bagdad et des travaux scientifiques des Arabes. Bull. di bibl. e di storia d. sc. mat. e fis. (Boncompagni), v. 1, p. 217.
1871. Des savants arabes et des savants d'aujourd'hui à propos de quelques rectifications. *Ibid.*, v. 4, p. 401.
1877. Histoire générale des Arabes. Leur empires, leur civilisation, leurs écoles philosophiques, scientifiques et littéraires. 2d ed. 2 vols. Maisonneuve & Cie, Paris.

SEEFELDER, R.
1909. Untersuchungen über die Entwicklung der

Netzhautgefässe des Menschen. Arch. f. Ophth. (Graefe), v. 70, p. 448.

1910. Beiträge zur Histogenese und Histologie der Netzhaut, des Pigmentepithels und des Sehnerven (nach Untersuchungen am Menschen). *Ibid.*, v. 73, p. 419.

1921. Ueber die Entwicklung des Sehnerveneintritts beim Menschen, zugleich ein Beitrag zur Frage der Faltenbildungen in der embryonalen Netzhaut. *Ibid.*, v. 106, p. 114

1930. Die Entwicklung des menschlichen Auges. *In:* SCHIECK & BRÜCKNER, Kurzes Handb. d. Ophth., v. 1, p. 476. J. Springer, Berlin.

SEELIG, M. G.
1925. Medicine, an historical outline. Williams & Wilkins Co., Baltimore.

SEEMANN, H. J.
1930. Eilhard Wiedemann. Isis, v. 14, p. 166. (*See* p. 171 for Wiedemann's bibliography.)

SEGALL (SEGAL), J.
1933. Versuche über Lichtreaktionen und Lichtempfindlichkeit beim Regenwurm. Ztschr. f. vergl. Physiol., v. 19, p. 94.

1946. L'évolution des quantités liminaires en fonction du temps dans l'excitation électrotactile. Compt. rend. Soc. de biol., v. 140, p. 433.

1946. La signification de la loi parabolique des quantités liminaires (loi de Piéron). *Ibid.*, p. 718.

1949. La couleur des sensations chromatiques élémentaires. *Ibid.*, v. 143, p. 1314.

1950. Localisation du pigment maculaire de la rétine. *Ibid.*, v. 144, p. 1630.

1951. La nature chimique du pigment maculaire rétinien. *Ibid.*, v. 145, p. 43.

1951. Les fonctions corticales dans la sensation chromatique. Année psychol., v. 50, p. 145·

SEGGERN, H.
1923. Achromatopsie bei homonymer Hemianopsie mit voller Sehschärfe. Klin. Monatsbl. f. Augenh., v. 71, p. 101.

SEGI, M.
1923. Ein anatomisch untersuchter Fall von doppelseitiger homonymer Hemianopsie. Ztschr. f. d. ges. Neurol. u. Psychiat., v. 85, p. 467.

SÉGUIN, E. C.
1886. Contribution à l'étude de l'hémianopsie d'origine centrale. Arch. de neurol., v. 11, p. 176.

1886. A contribution to the pathology of hemianopsia of central origin (cortex-hemianopsia). J. Nerv. & Ment. Dis., v. 13, p. 1.

1886. Clinical study of lateral hemianopsia. *Ibid.*, p. 445.

SÉGUY, E.
1936. Code universel des couleurs. P. Lechevalier, Paris.

SEIDEL, E.
1919. Experimentelle Untersuchungen über die Lage der Versorgungsgebiete der Nervenfasern des Sehnervenstammes in der Netzhaut des Menschen. Arch. f. Ophth. (Graefe), v. 100, p. 168.

SELLARS, R W
1938. An analytic approach to the mind-body problem. Phil. Rev., v. 47, p. 461.

SEMMES-BLUM, J., CHOW, K. L., & PRIBRAM, K. H.
1950. A behavioral analysis of the organization of the parieto-temporo-preoccipital cortex. J. Comp. Neurol., v. 93, p. 53.

SEMON, R. W.
1909. Die mnemischen Empfindungen in ihren Beziehungen zu den Originalempfindungen. W. Engelmann, Leipzig.

1911. Die Mneme als erhaltendes Prinzip im Wechsel des organischen Geschehens. W. Engelmann, Leipzig.

SEMPER, C.
1877. Ueber Schneckenaugen vom Wirbelthiertypus, etc. Arch. f. mikr. Anat., v. 14, p. 118.

SENÁ, J. A.
1932. El conducto óptico. Semana méd., v. 1, p. 702; *also* Arch. oftal. Buenos Aires, v. 7, p. 404. Abstr. in Zentralbl. f. d. ges. Ophth., v. 28, pp. 29, 492.

SENDEN, M. VON
1932. Raum- und Gestaltauffassung bei operierten Blindgeborenen vor und nach der Operation. J. Barth, Leipzig.

SENECA, LUCIUS ANNAEUS
Ca. A.D. 63–64. Physical science in the time of Nero, being a translation of the *Quaestiones naturales* of Seneca, by J. CLARKE, with notes on the treatise by Sir ARCHIBALD GEIKIE. Macmillan & Co., London, 1910.

SENN, D.
1942. L'area striata de l'écorce visuelle. Étude myéloarchitectonique. Thèse. Imprimerie commerciale, Lausanne.

SENNERT (SENNERTUS), DANIEL; *see* catalogue of Bibliothèque Nationale, v. 170, p. 750.

SEPP, E. K.
1928. Die Dynamik der Blutzirkulation im Gehirn. J. Springer, Berlin.

SEPPILLI, G.
1892. Sui rapporti della cecità bilaterale colle affezioni dei lobi occipitali. Riv. sper. di freniat., v. 18, p. 245.

ŠERCER, A.
  1951. Otolaringologija (Otolaryngology; in Croatian). Med. Knjiga, Beograd & Zagreb (Yugoslavia), v. 1.
SERGI, S.
  1904. Un cervello di Giavanese. Atti Soc. rom. antropol., v. 10, p. 214.
  1908. Sulla morfologia del cervello degli Herero. *Ibid.*, v. 14, p. 71.
  1908. Osservazioni su due cervelli di Ovambo ed uno di Ottentotta. *Ibid.*, p. 139.
  1909. Cerebra Hererica. *In:* L. SCHULTZE, Zoologische und anthropologische Ergebnisse einer Forschungsreise im westlichen und zentralen Südafrika ausgeführt in den Jahren 1903–05. ("Denkschriften d. med.-naturwiss. Gesellsch. z. Jena," v. 15.) G. Fischer, Jena.
SÉRIEUX, P., & MIGNOT, R.
  1902. Hallucinations de l'ouïe. Nouv. iconog. Salpêtr., v. 15, p. 286.
SERNOW (SERNOFF, ZERNOV), D. M.
  1877. Die typischen Variationen der Gehirnwindungen. Moskau.
  1878. Differences in the convolutions of the brain, considered as a racial indication (in Russian). Bull. Imper. Soc. of Lovers of Natural Sc., Anthropol. & Ethnog. in connection with the Imperial University, Moscow, v. 31 (appendix), p. 17. (*Cf.* Catalogue of scientific papers of the Royal Society of London, v. 12, p. 802.)
SEROG
  1910. Rechtsseitige homonyme Hemianopsie. Deutsch. med. Wchnschr., v. 36, p. 779.
SERRA, M.
  1922. Nota sobre las gliofibrillas de la neuroglia de la rana. Trab. (Trav.) del lab. de invest. biol. Madrid, v. 19, p. 217.
SERRES, A.-E.-R.-A.
  1824–26. Anatomie comparée du cerveau dans les quatre classes des animaux vertébrés. Gabon & Cie, Paris.
  1826. Ueber die Augen der Insecten. Aus dem Französischen, VON J. F. DIEFFENBACH. T. C. F. Enslin, Berlin.
SETON, E. T.
  1909. Life-histories of northern animals. An account of the mammals of Manitoba., v. 2 (Insectivora), p. 1089. Charles Scribner's Sons, New York.
SETTLAGE, P. H.
  1939. The effect of occipital lesions on visually-guided behavior in the monkey. I. Influence of the lesions on final capacities in a variety

of problem situations. J. Comp. Psychol., v. 27, p. 93.
SEWERTZOFF, A. N.
  1929. Directions of evolution. Acta zool., v. 10, p. 58.
SGONINA, K.
  1933. Das Helligkeitsunterscheidungsvermögen der Elritze (*Phoxinus laevis*). Ztschr. f. vergl. Physiol., v. 18, p. 516.
  1936. Ueber das Farben- und Helligkeitssehen des Meerschweinchens. Ztschr. f. wissensch. Zool., v. 148, p. 350.
SHAAD, D. J.
  1938. Binocular vision and orthoptic procedure. Arch. Ophth., v. 20 (77), p. 477.
SHAFIK ABD-EL-MALEK
  1937–38. On the localization of nerve centres of the extrinsic ocular muscles in the oculomotor nucleus. J. Anat., v. 72, p. 518.
  1937–38. On the presence of sensory fibres in the ocular nerves. *Ibid.*, p. 524.
SHANES, A. M.
  1952. Ionic transfer in nerve in relation to bioelectrical phenomena. Ann. New York Acad. Sc., v. 55, art. 1.
SHANKLIN, W. M.
  1930. The central nervous system of *Chameleon vulgaris*. Acta zool., v. 11, p. 425.
  1933. The comparative neurology of the nucleus opticus tegmenti with special reference to *Chameleon vulgaris*. *Ibid.*, v. 14, p. 163.
SHANNON, C. E. G., & EDGERTON, A. E.
  1931. A case of hemiachromatopsia. Am. J. Ophth., ser. 3, v. 14, p. 41.
SHAPLEY, H.
  1953. On climate and life. *In:* H. SHAPLEY *et al.*, Climatic change. Evidence, causes, and effects. Harvard University Press, Cambridge.
SHARKEY, S. J.
  1897. The representation of the function of vision in the cerebral cortex of man. Lancet, v. 1, p. 1399.
SHARPE, E.
  1937. An eight-hundred-year-old book of Indian medicine and formulas. Translated from the original very old Hindi into Gujarati character and thence into English. (*Cf.* Waghji Muni.) Luzac & Co., London.
SHARPLEY, F. W.
  1946. Relation between illumination and extent of the visual field. J. Physiol., v. 105, p. 215.
SHASTID, T. H.
  1926. An outline history of ophthalmology. Am. J. Physiol. Opt., v. 7, p. 568; *also* Am. Encycl. & Dict. of Ophth., v. 2, p. 8524, 1917.

SHAXBY, J. H.
1946. Colour vision. Phil. Mag., ser. 7, v. 32, p. 33.

SHEEHAN, D.
1941. The autonomic nervous system. Ann. Rev. Physiol., v. 3, p. 399.
1941. Spinal autonomic outflows in man and monkey. J. Comp. Neurol., v. 75, p. 341.

SHELFORD, V. E.
1944. Deciduous forest man and the grassland fauna. II. Science, v. 100, p. 100.

SHELLSHEAR, J. L.
1920. The basal arteries of the forebrain and their functional significance. J. Anat., v. 55, p. 27.
1926. The occipital lobe in the brain of the Chinese with special reference to the sulcus lunatus. Ibid., v. 61, p. 1.
1927. The arteries of the brain of the orang-utan. Ibid., p. 167.
1927. The evolution of the parallel sulcus. Ibid., p. 267.
1927. A contribution to our knowledge of the arterial supply of the cerebral cortex in man. Brain, v. 50, p. 236.
1931. The arterial supply of the cerebral cortex in the chimpanzee (*Anthropopithecus troglodytes*). J. Anat., v. 65, p. 45.
1933. The arterial supply of the cerebral cortex. Proc. Kon. Akad. Wetensch. Amsterdam, v. 36, p. 700.
1934. The primitive features of the cerebrum, with special reference to the brain of the bushwoman described by Marshall. Phil. Tr. Roy. Soc. London, ser. B, v. 223, p. 1.
1934. A comparative study of the endocranial cast of *Sinanthropus. Ibid.*, p. 469.
1936. The brain as an index of race. (Anderson Stuart Oration, University of Sydney.) Year Book Roy. Prince Alfred Hosp. Med. Officers' A., Sydney, Australia, p. 21.
1937. The brain of the aboriginal Australian. Phil. Tr. Roy. Soc. London, ser. B, v. 227, p. 293.
1937. Grafton Elliot Smith (obituary). M. J. Australia, p. 307.
1939. The brain of a girl, aged 12, said to be that of an aboriginal Australian. J. Anat., v. 73, p. 327.

SHELLSHEAR, J. L., & SMITH, G. E.
1934. A comparative study of the endocranial cast of *Sinanthropus.* Phil. Tr. Roy. Soc. London, ser. B, v. 223, p. 469.

SHENKIN, H. A., HARMEL, M. H., & KETY, S. S.
1948. Dynamic anatomy of the cerebral circulation. Arch. Neurol. & Psychiat., v. 60, p. 240.

SHENKIN, H. A., & LEOPOLD, I. H.
1945. Localizing value of temporal crescent defects in the visual fields. Arch. Neurol. & Psychiat., v. 54, p. 97.

SHEPHERD, W. T.
1910. Some mental processes of the rhesus monkey. Psychol. Monog., v. 12, No. 5.

SHEPPARD, H.
1920. Foveal adaptation to color. Am. J. Psychol., v. 31, p. 34.

SHERRINGTON, C. S.
1894. Experimental note on two movements of the eye. J. Physiol., v. 17, p. 27.
1906. The integrative action of the nervous system. (Silliman Memorial Lect.) Constable & Co., London.
1918. Observations on the sensual role of the proprioceptive nerve-supply of the extrinsic ocular muscles. Brain, v. 41, p. 332.
1934. The brain and its mechanism. Cambridge University Press, Cambridge.
1946. The endeavour of Jean Fernel. Macmillan Co., New York & London.

SHERRINGTON, C. S., & GRÜNBAUM, A. S. F. (*see* GRÜNBAUM & SHERRINGTON; LEYTON & SHERRINGTON)

SHIKINAMI, J.
*1930(?) A study of the development of the eyeball of *Hynobius* (in Japanese).

SHILLABER, C. P.
1947. Photomicrography in theory and practice. John Wiley & Sons, New York.

SHIRAS, G., 3d
1935. Hunting wild life with camera and flashlight. 2 vols. National Geographic Society, Washington, D.C.

SHLAER, S.
1938. The relation between visual acuity and illumination. J. Gen. Physiol., v. 21, p. 165.

SHLAER, S., SMITH, E. L., & CHASE, A. M.
1942. Visual acuity and illumination in different spectral regions. J. Gen. Physiol., v. 25, p. 553.

SHORTT, T. M.
1946. Arctic mammals. Canad. Naturalist, v. 8, p. 12.

SHULL, A. F.
1907. Habits of the short-tailed shrew, *Blarina brevicauda* (Say). Am. Naturalist, v. 41, p. 495.

SHUMWAY, W.
1942. Introduction to vertebrate embryology. 4th ed. John Wiley & Sons, New York; Chapman & Hall, London.

SIBREE, J.
1915. A naturalist in Madagascar. J. B. Lippincott Co., Philadelphia; Seeley, Service & Co., London.

SICHEL
1866. Nouveau recueil de pierres sigillaires d'oculistes romains. Ann. d'ocul., v. 56, pp. 97, 216.
1868. Historische Notiz über die Operation des grauen Staares durch die Methode des Aussaugens oder der Aspiration. Arch. f. Ophth. (Graefe), v. 14 (3), p. 1.

SICKENBERG, O.
1934. Kontinentalverschiebung, Klimawechsel und Verbreitung der tertiären landbewohnenden Säugetiere. Biol. gen., v. 10, p. 267.

SIEGRIST
1899. Discussion on chiasma. Ber. d. Deutsch. ophth. Gesellsch. Heidelberg, v. 27, p. 105.

SIEMERLING, E.
1888. Ein Fall von gummöser Erkrankung der Hirnbasis mit Betheiligung des Chiasma nervorum opticorum. Ein Beitrag zur Lehre vom Faserverlauf im optischen Leitungsapparat. Arch. f. Psychiat., v. 19, p. 401.
1890. Ein Fall von sogenannter Seelenblindheit nebst anderweitigen cerebralen Symptomen. *Ibid.*, v. 21, p. 284.
1898. Ueber Markscheidenentwickelung des Gehirns und ihre Bedeutung für die Lokalisation. Berlin. klin. Wchnschr., v. 35, p. 133.

SIGERIST, H. E.
1951. A history of medicine. Vol. 1: Primitive and archaic medicine. ("Publications of the Historical Library, Yale Medical Library," No. 27.) Oxford University Press, New York.

SILBERMANN, M., & TAMARI, M.
1933. Audiometrische Untersuchungen bei Erkrankungen des Temporallappens. Jahrb. f. Psychiat., v. 50, p. 98.

SILEX, P.
1899. Ueber die centrale Innervation der Augenmuskeln. Ber. d. Deutsch. ophth. Gesellsch. Heidelberg, v. 27, p. 84.

SILVER, M. L.
1942. The glial elements of the spinal cord of the frog. J. Comp. Neurol., v. 77, p. 41.

SIMHAJĪ, SHREE BHAGAVAT SINH JEE
1895 (1927). A short history of Aryan medical science. Bhagavat Sinh Jee Electric Printing Press, Gondal, India.

SIMON, J. R.
1946. Wyoming fishes. Bull. Wyoming Game & Fish Dept., No. 4.

SIMON, M.
1906. Sieben Bücher Anatomie des Galen. 2 vols. J. C. Hinrichs'sche Buchhandlung, Leipzig.

SIMON, R.
1907. Berichtigung zu der Arbeit des Herrn Dr. May "Ein Fall totaler Farbenblindheit." Ztschr. f. Psychol. u. Physiol. d. Sinnesorg., v. 42, p. 154.

SIMPSON, D. A.
1949. The epiphyseal complex in *Trachysaurus rugosus*. Tr. Roy. Soc. South Australia, v. 73, p. 1.

SIMPSON, G. G.
1928. Further notes on Mongolian cretaceous mammals. Am. Mus. Novitates, No. 329.
1928. Affinities of the Mongolian cretaceous insectivores. *Ibid.*, No. 330.
1931. A new insectivore from the Oligocene of Manchuria. *Ibid.*, No. 505, p. 1.
1931. A new classification of mammals. Bull. Am. Mus. Nat. Hist., v. 59, p. 259.
1937. The beginning of the age of mammals. Biol. Rev., v. 12, p. 1.
1947. Tempo and mode in evolution. Columbia University Press, New York.
1948. The beginning of the age of mammals in South America. Bull. Am. Mus. Nat. Hist., v. 91, p. 1.
1949. Rates of evolution in animals. *In:* JEPSEN *et al.*, Genetics, paleontology, and evolution, p. 205.
1949. The meaning of evolution. A study of the history of life and of its significance for man. Yale University Press, New Haven.
1950. Some principles of historical biology bearing on human origins. Cold Spring Harbor Symp. Quant. Biol., v. 15, p. 55.
1953. Life of the past. Yale University Press, New Haven. (Review by J. S. Huxley, Scient. Amer., v. 189, p. 88.)
1953. The major features of evolution. Columbia University Press, New York.

SINCLAIR, J. G.
1945. The lens in accommodation. Am. J. Ophth., v. 28, p. 38.

SINGER, C.
1914. Notes on the early history of microscopy. Proc. Roy. Soc. Med., v. 7 (2), Sec. Hist. Med., p. 247.
1915. The dawn of microscopical discovery. J. Roy. Micr. Soc., p. 317.
1917. A study in early Renaissance anatomy, with a new text: The *Anothomia* of Hieronymo Manfredi, transcribed and translated by A. MILDRED WESTLAND. *In:* C. SINGER,

Studies in the history and method of science, v. 1, p. 79. (*See also* p. 118, The eye.)

1917–21. Studies in the history and method of science. 2 vols. Clarendon Press, Oxford.

1921. Greek biology and its relation to the rise of modern biology. *In:* C. Singer, Studies in the history and method of science, v. 2, p. 1.

1921. Steps leading to the invention of the first optical apparatus. *Ibid.*, p. 385.

1922. Greek biology and Greek medicine. Clarendon Press, Oxford.

1925. The evolution of anatomy. K. Paul, Trench, Trübner & Co., London.

1925. The *Fasciculo di medicina*, Venice 1493, with an introduction by C. Singer. 2 parts. ("Monumenta medica," v. 2.) R. Lier & Co., Florence. (*See also* Ketham; Mondino de' Luzzi.)

1928. From magic to science. Boni & Liveright, New York.

1928. A short history of medicine. Oxford University Press, New York.

1931. A short history of biology; a general introduction to the study of living things. Clarendon Press, Oxford.

1941. A short history of science to the nineteenth century. Clarendon Press, Oxford; Oxford University Press, London.

1942. To Vesalius on the fourth centenary of his *De humani corporis fabrica*. J. Anat., v. 77, p. 261. (*See also* his trans. of Vesalius' chapters on the brain, 1952.)

Singer, C., & Rabin, C.

1946. A prelude to modern science, being a discussion of the history, sources and circumstances of the *Tabulae anatomicae sex* of Vesalius. Cambridge University Press, Cambridge.

Singer, C., & Singer, D. W.

1925. The school of Salerno. History, N.S., v. 10, p. 242.

Singer, J., & Münzer, E.

1889. Beiträge zur Kenntniss der Sehnervenkreuzung. Denkschr. d. Kaiserl. Akad. d. Wissensch., math.-naturw. Cl., v. 55 (2), p. 163.

Sinkler, W.

1893. Tumor of the optic thalamus. Tr. Am. Neurol. A., p. 48.

Sinno, A.

*1941. Regimen sanitatis flos medicinae scholae Salerni. Traduzione e note di A. Sinno.

Sinnott, E. W.

1950. Principles of genetics. 4th ed. McGraw-Hill Book Co., New York.

Sirturus, H.

1618. Hieronymi Sirturi Mediolanensi *TELESCOPIUM:* Ars Perficiendi Novum Illud Galilaei Visorium Instrumentum ad Sydera In Tres Partes Divisa. Quarum prima exactissimam perspicillorum artem tradit, Secunda Telescopii Galilaei absolutam constructionem, & artem aperte docet. Tertia alterius Telescopii faciliorem usum: & admirandi sui Adinventi sui arcanum patefacit. AD SERENISSIMUM COSIMUM II. MAGNUM ETRURIAE DUCEM. Francofurti. Typis Pauli Iacobi. Impensis Lucae Iennis. M.D.C.XVIII.

Sisarić, I.

1921. Ein Fall von plötzlicher Erblindung durch Tuberkel im Chiasma nervi optici. Wien. med. Wchnschr., v. 71, p. 445.

Sisilacera; *see* Saralacera

Sisson, R. F.

1950. Lake Sunapee's golden trout. Nat. Geog. Mag., v. 98, p. 529.

Sittig, O.

1914. Klinische Beiträge zur Lehre von der Lokalisation der sensiblen Rindenzentren. Prager med. Wchnschr., v. 39, p. 548.

1916. Ein weiterer Beitrag zur Lehre von der Lokalisation der sensiblen Rindenzentren. Neurol. Centralbl., v. 35, p. 408.

1923. Nachweis der temporalen Sichel in einem Migräneskotom. Med. Klin., v. 19, p. 204.

1931. Ueber Apraxie. S. Karger, Berlin.

Sjaaff, M.

1923. Vezelverloop in netvlies en oogzenuw. Academisch proefschrift. Buijten & Schipperheijn, Amsterdam.

Sjaaff, M., & Zeeman, W. P. C.

1924. Ueber den Faserverlauf in der Netzhaut und im Sehnerven beim Kaninchen. Arch. f. Ophth. (Graefe), v. 114, p. 192.

Sjögren, V. H.

1928. De la valeur diagnostique de l'intégrité maculaire dans l'hémianopsie homonyme. Acta psychiat. et neurol., v. 3, p. 233.

Skinner, H. A.

1949. The origin of medical terms. Williams & Wilkins Co., Baltimore.

Skoglund, C. R.

1942. The response to linearly increasing currents in mammalian motor and sensory nerves. Acta physiol. Scandinav., v. 4, suppl. XII.

1945. The electrotonic changes of excitability in nerve and their relation to accommodation. K. svensk. vetensk. handl., 3d ser., v. 21, No. 9.

Skolnick, A.
  1940. The role of eye movements in the autokinetic phenomenon. J. Exper. Psychol., v. 26, p. 373.
Sleggs, G. F.
  1926. The functional significance of the inversion of the vertebrate retina. Am. Naturalist, v. 60, p. 560.
Sloan, L. L.
  1942. The use of pseudo-isochromatic charts in detecting central scotomas due to lesions in the conducting pathways. Am. J. Ophth., ser. 3, v. 25, p. 1352.
  1946. A case of atypical achromatopsia. *Ibid.*, v. 29, p. 290.
  1950. The threshold gradients of the rods and the cones: in the dark-adapted and in the partially light-adapted eye. *Ibid.*, v. 33, p. 1077.
Slonaker, J. R.
  1897. A comparative study of the area of acute vision in vertebrates. J. Morphol., v. 13, p. 445.
  1902. The eye of the common mole, *Scalops aquaticus machrinus*. J. Comp. Neurol., v. 12, p. 335.
  1918. A physiological study of the anatomy of the eye and its accessory parts of the English sparrow (*Passer domesticus*). J. Morphol., v. 31, p. 351.
  1921. The development of the eye and its accessory parts in the English sparrow (*Passer domesticus*). *Ibid.*, v. 35, p. 263.
Smallwood, W. M.
  1930. The nervous structure of the annelid ganglion. J. Comp. Neurol., v. 51, p. 377.
Smallwood, W. M., & Holmes, M. T.
  1927. The neurofibrillar structure of the giant fibers in *Lumbricus terrestris* and *Eisenia foetida*. J. Comp. Neurol., v. 43, p. 327.
Smaltino, M.
  1937. Ricerche anatomiche e cliniche sulla topografia dell'inserzione dei muscoli obliqui nell'occhio. Ann. di ottal., v. 65, p. 585.
Smart, W. M.
  1951. The origin of the earth. Cambridge University Press, New York.
Smeesters, J.
  1921. Le champ visuel des névroses traumatiques. Clin. opht., v. 16, p. 123.
Smith, G. Elliot (*see also* Campion & G. Elliot Smith 1934)
  1900–1903. On the morphology of the brain in the mammalia, with special reference to that of the lemurs, recent and extinct. Tr. Linnean Soc. London, 2d ser., v. 8, p. 319, 1902.

  1902. On the homologies of the cerebral sulci. J. Anat., v. 36, p. 309.
  1904. The so-called "Affenspalte" in the human (Egyptian) brain. Anat. Anz., v. 24, p. 74.
  1904. Note on the so-called "transitory fissures" of the human brain, with special reference to Bischoff's "Fissura perpendicularis externa." *Ibid.*, p. 216.
  1904. The morphology of the occipital region of the cerebral hemisphere in man and the apes. *Ibid.*, p. 436.
  1904. Studies on the morphology of the human brain, etc. The occipital region. Rec. Egypt. Gov. School Med., v. 2, p. 123.
  1904. The fossa parieto-occipitalis. J. Anat., v. 38, p. 164.
  1904. The morphology of the retrocalcarine region of the cortex cerebri. Proc. Roy. Soc. London, v. 73, p. 59.
  1904. The persistence in the human brain of certain features usually supposed to be distinctive of apes. Rep. Brit. A. Adv. Sc., Cambridge, p. 715.
  1907. On the asymmetry of the caudal poles of the cerebral hemispheres and its influence on the occipital bone. Anat. Anz., v. 30, p. 574.
  1907. New studies on the folding of the visual cortex and the significance of the occipital sulci in the human brain. J. Anat., v. 41, p. 198.
  1907. A new topographical survey of the human cerebral cortex, being an account of the distribution of the anatomically distinct cortical areas and their relationship to the cerebral sulci. *Ibid.*, p. 237.
  1907. On the relationship of lemurs and apes. Nature, v. 76, p. 7. (*See also* Standing.)
  1908. On the form of the brain in the extinct lemurs of Madagascar, with some remarks on the affinities of the Indrisinae. Tr. Zoöl. Soc. London, v. 18, p. 163.
  1909. The zoölogical position of *Tarsius*. Nature, v. 80, p. 38.
  1909. The localisation of the human cerebral cortex. Rep. 78th meet. Brit. A. Adv. Sc., p. 876.
  1910. Some problems relating to the evolution of the brain. (Arris and Gale Lect.) Lancet, v. 1, pp. 1, 147, 221.
  1911. Discussion on the origin of mammals. Rep. Brit. A. Adv. Sc. Portsmouth, p. 424, 1912.
  1919. Discussion on the zoölogical position and affinities of *Tarsius*. Proc. Zoöl. Soc. London, p. 465. (*See also* pp. 476, 491, 494, 495, 496, 497.)

SMITH, G. ELLIOT—*Continued*

1919. The significance of the cerebral cortex. Brit. M. J., v. 1, pp. 758, 796; v. 2, p. 11.

1919. A preliminary note on the morphology of the corpus striatum and the origin of the neopallium. J. Anat., v. 53, p. 271.

1921. Exhibition of, and remarks upon, photographs of a living example of *Tarsius.* Proc. Zoöl. Soc. London, p. 184.

1923. The old and the new phrenology. (W. R. Henderson Trust Lect., No. 1, delivered at the University of Edinburgh, January 26, 1923.) Oliver & Boyd, Edinburgh & London, 1924.

1925. Anthropology. *In:* Evolution in the light of modern knowledge. Blackie & Son, London.

1926. Vision and evolution. West London M. J., v. 31, p. 97.

1927. The evolution of man. *In:* Essays. 2d ed. Oxford University Press, H. Milford, London.

1928. The new vision. Nature, v. 121, p. 680.

1928. Endocranial cast obtained from the Rhodesian skull. *In:* W. P. PYCRAFT, G. E. SMITH, *et al.,* Rhodesian man and associated remains, p. 52. British Museum (Natural History), London.

1929. The variations in the folding of the visual cortex in man. *In:* Mott memorial vol , p. 57. H. K. Lewis & Co., London.

1930. The classification of the primates. Nature, v. 125, p. 270.

1930. New light on vision. *Ibid.,* p. 820.

1930. The cortical representation of the macula. J. Anat., v. 64, p. 477.

1930. Human history. Jonathan Cape, London.

1932. The evolution of the instruments of vision. Tr. Ophth. Soc. United Kingdom, v. 51, p. 399.

1937. Obituary. *See* J. L. Shellshear, M. J. Australia, v. 24 (Part 1), p. 307.

SMITH, H. M.

1946. Handbook of lizards. Lizards of the United States and of Canada. Comstock Publishing Co., Ithaca, N.Y. (Part of series entitled "Handbooks of American Natural History," ed. A. H. WRIGHT.)

SMITH, J. E.

1945. The role of the nervous system in some activities of starfishes. Biol. Rev. Cambridge Phil. Soc., v. 20, p. 29.

SMITH, J. P.

1900. The biogenetic law from the standpoint of paleontology. J. Geol., v. 8, p. 413.

SMITH, K. U.

1936. Visual discrimination in the cat. IV. The visual acuity in the cat in relation to stimulus distance. J. Genet. Psychol., v. 49, p. 297.

1937. The postoperative effects of removal of the striate cortex upon certain unlearned visually controlled reactions in the cat. *Ibid.,* v. 50, p. 137,

1937. Visual discrimination in the cat. V. The postoperative effects of removal of the striate cortex upon intensity discrimination. *Ibid.,* v. 51, p. 329.

1937. The relation between visual acuity and the optic projection centers of the brain. Science, v. 86, p. 564.

1940. The neural centers concerned in the mediation of apparent movement vision. J. Exper. Psychol., v. 26, p. 443.

SMITH, K. U., KAPPAUF, W. E., & BOJAR, S.

1940. The functions of the visual cortex in optic nystagmus at different velocities of movement in the visual field. J. General Psychol., v. 22, p. 341.

SMITH, O. W.

1922. The book of the pike. Stewart Kidd Co., Cincinnati.

SMITH, P.

1917–18. The blood-pressure in the eye and its relation to the chamber-pressure. Brit. J. Ophth., v. 1, pp. 4, 657; v. 2, p. 257.

SMITH, R.

1876. Transitory hemiopia and hemidysaesthesia. M. Times & Gaz., v. 2, p. 676.

SMITH, ROBERT

1738. A compleate system of opticks, etc. 2 vols. Cambridge. French trans.: Cours complet d'optique. Avignon & Paris, 1767.

SMITH, T. E.

1932. Article: Optics, Encyclopaedia Britannica, 14th ed., v. 16, p. 815.

SMITH, W. K.

1936. Ocular responses elicited by electrical stimulation of the cerebral cortex. Anat. Rec., v. 64 (suppl.), p. 45.

1938. The representation of respiratory movements in the cerebral cortex. J. Neurophysiol., v. 1, p. 55.

1941. Vocalization and other responses elicited by excitation of the regio cingularis in the monkey. Am. J. Physiol., v. 133, p. P451.

SMOKEY, G.

1944. Shrews are like that. South Dakota Conserv. Digest, Pierre, v. 11, pp. 7, 11.

1944. Most secretive mammals (moles). *Ibid.,* p. 10.

SNELL, WILLEBRORD
1626. Risneri optica cum annotationibus W. Snellii. Pars prima librum primum continens, ed. J. A. VOLLGRAFF. Ghent, 1918. (*See* Isis, v. 29, p. 491.)

SNIDER, R. S., & STOWELL, A.
1944. Receiving areas of the tactile, auditory, and visual systems in the cerebellum. J. Neurophysiol., v. 7, p. 331.

SOBOTTA, J.
1929. Atlas der Histologie und mikroskopischen Anatomie des Menschen. J. F. Lehmann's Verlag, München.

SÖLDER, F.
1898. Zur Anatomie des Chiasma opticum beim Menschen. Wien. klin. Wchnschr., v. 11, p. 996.

SOEMMERRING, D. W.
1818. De oculorum hominis animaliumque sectione horizontali commentatio. Goettingae, ap. Vandenhoeck et Ruprecht.

SOEMMERRING, S. T.
1778. De basi encephali et originibus nervorum cranio egredientium. Goettingae, apud A. Vandenhoeck.
1788. Vom Hirn und Rückenmark. P. A. Winkopp, Mainz.
1795. On the central foramen (German). Götting. Anz. v. gelehrt. Sachen, Stück 140, v. 2, p. 1401. *Also* J. d. Erfindungen, Theorien u. Widersprüche, Stück 14, p. 117, 1796; and Salzburg. med. Ztschr., v. 3, p. 415.
1795–98. De foramine centrali limbo luteo cincto retinae humanae. Comment. Soc. reg. Sc. Gotting., v. 13, p. 3, 1799.
1796. Ueber das Organ der Seele. F. Nicolovius, Koenigsberg. (*See* letter by E. Kant, p. 81.)
1800. Lehre vom Hirn und von den Nerven. Varrentrapp & Wenner, Frankfurt a.M. (First ed. either 1788 or 1791.)
1801. Abbildungen des menschlichen Auges. Varrentrapp & Wenner, Frankfurt a.M.
1839–45. Vom Baue des menschlichen Körpers, ed. W. T. BISCHOFF, J. HENLE, E. HUSCHKE, F. W. THEILE, G. VALENTIN, J. VOGEL, and R. WAGNER. 8 vols. L. Voss, Leipzig. Earlier German ed., 1791–96, Varrentrapp & Wenner, Frankfurt a.M. Latin ed.: De corporis humani fabrica. Trajecti ad Moenum, 1794–1801.

SOEMMERRING, S. T., & NOETHIG
*1786. Dissertatio de decussatione nervorum opticorum, Maguntiae. Also *in:* LUDWIG, Scripta neurol. minor., v. 1, p. 127, 1791. Lipsiae.

SOLMIS, E.
1905. Nuovi studi sulla filosofia naturale di Leonardo da Vinci. Leonardo da Vinci e la teoria della visione. Atti e mem. d. r. Accad. Virgil. di Mantova, p. 137.

SOLNITZKY, O.
1938. The thalamic nuclei of *Sus scrofa*. J. Comp. Neurol., v. 69, p. 121.
1939. The lenticulostriate and lenticulo-optic arteries. Anat. Rec., v. 73 (suppl.), p. 48.
1940. The angioarchitecture of the cerebral cortex of *Macacus rhesus*. *Ibid.*, v. 76 (suppl. 2), p. 52. (Abstr.)
1945. Volumetric and reconstruction studies of the mammalian lateral geniculate nucleus. *Ibid.*, v. 91, p. 300. (Abstr.)

SOLNITZKY, O., & HARMAN, P. J.
1943. The lateral geniculate complex of *Ateles ater*. Anat. Rec., v. 85, p. 339. (Abstr.)
1943. The lateral geniculate complex in the spider monkey, *Ateles ater*. Yale J. Biol. & Med., v. 15, p. 615.
1946. The regio occipitalis of the lorisiform lemuroid *Galago demidovii*. J. Comp. Neurol., v. 84, p. 339.
1946. Photomicrographs showing structural differences between the peripheral and central sectors of the visual cortex of primates. Anat. Rec., v. 94, p. 548. (Abstr.)
1946. A comparative study of the central and peripheral sectors of the visual cortex in primates, with observations on the lateral geniculate body. J. Comp. Neurol., v. 85, p. 313.

SOLNITZKY & TRUSCOTT
1944. The lateral geniculate complex of *Macaca mulatta*. Anat. Rec., v. 88, p. 458. (Abstr.)

SOMMER, R.
1891. Ueber das Begriffscentrum. Sitzungsb. d. physiol.-med. Gesellsch. Würzburg, pp. 102, 113.

SOMMERFELT, A.
1938. Les formes de la pensée et l'évolution des catégories de la grammaire. J. de psychol., v. 35, p. 170.

SOMMERS, I. G.
1949. Histology and histopathology of the eye and its adnexa. Grune & Stratton, New York.

SOMYA, R.
1897. Kleiner Beitrag zum Capitel "Flimmerskotom." Klin. Monatsbl. f. Augenh., v. 35, p. 164.

SONDERMANN, R.
1930. Beitrag zur Entwicklung und Morphologie des Schlemmschen Kanals. Arch. f. Ophth. (Graefe), v. 124, p. 521.
1933. Ueber Entstehung, Morphologie und Funk-

tion des Schlemmschen Kanals. Acta ophth. Scandinav., v. 11, p. 280.

SONNTAG, C. F.
1924. The morphology and evolution of the apes and man. J. Bale, Sons & Danielsson, London.

SONNTAG. C. F., & WOOLLARD, H. H.
1925. A monograph of *Orycteropus afer*. II. Nervous system, sense-organs and hairs. Proc. Zoöl. Soc. London, p. 1185.

SOPER, J. D.
1944. Notes on the large short-tailed shrew at Fort Garry, Manitoba. Canad. Field-Naturalist, v. 58, p. 104.

SORSBY, A.
1939. Vital staining of the retina. Brit. J. Ophth., v. 23, p. 20; and Tr. Ophth. Soc. United Kingdom, v. 59 (2), p. 727.
1948. A short history of ophthalmology. Staples Press, London.
1951. Genetics in ophthalmology. Butterworth, London; Mosby & Co., St. Louis.

SORSBY, A., *et al.*
1937. Experimental staining of the retina in life. Proc. Roy. Soc. Med., v. 30 (2), p. 1271; Brit. M. J., v. 1, p. 129.

SOUQUES, A.
1917. Localisation corticale circonscrite de la macula. Rev. neurol., v. 32 (2), p. 346.

SOUQUES, A., & BARUK, H.
1930. Autopsie d'un cas d'amusie (avec aphasie) chez un professeur de piano. Rev. neurol., v. 1, p. 545.

SOUQUES, A., & BERTRAND, I.
1931. Études des voies optiques dans un cas d'anophtalmos congénital. Rev. neurol., v. 2, p. 1.

SOUQUES, A., & ODIER, C.
1917. Localisation corticale circonscrite de la macula. À propos d'un cas d'hémianopsie maculaire. Rev. neurol., v. 32 (2), p. 45.

SOURY, J.
1895. La vision mentale. Rev. phil. de France et de l'étrang., v. 39, pp. 1, 163.
1895–96. Le lobe occipital et la vision mentale. *Ibid.*, v. 40, p. 561; v. 41, pp. 145, 285.
1896. Cécité corticale: vision des couleurs, mémoire des lieux, idées d'espace. *Ibid.*, v. 42, p. 242.
1896. The occipital lobe and mental vision. Brain, v. 19, p. 432.
1899. Le système nerveux central. 2 vols. G. Carré & C. Naud, Paris.
1901. Anatomie cérébrale et psychologie. Arch. de neurol., ser. 2, v. 12, p. 97.

SOUTHALL, J. P. C.
1922. The beginnings of optical science. J. Opt. Soc. Amer., v. 6, p. 293.
1922. Early pioneers in physiological optics. *Ibid.*, p. 827.
1933. Mirrors, prisms, and lenses. 3d ed. Macmillan Co., New York.
1937. Introduction to physiological optics. Oxford University Press, London, New York & Toronto.

SPAETH, E. B.
1941. Principles and practice of ophthalmic surgery. 2d ed. Lea & Febiger, Philadelphia.

SPALLANZANI, L.
1792–97. Viaggi alle Due Sicilie e in alcune parti dell'Appennino. 6 vols. Stamperia di B. Comini, Pavia. French trans.: Voyage dans les Deux Siciles et dans quelques parties des Appennins. 5 vols. E. Haller, Bern.

SPALTEHOLZ, W.
1926. Hand-atlas of human anatomy. Lippincott Co., Philadelphia. Also a 15th German ed., 1953.

SPATZ, H.
1939. Pathologische Anatomie der Kreislaufstörungen des Gehirns. Zentralbl. f. d. ges. Neurol. u. Psychiat., v. 94, p. 347.

SPEARMAN, C. E.
1937. The confusion that is Gestalt-psychology. Am. J. Psychol., v. 50, p. 369.

SPEIDEL, C. C.
1940. Studies of living nerves. VI. Effects of metrazol on tissues of frog tadpoles with special reference to the injury and recovery of individual nerve fibers. Proc. Am. Phil. Soc., v. 83, p. 349.
1941. Adjustments of nerve endings. Harvey Lect., ser. 36, p. 126.
1942. Studies of living nerves. VII. Growth adjustments of cutaneous terminal arborizations. J. Comp. Neurol., v. 76, p. 57.
1942. Studies of living nerves. VIII. Histories of nerve endings in frog tadpoles subjected to various injurious treatments. Proc. Am. Phil. Soc., v. 85, p. 167.
1944. The trophic influence of specific nerve supply on special sensory organs, as revealed by prolonged survival of denervated lateral-line organs. Anat. Rec., v. 88, p. 459. (Abstr.)
1947. Living cells in action. Sc. in Prog., 5th ser., p. 280. Yale University Press, New Haven.
1947. Correlated studies of sense organs and nerves of the lateral-line in living frog tadpoles. I. Regeneration of denervated organs. J. Comp. Neurol., v. 87, p. 29.

SPEMANN, H.
1927. Neue Arbeiten über Organisatoren in der tierischen Entwicklung. Naturwiss., v. 15, p. 946.
1936. Experimentelle Beiträge zu einer Theorie der Entwicklung. J. Springer, Berlin.
1938. Embryonic development and induction. Yale University Press, New Haven. (Also in German.)

SPENCE, K. W.
1934. Visual acuity and its relation to brightness in chimpanzee and man. J. Comp. Psychol., v. 18, p. 333.

SPENCE, K. W., & FULTON, J. F.
1936. The effects of occipital lobectomy on vision in chimpanzee. Brain, v. 59, p. 35.

SPENCER, W. B.
1887. On the presence and structure of the pineal eye in Lacertilia. Quart. J. Micr. Sc., v. 27, p. 165.

SPERRY, R. W.
1942. Reestablishment of visuomotor coordinations by optic nerve regeneration. Anat. Rec., v. 84, p. 470. (Abstr.)
1943. Effect of 180 degree rotation of the retinal field on visuomotor coördination. J. Exper. Zoöl., v. 92, p. 263.
1943. Visuomotor coordination in the newt (*Triturus viridescens*) after regeneration of the optic nerve. J. Comp. Neurol., v. 79, p. 33.
1944. Optic nerve regeneration with return of vision in anurans. J. Neurophysiol., v. 7, p. 57.
1945. Restoration of vision after crossing of optic nerves and after contralateral transplantation of eye. *Ibid.*, v. 8, p. 15.
1945. The problem of central nervous reorganization after nerve regeneration and muscle transposition. Quart. Rev. Biol., v. 20, p. 311.
1945. Horizontal intracortical organization in the cerebral control of limb movement. Proc. Soc. Exper. Biol. & Med., v. 60, p. 78.
1945. Centripetal regeneration of the 8th cranial nerve root with systematic restoration of vestibular reflexes. Am. J. Physiol., v. 144, p. 735.
1947. Cerebral regulation of motor coordination in monkeys following multiple transection of sensorimotor cortex. J. Neurophysiol., v. 10, p. 275.
1948. Orderly patterning of synaptic associations in regeneration of intracentral fiber tracts mediating visuomotor coordination. Anat. Rec., v. 102, p. 63.
1948. Patterning of central synapses in regenera-

tion of the optic nerve in teleosts. Physiol. Zoöl., v. 21, p. 351.
1949. Reimplantation of eyes in fishes (*Bathygobius soporator*) with recovery of vision. Proc. Soc. Exper. Biol. & Med., v. 71, p. 80.
1950. Myotopic specificity in teleost motoneurons. J. Comp. Neurol., v. 93, p. 277.
1950. Neural basis of the spontaneous optokinetic response produced by visual inversion. J. Comp. & Physiol. Psychol., v. 43, p. 482.
1950. Neuronal specificity. *In:* P. WEISS, Genetic neurology, p. 232. University of Chicago Press, Chicago.
1951. Mechanisms of neural maturation. *In:* STEVENS, Handbook of Experimental Psychology, p. 236. John Wiley & Sons, New York.
1951. Regulative factors in the orderly growth of neural circuits. Growth (Symp.), v. 10, p. 63.
1951. Developmental patterning of neural circuits. Chicago M. School Quart., v. 12, p. 66.
1952. Neurology and the mind-brain problem. Am. Scientist, v. 40, p. 291.

SPERRY, R. W., & CLARK, E.
1949. Interocular transfer of visual discrimination habits in a teleost fish. Physiol. Zoöl., v. 22, p. 372.

SPERRY, R. W., & MINER, N.
1949. Formation within sensory nucleus V of synaptic associations mediating cutaneous localization. J. Comp. Neurol., v. 90, p. 403.

SPIEGEL, E. A.
1928. Die Zentren des autonomen Nervensystems. Monog. a. d. Gesamtgeb. d. Neurol. u. Psychiat., Heft 54. J. Springer, Berlin.
1932. The centers of the vegetative nervous system. Bull. Johns Hopkins Hosp., v. 50, p. 237.
1932. Physiopathology of the voluntary and reflex innervation of ocular movements. Arch. Ophth., v. 8, p. 738.

SPIEGEL, E. A., & NAGASAKA, G.
1927. Experimentelle Studien am Nervensystem. VI. Ueber die Beziehungen des Pupillenreflexbogens zum vorderen Vierhügel. Arch. f. d. ges. Physiol. (Pflüger), v. 215, p. 120.

SPIEGEL, E. A., & SCALA, N. P.
1936. The cortical innervation of ocular movements. Arch. Ophth., v. 16, p. 967.
1937. Ocular disturbances associated with experimental lesions of the mesencephalic gray matter. With special reference to vertical ocular movements. *Ibid.*, v. 18, p. 614.
1940. Role of the cervical sympathetic nerve in the light reflex of the pupil. *Ibid.*, v. 23, p. 371.

SPIEGEL, E. A., & SOMMER, I.
1944. Neurology of the eye, ear, nose and throat. Grune & Stratton, New York.

SPIEGEL, E. A., WESTON, K., & OPPENHEIMER, M. J.
1943. Postmotor foci influencing the gastro-intestinal tract and their descending pathways. J. Neuropath. & Exper. Neurol., v. 2, p. 45.

SPIELER, F.
1902. Ein Lipom der Vierhügelgegend. Arb. a. d. Neurol. Inst. Wien (Obersteiner), v. 8, p. 221.

SPIELMANN, M. H.
1925. The iconography of Andreas Vesalius (André Vésale), anatomist and physician, 1514–1564. J. Bale, Sons & Danielsson, London.

SPIELMEYER, W.
1922. Histopathologie des Nervensystems. J. Springer, Berlin.
1929. Degeneration und Regeneration am peripherischen Nerven. In: BETHE et al., Handbuch d. norm. u. path. Physiol., v. 9, p. 285.
1931. The significance of local factors for electivity in central nervous system disease processes. Medicine, v. 10, p. 243.

SPILLER, W. G.
1901. A case of complete absence of the visual system in an adult. Brain, v. 24, p. 631.
1907. Paralysis of upward associated ocular movements. (Blicklähmung.) Arb. a. d. Neurol. Inst. Wien (Obersteiner), v. 15, p. 352.

SPITZER, A.
1910. Ueber die Kreuzung der zentralen Nervenbahnen und ihre Beziehungen zur Phylogenese des Wirbeltierkörpers. Urban & Schwarzenberg. Leipzig & Wien.
1924. Anatomie und Physiologie der zentralen Bahnen des Vestibularis. Arb. a. d. Neurol. Inst. Wien (Obersteiner), v. 25, p. 423.
1925. Ueber die Funktionen der Bogengänge des Ohrlabyrinths. Monatsschr. f. Ohrenh. u. Laryng.-Rhinol., v. 59, p. 1.

SPITZKA, E. A.
1902. Three Eskimo brains from Smith Sound. Am. J. Anat., v. 2, p. 25.
1908. A study of the brains of six eminent scientists and scholars belonging to the American Anthropometric Society, together with a description of the skull of Professor E. D. Cope. Tr. Am. Phil. Soc., N.S., v. 21, p. 175.

SPOFFORD, W. R.
1942. A study of optic nerve terminals (boutons terminaux) in the lateral geniculate nucleus in the cat. Anat. Rec., v. 82, p. 449. (Abstr.)

1942. The central endings of the retino-geniculate tract of section of one optic nerve. Ibid., p. 490. (Abstr.)

SPRATT, N. T.
1940. An in vitro analysis of the organization of the eye-forming area in the early chick blastoderm. J. Exper. Zoöl., v. 85, p. 171.

SPRONG, W.
1035. Santiago Ramón y Cajal. Arch. Neurol. & Psychiat., v. 33, p. 156.

SPRUCE, R.
1908. Notes of a botanist on the Amazon & Andes: being records of travel on the Amazon and its tributaries, the Trombetas, Río Negro, etc., during the years 1849–1864, ed. A. R. WALLACE. Macmillan & Co., London.

SPURZHEIM, J. G.
1833. Phrenology, in connexion with the study of physiognomy. Illustration of characters. To which is prefixed a biography of the author by Nahum Capen. Marsh, Capen & Lyon, Boston.
1834. The anatomy of the brain, with a general view of the nervous system. By J. G. Spurzheim, M.D., of the University of Vienna and Paris; Licenciate of the Royal Col. of Phys. in London. Trans. from the unpublished French MS by R. WILLIS, member of the Royal College of Surgeons, London. First Amer. ed., rev. by C. H. STEDMAN. Marsh, Capen & Lyon, Boston.

SQUIRES, P. C.
1930. A criticism of the configurationist's interpretation of "structuralism." Am. Jour. Psychol., v. 42, p. 134.

STADERINI, R.
1917. Notevole fascio di fibre nervose che dal chiasma ottico si prolunga nella lamina terminale. Mon. zool. ital., v. 28, p. 149.
1928. Di un sistema di vie nervose presumibilmente ottiche aventi rapporto col chiasma, col nervo e col tratto ottico. Ibid., v. 39, p. 269.
1934. Particolarità riguardanti lo sviluppo, la struttura e i rapporti del nervo ottico, del tratto ottico, del chiasma e della lamina terminale. Arch. ital. di anat. e di embriol., v. 33, p. 1.
1937. Aspetti nuovi della costituzione anatomica e delle connessioni del chiasma, del tratto ottico e del nervo ottico. Mon. zool. ital., v. 47, suppl., p. 151.

STALLARD, H. B.
1947. Eye surgery. Williams & Wilkins Co., Baltimore.

STAMBUL, J.
1952. The mechanisms of disease. A study of the autonomic nervous system, the endocrine system and the electrolytes in their relationship to clinical medicine. Froben Press, New York.

STANCULÉANU, G.
1902. Rapports anatomiques et pathologiques entre les sinus de la face et l'appareil orbito-oculaire. Thèse de Paris. G. Steinheil, Paris.

STANDING, H. B.
1908. On recently discovered subfossil primates from Madagascar. With an appendix: On the form of the brain in the extinct lemurs of Madagascar, with some remarks on the affinities of the Indrisinae, by G. ELLIOT SMITH. Tr. Zoöl. Soc. London, v. 18, p. 59.

STANGIER, H.
1937. Die Furchen der Grosshirnrinde beim Schimpansen. Ztschr. f. Anat. u. Entw., v. 107, p. 467.

STARLING, E. H.
1949. Principles of human physiology. 10th ed. J. & A. Churchill, London.

STAROKOTLITZKI, N.
1903. Das untere Längsbündel des menschlichen Grosshirns. Inaug.-Diss. Breslau. R. Nischkowsky, Breslau.

STARR, M. A.
1884. The visual area in the brain determined by a study of hemianopsia. Am. J. M. Sc., v. 87, p. 65.
1884. Cortical lesions of the brain. A collection and analysis of the American cases of localized cerebral disease. *Ibid.*, p. 366; v. 88, p. 114.

STAUFFENBERG, W. VON
1911. Beitrag zur Lokalisation der Apraxie. Ztschr. f. d. ges. Neurol. u. Psychiat. (Orig.), v. 5, p. 434.
1914. Ueber Seelenblindheit (opt. Agnosie), nebst Bemerkungen zur Anatomie der Sehstrahlung. Arb. a. d. hirnanat. Inst. Zürich, v. 8, p. 1.

STAVRAKY, G. W.
1936. Response of cerebral blood vessels to electric stimulation of the thalamus and hypothalamic regions. Arch. Neurol. & Psychiat., v. 35, p. 1002.

STEELE, R.
1921. Roger Bacon and the state of science in the thirteenth century. *In:* C. SINGER, Studies in the history and method of science, v. 2, p. 121. Clarendon Press, Oxford.

STEFFAN, P.
1897. Ueber sensorische Anopsie (Seelenblindheit) im physiologischen und pathologischen Sinne. Arch. f. Ophth. (Graefe), v. 43, p. 643.

STEIN, H., & WEIZSÄCKER, V. VON
1927. Der Abbau der sensiblen Funktionen. Deutsch. Ztschr. f. Nervenh., v. 99, p. 1.

STEIN, J.
1928. Ueber die Veränderung der Sinnesleistungen und die Entstehung von Trugwahrnehmungen. *In:* MAYER-GROSS & STEIN, Pathologie der Wahrnehmung, in BUMKE, Handb. d. Geisteskrankh., v. 1, p. 352.
1931. Zur Symptomatologie der Stirnhirnläsionen. Deutsch. Ztschr. f. Nervenh., v. 117-19, p. 623.

STEIN, R.
1932. Beiträge zur Topographie und Anatomie der Ora serrata und des Orbiculus ciliaris. Arch. f. Augenh., v. 106, p. 145.

STEIN, S. A. W.
1834. De thalamo et origine nervi optici in homine et animalibus vertebratis dissertatio anatomica, quam, ad summos in arte medica honores rite capessendos, die II. aprilis, H. L. S. defendere studebit Sophus Augustus Wilhelmus Stein, chirurgiae et medicinae candidatus, chirurgus legionarius; respondente Severino Eskildsen Larsen, Viro doctissimo, chirurgiae candidato, in Academia Chirurgorum Regia docente. Hauniae (Copenhagen). Typis excudebat S. Trier. MDCCCXXXIV.

STEINACH, E.
1890. Untersuchungen zur vergleichenden Physiologie der Iris. I. Mitt. Ueber Irisbewegung bei den Wirbelthieren und über die Beziehung der Pupillarreaction zur Sehnervenkreuzung im Chiasma. Arch. f. d. ges. Physiol. (Pflüger), v. 47, p. 289.

STEINDORFF, G.
1940. Physicians and medicine in ancient Egypt. Ciba Symp., v. 1, No. 10.

STEINER, J.
1885-1900. Die Functionen des Centralnervensystems und ihre Phylogenese. 4 parts. (1, frog; 2, fishes; 3, invertebrates; 4, reptiles & misc.). F. Vieweg & Sohn, Braunschweig.
1888. Les fonctions du système nerveux et leur phylogenèse. Compt. rend. Soc. de biol., v. 40, p. 566.
1891. Sinnessphären und Bewegungen. Arch. f. d. ges. Physiol. (Pflüger), v. 50, p. 603.
1895. Ueber die Entwickelung der Sinnessphären, insbesondere der Sehsphäre auf der Grosshirnrinde des Neugeborenen. Akad. d. Wissensch. Berlin, p. 303.

STEINITZ, E.
1906. Ueber den Einfluss der Elimination der embryonalen Augenblasen auf die Entwicklung des Gesamtorganismus beim Frosche. Arch. f. Entwicklungsmech. d. Org., v. 20, p. 537.

STEINSCHNEIDER, M.
1893. Die hebraeischen Uebersetzungen des Mittelalters und die Juden als Dolmetscher. 2 vols, Bibliog. Bureau, Berlin.
1905. Die europäischen Uebersetzungen aus dem Arabischen bis Mitte des 17. Jahrhunderts. Sitzungsb. phil.-hist. Kl. d. Kaiserl. Akad. d. Wissensch. Wien, v. 149, chap. 4.

STENGEL, E.
1924. Vergleichend-anatomische Studien über die Kerne an der hinteren Commissur und im Ursprungsgebiete des hinteren Längsbündels. Arb. a. d. Neurol. Inst. Wien, v. 26, p. 419.
1930. Morphologische und cytoarchitektonische Studien über den Bau der unteren Frontalwindung bei Normalen und Taubstummen. Ihre individuellen und Seitenunterschiede. Ztschr. f. d. ges. Neurol. u. Psychiat., v. 130, p. 631.

STENGER, C.
1882. Die cerebralen Sehstörungen der Paralytiker. Arch. f. Psychiat. u. Nervenkr. v. 13, p. 218.

STENIUS, S.
1941. Dark-adaptation and the platinum chloride method of staining visual purple. Acta physiol. Scandinav., v. 1, p. 380.

STENO (STENSEN), NIELS
1668. A dissertation on the anatomy of the brain by M. Steno read in the assembly at M. Thevenot's house in the year 1668. *In:* WINSLOW, An anatomical exposition of the structure of the human body, sec. 10, §10, p. 56, 1773.

STENSEN; *see* STENO

STENVERS, H. W.
1924. Ueber die klinische Bedeutung des optischen Nystagmus für die zerebrale Diagnostik. Schweiz. Arch. f. Neurol. u. Psychiat., v. 14, p. 279.

STEPHANUS (ESTIENNE), CAROLUS
1545. De dissectione partium corporis humani libri tres. Apud S. Colinoeum, Parisiis.
1546. La dissectione des parties du corps humain, divisée en trois livres, avec les figures et declaration des incisions. Composée par Estienne de la Rivière. S. de Colines, Paris.

STERN, F., & LEHMANN, W.
1929. Ueber einen Tumor des linken Hinterhauptlappens mit mehrfachen Rezidiverscheinungen. Arch. f. Psychiat. u. Nervenkr., v. 86, p. 539.

STERN, R.
1905. Ueber Sehpurpurfixation. Arch. f. Ophth. (Graefe), v. 61, p. 561.

STERZ, G.
1925. Encephalitis und Lokalisation psychischer Störungen. Arch. f. Psychiat. u. Nervenkr., v. 74, p. 288.
1929. Die Symptomatologie der Tumoren im Bereich des Zwischenhirns (Zwischenhirnsyndrom). Ein Beitrag zur Lokalisation psychischer Störungen. *Ibid.*, v. 88, p. 794.

STEVENS, S. S., & DAVIS, H.
1938. Hearing. Its psychology and physiology. John Wiley & Sons, New York.

STEWART, T. D.
1950. The problem of the earliest claimed representatives of *Homo sapiens*. Cold Spring Harbor Symp. Quant. Biol., v. 15, p. 97.

STIEDA, L.
1870. Studien über das centrale Nervensystem der Wirbelthiere. Ztschr. f. wissensch. Zool., v. 20, p. 273.
1899. Geschichte der Entwickelung der Lehre von den Nervenzellen und Nervenfasern während des 19. Jahrhunderts. I. Teil. Von Sömmering bis Deiters. *In:* Festschrift z. siebenzigsten Geburtstag v. Carl von Kupffer, p. 79, Pls. X and XI. G. Fischer, Jena.
1907. Das Gehirn eines Sprachkundigen. Ztschr. f. Morphol. u. Anthropol., v. 11, p. 83.

STILES, W. S.
1939. The directional sensitivity of the retina and the spectral sensitivities of the rods and cones. Proc. Roy. Soc. London, ser. B, v. 127, p. 64.
1946. Separation of the "blue" and "green" mechanisms of foveal vision by measurements of increment thresholds. *Ibid.*, v. 133, p. 418.

STILES, W. S., THOMSON, L. C., & PIRENNE, M. H.
1945. Colour vision of the fovea centralis. Nature, v. 155, p. 177.

STILLE, W. T.
1950. Nocturnal anurans of the sand dunes of Indiana. Thesis, University of Chicago.

STILLING, B.
1859. Neue Untersuchungen über den Bau des Rückenmarks. H. Hotop, Cassel.

STILLING, J.
1879. Notiz über die Bedeutung der Occipitallappen des Gehirns für das Sehen. Centralbl. f. pr. Augenh., v. 3, p. 33.

1880. Ueber die centralen Endigungen des *Nervus opticus*. Arch. f. mikr. Anat., v. 18, p. 468.

1882. Untersuchungen über den Bau der optischen Centralorgane. Chiasma und Tractus opticus. T. Fischer, Kassel & Berlin.

STILLWELL, R.

1944. Greece—the birthplace of science and free speech. Nat. Geog. Mag., v. 85, p. 273.

STIRLING, W.

1902. Some apostles of physiology, being an account of their lives and labours, etc. Waterlow & Sons, London.

STÖHR, P., JR.

1928. Die peripherische Nervenfaser. *In:* W. VON MÖLLENDORFF, Handb. d. mikr. Anat. d. Mensch., v. 4 (1), p. 143.

1937. Mikroskopische Studien zur Innervation des Magen-Darmkanales. Ztschr. f. Zellforsch. u. mikr. Anat., v. 27, p. 341.

STÖRRING, G. E.

1939. Die Apoplexien in relativ jugendlichem Alter. Zentralbl. f. d. ges. Neurol. u. Psychiat., v. 94, p. 350.

STOFFELS, J.

1939. Organisation du thalamus et du cortex cérébral chez le lapin. J. belge de neurol. et psychiat., v. 39, p. 557.

STOLL, M. R.

1950. Pericentral ring scotoma. Arch. Ophth., ser. 2, v. 43, p. 66.

STONE, L. S.

1942. Transplantations of the salamander eye four times showing return of vision after each operation. Anat. Rec., v. 82, p. 494. (Abstr.)

1942. Return of vision four times in the same adult salamander eye repeatedly transplanted. *Ibid.*, v. 84, p. 483. (Abstr.)

1944. Functional polarization in retinal development and its reestablishment in regenerating retinae of rotated grafted eyes. Proc. Soc. Exper. Biol. & Med., v. 57, p. 13.

1946. Return of vision in transplanted adult salamander eyes after seven days of refrigeration. Arch. Ophth., ser. 2, v. 35, p. 135.

1946. Motion picture showing reestablishment of the functional quadrants in regenerated retinae of rotated salamander eyes. Anat. Rec., v. 94, p. 551. (Abstr.)

1947. Return of vision and functional polarization in retinae of transplanted salamander eyes. J. Anat., v. 81, p. 398. (Abstr. of motion picture.)

1947. Return of vision and functional polarization in the retinae of transplanted eyes. Tr. Ophth. Soc. United Kingdom, v. 67, p. 349.

1948. Experiments on return of vision in transplanted eyes of salamanders. Anat. Rec., v. 101, p. 697. (Abstr.)

1950. Neural retina degeneration followed by regeneration from surviving retinal pigment cells in grafted adult salamander eyes. *Ibid.*, v. 106, p. 89.

1950. A color motion picture showing functional polarization in the retina of transplanted embryonic eyes of *Amblystoma punctatum* and *A. tigrinum*. *Ibid.*, p. 398. (Abstr.)

STONE, L. S., & ELLISON, F. S.

1945. Return of vision in eyes exchanged between adult salamanders of different species. J. Exper. Zoöl., v. 100, p. 217.

STONE, L. S., & ZAUR, I. S.

1940. Reimplantation and transplantation of adult eyes in the salamander (*Triturus viridescens*) with return of vision. J. Exper. Zoöl., v. 85, p. 243.

STONE, L. S., ZAUR, I. S., & FARTHING, T. E.

1933–34. Grafted eyes of adult *Triturus viridescens* with special reference to repeated return of vision. Proc. Soc. Exper. Biol. & Med., v. 31, p. 1082.

STOPFORD, J. S. B.

1916–17. The arteries of the pons and medulla oblongata. J. Anat., v. 50, pp. 131, 255; v. 51, p. 250.

STORER, J. H.

1948. The flight of birds analyzed through slow-motion photography. Bull. Cranbrook Inst. Sc., No. 28. Bloomfield Hills, Michigan.

STORER, T. I.

1943. General zoölogy. McGraw-Hill Book Co., New York.

STORT; *see* GENDEREN, S.

STORY, H. E.

1951. The carotid arteries in the Procyonidae. Fieldiana: Zoöl. (Chicago Nat. Hist. Mus.), v. 32, p. 475.

STOUGH, H. B.

1926. Giant nerve fibers of the earthworm. J. Comp. Neurol., v. 40, p. 409.

STRAET

Ca. 1600. Nova Reperta, with engravings by Ioan. Stradanus, Ioan. Collaert, and Phls. Galle. (*See* Fig. 14 representing an optometrist's shop, with the legend *Conspicilla. Inventa conspicilla sunt, quae luminum Obscuriores detegunt caligines.*) Antwerp. Newberry Library, Chicago.

STRAHL, H.

1898. Zur Entwickelung des menschlichen Auges. Anat. Anz., v. 14, p. 298.

STRASSBURGER, E.
1941. Die Arbeitsteilung in der menschlichen Grosshirnrinde. Monatsschr. f. Psychiat., v. 104, p. 73.

STRASSER, H.
1893. Alte und neue Probleme der entwicklungsgeschichtlichen Forschung auf dem Gebiete der Nervensystems. Ergebn. d. Anat. u. Entw. (Merkel & Bonnet), v. 2, p. 565.

STRAUB, M.
1908. Eine bisher nicht veröffentlichte Schrift von Christian Huygens über das Auge und das Sehen. Klin. Monatsbl. f. Augenh., N.F., v. 5, p. 295.

STRAUS, W. L., JR.
1940. The posture of the great ape hand in locomotion, and its phylogenetic implications. Am. J. Phys. Anthropol., v. 27, p. 199.
1941. Locomotion of gibbons. *Ibid.*, v. 28, p. 354.
1942. Rudimentary digits in primates. Quart. Rev. Biol., v. 17, p. 228.
1949. Recent discoveries of fossil primates and their alleged bearing on human evolution. Anat. Rec., v. 103, p. 509. (Abstr.)
1949. The riddle of man's ancestry. Quart. Rev. Biol., v. 24, p. 200.
1950. On the zoölogical status of *Telanthropus capensis*. Am. J. Phys. Anthropol., v. 8, N.S., p. 405.

STRAUSS, E.
1909. Das Gammaridenauge. Studien über ausgebildete und rückgebildete Gammaridenaugen. G. Fischer, Jena.

STRAUSS, H.
1925. Die diagnostische Bedeutung des optomotorischen (Eisenbahn-) Nystagmus für die Neurologie. Ztschr. f. d. ges. Neurol. u. Psychiat., v. 98, p. 93.
1925. Ueber Sensibilitätsstörungen an Hand und Gesicht, Geschmacksstörungen und ihre lokalisatorische Bedeutung. Monatsschr. f. Psychiat. u. Neurol., v. 58, p. 265.

STRAUSS, I., & KESCHNER, M.
1935. Mental symptoms in cases of tumor of the frontal lobe. Arch. Neurol. & Psychiat., v. 33, p. 986.

STREBEL, J.
1924. Ueber Hemianopien. Arch. f. Augenh., v. 94, p. 27.

STREETER, G. L.
1906. The cortex of the brain of the human embryo during the fourth month, etc. Am. J. Anat., v. 7, p. 337.
1912. The development of the nervous system. *In:* Manual of human embryol., ed. KEIBEL &

MALL. J. B. Lippincott Co., Philadelphia & London.

STRESEMANN, E.
1934. Sauropsida: Aves. *In:* W. KÜKENTHAL & T. KRUMBACH, Handb. d. Zool., v. 7 (2). W. de Gruyter, Berlin & Leipzig.

STREULI, H.
1925. Die Akkommodation des Wirbeltierauges. Naturwiss., v. 13, p. 477.

STRICHT, O.
1922. La structure de la rétine. La membrane limitante externe, etc. Compt. rend. Soc. de biol., v. 74 (1), p. 266.
1922. Étude de la rétine par l'ancienne méthode d'imprégnation au nitrate d'argent. Arch. de biol., v. 32, pp. 173, 345.

STRICKER, S.
1870–73. Handbuch der Lehre von den Geweben des Menschen und der Thiere. 2 vols. W. Engelmann, Leipzig. English trans.: Manual of human and comparative histology. 3 vols. New Sydenham Society, London.

STRÖER, W. F. H.
1939. Zur vergleichenden Anatomie des primären optischen Systems bei Wirbeltieren. Ztschr. f. Anat. u. Entwgesch., v. 110, p. 301.
1939. Ueber den Faserverlauf in den optischen Bahnen bei Amphibien. Proc. Kon. nederl. Akad. Wetensch. Amsterdam, v. 42, p. 649.
1940. Das optische System beim Wassermolch (*Triturus taeniatus*). Acta neerl. morphol., v. 3, p. 178.
1940. Experimental investigation of the optic pathways. Anat. Rec., v. 76, suppl. 2, p. 53. (Abstr.)

STRONG, O. S.
1895. The cranial nerves of the amphibia. A contribution to the morphology of the vertebrate nervous system. J. Morphol., v. 10, p. 1.

STRONG, O. S., & ELWYN, A.
1943. Human neuroanatomy. Williams & Wilkins Co., Baltimore.

STUDNIČKA, F. K.
1898. Untersuchungen über den Bau des Sehnerven der Wirbelthiere. Jena. Ztschr. f. Naturwiss., v. 31, p. 1.
1900. Untersuchungen über den Bau des Ependyms der nervösen Centralorgane. Anat. Hefte, v. 15, p. 301.
1905. Die Parietalorgane. *In:* A. OPPEL, Lehrb. d. vergl. mikr. Anat. d. Wirbeltiere, v. 5. G. Fischer, Jena.
1912. Ueber die Entwicklung und die Bedeutung

der Seitenaugen von Ammocoetes. Anat. Anz., v. 41, p. 561.

1913. Die primäre Augenblase und der Augenbecher bei der Entwickelung des Seitenauges der Wirbeltiere. *Ibid.*, v. 44, p. 273.

1918. Das Schema der Wirbeltieraugen. Zool. Jahrb. (Anat. & Ontog.), v. 40, p. 1.

1927. Joh. Ev. Purkinjes und seiner Schule Verdienste um die Entdeckung tierischer Zellen und um die Aufstellung der "Zellen"-Theorie. Práce Morav. Přír. Spol. (Acta Soc. sc. nat. Morav.), v. 4. Brno, Czechoslovakia.

1933. Ueber die Struktur des frischen Glaskörpers. Anat. Anz., v. 76, p. 28.

1934. Mikroskopische und ultramikroskopische Untersuchungen über den Bau des Glaskörpers. Ztschr. f. mikr.-anat. Forsch., v. 36, p. 267.

STUDNICZKA, F.

1908. Das Bildnis des Aristoteles. A. Edelmann, Leipzig.

STUDNITZ, G. VON

1936–37. Die retinale Säurebildung. Arch. f. d. ges. Physiol. (Pflüger), v. 238, p. 802.

1937–38. Weitere Studien an der Zapfensubstanz. *Ibid.*, v. 239, p. 515.

1940. Die Duplizitätstheorie. Naturwiss., v. 28, pp. 129, 152.

1940. Die Oelkugeln der Zapfen und des Pigmentepithels und die Regeneration von Zapfensubstanz und Sehpurpur. Arch. f. d. ges. Physiol. (Pflüger), v. 243, p. 181.

1940. Grundvorgänge des Sehens—100 Jahre Sehstoffe. Nova acta Leopold., N.F., v. 9, p. 53.

1940. Das Absorptionsspektrum der Zapfensubstanz. Ztschr. f. vergl. Physiol., v. 28, p. 153.

1940. Bleichung und Regeneration von Zapfensubstanz und Sehpurpur in Lösung. Arch. f. d. ges. Physiol. (Pflüger), v. 243, p. 651.

1941. Zapfensubstanz und Sehpurpur. Naturwiss., v. 29, p. 65.

1950. Review of The retina by S. L. POLYAK. *Ibid.*, v. 37, p. 216.

1952. Physiologie des Sehens. Retinale Primärprozesse. *In:* RIES & WETZEL (eds.), Probleme der Biologie, v. 3. Akademische Verlagsgesellschaft Geest & Portig K.-G., Leipzig.

STUDNITZ, G. VON, & LOEVENICH, H. K.

1946. Zur medikamentösen Beeinflussung des Farbensinns. Naturwiss., v. 33, p. 189.

STUDNITZ, G. VON, LOEVENICH, H. K., & NEUMANN, H. J.

1942. Ueber die Loeslichkeit und Trennbarkeit

der Farbensubstanzen. Ztschr. f. vergl. Physiol., v. 30, p. 71.

STUDNITZ, G. VON, NEUMANN, H. J., & LOEVENICH, H. K.

1943. Die Natur der Oelkugeln und Sehstoffe. Arch. f. d. ges. Physiol. (Pflüger), v. 246, p. 652.

STUDNITZ, G. VON, WIGGER, H., & LOEVENICH, H. K.

1943–44. Ueber die Wirkungsbereiche der Farbsubstanzen. Arch. f. d. ges. Physiol. (Pflüger), v. 247, p. 353.

STUMPF, F. G. A.

1841. Historia nervorum cerebralium ab antiquissimis temporibus usque ad Willisium nec non Vieussensium. Inaug.-Diss., Berlin.

STUMPF, H.

1952. Elektrophysiologische Untersuchung des Farbensehens von Fliegen (*Calliphora*). Naturwiss., v. 39, p. 574.

STURM, J. C.

1699. Dissertatio Visionis Sens. Nobiliss. ex Obscurae Camerae Tenebris illustrans, etc. *In:* Disput. select., ed. A. HALLER, v. 4, p. 163.

STUTTERHEIM, N. A.

1946. Squint and convergence: a study in di-ophthalmology. H. K. Lewis, London.

SUDHOFF, K.

1907. Augenanatomiebilder im 15. und 16. Jahrhundert. Stud. z. Gesch. d. Med. (Sudhoff), Fasc. 1, p. 19.

1907. Zur Anatomie des Lionardo da Vinci. Arch. f. Gesch. d. Med., v. 1, p. 67. (*See* M. Holl, Arch. f. Anat. u. Entw., p. 111, 1905.)

1912. Medizinische Fachillustrationen aus der Antike in mittelalterlicher Ueberlieferung. Mitt. d. Deutsch. Gesellsch. Leipzig, v. 10, p. 96.

1914. Weitere Beiträge zur Geschichte der Anatomie im Mittelalter. Augendurchschnittsbilder aus Abendland und Morgenland. Arch. f. Gesch. d. Med. (Sudhoff), v. 8, p. 1.

1914. Die kurze "Vita" und das Verzeichnis der Arbeiten Gerhards von Cremona, von seinen Schülern und Studiengenossen kurz nach dem Tode des Meisters (1187) zu Toledo verabfasst. *Ibid.*, p. 73.

1921. Andreas Vesalius zu Ehren zum vierhundertjährigen Gedächtnis seiner Geburt gesprochen. Verhandl. d. Ges. deutsch. Naturforsch. u. Aerzte, v. 86, p. 162.

1926. Essays in the history of medicine, ed. F. H. GARRISON. Medical Life Press, New York.

1928. Master minds in medicine. Medical Life Press, New York.

Sudhoff, K.—*Continued*

1930. Toledo. Arch. f. Gesch. d. Med. (Sudhoff), v. 23, p. 1.

1932. Constantin, der erste Vermittler muslimischer Wissenschaft ins Abendland und die beiden salernitaner Frühscholastiker Maurus und Urso, als Exponenten dieser Vermittlung. Archeion, v. 14, p. 359.

Sudhoff, W.

1914. Die Lehre von den Hirnventrikeln in textlicher und graphischer Tradition des Altertums und Mittelalters. Arch. f. Gesch. d. Med., v. 7, p. 149.

Sugar, H. S.

1942. Anatomic factors influencing anterior chamber depth. Am. J. Ophth., v. 3, p. 1341.

Sugar, O., & Gerard, R. W.

1938. Anoxia and brain potentials. J. Neurophysiol., v. 1, p. 558.

Sumner, F. B.

1940. Quantitative changes in pigmentation, resulting from visual stimuli in fishes and amphibia. Biol. Rev., v. 15, p. 351.

Surber, T.

1940. Propagation of minnows. Spec. Bull. Minnesota Div. Game & Fish.

1946. Mammals that eat insects: the shrews, moles, and bats. Conserv. Volunteer, v. 9, July–August, p. 20. St. Paul, Minnesota.

Suśruta

Ca. 1st cent. Suśruta Saṃhitā. English trans. by Kaviraj K. L. Bhiśagratna. 3 vols. Calcutta, 1907–16. (*See also* Esser 1934; Bidyādar 1939.)

Suter, H.

1897. Die Araber als Vermittler der Wissenschaften in deren Uebergang vom Orient in den Occident. H. R. Sauerlander & Co., Aarau (Switzerland).

1900. Die Mathematiker und Astronomen der Araber und ihre Werke. Abh. z. Gesch. d. math. Wissensch., Fasc. 10 (suppl. z. 45. Jahrg. d. Ztschr. f. Math. u. Phys.). B. G. Teubner, Leipzig.

Suttie, I. D.

1926. A theory of decussation. Note on a possible adaptive significance of the translateration of the upper motor and sensory neurones. J. Neurol. & Psychopath., v. 6, p. 267.

Svedberg, T., *et al.*

1939. A discussion on the protein molecule. Proc. Roy. Soc. London, ser. A, v. 170, p. 40.

Sverdlick, J.

1940. Conos y bastoncitos. A. Lopez, Buenos Aires.

1942. Influencia de la hipófisis y de la suprarrenal sobre el pigmento retiniano del "Bufo arenarum" Hensel. Rev. Soc. argent. de biol., v. 18, p. 207, 1943.

1944. Fenomenos de actividad secretora en el epitelio de los procesos ciliares. Arch. de histol. norm. y pat., v. 2, p. 247.

Sverdrup, H. U., Johnson, M. W., & Fleming, R. H.

1942. The oceans. Their physics, chemistry, and general biology. Prentice-Hall, Inc., New York.

Swammerdam, J.

1675. Ephemeri vita, etc. A. Wolfgang, Amsterdam.

1682. Histoire generale des insectes, etc. Guillaume de Walcheren, Utrecht.

1685. Historia insectorum generalis, etc. J. Luchtmans, Lugd. Batavorum (Leyden).

1737–38. Bybel der natuure, etc. I. Severinus, and B. & P. Vander Aa, Leyden.

Swan, K. C.

1948. Some aspects of studying binocular vision. Am. J. Ophth., v. 31, p. 845.

Swann, W. F. G.

1930. Contemporary theories of light. J. Opt. Soc. Amer., v. 20, p. 484.

Swedenborg, E.

1740. Oeconomia regni animalis. Chauguion, London. (*See also* O. M. Ramstrom: Swedenborg on the cerebral cortex as the seat of psychical activity. Tr. Internat. Swedenborg Cong., p. 56, 1930.)

1882–87. The brain considered anatomically, physiologically and philosophically. 2 vols. J. Speirs, London.

1938. Three transactions on the cerebrum. A posthumous work. 3 vols. Swedenborg Scientific Association, Philadelphia.

Swinne, J. R.

1924. Die Anfänge der optischen Glasschmelzkunst. Keramische Rundschau., v. 32, May 22.

Sylvius, F. (De Le Boë)

1680. Opera medica. 2d ed. Amstelodami, ap. D. Elsevirum, & A. Wolfgang.

Sylvius (Dubois), Jacobus (Jacques)

1555. Introduction sur l'anatomique partie de la phisiologie d'Hippocras et Galien. J. Hulpeau, Paris. Other French and Latin eds.

Symington, J.

1916. Endocranial casts and brain form: a criticism of some recent speculations. J. Anat., v. 50, p. 111.

Symonds, J. A.

1875–86. Renaissance in Italy. 7 vols. Smith, Elder & Co., London.

SYMONDS, J. A., & SMITH, P.
 1932. Article: The Renaissance, Encyclopaedia Britannica, 14th ed., v. 19, p. 122.

SYMPOSIUM ON BLOOD SUPPLY
 1938. The circulation of the brain and spinal cord. Research Pub. A. Research Nerv. &. Ment. Dis., v. 18.

SYMPOSIUM ON BLOOD SUPPLY (German)
 1939. Jahresversammlung der Gesellschaft Deutscher Neurologen und Psychiater, Wiesbaden. Zentralbl. f. d. ges. Neurol. u. Psychiat., v. 94, pp. 337-60.

SYMPOSIUM ON HYDROBIOLOGY (University of Wisconsin)
 1940. Addresses in honor of Edw. A. Birge, etc. University of Wisconsin Press, Madison.

SYMPOSIUM ON ORIGIN AND EVOLUTION OF MAN
 1950. Cold Spring Harbor Symposia on Quantitative Biology, vol. 15 (Origin and evolution of man). Cold Spring Harbor, L.I., New York.

SZENTÁGOTHAI, J.
 1942. Die innere Gliederung des Oculomotoriuskernes. Arch. f. Psychiat. u. Nervenkr., v. 115, p. 127.

SZENT-GYÖRGYI, A.
 1941. The study of energy-levels in biochemistry. Nature, v. 148, p. 157.

SZEPSENWOL, J.
 1938. Transplantation des yeux chez un poisson adulte et son effet sur les chromatophores. Compt. rend. Soc. de biol., v. 129, p. 1265.
 1945. The influence of the eyes on the melanophores in amphibian. Anat. Rec., v. 93, p. 185.

SZILY, A. VON
 1907. Ueber atypische Sehnervenfasern. Anat. Anz., v. 30, p. 363.
 1912. Ueber die einleitenden Vorgänge bei der ersten Entstehung der Nervenfasern im Nervus opticus. Arch. f. Ophth. (Graefe), v. 81, p. 67.
 1918. Atlas der Kriegsaugenheilkunde samt begleitendem Text. Sammlung der kriegsophthalmologischen Beobachtungen und Erfahrungen aus der Universitäts-Augenklinik in Freiburg i.Br. Mit einem Begleitwort von Herrn Gehr. Prof. Dr. Th. Axenfeld. F. Enke, Stuttgart.
 1921-22. Die Deutung der Zusammenhänge der wichtigsten Entwicklungsphasen des Wirbeltierauges, etc. Typus "Säuger," Arch. f. Ophth. (Graefe), v. 106, p. 195.
 1922. Vergleichende Entwicklungsgeschichte der Papilla nervi optici und der sog. axialen Gebilde. *Ibid.*, v. 107, p. 317; v. 109, p. 3.

 1927. Zur vergleichend-morphologischen Ausgestaltung der Chiasmagegend. Klin. Monatsbl. f. Augenh., v. 78, p. 876; Ber. d. Deutsch. ophth. Gesellsch. Heidelberg, v. 46, p. 147.

SZÜTS, A.
 1915. Studien über die feinere Beschaffenheit des Nervensystems des Regenwurmes, nebst Bemerkungen über die Organisierung des Nervensystems. Arch. f. Zellforsch., v. 13, p. 270.

T

TABOADA, R. P.
 1927-28. Note sur la structure du corps genouillé externe. Trav. du lab. de rech. biol. Madrid, v. 25, p. 319.
 *(?) Studios sobre las vías ópticas. Arch. hispanoam. de oftal.

TAFANI, A.
 1878. Nouvelles recherches sur la structure intime de la rétine chez les oiscaux. J. de micr., v. 2, pp. 164, 210.
 1883. Parcours et terminaison du nerf optique dans la rétine des crocodiles (*Champsa lucius*). Arch. ital. de biol., v. 4, p. 210.

TAGAWA, S.
 1928. Ueber die Dispersion der brechenden Medien des Auges. Arch. f. Augenh., v. 99, p. 587.

TAKAHASHI, H.
 1925. Studien über den Degenerationsprozess der Netzhaut und die Stromwege der Binnenflüssigkeit des Bulbus bei Anwendung einer vitalen Färbung. Arch. f. Ophth. (Graefe), v. 115, p. 305; *also* Nippon Ganka Gakkai Zassi, 1923.

TAKAHASHI, KEN
 1930. Ueber den Verschluss der fötalen Augenbecherspalte bei *Uroloncha domestica* Flower. Arb. a. d. med. Univ. Okayama, v. 2, Heft 1, p. 1.
 1930. Ueber die Morphogenese der fötalen Augenbecherspalte bei *Megalobatrachus japonicus*. Folia anat. japon., v. 8, p. 401.
 1931. Pri la genezo de la papilo de nervo optika ĉe *Sus scrofa domesticus. Ibid.*, v. 9, p. 149.

TALBOT, S. A.
 1942. A lateral localization in the cat's visual cortex. Fed. Proc., v. 1, p. 84.
 1951. Recent concepts of retinal color mechanisms. I and II. J. Opt. Soc. Amer., v. 41, pp. 895, 918.

TALBOT, S. A., & MARSHALL, W. H.
 1941. Physiological studies on neural mechanisms of visual localization and discrimination. Am. J. Ophth., ser. 3, v. 24, p. 1255.

TALIAFERRO, W. H.
1917. Orientation to light in planaria n. sp. and the function of the eyes. Anat. Rec., v. 11, p. 524.
1920. Reactions to light in *Planaria maculata*, with special reference to the function and structure of the eyes. J. Exper. Zoöl., v. 31, p. 59.

TALKO, J.
1869. Ueber die Siegel Römischer Oculisten in der Krimm und Transkaukasien. Klin. Monatsbl. f. Augenh., v. 7, p. 60.

TAMBURINI, A.
1880. Sulla genesi delle allucinazioni. Riv. sper. di freniat., v. 6, p. 126.
1880. Rivendicazione al Panizza della scoperta del centro visivo corticale. *Ibid.*, p. 153.

TANASESCO, J. C.
1905. Situation, rapports et branches de la carotide interne dans le sinus caverneux. Bull. et mém. Soc. anat. de Paris, ser. 6, v. 7, p. 834.

TANDLER, J.
1926–29. Lehrbuch der systematischen Anatomie, vols. 3 & 4. F. C. W. Vogel, Leipzig.

TANDLER, J., & RANZI, E.
1920. Chirurgische Anatomie und Operationstechnik des Zentralnervensystems. J. Springer, Berlin.

TANNERY, P.
1930. Pour l'histoire de la science hellène. 2d ed. Gauthier-Villars & Cie, Paris. 1st ed., F. Alcan, Paris, 1887.

TANSLEY, K.
1931. The regeneration of visual purple: its relation to dark adaptation and night blindness. J. Physiol., v. 71, p. 442.
1933. Factors affecting the development and regeneration of visual purple in the mammalian retina. Proc. Roy. Soc. London, ser. B, v. 114, p. 79.
1947. On degeneration of the inner layers of the retina in a case where central artery was interrupted, quoted by R. GRANIT in Sensory mechanisms of the retina, 1947, p. 204, footnote. (*See also* Nicholls in Brit. J. Ophth., v. 22, p. 672.)
1950. Visual purple. Doc. ophth., v. 4, p. 116.
1950. Retinal oxygen supply and macular pigmentation. Nature, v. 165, p. 524.

TANSLEY, K., DARTNALL, H. J. A., & THOMSON, L. C.
1950. Retinal oxygen supply and macular pigmentation. Nature. v. 165, p. 524.

TANZI, E.
1901. Una teoria dell'allucinazione. Riv. di pat. nerv., v. 6, p. 529.
1922. A che servano gli axoni centrifughi sulle vie di senso? *In:* Libro en honor de D. S. Ramón y Cajal, v. 1, p. 93.

TARKHAN, A. A.
1934. The innervation of the extrinsic ocular muscles. J. Anat., v. 68, p. 293.

TARTUFERI, F.
1878. Sull'anatomia microscopica e la morfologia cellulare delle eminenze bigemine dell'uomo e degli altri mammiferi. Riv. sper. di freniat., v. 4, pp. 52, 281.
1878. Sulla minuta tessitura delle eminenze bigemine anteriori dell'uomo. *Ibid.*, p. 304.
1879. Sull'anatomia minuta dell'eminenze bigemine anteriori delle scimmie. *Ibid.*, v. 5, p. 157.
1880. Il tratto ottico ed i centri visivi mesencefalici e corticali. *Ibid.*, v. 6, p. 380.
1880. Sulla struttura dei corpi genicolati. *Ibid.*, p. 381.
1882. Studio comparativo del tratto ottico e dei corpi genicolati nell'uomo, nella scimmia e nei mammiferi inferiori. *Ibid.*, v. 8, pp. 1, 196.
1885. Sull'anatomia minuta dell'eminenze bigemine anteriori dell'uomo. Arch. ital. per le mal. nerv., v. 22, p. 3.
1887. Sull'anatomia della retina. Arch. per le sc. med., v. 11, p. 335; Internat. Monatsschr. f. Anat. u. Phys., v. 4, p. 421.

TATE, G. H. H.
1935. Observations on the big-tailed shrew (*Sorex dispar* Batchelder). J. Mammal., v. 16, p. 213.
1944. A list of the mammals of the Japanese war area. 1. New Guinea, etc. 2. Greater Sunda area (Sumatra, Java, etc.). 3. Lesser Sunda Islands. 4. Borneo, etc. American Museum of Natural History, New York.
1946. Geographical distribution of the bats in the Australasian archipelago. Am. Mus. Novitates, No. 1323, p. 1.
1947. Mammals of eastern Asia. Macmillan Co., New York.

TATERKA, H.
1926. Beitrag zur Symptomatologie und Lokalisation der Sensibilitätsstörungen vom cerebralen Typus. Deutsch. Ztschr. f. Nervenh., v. 90, p. 193.

TAYLOR, C. L.
*(?) Andreas Vesalius. Longmans, Green & Co., New York. Announced, but not certain whether ever published. (*Cf.* Brit. M. J., v. 1, p. 34, 1920.) (*See* J. M. Ball 1910; and H. Cushing, A bio-bibliography of A. Vesalius, 1943, p. xxxvii.)

TAYLOR, F. S.
1939. The march of mind. A short history of science. Macmillan Co., New York.

TAYLOR, H. D., KNOCHE, L., & GRANVILLE, W. C.
1950. Descriptive color names dictionary. Container Corp. of America, New York.

TAYLOR, H. L.
1924. The antiquity of lenses. J. Physiol. Opt., v. 5, p. 514.

TAYLOR, II. O.
1922. Greek biology and medicine. Marshall Jones Co., Boston.

TAYLOR, W. P.
1943. The biologist and the war. Audubon Mag., v. 45, p. 71.

TEALE, E. W.
1937. Grassroot jungles. A book of insects. Dodd, Mead & Co., New York.

TEILHARD DE CHARDIN, P.
1921. La présence d'un tarsier dans les phosphorites du Quercy et sur l'origine tarsienne de l'homme. Anthropologie, v. 31, p. 329.
1952. On the zoölogical position and the evolutionary significance of australopithecines. Tr. New York Acad. Sc., v. 14 (ser. II), p. 208.

TEITELBAUM, H. A., LANGWORTHY, O. R., & KING, A. B.
1942. Apraxia. Report of a case, with autopsy. Arch. Neurol. & Psychiat., v. 48, p. 469.

TELESIO, B.
1925. Le osservazioni anatomo-fisiologiche di Bernardino Telesio sugli organi di senso della visione e dell'udito, by G. Calogero. Arch. di ottal., v. 32, p. 312.

TELLO, J. F.
1904. Disposición macroscópica y estructura del cuerpo geniculado externo. Trab. (Trav.) del lab. de invest. biol. Madrid, v. 3, p. 39.
1922. Los diferenciaciones neuronales en el embrión de polo, durante los cuatro primeros días de la incubación. *In:* Libro en honor de D. S. Ramón y Cajal, v. 1, p. 205.
1930. El retículo de las células ciliadas del laberinto y su relación con los terminaciones nerviosas. Bol. Soc. españ. de hist. nat., v. 30, p. 357.
1931. Le réticule des cellules ciliées du labyrinthe chez la souris et son indépendance des terminaisons nerveuses de la VIIIᵉ paire. Trav. du lab. de rech. biol. Madrid, v. 27, p. 151.
1935. Santiago Ramón y Cajal, 1852–1934. Sa formation et son œuvre. Résumé de son autobiographie. *Ibid.*, v. 30, p. 1; *also* Anat. Anz., v. 80, p. 46.

TEMKIN, O.
1933. The doctrine of epilepsy in the Hippocratic writings. Bull. Inst. Hist. Med. Johns Hopkins Univ., v. 1, p. 277.

TEN CATE, J.
1939. Bedingte Reflexe auf Lichtreize bei einer Katze nach beiderseitigen Exstirpation der Area striata. Arch. néerl. de physiol., v. 24, p. 61.

TEN DOESSCHATE, G.
1946. Some historical notes on spectacles and on beryllus. Brit. J. Ophth., v. 30, p. 660.

TEN DOESSCHATE, J., & FISCHER, F. P.
1948. Die mechanischen Eigenschaften des Auges und seiner Gewebe. Doc. ophth., v. 2, p. 193.

TEPLJASCHIN, A.
1894. Zur Kenntniss der histologischen Veränderungen der Netzhaut nach experimentellen Verwundungen. Arch. f. Augenh., v. 28, p. 353.

TERRIEN, F., & VINSONNEAU
1915. Hémianopsie par blessures de guerre. Arch. d'opht., v. 34, p. 785.
1916. Note complémentaire sur les hémianopsies par blessures de guerre. *Ibid.*, v. 35, p. 286.

TERTULLIAN (QUINTUS SEPTIMIUS FLORENS TERTULLIANUS CARTHAGINIENSIS) *ca.* 210 A.D.; *see* A. C. COXE; J. H. WASZINK

TESTELIN
1866–67. Note sur l'hémianopie. J. de méd., chir. & pharm. Bruxelles, v. 42, p. 334. German trans.: Notiz über Hemiopie. Klin. Monatsbl. f. Augenh., v. 5, p. 331, 1867.

THAUER, R., & PETERS, G.
1938. Sensibilität und Motorik bei lange überlebenden Zwischen-Mittelhirn-Tauben. Arch. f. d. ges. Physiol. (Pflüger), v. 240, p. 503.

THAUER, R., & STUKE, F.
1940. Ueber die funktionelle Bedeutung der motorischen Region der Grosshirnrinde für den Sehakt des Hundes. Arch. f. d. ges. Physiol. (Pflüger), v. 243, p. 347.

THERMAN, P. O.
1938. The neurophysiology of the retina in the light of chemical methods of modifying its excitability. Acta Soc. sc. Fennicae, new ser. B, v. 2, No. 1.

THIELE, R.
1927. Ueber Griesingers Satz: "Geisteskrankheiten sind Gehirnkrankheiten." Monatsschr. f. Psychiat. u. Neurol., v. 63, p. 294.

THIENEMANN, A.
1925. Der See als Lebenseinheit. Naturwiss., v. 13, p. 589.

THIENEMANN, A.—*Continued*
1939. Grundzüge einer allgemeinen Oekologie. Arch. f. Hydrobiol., v. 35, p. 267.

THOMAS, ANDRÉS
1903. Recherches sur le faisceau longitudinal postérieur et la substance réticulée bulbo-protubérantielle, le faisceau central de la calotte et le faisceau de Helweg. Rev. neurol., v. 11, p. 94.
1928. Tumeur de l'extrémité antérieure du lobe temporal gauche. *Ibid.*, v. 35 (2), p. 207.

THOMAS, B.
1937. The Arabs. T. Butterworth, London.

THOMAS, O.
1892. On some new mammalia from the East Indian archipelago. Ann. Mag. Nat. Hist., ser. 6, v. 9, p. 250.
1896. *Tarsius philippinensis.* Tr. Zoöl. Soc. London, v. 14, p. 381.

THOMAS, O., & WROUGHTON, R. C.
1909. On mammals from the Rhio archipelago and Malay peninsula collected by Messrs. H. C. Robinson, C. Boden Kloss, and E. Seimund, and presented to the National Museum by the government of the Federated Malay States, with notes by the collectors. J. Fed. Malay Mus., v. 4, p. 99.

THOMPSON, A. R.
1033. Nature by night. R. O. Ballou, New York.

THOMPSON, E. L.
1942. The dorsal longitudinal fasciculus in *Didelphis virginiana.* J. Comp. Neurol., v. 76, p. 239.

THOMPSON, R. C.
1923. Assyrian medical texts from the originals in the British Museum. Oxford University Press, London. *Also* Proc. Roy. Soc. Med., London, v. 17 and v. 19.
1924–26. Assyrian medical texts. Proc. Roy. Soc. Med. London, v. 17 (sec. hist. med.), p. 1; v. 19 (sec. hist. med.), p. 29.

THOMPSON, R. K., & SMITH, G. W.
1951. Experimental occlusion of the middle cerebral artery during arterial hypotension. Tr. Am. Neurol. A. (76th ann. meet.), p. 203.

THOMPSON, W. G., & BROWN, S.
1890. The center for vision, being an investigation into the occipital lobes of the dog, cat and monkey. Researches of Loomis Lab., Med. Dept. Univ. of City of New York, v. 1, p. 13.

THOMSON, D. F.
1948. An Arnhem adventure. Nat. Geog. Mag., v. 93, p. 403.

THOMSON, L. C.
1947. The effect of change of brightness level upon the foveal luminosity curve measured with small fields. J. Physiol., v. 106, p. 368.
1949. Intensity discrimination of the central fovea measured with small fields. *Ibid.*, v. 108, p. 78.
1949. The photopic luminosity curve and visual purple. Brit. J. Ophth., v. 33, p. 505.
1951. Studies on action currents of mammalian optic nerve fibers following retinal stimulation by light. Tech. Rep. ONRL-61-51, Office of Naval Research, London, England. (Am. Embassy.)
1951. The spectral sensitivity of the central fovea. J. Physiol., v. 112, p. 114.

THOMSON, L. C., & WRIGHT, W. D.
1947. The colour sensitivity of the retina within the central fovea of man. J. Physiol., v. 105, p. 316.

THOMSON, W.
1876. Case of sector-like defect of field of vision. Tr. Am. Ophth. Soc., 11th meet., p. 337.

THOMSON, W. E.
1897. Sensory aphasia, with sector-shaped homonymous defect of the fields of vision, a study in localization. Edinburgh M. J., N.S., v. 1, p. 512.

THONE, F.
1946. Down from the trees. Science News Letter, v. 50, p. 254.

THOREK, M.
1949. Modern surgical technic, vol. 1 (general, head & neck, including orbit & eye). 2d ed. J. B. Lippincott Co., Philadelphia.

THORINGTON, J.
1939. Refraction of the human eye and methods of estimating the refraction. 3d ed. Blakiston's Son & Co., Philadelphia.

THORNDIKE, L.
1923–41. A history of magic and experimental science. 6 vols. Macmillan Co. & Columbia University Press, New York.

THORNER, W.
1910. Die Grenzen der Sehsphäre. Klin. Monatsbl. f. Augenh., N.F., v. 9, p. 590.

THROCKMORTON, T. B.
1921. Homonymous hemianopia as an early symptom of brain tumor. J. Am. Med. Assoc., v. 76, p. 1815.

THUMA, B. D.
1928. Studies on the diencephalon of the cat. I. The cytoarchitecture of the corpus geniculatum laterale. J. Comp. Neurol., v. 46, p. 173.

TIEDEMANN, F.
1821. Icones cerebri simiarum et quorundam mammalium rariorum. Mohr & Winter, Heidelbergae.

1823. Anatomie du cerveau, contenant l'histoire de son développement dans le fœtus, avec une exposition comparative de sa structure dans les animaux. J.-B. Baillière, Paris.

1837. Das Hirn des Negers mit dem des Europäers und Orang-Outangs verglichen. K. Winter, Heidelberg. English trans.: On the brain of the Negro, compared with that of the European and the orang-outang. Phil. Tr. Roy. Soc. London, v. 126, p. 497.

TIEGS, O. W.

1926. On the inadequacy of the conception of the neurone, etc. Australian J. Exper. Biol. & M. Sc., v. 3, p. 45.

1926. The structure of the neurone junctions of the spinal cord. *Ibid.*, p. 69.

1927. A further note on the structure of the neurone junctions of the spinal cord. *Ibid.*, v. 4, p. 25.

1927. The structure of the neurone junctions in sympathetic ganglia, etc. *Ibid.*, p. 79.

1927. A critical review of the evidence on which is based the theory of discontinuous synapses in the spinal cord. *Ibid.*, p. 193.

1927. On the neurofibrillar structure of the nerve cell. *Ibid.*, v. 6, p. 111.

1931. A study of the neurofibril structure of the nerve cell. J. Comp. Neurol., v. 52, p. 189.

TIGERSTEDT, R. A. A.

1921–23. Die Physiologie des Kreislaufes. 2d ed. 4 vols. W. de Gruyter, Berlin & Leipzig.

TILLYARD, R. J.

1917. The biology of dragonflies. Cambridge University Press, Cambridge.

TILMANN, H.

1915. Schädelschüsse. Beitr. z. klin. Chir., v. 96, p. 454.

TILNEY, F.

1927. The brain of prehistoric man: a study of the psychologic foundations of human progress. Arch. Neurol. & Psychiat., v. 17, p. 723.

1927. The brain stem of Tarsius. A critical comparison with other primates. J. Comp. Neurol., v. 43, p. 371.

1928. The brain from ape to man. A contribution to the study of the evolution and development of the human brain. 2 vols. P. B. Hoeber, New York.

TINBERGEN, N.

1953. Social behaviour in animals. Methuen & Co., London; John Wiley & Sons, New York.

TODD, R. B., & BOWMAN, W.

1859. The physiological anatomy of man. 2 vols. J. W. Parker & Sons, London. (*See also* W. Bowman 1847.)

TÖNNIES, J. F.

1934. Die unipolare Ableitung elektrischer Spannungen vom menschlichen Gehirn. Naturwiss., v. 22, p. 411.

TÖNNIS, W.

1939. Zirkulationsstörungen bei krankhaftem Schädelinnendruck. Zentralbl. f. d. ges. Neurol. u. Psychiat., v. 94, p. 354.

TÖPLY, R. VON

1898. Studien zur Geschichte der Anatomie im Mittelalter. F. Deuticke, Leipzig & Wien.

TÖRÖK, A.

1881. Die Orbita bei den Primaten und die Methode ihrer Messung. Correspondenzbl. Anthropol., Ethnol. & Urgesch., p. 146.

TOLDT, C.

1904. An atlas of human anatomy, v. 6. Rebman Co., New York. Also German eds.

TOMASCHEWSKI, B.

1899. Ueber die Localisation der corticalen sensorischen Centren. Neurol. Centralbl., v. 8, p. 213.

TOMLINSON, H. M.

1920. The sea and the jungle. E. P. Dutton & Co., New York.

TONCRAY, J. E., & KRIEG, W. J. S.

1946. The nuclei of the human thalamus: a comparative approach. J. Comp. Neurol., v. 85, p. 421.

TONNER, F.

1943–44. Die Messung der Empfindungsfläche und Sehschärfe unter variablen Bedingungen im gleichen Versuch. Arch. f. d. ges. Physiol. (Pflüger), v. 247, p. 149.

1943–44. Die sphärische Aberration als begrenzender Factor der Abbildungsschärfe. *Ibid.*, p. 160.

1943–44. Die Grösse der Empfindungsfläche eines Lichtpunktes und der Zapfenraster. *Ibid.*, p. 168.

1943–44. Die Sehschärfe. *Ibid.*, p. 183.

TONNER, F., & WEBER, H. H.

1943–44. Die Grundlagen der Deutung der Sehschärfe. Arch. f. d. ges. Physiol. (Pflüger), v. 247, p. 145.

TOPOLANSKI, A.

1898. Das Verhalten der Augenmuskeln bei centraler Reizung. Das Coordinationscentrum und die Bahnen für coordinirte Augenbewegungen. Arch. f. Ophth. (Graefe), v. 46, p. 452.

TORNATOLA, S.

*1889. Contributo alla conoscenza della struttura del chiasma. G. Crupi, Messina.

1904. Sulla membrana limitante interna della

retina nei vertebrati. Anat. Anz., v. 24, p. 536.

TORREY, T. W.
1946. Phylogenetic interpretations in the teaching of comparative vertebrate anatomy. Proc. Indiana Acad. Sc., v. 55, p. 206; Turtox News, v. 25, p. 152.

TOUCHE
1900. Cécité corticale; hallucination de la vue. Compt. rend. Soc. de biol., v. 52, p. 390.

TOULOUSE, E., & MARCHAND, L.
1907. Cécité par ramollissement symétrique des sphères visuelles. Bull. et mém. Soc. anat. de Paris, v. 82, p. 646.

TOWER, S.
1940. Units for sensory reception in cornea; with notes on nerve impulses from sclera, iris and lens. J. Neurophysiol., v. 3, p. 486.

TOWER, S. S., & HINES, M.
1935. Dissociation of the pyramidal and extrapyramidal functions of the frontal lobe. Science, v. 82, p. 376.

TRABER, Z.
1675. *Nervus Opticus* sive tractatus theoricus, in tres libros opticam, catoptricam, dioptricam distributus. In quibus radiorum a lumine, vel objecto per medium diaphanum processus, natura, proprietates, et effectus, selectis, et rarioribus experientijs, figuris, demonstrationibusque exhibentur. Viennae Austriae, Typis J. Chr. Cosmerovij. Another ed., 1690.

TRACY, H. C.
1926. The development of motility and behavior reactions in the toadfish (*Opsanus tau*). J. Comp. Neurol., v. 40, p. 253.

TRAQUAIR, H. M.
1917. Bitemporal hemiopia: the later stages and the special features of the scotoma. Brit. J. Ophth., v. 1, pp. 216, 281, 337.
1922. The course of the geniculo-calcarine visual path in relation to the temporal lobe. *Ibid.*, v. 6, p. 251.
1923. The differential characters of scotomata and their interpretation. Tr. Ophth. Soc. United Kingdom, v. 43, p. 480.
1925. The special vulnerability of the macular fibres and "sparing of the macula." Brit. J. Ophth., v. 9, p. 53.
1931. Perimetry in study of glaucoma. Tr. Ophth. Soc. United Kingdom, v. 51, p. 585.
1939. Clinical detection of early changes in the visual field. Arch. Ophth., v. 22 (O.S., v. 79), p. 947.
1944. The nerve-fibre bundle defect. Tr. Ophth. Soc. United Kingdom, v. 64, p. 3.

1946. An introduction to clinical perimetry. 5th ed. H. Kimpton, London; C. V. Mosby Co., St. Louis.
1948. Clinical ophthalmology for general practitioners and students. C. V. Mosby, St. Louis.

TRAQUAIR, H. M., DOTT, N. M., & RUSSELL, R.
1935. Traumatic lesions of the optic chiasma. Brain, v. 58, p. 398.

TRAUTMANN, M. B., & HUBBS, C. L.
1935. When do pike shed their teeth? Am. Fish. Soc., v. 65, p. 261.

TRAVER, J. R.
1929. The habits of the black-nosed dace, *Rhinichthys atronasus* (Mitchill). J. Elisha Mitchell Sc. Soc., v. 45, p. 101.

TREITEL, T.
1879. Ueber den Werth der Gesichtsfeldmessung mit Pigmenten für die Auffassung der Krankheiten des nervösen Sehapparates. Arch. f. Ophth. (Graefe), v. 25 (2), p. 29; (3), p. 1.
1887. Ueber das Wesen der Lichtsinnstörungen. *Ibid.*, v. 33 (1), p. 31.
1890–91. Weitere Beiträge zur Lehre von den Functionsstörungen des Gesichtssinnes. *Ibid.*, v. 36 (3), p. 99; v. 37 (2), p. 151.

TRENDELENBURG, W.
1904. Quantitative Untersuchungen über die Bleichung des Sehpurpurs in monochromatischem Licht. Ztschr. f. Psychol. u. Physiol. d. Sinnesorg., v. 37, p. 1.
1943. Der Gesichtssinn. Grundzüge der physiologischen Optik. Springer-Verlag, Berlin.

TRENDELENBURG, W., & SCHMIDT, I.
1930. Untersuchungen über das Farbensystem der Affen. (Spektrale Unterschiedsempfindlichkeit und spektrale Farbenmischung bei Helladaptation). Ztschr. f. vergl. Physiol., v. 12, p. 249.

TRETJAKOFF, D. K.
1909. Das Nervensystem von Ammocoetes. I. Das Rückenmark. II. Das Gehirn. Arch. f. mikr. Anat., v. 73, p. 607; v. 74, p. 636.
1913. Zur Anatomie des Auges der Kröte. Ztschr. f. wissensch. Zool., v. 105, p. 537.
1915. Die Parietalorgane von *Petromyzon fluviatilis*. *Ibid.*, v. 113, p. 1.
1915. The sense organs of *Lampetra fluviatilis* (in Russian). Bull. phys.-math. Dept. Imp. Novoross. Univ. Odessa.

TREVIRANUS, G. R.
1828. Beiträge zur Anatomie und Physiologie der Sinneswerkzeuge des Menschen und der Thiere. Fasc. 1. Beiträge zur Lehre von den Gesichtswerkzeugen und dem Sehen des

Menschen und der Thiere. J. G. Heyse, Bremen.

1831–32. Die Erscheinungen und Gesetze des organischen Lebens. 2 vols. J. G. Heyse, Bremen. (*See* v. 2, p. 69, "Das Gesicht.")

1835–38. Beiträge zur Aufklärung der Erscheinungen und Gesetze des organischen Lebens, v. 1 (1), pp. 7, 41, 69; (2), p. 42; (3), pp. 51, 91; (4). J. G. Heyse, Bremen.

1837. Nachträge zu den Beobachtungen des Verfassers über den innern Bau der Retina. *In:* his Beitr. z. Aufkl. d. Ersch. u. Ges. d. org. Lebens, v. 1 (3), p. 91.

1837. Neue Untersuchungen über die Structur und Ausbreitung der Retina des Menschen. Ztschr. f. d. Ophth. (Ammon), v. 5, p. 489.

1838. Tafeln zur Erläuterung der neuen Untersuchungen über die organischen Elemente der thierischen Körper und deren Zusammensetzungen. *In:* his Beitr. z. Aufkl. d. Ersch. u. Ges. d. org. Lebens (ed. C. T. TREVIRANUS), v. 1 (4).

TRIANT, A.
*1874. Recherches sur le chiasma des nerfs optiques dans les différentes classes des animaux vertébrés. Thèse de Nancy.

TRICOMI-ALLEGRA, G.
1907. Sulle connessioni dei tubercoli bigemini posteriori. Vie corte. Anat. Anz., v. 31, p. 335.

TRIEPEL, H.
1920. Ein doppelseitiger Anophthalmus. Weitgehende Selbstdifferenzierung. Arch. f. Entwicklungsmech. d. Org., v. 47, p. 25.

TROCELLO, E.
1920. I rapporti topografici delle retine oculari con la corteccia cerebrale. Ann. d. med. nav. e colon., v. 26, p. 1.

TROLAND, L. T.
1917. The nature of the visual receptor process. J. Opt. Soc. Amer., v. 1, p. 3.

1920–21. The enigma of color vision. Am. J. Physiol. Opt., v. 1, p. 317; v. 2, p. 23.

1924. The optics of the nervous system. J. Opt. Soc. Amer., v. 8, p. 389.

1929. Optics as seen by a psychologist. *Ibid.*, v. 18, p. 223.

1929–32. The principles of psychophysiology. 3 vols. D. Van Nostrand Co., New York.

TROLARD, P.
1906. Le faisceau longitudinal inférieur du cerveau. Rev. neurol., v. 14, p. 440.

TRONCOSO, M. U.
1942. Microanatomy of the eye with the slitlamp microscope. II. Comparative anatomy of the ciliary body, zonula and related structures in mammalia. Am. J. Ophth., v. 25, p.

1. (*See,* for Part I, Troncoso & Castroviejo 1936.)

TRONCOSO, M. U., & CASTROVIEJO, R.
1936. Microanatomy of the eye with the slitlamp microscope. I. Comparative anatomy of the angle of the anterior chamber in living and sectioned eyes of mammalia. Am. J. Ophth., v. 19, p. 371.

TROUESSART, E.-L.
1898–99. Catalogus mammalium tam viventium quam fossilium. 2 vols. R. Friedländer & Sohn, Berolini.

1922. La distribution géographique des animaux. O. Doin, Paris.

TROUGHTON, E. L.
1947. Furred animals of Australia. Charles Scribner's Sons, New York.

TRUETA, J.
1952. Ramón y Cajal. The first centenary of his birth. Lancet, v. 2, p. 281.

TRUEX, R. C., & KELLNER, C. E.
1948. Detailed atlas of the head and neck. Oxford University Press, New York.

TRUMP, R. J.
1923–24. Binocular vision and the stereoscopic sense. Tr. Opt. Soc. London, v. 25, p. 261.

TRYON, C. A., JR.
1943. The great gray owl as a predator on pocket gophers. Wilson Bull. (Ann Arbor), v. 55, p. 130.

TSAI, CHIAO
1925. The optic tracts and centers of the opossum, *Didelphis virginiana*. J. Comp. Neurol., v. 39, p. 173.

TSANG, YÜ-CHÜAN
1934–36. The functions of the visual areas of the cerebral cortex of the rat in the learning and retention of the maze. I, II. Comp. Psychol. Monog., v. 10, No. 4 (50); v. 12, No. 2 (57).

1935. The blood supply of the lateral geniculate body in the rat. J. Comp. Neurol., v. 61, p. 553.

1936. Vascular changes in the lateral geniculate body following extirpation of the visual cortex. Arch. Neurol. & Psychiat., v. 36, p. 569.

1937. Visual centers in blinded rats. J. Comp. Neurol., v. 66, p. 211.

1937. Visual sensitivity in rats deprived of visual cortex in infancy. J. Comp. Psychol., v. 24, p. 255.

TSCHERMAK (TSCHERMAK-SEYSENEGG), A. VON
1902. Studien über das Binokularsehen der Wirbeltiere. Arch. f. d. ges. Physiol. (Pflüger), v. 91, p. 1.

1905. Ueber die Grundlagen der optischen Lokalisation nach Höhe und Breite. Ergebn. d. Physiol. (Asher & Spiro), v. 4, p. 517.

1909. Die Physiologie des Gehirns. *In:* NAGEL, Handb. d. Physiol. d. Mensch., v. 4, p. 1.

1914. Wie die Tiere sehen, verglichen mit dem Menschen. Vorträge des Vereins z. Verbr. naturwiss. Kenntn. in Wien, 54. Jahrg., p. 335.

1915. Das Sehen der Fische. Naturwiss., v. 3, p. 177.

1921. Der exakte Subjektivismus in der neuen Sinnesphysiologie. Arch. f. d. ges. Physiol. (Pflüger), v. 188, p. 1.

1927. Binokularsehen und Sehnervenkreuzung. Ztschr. f. Augenh., v. 61, p. 205.

1929. Licht- und Farbensinn. *In:* BETHE *et al.*, Handb. d. norm. u. path. Physiol., v. 12 (1), p. 295.

1930. Drei- oder Vierfarbenlehre? (Zugleich eine Darstellung der Rezeptor-Reagententheorie des Farbensehens.) Naturwiss., v. 18, p. 589.

1931. Optischer Raumsinn. *In:* BETHE *et al.*, Handb. d. norm. u. path. Physiol., v. 12 (2), p. 834.

1931. Augenbewegungen. *Ibid.*, p. 1000.

1937. Methodik des optischen Raumsinnes und der Augenbewegungen. *In:* E. ABDERHALDEN, Handb. d. biol. Arbeitsmeth., Abt. V, Teil 6 (2), p. 1427.

1942. Einführung in die physiologische Optik. J. F. Bergmann, München; Springer-Verlag, Berlin & Wien.

1948. Physiologisch-optische Studien. Doc. ophth., v. 2, p. 10.

TSCHERNING, M.

1922. La théorie de Th. Young sur la vision des couleurs. Arch. néerl. de physiol., v. 7, p. 450.

TSCHUDI, J. J. VON

1845–46. Peru. Reiseskizzen aus den Jahren 1838–42. 2 vols. in 1. Scheitlin & Zollikofer, St. Gallen. English trans.: Travels in Peru, during the years 1838–42. D. Bogue, London.

1866–69. Reisen durch Südamerika. 5 vols. Brockhaus, Leipzig.

TSUCHIDA, U.

1906. Ueber die Ursprungskerne der Augenbewegungsnerven und über die mit diesen in Beziehung stehenden Bahnen im Mittel- und Zwischenhirn. Arb. a. d. hirnanat. Inst. Zürich (Monakow), v. 2, p. 1.

1907. Ein Beitrag zur Anatomie der Sehstrahlungen beim Menschen. Arch. f. Psychiat. u. Nervenkr., v. 42, p. 212.

TÜRCK, L. (*see also* NEUBURGER 1910)

1849. Mikroskopischer Befund des Rückenmarkes eines paraplegischen Weibes. Ztschr. f. d. Gesellsch. d. Aerzte zu Wien, v. 5 (1), p. 173; *also* Jahrb. f. Psychiat., v. 31, p. 30, 1910.

1850. Ueber ein bisher unbekanntes Verhalten des Rückenmarkes bei Homiplegie. Ztschr. f. d. Gesellsch. d. Aerzte zu Wien, v. 6 (1), p. 6; *also* Jahrb. f. Psychiat., v. 31, p. 37, 1910.

1851. Ueber secundäre Erkrankung einzelner Rückenmarksstränge und ihrer Fortsetzungen zum Gehirne. Sitzungsb. d. Akad. d. Wissensch. Wien, math.-naturw. Kl., v. 6, p. 288; Ztschr. f. d. Gesellsch. d. Aerzte zu Wien, v. 8 (2), p. 511, 1852; *also* Jahrb. f. Psychiat., v. 31, p. 64, 1910.

1910. Ludwig Türcks gesammelte neurologische Schriften. Jahrb. f. Psychiat. u. Neurol., v. 31, pp. 23–194.

TUMBELAKA, R.

1915. Das Gehirn eines Affen, worin die interhemisphäriale Balkenverbindung fehlt. Folia neuro-biol., v. 9, p. 1.

TUREEN, L. L.

1938. Circulation of the spinal cord and the effect of vascular occlusion. *In:* The circulation of the brain and spinal cord, Research. Pub. A. Research Nerv. & Ment. Dis., v. 18, p. 394.

TURNER, J. P.

1940. The question of the cell theory. Science, v. 91, p. 404.

TURNER, O. A.

1948. Growth and development of the cerebral cortical pattern in man. Arch. Neurol. & Psychiat., v. 59, p. 1.

TURNER, W.

1865–66. Notes more especially on the bridging convolutions in the brain of the chimpanzee. Proc. Roy. Soc. Edinburgh, v. 5, p. 578.

1866. Convolutions of the human cerebrum topographically considered. Edinburgh M. J., v. 11, p. 1105.

TURNER, W. A.

1898. A note on conjugate movements of the eyeballs. Tr. Ophth. Soc. United Kingdom, v. 18, p. 395.

TWYMAN, F.

1932. Article: Lens, Encyclopaedia Britannica, 14th ed., v. 13, p. 919.

U

UEBERHORST, C.

1876. Die Entstehung der Gesichtswahrnehmung. Versuch der Auflösung eines Problems der physiologischen Psychologie. Vanderhoeck & Ruprecht's Verlag, Göttingen.

UEXKÜLL, J. VON
1921. Umwelt und Innenwelt der Tiere. J. Springer, Berlin.
1926. Theoretical biology. Kegan Paul, Trench, Trubner & Co., London; Harcourt, Brace & Co., New York.
1931. Die Rolle des Subjekts in der Biologie. Naturwiss., v. 19, p. 385.

UEXKÜLL, J. VON, & BROCK, F.
1927. Atlas zur Bestimmung der Orte in den Sehräumen der Tiere. Ztschr. f. vergl. Physiol., v. 5, p. 167.

UEXKÜLL, J. J. VON, & KRISZAT, G.
1934. Streifzüge durch die Umwelten von Tieren und Menschen. J. Springer, Berlin.

UHTHOFF, W.
1880. Beitrag zur Sehnervenatrophie. Arch. f. Ophth. (Graefe), v. 26 (1), p. 244.
1886. Ueber das Abhängigkeitsverhältniss der Sehschärfe von der Beleuchtungsintensität. *Ibid.*, v. 32 (1), p. 171.
1886-87. Untersuchungen über den Einfluss des chronischen Alkoholismus auf das menschliche Sehorgan. *Ibid.*, (4), p. 95; v. 33 (1), p. 257.
1890. Weitere Untersuchungen über die Abhängigkeit der Sehschärfe von der Intensität sowie von der Wellenlänge im Spektrum. *Ibid.*, v. 36 (1), p. 33.
1890. Untersuchungen über die bei der multiplen Herdsklerose vorkommenden Augenstörungen. Arch. f. Psychiat., v. 21, p. 303.
1899. Ueber Gesichtshallucinationen bei Erkrankungen des Sehorgans. Ber. d. Deutsch. ophth. Gesellsch. Heidelberg, v. 27, p. 39.
1899. Kurzer Bericht über die Untersuchung eines Falles von congenitaler totaler Farbenblindheit. *Ibid.*, p. 158.
1899. Ein Beitrag zur congenitalen totalen Farbenblindheit. Ztschr. f. Psychol. u. Physiol. d. Sinnesorg., v. 20, p. 326. (*See* König 1899.)
1900. Ueber einen Fall von einseitiger erworbener totaler Farbenblindheit auf Grundlage einer peripheren neuritischen Erkrankung des Opticus-Stammes bei fast voller Sehschärfe (S= 5/6). Verhandl. d. Gesellsch. deutsch. Naturforsch. u. Aerzte, 71. Versamml., p. 332.
1902. Ein Beitrag zur Kenntniss der Sehstörungen nach Hirnverletzung nebst Bemerkungen über das Auftreten functioneller nervöser Störungen bei anatomischen Hirnläsionen. Ber. d. Deutsch. ophth. Gesellsch. Heidelberg, v. 30, p. 185.

1908. Ueber das Sehen und über Sehstörungen in ihren Bezichungen zum Gehirn. Inaugural lecture. G. Fischer, Jena.
1915. Beiträge zu den hemianopischen Gesichtsfeldstörungen nach Schädelschüssen, besonders solchen im Bereich des Hinterhauptes. Klin. Monatsbl. f. Augenh., v. 55, p. 105.
1916. Kriegs-ophthalmologische Erfahrungen und Betrachtungen. Berlin. klin. Wchnschr., v. 53, p. 5.
1922. Die Verletzungen der zentralen optischen Bahnen und des Sehzentrums bei Schädelschüssen, speziell Hinterhauptschüssen. *In:* SCHJERNING, Handb. d. ärztl. Erfahr. i. Weltkriege 1914–18, v. 5 (Augenheilkunde, ed. AXENFELD). J. A. Barth, Leipzig.
1923. Ueber einen Fall von binasaler Hemianopsie. Klin. Monatsschr. f. Augenh., v. 70, p. 138.
1925. Zu den arteriellen und venösen Zirkulationsstörungen der Netzhaut. Ber. d. Deutsch. ophth. Gesellsch. Heidelberg, v. 45, p. 63.
1927. Ueber Hemianopie und Flimmerskotom. Klin. Monatsbl. f. Augenh., v. 78, p. 305.
1927. Vergleich zwischen den embolischen und thrombotischen Vorgängen in den Netzhautgefässen und denen des Gehirns. *Ibid.*, suppl., p. 1.

ULLRICH, F.
1919. Die anatomische und vivisektorische Technik des Galenos. Inaugural-Dissertation zur Erlangung der medizinischen Doktorwürde an der Universität zu Leipzig vorgelegt von F. U. aus Wendischcarsdorf, approb. Arzt. Buch- und Kunstdruckerei Julius Booch, Werdau i.Sa. (Inhaber: Otto Landgraf), 1919.

UNGER, L.
1906. Untersuchungen über die Morphologie und Faserung des Reptiliengehirnes. I. Das Vorderhirn des Gecko. Anat. Hefte (Merkel & Bonnet), v. 31, p. 269.

UNITED STATES ADJUTANT-GENERAL'S OFFICE
1948. Studies in visual acuity. Government Printing Office, Washington, D.C.

UNZER, J. A.
*1746. Gedanken vom Einflusse der Seele in ihren Körper. Halle.
*1768. Grundriss eines Lehrgebäudes von der Sinnlichkeit der thierischen Körper. Rinteln.
*1771. Erste Gründe einer Physiologie der eigentlichen thierischen Natur der thierischen Körper. Weidmanns Erben u. Reich, Leipzig.

URY, B., & OLDBERG, E.
  1940. Effect of cortical lesions on effective pupillary reactions. J. Neurophysiol., v. 3, p. 201.
USHER, C. H.
  1906. A note on the choroid at the macular region. Tr. Ophth. Soc. United Kingdom, v. 26, p. 107.
USHER, C. H., & DEAN, G.
  1896. Experimental research on the course of the optic nerve fibres. Brit. M. J., v. 2, p. 71.
UYAMA, Y.
  1926. Untersuchungen über die Verbreitung der Neurofibrillen in der Netzhaut bei den Wirbeltieren. Folia anat. japon., v. 3, p. 389.
  1927. Ein Beitrag zur Kenntnis der Anatomie der Sehzellen in der Netzhaut bei Affen und Meerschweinchen. Arch. f. Ophth. (Graefe), v. 118, p. 723.
  1934. Regionäre Verschiedenheiten der Horizontalzellen. *Ibid.*, v. 132, p. 10.
UYAMA, Y., & MIYAKE, T.
  1934. Weitere Mitteilung über die Verbreitung der Neurofibrillen in der Netzhaut. Arch. f. Ophth. (Graefe), v. 133, p. 157.

V

VAIL, D.
  1948. The blood supply of the optic nerve and its clinical significance. Am. J. Ophth., ser. 3, v. 31, p. 1.
VALDÉS; *see* DAZA DE VALDÉS
VALENTIN, G.
  1837–45. Retina (Jacobsche Membran, Bau der Netzhaut). *In*: G. VALENTIN (ed.), Repertorium f. Anat. u. Physiol., v. 1, p. 161; v. 2, pp. 249, 250; v. 4, p. 66; v. 5, p. 150; v. 6, p. 140; v. 7, p. 169; v. 8, p. 188.
VALETON, M. T.
  1908. Beitrag zur vergleichenden Anatomie des hinteren Vierhügels des Menschen und einiger Säugetiere. Arb. a. d. Neurol. Inst. Wien (Obersteiner), v. 14, p. 29.
VALIÈRE-VIALEIX
  1927. A propos de la cécité corticale. Considérations sur la symptomatologie de certaines lésions de la voie optique centrale: modifications de la vision maculaire et du champ visuel. Ann. d'ocul., v. 164, p. 34.
VALKENBURG; *see* VAN VALKENBURG
VALLOIS, H. V.
  1946. Les nouveaux pithécanthropes et le problème de l'origine de l'homme. Nature (Paris), No. 3125, p. 307.
VALSALVA, A. M.
  1740. Viri celeb. A. M. Valsalvae Opera, etc.

Tract. de Aure, etc., et Dissertationes Anatomicae, etc., Ad Oculos, etc. 2 vols. Venetiis, ap. F. Pitteri.
VALUDE, E., & SCHIFF-WERTHEIMER, S.
  1923. Sur un cas d'amaurose définitive sans lésions ophtalmoscopiques. Diagnostic différentiel entre tumeur cérébrale et encéphalite épidémique. Ann. d'ocul., v. 160, p. 731.
VALVERDA, J.
  1589. Anatome Corporis Humani, auctore Joh. Valverdo, nunc primum a. Mich. Columbo latine reddita. Venetiis.
VAN BOGAERT, L.
  1926. Sur les hallucinations visuelles. Encéphale, v. 21, p. 657.
  1928. Attaques de microtéléopsie. Attaques uncinées avec hémianopsie quadrantale homonyme par gliome de la région temporal. J. de neurol., v. 28, p. 61.
  1930. Le diagnostic des tumeurs suprasellaires et en particulier des tumeurs de la poche pharyngienne de Rathke. Concil. Ophth. XIII, 1929, v. 3 (Part 3), p. 1.
VAN BOGAERT, L., & MARTIN, P.
  1929. Sur deux signes du syndrome de déséquilibration frontale: l'apraxie de la marche et l'atonie statique. Encéphale, v. 24, p. 11.
VAN CAMPENHOUT, E.
  1931. Intraocular optic nerves in embryos of *Rana pipiens*. Anat. Rec., v. 61, p. 351.
VAN CLEAVE, H. J., & MARKUS, H. C.
  1929. Studies on the life history of the blunt-nosed minnow. Am. Naturalist, v. 63, p. 530.
VANDEL, A.
  1949. L'homme et l'évolution. ("L'avenir de la science," v. 28.) Librairie Gallimard, Paris.
VANDER EECKEN, H. M., FISHER, M., & ADAMS, R. D.
  1951. The arterial anastomoses of the human brain and their importance in the delimitation of infarcts. Am. A. Neuropath. (prog. of ann. meet.), p. 16.
VAN DER HOEVE, J.
  1912. The size of the blind spot and its distance from the point of fixation in the emmetropic eye. Arch. Ophth., v. 41, p. 350. (*See* Arch. f. Augenh., v. 70, No. 2, 1911.)
  1919–20. Die Bedeutung des Gesichtsfeldes für die Kenntnis des Verlaufs und der Endigung der Sehnervenfasern in der Netzhaut. Arch. f. Ophth. (Graefe), v. 98, p. 243; v. 102, p. 184.
  1922. Optic nerve and accessory sinuses. Ann. otol., rhin. & laryng., v. 31, p. 297.

VAN DER HORST, C. J.
 1933. The optics of the insect eye. Acta zool., v. 14, p. 101.
 1946. Some remarks on the biology of reproduction in the female of *Elephantulus*, the holy animal of Set. Tr. Roy. Soc. South Africa, v. 31, p. 181.

VAN DER KLAAUW, C. J.
 1929. On the development of the tympanic region of the skull in the Macroscelididae. Proc. Zool. Soc. London, p. 491.

VAN DER KLEIJ, J. J.
 1914. Von wo stammen die Vorfahren von Vesalius her? Janus, v. 19, p. 523.

VAN DER VELDEN, H. A.
 1944. Over het aantal lichtquanta dat nodig is voor een lichtprikkel bij het menselijk oog. Physica, v. 11, p. 179.

VAN GEHUCHTEN, A.
 1900. Anatomie du système nerveux de l'homme. 3d ed. Imprimerie Trois Rois (Soc. Anon.), Louvain.

VAN GEHUCHTEN, A., & GORIS, C.
 1902. La surdité verbale pure. Névraxe, v. 3, p. 63.

VAN HEUVEN, G. J.
 1929. Experimenteel-anatomisch onderzoek omtrent de corticale optische projectie bij den Java-aap. Doctor's thesis. P. H. Vermeulen, Amsterdam. (Abstr. in Am. J. Ophth., ser. 3, v. 13, p. 929.)

VAN HEUVEN, J. A., & FISCHER, F. P.
 1935. The water-binding of the retina. Brit. J. Ophth., v. 19, p. 390.

VAN LEERSUM, E. C.
 1914. André Vésale. Janus, v. 19, p. 397.

VAN OOSTEN, J.
 1946. The pikes. U.S. Dept. Interior, Fish & Wildlife Serv., Fishery Leaflet No. 166.

VAN VALKENBURG, C. T.
 1908. Zur Anatomie der Projektions- und Balkenstrahlung des Hinterhauptlappens sowie des Cingulums. Monatsschr. f. Psychiat., v. 24, p. 320.
 1908. Zur Kenntnis der gestörten Tiefenwahrnehmung. Deutsch. Ztschr. f. Nervenh., v. 34, p. 322 (*see also* v. 35, p. 472).
 1908. Kurze Erwiderung auf die "Bemerkungen" des Herrn Dr. E. Niessl von Mayendorf zu meinem Aufsatz: "Zur Kenntnis der gestörten Tiefenwahrnehmung." *Ibid.*, v. 35, p. 472.
 1911. Contribution à l'étude de la constitution de la substance blanche temporo-occipital de l'homme. Psychiat. en neurol. bl., v. 15, p. 374.
 1911. De oorsprong der vezels van het corpus callosum en het psalterium. Verslag kon. Akad. v. Wetensch. Amsterdam, wis. & nat. afd. v. 19 (2), p. 1337. English trans.: The origin of the fibres of the corpus callosum and the psalterium. Proc. kon. Akad. v. Wetensch. Amsterdam, sc. sec., v. 14 (1), p. 12.
 1913. On the occurrence of a monkey-slit in man. *Ibid.*, v. 15, p. 1040.
 1913. Experimental and pathologico-anatomical researches on the corpus callosum. Brain, v. 36, p. 119.
 1916. Sensibilitätsspaltung nach dem Hinterstrangtypus infolge von Herden der Regio rolandica. Zur Kenntnis der Lokalisation und des Aufbaues der Sensibilität im Grosshirn. Ztschr. f. d. ges. Neurol. u. Psychiat., v. 32, p. 209.
 1926. Bemerkung zu Dr. S. Poljaks Aufsatz über: "Die Verbindungen der Area striata bei der Katze." *Ibid.*, v. 103, p. 322.
 1929. Zur Pathologie mnestischer Störungen allgemeiner und besonderer Natur (Farbensinn) nach Hirntrauma. Schweiz. Arch. f. Neurol. u. Psychiat., v. 23, p. 266.

VAN WAGONEN, W. P., & HERREN, R. Y.
 1940. Surgical division of commissural pathways in the corpus callosum: relation to spread of an epileptic attack. Arch. Neurol. & Psychiat., v. 44, p. 740.

VARDEN, L. E.
 1942. The visual mechanism and pictorial photography. Am. Ann. Photog., v. 56, p. 7.

VAROLIUS (VAROLI), C.
 1573. Constantii Varolii medici bononiensis *De Nervis Opticis* nonnullisque aliis praeter communem opinionem in Humano capite observatis. Ad Hieronymum Mercurialem. Patavij, apud Paulum & Antonium Meiettos fratres. 1573.
 1591. Anatomiae, sive de resolutione corporis humani . . . libri IIII a. J. B. Cortesio . . . nunc primum editi. Ejusdem V. e H. Mercurialis de nervis opticis epistolae. Apud J. Wechelum et P. Fischerum. Francofurti.

VATER, A., & HEINICKE, J. C.
 1723. Dissertatio inauguralis medica qua visus vitia duo rarissima alterum duplicati, alterum dimidiati physiologice et pathologice considerata, etc. Wittenbergae, Literis Viduae Gerdesiae.

VAYSSIÈRE, E.
 1896. Étude sur l'organisation du nautile (caractères zoologiques, dimorphisme sexuel, tentacules et spadice). Ann. d. sc. nat. zool. et paleontol., v. 2, p. 137.

VEIT, O.
    1924. Beiträge zur Kenntnis des Kopfes der Wir-
        beltiere. II. Frühstadien der Entwicklung
        des Kopfes von *Lepidosteus osseus* und ihre
        prinzipielle Bedeutung für die Kephaloge-
        nese der Wirbeltiere. Morphol. Jahrb.
        (Gegenbaur), v. 53, p. 319.

VELHAGEN
    1902. Ein seltsamer Befund in einer nach Golgi
        behandelten Netzhaut. Arch. f. Ophth.
        (Graefe), v. 53, p. 499.

VELHAGEN, K.
    1943. Sehorgan und innere Sekretion. J. F. Berg-
        mann, München; Springer Verlag, Berlin &
        Wien. (Augenheilkunde der Gegenwart, v.
        2.)

VELTER, E.
    1916. Étude clinique de cinq cas d'hémianopsie
        par blessure de guerre. Arch. d'opht., v. 35,
        p. 151.
    1918. Les troubles oculaires dans les blessures du
        crâne. *Ibid.*, v. 36, p. 17.

VENDERÓVICH (WENDERÓWIČ), E. L.
    1915. Der Verlauf der sensiblen, akustischen und
        mancher anderer Systeme auf Grund eines
        Falles von Bluterguss in die basalen He-
        misphärenabschnitte. Arch. f. Psychiat. u.
        Nervenkr., v. 55, p. 486.
    1916. Nóvyia dánnyia o hódye choovstvítelynoy,
        sloohovóy i výdnoy sistém, etc. (New facts
        on the course of somesthetic, auditory, and
        visual systems in the hemisphere, etc., in
        Russian.) Government Press, Petrograd-
        Leningrad.
    1928. Irritatives Syndrom des architektonischen
        Feldes "19" Brodmann. Arch. f. Psychiat.
        u. Nervenkr., v. 84, p. 759.
    1930. Das myelogenetische Studium des Nerven-
        systems nach Flechsig als eine der Grund-
        lagen zur Erkenntnis seiner Struktur und
        Funktionen u. a. des Verhaltens und über
        die Beziehungen zwischen physiologischer
        und morphologischer Untersuchung. *Ibid.*,
        v. 90, p. 789.
    1933. Sind die sensorischen kortikalen Projek-
        tionszonen kompakt oder diffus? Lassen sie
        sich bei territorial begrenzten operativen
        Eingriffen völlig exstirpieren? Stellt die
        Rinde der grossen Hemisphären den einzi-
        gen Ort für die Formierung der bedingten
        Reflexe vor? Monatsschr. f. Psychiat. u.
        Neurol., v. 85, p. 145.

VENDRYES, J.
    1925. Language. A linguistic introduction to his-
        tory. A. A. Knopf, New York.

VERHOEFF, F. H.
    1942. Simple quantitative test for acuity and re-
        liability of binocular stereopsis. Arch.
        Ophth., v. 28, p. 1000.
    1943. A new answer to the question of macular
        sparing. *Ibid.*, v. 30, p. 421.

VERJAAL, A.
    1939. Klinische Betrachtungen über Bewusst-
        sein, Wahrnehmung und Erinnerung. Ztschr.
        f. d. ges. Neurol. u. Psychiat., v. 164, p. 63.

VERMES, L.
    1905. Ueber die Neurofibrillen der Retina. Anat.
        Anz., v. 26, p. 601.

VERNE, J.
    1925. Les pigments dans l'organisme animal.
        Doin, Paris.

VERNON, M. D.
    1937. Visual perception. Cambridge University
        Press, Cambridge.
    1952. A further study of visual perception. Cam-
        bridge University Press, Cambridge.

VERREY
    1888. Hémiachromatopsie droite absolue. Arch.
        d'opht., v. 8, p. 289.

VERRIER, M.-L.
    1927. Détermination de l'étendue des champs de
        vision anatomique chez quelques té-
        léostéens. Bull. Soc. zool. de France, v. 52,
        p. 320.
    1927. Sur la réfraction statique de l'œil chez les
        poissons. Compt. rend. Acad. d. sc., v. 185,
        p. 1070.
    1928. Recherches sur les yeux et la vision des pois-
        sons. Bull. biol. de France et de Belgique,
        Suppl. XI.
    1928. Sur la présence et la structure d'une *fovea*
        rétinienne chez un percidé: *Serranus cabrilla*
        L. Compt. rend. Acad. d. sc., v. 186, p. 457.
    1928. Le sens visuel chez les vertébrés. J. de psy-
        chol. norm. et path., p. 74.
    1929. Sur la structure des yeux et la physiologie
        de la vision chez les sélaciens. Compt. rend.
        Acad. d. sc., v. 188, p. 1695.
    1930. Sur la structure de la rétine d'une agamide:
        Agama tournevillii Lat. Présence d'une
        fovéa. *Ibid.*, v. 190, p. 517.
    1930. Contribution à l'étude de la vision chez les
        sélaciens. Ann. sc. nat. (zool.), 10th ser.,
        v. 13, p. 5.
    1932. Sur les rapports entre la structure des yeux
        et le comportement. Indications fournies par
        l'étude des reptiles. Arch. zool. expér. et
        gén., v. 74, p. 305.
    1932. Physiologie comparée des cônes et des bâ-
        tonnets. Indications fournies par l'étude du

comportement. Compt. rend. Acad. d. sc., v. 195, p. 1333.

1933. Étude des yeux d'un bleniide: *Pholis gunellus* L. Présence d'une fovéa. Bull. Soc. zool. de France, v. 58, p. 62.

1933. Recherches sur la vision des reptiles. Étude comparée de la morphologie des cellules visuelles et du pouvoir séparateur de la rétine. Bull. biol., v. 67, p. 350.

1933. Recherches sur les fovéae des poissons. Étude des yeux de *Julis giofredi* Risso. Compt. rend. Soc. de biol., v. 113, p. 134.

1933. Les yeux et la vision de *Cerastes vipera* Wagl., et de *Vipera aspis* L. Compt. rend. Acad. d. sc., v. 196, p. 723.

1933. Réfraction statique de l'œil des céphalopodes. *Ibid.*, p. 1435.

1934. Pigments mélaniques, pourpre rétinien et cellules visuelles. Compt. rend. Soc. de biol., v. 115, p. 1590.

1934. L'action de la lumière sur le pourpre rétinien. Compt. rend. Acad. d. sc., v. 198, p. 1806.

1934. Les yeux de deux colubridés: *Hypsirhina enhydris* Schneider et *Tropidonotus piscator* Schneider et leur rapports avec les yeux des autres reptiles. Bull. Soc. zool. de France, v. 59, p. 363.

1934. Dualité de la vision et comportement. *Ibid.*, p. 367.

1934. La réfraction de l'œil des poissons. *Ibid.*, p. 535.

1935. Les fovéae des reptiles, à propos de la rétine d'*Iguana tuberculata* Laurenti et de *Varanus arenarius* Dumeril et Bibron. *Ibid.*, v. 60, p. 187.

1935. Les variations de la forme des cellules visuelles et la théorie de la dualité de la vision. *Ibid.*, p. 193.

1935. Les paupières des reptiles et leur signification. *Ibid.*, p. 443.

1935. Recherches sur l'histophysiologie de la rétine des vertébrés et les problèmes qu'elle soulève. Bull. biol. de France et de Belgique, suppl., v. 20.

1935. La morphologie comparée des cellules visuelles et la théorie de la dualité de la vision. Compt. rend. Acad. d. sc., v. 200, p. 261.

1935. Les variations morphologiques de la rétine et leurs conséquences physiologiques; à propos de la rétine d'une musaraigne (*Crocidura mimula* Miller). Ann. sc. nat. (zool.), Paris, 10th ser., v. 18, p. 205.

1936. Les cellules visuelles des oiseaux diurnes et le pourpre rétinien. Compt. rend. Soc. de biol., v. 121, p. 383.

1936. Étude spectrophotométrique des boules colorées de la rétine de quelques oiseaux. *Ibid.*, p. 705.

1936. La rétine des oiseaux diurnes et la théorie de la dualité de la vision. Compt. rend. Acad. d. sc., v. 202, p. 159.

1936. Pourpre et cellules visuelles de la fovéa des oiseaux nocturnes et des autres vertébrés. *Ibid.*, p. 2012.

1936. Recherches sur la vision des oiseaux diurnes. Bull. biol., v. 70, p. 197.

1936. Étude biologique de la rétine des vertébrés. Arch. d'opht., v. 53, pp. 281, 363.

1937. Nouvelles recherches sur la rétine des vertébrés. Bull. biol., v. 71, p. 238.

1938. Les yeux de quelques mammifères et les théories de la vision. *Ibid.*, v. 72, p. 355.

1938. Les yeux et la vision. F. Alcan, Paris.

1939. Les facteurs rétiniens de l'acuité visuelle des vertébrés. Compt. rend. Acad. d. sc., v. 209, p. 845.

1940. Vision du relief et vision binoculaire. A propos de la double fovéa des oiseaux rapaces diurnes. Bull. biol., v. 74, p. 88.

1945. Biologie de la vision. Libr. A. Colin, Paris.

VERRIER, M.-L., & ESCHER-DESRIVIÈRES, J.
1936. Modalités de la vision et cellules visuelles. J. de psychol. norm. et path., v. 33, p. 184.

1937. Recherches sur la sensibilité lumineuse des poissons. Bull. Soc. zool. de France, v. 62, p. 126.

VERRIER, M.-L., & PANNIER, R.
1936. Recherches sur la nature du pourpre rétinien. Compt. rend. Soc. de biol., v. 122, p. 600.

1936. Recherches sur la composition du pourpre rétinien et ses rapports avec les cellules visuelles. Compt. rend. Acad. d. sc., v. 202, p. 1614.

1936. Recherches sur les constituants chimiques de la rétine, leurs rapports avec le pourpre rétinien et la théorie de la dualité de la vision. Bull. Soc. d'opht. de Paris, v. 48, p. 569.

VERSARI, R.
1909. Ueber die Entwicklung der Blutgefässe des menschlichen Auges. Anat. Anz., v. 35, p. 105.

VERWORN, M.
1900. Das Neuron in Anatomie und Physiologie. Verhandl. d. Gesellsch. Deutsch. Naturforsch. u. Aerzte, v. 72, p. 191. Also as a monograph pub. by G. Fischer, Jena.

1904. Naturwissenschaften und Weltanschauung. J. A. Barth, Leipzig.

1334 *The Vertebrate Visual System*

VERWORN, M.—*Continued*

1905. Prinzipienfragen in der Naturwissenschaft. G. Fischer, Jena.

1910. Die Mechanik des Geisteslebens. 2d ed. B. G. Teubner, Leipzig. (1st ed. 1907; 4th ed. 1919.)

VESALIUS, A.

1538. Tabulae Anatomicae Sex. *In:* C. SINGER & C. RABIN, A prelude to modern science. Cambridge University Press, Cambridge, 1946.

*1543. De Humani Corporis Fabrica. J. Oporinus, Basel.

1543. The epitome of Andreas Vesalius. Trans. L. R. LIND. Macmillan Co., New York, 1949.

1555. Andreae Vesalii Bruxellensis, invictissimi Caroli V. Imperatoris medici, *De Humani Corporis Fabrica* Libri septem. Cum Caesareae Maiest. Galliarum Regis, ac Senatus Veneti gratia & privilegio, ut in diplomatis eorundem continetur. Basileae, Per Iohannem Oporinum.

1568. De humani corporis fabrica, etc. Venetiis, ap. F. Franciscium, & I. Criegher, 1568.

1725. Opera omnia anatomica & chirurgica, cura H. Boerhaave & Bernhardi Siegfried Albini. Apud Joannem du Vivie, et Joan. & Herm. Verbeek. 2 vols. Lugduni Batavorum.

1934. A. Vesalii Bruxellensis Icones Anatomicae. McFarlane, Warde, McFarlane, New York.

1943. The four hundredth anniversary celebration of the *De humani corporis fabrica* of Andreas Vesalius. Pub. No. 7, Historical Library, Yale University School of Medicine, New Haven.

1950. The illustrations from the works of Andreas Vesalius of Brussels. By J. B. DEC. M. SAUNDERS & C. D. O'MALLEY. World Publishing Co., Cleveland and New York.

1952. Vesalius on the human brain. Trans. by C. Singer. Oxford University Press, London.

VESEY, F. A.

1950. Congruous homonymous hemianopia with macular sparing. Am. J. Ophth., ser. 3, v. 33, p. 590.

VESLING, J.

1696. Joannis Veslingii Equitis, Professoris quondam Patavini, &c. *Syntagma Anatomicum*, Commentario atque Appendice Ex Veterum, Recentiorum, Propriisque Observationibus, Illustratum & auctum A. Gerardo Leon. Blasio Med. Doct. & in Illustri Athenaeo Amstel. Profess. Editio Novissima Priori emendatior, & locupletior. Trajecti ad Rhenum (Utrecht), Apud Antonium Schou-

ten CIↃ IↃC XCVI. (First edition apparently 1666, the one of 1696 being the sixth.)

VIALET, N.

1893. Les centres cérébraux de la vision et l'appareil nerveux visuel intra-cérébral. Thèse, Paris. *Also* Ann. d'ocul., v. 111, p. 161.

1894. Considérations sur le centre visuel cortical; à propos de deux nouveaux cas d'hémianopsie corticale suivis d'autopsie. Arch. d'opht., v. 14, p. 121.

VIAUD, G.

1938. Recherches expérimentales sur le phototropisme des daphnies. Étude de psychologie animale. ("Pub. Fac. des Lettres de Strasbourg," 2d ser., Fasc. 84.) Soc. d'Édit. Les belles Lettres, Paris.

1938. Le phototropisme animal. Exposé critique des problèmes et des théories. ("Pub. Fac. des Lettres de Strasbourg," 2d ser., Fasc. 85.) Soc. d'Édit. Les belles Lettres, Paris.

VICQ-D'AZYR, F.

*1786–89. Traité d'anatomie et de physiologie, v. 1: Anatomie et physiologie du cerveau; v. 2: Planches anatomiques. F.-A. Didot, Paris.

1805. Œuvres de Vicq-d'Azyr, ed. J. L. MOREAU DE LA SARTHE. Ornées d'un volume de planches pour les œuvres de Vicq-d'Azyr. 6 vols. L. Duprat-Duverger, Paris.

VICTOR, S. A.

1948. Crossed cerebral lesions: left hemiparesis and right homonymous hemianopsia. Arch. Neurol. & Psychiat., v. 59, p. 843.

VICTORIA, M., & BALADO, M.

1929. Afasia por lesión del gyrus supramarginalis. (Nominal defects de Head.) Bol. d. Inst. clín. quir., Buenos Aires, v. 5, p. 53.

VIDAL, F., & DAMEL, C. S.

1944. The ocular neurovegetative system: normal intraocular tension. Arch. de oftal. de Buenos Aires, v. 19, p. 212. (Abstr. in Arch. Ophth., v. 35, p. 452, 1946.)

VIDAL, F., & MALBRAN, J. L.

1942. Recorrido de las fibras homolaterales periféricas inferiores en el gato. Microlesión retiniana. Arch. de oftal. de Buenos Aires, v. 17, p. 521.

1942. Disposición de las fibras ópticas homolaterales superiores en el gato (estudio experimental). *Ibid.*, p. 626.

1942. Disposición de las fibras mielínicas en el quiasma del gato (estudio experimental). *Ibid.*, p. 682.

1942. Disposición de las fibras mielínicas en el tractus ópticus del gato (estudio experimental). *Ibid.*, p. 733.

1943. Distribución de las fibras ópticas primárias mielínicas en el area pretectal del gato (estudio experimental). *Ibid.*, v. 18, p. 125.

VIEILLARD, C.
1903. La médecine néo-latine au VIᵉ siècle d'après Cassiodore. Bull. Soc. franç. d'hist. de la méd., v. 2, p. 516.

VIERORDT, K.
1863. Ueber die Messung der Sehschärfe. Arch. f. Ophth. (Graefe), v. 9 (1), p. 161, and (3), p. 219.

VIEUSSENS, R.
1685. Raymundi Vieussens Doctoris Medici Monspeliensis *NEVROGAPHIA* Universalis. Hoc est, Omnium Corporis Humani Nervorum, simul & cerebri, medullaeque spinalis Descriptio Anatomica; eaque integra et accurata, variis iconibus fideliter & ad vitam delineatis, aeréque incisis illustrata: Cum Ipsorum Actione Et Usu, Physico discursu explicatis. Editio Nova. Lugduni, Apud Joannem Certe, in vico Mercatorio sub signo Trinitatis. M.DC.LXXXV. Cum privilegio Regis.

VILLARET, M., & RIVES, A.
1916. L'hémianopsie bilatérale homonyme en quadrant, seul reliquant de blessures graves du lobe occipital. Paris méd., v. 19, p. 20.

VILLAVERDE, J. M.
1921. Estudios anatómico-experimentales sobre el curso y terminación de las fibras callosas. Trab. (Trav.) del lab. de invest. biol. Madrid, v. 19, p. 37.
1921. Sobre el origen de las fibras callosas en el area gigantopyramidalis del conejo. *Ibid.*, p. 195.
1924. Les connexions commissurales des régions postérieures du cerveau du lapin. Trav. du lab. de rech. biol. Madrid, v. 22, p. 99.
1931. Ueber die Endigung der Balkenfasern in der Hirnrinde. Proc. First Internat. Neurol. Cong. Berne, p. 243.
1935. Santiago Ramón y Cajal†. Ztschr. f. d. ges. Neurol. u. Psychiat., v. 152, p. 617.

VINCI; *see* LEONARDO DA VINCI

VINSONNEAU
1916. La vision maculaire chez les hémianopsiques à zone maculaire intacte. Arch. d'opht., v. 35, p. 287.

VINT, F. W.
1934. The brain of the Kenya native. J. Anat., v. 68, p. 216.

VINTON, K. W.
1938. A frog that eats bats and snakes. Nat. Geog. Mag., v. 73, p. 657.

VINTSCHGAU, M.
1853. Ricerche sulla struttura della retina dell'uomo, degli animali vertebrati e dei cefalopodi. Sitzungsb. d. Kaiserl. Akad. d. Wissensch., Wien, math.-naturw. Cl., v. 11, p. 943.

VIRCHOW, H.
1881. Ueber die Gefässe im Auge und in der Umgebung des Auges beim Frosche. Ztschr. f. wissensch. Zool., v. 35, p. 247.
1882. Ueber die Glaskörper- und Netzhautgefässe des Aales. Morphol. Jahrb., v. 7, p. 573.
1882. Beiträge zur vergleichenden Anatomie des Auges. Habilitationsschrift. A. Hirschwald, Berlin.
1901. Fächer, Zapfen, Leiste, Polster, Gefässe im Glaskörperraum von Wirbeltieren sowie damit in Verbindung stehende Fragen. Ergebn. d. Anat. u. Entw. (Merkel & Bonnet), v. 10, p. 720.
1901. Ueber die Netzhaut von *Hatteria punctata*. Arch. f. Physiol., p. 355.

VITELLO (WITELO)
*Ca. 1270–78. Vitellionis mathematici doctissimi Περί 'οπτικῆς, id est de natura, ratione & proiectione radiorum visus, luminum, colorum atque formarum, quam vulgo Perspectivam vocant, libri X, etc. Norimbergae apud Io. Petreium, Anno 1535.
Ca. 1270–78. Opticae Libri Decem. Etc. F. Risner, Basileae (Basel), 1572. Published in one volume with Alhazen's Thesaurus. Also two earlier printed eds., 1535 and 1551, Nuremberg. (*Cf.* Ibn al-Haitham.)

VITZOU, A. N.
1888. Contribution à l'étude du centre cérébro-sensitif visuel chez le chien. Compt. rend. Acad. d. sc., v. 107, p. 279.
1893. Effets de l'ablation totale des lobes occipitaux sur la vision, chez le chien. Arch. de physiol., v. 25 (5th ser., v. 5), p. 688.
1897. La néoformation des cellules nerveuses dans le cerveau du singe consécutive à l'ablation complète des lobes occipitaux. *Ibid.*, v. 29 (5th ser., v. 9), p. 29.
1898. Récupération de la vue perdue à la suite d'une première ablation totale des lobes occipitaux chez les singes. J. Physiol., v. 23 (suppl.), Proc. 4th Internat. Cong. [p. 57].

VOGELSANG, K.
1925. Ueber das foveale Purkinjesche Phänomen. Arch. f. d. ges. Physiol. (Pflüger), v. 207, p. 117.

VOGL, S.
1906. Die Physik Roger Bacons. Inaug.-Diss. Erlangen. Junge & Sohn, Erlangen.

VOGL, S.—*Continued*
1914. Roger Bacons Lehre von der sinnlichen Spezies und vom Sehvorgange. *In:* A. G. LITTLE, Roger Bacon Essays, etc., p. 205. Clarendon Press, Oxford.

VOGT, A.
1918. Ueber eine vertikale lineare Streifung, welche an der Vorderfläche der Netzhaut jüngerer Individuen im rotfreien Licht wahrgenommen wird. Klin. Monatsbl. f. Augenh., v. 60, p. 47.
1918. Zur Farbe der Macula retinae. *Ibid.*, p. 449.
1918. Weitere ophthalmoskopische Beobachtungen im rotfreien Licht, etc. *Ibid.*, v. 61, p. 379.
1919. Zur Technik der Ophthalmoskopie im rotfreien Licht. Arch. f. Ophth. (Graefe), v. 99, pp. 195, 296.
1921. Ophthalmoskopische Untersuchungen der Macula lutea im rotfreien Licht. Klin. Monatsbl. f. Augenh., v. 66, p. 321.
1921. Die Nervenfaserzeichnung der menschlichen Netzhaut im rotfreien Licht. *Ibid.*, p. 718.
1921. Die Reflexion der Netzhautvorderfläche im rotfreien Licht, etc. *Ibid.*, p. 838.
1930–42. Lehrbuch und Atlas der Spaltlampenmikroskopie des lebenden Auges mit Anleitung zur Technik und Methodik der Untersuchung. J. Springer, Berlin.
1935. Canalis hyaloideus mit Area Martegiani und symmetrisches Foramen hyaloideae posterius. Ztschr. f. Augenh., v. 88, p. 1.
1937. Untersuchungen des Auges im rotfreien Licht. *In:* E. ABDERHALDEN, Handb. d. biol. Arbeitsmeth., Abt. 5, Teil 6 (1), p. 365.
1941. Handbook and atlas of the slit lamp microscopy of the living eye. Schweizer Druck- u. Verlagshaus, Zürich.
1947. Slit lamp microscopy of the living eye: iris, vitreous body, conjunctiva. Stechert-Hafner, New York.

VOGT, C.
1900. Étude sur la myélinisation des hémisphères cérébraux. Steinheil, Paris.
1909. La myéloarchitecture du thalamus du cercopithèque. J. f. Psychol. u. Neurol., v. 12, p. 285.
1926. Die topistisch-pathoarchitectonische Forschung in der Psychiatrie. Ztschr. f. d. ges. Neurol. u. Psychiat., v. 100, p. 63.

VOGT, C., & VOGT, O. (*see also* J. OLSZEWSKI 1950)
1904. Die Markreifung des Kinderhirns während der ersten vier Lebensmonate und ihre methodologische Bedeutung. Neurobiol. Arb., vols. 1 and 2. Denkschriften med.-

naturwissensch. Gesellsch. Jena, 1. ser., v. 9, Part II, p. 147. G. Fischer, Jena.
1906–7. Zur Kenntnis der elektrisch erregbaren Hirnrindengebiete bei den Säugetieren. J. f. Psychol. u. Neurol., v. 8, p. 277.
1919. Allgemeinere Ergebnisse unserer Hirnforschung. *Ibid.*, v. 25, p. 279.
1926. Die vergleichend-architektonische und die vergleichend-reizphysiologische Felderung der Grosshirnrinde unter besonderer Berücksichtigung der menschlichen. Naturwiss., v. 14, p. 1190.
1936. Sitz und Wesen der Krankheiten im Lichte der topistischen Hirnforschung und des Variierens der Tiere. J. f. Psychol. u. Neurol., v. 47, p. 237.

VOGT, H.
1902. Ueber Neurofibrillen in Nervenzellen und Nervenfasern der Retina. Monatsschr. f. Psychiat. u. Neurol., v. 11, p. 167.

VOGT, M.
1929. Ueber fokale Besonderheiten der Area occipitalis im cytoarchitektonischen Bilde. J. f. Psychol. u. Neurol., v. 39, p. 506.

VOGT, O.
1894. Ueber Fasersysteme in den mittleren und caudalen Balkenabschnitten. Veit & Co., Leipzig. *Also* Neurol. Centralbl., v. 14, pp. 208, 253, 1895.
1900. Flechsig's Associationscentrenlehre im Lichte vergleichend-anatomischer Forschung. Neurol. Centralbl., v. 19, p. 334.
1902. Beiträge zur Hirnfaserlehre. ("Neurobiol. Arb.," v. 1.) G. Fischer, Jena.
1903–4. Zur anatomischen Gliederung des Cortex cerebri. J. f. Psychol. & Neurol., v. 2, p. 160.
1906. Der Wert der myelogenetischen Felder der Grosshirnrinde. Anat. Anz., v. 29, p. 273.
1906. Ueber strukturelle Hirncentra, mit besonderer Berücksichtigung der strukturellen Felder des Cortex pallii. *Ibid.* (Verhandl.), v. 29, Ergänzungsh., p. 74.
1919. Korbinian Brodmann. J. f. Psychol. u. Neurol., v. 24, p. I.
1943. Der heutige Stand der cerebralen Organologie und die zukünftige Hirnforschung. Eine Huldigung für Theodor Meynert anlässlich der 50. Wiederkehr seines Todestages. Anat. Anz., v. 94, p. 49.

VOGT, O., & VOGT, C.
1906. Der Wert der myelogenetischen Felder der Grosshirnrinde (Cortex pallii). Anat. Anz., v. 29, p. 273.

VOGT, W.
1925–29. Gestaltanalyse am Amphibienkeim mit örtlicher Vitalfärbung. I. Methodik, etc. II.

Gastrulation, etc. Arch. f. Entw.-mech. (Roux), v. 106, p. 542; v. 120, p. 384.

VOGTHERR, H.

1539. Eyn Newes hochnutzlichs Buechlin und Anothomi eynes auffgethonen augs, auch seiner erklacrung, bewerten purgation, Pflaster, Collirien, Saelblin pulvern und wassern, wie mans machen und brauchen sol. Getruckt zu Strassburg durch Heinrichen Vogtherren. Anno M.D.XXXIX.

VOLKMANN

1926. Vergleichende Untersuchungen an der Rinde der "motorischen" und "Sehregion" von Nagetieren. Anat. Anz. (Verhandl.), v. 61, Ergänzungsh., p. 234.

VOLKMANN, A. F.

*1836. Neue Beiträge zur Physiologie des Gesichtssinnes. Breitkopf & Härtel, Leipzig.

VOLKMANN, A. W.

1846. Sehen. *In:* R. WAGNER, Handwörterbuch der Physiologie, v. 3 (1), p. 265. F. Vieweg, Braunschweig.

1859. Die stereoskopischen Erscheinungen in ihrer Beziehung zu der Lehre von den identischen Netzhautpunkten. Arch. f. Ophth. (Graefe), v. 5 (2), p. 1.

1866. Weitere Untersuchungen über die Frage, ob die Zapfen der Netzhaut als Raumelemente beim Sehen fungiren. Arch. f. Anat., Physiol. u. wissensch. Med., p. 649.

VOLKMANN, R.

1936. Kleistsche Hypothese, Vertretung der temporalen Sichel in der Sehrinde und vermutliche Endigungsweise des Fasciculus corp. callosi cruciatus. Ztschr. f. d. ges. Neurol. u. Psychiat., v. 155, p. 631.

VOLTA, A.

*1816. *See:* ANTINORI, Collezione delle opere del cav. conte Alessandro Volta.

VOLZ, W.

1905. Zur Kenntnis des Auges von *Periophthalmus* und *Boleophthalmus*. Zool. Jahrb. (Anat.), v. 22, p. 331.

1922. Im Dämmer des Rimba. Sumatras Urwald und Urmensch. 2d ed. F. Hirt, Breslau.

VONWILLER, P.

1945–46. Études sur la rétine. Acta anat., v. 1, p. 191.

VORÓNIKHIN, N. N.

1945. Rastítel'nyi mir okeána (Ocean's plant life, in Russian). Izdátel'stvo- Akadémiyi Naúk SSSR, Moskvá.

VORSTER

1893. Ueber einen Fall von doppelseitiger Hemianopsie mit Seelenblindheit, Photopsien und Gesichtstäuschungen. Allg. Ztschr. f. Psychiat., v. 49, p. 227.

VOSS, G.

1917. Nervenärztliche Erfahrungen an 100 Schädelverletzten. München. med. Wchnschr., v. 64, p. 881.

VOSSIUS, A.

1882. Ein Fall von beiderseitigem centralem Scotom mit pathologisch-anatomischem Befund. Beitrag zur Kenntniss des Verlaufs der Maculafasern im N. opticus, Chiasma und Tractus opticus. Arch. f. Ophth. (Graefe), v. 28 (3), p. 201.

1883. Beiträge zur Anatomie des N. opticus. *Ibid.,* v. 29 (4), p. 119.

1896. Beiderseitige Hemianopsie mit Erhaltung eines kleinen centralen Gesichtsfeldes. Neurol. Centralbl., v. 15, p. 997.

VRIES, E.; *see* DE VRIES

VRIES, I.

1912. Ueber die Zytoarchitektonik der Grosshirnrinde der Maus und über die Beziehungen der einzelnen Zellschichten zum Corpus callosum auf Grund von experimentellen Laesionen. Folia neuro-biol., v. 6, p. 289.

VUJIĆ, V.

1929. Halluzinatorisches Farbenhören. Jahrb. f. Psychiat., v. 46, p. 262.

VULPIAN, A.

1866. Leçons sur la physiologie générale et comparée du système nerveux. G. Baillière, Paris.

1887. Éloge historique de Flourens. Rev. scient., 3d ser., v. 13 (tot. v. 39), p. 1.

W

WAARDENBURG, P. J.

1932. Das menschliche Auge und seine Erbanlagen. ("Bibliog. genet.," v. 7.) Martinus Nynhoff, 'S-Gravenhage.

WADDINGTON, C. H.

1936. How animals develop. W. W. Norton & Co., New York.

1940. Organizers and genes. Cambridge University Press, Cambridge.

WADDINGTON, C. H., & COHEN, A.

1936. Experiments on the development of the head of the chick embryo. J. Exper. Biol., v. 13, p. 219.

WADDY, R. G.

1915. A case of destruction of cortical visual centers by a rifle bullet. Ophthalmoscope, v. 13, p. 175.

WADSWORTH, O. F.

1880. Photograph of the fovea centralis of the

retina. Tr. Am. Ophth. Soc., 16th meet., p. 174.

1881. The fovea centralis in man. *In:* Beiträge zur Ophthalmologie, als Festgabe Friedrich Horner, etc. Wiesbaden.

WAELCHLI, G.

1881. Mikrospektroskopische Untersuchungen der gefärbten Kugeln in der Retina von Vögeln. Arch. f. Ophth. (Graefe), v. 27 (2), p. 303.

1883. Zur Topographie der gefärbten Kugeln der Vogelnetzhaut. *Ibid.*, v. 29 (3), p. 205.

WAGENMANN, A.

1890. Experimentelle Untersuchungen über den Einfluss der Circulation in den Netzhaut- und Aderhautgefässen auf die Ernährung des Auges, insbesondere der Retina, und über die Folgen der Sehnervendurchschneidung. Arch. f. Ophth. (Graefe), v. 36 (4), p. 1.

WAGHJI, M.

1937. An eight-hundred-year-old book of Indian medicine and formulas. Luzac & Co., London. (*Cf.* E. Sharpe.)

WAGNER, H.

1931. Bestimmung der linearen Masse auf der Bulbusoberfläche vom Limbus zur Ora serrata, zum hinteren Pol und zur Papille. Arch. f. Ophth. (Graefe), v. 127, p. 103.

1932. Ueber den Farbensinn der Eidechsen. Ztschr. f. vergl. Physiol., v. 18, p. 378.

WAGNER, R.

1833. Untersuchungen über die Endigung der Netzhaut, etc. Ztschr. f. d. Ophth. (Ammon), v. 3, p. 277.

1837. Beiträge zur Anatomie der Vögel. Abh. d. math.-phys. Kl. d. Akad., München, v. 2, p. 271.

1842–53. Handwörterbuch der Physiologie, mit Rücksicht auf physiologische Pathologie. 4 vols. in 5. F. Vieweg & Sohn, Braunschweig.

1860. Ueber die typischen Verschiedenheiten der Windungen der Hemisphären und über die Lehre vom Hirngewicht mit besondrer Rücksicht auf die Hirnbildung intelligenter Männer. Dieterichsche Buchhandlung, Göttingen.

1860–62. Vorstudien zu einer wissenschaftlichen Morphologie und Physiologie des menschlichen Gehirns als Seelenorgan. 1. Abh. Ueber die typischen Verschiedenheiten der Windungen der Hemisphären und über die Lehre vom Hirngewicht, mit besondrer Rücksicht auf die Hirnbildung intelligenter Männer. 2. Abh. Ueber den Hirnbau der Mikrocephalen mit vergleichender Rück-

sicht auf den Bau des Gehirns der normalen Menschen und der Quadrumanen. Göttingen, Verlag der Dieterichschen Buchhandlung.

WAGNER, W.

1937. Scheitellappensymptome und das Lokalisationsprinzip. (Untersuchung über Apraxie und verwandte Symptome.) Ztschr. f. d. ges. Neurol. u. Psychiat., v. 157, p. 160.

WALD, G.

1936. Carotenoids and the visual cycle. J. Gen. Physiol., v. 19, p. 351.

1938. On rhodopsin in solution *Ibid.*, v. 21, p. 795.

1939. The porphyropsin visual system. *Ibid.*, v. 22, p. 775.

1942. Visual systems and the vitamins A. *In:* Visual mechanisms, Biol. symp., v. 7, p. 43. J. Cattell Press, Lancaster, Pa.

1943. The photoreceptor function of the carotenoids and vitamins A. *In:* Vitamins and hormones, v. 1, p. 195. Academic Press, New York.

1944. The molecular organization of visual processes. *In:* J. ALEXANDER, Colloid chemistry, v. 5, p. 752.

1945. Human vision and the spectrum. Science, v. 101, p. 653.

1945. The spectral sensitivity of the human eye. J. Opt. Soc. Amer., v. 35, p. 187.

1945–46. The chemical evolution of vision. Harvey Lect., ser. 41, p. 117.

1948. The synthesis from vitamin A_1 of "retinene$_1$" and of a new 545 mμ chromogen yielding light-sensitive products. J. Gen. Physiol., v. 31, p. 489.

1948. Selig Hecht (1892–1947). *Ibid.*, v. 32, p. 1.

1950. Eye and camera. Scient. Amer., v. 183 (2), p. 32.

WALD, G., & BURIAN, H. M.

1944. The dissociation of form vision and light perception in strabismic amblyopia. Am. J. Ophth., v. 27, p. 950.

1945. Dissociation of form and light perception in patients with amblyopia ex anopsia. Arch. Ophth., ser. 2, v. 33, p. 160.

WALD, G., & CLARK, A.-B.

1938. Visual adaptation and chemistry of the rods. J. Gen. Physiol., v. 21, p. 93.

WALD, G., & GRIFFIN, D. R.

1947. The change in refractive power of the human eye in dim and bright light. J. Opt. Soc. Amer., v. 37, p. 321.

WALD, G., & ZUSSMAN, H.

1938. Carotenoids of the chicken retina. J. Biol. Chem., v. 112, p. 449.

WALDEYER (WALDEYER-HARTZ), W. VON

1863. Untersuchungen über den Ursprung und den Verlauf des Axencylinders bei Wirbellosen und Wirbelthieren, sowie über dessen Endverhalten in der quergestreiften Muskelfaser. Henle & Pfeufer's Ztschr. f. rat. Med., 3d ser., v. 20, p. 193.

1891. Ueber die "Insel" des Gehirns der Anthropoiden. Korresp.-Bl. d. Deutsch. Gesellsch. f. Anthropol., Ethnol. u. Urgesch., v. 22, p. 110.

1891. Das Gibbon-Hirn. Internat. Beitr. z. wissensch. Med., v. 1, p. 1. (Festschr. R. Virchow.) A. Hirschwald, Berlin.

1891. Ueber einige neuere Forschungen im Gebiete der Anatomie des Centralnervensystems. Deutsch. med. Wchnschr., v. 17, pp. 1213, 1244, 1267, 1287, 1331, 1352.

1891. Sylvische Furche und Reilsche Insel des Genus *Hylobates*. Sitzungsb. d. Preuss. Akad. d. Wissensch., v. 1, p. 265.

1894. Ueber einige anthropologisch bemerkbaren Befunde an Negerhirnen. *Ibid.*, p. 1213.

1895. Hirnfurchen und Hirnwindungen. Ergebn. d. Anat. u. Entw. (Merkel & Bonnet), v. 5, p. 146; v. 6, p. 171.

1895. Die neueren Ansichten über den Bau und das Wesen der Zelle. Deutsch. med. Wchnschr., v. 21, pp. 703, 727, 764, 776, 800, 846.

1906. Albert v. Koelliker zum Gedächtnis. Anat. Anz., v. 28, p. 539.

1909. Darwins Lehre, ihr heutiger Stand und ihre wissenschaftliche und kulturelle Bedeutung. Deutsch. med. Wchnschr., v. 35, p. 345.

1920. Lebenserinnerungen. F. Cohen, Bonn.

WALKER, A. E.

1937. The projection of the medial geniculate body to the cerebral cortex in the macaque monkey. J. Anat., v. 71, p. 319.

1938. The primate thalamus. University of Chicago Press, Chicago.

1940. A cytoarchitectural study of the prefrontal area of the macaque monkey. J. Comp. Neurol., v. 73, p. 59.

WALKER, A. E., & FULTON, J. F.

1937. The external configuration of the cerebral hemispheres of the chimpanzee. J. Anat., v. 71, p. 105.

1938. The thalamus of the chimpanzee. III. Metathalamus, normal structure and cortical connections. Brain, v. 61, p. 250.

1938. Hemidecortication in chimpanzee, baboon, macaque, potto, cat and coati: a study in encephalization. J. Nerv. & Ment. Dis., v. 87, p. 677.

WALKER, A. E., & GREEN, H. D.

1938. Electrical excitability of the motor face area: a comparative study in primates. Jour. Neurophysiol., v. 1, p. 152.

WALKER, A. E., KOLLROS, J. J., & CASE, T. J.

1944. The physiological basis of concussion. J. Neurosurg., v. 1, p. 103.

WALKER, A. E., & WEAVER, T. A.

1940. Ocular movements from the occipital lobe in the monkey. J. Neurophysiol., v. 3, p. 353.

WALKER, A. E., WOOLF, J. I., HALSTEAD, W. C., & CASE, T. J.

1943. Mechanism of temporal fusion effect of photic stimulation on electrical activity of visual structures. J. Neurophysiol., v. 6, p. 213.

1944. Photic driving. Arch. Neurol. & Psychiat., v. 52, p. 117.

WALKER, A. E., *et al.*

1951. A history of neurological surgery. Williams & Wilkins Co., Baltimore.

WALKER, C. B.

1913. Some new instruments for measuring visual-field defects. Arch. Ophth., v. 42, p. 577.

1915. A contribution to the study of bitemporal hemianopsia with new instruments and methods for detecting slight changes. *Ibid.*, v. 44, p. 369.

1917. Neurological perimetry and a method of imitating daylight with electric illumination. Tr. Am. Med. Assoc., 68th ann. sess., sec. on ophth., p. 189.

1917. Quantitative perimetry: practical devices and errors. Arch. Ophth., v. 46, p. 537.

1921. The value of quantitative perimetry in the study of post-ethmoidal sphenoidal sinusitis causing visual defects. Boston M. & Surg. J., v. 185, p. 321.

1929. The time element in quantitative perimetry. Arch. Surg., v. 18, p. 102.

1930. Lesions of the chiasmal region. Am. J. Ophth., v. 13, p. 198.

1944. Necrology. Tr. Am. Soc. Ophth., v. 80, p. 17.

WALKER, C. B., & CUSHING, H.

1916. Studies of optic-nerve atrophy in association with chiasmal lesions. Arch. Ophth., v. 45, p. 407.

1918. Chiasmal lesions, with especial reference to homonymous hemianopsia with hypophyseal tumor. *Ibid.*, v. 47, p. 119.

WALKER, E. P.

1939. Eyes that shine at night. Smithsonian Inst. Rep. for 1938, p. 349.

WALKER, E. P.—*Continued*

1947. "Flying" squirrels, nature's gliders. Nat. Geog. Mag., v. 91, p. 662.

1953. Tarsiers—night prowlers of Asian islands. Nature Mag., v. 46, p. 193.

1954. The monkey book. Macmillan Co., New York.

WALKER, H.

1949. Cruise to stone age Arnhem Land. Nat. Geog. Mag., v. 96, p. 417.

WALKER, L. W.

1945. Photoflashing western owls. Nat. Geog. Mag., v. 87, p. 475.

WALL, P. D., & PRIBRAM, K. H.

1950. Trigeminal neurotomy and blood pressure responses from stimulation of lateral cerebral cortex of *Macaca mulatta*. J. Neurophysiol., v. 13, p. 409.

WALLACE, A. R. (*see* biography by J. MARCHANT 1916)

1853. A narrative of travels on the Amazon and Río Negro, with an account of the native tribes, and observations on the climate, geology, and natural history of the Amazon Valley. Reeve & Co., London. Also later ed.

1860. On the zoölogical geography of the Malay Archipelago. Communicated by Charles Darwin (read November 3, 1859). J. Proc. Linnean Soc. (London), Zoöl., v. 4, p. 172.

1869. The Malay Archipelago. 2 vols. Macmillan & Co., London. Also later eds.

1871. Contributions to the theory of natural selection. A series of essays. Macmillan Co., New York.

1876. The geographical distribution of animals. With a study of the relations of living and extinct faunas as elucidating the past changes of the earth's surface. 2 vols. Harper & Bros., New York.

1881. Island life or, the phenomena and causes of insular faunas and floras including a revision and attempted solution of the problem of geological climates. Harper & Bros., New York.

1905. Darwinism, an exposition of the theory of natural selection with some of its applications. Macmillan & Co., New York and London. Also other eds.

1916. The world of life. A manifestation of creative power, directive mind and ultimate purpose. Moffat, Yard & Co., New York.

WALLACE, A. R., & DYER, V. T. T.

1885. The distribution of life, animal and vegetable, in space and time. ("Humboldt Library of Science," No. 64.) Humboldt Publishing Co., New York.

WALLACE, W. C.

1836. The structure of the eye with reference to natural theology. Wiley & Long, New York.

WALLENBERG, A.

1898. Das mediale Opticusbündel der Taube. Neurol. Centralbl., v. 17, p. 532.

1904. Neue Untersuchungen über den Hirnstamm der Taube. Anat. Anz., v. 24, p. 142.

1904. Notiz zur Anatomie des Tractus peduncularis transversus beim Meerschweinchen. *Ibid.*, p. 199.

1910. Beitrag zur Lehre des Levator palpebrae superioris und seiner angeblichen Beziehung zur Gehirnrinde. Neurol. Centralbl., v. 29, p. 402.

1913. Beitrag zur Kenntnis der Sehbahnen der Knochenfische. Névraxe, v. 14, p. 251.

1926. Einige Aufgaben der Nervenanatomie und ihre Behandlung in den letzten 50 Jahren. Arch. f. Psychiat., v. 76, p. 21.

1931. Beiträge zur vergleichenden Anatomie des Hirnstammes. Deutsch. Ztschr. f. Nervenh., v. 117–19, p. 677.

1934. Ueber Verbindungen des Tractus occipito-mesencephalo-bulbaris mit einem Vestibularis-Endkern bei der Saatkrähe (*Corvus frugilegus* L.). Anat. Anz., v. 78, p. 438.

1934. Einige Notizen zur Kenntnis vom Bau des Zentralnervensystems der Selachier, Teleostier und Vogel. Psychiat. en neurol. bl., v. 38, p. 561.

1934. Bemerkenswerte Endstätten der Grosshirnfaserung bei Säugern. Jahrb. f. Psychiat. u. Neurol., v. 51, p. 295.

WALLER, W. H.

1940. Thalamic degeneration induced by temporal lesions in the cat. J. Anat., v. 74, p. 528.

WALLER, W. H., & BARRIS, R. W.

1937. Pupillary inequality in the cat following experimental lesions of the occipital cortex. Am. J. Physiol., v. 120, p. 144.

WALLIS, G. F. C.

1917. Some observations upon the anatomical relations of the optic nerves and chiasma to the sphenoid bone. Practitioner (London), v. 98, p. 41.

WALLS, G. L.

1928. The photo-mechanical changes in the retina of mammals. Science, v. 67, p. 655.

1928. An experimental study of the retina of the brook lamprey, etc. J. Comp. Neurol., v. 46, p. 465.

1932. Pupil shapes in reptilian eyes. Bull. Antiven. Inst. Amer. (Glenolden), v. 5, p. 68.

1934. Human rods and cones. Arch. Ophth., v. 12, p. 914.

1934. The reptilian retina. Am. J. Ophth., 3d ser., v. 17, p. 892.

1934. The significance of the reptilian "spectacle." Am. J. Ophth., *Ibid.*, p. 1045.

1934. The visual cells of the white rat. J. Comp. Psychol., v. 18, p. 363.

1934. Interpretation of the stripe-formed optic papilla. Arch. Ophth., v. 11, p. 292.

1935. The visual cells of lampreys. Brit. J. Ophth., v. 19, p. 129.

1937. Significance of the foveal depression. Arch. Ophth., v. 18, p. 912; *see also* v. 23, p. 831.

1939. The significance of the "Kolmer's droplets" of the vertebrate retina. Anat. Rec., v. 73, p. 373.

1939. Notes on the retinae of two opossum genera. J. Morphol., v. 64, p. 67.

1939. The fish with the magic eye. Chicago Naturalist, v. 2, p. 73.

1939. Origin of the vertebrate eye. Arch. Ophth., v. 22, p. 452.

1940. The pigment of the vertebrate lens. Science, v. 91, p. 172.

1940. Postscript on image expansion by the foveal clivus. Arch. Ophth., v. 23, p. 831.

1940. Ophthalmological implications for the early history of the snakes. Copeia, No. 1, p. 1.

1942. The visual cells and their history. *In:* Visual mechanisms, ed. H. KLÜVER. Biol. Symp., v. 7, p. 203. J. Cattell Press, Lancaster, Pa.

1942. The vertebrate eye and its adaptive radiation. Cranbrook Inst. Sc., Bull. 19. Cranbrook Press, Bloomfield Hills, Mich.

1943. The history of the human eye. Ciba Symp., v. 5, p. 1586.

1943. Factors in human visual resolution. J. Opt. Soc. Amer., v. 33, p. 487.

1951. The problem of visual direction. (Monog. No. 117.) Am. J. Optom., etc., Minneapolis, Minn.

1951. A theory of ocular dominance. Arch. Ophth., v. 45, p. 387.

1953. The lateral geniculate nucleus and visual histophysiology. ("University of California Pub. Physiol.," v. 9, No. 1.) University of California Press, Berkeley & Los Angeles.

WALLS, G. L., & JUDD, H. D.
1933. The intra-ocular colour-filters of vertebrates. Brit. J. Ophth., v. 17, pp. 641, 705.

WALSH, F. B.
1947. Clinical neuro-ophthalmology. Williams & Wilkins Co., Baltimore.

WALSH, F. B., & FORD, F. R.
1940. Central scotomas. Their importance in topical diagnosis. Arch. Ophth., v. 24, p. 500.

WALSH, J.
1925. Galen's discovery and promulgation of the function of the recurrent laryngeal nerve. Ann. M. Hist., v. 8, p. 176, 1926; *also* Tr. College of Physicians, Philadelphia, 3d ser., v. 47, p. 677.

1927. Galen visits the Dead Sea and the copper mines of Cyprus (166 A.D.). Bull. Geog. Soc. Philadelphia, v. 25, p. 93.

1927. Galen's studies at the Alexandrian school. Ann. M. Hist., v. 9, p. 132.

1928. Galen clashes with the medical sects at Rome. M. Life, v. 35, p. 408.

1929. Date of Galen's birth. Ann. M. Hist., N.S., v. 1, p. 378.

1930. Galen's second sojourn in Italy and his treatment of the family of Marcus Aurelius. M. Life, v. 37, p. 473.

1930. Galen's exhortation to the study of the arts, especially medicine. *Ibid.*, p. 507.

1931. Refutation of the charges of cowardice made against Galen. Ann. M. Hist., N.S., v. 3, p. 195.

WALSHE, F. M. R.
1947. Diseases of the nervous system. 5th ed. Williams & Wilkins Co., Baltimore.

WALTER, H. E.
1949. Biology of the vertebrates. 3d ed. Macmillan Co., New York.

WALTERS, H. V., & WRIGHT, W. D.
1943. The spectral sensitivity of the fovea and extrafovea in the Purkinje range. Proc. Roy. Soc. London, ser. B, v. 131, p. 340.

WALTON, W. E., & BORNEMEIER, R. W.
1938. Further evidence of color discrimination in rodents. J. Genet. Psychol., v. 52, p. 165.

1939. Color discrimination in rats. J. Comp. Psychol., v. 28, p. 417.

WARD, H. B., & WHIPPLE, G. C.
1918. Fresh-water biology. John Wiley & Sons, New York.

WARDEN, C. J., JENKINS, T. N., & WARNER, L. H.
1934. Introduction to comparative psychology. Ronald Press Co., New York.

1935–40. Comparative psychology. 3 vols. Ronald Press Co., New York.

WARNER, F. J.
1931. The cell masses in the telencephalon and diencephalon of the rattlesnake, *Crotalus atrox*. Proc. Kon. Akad. v. Wetensch. Amsterdam, v. 34, p. 1156.

WARNER, L. H.
1931. The problem of color vision in fishes. Quart. Rev. Biol., v. 6, p. 329.

WARREN, J.
1910–11. The development of the paraphysis and pineal region in reptilia. Am. J. Anat., v. 11, p. 313.

WARSCHAWSKI, J.
1927. Zur Frage der präzisen Lokalisation der einzeläugigen Gesichtsfelder in der Sehrinde. Klin. Monatsbl. f. Augenh., v. 79, p. 216.

WASHBURN, M. F.
1936. The animal mind. 4th ed. Macmillan Co., New York.

WASHBURN, M. F., & ABBOTT, E.
1912. Experiments on the brightness value of red for the light-adapted eye of the rabbit. J. Anim. Behavior, v. 2, p. 145.

WASHBURN, M. F., & BENTLEY, I. M.
1906. The establishment of an association involving color-discrimination in the creek chub, *Semotilus atromaculatus*. J. Comp. Neurol., v. 16, p. 113.

WASHBURN, S. L.
1950. The analysis of primate evolution with particular reference to the origin of man. Cold Spring Harbor Symp. Quant. Biol., v. 15, p. 67.

WASMUND, C. W.
1948. A study of the angle of bifurcation of retinal vessels. Am. J. Ophth., ser. 3, v. 31, p. 12.

WASSENAAR, T.
1914. Optical illusions. Folia neuro-biol., v. 8, p. 281.

WASZINK, J. H.
1933. Tertullian, *De anima*. Mit Einleitung, Uebersetzung, und Kommentar. H. J. Paris, Amsterdam.

WATANABE, Y.
1930. The location of the ciliary ganglion. Acta Soc. ophth. japon., v. 34, p. 255.

WATERHOUSE, G. R.
1849. Description of a new species of *Tupaia* discovered in continental India by Walter Elliot, Esq. Proc. Zoöl. Soc. London, p. 106.

WATERHOUSE, J.
1902. Notes on early tele-dioptric lens-systems, and the genesis of telephotography. Photog. J., v. 42, p. 4.
1903. The beginnings of photography. A chapter in the history of the development of photography with the salts of silver. *Ibid.*, v. 43, p. 159; *also* Smithsonian Inst. Ann. Rep., 1903.
1932. Article: Camera obscura, Encyclopaedia Britannica, 14th ed., v. 4, p. 658.

WATKINSON, G. B.
1906. The cranial nerves of *Varanus bivittatus*. Morphol. Jahrb., v. 35, p. 450.

WATSON, D. M. S.
1919. The structure, evolution and origin of the amphibia. Phil. Tr. Roy. Soc. London, ser. B, v. 209, p. 1.
1926. The evolution and origin of the amphibia. *Ibid.*, v. 214, p. 189.
1932. Article: Zoölogical regions, Encyclopaedia Britannica, 14th ed., v. 23, p. 964.
1949. The evidence afforded by fossil vertebrates on the nature of evolution. *In:* JEPSEN *et al.*, Genetics, paleontology, and evolution, p. 45.

WATSON, G. A.
1907. The mammalian cerebral cortex, with special reference to its comparative histology. I. Order insectivora. Arch. Neurol. (Mott), v. 3, p. 49.

WATSON, J. B.
1909. Some experiments bearing upon color vision in monkeys. J. Comp. Neurol., v. 19, p. 1.
1914. Behavior. An introduction to comparative psychology. Henry Holt & Co., New York.
1915. Studies on the spectral sensitivity of birds. Papers Dept. Marine Biol. Carnegie Inst. Washington, v. 7, p. 85. (Carnegie Inst. Washington Pub. No. 211, p. 85.)

WATSON, J. B., & WATSON, M. I.
1913. A study of the responses of rodents to monochromatic light. J. Anim. Behavior, v. 3, p. 1.

WEAKLEY, A. L.
1919. Homonymous hemianopia occurring in a case of malignant malaria. Brit. J. Ophth., v. 3, p. 300.

WEALE, R. A.; *see also* DARTNALL & THOMSON 1949
1951. The foveal and para-central spectral sensitivities in man. J. Physiol., v. 114, p. 435.
1953. Spectral sensitivity and wave-length discrimination of the peripheral retina. *Ibid.*, v. 119, p. 170.
1953. Cone-monochromatism. *Ibid.*, v. 121, p. 548.

WEAVER, K. S.
1937. The visibility of radiation at low intensities. J. Opt. Soc. Amer., v. 27, p. 36.

WEAVER, T. A., JR.
1936. Anatomical relations of the commissures of Meynert and Gudden in the cat. J. Comp. Neurol., v. 66, p. 333.

WEBER
1905. Note sur la dégénérescence secondaire consécutive à un foyer de ramollissement de la région calcarine. Arch. de neurol., 2d ser., v. 19, p. 177.

WEBER, A.
1945. Fibres centrifuges dans le nerf optique de l'axolotl. Schweiz. med. Wchnschr., v. 75, p. 631.

WEBER, D., & ACKERMANN
1805. Anatomisch-physiologische Erklärung der Sinnesverrichtung des Gesichts. Arch. f. d. Physiol. (Reil), v. 6, p. 282.

WEBER, E. H.
1849. Die Lehre vom Tastsinne und Gemeingefühle, auf Versuche gegründet für Aerzte und Philosophen. Vieweg, Braunschweig. Reprint from WAGNER, Handwörterbuch der Physiologie, v. 3, article Tastsinn, p. 531.
1852. Ueber den Raumsinn und die Empfindungskreise in der Haut und im Auge. Ber. ü. d. Verhandl. d. kgl. sächs. Gesellsch. d. Wissensch. zu Leipzig, math.-phys. Cl., v. 4, p. 85.

WEBER, M. W. C.
1886–98. Studien über Säugethiere. 2 vols. G. Fischer, Jena.
1890. Mammalia from the Malay Archipelago. Zoologische Ergebnisse einer Reise in Niederländisch Ost- Indien, Fasc. 1, p. 93. E. J. Brill, Leiden.
1927–28. Die Säugetiere. Einführung in die Anatomie und Systematik der recenten und fossilen Mammalia. 2d ed. 2 vols. G. Fischer, Jena.

WEBER, R.
1900. Un cas de tumeur du lobe occipital. Rev. méd. de la Suisse Rom., v. 20, p. 135.

WECHSLER, I. S.
1943. A textbook of clinical neurology with an introduction to the history of neurology. W. B. Saunders Co., Philadelphia.

WEDEL, C.
1700. Epistola anatomica, etc. De oculorum tunicis. *In:* RUYSCH, Opera omnia, v. 2, 1737.

WEDEL, J. A.
1714. De visione quae oculo fit gemino. *In:* A. HALLER, Disput. An. Sel., v. 4, p. 209.

WEED, A. C.
1927. Pike, pickerel and muskalonge. ("Zoöl. Leaflets," No. 9.) Field Museum of Natural History, Chicago.

WEEKERS, L.
1928. Hémianopsie double avec intégrité de la vision centrale. Topographie du centre cortical de la vision maculaire et des radiations optiques correspondantes. J. de neurol. et de psychiat., v. 28, p. 685.

WEEKS, J. E.
1940. Scintillating scotoma and other subjective visual phenomena. Am. J. Ophth., ser. 3, v. 23, p. 513.

WEEL, P. B. VAN
1937. Die Ernährungsbiologie von *Amphioxus lanceolatus.* Pub. staz. zool. Napoli, v. 16, p. 221.

WEGEFAHRT, P. S.
1914. The drainage of intraocular fluids. J. M. Research., v. 31, p. 119.
1914. Establishment of drainage of intraocular and intracranial fluids into the venous system. *Ibid.,* p. 149.

WEGEFAHRT, P. S., & WEED, L. H.
1914. Analogous processes of cerebral and ocular fluids. J. M. Research, v. 31, p. 167.

WEGENER, A. L.
1941. Die Entstehung der Kontinente und Ozeane. F. Vieweg & Sohn, Braunschweig. English trans.: The origin of continents and oceans. E. P. Dutton & Co., New York, 1924.

WEGNER, R. N.
1939. Das Anatomenbildnis. Seine Entwicklung im Zusammenhang mit der anatomischen Abbildung. B. Schwabe & Co., Basel.
1953–54. Das anatomische Institut und Museum der Universität Greifswald. Wissensch. Ztschr. d. Univ. Greifswald, v. 3, p. 49 (math.-naturw. R. No. 1).

WEHRLI, E.
1906. Ueber die anatomisch-histologische Grundlage der sog. Rindenblindheit und über die Lokalisation der corticalen Sehsphäre, der Macula lutea und die Projektion der Retina auf die Rinde des Occipitallappens. Arch. f. Ophth. (Graefe), v. 62, p. 286.

WEICHERT, C. K.
1951. Anatomy of the chordates. McGraw-Hill Book Co., New York.

WEIDENREICH, F.
1924. Die Sonderform des Menschenschädels als Anpassung an den aufrechten Gang. Ztschr. f. Morphol. u. Anthropol., v. 24, n p. 157.
1928. Entwicklungs- und Rassetypen des *Homo primigenius.* Natur u. Museum, v. 58, pp. 1, 51.
1930. Ein neuer *Pithecanthropus* Fund in China. *Ibid.,* v. 60, p. 546.
1932. Ueber pithekoide Merkmale bei *Sinanthropus pekinensis* und seine stammesgeschichtliche Beurteilung. Ztschr. f. Anat. u. Entw., v. 99, p. 212.
1934. Das Menschenkinn und seine Entstehung. Ergebn. d. Anat. u. Entw., v. 31, p. 1.
1935. The *Sinanthropus* population of Choukou-

tien, etc. Bull. Geol. Soc. China, v. 14, p. 427.

1936. Observations on the form and proportions of the endocranial casts of *Sinanthropus pekinensis*, other hominids and the great apes: a comparative study of brain size. Paleont. Sinica, ser. D., v. 7 (4), p. 1.

1936. *Sinanthropus pekinensis*—a distinct primitive hominid. Proc. Joint Meet. Anthropol. Soc. in Tokyo and Jap. Soc. Ethnol., 1st sess., p. 13.

1936. Ueber das phylogenetische Wachstum des Hominidengehirns. Kaibôgaku Zasshi, v. 9 (5). (*Cf.* Anat. Bericht, v. 35, p. 24.)

1937. The relation of *Sinanthropus pekinensis* to *Pithecanthropus*, *Javanthropus* and Rhodesian man. J. Roy. Anthropol. Inst., v. 67, p. 51.

1938. *Pithecanthropus* and *Sinanthropus*. Nature, v. 141, p. 378.

1939. On the earliest representatives of modern mankind recovered on the soil of East Asia. Peking Nat. Hist. Bull., v. 13, Part 3, p. 161.

1939. Six lectures on *Sinanthropus pekinensis* and related problems. Bull. Geol. Soc. China, v. 19, p. 1.

1940. Man or ape? Nat. Hist. Mag., v. 45, p. 32.

1940. Some problems dealing with ancient man. Am. Anthropologist, v. 42, p. 375.

1940. The Upper Paleolithic man of the upper cave of Choukoutien and his bearing on the problem of the provenance of the American Indians. Proc. 6th Pacific Sc. Cong. Berkeley, v. 4, p. 165.

1941. The brain and its role in the phylogenetic transformation of the human skull. Tr. Am. Phil. Soc., N.S., v. 31, p. 321.

1942. Early man in Indonesia. Far East. Quart., v. 2, p. 58.

1943. The "Neanderthal man" and the ancestors of "Homo sapiens." Am. Anthropologist, v. 45, p. 39.

1943. The skull of *Sinanthropus pekinensis;* a comparative study on a primitive hominid skull. Paleont. Sinica, N.S. D, No. 10 (whole ser. No. 127). Geological Survey of China, Pehpei, Chungking.

1945. Giant early man from Java and South China. Anthropol. Papers Am. Mus. Nat. Hist., v. 40, Part 1.

1946. Apes, giants, and man. University of Chicago Press, Chicago.

1946. Size, special form and pattern of the human brain in the light of evolution. Anat. Rec., v. 94, p. 503. (Abstr.)

WEIGERT
1927. Nervenfasern, Markscheide. *In:* R. KRAUSE, Enzyklopädie der mikr. Technik, v. 3, p. 1622. (*See also* S. Polyak, The retina.)

WEIGERT, F.
1932. Photochemisches zur Theorie des Farbensehens. *In:* BETHE *et al.*, Handb. d. norm. u. path. Physiol., v. 18, p. 314.

WEIL, A.
1929. Measurements of cerebral and cerebellar surfaces. Am. J. Phys. Anthropol., v. 13, p. 69.

1933. A text-book of neuropathology. Lea & Febiger, Philadelphia. 2d ed., 1945.

WEINBERG, R.
1896. Das Gehirn der Letten. T. G. Fischer & Co., Kassel.

1896. Die Gehirnwindungen bei den Esten. ("Biblioth. Med.," Abt. A, Heft 1.) T. G. Fischer, Kassel.

1905. Die Gehirnformen der Polen. Ztschr. f. Morphol. u. Anthropol., v. 8, pp. 123, 279.

1907. Weitere Untersuchungen zur Anatomie der menschlichen Gehirnoberfläche. Arch. f. Psychiat. u. Nervenkr., v. 42, p. 107.

1926. Ungekreuzte Sehnervenfasern. Ztschr. f. Anat. u. Entw., v. 79, p. 433.

WEINERT, H.
1925. Der Affenmensch von Java in neuer Darstellung. Naturwiss., v. 13, p. 188.

1932. Das heutige "missing link." Jena. Ztschr. f. Naturwiss., v. 67, p. 245.

1948. Ueber die Heimat der Menschenrassen. Natur u. Volk (Ber. d. Senckenberg. naturforsch. Gesellsch.), v. 78, p. 13.

1951. Der geistige Aufstieg der Menschheit vom Ursprung bis zur Gegenwart. F. Enke, Stuttgart.

WEINSTEIN, B.
1945. The evolution of intelligent behavior in rhesus monkeys. Genet. Psychol. Monog., v. 31, p. 3.

WEINSTEIN, B., & GRETHER, W. F.
1940. A comparison of visual acuity in the rhesus monkey and man. J. Comp. Psychol., v. 30, p. 187.

WEINSTEIN, E. A., & BENDER, M. B.
1948. The mid-position phenomenon in eye movements. Tr. Am. Neurol. A., 73d meet., p. 163.

WEINSTEIN, P., & FORGÁCS, J.
1947. Circulatory studies of the fundus of the eye. Brit. J. Ophth., v. 31, p. 238.

WEISS, E.
1927. Weber-Fechnersches Gesetz und Adapta-

tion. Ber. d. Deutsch. ophth. Gesellsch. Heidelberg, v. 46, p. 308.

WEISS, P.

1934. In vitro experiments on the factors determining the course of the outgrowing nerve fiber. J. Exper. Zoöl., v. 68, p. 393.

WEISS, P., & HSI WANG

1936. Neurofibrils in living ganglion cells of the chick, cultivated in vitro. Anat. Rec., v. 67, p. 105.

WEISS, S.

1938. The regulation and disturbance of the cerebral circulation through extracerebral mechanism. *In:* The circulation of the brain and spinal cord. Research Pub. A. Research Nerv. & Ment. Dis., v. 18, p. 571.

WEISSBERGER, A.

1946. Physical methods of organic chemistry. 2 vols. Interscience Publishers, Inc., New York.

WEISZ, S.

1929. Ueber propriozeptive Körperreaktionen in der topischen Hirndiagnostik. Ztschr. f. d. ges. Neurol. u. Psychiat., v. 118, p. 167.

WEIZSÄCKER, V. VON

1925. Ueber eine systematische Raumsinnstörung. Deutsch. Ztschr. f. Nervenh., v. 84, p. 179.

1925. Einleitung zur Physiologie der Sinne. *In:* BETHE *et al.*, Handbuch d. norm. u. path. Physiol., v. 11, p. 1.

1927–28. Pathophysiologie der Sensibilität. Zentralbl. f. d. ges. Neurol. u. Psychiat., v. 47, p. 774; *also* Deutsch. Ztschr. f. Nervenh., v. 101, p. 184.

1930. Funktionswandel bei Störung räumlicher Leistungen in der Wahrnehmung und Bewegung. Deutsch. Ztschr. f. Nervenh., v. 116, p. 59.

1931. Kasuistische Beiträge zur Lehre vom Funktionswandel bei stato-opto-sensiblen Syndromen. *Ibid.*, v. 117–19, p. 716.

1934. Was lehrt die neue Pathologie der Sinnesorgane für die Physiologie der Sinnesleistungen? Ztschr. f. Sinnesphysiol., v. 64, p. 79.

WELCKER, H.

1863. Untersuchung der Retinazapfen und des Riechhautepithels, bei einem Hingerichteten. Ztschr. f. rat. Med., 3d ser., v. 20, p. 173.

WELLS, H. G., HUXLEY, J., & WELLS, G. P.

1931. The science of life. Cassel & Co., London.

WELLS, M. M.

1926. Collecting *Amphioxus.* Science, v. 64, p. 187.

WELLS, W. C.

1792. An essay on single vision with two eyes. T. Cadell, London.

1811. Observations and experiments on vision. Phil. Tr. Roy. Soc. London, v. 101, p. 378. German trans. by M. ROHR in Ztschr. f. ophth. Optik, v. 11, p. 170, 1923.

1818. Two essays: one upon single vision with two eyes; the other on dew. Etc. Edinburgh, London. German trans. in Ztschr. f. ophth. Optik, v. 10, pp. 12, 38, 68, 97.

WELSH, J. H.

1938. Diurnal rhythms. Quart. Rev. Biol., v. 13, p. 123.

WELSH, J. H., & OSBORN, C. M.

1937. Diurnal changes in the retina of the catfish, *Ameiurus nebulosus.* J. Comp. Neurol., v. 66, p. 349.

WEN, I. C.

1933. A study of the occipital region of the Chinese fetal brain. J. Comp. Neurol., v. 57, p. 477.

WENDENBURG, K.

1909. Ein Tumor des rechten Hinterhauptlappens mit ungewöhnlichen klinischen Begleiterscheinungen. Monatsschr. f. Psychiat. u. Neurol., v. 25, p. 428.

WENDT, G. R., & DODGE, R.

1938. Practical directions for stimulating and for photographically recording eye-movements of animals. J. Comp. Psychol., v. 25, p. 9.

WENTSLER, N. E.

1936. Microscopic study of the superficial cerebral vessels of the rabbit by means of a permanently installed transparent cranial chamber. Anat. Rec., v. 66, p. 423.

WENTWORTH, H. A.

1930. A quantitative study of achromatic and chromatic sensitivity from center to periphery of the visual field. Psychol. Monog., v. 40 (3), p. 1.

WENZEL, J., & WENZEL, K.

1812. De penitiori structura cerebri hominis et brutorum. Apud Cottam, Tubingae.

WEPFER, J. J.

1658. Observationes anatomicae ex cadaveribus eorum, quos sustulit apoplexia, cum exercitatione de eius loco affecto. J. C. Suteri, Schafhausen.

*1727. Observationes medico-practicae de affectibus capitis internis et externis. J. A. Ziegleri, Scaphusii.

*1664. De dubiis anatomicis epistola qua objectiones nonnullas contra Bilsii doctrinam proponit. Nürnberg. Another ed., Strassburg, 1665.

WERNER, H.
1942. Binocular vision—normal and abnormal. Arch. Ophth., v. 28, p. 834.

WERNER, O.
1910. Zur Physik Leonardo da Vincis. Inaug.-Diss. Junge & Sohn, Erlangen.

WERNICKE, C.; for obituary *see* Arch. f. Psychiat., v. 40, p. 1016
1875. Das Urwindungssystem des menschlichen Gehirns. Arch. f. Psychiat. u. Nervenkr., v. 6, p. 298.
1879. Die Theorie des apoplectischen Insultes, eine nothwendige Voraussetzung der klinischen Gehirnlocalisation. Deutsch. med. Wchnschr., v. 5, pp. 343, 355.
1881. Lehrbuch der Gehirnkrankheiten für Aerzte und Studirende. 2 vols. T. Fischer, Kassel.
1884. Ueber die motorische Sprachbahn und das Verhältniss der Aphasie zur Anarthrie. Fortschr. d. Med., v. 2, pp. 1, 405.
1890. Aphasie und Geisteskrankheit. Deutsch. med. Wchnschr., v. 16, p. 445.
1892–95. Arbeiten aus der psychiatrischen Klinik in Breslau. 2 vols. G. Thieme, Leipzig.
1893. Monoplegia brachialis mit Hemianopsie durch Stichverletzung des Hirnschenkels bedingt. Allg. Wien. med. Ztg., v. 38, pp. 544, 553.
1895. Zwei Fälle von Rindenläsion. Ein Beitrag zur Localisation der Vorstellungen. Arb. a. d. psychiat. Klin. Breslau, Fasc. 2, p. 33.
1903. Angeborene Wortblindheit. Centralbl. f. prakt. Augenh., v. 27, p. 264.
1906. Grundriss der Psychiatrie in klinischen Vorlesungen. G. Thieme, Leipzig.
1906. Der aphasische Symptomencomplex. Deutsch. Klinik, v. 6 (1), Nervenkrankheiten, p. 487. Urban & Schwarzenberg, Berlin, Wien. First ed.: Der aphasische Symptomencomplex. Eine psychologische Studie auf anatomischer Basis. Cohn & Weigert, Breslau, 1874.

WERNICKE, O.
1903. Angeborene Wortblindheit. Centralbl. f. prakt. Augenh., v. 27, p. 264.

WERTHEIM, T.
1887. Ueber die Zahl der Seheinheiten im mittleren Theile der Netzhaut. Arch. f. Ophth. (Graefe), v. 33 (2), p. 137.
1894. Ueber die indirekte Sehschärfe. Ztschr. f. Psychol. u. Physiol. d. Sinnesorg., v. 7, p. 172.

WERTHEIM SOLOMONSON, J. K. A.
1918. La photographie du fond de l'œil. Arch. néerl. de physiol., v. 3, p. 391.

WESENBERG-LUND, C.
1939. Biologie der Süsswassertiere (wirbellose Tiere). J. Springer, Wien.

WESTOLL, T. S.
1943. The origin of the tetrapods. Biol. Rev., v. 18, p. 78.

WESTPHAL, C.
1874. Aphasie. Verhandl. d. Berlin. Gesellsch. f. Anthropol., p. 94.
1879. Zur Frage der Localisation der unilaterale Convulsionen und Hemianopsie bedingenden Hirnerkrankungen. Charité-Ann., v. 6, p. 342, 1881.
1879. A case of homonymous hemianopia (in German). Centralbl. f. prakt. Augenh., v. 3, p. 181.
1880. Zur Localisation der Hemianopsie und des Muskelgefühls beim Menschen. Charité-Ann., v. 7, p. 466, 1882.
1881. Case of hemianopia with autopsy (in German). Arch. f. Psychiat. u. Nervenkr., v. 11, p. 822.
1887. Ueber einen Fall von chronischer progressiver Lähmung der Augenmuskeln (Ophthalmoplegia externa) nebst Beschreibung von Ganglienzellengruppen im Bereiche des Oculomotoriuskerns. *Ibid.*, v. 18, p. 846.
1908. Ueber einen Fall von motorischer Apraxie (mit Sektionsbefund). Med. Klin., v. 4, p. 283.

WETMORE, A.
1933. The eagle, king of birds, and his kin. Nat. Geog. Mag., v. 64, p. 43.

WEVE, H.
1919. Ein Fall kompletter, homonymer Hemianopsie im Wochenbett. Psychiat. en neurol. bl., v. 23, p. 39.

WEYGANDT, W.
1900. Psychologie und Hirnanatomie mit besonderer Berücksichtigung der modernen Phrenologie. Deutsch. med. Wchnschr., v. 26, p. 657.
1901. Hirnanatomie, Psychologie und Erkenntnisstheorie. Centralbl. f. Nervenh., v. 24, p. 1.
1927. Kraepelins psychologische Forschertätigkeit. Psychol. Arb., v. 9, p. 359.

WEYL, H.
1934. Universum und Atom. Naturwiss., v. 22, p. 145.

WEYMOUTH, F. W. *et al.* (*see also* ANDERSEN & WEYMOUTH; AVERILL & WEYMOUTH)
1928. Visual acuity within the area centralis and its relation to eye movements and fixation. Am. J. Ophth., v. 11, p. 947.

WHARTON, C. H.
1948. Seeking Mindanao's strangest creatures. Nat. Geog. Mag., v. 94, p. 389.
1950. The tarsier in captivity. J. Mammal., v. 31, p. 260.
1950. Notes on the life history of the flying lemur. *Ibid.*, p. 269.
1950. Notes on the Philippine tree shrew, *Urogale everetti* Thomas. *Ibid.*, p. 352.

WHEATSTONE, C.
1838. Contributions to the physiology of vision. Part the first. On some remarkable, and hitherto unobserved, phenomena of binocular vision. Phil. Tr. Roy. Soc. London, Part 1, v. 128, p. 371; Proc. Roy. Soc. London, v. 4, p. 76; and the Scientific papers of Sir Charles Wheatstone, p. 225. Taylor & Francis, London, 1879.

WHEELER, J. R.
1946. History of ophthalmology through the ages. Brit. J. Ophth., v. 30, p. 264.

WHEELER, W. M.
1918. A study of some ant larvae, with a consideration of the origin and meaning of the social habit among insects. Proc. Am. Phil. Soc., v. 57, p. 293.

WHITE, G. M.
1919. Association and color discrimination in mudminnows and sticklebacks. J. Exper. Zoöl., v. 27, p. 443.

WHITE, J. C., & SMITHWICK, R. H.
1941. The autonomic nervous system. Macmillan Co., New York.

WHITHEAD 1879; *see* O. THOMAS, Ann. Mag. Nat. Hist., ser. 6, v. 9, p. 250, 1892

WHITMAN, C. O.
1892. The metamerism of *Clepsine*. Festschr. z. siebz. Geburtst. Rudolf Leuckarts, etc., p. 385. W. Engelmann, Leipzig.
1893. A sketch of the structure and development of the eye of *Clepsine*. Zool. Jahrb. (Anat. & Ontog.), v. 6, p. 616.
1899. Animal behavior. Biological lectures from the Marine Biological Laboratory, Woods Hole, for 1898, p. 285. Boston.

WHITNALL, S. E.
1932. The anatomy of the human orbit and accessory organs of vision. H. Milford, Oxford University Press, London.

WHITNEY, W. D., & LANMAN, C. R.
1905. Atharva-Veda Saṁhitā. ("Harvard Orient. Ser.," vols. 7, 8.) Cambridge, Mass.

WHYTT, R.
1751. An essay on the vital and other involuntary motions of animals. Printed by Hamilton, Balfour, & Neill, Edinburgh. 2d ed. printed for Balfour, Edinburgh, 1763.
1755. Physiological essays containing an inquiry into the causes which promote the circulation of the fluids in the very small vessels of animals, with observations on the sensibility and irritability on the parts of man and other animals. Hamilton, Balfour & Neill, Edinburgh. 2d ed., Hamilton, Balfour & Neill, Edinburgh, 1761; 3d ed., J. Balfour Edinburgh, 1766.

WIBERG, J.
1914. The anatomy of the brain in the works of Galen and ᶜAli ᶜAbbas; a comparative historical-anatomical study. Janus, v. 19, pp. 17, 84.

WICHERN
1911. Ein Fall von totaler Rindenblindheit bei perniziöser Anämie (mit Sektionsbefund). München. med. Wchnschr., v. 58, p. 2307.

WICK, W. M.
1923. Zum Schema der reflektorischen Pupillenstarre. Klin. Monatsbl. f. Augenh., v. 70, p. 505.
1924. Funktionsprüfungen des Auges. S. Karger, Berlin.

WIDMARK, J.
1897. Om läget af det papillo-makulära knippet. Nord. med. ark., v. 30 (Festband), No. 25; review in Neurol. Centralbl., v. 18, p. 320, 1899.

WIECZOREK, A.
1935. The structure of the bony orbit (Polish with a French summary). Klin. oczna, v. 13, p. 39.

WIED-NEUWIED, MAXIMILIAN PRINZ ZU
1825. Reise nach Brasilien in den Jahren 1815 bis 1817. 3 vols. Kaulfuss & Krammer, Wien.

WIEDEMANN, E. (*see also* H. J. SEEMANN 1930)
1876. Beiträge zur Geschichte der Naturwissenschaften bei den Arabern. Ann. d. Phys. u. Chem. (Poggendorff), 6th ser., v. 9 (159), p. 656. Italian trans. in Bull. di bibl. e di storia d. sc. mat. e fis. (Boncompagni), v. 12, p. 873. (*See also* Isis, v. 14, p. 171.)
1881. Sull'ottica degli Arabi. Bull. di bibl. e di storia d. sc. mat. e fis. (Boncompagni), v. 14, p. 219.
1883. Ueber "Die Darlegung der Abhandlung über das Licht" von Ibn al Haiṭam. Ann. d. Phys. u. Chem. (Poggendorff-Wiedemann), N.F., v. 20, p. 337.
1890. Zur Geschichte der Brennspiegel. *Ibid.*, v. 39, p. 110.

WIEDEMANN, E.—*Continued*

1890. Zur Geschichte der Lehre vom Sehen. *Ibid.*, p. 470.

1890. Ueber das Sehen durch eine Kugel bei den Arabern. *Ibid.*, p. 565.

1906. Ibn al Haitham, ein arabischer Gelehrter. Festschr. J. Rosenthal, v. 1, p. 147. G. Thieme, Leipzig.

1910. Ueber die Erfindung der Camera obscura. Verhandl. d. Deutsch. physik. Gesellsch., v. 12, p. 177.

1910. Ueber die erste Erwähnung der Dunkelkammer durch Ibn al Haitam. Jahrb. f. Photog. u. Repr., v. 24, p. 12.

1910. Eine Zeichnung des Auges bei dem Bearbeiter der Optik von Ibn al Haitam, Kamâl al Dîn al Fârisî, etc. Centralbl. f. prakt. Augenh., v. 34, p. 204.

1911. Zur Optik von Kamâl al-Dîn. Arch. f. d. Gesch. d. Naturwiss. u. d. Tech., v. 3, p. 161.

1911. Ueber das Leben von Ibn al Haitam und al Kindî. Jahrb. f. Photog. u. Repr., v. 25, p. 6.

1912. Zu Ibn al Haitams Optik. Arch. f. d. Gesch. d. Naturwiss. u. d. Tech., v. 3, p. 1.

1913. Ibn Sīnā's Anschauung vom Sehvorgang. *Ibid.*, v. 4, p. 239.

1914. Roger Bacon und seine Verdienste um die Optik. *In:* A. G. LITTLE, Roger Bacon, Essays, etc., p. 185.

1915. Ueber die *Camera obscura* bei Ibn al Haitam. Sitzungsb. d. phys.-med. Soc. zu Erlangen (1914), v. 46, p. 155.

*1915. Die Naturwissenschaften bei den orientalischen Völkern. *In:* Erlangen in der Kriegszeit. 1. Ein Gruss der Universität an ihre Studenten. T. Krische, Erlangen.

WIEDERSHEIM, R.

1886. Lehrbuch der vergleichenden Anatomie der Wirbelthiere auf Grundlage der Entwicklungsgeschichte. 2d ed. G. Fischer, Jena.

1907. Grundriss der vergleichenden Anatomie der Wirbeltiere. 7th ed. G. Fischer, Jena. Also earlier and later eds.

WIEMAN, H. L.

1949. An introduction to vertebrate embryology. McGraw-Hill Book Co., New York.

WIENER, M., & ALVIS, B. Y.

1939. Surgery of the eye. W. B. Saunders Co., Philadelphia.

WIESLI, P.

1928. Eine Methode zur Frühdiagnose der bitemporalen Hemianopsie bei Hypophysentumoren. Schweiz. med. Wchnschr., v. 58, p. 479.

WIETHE, T.

1884. Ein Fall von plötzlicher Amaurosis mit nachfolgender Hemianopia homonyma superior. Arch. f. Augenh., v. 13, p. 387.

WIETING, J.

1898. Zur Anatomie des menschlichen Chiasma. Arch. f. Ophth. (Graefe), v. 45 (1), p. 75.

WIGGER, H.

1937–38. Versuche zur Kausalanalyse der retinomotorischen Erscheinungen. Arch. f. d. ges. Physiol. (Pflüger), v. 239, p. 215.

1939. Vergleichende Untersuchungen am Auge von Wild- und Hausschwein unter besonderer Berücksichtigung der Retina. Ztschr. f. Morphol. u. Oekol. d. Tiere, v. 36, p. 1.

WIGGLESWORTH, V. B.

1939. The principles of insect physiology. E. P. Dutton Co., New York.

WILBRAND, H.

1878. Ueber Neuritis axialis. Klin. Monatsbl. f. Augenh., v. 16, p. 505.

1881. Ueber Hemianopsie und ihr Verhältnis zur topischen Diagnose der Gehirnkrankheiten. A. Hirschwald, Berlin.

1885. Ein Fall von rechtsseitiger lateraler Hemianopsie mit Sectionsbefund. Arch. f. Ophth. (Graefe), v. 31, p. 119.

1887. Die Seelenblindheit als Herderscheinung und ihre Beziehungen zur homonymen Hemianopsie, zur Alexie und Agraphie. J. F. Bergmann, Wiesbaden.

1890. Die hemianopischen Gesichtsfeld-Formen und das optische Wahrnehmungszentrum. J. F. Bergmann, Wiesbaden.

1892. Ein Fall von Seelenblindheit und Hemianopsie mit Sectionsbefund. Deutsch. Ztschr. f. Nervenh., v. 2, p. 361.

1895. Die Doppelversorgung der Macula lutea und der Förster'sche Fall von doppelseitiger homonymer Hemianopsie. Arch. f. Augenh., v. 31, Ergh. (Beitr. z. Augenh.-Festschr. f. R. Förster), p. 93.

1907. Ueber die makulär-hemianopische Lesestörung und die v. Monakowsche Projektion der Makula auf die Sehsphäre. Klin. Monatsbl. f. Augenh., v. 45 (N.F., v. 4), p. 1.

1913. Die Theorie des Sehens. Zwei Vorträge gehalten während der akademischen Ferienkurse zu Hamburg. J. F. Bergmann, Wiesbaden.

1925. Ueber die Organisation der kortikalen Fovea und die Erklärung einiger Erscheinungen aus dem Symptomenkomplex der homonymen Hemianopsie. Ztschr. f. Augenh., v. 54, p. 1.

1925. Gedanken über die Notwendigkeit einer Partialkreuzung der Sehnervenfasern im Chiasma. *Ibid.*, v. 55, p. 371.

1926. Ueber die Bedeutung kleinster homonym-hemianopischer Gesichtsfelddefekte. *Ibid.*, v. 58, p. 197.

1926. Ueber die makuläre Aussparung. *Ibid.*, p. 261.

1926. Schema des Verlaufs der Sehnervenfasern durch das Chiasma. *Ibid.*, v. 59, p. 135.

1929. Der Faserverlauf durch das Chiasma und die intrakraniellen Sehnerven. S. Karger, Berlin.

1930. Ueber die wissenschaftliche Bedeutung der Kongruenz und Inkongruenz der Gesichts-felddefekte. J. f. Psychol. u. Neurol., v. 40, p. 133.

WILBRAND, H., & BEHR, C.

1927. Die Neurologie des Auges in ihrem heutigen Stande; zugleich ein Ergänzungsband zur Neurologie des Auges von Wilbrand & Saenger. Bearbeitet von H. Wilbrand und C. Behr. J. F. Bergmann, München.

1927. Lider-, Tränensekretion, Trigeminus, Pupille, Akkommodation, Heterochromie, Sympathikus. Suppl. vol. of WILBRAND & SAENGER, Die Neurologie des Auges. J. F. Bergmann, München.

WILBRAND, H., & SAENGER, A.

1899–1927. Die Neurologie des Auges. Ein Handbuch für Nerven- und Augenärzte. V. 1: Die Beziehungen des Nervensystems zu den Lidern, 1899. V. 2: Die Beziehungen des Nervensystems zu den Tränenorganen, zur Bindehaut und zur Hornhaut, 1922. V. 3 (1): Anatomie und Physiologie der optischen Bahnen und Zentren, 1904. V. 3 (2): Allgemeine Diagnostik und Symptomatologie der Sehstörungen, 1906. V. 4 (1): Die Pathologie der Netzhaut, 1909. V. 4 (2): Die Erkrankungen des Sehnervenkopfes, 1912. V. 5: Die Erkrankungen des Opticusstammes, 1913. V. 6: Die Erkrankungen des Chiasmas, 1915. V. 7: Die homonyme Hemianopsie nebst ihren Beziehungen zu den anderen cerebralen Herderscheinungen, 1917. V. 8: Die Pathologie der Bahnen und Centren der Augenmuskeln, 1921. V. 9: Die Störungen der Akkommodation und der Pupillen, 1922. V. 10: Gesamtregister, 1922. Suppl. vols. by H. WILBRAND & C. BEHR, Lider-, Tränensekretion, Trigeminus, Pupille, Akkommodation, Heterochromie, Sympathikus, 1927, and Die Neurologie des Auges in ihrem heutigen Stande, 1927. J. F. Bergmann, Wiesbaden-München.

1918. Die Verletzungen der Sehbahn des Gehirns mit besonderer Berücksichtigung der Kriegsverletzungen. J. F. Bergmann, Wiesbaden.

1921. Die Pathologie der Bahnen und Centren der Augenmuskeln. *In:* their Die Neurologie des Auges, v. 8. J. F. Bergmann, Wiesbaden & München.

1922. Die Störungen der Akkommodation und der Pupillen. *In:* their Die Neurologie des Auges, v. 9. J. F. Bergmann, Wiesbaden & München.

WILCKE, G.

1938. Freilands- und Gefangenschaftsbeobachtungen an *Sorex araneus* L. Ztschr. f. Säugetierk., v. 12, p. 332.

WILCOX, W. W.

1932. The basis of the dependence of visual acuity on illumination. Proc. Nat. Acad. Sc., v. 18, p. 47.

WILCOX, W. W., & PURDY, D. M.

1933. Visual acuity and its physiological basis. Brit. J. Psychol., v. 23, p. 233.

1933. Zum Problem der optischen Intensitäts-wahrnehmung. Ztschr. f. Psychol. u. Physiol. d. Sinnesorg., v. 63, p. 253.

WILCZEK, M.

1947. The lamina cribrosa and its nature. Brit. J. Ophth., v. 31, p. 551.

WILDE, E.

1838–43. Geschichte der Optik. 2 vols. Rücker & Püchler, Berlin.

WILDER, J.

1928. Ueber Schief- und Verkehrtsehen. Deutsch. Ztschr. f. Nervenh., v. 104, p. 222.

WILE, I. S.

1942. Eye dominance: its nature and treatment. Arch. Ophth., v. 28, p. 780.

WILKINSON, H. J.

1930. Observations on the sole-plates of motor end-organs. J. Comp. Neurol., v. 50, p. 133.

1931. L'innervation du muscle strié. Bull. d'histol., v. 8, p. 117.

1934. Further experimental studies on the innervation of striated muscle. J. Comp. Neurol., v. 59, p. 221.

WILLARD, W. A.

1915. The cranial nerves of *Anolis carolinensis*. Bull. Mus. Comp. Zoöl. Harvard, v. 59, p. 15.

WILLEY, A.

1894. *Amphioxus* and the ancestry of the vertebrates. Macmillan Co., New York & London.

1895. In the home of the Nautilus. Nat. Sc., v. 6, p. 405.

WILLIAMS, D.
1948. Subjective disorders of vision. Tr. Ophth. Soc. United Kingdom, v. 68, p. 13.

WILLIAMS, E.
1875. Binocular temporal hemiopia. Tr. Am. Ophth. Soc., 11th meet., p. 298, 1876.

WILLIAMS, H. W.
1889. Franciscus Cornelius Donders. Proc. Am. Acad. Arts & Sci., v. 24, p. 105.

WILLIAMSON, W. P.
1945. After-image perimetry, a rapid method of obtaining visual fields; preliminary report. Arch. Ophth., ser. 2, v. 33, p. 40.

WILLIS, T.
1664. Cerebri anatome. Londini, typ. Ja. Flesher, imp. Jo. Martyn & Ja. Allestry.
1682. De anima brutorum. *In:* his Opera omnia.
1682. Opera omnia. Amstelaedami, ap. H. Wetstenium.

WILLISTON, S. W.
1914. Water reptiles of the past and present. University of Chicago Press, Chicago.

WILLMER, E. N.
1944. Colour of small objects. Nature, v. 153, p. 774.
1946. Retinal structure and colour vision. A restatement and an hypothesis. Cambridge University Press, Cambridge.
1946. Observations on the central fovea of certain red-green-blind subjects. Proc. Physiol. Soc., J. Physiol., v. 105, p. 38P.
1949. Deuteranopia and the sensitivity of the "red receptor." *Ibid.*, v. 109, p. 28P.
1949. Some evolutionary aspects of mammalian colour vision. Proc. Linnean Soc. London, sess. 161 (2), p. 97.
1949. Comment on photoreceptors. Doc. ophth., v. 3, p. 42.
1949. Colour vision conference, Cambridge, 1947. Comments by E. N. Willmer. *Ibid.*, p. 47.
1949. Colour vision in the central fovea. *Ibid.*, p. 194.
1949. The monochromatism of the central fovea in red-green-blind subjects. J. Physiol., v. 110, p. 377.
1949. Further observations on the properties of the central fovea in colour-blind and normal subjects. *Ibid.*, p. 422.
1949. Low threshold rods and the perception of blue. *Ibid.*, v. 111, p. 17P.
1950. Interaction between lights of different wavelength in the central fovea. *Ibid.*, p. 69.
1950. The relationship between area and threshold in the central fovea for lights of different

colours. Quart. J. Exper. Psychol., v. 2 (2), p. 53.

WILLMER, E. N., & WRIGHT, W. D.
1945. Colour sensitivity of the fovea centralis. Nature, v. 156, p. 119.

WILMER, H. A., & SCAMMON, R. E.
1950. Growth of the components of the human eyeball. Parts I, II. Diagrams, computations and reference tables. Arch. Ophth., v. 43, pp. 599, 620.

WILMER, W. H.
1934. Atlas fundus oculi. Macmillan Co., New York.

WILSKA, A., & HARTLINE, H. K.
1941. The origin of "off-responses" in the optic pathway. Am. J. Physiol., v. 133, p. 491.

WILSON, F. H.
1939. Preliminary experiments on the color changes of *Anolis carolinensis* (Cuvier). Am. Naturalist, v. 73, p. 190.

WILSON, G.
1855. On the extent to which the received theory of vision requires us to regard the eye as a camera obscura. Tr. Roy. Soc. Edinburgh, v. 21, p. 327, 1857.

WILSON, J.
1704. The description and manner of using a late invented set of small pocket-microscopes, etc. Phil. Tr. Roy. Soc. London, v. 23, p. 1241.

WILSON, J. A.
1919. Gunshot injuries of the cortical visual areas. Brit. J. Ophth., v. 3, p. 453.

WILSON, R. B.
1933. The anatomy of the brain of the whale (*Balaenoptera sulfurea*). J. Comp. Neurol., v. 58, p. 419.

WILSON, S. A. K.
1908. A contribution to the study of apraxia with a review of the literature. Brain, v. 31, p. 164.
1917. Concussion injuries of the visual apparatus in warfare, of central origin. Lancet, v. 2, p. 1.
1940. Neurology. Ed. A. N. BRUCE. 2 vols. Williams & Wilkins Co., Baltimore. 2d ed., 1954–55.

WILSON, S. A. K., & GERSTLE, M.
1929. The Argyll Robertson sign in mesencephalic tumors. Arch. Neurol. & Psychiat., v. 22, p. 9.

WILSON, W. H., & SMITH, G. ELLIOT
1909. The interpretation of the results obtained from the study of cerebral localisation in the prosimiae. Rep. 78th meet. Brit. A. Adv. Sc., p. 875.

WINCHESTER, A.
1947. Zoölogy, the science of animal life. D. Van Nostrand Co., New York.

WINCKLER, G.
1937. Aspect morphologique et structure du muscle orbiculaire des paupières chez l'homme. Arch. d'anat., v. 24, p. 183.
1937. Les gaines des muscles extrinsèques de l'œil et la capsule de Tenon chez l'homme. *Ibid.*, p. 295.

WINDAR, F.
1925. Die Quintessenz des Darwinismus. Biol. Zentralbl., v. 45, p. 303.

WINDELS, F.
1948. Lascaux, "Chapelle Sixtine" de la préhistoire. Introduction de l'abbé H. Breuil. Centre d'études et de documentation préhistoriques. Montignac-sur-Vézère, Dordogne, France.
1948. Lascaux. (Summary by G. E. Daniel in Man, v. 49, p. 106; an English translation announced.)

WINDLE, W. F., & CLARK, S. L.
1928. Observations on the histology of the synapse. J. Comp. Neurol., v. 46, p. 153.

WING, K. G., & SMITH, K. U.
1942. The role of the optic cortex in the dog in the determination of the functional properties of conditioned reactions to light. J. Exper. Psychol., v. 31, p. 478.

WINGE, H.
1941. The interrelationships of the mammalian genera, v. 1. C. A. Reitzels Forlag, København.

WINKELMAN, J. E.
1949. The motor impulse elicited by the retinal stimulus and the binocular optical reflexes. Brit. J. Ophth., v. 33, p. 629.

WINKLER, C.
1910. De achterhoofdskwab en de halfblindheid. Psychiat. en neurol. bl., v. 14, p. 9. Le lobe occipital et l'hémianopsie, in his Opera omnia, v. 5, p. 183.
1911. A tumour in the pulvinar thalami optici. A contribution to the knowledge of the vision of forms. Proc. Kon. Akad. Wetensch. Amsterdam, sc. sec., v. 13, p. 928; Opera omnia, v. 5, p. 231; Folia neuro-biol., v. 5, p. 708.
1913. On localised atrophy in the lateral geniculate body causing quadrantic hemianopsia of both the right lower fields of vision. Proc. Kon. Akad. Wetensch. Amsterdam, v. 15, p. 840; Folia neuro-biol., v. 7 (suppl.), p. 1; Opera omnia, v. 5, p. 333.

1918–29. Manuel de neurologie. 3 vols. De Erven F. Bohn, Haarlem.
1918–33. Opera omnia. 10 vols. De Erven F. Bohn, Haarlem.
1923. Die Bedeutung der Arbeit Constantin von Monakow's für die Wissenschaft. Schweiz. Arch. f. Neurol. u. Psychiat., v. 13, p. 11.
1928. De localisatie der psyche. Psychiat. en neurol. Bl., v. 32, p. 251.

WINKLER, C., & POTTER, A.
1911. An anatomical guide to experimental researches on the rabbit's brain. W. Versluys, Amsterdam.
1914. An anatomical guide to experimental researches on the cat's brain. W. Versluys, Amsterdam.

WINSLOW, J. B.
1773. An anatomical exposition of the structure of the human body. 2 vols. London.
1776. Exposition anatomique de la structure du corps humain. 4 vols. Paris.

WINSOR, C. P., & CLARK, A.-B.
1936. Dark adaptation after varying degrees of light adaptation. Proc. Nat. Acad. Sc., v. 22, p. 400.

WINTERSTEIN, HANS
1910–24. Handbuch der vergleichenden Physiologie. G. Fischer, Jena.
1929. Der Stoffwechsel des Zentralnervensystems. *In:* BETHE, Handb. d. norm. u. path. Physiol., v. 9, p. 515.
1931. Elektrische Reizung und physiologische Erregung. Naturwiss., v. 19, p. 247.
1933. Die chemischen Grundlagen der Nervenerregung. *Ibid.*, v. 21, p. 21.
1933. Der Mechanismus der Nerventätigkeit. *Ibid.*, p. 702.

WISLOCKI, G. B.
1940. Some peculiarities of the cerebral blood vessels in the hypothalamus of the opossum (*Didelphys virginiana*). Anat. Rec., v. 76, suppl. 2, p. 97. (Abstr. of demonstration.)
1940. Peculiarities of the cerebral blood vessels of the opossum: diencephalon, area postrema and retina. *Ibid.*, v. 78, p. 119.

WISLOCKI, G. B., & SIDMAN, R. L.
1954. The chemical morphology of the retina. J. Comp. Neurol., v. 101, p. 53.

WITELO; *see* ALHAZEN & VITELLO; VITELLO

WITHINGTON, E. T.
1921. The Asclepiadae and the priests of Asclepius. *In:* C. SINGER, Studies in the history and method of science, v. 2, p. 192. Clarendon Press, Oxford.

WITKOWSKI, L.
1881. Ueber einige Bewegungserscheinungen an

den Augen. Arch. f. Psychiat. u. Nervenkr., v. 11, p. 507.

WITTICH
1863. Studien über den blinden Fleck. Arch. f. Ophth. (Graefe), v. 9 (3), p. 1.

WLASSAK, R.
1893. Die optischen Leitungsbahnen des Frosches. Arch. f. Anat. u. Physiol. (Du Bois-Reymond), suppl., p. 1.

WLASSAK, R., & SACHS, M.
1899. Die optische Localisation der Medianebene. Verhandl. d. Gesellsch. Deutsch. Naturforsch. u. Aerzte, v. 71, p. 490.

WÖLFFLIN, E.
1922. Urkunde über älteste ägyptische Augenärzte. Klin. Monatsbl. f. Augenh., v. 68, p. 635.

WOERDEMAN, M. W.
1929. Experimentelle Untersuchungen über Lage und Bau der augenbildenden Bezirke in der Medullarplatte beim Axolotl. Arch. f. Entwicklungsmech. d. Org. (Roux), v. 116, p. 220.
1948–50. Atlas of human anatomy, descriptive and regional. Williams & Wilkins Co., Baltimore.

WOERKOM
1923. Sur l'état psychique des aphasiques. Encéphale, v. 18, p. 286.

WOJTUSIAK, R. J.
1933. Ueber den Farbensinn der Schildkröten. Ztschr. f. vergl. Physiol., v. 18, p. 393.

WOLCOTT, R. H.
1946. Animal biology. 3d ed. McGraw-Hill Book Co., New York & London.

WOLF, A.
1935. A history of science, technology, and philosophy in the 16th & 17th centuries. Allen & Unwin, London.
1939. A history of science, technology, and philosophy in the eighteenth century. Macmillan Co., New York.

WOLF, E.
1942. Spacial relations of ommatidia in insects and differential sensitivity to moving visual stimuli. Anat. Rec., v. 84, p. 469. (Abstr.)

WOLFF, E.
1940. The external limiting membrane of the retina and its relation to "Verhoeff's membrane." Tr. Ophth. Soc. United Kingdom, v. 60, p. 61.
1941. The differential staining of rods and cones. *Ibid.*, v. 61, p. 81.
1948. The anatomy of the eye and orbit, including the central connections, development, and comparative anatomy of the visual apparatus. Blakiston Co., Philadelphia & Toronto.

WOLFF, H.
1925. Das Farbenunterscheidungsvermögen der Ellritze. Ztschr. f. vergl. Physiol., v. 3, p. 279.

WOLFF, H. G.
1936. The cerebral circulation. Physiol. Rev., v. 16, p. 511.
1938. The cerebral blood vessels—anatomical principles. *In:* The circulation of the brain and spinal cord. Research Pub. A. Research Nerv. & Ment. Dis., v. 18, p. 29.

WOLFF, M.
1909. Ueber das Wesen des Neurons. Monatsschr. f. Psychiat. u. Neurol., v. 26 (Ergh.), p. 343.

WOLFRUM, M.
1908. Untersuchungen über die Macula lutea der höheren Säugetiere. Ber. d. Deutsch. ophth. Gesellsch. Heidelberg, v. 35, p. 206; Klin. Monatsbl. f. Augenh., v. 71, p. 221, 1923.
1908. Beiträge zur Anatomie und Histologie der Aderhaut beim Menschen und bei höheren Wirbeltieren. Arch. f. Ophth. (Graefe), v. 67, p. 307.

WOLLASTON, W. H.
1804. On an improvement in the form of spectacle glasses. London, Edinburgh & Dublin Phil. Mag., v. 17, p. 327; J. Nat. Phil., Chem. & Arts, v. 7, p. 143.
1824. On semi-decussation of optic nerves. Phil. Tr. Roy. Soc. London, v. 114 (1), p. 222. French trans. in Ann. de chem. et de phys., v. 27, p. 102, 1924. (*See also* Brewster in Phil. Mag., ser. 4, v. 29, p. 503, 1865.)

WOLLENHAUPT, K.
1934–35. Ueber feinere histologische Verhältnisse des Zentralnervensystems und der Epidermis bei *Branchiostoma lanceolatum* Costa. Jena. Ztschr. f. Naturwiss., v. 69, p. 193.

WOLPERT, I.
1924. Die Simultanagnosie (Störung der Gesamtauffassung). Ztschr. f. d. ges. Neurol. u. Psychiat., v. 93, p. 397.

WOLTERECK, R.
1940. Grundzüge einer allgemeinen Biologie. Die Organismen als Gefüge/Getriebe, als Normen und als erlebende Subjekte. 2d ed. F. Enke, Stuttgart.

WONG (WANG), K. C., & WU LIEN-TEH
1936. History of Chinese medicine. Being a chronicle of medical happenings in China from ancient times to the present period. Nat. Quarantine Serv., Shanghai, China.

Wood, C. A.
1915. Shrapnel wound of the occipital region with involvement of the visual centers. Ophth. Rec., v. 24, p. 392.
1917. The fundus oculi of birds especially as viewed by the ophthalmoscope. Lakeside Press, Chicago.
1924. Sketches from the notebook of a naturalist-traveler in Oceania during the year 1923. Ann. Rep. Smithsonian Inst., p. 379.

Wood, E. H.
1948. Normal optic nerve. I. Classification of the optic disk based on branching of the central retinal artery. Arch. Ophth., ser. 2, v. 39, p. 305.

Wood, R. W.
1906. Fish-eye views and vision under water. London, Edinburgh, & Dublin Phil. Mag., ser. 6, v. 12, p. 159.
1934. Physical optics. 3d ed. Macmillan Co., New York.

Woodburne, R. T.
1939. Certain phylogenetic anatomical relations of localizing significance for the mammalian central nervous system. J. Comp. Neurol., v. 71, p. 215.

Woodburne, R. T., & Crosby, E. C.
1938. The basis of cortical localization. Anat. Rec., v. 70, suppl., p. 84.

Woodburne, R. T., Crosby, E. C., & McCotter, R. E.
1946. The mammalian midbrain and isthmus regions. II. The fiber connections. A. The relations of the tegmentum of the midbrain with the basal ganglia in *Macaca mulatta*. J. Comp. Neurol., v. 85, p. 67.

Woodruff, L. L.
1939. Microscopy before the nineteenth century. Am. Naturalist, v. 73, p. 485.
1941. The development of the sciences. 2d ser. Yale University Press, New Haven.
1941. Foundations of biology. Macmillan Co., New York.

Woods, A. H.
1941. Discussion on bioelectric phenomena. Tr. Am. Neurol. A., 67th meet., pp. 150, 151.

Woodward, A. S., Smith, G. E., Hill, J. P., Wood-Jones, F., Pocock, R. I., Cunningham, J. T., Mitchell, P. C., & MacBride, E. W.
1919. Discussion on the zoölogical position and affinities of *Tarsius*. Proc. Zoöl. Soc. London, p. 465.

Woodyatt, N.
1922. My sporting memories. H. Jenkins, London.

Woolf, J. I., Walker, A. E., Knox, G. W., & Halstead, W. C.
1945. The effect of lesions of the visual system on photic driving. J. Neuropath. & Exper. Neurol., v. 4, p. 59.

Woollard, H. H.
1925. The anatomy of *Tarsius spectrum*. Proc. Zoöl. Soc. London, p. 1071.
1925. The cortical lamination of *Tarsius*. J. Anat., v. 60, p. 86.
1926. Notes on the retina and lateral geniculate body in *Tupaia, Tarsius, Nycticebus* and *Hapale*. Brain, v. 49, p. 77.
1927. The differentiation of the retina in the primates. Proc. Zoöl. Soc. London, p. 1.
1929. The Australian aboriginal brain. J. Anat., v. 63, p. 207.
1938. An outline of Elliot Smith's contributions to neurology. *Ibid.*, v. 72, p. 280.

Woollard, H. H., & Beattie, J.
1927. The comparative anatomy of the lateral geniculate body. J. Anat., v. 61, p. 414.

Woollard, H. H., & Harpman, A.
1939. The cortical projection of the medial geniculate body. J. Neurol. & Psychiat., v. 2 (N.S.), p. 35.
1939. Discontinuity in the nervous system of coelenterates. J. Anat., v. 73, p. 559.

Woollard, H. H., & Weddell, G.
1935. The composition and distribution of vascular nerves in the extremities. J. Anat., v. 69, p. 165.

Woolsey, C. N., Marshall, W. H., & Bard, P.
1942. Representation of cutaneous tactile sensibility in the cerebral cortex of the monkey as indicated by evoked potentials. Bull. Johns Hopkins Hosp., v. 70, p. 399.

Woolsey, C. N., & Walzl, E. M.
1942. Topical projection of nerve fibers from local regions of the cochlea to the cerebral cortex of the cat. Bull. Johns Hopkins Hosp., v. 71, p. 315.

Worms, G.
1923. Les troubles visuels subjectifs chez les blessés crânio-cérébraux. Ann. d'ocul., v. 160, p. 456.

Wright, A. H., & Wright, A. A.
1949. Handbook of frogs and toads of the United States and Canada. Comstock Pub. Co., Ithaca, N.Y.

Wright, S.
1939. Statistical genetics in relation to evolution. Hermann & Cie, Paris.
1949. Adaptation and selection. *In:* Jepsen *et al.*, Genetics, paleontology, and evolution, p. 365.

WRIGHT, W. D.
   1939. A colorimetric equipment for research on vision. J. Scient. Instr., v. 16, p. 10.
   1940. The response of the eye to light in relation to the measurement of subjective brightness and contrast. Brit. J. Ophth., v. 24, p. 1; Tr. Illumin. Engin. Soc. (Brit.), v. 4, 1939.
   1942. Research on colour physics at South Kensington, 1877–1942. Proc. Phys. Soc., v. 54, p. 303.
   1942. A survey of modern researches on colour vision. Refractionist, v. 31, p. 53.
   1943. Spectral sensitivity of the retinal receptors. Nature, v. 151, p. 726.
   1944. The measurement of colour. A. Hilger, London.
   1947. Researches on normal and defective colour vision. C. V. Mosby Co., St. Louis; H. Kimpton, London.

WRIGHT, W. D., & GRANIT, R.
   1938. On the correlation of some sensory and physiological phenomena of vision. Brit. J. Ophth., Monog. Suppl. IX.

WÜRSCHMIDT, J.
   1914. Roger Bacons Art des wissenschaftlichen Arbeitens, dargestellt nach seiner Schrift *De Speculis*. *In:* A. G. LITTLE, Roger Bacon, Essays, etc., p. 229. Clarendon Press, Oxford.
   1915. Zur Theorie der *Camera obscura* bei Ibn al Haitham. Sitzungsb. d. phys.-med. Soz. Erlangen, v. 46, p. 151.
   1915. Zur Geschichte, Theorie und Praxis der *Camera obscura*. Ztschr. f. math. u. naturwiss. Unterricht, v. 46, p. 466.

WÜSTENFELD, F.
   1840. Geschichte der arabischen Aerzte und Naturforscher nach den Quellen bearbeitet von F. W., Doctor der Philosophie etc. Lehrer der orientalischen Sprachen an der Universität zu Göttingen. Göttingen, bei Vandenhoeck & Ruprecht.
   1877. Die Uebersetzungen arabischer Werke in das lateinische seit dem XI. Jahrhundert. Abh. d. kgl. Gesellsch. d. Wissensch. zu Göttingen, v. 22.

WUNDER, W.
   1926. Physiologische und vergleichend-anatomische Untersuchungen an der Knochenfischnetzhaut. Ztschr. f. vergl. Physiol., v. 3, p. 1.
   1926. Die Bedeutung des Adaptationszustandes für das Verhalten der Sehelemente und des Pigmentes in der Netzhaut von Knochenfischen. *Ibid.*, p. 595.
   1926. Ueber den Bau der Netzhaut bei Süsswasserfischen, die in grosser Tiefe leben (Coregonen, Tiefseesaibling). *Ibid.*, v. 4, p. 22.
   1927. Sinnesphysiologische Untersuchungen über die Nahrungsaufnahme bei verschiedenen Knochenfischarten. *Ibid.*, v. 6, p. 67.
   1930. Bau und Funktion der Netzhaut beim Zander (*Lucioperca sandra* Cuv. und Val.) und einigen anderen im Balatonsee häufigen Fischarten. *Ibid.*, v. 11, p. 749.

WUNDT, W. M.
   1900–1910. Völkerpsychologie. 4 parts. W. Engelmann, Leipzig. Also later revisions and expansions (vols. 5–10).
   1908–11. Grundzüge der physiologischen Psychologie. 6th ed. W. Engelmann, Leipzig.
   1919. Vorlesungen über die Menschen- und Tierseele. 6th ed. L. Voss, Leipzig.

WYBAR, K. C.
   1945. Branch thrombosis of middle cerebral artery. Brit. J. Ophth., v. 29, p. 355.

WYSS, O. A. M., & OBRADOR, S.
   1937. Adequate shape and rate of stimuli in electrical stimulation of the cerebral motor cortex. Am. J. Physiol., v. 120, p. 42.

Y

YASKIN, J. C., & SPAETH, E. B.
   1945. Acute cortical blindness with recovery: report of a case. Arch. Neurol. & Psychiat., v. 54, p. 70.

YEALLAND, L. R.
   1916. Case of gunshot wound involving visual centre, with visual disorientation. Proc. Roy. Soc. Med. (sec. ophth.), v. 9 (3), p. 97.

YERKES, R. M.
   1903. Reactions of *Daphnia pulex* to light and heat. E. L. Mark anniv. vol., p. 359. Henry Holt & Co., New York.
   1903. The instincts, habits and reactions of the frog. Psychol. Rev. Monog., v. 4, p. 579.
   1905–6. The sense of hearing in frogs. J. Comp. Neurol., v. 15, p. 279; v. 16, p. 167. (*See* letter by Edinger in v. 16, p. 166.)
   1915. Color vision in the ring-dove, *Turtur risorius*. Proc. Nat. Acad. Sc., v. 1, p. 117.
   1916. The mental life of monkeys and apes. Behavior Monog., v. 3, No. 1 (ser. No. 12).
   1925. Almost human. Century Co., New York & London.
   1927–28. The mind of a gorilla. Genet. Psychol. Monog., v. 2, pp. 1, 375; Comp. Psychol. Monog., v. 5, No. 24.
   1943. Chimpanzees. A laboratory colony. Yale University Press, New Haven.
   1951. Gorilla census and study. J. Mammal., v. 32, p. 429.

YERKES, R. M., & PETRUNKEVITCH, A.
1925. Studies of chimpanzee vision by Ladygin-Kohts. J. Comp. Psychol., v. 5, p. 99.

YERKES, R. M., & WATSON, J. B.
1911. Methods of studying vision in animals. Behavior Monog., v. 1, No. 2 (ser. No. 2).

YERKES, R. M., & YERKES, A. W.
1929. The great apes. A study of anthropoid life. Yale University Press, New Haven.

YONGE, C. M.
1949. The sea shore. Collins, London.

YOSHIMURA, K.
1909. Ueber die Beziehungen des Balkens zum Sehakt. Arch. f. Physiol. (Pflüger), v. 129, p. 425.

YOUMANS, W. B., & HUCKINS, A. R.
1951. Hemodynamics in failure of the circulation. Charles C Thomas, Springfield, Ill.

YOUNG, C. B. F., & COONS, K. W.
1945. Surface active agents: theoretical aspects and applications. Chemical Pub. Co., Brooklyn, N.Y.

YOUNG, G.
1922. The relations of the optic and Vidian nerves to the sphenoidal sinus. J. Laryng. & Otol., v. 37, p. 613.

YOUNG, J. Z.
1935. The photoreceptors of lampreys. II. The functions of the pineal complex. J. Exper. Biol., v. 12, p. 254.
1936. Structure of nerve fibres and synapses in some invertebrates. Cold Spring Harbor Symp. Quant. Biol., v. 4, p. 1.
1937. The physical and chemical properties of nerve fibres and the nature of synaptic contacts. Tr. Faraday Soc., v. 33, p. 1035.
1939. Fused neurons and synaptic contacts in the giant nerve fibres of cephalopods. Phil. Tr. Roy. Soc. London, ser. B, v. 229, p. 465.
1942. The functional repair of nervous tissue. Physiol. Rev., v. 22, p. 318.

YOUNG, S. P., & GOLDMAN, E. A.
1946. The puma, mysterious American cat. Am. Wildlife Inst., Washington, D.C.

YOUNG, THOMAS
1800. On the mechanism of the eye. Phil. Tr. Roy. Soc. London, v. 91, p. 23, 1801; A course of lectures on natural philosophy, v. 2, p. 573; Miscellaneous works, v. 1, p. 12.
1801. Zwei Abhandlungen von Thomas Young, by M. ROHR. Ztschr. f. ophth. Optik, v. 11, p. 102, 1923.
1802. On the theory of light and colours. Phil. Tr. Roy. Soc. London, v. 92, p. 12; A course of lectures on natural philosophy, v. 2, p. 613; Miscellaneous works, v. 1, p. 140. German trans. in Ann. d. Physik, v. 39, p. 156.
1802. An account of some cases of the production of colours. Phil. Tr. Roy. Soc. London, v. 92, p. 387; A course of lectures on natural philosophy, v. 2, p. 633; Miscellaneous works, v. 1, p. 170. German trans. in Ann. d. Physik, v. 39, p. 206, 1811.
1803. Experiments and calculations relative to physical optics. Phil. Tr. Roy. Soc. London, v. 94, p. 1, 1804; A course of lectures on natural philosophy, v. 2, p. 639. German trans. in Ann. d. Physik, v. 39, p. 262, 1811.
1807. A course of lectures on natural philosophy and mechanical arts. 2 vols. J. Johnson; W. Savage, London.
1855. Miscellaneous works of the late Thomas Young, etc., edited by G. PEACOCK, and J. LEITCH. 3 vols. J. Murray, London. (*Cf. also* article: Chromatics, Encyclopaedia Britannica, 6th ed.)
1855. Life of Thomas Young, etc. By GEORGE PEACOCK, etc., Dean of Ely. John Murray, London.

Z

ZACHARIAS (MAGISTER ZACHARIAS)
12th cent. Magistri Zacharie tractatus de passionibus oculorum qui vocatur Sisilacera, id est Secreta Secretorum, compilatus circa annos 1143–1180. *In:* P. PANSIER, "Collectio ophtalmologica veterum auctorum," v. 2, p. 57. J.-B. Baillière & Fils, Paris, 1907.
12th cent. Liber de oculis, qui vocatur Salaracer, id est secreta secretorum. A 14th cent. manuscript, Brit. Mus., Sloane Coll., MS 981, London. (*See* Sudhoff, Arch. f. Gesch. d. Med., v. 8, p. 1, 1915.)

ZACHER, J.
1874. Blind. Staar. Eine sprachwissenschaftliche Studie. Klin. Monatsbl. f. Augenh., v. 12, p. 277.

ZADE, M.
1916–19. Periphere Ringskotome. Arch. f. Ophth. (Graefe), v. 91, p. 159; v. 100, p. 129.

ZAGÓRSKI, A.
1867. Ein Fall von gleichseitiger Hemiopie nach apoplectischem Insult mit vollständiger Restitution. Klin. Monatsbl. f. Augenh., v. 5, p. 322.

ZAHL, P. A.
1950. Blindness; modern approach to the unseen environment. Princeton University Press, Princeton.
1953. Exotic birds in Manhattan's Bowery. Nat. Geog. Mag., v. 103, p. 77.

ZAHN, J.

1685–86. Oculus Artificialis Teledioptricus sive Telescopium, etc. Herbipoli (Bamberg), sumpt. Q. Heyl.

ZAHN, W.

1942. Die Reisen, Streifen und Spitznasenhörnchen der orientalischen Region. Ztschr. f. Säugetierk., v. 16, p. 1.

ZANDER, R.

1890. Beiträge zur Kenntnis der mittleren Schädelgrube mit besonderer Berücksichtigung der Lage des Chiasma opticum. Anat. Anz., v. 12, p. 457.

ZAWARZIN, A.

1912–14. Histologische Studien über Insekten. II. Das sensible Nervensystem der Aeschnalarven. Ztschr. f. wissensch. Zool., v. 100, p. 245. III. Ueber das sensible Nervensystem der Larven von *Melolontha vulgaris*. *Ibid.*, p. 447. IV. Die optischen Ganglien der Aeschna-Larven. *Ibid.*, v. 108, p. 175.

ZEBRAWSKI, T.

1879. Quelques mots au sujet de la note de M. Maximilien Curtze sur l'ortographe du nom et la patrie de Witelo. Bull. bibl. e di storia d. sc. mat. e fis. (Boncompagni), v. 12, p. 315.

ZEEMAN, W. P. C.

1925. Distribution des fibres optiques dans les voies optiques et les centres primaires. Bull. et mém. Soc. franç. d'opht., v. 38, p. 632.

1925. Erweichungsherd im Chiasma und Chiasmastruktur. Arch. f. Augenh., v. 95, p. 244.

1925. Zur Methodik der Gesichtsfelduntersuchung. *Ibid.*, v. 96, p. 1.

ZEEMAN, W. P. C., & TUMBELAKA, R.

1916. Das zentrale und periphere optische System bei einer kongenital blinden Katze. Arch. f. Ophth. (Graefe), v. 91, p. 242.

ZEHENDER, W.

1864. Historische Notiz zur Lehre vom blinden Fleck. Arch. f. Ophth. (Graefe), v. 10 (1), p. 152.

1897. Das sichelförmige Flimmerskotom Listing's. Klin. Monatsbl. f. Augenh., v. 35, p. 25.

ZELEBOR, J.

1869. Säugethiere. *In:* Reise der österreichischen Fregatte *Novara* um die Erde in den Jahren 1857, 1858, 1859. Zool. Theil, v. 1 (Heft 1), p. 1, Pls. 1–3. Gerold's, Wien.

ZELIONY, G.

1913. Observations sur des chiens auxquel on a enlevé les hémisphères cérébraux. Compt. rend. Soc. de biol., v. 65, p. 707.

ZELLER, E.

1920–23. Die Philosophie der Griechen in ihrer geschichtlichen Entwicklung. 4th ed. 3 vols. in 6 parts. O. R. Reisland, Leipzig.

ZENTMAYER

1912. Visual disturbances from distant haemorrhage. J. Am. Med. Assoc., v. 59, p. 1050.

ZERBI, G. DE

1502. Liber anatomiae corporis humani et (ac?) singulorum membrorum illius: Editum (or Editio?) per excellentissimum philosophum ac medicum. D. (Dominum?) Gabrielem de Zerbis Veronensem. Cum Gratia.

ZERNOV, D.; *see* SERNOW

ZEUNER, F. E.

1940. Geochronological table No. 2. The age of Neanderthal man, with notes on the Cotte de St. Brelade, Jersey, C.I. No. 3. University of London, Inst. of Archeology.

1944. *Homo sapiens* in Australia contemporary with *Homo neanderthalensis* in Europe. Nature, v. 153, p. 622.

1944. The Pleistocene period, its climate, chronology and faunal successions. Printed for the Ray Society, London.

1946. Time and the geologist. Discovery, v. 7, p. 104.

1946. Time and the biologist. *Ibid.*, p. 242.

1952. Dating the past. An introduction to geochronology. Methuen & Co., London. 3d ed. by Longmans, Green & Co., New York, 1951.

ZEWI, M.

1939. On the regeneration of visual purple. Acta Soc. sc. Fennicae, new ser. B, v. 2, No. 4.

1941. Evidence for two phases in the regeneration of visual purple. Acta physiol. Scandinav., v. 1, p. 271.

ZIEHEN, G. T.

1892. Introduction to physiological psychology, translated from the German by C. C. VAN LIEW & O. W. BEYER. S. Sonnenschein & Co., London.

1896. Ueber die Grosshirnfurchung der Halbaffen und die Deutung einiger Furchen des menschlichen Gehirns. Arch. f. Psychiat. u. Nervenkr., v. 28, p. 898.

1896. Die Grosshirnfurchen des Hylobates- und Semnopithecusgehirnes nebst Bemerkungen über die Fissura parieto-occipitalis und den sog. Sulcus tempor. III. Anat. Anz., v. 11, p. 470.

1898–1908. Das Zentralnervensystem der Monotremen und Marsupialier. Semon's Zool. Forschungsreisen in Australien, etc., v. 3 (1), pp. 1, 677; v. 3 (2), pp. 229, 789. ("Denkschriften d. med.-naturwiss. Gesellsch. Jena," v. 6.) G. Fischer, Jena.

1902. Ueber die allgemeinen Beziehungen zwischen Gehirn und Seelenleben. J. A. Barth, Leipzig.

1903. Einiges über den Faserverlauf im Mittel- und Zwischenhirn von *Tarsius spectrum*. Monatsschr. f. Psychiat., v. 14, p. 54.

1903. Der Faserverlauf des Gehirns von *Galeopithecus volans*. *Ibid.*, p. 289.

1903. Ueber den Bau des Gehirns bei den Halbaffen und bei *Galeopithecus*. Anat. Anz., v. 22, p. 505.

1903–34. Centralnervensystem. *In:* K. VON BARDELEBEN & H. VON EGGELING, Handb. d. Anat. d. Mensch., vol. 4 (1) and (2). G. Fischer, Jena.

1904. On the development of the brain in *Tarsius spectrum*. Proc. Kon. Akad. Wetensch. Amsterdam, sec. sc., v. 7, p. 331.

1924. Das Leib-Seele-Problem. Deutsch. med. Wchnschr., v. 50, p. 1267.

1924. Leitfaden der physiologischen Psychologie. G. Fischer, Jena. Also other eds.

ZIEHL

1895. Ueber einen Fall von Alexie mit Farbenhemiopie. Neurol. Centralbl., v. 14, p. 892.

ZIELINSKI, T.

1931. Histoire de la civilisation antique. Payot, Paris.

ZIGLER, M. J., COOK, B., MILLER, D., & WEMPLE, L.

1930. The perception of form in peripheral vision. Am. J. Psychol., v. 42, p. 246.

ZIKULENKO, K.

1926. Ueber die Rolle des Pigmentepithels der Netzhaut im Sehakt. Arch. f. Augenh., v. 97, p. 190.

ZILBOORG, G.

1935. The medical man and the witch during the Renaissance. Portrait. Johns Hopkins Press, Baltimore.

ZILBOORG, G., & HENRY, G. W.

1941. A history of medical psychology. W. W. Norton & Co., New York.

ZIMMER, H. R.

1948. Hindu medicine. Johns Hopkins Press, Baltimore.

ZINGERLE, H.

1911. Ueber einseitigen Schläfenlappendefekt beim Menschen. J. f. Psychol. u. Neurol., v. 18, p. 205.

ZINN, J. G.

*1749. Experimenta circa corpus callosum, cerebellum, duram meningem in vivis animalibus instituta. A. Vandenhoeck, Gottingae. *See also* A. Haller's Disputationes anatomicae, v. 7, p. 4.

1753. Observationes anatomicae de tunicis et musculis oculorum. Comment. Soc. reg. sc. Goetting. (= Gesellsch. d. Wissensch. zu Göttingen), v. 3, p. 115.

*1753. (Programma) de ligamentibus ciliaribus. J. C. L. Schulzii, Gottingae.

1754. De differentia fabricae oculi humani et brutorum. Comment. Soc. reg. sc. Goetting., v. 4, p. 247 (mistakenly printed p. 191).

1780. Johannis Gottfried Zinn professoris quondam medici in Universitate Goettingensi *Descriptio anatomica oculi humani* iconibus illustrata, nunc altera vice edita, et necessario supplemento, novisque tabulis aucta ab Henr. Aug. Wrisberg, anatomes professore Goettingensi. Goettingae, apud viduam b. Abrami Vandenhoeck. MDCCLXXX. First ed., 1755.

ZINN, W.

1892. Das Rindenfeld des Auges in seinen Beziehungen zu den primären Optikuscentren. München. med. Wchnschr., v. 39, pp. 493, 516.

ZIPSE, W.

1935. Können unsere heimischen Frösche und echte Kröten ultraviolettes Licht sehen? Zool. Jahrb. (Allg. Zool. u. Physiol.), v. 55, p. 487.

ZOLLINGER, R.

1935. Removal of left cerebral hemisphere. Arch. Neurol. & Psychiat., v. 34, p. 1055.

ZOLOTNITSKY, N.

1901. Les poissons distinguent-ils les couleurs? Arch. de zool. expér., 3d ser., v. 9, p. i.

ZONDEK, H.

1933. Rapports du système hypophyso-diencéphalique avec l'œil. Ann. de méd., v. 33, p. 292.

ZOOND, A., & EYRE, J.

1934. Studies in reptilian colour response. I. The binomics and physiology of pigmentary activity of the chameleon. Phil. Tr. Roy. Soc. London, ser. B, v. 223, p. 27.

ZOOND, A., & BOKENHAM, N. A. H.

1935. Studies in reptilian colour response. II. The role of retinal and dermal photoreceptors in the pigmentary activity of the chameleon. J. Exper. Biol., v. 12, p. 39.

ZOTH, O.

1899. Ueber den Einfluss der Blickrichtung auf die scheinbare Grösse der Gestirne und die scheinbare Form des Himmelgewölbes. Arch. f. d. ges. Physiol. (Pflüger), v. 78, p. 363.

1923. Alte und neue Anschauungen über die

Energieumwandlung in der Netzhaut. Ergebn. d. Physiol., v. 22, p. 345.

ZUCKERKANDL, E.

1902–5. Zur Morphologie des Affengehirnes. Ztschr. f. Morphol. u. Anthropol., v. 4, p. 463; v. 6, p. 285; v. 7, p. 223; v. 8, p. 100.

1903. Zur vergleichenden Anatomie des Hinterhauptlappens. Arb. a. d. Neurol. Inst. Wien (Obersteiner), v. 10, p. 297.

1904. Ueber die Collateralfurche. Ibid., v. 11, p. 407.

1905. Ueber die Affenspalte und das Operculum occipitale des menschlichen Gehirns. Ibid., v. 12, p. 207.

1906. Zur Anatomie der Fissura calcarina. Ibid., v. 13, p. 25.

1906. Zur Anatomie der Uebergangswindungen. Ibid., p. 141.

1906. Zur Orientierung über den Hinterhauptlappen. Jahrb. f. Psychiat., v. 27, p. 1.

1908. Zur Anatomie der Fissura parietooccipitalis medialis und des Sulcus intraparietalis. Sitzungsb. d. Kaiserl. Akad. d. Wissensch. Wien, math.-naturw. Kl., v. 117 (Abt. III), p. 411.

1910. Zur Oberflächenmodellierung des Atelesgehirns. Arb. a. d. Neurol. Inst. Wien (Obersteiner), v. 18, p. 60.

ZUCKERMAN, S.

1932. The social life of monkeys and apes. Kegan Paul, Trench, Trubner & Co., London.

1933. Functional affinities of man, monkeys, and apes. A study of the bearings of physiology and behaviour on the taxonomy and phylogeny of lemurs, monkeys, apes, and man. Harcourt, Brace & Co., New York.

1940. Human genera and species. Nature, v. 145, p. 510.

1944. Life and mentality of the chimpanzee. Review of R. M. YERKES, Chimpanzees. Ibid., v. 153, p. 65.

1950. Taxonomy and human evolution. Biol. Rev. (Cambridge), v. 25, p. 435.

1950. Review of R. BROOM, Finding the missing link. Man, v. 50, p. 92.

ZUCKERMAN, S., & FISHER, R. B.

1937. Growth of the brain in the rhesus monkey. Proc. Zoöl. Soc. London, ser. B, v. 107, p. 529.

ZUCKERMAN, S., & FULTON, J. F.

1934. The nomenclature of primates commonly used in laboratory work. Tuttle, Morehouse & Taylor Co., New Haven, Conn.

1940–41. The motor cortex in *Galago* and *Perodicticus*. J. Anat., v. 75, p. 447.

ZUCKERMAN, S., & WALLACE, H. M.

1932. The responses of a Chacma baboon (*P. porcarius*) in brightness and colour discrimination tests. Proc. Zoöl. Soc. London, p. 593.

ZÜRN, J.

1902. Vergleichend histologische Untersuchungen über die Retina und die Area centralis retinae der Haussäugetiere. Arch. f. Anat. u. Entw., suppl., p. 99.

ZUTT, J.

1930. Ueber einen Fall von halbseitigen Halluzinationen im hemianopischen Gesichtsfeld bei einer Herderkrankung im Occipitallappen. Zentralbl. f. d. ges. Neurol. u. Psychiat., v. 56, p. 477.

ZWANENBURG, S.

1915. Quantitatief onderzoek over den bouw van het netvlies. Acad. proefschr. (diss.). J. van Boekhoven, Utrecht-Amsterdam.

ZWEIG, H.

1931. Das Leib-Seelenproblem und seine Auswirkung in der Medizin. Zentralbl. f. d. ges. Neurol. u. Psychiat., v. 61, p. 1.

ZWORYKIN, V. K., MORTON, G. A., RAMBERG, E. G., HILLIER, J., & VANCE, A. W.

1945. Electron optics and the electron microscope. John Wiley & Sons, New York.

Index

Italicized page numbers indicate the principal discussion of the subject

Abbé, Ernst, Fig. 51
  contribution to microscopy by, 541
Abbie
  on arterial supply of optic chiasma, 605
  on blood supply of visual radiation, 608, 623
  lateral striate artery of, 607
  medial striate artery of, 606
Abbott & Kloss, 876
Aborigines of Australia, cortical visual centers of, 474
Accessory neuroglia of retina, *257*
Achillini, 87
Achromatopia, cerebral, *667*
Achúcarro on neuroglial cells, 258
Ackermann, 115
Acuity; see Visual acuity
Affenspalte, 465
Aggressiveness of Man, 1041
Agnosia; see also Mental blindness
  visual, discovery of, 150
  with field defect, 653
Agrammatism, functional cerebral localization and, 457, Fig. 274
Agraphia, functional cerebral localization and, 457, Fig. 274
Aguilonius, 23, Fig. 20
Aitken, 606
Akeley, Carl Ethan, 998, 999, Fig. 523
Akeley, Mrs. M. L. Jobe (Mrs. Carl), 1001
Akkeringa, on neuroglial cells, 258
Alcoatin, 43, 87
Alexander, J., 569
Alexander, L., 623
Alexander of Aphrodisías, 12
Alexia
  functional cerebral localization and, 457, Fig. 274
  with visual field defect, 653
Al-Fārābī, 18
Alhazen; see Ibn al-Haitham
ᶜAlī ibn al-ᶜAbbās, 42
ᶜAlī ibn ᶜĪsā, 42, 43
  description of visual system by, 84
  treatise on ophthalmology by, 15
Alison, and partial decussation in optic chiasma, 158
Alkmaíon of Croton, 76
  first dissection of human bodies by, 74
Al-Rāzī, 18
  description of visual system by, 84
Alzheimer, on neuroglia, 258

Amacrine cells, *249*
  in intraretinal integration system, 255, 587
  neuroglial, 257
  and rod system of neurons, 582
  synapses of, with midget bipolars, 237
  varieties of, 250
Amaurosis, epileptic, 645
Amblyopia, cerebral, 667
ᶜAmmār, treatise on ophthalmology by, 15
Amphibians
  anural, retinal blood supply in, 601
  in Carboniferous Period, 955
  central area of, 282
  chiasma of optic nerves in, 158, 310, 323
  eyes of, 958
  optic nerves in, decussation of, 779
Amphioxus, 559, Fig. 445
  in phylogenetic study of vertebrate eye, 769
Anagale, 892
Anaptomorphidae, 934
Anathana, Fig. 483
Anatomical axis of eye, 209
Anatomy
  beginnings of, *73*
  in early Europe, *86*
  and physiology of brain, post-Vesalian period, 96–100
  Vesalius and reform in, *92*
Anatomy of visual system, early modern contributions to, *97*
Anaxagóras of Klazomenai, first dissection of brain by, 74
Ancestors, earliest vertebrate, speculations on, 769
Andral, and functional cerebral localization, 147
Angel, M. F., 845
Anguillidae, retinal blood supply in, 601
Animals, primitive, probable photic environment of, *769*
Annelids, vesicular eyes of, 786
Anole, 838–47
  brain of, Fig. 465
  character and habits of, 838
  eye of, *841*, 958
  head of, showing eye movements, Fig. 464
  physiological considerations of, 843
  retina of, 841
  taxonomy of, *838*

use of visual apparatus by, Figs. 463, 464
  various views of, Fig. 462
  visual centers of, *841*
Anophthalmia, congenital, brain in, Fig. 108
Anthony, H. E., 896, 897, 898
  on Shrew, 866
Anthony, R., 475
Anthropods, ocelli of, 786
Aotes, retinal blood vessels in, 599, 601
Apatemys, 1040
Apáthy, 542, 543, 558
  and knowledge of neurofibrils, 543
Apes
  Anthropomorphous
    and ancestry of Man, 986
    cortical visual centers of, 478
    cuneolingual fold in, 480
    striate area in
      blood supply of, 615
      location and extent of, 490
    blood supply in, 615–17
    calcarine fissure in, 460
    calcarine sulcus in, lateral, 465
    central area and fovea in, 281, 285
    color vision in, 970
    cortical visual centers of, *470*
    Monkeys and, hands and feet of, Fig. 540
    and origin of Man, *1021*
    retinal arteries in, 599
    retinal blood supply of, 600
    striate area of
      blood supply of, 609
      histological characteristics of, 496
      nerve cell stratification of, 497
      visuo-sensory and visuo-psychic areas in, compared with Man, Fig. 298
  Taungs, 1034
Aphasia
  motor, functional cerebral localization and, 458, Fig. 274
  sensory, functional cerebral localization and, 457, Fig. 274
Aphrodite of Cnidos, Fig. 541
Aquapendente, G. F. d', 23, 95, Fig. 21
  on optic chiasma, 109
Aqueduct of Sylvius, 398
Aqueous humor of eye, 209
Arab arts and sciences, introduction into Europe of, 21–27
Arab civilization
  influence during Middle Ages of, on knowledge of visual system, 83–86
  rise of, and learning, *14*

Arab knowledge
  of eye; *see also* Alhazen; Baward; etc.
  of structure and function of eye, 14–21, Figs. 2, 3, 4, 5, 6, 10

Arab learning, and European Renaissance, *21*

Arab science, influence of Galen on, *77*

Arabs, as heirs of Greek science and medicine, *83*

Aranzi, 97
  retinal image experiment of, 38

Arboreal habit
  abandonment of, in evolutionary progress, *980*
  diurnality and visual acuity and, *969*
  evolution of colored fruits and, *973*

Arboreal life, its consequences in early evolution, 1027

Archambault, 178, 196

Archimédes, and light, 13

Area OC of Economo, 390; *see also* Striate area

Argyll Robertson, Douglas, Fig. 224

Argyll-Robertson sign, 382

Argyropelecus affinis, telescopic eye of, compared with Owl eye, Fig. 459

Ariëns Kappers and lateral calcarine sulcus in Apes, 465

Aristophanes, 14

Aristotle, 5, 79, 1027, 1053, Fig. 1
  concept of cerebral cortex by, 117
  discussion of eye by, 9
  knowledge of optic nerves and their connections by, *75*
  theory of vision by, 12

Armato degli Armati, S. d', and invention of eyeglasses, 29

Arndt, 195

Arnold, Friedrich, Fig. 91
  and central fovea, 280
  in early investigations of subcortical visual systems, 132
  and partial decussation, 116

Arterial anastomoses in central sparing, 619

Artery(ies)
  angular, 597
  auditory, point of origin of, 604
  of base of brain, *602*
    topographical arrangement of, 603
  basilar, 603
  calcarine, 462, 611–15, Fig. 278
    effect of obstruction of, 619
    effect of occlusion of, 614
    inferior, *612*, 613
    origin and distribution of, *611*
    principal, 613
      or axial, 612
    superior or principal, 612
  carotid
    in blood supply of orbital contents, 597
    internal, and cerebral artery, 604

cerebellar
  anterior, inferior, 603
  inferior, rostral, 604
  posterior, inferior, 603
  superior, origin and course of, 604
cerebral
  anterior, 394
    origin and course of, 606
    distribution of, Fig. 374
  middle, 594, 613
    in human fetus, 615
    long cortical branches of, *607*
    short subcortical branches of, *607*
    and its subsidiaries, 607–9
  origin of, 602–7
  posterior, 594, 613, Fig. 372
    effect of occlusion of, 613, 619
    in human fetus, 615
    mesencephalic branches of, 610
    obstruction of, central sparing and, 692
    origin and course of, 604
    origin and topography of, *609*
    subdivisions of, *610*
    and its subsidiaries, 609–11
chorioid
  anterior, effect of occlusion of, 619
  and hippocampal, *610*
  lateral, 610, 611
  origin and course of, 606
  posterior, 604, 610
ciliary
  and blood supply of optic nerve and eyeball, 597
  in blood supply of retina, 598
communicating
  anterior, 604
  posterior, 604
cuneal
  anterior, 612
  middle, 612
  posterior, 612, 613, 614
dorsal-nasal, 597
hippocampal, 610
isthmal, 611
lateral striate, 607
of left occipital lobe, Figs. 373, 374
lenticular or lenticulo-capsular, 608
macular, 598
  origin of, 599
maxillary
  facial or external, 597
  internal, 597
meningeal, middle, 597
nasal, 598
nasofrontal, in blood supply of orbital contents, 597
ophthalmic
  and blood supply of optic nerve and eyeball, 597
  in blood supply of orbital contents, 597
  origin and course of, 605
optic, deep, 607
paracalcarine, 612
parietal, posterior, *611*
parieto-occipital, 611
pontine, 604
posterior perforate, 610
precuneal, *611*

retinal
  in blood supply of optic nerve, 597
  central
    and blood supply of optic nerve and eyeball, 597
    in blood supply of retina, 598
    course of, 598
    obstruction of, 618
    origin of, 605
  spinal, anterior, 603
  splenial, 611
  striate, medial, 606
  supracalcarine and precuneal, *611*
  Sylvian
    effect of occlusion of, 614, 619
    temporo-occipital, superior, *610*, 613, 614
    visual system and, 609
  temporal, 598
    medial, 610
  terminal
    effect of obstruction of, 618
    of retina, 599
  vertebral, at base of brain, 603

Arthropods
  eyes of, 801
  in phylogenetic study of vertebrate eye, 769

Ascidians, in phylogenetic study of vertebrate eye, 769

Asclepios, Fig. 544

Association areas of brain, Flechsig's myelogenitical study of, *173*

Association areas of cortex
  discovery by Flechsig of, *174*
  of Flechsig, 470
  function of, 176
  identification by Flechsig of, 175

Association cells of retina, 246–50

Assyrians, and knowledge of visual system, 73

Astrocytes of retina, 257
  fibrous, 258
  protoplasmic, 258

Ateles, in phylogenesis of cortical visual centers, 470

Auditory center, location of, 174

Auditory nerve fibers, number of, 300

Auditory perceptions, cerebral cortical center of, 455

Auditory radiation
  blood supply of, 608, 609
  cortical termination of, 457, Fig. 274
  in relation to visual radiation, 400

Audubon, John James, Fig. 522

Aurignacian race, 1034

Australian aborigines, cortical visual centers of, 474

Australopithecus, 1031, 1034
  diet of, 1040
  mind of, 1040
  and origin of Man, 1038–46

Australopithecus africanus, 1034, *1035*
  cortical visual centers in, 472

Avalanche, mechanism of, *579*

Avicenna, on optic chiasma, 109

Axial vision, midget ganglions in, 587

Axis cylinders; *see also* Axons
discovery of, 60
function of, 570
in neuron theory, 66

Axolotl, efferent axons in, 292

Axonal process of brush and flat bipolars, 231

Axons
collateral branches of, 548
discovery of, 60
nervous impulses and, 550
neuron theory and, 548
in neuron theory, 66

Aye-Aye, 1041

Baboon
and ancestry of Man, 986
in captivity, character and habits of, *1003*
character, habitat, and behavior of, *989*
Guinea, various views of, Figs. 526, 527
intelligence of, 993, 994
locomotion of, 980
occipital operculum in, 470
simian sulcus in, 470
vocal expression of, 994

Babylonians, ancient, and knowledge of visual system, 73

Bacillary expansions, outer, *220*

Bacillary layer of retina, 214
role of
in dynamics of retinal structures, 587
in photoreception, 215, 275
topography of, 581

Bacon, Roger, 87, 122
geometrical eye diagram by, Figs. 7, 8
and invention of eyeglasses, 29
treatise on optics by, 22

Baer, K. E. von, 763–67

Bailey, V., on Shrew, 865

Baillarger, J. P., 195, Fig. 86A
in early investigation of cerebral cortex, 132
and functional cerebral localization, 143
outer stripe of, 398
on structure of cerebral cortex, Figs. 87, 88

Balado & Franke, 194
experiments on visual system by, 192

Balanoglossus, in phylogenetic study of vertebrate eye, 769

Balbuena, and midget bipolars, 234

Balfour, 542

Bandar, 987

Bangs Red Squirrel, 896; *see also* Squirrel

Barbaro, Daniello, 35

Barris, experiments on visual system by, 192, 193

Bartelmez & Hoerr, on neurofibrils, 544

Bartholin, T., 38

Basal nuclei of brain, 394

Bat
flight of, 953
Flying, visual behavior of, 952
Fruit-eating, striate area of, shape, extent, and location of, Fig. 309
hearing of, 953
Insectivorous
retinal blood supply in, 601
visual behavior of, *945*, 952

Bates, H. W., 973

Bauhin, on optic chiasma, 109

Baumgarten, 165

Bāward, visual system diagram by, Fig. 59

Beauvieux, 598, 611, 613

Bechterev (Béhterev, Vladímir Miháilovich), 185, Fig. 119

Beevor & Collier, 183

Bell, Charles, 117, 552, 1025
and cerebral functional organization, 122

Beneke, contribution to histology by, 170

Berengario da Carpi, 87

Bergmann and foveal structure and function, 280

Berlin, 195

Bernheimer, 155

Bethe, 542, 558
and knowledge of neurofibrils, 543

Betweenbrain
brain stem and, visual system in, Fig. 184
cross-section through, Fig. 209
visual system and, 290, 318, Fig. 183

Betz, 195

Bichat, on cerebral cortex, 117

Bidder, 51
and catoptrics of rod function, 48

Bidloo, 106
on cerebral cortex, 117

Bielschowsky
contribution to histology by, 171
and knowledge of neurofibrils, 543
staining method of, in striate area of cortex, 510

Bierens de Haan, 987

Bierens de Haan & Frima, 970

Bingham, 998, 999, 1001

Bioelectrical currents, mode of action of, 561

Bipedality
in Birds, 975
earliest Primate with, 1035, 1038
evolutionary consequences of, 1039, 1044
evolutionary development of, 980, 981
motivation for, *981*
in Mammals, 975
in Man, evolutionary role of, 975
of Simians, role of, in human evolution, *978*
of Tarsier, and manipulative ability, *976*

Bipolar cells of retina, 228–37; *see*

also under Brush and flat-top; Centrifugal; Midget; Mop
brush and flat-top, 230
centrifugal, in retinal integration, 587
centripetal
in relation to cone system, 583
synaptical relationships of, 582
excitation of
course of, 587
quality of, 577
transmission of, 573
in excitation of midget ganglions, 575
freak cells among, 292
in function of cone system, 252
functional specificity of, 577
general features of, *228*
midget, 233
in cone system of neurons, 583
and rod system of neurons, 582
monosynaptic, 228
mop, *228*
synaptical relationship of, with cone pedicles, 563
polysynaptic, 228
and retinal impulses, Figs. 178, 179
in retinal response, 255

Birds
binocular-stereoscopic vision of, *947*
bipedality of, *975*
central area in, 282
chiasma of optic nerves in, 158, 310, 323
color vision in, 970, 971
efferent axons in, 292
eyes of, 958
first appearance of, 894
fovea in, 233, 283
foveal synapses of, 285
optic nerves of, decussation of, 779, 780
with panoramic vision, *946*
of Paradise, color vision and, 974
retina of, regional structures of, *283*
retinal blood supply in, 598
visual pathway of, 250
visual system of, 313

Blarina; *see also* Shrew
in early mammalian ancestry, 891
olfactory bulbs of, 933

Blind spot
optic papilla and, 260
Soemmerring and, 279

Blindness
complete, 630
cortical
definition of, *151*
discovery of, 149–52, *150*
first case testing Munk's theory of, 183
mental
discovery of, 149–52, *150*
horizontal hemianopia and, case report of, 724–32, Figs. 417–22
relative, visual fields in, 630
scintillating, factors responsible for, 620

Blood supply
of brain, Figs. 366–70
of central fovea, Fig. 364

Blood supply—*Continued*
  cerebral, and central sparing in
    hemianopia, *620*
  of cerebrum, sources and charac-
    ter of, *594*
  of eye, general remarks on, 593–97
  of eyeball, Fig. 365
  in fetus, 615–17
  of head and brain, sources of,
    Fig. 362
  of occipital lobe at various levels,
    Fig. 377
  of retina, *598*
    central-retinal, 600
    ciliary-chorioidal, 600
  role of, in central sparing, 691–92
  of visual system, 593–625, Fig. 371
    character of, *618*
    importance of, 3
    physiologic and pathophysio-
      logic implications of, 617–23
    summary of, 623–25

Blood vessels; *see also* Artery(ies);
    Vein(s)
  in central area, 294
  of eye and optic nerve, 597–602
  in optic papilla, 260
  retinal, central
    examination of, 598
    variations in course and size of,
      599
  in retinal membrane, 214
  of striate area, 535

Blue arcs of retina, 295

Blue Jay, visual behavior of, 949

Bluegill; *see* Sunfish

Blum, contribution to histology by,
    170

Bochenek, accessory optic tracts of,
    303, 310

Bochenek and Tsai, posterior acces-
    sory optic bundle of, 317

Bock & Watson, 768

Bodian
  experiments on visual system by,
    194
  on neurofibrils, 544
  staining method of, in striate area
    of cortex, 510
  on visual system of Opossum, 200

Böttcher, contribution to histology
    by, 170

Boll, 571
  discovery of rhodopsine by, 52
  and visual purple, 223, 225

Bolton and Campbell, visuo-sensory
    area of; *see* Striate area

Bonnet, 118, 552
  on cerebral functional organiza-
    tion, 122

Bontekoe, 118

Bouillaud, Jean, Fig. 94
  and cerebral cortex, 451
  discovery of motor speech center
    by, *138*
  and functional cerebral localiza-
    tion, 147
  and organization of cerebral cor-
    tex, *140*

Bouin
  on efferent axons, 292

on exogenous or centrifugal fibers,
    250

Bouquet of central cones, 269, 272

Boveri, T., 767

Bowman, William, 4, 51, Fig. 45
  description of retinal layers by, 50

Bozler, 558

Bradypus; *see* Sloth

Brain; *see also* Cerebral hemispheres
  anatomy of, Greek, *74*
  anatomy and physiology of, post-
    Vesalian period in, 96–100
  arteries of, Figs. 366–70
  arteries of, as terminal arteries,
    618
  association areas of, function of,
    176
  back view of, Fig. 288
  base of, and its arteries, *602*
  blood supply of, *594*
  coronal section through, Fig. 230
  course of retinal excitations to,
    587
  description of, *446*
  diagram of visual system and out-
    line of, Fig. 180
  embryonic development of, *763*,
    Figs. 434, 435
  fetal, sulci and fissures of, neopal-
    lial, *447*
  fiber systems of
    discovery of, 133
    Gratiolet's investigations of,
      135
  function of, Vesalius and Galen
    on, *96*
  functional centers of, 457, Figs.
    274, 275
  functional organization of
    early physiological experiments
      on, *126*
    early speculations on, *122*
    plurality doctrine of, 122–26
  Galen on importance of, 80
  growth of, in origin of Man, 1028,
    1029
  hemisphere(s) of, in fetus, Fig. 270
  hemispheres of, visual system and,
    Fig. 182
  lateral ventricles of, 398
  lobes of, *448; see also under* Fron-
    tal; Occipital; Parietal; Tempo-
    ral
    left occipital, Fig. 278
    occipital, sections through, Fig.
      229
  major subdivisions of, Fig. 272
  mechanisms of, sixteenth-century
    diagram of, Fig. 81
  nervous function of, *560*
  phylogenesis of, 446
  physiology of, dawn of modern,
    119–21
  pithecoid conditions in, 475, Fig.
    294
  as repository of "animal spirit"
    and "reasoning soul," Galen
    and, *79*
  role of, in evolution of Man, 1026
  as seat of "general sense," 98
  as "seat of soul," 118
  sections of, showing topographical
    relations of structures, Figs.
    231, 232, 233

sulci and gyri of, Fig. 271
  structures of
    horizontal   section   showing,
      Figs. 226, 227
    vertical section showing, Fig.
      228
  topographical retinal representa-
    tion in, Cartesian hypothesis
    of, *102*
  tumor of
    homonymous hemianopia from,
      case report of, *698*
    quadrantic homonymous hemi-
      anopia from, case report of,
      707
  ventral aspect of, with infranu-
    clear division of visual system,
    Fig. 181
  visual, in embryonic life, 764
  visual centers of, pathology of,
    629–759
  visual pathways of, pathology of,
    629–759

Brain research
  modern history of, Meynert and,
    171
  role of improved laboratory tech-
    nique in, *170*

Brain stem and betweenbrain, visual
    system in, Fig. 184

Brain tissues, methods of revealing,
    391

Brehm, A., 848, 869, 991, 994
  on biology of Shrews, 863

Brewster, Sir David, 1

Briggs, W., 45, 106, 107
  on optic chiasma, 109
  and space perception, 334
  on structure of retina, 279
  visual system according to, Fig. 74

Broca, Paul, Fig. 95
  discovery of motor speech center
    by, 143, 451
  motor aphasia of, functional cere-
    bral localization and, 458, Fig.
    274

Brodmann, Korbinian, 499, 504,
    Fig. 299
  charts of cerebral cortex by, Fig.
    300
  deep internal granular lamina of;
    see Granular layer of striate
    area, inner, inner lamina of
  external granular lamina of, 502;
    see also Striate area, outer gran-
    ular layer of
  field 17 of, 390, 404, 414, 452; *see
    also* Striate area
  fields 18 and 19 of, 397, 453
  ganglion lamina of; *see* Ganglion
    cell layer of striate area
  multiform lamina of; *see* Striate
    area, multiform cell layer of
  pyramidal lamina of; *see* Pyrami-
    dal cell layer of striate area
  superficial internal granular lami-
    na of; *see* Granular layer of
    striate area, inner, outer lami-
    na of

Brody, 161, 335
  experiments on visual system by,
    191

Brook Trout; *see* Trout

Broom, R., 472, 1034, 1036

Broom & Robinson, 1039

Brouwer, Bernardus, 674, 686, Fig. 121

Brouwer, Van Heuven & Biemond, experiments on visual system by, 200

Brouwer & Zeeman, 160, 161
  experiments on visual system by, *190*
  on foveal representation in brain, 341
  on lateral geniculate nucleus, 366

Brouwer, Zeeman & Houwer, 335

Brücke, 51

Bruesch & Arey, on optic nerve fibers, 300, 301

Brush and flat-top bipolars, *231*
  distribution and history of, *233*
  in function of rod system, 252
  and rod system of neurons, 582
  synapses of, Fig. 177
    with ganglion cells, 231
    with midget ganglion, 242
    with photoreceptors, *231*
    with shrub ganglion, 239
    with umbrella ganglion, 239

Buddenbrock, 799

Buffon, G. L. L. de, 903

Bullhead, 831–39
  biology of, *836*
  characteristics of, 831
  eyeball of, *831*
  habits of, *831*
  nervous system of, *835*
  Northern Brown
    brain of, Figs. 456, 458
    field of view of, 787, Fig. 457
  photoreceptors in, 834
  retina of, *831*
  sight of, *831*
  taxonomy of, *831*

Bunge, on macular bundle, 160

Bunsen, brain of, 475

Burdach, Karl Friedrich, 113, 116, 154, 156, 178, Fig. 90
  on brain in visual function, 113
  on cerebral cortex, 117
  and cerebral functional organization, 122
  in early investigations of subcortical fiber systems, 132
  inferior longitudinal fascicle of, 395, 400, 405
  and lateral geniculate nucleus, 115
  on optic nerves, 116
  and pulvinar of thalamus, 115

Burmeister, 907

"Bushman," the Gorilla; *see* Gorilla

Bushmen, lunate sulcus in brains of, 474

Buzzi, 38
  discovery of yellow spot by, 45, 279

Caesalpinus, and optic chiasma, 109

Caesar, Gaius Julius, Fig. 546

Cahn, A. R., 803

Cajal; *see* Ramón y Cajal

Calcar avis, 394, 400

Calcarine artery; *see* Artery, calcarine

Calcarine cortex
  representation of visual fields in, Fig. 124
  visual radiation and, 520

Calcarine fissure, Fig. 289
  anatomy of, 460
  anterior portion of, 460
  configuration of, 461
  cortical lesion along, hemianopia due to, Fig. 112
  and crescentic field defect, 678
  damage to, central sparing and, 693
  discovery of role of vision in relation to, *166*
  divisions of, 400
  in fetus, 448
  of infant, asteriform cells in, Fig. 319
  inner configuration of, Fig. 278
  lesion of, case report of, 750–55
  lesion in lip of, case report of, Figs. 429, 430, 431
  in Man and Chimpanzee, 480
  medial, tumors of, central sparing and, 693
  morphology of, *460*
  phylogeny of, 467–86, 471
  posterior polar segment of, in phylogeny, 484
  posterior portion of, 460
    phylogenesis of, 480
  of Rhesus Macaque, experimental lesion of, Figs. 245, 246, 247
  simian, morphology of, *462*
  topography of, Figs. 231, 232, 233

Calcarine layer, 394

Calcarine sulcus, 451, Figs. 291–95; *see also* Calcarine fissure
  anatomy of, 460
  anterior, 461
  blood supply of, 612, 614
  encephalomalacia in, case report of, 755–59
  evolution of, 470, Fig. 282
  external or lateral, phylogenesis of, 481
  lateral, in phylogenesis of calcarine fissure, 471
  lateral or posterior, 461
  medial
    in evolutionary process, 484–95
    in phylogenesis of calcarine fissure, 471
  medial or anterior, 461
  parieto-occipital and, encephalomalacia in, case report of, Figs. 432, 433
  posterior, 461
    in incipient human races, 472
  prestriate; *see* Calcarine fissure, medial or anterior

Camera obscura; *see* Dark chamber

Campbell
  visuo-psychic area of, 470
  visuo-sensory area of, 390

Campbell, Alfred Walter, Fig. 297

Campbell, J., 38

Camper, Pieter, Fig. 82

Cantonnet, 183

Cantor, on Tree Shrew, 876

Capsule
  circumgeniculate, 356
  internal, of brain, 394

Carboniferous Period, 894, 955

Carnivora
  decussation of optic nerve fibers in, 788
  optic nerves of, decussation of 780
  retinal blood supply of, 601

Carnivorous habit, as deterrent to evolution of Australopithecus, 1040

Carp, fields of view of, 787

Carpensis, 87

Carpenter, L. S., 1021

Carpolestes, 1040

Carrière, 542

Carus, and lateral geniculate nucleus, 115

Castelain, Morax, Moreau &, 183

Cat
  and color vision, 886
  decussation of optic nerve fibers in, 788
  fovea of, 282
  lateral geniculate nucleus of
    coronal section through, Fig. 217
    inferior segment of, Fig. 218
    structure of, Fig. 216
  optic chiasma in, 158, 310, 323, 324
  retinal projection in, 353
  striate area of, O'Leary on, 510
  visual behavior of, 951
  visual cortex of
    layer of asteriform cells in, Figs. 323, 324
    neurons in deep layers of, Fig. 326
  visual system of, *319*
    infranuclear and nuclear divisions of, Fig. 192
  yellow spot in, investigation for, 261

Cataract, operation for
  by Arabs, 17
  first, 9

Catarrhines
  cortical visual centers of, 470
  occipital lobe in, 465
  occipital operculum in, 470
  simian sulcus in, 470
  striate area of, location and extent of, 490

Catchpole & Fulton, Tarsiers and, 909

Catoptrics
  Greek, *13*
  of rod function, hypothesis of, *48*

Caucasians
  calcarine fissure in, 476
  lunate sulcus in brains of, 474
  representative types of, Figs. 541–46

Cave-dwelling species, eyes of, 958

Cazauvieilh, in early investigations of cerebral cortex, 132

Cebus Monkey, color vision in, 970

Cell body
   and nervous impulses, 550
   in neuron theory, 548
Cells, star-shaped, in inner granular
      layer of striate area, 512, 513,
      515
Celsus, Aulus Cornelius, 10, 75, 76
Cenozoic Period, 872
Central area
   blood vessels of, 599
   boundary of, experiments with le-
      sions on, *344*
   and fovea
      blood supply of, 598
      in course of retinal excitations
         to brain, 588
      monosynaptic cone system in,
         584
      relationship of, 281
         to visual radiation, 407
      studies of minute structures of,
         285
   inner photoreceptor fibers in, 226
   lesions in, experiments with, *342*
   relations of fovea to, *281*
   representation of, in striate area
      419
      of retina, 260
      experiments with lesions in,
         Figs. 204, 205, 206
Central foramen of Soemmerring,
      279
Central fovea, 259, *262*, Fig. 161
   blood supply of, Fig. 364
   comparative studies on, *281*
   connections of, with pregeniculate
      gray nucleus, *341*
   discovery of, *278*
   inner layers of, *272*
   lesion in, experiment with, *339*
   representation of
      cerebral, 673
      cortical, scotomas and, *673*
      in divisions of visual system,
         388
      in lateral geniculate nuclei, *339*
      in optic chiasma, *339*
      in optic nerves, *339*
      in optic tracts, *339*
      in striate area, 419
   of Reptiles, Fishes, and Cephalo-
      pods, *284*
Central nervous system, affections
      of, pupillary reflex in, 382
Central orifice; *see* Central foramen
Central and peripheral nervous sys-
      tems, *560*
Central rests, 660
Central sparing, 614
   case of incomplete homonymous
      hemianopia with, 747–50
   vs. central pseudo-sparing, 688
   explanations of, Fig. 400
   extent of, 649
   in hemianopia
      cerebral blood supply and, *620*
      Ferrier on, *148*
      functional and anatomical fac-
         tors underlying, 687–94
      origin of concept of, *680*
      testing of fields of view in, *687*
   in homonymous hemianopia, 330,
      683

anatomical factors responsible
      for, *691*
basic concepts regarding, *689*
hypothesis on
   of asymmetric division of de-
      cussating and nondecussat-
      ing fibers in chiasma, *684*
   of bilateral connections of fo-
      veal photoreceptors with
      brain, *682*, 689
   of causation by multiple ar-
      terial supply of occipital
      pole, *685*
   of causation by protected lo-
      cation of foveal macular
      fibers in visual radiation,
      685
   of intraretinal decussation of
      foveal-macular fibers, *680*
   of midbrain decussation of
      "macular" fibers, *683*
   recent, *686*
   of special form of hemiam-
      blyopia, *685*
   and speculations on, 680–87
in incomplete homonymous hemianopia, 648–49
role of arterial anastomoses in,
   619
Wilbrand's hypothesis on, final
   verdict on, *684*
Centrifugal bipolars, *246*
   dynamic orientation on, 248
   and facilitation or inhibition
      mechanism, 579
   function of, 255
   and functional polarity of neu-
      rons, 550
   in integration system, 255
   in retinal integration, 587
   synapses of, with midget bipolars,
      237
   various types of, Fig. 142
Centripetal bipolars; *see under* Bipolar; Brush; Flat-top; Midget
Cephalopods, central fovea of, *284*
Cercopithecidae
   occipital operculum in, 470
   simian sulcus in, 470
Cerebellum; *see* Brain
Cerebral artery, posterior, origin of,
   604
Cerebral cortex
   anatomy and physiology of, in
      seventeenth and eighteenth
      centuries, 117–18
   association areas of, Flechsig's,
      174
   Baillarger's figure showing struc-
      ture of, Figs. 87, 88
   blood supply of, 609
   Brodmann's charts of, Figs. 300,
      302, 306
   and color vision, 667
   cytoarchitectural charts of, Figs.
      300, 301, 302, 306
   discovery of dependence of vision
      on, *129*
   discovery of functional signifi-
      cance of, *176*
   and doctrine of functional om-
      nivalence, 126–30
   early investigations of, 130–37
   Economo's charts of, Fig. 301

functional localization in, 451,
      457, Figs. 274, 275
functional organization of, Flechsig's concept of, *176*
functional significance of, old
   anatomists' beliefs of, *117*
hemiretinal representation in, first
   demonstration of, 168
hypothesis of bilateral representation of fovea in, *683*
investigation of, concept of "soul"
   as deterrent to, 118
and lateral geniculate nucleus, figure experiments on, *424*
localization of visual function in
   early attempts at, 147–49
   early modern attempts at, 163–
      69
map of, showing motor, sensory
   and mental faculties, Fig. 275
minute structure of, modern investigation of, *195*
myelogenetical sensory regions in,
   174
omnivalence doctrine in, and
   unity of "soul" or mind, 129
organization of, Bouillaud's concept of, *140*
projection centers and association
   areas of, 170–79
retinal image and, 420–25
retinal representation in, early research on, *179*
role of, in early evolution, 1027
structure of, Gennari's figure on,
   Fig. 86
topographical retinal representation in, history of theory of,
   179–84
visual radiation terminal area in,
   404
Cerebral disease, visual disturbances
   with, early reports of, 164
"Cerebral eye," 432
Cerebral function, "vicarious" doctrine of, 149
Cerebral hemispheres
   configuration of, 446–59
   functional organization of, 446–59
   subdivisions of, *448*
   visual pathway and, 391–98
   visual radiation and, 391–98
Cerebral localization, functional
   Bouillaud's concept of, 142
   early attempts at, 118
   evidence for and against, *119*
   Flourens and, 128
   founding of concept of, 128
   Haller's verdict against, *121*
   revival of doctrine of, 138–46
   superseding omnivalence doc-
      trine, *145*
Cerebral ventricles, 391
Cerebrospinal fluid, course of, 398
Chacko, 619
Chaetognates, eyes of, 786
Chaillou, F. H., report of homonymous hemianopia by, 147, 163
Chamber eye
   inception of, in phylogenesis of
      visual system, 786
   and organization of visual system,
      in evolutionary process, 786

Chambers of eye, structure and function of, *211*

Chameleon, American; *see also* Anole
central fovea of, *285*
eyes of, 958
foveal synapses of, 285
Old World, *845*

Champion, F. W., 996

Chanet, on cerebral functional localization, 122

Charcot, 105, 683
and functional cerebral localization, 143
on midbrain decussation of optic nerve fibers, *160*

Chatelin, Marie &, 183

Chauliac, Guy de, 87
and reading glasses, 29

Chiasma of optic nerves, 289
blood supply of, 605
summary of, *623*
central foveal representation in, *339*
decussation in
evidence of, 330
partial vs. complete, *156*
solution of problem of, *158*
displacement of, by pituitary tumor, case report of, 696–97
in early nineteenth century, 115
fascicular composition of, Figs. 193, 194, 195
fibers of, 673
course of, 386, *301*
hypothesis of role of, in central sparing, *684*
Galen's functional interpretation of, 80–81
histology of, 297–301
and homonymous hemianopia, Landoldt's hypothesis on, 160
and hypothalamic region
course of nerve fibers in, Fig. 196
topography of, Fig. 197
lesions of, visual field defects after, 639
after obstruction to blood supply, 619
partial decussation in, earliest announcement of, *109*
pathology of, scotomas in, 639
in pathway from retina to lateral geniculate nuclei, 323–34
in Pigeon, 313
in stereoptic vision, 441
structure of, 299
fascicular, *324*
in Inframammalian Vertebrates, *310*
in various Vertebrates, Fig. 188
structure and function of
historical confusion on, *108*
in late eighteenth and early nineteenth centuries, 113
topography of, *442*
Vesalius on structure of, *95*

Chickadee
visual acuity of, 967
visual behavior of, 947, 948

Chickaree, Fig. 494; *see also* Squirrel, Red

Chickens, visual behavior of, 947, 951

Chimney Swift, visual behavior of, 951

Chimpanzee
calcarine fissure in, 480
cerebral hemispheres of, external configuration of, Fig. 284
character, habitat, and behavior of, *997*
character and habits of, in captivity, *1007*
cortical visual centers in, 478
extent and location of, Figs. 284, 285
eye of
dimensions of, 209
fundus of, Fig. 166
ganglion cells of retina of, Figs. 136, 137
lateral geniculate nuclei of, Fig. 214
middle cerebral artery in, 615
occipital lobe of, blood supply of, in relation to striate area, Fig. 376
in phylogenesis of cortical visual centers, 470
retina of, 250
ganglion and bipolar cells in, Fig. 139
nerve cells from central area in, Fig. 138
striate area of, blood supply of occipital lobe and, Fig. 376
synaptical organelles of, 566
various views and attitudes of, Figs. 532, 533
vision of, 1010

China, ancient, and knowledge of visual system, 73

Chinese, lunate sulcus in brains of, 474

Chipmunks, 895
behavior of, eyesight in, 900
Eastern, 896
habits of, *896*, 897
visual behavior of, 948
Western, 896, Fig. 493
behavior of, *898*
habits of, 897

Chiroptera, eyes of, 958

Chlamidomonas, eyespot in, 796

Chopart, 118

Chordate Phylum, photoreceptors in rise of, 873

Chordates, in phylogenetic study of vertebrate eye, 769

Chorioid fissure, 357

Chorioid membrane, 207
in blood supply of optic nerve and eyeball, 597
in blood supply of retina, 598

Chorioretinitis, defects of visual field in, 638

Christiansen, 183

Chromic acid, first use in histology of, 49

Chrysochlorids, 939

Church, 768

Ciliary body, 210

Cingular gyrus in adult, 449

Cingular sulcus in fetus, 448

Clark, W. E. Le Gros, 889, 891, 892, 1035, Fig. 310
& Leakey, 1034
& Penman, 158, 161, 684
experiments on visual system by, *191*, 192, 194
on projection of retinal quadrants, 335
on Tarsier, 908

Cleomédes, and theory of vision, 12

Coelenterates
nervous pathways in, 572
nervous system of, 544, 560

Cog or jobble synapse of Ramón y Cajal, 236

Cohnheim, 599, 618

Colliculus, superior, 290, 308

Collier, Beevor &, 183

Color, in sexual selection by Birds, 972

Color blindness; *see also* Achromatopia; Hemiachromatopia
in nocturnal species, 886

Color of fruits, animals and, *972*

Color mixing, binocular, 375, 376

Color perception, as basic quality of vision, *971*

Color vision
in acquisition of food, 972
cerebral cortex and, 667
and color of fruits, *972*
in evolution of Primates, *969*
four-color theory of, 376
impairment of, homonymous, 665
midget ganglions in, 574, 587
retinal structures in, 71
in rise of Primates, 902
in Squirrel, 886
striate area and, 453
in struggle of animals for survival, *970*
in Tree Shrew, 886
trichromatic theory of, 376

Coloring of fruits
biological effects and, Fig. 518A
in evolution, 973
evolution of, and arboreal habit, *973*

Common pathway mechanism in retina, *578*

Common pathway for nerve impulses, 255

Common Shrew; *see* Shrew

Cone bipolars; *see also* Midget bipolars
polysynaptic, 236
of Ramón y Cajal, 233

Cone mosaic, foveal, 269, Fig. 156

Cone pedicles, 217, 218, *227*

Cone system, 582
of central area and fovea
excitation currents in, 584
monosynaptic, 584
complete, receptor and conductor units in, arrangement of, 584
functional relationship of, to rod system, 583

Cone system—*Continued*
  individual or monosynaptic mechanism in, 584
  monosynaptical, excitation currents in, 585
  of neurons, *583*
  pure, in retinal response, *252, 253*
Cones
  in central fovea, 266–72
  discovery of, *47*
  in dynamics of retina, 589
  excitation of
    channels of, *572*
    course of, 584
    quality of, 573
  in excitation of bipolars, 577
  light stimulation and, 565
  and photomediator substance, 223
  in Pike, 820
  relationship of, to bipolar cells, 576
  and rod system of neurons, 582
  rods and, general features of, *220*
  synaptical relationships of, functions of, 576
  in Trout, 829
Cook, Captain, and Tree Shrew, 876
Cook, N., on Tarsier's sight, 909
Cope, 934
Corbett, J., 997
Cormorant and Swallow, visual apparatus of, 853
Cornea in dioptrics, 212
  nutritive fluids of, 597
  structure of, 207, *209*
Corona radiata, discovery of, *132*
Corpus callosum, as "seat of soul," 118
Corpus striatum, as "seat of soul," 118
Corti, 541
  investigation of retinal structure by, 50
Cortical visual centers; *see* Visual centers, cortical
Corticonigral tracts, 394
Corticopontine tracts, 394
Craniates, in studies of origin of vertebrate eye, 771
Craniognomy, 125
Crappie, Black, 813
Crayfish, in experiments on nervous system, 559
Creodonts, 936
Cretaceous Period, 869, 872, 873, 892, 893, 926, 937, 963
  heads and skulls of placental Mammals in, Fig. 477
  Upper, 926
Critchley, M., 606, 607
  and branches of anterior cerebral artery, 606, 607
Crocidura, in early mammalian ancestry, 891
Cro-Magnon Race, 1034
Crow, and Swallow
  visual apparatus of, 853
  visual behavior of, 949
Crusius, 118

Crustaceans, eyes of, 801
Cruveillier, Jean, Fig. 378
Crystalline lens, *212*
Cuckoo, Yellow-billed
  fundus of eye of, Fig. 176
  various views of, Fig. 472
Culpeper & Scarlet, microscope by, Fig. 40
Cuming, H., 907
Cuneolingual fold in evolutionary process, 480
Cunningham, 488
  cuneolingual gyri of, 462
  external calcarine sulcus of, 465
Curschmann, 165
Cusanus, Nicolaus, and concave eyeglasses, 31
Cushing, H.
  and temporal loop of Flechsig, 178
  visual radiation studies of, 405
Cuttlefish, eyes of, 786
Cuvier
  on cerebral cortex, 117
  and lateral geniculate nucleus, 115
Cyclopean eye, 81
  early concept of, 109
  primordial, 774
  visual function and, 792
Cyclostomes, eye of, 768
Cyprinidae, 803

Dalén, on macular bundle, 160
Damselfly
  head and eyes of, Fig. 444
  visual behavior of, 945
Dark Ages, science in Europe during, *83*
Dark chamber
  in Arab optics, 20
  eye as, 212
  in formation of retinal image, 787
  origin of, 799
  in phylogeny of visual decussation, 783
Darner, Big Green, head and eyes of, Fig. 444
Dart, R. A., 472, 1031, 1034, 1035, 1037, 1052
Dartians, 1035; *see also* Australopithecus
Dartnall
  and photoreceptive substances, 222
  on role of visual purple, 223
Darwin, Charles R., 802, 901, 941, 954, 972, 1007, 1028, 1044, Figs. 519, 520
  on origin and pre-eminence of Man, 1023–26
Dasypus, retinal blood supply in, 601
Davenport, staining method of, in striate area of cortex, 510
Davis & Joeris, on Short-tailed Shrew, 867
Dayaks of Borneo, lunate sulcus in brains of, 474
Deafness, central, temporal gyrus and, 457, Fig. 274

Dean, Usher &, experiments on visual system by, 189
Decussation
  of optic nerves, in image formation, 787
  of visual system
    phylogenesis of, *784*
    phylogenetic origin of, Ramón y Cajal diagram explaining, Figs. 437, 438
    and significance of, 770–93
    probable causes of, *783*
    ultimate causes and consequences of, *792*
Degeneration
  transsynaptic, 548
  transsynaptic or transneuronal, 331, 355, 364
Deiters, 541, 543
  on histologic structure of nervous tissue, 60
  protoplasmic expansions of, 66
Dejerine, 183
  and pregeniculate gray nucleus, 192
Deltatheridium, 892
Demócritos of Abdera, 76
  description of eye by, 9
  theory of vision by, 12
Dendrites
  discovery of, 60
  and nervous impulses, 550
  in neuron theory, 66, 548
Dendritic bouquet of midget bipolars, 233, 234
Dendritic expansion
  of brush and flat-top bipolars, 231
  of mop bipolar, 228, 233
Derscheid, 1002
Des Cartes, René, 37, Fig. 69
  and anatomical basis of vision, *100*
  and "animal spirit" concept, 96
  on optic chiasma, 109
  on pineal gland function, 118
  retinal image diagram by, Fig. 33
  and space perception, 335
  speculations of, mistakes and merits in, *104*
  visual system according to, Fig. 70
  working of, Fig. 71
Des Cartes to von Haller, knowledge of visual pathways and centers from, 105–12
Detwiler, 944
Devonian Period, 893
Diatryma, rise of, 936
Diemerbroeck, 106
  on optic chiasma, 109
Diencephalon; *see* Betweenbrain
Diet; *see* Carnivorous habit; Omnivorous habit
Dimmer, 155
  outer fovea of, 266
Dinoflagellates, ocelli of, 796
Dinosaurs
  as impediment in evolution, 959
  in struggle for survival, 869
Diodóros of Sicily, 73

Dioptrics
early modern, Italian Renaissance
and, *31*
of eye, 207, 212
Greek, *13*
and landmarks of eyeball, 209
mechanism of, Fig. 31

Diurnality
and nocturnality, in evolutionary
progress, *954*
role of, in evolution, 968, 969,
1030
and visual acuity of advanced
Vertebrates, *968*

Doellinger, membrane of; *see* Bacillary layer

Dog
fovea of, 282
retinal representation in cortex of,
180, 181
according to Munk, Figs. 99,
100
yellow spot in, investigation for,
261

Dogiel, 542, 543
on efferent axons, 292
granular clods of, 234
in Tree Shrew, 885
and retinal structure, 67

Dogiel's cells, 237, 292

Dolecek & Launay, and blue arcs,
295

Donders, Frans Cornelius, Fig. 358

Dormouse, retinal blood supply in,
601

Douroucouli, fovea in, 281

Dragonfly
head and eyes of, Fig. 444
visual behavior of, *945*

Drelincourt, 118

Drill; *see also* Baboon
character, habitat, and behavior
of, *997*

Duck, Mallard, visual behavior of,
948

Du Laurens, André, Fig. 68
and "animal spirit" concept, 96
and brain and seat of "general
sense," 98
on function of "visual spirit," 99
on locus of visual perception, *100*

Duplexity theory, *71*

Dura mater, 391

Duret, 604, 605
concept of lenticulo-optic artery
by, 606

Dutt, 9

Duval, M., 571

Eadie, 866

Eagle
American Golden, central fovea
of retina of, vertical section
through, Fig. 171
Bald
fundus of eye of, Fig. 172
visual behavior of, 950
chiasma of optic nerves in, Fig.
189
fields of view of, 787

Golden
cones in, 226
fovea in, 283
optic chiasma in, 310
structure of, Fig. 188
and Swallow, visual apparatus of,
853
visual function of, 789

Early China Man, endocranial casts
of, Fig. 287

Earth, age of, 768

Earthworm
in experiments on nervous system,
559
photosensitive cells in, 799

Echidna, retinal blood supply in,
601

Eckman, and Tarsiers, 909

Economo, 504
area OC of, 390
charts of cerebral cortex by, Fig.
301
deep internal granular lamina of;
see Granular layer of striate
area, inner, inner lamina of
ganglion layer of; *see* Ganglion
cell layer of striate area
and innermost layer of striate
area, 507
and koniocortex, 497
molecular layer of, 499; *see also*
Plexiform layer of striate area
outer granular layer of, 502; *see
also* Striate area, outer granular
layer of
superficial internal granular lamina; *see* Granular layer of striate
area, inner, outer lamina of

Eddy & Surber, 803, 805, 810, 826

Edentates, retinal blood supply in,
601

Edinger, Ludwig, Fig. 446

Edwin Smith papyrus, 73

Eel, retinal blood supply in, 601

Efferent fibers of retina, 250–52

Egyptian fellahs, lunate sulcus in
brains of, 474

Egyptians, ancient, and knowledge
of visual system, 73

Ehrenberg, 541
on cerebral cortex, 117

Ehrlich, P., 543
contribution to histology by, 171
discovery of vital methylene blue
stain by, 62
staining method of, in striate area
of cortex, 510

Elephant, retinal blood supply in,
601

Elephant Shrew, 873, 962
African, various views of, Figs.
478, 479
brain of, Figs. 480, 481
cortical visual centers of, 469
optic nerves of, 886
in primate phylogenesis, 890

Ellis, 876

Elze, 178
visual radiation studies of, 405

Embryos, in early stages, showing

development of eye and brain,
Figs. 434, 435

Empedoclés, 11

Encephalomalacia, thrombotic, homonymous hemianopia from,
case report of, 717–24

Engelhardt, 157

Engelmann, 571

English
fundus of eye of, Fig. 148
lunate sulcus in brains of, 474

Eocene Epoch, 860, 893, 902, 904,
935, 1038, 1041
Creodonts in, 936
Late, Miacids in, 936
Lemurs in, 934
Lower
American, 937
Sciurides and, 895
of North America and Europe,
936
Tarsier in, 934, 936
Upper
European, Tarsioids of, 934
Sciurides and, 895

Eocene Tarsioids, 1040

Eohippus, 937

Epícuros, theory of vision by, 12

Equator of eyeball, 209

Erasístratos, vivisection by, 76

Erinaceoids, 939

Erlanger, 567

Erythropsin, 222
discovery of, 52

Eskimo, diet of, 1043

Esocidae, sense of sight in, 825

Esquirol, as creator of science of
psychiatry, 132

Euclid
and light, 13
and physiology of vision, 12

Euglena, eyespots in, 796

Europe, Western, knowledge of visual system during Renaissance
in, 86–92

European Renaissance, 21–27

Eustachio, Bartolommeo, Fig. 66
first depiction of visual pathway
by, 97

Eutherians, 892

Exner, plexus of, 510

Exogenous fibers
of extraretinal origin, 255
of retina, 250

Extra-areal periphery of retina, 259
lesions in, experiments with, *345*,
Figs. 207, 208

Extra-areal regions of retina, 275
rod and cone fibers in, 226

Extrafoveal regions, structural features of, 275

Eye
accessory organs of, *212*
anatomical axis of, 209
anatomy of
Alexandrine, 10, 11
ancient, *9*
Arab, *16*
Early European, *22*

Eye—*Continued*
    anatomy of —*Continued*
        first description of, 10
        Galenian, 10, 11
        Arab interest in, 15
        blood vessels of, 597
        diagrams of
            by Aguilonius, Fig. 20
            by Arabs, Figs. 2, 3, 4, 5, 6
            by Roger Bacon, Figs. 7, 8
            Early Western, *22*
            by Ibn al-Haitham, Figs. 10, 18
            by John Peckham, Fig. 9
            by Platter, Fig. 19
            by Reisch, Fig. 12
            by Walter H. Ryff, Fig. 14
            by Scheiner, Fig. 22
            by Vesalius, Figs. 16, 17
            by Vitello, Figs. 11, 18
            by Heinrich Vogtherr, Fig. 13
        dioptrics of, 212
        embryonic development of, Figs. 434, 435
        function of, structure and, 207–12
        fundus of, Figs. 148, 363
        horizontal section through, Fig. 125
        of Invertebrates, in origin of vertebrate eye, 799
        investigations of, earliest, 9–12
        ontogenesis of, 763–67
        ontogeny and phylogeny of, interdependence of, 765
        optical axis of, 209
        origin and development of, 763–93
        phylogenesis of, 768–78
        probable stages in, Fig. 436
        physiology of, Early European, *22*
        stages in evolution of, *774*
        structure of, early modern knowledge of, *27*
        structure and function of, 207–12
        Arab knowledge of, 14–21
        history of investigation of, 9–62
        investigators of, 799
        types of, and their use, *798*
Eye socket, contents of, blood supply of, 597
Eyeball
    blood supply of, 597, Fig. 365
        summary of, 623
    dimensions of, *209*
    dioptrical landmarks of, *209*
    topographical relationships of, *442*
    tunics of, vertical section through, Fig. 127
Eyeglasses
    concave, earliest mention of, 31
    earliest mention of, 29
    earliest picture of, 31
    fitting of, in seventeenth century, Fig. 25
    invention of, *28*
    in seventeenth century, Figs. 25, 26
    in sixteenth century, Figs. 24, 37
Eyesight; *see* Diurnality; Nocturnality; Vision; etc.

Fabricius ab Aquapendente, 23, 95, Fig. 21
Facilitation or inhibition mechanism, *579*

Falcon, and Swallow, visual apparatus of, 853
Falconiform Order, rise of, 936
Fallopius, 97
Falx of cerebrum, 391
Feline Douroucouli, 281
Fernel, 90
Ferrier, David, 683, Fig. 97
    experiments on localization of vision by, 147
    significance of, *149*
Fetus
    blood supply in, 615–17
    development of eye and brain in, Figs. 434–35
    retinal elements in, Fig. 143
Fiber systems
    of brain
        discovery of, *133*
        Gratiolet's investigations of, *135*
    of striate area, 507–10
        S. Ramón y Cajal on, *518*
Fibers
    afferent, in striate area, variety of, 533
    association, and stripe of Gennari, 521
    of striate area
        centrifugal, 518
        centripetal, 518
Fibrillar baskets in retina, 257
Fibrous astrocytes in retina, 258
Field 17 of Brodmann, 390, 404, 414;
    see also Striate area
Field 18 of Brodmann, 397
Field 19 of Brodmann, 397
Field defects
    in achromatopia, 666
    in amblyopia, 666
    crescentic, interpretation of, 668–80
    hemianopic, asymmetry and incongruity in, 679
    interpretation of, 668–80
    minute, theoretical importance of, 671
Field plotting, 646
Field rests
    central, cerebral symptoms accompanying, 675
    and color vision, 674, 676
    hemianopic, *674*
        central, interpretation of, 674
        homonymous, causes of, 675
        peripheral, interpretation of, 674
        types of, 674
    interpretation of, 668–80
    pathologic basis of, 675
    and visual acuity, 674, 676
Fields of view
    and landmarks of, Fig. 381
    testing and interpretation of, in central sparing, *687*
    topographic representation of, in visual pathways and centers, Fig. 259
Finches, visual behavior of, 947
Fingerman, 801
Fire, first making of, 1036

Fish; *see also* Pike; Silverside; Sunfish; etc.
    central area of, 282
    central fovea of, *284*
    chiasma of optic nerves in, 310, 323
    diurnal, 971
    earliest, appearance of, 768
    early, photoreceptors of, in evolutionary progress, 954
    eye of, 768, 958
    monocular fields in, *787*
    nocturnal, 971
    optic chiasma in, 158
    optic nerves in, decussation of, 779, 780
    retina of, visual violet in, 222
    retinal projection in, 353
    visual acuity in, 816
Fissure, calcarine; *see* Calcarine fissure
    simian, 465
Fixation points, foveal cortex and, 432
Fixation techniques, early, 132
Flat-top bipolars, synaptical relationship of
    with garland ganglion, 239
    with shrub ganglion, 239
    with umbrella ganglion, 239
Flatworms, vesicular eyes of, 786
Flechsig, Paul Emil, 155, 662, 683, Fig. 114
    association area of, *174*, 470, 484
    on course of visual radiation, 178
    discovery of myelogenesis by, 172
    discovery of origin of visual radiation by, *177*
    fundamental law of myelogenesis of, 173
    role of, in advancement of knowledge, 178
    sensory and association areas of, Fig. 115
    study of fiber tracts by, *173*
    temporal loop of, discovery of, 178
    visual radiation studies of, 405
Flemming, 543
Flicker, dissected head of, Fig. 471
Flourens, Marie Jean Pierre, 543, Fig. 85
    brain experiments of, *126, 127*
    and cerebral functional omnivalence, *129*
    and role of cerebral cortex in vision, *129*
Flycatcher, visual behavior of, 947
Flying ability, development of, 937
Foerster, O., 687
    experiments on visual system by, 200
Förster, R., 164, 633, 646, 680, 685, 694, Fig. 104
    case of, testing Munk's theory of "cortical blindness," 183
    invention of perimeter by, 153, 163
Foix, 607
Fontana, Felix, 541
    and functional organization of brain, 126
    observation of retina by, 45
    on structure of retina, 279

Foramen
central retinal, of Soemmerring, 279
of Monroe, 398
Forbes & Richardson, 805
Forebrain, Ibn al-Haitham on, 85
Forel, 154
commissure of, 303
and neuron theory, 65
Form perception in achromatopia, 665
Fornicate sulcus; *see* Cingular sulcus
Fovea,
in Birds, 233
blood vessels of, 599
central; *see also* Central fovea
inner layers of, *272*
radial fibers in, 257
cone system in, 252
pure, 254
diameter of, 264
neurons in, synaptical relationships of, 285
outer, 272
pseudo-, 688
representation in brain of, 339
simian, 233
terminology of, clarification of, 266
Foveal cortex
collateral circulation in, 616
and fixation points, 432
Foveal depression, functional significance of, *275*
Foveal-macular fibers, intraretinal decussation of, hypothesis on, *680*
Foveal photoreceptors, and brain, bilateral connections between, hypothesis of, *682, 689*
Foveal reflex, 264
Foveal representation in cortex, bilateral, hypothesis of, *683*
Foveola, *262, 272*
terminology of, clarification of, 266
Foville & Pinel-Grandchamp, and functional cerebral localization, 143
Foxes, Flying
retinal blood supply in, 601
striate area of, shape, extent, and location of, Fig. 309
Franke, Balado &, experiments on visual system by, 192
Franz, V., 768, 799
on neuroglial cells, 258
Frauenlob, Heinrich, earliest mention of reading glasses by, 29
Frequency modulation, in functioning of visual pathway, 575
Frey, hypothalamic optic root of, 315
Friedemann, and pregeniculate gray nucleus, 192
Friedman, B., and blue arcs, 295
Frima, Bierens de Haan &, 970
Fritsch
and cerebral cortex, 451
on cone distribution in central fovea, 269

and discovery of somatomotor area, 143
Frog
Meadow or Leopard, head of, dissected to show brain and eyes, Fig. 461
retinal blood supply in, 601
Tree, retinal blood supply in, 601
Frontal lobe, anatomy of, 449
Froriep, 768
Fruits, samples of American Midwestern, Fig. 518A
Fuchs, W., 688
Fulton, Catchpole &, Tarsiers and, 909
Functional centers of human brain, Figs. 274, 275
Functional localization in human cerebral cortex, 451–58

Galagos; *see* Lemur
Galagos monteiri
retinal blood supply of, 601
survival of, 939
Galen, 11, 76, 789
anatomy and physiology of the visual system by, 77–78
and "animal spirit," *79*
description of nerves related to eye by, *77*
on function of brain, during post-Vesalian period, *96*
functional interpretation of optic nerves by, 80–81
on importance of brain, 80
influence on Arab and early Western science of, *77*
influence on Vesalius' views of, *96*
mistakes of, *82*
on optic chiasma, 109
physiology of visual system by, 78–80
compared with modern view, *82*
evaluation and critique of, 82–83
and "pneuma" or "spirit" as life's principle, *78, 79*
on properties of "soul," 122
and "reasoning soul," 79
on retinal substance and brain, 41
Galileo, Galilei, Fig. 349
Gall, F. J., 117, 154, Figs. 83, 84
and cerebral cortex, 451
on cerebral functional localization, *122, 123*
Gall & Spurzheim, 116
in early investigations of subcortical fiber systems, 132
and lateral geniculate nucleus, 115
Ganglion cell layer
of retina, *219*
of striate area, *506*, Fig. 314
minute structure of, *515*
Ganglion cells; *see also under* Garland; Giant; Midget; Parasol; Shrub; Small diffuse
of retina, 237–46
classification of, *237*
in cone system of neurons, 583, 585
after cutting or destroying optic nerve, tract, or nucleus, 292

degeneration of, 292
diffuse, synapses of, Fig. 177
discovery of, *47*
displaced, 292; *see also* Dogiel's cells
excitation of
course of, 587
quality of, 586
in function of cone system, 252
in function of rod system, 252
investigation of, history of, *242*
and retinal impulses, Figs. 178, 179
in retinal response, 255
in rod system of neurons, 582
synapses of
with brush and flat-top bipolars, *231*
with midget bipolars, 236
with mop bipolars, *230*
in striate area, 527
Ganser, 154
commissure of, 303
Garland ganglion, *239*
Gastropods, eyes of, 786
Gaul, head of a, Fig. 542
Gautrand, Monbrun &, 183
Genderen Stort, 571
Geniculo-calcarine tract; *see* Visual radiation
Gennari
in early investigation of cerebral cortex, 132
hardening technique of, 132
stripe of, 390, 394, 398, 414, 415, Fig. 86
and association fibers, 521
formation of, 520
identification of, 518
and striate cortex, 497
Geometrical axis of eyeball, 209
Gerard of Cremona, 22
Gerlach, 60, 541, 542
contribution to histology by, 170
introduction of carmine stain by, 61
on organization of nervous system, 63, 541
Germans, lunate sulcus in brains of, 474
Giambattista della Porta, Fig. 27
and early modern dioptrics, 35
Giant cells of striate area, 505, 506
Giant ganglions of retina, *239*
Gibbon
character and habits of, in captivity, *1004*
intelligence of, 987
in phylogenesis of cortical visual centers, 470
posture of, and evolution, 1029
use of hands and feet by, Fig. 531
various views of, Figs. 528, 529, 530, 531
vocalization of, 1006
White-handed, fundus of eye of, Fig. 167
Gifford, B. L., 335
Giovanardi
on brain in congenital anophthalmia, Fig. 108

Giovanardi—*Continued*
  and occipital localization of visual
    center, 165
Girardi, and medial geniculate nu-
    cleus, 115
Glassfish; *see* Silverside
Glaucoma, scotomas in, 638, 639
Glees, 558
Glees & Clark, on lateral geniculate
    nucleus, 369
Glioblastoma of brain
  complete homonymous hemiano-
    pia from, case report, 698–702,
    Figs. 403, 404, 405
  incomplete homonymous hemi-
    anopia from, case report of,
    702–7, Figs. 406, 407, 408
  quadrantic homonymous hemi-
    anopia from, case report of,
    707–10, Figs. 409, 410
Gnosis, musical, and functional cere-
    bral localization, 458, Fig. 275
Goat, striate and peristriate area of,
    shape, extent, and location of,
    Fig. 309
Goatsuckers, visual behavior of, 952
Godding, visual purple and, 222
Goldstein, 646
Golgi, Camillo G., 541, Fig. 344
  contribution to histology by, 171
  introduction of new histoanalyti-
    cal method by, 61
Golgi cells
  type I, 523
  type II, 523
Golgi method
  discovery of, influence on ad-
    vances in knowledge of, *62*
  introduction of, 61
  staining method of
    in identifying neuroglial cells of
      striate area, 536
    in striate area, 510
Golgi technique in study of striate
    area, 523
Goltz
  and cortical equivalence doctrine,
    149
  experiments on cerebral function
    by, 149
  Munk's critique of, *149*
Goodeve & Lythgoe, and visual
    purple absorption curve, 223
Gophers, visual behavior of, 948
Gordon
  and lateral geniculate nucleus, 115
  and pulvinar of thalamus, 115
Gordon, Bernhard, and reading
    glasses, 29
Gorilla
  arterial supply of occipital oper-
    culum in, 616
  "Bushman," 1018, 1020
    portrait and attitudes of, Fig.
      538
  character, habitat, and behavior
    of, *997*
  character and habits of, in cap-
    tivity, *1014*
  cortical visual center in, 478
  eye of, dimensions of, 209

Mountain, habitat and habits of,
    999
  in phylogenesis of cortical visual
    centers, 470
  sanctuary for, 1002
  striate areae in, topographical re-
    lationships of, Fig. 286
  use of hands and feet by, Figs.
    539, 540
  various views of, Figs. 536, 537,
    538, 539, 540
Graefe, Albrecht von, Fig. 103
  first interpretation of homony-
    mous hemianopia by, 156
  introduction of plotting of visual
    fields by, 153, 163, 633
Granit, Ragnar Arthur, Fig. 360
  on role of visual purple, 223
Granular cell(s)
  compared with solitary cell of
    Meynert, Fig. 337
  of striate area, 513, 527, Fig. 339
Granular clods of Dogiel, 234
Granular layer of striate area
  inner
    inner lamina of, 506
    lesion in, lateral geniculate nu-
      cleus and, 533
    middle lamina of, *504*
    minute structure of, *512*
    outer lamina of, *503*
  outer, *502*, Fig. 314
    minute structure of, *511*
Granular lines of Ramón y Cajal
Granules, inner, in striate area, 513
Grassus, Benevenutus, 43
Gratiolet, Louis-Pierre, 154, 470,
    Fig. 92
  discovery of visual radiation by,
    135, 147
  dissection of visual pathway by,
    Fig. 93
  external or perpendicular fissure
    of, 465
  investigation of fiber systems of
    brain by, *135*, 147
  and visual radiation termination,
    165
Gratiolet's radiation; *see* Visual ra-
    diation
Gray Shrew, 866
Gray or white, sensations of, rods
    and, 578
Great Northern Pike; *see* Pike
Greek anatomy of brain and visual
    system, *74*
Greek catoptrics, *13*
Greek dioptrics, *13*
Greeks
  early, and anatomy of eye, 9
  "emanation hypothesis of," end
    of, 100
  late, and anatomy of eye, 10
  pneuma hypothesis of, *78*
Gregory, W. K., 768
Gregory & Raven, 1001
Grether, 987
Ground Hog, visual behavior of, 948
Grünbaum, 605
Gudden, Bernhard von, 154, Fig.
    105

commissure of, 303
  on lateral geniculate nucleus, 368
  transverse peduncular tract of,
    303, 310, 317
Guenther, K., 973
Guinea Pig
  chiasma of optic nerves in, 323
  and color vision, 886
  optic chiasma structure in, Fig.
    188
  visual behavior of, 948
  visual system of, *318*
Gull and Swallow, visual apparatus
    of, 853
Gunderson & Hastings, 1043
Gustatory center, location of, 174
Gymnura, 873
  Tree Shrew and, 892
Gymnurinae, 962
  Malayan, 936, 939
Gyrus(i)
  angular, localization of visual cen-
    ter in, *147*
  annectent, 470
  cortical, in fetus, Fig. 270
  cuneolingual, 462, Fig. 278
    evolution of, 471
  posterior
    in evolutionary process, 480
    in Man and Chimpanzee, 478
  and sulcus(i) of brain, Fig. 271

Haab, on visual disturbance due to
    lesions of calcarine region of oc-
    cipital lobes, Fig. 109
Haab & Huguenin, and occipital lo-
    calization of visual center, 165
Haberlandt, 796
Haeckel, Ernst Heinrich, 765, Fig.
    521
  biogenetical law of, 173
  monerans of, 569
Hagfish, eye of, 768
Haller, A., 38, 112, 118, 771, Fig. 80
  arterial circle of, 598
  on cerebral function, *119*, *121*
  on cerebral functional localiza-
    tion, 122
  and functional organization of
    brain, 126
  on "seat of soul," 118
Haller, B., 542
Hamberger, 37
Hamilton, on Shrew, 867
Hand-clasp synapse of Herrick, 236
Hands, grasping ability of, in pri-
    mate evolution, 938
Hannover, 51, 680
  contribution to histology by, 49,
    170
  in early investigation of cerebral
    cortex, 132
  and tissue fixation, 541
Hannover & Obersteiner, ansate
    commissure of, 303
Hansemann, 475
Hanström, 801
Hardesty on neuroglial cells, 258
Harpman, 558
Hastings, Gunderson &, 1043

Hawk
  fields of view of, 787
  Red-tailed, visual behavior of, 950
  Sparrow, visual behavior of, 950
  and Swallow, visual apparatus of, 853
  vision of, 947
Hayashi, Polyak &, experiments on visual system by, 200
Head, X-ray of, showing topographic relationships of visual system, Fig. 269
Head and brain, blood supply of, sources of, Fig. 362
Hearing
  role of, in Man's pre-eminence, 985
  sense of, cerebral cortical center of, 453
Heart, as "seat of soul," 75
Hechst, experiments on visual system by, 192
Heck, L., 863, 991
Hedgehog, 873
  ancient, head and skull of, Fig. 477
  cortical visual center of, 469
  European
    cortical visual centers in, Fig. 309
    striate area of, location and extent of, 490
  vision of, in evolutionary progress, 961
Hegemonikón, 74
Heidenhain, 561
Heine, 683
  decussating callosal bundle of, 428
  on the extent of central sparing, 649
  hypothesis of macular projection as advocated by, Fig. 401
Heinicke, Vater &, 156
  first correct interpretation of homonymous hemianopia by, 114
Held, 542, 543
  on neuroglial cells, 258
  on peripheral nervous system, 544
Heliodóros
  and light, 13
  and theory of vision, 12
Helmholtz, Hermann Ludwig Ferdinand, 51, 792, Figs. 101, 356
  brain of, 475
  discovery of ophthalmoscope by, 152
  on histologic structure of nervous tissue, 60
  investigation of retinal structure by, 50
  ophthalmoscope invented by, Fig. 102
Hemiachromatopia, 665–68
  complications in, 666
  homonymous, bilateral, 667
  pathoanatomical basis of, 666
  pathophysiological deducations from, 667
  quadrantic homonymous hemianopia with, case report of, 717–24, Figs. 413, 414, 415, 416

Hemiagnosia, visual, 666
Hemiamblyopia, 665
  bilateral, 667
  central sparing as special form of, 685
  complications in, 666
  homonymous
    crescentic hemianopia in, 676
    right, with temporal crescent scotoma, Fig. 399
  pathoanatomical basis of, 666
Hemianopia(s)
  absolute congruity in, 679
  asymmetry and incongruity in, 679
  bilateral incomplete, from cystic multiform glioblastoma, case report of, 707
  binasal, due to lesions of optic chiasma, 639
  bitemporal, due to lesions of optic chiasma, 639
  central sparing in
    Ferrier on, 148
    functional and anatomical factors underlying, 687–94
    origin of concept of, 680
    recent speculations regarding, 686
  cerebral blood supply and central sparing in, 620
  crescentic, 676
    left temporal, Fig. 398
    optic chiasma in, 641
  differential diagnostic tests in, 646
  early modern investigation of, 156
  as evidence of partial crossing in the chiasma, 330
  heteronymous, due to lesions of optic chiasma, 639
  homonymous
    basic types of, 646
    bilateral
      with central sparing, 674
      left complete, with right central sparing, Fig. 397
      visual fields in, Fig. 392
      wedge-shaped rests in, Fig 392
    causes of, 643
    central pseudo-sparing in, 688
    central sparing in, 614, 673, 680–87
      anatomical factors responsible for, 691
      attempted explanations of, Fig. 400
      Ferrier on, 148
    without central sparing, case report of, 698
    combined left, visual fields in, Fig. 391
    complete, 646, 647
      case report of, 698–702, Figs. 403, 404, 405
      visual fields in, Fig. 385
    complications in, 646, 650
    definition of, 642
    detection of, 646
    earliest correct interpretation of, 114
    first interpretation of, 156
    general remarks on, 642
    incomplete, 646, 648

case report of, 702–7, 747–50, Figs. 406, 407, 408
  with central sparings, case report of, Fig. 428
  progression of, 653
  transformed into bilateral incomplete, Fig. 387
  visual fields in, Fig. 386
due to lesions of optic tracts, 643
in migraine, vascular pathology of, 620
partial left-sided, visual fields in, Fig. 393
quadrantic, 654
  anatomical basis of, 294, 655
  case report of, 707–10
  due to cortical lesion along calcarine fissure, Fig. 112
  expanding into bilateral incomplete, case report of, 707–10, Figs. 409, 410
  with hemiachromatopia, case report of, 717–24, Figs. 413, 414, 415, 416
  incomplete, case report of, 710–17, Figs. 411, 412
  as symptom of brain damage, 655
  theoretical interpretation of, 655
with sparing of peripheral monocular crescent, 674
subjective experience in, 645
as symptom of organic brain damage, 653
types of, anatomical basis of, 647–54
horizontal or altitudinal, 664
  and mental blindness, case report of, 724–32, Figs. 417, 418, 419, 420, 421, 422
incomplete, bilateral
  bitemporal, and complete binasal, Fig. 384
  case report of, 707–10
  from quadrantic homonymous, case report of, 707–10, Figs. 409, 410
  scotoma in, 660
incongruous, 679
  anatomic explanation of, 636
inferior horizontal or altitudinal
  with central sparings, Fig. 395
  visual fields in, Fig. 389
lateral; see Hemianopia, homonymous
nasal or binasal
  and incomplete bitemporal, visual field in, Fig. 384
  optic chiasma in, 640
  unilateral, due to lesions of optic chiasma, 639
and nerve fiber arrangement, 386
partial, and their anatomical basis, 654–65
quadrantic
  and organization of visual radiation, 657
  superior, interpretation of, 662
reorganization of vision in, 646
surplus, 648
temporal or bitemporal
  optic chiasma in, 640
  unilateral, due to lesions of optic chiasma, 639

Hemianopia(s)—*Continued*
transient, 645
vertical; *see* Hemianopia, homonymous
Wollaston and, 156
Henle, Jakob, 154, 156, Fig. 49A
inner fiber layer of, 219
inner ganglion layer of, 219; *see also* Ganglion cell layer
outer fiber layer of, 217, 272
pigment in, 260
outer ganglion layer of, 218
posterior or horizontal occipital sulcus of, 451
Henschen, Salomon Eberhard, 619, 674, Fig. 117
and functional organization of visual pathway, 181
on intrinsic organization of visual system, *182*
on lateral geniculate nucleus, 366
on location and functional organization of cortical visual center, *183*
and organization of visual cortical area, 181
on retinotopical organization of infranuclear division of visual system, *161*
and space perception, 335
Hensen, 542
Hercules, Fig. 542
Herder, J. G. von, on cerebral functional localization, 122
Hering, Ewald H., 792, Fig. 357
on binocular color mixing, 375
Heródotos of Halicarnassós, 73
Héron of Alexandria
and light, 13
and theory of vision, 12
Heróphilos
anatomy of eye by, 10
description of eye by, 10
and "dominant spirit," 79
and retina, 43
vivisection by, 76
Herrenheiser, Pick &, experiments on visual system by, 189
Herrick, C. J., 544, Fig. 460
hand-clasp synapse of, 236
on visual system of Newts and Catfish, 353
Herrick, C. L., on Shrews, 865
Heschl, transverse temporal gyri of, 400, 449, 457, Fig. 274
Hess, C., on pupillary reflex, 382
Hesse, R., 769, 799
Heubner's artery, 606
Hevermann, 279
Hindus, ancient
and anatomy of eye, 9
and knowledge of visual system, 73
Hipparchos of Nicea, and physiology of vision, 12
Hippocampal gyrus, 400
Hippocampus, 357
Hippocampus minor, 394
Hippocrátes of Cos, 5, 74
description of ocular structures by, 9

Hire, De la, 38
His, Wilhelm, 546, Fig. 343
embryological studies of, 64
Hitzig, Julius Eduard, Fig. 96
and cerebral cortex, 451
discovery of somatomotor area by, *143*
Hösel, 178
experiments on visual system by, 196
Hogarth, 31
Holmes, Gordon Morgan, 183, 686, Fig. 123
anatomical interval of radiation of, 429
experiments on visual system by, 200
on organization of visual radiation, 197
on retinal representation in cortex, 199
Holmes & Lister, 183, 685
Holocene Epoch, 1038
Holzer, on neuroglial cells, 258
Homo soloensis, cortical visual centers in, 472
Hoogstraal, 907
on Philippine Tarsier, 909
Horizontal cells and functional polarity of neurons, 550
of retina, *246*, 218
excitation of, course of, 587
and facilitation or inhibition mechanism, 579
in intraretinal integration system, 255, 587
and rod system of neurons, 582
synaptical relationships of, *246*, 255
Horn, 38
Horned Pout; *see* Bullhead
Horse
evolution of, 937
optic chiasma in, 158
retinal blood supply in, 601
Horst, W., 996
Hosch, 165
House Wren, visual behavior of, 948
Housefly, Fig. 443
Hubbs & Lagler, 803, 804, 810
Huguenin, 154, 165
on cortical area in visual function, 165
Haab &, and occipital localization of visual center, 165
and visual radiation termination, 165
Humboldt, A. von, 973
Hummingbirds, color vision and, 974
Humor(s) of eye, *211*
aqueous, 209
vitreous, 209, 212
Hun, Henry, Fig. 111
case of quadrantic homonymous hemianopia recorded by, Fig. 112
and localization of visual center, 168

Hunain ibn Isḥāḳ, 42
concept of visual pathway by, 84
eye diagram by, Figs. 2, 3
treatise on ophthalmology by, 15
Huxley, Thomas Henry, Fig. 276
calcarine sulcus of, 451; *see also* Calcarine sulcus
external or perpendicular fissure of, 465
Huygens, Christiaan, 37, Fig. 351
Hydrocephalus, hemianopia in, binasal, 641
Hypophysis, adenoma of, case report of, *696*, Fig. 402
Hypothalamus
optic chiasma and, course of nerve fibers in region of, Fig. 196
optic chiasma and, topography of visual system in region of, Fig. 197
pathology of, visual field changes due to, 640
topographical relationship of
to optic chiasma, 443
to optic tracts, 444
Hyrax, retinal blood supply in, 601
Hystrix, retinal blood supply in, 601

Ibn Abī Usaibiʿah, treatise on ophthalmology by, 15
Ibn al-Haitham
description of visual system by, 84
eye diagram by, Figs. 10, 18
on functional organization of visual system, *85*
oldest manuscript by, Fig. 5
on physiology of vision, 17
and topographical representation of retina, 334, 335
treatise on optics by, 15
visual system diagram by, Figs. 56, 58
Ibn Rushd, 35
Ibn Sīnā, 18, 42, 43
description of visual system by, 84
Ice Age, 1038
Igersheimer, 685
Image formation in eye, 209
Incongruity in defects of visual fields, 636
India, ancient, and knowledge of visual system, 73
Indian Rhesus Macaque, 987
Indians, North American, living habits of, 1043
Indonesians, cortical visual centers in, 474
Infant
calcarine fissure of, asteriform cells in, Fig. 319
granular cells from cortex of, Fig. 321
retinal elements in, Fig. 144
striate cortex of
fiber plexus in stripe of Gennari of, Fig. 328
neurons from inner nuclear layer of, Fig. 322
teledendrons in 1st and 2d layers of, Fig. 318
visual radiation and, Fig. 327

visual cortex of
neurons from 4th layer of, Fig. 320
neurons from 5th and 6th layers of, Fig. 325
Infectious diseases, scotomas from, 669
Infraprimates, origin of primate vision from, 965
Ingalls, and lateral calcarine sulcus, 465
Ingram, experiments on visual system by, 193
Inhibition or facilitation mechanism, *579*
Injuries to visual system
bilateral, character of symptoms of, 651
unilateral, character of symptoms of, 651
Inner fiber layer of Henle, 219
Inner ganglion layer of Henle, 218; *see also* Ganglion cell layer
Inner limiting membrane of retina, *219*
Inner nuclear layer
of retina, *218*
of striate cortex, in infant, Fig. 322
Inner plexiform layer of retina, *218*
Inouye, 183
war injuries to occiput reported by, 198
Insectivores
early, adaptation of, to arboreal life, 937
eyes of, 958
in phylogeny of vision, 959
Insectivorous Mammals in primate evolution, 936
Insects
eyes of, 801
nervous system of, 558
winged, first appearance of, 894
Integration system of neurons in retina, *255*, 582
Intellect, evolutionary development of, 985
Intellect of Man, evolutionary role of stereopsis in, 965
Intelligence
evolutionary emergence of
factors fostering, 1039
factors inhibiting, 1040
human, development of, *1030*
vision in evolution of, 957
Intraretinal association system of neurons, *255*
Invertebrates
nervous system of, 558
in study of vertebrate history, 770
Iodopsin, 223
Iris
light rays and, 209
structure and function of, *210*
Italian boy, occipital lobe of, Fig. 296

Jackson, H. H. T., on Shrew, 867
Jackson, J. Hughlings, 164, 645, Fig. 106

and functional cerebral localization, 143, 163
Jacob's membrane; *see* Bacillary layer
Jacobsohn-Lask, 783
Jagor, 907, 908
Japanese, lunate sulcus in brains of, 474
Jatzow, 161
on macular bundle, 160
Java Ape-Man; *see* Pithecanthropus erectus
Java Macaque, 987
fundus of eye of, Fig. 168
Javanese, lunate sulcus in brains of, 474
Jews, Ashkenazic, lunate sulcus in brains of, 474
Joeris, Davis &, on Short-tailed Shrew, 867
Johnson, G. L., 601
Jones, T. Wharton, 214
Joseph, 769
on neuroglial cells, 258
Juba, experiments on visual system by, 192, 200
Judd, and blue arcs, 295
Jurassic Period, 868, 869, 872, 892, 893, 894, 936, 963

Kaes & Bechterew's plexus, 509
Kamāl al-Dīn Abu'l-Ḥasan al-Fārisī
on binocular stereoscopic vision, Fig. 348
eye diagram by, Figs. 4, 6
treatise on optics by, 16
visual system according to, Figs. 57, 348
Kangaroo, striate and peristriate areae of, shape, extent, and location of, Fig. 309
Kant, Immanuel, Fig. 353
Kappers, Cornelius Ubbo Ariëns, Fig. 467
Karplus & Kreidl, and pupillary reflex, 381
Katydid, Fig. 443
Keen & Thomson, 165, 680
Keith, Sir Arthur, 1035
Kellogg & Kohler, 850
Kepler, Johannes, 100, Fig. 29
and "animal spirit" concept, 96
evidence of retinal image by, *36*, 38
on structure of retina, 279
Khalīfa
treatise on ophthalmology by, 15
visual system according to, Fig. 60
Kingbird, visual behavior of, 947
Kingfisher, British
fovea of, 282
fundus of eye of, Fig. 174
Kinkajou, cortical visual centers in, Fig. 308
Kipp, F., 972
Kircher, Athanasius, 38, Fig. 32
retinal image diagram by, Fig. 33

Kleiss, classification of branches of anterior cerebral artery, 607
Kloss, 876
Klossowski, 683
Klüver, Heinrich, 148, 199, 271, 355, 929, 987, 988, 995, 1042, Fig. 522A
on visual functions after removal of striate areae, 308
Klüver stain in study of striate area, 531
Knapp, on binasal hemianopia, 157
Knoll, Birukow &, 869
Kölliker (Koelliker), Rudolf Albert, 4, 541, 543, 682, Fig. 47
description of retina by, 67
description of retinal layers by, 50
in early investigation of cerebral cortex, 132
experiments on visual system by, 194
on histologic structure of nervous tissue, 60
on lateral geniculate nucleus, 365
and Müller's fibers, 51
and pregeniculate gray nucleus, 192
on retinal cells and their relationships, Fig. 48
Koeppe, on cones in central fovea, 269
Kohler, Kellogg &, 850
Kohlrausch, 575
Kolmer, 601, 799
on cone distribution in central fovea, 269
on eyes of European Shrews, 863
Krause, W., on number of optic nerve fibers, 300
Kries, 71
duplex retina theory of, 61, 222
Kronfeld, P. C., 335
Kühne, 571
optograms of, 223
Kuhlenbeck, and calcarine fissure, 465
Kuhnt, outer fovea of, 266
Kupffer, 543
Kurzveil, 185

Laboratory technique, introduction of improved, 170
Ladd-Franklin and blue arcs, 295
Lagler, Hubbs &, 803, 804, 810
Lamarck, on cerebral cortex, 17
Lampman, 868
Lamprey, eye of, 768
Lancelet, Fig. 445
gastrula of, as example of vertebrate evolution, 785, 786
Lancisi, 98, 118
Landau, and lateral calcarine sulcus in Apes, 465
Landi, 87
Landolt, E., 683
on midbrain decussation of optic nerve fibers, *160*
Landolt, M., 14

Language; *see* Speech
Langur, 997
　cortical visual center of, 470
　striate area of, Fig. 304
La Peyronie, 118
Laqueur, 183, 694
Laqueur & Schmidt, 694
　case of, testing Munk's theory of
　　"cortical blindness," 183
La Salle d'Archambault, 178, 196,
　405
Lashley, Karl Spencer, 38, Fig. 359
　on visual system of rats, 200
Lauber, on optic nerve fibers in
　hemianopia, 330
Lauber's symptom, 647
Leakey, L. S. B., 1038
　Le Gros Clark and, 1034
Leber, 599
　arterial circle of, 598
　on avascular foveal area, 599
Le Cat, 38
　on cerebral cortex, 117
Lederer, 571
Leech, in experiments on nervous
　system, 559
Leeuwenhoek, Antoni van, 117, Fig.
　34
　first microscopic investigation of
　　retina by, 43
　microscope of, Fig. 35
Le Gros Clark; *see* Clark, W. E. Le
　Gros
Lehot, 38
Leitz's Ultropak in study of striate
　area, 523
Lemur, Fig. 525
　cortical visual centers of, *469*, Fig.
　　307
　Mouse, cortical visual center of,
　　Fig. 279
　retinal blood supply of, 601
　survival of, 939
　Tree Shrew and, 892
Lemur coronatus, retinal blood sup-
　ply of, 601
Lenhossék, and neuron theory, 65
Lens(es)
　ancient, 13, 28
　crystalline, 209, *212*
　　in dioptrics, 212
　　structure and function of, *212*
　of Volvox, size of, 796
Lenz, 183, 683
　experiments on visual system by,
　　192
　and pupillary light reflex, 381
Leonardo da Vinci, Fig. 61
　on base of brain and cerebral
　　ventricles, Fig. 63
　and early modern dioptrics, 33
　knowledge of visual pathways and
　　centers by, *89*
　on relationship of eyes to brain,
　　Fig. 62
　sketches of eye by, 23
Leptocinclis, eyespot in, 796
Leptomeninges, 391
Leuckart, 799

Levick, 165
Levin, 475
Lewis, G. C., on Tarsier's eyes, 908
Leydig, 543
　punctate substance of, 541, 544
Life
　factors essential for, 769
　Galen's "pneuma" or "spirit" as
　　principle of, *78*
　time since beginning of, 768
　vertebrate, general considerations
　　of, *194*
Light
　discovery of rectilinear propaga-
　　tion of, *13*
　as initiator of life on earth, 1046
　and orientation in space, *795*
　properties of
　　utilized by animals, 796
　　utilized by plants, 796
　in rise of life, 769
　utilization of, by Vertebrate An-
　　cestors, *770*
Light perception
　in achromatopia, 665
　retinal structures in, *71*
　striate area and, 453
Light rays, focus on retina of, 209
Limnopithecus, 1034
Linné, 1053
Lister, Holmes &, 183
Lizard, Collared
　eyes of, 958
　fovea of, 284
　optic chiasma structure in, Fig.
　　188
　retinal blood supply in, 598
　visual function of, 789
Lobé, 279
Locher, 886
Löwenstein, K., 178
　experiments on visual system by,
　　196
Lorente de Nó, 368
Lorenz, 891
Loris; *see also* Lemur
　Indian, cortical visual center of,
　　Fig. 307
　Slender, Figs. 500, 524
　survival of, 939
Lorry, and functional organization
　of brain, 122, 126
Lubsen
　experiments on visual system by,
　　190
　on retinal projection in Fish, 353
Lugaro, 543
Luschka, foramens of, 398
Lythgoe, and visual purple absorp-
　tion curve, 223

Macaque; *see also* Java Macaque and
　Rhesus Macaque
　occipital operculum in, 470
　simian sulcus in, 470
　striate area in, location and extent
　　of, 490
　synaptical organelles of, 566
Mach, 36

Mackenzie, Meighan & Pollock, ex-
　periments on visual system by,
　200
Maclatchy, Malbrant &, 862, 997,
　1001
Macrochiroptera, retinal blood sup-
　ply in, 601
Macroscelidids, 939, 962
Macula
　bilateral representation of, 680
　terminology of, clarification of,
　　266
Macula flava; *see* Yellow spot
Macula lutea; *see* Yellow spot
Macular bundle
　in chiasma, 325
　early modern investigation of, 160
　relation of, to visual radiation,
　　407
Macular fibers, hypothesis of mid-
　brain decussation of, in central
　sparing, *683*
Macular sparing; *see* Central spar-
　ing
Magendie, 38
　and cerebral functional organiza-
　　tion, 122
　foramens of, 398
Magness, J. R., 973
Magnus, Albertus, 89, 122
Magnus, H., 9, 598, 599
Magoun & Ranson, and pupillary
　reflex, 381
Maître-Jan, 45
　on structure of retina, 279
Malacarne, and medial geniculate
　nucleus, 115
Malayans, lunate sulcus in brains
　of, 474
Malbrant and Maclatchy, 862, 997,
　1001
Mall, embryological studies of, 64
Mallory, F. B.
　brain of, 475, 737, 738, Figs, 425,
　　426, 427
　case report of patient, 735–47,
　　Figs. 424, 425, 426, 427
Malpighi, 104, 106, 117, Fig. 36
　fixation and hardening technique
　　of, 132
Mammalian orders, evolutionary di-
　urnality and nocturnality of,
　955
Mammals
　bipedality of, *975*
　central area of, 282
　chiasma of optic nerves in, 323
　early
　　evolutionary progress of, fac-
　　　tors responsible for, 962
　　living habits of, visual acuity
　　　and, *968*
　evolution of, impediments in, *959*
　evolutionary rise of, 869
　Infraprimate
　　retinal blood supply in, 598
　　use of forelimbs by, *975*
　lower, visual behavior of, 948
　optic nerves of, decussation of,
　　780

primitive
experiments on visual system of, *194*
optic chiasma in, 158
vision in origin of, *959*
Man
adaptability of, 1044
ancestors of
Infrahuman Primates illustrating, 985–1002
intellectual advancement of, role of living habits in, *1042*
preceding erect posture and bipedality, 1033–38
birthplace of, 1045
derivation of, from infrahuman ancestors, *986*
development of, role of vision in, *1032*
evolution of, mental
duration of, 1032
prime initiating factors in, 1026
sequence of factors in, 1033
future of, 1051
and lesser Primates, comparison of character of, *995*
origin of, 974–85
Apes and Monkeys and, *1021*
Australopithecus and, 1038–46
Darwin on, 1023–26
factors responsible for, 1026–33
role of vision and other factors in, 1046–55
Tarsier and, 978
primeval, physical character, habit, and habitat of, *983*
rise of
omnivorous habit as incentive to, *1041*
prime factor in, 982
processes responsible for, *1032*
Mandrill; *see also* Baboon
character, habitat, and behavior of, *997*
Manfredi, Hieronymo, 87, 122
Mangabey
occipital operculum in, 470
simian sulcus in, 470
Mankind; *see* Man
Marchand, on quadrantic representation, 161
Marchi, contribution to histology by, 171
Marchi method of study of nerve fibers, 301
Marie, Pierre
& Chatelin, 183
on foveal representation in brain, 341
& Leri, residual bundle of, 303
Mariotte, 38, 552
blind spot of, 260, 279
Markat, 987
Marmoset, cortical visual center of, 470, Figs. 306, 307
Marshall, double reflecting microscope of, Fig. 40
Marsupials
optic chiasma in, 158
retinal blood supply in, 601
Marten, 863

Martin, Purple; *see also* Swallow
visual behavior of, *944*
Marx & Trendelenburg, 688
Masai tribe of Kenya, diet of, 1043
Massa, 87
Mast, S. O., 796
Mathews, F. S., 899
Maurolycus of Messina, and early modern dioptrics, 35
Mayer, 38
Mayer, J. C. A., on cerebral functional localization, 118, 122
Mayer, L. L., 178
Meckel, 395
in early investigation of cerebral cortex, 132
and lateral geniculate nucleus, 115
and pulvinar of thalamus, 115
Medulla oblongata and vertebral arteries, 603
Medusa, eyespots of, 786
Megahippus, 937
Meninges, *391*
Meningitis, chronic, pupillary reflex in, 382
Mental blindness; *see* Agnosia; Blindness; etc.
Menzel, brain of, 475
Mercatus, on optic chiasma, 109
Meridians, 209
extent of central sparing along, 649
horizontal, localization of, in visual radiation, *658*
Merriam, C. H., on Shrew, *864*, 866
Mery, 38
Mesencephalon; *see* Midbrain
Mesozoic Era, 869, 937, 939
Metathalamus, 355
Metz, on neuroglial cells, 258
Meyer, A., 178
and temporal loop of Flechsig, 178
visual radiation studies of, 405
Meyerhof, 15
Meynert, Theodor Hermann, 154, 156, 179, 195, 505, 506, 507, Figs. 113, 311
commissure of, 303
contribution to histology by, 170
and functional cerebral localization, 143
initiation of modern brain research by, 171
and relation of vision to cerebral cortex, 147
solitary cell of, Figs. 337, 338
compared with granular cell, Fig. 337
in inner granular layer of striate area, 512
Miacids, 936
Michaelis
and concept of partial decussation, 114
and foveal structure and function, 280
Microglia of Río-Hortega, 258

Microglial cell of striate cortex, Fig. 339
Micropia, functional cerebral localization and, 457, Fig. 274
Microscope(s)
compound, of John Cuff, Fig. 41
double reflecting, of Marshall, Fig. 40
early eighteenth-century, Figs. 35, 38, 39, 40, 41
objects observed with, Figs. 42, 43, 44
of Leeuwenhoek, Fig. 35
of Seneca, 14
single pocket, of Wilson, Fig. 39
Microscopy
early
and cerebral cortex, 117
and investigation of retina, *43*
modern, rise of, *46*
Midbrain, and betweenbrain
optic nerves in relation to, Fig. 183
visual system and, 290
Middle Ages, knowledge of retina in, *42*
Midget bipolar, *233*
in cone system of neurons, 583
discovery of, *237*
in function of cone system, 252
historical note on, 236
and retinal impulses, Figs. 178, 179
and rod system of neurons, 582
synaptical relationships of, 564
synapses of, 564, Fig. 177
with amacrine cells, 237
with centrifugal bipolars, 237
with ganglion cells, *236*, *237*
with garland ganglion, 239
multiple, 236
with photoreceptors, *233*
functional significance of, 236
with rods and cones, 233
with shrub ganglion, 239
with umbrella ganglion, 239
Midget ganglions of retina, *239*
character of, 370
and color vision, 574, 587
dynamic response of, 572
dynamical states elicited in, 573
and spatial vision, 587
synapses of, Fig. 177
with brush and flat-top bipolars, 242
with midget bipolars, 242
functional significance of, 242
with mop bipolars, 242
synaptical relationships of, functional significance of, *242*
terminations of, in lateral geniculate nucleus, *374*
in transmission of bipolar excitation, 573
and visual acuity, 574, 587
Mieg, 118
Minimum visibile, foveal cone mosaic and, 271
Minkowski, Mieczyslaw, 161, 185, 331, Fig. 122
experiments on visual system by, 192, *196*, 200
on lateral geniculate nucleus, 366

Minnesota Red Squirrel, 896; *see also* Squirrel

Miocene Epoch, 902, 1038
  Early, 1039
  Late, 1045
  South American, 936
  Upper, Sciurides and, 895

Miocene Hominoids, 1034

Miosis, pupillary, 384

"Missing links," 1034

Moehring, 279

Mooli, 303

Moles, 939
  vision of, in evolutionary progress, 961

Molinetti, 118
  on cerebral functional organization, 122

Mollusks
  in phylogenetic study of vertebrate eye, 769
  vesicular eyes of, 786

Molyneaux, 37

Mommsen, brain of, 475

Monakow, Constantin von, 154, 178, 686, Figs. 118, 379
  brain of, 475
  intercalated cells of, in lateral geniculate nucleus, 364, 365
  and motor speech center, 458
  principal cells of, in lateral geniculate nucleus, 361
  on retinal representation in cortex, *184*
  on Wilbrand's central sparing hypothesis, 684

Monbrun, 183, 687
  & Gautrand, 183
  on organization of visual radiation, 197

Mondino de'Luzzi, 87

Monkey(s)
  American, diet of, 1043
  and Apes
    in captivity, 1003–23
    cortical visual centers of, *470*
    hands and feet of, Fig. 540
    and origin of Man, *1021*
  behavior of, under natural conditions, *996*
  blood supply of brain in, 615–17
  brain of, cytoarchitectural charts of, Fig. 302
  calcarine fissure in, 460, 462, 465, Fig. 315
  central area and fovea in, 281, 285
  color vision in, 970
  cuneolingual fold in, 480
  diet of, 1043
  Dog-faced; *see* Baboon
  extra-areal striatal cortex of, peripheral, position of, 491
  foveal cones in, 226
  giant cells of striate cortex in, 505, 506
  Hanuman, striate area of, Fig. 304
  lower
    cortical visual centers of, *469*
    pole of occipital lobe in, 480
  midget bipolar in retina of, 233
  Old World, striate area in, location and extent of, 490

optic chiasma in, 158, 310, 323, 324
plexiform layer of striate area in, 499
Red Spider
  brain of, external configuration of, Fig. 282
  calcarine fissural complex in, topographical relationships of, Fig. 283
retinal arteries in, 599
retinal blood supply of, 600
South American Marmoset, cerebral cortex of, cytoarchitectural charts of, Fig. 306
South American Night, retina of, 929
South American Woolly, striate area of, Fig. 305
Spider
  cortical visual center of, 470, 478
  fundus of eye of, Fig. 169
striate area of
  blood supply of, 609
  histological characteristics of, 496
  multiform cell layer of, 507
  nerve cell stratification of, 497
  visual radiation in
    termination of, Fig. 315
    ventral fibers of, 663

Monocular crescent, localization by Wilbrand & Saenger of, 184

Monosynaptic receptor-conductor channel, 242

Monro
  fixation and hardening technique of, 132
  foramens of, 308

Mop bipolar, *228*
  in common pathway mechanism, 578
  distribution and history of, *230*
  in function of cone system, 252
  in function of rod system, 252
  and rods and cones, neuronal relationship of, 578
  in summation mechanism, 578
  synapses of, Fig. 177
    with cone pedicles, 564
    with ganglion cells, *230*
    with garland ganglion, 239
    with midget ganglion, 242
    with photoreceptors, *228*, *230*
    with rods and cones, 578
    with shrub ganglion, 239
    with umbrella ganglion, 239

Morax, 183, 682
  on measurements of extent of central sparing, 649

Morden, 865

Moreau, 183

Morgagni, Giovanni Battista, 45, 156, Fig. 79
  first case report of homonymous hemianopia by, 114
  on structure of retina, 279

Morgan, A. H., 942

Morton, R. A., 222

Motor and sensory centers, Bouillaud's concept of, 140

Mountford, C. P., 1042

Mouse, optic chiasma in, 158

Mühlbach, 38

Müller, D. E.
  on bitemporal hemianopia, 157
  on macular bundle, 160

Müller, Heinrich, 4, 541, Fig. 46
  and blue arcs, 295
  and central area, 281
  conception of retinal cells and their relationships by, Fig. 48
  contribution to histology by, 170
  description of retina and retinal layers by, 50
  discovery of radial fibers by, 51, 52
  and foveal structure and function, 280
  radial fibers of, 218, 219, 255, 257, 269
  solution of, in histology, 50

Müller, Johannes Peter, 552, Fig. 355
  on optic chiasma and stereoptical vision, 310
  and partial decussation, 116
  theory of identical or conjugate points of, 109, 116

Müller, S., 907

Müller, W.
  and ganglion of optic nerve, 219; *see also* Ganglion cell layer
  and ganglion of retina, 218
  interstitial spongioblasts of, 257

Multiform cell layer of striate area *518*, Fig. 314

Munk, Hermann, Fig. 98
  on cortical blindness, 151
  discovery of mental or psychic blindness by, *150*
  experiments on visual cortical function by, 149–52
  on Goltz's cerebral function experiments, *149*
  on retinal representation in cortex, 179, 334
  on retinal representation in Dog, Figs. 99, 100

Muskellunge, 814, 816

Mussels, vesicular eyes of, 786

Myelin sheaths, of optic nerve fibers within eyeball, 239

Myelogenesis
  discovery of, *172*
  fundamental law of, 173

Myoxus, retinal blood supply in, 601

Nautilus
  dark chamber of, 800
  Pearly, chamber eye of, 786

Neanderthal Man, 1034

Negro, American
  cortical visual center of, Figs. 290, 291, 292
  occipital lobes of, Fig. 290
  lunate sulcus in brains of, 474

Nemesius, 122
  concept of cerebral cells of, 89

Neolithic Period, 1042

Nero, Emperor, correction of myopia of, 14

Nerve cells and fibers of retina in pre-Golgi period, Fig. 50

Nerve fiber(s)
  in neuron theory, 66
  neuron theory and, 548
  retinal, discovery of course of, *280*

Nerve net; *see* Neuroreticulum

Nervous centers, organization of
  dynamical factors in, *562*
  intrinsic, *560*
  minute, 560–63

Nervous system(s)
  anatomy of, Vesalius and, *92*
  earliest systematic description of, 76
  organization of, principles of, *540*
  peripheral and central, comparison of, *560*
  and visual function, theory of organization of, 540–92

Nervous tissue, study of, first histo-analytic method of, *61*

Net, nerve; *see* Neuroreticulum

Neurencytium
  concept of, 63
  hypothesis of, *542*

Neuroanatomy, Vesalius and, 92

Neurobiotaxis, hypothesis of, 783

Neuroblasts, 545, 548

Neurofibrils
  and neuroreticulum, *542*
  role of, 543

Neuroglia
  as insulator, 258
  interrelationships of, 258
  of retina, 213, 255
    accessory, 256, *257*
    functions of, 258
  of striate area, 535
  structural independence of, 258

Neuroglial sheaths, absence of, 258

Neuroglial syncytium, 258

Neurohistology in mid-nineteenth century, 541

Neurohumors, problem of, 561

Neuron(s); *see also* Axis cylinder; Dendrites; Perikaryon; Teledendrons; etc.
  analytical mechanism of, 576
  as complex functional organism, 564
  cone system of, *583*
  dynamical activation of, 563
  dynamical states of, 554
  emissive parts of, 570
  excitation of, 554, 570
  expansions of, 548
  integrator, and cone systems, 584
  interlocking of, *552; see also* Synapses, and under names of specific neuron cells
  intermediary, modification of nervous activity by, *573*
  intraretinal association system of, *255*
  origin and development of, 545
  in phylogenetical perfection of nervous centers, *575*
  polarity of, functional, 66, 550, 570
  ramifications of, 548
  receptive parts of, 570

relationships between, *552*, *572*–75; *see also* Synapses, and under names of specific neurons
  plasticity of, 571
  stability of, 571
  of retina; *see also* Bipolar cells; Ganglion cells; Photoreceptors; etc.
    after light stimulation, 565
    synaptical relationships of, *67*
    systems of, *581*
    varieties of, *67*
  rod system of, *582*
  specificity of, 66, *552*
    functional, 566, 573
    in phylogenetical perfection of nervous centers, 575
  synaptical grouping of, *572*
  synaptical relationships of, elemental, 575
  topographical relations of, *580*

Neuron theory, 545–59
  modifications of, *558*
  origin of, 64, 545
  and retinal structure and function, 67–72
  summary of, *557*
  tenets of, *65*, *548*

Neuronal associations, elemental, and probable function, 575–81

Neuronal response to stimulation, kind and amount of, summary of, 570

Neuropil, 544, 561

Neuroreticulum
  hypothesis of, 64, 541–45
    critique of, *543*
    tenets of, *542*
    neurofibrils and, *542*

Neurosensory cells, phylogenesis of, 772

Neurosyphilis, pupillary reflex in, 382

Newhall, and blue arcs, 295

Newton, Isaac, 37, Figs. 76, 350
  and decussation in optic chiasma, *109*

Nichols, L. N., 848

Niemeyer, fixation and hardening technique of, 132

Niessl von Mayendorf, 178, 183, 196, 683
  decussating callosal bundle of, 428
  and visual radiation, 403

Nighthawk
  flight of, 953
  visual behavior of, 951, 952

Nissl, 542
  contribution to histology by, 171
  description of lateral geniculate nucleus by, 290
  and pregeniculate nucleus, 192
  staining method of, in striate area, 510

Nocturnality, and diurnality
  in evolutionary process, 954
  as inhibitor in evolution, 1030
  role of, in evolution, 968

Northern Brook Silverside; *see* Silverside

Nothnagel, 165

Nubian, fundus of eye of, Fig. 165

Nucleus(i)
  geniculate, discovery of, *115*
  lateral geniculate, 290
    association cells of, *369*
    axis cylinders of, 531
    axonal terminations in, general remarks on, *370*
    blood supply of, 606
      summary of, *623*
    central foveal representation in, *339*
    cerebral axonal terminations in, *374*
    and cerebral cortex, figure experiments on, *424*, Figs. 256, 257, 258
    coronal sections through, Fig. 215
    cutting of, ganglion after, 292
    damage to, 619
    destruction of, hemianopia after, 648
    discovery of, 115
    foveal representation in, 388
    histoanalytic study of, history of, *365*
    injury to, unilateral, 651
    lamination of, *357*
    lesions of, visual disturbances after, *644*
    microphotographs of sections of, Figs. 212, 213
    midget ganglion terminations in, *374*
    minute structure of, 354–64
    nerve cells of, *361*
    nerve fiber terminations in, *364*
    nerve fibers in, 673
    neuron theory and, 548
    optic nerve fibers in, termination of, *331*
    and optic tracts, retinotopical organization of, *386*
    organization of, *374*
    as origin of visual radiation, discovery of, *177*
    phylogenetic development of, 333
    principal nerve cells of, *369*
    retinal representation in, 323–34
    of Rhesus Macaque, after experimental lesions, Fig. 251
    role of, in vision, 589
    shape and topographical relation of, *355*
    shrub ganglion terminations in, *372*
    and stripe of Gennari, 533
    structure of
      histological, 354–64
      historical review of, *365*
    synaptical relationships of cells of, 367
    termination of optic nerve fibers in, functional significance of, *333*
    topographic representation of, in visual radiations and striate areae, Fig. 260
    topography of, Fig. 233
    umbrella ganglion terminations in, *372*
    vascular pathology of, 619
    and visual radiation, *398*, 416

Nucleus(i)—*Continued*
  medial geniculate, 290, 357
    blood supply of, 610, 611
  parageniculate, 305
  posterior thalamic, 357
  pregeniculate, 290, 305
    connections of, *379*
    discovery of, 192
    function of, *381*
    and pupillary reflex pathway, 376–84
    structure and relationships of, *378*
Nuthatch, visual behavior of, 948

Occipital lobe
  anatomy of, 449
  pole of, in evolutionary process, 480
  sagittal fiber layers of, *394*
Occipital operculum in phylogenesis of cortical visual centers, 470
Ocelli
  of Dinoflagellates, 796
  of Volvox globator, structure of, Fig. 440
Octopus, eyes of, 786
Odier, Souques &, 183
Odonates, 946
O'Leary, 194, 579
  on lateral geniculate nucleus, 366, 368
  on striate area of cat, 366, 510
Olfactory system in rise of Primates, 891
Oligocene Epoch, 892, 934, 1034, 1038, 1039
  American, 1040
  Miacids in, 936
  in North America, 936
Oligodendroglia
  in retina of Primates, 258
  in striate area, 539
Omnivorous habit, as incentive to rise of Man, *1041*
Onychophors, vesicular eyes of, 786
Operculum
  lunate, in living primitive races, 474
  occipital, Fig. 288
    in American Negro, Fig. 290
    anthropological significance of, 475
    evolutionary origin of, 470
    in incipient human races, 472
    in phylogenesis of cortical visual centers, 470
Ophthalmencephalon, 764
Ophthalmology
  Arab interest in, 15
  modern, founder of, 156
Ophthalmoneurology, beginnings of modern, *152*
Ophthalmoscope
  discovery of, 152
  invented by Helmholtz, Fig. 102
Opossum
  optic chiasma in, 158
  retinal blood supply in, 601
  retinal projection in, 353

visual system of, experiments on, 194
Optic chiasma; *see* Chiasma of optic nerves
Optic colliculus; *see* Optic papilla
Optic nerve(s), 219, 289, *297*
  axis cylinders of, unsolved problem regarding, 292
  blood supply of, 605
    sources of, *597*
    summary of, *623*
  blood vessels of, 597–602
  central foveal representation in, *339*
  chiasma and tracts and histology of, 297–301
  close to eyeball, cross-section of, Fig. 185
  course and termination of, procedures for study of, *301*
  decussation of
    experimental evidence of, *323*
    origin and significance of, 779–93
  and eyeball, blood supply of, *597*
  Galen's description of, *77*
  histology of, 297–301
  knowledge by Aristotle of, *75*
  lesions of
    visual disturbances after, 636–42
    visual field defects due to, *638*
  of missing eye, 251
  "origin" of
    in early nineteenth century, 115
    in eighteenth and nineteenth centuries, *112*
  origin and course of, 292–97
  in relation to mid- and between-brain, Fig. 183
  and scotomas, 669
  segregation of optic tracts from, *115*
  structure of, *297*
  topical relationships of, *443*
  transection of, ganglion cell degeneration after, 292, 330
  Vesalius and, *92*
Optic nerve fiber layer, 219
Optic nerve fibers
  afferent, tectal decussation of, 322
  arching perifoveal, significance of, *295*
  bifurcation of, 327
  in chiasma, course of, 325
  course of, *301*
    and arrangement of, *385*
    in chiasma and tracts, *386*
    in retina, *292*
  diagram by John Taylor of, Fig. 78
  of infranuclear division, course and termination of, 301–9
  in Monkeys, experimentation on, 292
  monocular, 303
  number of, in various Vertebrates, *300*
  in optic nerve, course and arrangement of, *385*
  optotectal connection of, 322
  origin and functional significance of, *292*
  in papilla, course and arrangement of, *385*

in retina
  course and arrangement of, *385*
  separation of, *330*
retinal origin of, 385
retinal, terminations of, 304
termination of
  in laminated lateral geniculate nucleus, *304*
  in lateral geniculate nuclei, *331*
    functional significance of, *333*
  in pregeniculate and paragenic-ulate gray nuclei, *305*
  in pulvinar of thalamus, *306*
  in superior colliculus of mid-brain, *306*
Optic papilla(e) or disk, *259*
  atrophy of, hemianopic, 644
  composition of, 295
  in interpretation of visual field defects, 638
  optic nerve fibers in, course and arrangement of, 385
Optic tract(s), 289
  blood supply of, 605, 606
    summary of, *623*
  central foveal representation in, *339*
  fibers of, course of, *301*
  histology of, 297–301
  interruption of, hemianopia after, 648
  interruption of, retinal ganglion cells after, 292
  and lateral geniculate nuclei, reti-notopical organization of, *386*
  lesions of, visual disturbances due to, *643*
  nerve fibers in, 673
    arrangement of, *328*
    course of, 386
  after obstruction to blood supply, 619
  segregation of optic nerves from, *115*
  structure of, *299*
  topography of, *444*
Optical axis of eye, 209
Optical sciences, history of development of, 9–62
Optics
  Arab knowledge of, 14–21, *19*
  Arab treatises on, 15
  beginnings of, 9–12
    among early civilized nations, 13–14
  early modern, 27–39
  Early Western, advancement of, *27*
  Early Western European treatises on, *21*
Optogram, 38
Ora serrata, 259, 275
Ora terminalis, 259
Orangutan, Figs. 534, 535
  and ancestry of Man, 1013
  character and habits of, in captivity, 1010
  in phylogenesis of cortical visual centers, 470
  striate area of, Fig. 303
Orbital sulci and gyri, 449
Organelles, synaptical, 566
Orione, J., 965

Orlando, experiments on visual system by, 192

Ostracoderms, fossils of, evidence of eye in, 768

Outer bacillary expansions in retina, *220*

Outer fiber of photoreceptor cell, 220

Outer fiber layer of Henle, 217, 272

Outer fovea, 272

Outer limiting membrane, structure and function of, *215*

Outer nuclear layer of retina, 272 structure and function of, *215*

Outer plexiform layer, in structure and function of retina, *215*

Ovio, on optic chiasma and stereoptical vision, 311

Owl
 Barred, visual behavior of, 952
 binocular vision in, 853
 eye of, compared with that of Argyropelecus, Fig. 459
 fields of view of, 787
 Great Gray, visual behavior of, 952
 Great Horned, visual behavior of, 952
 Saw-Whet
  various views of, Figs. 473, 474
  visual behavior of, Figs. 473, 474
 Screech, visual behavior of, 951
 visual behavior of, 953

Ox, Indian, fundus of eye of, Fig. 170

Pachymeninx; *see* Dura mater

Pacini
 description of retinal layers by, 50
 inner limiting membrane of, 219

Paleocene Epoch, 893, 902, 904, 936, 937, 1038, 1040
 Creodonts in, 936
 Lemurs in, 934
 Tarsier in, 934, 936

Paleolithic Period, 1042

Panizza, 154
 experiments on visual system by, 143, 147, 163

Panoramic vision
 fields of view in, 787
 functional comparison of stereoscopic vision with, 791
 optic nerve fibers in, 780

Pantotheria, 892, 893
 Shrew and, 861

Papez, anatomical investigation of visual system by, 196

Papilla; *see* Optic papilla

Papilledema, receded, ophthalmological findings in, *698*

Papillomacular bundle, 292, 297
 course and arrangement of, 385
 interruption of, experiments with, *335*, Figs. 201, 202, 203
 position of, effect of, 295

Paranthropus, 1034

Paranthropus robustus, cortical visual centers in, 472

Para-peristriate area of Rhesus Macaque, experimental lesion of, Figs. 267, 268

Parasol ganglion; *see* Umbrella ganglion

Parastriate area
 cell arrangement in, Figs. 312, 313
 of various Mammals, shape, extent, and location of, Figs. 308, 309

Parietal lobe, anatomy of, 449

Parieto-occipital lobe, tumor in, case report of, *698*

Parieto-occipital sulcus; *see* Sulcus

Parinaud, duplex retina theory of, 61, 71, 222

Parrot, and Swallow, visual apparatus of, 853

Parsons, 645

Parsons, H., experiments on visual system by, 189

Pasinus, 95

Pathway, common, 255, *578*

Peckham, John, 87
 eye diagrams by, Fig. 9
 treatise on optics by, 22

Pecten of Birds in retinal blood supply, 598

Penfield & Rasmussen, temporal area of speech arrest of, 457, Fig. 274

Perikaryon; *see also* Cell body
 function of, 570
 in neuron theory, 548

Perimeter
 effect on neuro-ophthalmology of, *163*
 invention of, 153

Peripheral and central nervous systems, *560*

Péterfi, 542

Petrarca, Francesco, and reading glasses, 29

Pfeifer, R. A., 178, 683, 694
 decussating callosal bundle of, 428
 experiments on visual system by, 196, 200
 sagittal layer of, 397
 and visual radiation, 403, 405

Phagus, eyespot in, 796

Philippine Tarsier; *see* Tarsier

Philippine Tree Shrew; *see* Tree Shrew

Philólaos of Croton, 74

Phororhacos, rise of, 936

Photomas, functional cerebral localization and, 457, Figs. 274, 275

Photomechanical response, 571

Photopic cone vision, 223

Photopic vision, scotopic and, in vertebrate evolution, 954

Photoreception
 initial process of, 225–26
 mechanics of, *225*, 275
 role of bacillary layer in, 215
 unsolved problems in, 225–26

Photoreceptor layer of retina, blood supply of, 605

Photoreceptor mosaic, *222*

Photoreceptors 220–28; *see also* Cones; Rods
 central, *266*
 foveal, *266*
 insulation of, 257
 in lower animals, 799
 and origin of central nervous system, 1047
 peripheral, synaptical relationships of, *572*
 photomechanical response of, 571
 phylogenetic advancement of, 799
 phylogenetic inception of, 772
 synapses of
  with brush and flat-top bipolars, *231*
  with midget bipolar, 233
   functional significance of, 236
  with mop bipolar, *228*
 true, 540
 rods and cones as, 51

Photosensitive substances
 distribution of, 225
 questions concerning, 225
 of rods and cones, *222*

Phrenology, origin of, 125

Phylogenetical role of vertebrate visual system, *957*

Pia mater, 391

Pick
 agrammatism of, functional cerebral localization and, 457, Figs. 274, 275
 experiments on visual system by, 189
 & Herrenheiser, experiments on visual system by, 189

Pickerel; *see* Pike

Pickford, on color mixing, 376

Pigeon
 optic nerve fibers in, 300, 313
 visual apparatus of, 853
 visual behavior of, 946
 visual system of, *313*, Fig. 190

Pigment
 and light intensity, 214
 macular, function of, 260

Pigment epithelium of retina
 derivation of, 213
 function of, 207
 photomechanical response in, 571
 structure and function of, *214*

Pigmy Shrew, 866

Pike, 814–25, Fig. 450
 binocular vision of, 822
 biological considerations of, 824
 brain of, 823, 824, Fig. 454
  in struggle for survival, 814
 cornea of, *817*
 description of, *814*
 eyeball of, *817*
  structure of, Fig. 452
 eyes and sighting grooves of, Fig. 451
 fields of view of, 787
 habits of, *816*
 head of, dissected, Fig. 453
 internal eye structures of, *818*
 lens of, *817*, 818

Pike—*Continued*
optic chiasma in, 310
optic nerves and centers of, *822*
as predator of Sunfish, 813
retina of, *820*
sighting groove of, 817
synaptical organelles of, 566
taxonomy of, 814
visual acuity in, 816, 820, 821

Pince-nez eyeglasses, in sixteenth century, Fig. 24

Pineal gland, and vision, Des Cartes's views on, 102

Pinel-Grandchamp, Foville &, and functional cerebral localization, 143

Pinnipedia, retinal blood supply of, 601

Pithecanthropus erectus
cortical visual centers in, 472
endocranial casts of, Fig. 287

Pithecanthropus-Sinanthropus, 1034

Pithecoid Primates, Tarsier and, 918

Pitjendadjara tribe, 1042

Pituitary
tumor of, and displacement of chiasma, case report of, 696–97
visual fields in, 640

Placental Mammals, primitive living, 868

Plagge, 38

Plants, properties of light utilized by, 796

Plate, 799

Plato, 79
hypothesis of "synaugy" of, 12

Platter, Felix, 98, 99, 100, Fig. 28
and "animal spirit" concept, 96
diagram of eye by, 23, Fig. 19
discovery of photoreceptor role of retinal membrane by, *35*

Platyrrhines
advanced, cortical visual centers of, 470, 478
occipital operculum in, 470
simian sulcus in, 470
striate area of, location and extent of, 490

Pleistocene Epoch, 1037, 1038
Man in, 1038

Plemp, on optic chiasma, 109

Plesiadapis, 1040

Plesianthropus, 1034

Plesianthropus transvaalensis, cortical visual centers in, 472

Plexiform layer of striate area, *499*, Fig. 314
minute structure of, *511*

Pliny the Elder, 14

Pliocene Epoch, 937, 1037, 1038, 1045
Man in, 1038
Upper, 1038

Plover, Black-bellied, fundus of eye of, Fig. 175

"Pneuma," concept of
Greek hypothesis of, *78*
last manifestation of, *119*
during post-Vesalian period, 96

Pötzl, Otto, Fig. 380

Poles, lunate sulcus in brains of, 474, 475, Figs. 288, 289

Polyak, Stephen, Fig. 131A

Polysynaptic receptor-conductor channel of retina, 242

Pons, as "seat of soul," 118

Pooley, 165

Porphyropsin, 222

Porpoise, hearing in, 850

Porta, on optic chiasma, 100

Postglacial Epoch, 1038

Posture, erect
earliest Primate with, 1035, 1038
evolution of, *981*
evolutionary consequences of, 1039
role of, in human evolution, *1028*

Potamogale, 873

Pottos, survival of, 939

Pourfour du Petit, and functional organization of brain, 126

Pout, Horned; *see* Bullhead

Pregeniculo-mesencephalic system, 380
function of, *381*
pathologic processes and, 382
and pupillary reflex, *381*

Prevertebrate
evolution of, 770, 771
optic primordia of, *773*

Primates
arboreal life of, bodily adaptations caused by, *938*
color vision in, 972
evolutionary interdependence of colored fruits and, *973*
decussation of optic nerve fibers in, 788
dominance of vision in, 1032
evolution of; *see also* Primates, origin of
abandonment of arboreal habit in, *980*
color vision in, *969*
diurnality in, 938
grasping ability in, 938
insectivorous phase of, *936*
intellectual pre-eminence in, *939*
uncertainties about causes of, *940*
foveal synapses of, 285
Infrahuman
diet of, 1043
factors in origin of Man from, 1026–33
illustrating Man's Ancestors, 985–1002
lateral calcarine sulcus of, in phylogenesis of calcarine fissure, 480
origin of Man from, role of vision in, *1032*
striate area of, blood supply of, 609
and Infraprimates, comparison of visual systems of, *321*
lesser, humans and, comparison of character of, *995*
origin of
arboreal life and, *893, 937*

and arboreal habit of Squirrel, 901
Insectivores in, 963
role of vision in, 957
Shrews and, *868*
Tarsier and, *934*
Tree Shrews in, *889*
vision in, character of, *963*
retina of
functional grouping of neurons of, Fig. 145
neurons and synaptical relationships of, Figs. 146, 147
rise of, 861
aerial life and, 961
role of arboreal habits in, 902
role of vision in, 902, 963–74
subterranean life and, 961
rods and cones in, 224
senses of, 981
stereopsis in, evolution of, 964
striate area in, 507–10
vision of
foundations of, *963*
origin of, author's view on, *965*
phylogeny of, acuity in, *967*
visual acuity of, diurnality and arboreal habit and, *969*

Probst, experiments on visual system by, 196

Proconsul, 1034

Proechidna, retinal blood supply in, 601

Projection areas
of brain, Flechsig's myelogenetical study of, *173*
cortical, discovery by Flechsig of, *174*

Protovertebrate, evolution of, 771

Psychiatry, creator of science of, 132

Psychology, early speculative, *118*

Psychophysical parallelism, 540

Pterosaurs, as impediment in evolution, 959

Ptolemy
and light, 13
and optical phenomena, 14
and theory of vision, 12

Pütter, 799

Pulvinar of thalamus, discovery of, *115*

Punctate substance, 561

Pupil
light rays and, 209
structure and function of, *210*

Pupillary light reflex, pregeniculo-mesencephalic system and, *381*

Pupillary light reflex pathway, 342
diagram of, Fig. 223

Pupillary reaction, hemianopic, 646

Pupillary reflex pathway, pregeniculate nucleus and, 376–84

Purkinje, Johannes Evangelista, 599, 601, Fig. 354
and blue arcs of retina, 295

Purkinje phenomenon, 223

Purkinje shift, 223

Purple Martin
flight of, 953
visual behavior of, 951

Purtscher, on macular bundle, 160
Putnam, 623
  experiments on visual system by, 196
Pyramidal cell layer of striate area, *502*, Fig. 314
  minute structure of, *512*
Pyramidal cells
  in ganglion cell layer of striate area, 515
  in inner granular layer of striate area, 513, 515
Pyramidal tracts, 394
Pythágoras, hypothesis of vision by, 12

Quadrantanopia, *654*
Quadrants of eye, 209
Quadrumana, 978
Quadrupedality, evolution of bipedality from, 980
Quaternary Period, 1038

Rabbit
  chiasma of optic nerves in, 158, 310, 323
  cortical visual centers in, Fig. 308
  optic chiasma in, Fig. 188
  optic nerve fibers in, 279
  retinal projection in, 353
Rabl-Rückhardt, 571
Raccoon, retinal blood supply in, 601
Radial fibers of retina, 255, *256; see also* Müller, Heinrich
  in central fovea, 257
Radiations; *see* Auditory radiation; Somesthetic radiation; Visual radiation
Rádl, 783
Raffles, 907
Ramón y Cajal, 571, 682, 781, 785, 786, 801, 841, Figs. 52, 131, 317
  and amacrine cells, 249
  and avalanche or conduction mechanism, 579
  and centrifugal fibers, 250
  and cog or jobble synapse, 236
  and cone bipolars, 233
  on dendrites of midget bipolars in Birds, 233
  diagram explaining decussation of visual system by, Figs. 437, 438
  diagrams of neurons of eye by, Figs. 53, 54, 55
  on efferent axons, 292
  experiments on visual system by, 194
  and granular lines, 218
  interpretation of retinal structures by, 71
    critique of, *71*
  introduction of new staining methods by, 171
  investigations of, on striate area, comment on, *523*
  and knowledge of neurofibrils, 543
  on lateral geniculate nucleus, 365, 367
  on minute structure of striate area, 510, *511*

on nervous system of Insects, 558
on neurofibrils, 544
on neuroglial cells, 258
and neuron theory, 65
on neuroreticulum hypothesis, 544
and organization of nervous system, 541
on phylogenetical inception of decussation of optic nerves, 780
and rod bipolar, 231
staining method of, in striate area, 510
on structure and function of retina, 67
and study of foveal synapses, 285
on visual decussation, phylogenetic origin of, 780
Ranson, experiments on visual system by, 193
Ranson & Magoun
  on pupillary light reflex pathway, 342
  and pupillary reflex, 381
Raphé of retinal nerve fibers, *294*
Rasmussen, 178
  on auditory nerve fibers, 300
  experiments on visual system by, 196
  visual radiation studies of, 405
Rat
  chiasma of optic nerves in, 158, 323
  retinal projection in, 353
  visual behavior of, 948
  visual system of, *315*
    infranuclear and nuclear divisions of, Fig. 191
Raven
  Gregory &, 1001
  on Tarsier, 908
Raven, and Swallow, visual apparatus of, 853
Read, Carveth, 1038
Reade, 38
Receptor-conductor system, function of, 582
Red Squirrel; *see* Squirrel
Red-free light in examining course of optic nerve fibers, 295
  yellow spot in, 260, 261
Redlich, experiments on visual system by, 196
Redstart, visual behavior of, 948
Reflex of the foveola, 264
Refraction, laws of, formulation of, 809
Reich, 820
Reichenow, E., 998, 999, 1000
Reil, Johann Christian, 116, Fig. 89
  contribution to histology by, 170
  and corona radiata, 133
  in early investigations of subcortical fiber systems, 132
  fixation and hardening technique of, 132
  and geniculate bodies, 115
Reisch, Gregor
  diagram of brain mechanisms from, Fig. 81
  eye diagram by, Fig. 12

Remak, 543
  on histologic structure of nervous tissue, 60
Renaissance
  European, role of Arab learning in, *21*
  Italian, and early modern dioptrics, *31*
Reptiles
  central area of, 282
  central fovea of, *284*
  chiasma of optic nerves in, 158, 310, 323
  downfall of, 869
  eyes of, 958
  optic nerves of, decussation of, 779, 780
Research, need for
  in anatomophysiology of Swallow's eye, 860
  on arterial supply of foveal portion of striate area, 617
  on behavior of Tree Shrew, 890
  on biological needs of Elephant Shrew, 887
  on categories of fibers in visual radiation, 592
  on centrifugal retinal fibers in Birds, 250
  on coloring in nature, 973
  on co-ordination in Lizards, 845
  on the finer synaptical structures of visual centers, 801
  on functions of auditory and visual organs of Birds, 950
  on neuronal groupings in the visual system, 581
  on the occurrence of panoramic visual systems in various animal forms, 787
  on the refractive index of the cornea of Fish, 817
  on role of amacrine cells of retina, 587
  on role of laminated lateral geniculate nucleus, 591
  on selectivity in responses to photic stimuli, 796
  on sensory systems of Bats, 953
  on stereoscopic visions in Birds, 965
  summary of, 203
  on Tarsier, 907
  on topographical relations of neurons in terms of basic functions, 581
  on vascular systems of nervous organs, 594
  on vision of modern Prosimians, 968
  on visual apparatus of Pike, 822
  on visual apparatus of principal vertebrate subdivisions, 802
  on visual mechanisms in the Pigeon, 947
  on visual physiology of Silversides, 809
Rests, central, 660
  minute hemianopic, Fig. 397
Retina
  as analyzer and integrator, 589
  areal ratio of, to striate area, 490
  association cells of, 246–50
  avascular foveal area of, 599

Retina—*Continued*
bipolar cells of, 228–37
nervous impulses and, 550
blood supply of, *598*
summary of, 623
blood vessels of, entoptic view of, 601
blue arcs of, 295
central fovea of, Fig. 161
cerebral representation of, first definition of problem of, 152
color of, 211
description of, *211*
differentiation of, in ontogenesis, *764*
in dioptrics, 212
duplex, theory of, 61
early investigations of, 40–46
efferent fibers of, 250–52
embryonic development of, 211, *763, 764*
excitation in, probable course of, 587
exogenous fibers of, 250–52
foci in, scotomas from, 669
function of, early modern investigation of, 46–58
functional response of, *252, 255*
anatomical factors in, 255
factors determining, *252*
physical factors in, 255
physiological factors in, 255
ganglion cells of, 237–46
intrinsic organization of, modern studies of, 59–66
investigation of
during classical antiquity, *40*
early microscopic, *43*
lesions of, visual disturbances after, 636–42
nerve cells of, according to H. Müller and Kölliker, Fig. 48
nerve fibers of
in pre-Golgi period, Fig. 50
separation of nasal from temporal, *330*
neuroglia of, 213
neuronal elements in, Figs. 143, 144; *see also* under names of neurons
neurons in
functional grouping of, 252–55, 581–92
and synaptical relationships, Figs. 53, 54, 55, 177, 178, 179
types of, Fig. 347
optic nerve fibers in, course and arrangement of, *385*
origin of term, 42, 43
outer nuclear layer of, blood supply of, 605
outer plexiform layer of, blood supply of, 605
papillomacular fibers in, interruption of, experiments on, *335*
pathology of, 629–759
photoreceptor layer of, blood supply of, 605
pigment epithelium of, 207
representation of; *see* Retinal projection
simian, fovea in, 233
structure of, 207–87
critique of Ramón y Cajal's interpretation of, *71*

early modern investigation of, 46–58
and function of, neuron theory and, 67–72
histological, *213*
interpretation of, *71*
regional and comparative characteristics of, 278–87
supporting, 255–59
functional significance of, *258*
history of investigations of, 258
variations in, *259*
in vertical sections through, Figs. 127, 128
surface area of, 490
synaptical relationships in, scheme of, Fig. 177
topographical representation of, Taylor and, 110
visual fields of, *629*
vitreal half of, blood supply of, 605
Retinal image
diagrams of, by Kircher and Des Cartes, Fig. 33
discovery of, 27–39
Kepler's evidence of, *36*
Scheiner's demonstration of, *37*
transmission of, to cerebral cortex, 420–25
Retinal impulses, course of, Figs. 178, 179
in striate area, 533
Retinal integrators, *587*
Retinal layers, discovery of true order of, *49*
Retinal membrane
knowledge in Middle Ages of, *42*
as photoreceptor, 540
discovery of, *35*
Retinal nerve fibers, temporal raphé of, *294*
Retinal projection
in brain, Cartesian hypothesis of, *102*
in cortex
early research on, 179
history of theory of, 179–84
in infranuclear and nuclear divisions, 334–53
in Infraprimates, 353
in lateral geniculate nuclei, 323–34
of monocular crescent, in striate area, 678
in striate area
experiments on, *421, 424*
in phylogenesis of visual system, 481
subcortical, 334–53
in supranuclear division, *409*
in visual pathway, significance of, 673
in visual radiation, 410, 414, 415, 420, 421
experiments on, *421, 424*
Retzius, 541
and neuron theory, 65
Révész, 987
Rhazes, on optic chiasma, 109
Rhesus Macaque
and ancestry of Man, 987

bipolar cells of retina of, Fig. 132
synapses of, Fig. 134
bipolar and horizontal cells of retina of, Fig. 133
calcarine fissure in, 462
experimental lesion of, Figs. 245, 246, 247
calcarine sulci of, Fig. 281
central area of retina of, experiments with lesions in, Figs. 204, 205, 206
central fovea of retina of, Figs. 150, 151, 152, 153, 154, 155, 157
cerebral arterial tree in, 615
character, habitat, and behavior of, *987*
character and habits of, in captivity, *1003*
cortical visual centers of, 478
emerging moral sense in, 987
experimental lesions in visual radiation of, Figs. 237, 238, 239, 240, 241, 242, 243, 244
eye of, dimensions of, 209
eyeball of, horizontal section through, Fig. 126
fear manifestations in, 987
fovea of, 261, 264, 266, 269, 272
ganglion cells of retina of, Fig. 135
intelligence of, 987
lateral geniculate nuclei of, Figs. 210, 211, 234
association cell from, Fig. 219
optic nerve fiber terminations in, Fig. 220
retinal representation in, Fig. 200
topographic representation of, Fig. 260
after various experimental lesions, Fig. 251
nervous system of, 987
optic chiasma of, fascicular composition of, Figs. 198, 199
optic nerve fiber terminations in, Fig. 187
papillomacular bundle of optic nerve in, Figs. 201, 202, 203
pregeniculate nucleus of, Figs. 221, 222
pyramidal cell from striate area of, Fig. 336
retina of
bacillary and outer nuclear layers of, Fig. 130
central areal photoreceptors of, Fig. 160
fundus of, Fig. 162
outer plexiform layer of, structures of, Fig. 141
para-peristriate area of, experimental lesion of, Figs. 267, 268
photoreceptors at foveal periphery in, Figs. 158, 159
synapses in, Fig. 140
retinal representation in infranuclear and nuclear divisions in visual system of, Fig. 225
retinal structure of, regional variation of, Fig. 129
striate area(e) of, Fig. 281
experimental cortical lesions in, Figs. 261, 262, 263, 264, 265, 266
experimental lesion in, Figs.

248, 249, 250, 252, 253, 254, 255
extent and location of, Fig. 280
foveal portion of, 533
    nerve cells in, Figs. 329, 330, 331, 332, 333
    granular cell in, Fig. 339
        compared with solitary cell, Fig. 337
    inner granular neuron from, Fig. 340
    microglial cell in, Fig. 339
    pyramidal cell from, Figs. 336, 341
    solitary cell of Meynert in, Figs. 337, 338, 341
        compared with granular cell, Fig. 337
    terminal arborizations in, Figs. 334, 335
    thickness of, 496
vision of, 987
visual radiation of, Fig. 234
visual system of, 987
    infranuclear and nuclear divisions of, Fig. 186
vocal expression of, 995
Rhinoceros, retinal blood supply in, 601
Rhodesian Man
    occipital lobes of, 1032
    temporal lobes of, 1032
Rhodopsin, 222
    discovery of, 52
Richardson, Forbes &, 805
Ridley, H. N., 876, 973, 997
Río-Hortega
    mesodermal microglia of, in striate area, 539
    microglia of, 258
    on neuroglial cells, 258
Riolan, on optic chiasma, 109
Ristich-Goelmino, 611, 613
Ristitch, 598
Robin, American, visual behavior of, 946, 949, 951
Robinson, 1034
Robinson, Broom &, 1039
Robinson & Kloss, 876
Rochon-Duvigneaud, André, 799, 846, 847, 852, 860, 862, 945, 946, 965, 966, Fig. 163
    on visual apparatus of Old World Chameleon, 845
    visual trident of, 284
Rod bipolar of Ramón y Cajal, 231
Rod and cone system, common or duplex, 585
Rod function, "catoptric hypothesis" of, 48
Rod segments, photoreceptor role of, 223
Rod spherules, 218, 227
Rod system of neurons, 582
    in function of retina, 252
    functional relationship of, to cone system, 583
Rodents
    and Cat, visual systems of, comparison of, 319, 321
    cone mosaic of, 283

optic chiasma in, 158
optic nerves of, decussation of, 780
retinal blood supply in, 601
visual system of, functional organization of, 788
Rods
    discovery of, 47
    in dynamics of retina, 589
    excitation in, course of, 582, 587
    in Pike, 820
    and sensations of white or gray, 578
    synaptical relationships of, 582
Rod(s) and cones
    in common pathway mechanism, 578
    differential characteristics of, 222, 224
    in extrafoveal regions, 275
    fibers of, 226
    general features of, 220
    inner expansions of, 226
    inner terminations of, 227
    and mop bipolar, neuronal relationship of, 578
    photosensitive substances of, 222
    of Primates, 224
    proper, 221, 222
    in structure and function of retina, 215
    in summation mechanism, 578
    synaptical relationship of, with mop bipolars, 578
    transmission of impulses by, Fig. 178
    as true photoreceptors, recognition of, 51
Rønne, Hennig Kristian Trappand, 161, 685, 686, Fig. 120
    on cause of quadrantic hemianopia, 295
    investigation of infranuclear division of visual system by, 189
    and representation of the retina in infranuclear division of visual system, 335
Rohr, 14
Rolando, 144
    central sulcus of, 400
    in fetus, 448
    in early investigations of subcortical fiber systems, 132
    and functional organization of brain, 126
Romer, A. S., 937, 1045
Rorig, 863
Rosenberg, H., 907
Rucker, C. W., 600
Rudolphi, and concept of partial decussation, 114
Rüdinger and simian sulcus or fissure, 465
Rûfos of Ephésos, 11
    earliest systematic description of nervous system by, 76
Ruminants
    central area of, 283
    retinal blood supply in, 601
Russians, lunate sulcus in brains of, 474

Ruysch, 117
    on cerebral cortex, 117
    description of retina by, 44
    fixation and hardening technique of, 132
    membrane of; see Bacillary layer
Ryerson, F. S., 335, 927
Ryff, Walter H., eye diagram by, Fig. 14

Sabouraut, on cerebral functional organization, 122
Sachs, H., 694
    on organization of visual radiation, 178
    sagittal fiber layers of, 394, 400
Saenger, Wilbrand &, 161, 184
    on retinal representation in cortex, 199
Sagittal fiber layers, 394, 400
    visual radiation and, 390
St. Augustin, 122
Saint-Yves, 38
Ṣalāḥ al-Dīn, 18
    treatise on ophthalmology by, 15
Salpa, in phylogenetic study of vertebrate eye, 769
Samelsohn, 161
    on macular bundle, 160
Sánchez, 801, 841
Sanford & Bair, 684
Sántha, experiments on visual system by, 192
Santorini, and geniculate bodies, 115
Santorio, 38
Saucerotte, on cerebral functional organization, 122
Saurians, as impediment in evolution, 959
Scarlet, Culpeper &, microscope by, Fig. 40
Schäfer, Edward Albert, Fig. 116
    demonstration of retinal representation in cortex by, 180
    and organization of visual cortical area, 181
Scheiner, Christopher, 23, 100, Fig. 30
    and "animal spirit" concept, 96
    demonstration of retinal image by, 37
    diagram of dioptrical mechanism by, Fig. 31
    eye diagram by, Fig. 22
    retinal image experiments of, 38
Schepers, 1036
Schmidt, Laqueur &, case of, testing Munk's theory of "cortical blindness," 183
Schmidt-Rimpler, on macular bundle, 160
Schneider, and "animal spirit" concept, 96
Schneider, E. E., and visual photosensitivity, 223
Schoolcraft, 1024
Schroeder, experiments on visual system by, 192
Schultze, H., 543

Schultze, Max Johann Sigismund, 4, 71, 258, 543, Fig. 49
  on foveal photoreceptor mosaic, 269
  on histologic structure of nervous tissue, 60
  investigation of retina by, 61, 67, 215
  on nervous system organization, 541
  on rod and cone functions, 222
Schultze, O., 542
Schusterkugeln, 14
Schwalbe, 61
Schwann, 542
Schweigger, 164, 664
Sclera, 207, *209*
  blood supply of, 597, 598
Scotoma(s), 618
  absolute, definition of, 668
  amblyopic, definition of, 668
  annular or ring-shaped, retinal pathology in, 638
  central
    definition of, 668
    hemianopic, 670
      homonymous
        case report of, 733–35, Fig. 423
        in patient Mallory, 735–47, Figs. 424, 425, 426, 427
    due to retinal lesions, 637
    theoretical importance of, 671
  classification of, *668*
  and cortical representation of central fovea, *673*
  crescentic, monocular, 676
  extracentral, definition of, 668
  and functional cerebral localization, 457, Fig. 274
  with hemianopia, 646
  in hemianopia, incomplete, 660
  hemianopic, central, 670
    homonymous
      causes of, 669
        with central sparings, Fig. 396
        field defects in, 669
        irregular, of right fields, Fig. 394
  in horizontal or altitudinal hemianopia, 664
  interpretation of, 668–80
  neuroanatomical basis of, *668*
  paracentral, definition of, 668
  pathophysiology of, *670*
  peripheral, definition of, 668
  relative, definition of, 668
  scintillating, blood supply of striate area and, 620
  theoretical significance of, *671*
  transient, interpretation of, *670*
  wedge-shaped additive, visual fields in, Fig. 390
Scotopic vision
  photopic and, in vertebrate evolution, 954
  visual purple in, 223
Scott, Sir Walter, 1
Segal, and yellow pigment in outer fiber layer of retina, 260
Séguin, 680
Seitz, fissure extrema of, 481

Selachii, ganglion cells in, 558
Sella turcica, topographical relationship of, to optic chiasma, 443
Seneca's microscopes, 14
Sennertus, on optic chiasma, 109
Senses
  adjustment of, twenty-four-hour cyclic, 949
  cortical localization of, discovery of, 130
  role of
    in early evolution, 1027
    in Man's pre-eminence, 985
    in primate evolution, 937
Sensory centers, Bouillaud's concept of, 140
Sensory pathways, crossroad of, 400
Seton, on Shrew, 865, 866
Shellshear, 606, 616
Shepherd, 987, 988
Sherrington, 576, 605
Shrew, 860–74, Figs. 475, 476
  African Jumping, striate area of, location and extent of, 490
  Anthony's observations on, 866
  characteristics of, *862*
  Cope's observations on, 865
  Elephant; see Elephant Shrew
  European, 863
  eyes of, 862
  habits of, *863*
  hearing in, 865, 866
  Jackson's observations of, 867
  Jumping, cortical visual centers of, 469, Fig. 279
  Merriam's observations on, *864*, 866
  North American genera of, 861
  Old World species of, 861
  and origin of Primates, *868*
  physiology of, 863
  Seton's observations on, 865, 866
  Short-tailed, 866, 867
  Shull's observations on, *864*
  Soricide, cortical visual centers of, 469
  Surber's observations on, 866
  taxonomy of, 860
  Tree; see Tree Shrew
  vision of, in evolutionary progress, 961
  Water, 864, 866, 867, 873
    sense of vision of, 868
Shrub ganglion, *239*
  in cone system of neurons, 585
  synaptical relationships of, 239
  terminations of, in lateral geniculate nucleus, *372*
Shull, A. T., on Shrew, *864*
Silverside, 803–10, Fig. 447
  in confinement, eye movements of, *807*
  description of, *805*
  and Minnows, comparison of, 803
  in nature, behavior of, *807*
  taxonomy and habits of, *803*
  vision of, physiological considerations of, *809*
  visual apparatus, of *805*, 808
  visual behavior of, 952
Simarro, 543

Simian fossa in phylogenesis of cortical visual center, 470
Simians
  bipedality and manipulative ability of, *978*
  occipital lobe in, 465
  striate area in, structure of, 490
Simpson, G. G., 1051
Sinanthropus pekinensis
  cortical visual centers in, 472
  endocranial casts of, Fig. 287
Sinclairella, 1040
Sinus
  cavernous, and venous blood from orbital contents, 597
  petrosal, superior, and venous blood from orbital contents, 597
Sloth, 894
Small diffuse ganglion of retina, *239*
Smell, sense of, cerebral cortical center of, 455
Smith, Grafton Elliot, 2, 891, 903, 935, 940, 1026, 1027, 1028, 1030, 1031, 1032, 1033, 1045, Fig. 277
  and calcarine fissure, 465
  and lateral calcarine sulcus, 465
  para-peristriate area of, 397, 453
  on role of vision in rise of Primates, *964*
  striate area of, 390, 404
  on Tarsier in primate origin, 934, 935
Snails, eyes of, phylogenetical stages of, Fig. 441
Snell, Willebrord, 37, 809
Soemmerring, Samuel Thomas von, Fig. 37
  on brain in visual function, 113
  and central fovea, 279
  on function of cerebrospinal fluid, 119
  and geniculate bodies, 115
  maculanigra of, 263
  and yellow spot, 45
Solenodontids, 939
Somatomotor function, cerebral cortical center of, 455
Somesthetic radiation, 400
Somesthetic sense, cerebral cortical center of, 455, Fig. 274
Somesthetic and somatomotor centers, location of Flechsig's, 174
Soul
  cerebrospinal fluid as seat of, 119
  concept of, as deterrent to investigation of cortex, *118*
  in cortical omnivalence doctrine, *129*
  relation to brain of, speculations on, *118*
Souques, 183
Souques & Odier, 183
Southern Ape, *1035*; see also Australopithecus
Space orientation, disorders of, with visual field defect, 653
Space perception
  and arrangement of optic fibers, 335
  striate area and, 453

Sparing; *see also* Central sparing
  macular; *see* Central sparing
  phenomenon of, 614
  pseudo-, central, 688
Sparrow
  synaptical organelles of, 566
  visual apparatus of, 853
  visual behavior of, 946, 949, 951
Spatial fusion, 578
Spatial summation, 578
Spatial vision, midget ganglions in, 587
Spatz on neuroglial cells, 258
Spectacles; *see also* Eyeglasses
  earliest picture of, Fig. 23
Speech
  cerebral cortex and, 456
  impairment of, with right homon-ymous hemianopia, 653
  origin of, 994, *1030*
    manipulative ability and, 1030
Speech center
  discovery of, 138, 451
  motor, 458, Figs. 274, 275
Sperry, experiments on Salamanders
  and Frogs by, 353
Spiders, eyes of, 801
Spielmeyer, 542
Spina, A., and invention of eye-glasses, 29
Spinal cord
  motor nerve cells of, synaptical
    relationships of, 576
  as "seat of soul," 118
Spitzer, 782, 783
Spongioblasts of retina, interstitial, 257
Spurzheim, 125
  Gall &, 116
  and lateral geniculate nucleus, 115
Squid
  eyes of, 786
  giant axons in, 558
Squirrel, 895–902
  arboreal, visual behavior of, 948
  arboreal habit of, and origin of
    Primates, *901*
  behavior of, *900*
  color vision in, 886
  Eastern Gray, 898
    behavior of, *900*
  European Ground, cortical visual
    center of, Fig. 308
  Flying, 898, Fig. 496
  Fox, 898
  Ground, visual behavior of, 948
  habits of, *896*
  Red, 896, Figs. 494, 495
    behavior of, *900*
    brain of, 887
    habits of, 897
    optic nerves of, *886*
    retina of, *886*
  retinal blood supply of, 601
  taxonomy of, *895*
  Tuft-eared, 898
  visual behavior of, 948
Staining procedures, introduction
  of, 171
Starfish, eyespots of, 786

Starr, M. Allen, Fig. 110
  on pathophysiology of visual
    pathways, *165*
Stauffenberg, 178
  experiments on visual system by, 196
Stein, 154
Steno, 108
Stensen, and "animal spirit" con-cept, 96
Stensen, Niels, Fig. 72
Stereopsis
  in arboreal life, 894
  inframammalian, *966*
  in Inframammalian Vertebrates,
    mechanism of, 965
  in Man, mechanism of, 965
  mechanism of, 311, 313, 315, 965
  in Primates, development of, 788
  role of, in origin of Man, 1033
  in Silversides, 809
  of Tarsier, 933
Stereoscopic vision
  binocular, as explained in fif-teenth-century Persia, Fig. 348
  compared with panoramic vision, 791
  definition of, 964
  optic nerve fibers in, 781
  phylogeny of, *964*
Stilling, B.
  contribution to histology by, 170
  on histologic structure of nervous
    tissue, 60
Stilling, J., 154
Stöhr, Jr., 543
Stone experiments on Salamanders
  and Frogs, 353
Stone Marten, cortical visual cen-ters in, Fig. 308
Straus, Jr., W. L., 1003
Striate area(e), 394; *see also* Field 17
  of Brodmann
  afferent fibers in, variety of, 533
  asymmetry of, 488
  blood supply of, 607, 609, 614
    summary of, 623
    and scintillating scotoma, *620*
  blood vessels of, 535
  cell arrangement in margin of,
    Fig. 312, 313
  cell layers of human, 496–507,
    Fig. 314
  central foveal-areal representation
    in, 419
  in central sparing, 692
  connections of
    evaluation of, *437*
    with other parts of brain, 434–42
  damage to, scotomas from, 669
  evolution of, Fig. 282
  extension of, anthropological sig-nificance of, 475
  fiber systems of, 507–10
    S. Ramón y Cajal on, *518*
  in first stage of phylogenesis of
    visual centers, 469
  in fourth stage of phylogenesis of
    visual centers, 470
  foveal-areal portions of, in trans-

mission of gnostic retinal im-pulses, 483
functional organization of, 409–20
  experimental evidence of, *200*
ganglion cell layer of, *506*
  minute structure of, *515*
giant cells of, 505
granular layer of
  inner
    inner or deep lamina of, *506*
    middle lamina of, *504*
    minute structure of, *512*
    outer lamina of, *503*
  outer, 502
    minute structure of, *511*
in human brains, 480
of infant, fiber plexus in stripe of
  Gennari in, Fig. 328
  neurons from inner nuclear lay-er of, Fig. 322
  teledendrons in, Fig. 318
injury to
  bilateral, 652
  hemianopia after, 648
  unilateral, 651
layers of, *497*
lesions of, visual disturbances
  after, *644*
locality of, in relation to central
  foveae, 491
location and extent of, in Infra-human Primates and other
  Mammals, *490*
location, extent, and general char-acteristics of, *487–95*
method of study of, 523
in Monkeys and Apes, blood sup-ply of, 609
multiform cell layer of, *507*
  minute structure of, *518*
myelinated fibers in, 507
nerve cell stratification in, *497*
nerve terminations in, 533
neuroglia of, 535
neurons in, types and synaptical
  relationships of, Fig. 342
after occlusion of calcarine ar-tery, 614
  of posterior cerebral artery, 614
  of posterior temporo-occipital
    artery, 614
outer granular layer of, *502*
phylogeny of, 467–86
plexiform layer of, *499*
  minute structure of, *511*
of Primates, histological charac-teristics of, *496*
problems for future research on,
  534, 535
pyramidal cell layer of, 502, *503*
  minute structure of, *512*
Ramón y Cajal's investigations
  of, comment on, *523*
retinal impulses in, course of, 533
retinal representation in, experi-ments on, *421, 424*
  and monocular crescent, 678
  topographic organization of,
    673
of Rhesus Macaque
  experimental cortical lesions in,
    Figs. 263, 264, 265, 266
  experimental lesions in, Figs.
    248–58, 261–62
role of, in vision, 589
section through, showing stratifi-

Striate area(e)— *Continued*
  cation of nerve cells and fibers, Fig. 316
  in sixth stage of phylogenesis of cortical visual center, 476
  staining methods for, 510
  in stereoptic vision, 441
  structure of, *490*
    minute, 510–39
    Ramón y Cajal's investigation of, *511*
  surface area of, 488
  synaptical relationships of, 510
  as terminus of visual radiation, according to Flechsig, 178
  thickness of, 496
  in third stage of phylogenesis of visual center, 470
  topographic arrangement of, functional significance of, 581
  topography of, *444*, Figs. 231, 232, 233
  in transmission of gnostic retinal impulses, 483
  of various Mammals, shape, extent, and location of, Figs. 308, 309
  and vision, 452
  as visual center, earliest suggestion of, *165*
  visual radiation fibers and, 403
  visual radiation fibers into, of infant, Fig. 327
Ströer, on retinal projection in Newt, 353
Studnička, 767
Studnitz, and cone substance, 223
Subcortical fiber systems, early investigations of, 130–37
Subthalamus and lateral geniculate nucleus, 354, 357
Sudanese, lunate sulcus in brains of, 474
Sulcus(i); *see also* Fissure(s)
  calcarine, 451
    anatomy of, 460
    external, 465
    lateral or posterior, 461, 465
    medial or anterior, 461
    and parieto-occipital, encephalomalacia in, case report of, Figs. 432, 433
  central, of Rolando, in fetus, 448
  cingular
    in adult, Fig. 271
    in fetus, 448, Fig. 270
  cortical, in fetus, Fig. 270
  and fissures, neopallial, of fetal brain, *447*
  fornicate; *see* Sulcus, cingular
  and gyri
    of brain, Fig. 271
    in adult, *448*
    orbital, 449
  horizontal occipital, 465
  lateral intrastriate, 465
  lunate, Figs. 288, 289, 290
    anthropological significance of, 475
    in incipient human races, 472
    in living primitive races, 474, 475
    in modern Man, 475
  occipital diagonal, 465

occipital horizontal, 465
occipital superior, 465
opercular, 465
paracalcarine
  lateral inferior, 462
  lateral superior, 462
  medial inferior, 462
  medial superior, 462
parieto-occipital, encephalomalacia in
  case report of, 755–59
  in fetus, 448
  lateral, in Simians, 465
simian, 465
  evolutionary origin of, 470
superior occipital, 465
triradiate, 465
x, 465
ypsiliform, 465
Sumerians, ancient, and knowledge of visual system, 73
Summation
  mechanism of, *578*
  physiological or temporal, 578
  spatial, 578, 579
Sun, rise of life and, 769
Sunfish, 810–14, Fig. 448
  brain of, in struggle for survival, 814
  description of, 810
  physiological and biological considerations of, 813
  predatory enemies of, 813
  taxonomy of, *810*
  visual apparatus of, *810*
Surber, Eddy &, 803, 805, 810, 826
Surber, Thaddeus, on Shrew, 866
Suśruta, description of eye by, 9
Swallow, 847–60
  Barn
    brain of, Fig. 470
    flight of, 953
    head of, horizontal section through, showing dioptrical apparatus, Fig. 469
    various views of, Fig. 468
    visual behavior of, 951, 952
  binocular vision in, 853
  biological considerations of, *858*
  cornea of, *853*
  description of, *848*
  European Chimney, fundus of eye of, Fig. 173
  eye movements of, *850*
  eyeball of, *852*
  fields of view of, 787
  food of, *848*
  fovea of, 282
    central, *856*
    lateral, *856*
  habits of, *848*
  lens of, *853*
  nervous system of, *858*
  pupillary movement in, *852*
  retina of, *853*
  sclera of, *853*
  sense of sight of, *850*
  taxonomy of, 847
  visual acuity of, 967
  visual behavior of, 947
  visual function of, 789
Swedenborg, E., 117
Swedes, lunate sulcus in brains of, 474

Sylvian artery(ies), 608
  central, 608
  frontal, 608
  parieto-occipital, 608
  temporal, anterior, 608
  temporo-occipital, 608
    inferior, 608
    superior, 608
    origin and course of, 609
Sylvian fossa, 400
  development of, 448
  and middle cerebral artery, 608
Sylvius, aqueduct of, 398
Sylvius de la Boë, F., 38
Synapses; *see also* under names of specific cells
  of amacrine cells, *250*
  of brush and flat-top bipolars, *230, 231*, Fig. 177
  of centrifugal bipolar, *246*
  in common pathway mechanism of retina, 578
  of diffuse ganglion cells, Fig. 177
  in dynamical activation of neurons, 563
  function of, *550, 563–72*
  functional polarity of, *570*
  of garland ganglion, *239*
  of horizontal cells, *246*
  of midget bipolar, *233, 236*, Fig. 177
  of midget ganglion, *242*, Fig. 177
  of mop bipolar, *228, 230*, Fig. 177
  in neuron theory, 66
  of shrub ganglion, *239*
  of small diffuse ganglion, *239*
  stability or plasticity of, *570*
  structure of, *566*
    and function of, 563–72
  of umbrella ganglion, *239*
Synaptical membrane, 567
  influences transmitted across, *568*
Synaptical organelles, 566
Synaptical relationships
  functions of, 576
  scheme of, in Primate retina, Fig. 177
Synaugy, Plato's hypothesis of, 12, 79
Syncytium, neuroglial, 258

Taboada, 194
  on lateral geniculate nucleus, 366
Tactile sense, E. H. Weber's test for, 172
Talpidae, 939
Tansley, and visual purple, 222, 223
Tapetum of sagittal fiber layers in occipital lobe, 394, 397
Tapir, retinal blood supply in, 601
Tarsier, 903–41, Fig. 515
  behavior of, in captivity, *912*
  bipedality and manipulative ability of, *976*
  brain of, 929, Figs. 516, 517, 518
    in Primate origin, 934
  central fovea in, 788
    structure of, Fig. 512
  color vision in, 886, 971
  cortical visual centers of, *469*, Fig. 279

as example of supremacy of sight, 933
eye, ear, and head movements of, *916*
eyeball of, *920*
eyes of, Fig. 512
and facial expressions and poses, Figs. 509, 510
feet, auricles, and hands of, Fig. 514
fovea in, 261, 262, 281
fright in, 909
fundus of eye of, Fig. 149
general character of, *904*
habits of, *907*
food and eating, *916*
as inhibition to evolution, 1030
hands of, Figs. 513, 514
macular arteries in, 599
nocturnality of
evolutionary progress and, *935*
evolutionary stagnation and, 936
olfactory system in, 933
ophthalmoscopic examination of, 927
optic chiasma in, 788
optic nerves of, *929*
retina of, *922*
retinal blood supply in, 599, 600, 601
senses of, relative importance of, *933*
Spectral, 904
survival of, 939
taxonomy of, *903*
use of limbs by, *918*
in various attitudes and positions, Figs. 497, 498, 499, 501, 502, 503, 504, 505, 506, 507, 508, 509, 510
vision in, 788
as a "visual animal," 933
visual pathways and centers of, *929*
yellow spot in, 261, 281
Tarsioidea, 934
Tartuferi, 154, 542
and brush and flat-top bipolars, 233
and mop bipolar, 231
and retinal structure, 67
Taste, sense of, cerebral cortical center of, 455
Taungs Ape, 1034
Taylor, John, 38, Fig. 77
diagram of optic nerve fibers by, Fig. 78
on functional organization of optic nerve fibers, 109
and homonymous hemianopia, 114
and topographical representation of the retina, 334, 335
Teledendron
of axon, nervous impulses and, 550
in neuron theory, 66, 548
Teleosteans, eyes of, 958
Tello, 194, 579
on lateral geniculate nucleus, 365
on neurofibrils, 544
Temporal crescent in defects of visual field, 636

Temporal lobe, anatomy of, 449
Tentorium, 391
Tertiary Period, 893, 936, 937, 1038
Tertullian, 75
Testing, inadequate, and complete homonymous hemianopia, 648
Tetonius, 1040
Tetrantanopia, *654*
Thalamus(i), 394
pulvinar of, discovery of, *115*
Théon of Alexandria, and physiology of vision, 12
Thomsen, on macular bundle, 160
Thomson, Keen &, 165, 680
Titmouse
visual acuity of, 967
visual behavior of, 947
Toads, retinal blood supply in, 601
Tommaso di Modena, earliest picture of eyeglasses by, 31
Trachelomonas, eyespots in, 796
Trajanus, Marcus Ulpius, Fig. 545
Transparent media of eye, 209
Traquair, 178
experiments on visual system by, 196
Tree Frogs, visual behavior of, *941*
Tree Shrew, 281, 873, 874–95, Fig. 483
behavior of, *880*
brain of, 894, Figs. 490, 491, 492
compared with other Mammals, *887*, 890
in captivity, *876*
central area of, 282
cerebellum of, 890
characteristics of, *875*
climbing ability of, *883*
color vision in, 886
cortical visual centers of, *469*, Fig. 279
diurnality of, 935
eyeball and retina of, *884*
field of vision of, *884*
habits of, 876
Long-nosed, Fig. 482
olfactory sense of, 933
optic nerves of, compared with other Mammals, *886*
optic pathways and brain centers of, *888*
Pen-tailed, Fig. 484
cortical visual center of, Fig. 279
Philippine, Fig. 485
brain of, Figs. 490, 491, 492
eyes of, Fig. 489
head and physiognomy of, Fig. 488
retinal blood supply of, 601
various views of, Figs. 486, 487
phylogenetical affinities of, *889*
prehistory of, *892*
retina of, 890
compared with other Mammals, *886*
specific features of, 875
taxonomy of, *874*
use of limbs of, *880*
vision of, *883*
visual acuity of, 885

Tree Squirrel; *see* Squirrel
Trendelenburg, and visual purple absorption curve, 223
Treviranus
description of retina by, 47, 67
and lateral geniculate nucleus, 115
and microscopy of retina, 46
and partial decussation, 116
retinal structures observed by, Figs. 42, 43, 44
Triassic Period, 869, 893, 962
Trout, 825–30
behavior of, 827
characteristics of, *826*
eye of, *828*
fields of view of, 787
Northern Brook, Fig. 455
physiological considerations of, *829*
retina of, *828*
taxonomy of, 825
visual acuity in, 830
visual apparatus of, 827
Tsai, tegmental optic nucleus of, 318
Tschermak, 787
Tubular vision, after war injuries to striate area, 652
Türck, contribution to histology by, 170
Türck's fiber bundle, origin of, 457, Fig. 274
Tupaia, in primate phylum, 891, 892
Turtle, Painted
dissected head of, showing brain and eyes, Fig. 466
visual behavior of, *942*

Uexküll, 788
Uhthoff, 183
on macular bundle, 160
Umbrella ganglions of retina, *239*
character of, 370
synapses of, with bipolars, 239
terminations of, in lateral geniculate nucleus, *372*
Urogale, in early mammalian ancestry, 891
Urogale everetti, Fig. 485; *see also* Tree Shrew, Philippine
retinal blood supply of, 601
Usher & Dean, experiments on visual system by, 189
Uvea
blood supply of, 597
structure and function of, 210
veins of, 598

"Vacuoles" in retina, 224
Valsalva, 45
on structure of retina, 279
Valverda, 95
on optic chiasma, 109
Van der Horst, 801
Van Eyck, Jan, and eyeglasses, 31
Van Gehuchten, 541
on lateral geniculate nucleus, 365
and neuron theory, 65
Van Heuven, experiments on visual system by, 200

Van Soest, Conrad, and early pictures of eyeglasses, 31

Varoli (Varolius)
  basal aspect of brain according to, Fig. 67
  first adequate depiction of infranuclear visual pathways by, 98

Vascular cone of Lizards in retinal blood supply, 598

Vascular disturbances, scotomas from, 669

Vater & Heinicke, 156
  first correct interpretation of homonymous hemianopia by, 114

Vein(s)
  facial, common, 597
  jugular, and venous blood from orbital contents, 597
  macular, 598
  nasal, 598
  nasofrontal, and venous blood from orbital contents, 597
  ophthalmic, 597
  palatine, 597
  retinal, central, course of, 598
  temporal, 598

Venderovich, experiments on visual system by, 196

Ventricles, lateral, topography of, Figs. 231, 232, 233

Verrier, 799

Vertebrate Ancestors and utilization of light, *770*

Vertebrate life, general considerations of, *794*

Vertebrates, Inframmalian, retinal blood supply in, 598, 601

Vesalius, Andreas, 90, Figs. 15, 64
  and anatomy and physiology of visual pathways, 92–96
  base of brain according to, Fig. 65
  eye diagrams by, 23, Figs. 16, 17
  influence of Galen's views on, *96*
  on optic chiasma, 109
  reform in anatomy introduced by, *92*

Vesling, on optic chiasma, 109

Vicq-d'Azyr
  in early investigation of cerebral cortex, 132
  fiber layer of; *see* Granular layer
  fixation and hardening technique of, 132
  hippocampus minor of, 394
  and lateral geniculate nucleus, 115
  on optic nerve, 115
  and pulvinar, 115
  stripe of, 390, 394, 398, 414, 415, Fig. 86; *see also* Gennari, stripe of
  identification of, 518

Vieussens, Raymond, 106, 116, 117, 394, Fig. 75
  and "animal spirit" concept, 96, 122
  and corona radiata, 133
  and earliest intimation of visual radiation, 107
  fixation and hardening technique of, 132

on optic nerve, 115
and "seat of soul," 118

Vintschgau, description of retinal layers by, 50

Vision; *see also* Visual function
  anatomical substratum of, *540*
  Arab interest in, 15
  biological problems of, *3*
  color, impairment of; *see* Achromatopia; Hemiachromatopia
  dependence of Vertebrates on, *959*
  disturbances of, 629–94; *see also* Visual fields, defects of
    due to lesions in calcarine region of occipital lobes, first verified case of, Fig. 109
    due to lesions of lateral geniculate nuclei, *644*
    due to lesions of optic tracts, *643*
    due to optic nerve pathology, 636–42
    due to pathology of optic chiasma, 636–42
    due to retinal pathology, 636–42
    due to suprachiasmal pathology, 642–46
    earliest anatomically verified clinical cases of, 163
  dullness of; *see* Hemiamblyopia
  duplexity theory of, 61
  in economy of Vertebrates, *957*
  epicritic, 645
    chamber eye and, 786
  evolutionary adaptations of, 959
  fields of; *see* Visual fields
  interest in, 1
  localization in cerebral cortex of, early attempts at, 147–49
  occipital lobe localization of, history of, 149–52
  and origin of Mammals, *959*
  physiology of
    Arab, 17
    Greek, *11*
  of Primates
    character of, and origin of Primates, *963*
    foundations of, *963*
    origin of, *965*
  problem of, *1*
  protopathic, 645
  role of
    in evolution of Man, *1032*
    in evolution of Primates, 873
    in maintenance of animal life, 794–803
    in Man's pre-eminence, *984*
    in origin of Man, 957–1055,
    in origin of Primates, 957
  sense of, and brain, 452
  tubular, after war injuries to striate area, 652
  vascular factors in, 594

Visual acuity, 278
  in achromatopia, 665
  central, in homonymous hemianopia, 650
  cones in, 584
  definition of, 967
  diurnality and, *968*
  of early Mammals, living habits and, *968*
  midget ganglions in, 574, 587

role of, in evolutionary progress, 969
visual radiation and, 441

Visual adjustment, mechanism of, 288

Visual area, cortical, Munk's conclusions on retinotopical organization of, *152*

Visual behavior
  of animals 941–56; *see also* under names of specific animals
  twenty-four-hour variations in, *949*

Visual blue, 222

Visual cells, 220–28

Visual center(s)
  accessory subcortical, discovery of, 192
  blood supply of, general remarks on, 593–97
  cortical, 446–539
    of advanced Monkeys and Apes, *470*
    anatomy of, gross, 460–66
    definition of, *487*
    evolution of, phylogenetic factors responsible for, *478*
    first evidence of retinotopical organization of, *199*
    gross anatomy of, 460–66
    Henschen on location and functional organization of, 183
    of infant
      neurons from 4th layer of, Fig. 320
      neurons from 5th and 6th layers of, Fig. 325
    of modern Man, *474*
    phylogeny of
      1st stage in, 469
      2d stage in, 469
      3d stage in, 470
      4th stage in, 470
      5th stage in, 472
    in prehistoric humans, *472*
    racial characteristics in, 476
    section through, showing stratification of nerve cells and fibers, Fig. 316
    in stages of evolution of Primate Mammals, Fig. 279
  location of, 174
  occipital, historical establishment of, 168
  organization of, hypothesis of "diffuse" or "plastic," 184–88
  pathophysiology of, *629*
  subcortical, 250
    early modern search for, *154*
    organization of, 290
    retinal representation in, 334–53

Visual cortex
  association fibers of, *435*
  connection of, with other parts of brain, 434–42

Visual field(s)
  disturbances of, case reports of, clinical and pathoanatomical, 695–759
  and landmarks of, Fig. 381
  plotting of, introduction of, 152
  and relation to retinal surface, *629*

representation of, in calcarine cortex, Fig. 124
testing of
  in drivers, 633
  by flicker-campimeter, 688
  importance of, *633*
  and interpretation of, in central sparing, *687*
Visual field(s), defects of
  due to combined cortical and subcortical lesions, *660*
  due to damage to cortical visual center, 638
  due to damage to striate area, 638
  due to lesions of optic chiasma, *639*
  due to lesions of optic nerve, *638*
  hemianopic zonal type of, Fig. 388
  incongruity in, 636
  principal
    in lesions affecting suprachiasmal visual system, Fig. 383
    in lesions of peripheral visual system, Fig. 382
  types of, *629*
  wedge-shaped, 638
Visual function(s), 207, 212, 255
  localization of, early modern attempts at, 163–69
  in Monkey and Cat, 308
  nervous system organization and, 540–92
  occipital localization of, first verified cases suggesting, *165*
  role of superior temporo-occipital Sylvian artery in, 609
  unsolved problem regarding, 292
Visual memory, striate area and, 453
Visual nuclei, subcortical, fibers of, course of, *301*
Visual pathway(s), afferent, *288*
  anatomy and physiology of, Vesalius and, 92–96
  of Baboon, Gratiolet's dissection of, Fig. 93
  blood supply of, general remarks on, 593–97
  of Capuchin Monkey, Gratiolet's dissection of, Fig. 93
  and centers
    anatomy and physiology of
      from Des Cartes to von Haller, 105–12
      during Middle Ages, 83–86
    investigation of
      from antiquity to early modern scientific era, 73–161
      in early modern brain research, 117–63
    Leonardo da Vinci's knowledge of, *89*
    modern investigation of, 163–201
  and cerebral hemispheres, 391–98
  first depiction of, 97
  foveal-areal portions of, in transmission of gnostic retinal impulses, 483
  function of, 207
  functional organization of, first attempts to reveal, *181*
  infranuclear division of, first adequate depiction of, 98
  pathology of, 629–759
  pathophysiology of, *629*

Starr's pathophysiological analysis of, *165*
suprachiasmal
  damage to, scotomas from, 669
  functional character of, 642
supranuclear divisions of, nerve fibers of, 292
Visual pathway, efferent, 250
Visual perception
  Du Laurens on locus of, *100*
  of light, color, and form, homonymous impairment of, 665
Visual purple
  absorption curve of, 223
  bleaching of, 222
  chemical and physiological properties of, 223
  demonstration of, 223
  discovery of, 52
  regeneration of, 222
Visual radiation, 390–445
  axial segment of, origin, course, and termination of, *415*
  blood supply of, 608, 609
    summary of, 623
  in central sparing, 692
  and cerebral hemispheres, 391–98
  composition of, 420–25
  course of
    according to Flechsig, *178*
    and topical relationships, *399*
  and crescentic field defect, 678
  discovery of, *135*
  dissection to demonstrate, 405, Figs. 235, 236
  functional organization of, 409–20
  functional segmentation of, *402*
  general characteristics of, *390*
  horizontal meridians in, localization of, *658*
  injuries to, hemianopia after, 648
  intermediate segment of, origin, course, and termination of, *415*
  interruption of, 405
  lesion of
    unilateral, 651
    visual disturbances after, 644
  lower segment of, origin, course, and termination of, *416*
  myelogenetic investigation of, 177–79
  organization of, quadrantic hemianopia and, 657
  origin of, *398*
    in Rhesus Macaque, Fig. 234
  origin, course, and termination of, *390*
  in relation to auditory radiation, 400
  relationship of
    to central area and fovea, 407
    to macular bundle, 407
  representation of wedge-shaped segments and beltlike zones in, *659*
  retinal representation in, 414, 415, 420, *421*
    experiments on, *421, 424*
  retinotopical organization of, *417*
    evidence of, *420*
  of Rhesus Macaque, experimental lesions of, Figs. 237, 238, 239, 240, 241, 242, 243, 244, 315
  role of, in vision, 591
  secondary, of Flechsig, 178

shape of, 400
and striate cortex of infant, Fig. 327
temporal loop of, and superior quadrantic hemianopia, *662*
termination of, *404*, 520
  according to Flechsig, 178
topography of, Figs. 231, 232, 233
  in transmission of retinal image, 420–25
unilaterality of, *403*
upper segment of, origin, course, and termination of, *411*
vacular pathology of, 619
Visual red, 222
Visual sensations, striate area and, 453
Visual space perception, 278
  retinal structures and, *71*
  visual radiation and, 441
"Visual spirit"
  Du Laurens' views on, *99*
  of Galen's physiology, *79*
  during post-Vesalian period, 96
Visual trident, 284
Visual violet in Fish retina, 222
Visual yellow, 222
Visuo-sensory area; *see also* Striate area
  of Campbell, 390
  and visuo-psychic area, of Man, compared with Ape, Fig. 298
Vitamin A, 222
Vitamin B₂, 222
Vitello, 43, 87, 89
  eye diagram by, Figs. 11, 18
  treatise on optics by, 222
Vitreal cavity, 212
Vitreous humor of eye, 209, 212
Vogt, and pregeniculate gray nucleus, 192
Vogtherr, Heinrich, eye diagram by, Fig. 13
Volkmann, and partial decussation, 116
Volvox globator, cells of, showing eyespots, 796, Fig. 440
von Economo; *see* Economo
von Mayendorf; *see* Niessl von Mayendorf
Vossius, on macular bundle, 160

Wald, and photosensitive substances, 222, 223
Waldeyer, Wilhelm, Fig. 345
  contribution to histology by, 170
  and neuron theory, 65
Walker & Fulton, experiments on visual system by, 200
Wallace, A. R., 973
Wallace, W. C., first description of arching course of optic nerve fibers in retina by, 280
Walls, Gordon Lynn, 767, 768, 799, 885, 886, 970, Fig. 164
  foveal excavation hypothesis of, 275
  on optic chiasma and stereoscopic vision, 311

War injuries
  to striate area, 652
  and study of visual system, *197*
Warblers, visual behavior of, 948
Water, and origin of life, 769
Weber, A., on efferent axons, 292
Weber, D., and partial decussation, 115
Weber, E. H., 179
  and modern brain research, 172
Weigert
  contribution to histology by, 171
  myelin stain of, 173
Weiss, P., resonance hypothesis of, 543, 555
Wells, L. H., 1037
Wenzel brothers, and concept of partial decussation, 114
Wepfer, and "animal spirit" concept, 96
Wernicke
  auditory area of, 457, 458, Fig. 274
  sensory aphasia of, 457, Fig. 274
  and termination of visual radiation, 165
  triangular field of, 400
Westphal, 165
  on lateral geniculate nucleus, 368
Wharton, Charles H.
  on Tarsier's habits, 907, 909
  on Tree Shrew, 876
White or gray, sensations of, rods and, 578
Whytt, R., on habitat of soul, 118
Widmark, on macular bundle, 160
Wilbrand, Hermann, 154, 335, 644, 674, 679, 682, 684, Fig. 107
  anterior knee of, 325
  central sparing hypothesis, final verdict on, 684
  and functional organization of visual pathway, *181*
  hypothesis of macular projection as advocated by, Fig. 401
  on measurements of central sparing, 649

and occipital localization of vision, 165
theory of syndynamical homonymous conductor units by, 109, 181
Wilbrand & Saenger, 161, 184, 683
  on retinal representation in cortex, 199
William of Saliceto, 87
Willis, Thomas, 116, Fig. 73
  and "animal spirit" concept, 96
  arterial circle of, 594, *604*
    composition of, 604
    function of, 605
    and origin of cerebral arteries, 602–7
    parts of visual system supplied by, *605*
    and its topographical relations, Fig. 368
  on cerebral functional localization, 122
  and corona radiata, 133
  earliest post-Renaissance presentation of anatomy of brain by, *105*
  and medial geniculate nucleus, 115
  and "seat of soul," 118
Wilson, single pocket microscope of, Fig. 39
Winslow, 45
  and "animal spirit" concept, 96
Wolff, E., 598
Wollaston, W. H.
  and interpretation of "half-vision," 156
  on partial decussation, binocular vision, and homonymous hemianopia, 115
  on semidecussation in optic chiasma, 158
Wood, A. C., 15
Woodchuck, visual behavior of, 948
Woodpecker
  Downy, visual behavior of, 948
  Hairy, visual behavior of, 948

Woollard, 558, 885, 890, 907
  on Tarsier in primate evolution, 934
Worms, Annelide
  eyes of, phylogenetical stages of, Figs. 441, 442
  in phylogenetic study of vertebrate eye, 769
Wren, Sir Christopher, 105
Wright, Chancey, 1023
Wrisberg, 118
Wundt, 782

Yellow spot, 259, *260*
  comparative studies on, *281*
  discovery of, 45, *278*
  history of theories on, 281
  terminology of, clarification of, 266
Yerkes, R. M., 999, 1001, 1015
Young, J. Z., 550, 558
Young, Thomas, Fig. 352
Young and Helmholtz theory of color vision, 376

Zarrīn-Dast, treatise on ophthalmology by, 15
Zeeman, Brouwer &, experiments on visual system by, *190*
Zeuner, 768, 869
  on duration of geological periods, 1038
Zingerle, 178, 196
Zinn, 45
  arterial circle of, 598
  and functional organization of brain, 126
  on "seat of soul," 118
  on structure of retina, 279
  and topographical representation of retina, 111, 334
Zinn's zonule, 210
Zuckerman, S., 994, 1042